CHILTON®

GENERAL MOTORS
SERVICE MANUAL
2010 EDITION
VOLUME II

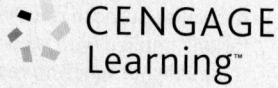
CENGAGE
Learning™

Australia • Brazil • Japan • Korea • Mexico • Singapore • Spain • United Kingdom • United States

CHILTON®
General Motors Service Manual
2010 Edition
Volume II

Vice President,
Technology Professional
Business Unit:
Gregory L. Clayton

Publisher,
Technology Professional
Business Unit:
David Koontz

Director of Marketing:
Beth A. Lutz

Production Director:
Carolyn Miller

Production Manager:
Andrew Crouth

Marketing Manager:
Jennifer Barbic

Marketing Coordinator:
Rachael Conover

Editorial Assistant:
Tracey Gates

Chilton Content Specialist:
Paula Baillie

Graphical Designer:
Melinda Possinger

Art Director:
Benj Gleeksman

Sr. Content Project Manager:
Elizabeth C. Hough

Managing Editor:
Terry L. Blomquist

Senior Editor:
Christine L. Sheeky

Editors:
Ken Burdette

Nick D'Andrea

Eugene F. Hannon, Jr., A.S.E.

Kyla Nyjordet

Lance Williams

For product information and technology assistance, contact us at
Professional & Career Group Customer Support, 1-800-648-7450.
For permission to use material from this text or product,
submit all requests online at
www.cengage.com/permissions.
Further permissions questions can be e-mailed to
permissionrequest@cengage.com.

ISBN-13: 978-1-1110-3659-1
ISBN-10: 1-1110-3659-4
ISSN: 1939-621X

Delmar
5 Maxwell Drive
Clifton Park, NY 12065-2919
USA

Cengage Learning is a leading provider of customized learning solutions with office locations around the globe, including Singapore, the United Kingdom, Australia, Mexico, Brazil, and Japan. Locate your local office at: **international.cengage.com/region**

Cengage Learning products are represented in Canada by Nelson Education, Ltd.

NOTICE TO THE READER

Publisher does not warrant or guarantee any of the products described herein or perform any independent analysis in connection with any of the product information contained herein. Publisher does not assume, and expressly disclaims, any obligation to obtain and include information other than that provided to it by the manufacturer.

The reader is expressly warned to consider and adopt all safety precautions that might be indicated by the activities described herein and to avoid all potential hazards. By following the instructions contained herein, the reader willingly assumes all risks in connection with such instructions.

The publisher makes no representations or warranties of any kind, including but not limited to, the warranties of fitness for particular purpose or merchantability, nor are any such representations implied with respect to the material set forth herein, and the publisher takes no responsibility with respect to such material. The publisher shall not be liable for any special, consequential, or exemplary damages resulting, in whole or part, from the readers' use of, or reliance upon, this material.

Printed in the United States of America
1 2 3 4 5 6 7 13 12 11 10 09

these instructions may result in personal injury.

• Observe all applicable safety precautions when working around fuel. Whenever servicing the fuel system, always work in a well-ventilated area. Do not allow fuel spray or vapors to come in contact with a spark, open flame, or excessive heat (a hot drop light, for example). Keep a dry chemical fire extinguisher near the work area. Always keep fuel in a container specifically designed for fuel storage; also, always properly seal fuel containers to avoid the possibility of fire or explosion. Do not smoke or carry lighted tobacco or open flame of any type when working on or near any fuel-related components.

• Fuel injection systems often remain pressurized, even after the engine has been turned OFF. The fuel system pressure must be relieved before disconnecting any fuel lines. Failure to do so may result in fire and/or personal injury.

• The evaporative emissions system contains fuel vapor and condensed fuel vapor. Although not present in large quantities, it still presents the danger of explosion or fire. Disconnect the battery ground cable from the battery to minimize the possibility of an electrical spark occurring, possibly causing a fire or explosion if fuel vapor or liquid fuel is present in the area. Failure to follow these instructions can result in personal injury.

• The EPA warns that prolonged contact with used engine oil may cause a number of skin disorders, including cancer! You should make every effort to minimize your exposure to used engine oil. Protective gloves should be worn when changing oil. Wash your hands and any other exposed skin areas as soon as possible after exposure to used engine oil. Soap and water, or waterless hand cleaner should be used.

• Some vehicles are equipped with an air bag system, often referred to as a Supplemental Restraint System (SRS) or Supplemental Inflatable Restraint (SIR) system. The system must be disabled before performing service on or around system components, steering column, instrument panel components, wiring and sensors. Failure to follow safety and disabling procedures could result in accidental air bag deployment, possible personal injury and unnecessary system repairs.

• Always wear safety goggles when working with, or around, the air bag system. When carrying a non-deployed air bag, be sure the bag and trim cover are pointed away from your body. When placing a non-deployed air bag on a work surface, always face the bag and trim cover upward, away from the surface. This will reduce the motion of the module if it is accidentally deployed.

• Electronic modules are sensitive to electrical charges. The ABS module can be damaged if exposed to these charges.

• Brake pads and shoes may contain asbestos, which has been determined to be a cancer-causing agent. Never clean brake surfaces with compressed air. Avoid inhaling brake dust. Clean all brake surfaces with a commercially available brake cleaning fluid.

• When replacing brake pads, shoes, discs or drums, replace them as complete axle sets.

• When servicing drum brakes, disassemble and assemble one side at a time, leaving the remaining side intact for reference.

• Brake fluid often contains polyglycol ethers and polyglycols. Avoid contact with the eyes and wash your hands thoroughly after handling brake fluid. If you do get brake fluid in your eyes, flush your eyes with clean, running water for 15 minutes. If eye irritation persists, or if you have taken brake fluid internally, immediately seek medical assistance.

• Clean, high quality brake fluid from a sealed container is essential to the safe and proper operation of the brake system. You should always buy the correct type of brake fluid for your vehicle. If the brake fluid becomes contaminated, completely flush the system with new fluid. Never reuse any brake fluid. Any brake fluid that is removed from the system should be discarded. Also, do not allow any brake fluid to come in contact with a painted or plastic surface; it will damage the paint.

• Never operate the engine without the proper amount and type of engine oil; doing so will result in severe engine damage.

• Timing belt maintenance is extremely important! Many models utilize an interference-type, non-freewheeling engine. If the timing belt breaks, the valves in the cylinder head may strike the pistons, causing potentially serious (also time-consuming and expensive) engine damage.

• Disconnecting the negative battery cable on some vehicles may interfere with the functions of the on-board computer system (s) and may require the computer to undergo a relearning process once the negative battery cable is reconnected.

• Steering and suspension fasteners are critical parts because they affect performance of vital components and systems and their failure can result in major service expense. They must be replaced with the same grade or part number or an equivalent part if replacement is necessary. Do not use a replacement part of lesser quality or substitute design. Torque values must be used as specified during reassembly.

USING THIS INFORMATION

Organization

To find where a particular model section or procedure is located, look in the Table of Contents. Main topics are listed with the page number on which they may be found. Following the main topics is an alphabetical listing of all of the procedures within the section and their page numbers.

Manufacturer and Model Coverage

This product covers 2008 – 2010 General Motors models that are produced in sufficient quantities to warrant coverage, and which have technical content available from the vehicle manufacturers before our publication date. Although this information is as complete as possible at the time of publication, some manufacturers may make changes which cannot be included here. While striving for total accuracy, the publisher cannot assume responsibility for any errors, changes, or omissions that may occur in the compilation of this data.

Part Numbers and Special Tools

Part numbers and special tools are recommended by the publisher and vehicle manufacturer to perform specific jobs. Before substituting any part or tool for the one recommended, you must be completely satisfied that neither your personal safety, nor the performance of the vehicle will be endangered.

ACKNOWLEDGEMENT

Portions of materials contained herein have been reprinted under license from General Motors Company, Service and Parts Operations License Agreement #0510757.

PRECAUTIONS

Before servicing any vehicle, please be sure to read all of the following precautions, which deal with personal safety, prevention of component damage, and important points to take into consideration when servicing a motor vehicle:

• Always wear safety glasses or goggles when drilling, cutting, grinding or prying.

• Steel-toed work shoes should be worn when working with heavy parts. Pockets should not be used for carrying tools. A slip or fall can drive a screwdriver into your body.

• Work surfaces, including tools and the floor should be kept clean of grease, oil or other slippery material.

• When working around moving parts, don't wear loose clothing. Long hair should be tied back under a hat or cap, or in a hair net.

• Always use tools only for the purpose for which they were designed. Never pry with a screwdriver.

• Keep a fire extinguisher and first aid kit handy.

• Always properly support the vehicle with approved stands or lift.

• Always have adequate ventilation when working with chemicals or hazardous material.

• Carbon monoxide is colorless, odorless and dangerous. If it is necessary to operate the engine with vehicle in a closed area such as a garage, always use an exhaust collector to vent the exhaust gases outside the closed area.

• When draining coolant, keep in mind that small children and some pets are attracted by ethylene glycol antifreeze, and are quite likely to drink any left in an open container, or in puddles on the ground. This will prove fatal in sufficient quantity. Always drain the coolant into a sealable container.

• To avoid personal injury, do not remove the coolant pressure relief cap while the engine is operating or hot. The cooling system is under pressure; steam and hot liquid can come out forcefully when the cap is loosened slightly. Failure to follow these instructions may result in personal injury. The coolant must be recovered in a suitable, clean container for reuse. If the coolant is contaminated it must be recycled or disposed of correctly.

• When carrying out maintenance on the starting system be aware that heavy gauge leads are connected directly to the battery. Make sure the protective caps are in place when maintenance is completed. Failure to follow these instructions may result in personal injury.

• Do not remove any part of the engine emission control system. Operating the engine without the engine emission control system will reduce fuel economy and engine ventilation. This will weaken engine performance and shorten engine life. It is also a violation of Federal law.

• Due to environmental concerns, when the air conditioning system is drained, the refrigerant must be collected using refrigerant recovery/recycling equipment. Federal law requires that refrigerant be recovered into appropriate recovery equipment and the process be conducted by qualified technicians who have been certified by an approved organization, such as MACS, ASI, etc. Use of a recovery machine dedicated to the appropriate refrigerant is necessary to reduce the possibility of oil and refrigerant incompatibility concerns. Refer to the instructions provided by the equipment manufacturer when removing refrigerant from or charging the air conditioning system.

• Always disconnect the battery ground when working on or around the electrical system.

• Batteries contain sulfuric acid. Avoid contact with skin, eyes, or clothing. Also, shield your eyes when working near batteries to protect against possible splashing of the acid solution. In case of acid contact with skin or eyes, flush immediately with water for a minimum of 15 minutes and get prompt medical attention. If acid is swallowed, call a physician immediately. Failure to follow these instructions may result in personal injury.

• Batteries normally produce explosive gases. Therefore, do not allow flames, sparks or lighted substances to come near the battery. When charging or working near a battery, always shield your face and protect your eyes. Always provide ventilation. Failure to follow these instructions may result in personal injury.

• When lifting a battery, excessive pressure on the end walls could cause acid to spew through the vent caps, resulting in personal injury, damage to the vehicle or battery. Lift with a battery carrier or with your hands on opposite corners. Failure to follow

Model Index

Table of Contents

CADILLAC

CTS • CTS-V • DTS

SPECIFICATIONS AND MAINTENANCE CHARTS

ENGINE AND VEHICLE IDENTIFICATION

Code ①	Liters (cc)	Cu. In.	Cyl.	Fuel Sys.	Engine Type	Eng. Mfg.
V	3.6 (3600)	217	6	SDI	DOHC	GM
7	3.6 (3564)	217	6	SMFI	DOHC	GM
Y	4.6 (4565)	279	8	SMFI	DOHC	GM
9	4.6 (4565)	279	8	SMFI	DOHC	GM
W	6.2 (6194)	376	8	SFI	OHV	GM

Code ②	Year
8	2008
9	2009

SDI: Sequential Direct Injection

SMFI: Sequential Multi-port Fuel Injection

SFI: Sequential Fuel Injection

DOHC: Dual Overhead Camshaft

① 8th position of VIN

② 10th position of VIN

36616_CCTS_C0001

GENERAL ENGINE SPECIFICATIONS

Year	Model	Engine Displacement Liters	Engine Series (VIN)	Fuel System	Net Horsepower @ rpm	Net Torque @ rpm (ft. lbs.)	Bore x Stroke (in.)	Com-pression Ratio	Oil Pressure @ rpm
2008	CTS	3.6	V	SDI	304@6400	273@5200	3.70x3.37	11.4:1	20@2000
	CTS	3.6	7	SMFI	263@6400	253@3100	3.70x3.37	10.2:1	20@2000
	DTS	4.6	Y	SMFI	275@6000	295@4400	3.66x3.31	10.0:1	35@2000
	DTS	4.6	9	SMFI	292@6300	288@4500	3.66x3.31	10.0:1	35@2000
2009	CTS	3.6	V	SDI	304@6400	273@5200	3.70x3.37	11.4:1	20@2000
	CTS	3.6	7	SMFI	263@6400	253@3100	3.70x3.37	10.2:1	20@2000
	DTS	4.6	Y	SMFI	275@6000	295@4400	3.66x3.31	10.0:1	35@2000
	DTS	4.6	9	SMFI	292@6300	288@4500	3.66x3.31	10.0:1	35@2000
	CTS-V	6.2	W	SFI	556@6100	551@3800	4.00x3.62	9.1:1	①

SDI: Sequential Direct Injection

SMFI: Sequential Multi-port Fuel Injection

SFI: Sequential Fuel Injection

① 6psi @ 1000RPM

  18psi @ 2000RPM

  24psi @ 4000RPM

36616_CCTS_C0002

ENGINE TUNE-UP SPECIFICATIONS

Year	Engine Displacement Liters	Engine VIN	Spark Plug Gap (in.)	Ignition Timing (deg.)	Fuel Pump (psi)	Idle Speed (rpm)	Valve Clearance In.	Valve Clearance Ex.
2008	3.6	V	0.043	①	NA	①	HYD	HYD
	3.6	7	0.043	①	NA	①	HYD	HYD
	4.6	Y	0.050	①	NA	①	HYD	HYD
	4.6	9	0.050	①	NA	①	HYD	HYD
2009	3.6	V	0.043	①	NA	①	HYD	HYD
	3.6	7	0.043	①	NA	①	HYD	HYD
	4.6	Y	0.050	①	NA	①	HYD	HYD
	4.6	9	0.050	①	NA	①	HYD	HYD
	6.2	W	0.040	①	NA	①	HYD	HYD

NOTE: The Vehicle Emission Control Information label often reflects specification changes made during production.

The label figures must be used if they differ from those in this chart.

HYD: Hydraulic

NA: Information not available

① Refer to Vehicle Emission Control Information label

36616_CCTS_C0003

CAPACITIES

Year	Model	Engine Displacement Liters	Engine VIN	Engine Oil with Filter (qts.)	Transmission (pts.) Auto.	Transmission (pts.) Man.	Drive Axle Rear (pts.)	Fuel Tank (gal.)	Cooling System (qts.)
2008	CTS	3.6	V	6.0	13.4	3.8	2.2	18.0	10.6
	CTS	3.6	7	6.0	13.4	3.8	2.2	18.0	10.3
	DTS	4.6	Y	7.5	14.8	NA	NA	18.5	12.6
	DTS	4.6	9	7.5	14.8	NA	NA	18.5	12.6
2009	CTS	3.6	V	6.0	13.4	3.8	2.2	18.0	10.6
	CTS	3.6	7	6.0	13.4	3.8	2.2	18.0	10.3
	DTS	4.6	Y	7.5	14.8	NA	NA	18.5	12.6
	DTS	4.6	9	7.5	14.8	NA	NA	18.5	12.6
	CTS-V	6.2	W	6.0	13.4	8.0	2.2	18.0	13.4

NOTE: All capacities are approximate. Add fluid gradually and ensure a proper fluid level is obtained.

NA: Information not available

36616_CCTS_C0004

FLUID SPECIFICATIONS

Year	Model	Engine Displacement Liters (VIN)	Engine Oil	Auto. Trans.	Drive Axle	Power Steering Fluid	Brake Master Cylinder
2008	CTS	3.6 (V)	5W-30	DEXRON®-VI ATF Fluid	75W-90 Synthetic	GM Power Steering Fluid	DOT 3
	CTS	3.6 (7)	5W-30	DEXRON®-VI ATF Fluid	75W-90 Synthetic	GM Power Steering Fluid	DOT 3
	DTS	4.6 (Y)	5W-30	DEXRON®-VI ATF Fluid	NA	GM Power Steering Fluid	①
	DTS	4.6 (9)	5W-30	DEXRON®-VI ATF Fluid	NA	GM Power Steering Fluid	①
2009	CTS	3.6 (V)	5W-30	DEXRON®-VI ATF Fluid	75W-90 Synthetic	GM Power Steering Fluid	DOT 3
	CTS	3.6 (7)	5W-30	DEXRON®-VI ATF Fluid	75W-90 Synthetic	GM Power Steering Fluid	DOT 3
	DTS	4.6 (Y)	5W-30	DEXRON®-VI ATF Fluid	NA	GM Power Steering Fluid	DOT 3
	DTS	4.6 (9)	5W-30	DEXRON®-VI ATF Fluid	NA	GM Power Steering Fluid	DOT 3
	CTS-V	6.2 (W)	5W-30	DEXRON®-VI ATF Fluid	75W-90 Synthetic	GM Power Steering Fluid	DOT 3

① Delco Supreme 11 Brake Fluid or DOT-3 equivalent

DOT: Department Of Transportation

NA: Information Not Available

36616_CCTS_C0005

VALVE SPECIFICATIONS

Year	Engine Displacement Liters	Engine VIN	Seat Angle (deg.)	Face Angle (deg.)	Spring Test Pressure (lbs. @ in.)	Spring Installed Height (in.)	Stem-to-Guide Clearance (in.) Intake	Stem-to-Guide Clearance (in.) Exhaust	Stem Diameter (in.) Intake	Stem Diameter (in.) Exhaust
2008	3.6	V	45	44.25	61@1.378	1.378	0.0010-0.0026	0.0014-0.0030	0.2344-0.2352	0.2341-0.2348
	3.6	7	45	44.25	61@1.378	1.378	0.0010-0.0026	0.0014-0.0030	0.2344-0.2352	0.2341-0.2348
	4.6	Y	45.75	45	52.4@1.378	1.378	0.0011-0.0027	0.0020-0.0039	0.2331-0.2339	0.2331-0.2339
	4.6	9	45.75	45	52.5@1.378	1.378	0.0011-0.0027	0.0020-0.0039	0.2331-0.2339	0.2331-0.2339
2009	3.6	V	45	44.25	61@1.378	1.378	0.0010-0.0026	0.0014-0.0030	0.2344-0.2352	0.2341-0.2348
	3.6	7	45	44.25	61@1.378	1.378	0.0010-0.0026	0.0014-0.0030	0.2344-0.2352	0.2341-0.2348
	4.6	Y	45.75	45	52.4@1.378	1.378	0.0011-0.0027	0.0020-0.0039	0.2331-0.2339	0.2331-0.2339
	4.6	9	45.75	45	52.5@1.378	1.378	0.0011-0.0027	0.0020-0.0039	0.2331-0.2339	0.2331-0.2339
	6.2	W	45	45	90@1.800	1.800	0.0010-0.0026	0.0010-0.0026	0.3130-0.3140	0.3130-0.3140

36616_CCTS_C0006

CAMSHAFT AND BEARING SPECIFICATIONS

All measurements are given in inches.

Year	Engine Displacement Liters	Engine VIN	Journal Diameter	Brg. Oil Clearance	Shaft End-play	Runout	Journal Bore	Lobe Lift	
								Intake	Exhaust
2008	3.6	V	①	0.0016-0.0033	0.0018-0.0085	②	③	1.6687-1.6805	1.6703-1.6821
	3.6	7	①	0.0016-0.0033	0.0018-0.0085	②	③	1.6687-1.6805	1.6703-1.6821
	4.6	Y	1.0610-1.0619	0.0020-0.0030	0.0050-0.0087	0.002	NA	0.2421	0.2339
	4.6	9	1.0610-1.0619	0.0020-0.0030	0.0050-0.0087	0.002	NA	0.2173	0.2168
2009	3.6	V	①	0.0016-0.0033	0.0018-0.0085	②	③	1.6687-1.6805	1.6703-1.6821
	3.6	7	①	0.0016-0.0033	0.0018-0.0085	②	③	1.6687-1.6805	1.6703-1.6821
	4.6	Y	1.0610-1.0619	0.0020-0.0030	0.0050-0.0087	0.002	NA	0.2421	0.2339
	4.6	9	1.0610-1.0619	0.0020-0.0030	0.0050-0.0087	0.002	NA	0.2421	0.2339
	6.2	W	2.1640-2.1660	0.0009-0.0038	0.0010-0.0012	0.002	2.1678-2.1688	0.2830	0.2830

NA: Information not available

① Front Journal Number 1: 1.3754 - 1.3764 in.
 Middle and Rear Journals Number 2 - 4: 1.0605 - 1.0614 in.

③ Front Number 1: 1.3779-1.3787 in.
 Middle and Rear Number 2-4: 1.0630-1.0638 in.

② Front / Rear Number 1 & 4: 0.0010 in.
 Middle Numbers 2 & 3: 0.0020 in.

36616_CCTS_C0007

CRANKSHAFT AND CONNECTING ROD SPECIFICATIONS

All measurements are given in inches.

Year	Engine Displacement Liters	Engine VIN	Crankshaft				Connecting Rod		
			Main Brg. Journal Dia.	Main Brg. Oil Clearance	Shaft End-play	Thrust on No.	Journal Diameter	Oil Clearance	Side Clearance
2008	3.6	V	2.6768-2.6775	0.0004-0.0024	0.0039-0.0130	2	2.2044-2.2050	0.0004-0.0028	0.0037-0.0140
	3.6	7	2.6768-2.6775	0.0004-0.0024	0.0039-0.0130	2	2.2044-2.2050	0.0004-0.0028	0.0037-0.0140
	4.6	Y	2.5335-2.5341	0.0006-0.0025	0.0020-0.0197	3	2.1239-2.1245	0.0010-0.0030	0.0079-0.0197
	4.6	9	2.5335-2.5341	0.0006-0.0025	0.0020-0.0197	3	2.1239-2.1245	0.0010-0.0030	0.0079-0.0197
2009	3.6	V	2.6768-2.6775	0.0004-0.0024	0.0039-0.0130	2	2.2044-2.2050	0.0004-0.0028	0.0037-0.0140
	3.6	7	2.6768-2.6775	0.0004-0.0024	0.0039-0.0130	2	2.2044-2.2050	0.0004-0.0028	0.0037-0.0140
	4.6	Y	2.5335-2.5341	0.0006-0.0025	0.0020-0.0197	3	2.1239-2.1245	0.0010-0.0030	0.0079-0.0197
	4.6	9	2.5335-2.5341	0.0006-0.0025	0.0020-0.0197	3	2.1239-2.1245	0.0010-0.0030	0.0079-0.0197
	6.2	W	2.5580-2.5590	0.0008-0.0025	0.0015-0.0078	3	2.0991-2.0999	0.0009-0.0025	0.0043-0.0200

36616_CCTS_C0008

PISTON AND RING SPECIFICATIONS

All measurements are given in inches.

Year	Engine Displacement Liters	Engine VIN	Piston Clearance	Ring Gap			Ring Side Clearance		
				Top Compression	Bottom Compression	Oil Control	Top Compression	Bottom Compression	Oil Control
2008	3.6	V	0.0010-0.0021	0.0059-0.0118	0.0110-0.0189	0.0059-0.0236	0.0012-0.0026	0.0006-0.0024	0.0012-0.0067
	3.6	7	0.0010-0.0021	0.0059-0.0118	0.0110-0.0189	0.0059-0.0236	0.0012-0.0026	0.0006-0.0024	0.0012-0.0067
	4.6	Y	0.0008-0.0020	0.0098-0.0157	0.0138-0.0020	0.0098-0.0299	0.0016-0.0037	0.0016-0.0037	①
	4.6	9	0.0008-0.0020	0.0098-0.0157	0.0138-0.0020	0.0098-0.0299	0.0016-0.0037	0.0016-0.0037	①
2009	3.6	V	0.0010-0.0021	0.0059-0.0118	0.0110-0.0189	0.0059-0.0236	0.0012-0.0026	0.0006-0.0024	0.0012-0.0067
	3.6	7	0.0010-0.0021	0.0059-0.0118	0.0110-0.0189	0.0059-0.0236	0.0012-0.0026	0.0006-0.0024	0.0012-0.0067
	4.6	Y	0.0008-0.0020	0.0098-0.0157	0.0138-0.0020	0.0098-0.0299	0.0016-0.0037	0.0016-0.0037	①
	4.6	9	0.0008-0.0020	0.0098-0.0157	0.0138-0.0020	0.0098-0.0299	0.0016-0.0037	0.0016-0.0037	①
	6.2	W	0.0028	0.0090-0.0196 ②	0.0173-0.0300 ②	0.0070-0.0320 ②	0.0016-0.0034	0.0016-0.0031	0.0005-0.0078

① None - Side Sealing

② Measured in Cylinder Bore

36616_CCTS_C0009

TORQUE SPECIFICATIONS
All readings in ft. lbs.

Year	Engine Displacement Liters	Engine VIN	Cylinder Head Bolts	Main Bearing Bolts	Rod Bearing Bolts	Crankshaft Damper Bolts	Flywheel Bolts	Manifold Intake	Manifold Exhaust	Spark Plugs	Oil Pan Drain Plug
2008	3.6	V	①	②	③	④	⑤	17	18	15	15
	3.6	7	⑥	②	③	④	⑤	17	18	15	15
	4.6	Y	⑥	⑦	③	⑧	⑨	⑩	18	11	15
	4.6	9	⑥	⑦	③	⑧	⑨	⑩	18	11	15
2009	3.6	V	①	②	③	④	⑤	17	18	15	15
	3.6	7	⑥	②	③	④	⑤	17	18	15	15
	4.6	Y	⑥	⑦	③	⑧	⑨	⑩	18	11	15
	4.6	9	⑥	⑦	③	⑧	⑨	⑩	18	11	15
	6.2	W	⑪	⑫	⑬	⑭	⑮	⑯	⑰	11	15

① M11 bolts:
Step 1: 22 ft. lbs.
Step 2: Rotate 150 degrees
M8 bolts:
Step 1: 11 ft. lbs.
Step 2: Rotate 75 degrees

⑤ Step 1: 22 ft. lbs.
Step 2: Rotate 45 degrees

⑨ Step 1: 22 ft. lbs.
Step 2: Rotate 50 degrees

⑬ Step 1: 15 ft. lbs.
Step 2: Rotate 85 degrees

⑰ Step 1: 11 ft. lbs.
Step 2: 15 ft. lbs.

② Inner:
Step 1: 15 ft. lbs.
Step 2: Rotate 80 degrees
Outer:
Step 1: 10 ft. lbs.
Step 2: Rotate 110 degrees
Side:
Step 1: 22 ft. lbs.
Step 2: Rotate 60 degrees

⑥ Step 1: 22 ft. lbs.
Step 2: Rotate 70 degrees
Step 3: Rotate 60 degrees
Step 4: Rotate 45 degrees

⑩ Step 1: 89 inch lbs.

⑭ Step 1: 110 ft. lbs.
Step 2: Loosen 360 degrees
Step 2: 37 ft. lbs.
Step 2: Tighten 230 degrees

③ Step 1: 22 ft. lbs.
Step 2: Back off to zero
Step 3: 18 ft. lbs.
Step 4: Rotate to 110 degrees

⑦ Step 1: M11 bolts to 15 ft. lbs.
Step 2: Rotate 65 degrees
Step 3: M8 bolts to 22 ft. lbs.

⑪ Step 1: M11 bolts to 37 ft. lbs.
Step 2: M11 bolts plus 80 degrees
Step 3: M11 bolts plus 55 degrees
Step 4: M8 bolts to 22 ft. lbs.

⑮ Step 1: 15 ft. lbs.
Step 2: 37 ft. lbs
Step 2: 74 ft. lbs.

④ Step 1: 74 ft. lbs.
Step 2: Rotate 150 degrees

⑧ Step 1: 37 ft. lbs.
Step 2: Rotate 150 degrees

⑫ Inner:
Step 1: 15 ft. lbs.
Step 2: Rotate 80 degrees
Outer:
Step 1: 15 ft. lbs.
Step 2: Rotate 51 degrees
Side:
Step 1: 18 ft. lbs.

⑯ Step 1: 44 ft. lbs.
Step 2: 89 inch lbs.

36616_CCTS_C0010

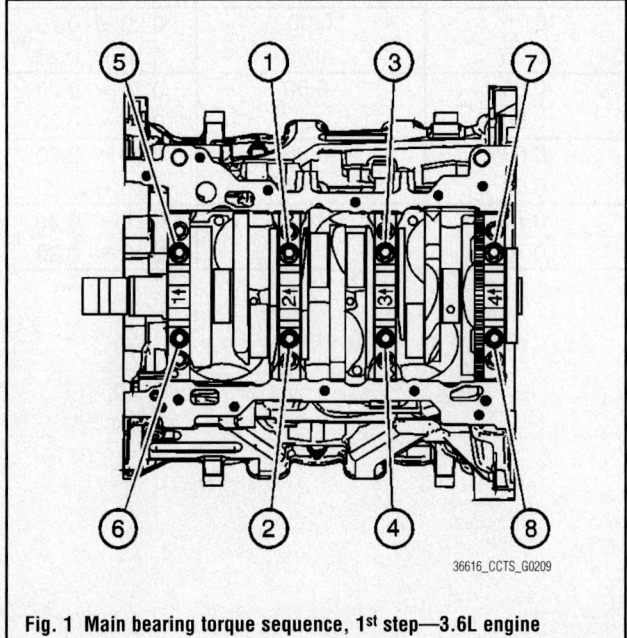

Fig. 1 Main bearing torque sequence, 1st step—3.6L engine

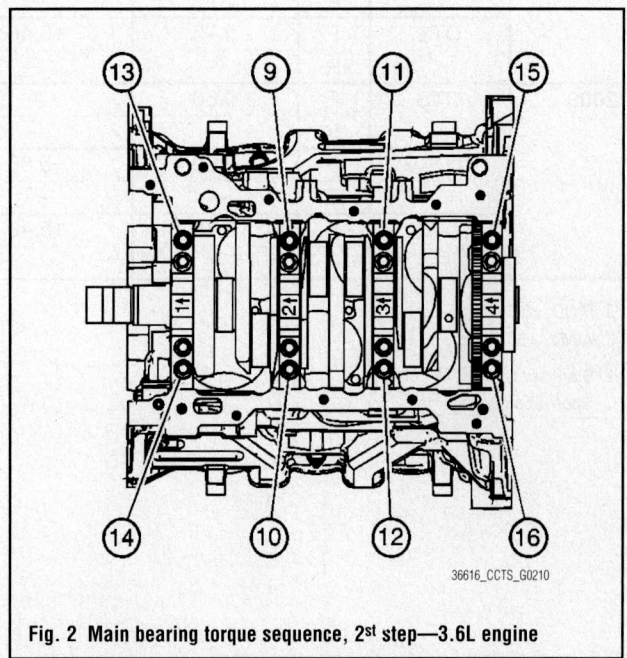

Fig. 2 Main bearing torque sequence, 2nd step—3.6L engine

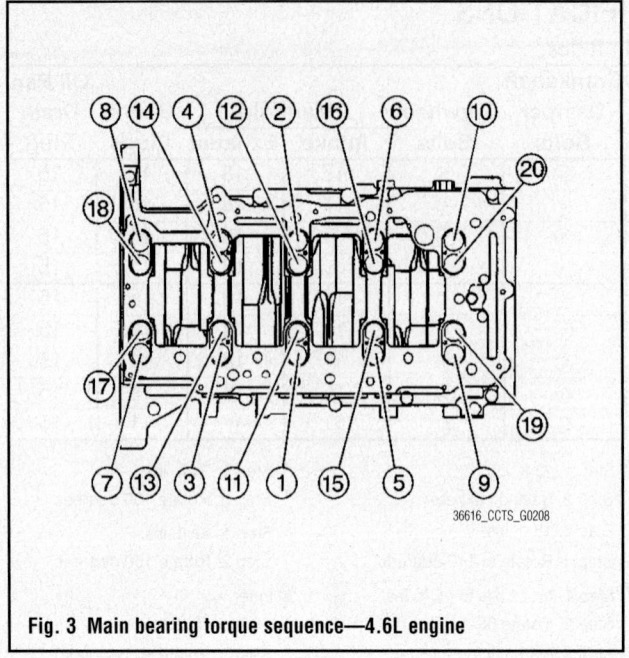

Fig. 3 Main bearing torque sequence—4.6L engine

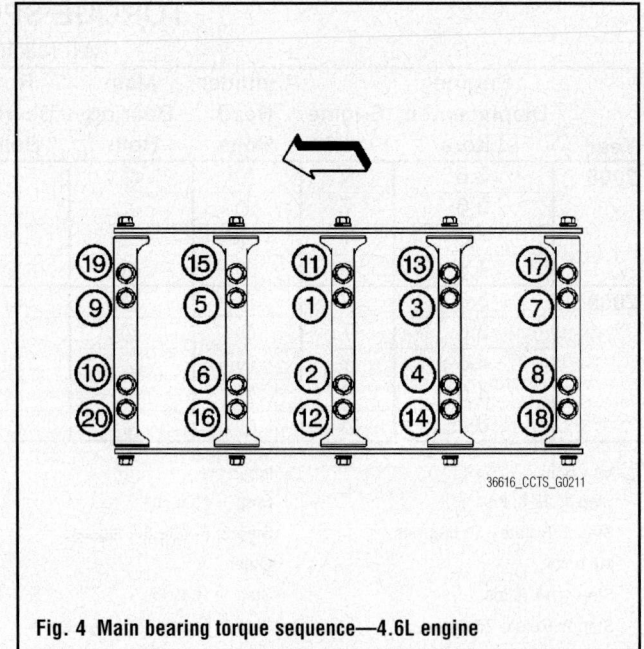

Fig. 4 Main bearing torque sequence—4.6L engine

WHEEL ALIGNMENT

Year	Model		Caster Range (+/-Deg.)	Caster Preferred Setting (Deg.)	Camber Range (+/-Deg.)	Camber Preferred Setting (Deg.)	Toe-in (in.)
2008	CTS	F	0.60	①	0.60	-0.50	0.20 +/- 0.20
		R	—	—	0.60	②	0.20 +/- 0.20
	DTS	F	0.75	+5.40	0.75	0.00	0.20 +/- 0.20
		R	—	—	0.75	-0.05	0.10 +/- 0.20
2009	CTS	F	0.60	①	0.60	-0.50	0.20 +/- 0.20
		R	—	—	0.60	②	0.20 +/- 0.20
	CTS-V	F	0.60	+5.80	0.60	-0.90	0.20 +/- 0.20
		R	—	—	0.60	-1.40	0.20 +/- 0.20
	DTS	F	0.75	+5.40	0.75	0.00	0.20 +/- 0.20
		R	—	—	0.75	-0.05	0.10 +/- 0.20

① RWD: +5.60 deg.
   AWD: +5.40 deg.

② Standard Shocks: +1.00 deg.
   Sport Shocks: -1.4 deg.

36616_CCTS_C0011

TIRE, WHEEL AND BALL JOINT SPECIFICATIONS

Year	Model	OEM Tires		Tire Pressures (psi)		Wheel Size	Ball Joint Inspection	Wheel Lug Nut Torque (ft. lbs.)
		Standard	Optional	Front	Rear			
2008	CTS	P235/55R17	NA	①	①	NA	0.125 in. ②	140
	DTS	P235/55R17	P245/50R18	①	①	NA	0.063 in. ②	103
2009	CTS	P235/55R17	NA	①	①	NA	0.125 in. ②	140
	CTS-V	③	NA	①	①	NA	0.125 in. ②	140
	DTS	P235/55SR17	P245/50HR18	①	①	NA	0.063 in. ②	103

NA: Information not available

OEM: Original Equipment Manufacturer

PSI: Pounds Per Square Inch

① See placard on vehicle

② Replace if vertical or horizontal movement exceeds specification

③ Front: P255/40ZR19

   Rear: P285/35ZR19

36616_CCTS_C0012

BRAKE SPECIFICATIONS
All measurements in inches unless noted

Year	Model		Brake Disc			Minimum Lining Thickness	Brake Caliper	
			Original Thickness	Minimum Thickness	Maximum Runout		Bracket Bolts (ft. lbs.)	Mounting Bolts (ft. lbs.)
2008	CTS	F	1.181	1.122	0.002	NA	166	20
		R	0.906	0.846	0.002	NA	96	20
	DTS	F	1.181	1.126	0.002	NA	133	27
		R	0.472	0.413	0.002	NA	94	25
2009	CTS	F	1.181	1.122	0.002	NA	170	46
		R	0.906	0.846	0.002	NA	100	44
	CTS-V	F	1.338	1.259	0.002	NA	129	NA
		R	1.102	1.023	0.002	NA	96	NA
	DTS	F	1.181	1.126	0.002	NA	133	27
		R	0.472	0.413	0.002	NA	94	25

F: Front

R: Rear

NA: Information not available

36616_CCTS_C0013

MAINTENANCE SERVICE SCHEDULE
Cadillac CTS, CTS-V, DTS

When the CHANGE ENGINE OIL light appears, certain services and inspections are required.

Service	Maintenance
Change the engine oil and filter. Reset the oil life system.	✓
Visually inspect the vehicle for leaks or damage. A fluid loss in the vehicle system could indicate a problem. Inspected, repair and add fluid to the system if necessary.	✓
Inspect the engine air cleaner filter. If necessary, replace the filter.	✓
Rotate the tires. Inspect the tire inflation pressures and the tire wear.	✓
Visually inspect the brake lines and hoses for proper hook-up, binding, leaks, cracks, chafing, etc. Inspect the disc brake pads for wear and the rotors for surface condition. Inspect the drum brake linings for wear or cracks. Inspect other brake parts, including drums, wheel cylinders, calipers, parking brake, etc. Inspect the parking brake adjustment.	✓
Inspect the engine coolant and the windshield washer fluid levels. Add fluid as needed.	✓
Inspect the suspension and steering components. Inspect the front and rear suspension and the steering system for damaged, loose or missing parts, or signs of wear. Inspect the power steering lines and the hoses for proper hook-up, binding, leaks, cracks,	✓
Visually inspect the coolant hoses and replace the hoses if they are cracked, swollen or deteriorated. Inspect all pipes, fittings and clamps; replace with GM parts as needed. To help ensure proper operation, a pressure test of the cooling system and pressure cap and cleaning the outside of the radiator and air conditioning condenser is recommended at least once a year.	✓
Inspect the wiper blades for wear, cracking or contamination. Replace any blades that are worn or cracking.	✓
Inspect the restraint system components. Make sure the safety belt reminder light and safety belt assemblies are working properly. Look for any other loose or damaged safety belt system parts. Replace any torn or frayed belts.	✓
Lubricate the body components.	✓
Inspect the front and rear suspension and the steering system for damaged, loose or missing parts, or signs of wear. Inspect power steering lines and hoses for proper hook-up, binding, leaks, cracks, chafing, etc.	✓
Inspect the throttle system for interference or binding and for damaged or missing parts. Replace the parts as needed. Replace any components that have high effort or excessive wear. Do not lubricate the accelerator or the cruise control cables.	✓
Replace the passenger compartment air filter.	✓

36616_CCTS_C0014

ADDITIONAL MAINTENANCE SERVICES
Cadillac CTS, CTS-V, DTS

TO BE SERVICED	TYPE OF SERVICE	VEHICLE MILEAGE INTERVAL (x1000)					
		25	50	75	100	125	150
Fuel system	I	✓	✓	✓	✓	✓	✓
Exhaust system	I	✓	✓	✓	✓	✓	✓
Engine air cleaner	R		✓		✓		✓
Passenger compartment air filter	R	✓	✓	✓	✓	✓	✓
Automatic transmission fluid/filter	R				✓		
6-speed manual transmission fluid (CTS-V)	R		✓		✓		✓
Transfer case fluid (AWD)	R				✓		
Hydraulic clutch fluid (CTS-V)	R	✓	✓	✓	✓	✓	✓
Brake fluid (CTS-V)	R	✓	✓	✓	✓	✓	✓
Spark plugs	R				✓		
Intercooler system service (6.2L engine)	S/I						✓
Engine accessory drive belt	I						✓
Supercharger drive belt, if equipped	I				✓		

R: Replace   S/I: Inspect and service, if necessary

36616_CCTS_C0015

PRECAUTIONS

Before servicing any vehicle, please be sure to read all of the following precautions, which deal with personal safety, prevention of component damage, and important points to take into consideration when servicing a motor vehicle:

• Never open, service or drain the radiator or cooling system when the engine is hot; serious burns can occur from the steam and hot coolant.

• Observe all applicable safety precautions when working around fuel. Whenever servicing the fuel system, always work in a well-ventilated area. Do not allow fuel spray or vapors to come in contact with a spark, open flame, or excessive heat (a hot drop light, for example). Keep a dry chemical fire extinguisher near the work area. Always keep fuel in a container specifically designed for fuel storage; also, always properly seal fuel containers to avoid the possibility of fire or explosion. Refer to the additional fuel system precautions later in this section.

• Fuel injection systems often remain pressurized, even after the engine has been turned **OFF**. The fuel system pressure must be relieved before disconnecting any fuel lines. Failure to do so may result in fire and/or personal injury.

• Brake fluid often contains polyglycol ethers and polyglycols. Avoid contact with the eyes and wash your hands thoroughly after handling brake fluid. If you do get brake fluid in your eyes, flush your eyes with clean, running water for 15 minutes. If eye irritation persists, or if you have taken brake fluid internally, IMMEDIATELY seek medical assistance.

• The EPA warns that prolonged contact with used engine oil may cause a number of skin disorders, including cancer. You should make every effort to minimize your exposure to used engine oil. Protective gloves should be worn when changing oil. Wash your hands and any other exposed skin areas as soon as possible after exposure to used engine oil. Soap and water, or waterless hand cleaner should be used.

• All new vehicles are now equipped with an air bag system, often referred to as a Supplemental Restraint System (SRS) or Supplemental Inflatable Restraint (SIR) system. The system must be disabled before performing service on or around system components, steering column, instrument panel components, wiring and sensors. Failure to follow safety and disabling procedures could result in accidental air bag deployment, possible personal injury and unnecessary system repairs.

• Always wear safety goggles when working with, or around, the air bag system. When carrying a non-deployed air bag, be sure the bag and trim cover are pointed away from your body. When placing a non-deployed air bag on a work surface, always face the bag and trim cover upward, away from the surface. This will reduce the motion of the module if it is accidentally deployed. Refer to the additional air bag system precautions later in this section.

• Clean, high quality brake fluid from a sealed container is essential to the safe and proper operation of the brake system. You should always buy the correct type of brake fluid for your vehicle. If the brake fluid becomes contaminated, completely flush the system with new fluid. Never reuse any brake fluid. Any brake fluid that is removed from the system should be discarded. Also, do not allow any brake fluid to come in contact with a painted surface; it will damage the paint.

• Never operate the engine without the proper amount and type of engine oil; doing so WILL result in severe engine damage.

• Timing belt maintenance is extremely important. Many models utilize an interference-type, non-freewheeling engine. If the timing belt breaks, the valves in the cylinder head may strike the pistons, causing potentially serious (also time-consuming and expensive) engine damage. Refer to the maintenance interval charts for the recommended replacement interval for the timing belt, and to the timing belt section for belt replacement and inspection.

• Disconnecting the negative battery cable on some vehicles may interfere with the functions of the on-board computer system(s) and may require the computer to undergo a relearning process once the negative battery cable is reconnected.

• When servicing drum brakes, only disassemble and assemble one side at a time, leaving the remaining side intact for reference.

• Only an MVAC-trained, EPA-certified automotive technician should service the air conditioning system or its components.

BRAKES

GENERAL INFORMATION

PRECAUTIONS

• Certain components within the ABS system are not intended to be serviced or repaired individually.

• Do not use rubber hoses or other parts not specifically specified for and ABS system. When using repair kits, replace all parts included in the kit. Partial or incorrect repair may lead to functional problems and require the replacement of components.

• Lubricate rubber parts with clean, fresh brake fluid to ease assembly. Do not use shop air to clean parts; damage to rubber components may result.

• Use only DOT 3 brake fluid from an unopened container.

• If any hydraulic component or line is removed or replaced, it may be necessary to bleed the entire system.

• A clean repair area is essential. Always clean the reservoir and cap thoroughly before removing the cap. The slightest amount of dirt in the fluid may plug an orifice and impair the system function. Perform repairs after components have been thoroughly cleaned; use only denatured alcohol to clean components. Do not allow ABS components to come into contact with any substance containing mineral oil; this includes used shop rags.

• The Anti-Lock control unit is a microprocessor similar to other computer units in the vehicle. Ensure that the ignition switch is **OFF** before removing or installing controller harnesses. Avoid static electricity discharge at or near the controller.

ANTI-LOCK BRAKE SYSTEM (ABS)

• If any arc welding is to be done on the vehicle, the control unit should be unplugged before welding operations begin.

WHEEL SPEED SENSORS

REMOVAL & INSTALLATION

CTS & CTS-V

Front

See Figure 5.

1. Raise and safely support the vehicle.
2. Remove the front wheel.
3. Disconnect the wheel speed sensor electrical connector.
4. Remove the wheel speed sensor wire harness clips from the vehicle frame, RWD models only.

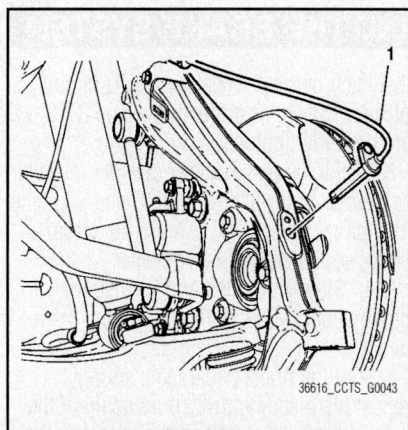

Fig. 5 Remove the wheel speed sensor (1) from the steering knuckle—2008–09 CTS & CTS-V RWD Models shown

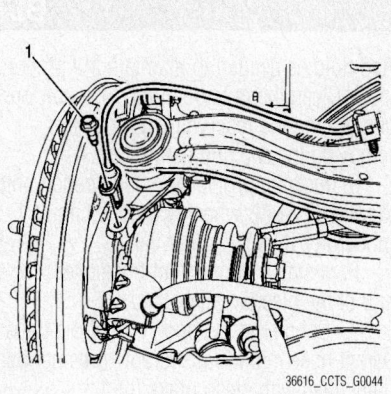

Fig. 6 Remove the wheel speed sensor bolt (1) and speed sensor from the knuckle—2008–09 CTS & CTS-V models

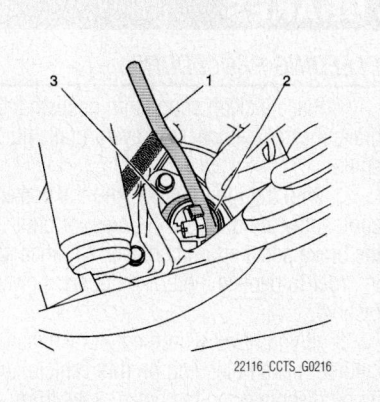

Fig. 8 Wheel speed sensor installation with special tool J 44252—2008–09 DTS Models.

5. Remove the wheel speed sensor wire harness clip from the stabilizer bar bracket, AWD models only.

6. Remove the wheel speed sensor wire harness clip from the steering knuckle.

7. Thoroughly clean the wheel speed sensor mounting area of the steering knuckle of any dirt and debris.

8. Remove the wheel speed sensor bolt.

9. Remove the wheel speed sensor from the steering knuckle.

10. Installation is the reverse order of removal. Tighten the sensor mounting bolt to 80 inch lbs. (9 Nm).

Rear

See Figure 6.

1. Raise and safely support the vehicle.

2. Remove the rear wheel.

3. Remove the wheel speed sensor wire harness clips from the upper control arm and vehicle frame.

4. Disconnect the wheel speed sensor electrical connector.

5. Thoroughly clean the wheel speed sensor mounting area of the suspension

6. Remove the wheel speed sensor bolt and the wheel speed sensor.

7. Installation is the reverse order of removal. Tighten the sensor mounting bolts to 80 inch lbs. (9 Nm).

DTS

Rear

See Figures 7 and 8.

1. Before servicing the vehicle, refer to the Precautions Section.

2. Turn **OFF** the ignition.

3. Raise the vehicle.

4. Remove the rear wheel.

5. Remove the wheel speed sensor connector (1) from the wheel speed sensor (2).

6. Remove and discard the wheel speed sensor (2).

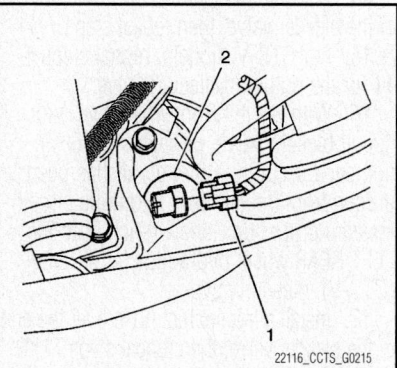

Fig. 7 Rear ABS wheel speed sensor (2), connector (1)—2008–09 DTS Models.

➡ Do not reuse the wheel speed sensor after it has been removed.

To install:

➡ The connector of the wheel speed sensor must point toward the brake caliper.

7. Insert the wheel speed sensor (1) onto the hub assembly.

8. Install the ring (2) of the J 44252 installer onto the wheel speed sensor.

9. Insert the J 44252 (1) onto the wheel speed sensor (3).

10. Pull the J 44252 (1) to seat the wheel speed sensor (3).

11. Test the output of the new wheel speed sensor as follows:

a. Connect the DMM to the wheel speed sensor connector.

b. Set the DMM to AC voltage.

c. By hand, spin the wheel.

d. For a proper wheel speed sensor signal, the AC voltage will measure greater than 100 mV while the wheel is spinning.

12. Install the wheel speed sensor connector (1) to the wheel speed sensor.

13. Install the rear wheel.

14. Lower the vehicle.

BLEEDING PROCEDURE

1. Place a clean shop cloth beneath the brake master cylinder to prevent brake fluid spills.

2. With the ignition OFF and the brakes cool, apply the brakes 3-5 times, or until the brake pedal effort increases significantly, in order to deplete the brake booster power reserve.

3. If you have performed a brake master cylinder bench bleeding on this vehicle, or if you disconnected the brake pipes from the master cylinder, you must perform the following steps:

  a. Ensure that the brake master cylinder reservoir is full to the maximum-fill level. If necessary, add Delco Supreme 11®, or equivalent DOT-3 brake fluid from a clean, sealed brake fluid container. If removal of the reservoir cap and diaphragm is necessary, clean the outside of the reservoir on and around the cap prior to removal.

  b. With the rear brake pipe installed securely to the master cylinder, loosen and separate the front brake pipe from the front port of the brake master cylinder.

  c. Allow a small amount of brake fluid to gravity bleed from the open port of the master cylinder.

  d. Reconnect the brake pipe to the master cylinder port and tighten securely.

  e. Have an assistant slowly depress the brake pedal fully and maintain steady pressure on the pedal.

  f. Loosen the same brake pipe to purge air from the open port of the master cylinder.

  g. Tighten the brake pipe, then have the assistant slowly release the brake pedal.

  h. Wait 15 seconds, then repeat until all air is purged from the same port of the master cylinder.

  i. With the front brake pipe installed securely to the master cylinder - after all air has been purged from the front port of the master cylinder - loosen and separate the rear brake pipe from the master cylinder, then repeat steps 3-8.

  j. After completing the final master cylinder port bleeding procedure, ensure that both of the brake pipe-to-master cylinder fittings are properly tightened.

4. Fill the brake master cylinder reservoir with Delco Supreme 11®, or equivalent DOT-3 brake fluid from a clean, sealed brake fluid container. Ensure that the brake master cylinder reservoir remains at least half-full during this bleeding procedure.

Add fluid as needed to maintain the proper level. Clean the outside of the reservoir on and around the reservoir cap prior to removing the cap and diaphragm.

5. Install a proper box-end wrench onto the RIGHT REAR wheel hydraulic circuit, inboard (CTS-V), bleeder valve.

6. Install a transparent hose over the end of the bleeder valve.

7. Submerge the open end of the transparent hose into a transparent container partially filled with clean brake fluid.

8. Have an assistant slowly depress the brake pedal fully and maintain steady pressure on the pedal.

9. Loosen the bleeder valve to purge air from the wheel hydraulic circuit.

10. Tighten the bleeder valve, then have the assistant slowly release the brake pedal.

11. Wait 15 seconds, then repeat until all air is purged from the same wheel hydraulic circuit.

12. For CTS-V models, repeat steps 5-11 for the outboard bleeder valve.

13. With the right rear wheel hydraulic circuit bleeder valve, or valves (CTS-V), tightened securely - after all air has been purged from the right rear hydraulic circuit - install a proper box-end wrench onto the LEFT FRONT wheel hydraulic circuit, inner (CTS-V), bleeder valve.

14. Install a transparent hose over the end of the bleeder valve, then repeat steps 7-11.

15. For CTS-V models, repeat steps 5-11 for the outboard bleeder valve.

16. With the left front wheel hydraulic circuit bleeder valve, or valves (CTS-V), tightened securely - after all air has been purged from the left front hydraulic circuit - install a proper box-end wrench onto the LEFT REAR wheel hydraulic circuit, inner (CTS-V), bleeder valve.

17. Install a transparent hose over the end of the bleeder valve, then repeat steps 7-11.

18. For CTS-V models, repeat steps 5-11 for the outboard bleeder valve.

19. With the left rear wheel hydraulic circuit bleeder valve, or valves (CTS-V), tightened securely - after all air has been purged from the left rear hydraulic circuit - install a proper box-end wrench onto the RIGHT FRONT wheel hydraulic circuit, inner (CTS-V), bleeder valve.

20. Install a transparent hose over the end of the bleeder valve, then repeat steps 7-11.

21. For CTS-V models, repeat steps 5-11 for the outboard bleeder valve.

22. After completing the final wheel hydraulic circuit bleeding procedure, ensure

that each of the 4 wheel hydraulic circuit bleeder valves, or 8 bleeder valves (CTS-V), are properly tightened.

23. Fill the brake master cylinder reservoir to the maximum-fill level with Delco Supreme 11®, or equivalent DOT-3 brake fluid from a clean, sealed brake fluid container.

24. Slowly depress and release the brake pedal. Observe the feel of the brake pedal.

25. If the brake pedal feels spongy, repeat the bleeding procedure again. If the brake pedal still feels spongy after repeating the bleeding procedure, perform the following steps:

26. Inspect the brake system for external leaks.

27. Pressure bleed the hydraulic brake system in order to purge any air that may still be trapped in the system.

28. Turn the ignition key ON, with the engine OFF. Check to see if the brake system warning lamp remains illuminated.

29. DO NOT allow the vehicle to be driven until it is diagnosed and repaired.

30. If the brake system warning lamp remains illuminated, diagnose the cause and repair as necessary.

BLEEDING THE ABS SYSTEM

1. Raise and safely support the vehicle.

2. Remove all four wheels.

3. Inspect the brake system for leaks and visual damage.

4. Lower the vehicle.

5. Install a scan tool.

6. Turn the ignition ON, with the engine OFF.

7. With the scan tool, establish communications with the ABS system. Select Special Functions. Select Automated Bleed from the Special Functions menu.

8. Following the directions given on the scan tool, pressure bleed the base brake system. For additional information, refer to the following section, "Bleeding the Brake System, Bleeding Procedure."

9. Follow the scan tool directions until the desired brake pedal height is achieved.

10. If the bleed procedure is aborted, a malfunction exists. Perform the following steps before resuming the bleed procedure:

- If a Diagnostic Trouble Code (DTC) is detected, diagnose and repair the appropriate DTC.
- If the brake pedal feels spongy, perform the conventional brake

bleed procedure again. For additional information, refer to the following section, "Bleeding the Brake System, Bleeding Procedure."

11. When the desired pedal height is achieved, press the brake pedal to inspect for firmness.

12. Remove the scan tool.

13. Install all four wheels.

14. Lower the vehicle and inspect the brake fluid level.

15. Road test the vehicle while inspecting that the pedal remains high and firm.

BRAKES

FRONT DISC BRAKES

BRAKE CALIPER

REMOVAL & INSTALLATION

2008–09 CTS

1. Before servicing the vehicle, refer to the Precautions Section.

2. Disconnect the negative battery cable.

3. If the brake fluid in the cylinder reservoir is above the midpoint, remove brake fluid to the midway of the cylinder reservoir.

4. Raise and safely support the vehicle.

5. Remove the front wheel.

6. Using a large C-clamp against the outer pad and the rear of the brake caliper body.

7. Compress the caliper piston into the caliper to provide clearance during removal.

8. Place a catch pan under the caliper.

9. Remove the caliper mounting bolts and remove the caliper from the vehicle.

10. Disconnect the brake hose from the caliper. Cap the line to prevent excessive fluid loss or contamination.

11. Remove the caliper assembly.

12. Inspect the mounting bolts; sleeves and boots for wear and/or damage. Replace parts as necessary.

To install:

13. Before installing the caliper, make sure the piston is fully seated in the bore and the brake pads are properly seated.

14. Lubricate the mounting bolt shafts and inner diameter of the sleeves with silicone grease.

15. Install the caliper in the caliper mounting bracket and install the mounting bolts. Torque the mounting bolts to 46 ft. lbs. (63 Nm).

16. Connect the brake hose with the bolt and new gaskets. Torque the brake hose bolt to 37 ft. lbs. (50 Nm).

17. Refill the master cylinder and bleed the brake system.

18. Install the wheel and tire assembly.

19. Connect the negative battery cable.

20. Road test the vehicle for proper brake system operation.

2009 CTS-V

See Figure 9.

1. Before servicing the vehicle, refer to the Precautions Section.

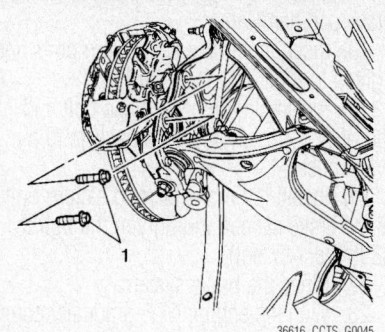

Fig. 9 Remove the caliper mounting bolts—2009 CTS-V Models

2. If the brake fluid level is midway between the maximum-full point and the minimum allowable level, no brake fluid needs to be removed from the reservoir before proceeding.

3. If the brake fluid level is higher than midway between the maximum-full point and the minimum allowable level, remove brake fluid to the midway point before proceeding.

4. Raise and safely support the vehicle.

5. Remove the front wheel.

6. Remove the brake pads. For additional information, refer to the following section, "Disc Brake Pads, Removal & Installation."

7. Remove the brake hose and copper gaskets from the brake caliper. Cap the ine to prevent excessive fluid loss or contamination.

8. Remove the caliper-to-knuckle mounting bolts.

9. Remove the brake caliper.

To install:

10. Apply threadlocker to two-thirds of the threaded length of the caliper to knuckle mounting bolts.

11. Apply a thin coat of high temperature silicone brake lubricant to the brake caliper pin.

12. Install the brake caliper. Tighten the mounting bolts to 129 ft. lbs. (175 Nm).

13. Connect the brake hose with the bolt and new gaskets. Tighten the bolt to 36 ft. lbs. (49 Nm).

14. Install the brake pads.

15. Refill the master cylinder and bleed the brake system.

16. Install the wheel.

17. Road test the vehicle for proper brake system operation.

DTS

JL9 Brake System

See Figure 10.

1. Before servicing the vehicle, refer to the Precautions Section.

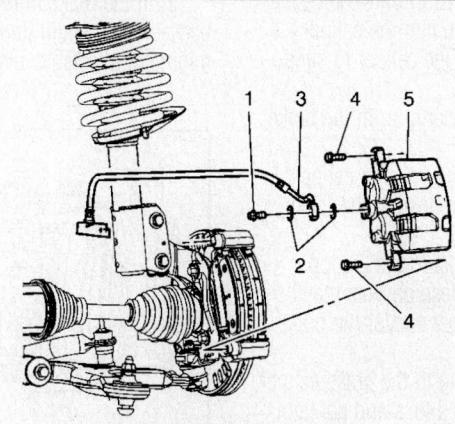

1. Brake hose fitting bolt
2. Brake hose gaskets
3. Brake hose
4. Brake caliper guide pin bolt
5. Brake caliper

Fig. 10 Brake caliper assembly—2008–09 DTS JL9 System

2. Raise and safely support the vehicle.

3. Remove the front wheel.

4. Remove the brake hose fitting bolt and gasket, and cap the brake hose to prevent fluid leakage and contamination.

5. Remove the guide pin bolts and remove the brake caliper assembly.

To install:

6. Install the caliper assembly and tighten the guide pin bolts to 27 ft. lbs (36 Nm).

7. Install the brake hose with new gaskets and tighten the bolt to 30 ft. lbs. (40 Nm).

8. Bleed the brake system.

9. Install the wheel.

10. Road test the vehicle for proper brake system operation.

J55 Brake System

1. Inspect the fluid level in the brake master cylinder reservoir.

2. If the brake fluid level is midway between the maximum-full point and the minimum allowable level, no brake fluid needs to be removed from the reservoir before proceeding.

3. If the brake fluid level is higher than midway between the maximum-full point and the minimum allowable level, remove brake fluid to the midway point before proceeding.

4. Raise and safely support the vehicle.

5. Mark the relationship of the wheel to the axle flange.

6. Remove the front wheel.

7. Install a large C-clamp over the body of the brake caliper with the C-clamp ends against the rear of the caliper body and against the outer brake pads.

8. Tighten the C-clamp until the caliper pistons are compressed into the caliper bores enough to allow the caliper to slide past the brake rotor.

9. Remove the C-clamp from the brake caliper.

10. Remove the brake hose to caliper bolt attaching the brake hose to the brake caliper.

11. Remove and discard the 2 copper brake hose gaskets. These gaskets may be stuck to the brake caliper and/or the brake hose end.

12. Plug the opening in the brake caliper and pipe to prevent fluid loss and contamination.

13. Remove the brake caliper pin bolts.

14. Remove the brake caliper.

To install:

15. If reusing the brake caliper pin bolts and retainers, clean the brake caliper pin

bolts and retainers using denatured alcohol, or equivalent.

16. Dry the brake caliper pin bolts and retainers, using non-lubricated, filtered air.

17. Install the brake caliper over the brake pads and into the brake caliper bracket.

18. Apply a thin coat of high temperature silicone brake lubricant to the brake caliper pin bolts: do NOT apply lubricant to the brake pad hardware.

19. Install the brake caliper pin bolts and tighten to 83 ft. lbs. (113 Nm).

20. Assemble the brake hose bolt and the NEW copper brake hose gaskets to the brake hose.

21. Install the brake hose to caliper bolt to the brake caliper and tighten the bolt to 33 ft. lbs. (45 Nm).

22. Bleed the brake system.

23. With the engine OFF, gradually apply the brake pedal to approximately 2/3 of its travel distance.

24. Slowly release the brake pedal.

25. Wait 15 seconds, then repeat these steps until a firm brake pedal apply is obtained; this will properly seat the brake caliper pistons and brake pads.

26. Install the front wheel and lower the vehicle.

27. Road test the vehicle for proper brake system operation.

DISC BRAKE PADS

REMOVAL & INSTALLATION

2008–09 CTS

See Figure 11.

1. Inspect the fluid level in the brake master cylinder reservoir.

2. If the brake fluid level is midway between the maximum full point and the minimum allowable level, no brake fluid

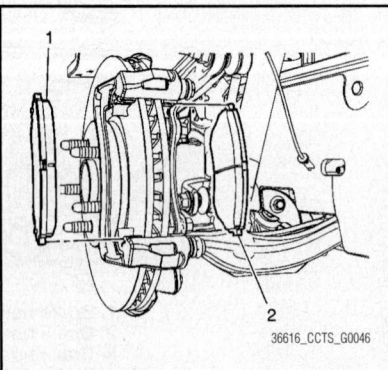

Fig. 11 Removing the outer pad (1) and inner pad (2) and pad springs—2008–09 CTS Models

36616_CCTS_G0046

needs to be removed from the reservoir before proceeding.

3. If the brake fluid level is higher than midway between the maximum full point and the minimum allowable level, remove brake fluid to the midway point before proceeding.

4. Raise and safely support the vehicle.

5. Remove the front wheel.

6. Install a C-clamp against the outer brake pad and the rear of the brake caliper body.

7. Slowly tighten the C-clamp until the brake caliper pistons are compressed into the brake caliper bores.

8. Using a backup wrench on the brake caliper guide pin, remove the brake caliper guide pin bolts.

9. Support the brake caliper assembly with mechanic's wire to prevent damage to the brake hose.

10. Remove the caliper assembly.

11. Remove the brake pads and brake pad springs.

To install:

12. Install the brake pad springs.

13. Install the inner and outer pad.

14. Clean the caliper pin bolts if necessary. Apply threadlocker GM P/N 12345493 (Canadian P/N 10953488), or equivalent to 2/3 of the threaded length of the brake caliper guide pin bolts. Ensure there are no gaps in the threadlocker along the length of the filled area of the bolt. Allow the threadlocker to cure approximately 10 minutes before installation.

15. Install the caliper assembly and tighten the guide pins to 46 ft. lbs. (63 Nm).

16. Install the front wheel.

17. Refill the master cylinder reservoir to the proper level.

18. Road test the vehicle for proper brake system operation.

2009 CTS-V

See Figures 12 and 13.

1. Before servicing the vehicle, refer to the Precautions Section.

2. If the brake fluid level is midway between the maximum-full point and the minimum allowable level, no brake fluid needs to be removed from the reservoir before proceeding.

3. If the brake fluid level is higher than midway between the maximum-full point and the minimum allowable level, remove brake fluid to the midway point before proceeding.

4. Raise and safely support the vehicle.

5. Remove the front wheel.

6. Holding the lower end of the retainer down and using a hammer and

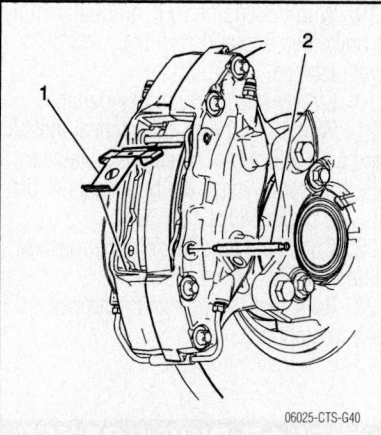

Fig. 12 Holding the lower end of the retainer (1) down and using a hammer and punch carefully tap the lower caliper guide pin (2) inward out of the caliper.–CTS-V Models

punch carefully tap the lower caliper guide pin inward out of the caliper.

7. Rotate the brake pad retainer upward and remove the retainer.

8. Using a hammer and punch tap the upper caliper to brake pad mounting pin inward out of the caliper.

9. Carefully insert a plastic flat-bladed trim tool between the rotor and inboard brake pad.

10. Carefully apply pressure to the inboard brake pad until both caliper inner pistons are fully compressed into the caliper piston bores.

11. Carefully insert a plastic flat-bladed trim tool between the rotor and outboard brake pad.

12. Carefully apply pressure to the outboard brake pad until both caliper outer pistons are fully compressed into the bores.

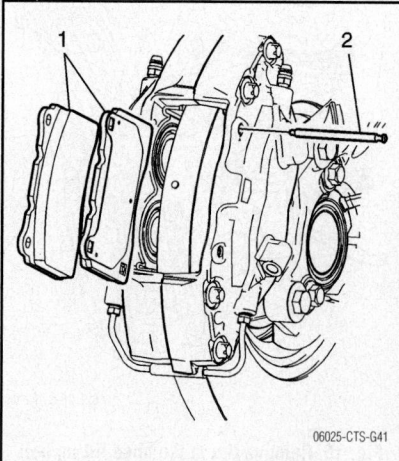

Fig. 13 Upper caliper pin-to-brake pad mounting pin (2)–CTS-V

13. Remove the brake pads from the caliper.

To install:

14. Install the brake pads to the caliper.

15. Install the upper caliper guide pin through the caliper, inner and outer brake pads.

16. Using a hammer and punch seat the upper guide pin to the outer caliper half. Ensure that the caliper guide pin is seated into the outer caliper pin seat.

17. Install the brake pad retainer under the upper caliper pin assembly.

18. Rotate brake pad retainer down.

19. Carefully apply pressure downward on the lower end of the brake pad retainer.

20. Carefully install the lower caliper guide pin through the caliper, inner and outer brake pads.

21. Using a hammer and punch seat the upper guide pin to the outer caliper half. Ensure that the caliper guide pin is seated into the outer caliper pin seat. Ensure that the brake pad retainer is centered retaining both brake pads.

22. Install the front wheel.

23. Pump the brake pedal several times to seat the brake pads.

24. Check the fluid level in the master cylinder and fill as necessary.

25. Road test the vehicle for proper brake operation.

DTS

JL9 Brake System

1. Inspect the fluid level in the brake master cylinder reservoir.

2. If the brake fluid level is midway between the maximum-full point and the minimum allowable level, no brake fluid needs to be removed from the reservoir before proceeding.

3. If the brake fluid level is higher than midway between the maximum-full point and the minimum allowable level, remove brake fluid to the midway point before proceeding.

4. Raise and safely support the vehicle.

5. Remove the front wheel.

6. Install an open end wrench to hold the caliper guide pin in line with the brake caliper while removing or installing the caliper guide pin bolts. DO NOT allow the open end wrench to contact the brake caliper.

➡ **Allowing the open end wrench to contact the brake caliper will cause a pulsation when the brakes are applied.**

7. Rotate the brake caliper up and to the rear until it rests on the mounting bracket and support with heavy mechanics wire or equivalent.

8. Place a block of wood or an old disc brake pad against the brake caliper pistons.

9. Using a suitable tool, slowly compress the brake caliper pistons squarely into the caliper bores.

10. Remove the brake pads.

To install:

➡ **If replacing the brake pads, new spring retainers must be used.**

11. Install the brake pads.

12. Install the brake caliper assembly and tighten the guide pin bolts to 27 ft. lbs. (36 Nm). Ensure the brake caliper guide pin seal is fully seated in the groove of the brake caliper guide pin and the guide pin slides freely in caliper bracket bore.

13. Install the front wheel and lower the vehicle.

14. With the engine OFF, gradually apply the brake pedal to approximately 2/3 of its travel distance.

15. Slowly release the brake pedal.

16. Wait 15 seconds, then repeat these steps until a firm brake pedal is obtained. This will properly seat the brake caliper pistons and brake pads.

17. Check the fluid level in the master cylinder and fill as necessary.

18. Road test the vehicle for proper brake operation.

J55 Brake System

1. Inspect the fluid level in the brake master cylinder reservoir.

2. If the brake fluid level is midway between the maximum-full point and the minimum allowable level, no brake fluid needs to be removed from the reservoir before proceeding.

3. If the brake fluid level is higher than midway between the maximum-full point and the minimum allowable level, remove brake fluid to the midway point before proceeding.

4. Raise and safely support the vehicle.

5. Mark the relationship of the wheel to the axle flange.

6. Remove the front wheel.

7. Install a large C-clamp over the body of the brake caliper with the C-clamp ends against the rear of the caliper body and against the outer brake pads.

8. Tighten the C-clamp until the caliper pistons are compressed into the caliper bores enough to allow the caliper to slide past the brake rotor.

9. Remove the C-clamp from the brake caliper.

10. Remove the brake caliper pin bolts.

11. Pivot the brake caliper upwards and

secure with heavy mechanics wire or equivalent.

12. Remove the inboard and outboard brake pads from the brake caliper mounting bracket.

13. Remove the brake pad retainers.

To install:

❈❈ WARNING

The brake rotor is coated with a corrosion inhibitor and must not be refinished.

BRAKES

BRAKE CALIPER

REMOVAL & INSTALLATION

2008–09 CTS

See Figures 14 and 15.

1. Before servicing the vehicle, refer to the Precautions Section.

2. Inspect the fluid level in the brake master cylinder reservoir.

3. If the brake fluid level is midway between the maximum full point and the minimum allowable level, no brake fluid needs to be removed from the reservoir before proceeding.

4. If the brake fluid level is higher than midway between the maximum full point and the minimum allowable level, remove brake fluid to the midway point before proceeding.

5. Release the electronic park brake cable tension, if equipped.

6. Raise and safely support the vehicle.

7. Remove the rear wheel.

8. Install a C-clamp against the outer brake pad and the rear of the brake caliper body.

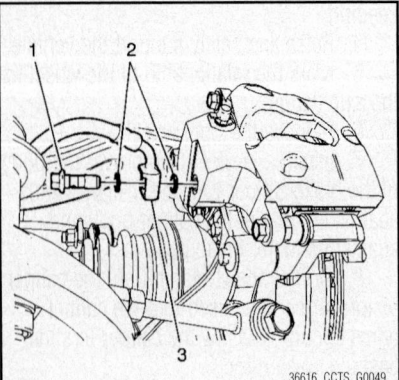

Fig. 14 Remove the brake hose filling bolt (1), gaskets (2) and brake hose (3)—2008–09 CTS Models

14. Install the brake pad retainers into the brake caliper bracket.

15. Pivot the brake caliper down over the brake pads and into the brake caliper bracket.

16. Apply a thin coat of high temperature silicone brake lubricant to the brake caliper pin bolts.

17. Install the brake caliper pin bolts and tighten to 83 ft. lbs. (113 Nm).

18. Install the front wheel and lower the vehicle.

9. Slowly tighten the C-clamp until the brake caliper piston is compressed into the brake caliper bore.

10. Remove the brake hose fitting bolt.

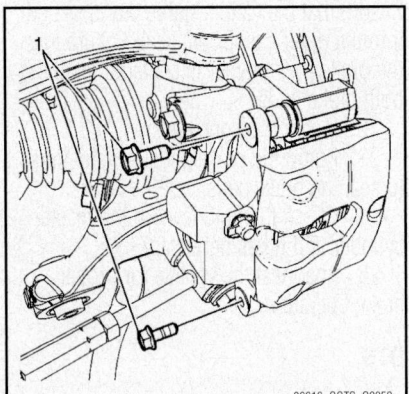

Fig. 15 Remove the rear brake caliper guide pin bolts (1)—2008–09 CTS Models

11. Remove the brake hose fitting gaskets and the brake hose. Discard the brake hose fitting gaskets.

12. Using a backup wrench on the brake caliper guide pin, remove the brake caliper guide pin bolts.

13. Remove the brake caliper.

To install:

14. Before installing the caliper, make sure the piston is fully seated in the bore and the brake pads are properly seated.

15. Lubricate the mounting bolt shafts and inner diameter of the sleeves with silicone grease.

16. Install the brake caliper and tighten the guide pin bolts to 44 ft. lbs. (60 Nm).

17. Assemble the brake hose fitting bolt and 2 new brake hose fitting gaskets to the brake hose.

18. Install the brake hose assembly to the caliper and tighten the fitting bolt to 36 ft. lbs. (49 Nm).

19. With the engine OFF, gradually apply the brake pedal to approximately 2/3 of its travel distance.

20. Slowly release the brake pedal.

21. Wait 15 seconds, then repeat these steps until a firm brake pedal is obtained. This will properly seat the brake caliper pistons and brake pads.

22. Check the fluid level in the master cylinder and fill as necessary.

23. Road test the vehicle for proper brake operation.

REAR DISC BRAKES

19. Refill the master cylinder and bleed the brake system.

20. Install the rear wheel.

21. Road test the vehicle for proper brake system operation.

2009 CTS-V

See Figures 16 and 17.

1. Before servicing the vehicle, refer to the Precautions Section.

2. If the brake fluid level is midway between the maximum-full point and the minimum allowable level, no brake fluid needs to be removed from the reservoir before proceeding.

3. If the brake fluid level is higher than midway between the maximum-full point and the minimum allowable level, remove brake fluid to the midway point before proceeding.

4. Raise and safely support the vehicle.

5. Remove the front wheel.

6. Remove the brake pads. For additional information, refer to the following

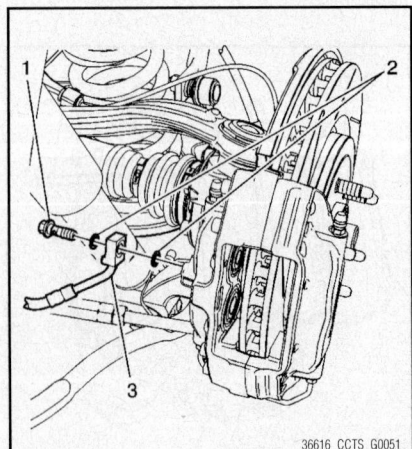

Fig. 16 Remove the brake hose fitting bolt (1), fitting gaskets (2) and brake hose (3)—2009 CTS-V Models

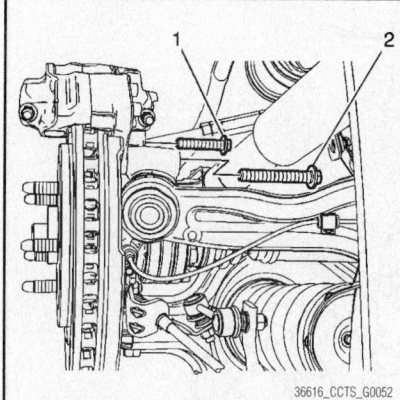

Fig. 17 Remove the upper (2) and lower (1) caliper bolt to remove the rear brake caliper—2009 CTS-V Models

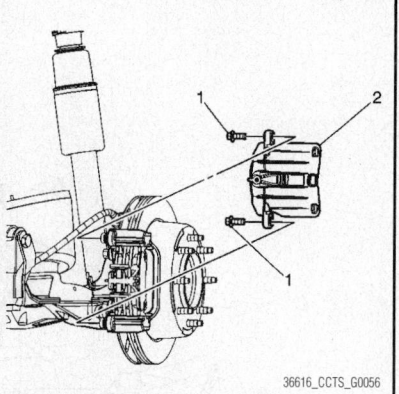

Fig. 18 Remove the caliper guide pin bolts (1) to remove the brake caliper (2)—2008–09 DTS Models

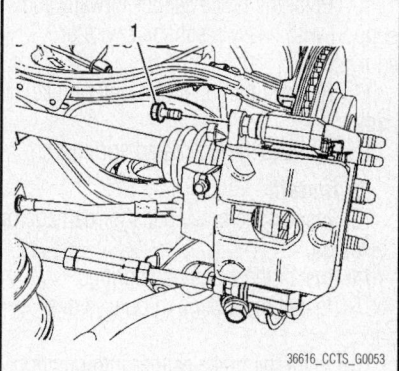

Fig. 19 Using a backup wrench on the brake caliper guide pin, remove the upper brake caliper guide pin bolt—2008-09 CTS & CTS-V Models

section, "Disc Brake Pads, Removal & Installation."

7. Remove the brake hose fitting bolt. Cap the brake caliper inlet port to prevent brake fluid loss and contamination.

8. Remove and discard the brake hose fitting gaskets from the brake hose. Cap the brake hose fitting to prevent brake fluid loss and contamination.

9. Remove the lower brake caliper bolt.

10. Remove the upper brake caliper bolt and the brake caliper.

To install:

11. Apply threadlocker to two-thirds of the threaded length of the caliper to knuckle mounting bolts.

12. Apply a thin coat of high temperature silicone brake lubricant to the brake caliper pin.

13. Install the brake caliper and hand tighten the upper and lower brake caliper bolts.

14. Tighten the brake caliper bolts to 96 ft. lbs. (130 Nm).

15. Assemble the brake hose fitting bolt and the 2 new brake hose fitting gaskets to the brake hose. Install the brake hose assembly to the brake caliper and tighten the brake hose fitting bolt to 36 ft. lbs. (49 Nm).

16. Install the brake pads.

17. Refill the master cylinder and bleed the brake system.

18. Install the rear wheel.

19. Road test the vehicle for proper brake system operation.

2008–09 DTS

See Figure 18.

1. Before servicing the vehicle, refer to the Precautions Section.

2. Raise and safely support the vehicle.

3. Remove the rear wheel.

4. Remove the brake hose from the brake caliper and cap the brake hose to prevent fluid leakage and fluid contamination.

5. Disconnect the parking brake cable from the caliper.

6. Remove the brake caliper guide pin bolts.

7. Remove the brake caliper assembly.

8. Install the caliper assembly. Tighten the guide pin bolts to 46 ft. lbs. (63 Nm).

9. Install the brake hose with new copper gaskets to the caliper assembly. Tighten the bolt as follows:

- J55 brake system: 33 ft. lbs. (45 Nm).
- JL9 brake system: 30 ft. lbs. (40 Nm).

10. Refill the master cylinder and bleed the brake system.

11. Connect the parking brake cable.

12. Install the rear wheel.

13. With the engine OFF, gradually apply the brake pedal to approximately 2/3 of its travel distance.

14. Slowly release the brake pedal.

15. Wait 15 seconds, then repeat these steps until a firm brake pedal is obtained. This will properly seat the brake caliper pistons and brake pads.

16. Road test the vehicle for proper brake system operation.

DISC BRAKE PADS

REMOVAL & INSTALLATION

CTS & CTS-V

See Figures 19 and 20.

1. Inspect the fluid level in the brake master cylinder reservoir.

2. If the brake fluid level is midway

between the maximum full point and the minimum allowable level, no brake fluid needs to be removed from the reservoir before proceeding.

3. If the brake fluid level is higher than midway between the maximum full point and the minimum allowable level, remove brake fluid to the midway point before proceeding.

4. Release the electronic park brake cable tension, if equipped.

5. Raise and safely support the vehicle.

6. Remove the rear wheel.

7. Install a C-clamp against the outer brake pad and the rear of the brake caliper body.

8. Slowly tighten the C-clamp until the brake caliper pistons are compressed into the brake caliper bores.

9. Using a backup wrench on the brake caliper guide pin, remove the upper brake caliper guide pin bolt.

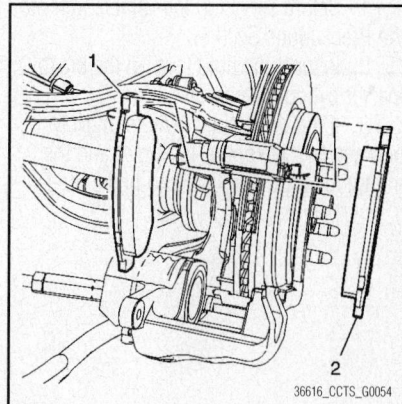

Fig. 20 Remove the inner (1) and outer (2) brake pads—2008-09 CTS & CTS-V Models

10. Pivot the brake caliper forward and support with heavy mechanics wire or equivalent.

11. Remove the inner and outer brake pads.

12. Remove the brake pad springs.

To install:

13. Inspect the brake pads for damage or corrosion.

14. Install the brake pad springs.

15. Install the inner and outer brake pads.

16. Pivot the brake caliper into position.

17. If reusing the caliper pin bolts, thoroughly clean any residue from the bolt threads.

18. Apply threadlocker GM P/N 12345493, or equivalent to 2/3 of the threaded length of the brake caliper guide pin bolt. Ensure there are no gaps in the threadlocker along the length of the filled area of the bolt. Allow the threadlocker to cure before installation.

19. Install the brake caliper guide pin and tighten to 44 ft. lbs. (60 Nm).

20. Install the rear wheel and lower the vehicle.

21. With the engine OFF, gradually apply the brake pedal to approximately 2/3 of its travel distance.

22. Slowly release the brake pedal.

23. Wait 15 seconds, then repeat the steps until a firm brake pedal apply is obtained. This will properly seat the brake caliper pistons and brake pads.

24. Refill the brake master cylinder reservoir to the proper level.

25. Set the electronic park brake cable tension, if equipped.

2008–09 DTS

See Figure 21.

1. Before servicing the vehicle, refer to the Precautions Section.

2. Inspect the fluid level in the brake master cylinder reservoir.

3. If the brake fluid level is midway between the maximum-full point and the minimum allowable level, no brake fluid

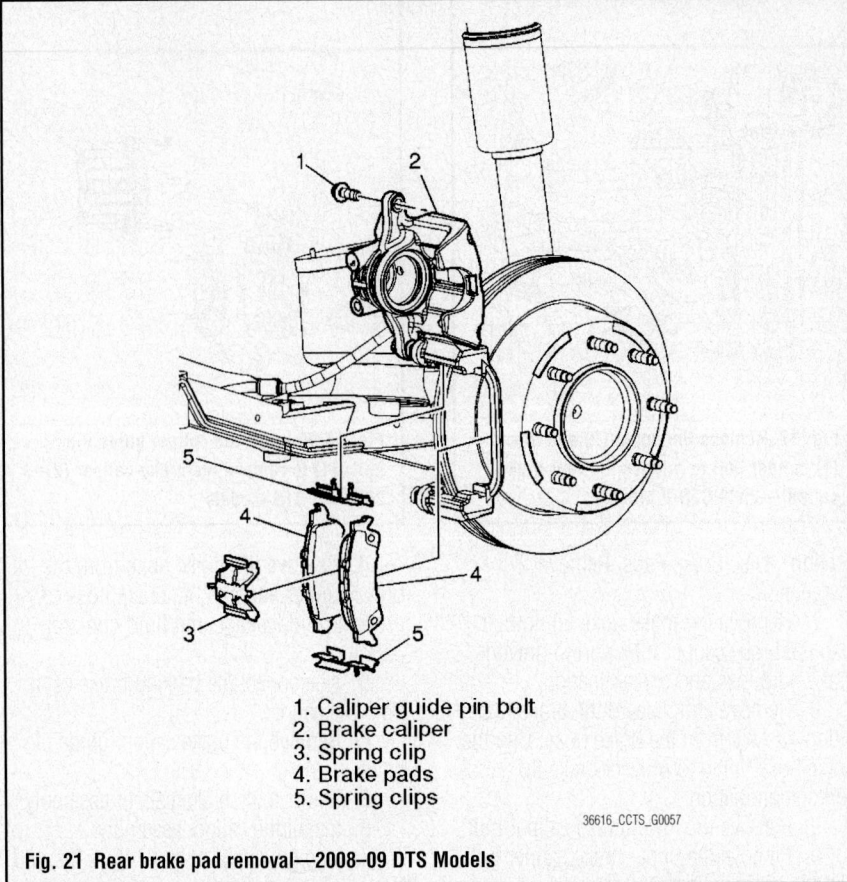

1. Caliper guide pin bolt
2. Brake caliper
3. Spring clip
4. Brake pads
5. Spring clips

36616_CCTS_G0057

Fig. 21 Rear brake pad removal—2008–09 DTS Models

needs to be removed from the reservoir before proceeding.

4. If the brake fluid level is higher than midway between the maximum-full point and the minimum allowable level, remove brake fluid to the midway point before proceeding.

5. Raise and safely support the vehicle.

6. Remove the rear wheel.

7. Remove the caliper guide pin bolt and rotate the brake caliper upward and secure with mechanics wire or equivalent.

8. Remove the brake pads and spring retainers.

To install:

9. Install the brake pads using new spring clips.

10. Rotate the brake caliper down and tighten brake caliper guide pin bolt as follows:

- J55 brake system: 46 ft. lbs. (63 Nm)
- JL9 brake system: 25 ft. lbs. (34 Nm)

11. With the engine OFF, gradually apply the brake pedal to approximately 2/3 of its travel distance.

12. Slowly release the brake pedal.

13. Wait 15 seconds, then repeat steps 2-3 until a firm brake pedal is obtained. This will properly seat the brake caliper pistons and brake pads.

14. Fill the master cylinder to the proper level.

15. Install the rear wheel and lower the vehicle.

16. Road test the vehicle for proper operation.

CHASSIS ELECTRICAL   **AIR BAG (SUPPLEMENTAL RESTRAINT SYSTEM)**

GENERAL INFORMATION

SERVICE PRECAUTIONS

Disconnect and isolate the battery negative cable before beginning any airbag system component diagnosis, testing, removal, or installation procedures. Allow system capacitor to discharge for two minutes before beginning any component service. This will disable the airbag system. Failure to disable the airbag system may result in accidental airbag deployment, personal injury, or death.

Do not place an intact undeployed airbag face down on a solid surface. The airbag will propel into the air if accidentally deployed and may result in personal injury or death.

When carrying or handling an undeployed airbag, the trim side (face) of the airbag should be pointing towards the body to minimize possibility of injury if accidental deployment occurs. Failure to do this may result in personal injury or death.

Replace airbag system components with OEM replacement parts. Substitute parts may appear interchangeable, but internal differences may result in inferior occupant protection. Failure to do so may result in occupant personal injury or death.

Wear safety glasses, rubber gloves, and long sleeved clothing when cleaning powder residue from vehicle after an airbag deployment. Powder residue emitted from a deployed airbag can cause skin irritation. Flush affected area with cool water if irritation is experienced. If nasal or throat irritation is experienced, exit the vehicle for fresh air until the irritation ceases. If irritation continues, see a physician.

Do not use a replacement airbag that is not in the original packaging. This may result in improper deployment, personal injury, or death.

The factory installed fasteners, screws and bolts used to fasten airbag components have a special coating and are specifically designed for the airbag system. Do not use substitute fasteners. Use only original equipment fasteners listed in the parts catalog when fastener replacement is required.

During, and following, any child restraint anchor service, due to impact event or vehicle repair, carefully inspect all mounting hardware, tether straps, and anchors for proper installation, operation, or damage. If a child restraint anchor is found damaged in any way, the anchor must be replaced. Fail-

ure to do this may result in personal injury or death.

Deployed and non-deployed airbags may or may not have live pyrotechnic material within the airbag inflator.

Do not dispose of driver/passenger/curtain airbags or seat belt tensioners unless you are sure of complete deployment. Refer to the Hazardous Substance Control System for proper disposal.

Dispose of deployed airbags and tensioners consistent with state, provincial, local, and federal regulations.

After any airbag component testing or service, do not connect the battery negative cable. Personal injury or death may result if the system test is not performed first.

If the vehicle is equipped with the Occupant Classification System (OCS), do not connect the battery negative cable before performing the OCS Verification Test using the scan tool and the appropriate diagnostic information. Personal injury or death may result if the system test is not performed properly.

Never replace both the Occupant Restraint Controller (ORC) and the Occupant Classification Module (OCM) at the same time. If both require replacement, replace one, then perform the Airbag System test before replacing the other.

Both the ORC and the OCM store Occupant Classification System (OCS) calibration data, which they transfer to one another when one of them is replaced. If both are replaced at the same time, an irreversible fault will be set in both modules and the OCS may malfunction and cause personal injury or death.

If equipped with OCS, the Seat Weight Sensor is a sensitive, calibrated unit and must be handled carefully. Do not drop or handle roughly. If dropped or damaged, replace with another sensor. Failure to do so may result in occupant injury or death.

If equipped with OCS, the front passenger seat must be handled carefully as well. When removing the seat, be careful when setting on floor not to drop. If dropped, the sensor may be inoperative, could result in occupant injury, or possibly death.

If equipped with OCS, when the passenger front seat is on the floor, no one should sit in the front passenger seat. This uneven force may damage the sensing ability of the seat weight sensors. If sat on and damaged, the sensor may be inoperative, could result in occupant injury, or possibly death.

DISARMING THE SYSTEM

1. Turn the steering wheel so that the vehicles wheels are pointing straight ahead.
2. Place the ignition in the OFF position.

➡**The SDM may have more than one fused power input. To ensure there is no unwanted SIR deployment, personal injury, or unnecessary SIR system repairs, remove all fuses supplying power to the SDM. With all SDM fuses removed and the ignition switch in the ON position, the AIR BAG warning indicator illuminates. This is normal operation, and does not indicate a SIR system malfunction.**

3. Locate and remove the fuse(s) supplying power to the Sensing and Diagnostic Module (SDM).
4. Wait 1 minute before working on the system.

ARMING THE SYSTEM

1. Place the ignition in the OFF position.
2. Install the fuse(s) supplying power to the SDM.
3. Turn the ignition switch to the ON position. The AIR BAG indicator will flash then turn OFF.
4. Perform the Diagnostic System Check - Vehicle if the AIR BAG warning indicator does not operate as described.

CLOCKSPRING CENTERING

See Figures 22 through 25.

1. Before servicing the vehicle, refer to the Precautions Section.
2. Verify the following before centering the Supplemental Inflatable Restraint (SIR) coil:

- The wheels on the vehicle are straight ahead.
- The block tooth of the steering shaft assembly is in the 12 o'clock position.
- The ignition switch is in the LOCK position.

3. If the front (5) of the SIR coil (Clockspring) has a centering window (4), and on the back side (2) a spring service lock (1), perform the following steps:

   a. Hold the SIR coil with the face up.
   b. While depressing the spring service lock, rotate the coil hub clockwise until the coil ribbon stops.

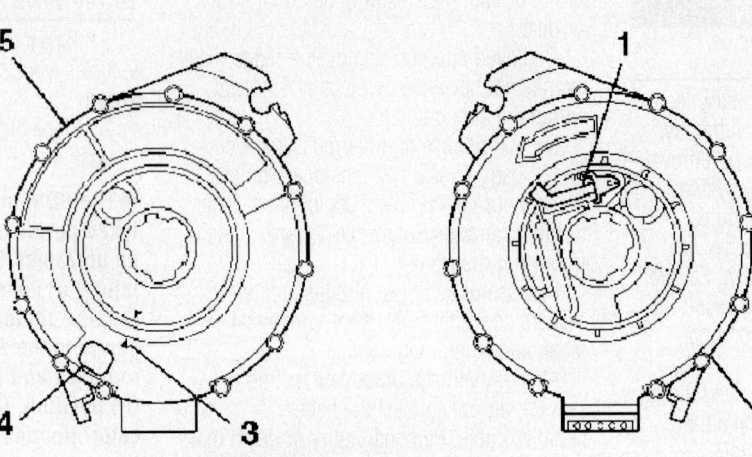

1. Spring service lock
2. Back side of clockspring
3. Alignment arrows
4. Centering window
5. Front of clockspring

22116_CCTS_G0120

Fig. 22 Clock spring view with front centering window and back side

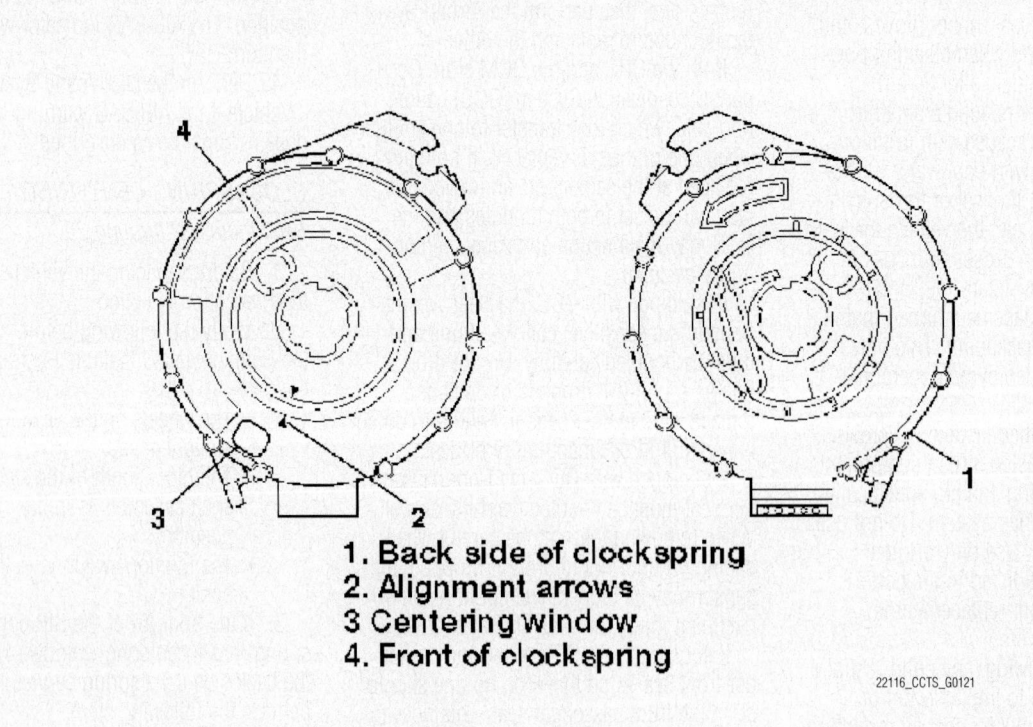

1. Back side of clockspring
2. Alignment arrows
3 Centering window
4. Front of clockspring

22116_CCTS_G0121

Fig. 23 Clock spring view with front centering window and no back side

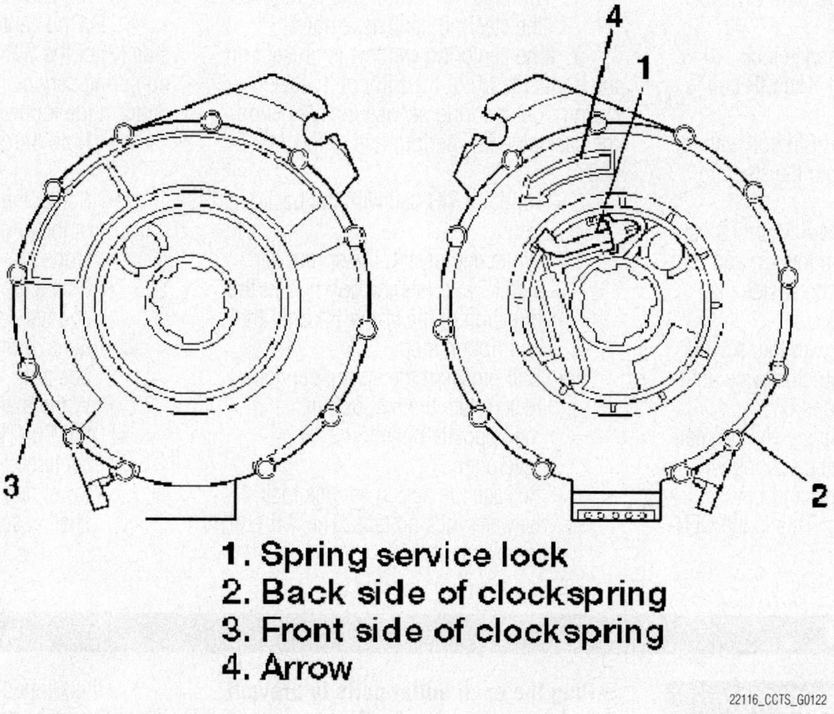
4
1
3
2
1. Spring service lock
2. Back side of clockspring
3. Front side of clockspring
4. Arrow
22116_CCTS_G0122

Fig. 24 Clock spring view with no front centering window and back side

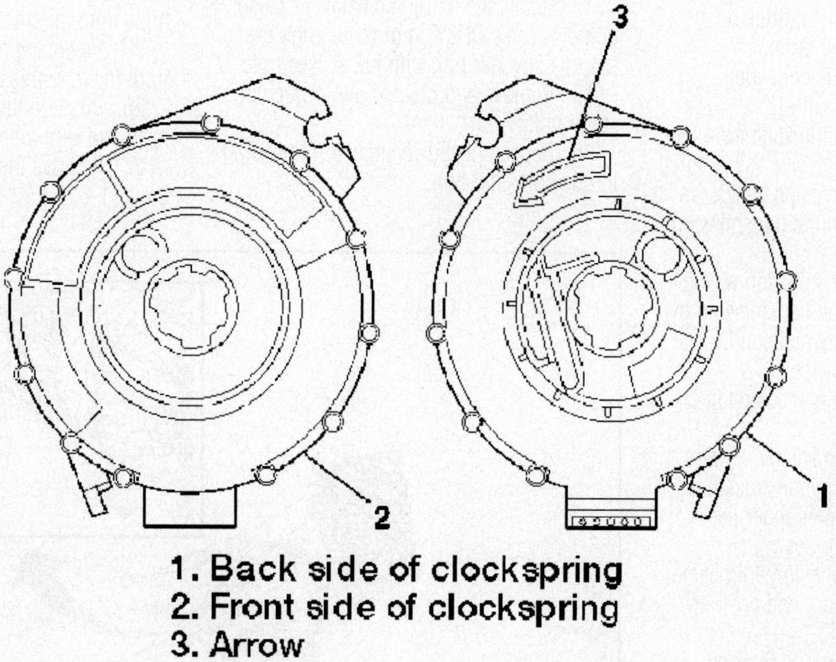
3
2
1
1. Back side of clockspring
2. Front side of clockspring
3. Arrow
22116_CCTS_G0123

Fig. 25 Clock spring view with no front centering window and no back side

c. Rotate the coil hub slowly, counterclockwise, until the centering window appears yellow and both arrows (3) line up.

d. Release spring service lock between the locking tab. The SIR coil is now centered.

e. Align the centered SIR coil with the horn tower and slide onto the steering shaft assembly.

4. If the front (4) of the SIR coil (Clockspring) has a centering window (3) and no spring service lock on the back side (1), perform the following steps:

- Hold the SIR coil with the face up.
- Rotate the coil hub clockwise until the coil ribbon stops.
- Rotate the coil hub slowly, counterclockwise until the centering window appears yellow and both arrows (2) line up. This is the CENTER position.

- While holding the coil hub in the CENTER position, align the SIR coil with the horn tower and slide onto the steering shaft assembly.

5. If no centering window is present on the front side (3) of the SIR coil (Clockspring), but a spring service lock (1) is on the back side (2), perform the following steps:

- Hold the SIR coil with the back side up.
- While depressing the spring service lock, rotate the coil hub in the direction of the arrow (4) until the coil ribbon stops.
- Still pressing the spring service lock, rotate the coil hub in the opposite direction 2 ½ revolutions.
- Release the spring service lock between locking tabs. The SIR coil is now centered.

- Align the centered SIR coil with the horn tower and slide onto the steering shaft assembly.

6. For no centering window on the front side (2) of the SIR coil (Clockspring) and no spring service lock on the back side (1), perform the following steps:

- Hold the SIR coil with the face up.
- Rotate the coil hub in the direction of the arrow (3) until the coil ribbon stops.
- Rotate the coil hub, slowly, counterclockwise, for 2 ½ revolutions. This is the CENTER position.
- While maintaining the coil hub in the CENTER position, align the centered SIR coil with the horn tower and slide onto the steering shaft assembly.

DRIVE TRAIN

AUTOMATIC TRANSMISSION ASSEMBLY

REMOVAL & INSTALLATION

2008–09 CTS

See Figure 26.

1. Disconnect the negative battery cable.
2. Remove the thermostat housing.
3. Remove the exhaust system.
4. Remove the catalytic converters.
5. Remove the driveshaft(s).
6. Disconnect the shift linkage from the transmission.
7. Remove the transmission vent hose from the retaining clips on the transmission support.
8. Disconnect the transmission wiring harness connector from the transmission by releasing the locking mechanism and rotating the latch counterclockwise.
9. Remove the wiring harness retainers from the transmission.
10. Remove the oxygen sensor wiring harness connector from the transmission.
11. Place an oil drain pan under the transmission fluid cooler pipes.
12. Remove the transmission fluid cooler pipes from the transmission, and position aside.
13. Remove and discard the O-rings.

✳✳ WARNING

Do NOT reuse the O-rings.

➡**Plug the open outlet ports to prevent fluid loss and contamination.**

14. Remove the transmission close out plug.
15. Mark the torque converter to flexplate/flywheel orientation to ensure proper realignment.
16. Remove the starter motor.
17. Rotate the harmonic balancer center bolt clockwise ONLY, in order to align the torque converter bolt with the access hole.
18. Remove and discard the torque converter bolt.
19. Repeat those two steps to remove all torque converter bolts.

20. If equipped with AWS, disconnect the intermediate shaft from the power steering gear.
21. Support the transmission with a suitable transmission jack.
22. Remove the transmission support.
23. Lower the transmission slightly.
24. Disconnect the transmission vent hose from the transmission vent pipe.
25. Remove the wiring harness retainers from the transmission.
26. Position the transmission wiring harness and vent tube out of the way.
27. Remove the transmission mounting bolts (1-6).

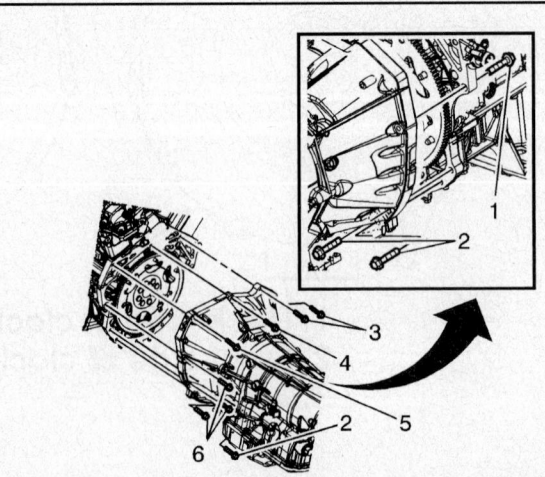

36616_CCTS_G0095

Fig. 26 Location of the transmission mounting bolts—2008–09 CTS RWD

28. Pull the transmission free from the engine dowels.

29. Ensure clearance is maintained between the transmission and the following:
   - The wiring harness
   - The vent tube
   - The cooler pipes

30. Carefully lower the transmission from the vehicle.

To install:

31. Using the transmission jack, carefully raise the transmission to the engine and align the transmission with the engine dowels.

32. Install the transmission mounting bolts and tighten to 37 ft. lbs. (50 Nm).

33. Position the engine wiring harness and harness retainers to the original location.

34. Connect the transmission vent hose to the transmission vent pipe.

35. Raise the transmission to the installed position.

36. Install the transmission support and tighten the bolts as follows:
   - AWD: 81 ft. lbs. (110 Nm)
   - RWD: 44 ft. lbs. (60 Nm)

37. Remove the jack from under the transmission.

38. Align the torque converter to flexplate/flywheel orientation marks made during the removal procedure.

➡ **Torque converter bolts are self locking and must be replaced with NEW torque converter bolts every time the bolts are removed.**

39. Rotate the harmonic balancer center bolt clockwise ONLY, in order to align the torque converter bolt holes in the flexplate/flywheel with the access hole in the engine block.

40. To aid in alignment of the torque converter to the flexplate/flywheel. Install all NEW torque converter bolts before fully tightening. Tighten the bolts to 46 ft. lbs. (63 Nm).

41. Install the starter motor.

42. Install the transmission close out plug.

43. Using NEW O-rings over the transmission fluid cooler pipes, install the transmission fluid cooler pipes to the transmission.

44. Install the oxygen sensor wiring harness connector from the transmission.

45. Install the wiring harness retainers to the transmission.

46. Connect the transmission wiring harness connector to the transmission by rotating the locking latch clockwise.

47. Install the transmission vent hose to the retaining clips (6) on the transmission support.

48. Install the shift linkage to the transmission.

49. Install the transmission manual shift shaft nut and tighten to 11 ft. lbs. (15 Nm).

50. Install the driveshaft.

51. Install the catalytic converters.

52. Install the exhaust system.

53. Lower the vehicle.

54. Install the thermostat housing.

55. Check the transmission fluid level and fill if necessary.

56. Adjust the shift control linkage as necessary.

AUTOMATIC TRANSAXLE ASSEMBLY

REMOVAL & INSTALLATION

DTS—4T80-E

See Figures 27 through 29.

1. Before servicing the vehicle, refer to the Precautions Section.

2. Disconnect the negative battery cable.

3. Remove the front compartment sight shield.

4. Remove the upper and lower air cleaner assemblies.

5. Disconnect the range selector cable terminal from the transaxle range selector lever.

6. Remove the nuts securing both the range selector cable bracket and heater pipe to the transaxle. Position the range selector cable bracket and heater pipe aside.

7. Remove the Magnasteer wire from the retaining clip.

8. Remove the brake master cylinder from the brake booster and position aside. Do not disconnect the brake lines.

9. Disconnect the master cylinder brake pipe retainers from the side rail.

10. Remove the brake pipe retainers from the side rail and using mechanics wire, support the brake pipes above the side rail.

11. Reposition the main wiring harness to gain access to the upper transaxle to engine bolts.

12. Remove the transaxle to engine bolts. The remaining bolt will temporally retain the transaxle and will be removed from the underside of the vehicle.

13. Place a drain pan under the vehicle.

14. Remove the upper transaxle oil cooler pipe retaining bolt from the radiator fan shroud.

15. Disconnect the upper transaxle oil cooler pipe from the radiator using the J 41623-B cooler quick connect tool . Install plugs in the oil cooler pipe and the radiator to prevent fluid loss and contamination.

16. Disconnect the lower transaxle oil cooler pipe from the transaxle and Install plugs in the oil cooler pipe and the transaxle to prevent fluid loss and contamination.

17. Disconnect the transaxle vent tube from the accelerator bracket.

18. Install the engine support fixture.

19. Raise and support the vehicle.

✳✳ CAUTION

To avoid any vehicle damage, serious personal injury or death when major components are removed from the vehicle and the vehicle is supported by a hoist, support the vehicle with jack stands at the opposite end from which the components are being removed and strap the vehicle to the hoist.

20. Secure the vehicle to the front hoist pads.

21. Remove the front tires and wheels.

22. Remove the bolts retaining the steering gear to the engine frame.

23. Remove the ball joints from the steering knuckle.

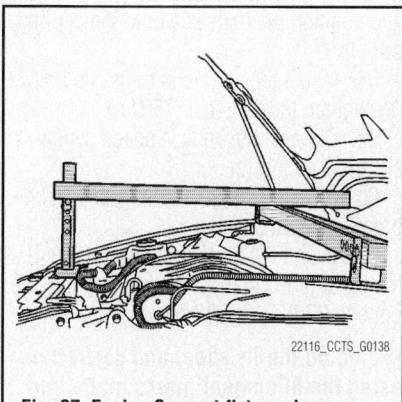

22116_CCTS_G0138
Fig. 27 Engine Support fixture shown

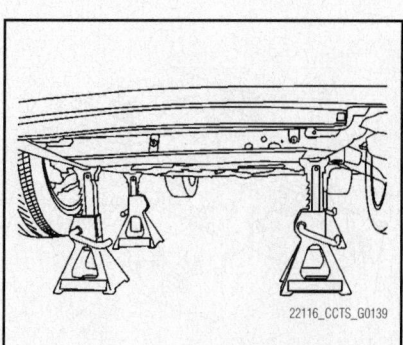

22116_CCTS_G0139
Fig. 28 Engine frame resting on suitable jack stands

24. Remove the front air deflector.

25. Remove the brake pressure modulator valve and bracket from the frame.

26. Disconnect the ESC sensor links from the lower control arm ball studs.

27. Do not remove the A.I.R pump assembly from the vehicle. Retain the pump to the body using mechanics wire.

28. Remove the steering gear heat shield fasteners in order to remove the steering gear heat shield and disconnect the electrical harness retainer that is mounted on the heat shield.

29. Disconnect the electrical harness from the heat shield.

30. Remove the brackets retaining the power steering line to the frame.

31. Remove the retainer, retaining the power steering line along the left side of the engine frame.

32. Using mechanics wire, retain the steering gear to the body.

33. Lower vehicle until the engine frame rests on the J 39580 or suitable jack stands.

34. Remove the fastener retaining the front engine mount to the engine frame.

35. Remove the fasteners retaining the rear transaxle mount to the engine frame.

36. Remove the engine frame insulator bolts.

37. Raise vehicle away from engine frame.

38. Remove the left transaxle mount and bracket from the transmission.

39. Support the transaxle using the J 41160 and a suitable transmission jack.

40. Secure the J 41160 to the transaxle.

41. Remove the bolt securing the left transaxle brace to the transaxle.

42. Loosen the nut securing the left transaxle brace to the engine.

43. Remove the left transaxle brace from the powertrain assembly.

44. Remove the 3 ground connections from the side of the transaxle.

45. Disconnect the transaxle main electrical harness connector.

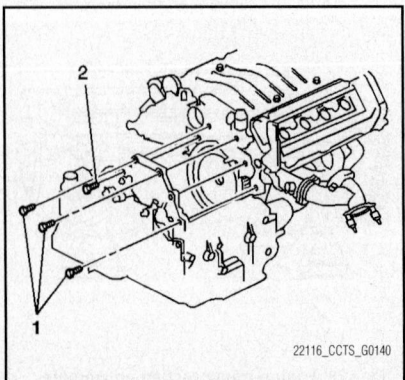

Fig. 29 Transaxle to engine bolts (1) and (2)

22116_CCTS_G0140

46. Remove the bolt securing the front transaxle brace to the transaxle.

47. Remove the nut securing the secondary AIR pipe to the transaxle.

48. Remove the nuts securing the vehicle speed sensor heat shield to the transaxle.

49. Remove the vehicle speed sensor heat shield from the vehicle.

50. Disconnect the vehicle speed sensor electrical connector.

51. Remove only the bolts securing the front transaxle brace to the transaxle.

52. Remove only the bolts securing the center transaxle brace to the transaxle.

53. Disengage the right and left drive shafts from the transaxle. The drive shafts do not have to be removed from the wheels.

54. Using mechanics wire, support the wheel drive shafts out of the way by tying them up to the strut spring.

55. Remove the torque converter cover.

➡**Mark the flywheel to torque converter position so that they can be assembled in the same position.**

56. Remove the flywheel to torque converter bolts.

57. Position the power steering gear pressure hose to the right side of the vehicle in order to clear the transaxle during removal.

58. Remove the remaining transaxle to engine bolt.

59. Separate the transaxle from the engine.

60. Tilt the transaxle using the support jack enough to allow clearance for the starter nose cone.

61. Carefully lower the transaxle from the vehicle.

To install:

62. Carefully raise the transaxle to the engine in a tilted position in order to clear the starter nose cone.

63. Align the transaxle with the engine and position the transaxle onto the engine dowels.

64. Install the engine to transaxle bolt (2), tighten to 55 ft. lbs. (75 Nm).

65. Connect the vehicle speed sensor electrical connector.

66. Install the engine to transaxle center brace and heat shield.

67. Install the bolts securing the front transaxle brace to the transaxle. Tighten the bolts to 37 ft. lbs. (50 Nm).

➡**Line up the flywheel and converter using the alignment marks made during disassembly.**

68. Install the flywheel to converter bolts. Tighten the bolts to 44 ft. lbs. (60 Nm).

69. Install the torque converter cover assembly.

70. Install the engine to transaxle bracket lower bolt and tighten to 37 ft. lbs. (50 Nm).

71. Install the right and left drive shafts to the transaxle.

72. Install the 3 ground connections to the side of the transaxle. Tighten the bolts to 37 ft. lbs. (50 Nm).

73. Connect the transaxle main electrical harness connector.

74. Install the left transaxle brace to the powertrain assembly.

75. Install the bolt securing the left transaxle brace to the transaxle. Tighten the left transaxle brace bolt to 37 ft. lbs. (50 Nm). Tighten the left transaxle brace nut to 30 ft. lbs. (41 Nm).

76. Remove the transmission jack and the J 41160.

77. Install the left transaxle mount and bracket to the transmission.

78. Lower the vehicle onto the engine frame.

79. Using dowel pins in the alignment holes, align the engine frame with the vehicle.

80. Install the engine frame insulator retainer bolts in order to retain the engine frame to the vehicle.

81. Tighten the retainers to 133 ft. lbs. (181 Nm).

82. Raise the vehicle away from the jack stands supporting the engine frame.

83. Install the fasteners in order to retain the rear transaxle mount to the bracket. Tighten the retainers to 37 ft. lbs. (50 Nm).

84. Install the fastener in order to retain the front engine mount to the engine frame. Tighten the fastener to 52 ft. lbs. (70 Nm).

85. Install the fasteners in order to retain the steering gear to the engine frame. Tighten the fastener to 70 ft. lbs. (95 Nm).

86. Install the bracket to retain the power steering line to the engine frame.

87. Install the clips retaining power steering line along engine frame rail.

88. Connect the wiring harness to the heat shield.

89. Install the steering gear heat shield to the vehicle. Tighten the retainers to 80 inch lbs. (9 Nm).

90. Install the brake pressure modulator valve.

91. Install the ESC sensor links to the lower control arm ball studs.

92. Install the front air deflector.

93. Install the ball joints to the steering knuckle.

94. Tighten the ball joint nut to 22 ft. lbs, (30 Nm). Then tighten the nut an additional 210 degrees.

95. Install the front tires and wheels.

96. Install the stabilizer shaft links.

97. Lower the vehicle.

98. Connect the lower transaxle oil cooler pipe to the transaxle.

99. Install the upper transaxle oil cooler pipe to the radiator.

100. Install the remaining transaxle to engine bolts, tighten to 55 ft. lbs. (75 Nm).

101. Remove the engine support fixture.

102. Install the range selector cable bracket to the studs on the transaxle.

103. Install the heater pipe to the stud on the transaxle.

104. Install the nuts that retain the heater pipe and the range selector cable bracket to the transaxle. Tighten the nuts to 18 ft. lbs. (25 Nm).

105. Connect the range selector cable terminal to the transaxle range selector lever.

106. Install the Magnasteer wire to the retaining clip.

107. Connect the transaxle vent tube to the accelerator bracket.

108. Install the Magnasteer wire to the retaining clip.

109. Connect the transaxle vent tube to the accelerator bracket.

110. Install the brake pipe retainers to the side rail.

111. Install the brake master cylinder to the brake booster.

112. Install the upper and lower air cleaner assemblies.

113. Install the front compartment sight shield.

114. Flush the transmission cooler.

115. Add DEXRON®VI transmission fluid as required.

116. Check the front suspension alignment, adjust the toe as necessary.

➡️**It is recommended that Transmission Adaptive Pressure (TAP) information be reset. Resetting the TAP values using a scan tool will erase all learned values in all cells. As a result, The ECM, PCM or TCM will need to relearn TAP values. Transmission performance may be affected as new TAP values are learned.**

117. Clear the TAP values.

118. Connect the negative battery cable.

119. Check the front wheel alignment.

120. Road test the vehicle and check for transaxle leaks.

CLUTCH DRIVEN DISC & PRESSURE PLATE

REMOVAL & INSTALLATION

2008–09 CTS

See Figures 30 and 31.

1. Remove the manual transmission. For additional information, refer to the following section, "Manual Transmission, Removal & Installation."

2. Remove the clutch pressure plate bolts.

3. Remove the clutch pressure plate and driven disc from the dowel pins on the flywheel.

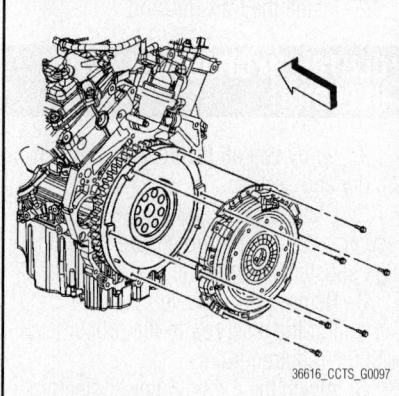

**Fig. 30 Removing the pressure plate and driven disc assembly from the transmission—CTS **

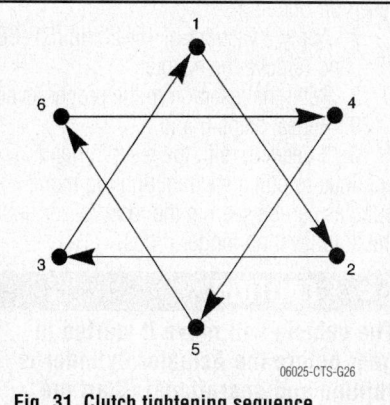

Fig. 31 Clutch tightening sequence

To install:

➡️**The splined portion of the driven plate protrudes out of the plate more on one side than the other. The side that protrudes out more is the transmission side. The arrow in the graphic indicates the front of the vehicle, or flywheel side of the driven plate.**

4. Install the clutch pressure plate and driven plate to the dowel pins on the flywheel.

5. Install the clutch pressure plate bolts finger tight.

6. Using a commercially available universal clutch alignment tool, align the clutch driven plate to the clutch pilot bearing.

7. Tighten the clutch pressure plate bolts in the sequence shown, starting with the number one and following in numerical order as follows:

a. Tighten all the clutch pressure plate bolts in sequence and evenly to 22 ft. lbs. (30 Nm).

b. Loosen bolts (1, 2, 3) 180 degrees. Re-torque bolts (1, 2, 3) in sequence and evenly 22 ft. lbs. (30 Nm).

c. Loosen bolts (4, 5, 6) 180 degrees. Re-torque bolts (4, 5, 6) in sequence and evenly 22 ft. lbs. (30 Nm) plus 20 degrees.

8. Install the manual transmission.

ADJUSTMENTS

The hydraulic clutch system requires no adjustments.

CLUTCH MASTER CYLINDER

REMOVAL & INSTALLATION

See Figure 32.

1. Remove the driver side instrument panel insulator.

2. Disconnect the clutch pedal position switch electrical connector.

3. Disconnect the clutch master cylinder push rod from the clutch pedal pin.

4. Remove the clutch fluid reservoir from the cowl.

5. Position the clutch fluid reservoir aside.

6. Remove the vacuum brake booster.

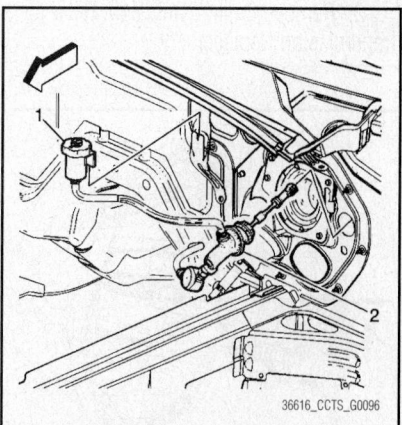

Fig. 32 Remove the clutch fluid reservoir (1) before removing the clutch master cylinder (2)—CTS Models

7. Rotate the clutch master cylinder clockwise ⅛ turn.

8. Remove the clutch master cylinder from the cowl.

To install:

9. With the clutch fluid reservoir connection at 2 o'clock position. Insert the clutch master cylinder into the cowl.

10. Align the keys of the clutch master cylinder housing with the tabs on the clutch pedal bracket.

11. Rotate the clutch master cylinder counter clockwise approximately ⅛ turn until fully seated. The clutch fluid reservoir hose connection will be at vertical 12 o'clock position when the clutch master cylinder is properly installed.

12. Install the vacuum brake booster.

13. Install the clutch fluid reservoir to the cowl.

14. Position the clutch master cylinder push rod to the clutch pedal pin.

15. Push the clutch master cylinder push rod onto the clutch pedal pin to secure.

16. Check for proper clutch pedal movement and operation.

17. Install the driver side instrument panel insulator.

18. Bleed the clutch hydraulic system.

CLUTCH SLAVE CYLINDER

REMOVAL & INSTALLATION

See Figure 33.

1. Before servicing the vehicle, refer to the Precautions Section.

2. Remove the transmission. Refer to Transmission Replacement.

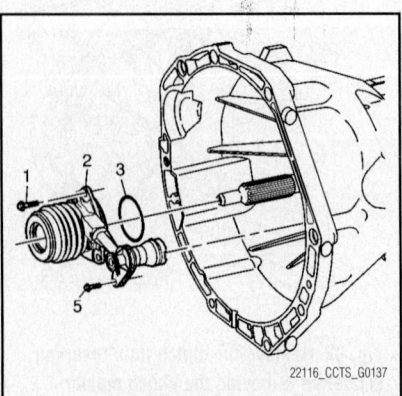

22116_CCTS_G0137

Fig. 33 Slave cylinder (2) removal shown

3. Remove the concentric actuator cylinder (Slave Cylinder) quick connect bolt.

4. Remove the 3 concentric actuator cylinder bolts.

5. Remove the concentric actuator cylinder.

6. Remove the O-ring.

To install:

7. Install the O-ring.

8. Install the concentric actuator cylinder.

9. Install the 3 concentric actuator cylinder bolts and the quick connect bolt.

10. Tighten the 3 concentric actuator cylinder bolts to 15 ft. lbs. (20 Nm)

11. Tighten the quick connect bolt to 89 inch. (10 Nm).

12. Install the transmission.

CLUTCH HYDRAULIC SYSTEM BLEEDING

1. Verify that all the lines and fittings are dry and secure.

2. Clean the dirt and grease from the reservoir cap in order to ensure that no foreign substances enter the system.

3. Remove the reservoir cap.

4. Fill the reservoir to the proper level with the required fluid.

5. Attach the J 43485 power steering bleeder adapter to the J 35555 metal Mityvac®, or equivalent.

6. Place and hold the adapter on the reservoir filler neck to ensure a tight fit. In some cases, the adapter will fit into the reservoir opening.

7. Apply a vacuum of 15–20 hg (51–68 kPa) and remove the adapter.

8. Refill the reservoir to the proper level.

9. Repeat steps 6 and 7.

10. If needed, refill the reservoir and continue to pull a vacuum until no more bubbles can be seen in the reservoir or until the fluid level no longer drops.

11. Pump the clutch pedal until firm (to refill actuator cylinder).

12. Add additional fluid if needed.

13. Test drive the vehicle to ensure proper operation.

FRONT HALFSHAFTS

REMOVAL & INSTALLATION

2008–09 CTS

Left Side

See Figure 34.

1. Before servicing the vehicle, refer to the Precautions Section.

2. Raise and safely support the vehicle.

3. Remove the left-front tire.

4. Remove the outer tie rod from the steering knuckle.

5. Insert a drift or punch in the brake rotor against the brake caliper mounting bracket to keep the wheel from rotating.

6. Using a breaker bar and proper size socket, loosen the drive shaft nut. Discard the nut.

7. Remove the wheel speed sensor.

8. Using the J 42129 remover, separate the wheel drive shaft from the wheel hub/bearing.

9. Remove the left upper control arm from the knuckle.

10. Using the J 2619-01 adapter , J 29794 extension , and the J 42943 separator , remove the halfshaft from the intermediate wheel drive shaft.

To install:

11. Install the new O-ring on the intermediate shaft.

12. Install the new retaining ring on the intermediate shaft.

13. Apply a small amount of grease to the intermediate wheel drive shaft splines.

14. Install the left front halfshaft in the intermediate shaft.

15. To ensure that the halfshaft is installed properly, grasp the inner tripod

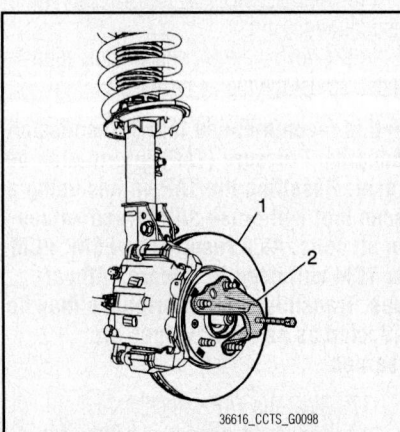

36616_CCTS_G0098

Fig. 34 Separate the halfshaft from the hub (1) using Special Tool J-42129 (2)— CTS Left Side Front Halfshaft

housing and pulling it outward. DO NOT pull on the axle shaft.

16. Install the halfshaft in the front knuckle.

17. Install the left upper control arm on the knuckle.

18. Hand start a NEW drive shaft nut. Apply threadlocker to the nut.

➡ **Ensure that there are no gaps in the threadlocker along the length of the filled area of the halfshaft. Allow the threadlocker to cure approximately 10 minutes before installation of the drive shaft nut.**

19. Using hand tools, tighten the NEW drive shaft nut until the halfshaft is fully seated in the wheel hub/bearing assembly.

20. Insert a drift or punch into the brake rotor and rotate the brake rotor until it rests against the caliper mounting bracket.

21. Tighten the halfshaft nut to 158 ft. lbs. (215 Nm).

22. The remainder of the installation is the reverse order of removal.

Right Side

See Figure 35.

1. Before servicing the vehicle, refer to the Precautions Section.

2. Raise and safely support the vehicle.

3. Remove the right front tire.

4. Remove the outer tie rod from the steering knuckle.

5. Insert a drift or punch in the brake rotor against the brake caliper mounting bracket to keep the wheel from rotating.

6. Using a breaker bar and proper size socket, loosen the drive shaft nut. Discard the nut.

7. Remove the wheel speed sensor.

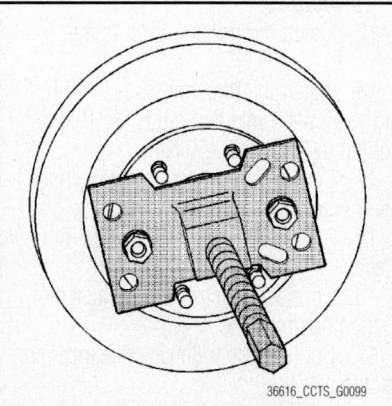

Fig. 35 Using Special Tool J 45859, remove the halfshaft from the steering knuckle—CTS

8. Using Special Tool J 45859, remove the halfshaft from the steering knuckle. Then remove J 45859 from the brake rotor.

9. Using the J 2619-01 hammer , J 29794 extension , and the J 42943 separator , remove the halfshaft from the differential enough to install J 44394 protector .

➡ **If the wheel drive shaft seal is found to be damage, replace the seal.**

10. Remove the halfshaft and the J 44394 protector from the vehicle.

To install:

11. Install the J 44394 protector in the differential assembly.

12. Install the halfshaft until the splines are past the J 44394 protector .

13. Remove the J 44394 protector from the halfshaft and continue to install the drive shaft until it is fully seated.

14. To ensure that the halfshaft is installed properly, grasp the inner tripod housing and pull it outward. DO NOT pull on the axle shaft.

15. Install the right front halfshaft into the wheel hub/bearing assembly.

16. Install the upper ball joint in the steering knuckle.

17. Hand start a NEW drive shaft nut. Apply threadlocker to the nut.

➡ **Ensure that there are no gaps in the threadlocker along the length of the filled area of the halfshaft. Allow the threadlocker to cure approximately 10 minutes before installation of the drive shaft nut.**

18. Using hand tools, tighten the NEW drive shaft nut until the halfshaft is fully seated in the wheel hub/bearing assembly.

19. Insert a drift or punch into the brake rotor and rotate the brake rotor until it rests against the caliper mounting bracket.

20. Tighten the halfshaft nut to 158 ft. lbs. (215 Nm).

21. The remainder of the installation is the reverse order of removal.

2008–09 DTS

See Figure 36.

1. Before servicing the vehicle, refer to the Precautions Section.

2. Raise and safely support the vehicle

3. Remove the tire and wheel assembly.

4. If equipped with road sensing suspension, disconnect the level sensor link from the ball stud on the lower control arm.

5. Disconnect the outer tie rod end from the steering knuckle. DO NOT loosen the tie rod end jam nut.

6. Insert a drift or punch into the brake

rotor and against the brake caliper in order to prevent the wheel hub and bearing from turning.

The front wheel drive axle nut must not be reused. Replace the front wheel drive axle nut with a NEW nut whenever it is removed.

7. Disconnect the electrical connector from the wheel speed sensor and reposition the wiring harness away from the ball joint.

8. Disconnect the lower ball joint from the steering knuckle.

9. Install the J 45859, CJ129 Universal Hub Puller or equivalent to the wheel bearing/hub.

10. Using the J 45859, CJ129 Universal Hub Puller or equivalent, carefully disengage the wheel drive shaft from the wheel bearing/hub.

11. Using an axle removal tool, carefully remove the wheel drive shaft axle.

To install:

12. Install the wheel drive shaft axle to the transaxle.

13. Verify that the wheel drive shaft is properly engaged to the transaxle by grasping the inner tripod housing and pulling outward. Do not pull on the wheel drive shaft bar.

14. Install the wheel drive shaft to the hub and bearing.

15. Connect the ball joint to the steering knuckle.

16. Tighten the ball joint nut to 22 ft. lbs, (30 Nm). Then tighten the nut an additional 210 degrees.

17. Connect the wheel speed sensor electrical connector.

18. Install the stabilizer shaft link. Tighten the stabilizer link nut to 13 ft. lbs. (17 Nm).

19. Insert a drift or punch into the rotor and against the caliper in order to prevent the hub and bearing from turning.

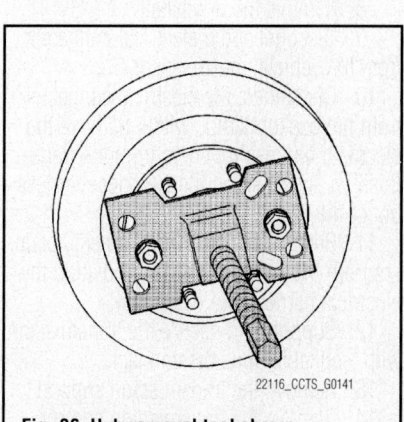

Fig. 36 Hub removal tool shown

20. Thoroughly clean the residue from the male threads of the wheel drive axle by using denatured alcohol or equivalent and allow to dry.

21. Apply threadlocker GM US P/N 12345493 (Canadian P/N 10953488), or equivalent to two-thirds of the threaded length of male threads of the wheel drive axles. Ensure that there are no gaps in the threadlocker along the length of the filled area of the threads.

22. Allow the threadlocker to cure approximately ten minutes before installation.

23. Install the new wheel drive shaft spindle nut to the wheel drive shaft.

24. Tighten the wheel drive shaft spindle nut to 170 ft. lbs. (230 Nm).

25. Connect the outer tie rod end to the steering knuckle.

26. Tighten the outer tie rod retaining nut to 35 ft. lbs. (47 Nm), and ⅛ additional turn.

27. Install the tire and wheel.

28. Lower the vehicle.

29. Adjust the front toe.

MANUAL TRANSMISSION ASSEMBLY

REMOVAL & INSTALLATION

2008–09 CTS

1. Turn the steering wheel so that the front wheels are pointing straight ahead.

2. Turn the ignition lock cylinder to the lock position and remove the key.

3. Lock the steering column through the access hole in the lower steering column trim cover using J 42640 .

4. Remove the transmission control lever knob.

5. Remove the manual transmission control mount plate assembly.

6. Remove the exhaust system.

7. Remove the catalytic converters.

8. Remove the driveshaft.

9. Disconnect the electrical connector from the vehicle speed sensor.

10. Disconnect the electrical connector from the backup lamp switch. Remove the electrical harness retainers from the transmission and position the electrical harness out of the way.

11. Remove the electrical harness retainers from the transmission and position the electrical harness out of the way.

12. Support and secure the transmission with a suitable transmission jack.

13. Remove the transmission support.

14. Remove the transmission control.

15. Remove the clutch hydraulic hose retaining clip from the clutch slave cylinder.

16. Disconnect the clutch hydraulic hose from the clutch slave cylinder. It is not necessary to plug the lower hose end or slave cylinder fitting as they are equipped with check valves. Only minimal fluid loss may be experienced.

17. Remove the transmission bolts (1-6).

18. Pull the transmission free from the engine dowels.

19. Ensure clearance is maintained between the transmission and the following:
   • The clutch assembly
   • The input shaft
   • The catalytic converters
   • The wiring harnesses
   • The driveshaft

20. Using the transmission jack, carefully lower the transmission from the vehicle.

To install:

21. Using the transmission jack, carefully raise the transmission to the vehicle.

22. Align the transmission with the engine dowels.

23. Install the transmission mounting bolts and tighten to 37 ft. lbs. (50 Nm).

24. Install the clutch hydraulic hose retaining clip to the clutch slave cylinder.

➡**Ensure the clutch hydraulic hose is routed in an upward direction above the clutch slave cylinder with no sharp bends, kinks, or downward loops. Ensure the clutch hydraulic hose does not come in contact with any sharp or potentially hot surfaces.**

25. Install the clutch hydraulic hose to the vehicle.

26. Align the clutch hydraulic hose locating tab with the notch in the slave cylinder hose fitting.

27. Push the clutch hydraulic hose into the clutch slave cylinder until a "click" is heard.

28. Tug gently on the clutch hydraulic hose to ensure proper retention to the clutch slave cylinder.

29. Install the transmission control.

30. Remove the transmission jack and install the transmission support.

31. Install the electrical harness retainers to the transmission.

32. Install the electrical harness retainers (1) to the transmission.

33. Connect the electrical connector (4) to the backup lamp switch.

34. Connect the electrical connector (5) to the vehicle speed sensor.

35. Install the propeller shaft. Refer to Rear Propeller Shaft Replacement.

36. Install the catalytic converters.

37. Install the exhaust system.

38. Inspect the transmission fluid level.

39. Lower the vehicle.

40. Install the manual transmission control mount plate assembly.

41. Install the transmission control lever knob.

42. Unlock the steering column by removing the J 42640 from the steering column lower trim cover access hole.

43. Bleed the clutch hydraulic system

2009 CTS-V

See Figure 37.

1. Before servicing the vehicle, refer to the Precautions Section.

2. Remove the exhaust system.

3. Remove the driveshaft from the vehicle.

4. Support the transmission with a uitable jack.

5. Remove the transmission mount.

6. Lower the transmission assembly to gain access to the top of the transmission.

7. Disconnect the shift control assembly from the transmission.

8. Disconnect the following electrical connectors:
   • Transmission fluid temperature (TFT) sensor
   • Backup lamp switch
   • Vehicle speed sensor (VSS)
   • Reverse lockout solenoid
   • Gear select/skip shift solenoid

9. Disconnect the clutch hydraulic hose.

10. Remove the transmission clutch housing to engine fasteners (1, 4).

11. Remove the transmission from the vehicle

To install:

12. Install the transmission to the vehicle.

13. Install the transmission clutch housing to engine bolts and studs (1, 4) and tighten to 37 ft. lbs. (50 Nm).

14. Connect the clutch hydraulic hose to the transmission.

15. Raise the transmission back into place.

16. Connect the shift control assembly to the transmission.

17. Connect the following electrical connectors:
   • TFT sensor
   • Backup lamp switch
   • Vehicle Speed Sensor

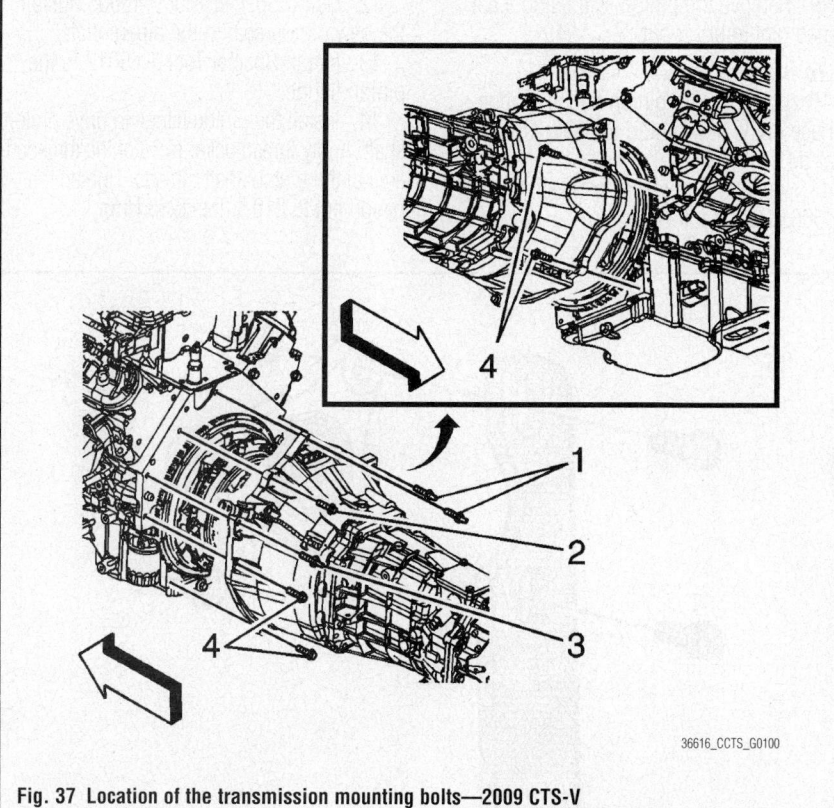

Fig. 37 Location of the transmission mounting bolts—2009 CTS-V

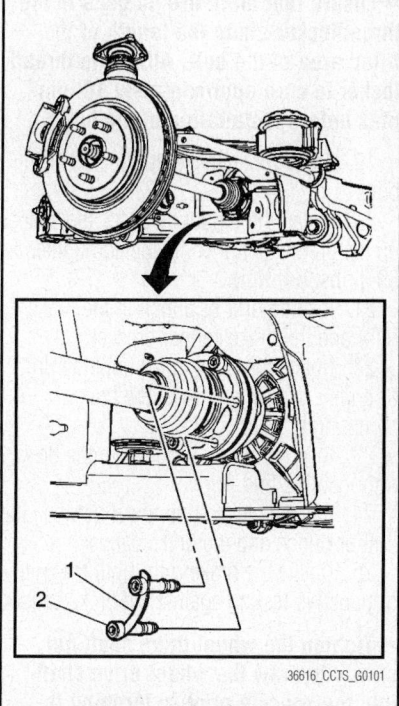

Fig. 39 Remove the halfshaft mounting bolts (2) and the spacer (1) from the differential drive flange—CTS

• Reverse lockout solenoid
• Gear select/skip shift solenoid
18. Raise the transmission assembly.
19. Install the transmission mount and remove the transmission jack.
20. Install the driveshaft.
21. Check the transmission fluid and fill as necessary.
22. Install the exhaust system.
23. Lower the vehicle.

REAR HALFSHAFTS

REMOVAL & INSTALLATION

See Figures 38 and 39.

1. Raise and safely support the vehicle.
2. Remove the rear wheel.
3. Insert a drift or punch in the brake rotor and the brake caliper bracket.
4. Rotate the brake rotor until the drift or punch is resting against the brake mounting bracket.
5. Insert a drift or a punch in the brake rotor cooling fins.
6. Place a clean shop towel between the drift or punch and the brake caliper.
7. Rotate the brake rotor until the drift or punch is resting against the brake caliper.
8. Using a breaker bar and the proper size socket, loosen the axle shaft nut. Remove and discard the wheel drive shaft retaining nut.

9. Using the J 45859 puller, separate the wheel drive shaft from the wheel bearing/hub assembly.
10. Support the knuckle assembly with a jack stand.

➡**Position the jack stand to the side to have enough access area to remove the wheel drive shaft.**

11. Remove the lower control arm.
12. Mark the relationship of the halfshaft to the output shaft flange.

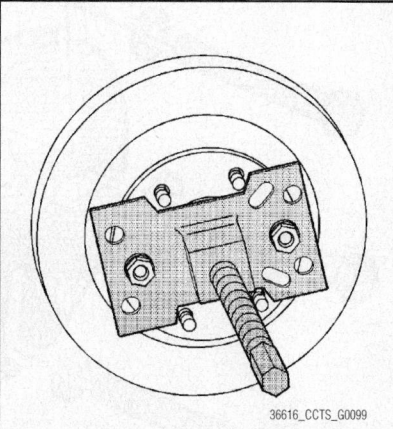

Fig. 38 Using the J 45859 puller, separate the wheel drive shaft from the wheel bearing/hub assembly.

13. Remove the halfshaft mounting bolts and the spacer from the differential drive flange.

➡**It may be necessary to use a flat bladed screw drive to separate the wheel drive shaft from the differential flange.**

14. Remove the halfshaft from the vehicle.

To install:

15. Install the halfshaft in the vehicle.
16. Apply threadlocker to the wheel drive shaft threads.

➡**Ensure that there are no gaps in the threadlocker along the length of the filled area of the wheel drive shaft threads. Allow the threadlocker to cure approximately 10 minutes before installation of the wheel drive shaft nut.**

17. Hand start the NEW wheel drive shaft retaining nut.
18. Align the reference marks on the wheel drive shaft and the output shaft flange.

➡**If reusing the halfshaft bolts, the threads must be free of debris prior to the application of the threadlocker to ensure the proper adhesion and retention. Thoroughly clean the threads using denatured alcohol or equivalent and allow to dry.**

➠Ensure that there are no gaps in the threadlocker along the length of the filled area of the bolt. Allow the threadlocker to cure approximately 10 minutes before installation of the bolts.

19. Apply threadlocker to the halfshaft bolts.

20. Install the mounting bolts and spacer on the differential drive flange and tighten to 59 ft. lbs. (80 Nm).

21. Insert a drift or punch in the brake rotor and the brake caliper bracket.

22. Rotate the brake rotor until the drift or punch is resting against the brake mounting bracket.

23. Insert a drift or a punch in the brake rotor cooling fins.

24. Place a clean shop towel between the drift or punch and the brake caliper.

25. Rotate the brake rotor until the drift or punch is resting against the brake caliper.

➠Tighten the wheel drive shaft nut slowly to draw the wheel drive shaft into the knuckle prior to torquing to specifications.

26. Tighten the wheel drive shaft nut to 158 ft. lbs. (215 Nm).

27. Install the lower control arm assembly.

28. Install the wheel and lower the vehicle.

REAR PINION SEAL

REMOVAL & INSTALLATION

CTS & CTS-V

See Figures 40 through 42.

1. Before servicing the vehicle, refer to the Precautions Section.

2. Remove the driveshaft coupler-to-differential flange bolts.

❊❊ WARNING

Do not remove the coupler from the propeller shaft.

3. Push the driveshaft toward the front of the vehicle in order to release the driveshaft coupler from the pinion flange.

4. Position the driveshaft out of the way.

5. Install the Pinion Holding Fixture J-45012 to the pinion flange.

6. While holding the Pinion Holding Fixture, remove the drive pinion nut.

7. Remove the Pinion Holding Fixture J-45012 from the flange.

8. Install Flange and Pinion Cage Remover J-45019 and remove the pinion flange.

9. Remove the pinion seal using a flat bladed tool to pry it out.

To install:

10. Lubricate the pinion flange sealing surface of the new pinion seal with synthetic gear oil.

11. Install the new seal to Special Tool J-45005 Seal Installer

12. Using Special Tool J-45005, install the new pinion seal to the differential.

13. Install Special Tool J-45012 to the pinion flange.

14. Install the pinion flange to drive pinion shaft. Apply threadlocker to ⅔ of the threaded area of the pinion shaft threads. Tighten the pinion nut to 210 ft. lbs. (285 Nm).

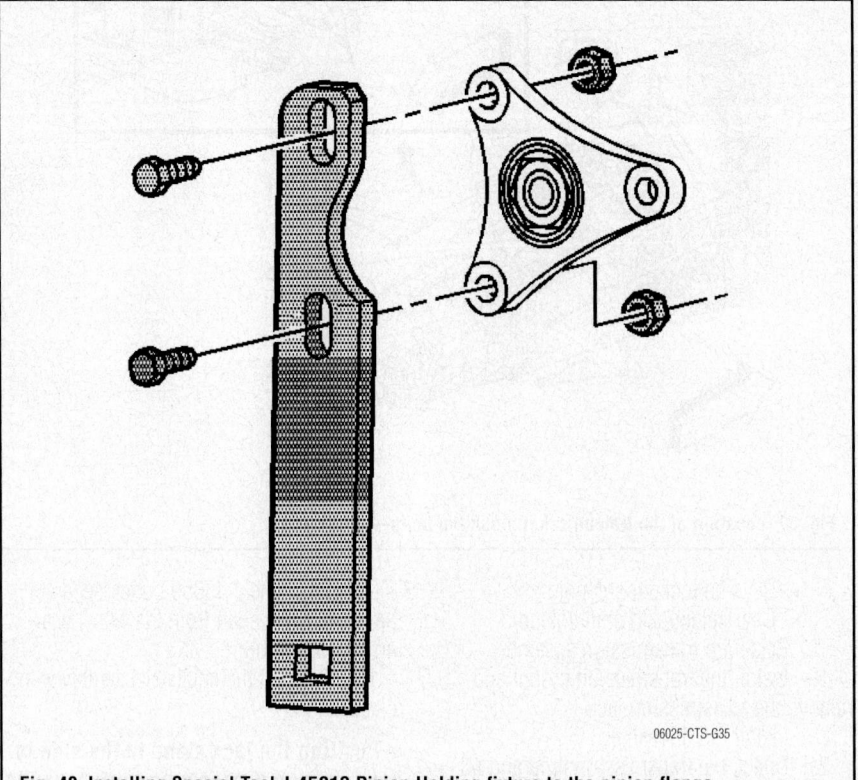

06025-CTS-G35

Fig. 40 Installing Special Tool J-45012 Pinion Holding fixture to the pinion flange

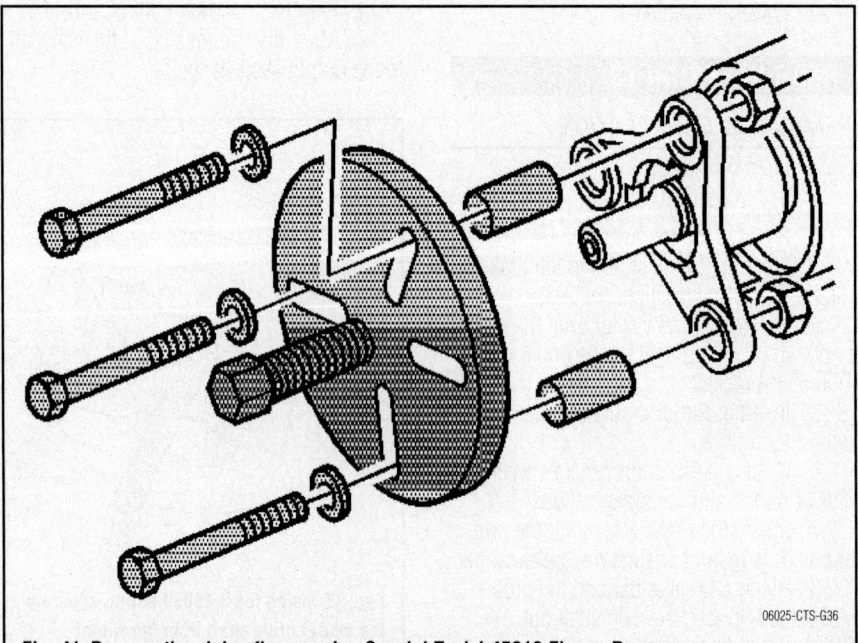

06025-CTS-G36

Fig. 41 Remove the pinion flange using Special Tool J-45019 Flange Remover

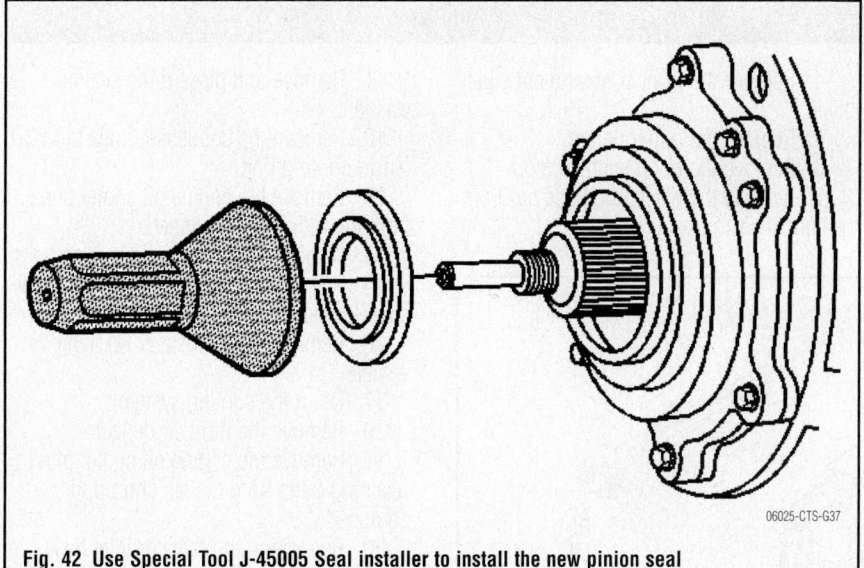

Fig. 42 Use Special Tool J-45005 Seal installer to install the new pinion seal

15. Install the driveshaft coupler-to-differential flange bolts. Tighten to 63 ft. lbs. (85 Nm).

16. Check the fluid level of the differential.

TRANSFER CASE ASSEMBLY

REMOVAL & INSTALLATION

CTS & CTS-V

See Figure 43.

1. Before servicing the vehicle, refer to the Precautions Section.

2. Drain the transfer case fluid, if necessary.

3. Remove the exhaust system.

4. Remove the rear driveshaft.

5. Support the transmission with a suitable screw jack and a block of wood.

6. Remove the transmission mount-to-body bolts.

7. Disconnect the shift linkage at the control lever.

8. Using the jack, lower the transmission enough to access the transmission mount-to-transfer case mounting bolts.

9. Remove the vent hose from the transmission mount assembly.

10. Remove the transmission mount-to-transfer case mounting bolts.

11. Remove the transmission mount assembly from the vehicle.

12. Remove the front driveshaft.

13. Disconnect the electrical connectors from the transfer case.

➡**Do not remove the jack and block of wood from under the transmission.**

14. Using another suitable adjustable jack, support the transfer case.

15. Remove the transfer case bolts.

16. Remove the transfer case dampener.

17. Remove the transfer case and transfer case gasket.

To install:

18. Apply grease GM P/N 1051344 (Canadian P/N 993037), or equivalent, on the input splines starting from the front edge to 10 mm inward in a continuous pattern around the inside diameter (ID) of the splines to completely fill the splines.

19. Install the transfer case gasket .

20. Install the transfer case and dampener.

21. Install the transfer case bolts and tighten to 44 ft. lbs. (60 Nm).

22. Remove the adjustable jack from the transfer case.

23. Connect the electrical connectors to the transfer case.

24. Install the transmission mount assembly. Refer to Transmission Mount Replacement.

25. Install the vent hose to the transmission mount assembly.

26. Remove the jack and block of wood from under the transmission.

27. Connect the shift linkage to the control lever.

28. Install the driveshafts.

29. Install the exhaust system.

30. Refill the transfer case with fluid.

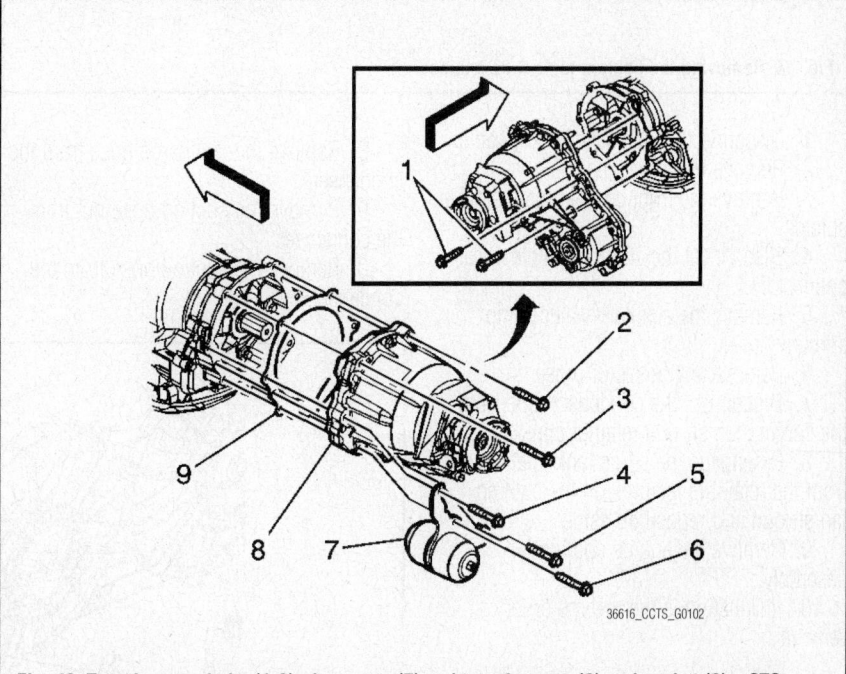

Fig. 43 Transfer case bolts (1-6), dampener (7) and transfer case (8) and gasket (9)—CTS

ENGINE COOLING

ENGINE FAN

REMOVAL & INSTALLATION

3.6L Engine

See Figure 44.

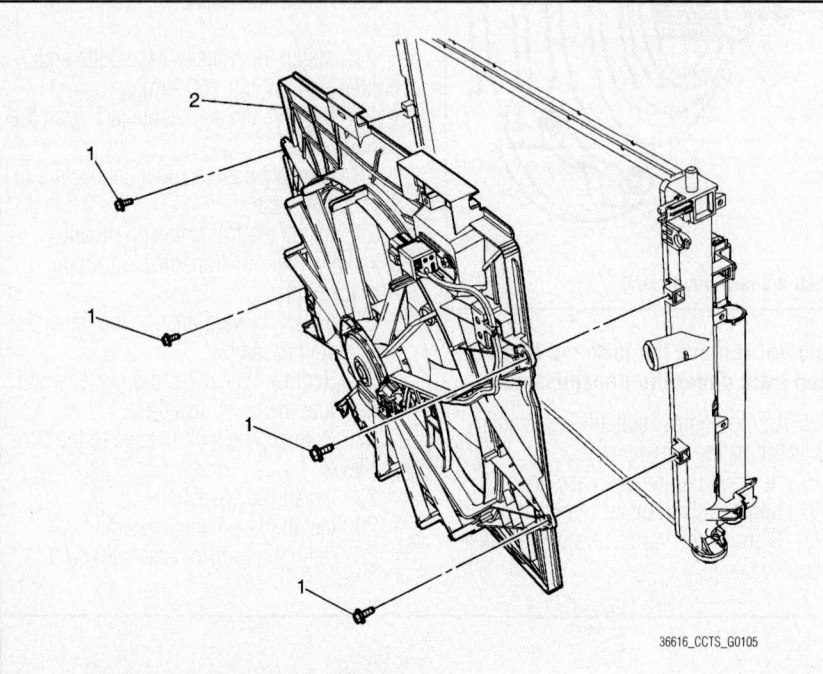

Fig. 44 Removing the coolant fan—3.6L engines

1. Disconnect the negative battery cable.
2. Remove the air cleaner.
3. Remove the front compartment sight shield.
4. Disconnect the cooling fan electrical connectors.
5. Remove the auxiliary water pump and any hoses.
6. Remove any hoses or pipes.
7. Disconnect the condenser tube from the cooling fan shroud retainer clip.
8. Disengage the surge tank inlet hose from the retaining features on the cooling fan shroud and reposition aside.
9. Remove the engine cooling fan assembly.
10. Installation is the reverse order of removal.

4.6L Engine

See Figures 45 and 46.

1. Before servicing the vehicle, refer to the Precautions Section.
2. Disconnect the battery negative cable.
3. Recover the refrigerant.

4. Remove the front compartment sight shield.
5. Remove the upper tie bar.
6. Remove the hood latch support.
7. Remove the discharge hose nut from the condenser.

8. Remove the discharge hose from the condenser.
9. Remove the suction hose nut from the condenser.
10. Remove the suction hose from the condenser.

11. Remove and discard the sealing washers.
12. Remove the condenser lines to radiator mounting bolt.
13. Remove the engine oil cooler lines from the radiator, if equipped.
14. Remove the condenser mounting bolts.
15. Remove the condenser from the radiator retainer.
16. Remove the condenser from the vehicle.
17. Drain the cooling system.
18. Remove the front air deflector.
19. Remove the engine oil cooler pipe retaining bolts from the fan shroud, if equipped.
20. Reposition the radiator inlet hose clamp.
21. Disconnect the radiator inlet hose from the radiator.
22. Remove the transmission lines from the radiator.
23. Disconnect the wiring harness electrical connectors from the cooling fan motors.
24. Remove the clips attaching the harness to the fan shroud.
25. Remove the electric cooling fan mounting bolts.

✳✳ WARNING

Care should be taken when removing the cooling fan assembly not to damage the lower attachment points of both the cooling fan assembly and radiator.

26. Remove the electric cooling fan assembly from the vehicle in the following order:

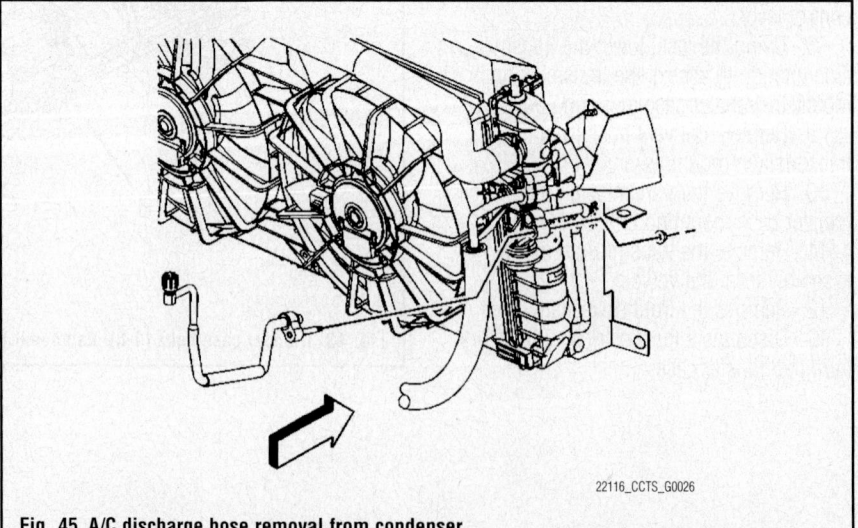

Fig. 45 A/C discharge hose removal from condenser

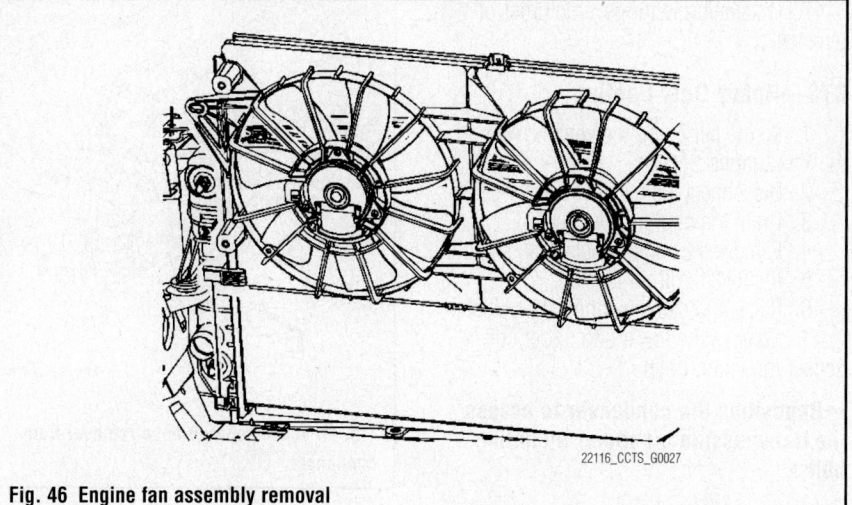

Fig. 46 Engine fan assembly removal

a. Position the cooling fan assembly towards the left side of the vehicle.

b. Pull upward on the right side of the fan assembly.

c. Position the fan assembly towards the right side of the vehicle.

d. Pull upward on the fan assembly removing the fan assembly from the vehicle.

To install:

27. Install the cooling fan assembly to the vehicle in the following order:

a. Position the cooling fan assembly behind the radiator.

b. Position the fan assembly towards the right side of the vehicle.

c. Push downward on the right side of the fan assembly.

d. Move the fan assembly into position, aligning the lower feet of the fan shroud to the mounting tabs on the radiator.

✳✳ WARNING

The bolts retaining the cooling fan to the radiator end tanks are a special length and should be the ONLY bolts used upon reinstallation. The use of longer bolts will damage the radiator end tanks.

28. Install the electric cooling fan mounting bolts and tighten to 53 inch lbs. (6 Nm).

29. Connect the wiring harness electrical connectors to the cooling fan motors.

30. Attach the wiring harness retaining clips to the fan shroud.

31. Push the upper transaxle oil cooler pipe into the radiator quick connect fitting, until a "click" is heard.

32. Tug gently on the cooler pipe to ensure proper retention.

33. Slide the plastic cap over the quick connect joint.

34. Install the transmission oil cooler pipe retaining bolts to the fan shroud. Tighten to 53 inch lbs. (6 Nm).

35. Install the radiator inlet hose to the radiator.

36. Reposition the radiator inlet hose clamp.

37. Raise the vehicle.

38. Install the engine oil cooler pipe retaining bolts to the fan shroud. Tighten the bolts to 53 inch lbs. (6 Nm).

39. Install the front air deflector

40. Lower the vehicle.

41. Install the condenser into the radiator retainer.

42. Install the condenser mounting bolts. Tighten the bolts to 80 inch lbs. (9 Nm).

43. Install the condenser line to radiator mounting bolt. Tighten the bolts to 53 inch lbs. (6 Nm).

44. Install the engine oil cooler lines to the radiator, if equipped.

45. Push the engine oil cooler lines into the radiator quick connect fitting, until a click is heard.

46. Tug gently on the cooler pipe to ensure proper retention.

47. Slide the plastic cap over the quick connect joint.

48. Install new sealing washers.

49. Install the suction hose to the condenser.

50. Install the suction hose nut to the condenser. Tighten the nut to 12 ft. lbs. (16 Nm).

51. Install the liquid line to the condenser.

52. Install the liquid line nut to the condenser. Tighten the nut to 15 ft. lbs. (20 Nm).

53. Install the hood latch bracket.

54. Install the upper tie bar.

55. Recharge the A/C system.

56. Leak test the fittings using a halogen leak detector.

57. Install the front compartment sight shield.

6.2L Engine

See Figure 47.

1. Before servicing the vehicle, refer to the Precautions Section.

2. Disconnect the battery negative cable.

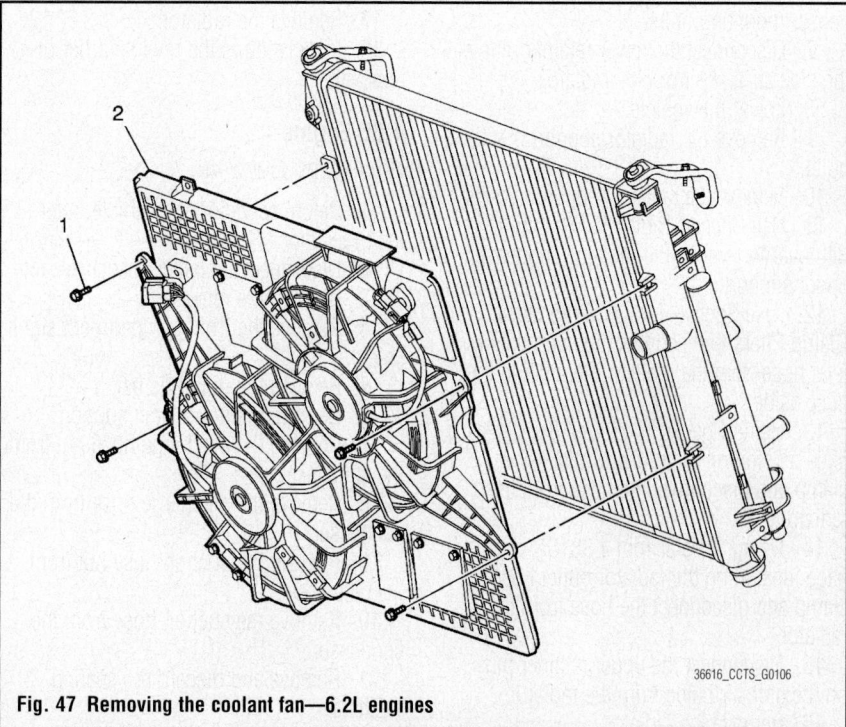

Fig. 47 Removing the coolant fan—6.2L engines

3. Remove the air cleaner. Refer to Air Cleaner Assembly Replacement.

4. Remove the air cleaner resonator outlet duct.

5. Remove the front compartment sight shield.

6. Remove the radiator inlet hose.

7. Disconnect the cooling fan electrical connectors.

8. Remove any hoses or pipes.

9. Disconnect the condenser tube from the cooling fan shroud retainer clip.

10. Disengage the surge tank inlet hose from the retaining features on the cooling fan shroud and reposition aside.

11. Remove the shroud radiator clip and remove the engine fan assembly.

12. Installation is the reverse order of removal.

RADIATOR

REMOVAL & INSTALLATION

CTS—Standard Duty Cooling

1. Before servicing the vehicle, refer to the Precautions Section.

2. Disconnect the battery negative cable.

3. Drain the cooling system.

4. Remove the electric cooling fan assembly. For additional information, refer to the following section, "Engine Fan, Removal & Installation."

5. Raise and safely support the vehicle.

6. Remove the lower and upper condenser mounting bolts.

7. Disconnect the lower retainer pins of the side air baffle from the radiator.

8. Lower the vehicle.

9. Remove the radiator support bracket bolts.

10. Remove the radiator support brackets.

11. Use Special Tool J 38778 Trim Clip Remover to remove the radiator/condenser upper support.

12. Use Special Tool J 38185 Hose Clamp Pliers to disconnect the surge tank inlet hose from the radiator. Reposition the hose aside.

13. Using Special Tool J 38185, disengage tension on the radiator inlet hose clamp and disconnect the hose from the radiator.

14. Using Special Tool J 38185, disengage tension on the radiator outlet hose clamp and disconnect the hose from the radiator.

15. Disconnect the upper retainer pins on the side air baffle from the radiator.

16. Remove the radiator.

17. Installation is the reverse order of removal.

CTS—Heavy Duty Cooling

1. Before servicing the vehicle, refer to the Precautions Section.

2. Disconnect the negative battery cable.

3. Drain the cooling system.

4. Remove the engine coolant fan shroud.

5. Remove the front fascia.

6. Raise and safely support the vehicle.

7. Remove the lower and upper condenser mounting bolts.

→**Reposition the condenser to access the transmission oil cooler mounting bolts.**

8. Remove the transmission oil cooler mounting bolts.

9. Disconnect the lower retainer pins of the side air baffle from the radiator.

10. Lower the vehicle.

11. Remove the radiator support bracket bolts and support brackets.

12. Use J 38778 to remove the radiator/condenser upper support.

13. Use J 38185 to disconnect the surge tank inlet hose from the radiator. Reposition the hose aside.

14. Using J 38185 disengage tension on the radiator inlet hose clamp and disconnect the hose from the radiator.

15. Using J 38185 disengage tension on the radiator outlet hose clamp and disconnect the hose from the radiator.

16. Disconnect the upper retainer pins on the side air baffle from the radiator.

17. Remove the radiator.

18. Installation is the reverse order of removal.

4.6L Engine

See Figures 48 and 49.

1. Before servicing the vehicle, refer to the Precautions Section.

2. Disconnect the battery negative cable.

3. Recover the refrigerant.

4. Remove the front compartment sight shield.

5. Remove the upper tie bar.

6. Remove the hood latch support.

7. Remove the discharge hose nut from the condenser.

8. Remove the discharge hose from the condenser.

9. Remove the suction hose nut from the condenser.

10. Remove the suction hose from the condenser.

11. Remove and discard the sealing washers.

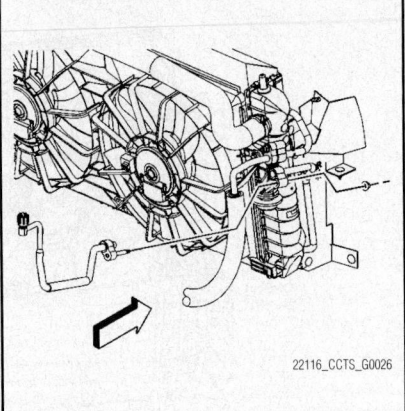

Fig. 48 A/C discharge hose removal from condenser

12. Remove the condenser lines to radiator mounting bolt.

13. Remove the engine oil cooler lines from the radiator, if equipped.

14. Remove the condenser mounting bolts.

15. Remove the condenser from the radiator retainer.

16. Remove the condenser from the vehicle.

17. Drain the cooling system.

18. Remove the front air deflector.

19. Remove the engine oil cooler pipe retaining bolts from the fan shroud, if equipped.

20. Reposition the radiator inlet hose clamp.

21. Disconnect the radiator inlet hose from the radiator.

22. Remove the transmission lines from the radiator.

23. Disconnect the wiring harness electrical connectors from the cooling fan motors.

24. Remove the clips attaching the harness to the fan shroud.

25. Remove the electric cooling fan mounting bolts.

✳✳ WARNING

Care should be taken when removing the cooling fan assembly not to damage the lower attachment points of both the cooling fan assembly and radiator.

26. Remove the electric cooling fan assembly from the vehicle in the following order:

   a. Position the cooling fan assembly towards the left side of the vehicle.

   b. Pull upward on the right side of the fan assembly.

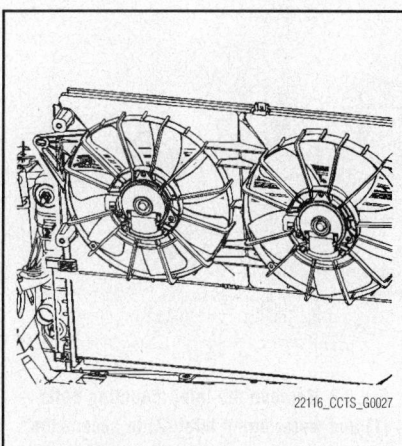

Fig. 49 Engine fan assembly removal

c. Position the fan assembly towards the right side of the vehicle.

d. Pull upward on the fan assembly removing the fan assembly from the vehicle.

To install:

27. Install the cooling fan assembly to the vehicle in the following order:

a. Position the cooling fan assembly behind the radiator.

b. Position the fan assembly towards the right side of the vehicle.

c. Push downward on the right side of the fan assembly.

d. Move the fan assembly into position, aligning the lower feet of the fan shroud to the mounting tabs on the radiator.

✸✸ WARNING

The bolts retaining the cooling fan to the radiator end tanks are a special length and should be the ONLY bolts used upon reinstallation. The use of longer bolts will damage the radiator end tanks.

28. Install the electric cooling fan mounting bolts and tighten to 53 inch lbs. (6 Nm).

29. Connect the wiring harness electrical connectors to the cooling fan motors.

30. Attach the wiring harness retaining clips to the fan shroud.

31. Push the upper transaxle oil cooler pipe into the radiator quick connect fitting, until a "click" is heard.

32. Tug gently on the cooler pipe to ensure proper retention.

33. Slide the plastic cap over the quick connect joint.

34. Install the transmission oil cooler pipe retaining bolts to the fan shroud. Tighten to 53 inch lbs. (6 Nm).

35. Install the radiator inlet hose to the radiator.

36. Reposition the radiator inlet hose clamp.

37. Raise the vehicle.

38. Install the engine oil cooler pipe retaining bolts to the fan shroud. Tighten the bolts to 53 inch lbs. (6 Nm).

39. Install the front air deflector

40. Lower the vehicle.

41. Install the condenser into the radiator retainer.

42. Install the condenser mounting bolts. Tighten the bolts to 80 inch lbs. (9 Nm).

43. Install the condenser line to radiator mounting bolt. Tighten the bolts to 53 inch lbs. (6 Nm).

44. Install the engine oil cooler lines to the radiator, if equipped.

45. Push the engine oil cooler lines into the radiator quick connect fitting, until a click is heard.

46. Tug gently on the cooler pipe to ensure proper retention.

47. Slide the plastic cap over the quick connect joint.

48. Install new sealing washers.

49. Install the suction hose to the condenser.

50. Install the suction hose nut to the condenser. Tighten the nut to 12 ft. lbs. (16 Nm).

51. Install the liquid line to the condenser.

52. Install the liquid line nut to the condenser. Tighten the nut to 15 ft. lbs. (20 Nm).

53. Install the hood latch bracket.

54. Install the upper tie bar.

55. Recharge the A/C system.

56. Leak test the fittings using a halogen leak detector.

57. Install the front compartment sight shield.

THERMOSTAT

REMOVAL & INSTALLATION

3.6L Engines

See Figures 50 and 51.

1. Before servicing the vehicle, refer to the Precautions Section.

2. Partially drain the cooling system.

3. Remove the upper intake manifold. For additional information, refer to the following section, "Intake Manifold, Removal & Installation."

4. Disconnect the surge tank outlet pipe from the thermostat.

5. Remove the coolant pipe/thermostat housing bolt.

6. Remove the coolant pipe upper bolt.

7. Remove the coolant inlet pipe from the thermostat.

8. Remove the thermostat mounting bolts.

9. Remove the thermostat and discard the gasket.

To install:

10. Install the thermostat with a new gasket.

11. Install the thermostat mounting bolts and tighten to 89 inch lbs. (10 Nm).

12. Install the coolant inlet pipe with a new seal. Tighten the mounting bolts to 16 ft. lbs. (22 Nm).

13. Connect the surge tank outlet pipe to the thermostat.

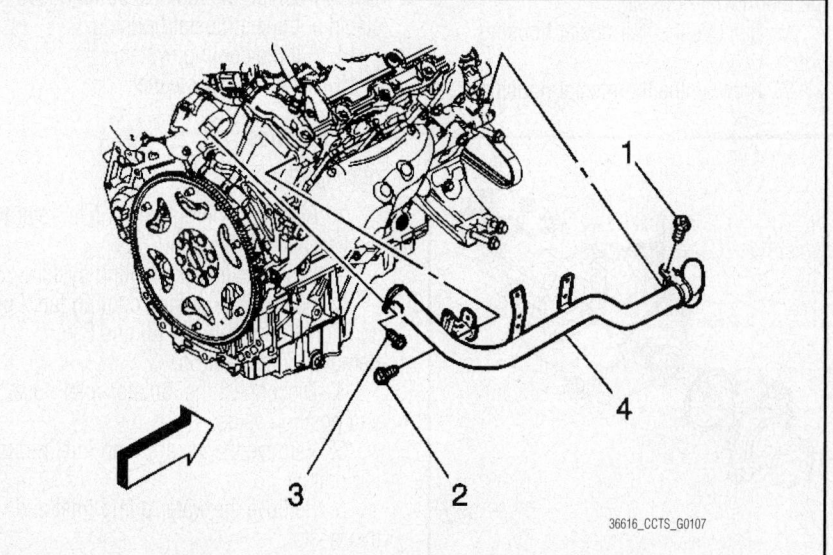

Fig. 50 Remove the coolant pipe bolts (1-3) to remove the coolant inlet pipe (4)—3.6L engines

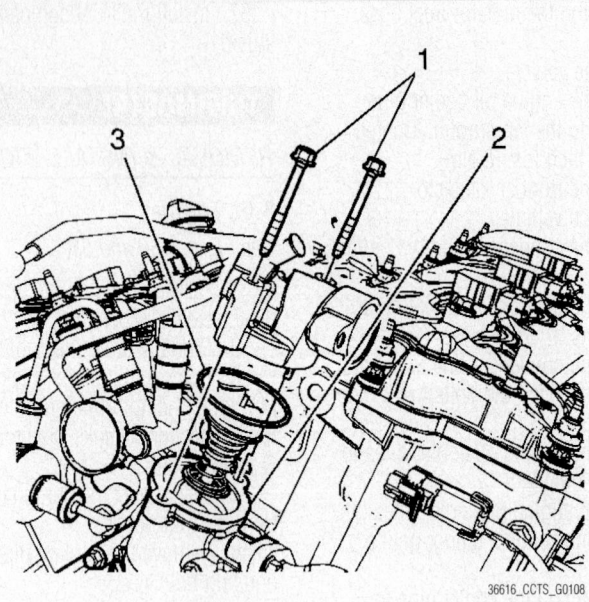

Fig. 51 Remove the mounting bolts (1) to remove the thermostat (2) and seal (3)—3.6L engines

14. Install the upper intake manifold.

15. Refill the cooling system to the correct level.

4.6L Engines

See Figure 52.

1. Before servicing the vehicle, refer to the Precautions Section.

2. Remove the air cleaner.

3. Drain the cooling system.

4. Reposition the radiator outlet hose clamp at the thermostat housing.

5. Remove the radiator outlet hose from the thermostat housing.

6. Remove the thermostat housing bolts.

7. Remove the thermostat housing,

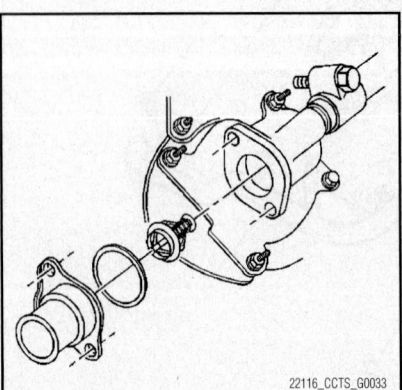

Fig. 52 Thermostat removal 4.6L engine

thermostat, and gasket from the water pump housing.

To install:

8. Install a NEW thermostat housing gasket into the water pump housing.

9. Install the thermostat into the water pump housing.

10. Install the thermostat housing.

11. Install the thermostat housing bolts. Tighten the bolts to 89 inch lbs. (10 Nm).

12. Install the radiator outlet hose to the thermostat housing.

13. Position the radiator outlet hose clamp at the thermostat housing.

14. Fill the cooling system.

15. Install the air cleaner.

6.2L Engines

See Figure 53.

1. Before servicing the vehicle, refer to the Precautions Section.

2. Drain the engine cooling system.

3. Remove the engine cooling fan. For additional information, "Engine Fan, Removal & Installation."

4. Disconnect the radiator inlet hose and position aside.

5. Remove the water pump inlet mounting bolts.

6. Remove the water pump inlet and thermostat.

7. Installation is the reverse order of removal. Install the thermostat with a

Fig. 53 Remove the inlet mounting bolts (1) and water pump inlet (2) to access the thermostat (3)—6.2L engine

NEW gasket and tighten the water pump inlet mounting bolts to 11 ft. lbs. (15 Nm).

WATER PUMP

REMOVAL & INSTALLATION

3.6L Engine

See Figure 54.

1. Before servicing the vehicle, refer to the Precautions Section.

2. Drain the cooling system.

3. Disconnect the negative battery cable.

4. Remove the alternator and water pump drive belt.

5. Install Water Pump holding tool EN-46104 to retain the water pump pulley.

6. Remove or disconnect the following:
   • Water pump pulley bolts
   • Water pump pulley
   • Water pump mounting bolts
   • Water pump

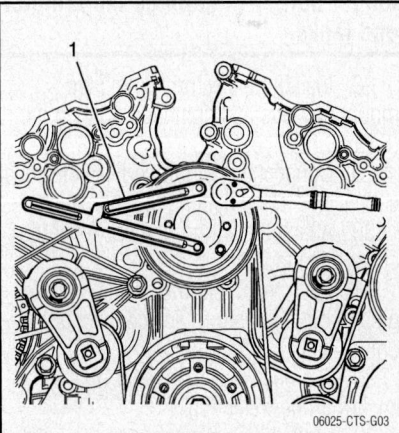

Fig. 54 Using special tool EN-46104 to retain the pulley when installing water pump pulley bolts—3.6L engine

To install:

7. Install or connect the following:
- Water pump with a NEW gasket. Tighten mounting bolts to 89 inch lbs. (10 Nm).
- Water pump pulley. Tighten pulley bolts to 106 inch lbs. (12 Nm).
- Drive belt
- Negative battery cable

8. Fill the cooling system to the correct level.

9. Start the engine and check for leaks.

4.6L Engine

See Figures 55 through 58.

1. Before servicing the vehicle, refer to the Precautions Section.
2. Drain the cooling system.
3. Remove the air cleaner.
4. Remove the fuel injector sight shield.
5. Remove the water pump drive belt.
6. Reposition the brake booster vacuum hose clamp at the water pump housing.
7. Remove the brake booster vacuum hose from the water pump housing.
8. Remove the oil level indicator tube nut.
9. Reposition the oil level indicator tube.
10. Remove the transaxle vent hose clip from the bracket.
11. Remove the throttle body bolts.
12. Remove the bracket.
13. Remove the throttle body.
14. Remove and discard the throttle body seal.
15. Loosen the throttle body plenum duct clamp.
16. Remove and discard the throttle body plenum duct.
17. Remove the fuel rail bracket nut at the rear left lift bracket.
18. Reposition the surge tank inlet hose clamp at the fitting.
19. Remove the surge tank inlet hose from the fitting.
20. Remove the engine coolant outlet fitting.
21. Remove the rear left lift bracket bolt.
22. Remove the rear left lift bracket.
23. Remove the exhaust gas recirculation (EGR) valve shield nuts.
24. Remove the EGR valve shield.
25. Remove the EGR valve bolts.
26. Remove the EGR valve.
27. Remove and discard the EGR valve gasket.
28. Disconnect the engine harness electrical connector from the engine valley electrical connector.
29. Raise and support the vehicle.
30. Disconnect the EGR inlet pipe nut from the exhaust manifold front pipe.

31. Lower the vehicle.
32. Remove the EGR inlet pipe bolt from the water pump housing.
33. Remove and discard the EGR inlet pipe.
34. Remove the Evaporative Emission (EVAP) canister purge solenoid valve bolt.
35. Remove the EVAP canister purge solenoid valve.
36. Remove the MAP sensor bracket.
37. Remove the MAP sensor.
38. Reposition the radiator inlet hose clamp at the water pump housing.
39. Remove the radiator inlet hose from the water pump housing.
40. Reposition the radiator outlet hose clamp at the thermostat housing.
41. Remove the radiator outlet hose from the thermostat housing.

42. Remove the water pump belt tensioner studs.
43. Remove the water pump belt tensioner.
44. Reposition the heater outlet hose clamp at the heater pipe.
45. Remove the heater outlet hose from the heater pipe.
46. Remove the water pump cover bolt and studs.
47. Remove the water pump cover.
48. Loosen the water pump housing bolts.
49. Remove the water pump housing.
50. Remove the water pump housing gaskets and bolts.
51. With the water pump housing on the bench, remove the water pump bolts.
52. Remove the water pump from the water pump housing.

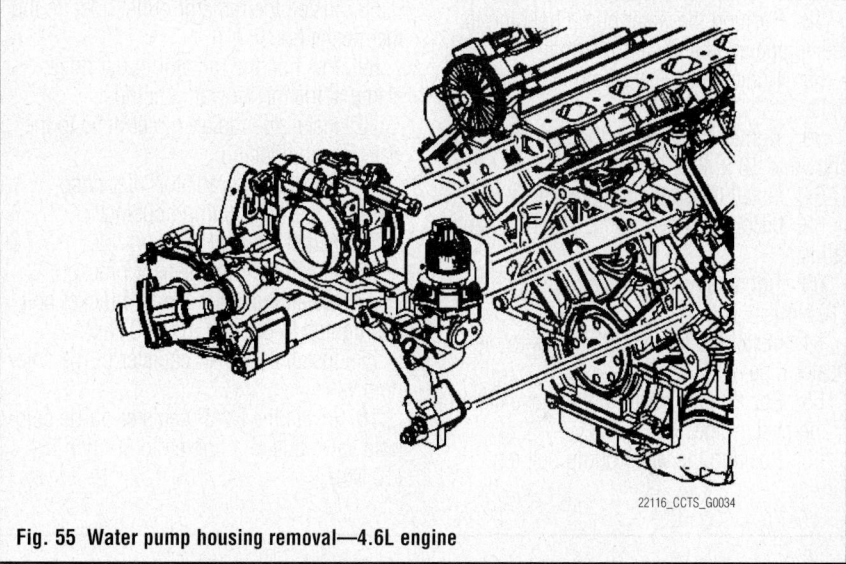

22116_CCTS_G0034

Fig. 55 Water pump housing removal—4.6L engine

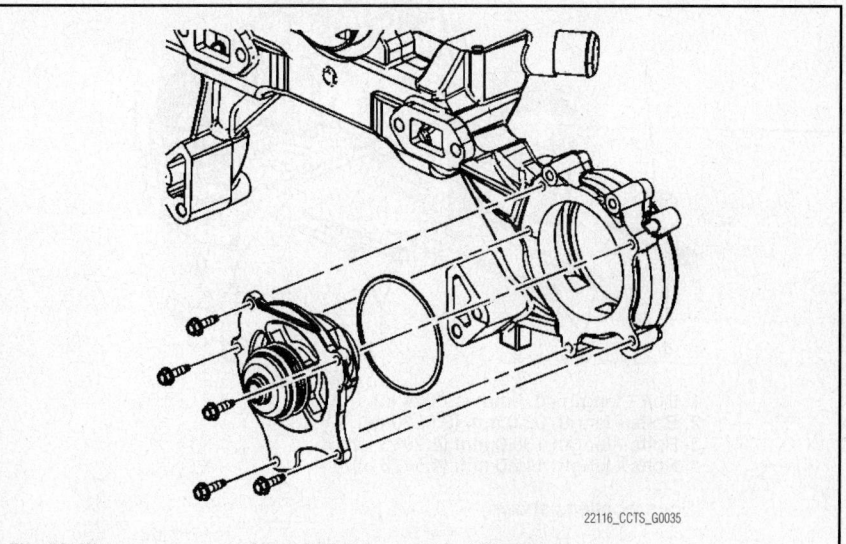

22116_CCTS_G0035

Fig. 56 Water pump removal from housing assembly 4.6L engine

53. Remove and discard the water pump O-ring.

To install:

54. Install a NEW water pump O-ring to the water pump.

55. Install the water pump and tighten mounting bolts to 89 inch lbs. (10 Nm).

56. With the water pump housing on the bench, install the bolts in the locations shown:

- Bolt (1) length 1.6024 inch (40.7 mm).
- Bolts (2) length 3.6220 inch (92.0 mm).
- Bolts (3) length 4.2913 inch (109.0 mm).
- Bolts (4) length 4.5276 inch (115.0 mm).

57. With the housing still on the bench, install the NEW water pump housing gasket onto the bolts.

58. Position the water pump housing to the engine and hand start the bolts.

59. Tighten the water pump housing bolts.

60. Tighten the bolts in the sequence shown to 18 ft. lbs. (25 Nm).

61. Install the water pump cover.

62. Install the water pump cover bolt and studs.

63. Tighten the bolt/studs to 89 inch lbs. (10 Nm).

64. Install the heater outlet hose to the heater pipe.

65. Position the heater outlet hose clamp at the heater pipe.

66. Position the water pump belt tensioner.

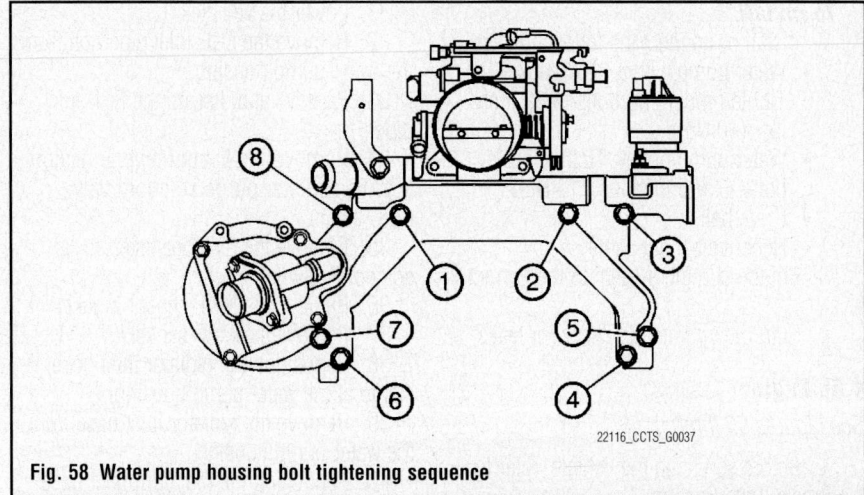

Fig. 58 Water pump housing bolt tightening sequence

67. Install the water pump belt tensioner studs and tighten to 89 inch lbs. (10 Nm).

68. Install the radiator outlet hose to the thermostat housing.

69. Position the radiator outlet hose clamp at the thermostat housing.

70. Install the radiator inlet hose to the water pump housing.

71. Position the radiator inlet hose clamp at the water pump housing.

72. Install the MAP sensor.

73. Install the MAP sensor bracket.

74. Install the MAP sensor bracket bolt and tighten to 89 inch lbs. (10 Nm).

75. Install the EVAP canister purge solenoid valve.

76. Install the EVAP canister purge solenoid valve bolt and tighten to 89 inch lbs. (10 Nm).

❄ WARNING

The EGR valve inlet pipe incorporates a crush seal connection at the water pump housing. The EGR valve inlet pipe must be replaced if disconnected from the water pump housing.

77. Hand start the NEW EGR inlet pipe nut at the exhaust manifold front pipe.

78. Install the EGR inlet pipe and bolt to the water pump housing. Tighten the nut to 44 ft. lbs. (60 Nm). Tighten the bolt to 18 ft. lbs. (25 Nm).

79. Raise and support the vehicle.

80. Tighten the EGR inlet pipe nut.

81. Tighten the nut to 44 ft. lbs. (60 Nm).

82. Lower the vehicle.

83. Connect the engine harness electrical connector (1) to the engine valley electrical connector.

84. Install the NEW EGR valve gasket.

85. Install the EGR valve.

86. Install the EGR valve bolts and tighten to 18 ft. lbs. (25 Nm).

87. Install the EGR valve shield.

88. Install the EGR valve shield nuts and tighten to 89 inch lbs. (10 Nm).

89. Position the rear left lift bracket to the water pump housing.

90. Install the rear left lift bracket bolt and tighten to 18 ft. lbs. (25 Nm).

91. Install the engine coolant outlet fitting, tighten the fitting to 35 ft. lbs. (47 Nm).

92. Install the surge tank inlet hose to the fitting.

93. Position the surge tank inlet hose clamp at the fitting.

94. Install the fuel rail bracket nut at the rear left lift bracket. Tighten the nut to 89 inch lbs. (10 Nm).

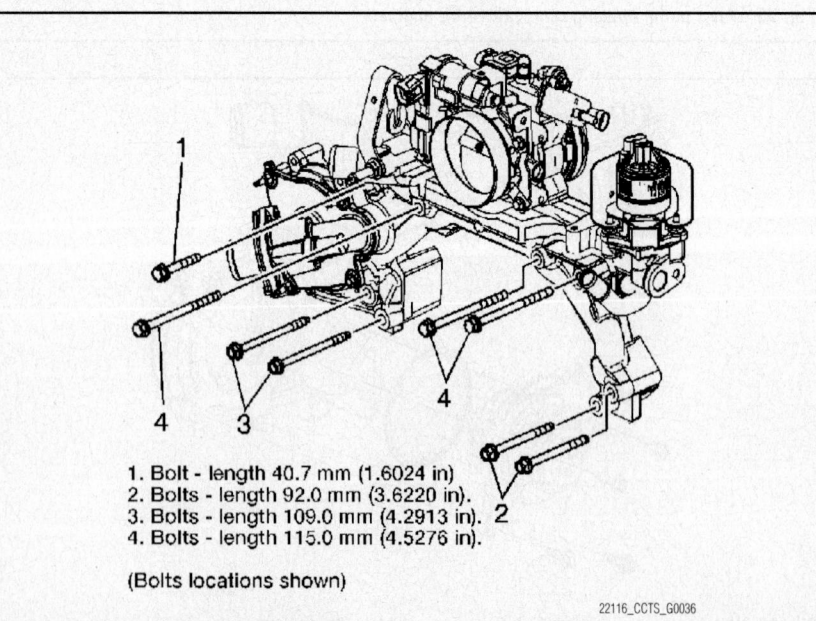

1. Bolt - length 40.7 mm (1.6024 in)
2. Bolts - length 92.0 mm (3.6220 in).
3. Bolts - length 109.0 mm (4.2913 in).
4. Bolts - length 115.0 mm (4.5276 in).

(Bolts locations shown)

Fig. 57 Water pump bolts locations shown

❋❋ **WARNING**

DO NOT use any type of sealant between the plenum and the water pump housing.

95. Install a NEW throttle body plenum duct.

96. Tighten the throttle body plenum duct clamp to 20 inch lbs. (2.25 Nm).

97. Install a NEW throttle body seal.

98. Install the throttle body.

99. Install the throttle body bracket.

100. Install the throttle body bolts and tighten to 89 inch lbs. (10 Nm).

101. Install the transaxle vent hose clip to the bracket.

102. Position the oil level indicator tube.

103. Install the oil level indicator tube nut and tighten to 89 inch lbs. (10 Nm).

104. Install the brake booster vacuum hose to the water pump housing.

105. Position the brake booster vacuum hose clamp at the water pump housing.

106. Install the water pump drive belt.

107. Install the air cleaner.

108. Fill the cooling system.

109. Install the fuel injector sight shield.

6.2L Engine

See Figure 59.

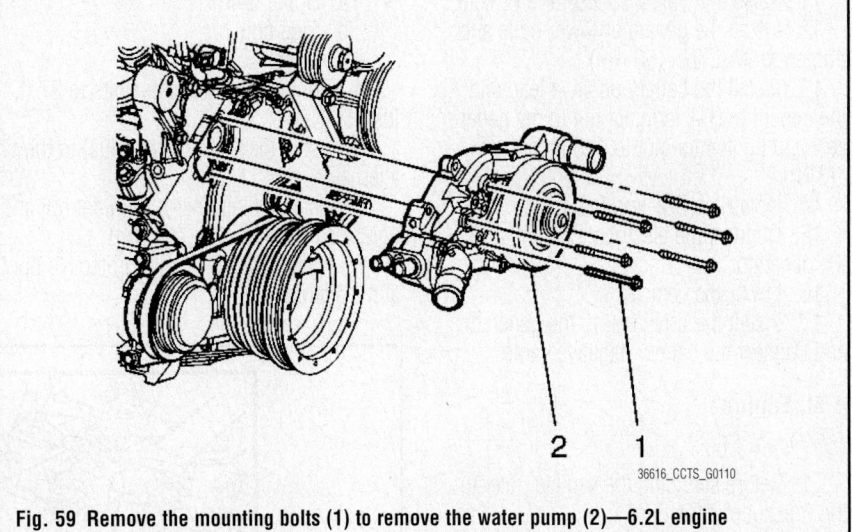

Fig. 59 Remove the mounting bolts (1) to remove the water pump (2)—6.2L engine

1. Remove the air cleaner outlet duct.
2. Drain the cooling system.
3. Remove the supercharger belt.
4. Remove the drive belt tensioner.
5. Remove the drive belt idler pulley.
6. Remove the supercharger belt idler pulley bracket.
7. Disconnect the radiator inlet hose from the water pump.
8. Disconnect the radiator outlet hose from the water pump.
9. Disconnect the heater inlet hose/pipe and heater outlet hose/pipe.
10. Remove the supercharger belt tensioner bracket.
11. Remove the water pump to block bolts.
12. Reposition the pump to access the oil cooler hose. Remove the clamp and pull the pump away from the hose.
13. Remove the water pump.
14. Installation is the reverse order of removal. Install the water pump with a new gasket and tighten the mounting bolts to 22 ft. lbs. (30 Nm).

ENGINE ELECTRICAL

CHARGING SYSTEM

ALTERNATOR

REMOVAL & INSTALLATION

3.6L Engine

See Figure 60.

1. Disconnect the battery negative cable.

2. Remove the drive belt from the generator.

3. Raise and safely support the vehicle.

4. Disconnect the electrical connector from the alternator.

5. Reposition the protective boot from the generator output BAT terminal for access.

6. Remove the alternator output BAT terminal nut and disconnect the battery positive lead from the alternator.

7. Remove the alternator lower bolts.

8. Lower the vehicle.

9. Remove the alternator upper bolt and remove the alternator from the engine.

To install:

10. Install the generator to the engine and install the generator upper bolt.

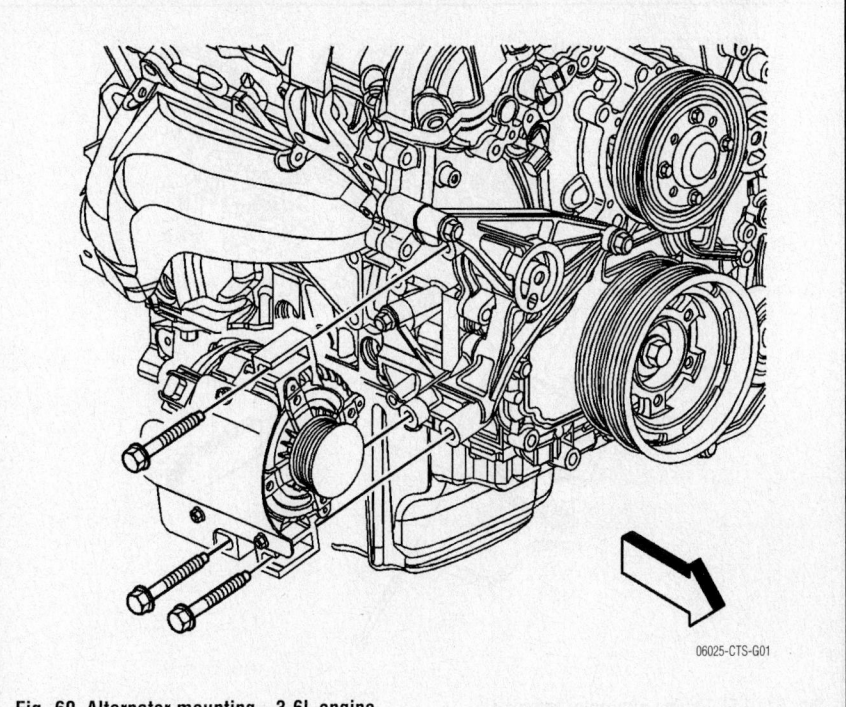

Fig. 60 Alternator mounting—3.6L engine

11. Raise and safely support the vehicle.

12. Install the generator lower bolts and tighten to 37 ft. lbs. (50 Nm).

13. Install the battery positive lead and the generator BAT terminal nut to the generator and tighten the nut to 115 inch lbs. (13 Nm).

14. Install the BAT terminal boot.

15. Connect the electrical connector to the generator.

16. Lower the vehicle.

17. Install the drive belt to the generator and connect the battery negative cable.

4.6L Engine

See Figure 61.

1. Before servicing the vehicle, refer to the Precautions Section.

2. Disconnect the negative battery cable.

3. Remove the radiator.

4. Remove the drive belt.

5. Disconnect the engine wiring harness electrical connector from the alternator.

6. Reposition the B+ cable protective boot at the alternator.

7. Remove the alternator terminal nut.

8. Remove the B+ cable terminal from the alternator.

9. Remove the alternator bolts.

10. Reposition the engine ground cable.

11. Remove the alternator.

To install:

12. Position the alternator to the engine.

13. Install the alternator bolts finger tight in the following sequence.

a. Upper bolt
b. Side bolt
c. Lower bolt

14. Tighten the alternator bolts to 37 ft. lbs. (50 Nm).

15. Install the B+ cable terminal to the alternator.

16. Install the alternator terminal nut and tighten to 106 inch lbs. (12 Nm).

17. Position the B+ cable protective boot at the alternator.

18. Connect the engine wiring harness electrical connector (5) to the generator.

19. Install the drive belt.

20. Install the radiator.

21. Connect the negative battery cable.

22. Refill the radiator and bleed cooling system.

6.2L Engine

See Figure 62.

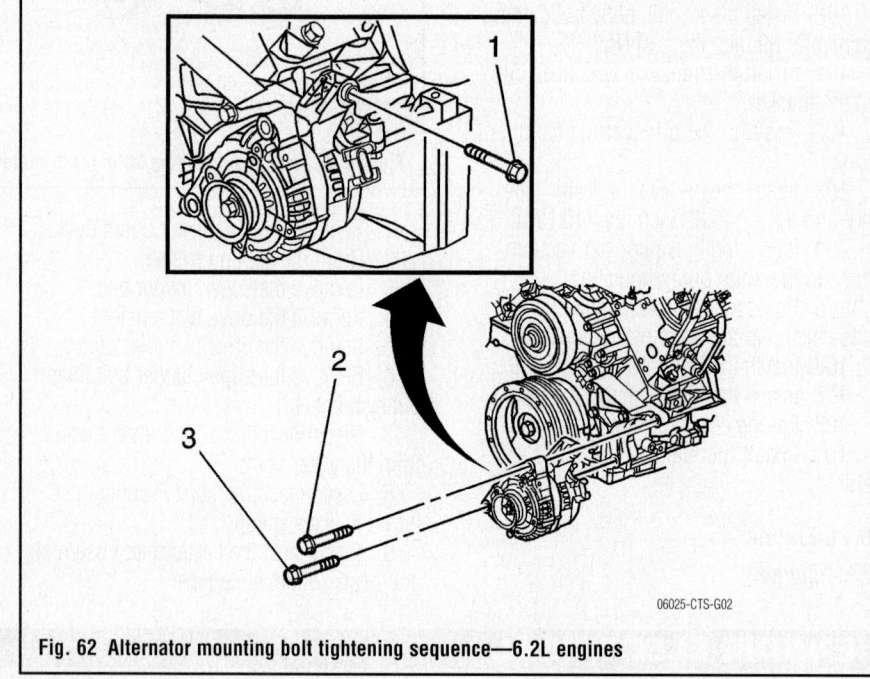

Fig. 62 Alternator mounting bolt tightening sequence—6.2L engines

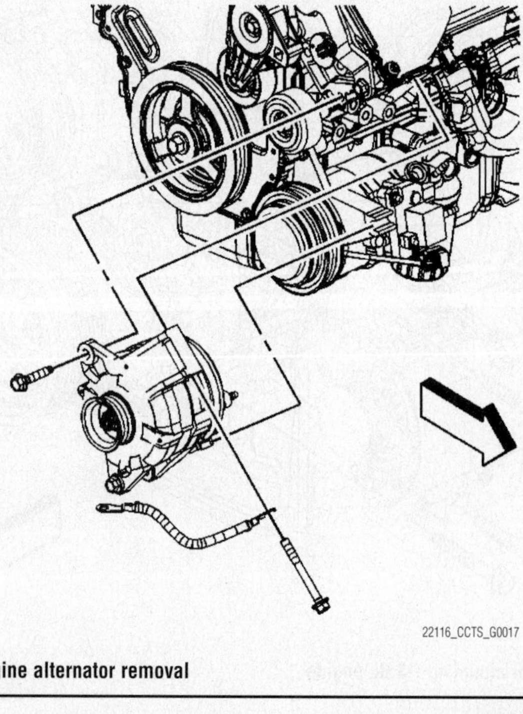

06025-CTS-G02

1. Before servicing the vehicle, refer to the Precautions Section.

2. Disconnect the battery negative cable.

3. Remove the air cleaner assembly.

4. Remove the radiator fan assembly.

5. Remove the accessory drive belt.

6. Remove the bolt securing the power steering pressure hose bracket to the alternator.

7. Remove the rear alternator mounting bolt.

8. Remove the front alternator mounting bolts.

9. Lift the generator off of the mounting bracket in order to gain access to the connector and the generator output BAT terminal nut.

10. Disconnect the wire harness electrical connector from the alternator.

11. Reposition the protective boot from the alternator output battery terminal for access.

12. Remove the alternator output battery terminal nut and disconnect the battery positive lead from the alternator.

Fig. 61 4.6L Engine alternator removal

22116_CCTS_G0017

13. Remove the alternator from the vehicle.

To install:

14. Position the alternator near the installed position.

15. Connect the battery positive lead to the alternator and install the alternator output battery terminal nut.

16. Tighten the alternator output battery terminal nut to 115 inch lbs. (13 Nm).

17. Press the protective boot on to the alternator output BAT terminal.

18. Connect the wiring harness connector to the alternator.

19. Position the alternator to the alternator bracket on the engine.

20. Install the front alternator mounting bolts, but do not tighten at this time.

21. Install the rear alternator mounting bolt.

22. Tighten the alternator mounting bolts in the following order:

- Tighten the front alternator mounting bolt to 37 ft. lbs. (50 Nm)

- Tighten the front alternator mounting bolt to 37 ft. lbs. (50 Nm)

- Tighten the rear alternator mounting bolt to 37 ft. lbs. (50 Nm)

23. Tighten the power steering pressure hose bracket nut to 80 inch lbs. (9 Nm).

24. Install the accessory drive belt

25. Install the radiator fan assembly.

26. Install the air cleaner assembly.

27. Connect the battery negative cable.

ENGINE ELECTRICAL

FIRING ORDERS

See Figures 63 and 64.

The Northstar V8 VIN Code 9 or Y is a 4.6L engine. The cylinders are arranged in 2 banks of 4 with a 90 degrees included angle. The left (front) bank of cylinders are number 2-4-6-8 and the right (rear) bank cylinders are 1-3-5-7. Engine firing order is 1-2-7-3-4-5-6-8.

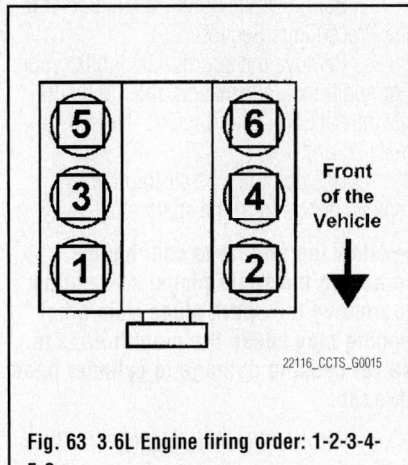

Fig. 63 3.6L Engine firing order: 1-2-3-4-5-6

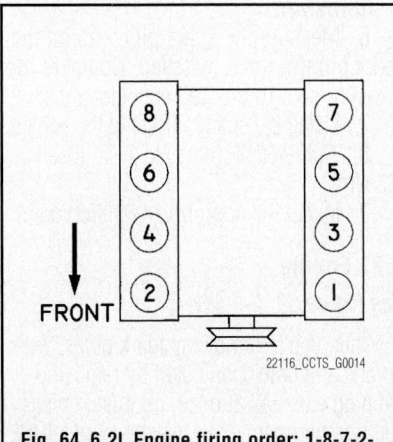

Fig. 64 6.2L Engine firing order: 1-8-7-2-6-5-4-3

IGNITION COIL

REMOVAL & INSTALLATION

3.6L Engines

1. Before servicing the vehicle, refer to the Precautions Section.

2. Turn the ignition **OFF**.

3. Remove the engine appearance cover.

4. Disconnect the air cleaner duct from the throttle body. Disconnect the positive crankcase ventilation (PCV) hose from the camshaft cover. Remove the intake manifold bolts, but do not separate the upper intake manifold from the lower intake manifold.

5. Remove the intake manifold brace bolts and the brace.

6. Remove and reposition the upper intake manifold with the lower intake manifold in order to gain sufficient clearance for ignition coil removal.

7. Remove the ignition coil electrical connector.

8. Remove the ignition coil bolt.

9. Remove the ignition coil(s).

To install:

10. Install the ignition coil(s).

11. Install the ignition coil bolt(s) and tighten to 89 inch lbs. (10 Nm).

12. Install the ignition coil electrical connector(s).

13. Install the intake manifold.

14. Install the engine cover.

4.6L Engine

See Figure 65.

1. Before servicing the vehicle, refer to the Precautions Section.

2. Remove the fuel injector sight shield.

3. Disconnect the individual ignition coil electrical connector, as required.

4. Remove the individual ignition coil bolt, as required.

IGNITION SYSTEM

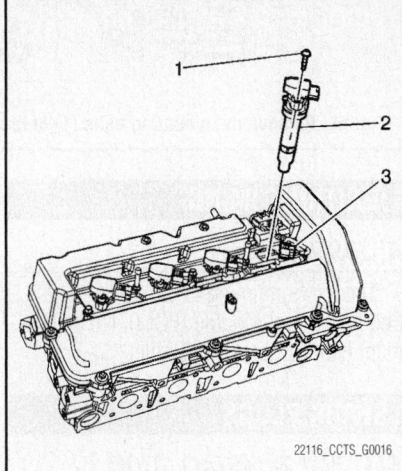

Fig. 65 Ignition coil (2) removal—4.6L engine

5. Remove the ignition coil, as required.

To install:

6. Install the ignition coil, as required.

7. Install the individual ignition coil bolt, as required.

8. Tighten the bolt to 89 inch lbs. (10 Nm).

9. Connect the individual ignition coil electrical connector, as required.

10. Install the fuel injector sight shield.

6.2L Engine

See Figure 66.

1. If replacing front coils, remove the front intake manifold cover.

2. If replacing rear coils, remove the front and rear intake manifold cover.

3. Remove the ignition coil mounting bolt.

4. Disconnect the ignition coil electrical connector and remove the ignition coil.

5. Installation is the reverse order of removal. Tighten the mounting bolts to 106 inch lbs. (12 Nm).

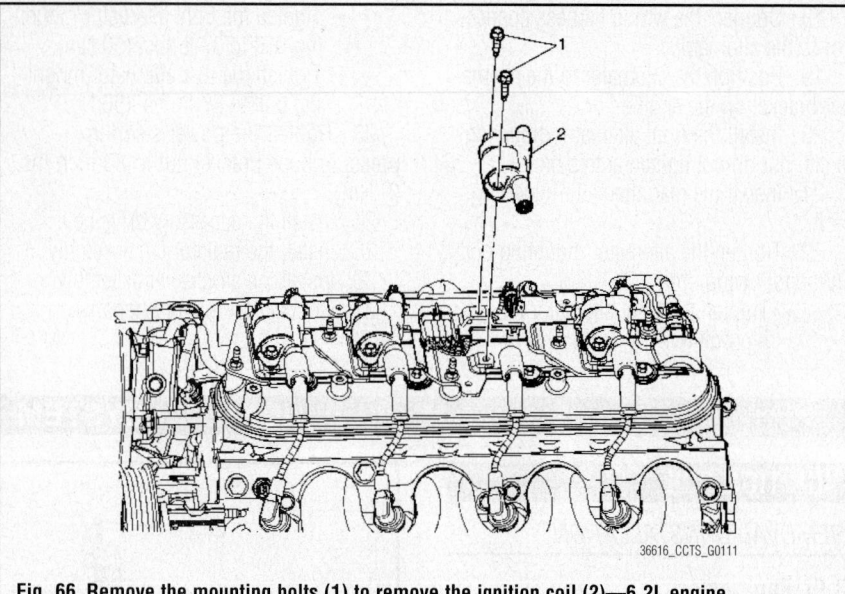

Fig. 66 Remove the mounting bolts (1) to remove the ignition coil (2)—6.2L engine

IGNITION TIMING

ADJUSTMENT

The ignition timing is controlled by the Engine Control Module (ECM). No adjustment is necessary or possible.

SPARK PLUGS

REMOVAL & INSTALLATION

3.6L Engines

See Figure 67.

1. Before servicing the vehicle, refer to the Precautions Section.
2. Turn the ignition OFF.
3. Remove the ignition coil.
4. Use compressed air in order to remove debris from the spark plug cavity.

➡Allow the engine to cool before removing the spark plugs. Attempting to remove the spark plugs from a hot engine may cause the plug threads to seize, causing damage to cylinder head threads.

5. Remove the spark plug.

To install:

➡Use only the spark plugs specified for use in the vehicle. Do not install spark plugs that are either hotter or colder than those specified for the vehicle. Installing spark plugs of another type can severely damage the engine.

6. Ensure that the spark plug gap is equivalent to the spark plug gap specification.
7. Install the spark plug.

8. Tighten the spark plug to 15 inch lbs. (20 Nm).
9. Install the ignition coil and mounting bolt.
10. Tighten the ignition coil bolt to 89 inch lbs. (10 Nm).

4.6L Engine

See Figure 68.

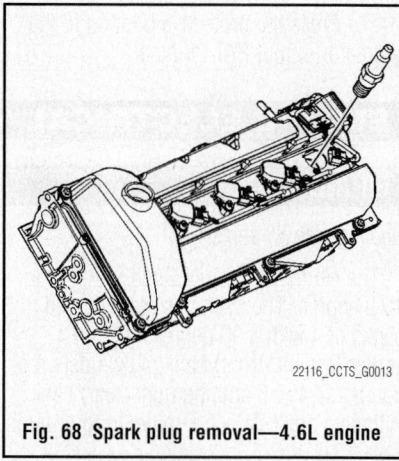

Fig. 68 Spark plug removal—4.6L engine

1. Before servicing the vehicle, refer to the Precautions Section.
2. Remove the appropriate ignition coil. For additional information, refer to the following section, "Ignition Coil Removal & Installation."
3. Use compressed air in order to remove debris from the spark plug cavity.

➡Allow the engine to cool before removing the spark plugs. Attempting to remove the spark plugs from a hot engine may cause the plug threads to seize, causing damage to cylinder head threads.

4. Remove the spark plug(s) from the engine.
5. Inspect the spark plugs.

To install:

6. Measure the spark plug gap on the spark plug(s) to be installed. Compare the measurement to the gap specifications.
7. Install the spark plug(s) to the engine.
8. Tighten the plug(s) to 11 ft. lbs. (15 Nm).
9. Install the appropriate ignition coil.

6.2L Engine

See Figure 69.

When you're removing spark plugs, work on one at a time. Don't start by removing the plug wires all at once, because, unless you number them, they may become mixed up. Take a minute before you begin and number the wires with tape.

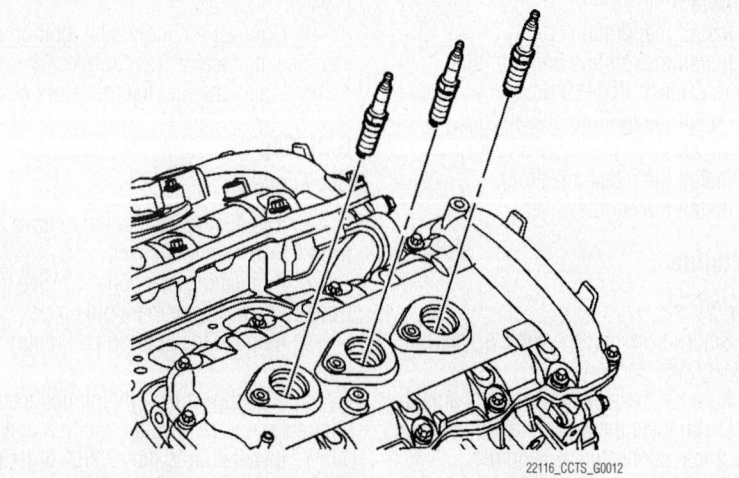

Fig. 67 Spark plug removal—3.6L engine

Always allow the engine to thoroughly cool before removing the spark plugs, or the threads in the cylinder head may be damaged.

1. Disconnect the negative battery cable, and if the vehicle has been run recently, allow the engine to thoroughly cool.

2. Carefully twist the spark plug wire boot to loosen it, then pull upward and remove the boot from the plug. Be sure to pull on the boot and not on the wire, otherwise the connector located inside the boot may become separated.

3. Using compressed air, blow any water or debris from the spark plug well to assure that no harmful contaminants are allowed to enter the combustion chamber when the spark plug is removed. If compressed air is not available, use a rag or a brush to clean the area.

➡Remove the spark plugs when the engine is cold, to prevent damage to the threads. If removal of the plugs is difficult, apply a few drops of penetrating oil or silicone spray to the area around the base of the plug, and allow it a few minutes to work.

4. Using a spark plug socket that is equipped with a rubber insert to properly hold the plug, turn the spark plug counterclockwise to loosen and remove the spark plug from the bore.

Be sure not to use a flexible extension on the socket. Use of a flexible

extension may allow a shear force to be applied to the plug. A shear force could break the plug off in the cylinder head, leading to costly and frustrating repairs.

5. Place the spark plugs in a tray labeled by cylinder number to help identify the spark plug and relate any unusual condition with the cylinder involved.

To install:

6. Inspect the spark plug boot for tears or damage. If a damaged boot is found, the spark plug wire must be replaced.

7. Using a wire feeler gauge, check and adjust the spark plug gap. When using a gauge, the proper size should pass between the electrodes with a slight drag. The next larger size should not be able to

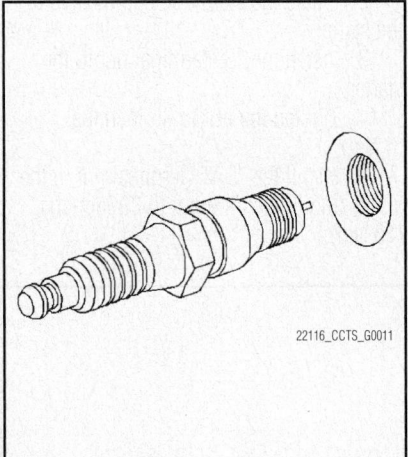

Fig. 69 Spark plug removal shown—6.2L engine

pass while the next smaller size should pass freely.

8. Carefully thread the plug into the bore by hand. If resistance is felt before the plug is almost completely threaded, back the plug out and begin threading again. In small, hard to reach areas, an old spark plug wire and boot could be used as a threading tool. The boot will hold the plug while you twist the end of the wire and the wire is supple enough to twist before it would allow the plug to crossthread.

Do not use the spark plug socket to thread the plugs. Always carefully thread the plug by hand or using an old plug wire to prevent the possibility of crossthreading and damaging the cylinder head bore.

9. Carefully tighten the spark plug. If the plug you are installing is equipped with a crush washer, seat the plug, then tighten about ¼ turn to crush the washer. If you are installing a tapered seat plug, tighten the plug to specifications provided by the vehicle or plug manufacturer. Tighten the spark plugs to 15 ft. lbs. (20 Nm).

10. Apply a small amount of silicone dielectric compound to the end of the spark plug lead or inside the spark plug boot to prevent sticking, then install the boot to the spark plug and push until it clicks into place. The click may be felt or heard, then gently pull back on the boot to assure proper contact.

ENGINE ELECTRICAL   STARTING SYSTEM

STARTER

REMOVAL & INSTALLATION

3.6L Engine

See Figure 70.

1. Before servicing the vehicle, refer to the Precautions Section.

2. Ensure the ignition is in the **OFF** position.

3. Disconnect the negative battery cable.

4. Remove the left catalytic converter.

5. Remove the starter solenoid electrical connector from the starter.

6. Remove the starter terminal nut and the engine harness from the starter.

7. Remove the starter mounting bolts and the starter.

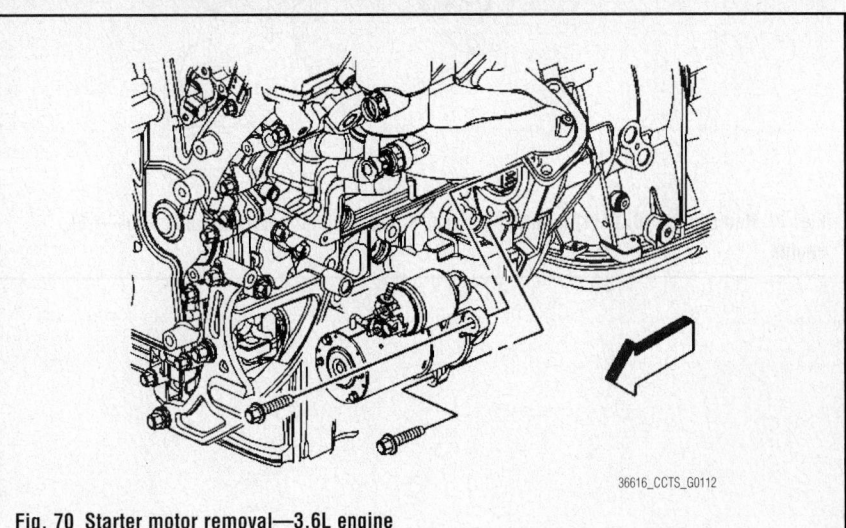

Fig. 70 Starter motor removal—3.6L engine

To install:

8. Install the starter motor and tighten the mounting bolts to 37 ft. lbs. (50 Nm).

9. Install the battery positive cable to the starter and install the starter terminal nut and tighten to 10 ft. lbs. (13 Nm).

10. The remainder of the installation is the reverse order of removal.

4.6L Engine

See Figures 71 and 72.

1. Before servicing the vehicle, refer to the Precautions Section.

2. Disconnect the negative battery cable.

3. Remove the intake manifold. Refer to Intake Manifold Replacement.

4. Remove the "BAT" terminal nut from the starter.

5. Remove the "S" terminal nut from the starter.

6. Remove the starter solenoid cable from the starter.

7. Remove the starter motor bolts.

8. Remove the starter motor.

To install:

9. Install the starter motor.

10. Install the starter motor bolts.

11. Tighten the bolts to 18 ft. lbs. (25 Nm).

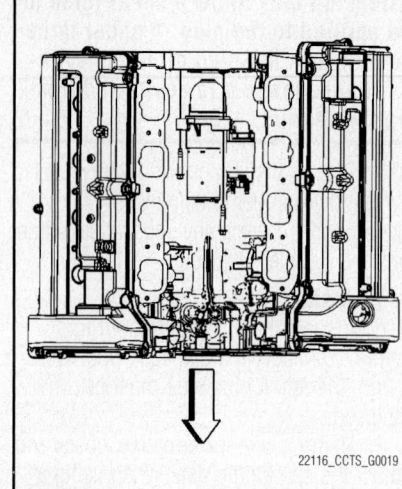

22116_CCTS_G0019

Fig. 72 Starter motor removal—4.6L engine

12. Install the starter solenoid cable to the starter.

13. Install the "S" terminal nut to the starter.

14. Tighten the nut to 35 inch lbs. (4 Nm).

15. Install the "BAT" terminal nut to the starter and tighten the nut to 89 inch lbs. (10 Nm).

16. Install the intake manifold. For additional information, refer to the following section, "Intake Manifold, Removal & Installation".

17. Connect the negative battery cable.

6.2L Engine

See Figure 73.

1. Before servicing the vehicle, refer to the Precautions Section.

2. Remove or disconnect the following:
   - Negative battery cable
   - Right side catalytic converter
   - Positive battery cable
   - Starter electrical connections
   - Starter motor mounting bolts
   - Starter motor

To install:

3. Install or connect the following:
   - Starter motor. Tighten the mounting bolts to 37 ft. lbs. (50 Nm).
   - Starter motor electrical connections
   - Positive battery cable
   - Right side catalytic converter
   - Negative battery cable

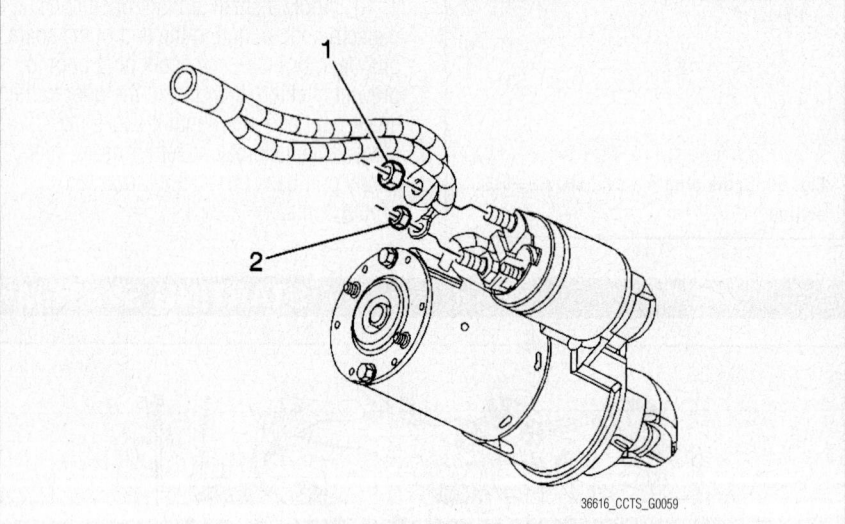

36616_CCTS_G0059

Fig. 71 Remove the "BAT" (1) terminal nut and "S" (2) terminal nut from the starter—4.6L engine

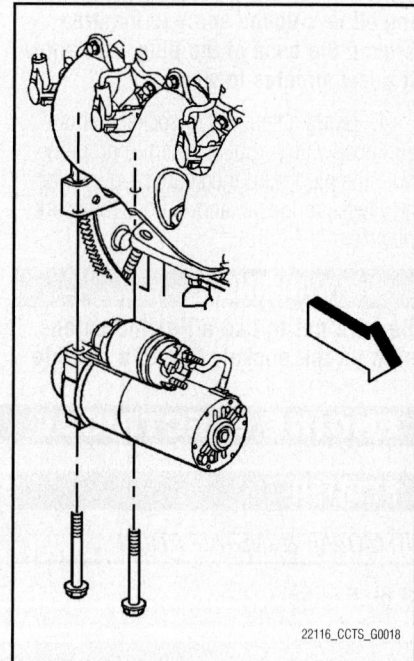

22116_CCTS_G0018

Fig. 73 Starter motor removal—6.2L engines

ENGINE MECHANICAL

ACCESSORY DRIVE BELTS

ACCESSORY BELT ROUTING

See Figures 74 through 77.

INSPECTION

Inspect the drive belt for signs of glazing or cracking. A glazed belt will be perfectly smooth from slippage, while a good belt will have a slight texture of fabric visible. Cracks will usually start at the inner edge of the belt and run outward. All worn or damaged drive belts should be replaced immediately.

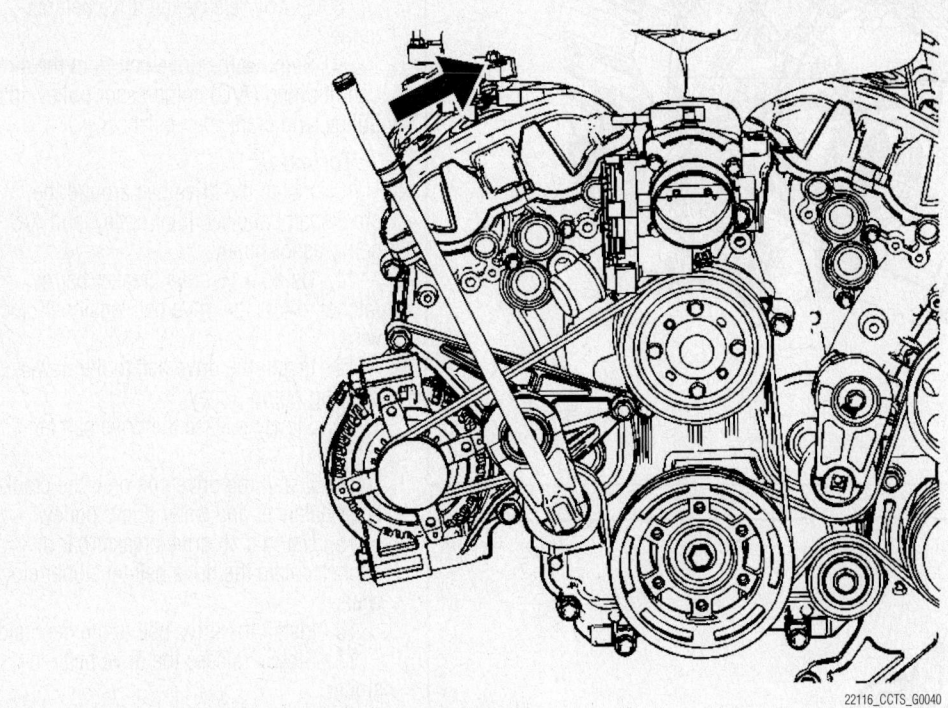

22116_CCTS_G0040

Fig. 74 Water pump and alternator belt routing—3.6L engines

22116_CCTS_G0039

Fig. 75 A/C and power steering belt routing—3.6L engines

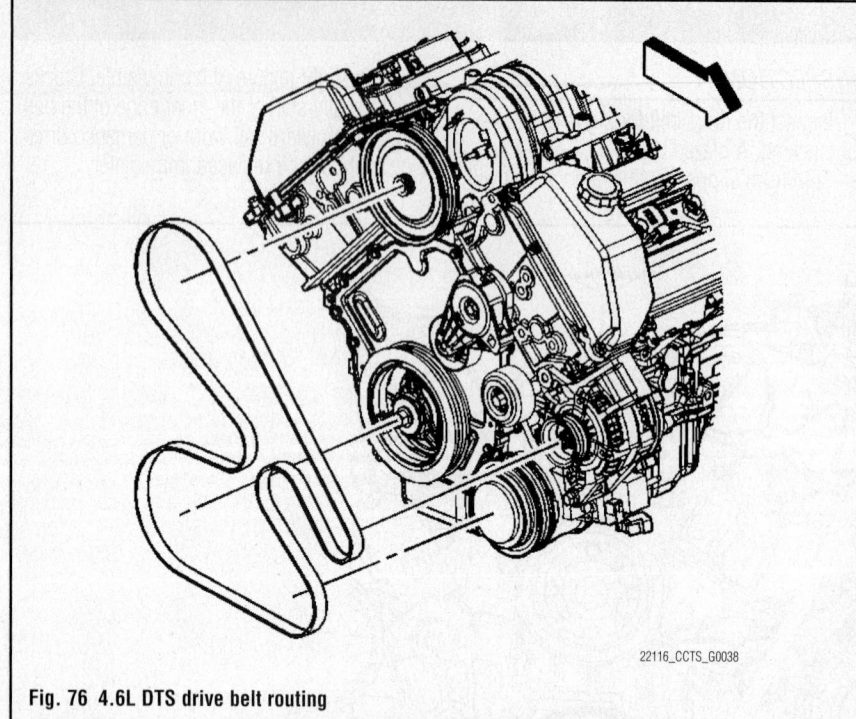

Fig. 76 4.6L DTS drive belt routing

22116_CCTS_G0038

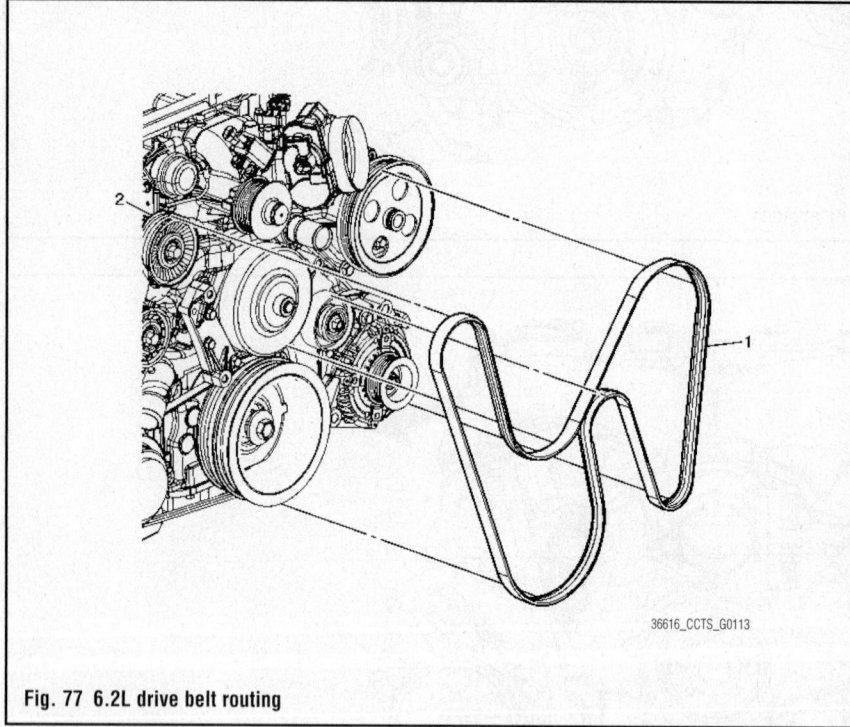

36616_CCTS_G0113

Fig. 77 6.2L drive belt routing

ADJUSTMENT

Belt tension is automatically adjusted by the belt tensioner. If tension is not within specification, the belt or the belt tensioner must be replaced.

REMOVAL & INSTALLATION

3.6L Engines

See Figures 74 and 75.

1. Before servicing the vehicle, refer to the Precautions Section.
2. Using a ½ drive breaker bar or ratchet, rotate the drive belt tensioner clockwise in order to release tension on the drive belt.
3. Remove the drive belt from the generator pulley.
4. Slowly release the drive belt tensioner.

5. Remove the drive belt from the water pump pulley and crankshaft balancer.
6. Using a ½ drive breaker bar or ratchet, rotate the drive belt tensioner clockwise in order to release tension on the drive belt.
7. Remove the drive belt from the power steering pump pulley.
8. Slowly release the drive belt tensioner.
9. Remove the drive belt from the air conditioning (A/C) compressor pulley, idler pulley, and crankshaft balancer.

To install:

10. Install the drive belt around the crankshaft balancer, idler pulley, and A/C compressor pulley.
11. Using a ½ drive breaker bar or ratchet, rotate the drive belt tensioner clockwise.
12. Install the drive belt to the power steering pump pulley.
13. Slowly release the drive belt tensioner.
14. Install the drive belt onto the crankshaft balancer and water pump pulley.
15. Using a ½ drive breaker bar or ratchet, rotate the drive belt tensioner clockwise.
16. Install the drive belt to the generator.
17. Slowly release the drive belt tensioner.
18. Ensure the drive belt is properly aligned and seated into the grooves of the accessory drive pulleys.

4.6L Engine

See Figure 76.

1. Before servicing the vehicle, refer to the Precautions Section.
2. Remove the right front wheelhouse liner.
3. Install a ½ inch drive breaker to the drive belt tensioner.
4. Push down on the breaker bar in order to release the tension.
5. Remove the drive belt from the power steering pump.
6. Slowly return the tensioner to the original position.
7. Remove the belt from the lower pulley and idlers.
8. Partially raise the vehicle.

To install:

9. Route the drive belt around all the pulleys except for the power steering pump.
10. Lower the vehicle.
11. Install a ½ inch drive breaker bar to the drive belt tensioner.
12. Push down on the breaker bar in order to release the tension and route the

belt around the power steering pump pulley. Ensure the belt is seated on all pulleys.

13. Slowly return the tensioner to its original position.

14. After drive belt installation, inspect the drive belt for the proper routing and correct alignment.

15. Install the right front wheelhouse liner.

16. Start the engine and check for proper belt and accessory operation.

6.2L Engine

See Figure 77.

1. Before servicing the vehicle, refer to the Precautions Section.

2. Remove the air cleaner resonator outlet duct.

3. Install a ½ inch drive breaker to the supercharger belt tensioner.

4. Push down on the breaker bar in order to release the tension and remove the supercharger belt.

5. Install a ½ inch drive breaker to the drive belt tensioner.

6. Push down on the breaker bar in order to release the tension and remove the drive belt.

To install:

7. Route the drive belt around all the pulleys except for the power steering pump.

8. Install a ½ inch drive breaker bar to the drive belt tensioner.

9. Push down on the breaker bar in order to release the tension and route the belt around the power steering pump pulley. Ensure the belt is seated on all pulleys.

10. Slowly return the tensioner to its original position.

11. After drive belt installation, inspect the drive belt for the proper routing and correct alignment.

12. Install a ½ inch drive breaker bar to the supercharger belt tensioner.

13. Push down on the breaker bar in order to release the tension and route the supercharger belt into its original position. Ensure the belt is seated on all pulleys.

14. Slowly return the tensioner to its original position.

15. Install the air cleaner resonator outlet duct.

CAMSHAFT AND VALVE LIFTERS

REMOVAL & INSTALLATION

3.6L Engine

See Figures 78 through 82.

1. Before servicing the vehicle, refer to the Precautions Section.

2. Ensure the ignition is in the **OFF** position.

3. Remove the upper intake manifold with the lower intake manifold. For additional information, refer to the following section, "Intake Manifold, Removal & Installation."

4. Disconnect the ignition coil electrical connectors.

5. Remove the wiring harness from the side of the camshaft cover by sliding the conduit down and outboard.

6. Remove the wiring conduit retainers from the camshaft cover by rotating the wiring harness conduit retainers counterclockwise.

➡**It is not necessary to disconnect the engine front cover electrical connectors.**

7. Remove the wiring harness from the front of the camshaft cover.

8. Reposition and secure the wiring harnesses away from the camshaft cover in order to provide clearance.

9. Remove the ignition coils.

10. Remove the camshaft cover. Remove and discard the camshaft cover seal and grommets.

11. Remove the camshaft position sensors. For additional information, refer to the following section, "Camshaft Position Sensor, Removal & Installation."

12. Rotate the crankshaft until the camshafts are in the neutral (low) position. The camshaft flats will be parallel with the camshaft cover rail.

13. Loosen the camshaft position actuator bolt.

14. Unscrew the timing chain retention tool so that the legs of the tool are retracted.

15. Insert the timing chain retention tool between the camshaft actuators, rearward of the timing chain until the bottom line that is scribed in the body of the tool is adjacent to the top surface of the cylinder head. This is the approximate installed position.

16. Ensure that the feet on the legs of the tool are facing the front of the engine.

17. Partially expand the legs of the timing chain retention tool by turning the T-shaped handle clockwise.

18. Insert the leg of the tool behind the timing chain guide.

19. Continue expanding the timing chain retention tool until the legs contact the timing chain. Do not tighten at this time.

20. Hand tighten the timing chain retention tool.

21. Use an open end wrench on the hex cast into the left intake and exhaust camshafts and rotate the camshafts toward each other in order to create slack in the chain between the actuators.

22. Mark the timing chain and the respective locations on the camshaft position actuators.

23. Remove the camshaft position actuator bolt.

24. Observe the markings on the bearing caps. Each bearing cap is marked in order to identify its location. The markings have the following meanings:

- The raised feature must always be oriented toward the center of the cylinder head.
- The I indicates the intake camshaft.
- The E indicates the exhaust camshaft.

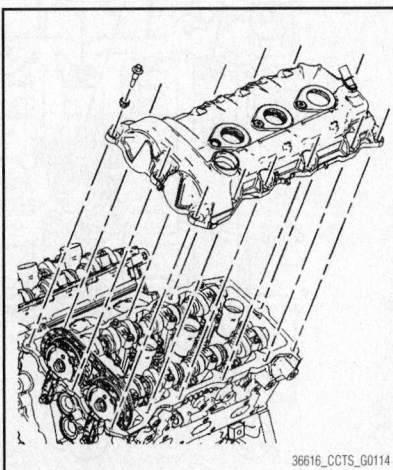

Fig. 78 Removing the camshaft cover, left side shown—3.6L engines

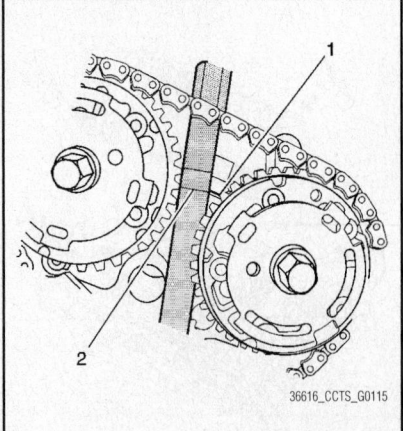

Fig. 79 Insert the timing chain retention tool between the camshaft actuators, rearward of the timing chain until the bottom line that is scribed in the body of the tool (2) is adjacent to the top surface of the cylinder head (1)—3.6L engine

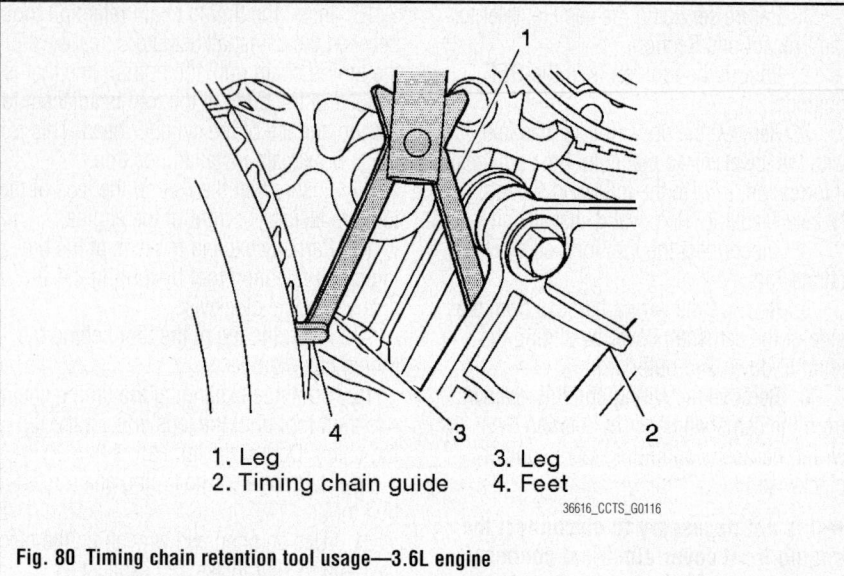

1. Leg
2. Timing chain guide
3. Leg
4. Feet

36616_CCTS_G0116

Fig. 80 Timing chain retention tool usage—3.6L engine

- The number indicates the journal position from the front of the engine.

25. Remove the camshaft bearing cap bolts and bearing caps.

➡**Matchmark the camshafts upon removal to ensure installation is in the correct position.**

26. Remove the camshafts.

To install:

27. Replace the camshaft bearing caps and bolts.

28. Ensure that the camshaft sealing rings are in place in the camshaft grooves. Camshaft sealing rings must be in place below the surface of the camshaft journal in order to avoid being pinched between the cylinder head and the camshaft caps.

29. Apply a liberal amount of lubricant GM P/N 12345501 (Canadian P/N 992704) or equivalent to the camshaft journals and the left cylinder head camshaft carriers.

30. Place the left intake and left exhaust camshafts in position in the left cylinder head.

➡**Observe the markings on the left cylinder head camshaft bearing caps. Each bearing cap is marked in order to identify its location.**

31. Apply a liberal amount of lubricant GM P/N 12345501 (Canadian P/N 992704) or equivalent to the camshaft bearing caps.

32. Install the camshaft bearing thrust cap in the first journal of the left cylinder head.

33. Install the remaining bearing caps with their orientation mark toward the center of the cylinder head.

34. Hand start all the camshaft bearing cap bolts.

35. Tighten the camshaft bearing cap bolts in the sequence shown and tighten to 89 inch lbs. (10 Nm).

36. Loosen the center intake camshaft bearing cap bolts and the center exhaust camshaft bearing cap bolts.

37. Retighten the center camshaft bearing cap bolts and retighten the camshaft bearing cap bolts to 89 lb in. (10 Nm).

38. Remove the timing chain retention tool.

39. Install and tighten the camshaft position actuators. Tighten the bolt to 43 ft. lbs. (58 Nm).

40. Install the intake camshaft position actuator solenoid. Tighten the actuator valve bolt to 89 inch lbs. (10 Nm).

41. Install the camshaft position sensors. For additional information, refer to the following section, "Camshaft Position Sensors, Removal & Installation."

42. Install the camshaft cover.

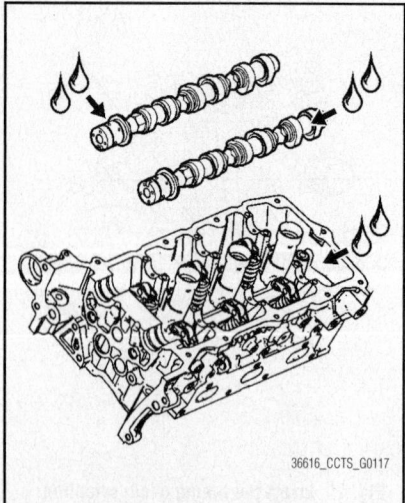

36616_CCTS_G0117

Fig. 81 Apply a liberal amount of lubricant GM P/N 12345501 (Canadian P/N 992704) or equivalent to the camshaft journals and the left cylinder head camshaft carriers.

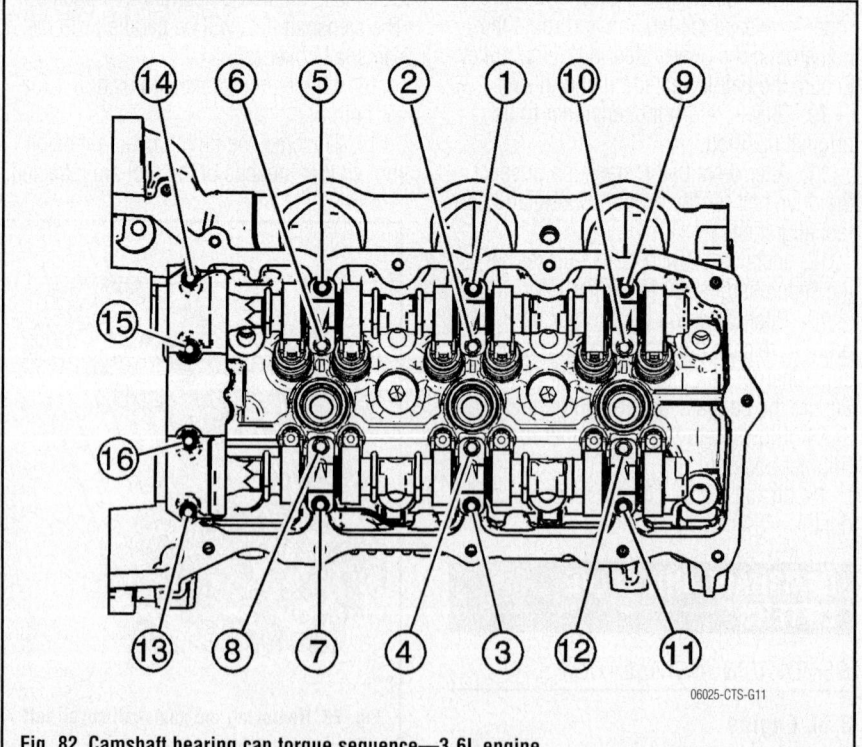

06025-CTS-G11

Fig. 82 Camshaft bearing cap torque sequence—3.6L engine

43. Install the upper intake manifold with the lower intake manifold.

44. Start the engine to verify proper operation and check for leaks.

4.6L Engine

See Figures 83 through 89.

1. Before servicing the vehicle, refer to the Precautions Section.

2. Remove the camshaft cover

3. Rotate the crankshaft to TDC of the no. 1 cylinders compression stroke, both camshaft sprocket drive pins should be at the top of their rotation.

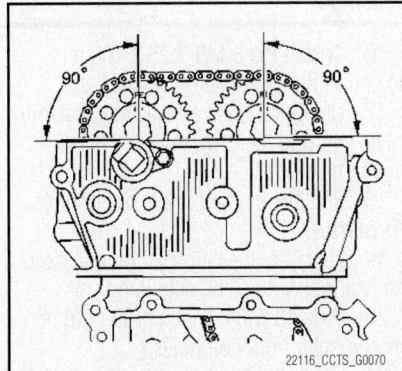

Fig. 83 Camshaft sprocket drive pins at the top of their rotation

4. Install the J 44212 holding tool over the camshafts.

5. Use a paint stick to create a mark (1) on the timing chain link adjacent to each camshaft sprocket timing mark (2, 3).

6. Install both EN 46327 camshaft sprocket and chain holding tools to the engine using the following step:

   a. Rotate the wing nut of the EN 46327 to the top of its travel.

7. Position the bottom retention tool on

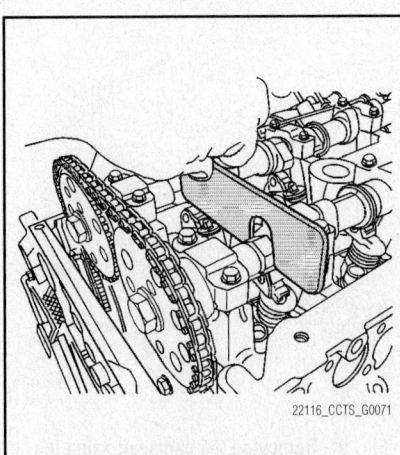

Fig. 84 Camshaft holding tool J 44212

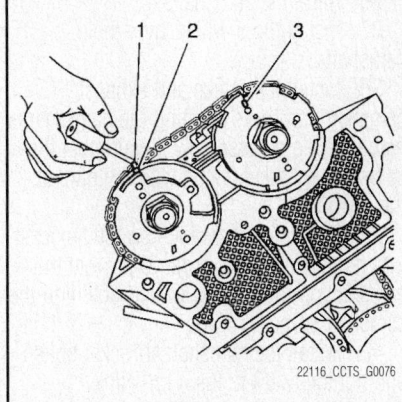

Fig. 85 Paint mark (1) timing marks (2) and (3)

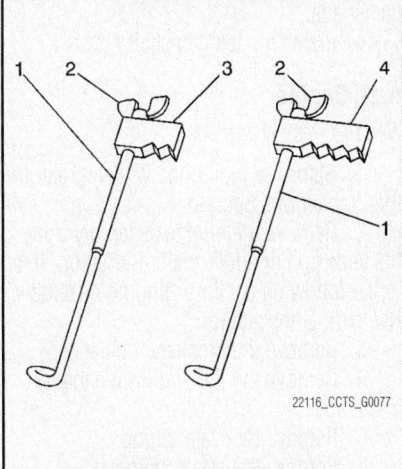

Fig. 86 EN 46327 holding tools shown

the cylinder head with the V-notch of the block (1) adjacent to the left exhaust camshaft sprocket and chain.

8. Insert the hook end into a secondary timing chain link as shown.

9. Rotate the wing nut until it contacts the retention tool block (1). DO NOT tighten the wing nut at this time.

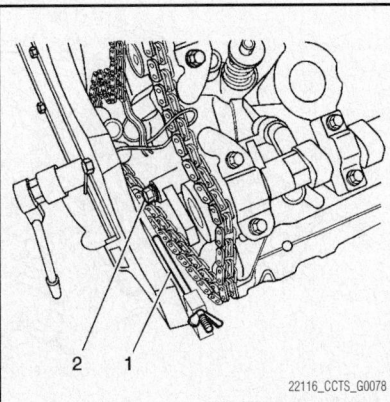

Fig. 87 Holding tool installed into timing chain

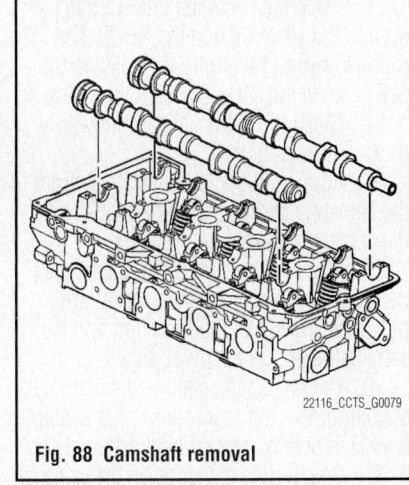

Fig. 88 Camshaft removal

10. Rotate the wing nut of the EN 46327 to the top of its travel.

11. Position the top retention tool on the cylinder head with the V-notch of the block (1) adjacent to the left intake camshaft sprocket and chain.

12. Insert the hook end into a secondary timing chain link as shown.

13. Rotate the wing nut until it contacts the retention tool block. Alternately tighten both wing nuts to retain the chain.

14. Use an open wrench on the hex cast into the camshafts in order to prevent the camshafts from rotating when removing the camshaft sprocket bolts.

15. Remove the camshaft sprocket bolts

16. Remove the camshaft sprockets.

17. Alternately loosen the camshaft bearing cap bolts a few turns at a time until all valve spring pressure has been released.

18. Remove the camshaft bearing caps.

19. Remove the J 44212 from the camshafts.

20. Remove the camshafts.

21. Remove the camshaft followers.

22. Remove the Stationary Hydraulic Lash Adjusters (SHLA) from the bores.

To install:

23. Fill the stationary hydraulic lash adjuster (SHLA) with clean engine oil.

24. Install the new SHLA's into the bores.

25. Apply a liberal amount of lubricant to the roller pivot pocket and valve slot areas of the camshaft followers.

✴✴ WARNING

The follower must be positioned squarely on the valve tip so that the full width of the roller will completely contact the camshaft lobe. If the followers are being reused you must put them back in their original location.

26. Place the camshaft followers in position on the valve tip and the SHLA. The rounded head of the follower goes on the SHLA, while the flat end goes on the valve tip.

27. Clean the camshaft carriers with a clean, lint-free cloth.

28. Apply a liberal amount of lubricant to the camshaft carriers, camshaft lobes and the camshaft journals.

29. Place the camshaft in the camshaft carriers with the camshaft sprocket drive pins near the top of their rotation and the camshaft lobes in a neutral position.

30. The camshafts can be identified by a stamping near the rear journal. For example: L-EXH is defined as Left bank Exhaust

31. Observe the markings on the camshaft bearing caps. Each camshaft bearing cap is marked in order to identify its location.

32. The markings have the following meanings:
- The arrow should point to the front of the engine.
- The number indicates the position from the front of the engine.
- The "E" indicates the exhaust camshaft.
- The "I" indicates the Intake camshaft.

33. Apply a liberal amount of lubricant to the camshaft bearing caps.

34. Install the camshaft bearing caps according to the identification marks.

35. Install the camshaft bearing cap bolts in sequence and tighten as follows:
  a. Alternately hand tighten the camshaft bearing cap bolts a few turns at a time until all caps are fully seated.
  b. Tighten the camshaft bearing cap bolts to 44 inch lbs. (5 Nm).
  c. Tighten the camshaft bearing cap bolts an additional 30 degrees using the J 45059 angle meter.

36. Align the camshafts.

37. Install the J 44212 over the camshafts.

38. Install the intake and exhaust camshaft sprockets aligning the paint marks made during disassembly. Ensure that the camshaft sprockets align with the pins of the camshafts.

39. Use an open wrench on the hex cast into the camshafts in order to prevent the camshafts from rotating when tightening the camshaft sprocket bolts.

40. Install the camshaft sprocket bolts and tighten to 89 ft. lbs. (120 Nm).

41. Remove the EN 46327 holding tool.

42. Verify the camshaft sprocket alignment.

43. Remove the J 44212 from the camshafts.

44. Install the left camshaft cover.

6.2L Engine

See Figures 90 and 91.

1. Before servicing the vehicle, refer to the Precautions Section.

2. Remove the engine assembly from the vehicle. For additional information, refer to the following section, "Engine Assembly, Removal & Installation."

3. Remove the crankshaft balancer.

4. Remove the left and right exhaust manifolds.

5. Remove the water pump.

6. Remove the supercharger.

7. Remove the left and right covers.

8. Remove the valve rocker arms and push rods.

9. Remove the left and right cylinder heads.

10. Remove the valve lifters.

11. Remove the engine front cover and gasket. Discard the old gasket.

12. Rotate the engine in order to align the timing marks.

13. Remove the camshaft sprocket bolts.

14. Remove the timing chain from the camshaft sprocket, and allow the timing chain to rest on the crankshaft sprocket.

15. Remove the camshaft retainer bolts and retainer.

❊❊ WARNING

All camshaft journals are the same diameter, so care must be used in removing or installing the camshaft to avoid damage to the camshaft bearings.

16. Install the 3 M8-1.25 x 100 mm bolts into the camshaft front bolt holes.

17. Using the bolts as a handle, carefully rotate and pull the camshaft out of the engine block.

18. Remove the bolts from the front of

To install:

19. Lubricate the camshaft journals and the bearings with clean engine oil.

20. Install 3 M8 - 4 inch (100 mm) in the camshaft front bolt holes.

21. Using the bolts as a handle, carefully install the camshaft into the engine block.

22. Remove the 3 bolts from the front of the camshaft.

23. Install the camshaft retainer. Tighten the bolts as follows:
  a. Hex head bolts to 18 ft. lbs (25 Nm)
  b. TORX® head bolts to 11 ft. lbs. (15 Nm)

24. CMP sensor. Tighten the bolt to 18 ft. lbs (25 Nm).

25. Align the camshaft sprocket alignment mark in the 6 o'clock position.

26. The remainder of the installation is the reverse order of removal.

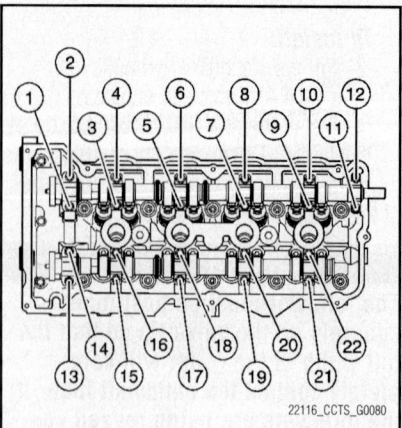

Fig. 89 4.6L–Camshaft bearing cap bolts tightening sequence

22116_CCTS_G0080

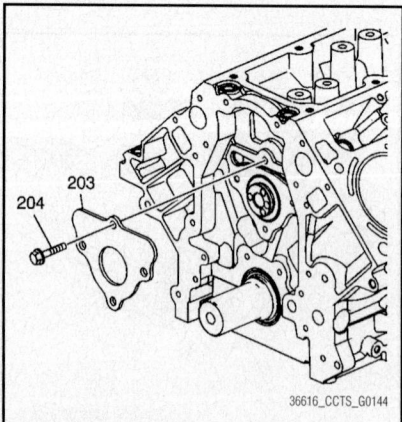

Fig. 90 Remove the camshaft retainer bolts (204) and retainer (203)—6.2L engine

36616_CCTS_G0144

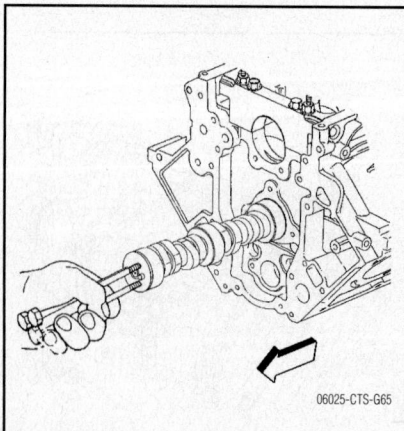

Fig. 91 Removing the camshaft using the bolts as a handle—6.2L engine

06025-CTS-G65

CATALYTIC CONVERTER

REMOVAL & INSTALLATION

3.6L Engine

See Figure 92.

1. Remove the fuel injector sight shield. Refer to Fuel Injector Sight Shield Replacement.
2. Remove the exhaust manifold heat shield bolts and heat shield.
3. Remove the upper exhaust manifold heat shield insulator from the oil level indicator tube, if necessary.
4. Remove the lower exhaust manifold heat shield insulator from the oil level indicator and exhaust gasket, if necessary.
5. Remove the catalytic converter nuts.
6. Raise and safely support the vehicle.
7. Disconnect the oxygen sensor electrical connector.
8. Disconnect the muffler pipe from the left and the right side catalytic converters.
9. Carefully remove the catalytic converter with the seal/heat shield and oxygen sensor from the exhaust manifold. Remove and discard the catalytic converter inlet seal/heat shield from the converter assembly. Do not reuse.

To install:

10. If replacing the catalytic converter, transfer the oxygen sensor to the new converter.
11. Install the NEW catalytic converter seal/heat shield to the catalytic converter.
12. Install the catalytic converter to the exhaust manifold.
13. Partially install the catalytic converter nuts to the exhaust manifold.
14. Connect the oxygen sensor electrical connector.
15. Install the exhaust pipe to the left

and the right side catalytic converters and tighten to 13 ft. lbs. (17 Nm).
16. Lower the vehicle.
17. Tighten the catalytic converter to exhaust manifold nuts to 37 ft. lbs. (50 Nm).
18. Install the exhaust manifold heat shield.
19. Start the engine and inspect the exhaust system for leaks.

4.6L Engine

See Figures 93 through 97.

1. Raise and safely support the vehicle.
2. Support the exhaust system near the resonator with a suitable jack.
3. Remove the oxygen sensor.

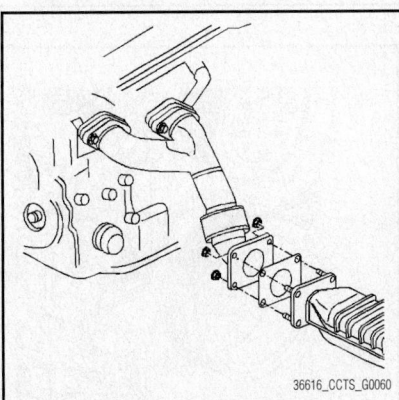

Fig. 93 Remove the nuts securing the catalytic converter to the exhaust manifold—DTS Models shown

➡**It is not necessary to disconnect the electrical connector.**

4. Remove the nuts securing the catalytic converter to the exhaust manifold.
5. Remove the bolts securing the center exhaust hangers to the rear suspension support brackets.

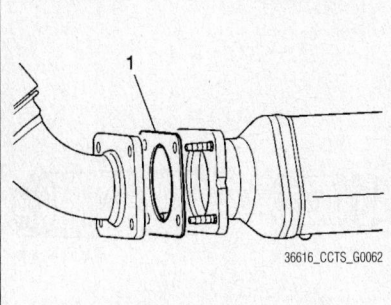

Fig. 95 Remove the catalytic converter gasket (1) and discard—DTS Models shown

6. Remove the catalytic converter from the manifold pipe.
7. Lower the exhaust system.
8. Remove the catalytic converter gasket and discard.
9. Cut the intermediate pipe 1.3 inches (34 mm) from the resonator weld.

To install:

10. Slide two service clamps over the catalytic converter assembly outlet pipe. Do not tighten at this time.
11. Slide the catalytic converter assembly outlet pipe over the intermediate pipe.
12. Place a new catalytic converter gasket over the catalytic converter studs.
13. Raise the exhaust system into position, aligning the catalytic converter with the exhaust manifold pipe.
14. Install the nuts securing the catalytic converter to the exhaust manifold pipe. Do not tighten the nuts at this time.
15. Install the bolts securing the center exhaust hangers to the rear suspension support brackets and tighten the bolts to 22 ft. lbs. (30 Nm).

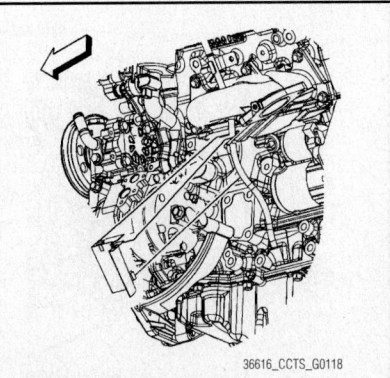

Fig. 92 Remove the lower exhaust manifold heat shield insulator from the oil level indicator and exhaust gasket, if necessary—3.6L engine

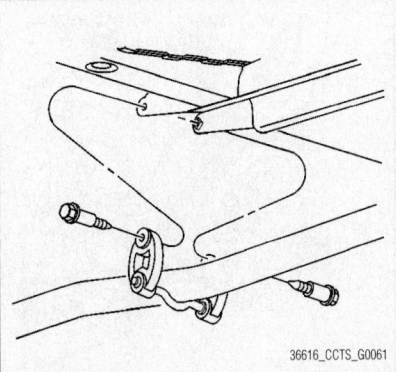

Fig. 94 Remove the bolts securing the center exhaust hangers to the rear suspension support brackets—DTS Models shown

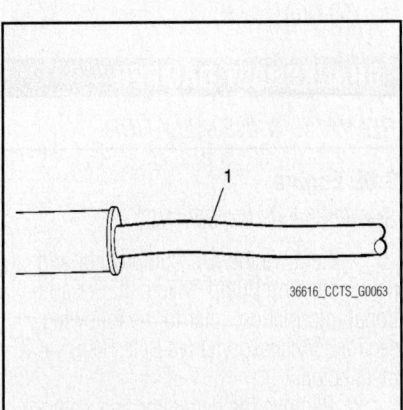

Fig. 96 Cut the intermediate pipe 1.3 inches (34 mm) from the resonator weld—DTS Models shown

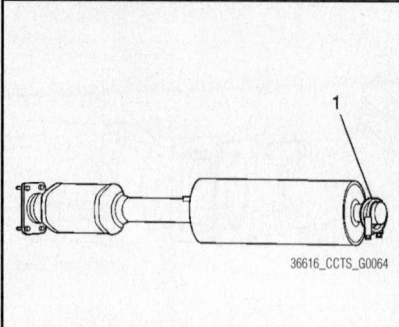

Fig. 97 Slide service clamps (1) over the outlet pipe

16. Tighten the catalytic converter nuts in a crisscross pattern to 18 ft. lbs. (25 Nm).

17. Position the service clamps midway on the catalytic converter assembly outlet pipe, as close together as possible.

18. Rotate the clamps so the fastening ends are pointing in opposite directions. Tighten the clamps to 40 ft. lbs. (54 Nm).

19. Lower the vehicle and check the exhaust system for leaks.

6.2L Engine

1. Raise and safely support the vehicle.

2. Support the exhaust system with a suitable screw jack.

3. Disconnect the exhaust system from the left and right side catalytic converters.

4. Using the screw jack, lower the exhaust system.

5. Disconnect the oxygen sensor electrical connectors.

6. Remove the left bank catalytic converter to exhaust manifold nuts.

7. Carefully remove the catalytic converter with the gasket and oxygen sensors from the exhaust manifold.

8. Installation is the reverse order of removal. Tighten the mounting nuts to 37 ft. lbs. (50 Nm).

CRANKSHAFT DAMPER

REMOVAL & INSTALLATION

3.6L Engine

See Figures 98 through 102.

1. Remove the A/C compressor and power steering pump drive belt. For additional information, refer to the following section, "Accessory Drive Belt, Removal & Installation."

2. Remove the generator and water pump drive belt. For additional information, refer to the following section, "Accessory Drive Belt, Removal & Installation."

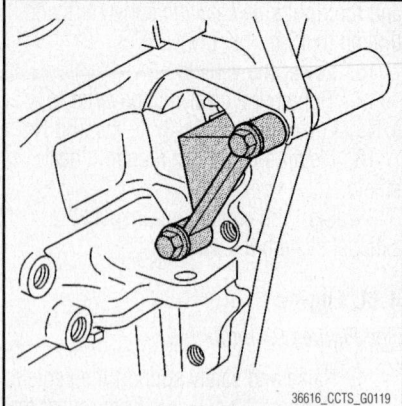

Fig. 98 Install the flywheel holding tool through the starter mounting hole—3.6L engine

Fig. 99 Install the crankshaft button in the nose of the crankshaft—3.6L engine

3. Raise and safely support the vehicle.

4. Remove the transmission bell housing inspection hole cover.

5. Install the EN-48018 flywheel holding tool.

Fig. 100 Install the harmonic balancer puller in order to remove the crankshaft balancer—3.6L engine

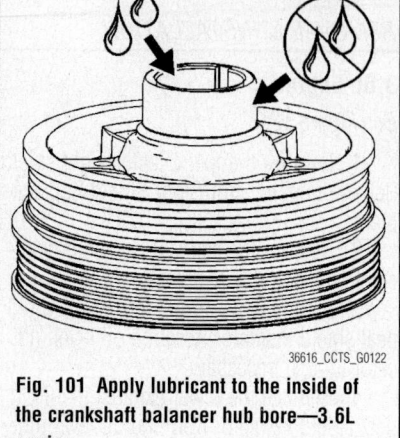

Fig. 101 Apply lubricant to the inside of the crankshaft balancer hub bore—3.6L engine

6. Remove the front air deflector.

7. Install the flywheel holding tool through the starter mounting hole.

8. Remove the crankshaft balancer bolt.

9. Install the J 38416-2 crankshaft button in the nose of the crankshaft.

10. Install the J 24420-C puller in order to remove the crankshaft balancer.

11. Pull the crankshaft balancer off by tightening the center bolt on the puller until the crankshaft balancer pulls off of the crankshaft end.

To install:

12. Leave the flywheel holding tool installed.

13. Apply lubricant to the **inside** of the crankshaft balancer hub bore.

14. Place the crankshaft balancer in position on the crankshaft.

15. Thread the J 41998-B installer in the crankshaft. Ensure you engage at least 10 threads of the J 41998-B installer before pressing the crankshaft balancer in place.

Fig. 102 Thread the J 41998-B installer in the crankshaft—3.6L engine

16. Push the crankshaft balancer into position by tightening the nut on the J 41998-B installer until the large washer bottoms out on the crankshaft end.

17. Remove the J 41998-B installer.

18. Install the crankshaft balancer bolt and tighten as follows:

    a. Tighten the bolt to 74 ft. lbs. (100 Nm).

    b. Tighten the bolt an additional 150°.

19. Remove the flywheel holding tool.

20. The remainder of the installation is the reverse order of removal.

4.6L Engine

See Figures 103 and 104.

1. Before servicing the vehicle, refer to the Precautions Section.

2. Remove the drive belt.

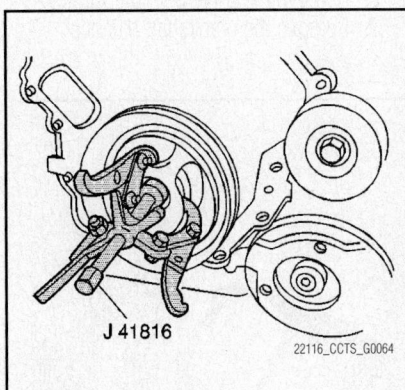

Fig. 103 Crankshaft balancer removal using the J 41816 puller.

3. Remove the transaxle to engine brace bolts.

4. Remove the transaxle to engine brace.

5. Remove the torque converter cover bolt.

6. Remove the torque converter cover.

7. Install the J 44214 flywheel holder.

8. Remove the crankshaft balancer bolt.

9. Remove the front fascia (Front Bumper).

10. Support the frame with a suitable adjustable jack.

11. Loosen the right side frame bolts.

12. Lower the frame in order to obtain clearance for the J 41816 puller below the body rail.

13. Place the remover pilot into the end of the crankshaft.

14. Remove the crankshaft balancer using the J 41816 puller.

To install:

15. Position the crankshaft balancer on the nose of the crankshaft.

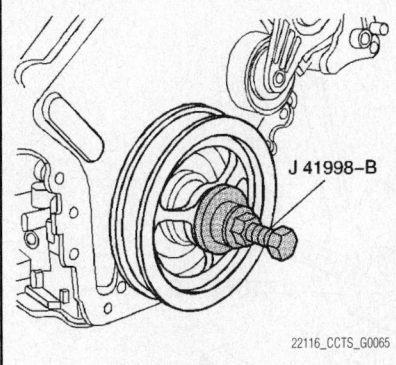

Fig. 104 Crankshaft balancer installation using the J 41998-B installer

16. Press the crankshaft balancer in place using the J 41998-B installer.

17. Clean the crankshaft balancer bolt threads.

18. Apply engine oil to the crankshaft balancer bolt threads.

19. Install the crankshaft balancer bolt and tighten as follows:

    a. Tighten the bolt a first pass to 37 ft. lbs. (50 Nm).

    b. Tighten the bolt a final pass an additional 120 degrees using the J 45059 angle meter.

20. Raise the frame into position.

21. Install the right side frame bolts and tighten to 133 ft. lbs. (181 Nm).

22. Install the front fascia (Front Bumper).

23. Remove the support(s) from the frame.

24. Remove the J 44214 flywheel holder.

25. Install the torque converter cover and tighten mounting bolts to 106 inch lbs. (12 Nm).

26. Install the transaxle to engine brace.

27. Install the transaxle to engine brace bolts and tighten to 35 ft. lbs. (47 Nm).

28. Install the drive belt.

6.2L Engine

See Figures 105 and 106.

1. Remove the air conditioning (A/C) drive belt.

2. Remove the power steering gear.

3. Remove the starter motor.

4. Remove the right transmission cover and bolt.

➡️If replacing the crankshaft balancer on manual transmission applications, note the location of any existing balance weights, if applicable. Crankshaft balance weights must be installed into the new balancer in the same location as the old balancer. A properly installed balance weight will be either

flush or below flush with the face of the balancer.

Do not use the crankshaft balancer bolt again. Install a NEW crankshaft balancer bolt during final assembly.

5. Install the flywheel holding tool and bolts. Use one M10 - 1.5 x 120 mm and one M10 - 1.5 x 45 mm bolt for proper tool operation. Tighten the flywheel holding tool bolts to 37 ft. lbs. (50 Nm).

6. Remove the crankshaft balancer bolt.

➡️**Do not discard the crankshaft balancer bolt. The balancer bolt will be used during the balancer installation procedure.**

7. Using a suitable puller, remove the crankshaft balancer.

To install:

8. Position the balancer on the end of the crankshaft as straight as possible.

9. Install the balancer onto the end of the crankshaft.

10. Use the Crankshaft Balancer Installer J-41665 and Oil Seal Installer J-41478 as follows:

    a. Assemble the threaded rod, nut, washer and the installer. Insert the smaller end of the installer into the front of the balancer.

    b. Use a wrench and hold the hex end of the threaded rod.

    c. Use a second wrench and rotate the installation tool nut clockwise until the balancer is started onto crankshaft.

    d. Remove the tool and reverse the installation tool. Position the larger end of the installer against the front of the balancer.

    e. Use a wrench and hold the hex end of the threaded rod.

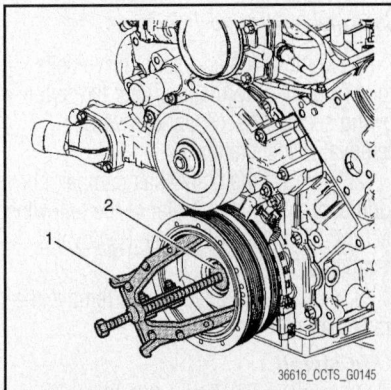

Fig. 105 Using a suitable puller, remove the crankshaft balancer—6.2L engine

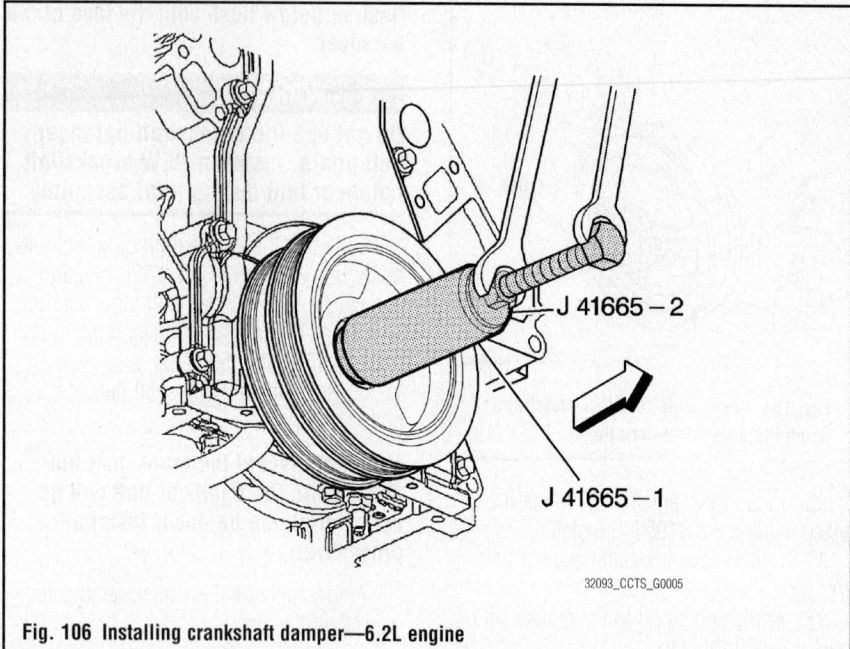

Fig. 106 Installing crankshaft damper—6.2L engine

    f. Use a second wrench and rotate the installation tool nut clockwise until the balancer is installed onto the crankshaft.

    g. Remove the balancer installation tools.

    11. Tighten the crankshaft bolt as follows:

    a. Tighten the crankshaft balancer bolt a first pass to 110 ft. lbs. (150 Nm).

    b. Loosen the crankshaft balancer bolt a second pass to 360 degrees.

    c. Tighten the crankshaft balancer bolt a third pass to 37 ft. lbs. (50 Nm).

    d. Tighten the crankshaft balancer bolt a final pass to 230 degrees.

    12. The remainder of the installation is the reverse order of removal.

CRANKSHAFT FRONT SEAL

REMOVAL & INSTALLATION

3.6L Engine

See Figures 107 and 108.

    1. Remove the accessory drive belts. For additional information, refer to the following section, "Accessory Drive Belt, Removal & Installation."

    2. Remove the crankshaft damper. For additional information, refer to the following section, "Crankshaft Damper, Removal & Installation."

    3. Use a flat-bladed tool to remove the crankshaft oil seal.

To install:

    4. Use Special Tool J-29184 or equivalent seal installer to install the crankshaft front oil seal.

    5. Install the crankshaft balancer.

    6. Install the accessory drive belts.

    7. Start the engine and check for leaks.

4.6L Engine

See Figures 110 through 112.

➡ The crankshaft front oil seal is not serviced as an individual component. When replacing the crankshaft front oil seal install a NEW engine front cover. In order to precisely align the crankshaft front oil seal to the crankshaft balancer and crankshaft balancer dust shield the engine front cover and the crankshaft front oil seal are sold as an assembly.

    1. Before servicing the vehicle, refer to the Precautions Section.

    2. Remove the drive belt idler pulley.

    3. Remove the crankshaft balancer.

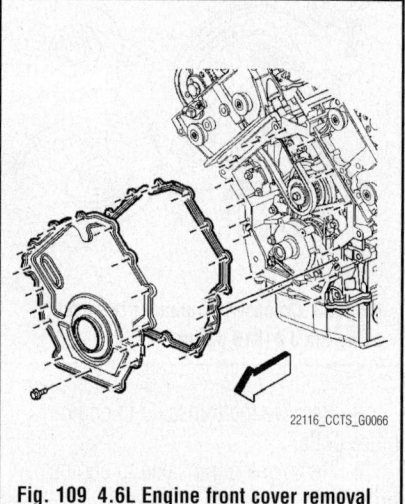

Fig. 107 Use a flat-bladed tool to remove the crankshaft oil seal—3.6L engine

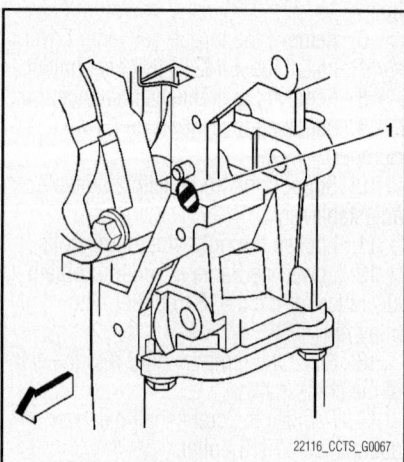

Fig. 109 4.6L Engine front cover removal

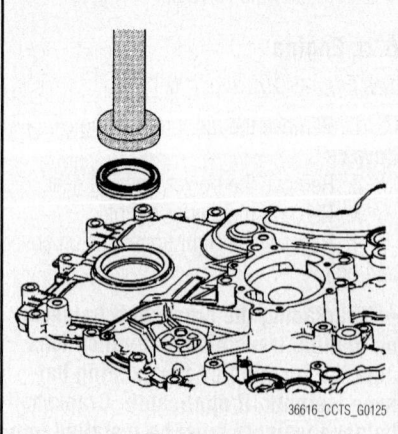

Fig. 108 Use Special Tool J-29184 or equivalent seal installer to install the crankshaft front oil seal—3.6L engine

Fig. 110 Sealant application at the split line shown

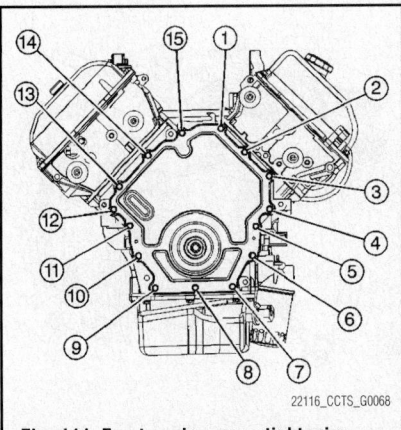

Fig. 111 Front engine cover tightening sequence

4. Remove the engine front cover bolts.

5. Remove the engine front cover and gasket. The gasket is reusable. Do not discard unless it is damaged.

To install:

6. Place a small amount of sealant at the split line of the upper and lower crankcases (1).

7. Place the engine front cover gasket over the crankcase dowel pins.

8. Place the engine front cover in position on the crankcase.

9. Apply threadlock to the engine front cover bolts.

10. Install the engine front cover bolts until snug.

11. Tighten the engine front cover bolts as follows:

   a. Tighten the bolts in the sequence to 89 inch lbs. (10 Nm)

12. Install the crankshaft balancer.

13. Install the drive belt idler pulley.

6.2L Engine

See Figures 112 and 113.

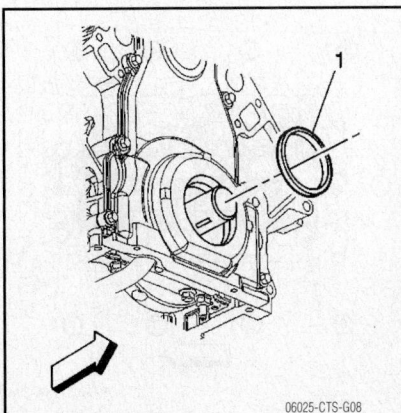

Fig. 112 Removing the front crankshaft seal—6.2L engine

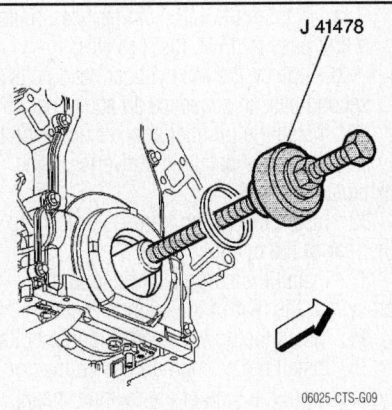

Fig. 113 Install the front crankshaft seal using Special Tool J-41478—6.2L engine

1. Remove the crankshaft damper. For additional information, refer to the following section, "Crankshaft Damper, Removal & Installation."

2. Use a flat-bladed tool to remove the crankshaft oil seal.

To install:

3. Lubricate the outer edge of the oil seal and front cover oil seal bore with clean engine oil.

4. Install the front oil seal onto Special Tool J-41478 Installer guide.

5. Install the J-41478 threaded rod into the end of the crankshaft.

6. Use a wrench to hold the hex on the installer tool.

7. Use a second wrench to rotate the installer nut clockwise until the seal bottoms out in the front cover oil seal bore.

8. Install the crankshaft damper.

9. Start the engine and check for leaks.

CYLINDER HEAD

REMOVAL & INSTALLATION

3.6L Engine

Left Side

See Figures 114 through 116.

1. Disconnect the negative battery cable.

2. Drain the engine oil.

3. Drain the engine cooling system.

4. Remove the engine front cover. For additional information, refer to the following section, "Timing Chain Cover & Seal, Removal & Installation."

5. Remove the left secondary timing chain. For additional information, refer to the following section, "Timing Chain, Removal & Installation."

6. Remove the oil level indicator from the oil level indicator tube.

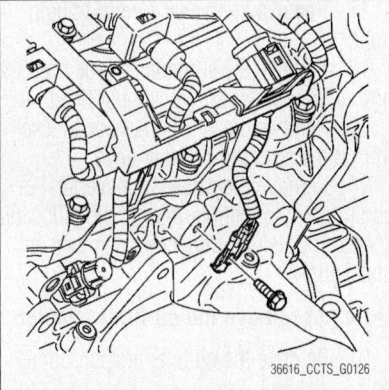

Fig. 114 Remove the wiring harness ground from the cylinder head—3.6L engine Left Side

7. Remove the top oil level indicator tube bolt.

8. Raise and safely support the vehicle.

9. Remove the knock sensor. For additional information, refer to the following section, "Knock Sensor, Removal & Installation."

10. Remove the heat shield clip from the oil level indicator tube.

11. Lower the vehicle.

12. Remove the oil level indicator tube up through the exhaust manifold.

13. Remove the heat shield from the coolant temperature sensor and disconnect the coolant temperature sensor electrical connector.

14. Remove the wiring harness ground from the cylinder head.

15. Disconnect the wiring harness electrical connector located at the side of the cylinder head.

16. Remove the wiring harness connector bracket from the side of the cylinder head.

➡DO NOT disconnect the power steering pipes and/or hoses.

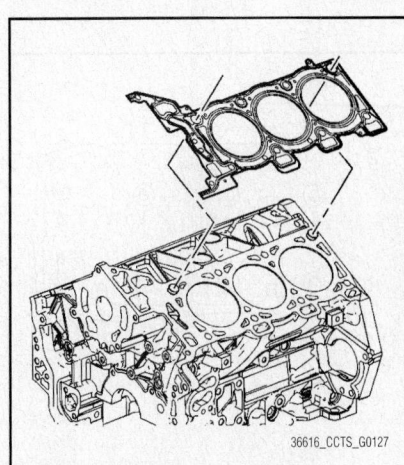

Fig. 115 Install a new cylinder head gasket—3.6L engine

17. Remove the power steering pump bolts.

18. Remove the surge tank hose from the bracket at the rear of the cylinder head.

19. Remove the wiring harness bracket from the rear of the cylinder head.

20. Remove the catalytic converter. For additional information, refer to the following section, "Catalytic Converter, Removal & Installation."

➡ **Do not remove the oil filter adapter.**

21. Remove the oil filter adapter upper bolt.

22. Remove the cylinder head with the exhaust manifold.

23. Remove and discard the cylinder head gasket.

To install:

24. Ensure the cylinder head locating pins are securely mounted in the cylinder block deck face.

25. Install a NEW left cylinder head gasket using the deck face locating pins for retention.

26. Align the left cylinder head with the deck face locating pins.

27. Place the left cylinder head in position on the deck face.

➡ **DO NOT allow oil on the cylinder head bolt bosses.**

➡ **DO NOT reuse the old cylinder head bolts.**

28. Install the NEW M11 cylinder head bolts as follows:

   a. Tighten the M11 cylinder head bolts a first pass in sequence to 22 ft. lbs. (30 Nm).

   b. Tighten the M11 cylinder head bolts a second pass in sequence an additional 150°.

29. Install the 2 NEW front M8 left cylinder head bolts as follows:

   a. Tighten the M8 cylinder head bolts a first pass to 11 ft. lbs. (15 Nm).

   b. Tighten the M8 cylinder head bolts a second pass in sequence an additional 75°.

30. Install the oil filter adapter upper bolt.

31. Install the catalytic converter to the exhaust manifold.

32. Install the wiring harness bracket to the rear of the cylinder head.

33. Install the surge tank hose to the bracket at the rear of the cylinder head.

34. Install the power steering pump bolts.

35. Install the wiring harness connector bracket from the side of the cylinder head.

36. Disconnect the wiring harness electrical connector located at the side of the cylinder head.

37. Install the wiring harness ground to the cylinder head and tighten the bolt to 89 inch lbs. (10 Nm).

38. Install the coolant temperature sensor electrical connector heat shield.

39. Install the oil level indicator.

40. Install the left bank secondary timing chain.

41. Refill the engine with coolant to the correct level.

42. Refill the engine with oil to the correct level.

43. Connect the negative battery cable.

44. Start the engine and check for leaks.

Right Side

See Figures 117 through 119.

1. Disconnect the negative battery cable.
2. Drain the engine oil.
3. Drain the engine cooling system.
4. Remove the engine front cover. For additional information, refer to the following section, "Timing Chain Cover & Seal, Removal & Installation."
5. Remove the right secondary timing chain. For additional information, refer to

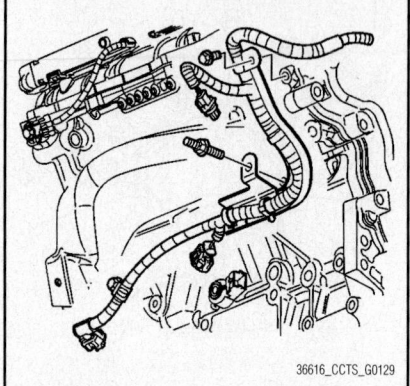

Fig. 118 Remove the wiring harness conduit upper bolt from the cylinder head and reposition the conduit—3.6L engine

the following section, "Timing Chain, Removal & Installation."

6. Remove the coolant inlet pipe bolts and reposition the coolant inlet pipe to provide access.

7. Remove the catalytic converter. For additional information, refer to the following section, "Catalytic Converter, Removal & Installation."

8. Remove the wiring harness ground from the side of the cylinder head.

9. Remove the wiring harness conduit upper bolt from the cylinder head and reposition the conduit to provide access.

10. Remove the battery cable from the cylinder head.

11. Remove the cylinder head with the exhaust manifold.

12. Remove and discard the cylinder head gasket.

To install:

13. Ensure the cylinder head locating pins are securely mounted in the cylinder block deck face.

14. Install a NEW right cylinder head

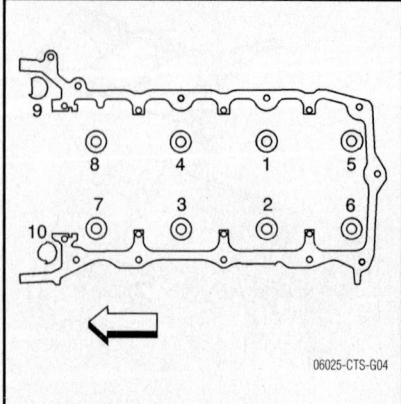

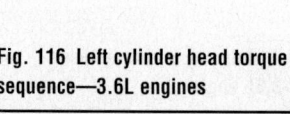

Fig. 116 Left cylinder head torque sequence—3.6L engines

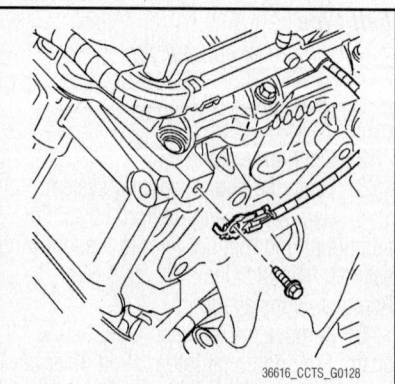

Fig. 117 Remove the wiring harness ground from the side of the cylinder head—3.6L engine Right Side

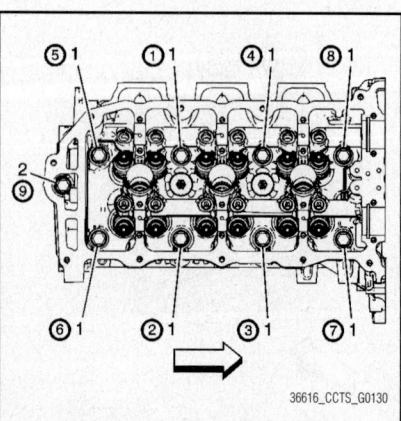

Fig. 119 Right cylinder head torque sequence—3.6L engines

gasket using the deck face locating pins for retention.

15. Align the right cylinder head with the deck face locating pins.

16. Place the right cylinder head in position on the deck face.

17. Install the NEW M11 cylinder head bolts as follows:

a. Tighten the M11 cylinder head bolts a first pass in sequence to 22 ft. lbs. (30 Nm).

b. Tighten the M11 cylinder head bolts a second pass in sequence an additional 150°.

18. Install the 2 NEW front M8 left cylinder head bolts as follows:

a. Tighten the M8 cylinder head bolts a first pass to 11 ft. lbs. (15 Nm).

b. Tighten the M8 cylinder head bolts a second pass in sequence an additional 75°

19. Connect the catalytic converter to the exhaust manifold.

20. Install the battery negative cable to the cylinder head.

21. Install the wiring harness conduit to the cylinder head. Tighten the wiring harness upper bolt to 89 inch lbs. (10 Nm).

22. Install the wiring harness ground to the side of the cylinder head. Tighten the wiring harness ground bolt to 89 inch lbs. (10 Nm).

23. Install the catalytic converter.

24. Install the coolant inlet pipe.

25. Install the right bank secondary timing chain.

26. Refill the engine with oil to the correct level.

27. Refill the cooling system to the correct level.

28. Connect the negative battery cable.

29. Start the engine and check for leaks.

4.6L Engine

Left Side

See Figures 120 and 121.

1. Before servicing the vehicle, refer to the Precautions Section.

2. Disconnect the negative battery cable.

3. Remove the left exhaust manifold.

4. Remove the engine mount strut bracket.

5. Remove the alternator.

6. Remove the water crossover.

7. Remove the intake manifold.

8. Remove the camshaft cover.

9. Remove the engine front cover.

10. Remove the left secondary camshaft drive chain.

11. Remove the 3 M6 cylinder head bolts.

12. Remove and discard the 10 M11 cylinder head bolts.

✳✳ WARNING

DO NOT reuse the M11 cylinder head bolts.

13. Remove the left cylinder head. Make sure that no locating pins are stuck in the cylinder head.

✳✳ WARNING

You must clean the thread sealant material from the cylinder head bolt holes in the cylinder block. Failure to do so could cause false torque readings during reassembly.

14. After removing the cylinder head, remove any remaining bolt thread sealant material from the threaded cylinder block holes.

15. Remove and discard the left cylinder head gasket.

16. Remove all remaining gasket material from the cylinder head and cylinder block.

17. Clean and inspect the cylinder head.

To install:

18. Make sure all the cylinder head locating pins are securely installed in the cylinder block deck face.

19. Make sure all old thread sealant material is removed from the cylinder head bolt holes in the cylinder block.

20. Install a NEW cylinder head gasket using the locating pins for retention.

21. Align the cylinder head with the locating pins.

22. Place the cylinder head in position on the cylinder block.

23. Install 10 NEW M11 cylinder head bolts until snug.

24. Install the 3 M6 cylinder head bolts until snug.

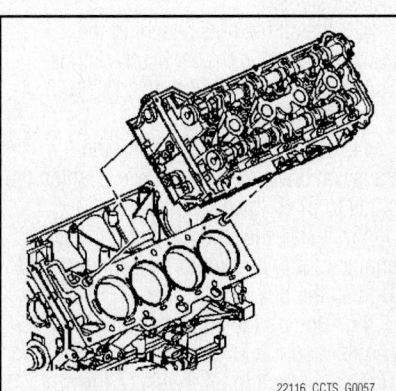

22116_CCTS_G0057
Fig. 120 Cylinder head removal

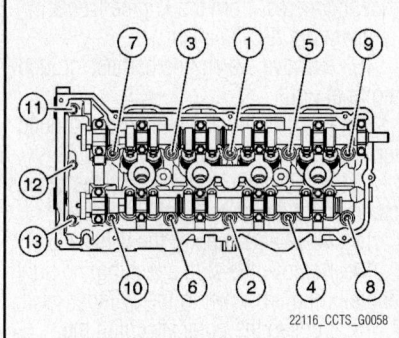

22116_CCTS_G0058
Fig. 121 Left cylinder head tightening sequence—4.6L engine

25. Tighten the 10 M11 cylinder head bolts as follows:

a. Tighten the bolts (1-10) a first pass in the sequence shown to 22 ft. lbs. (30 Nm).

b. Tighten the bolts a second pass in the sequence shown an additional 70 degrees using an angle meter.

c. Tighten the bolts a third pass in the sequence shown an additional 60 degrees using the angle meter.

d. Tighten the bolts a final pass in the sequence shown an additional 45 degrees (total 175 degrees) using the angle meter.

26. Tighten the 3 M6 bolts cylinder head bolts as follows:

a. Tighten the bolts (11-13) to 106 inch lbs. (12 Nm).

27. Install the left secondary camshaft drive chain.

28. Install the engine front cover.

29. Install the camshaft cover.

30. Install the intake manifold.

31. Install the water crossover.

32. Install the alternator.

33. Install the engine mount strut bracket.

34. Install the left exhaust manifold.

35. Connect the negative battery cable.

36. Fill the cooling system to the correct level.

37. Start the engine and check for leaks.

Right Side

See Figure 122.

1. Before servicing the vehicle, refer to the Precautions Section.

2. Disconnect the negative battery cable.

3. Remove the right exhaust manifold.

4. Remove the water crossover.

5. Remove the intake manifold.

6. Remove the camshaft cover.

7. Remove the engine front cover.

8. Remove the right secondary camshaft drive chain.

9. Disconnect the engine harness elec-

trical connector from the Engine Coolant Temperature (ECT) sensor.

10. Remove the engine harness ground terminal nut.

11. Remove the engine harness ground terminal.

12. Remove the stud attaching the exhaust manifold front pipe to the cylinder head.

13. Raise and support the vehicle.

14. Remove the stud attaching the right engine mount bracket to the cylinder head.

15. Loosen the bolts attaching the engine mount bracket to the transaxle.

16. Remove the bolt attaching the transaxle brace to the transaxle.

17. Lower the vehicle.

18. Remove the nuts attaching the transaxle brace to the lift bracket studs.

19. Remove the transaxle brace.

20. Remove the rear lift bracket studs.

21. Remove the rear lift bracket.

22. Remove the 3 M6 cylinder head bolts.

23. Remove and discard the 10 M11 cylinder head bolts.

24. Remove the right cylinder head. Make sure that no locating pins are stuck in the cylinder head.

✳✳ WARNING

You must clean the thread sealant material from the cylinder head bolt holes in the cylinder block. Failure to do so could cause false torque readings during reassembly.

25. After removing the cylinder head, remove any remaining bolt thread sealant material from the threaded cylinder block holes.

26. Remove and discard the right cylinder head gasket.

27. Remove all remaining gasket material from the cylinder head and cylinder block.

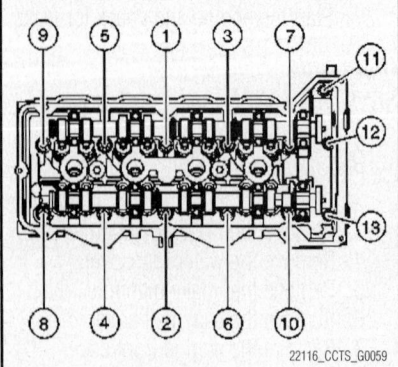

Fig. 122 Right cylinder head tightening sequence—4.6L engine

22116_CCTS_G0059

28. Place the cylinder head on a clean, flat surface with the combustion chambers face-up in order to prevent damage to the deck face.

29. Clean and inspect the cylinder head.

To install:

30. Make sure the locating pins are securely mounted in the cylinder block deck face.

31. Make sure any old thread sealant material is removed from the cylinder head bolt holes in the cylinder block.

32. Install a NEW cylinder head gasket using the locating pins for retention.

33. Align the cylinder head with the locating pins.

34. Place the cylinder head in position on the cylinder block.

35. Install NEW M11 cylinder head bolts until snug.

36. Install the 3 M6 cylinder head bolts until snug.

37. Tighten the 10 M11 cylinder head bolts as follows:

   a. Tighten the bolts (1-10) a first pass in the sequence shown to 22 ft. lbs. (30 Nm).

   b. Tighten the bolts a second pass in the sequence shown an additional 70 degrees using an angle meter.

   c. Tighten the bolts a third pass in the sequence shown an additional 60 degrees using the angle meter.

   d. Tighten the bolts a final pass in the sequence shown an additional 45 degrees (total 175 degrees) using the angle meter.

38. Tighten the 3 M6 bolts cylinder head bolts as follows:

   a. Tighten the bolts (11-13) to 106 inch lbs. (12 Nm).

39. Position the rear lift bracket to the cylinder head.

40. Install the rear lift bracket studs. Tighten the studs to 37 ft. lbs. (50 Nm).

41. Install the transaxle brace to the lift bracket studs.

42. Install the nuts attaching the transaxle brace to the lift bracket studs. Tighten the studs to 37 ft. lbs. (50 Nm).

43. Raise the vehicle.

44. Install the bolt attaching the transaxle brace to the transaxle. Tighten the studs to 37 ft. lbs. (50 Nm).

45. Install the stud attaching the right engine mount bracket to the cylinder head. Tighten the bolt to 54 ft. lbs. (73 Nm).

46. Tighten the bolts attaching the engine mount bracket to the transaxle. Tighten the bolt to 54 ft. lbs. (73 Nm).

47. Lower the vehicle.

48. Install the stud attaching the exhaust manifold front pipe to the cylinder head.

49. Install the engine harness ground terminal onto the stud.

50. Install the engine harness ground terminal nut. Tighten the nut to 13 ft. lbs. (17 Nm).

51. Connect the engine harness electrical connector to the ECT sensor.

52. Install the right secondary camshaft drive chain.

53. Install the engine front cover.

54. Install the camshaft cover.

55. Install the intake manifold.

56. Install the water crossover.

57. Install the right exhaust manifold.

58. Connect the negative battery cable.

59. Fill the cooling system to the correct level.

60. Start the engine and check for leaks.

6.2L Engine

Left Side

See Figure 123.

1. Remove the valve rocker arms and pushrods.

2. Remove the power steering pump bracket.

3. Remove the exhaust manifold.

4. Remove the supercharger.

5. Remove the engine wiring harness ground bolt from the rear of the left cylinder head.

6. Reposition the engine wire harness ground strap away from the cylinder head.

➡**The cylinder head bolts are NOT reusable.**

7. Remove the cylinder head bolts.

8. Remove the cylinder head.

✳✳ WARNING

After removal, place the cylinder head on 2 wood blocks in order to prevent damage to the sealing surfaces.

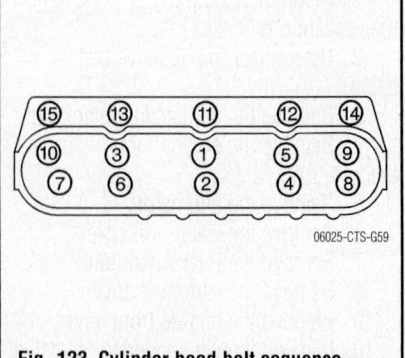

Fig. 123 Cylinder head bolt sequence— 6.2L engine

06025-CTS-G59

9. Remove the cylinder head bolts and discard.

To install:

10. Install the cylinder head with a new gasket. Tighten bolts in sequence as follows:

   a. Step 1: Tighten bolts 1-10 in to 37 ft. lbs. (50 Nm).

   b. Step 2: Tighten bolts 1-10 in an additional 80 degrees.

   c. Step 3: Tighten bolts 1-10 an additional 55 degrees.

   d. Step 4: Tighten bolts 11-15 to 22 ft. lbs. (30 Nm) alternating side-to-side working outward.

11. The remainder of the installation the reverse order of removal.

Right Side

See Figure 123.

1. Remove the valve rocker arms and pushrods.

2. Remove the supercharger belt tensioner bracket.

3. Remove the exhaust manifold.

4. Remove the oil level indicator tube bolt. Reposition the oil level indicator tube if necessary.

5. Remove the supercharger.

6. Remove the wiring harness from the clip of the rear of the cylinder head.

➡**The cylinder head bolts are NOT reusable.**

7. Remove the cylinder head bolts.

8. Remove the cylinder head.

❋❋ WARNING

After removal, place the cylinder head on 2 wood blocks in order to prevent damage to the sealing surfaces.

9. Remove the cylinder head bolts and discard.

To install:

10. Install the cylinder head with a new gasket. Tighten bolts in sequence as follows:

   a. Step 1: Tighten bolts 1-10 in to 37 ft. lbs. (50 Nm).

   b. Step 2: Tighten bolts 1-10 in an additional 80 degrees.

   c. Step 3: Tighten bolts 1-10 an additional 55 degrees.

   d. Step 4: Tighten bolts 11-15 to 22 ft. lbs. (30 Nm) alternating side-to-side working outward.

11. The remainder of the installation the reverse order of removal.

ENGINE ASSEMBLY

REMOVAL & INSTALLATION

3.6L Engine

See Figures 124 through 127.

1. Before servicing the vehicle, refer to the Precautions Section.

2. Drain the cooling system.

3. Drain the engine oil.

4. Position and secure the battery cables to the engine.

5. Remove the fuel injector sight shield.

6. Remove the air intake assembly.

7. Disconnect the cooling fan electrical connectors.

8. Remove the cooling fan wiring harnesses from the fan shroud.

9. Secure the wiring harnesses to the vehicle.

10. Disconnect the surge tank outlet hose from the surge tank.

11. Position and secure the surge hose to the engine.

12. Disconnect the surge tank inlet hose from the water outlet housing and the radiator.

13. Position and secure the surge tank inlet hose to the vehicle.

14. Disconnect the heater hoses from the heater core.

15. Disconnect the purge line from the purge solenoid.

16. Disconnect the fuel pipe from the fuel rail.

17. Plug the fuel pipe and cap the fuel rail to prevent fuel loss or contamination.

18. Properly recover the conditioning refrigerant.

19. Remove the wiper assembly. For additional information, refer to the following section, "Window Wipers & Washer, Removal & Installation."

20. Disconnect the air conditioning suction hose from the evaporator and remove the suction hose bracket from the shock tower. Position and secure the suction hose to the engine.

21. Disconnect the air conditioning pressure switch electrical connector and remove the liquid line.

22. Remove the radiator support brackets.

23. Disconnect the brake booster check valve and vacuum hose from the brake booster.

24. Position and secure the brake booster hose to the engine.

25. Disconnect all engine harness electrical connectors.

26. Remove the right side engine harness retaining clips.

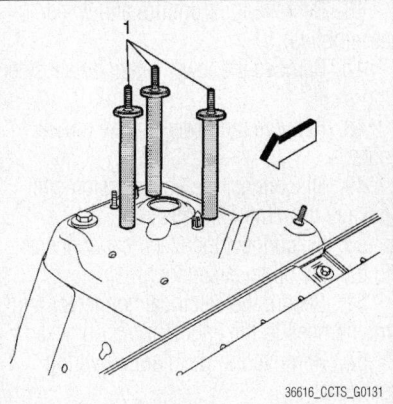

36616_CCTS_G0131

Fig. 124 Install Special Tool J-28467-550 Engine Support Beam Adapters in the location shown on the left and right shock towers—CTS 3.6L Engines

27. Remove the right side engine harness to valve cover retaining clips.

28. Remove the left side engine harness retaining clips.

29. Remove the bolt from the engine harness retainer.

30. Remove the engine harness to transmission retaining clips.

31. Remove the ground bolt and wire from the longitudinal rail.

➡**Do NOT disconnect the brake pipes from the master cylinder.**

32. Remove the master cylinder nuts and reposition and secure the master cylinder to the engine.

33. Properly relieve the fuel system pressure.

34. Raise and safely support the vehicle.

35. Remove the engine harness to transmission retaining clips.

36. Remove the muffler assembly.

37. Remove the driveshafts.

38. Remove the transfer case, if equipped.

39. Remove the air deflector.

➡**DO NOT remove the water bottle.**

40. Remove the washer bottle bracket.

41. Disconnect the side air baffles from the radiator.

42. Disconnect the left front brake pipe retainer along with the brake pipe from the longitudinal rail.

43. Remove the right front brake pipe from the brake pipe bundle retainer.

44. Disconnect the rear brake pipes from the brake pressure modulator valve (BPMV).

45. Plug the brake pipes and the brake modulator valve in order to minimize brake fluid loss.

46. Remove the front tire and wheel assemblies.

47. Remove the lower intermediate steering shaft.

48. Remove the lower engine mount nuts.

49. Disconnect the transmission shift linkage from the transmission.

50. Disconnect the electrical connector to the low oil level sensor.

51. Secure the electrical connector and the harness to the engine mount bracket.

52. Remove the headlamp leveling sensors.

53. Secure the shock modules to the lower control arms with a suitable strap in order to prevent damage to the front brake hoses.

54. Remove the upper mounting bolts from the right and left shock module.

55. Raise the vehicle enough to place a suitable lift table under the engine, transmission, front frame and front suspension assembly.

56. Position a suitable powertrain or engine lift table below the frame, engine and transmission.

57. Raise the lift table or lower the vehicle to support the frame, engine and transmission.

58. Remove the bolts which secure the transmission brace to the underbody.

59. Remove the front frame bolts.

➡Ensure that all the hoses, wires, pipes and shock modules clear the vehicle during the removal process.

60. With the aid of an assistant, lower the table or raise the vehicle to remove the engine, transmission, front frame and front suspension assembly from the vehicle.

➡Do NOT remove the oxygen sensors.

61. Remove the catalytic converters with the oxygen sensors.

62. Remove the thermostat housing with the heater pipes, heater hoses and surge tank outlet hose.

63. Remove the starter motor.

64. Remove the flywheel bolts.

65. Remove the heated oxygen sensor (HO2S) connector bracket from the left cylinder head.

66. Remove the engine wiring harness and related components.

67. Disconnect the transmission oil cooler pipes from the engine, radiator and the transmission.

68. Disconnect the radiator hoses from the water outlet housing and the coolant inlet pipe.

69. Disconnect the power steering cooler hoses from the condenser radiator and fan module (CRFM).

70. Plug the power steering hoses and pipes in order to prevent fluid loss and contamination.

71. Remove the CRFM with the radiator hoses from the frame.

72. Install Special Tool EN-46114 Engine Support Fixture to the engine as follows:

   a. Use a grade 10.9, M10 X 1.5 X 35 bolt, GM P/N 11519182, or equivalent, in order to install Special Tool J-36857 lift bracket, or equivalent, to the front of the left cylinder head in the location shown. Tighten the bolt to 48 ft. lbs. (65 Nm).

   b. Remove the shock module mounting stud and bolt from the left and right shock tower.

   c. Install the Engine Support Beam Adapters in the location shown on the left and right shock towers.

   d. Ensure the strut tower support assemblies are secured to the engine support beam adapters with wing nuts.

   e. Secure the strut tower tube to the strut tower support with quick release pins.

   f. Secure the strut tower tube to the radiator shelf tube with the cross bracket assembly.

   g. Tighten the cross bracket wing nuts.

   h. Assemble the lift hook wing nut and the lift hook bracket to the lift hook.

   i. Install lift hook assembly to the radiator shelf tube.

   j. Install lift hook assembly to left side engine lift hook bracket.

   k. Assemble the lift hook wing nut and the lift hook bracket to the lift hook.

   l. Install lift hook assembly to the strut tower tube.

   m. Hand tighten the lift hooks in order to remove all slack from the engine support fixture.

73. Connect a floor crane to the engine lift brackets and raise the floor crane to partially support the engine.

74. Position a second powertrain lift table below the transmission.

75. Remove the bolts that secure the transmission to the engine.

76. Remove the transmission from the engine.

77. Remove the accessory drive belts.

78. Remove the generator and the generator bracket.

79. Remove the A/C compressor.

80. Remove the power steering pump.

81. Remove the power steering reservoir from the engine.

82. Remove the oil level indicator.

83. Remove the left exhaust manifold.

84. Remove the oil filter adapter.

85. Remove the right exhaust manifold.

86. Remove the crankshaft balancer.

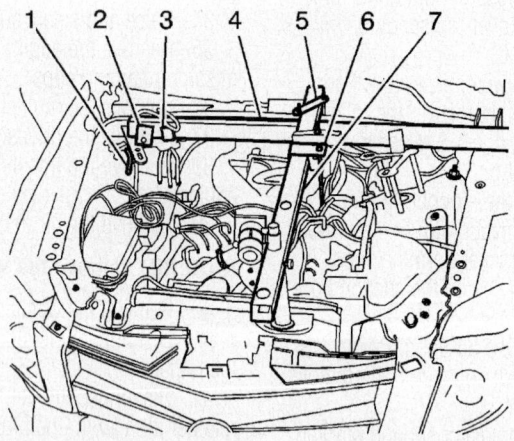

1. Engine support beam adapters
2. Strut tower support assemblies
3. Lift hook
4. Strut tower tube
5. Cross bracket assembly
6. Lift hook
7. Radiator shelf tube

36616_CCTS_G0132

Fig. 125 Engine support fixture—CTS 3.6L Engine

87. Remove the flywheel.

88. Remove the intake manifold.

89. Remove the water outlet.

90. Remove the block heater.

91. Remove the Engine Control Module (ECM) with the mounting bracket.

92. Remove the front drive shafts, if equipped.

93. Use a floor crane in order to remove the engine from the frame.

To install:

94. Use a floor crane in order to install the engine to the frame.

95. Install the front drive shafts, if equipped.

96. Install the ECM with the ECM bracket.

97. Install the water outlet and tighten the mounting bolts to 89 inch lbs. (10 Nm).

98. Install the block heater.

99. Install the flywheel.

100. Install the intake manifold.

101. Install the crankshaft balancer.

102. Install the right exhaust manifold.

103. Install the oil filter adapter.

104. Install the left exhaust manifold.

105. Install the oil level indicator.

106. Install the generator and the generator bracket.

107. Install the power steering pump.

108. Install the power steering reservoir to the engine.

109. Install the A/C compressor.

110. Install the A/C compressor and power steering drive belt tensioner.

111. Install the generator and water pump drive belt tensioner.

112. Install the drive belts.

113. Install the bolts that secure the transmission to the engine.

114. Install the starter motor.

115. Remove engine support fixture from the engine.

116. Install the CRFM with the radiator hoses to the frame.

117. Connect the power steering cooler hoses to the CRFM.

118. Connect the radiator hoses to the water outlet housing and the coolant inlet pipe.

119. Install the transmission oil cooler pipes to the engine, radiator and the transmission.

120. Install the engine wiring harness and related components.

121. Install the HO2S connector bracket to the left cylinder head.

122. Install the thermostat housing with the heater pipes, heater hoses and surge tank outlet hose.

123. Install the catalytic converters with the oxygen sensors.

124. Install the fuel lines to the fuel rail and the EVAP purge solenoid.

➡**Ensure that all the hoses, wires, pipes and shock modules clear the vehicle during the installation process.**

125. With the aid of an assistant, raise the table or lift the vehicle to install the engine, transmission, front frame and front suspension assembly to the vehicle.

126. Install the front frame bolts.

127. Install the transmission support to underbody bolts and remove the powertrain lift/support table.

128. Install the upper mounting bolts to the right and left shock module.

129. Secure the shock modules to the front frame with mechanics wire to avoid stretching the front brake hoses.

130. Install the headlamp leveling sensors.

131. Connect the transmission shift linkage to the transmission.

132. Connect electrical connector to the low oil level sensor.

133. Install the lower engine mount nuts.

134. Install the lower intermediate steering shaft.

135. Install the front tire and wheel assemblies.

136. Install the front brake pipes and retainers to the underbody.

137. Connect the rear brake pipes to the BPMV.

138. Install the washer bottle bracket.

139. Install the air deflector.

140. Install the transfer case, if equipped.

141. Install the driveshaft.

142. Install the muffler assembly.

143. Install the engine harness to transmission retaining clips.

144. Install the brake master cylinder.

145. Install the ground wire and bolt to the longitudinal rail and tighten the bolt to 89 inch lbs. (10 Nm).

146. Install the engine harness to transmission retaining clips.

147. Install the left side engine harness retaining clips.

148. Install the bolt to the engine harness retainer and tighten to 89 inch lbs. (10 Nm).

149. Install the right side engine harness to valve cover retaining clips.

150. Install the right side engine harness retaining clips.

151. Connect all engine harness electrical connectors.

152. Connect the brake booster vacuum hose to the brake booster.

153. Install the radiator support brackets and tighten the bolts to 80 inch lbs. (9 Nm).

154. Connect the purge line to the purge solenoid.

155. Connect the fuel pipe to the fuel rail.

156. Connect the heater hoses to the heater core.

157. Position and secure the surge tank inlet hose to the vehicle.

158. Connect the surge tank inlet hose to the water outlet housing and to the radiator.

159. Connect the outlet hose to the surge tank.

160. Connect the electrical connector for the air conditioning pressure switch and the liquid line to the evaporator.

161. Connect the air conditioning suction hose to the evaporator and install the suction hose bracket to the shock tower.

162. Install the air intake assembly.

163. Install the cooling fan wiring harnesses to the fan shroud.

164. Install the cooling fan electrical connectors.

165. Install the wiper assembly.

166. Install the fuel injector sight shield.

167. Connect the negative cable from the battery and the body at the top of the right strut tower.

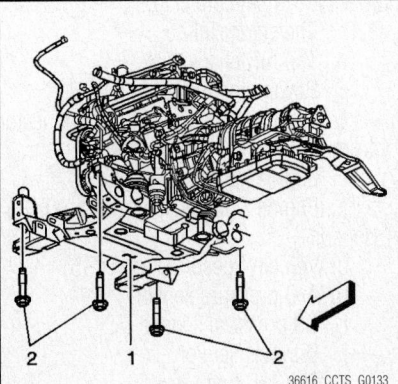

36616_CCTS_G0133

Fig. 126 Raise the engine assembly into the vehicle and install the front frame bolts (2)—CTS 3.6L Engine

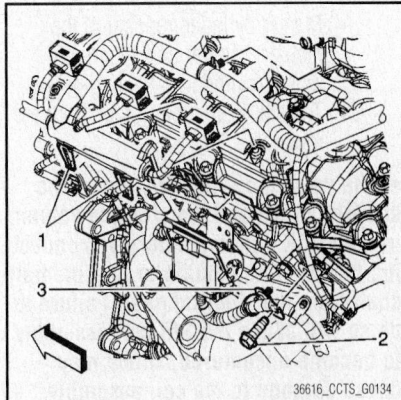

36616_CCTS_G0134

Fig. 127 Install the left side retaining clips (1), bolt (2) and engine wiring harness retainer (3)—CTS 3.6L Engine

168. Refill the engine cooling system to the correct level.

169. Properly charge the air conditioning system.

170. Refill the engine with oil to the correct level.

171. Bleed the rear brakes.

172. Start the engine to verify proper operation and check for leaks.

4.6L Engine

See Figure 128.

1. Before servicing the vehicle, refer to the Precautions Section.
2. Drain the cooling system.
3. Drain the engine oil.
4. Recover the A/C refrigerant.
5. Remove the fuel injector sight shield.
6. Relieve the fuel system pressure.
7. Remove or disconnect the following:
   - Booster vacuum hose
   - Fuel feed line
   - Evaporative emission (EVAP) line
   - Front compartment sight shield
   - Air cleaner
   - Starter cable from the BEC terminal and secure to the top of the engine
   - Engine harness electrical connector from the Transaxle Control Module (TCM)
   - Secure the TCM and engine harness wiring branches to the engine
   - Engine harness electrical connectors from the engine control module (ECM).
   - The junction block and bolts
   - Engine harness from the BEC
   - Right side frame rail ground strap, secure to engine
   - Transaxle shift cable from the bracket and position the cable aside
   - Radiator inlet and outlet hoses
   - Surge tank inlet hose
   - Heater hoses
   - Master cylinder, reposition the master cylinder and secure the master cylinder to the engine
   - Transaxle oil cooler pipes from the radiator

➡ **The wheels of the vehicle must be straight ahead and the steering column in the LOCK position before disconnecting the steering column or intermediate shaft from the steering gear. Failure to do so will cause the SIR coil assembly to become uncentered, which may cause damage to the coil assembly.**

8. Lock the steering column by installing the J 42640 into the underside of the steering column.

9. Remove the left and right side strut tower bolts.

10. Raise and support the vehicle.

11. Remove or disconnect the following:
   - Rear exhaust manifold pipe
   - Front wheels.
   - Engine harness grommet from frame rail
   - Engine harness clip from ride lever sensor
   - Electronic suspension front position sensor, if equipped
   - Front brake line brackets
   - Rear brake lines from front lines, plug the open brake lines
   - A/C compressor discharge and suction hoses at the condenser, secure to the engine and plug port

✳✳ WARNING

Failure to disconnect the intermediate shaft from the rack and pinion stub shaft can result in damage to the steering gear and/or damage to the intermediate shaft. This damage may cause loss of steering control which could result in personal injury.

   - Steering shaft cover
   - Intermediate shaft pinch bolt and shaft
   - The heated oxygen sensor (HO2S).
   - Transaxle brace bolts and brace
   - Torque converter cover

➡ **Mark the flywheel to torque converter relationship prior to removal of the bolts.**

   - Flywheel to torque converter bolts
12. Position the J 39580 engine cradle under the frame.
13. Lower the vehicle onto the J 39580.
14. If the J 39580 is not available. Support the powertrain with four suitable jackstands.

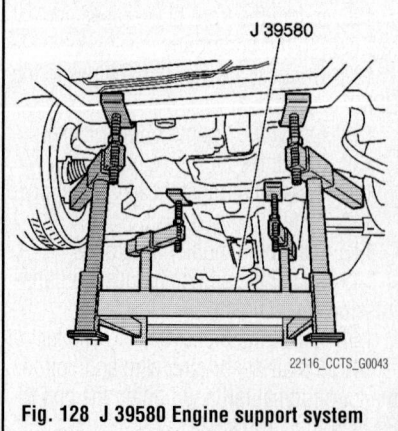

Fig. 128 J 39580 Engine support system

15. Place a 2 inch x 4 inch block of wood between the front of the engine oil pan and the engine frame.

✳✳ WARNING

To avoid any vehicle damage, serious personal injury or death when major components are removed from the vehicle and the vehicle is supported by a hoist, support the vehicle with jack stands at the opposite end from which the components are being removed and strap the vehicle to the hoist.

16. Secure the front hoist pads to the vehicle.

17. Remove the front fascia.

18. Remove the 6 bolts attaching the frame to the body.

19. Ensure clearance is maintained between the engine/transaxle assembly and the following:
   a. The A/C compressor components
   b. The brake pipes
   c. The heater hoses
   d. The radiator hoses
   e. The wheel speed sensor leads

20. Carefully raise the vehicle in order to clear the supported engine/transaxle assembly.

21. Remove secondary Air Injection (AIR) components.

22. Remove the Ignition Control Module (ICM) ground strap from the right cylinder head.

23. Disconnect the following engine harness electrical connectors from the front of the engine:
   a. The fuel injectors
   b. The Ignition Control Module (ICM)
   c. The Manifold Absolute Pressure (MAP) sensor
   d. The throttle actuator

24. Disconnect the following engine harness electrical connectors:
   a. The starter inline
   b. The AIR check valve
   c. Power steering sensor
   d. Engine harness electrical connector from the engine valley jumper
   e. Engine harness ground
   f. Engine Coolant Temperature (ECT) sensor
   g. Vehicle Speed Sensor (VSS)
   h. A/C pressure sensor
   i. Oil pressure sensor
   j. Oil level sensor
   k. The A/C compressor
   l. Alternator
   m. The AIR pump
   n. The brake modulator
   o. HO2S sensor

25. Remove all clips and retainers as needed.

26. Disconnect the engine harness electrical connector from the transaxle.

27. Remove all remaining engine harness ground bolts.

28. Gather all the branches of the engine harness and remove the engine harness from the engine.

29. Remove or disconnect the following:
- Power steering outlet hose from the reservoir
- Power steering inlet pipe fitting from the power steering pump
- A/C compressor discharge and suction hoses, plug ports
- Transaxle nuts, bolt and brace

30. Install an engine lift chain to the engine lift brackets and attach an engine lifting device.

31. Remove the rear engine mount to frame nut.

32. Remove the rear engine mount bracket bolts and stud.

33. Remove the rear engine mount bracket.

34. Remove the front engine mount to frame nut.

35. Remove the rear transaxle bolt.

36. Remove the upper transaxle bolts.

37. Separate the engine from the transaxle.

38. Raise the engine from the supported frame and transaxle assembly.

39. Remove the front engine mount bracket bolts/nuts.

40. Remove the front engine mount bracket.

41. Install the engine assembly to a suitable engine stand.

To install:

42. Install the front engine mount bracket.

43. Install the front engine mount bracket bolts/nuts and tighten to 37 ft. lbs. (50 Nm).

44. Install an engine lift chain to the engine lift brackets and attach an engine lifting device.

45. Remove the engine assembly from the engine stand.

46. Carefully position and install the engine to the supported frame and transaxle, aligning the engine dowel pins to the transaxle.

47. Install or connect the following:
- Upper transaxle bolts, Tighten to 55 ft. lbs. (75 Nm).
- Rear transaxle bolt. Tighten to 55 ft. lbs. (75 Nm).
- Front engine mount to frame nut. Tighten to 59 ft. lbs. (80 Nm).

- Rear engine mount bracket bolts and stud. Tighten the bolts/stud to 54 ft. lbs. (73 Nm).
- Rear engine mount to frame nut. Tighten the nut to 59 ft. lbs. (80 Nm).
- Transaxle brace
- Transaxle brace bolt. Tighten the bolt to 37 ft. lbs. (50 Nm).
- Front engine mount bracket nut with the transaxle brace behind it. Tighten the nut to 37 ft. lbs. (50 Nm).
- Transaxle brace to the engine and transaxle
- Transaxle brace bolts to the engine. Tighten the bolts to 37 ft. lbs. (50 Nm).
- Transaxle brace bolt/stud to the transaxle. Tighten the bolt/stud to 37 ft. lbs. (50 Nm).
- Transaxle brace to the lift bracket studs
- Transaxle brace bolt. Tighten the bolt/stud to 37 ft. lbs. (50 Nm). Tighten the nut to 37 ft. lbs. (50 Nm).
- A/C suction and discharge hoses. Remove plugs. Tighten to mounting nuts to 12 ft. lbs. (16 Nm).
- Power steering inlet pipe fitting to the power steering pump. Tighten the fitting to 20 ft. lbs. (27 Nm).
- Power steering inlet pipe bracket
- Power steering inlet pipe nut. Tighten the nut to 80 inch lbs. (9 Nm).
- Power steering outlet hose to the reservoir.
- Engine harness to the engine.
- Engine harness grounds. Tighten the bolts to 18 ft. lbs. (25 Nm).
- Engine harness electrical connector to the transaxle

48. Connect the engine harness electrical connectors to the following:
- a. HO2S
- b. The AIR pump
- c. The brake modulator
- d. The oil pressure sensor
- e. The oil level sensor
- f. The A/C compressor
- g. The alternator
- h. A/C pressure sensor.
- i. Vehicle Speed Sensor (VSS)
- j. Engine Coolant Temperature (ECT) sensor
- k. The power steering sensor
- l. Engine valley jumper harness electrical connector.

49. Connect the following engine harness electrical connectors to the top of the engine:
- a. The starter inline
- b. The AIR check valve

50. Connect the following engine harness electrical connectors to the front of the engine:
- a. The fuel injectors
- b. The ICM
- c. The MAP sensor
- d. The throttle actuator

51. Connect the following engine harness electrical connectors to the rear of the engine:
- a. The EVAP solenoid
- b. The EGR valve
- c. The fuel injectors
- d. The ICM

52. Install all clips and retainers as needed.

53. Install or connect the following:
- ICM ground strap bolt to the right cylinder head. Tighten the bolt to 18 ft. lbs. (25 Nm).
- Secondary air injection components.
- AIR pipe outlet pipe nut. Tighten the nut to 80 inch lbs. (90 Nm).
- Heater outlet pipe to the engine. Tighten the nut to 18 ft. lbs. (25 Nm).
- Heater outlet pipe at the water pump housing

54. Position the engine/transaxle assembly under the vehicle.

55. Ensure clearance is maintained between the engine/transaxle assembly and the following:
- a. The A/C compressor components
- b. The brake pipes
- c. The heater hoses
- d. The radiator hoses
- e. The wheel speed sensor leads
- f. The wiring harnesses

56. Carefully lower the vehicle over the engine/transaxle assembly, aligning the struts to the strut towers.

57. Install the 6 bolts attaching the frame to the body. Tighten the bolts to 141 ft. lbs. (191 Nm).

58. Install the front fascia.

59. Raise the vehicle off of the J 39580 or the jack stands.

60. Remove the J 39580 or jack stands from under the frame.

61. Align the flywheel with the marks made during the removal.

62. Install the flywheel to torque converter bolts. Tighten the bolts to 44 ft. lbs. (60 Nm).

63. Install or connect the following:
- Torque converter cover. Tighten the bolt to 106 inch lbs. (12 Nm).
- Transaxle brace. Tighten the bolts to 35 ft. lbs. (47 Nm).
- HO2S
- Oxygen sensor wiring harness heat shield

- Intermediate shaft to the steering gear. Tighten the pinch bolt to 33 ft. lbs. (45 Nm).
- Intermediate steering shaft cover
- A/C compressor suction and discharge hoses to the condenser. Remove plugs. Install new washers and tighten the nut to 12 ft. lbs. (16 Nm).
- Rear brake lines to the front brake lines. Remove plugs. Tighten the fittings to 15 ft. lbs. (20 Nm).
- Left and right brake pipe bracket to the body frame rail. Tighten the nut to 80 inch lbs. (9 Nm).
- Front air deflector
- Electronic suspension front position sensor, if equipped.
- Engine harness grommet
- Front wheels
- Rear exhaust manifold pipe

64. Lower the vehicle.
65. Remove the J 42640 from the steering column.
66. Install or connect the following:

- Transaxle oil cooler pipes to the radiator
- Upper transaxle oil cooler pipe bolt. Tighten the bolt to 53 inch lbs. (6 Nm).
- Master cylinder. Tighten the nuts to 22 ft. lbs. (30 Nm).
- Heater inlet and outlet hoses to the heater pipes
- Surge tank inlet hose
- Radiator inlet and outlet hoses
- Transaxle shift cable
- Engine ground strap at frame rail. Tighten the bolt to 18 ft. lbs. (25 Nm).
- Engine harness to the BEC.
- The junction block. Tighten the bolts to 58 inch lbs. (6.5 Nm).
- Engine harness electrical connectors to the ECM
- Engine harness electrical connector to the body harness electrical connector
- Engine harness electrical connector to the TCM

- Starter cable to the BEC terminal. Tighten the nut to 11 ft. lbs. (15 Nm)
- Junction block cover
- The air cleaner
- Front compartment sight shield
- Fuel feed hose
- EVAP line
- Brake booster vacuum hose

67. Connect the negative battery cable.
68. Fill the engine with oil.
69. Fill the cooling system.
70. Bleed the brake system.
71. Recharge the A/C refrigerant system.
72. Bleed the power steering system.
73. Check the wheel alignment.
74. Pre-lube the engine.
75. Install the fuel injector sight shield.
76. With the ignition OFF or disconnected, crank the engine several times. Listen for any unusual noises or evidence that any parts are binding.
77. Start the engine and listen for abnormal conditions.
78. Check the vehicle oil pressure gauge or light and confirm that the engine has acceptable oil pressure.
79. Run the engine at approximately 1000 RPM until the engine reaches normal operating temperature.
80. While the engine continues to idle raise and support the vehicle.
81. Inspect for oil, coolant and exhaust leaks while the engine is idling.
82. Lower the vehicle.
83. Perform the Crankshaft Position (CKP) system variation learn procedure.
84. Perform a final inspection for the proper engine oil and coolant levels.
85. Road test the vehicle.

6.2L Engine

See Figure 129.

1. Disconnect the negative battery cable.
2. Remove the intake manifold cover.
3. Discharge the air conditioning (A/C) system.
4. Raise and safely support the vehicle.
5. Remove the front wheels.
6. Remove the transmission.
7. Drain the supercharger cooling system.
8. Drain the engine cooling system.
9. Drain the engine oil from the oil pan and dry sump oil tank.
10. Remove the two drain plugs from the oil pan to drain.
11. Install the drain plugs to the oil pan and tighten.
12. Lower the vehicle.
13. Remove the air cleaner resonator outlet duct.

14. Disconnect the supercharger intercooler cooling hoses.
15. Remove the radiator inlet and outlet hoses.
16. Disconnect all necessary engine harness electrical connectors.
17. Install the engine support fixture.
18. Raise and safely support the vehicle.
19. Remove the front compartment lower noise shield.
20. Remove the electrical harness retainers (1) securing the engine harness (2) to the frame.
21. Remove the wheel speed sensor wire harness from the frame.
22. Remove the brake pipes from the frame.
23. Remove the brake pressure modulator valve (BPMV) from the bracket assembly.
24. Using mechanics wire, support the radiator and A/C condenser assembly to the vehicle body.
25. Remove the washer bottle bracket from the frame.
26. Loosen the stabilizer shaft mounting bolts. Mark the stabilizer shaft to ensure the correct position when reinstalling.
27. Remove the lower stabilizer shaft link from the lower control arm.
28. Remove the power steering gear mounting bolts.
29. Using mechanics wire, secure the power steering gear to the engine.
30. Separate the outer tie rod from the steering knuckle.
31. Disconnect the lower ball joint from the steering knuckle.
32. Remove the shock module yokes from the lower control arms.
33. Install the J 39580 Engine Support Stand under the frame.
34. Lower the vehicle to the frame support table.

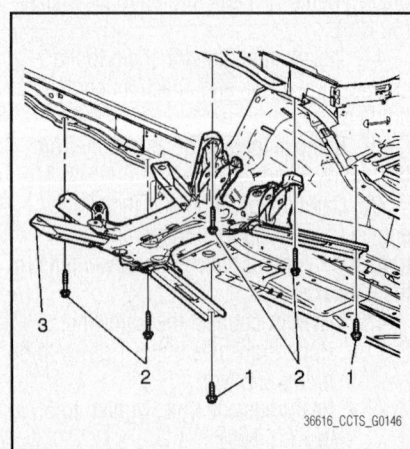

36616_CCTS_G0146

Fig. 129 Remove the frame mounting bolts (1, 2)—6.2L engine

35. Remove the frame mounting bolts (1, 2).

36. With the aid of an assistant, carefully raise the body from the frame.

37. Ensure when raising the body the following components are clear from the frame:
- Brake pipes
- Steering knuckle assembly
- Electrical wiring harness

38. Remove the stabilizer shaft.

39. With the aid of an assistant, remove the frame from the support fixture.

40. Remove the power steering rack from the vehicle.

41. Remove the engine mount brackets with the engine mounts.

42. With the aid of an assistant, lower the engine and disconnect the electrical connector as needed.

43. The installation is the reverse order of removal.

EXHAUST MANIFOLD

REMOVAL & INSTALLATION

3.6L Engine

See Figure 130.

1. Remove the fuel injector sight shield.

2. Remove the exhaust manifold heat shield bolts and heat shield.

3. Remove the upper exhaust manifold heat shield insulator from the oil level indicator tube, if necessary.

4. Remove the lower exhaust manifold heat shield insulator from the oil level indicator and exhaust gasket, if necessary.

5. Remove the oil level indicator and tube.

6. Remove the lower intermediate steering shaft.

7. Remove the catalytic converter.

8. Remove the exhaust manifold and discard the exhaust manifold gasket.

To install:

9. Install the exhaust manifold with a NEW gasket. Tighten the manifold bolts to 15 ft. lbs. (20 Nm).

10. The remainder of the installation is the reverse order of removal.

11. Start the engine and inspect for exhaust leaks.

4.6L Engine

Left Side

See Figure 131.

1. Before servicing the vehicle, refer to the Precautions Section.

> ※※ **WARNING**
>
> **Always wear protective goggles and gloves when removing exhaust parts as falling rust and sharp edges from worn exhaust components could result in serious personal injury.**

2. Remove the front engine mount bracket.

3. Remove the Connector Position Assurance (CPA) retainer.

4. Disconnect the engine harness electrical connector from the heated oxygen sensor (HO2S).

5. Remove the HO2S.

6. Remove the exhaust manifold front pipe bolts.

7. Remove the exhaust manifold bolts.

8. Remove the exhaust manifold.

9. Remove and discard the exhaust manifold gasket.

10. Remove and discard the front exhaust manifold pipe seal.

11. Remove the front exhaust manifold pipe flange.

To install:

12. Install the front exhaust manifold pipe flange and a NEW seal onto the exhaust manifold.

13. Insert the upper right exhaust manifold bolt to the manifold in this location.

14. Place the NEW exhaust manifold gasket over the bolt and against the manifold.

15. Insert the exhaust manifold into the front exhaust manifold pipe and against the cylinder head.

16. Finger start the exhaust manifold bolt.

17. Install the remaining exhaust manifold bolts and tighten all exhaust manifold bolts starting from right to left beginning with the bolt in this location. Tighten the bolts to 18 ft. lbs. (25 Nm).

18. Install the exhaust manifold front pipe bolts.

19. If reusing the old HO2S, coat the threads with anti-seize compound, GM P/N 12377953 or equivalent.

20. Install the HO2S and tighten to 30 ft. lbs. (41 Nm).

21. Connect the engine harness electrical connector to the HO2S.

22. Install the CPA retainer.

23. Install the front engine mount bracket.

Right Side

See Figures 132 through 134.

> ※※ **WARNING**
>
> **Always wear protective goggles and gloves when removing exhaust parts as falling rust and sharp edges from worn exhaust components could result in serious personal injury.**

1. Remove the Connector Position Assurance (CPA) retainer.

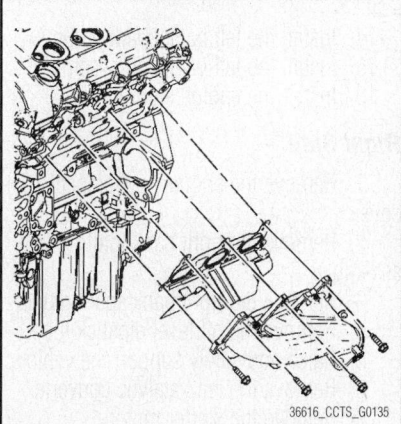

Fig. 130 Installing the exhaust manifold— 3.6L engine

36616_CCTS_G0135

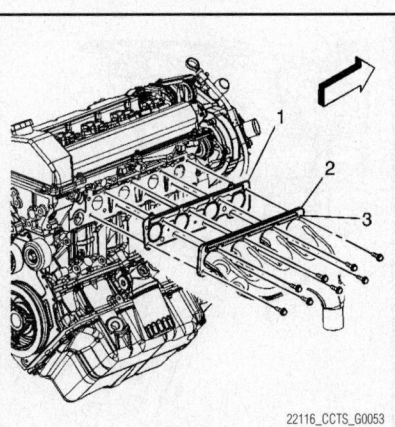

Fig. 131 View of the left exhaust manifold removal

22116_CCTS_G0053

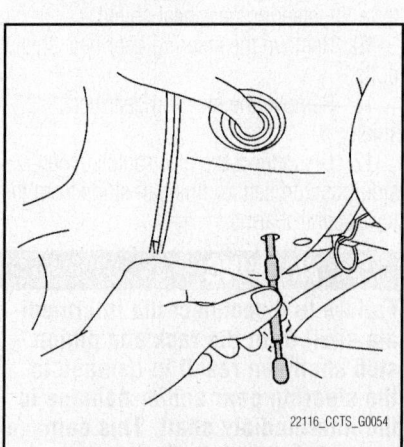

Fig. 132 Installing the J 42640 to lock steering column

22116_CCTS_G0054

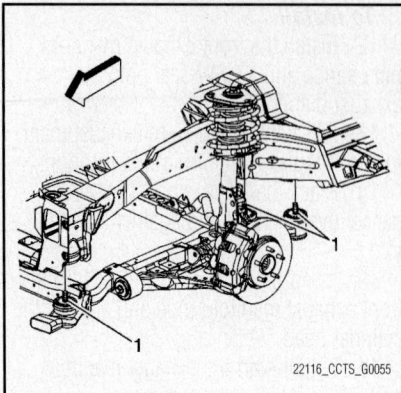

Fig. 133 View of engine frame being lowered, frame bolts (1) shown

2. Disconnect the engine harness electrical connector from the heated oxygen sensor (HO2S) .

3. Remove the HO2S clip from the secondary air injection (AIR) valve hose bracket.

➡**The wheels of the vehicle must be straight ahead and the steering column in the LOCK position before disconnecting the steering column or intermediate shaft from the steering gear. Failure to do so will cause the coil assembly in the steering column to become uncentered which will cause damage to the coil assembly.**

4. Lock the steering column by installing the J 42640 into the underside of the steering column.

5. Raise and support the vehicle.

6. Remove the rear exhaust manifold pipe.

7. Remove the AIR check valve.

8. Disconnect the engine harness clip from the steering gear heat shield.

9. Disconnect the engine harness clip from the steering gear heat shield.

10. Remove the steering gear heat shield bolts.

11. Remove the steering gear heat shield.

12. Disconnect the electronic suspension position sensor link ball studs from the lower control arms.

⁜⁜ WARNING

Failure to disconnect the intermediate shaft from the rack and pinion stub shaft can result in damage to the steering gear and/or damage to the intermediate shaft. This damage may cause loss of steering control which could result in personal injury.

13. Unsnap and remove the intermediate shaft seal.

14. Remove the intermediate shaft pinch bolt.

15. Separate the intermediate shaft from the steering gear.

16. Support the rear of the frame with a tall screw type jack.

17. Remove the rearward engine frame-to-body bolts.

18. Lower the screw type jack approximately 1.5 inch (4 cm) allowing the rear of the engine frame to lower.

19. Remove the HO2S.

20. Remove the exhaust manifold nuts.

21. Remove the exhaust manifold.

22. Remove and discard the exhaust manifold gasket.

To install:

23. Install a NEW exhaust manifold gasket onto the cylinder head studs.

24. Install the exhaust manifold and tighten the nuts to 18 ft. lbs. (25 Nm).

25. If reusing the old HO2S, coat the threads with anti-seize compound, GM P/N 12377953 or equivalent.

26. Install the HO2S and tighten to 30 ft. lbs. (41 Nm).

27. Raise the engine frame into position.

28. Install the 4 rearward engine frame-to-body bolts and tighten to 141 ft. lbs. (191 Nm).

29. Remove the screw type jack.

30. Connect the intermediate shaft to the steering gear.

31. Install the intermediate shaft pinch bolt and tighten to 33 ft. lbs. (45 Nm).

32. Install the intermediate shaft seal.

33. Connect the electronic suspension position sensor link ball studs to the lower control arms.

34. Install the steering gear heat shield.

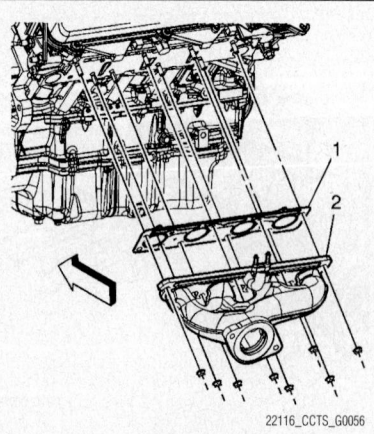

Fig. 134 View of exhaust manifold (2) and gasket (1) removal

35. Install the steering gear heat shield bolts and tighten to 80 inch lbs. (9 Nm).

36. Connect the engine harness clip to the steering gear heat shield.

37. Install the AIR check valve.

38. Install the rear exhaust manifold pipe.

39. Lower the vehicle.

40. Remove the J 42640 from the steering column.

41. Connect the engine harness electrical connector to the HO2S.

42. Install the HO2S clip to the AIR valve hose bracket.

43. Install the CPA retainer.

6.2L Engine

Left Side

1. Remove the engine appearance cover.

2. Remove the left bank ignition coil assembly.

3. Remove the left bank spark plugs.

4. Raise and safely support the vehicle.

5. Remove the left catalytic converter.

6. Disconnect the center steering shaft from the lower steering shaft. Separate the shafts and position aside to provide a removal envelope for the manifold. Refer to Intermediate Steering Shaft Replacement.

7. Lower the vehicle.

8. Remove the exhaust manifold bolts.

9. Remove the exhaust manifold, bolts, and gasket. Discard the gasket.

To install:

10. Position the exhaust manifold and a NEW gasket into place.

11. Install the exhaust manifold bolts and tighten as follows:

   a. Step 1: to 11 ft. lbs. (15 Nm).

   b. Step 2: to 15 ft. lbs. (20 Nm).

12. Using a flat punch, bend over the exposed edge of the exhaust manifold gasket at the rear of the left cylinder head.

13. Install the left catalytic converter and seal.

14. Install the left bank spark plugs.

15. Install the left bank coil assembly.

16. Install the engine sight shield.

Right Side

1. Remove the engine appearance cover.

2. Remove the right bank ignition coil assembly.

3. Remove the right bank spark plugs.

4. Remove the oil level dipstick tube.

5. Raise and safely support the vehicle.

6. Remove the left catalytic converter.

7. Remove the starter motor.

8. Remove the exhaust manifold bolts.

9. Remove the exhaust manifold, bolts, and gasket. Discard the gasket.

To install:

10. Position the exhaust manifold and a NEW gasket into place.

11. Install the exhaust manifold bolts and tighten as follows:

    a. Step 1: to 11 ft. lbs. (15 Nm).

    b. Step 2: to 15 ft. lbs. (20 Nm).

12. Install the starter motor.

13. Install the right catalytic converter.

14. Install the right bank spark plugs.

15. Install the right bank coil assembly.

16. Install the oil level dipstick tube.

17. Install the engine sight shield.

FLYWHEEL

REMOVAL & INSTALLATION

CTS

1. Before servicing the vehicle, refer to the Precautions Section.

2. Remove the transmission assembly. For additional information, refer to the following section, "Automatic Transmission, Removal & Installation."

3. Remove the flywheel bolts and flywheel.

4. Installation is the reverse order of removal.

4.6L Engine

See Figures 135 and 136.

1. Before servicing the vehicle, refer to the Precautions Section.

2. Remove the transmission assembly. For additional information, refer to the following section, "Automatic Transmission, Removal & Installation."

3. Install the J 44214 flywheel holder.

4. Loosen the flywheel bolts.

5. Remove all but one of the flywheel bolts, leaving the one bolt at the top of the crankshaft.

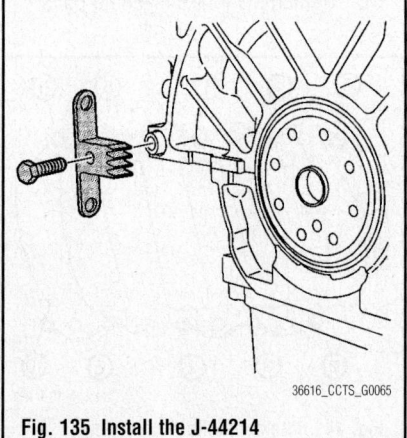

Fig. 135 Install the J-44214 flywheel holder.

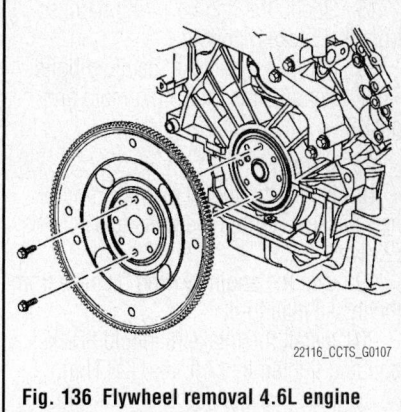

Fig. 136 Flywheel removal 4.6L engine

6. Grasp the engine flywheel with one hand and remove the remaining bolt. Do not drop the engine flywheel when removing the final bolt.

7. Clean and inspect the engine flywheel.

To install:

8. Apply sealant to the flywheel bolts.

9. Place the engine flywheel in position against the crankshaft.

10. Install the flywheel bolts.

11. Place the engine flywheel in position against the crankshaft.

12. Install the flywheel bolts and tighten as follows:

    a. Tighten the bolts a first pass to 22 ft. lbs. (30 Nm).

    b. Tighten the bolts a final pass an additional 50 degrees using the J 45059 angle meter.

13. Remove the J 44214 from the engine block.

14. Install the transaxle assembly.

INTAKE MANIFOLD

REMOVAL & INSTALLATION

3.6L Engine

VIN 7

See Figures 137 and 138.

1. Turn the ignition OFF.

2. Remove the fuel injector sight shield.

3. Remove the air outlet duct.

4. Disconnect the brake booster vacuum hose from the intake manifold.

5. Disconnect the purge solenoid valve electrical connector.

6. Disconnect the purge line from the purge solenoid valve.

7. Remove the wiring harness retainer.

8. Disconnect the throttle body electrical connector.

9. Remove the upper intake manifold brace stud (1), bolt (2), and brace.

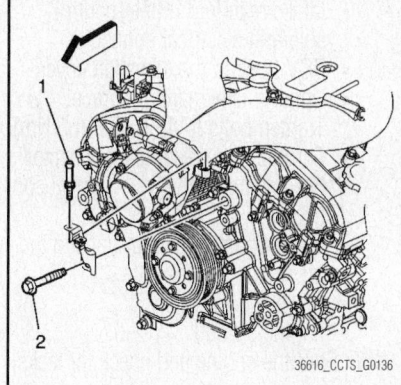

Fig. 137 Remove the upper intake manifold brace stud (1), bolt (2), and brace—3.6L engine VIN 7

10. Disconnect the positive crankcase ventilation (PCV) hose from the right bank camshaft cover.

11. Disconnect the barometric pressure sensor electrical connector.

12. Disconnect the intake manifold runner control solenoid electrical connector.

13. Remove the injector harness bracket bolt.

14. Remove the left bank ignition coil wiring harness from the bracket.

15. Remove the upper intake manifold bolts. Some deflection of the cowl panel may be necessary to extract the right rear bolt.

16. Remove the upper intake manifold with the throttle body.

To install:

17. Install the intake manifold with a new gasket. Tighten the bolts to 17 ft. lbs. (23 Nm).

18. Install or connect the following:

- Fuel injector harness bracket. Tighten bolt to 89 inch lbs. (10 Nm).
- Left bank ignition coil harness
- BARO sensor electrical connector

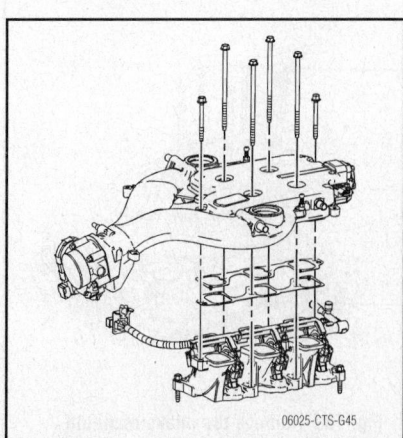

Fig. 138 View of the intake manifold—3.6L engine VIN 7

- Intake manifold runner control solenoid electrical connector
- PCV hose to the camshaft cover
- Upper intake manifold brace. Tighten bolts to 48 ft. lbs. (65 Nm).
- Throttle body electrical connector
- Purge solenoid valve electrical connector
- Brake booster vacuum hose to the manifold
- Air intake assembly
- Engine shroud

19. Start the engine and check for leaks.

VIN Y

See Figure 139.

1. Remove the cross vehicle brace.
2. Remove the fuel injection sight shield.
3. Remove the intake manifold insulator.
4. Remove the wiper transmission.
5. Remove the fuel pipe shield to intake manifold bolts.
6. Remove the fuel pipe shield to cylinder bolt.
7. Carefully remove the fuel pipe shield from the vehicle.
8. Remove the air outlet duct.
9. Disconnect the brake booster vacuum hose from the intake manifold.
10. Disconnect the positive crankcase ventilation (PCV) hose from the intake manifold.
11. Disconnect the purge line from the intake manifold.
12. Remove the purge solenoid bolt from the intake manifold and set the purge solenoid aside.
13. Disconnect the throttle body electrical connector.
14. Remove the intake manifold bracket bolt.

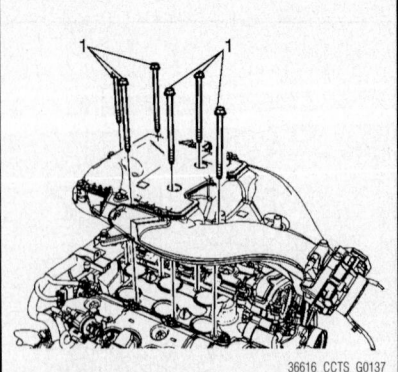

Fig. 139 Remove the intake manifold bolts (1) to remove the intake manifold—3.6L engine VIN Y

15. Unclip the engine wiring harness from the intake manifold.
16. Remove the intake manifold bolts.
17. Remove the intake manifold and gasket.

To install:

18. Install the intake manifold with a new gasket. Tighten the bolts to 17 ft. lbs. (23 Nm).
19. Clip the engine wiring harness from the intake manifold.
20. Install the intake manifold bracket bolt and tighten to 17 ft. lbs. (23 Nm).
21. Install or connect the following:
    - Throttle body connector
    - Purge solenoid bolt to the intake manifold
    - Purge line to the intake manifold
    - PCV hose to the intake manifold
    - Brake booster vacuum hose to the intake manifold
    - Air outlet duct
    - Fuel pipe shield

4.6L Engine

See Figures 140 and 142.

1. Before servicing the vehicle, refer to the Precautions Section.
2. Remove the fuel injector sight shield cover.
3. Remove the air cleaner outlet duct.
4. Disconnect the front ignition coil module engine harness electrical connector.
5. Disconnect the front fuel injectors engine harness electrical connectors.
6. Disconnect the rear ignition coil module engine harness electrical connector.
7. Disconnect the rear fuel injectors engine harness electrical connectors.
8. Disconnect the Positive Crankcase Ventilation (PCV) foul air tube quick connect fitting from the right camshaft cover.
9. Disconnect the PCV fresh air tube quick connect fitting from the camshaft cover.
10. Disconnect the fuel feed line quick connect fitting at the fuel rail.
11. Reposition the radiator surge tank inlet hose/pipe clamp at the surge tank.
12. Remove the surge tank inlet hose/pipe from the surge tank.
13. Reposition the radiator surge tank inlet hose/pipe clamp at the engine.
14. Remove the surge tank inlet hose/pipe from the engine fitting.
15. Remove the 2 push nuts securing the surge tank inlet hose/pipe to the fuel rail studs.
16. Remove the surge tank inlet hose/pipe from the fuel rail studs.
17. Remove the engine harness retainer from the fuel rail stud.

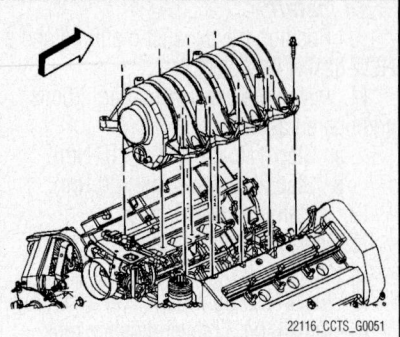

Fig. 140 View of the intake manifold removal—4.6L engine

18. Remove the coolant heater cord tabs from the fuel rail studs, if equipped.
19. Remove the fuel rail bracket nut at the rear left lift bracket.
20. Remove the fuel rail studs.
21. Remove the fuel rail.
22. Loosen the plenum duct clamp screw at the water pump housing.
23. Remove intake manifold bolts.
24. Position the power steering aside.
25. Remove the intake manifold.
26. Disconnect the PCV foul air tube quick connect fitting at the intake manifold.
27. Remove the PCV foul air tube from the retaining features on the intake manifold.
28. Remove and discard the old seals.
29. Clean and inspect the intake manifold.

To install:

30. Install the new intake manifold seals.
31. Connect the PCV foul air tube quick connect fitting at the intake manifold.
32. Install the PCV foul air tube to the retaining features on the intake manifold.
33. Lightly grease the inside edge of the rubber plenum duct on the water pump housing.
34. Install the intake manifold.
35. Install intake manifold bolts until snug.
36. Tighten the intake manifold bolts.

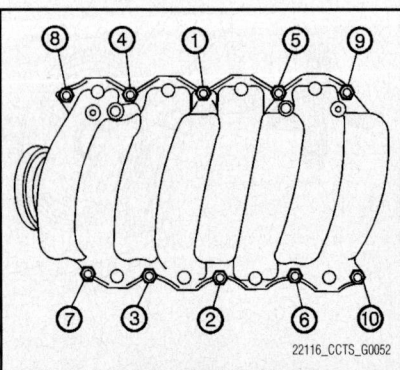

Fig. 141 Intake manifold tightening sequence—4.6L engine

37. Tighten the bolts in the sequence to 89 inch lbs. (10 Nm).

38. Ensure that the intake manifold is fully installed into the plenum duct on the water pump housing.

39. Install the power steering pump

40. Tighten the plenum duct clamp screw at the water pump housing to 24 inch lbs. (2.75 Nm).

41. Lubricate the fuel injector lower O-ring seals with clean engine oil.

42. Install the fuel rail.

43. Install the fuel rail studs and tighten to 89 inch lbs. (10 Nm).

44. Install the fuel rail bracket nut at the rear left lift bracket and tighten to 89 inch lbs. (10 Nm).

45. Install the coolant heater cord tabs to the fuel rail studs, if equipped.

46. Install the engine harness retainer to the fuel rail stud.

47. Install the surge tank inlet hose/pipe to the fuel rail studs.

48. Install the 2 push nuts securing the surge tank inlet hose/pipe to the fuel rail studs.

49. Install the surge tank inlet hose/pipe to the engine fitting.

50. Position the radiator surge tank inlet hose/pipe clamp at the engine.

51. Install the surge tank inlet hose/pipe to the surge tank.

52. Position the radiator surge tank inlet hose/pipe clamp at the surge tank.

53. Connect the fuel feed line quick connect fitting at the fuel rail.

54. Connect the PCV fresh air tube quick connect fitting to the camshaft cover.

55. Connect the PCV foul air tube quick connect fitting to the right camshaft cover.

56. Connect the rear fuel injectors engine harness electrical connectors.

57. Connect the rear ignition coil module engine harness electrical connector.

58. Connect the front fuel injectors engine harness electrical connectors.

59. Connect the front ignition coil module engine harness electrical connector.

60. Install the air cleaner outlet duct.

61. Install the fuel injector sight shield cover.

OIL PAN

REMOVAL & INSTALLATION

3.6L Engine

See Figures 142 through 145.

1. Before servicing the vehicle, refer to the Precautions Section.

2. Drain the engine oil.

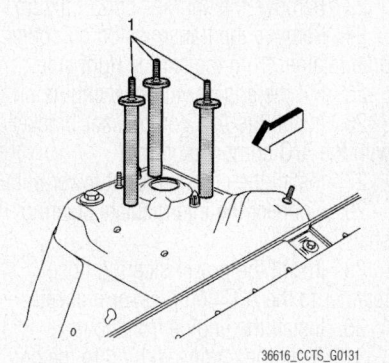

Fig. 142 Install Special Tool J-28467-550 Engine Support Beam Adapters in the location shown on the left and right shock towers—CTS 3.6L Engines

36616_CCTS_G0131

3. Remove the engine front cover. For additional information, refer to the following section, "Timing Chain Cover, Removal & Installation."

4. Remove the power steering hose retainer from the A/C compressor bracket.

5. Disconnect the intermediate steering shaft.

6. Remove the engine mount lower nuts.

➡**Do NOT disconnect the A/C pipes and/or hoses.**

7. Remove the A/C compressor bracket bolts and reposition aside.

8. Remove the transmission oil cooler pipe retainer from the engine right side.

9. Install Special Tool EN-46114 Engine Support Fixture to the engine as follows:

   a. Use a grade 10.9, M10 X 1.5 X 35 bolt, GM P/N 11519182, or equivalent, in order to install Special Tool J-36857 lift bracket, or equivalent, to the front of the left cylinder head in the location shown. Tighten the bolt to 48 ft. lbs. (65 Nm).

   b. Remove the shock module mounting stud and bolt from the left and right shock tower.

   c. Install the Engine Support Beam Adapters in the location shown on the left and right shock towers.

   d. Ensure the strut tower support assemblies are secured to the engine support beam adapters with wing nuts.

   e. Secure the strut tower tube to the strut tower support with quick release pins.

   f. Secure the strut tower tube to the radiator shelf tube with the cross bracket assembly.

   g. Tighten the cross bracket wing nuts.

   h. Assemble the lift hook wing nut and the lift hook bracket to the lift hook.

   i. Install lift hook assembly to the radiator shelf tube.

   j. Install lift hook assembly to left side engine lift hook bracket.

   k. Assemble the lift hook wing nut and the lift hook bracket to the lift hook.

   l. Install lift hook assembly to the strut tower tube.

   m. Hand tighten the lift hooks in order to remove all slack from the engine support fixture.

10. Tighten the support fixture wing nuts in order to provide clearance for the oil pan.

11. Remove the front differential carrier, if equipped.

12. Remove the oil pan bolts.

13. Using the pry points located at the edge of the oil pan separate the RTV sealant.

14. Remove the oil pan from the block

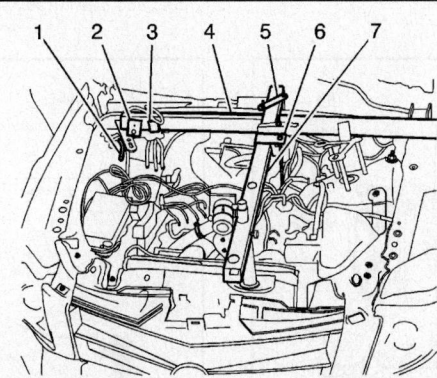

1. Engine support beam adapters
2. Strut tower support assemblies
3. Lift hook
4. Strut tower tube
5. Cross bracket assembly
6. Lift hook
7. Radiator shelf tube

36616_CCTS_G0132

Fig. 143 Engine support fixture—CTS 3.6L Engine

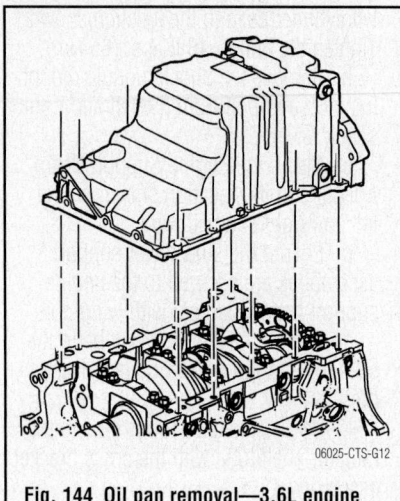

Fig. 144 Oil pan removal—3.6L engine

To install:

15. Install the 8 mm guides from the EN 46109 guide pin set into the center oil pan rail bolt hole on each side of the engine block.

16. Place a 0.118 in. (3 mm) bead of RTV sealant, GM P/N 12378521 (Canadian P/N 88901148) or equivalent, on the block pan rail and the crankshaft rear oil seal housing.

17. Position the oil pan onto the block.

18. Remove the guide pins from the engine block.

19. Loosely install the oil pan bolts.

20. Tighten the oil pan bolts in sequence as follows:

   a. Tighten the 0.30 in (8mm) bolts (1-11) to 17 ft. lbs. (23 Nm).

   b. Tighten the 0.23 in (6mm) bolts (12-13) to 89 inch lbs. (10 Nm).

21. Install the front differential carrier, if equipped.

22. Loosen the engine support fixture wing nuts in order to lower the engine and engage the engine mounts to the frame.

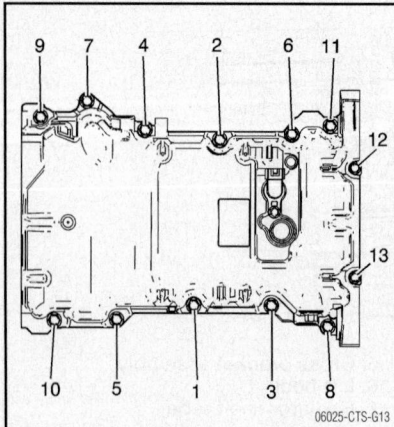

Fig. 145 Oil pan torque sequence—3.6L engine

23. Remove the engine support fixture.

24. Remove the transmission oil cooler pipe retainer from the engine right side.

25. Fill the engine with new engine oil.

26. Install the A/C compressor bracket with the A/C compressor.

27. Install the engine mount lower nuts.

28. Connect the intermediate steering shaft.

29. Install the power steering hose retainer to the A/C compressor bracket.

30. Install the engine front cover.

31. Refill the engine with oil to the correct level.

32. Start the engine and check for leaks.

4.6L Engine

See Figures 146 and 147.

1. Before servicing the vehicle, refer to the Precautions Section.

2. Drain the engine oil.

3. Remove the front exhaust manifold pipe.

4. Disconnect the engine harness electrical connector from the oil level sensor.

5. Loosen the oil pan bolts.

6. Remove the oil pan and discard the oil pan gasket.

7. Clean and inspect the oil pan, if necessary.

To install:

8. Completely fill and slightly overfill the oil pan seal groove with a continuous bead of RTV sealant.

9. Ensure the RTV sealant is higher than the oil pan sealing surface (1) by 0.118 inch (3 mm).

10. To prevent shifting of the oil pan, install one EN 46109 guide into the bolt hole in each side of the lower crankcase.

11. Position the oil pan to the lower crankcase and finger start the oil pan bolts.

Fig. 146 RTV 0.118 inch (3 mm) sealant installation shown

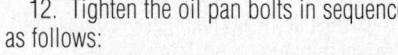

Fig. 147 Oil pan bolt tightening sequence—4.6L engine

12. Tighten the oil pan bolts in sequence as follows:

   a. Tighten the bolts a first pass to 71 inch lbs. (8 Nm).

   b. Tighten the bolts a final pass to 106 inch lbs. (12 Nm)

13. Connect the engine harness electrical connector to the oil level sensor.

14. Install the front exhaust manifold pipe.

15. Fill the engine with oil to the correct level.

16. Start the engine and check for leaks.

6.2L Engine

1. Remove the front frame assembly. For additional information, refer to the following section, "Engine Assembly, Removal & Installation."

2. Remove the oil filter.

3. Remove the starter assembly.

4. Reposition any oil cooler lines as needed.

5. Remove the oil pan mounting bolts and remove the oil pan and gasket.

To install:

➡The alignment of the structural oil pan is critical. The rear bolt hole locations of the oil pan provide mounting points for the transmission housing. To ensure the rigidity of the powertrain and correct transmission alignment, it is important that the rear of the block and the rear of the oil pan are flush or even.

✱✱ WARNING

The rear of the oil pan must NEVER protrude beyond the engine block and the transmission housing plane.

6. Apply a 5 mm (0.2 in) bead of sealant 20 mm (0.8 in) long to the engine block.

7. Apply the sealant directly onto the tabs of the front cover gasket that protrude into the oil pan surface.

8. Install the oil pan and tighten the bolts as follows:

    a. 12 short bolts: 18 ft. lbs. (25 Nm).

    b. 2 long bolts: 106 inch lbs. (12 Nm).

9. The remainder of the installation is the reverse order of removal.

OIL PUMP

REMOVAL & INSTALLATION

3.6L Engine

See Figure 148.

1. Before servicing the vehicle, refer to the Precautions Section.

2. Disconnect the negative battery cable.

3. Remove the engine front cover. For additional information, refer to the following section, 'Timing Chain Cover, Removal & Installation."

4. Removing the timing chain and crankshaft sprocket. For additional information, refer to the following section, "Timing Chain & Sprockets, Removal & Installation."

5. Remove the oil pump mounting and oil pump assembly.

To install:

6. Align the oil pump drive gear with the crankshaft flats and install the oil pump to the engine block.

7. Align the pump body with the mounting holes in the cylinder block.

8. Install the oil pump mounting bolts and tighten to 18 ft. lbs. (25 Nm).

9. Install the crankshaft sprocket and timing chain.

10. Install the engine front cover.

11. Refill the engine with oil to the correct level.

12. Start the engine and check for leaks.

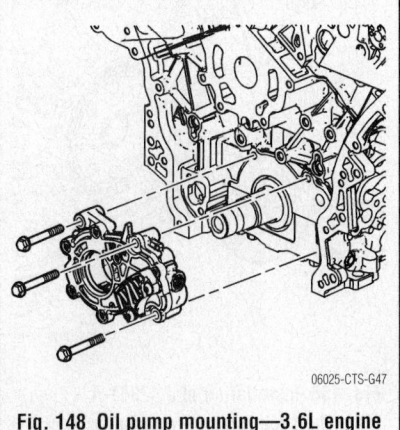

Fig. 148 Oil pump mounting—3.6L engine

06025-CTS-G47

4.6L Engine

See Figure 149.

1. Before servicing the vehicle, refer to the Precautions Section.

2. Disconnect the negative battery cable.

3. Remove the engine front cover.

4. Remove the 3 oil pump assembly retaining bolts (1, 2, 3) identified by the larger head size.

5. Slide the oil pump assembly off the nose of the crankshaft with the drive collar in place.

6. Clean and inspect the oil pump.

To install:

7. Install the oil pump drive spacer into the oil pump so that the drive flat engages the pump rotor.

8. Position the oil pump on the crankshaft.

9. Install the retaining bolts.

➡**Use the correct fastener in the correct location. Replacement fasteners must be the correct part number for that application. Fasteners requiring replacement or fasteners requiring the use of thread locking compound or sealant are identified in the service procedure. Do not use paints, lubricants, or corrosion inhibitors on fasteners or fastener joint surfaces unless specified. These coatings affect fastener torque and joint clamping force and may damage the fastener. Use the correct tightening sequence and specifications when installing fasteners in order to avoid damage to parts and systems.**

10. Apply upward pressure on the pump while tightening the three retaining bolts.

11. Tighten the bolts in the sequence (1, 2, and 3) shown as follows:

    a. First pass tighten the oil pump mounting bolts in sequence to 89 lb inch (10 Nm).

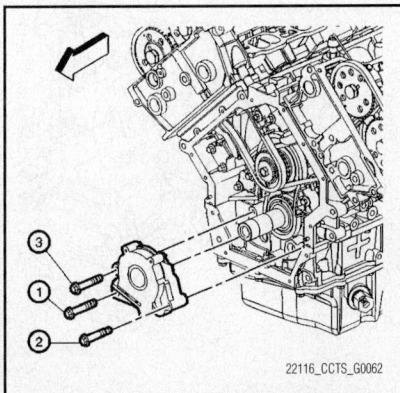

Fig. 149 Exploded view of the oil pump—4.6L engine

22116_CCTS_G0062

    b. Final pass tighten the oil pump mounting bolts in sequence an additional 35 degrees using the J 45059 angle meter.

12. Install the engine front cover.

13. Connect the negative battery cable.

14. Fill the engine with oil to the correct level using a NEW engine oil filter.

15. Start the engine and check for leaks.

6.2L Engine

1. Remove the engine front cover. For additional information, refer to the following section, "Timing Chain Cover, Removal & Installation."

2. Remove the oil pan. For additional information, refer to the following section, "Oil Pan, Removal & Installation."

3. Remove the oil pump screen bolt and nut.

4. Remove the oil pump screen and O-ring seal.

5. Remove the O-ring seal from the pump screen.

6. Discard the O-ring seal.

7. Remove the remaining crankshaft oil deflector nuts.

8. Remove the crankshaft oil deflector.

9. Remove the oil pump bolts and oil pump.

To install:

10. Align the splined surfaces of the crankshaft sprocket and the oil pump drive gear and install the oil pump.

11. Install the oil pump onto the crankshaft sprocket until the pump housing contacts the face of the engine block. Tighten the oil pump bolts to 18 ft. lbs. (25 Nm).

12. Install the crankshaft oil deflector and tighten the crankshaft oil deflector nuts to 18 ft. lbs. (25 Nm).

13. Lubricate a NEW oil pump screen O-ring seal with clean engine oil.

14. Install the NEW O-ring seal onto the oil pump screen.

➡**Push the oil pump screen tube completely into the oil pump prior to tightening the bolt. Do not allow the bolt to pull the tube into the pump.**

15. Align the oil pump screen brackets with the correct crankshaft bearing cap studs.

16. Install the oil pump screen and tighten the oil pump screen bolt and nut as follows:

    a. Tighten the oil pump screen bolt to 106 inch lbs. (12 Nm).

    b. Tighten the oil pump screen nut to 18 ft. lbs. (25 Nm).

17. Install the oil pan.

18. Install the engine front cover.

PISTON AND RING

POSITIONING

See Figures 150 through 152.

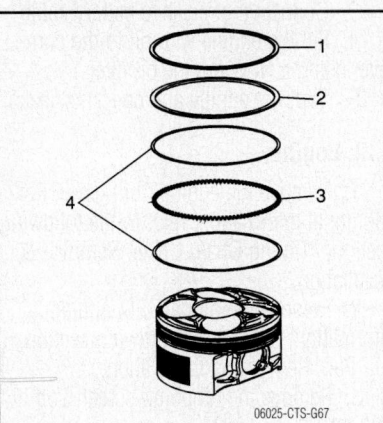

Fig. 150 Piston ring installation order—3.6L engine

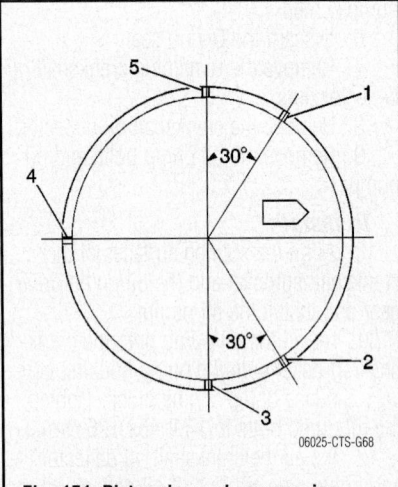

Fig. 151 Piston ring end-gap spacing—3.6L engine

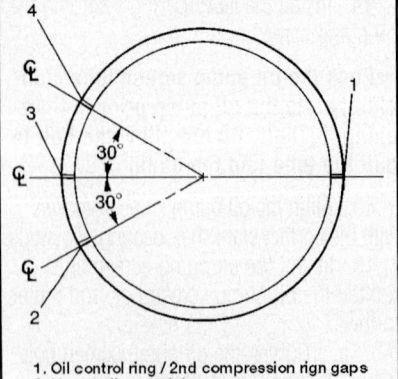

1. Oil control ring / 2nd compression rign gaps
2. Upper oil control ring gap
3. Top compression ring gap
4. Lower oil control ring gap

Fig. 152 Piston ring positioning—4.6L engine

REAR MAIN SEAL

REMOVAL & INSTALLATION

3.6L Engine

See Figures 153 and 154.

1. Before servicing the vehicle, refer to the Precautions Section.
2. Remove or disconnect the following:
   - Negative battery cable
   - Flywheel
   - Oil pan
   - Rear oil seal housing bolts
3. Using the pry point located at the edge of the crankshaft rear main seal housing, shear the RTV sealant.
4. Remove the rear main oil seal.

To install:

5. Install guide pins into the two crankshaft rear oil seal housing corner bolt hoses of the engine block.
6. Install the crankshaft rear seal installation tool onto the rear of the crankshaft flange.

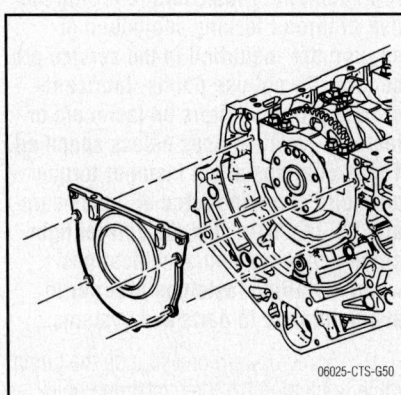

Fig. 153 Exploded view of the rear oil seal—2.8L and 3.6L engines

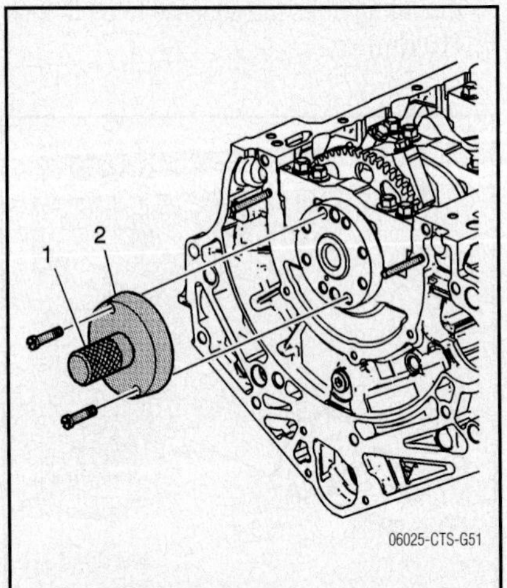

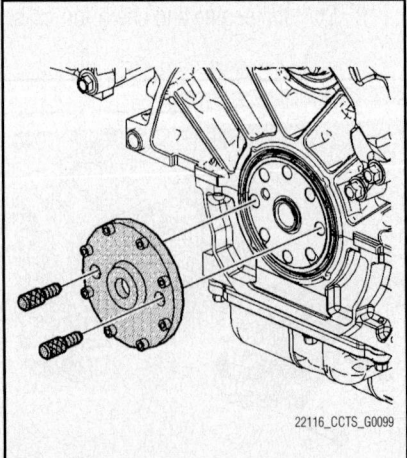

Fig. 154 Using the Crankshaft Rear Seal Installation Tool–2.8L and 3.6L engines

7. Apply a 0.2 inch (3mm) bead of silicone sealant to the rear oil seal housing.
8. Install the rear seal housing to the engine block.
9. Remove the guide pins and install the housing bolts. Tighten the bolts to 89 inch lbs. (10 Nm).
10. Remove the rear seal installation tool from the crankshaft flange.
11. Install or connect the following:
    - Oil pan
    - Flywheel
    - Negative battery cable
12. Start the engine and check for leaks.

4.6L Engine

See Figures 155 through 162.

1. Before servicing the vehicle, refer to the Precautions Section.
2. Remove the transaxle.
3. Remove the flywheel.
4. Place the J 42841-A crankshaft rear oil seal remover on to the crankshaft.
5. Install the J 42841-A retaining bolts.
6. Using a drill motor, variable speed preferred, with a socket adapter, install eight one-inch self-drilling screws into the seal using the guide holes in the removal tool. When drilling, make sure you reduce the drill speed when the screw begins threading into the seal.
7. With all eight removal screws installed, remove the J 42841-A retaining bolts.
8. Install the center screw to the J 42841-A.
9. Tighten the center screw on the J 42841-A to pull the seal assembly off the end of the crankshaft.

Fig. 155 Installation of J 42841-A crankshaft rear oil seal remover

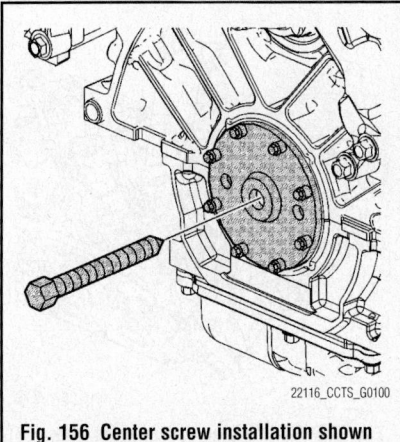

Fig. 156 Center screw installation shown

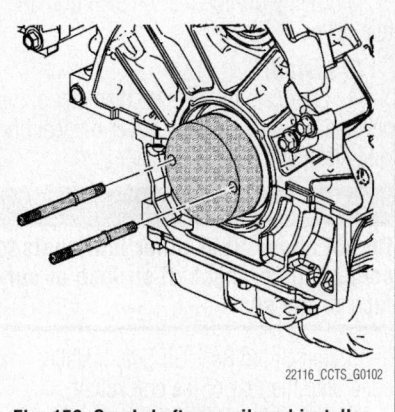

Fig. 158 Crankshaft rear oil seal installer

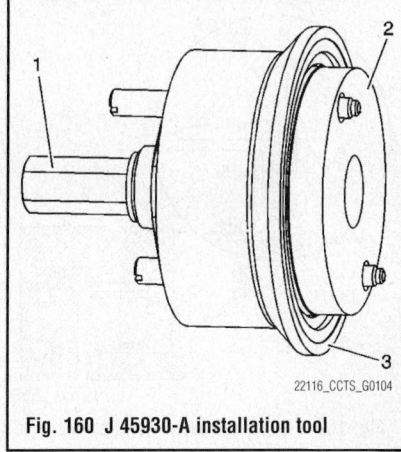

Fig. 160 J 45930-A installation tool

To install:

❋❋ WARNING

The EN-48072 must be used to ensure even application of the sealant in the bore and to prevent blockage of the drain back hole.

10. Inspect the engine block bore and the crankshaft flange for the damage. Repair or replace any damaged components.

11. Ensure the oil drain-back hole is clear of debris using a wire or an unbound plastic tie wrap.

➡**In order to ensure proper bonding of the sealant the bore must be clean and dry.**

12. Clean the bore in the block with cleaner solvent GM P/N 12378392 or 12346139 (Canadian P/N 88901247).

13. Remove the proper sized bolts from the J 45930-A. Use the bolts (8 mm) or the bolts (11 mm).

14. Install the EN-48072 pilot base onto the crankshaft. The hub on the crankshaft will fit into the recess on the inboard side of the EN-48072 pilot base.

15. Use the proper bolts from the J 45930-A to retain the EN-48072 pilot base in place.

16. Install the EN-48072 applicator housing over the EN-48072 pilot base. Ensure the EN-48072 applicator housing bottoms in the bore of the block.

➡**The sealant must not block the drain back hole. Blockage of the drain back hole can lead to oil leakage.**

17. Apply the sealant GM P/N 12378521 (Canadian P/N 88901148) to the bore outer diameter in the block. Ensure the sealant does not block the drain hole.

18. Using a suitable tool spread the sealant within the bore to ensure an even coating across the bore.

19. Using both hands, slowly and evenly, pull the EN-48072 applicator housing out of the bore and remove it from the EN-48072 pilot base.

20. Remove the J 45930-A bolts from the EN-48072 pilot base.

21. Remove the EN-48072 pilot base.

22. Ensure that the sealant is evenly spread across the bore of the block.

23. Ensure the drain back hole is clear of the sealant.

24. Ensure the proper size of bolt (8 mm) or (11 mm) is being installed in the J 45930-A.

25. Turn the center nut of the J 45930-A until the center hub protrudes approximately 0.591 inch (15 mm) beyond the outer plate.

➡**Do not lubricate any part of the new cassette style crankshaft rear oil seal.**

26. Install the new cassette style crankshaft rear oil seal onto the center hub of the J 45930-A.

27. Thread the two J 45930-A mounting bolts into the crankshaft flywheel bolt holes.

28. Tighten the two mounting bolts until the J 45930-A is firmly mounted on the crankshaft.

29. Install the new cassette style crankshaft rear oil seal by turning the nut of the J 45930-A until the drive portion of the J 45930-A bottoms against the crankcase.

30. Loosen the center nut to release pressure on the crankcase.

31. Loosen the two mounting bolts.

32. Remove the J 45930-A from the crankshaft.

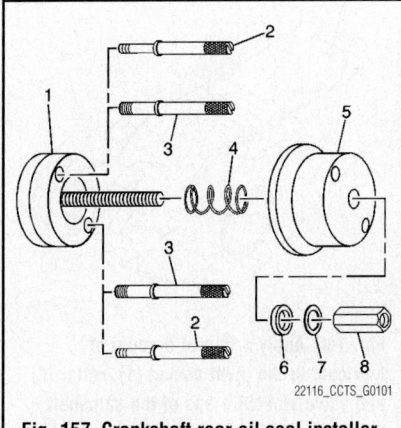

Fig. 157 Crankshaft rear oil seal installer

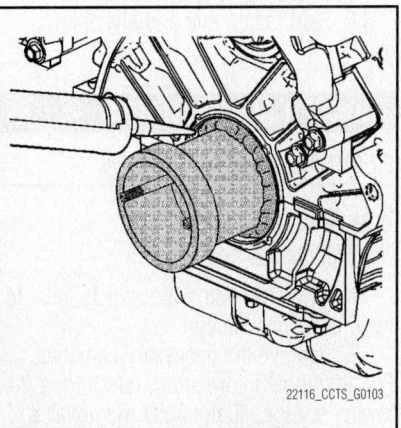

Fig. 159 Sealant application shown

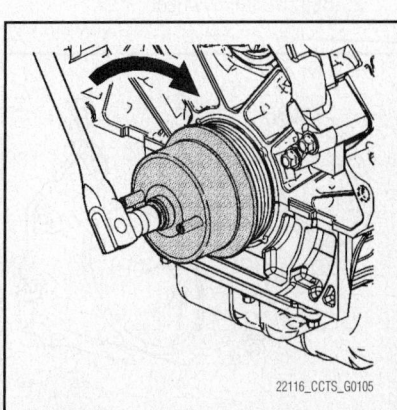

Fig. 161 Rear main seal installation using J 45930-A

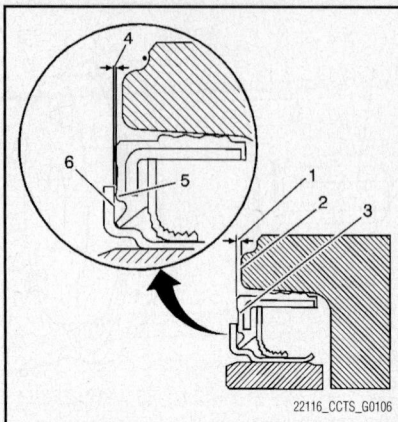

Fig. 162 View of properly installed rear main oil seal

33. Wipe off any excessive sealant from the block.

34. Ensure the new cassette style crankshaft rear oil seal is installed properly as follows:

- The outer surface of the seal (3) should be (0.500-0.800 mm) 0.0197-0.0315 inch (1) below the surface of the engine block (2).
- The inner surface of the sleeve (6) should be 0.0158-0.0354 inch (0.400-0.900 mm) (4) below the surface of the outer surface of the seal (5).
- The installed seal and sleeve need to be parallel to the block by 0.000-0.0197 inch (0.000-0.500 mm).

35. Clean all tools to remove any residual sealant.

36. Install the flywheel.

37. Install the transaxle.

6.2L Engine

See Figures 163 and 164.

1. Before servicing the vehicle, refer to the Precautions Section.

2. Remove the flywheel.

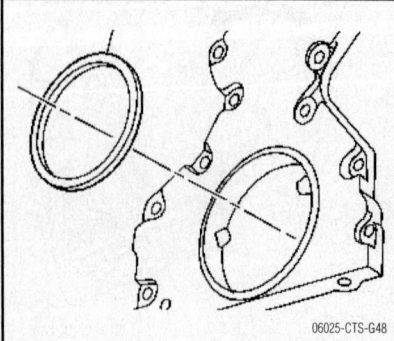

Fig. 163 View of the rear oil seal— 6.2L engine

3. Gently pry the rear oil seal from the rear cover.

To install:

4. Lubricate the outside diameter of the new rear oil seal and rear cover oil seal bore with clean engine oil.

✳✳ WARNING

Do not allow oil or other lubricants to contact the crankshaft surface or surface or the seal.

5. Install the Rear Oil Seal Installer cone onto the rear of the crankshaft.

6. Install the rear oil seal onto the tapered cone of the installer tool and push the seal to the rear cover bore.

7. Install the threaded rod Installation Tool into the tapered cone until the tool contacts the seal.

8. Rotate the handle of the tool clockwise until the seal enters the rear cover and bottoms into the cover bore.

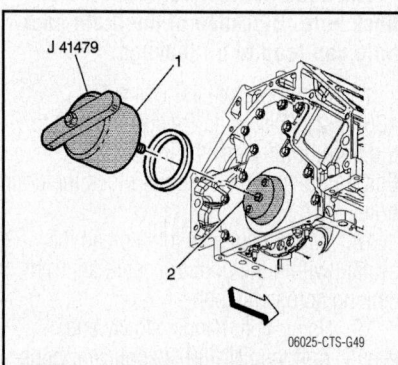

Fig. 164 Install the oil seal installer cone (2) onto the crankshaft. Install the threaded rod of the Oil Seal Installer (1) into the cone—6.2L engine

9. Remove the rear oil seal installer tool.

10. Install the flywheel.

11. Start the engine and check for leaks.

ROCKER ARMS/SHAFTS

REMOVAL & INSTALLATION

3.6L Engine

See Figures 165 and 166.

1. Before servicing the vehicle, refer to the Precautions Section.

2. Remove the necessary camshaft. For additional information, refer to the following section, "Camshafts, Removal & Installation."

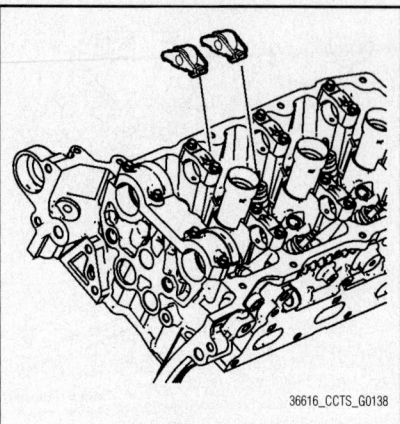

Fig. 165 Remove the rocker arms from the cylinder head—3.6L engine

3. Remove the valve rocker arms from the cylinder head. If the rocker arms are to be reused, keep in order so they can be reinstalled in the same position.

To install:

4. Apply a liberal amount of lubricant GM P/N 12345501 (Canadian P/N 992704) or equivalent to the pivot pocket (1), roller (2) and valve slot (3) areas of the camshaft followers.

➡ **The follower must be positioned squarely on the valve tip so that the full width of the roller will completely contact the camshaft lobe. If the followers are being reused you must put them back in their original location.**

5. Place the camshaft followers in position on the valve tip and stationary hydraulic lash adjuster (SHLA).

6. The rounded head end of the follower goes on the SHLA while the flat end goes on the valve tip.

7. Clean the camshaft journals and carriers with a clean, lint-free cloth.

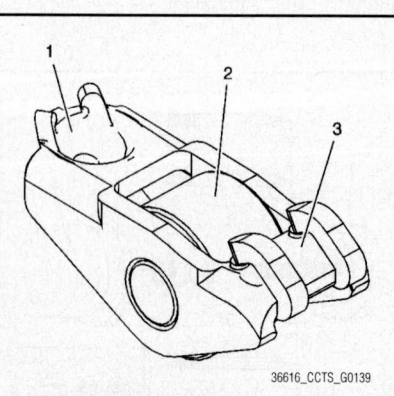

Fig. 166 Apply a liberal amount of lubricant to the pivot pocket (1), roller (2) and valve slot (3) areas of the camshaft followers—3.6L engine

6.2L Engine

1. Before servicing the vehicle, refer to the Precautions Section.

2. Remove the valve covers. For additional information, refer to the following section, "Valve Covers, Removal & Installation."

3. Remove the valve rocker arm bolts.

4. Remove the valve rocker arms.

5. Remove the valve rocker arm pivot support.

To install:

6. Lubricate the valve rocker arms and pushrods with clean engine oil.

7. Lubricate the flange of the valve rocker arm bolts with clean engine oil.

8. Install the valve rocker arm pivot support.

9. Install the rocker arms and bolts.

10. Rotate the crankshaft until number one piston is at top dead center of compression stroke.

11. With the engine in the number one firing position, tighten the following valve rocker arm bolts:

    a. Tighten exhaust valve rocker arm bolts 1, 2, 7, and 8 to 22 ft. lbs. (30 Nm).

    b. Tighten intake valve rocker arm bolts 1, 3, 4, and 5 to 22 ft. lbs. (30 Nm).

12. Rotate the crankshaft 360 degrees.

13. Tighten the following valve rocker arm bolts:

    a. Tighten exhaust valve rocker arm bolts 3, 4, 5, and 6 to 22 ft. lbs. (30 Nm).

    b. Tighten intake valve rocker arm bolts 2, 6, 7, and 8 to 22 ft. lbs. (30 Nm).

14. Install the valve rocker arm covers.

SUPERCHARGER

REMOVAL & INSTALLATION

6.2L Engine

See Figures 167 and 168.

1. Before servicing the vehicle, refer to the Precautions Section.

2. Remove the positive crankcase ventilation (PCV) - dirty air hose from the valley cover and supercharger.

3. Remove the supercharger cover bolts and the supercharger cover.

4. Remove the supercharger cover seal.

5. Remove the charge air cooler insulator.

6. Cover the supercharger rotors area to prevent dirt or debris contamination onto the rotors.

7. Remove the supercharger bolts.

8. Install the EN 48898 fixture to the supercharger and tighten the EN 48898 fixture studs and nuts until snug.

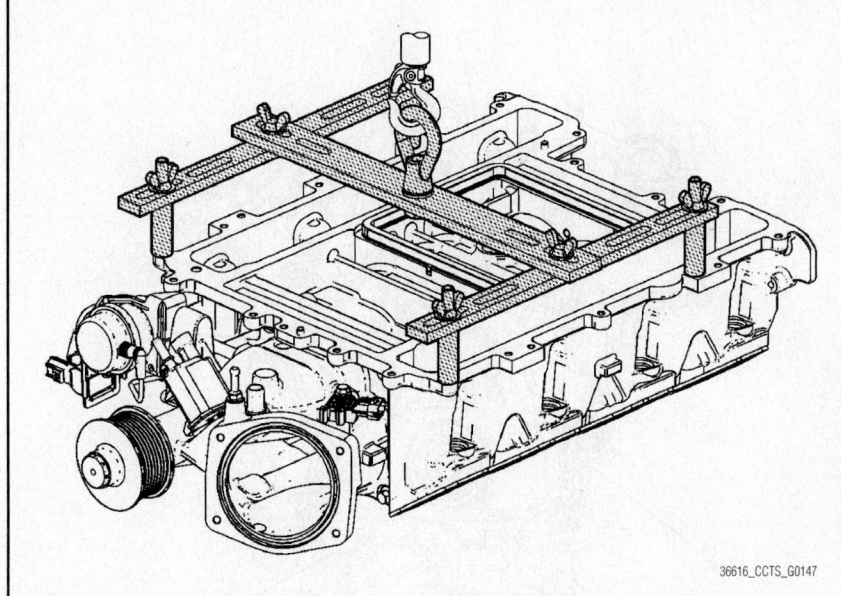

Fig. 167 Install the EN 48898 fixture to the supercharger to remove the supercharger— 6.2L engine

9. Using a lifting device, remove the supercharger from the engine.

To install:

10. If removed, reinstall the Install the EN 48898 fixture to the supercharger and tighten the EN 48898 fixture studs and nuts until snug.

11. Using the lifting device, install the supercharger onto the engine. Align the dowel pin at the right front of the supercharger to the cylinder head.

12. Install the supercharger mounting bolts and tighten in sequence as follows:

    a. Tighten the bolts a first pass in sequence to 44 inch lbs. (5 Nm).

    b. Tighten the bolts a final pass in sequence to 89 inch lbs. (10 Nm).

13. The remainder of the installation is the reverse order of removal.

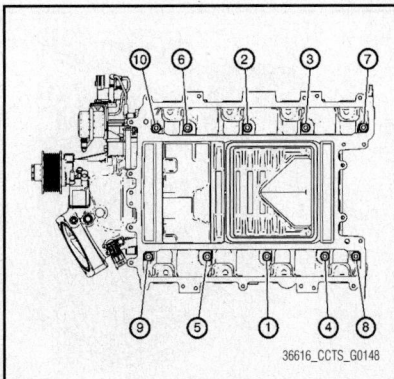

Fig. 168 Supercharger torque sequence— 6.2L engine

TIMING CHAIN COVER AND SEAL

REMOVAL & INSTALLATION

3.6L Engine

See Figures 169 through 174.

1. Before servicing the vehicle, refer to the Precautions Section.

2. Remove the engine appearance cover.

3. Remove the intake manifold.

4. Remove the camshaft covers.

5. Drain the cooling system.

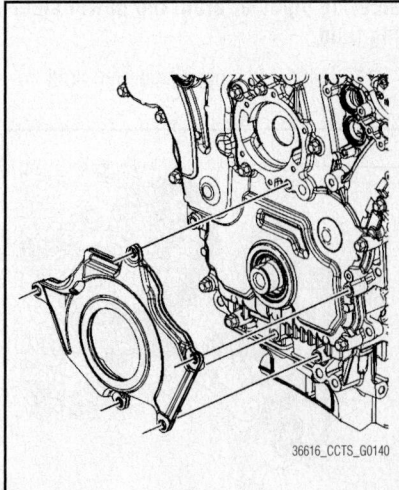

Fig. 169 Removing the engine front cover deadener—3.6L engine

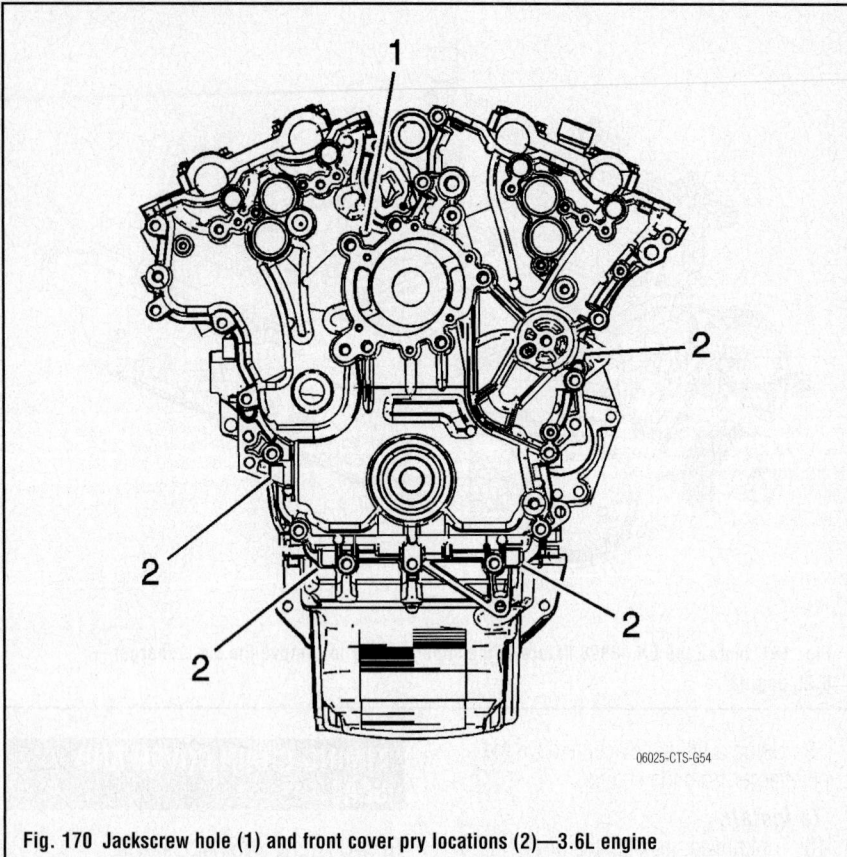

06025-CTS-G54

Fig. 170 Jackscrew hole (1) and front cover pry locations (2)—3.6L engine

6. Disconnect the purge vent hose from the water outlet.

7. Remove the water outlet with the radiator hose and reposition aside.

8. Remove the accessory drive belts.

9. Remove the A/C compressor and power steering belt tensioner.

10. Remove the generator bracket with the generator and the belt tensioner.

➡**Do not disconnect the power steering pipes or drain the power steering fluid.**

11. Remove the power steering fluid reservoir and reposition the power steering fluid reservoir in order to provide access.

12. Remove the power steering pump pulley.

➡**Do not disconnect the power steering pipes/hoses.**

13. Remove the power steering pump upper front bolt and loosen the remaining two bolts.

14. Remove the crankshaft balancer.

15. Remove the camshaft position sensors.

16. Remove the camshaft position actuator solenoid valves from the front cover.

17. Remove the engine front cover bolts that hold the engine front cover deadener into position.

18. Remove the engine front cover deadener.

➡**Engine front cover bolts in the number (2) location are model dependent and may have already been removed.**

➡**There are a total of 22 M8 bolts that must be removed and 3 optional M12 bolts that may need to be removed before the front cover will separate from the engine block.**

19. Remove the remaining engine front cover bolts.

❋❋ **CAUTION**

Do not use the jackscrew hole without first removing all engine front cover bolts. Failure to remove all engine front cover bolts before using the jackscrew hole could result in damage to components.

❋❋ **CAUTION**

Do not pry between the engine front cover and the camshaft position sensors or the camshaft position actuators in order to separate the RTV. Use the pry points and a bolt in the jackscrew hole in order to remove the engine front cover. Damage to the camshaft position sensors or the camshaft position actuators may occur if the camshaft position sensors or the camshaft position actuators are used to pry against in order to remove the engine front cover.

20. Loosely install a 10 x 1.5 mm bolt in the jackscrew hole.

21. Using the pry points located at the edge of the front cover and the jackscrew, separate the room temperature vulcanizing (RTV) sealant.

22. Remove the engine front cover.

To install:

23. Install the 8 mm guide pins into the cylinder block positions as shown.

24. Install the NEW engine front cover to cylinder block seal.

25. Apply a 0.12 inch (3mm) bead of silicone sealant on the front cover as shown.

26. Place the front cover into position on the engine block and remove the guide pins.

27. Hand start all of the engine front cover bolts.

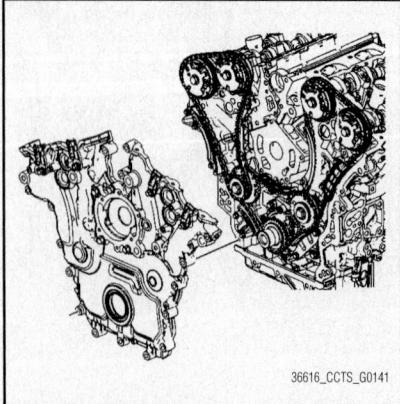

36616_CCTS_G0141

Fig. 171 Removing the engine front cover—3.6L engine

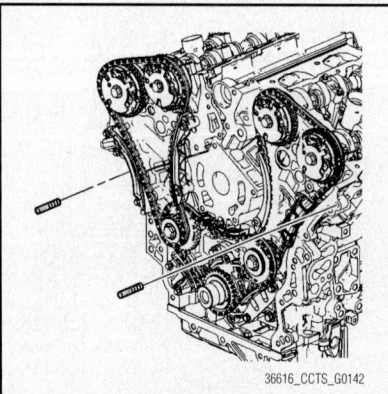

36616_CCTS_G0142

Fig. 172 Installing the guide pins into the cylinder block—3.6L engines

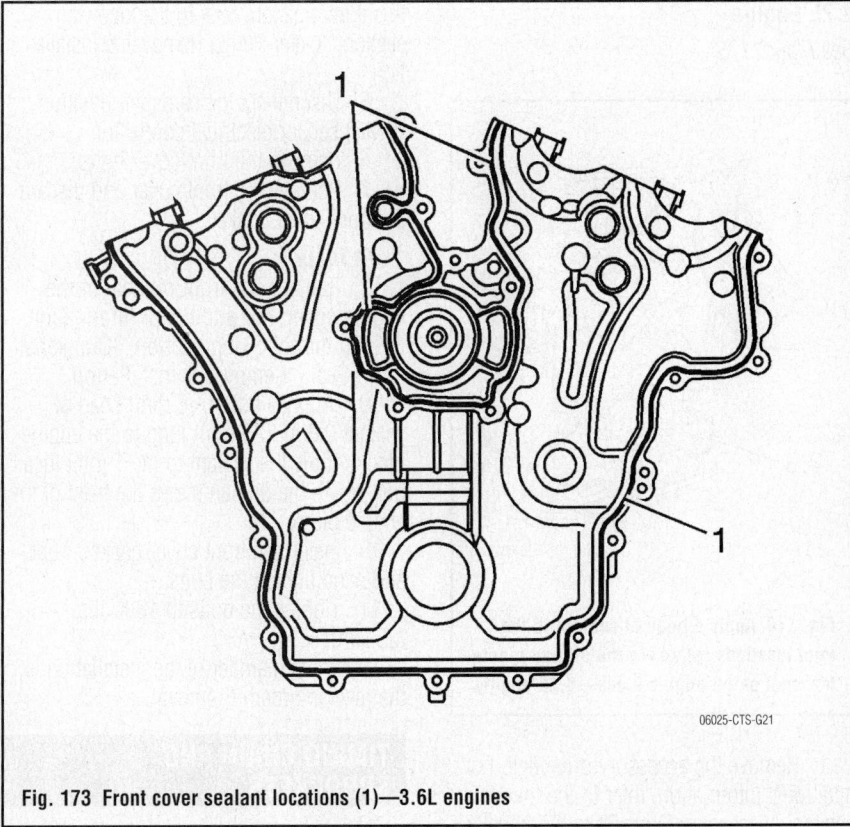

Fig. 173 Front cover sealant locations (1)—3.6L engines

06025-CTS-G21

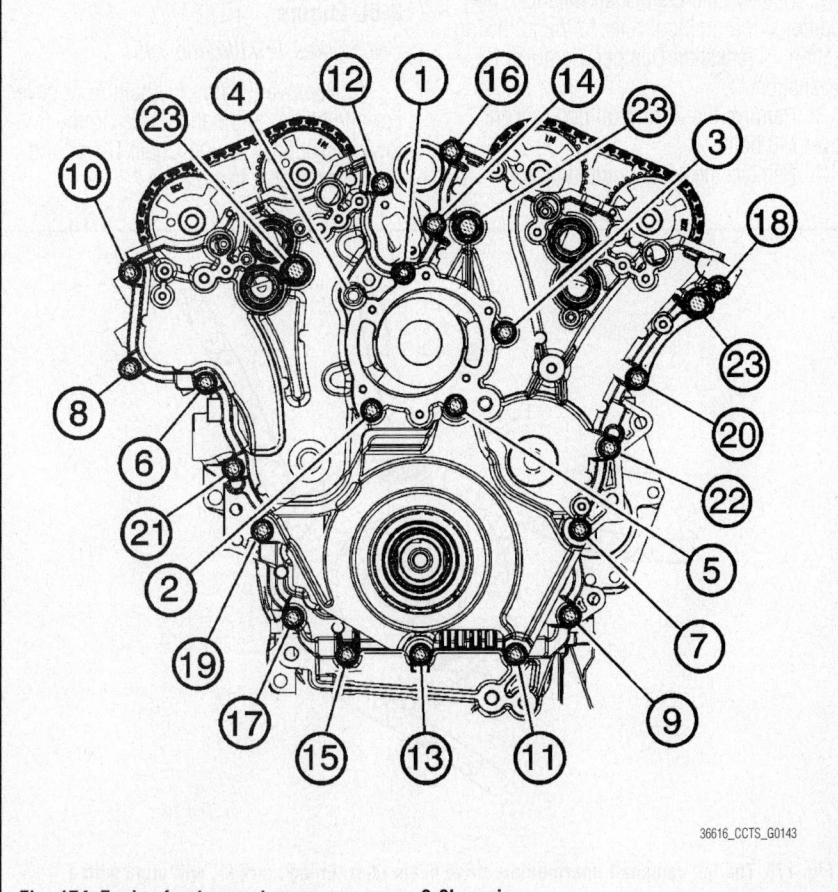

Fig. 174 Engine front cover torque sequence—3.6L engine

36616_CCTS_G0143

28. Install the engine front cover deadener.

➡ The front cover and deadener may vary in appearance depending on application but are retained by the same number of bolts.

29. Loosely install the engine front cover bolts to hold the engine front cover deadener into position.

30. Loosely install the remaining engine front cover bolts.

➡ Engine front cover bolts in the number (23) location are model dependent and may not apply.

31. Tighten the engine front cover bolts (1-22) in sequence shown to 14 ft. lbs. (20 Nm).

32. Tighten the engine front cover bolts (1-22) a second pass in sequence an additional 60 degrees.

33. Tighten the engine front cover bolt (23) to 48 ft. lbs. (65 Nm).

34. The remainder of the installation is the reverse order of removal.

35. Refill the engine cooling system to the correct level.

36. Start the engine and check for leaks.

4.6L Engine

See Figures 175 through 177.

1. Disconnect the negative battery cable.

2. Remove the drive belt tensioner. Refer to Drive Belt Tensioner Replacement.

3. Loosen the drive belt idler pulley bolt.

4. Remove the drive belt idler pulley.

5. Remove the crankshaft pulley. For additional information, refer to the following section, "Crankshaft Pulley, Removal & Installation."

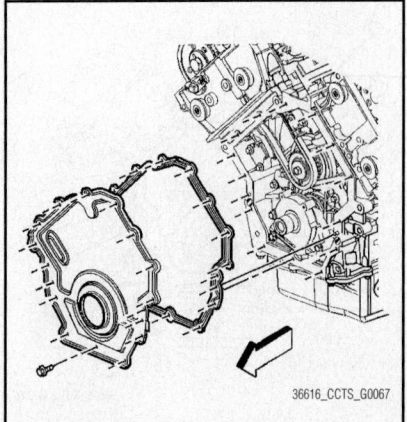

36616_CCTS_G0067

Fig. 175 Remove the timing chain cover and seal—4.6L engine

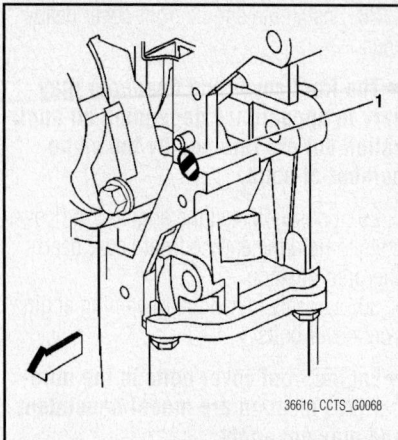

Fig. 176 Place a small amount of sealant at the split line of the upper and lower crankcases (1)—4.6L engines

6. Remove the timing chain cover mounting bolts.

7. Remove the timing chain cover and gasket.

➡ **The gasket is reusable unless it is damaged.**

To install:

8. Place a small amount of sealant at the split line of the upper and lower crankcases.

9. Place the timing chain cover gasket over the crankcase dowel pins.

10. Place the timing chain cover in position on the crankcase.

11. Apply threadlock to the engine front cover bolts.

12. Install the timing chain cover bolts until snug.

13. Tighten the timing chain cover bolts in sequence to 89 inch lbs. (10 Nm).

14. The remainder of the installation is the reverse order of removal.

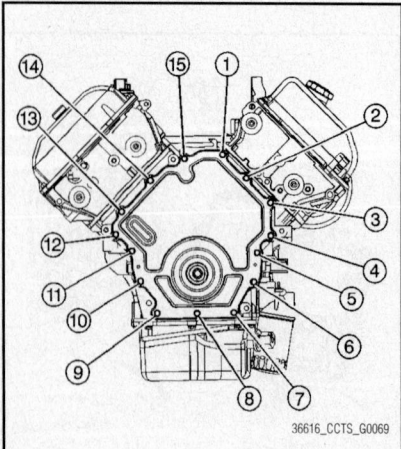

Fig. 177 Timing chain cover torque sequence—4.6L engines

6.2L Engine

See Figure 178.

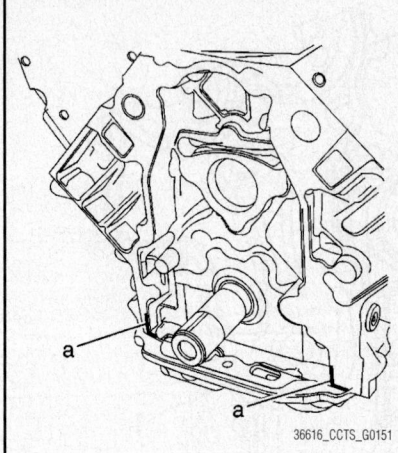

Fig. 178 Apply a bead of sealant to the T joint locations (a) where the oil pan meets the front of the engine block—6.2L engine

1. Remove the accessory drive belt. For additional information, refer to the following section, "Accessory Drive Belts, Removal & Installation."

2. Remove the crankshaft balancer. For additional information, refer to the following section, "Crankshaft Damper, Removal & Installation."

3. Remove the 2 front oil pan to front cover M8 bolts.

4. Remove the water pump. For additional information, refer to the following section, "Water Pump, Removal & Installation."

5. Disconnect the camshaft position (CMP) sensor electrical connector.

6. Remove the front cover bolts.

7. Remove the front cover and discard the front cover gasket.

To install:

8. Replace the front oil seal in the engine cover. For additional information, refer to the following section, "Crankshaft Front Seal, "Removal & Installation."

9. Apply a 0.2 in. (5 mm) bead of sealant 0.8 in. (20 mm) long to the engine block. Apply the sealant to the T joint location where the oil pan meets the front of the engine block.

10. Install the front cover gasket, front and hand tighten the bolts.

11. Tighten the bolts to 18 ft. lbs. (25 Nm).

12. The remainder of the installation is the reverse order of removal.

TIMING CHAIN AND SPROCKETS

REMOVAL & INSTALLATION

3.6L Engine

See Figures 179 through 188.

1. Remove the timing chain front cover. For additional information, refer to the following section, "Timing Chain Cover and Seal, Removal & Installation."

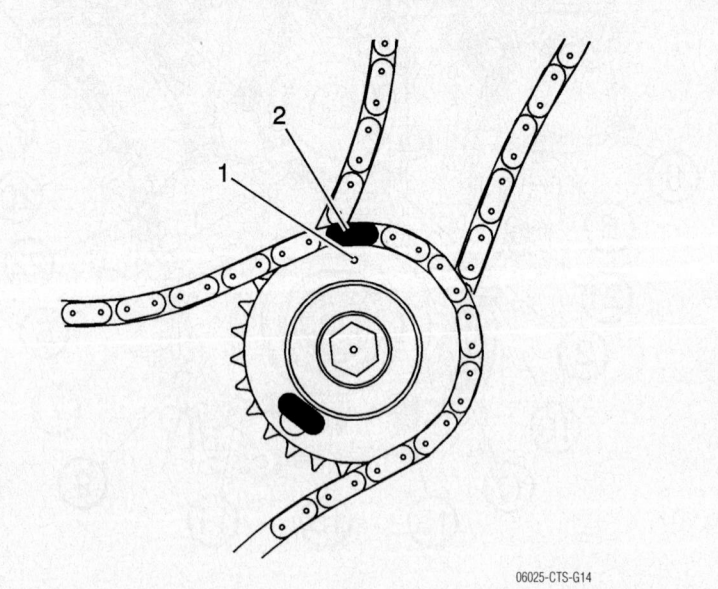

Fig. 179 The left camshaft intermediate drive chain idler timing mark (1) will align with a timing camshaft drive chain link (2)

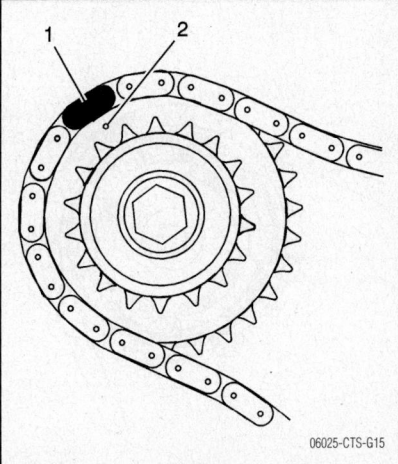

Fig. 180 The right camshaft intermediate drive chain idler timing mark (2) will align with a timing camshaft drive chain link (1).

2. Remove the right secondary camshaft drive chain tensioner bolts.

3. Remove the right secondary camshaft drive chain tensioner.

4. Remove and discard the right secondary camshaft drive chain tensioner gasket.

5. Remove the right secondary camshaft drive chain shoe bolt.

6. Remove the right secondary camshaft drive chain shoe.

7. Remove the right secondary camshaft drive chain guide bolts.

8. Remove the right secondary camshaft drive chain guide.

9. Remove the right secondary camshaft drive chain from the right camshaft position actuators and the right camshaft intermediate drive chain idler sprocket.

10. Remove the primary camshaft drive chain tensioner bolts.

11. Remove the primary camshaft drive chain tensioner.

12. Remove and discard the primary camshaft drive chain tensioner gasket.

13. Remove the primary camshaft drive chain upper guide bolts.

14. Remove the primary camshaft drive chain upper guides.

15. Remove the primary camshaft timing chain.

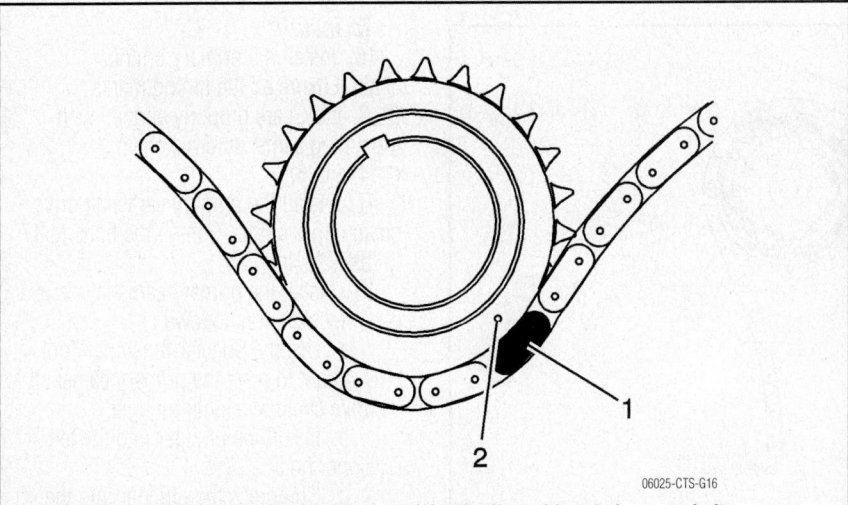

Fig. 181 The crankshaft sprocket timing mark (2) will align with a timing camshaft drive chain link (1).

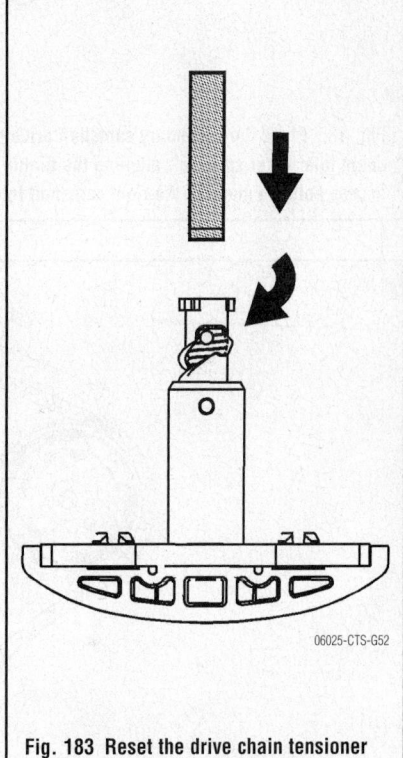

Fig. 183 Reset the drive chain tensioner plunger with Special Tool J-45027.

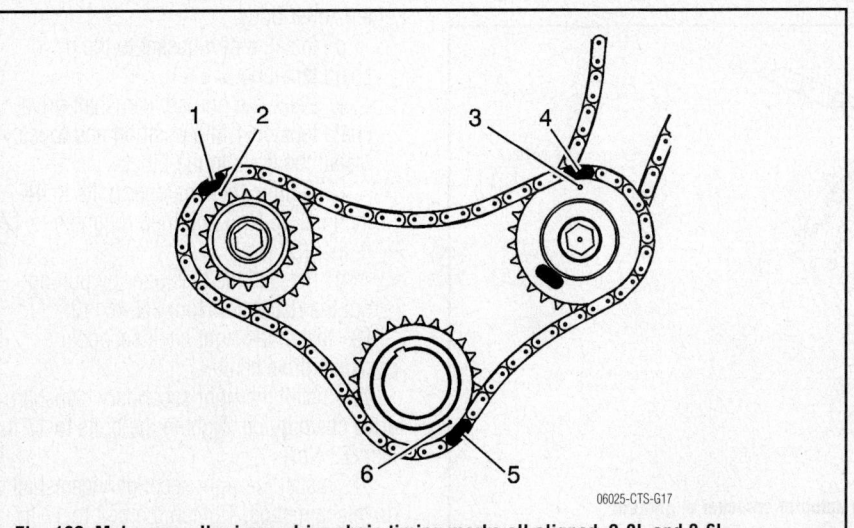

Fig. 182 Make sure all primary drive chain timing marks all aligned–2.8L and 3.6L

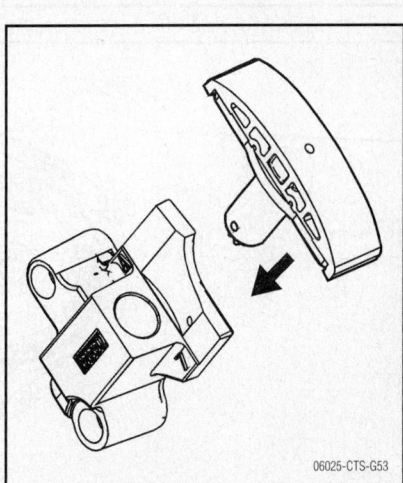

Fig. 184 Lock the tensioner with Special Tool EN-46112–2.8L and 3.6L

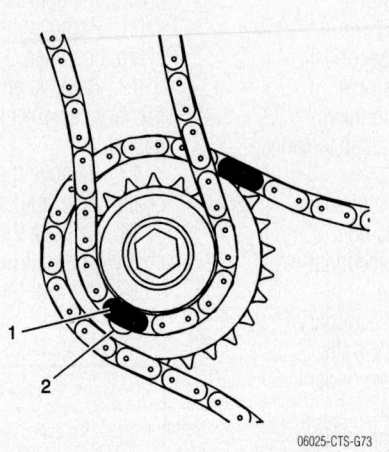

06025-CTS-G73

Fig. 185 Place the secondary camshaft drive chain around the right camshaft intermediate drive chain idler outer sprocket, aligning the timing camshaft drive chain link (1) with the alignment access hole (2) made in the right camshaft intermediate drive chain idler inner sprocket.

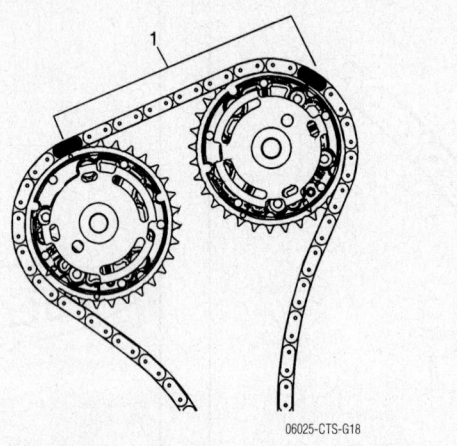

06025-CTS-G18

Fig. 186 Ensure there are 7 links (1) between the timing camshaft drive chain links for the camshaft position actuator sprockets

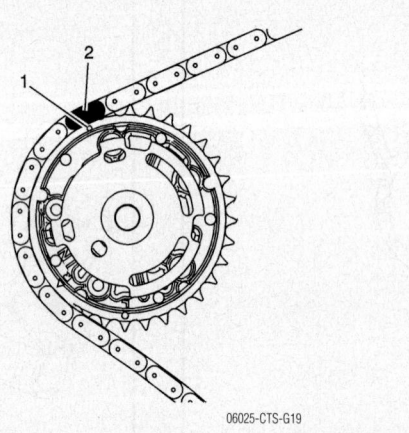

06025-CTS-G19

Fig. 187 Align the right exhaust camshaft position actuator sprocket alignment triangle mark (1) with the timing camshaft drive chain link (2).

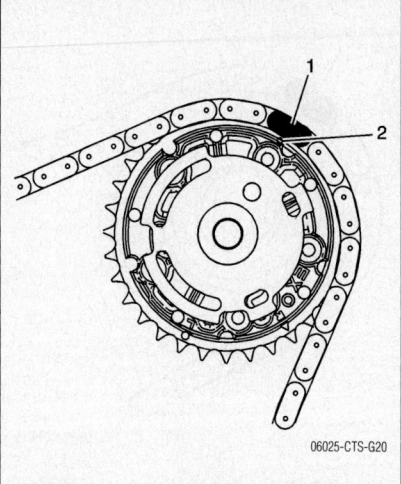

06025-CTS-G20

Fig. 188 Align the right intake camshaft position actuator sprocket alignment triangle mark (2) with the timing camshaft drive chain link (1).

To install:

16. Install the primary timing chain. Ensure all the timing marks (2, 3, and 6) are properly aligned with the timing camshaft drive chain links (1, 4, and 5).

17. Install the primary camshaft drive chain upper guide. Tighten the bolts to 17 ft. lbs. (23 Nm).

18. Install the primary camshaft drive chain tensioner as follows:

a. Use the Special Tensioner Tool J-45027 to reset the primary camshaft drive chain tensioner plunger.

b. Install the plunger into the tensioner body

c. Compress the plunger into the body and lock the tensioner by inserting the Special Retraction Tool EN-46112 into the access hole in the side of the tensioner body.

d. Install a new gasket to the drive chain tensioner.

e. Place the primary camshaft drive chain tensioner into position and loosely install the bolts to the block.

f. Tighten the tensioner bolts to 44 inch lbs. (5 Nm) and then retighten to 17 ft. lbs. (23 Nm).

g. Release the tensioner by pulling out the Retraction Tool EN-46112.

19. Install the right bank secondary camshaft drive chain.

20. Install the right secondary camshaft drive chain guide. Tighten the bolts to 17 ft. lbs. (23 Nm).

21. Install the right secondary camshaft drive chain shoe. Tighten the bolt to 17 ft. lbs. (23 Nm).

22. Install the right secondary camshaft drive chain tensioner as follows:

    a. Use the Special Tensioner Tool J-45027 to reset the primary camshaft drive chain tensioner plunger.

    b. Install the plunger into the tensioner body

    c. Compress the plunger into the body and lock the tensioner by inserting the Special Retraction Tool EN-46112 into the access hole in the side of the tensioner body.

    d. Install a new gasket to the drive chain tensioner.

    e. Place the primary camshaft drive chain tensioner into position and loosely install the bolts to the block.

    f. Tighten the tensioner bolts to 44 inch lbs. (5 Nm) and then retighten to 17 ft. lbs. (23 Nm).

    g. Release the tensioner by pulling out the Retraction Tool EN-46112.

23. Install the engine front cover.

4.6L Engine

See Figures 189 through 195.

1. Remove the timing chain front cover. For additional information, refer to the following section, "Timing Chain Cover and Seal, Removal & Installation."

2. Remove the oil pump. For additional information, refer to the following section, "Oil Pump, Removal & Installation."

3. Align the primary timing marks.

4. Remove the right secondary camshaft drive chain tensioner.

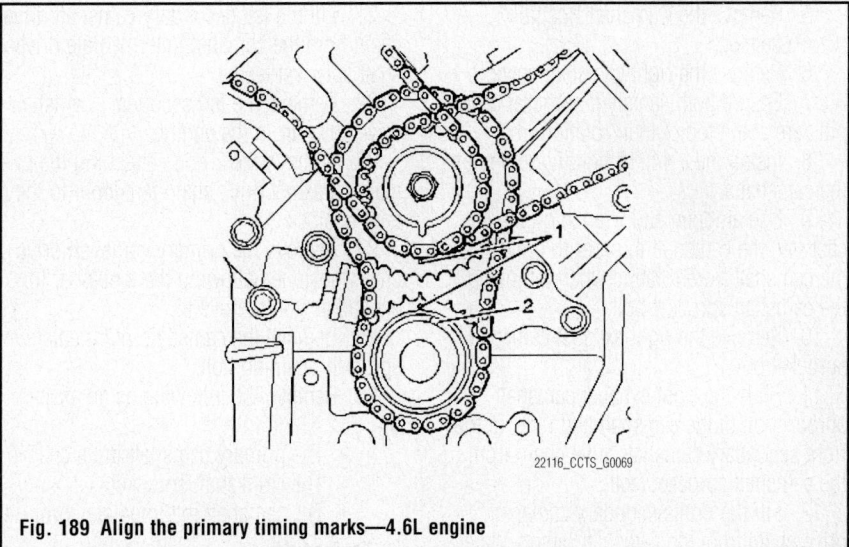

22116_CCTS_G0069

Fig. 189 Align the primary timing marks—4.6L engine

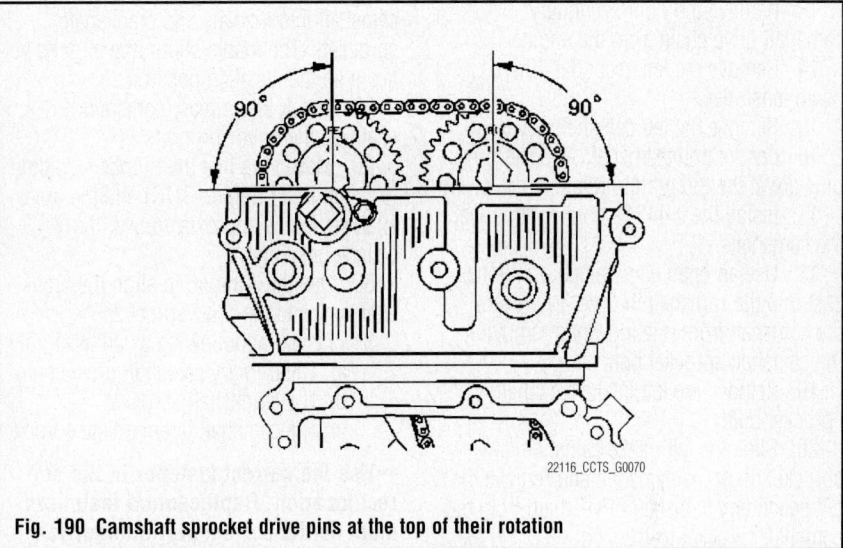

22116_CCTS_G0070

Fig. 190 Camshaft sprocket drive pins at the top of their rotation

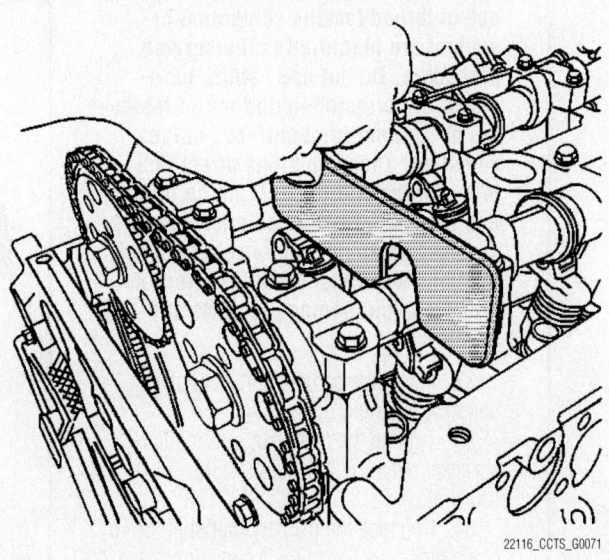

22116_CCTS_G0071

Fig. 191 Camshaft holding tool J 44212

5. Remove the Camshaft Position (CMP) sensor.

6. Remove the right camshaft cover.

7. Ensure both camshaft sprocket drive pins are at the top of their rotation.

8. Install the J 44212 holding tool over the camshafts.

9. Use an open end wrench on the hex cast into the camshaft in order to prevent the camshaft from rotating when removing the camshaft sprocket bolt.

10. Remove the right exhaust camshaft sprocket bolt.

11. Slide the right exhaust camshaft sprocket off of the camshaft and remove the right secondary camshaft drive chain from the camshaft sprocket teeth.

12. Lift the right secondary camshaft drive chain from the camshaft intermediate drive shaft sprocket teeth.

13. Remove the right secondary camshaft drive chain from the engine.

14. Remove the left secondary drive chain tensioner.

15. Remove the left camshaft cover.

16. Ensure both camshaft sprocket drive pins are at the top of their rotation.

17. Install the J 44212 holding tool over the camshafts.

18. Use an open end wrench on the hex cast into the camshaft in order to prevent the camshaft from rotating when removing the camshaft sprocket bolt.

19. Remove the left intake camshaft sprocket bolt.

20. Slide the left intake camshaft sprocket off of the camshaft and remove the left secondary camshaft drive chain from the camshaft sprocket teeth.

21. Lift the left secondary camshaft drive chain from the camshaft intermediate drive shaft sprocket teeth.

22. Remove the left secondary camshaft drive chain from the engine.

23. Remove the 2 bolts attaching the primary camshaft drive chain tensioner to the engine block.

24. Remove the primary camshaft drive chain tensioner, allowing the tensioner to expand as you remove it.

25. Remove the camshaft intermediate sprocket retaining bolt.

26. Remove the following as an assembly:
- The primary camshaft drive chain
- The crankshaft sprocket
- The camshaft intermediate sprocket

To install:

27. Align the timing marks (1) of the camshaft intermediate and crankshaft sprockets. The marks should be aligned vertically in the installed position.

28. Install the primary camshaft drive chain on the drive sprockets.

29. Make sure that the number 1 piston is at Top Dead Center (TDC) and the crankshaft keyway is approximately at the 1 o'clock position.

30. Use the J 39946 to align the crankshaft key with the drive sprocket.

31. Install the following as an assembly:
   a. The primary camshaft drive chain
   b. The crankshaft sprocket
   c. The camshaft intermediate sprocket

➡ Use the correct fastener in the correct location. Replacement fasteners must be the correct part number for that application. Fasteners requiring replacement or fasteners requiring the use of thread locking compound or sealant are identified in the service procedure. Do not use paints, lubricants, or corrosion inhibitors on fasteners or fastener joint surfaces unless specified. These coatings affect fastener torque and joint clamping force and may damage the fastener. Use the correct tightening sequence and specifications when installing fasteners in order to avoid damage to parts and systems.

32. Install the camshaft intermediate sprocket retaining bolt.

33. Tighten the camshaft intermediate sprocket retaining bolt to 44 ft. lbs. (60 Nm).

34. Collapse the primary camshaft drive chain tensioner using the following procedure:

   a. Rotate the ratchet release lever (2) clockwise and hold.
   b. Collapse the tensioner shoe (1) and hold.
   c. Release the ratchet lever (2).

35. Slowly release the pressure on the shoe (1), until the ratchet lever (2) moves to the first detent and a "click" is heard and felt.

36. Collapse the tensioner shoe (1) and hold.

37. Insert a pin through the hole in the release lever in order to lock the tensioner shoe in the collapsed position.

38. Install the primary camshaft drive chain tensioner and tighten mounting bolts to 18 ft. lbs. (25 Nm).

✲✲ WARNING

DO NOT remove the pin holding the tensioner until the secondary timing chains are installed.

39. Install the left secondary camshaft drive chain by sliding the chain down through the left cylinder head and placing the chain on the left exhaust camshaft sprocket.

40. Route the left secondary camshaft drive chain around the inner row of the camshaft intermediate drive shaft sprocket teeth.

41. Install the left intake camshaft sprocket into the left secondary camshaft drive chain.

42. Install the left intake camshaft sprocket onto the camshaft. The camshaft sprocket notch marked LI (left intake) engages the intake camshaft pin.

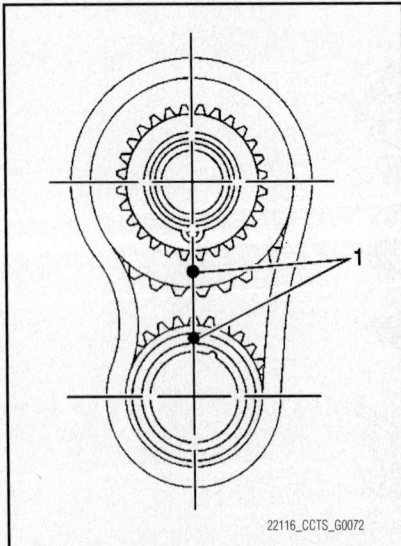

Fig. 192 Timing marks are shown aligned vertically

22116_CCTS_G0072

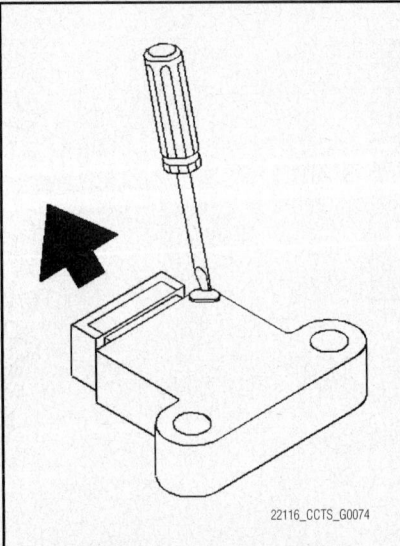

Fig. 193 Primary chain tensioner in the collapsed position.

22116_CCTS_G0074

43. Use an open end wrench on the hex cast into the camshaft in order to prevent the camshaft from rotating when tightening the camshaft sprocket bolt.

44. Install the left intake camshaft sprocket bolt. Tighten the camshaft sprocket bolt to 89 ft. lbs. (120 Nm).

45. Remove the J 44212 from the camshafts.

46. Install the left camshaft cover.

47. Collapse the left secondary camshaft chain tensioner using the following procedure:

    a. Rotate the ratchet release lever (2) counterclockwise and hold.

    b. Collapse the tensioner shoe (1) and hold.

    c. Release the ratchet lever (2).

48. Slowly release the pressure on the shoe (1), until the ratchet lever (2) moves to the first detent and a "click" is heard and felt.

49. Collapse the tensioner shoe (1) and hold.

50. Insert a pin through the hole in the release lever in order to lock the tensioner shoe in the collapsed position.

51. Install the left secondary drive chain tensioner and tighten mounting bolts to 18 ft. lbs. (25 Nm).

52. Remove the pin holding the tensioner to tighten any slack in the timing chain.

53. Install the right secondary camshaft drive chain by sliding the chain down through the right cylinder head and placing the chain on the right intake camshaft sprocket.

54. Route the right secondary camshaft drive chain around the outer row of the camshaft intermediate drive shaft sprocket teeth.

55. Install the right exhaust camshaft sprocket into the right secondary camshaft drive chain.

56. Install the right exhaust camshaft sprocket onto the camshaft. The camshaft sprocket notch marked RE (right exhaust) engages the exhaust camshaft pin.

57. Use an open end wrench on the hex cast into the camshaft in order to prevent the camshaft from rotating when tightening the camshaft sprocket bolt.

58. Install the right exhaust camshaft sprocket bolt and tighten to 89 ft. lbs. (120 Nm).

59. Collapse the right secondary camshaft chain tensioner using the following procedure:

    a. Rotate the ratchet release lever (2) counterclockwise and hold.

    b. Collapse the tensioner shoe (1) and hold.

    c. Release the ratchet lever (2).

60. Slowly release the pressure on the shoe (1), until the ratchet lever (2) moves to the first detent and a "click" is heard and felt.

61. Collapse the tensioner shoe (1) and hold.

62. Insert a pin through the hole in the release lever in order to lock the tensioner shoe in the collapsed position.

63. Install the right secondary drive chain tensioner and tighten mounting bolts to 18 ft. lbs. (25 Nm).

64. Remove the pin holding the tensioner to tighten any slack in the timing chain.

65. Remove the J 44212 from the camshafts.

66. Install the right camshaft cover.

67. Install the CMP sensor.

68. Remove the pin from the primary timing chain tensioner release lever.

69. Ensure the primary timing marks are aligned vertically.

70. Install the oil pump.

71. Install the engine front cover.

72. Install the crankshaft balancer.

73. Install the drive belt idler pulley.

74. Install drive belt.

75. Connect the negative battery cable.

6.2L Engine

See Figures 196 and 197.

1. Remove the oil pump. For additional information, refer to the following section, "Oil Pump, Removal & Installation."

2. Remove and discard the camshaft sprocket bolt.

3. Remove the camshaft sprocket and timing chain.

To install:

4. Compress the timing chain tensioner guide and install the timing belt tensioner retaining pin.

5. Install the camshaft sprocket, timing chain, and bolt.

6. Inspect the sprockets for proper alignment. The mark on the camshaft sprocket should be located in the 6 o'clock position and the mark on the crankshaft sprocket should be located in the 12 o'clock position.

7. Remove the tensioner retaining pin.

8. Tighten the camshaft sprocket bolt as follows:

    a. Tighten the bolt to 55 ft. lbs. (75 Nm).

    b. Tighten the bolt an additional 50 degrees.

9. The remainder of the installation is the reverse order of removal.

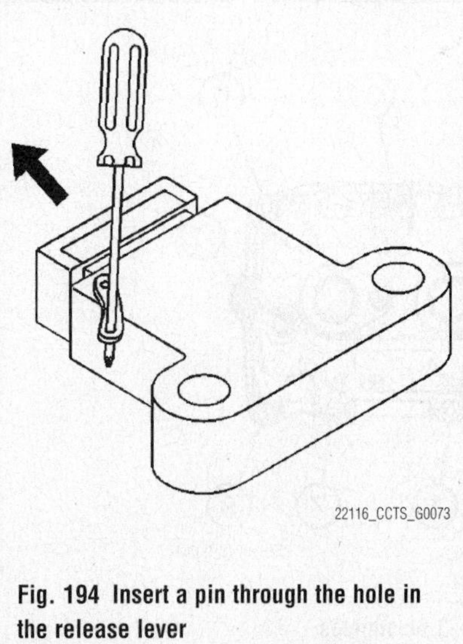

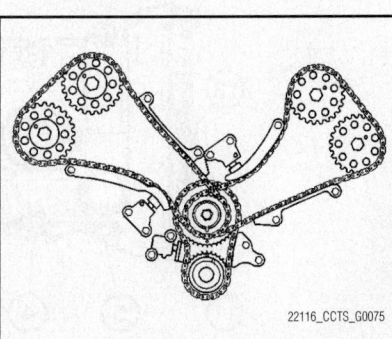

22116_CCTS_G0073

Fig. 194 Insert a pin through the hole in the release lever

22116_CCTS_G0075

Fig. 195 Timing chain components and marks—4.6L engine

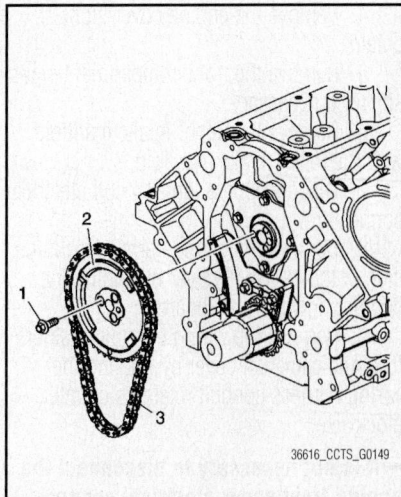

36616_CCTS_G0149

Fig. 196 Remove the camshaft sprocket bolt (1), camshaft sprocket (2) and timing chain (3)—6.2L engine

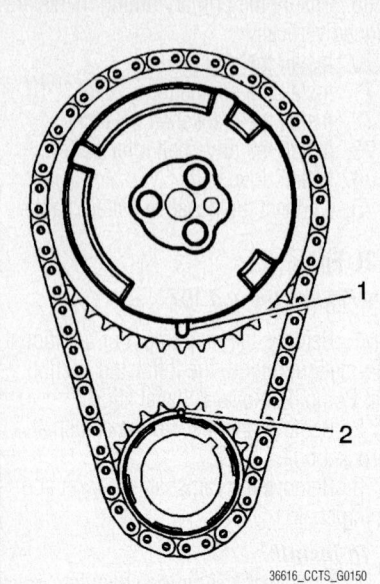

Fig. 197 The mark on the camshaft sprocket should be located in the 6 o'clock position and the mark on the crankshaft sprocket should be located in the 12 o'clock position—6.2L engine

VALVE COVERS

REMOVAL & INSTALLATION

3.6L Engine

See Figures 198 and 199.

1. Remove the cross car brace, if necessary.

2. Remove the oil fill cap.

3. Disengage the cover/shield from the ball studs by pulling up firmly on the right rear and left front of the engine cover.

4. Remove the engine cover/sight shield.

5. Remove the front compartment sight shield, if necessary.

6. Remove the upper intake manifold with the lower intake manifold.

7. Disconnect the ignition coil electrical connectors.

8. Remove the wiring harness from the side of the camshaft cover by sliding the conduit down and outboard.

9. Remove the wiring conduit retainers from the camshaft cover by rotating the wiring harness conduit retainers counterclockwise.

➡ It is not necessary to disconnect the engine front cover electrical connectors.

10. Remove the wiring harness from the front of the camshaft cover.

11. Reposition and secure the wiring harnesses away from the camshaft cover in order to provide clearance.

12. Remove the ignition coils.

13. Remove the camshaft cover and discard the camshaft cover seal and grommets.

To install:

14. Install a NEW camshaft cover seal and NEW grommets.

15. Wipe the camshaft cover sealing surface on the left cylinder head with a clean, lint-free cloth.

16. Place a bead 8 mm (0.3150 in) in diameter by 4 mm (0.1575 in) in height of RTV sealant, on the engine front cover split lines (1).

17. Place the camshaft cover into position onto the left cylinder head.

18. Loosely install the camshaft cover bolts.

19. Tighten the camshaft cover bolts in the sequence shown to 89 inch lbs. (10 Nm).

20. Install the NEW spark plugs into the left cylinder head and tighten to 15 ft. lbs. (20 Nm).

21. Install each ignition coil through the left camshaft cover into the spark plug tube taking care not to damage the spark plug and/or the seal in the left camshaft cover.

22. Install each ignition coil bolt and tighten to 89 inch lbs. (10 Nm).

23. The remainder of the installation is the reverse order of removal.

4.6L Engine

Left Side

See Figures 200 through 203.

1. Before servicing the vehicle, refer to the Precautions Section.

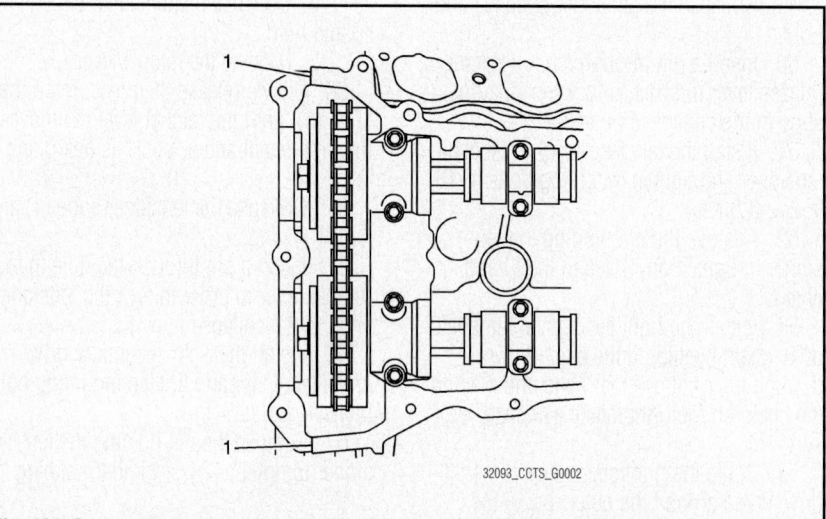

Fig. 198 Sealant application areas for camshaft cover installation—3.6L engines

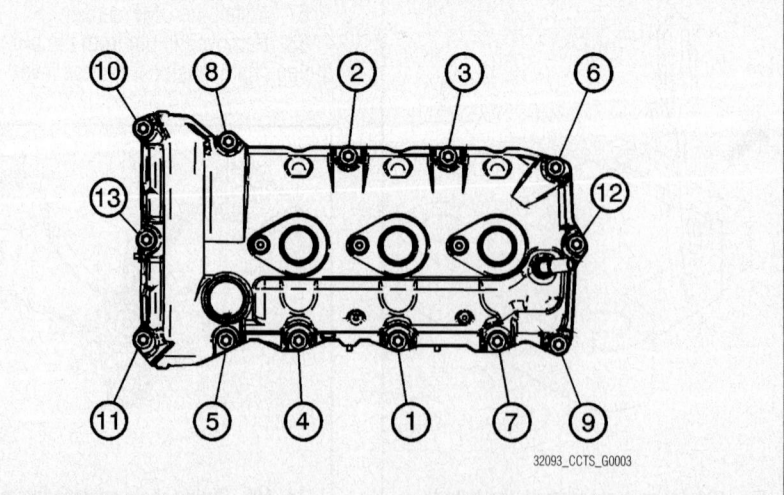

Fig. 199 Camshaft cover bolt tightening sequence—3.6L engines

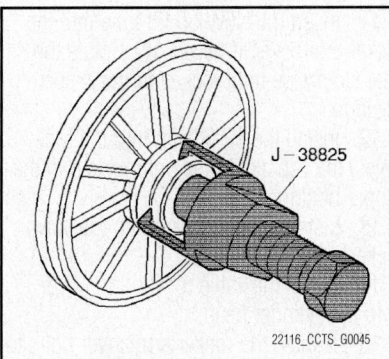

Fig. 200 Water pump pulley removal tool J 38825—4.6L engine

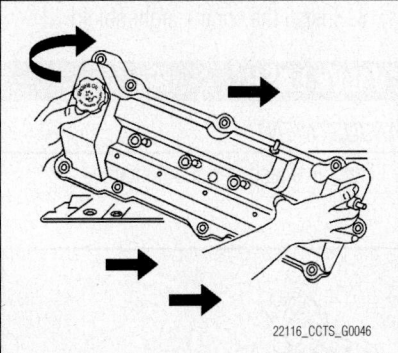

Fig. 201 Left camshaft cover removal— 4.6L engine

2. Remove the fuel injector sight shield.
3. Remove the upper tie bar.
4. Drain the cooling system.
5. Reposition the radiator inlet hose clamp.
6. Remove the radiator inlet hose from the water pump housing.
7. Disconnect the Positive Crankcase Ventilation (PCV) fresh air tube quick connect fitting from the camshaft cover.
8. Remove the ignition coils.
9. Remove the engine harness clips from the camshaft cover and position the harness aside.
10. Loosen the Ignition Control Module (ICM) wiring harness ground bolt from the camshaft cover.
11. Remove the ground wire terminal/bolt from the camshaft cover.
12. Remove the water pump drive belt tensioner shield bolt/nuts.
13. Remove the water pump drive belt shield.
14. Remove the water pump drive belt from the pulleys.
15. Remove the water pump drive belt tensioner studs.
16. Remove the water pump belt tensioner.
17. Remove the plastic dust cap from the end of the intake camshaft.

18. Remove the water pump pulley from the intake camshaft using the J 38825.
19. Remove the camshaft seal bolts.

➡**DO NOT reuse the camshaft seal.**

20. Remove and discard the camshaft seal.
21. Loosen the camshaft cover bolts.
22. Lift the camshaft drive end of the cover up.
23. Move the camshaft cover (valve cover) reward in order to clear the water pump drive shaft.
24. Discard the camshaft cover perimeter seals and spark plug seals if there is any evidence of damage or if the seal comes out of the groove in the cover during removal.
25. Clean and inspect the camshaft cover.

To install:

⁑ **WARNING**

Be careful to prevent the exposed section of the camshaft cover seal from being damaged by the edge of the cylinder head casting.

26. Install the camshaft cover seal as required.
27. Install the camshaft cover end over the intake camshaft end.
28. Work the camshaft cover into position by pivoting the cover down and to the left allowing the cover to clear the camshaft drive chain and then aligning the bolt holes.
29. Tighten the camshaft cover bolts to 89 inch lbs. (10 Nm).
30. Install a NEW camshaft seal as follows:
  a. Lubricate the camshaft seal lip with engine oil.
  b. Push the camshaft seal into position around the camshaft using the protective sleeve supplied with the seal.
  c. Coat the threads of the camshaft seal bolts with sealant.
  d. Install the camshaft seal bolts and tighten to 27 inch. lbs. (3 Nm).
31. Install the water pump drive pulley onto the intake camshaft.
32. Install the water pump pulley using the J 38823. During installation, the tool will bottom out on the camshaft at the proper depth.
33. Install the plastic dust cap into the end of the camshaft.
34. Position the water pump drive belt tensioner to the water pump housing.
35. Install the water pump drive belt tensioner studs and tighten to 89 inch lbs. (10 Nm).

36. Install the water pump drive belt over the pulleys.
37. Install the water pump drive belt shield over the tensioner studs.
38. Install the water pump drive belt shield bolt/nuts. Tighten to 89 inch lbs. 10 Nm).
39. Position the ground wire terminal/bolt to the camshaft cover.
40. Tighten the Ignition Control Module (ICM) wiring harness ground bolt to the camshaft cover.
41. Position the engine harness and install the engine harness clips to the camshaft cover.
42. Install the ignition coils.
43. Connect the PCV fresh air tube quick connect fitting to the camshaft cover.
44. Install the radiator inlet hose to the water pump housing.
45. Position the radiator inlet hose clamp.
46. Install the upper tie bar.
47. Fill the cooling system.
48. Install the fuel injector sight shield.

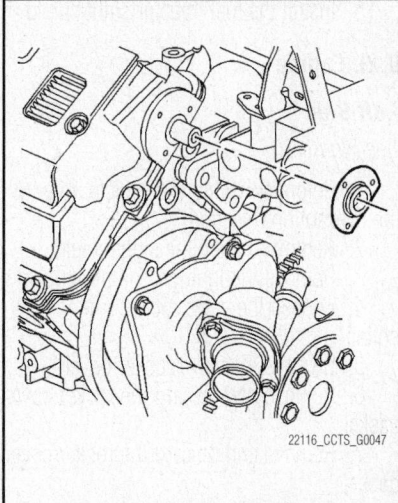

Fig. 202 New camshaft seal installation

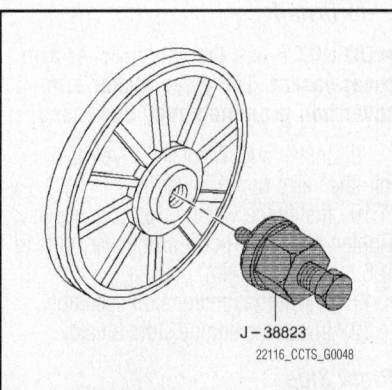

Fig. 203 Water pump pulley installation using the J 38823

Right Side

See Figure 204.

1. Remove the fuel injector sight shield.
2. Remove the secondary Air Injection (AIR) check valve.
3. Disconnect the Positive Crankcase Ventilation (PCV) foul air tube quick connect fitting from the camshaft cover.
4. Remove the ignition coils.
5. Loosen the camshaft cover (valve cover) bolts.
6. Remove the camshaft cover.
7. Discard the camshaft cover perimeter seals and spark plug seals if there is any evidence of damage or if the seal comes out of the groove in the cover during removal.
8. Clean and inspect the camshaft cover.
9. Install the camshaft cover seal as required.
10. Install the camshaft cover.
11. Tighten the camshaft cover bolts to 89 inch lbs. (10 Nm).
12. Install the ignition coils.
13. Connect the PCV foul air tube quick connect fitting to the camshaft cover.
14. Install the AIR check valve.
15. Install the fuel injector sight shield.

6.2L Engine

Left Side

See Figure 205.

1. Before servicing the vehicle, refer to the Precautions Section.
2. Remove the engine sight shield.
3. Remove the ignition coil assembly.
4. Loosen the valve rocker arm cover bolts.
5. Remove the valve rocker cover.
6. Remove and discard the rocker cover gasket.
7. Remove and discard the rocker cover gasket.
8. Clean and inspect the rocker arm cover.

To install:

➡ DO NOT reuse the valve rocker arm cover gasket. The valve rocker arm cover bolt grommets may be reused.

9. Install a NEW rocker cover gasket into the valve rocker cover lip.
10. Install the valve rocker arm cover. Tighten the valve rocker arm cover bolts to 106 inch lbs. (12 Nm).
11. Install the ignition coil assembly.
12. Install the engine sight shield.

Right Side

1. Before servicing the vehicle, refer to the Precautions Section.

2. Remove the fuel injector sight shield.
3. Remove the Positive Crankcase Ventilation (PCV) tube from the air cleaner outlet duct and rocker arm cover.
4. Remove the ignition coil assembly.
5. Loosen the valve rocker arm cover bolts.
6. Remove the valve rocker arm cover.
7. Remove and discard the rocker cover gasket.
8. Remove the oil fill cap from the oil fill tube.

➡ DO NOT remove the oil fill tube, unless replacement is necessary due to signs of leakage.

9. Clean and inspect the valve rocker arm cover.

To install:

10. Lubricate the O-ring seal of the NEW oil fill tube with clean engine oil, if removed.

11. Insert the NEW oil fill tube into the rocker arm cover, if necessary. Rotate the tube clockwise until locked in the proper position.
12. Install the oil fill cap into the tube. Rotate the cap clockwise until locked in the proper position.
13. Install a NEW gasket into the valve rocker cover lip.
14. Install the valve rocker arm cover onto the cylinder head.
15. Tighten the rocker arm cover bolts to 106 inch lbs. (12 Nm).
16. Install the ignition coil assembly.
17. Install the PCV tube to the air cleaner outlet duct and rocker arm cover.
18. Install the engine sight shield.

VALVE LASH

ADJUSTMENT

The valve lash is not adjustable.

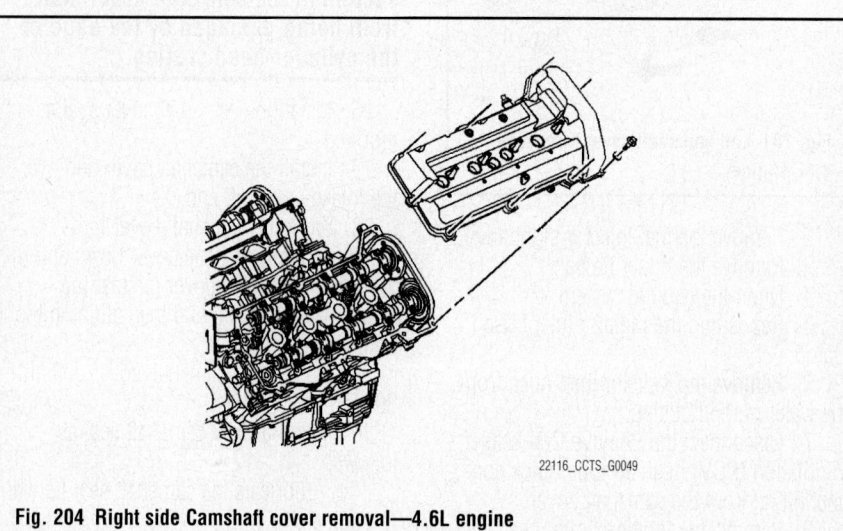

22116_CCTS_G0049

Fig. 204 Right side Camshaft cover removal—4.6L engine

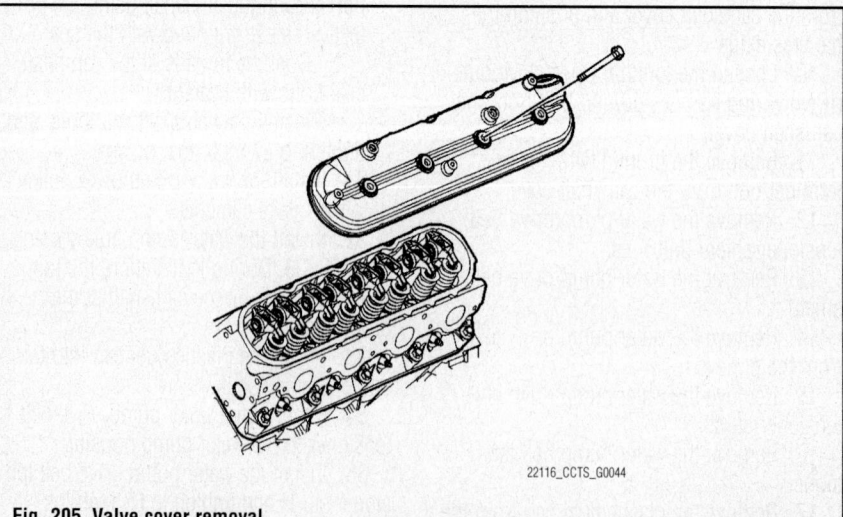

22116_CCTS_G0044

Fig. 205 Valve cover removal

ENGINE PERFORMANCE & EMISSION CONTROLS

ACCELERATOR PEDAL POSITION (APP) SENSOR

LOCATION

The Accelerator Pedal Position (APP) sensor is mounted at the top of the accelerator pedal and is part of the assembly.

REMOVAL & INSTALLATION

CTS Models

See Figure 206.

1. Remove the closeout/insulator panel from under the dashboard on the driver's side.

✳ WARNING

Handle the electronic throttle control components carefully. Use cleanliness in order to prevent damage. Do not drop the electronic throttle control components. Do not roughly handle the electronic throttle control components. Do not immerse the electronic throttle control components in cleaning solvents of any type.

2. Disconnect the Accelerator Pedal Position (APP) sensor electrical connector from the accelerator pedal module.

3. Remove the nuts from the APP sensor mounting plate and remove the APP sensor from the front of dash.

To install:

4. Install the APP sensor to the front of dash.

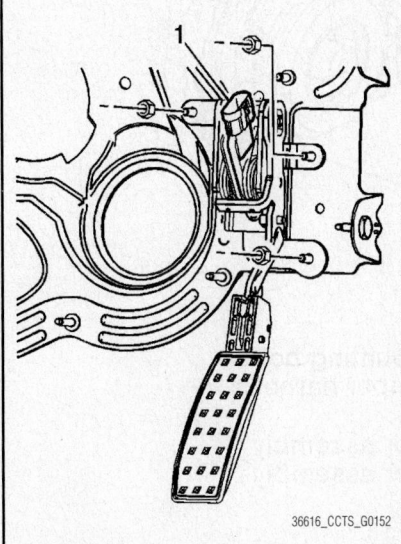

Fig. 206 Remove the APP sensor (1) from the front of the dash—CTS 3.6L Engine

5. Install the APP sensor mounting nuts and tighten to 80 inch lbs. (9 Nm).

6. Connect the APP sensor electrical connector.

7. Operate the accelerator pedal and observe the APP angles using a scan tool. The accelerator pedal should operate freely, without binding between closed throttle and wide open throttle.

8. Install the closeout/insulator panel.

4.6L Engine

See Figure 207.

1. Remove the left instrument panel sound insulator.

2. Disconnect the body harness electrical connector from the Accelerator Pedal Position (APP) sensor.

3. Remove the accelerator pedal mounting nuts and the pedal assembly.

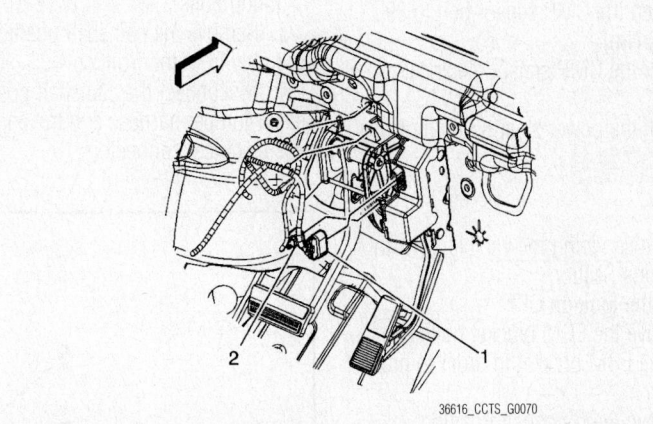

Fig. 207 Disconnect the body harness electrical connector (1)from the Accelerator Pedal Position (APP) sensor—DTS Models

4. Installation is the reverse order of removal.

CAMSHAFT POSITION (CMP) SENSOR

LOCATION

3.6L Engine

The Camshaft Position (CMP) Sensors are located in the cylinder head at the front of the engine, just below the valve covers.

4.6L Engine

See Figure 208.

The Camshaft Position (CMP) Sensor is located in the rear cylinder head, just below the valve cover.

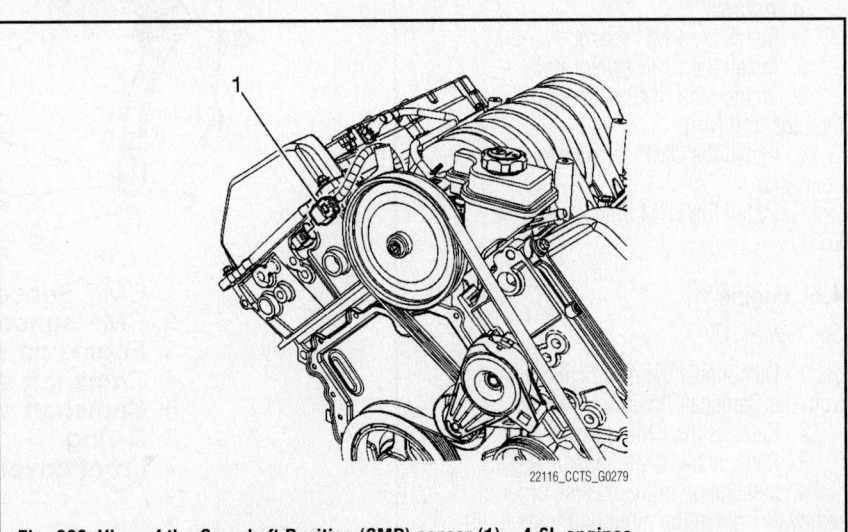

Fig. 208 View of the Camshaft Position (CMP) sensor (1)—4.6L engines

6.2L Engine

The Camshaft Position (CMP) Sensor is located at the front of the engine behind the crankshaft balancer.

REMOVAL & INSTALLATION

3.6L Engine

Left Bank

1. Before servicing the vehicle, refer to the Precautions Section.
2. Turn the ignition OFF.
3. Remove the power steering fluid reservoir bolts and reposition the power steering fluid reservoir in order to provide access.
4. Remove the Camshaft Position (CMP) sensor electrical connector.
5. Remove the CMP sensor bolt.
6. Remove the CMP sensor.

To install:

7. Install the CMP sensor.
8. Install the CMP sensor bolt.
9. Tighten the CMP sensor bolt to 89 inch lbs. (10 Nm).
10. Install the CMP sensor electrical connector.
11. Install the power steering fluid reservoir.

Right Bank

1. Before servicing the vehicle, refer to the Precautions Section.
2. Turn the ignition OFF.
3. Remove the ECM bracket bolts and reposition the ECM bracket in order to provide access.
4. Remove the Camshaft Position (CMP) sensor electrical connector.
5. Remove the CMP sensor bolt.
6. Remove the CMP sensor.

To install:

7. Install the CMP sensor.
8. Install the CMP sensor bolt.
9. Tighten the CMP sensor bolt to 89 inch lbs. (10 Nm).
10. Install the CMP sensor electrical connector.
11. Install the ECM bracket with the ECM.

4.6L Engine

See Figure 209.

1. Disconnect the electrical connector from the Camshaft Position (CMP) sensor.
2. Remove the CMP sensor bolt.
3. Remove the CMP sensor.
4. Installation is the reverse order of removal. Tighten the mounting bolts to 89 inch lbs. (10 Nm).

Fig. 209 Remove the mounting bolt to remove to CMP sensor—4.6L engine

6.2L Engine

See Figure 210.

1. Remove the alternator bracket assembly.
2. Remove the camshaft position sensor mounting bolts.
3. Remove the camshaft position sensor assembly from the front cover.
4. Disconnect the camshaft position sensor jumper harness and the engine harness electrical connectors.

5. Remove the camshaft sensor assembly.
6. Disconnect camshaft position sensor (CMP) from the jumper harness.

To install:

7. Reconnect the camshaft sensor and the jumper harness.
8. Install the O-ring on the camshaft sensor assembly.
9. Reconnect the camshaft position sensor assembly and the engine harness connector.

➡ Before installing the camshaft sensor assembly, apply a small amount of clean motor oil to the O-ring.

10. Install the camshaft position sensor assembly in the front cover.
11. Install the camshaft position sensor mounting bolts and tighten to 18 ft. lbs. (25 Nm).
12. Install the generator assembly.

CRANKSHAFT POSITION (CKP) SENSOR

LOCATION

3.6L Engine

See Figure 211.

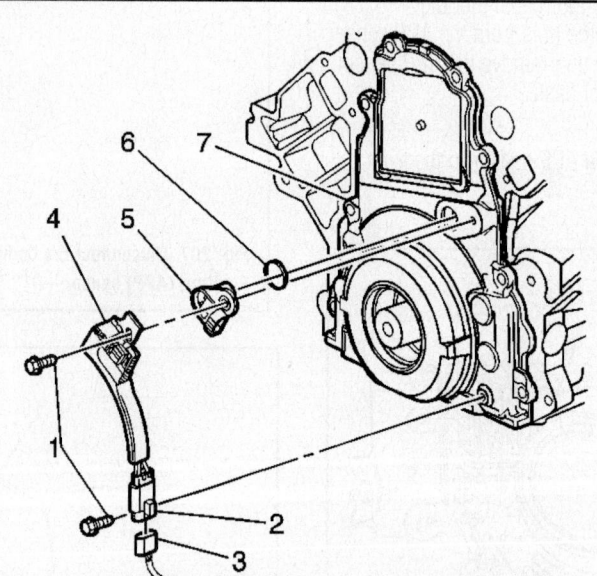

1. CMP Sensor mounting bolts
2. CMP sensor jumper harness
3. Engine harness
4. Camshaft sensor assembly
5. Camshaft sensor assembly
6. O-ring
7. Front cover

Fig. 210 CMP Sensor removal—6.2L engine

Fig. 211 Crankshaft Position sensor location—3.6L engine

The Crankshaft Position (CKP) sensor is mounted at the right rear of the engine block.

4.6L Engine

See Figure 212.

The Crankshaft Position (CKP) sensor is located under the intake manifold and is mounted in the engine block.

6.2L Engine

The Crankshaft Position (CKP) sensor is mounted in the engine block at the rear of the engine. The starter motor must be removed to access the sensor.

REMOVAL & INSTALLATION

3.6L Engine

1. Turn the ignition OFF.
2. Raise and safely support the vehicle.
3. Remove the exhaust manifold heat shield to obtain access.

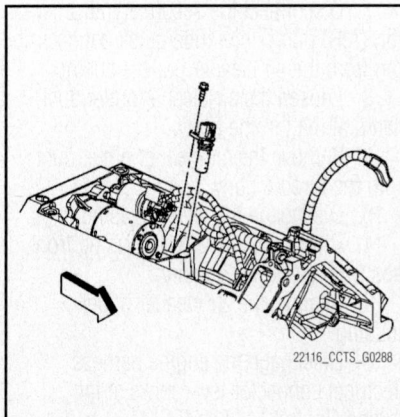

Fig. 212 Crankshaft Position (CKP) sensor location—4.6L engine

4. Disconnect the crankshaft position (CKP) electrical connector (3).
5. Remove the crankshaft sensor bolt.
6. Remove the crankshaft sensor.

To install:
7. Install the crankshaft position sensor and tighten the bolt to 89 inch lbs. (10 Nm).
8. Connect the CKP electrical connector (3).
9. Install the exhaust manifold heat shield and tighten to 89 inch lbs. (10 Nm).
10. Lower the vehicle

4.6L Engine

1. Remove the intake manifold. For additional information, refer to the following section, "Intake Manifold, Removal & Installation."
2. Disconnect the Crankshaft Position (CKP) sensor wiring harness electrical connector from the CKP sensor.
3. Remove the CKP sensor bolt. (cylinder heads shown removed, for clarity).
4. Remove the CKP sensor.

To install:
5. Lubricate the crankshaft sensor O-ring seal with clean engine oil.
6. Install the CKP sensor and tighten the mounting bolt to 89 inch lbs. (10 Nm).
7. Connect the CKP sensor wiring harness electrical connector to the CKP sensor.
8. Install the intake manifold.
9. Perform the CKP system variation learn procedure.

6.2L Engine

1. Disconnect the negative battery cable.
2. Raise and safely support the vehicle.
3. Remove the starter.
4. Disconnect the Crankshaft Position (CKP) sensor electrical connector.

➡ **Clean the area around the CKP before removal in order to avoid debris from entering the engine.**

5. Remove the CKP sensor retaining bolt.
6. Remove the CKP sensor.

To install:
7. Install the CKP sensor and tighten the retaining bolt to 18 ft. lbs. (25 Nm).
8. Connect the CKP sensor electrical connector.
9. Install the starter.
10. Lower the vehicle.
11. Connect the negative battery cable.
12. Perform the CKP System Variation Learn Procedure.

CRANKSHAFT POSITION SYSTEM VARIATION LEARN PROCEDURE

1. Install a scan tool.
2. Monitor the ECM for DTCs with a scan tool. If other DTCs are set, except DTC P0315, refer to Diagnostic Trouble Code (DTC) List - Vehicle for the applicable DTC that set.
3. With a scan tool, select the CKP system variation learn procedure within the Module Setup menu and perform the following:
4. Observe the fuel cut-off for the applicable engine.
5. Block the drive wheels.
6. Set the parking brake.
7. Place the vehicle's transmission in Park or Neutral.
8. Turn the air conditioning (A/C) OFF.
9. Cycle the ignition from OFF to ON.
10. Apply and hold the brake pedal for the duration of the procedure.
11. Start and idle the engine.
12. Accelerate to wide open throttle (WOT). The engine should not accelerate beyond the calibrated fuel cut-off RPM value noted in step 3.1. Release the throttle immediately if the value is exceeded.
13. Release the throttle when fuel cut-off occurs.
14. The scan tool displays Learn Status: Learned this Ignition. If the scan tool indicates that DTC P0315 ran and passed, the CKP variation learn procedure is complete. If the scan tool indicates DTC P0315 failed or did not run, or if any other DTCs set, refer to Diagnostic Trouble Code (DTC) List - Vehicle for the applicable DTC that set.
15. Turn OFF the ignition for 30 seconds after the learn procedure is completed successfully.

ELECTRONIC CONTROL MODULE (ECM)

LOCATION

3.6L Engine

The Electronic Control Module (ECM) is located to the left of the throttle body, and just above the drive belt.

4.6L Engine

See Figure 213.

The Engine Control Module (ECM) is located in the engine compartment next to the air cleaner housing.

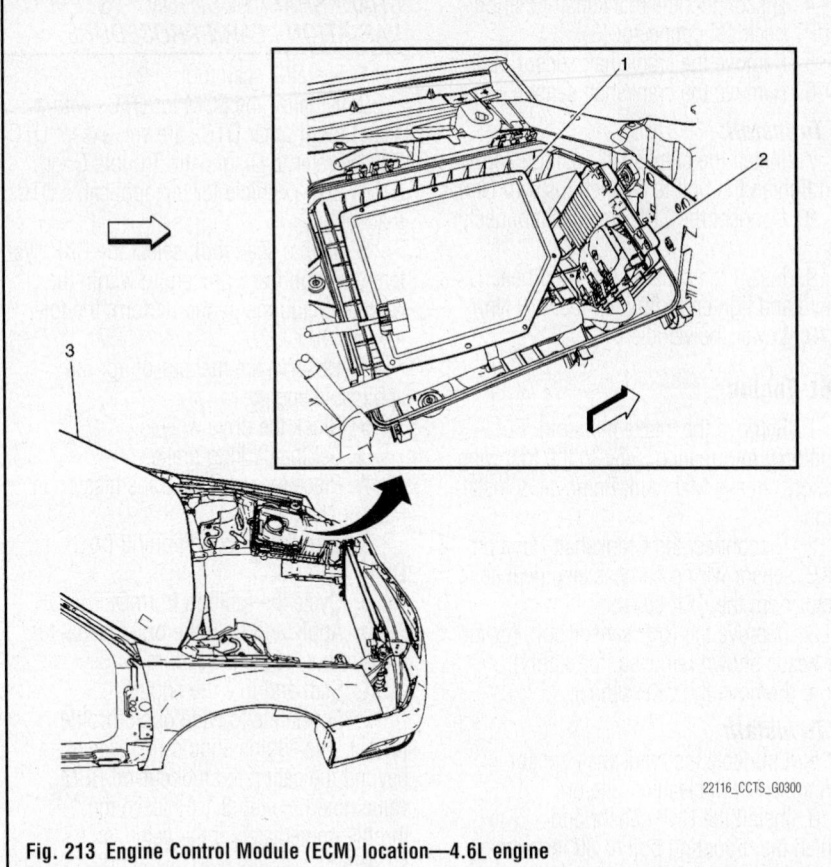

Fig. 213 Engine Control Module (ECM) location—4.6L engine

22116_CCTS_G0300

REMOVAL & INSTALLATION

3.6L Engine

See Figure 214.

1. Using a scan tool, retrieve the percentage of remaining engine oil and automatic transmission fluid life. Record the remaining engine oil and automatic transmission fluid life.

2. Disconnect the negative battery cable.

❊❊ WARNING

In order to prevent any possible electrostatic discharge damage to the ECM, do not touch the connector pins.

3. Unlock and disconnect the engine wiring harness electrical connectors from the Engine Control Module (ECM).

4. Use the tabs in order to disengage the retainers on the ECM bracket from the ECM and remove the ECM.

5. If replacing the ECM bracket perform the following steps, otherwise proceed to step 4 in the installation procedure.

6. Using a small flat-bladed tool, depress the locking tabs (1) on the ECM bracket.

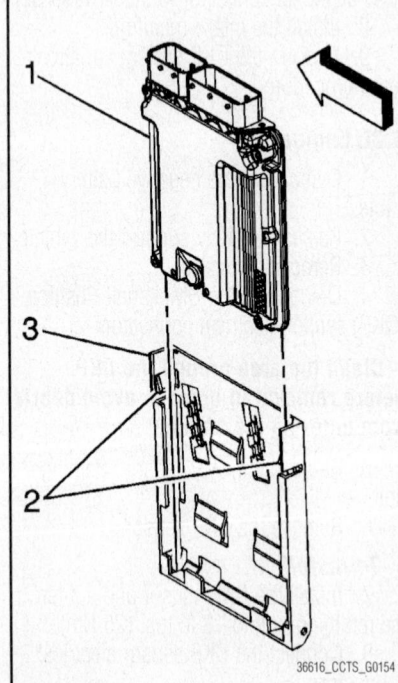

Fig. 214 Use the tabs (3) in order to disengage the retainers (2) on the ECM bracket from the ECM (1) and remove the ECM—3.6L engine

36616_CCTS_G0154

7. Slide up and remove the ECM bracket

To install:

8. If replacing the ECM bracket, perform the following:

  a. Slide down and install the ECM bracket.

  b. Ensure that the ECM bracket engages the locking tabs.

9. Slide the ECM into the ECM bracket, ensure that the ECM engages the bracket retainers.

❊❊ WARNING

In order to prevent any possible electrostatic discharge damage to the ECM, do not touch the connector pins.

10. Connect and lock the engine wiring harness electrical connectors to the ECM.

11. Connect the negative battery cable.

12. Program the ECM, if required.

13. Turn OFF the ignition for at least 5 seconds after the programming event is complete.

4.6L Engine

See Figure 215.

1. Using a scan tool, retrieve the percentage of remaining engine oil and automatic transaxle fluid life.

2. Record the remaining engine oil and transaxle fluid life.

3. Ensure that the ignition is in the OFF position.

4. Disconnect the negative battery cable.

5. Disconnect the engine harness electrical connector from the mass air flow/intake air temperature (MAF/IAT) sensor.

6. Disconnect the positive crankcase ventilation (PCV) fresh air tube quick connect fitting from the air duct.

7. Disconnect the secondary air injection (AIR) pump inlet tube quick connect fitting from the air cleaner upper housing.

8. Loosen the air cleaner outlet duct clamp at the throttle body.

9. Remove the air cleaner outlet duct from the throttle body.

10. Disengage the lower housing clips.

11. Disengage the upper housing front tabs from the lower housing.

12. Remove the air cleaner upper housing.

13. Disengage the engine harness electrical connector lever locks at the Engine Control Module (ECM).

14. Remove the engine harness electrical connectors from the ECM.

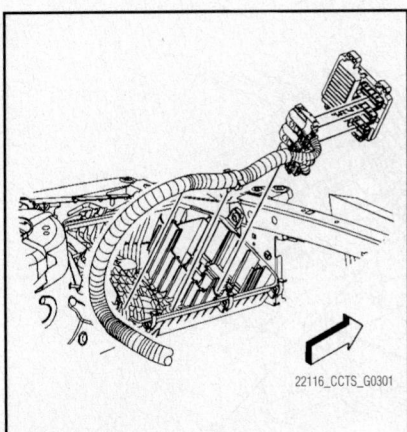

Fig. 215 Install the engine harness electrical connectors to the ECM—4.6L engine shown

15. Remove the ECM from the air cleaner lower housing.

To install:

16. Install the ECM to the lower air cleaner housing.

17. Install the engine harness electrical connectors to the ECM.

18. Engage the engine harness electrical connector lever locks at the ECM.

19. Install the air cleaner upper housing.

20. Engage the upper housing front tabs to the lower housing.

21. Engage the lower housing clips

22. The remainder of the installation is the reverse order of removal.

6.2L Engine

1. Using a scan tool, retrieve the percentage of remaining engine oil. Record the remaining engine oil life.

2. Turn OFF the Ignition.

3. Disconnect the ECM harness connectors. The ECM harness connectors are equipped with locking levers. Rotate the levers upward to the connectors to disengage the connector.

4. Disengage the ECM bracket retaining tabs.

5. Installation is the reverse order of removal.

ENGINE COOLANT TEMPERATURE (ECT) SENSOR

LOCATION

4.6L Engine

See Figure 216.

The ECT sensor is located in the front of the right cylinder head.

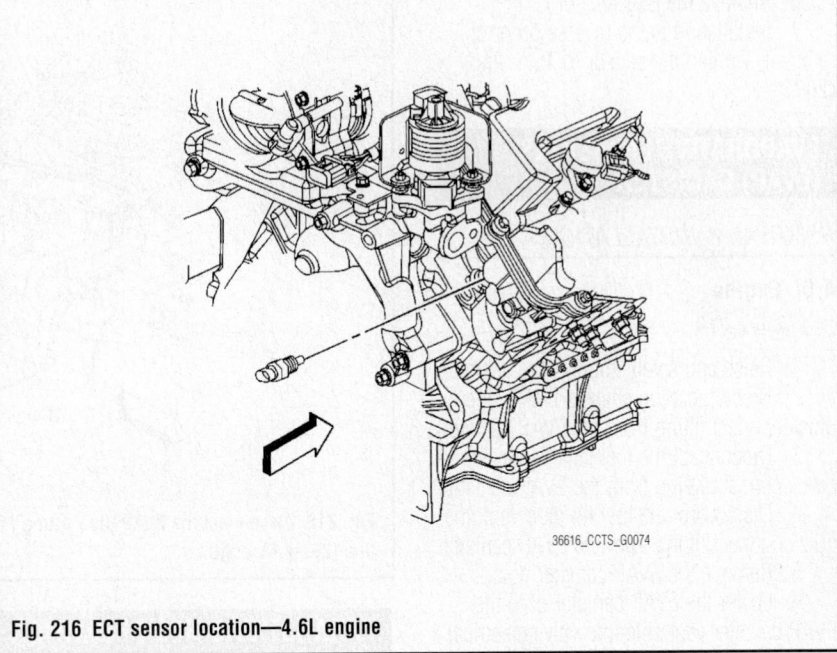

Fig. 216 ECT sensor location—4.6L engine

REMOVAL & INSTALLATION

3.6L Engine

See Figure 217.

1. Turn the ignition to the OFF position.

2. Remove the engine oil dipstick indicator.

3. Slide the electrical connector heat protector off the electrical connector.

4. Disconnect the coolant temperature sensor electrical connector.

5. Remove the coolant temperature sensor.

6. Installation is the reverse order of removal.

4.6L Engine

1. Remove the fuel injector sight shield.

2. Drain the cooling system. Refer to Cooling System Draining and Filling.

3. Disconnect the engine harness electrical connector from the Engine Coolant Temperature (ECT) sensor.

4. Remove the ECT sensor.

To install:

5. Apply sealant GM P/N 12346004 or equivalent to the threads of the ECT sensor.

6. Install the ECT sensor and tighten to 15 ft. lbs. (20 Nm).

7. Connect the engine harness electrical connector to the ECT sensor.

8. Refill the cooling system to the correct level.

9. Install the fuel inject sight shield.

6.2L Engine

1. Turn OFF the ignition.

2. Raise and safely support the vehicle.

3. Drain the engine coolant below the level of the Engine Coolant Temperature (ECT) sensor.

4. Lower the vehicle.

5. Disconnect the harness connector from the ECT sensor.

✳✳ WARNING

Use care when handling the coolant sensor. Damage to the coolant sensor will affect the operation of the fuel control system.

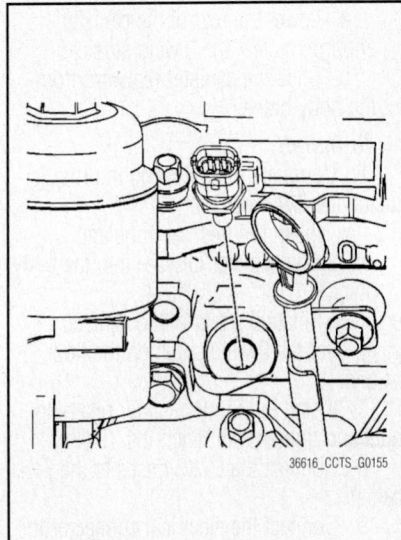

Fig. 217 Removing the coolant temperature sensor—3.6L engine

6. Remove the ECT sensor.

7. Installation is the reverse order of removal. Tighten the sensor to 15 ft. lbs. (20 Nm).

EVAPORATIVE EMISSIONS (EVAP) CANISTER

REMOVAL & INSTALLATION

4.6L Engine

See Figure 218.

1. Raise and safely support the vehicle.

2. Disconnect the chassis EVAP pipe quick connect fitting from the EVAP canister.

3. Disconnect the fuel tank vapor line quick connect fitting from the EVAP canister.

4. Disconnect the fuel fill pipe vent line quick connect fitting from the EVAP canister.

5. Remove the EVAP canister nuts.

6. Lower the EVAP canister until the EVAP canister vent solenoid valve electrical connector can be disconnected.

7. Disconnect the rear body harness electrical connector from the EVAP canister vent solenoid.

8. Remove the EVAP canister.

9. Installation is the reverse order of removal.

6.2L Engine

1. Remove the rear frame.

2. Disconnect the Evaporative Emission (EVAP) hoses from the EVAP canister.

3. Disconnect the electrical connector from the EVAP canister.

4. Remove the EVAP canister retaining nuts.

5. Complete the following in order to remove the EVAP canister:

a. Lower the rear of the canister enough to clear the 2 weld studs.

b. Slide the canister rearward from the body brace.

To install:

6. Complete the following in order to install the EVAP canister:

a. Insert the fresh air tube and tab on the canister forward into the body brace.

b. Rotate the rear of the canister up over the 2 weld studs on the floor pan.

7. Install the EVAP canister retaining nuts and tighten to 53 inch lbs. (6 Nm).

8. Connect the EVAP hoses to the EVAP canister.

9. Connect the electrical connector to the EVAP canister.

10. Install the rear frame.

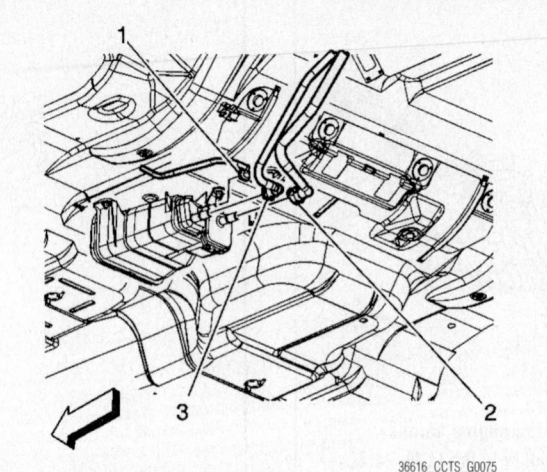

36616_CCTS_G0075

Fig. 218 Disconnect the EVAP pipe fitting (1), fuel tank vapor line fitting (3), and fuel fill vent line (2)—4.6L engines

EXHAUST GAS RECIRCULATION (EGR) VALVE

LOCATION

4.6L Engine

The Exhaust Gas Recirculation (EGR) Valve is located on the front of the engine, to the right of the throttle body.

REMOVAL & INSTALLATION

4.6L Engine

See Figure 219.

1. Disconnect the negative battery cable.

2. Remove the fuel injector sight shield.

3. Disconnect the engine harness electrical connector from the Exhaust Gas Recirculation (EGR) valve.

4. Remove the EGR bracket shield nuts.

5. Remove the EGR bracket shield.

6. Remove the EGR valve bolts.

7. Remove the EGR valve.

8. Remove and discard the EGR valve gasket.

To install:

9. Install the EGR valve with a new gasket.

10. Tighten the EGR valve mounting bolts to 18 ft. lbs. (24 Nm).

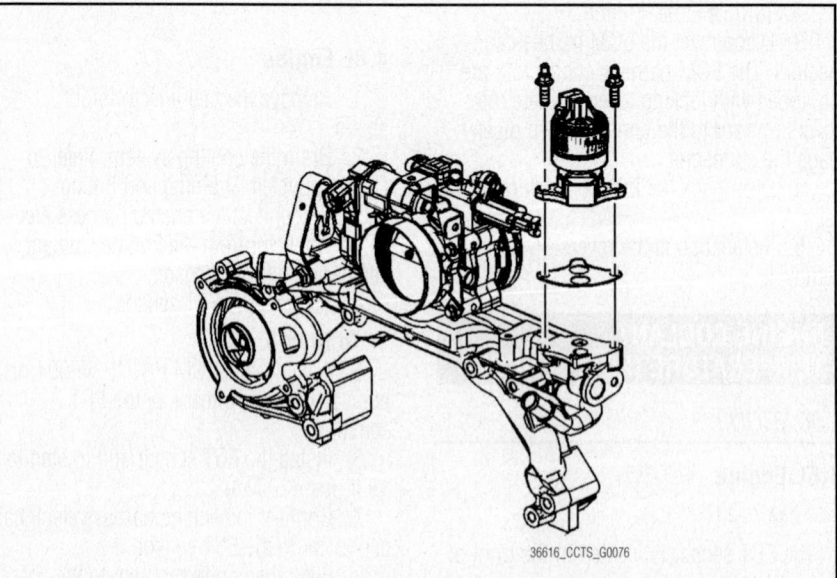

36616_CCTS_G0076

Fig. 219 Remove the EGR valve mounting bolts to remove the EGR valve—4.6L engines

11. Install the EGR bracket shield and tighten the nuts to 89 inch lbs. (10 Nm).
12. Connect the wiring harness electrical connector and install he fuel injector sight shield.

HEATED OXYGEN (HO2S) SENSOR

LOCATION

The Heated Oxygen Sensors (HO2S) are mounted in the exhaust system.

REMOVAL & INSTALLATION

3.6L Engine

Bank 1 Sensor 1

See Figure 220.

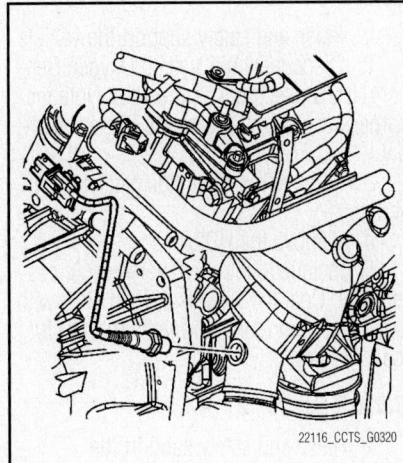

Fig. 220 Heated Oxygen Sensor (HO2S) Bank 1 Sensor 1 removal

1. Turn the ignition OFF.
2. Remove the fuel injector sight shield.
3. Disconnect the Heated Oxygen Sensor (HO2S) electrical connector.
4. Remove the HO2S electrical connector from the wiring harness bracket.
5. Raise and safely support the vehicle.

➡Removal of the oxygen sensor is easier when the engine temperature is above 48°C (120°F).

6. Remove the HO2S from the catalytic converter.
7. Installation is the reverse order of removal. Tighten the HO2S to 30 ft. lbs. (40 Nm).

Bank 1 Sensor 2

See Figure 221.

1. Turn the ignition OFF.

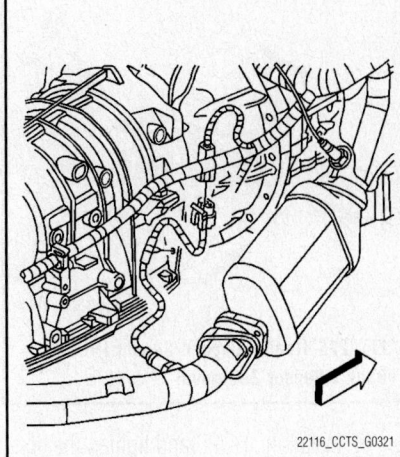

Fig. 221 Heated Oxygen Sensor (HO2S) Bank 1 Sensor 2 removal

2. Raise and safely support the vehicle.
3. Disconnect the Heated Oxygen Sensor (HO2S) electrical connector.
4. Remove the HO2S wiring harness from the transmission case.

➡Removal of the oxygen sensor is easier when the engine temperature is above 48°C (120°F).

5. Remove the HO2S.
6. Installation is the reverse order of removal. Tighten the HO2S to 30 ft. lbs. (40 Nm).

Bank 2 Sensor 1

See Figure 222.

1. Turn the ignition OFF.

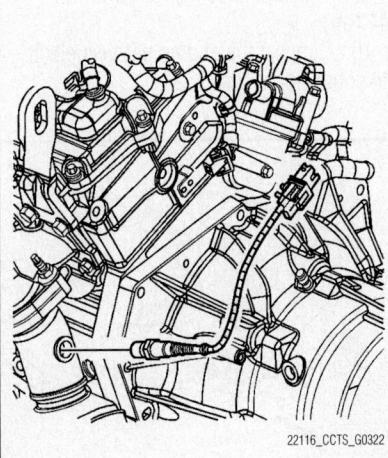

Fig. 222 Heated Oxygen Sensor (HO2S) Bank 2 Sensor 1 removal

2. Remove the fuel injector sight shield, if necessary.
3. Raise and safely support the vehicle.
4. Disconnect the Heated Oxygen Sensor (HO2S) electrical connector.
5. Remove the HO2S electrical connector from the wiring harness bracket.

➡Removal of the oxygen sensor is easier when the engine temperature is above 48°C (120°F).

6. Remove the HO2S.
7. Installation is the reverse order of removal. Tighten the HO2S to 30 ft. lbs. (40 Nm).

Bank 2 Sensor 2

See Figure 223.

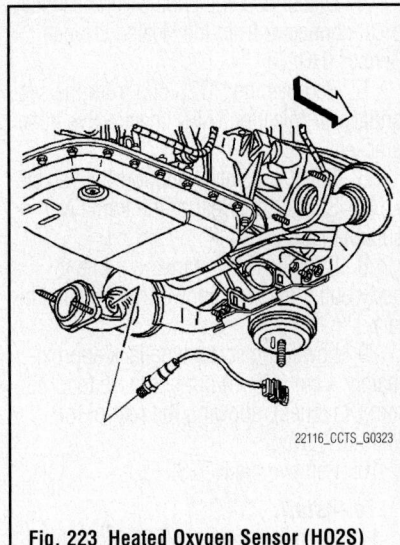

Fig. 223 Heated Oxygen Sensor (HO2S) Bank 2 Sensor 2 removal

1. Turn the ignition OFF.
2. Raise and safely support the vehicle.
3. Disconnect the Heated Oxygen Sensor (HO2S) electrical connector.
4. Remove the HO2S wiring harness from the transmission case.

➡Removal of the oxygen sensor is easier when the engine temperature is above 48°C (120°F).

5. Remove the HO2S.
6. Installation is the reverse order of removal. Tighten the HO2S to 30 ft. lbs. (40 Nm).

4.6L Engine

Bank 1 Sensor 1

See Figure 224.

1. Before servicing the vehicle, refer to the Precautions Section.

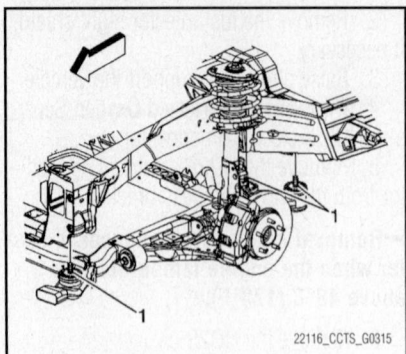

Fig. 224 Remove the four rearward frame-to-body bolts (1)

2. Remove the fuel injector sight shield.

3. Remove the Connector Position Assurance (CPA) retainer.

4. Disconnect the engine harness electrical connector from the Heated Oxygen Sensor (HO2S).

5. Remove the HO2S clip from the secondary air injection (AIR) check valve hose bracket.

6. Raise and safely support the vehicle.

7. Support the rear of the frame with a suitable jack.

8. Remove the 4 rearward frame to body bolts (left side shown, right side similar).

9. Lower the screw type jack approximately 4 cm (1.5 in) but not more than 76 mm (3 inches), allowing the rear of the frame to lower.

10. Remove the HO2S.

To install:

11. If reusing the old HO2S, coat the threads with anti-seize compound.

12. Install the sensor and tighten to 30 ft. lbs. (41 Nm).

13. Raise the engine frame into position and tighten the frame-to-body bolts to 141 ft. lbs. (191 Nm).

14. The remainder of the installation is the reverse order of removal.

Bank 1 Sensor 2

See Figure 225.

1. Before servicing the vehicle, refer to the Precautions Section.

2. Remove the oxygen sensor wiring harness heat shield..

3. Disconnect the engine harness electrical connector from the Heated Oxygen Sensor (HO2S).

4. Remove the HO2S.

To install:

5. If reusing the old HO2S, coat the threads with anti-seize compound, GM P/N 12377953 or equivalent.

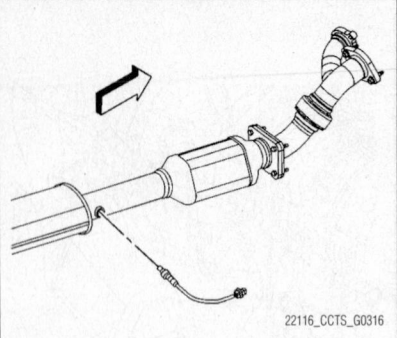

Fig. 225 Heated Oxygen Sensor (HO2S) Bank 1 Sensor 2 removal

6. Install the HO2S and tighten the sensor to 30 ft. lbs. (41 Nm).

7. Connect the engine harness electrical connector to the HO2S.

8. Install the oxygen sensor wiring harness heat shield.

Bank 2 Sensor 1

See Figure 226.

1. Before servicing the vehicle, refer to the Precautions Section.

2. Remove the air deflector

3. Remove the Connector Position Assurance (CPA) retainer.

4. Disconnect the engine harness electrical connector from the heated oxygen sensor (HO2S).

5. Remove the HO2S clip from the engine bracket.

6. Remove the HO2S.

To install:

7. If reusing the old HO2S, coat the threads with anti-seize compound, GM P/N 12377953 or equivalent.

8. Install the HO2S.

9. Tighten the sensor to 30 ft. lbs. (41 Nm).

10. Connect the engine harness electrical connector to the HO2S.

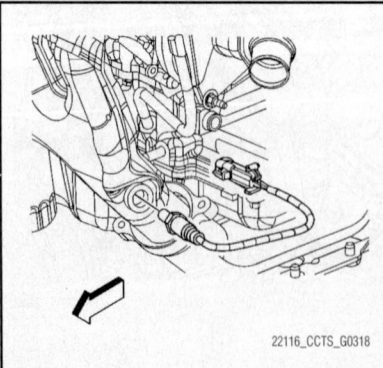

Fig. 226 Heated Oxygen Sensors (HO2S) Bank 2 Sensor 1 removal

11. Install the CPA retainer.

12. Install the HO2S clip to the engine bracket.

13. Install the air deflector.

6.2L Engine

Bank 1 Sensor 1 & 2

1. Raise and safely support the vehicle.

2. Disconnect the Heated Oxygen Sensor (HO2S) electrical connector.

3. Remove any wire harness retainers and note the wire harness routing for reassembly.

4. Carefully remove the HO2S.

5. Installation is the reverse order of removal. Coat the threads of the HO2S with anti-seize compound and tighten to 30 ft. lbs. (41 Nm).

Bank 2 Sensor 1

1. Raise and safely support the vehicle.

2. Disconnect the Heated Oxygen Sensor (HO2S) electrical connectors. Note the harness routing and retainers for reassembly.

3. Remove the right side catalytic converter.

4. Remove the HO2S.

5. Installation is the reverse order of removal. Coat the threads of the HO2S with anti-seize compound and tighten to 30 ft. lbs. (41 Nm).

Bank 2 Sensor 2

1. Raise and safely support the vehicle.

2. Disconnect the Heated Oxygen Sensor (HO2S) electrical connector.

3. Remove any wire harness retainers and note the wire harness routing for reassembly.

4. Carefully remove the HO2S.

5. Installation is the reverse order of removal. Coat the threads of the HO2S with anti-seize compound and tighten to 30 ft. lbs. (41 Nm).

KNOCK SENSOR (KS)

LOCATION

3.6L Engine

The Knock Sensors (KS) are located on both sides of the engine block toward the rear.

4.6L Engine

The Knock Sensor (KS) are located in the engine block, under the intake manifold.

REMOVAL & INSTALLATION

3.6L Engine

Bank 1

See Figure 227.

1. Before servicing the vehicle, refer to the Precautions Section.
2. Turn the ignition OFF.
3. Raise and safely support the vehicle.
4. Reposition the wiring harness heat shield to obtain access.
5. Remove the Knock Sensor (KS) electrical connector.
6. Remove the KS bolt.
7. Remove the KS.
8. Installation is the reverse order of removal. Tighten the sensor bolt to 17 ft. lbs. (23 Nm).

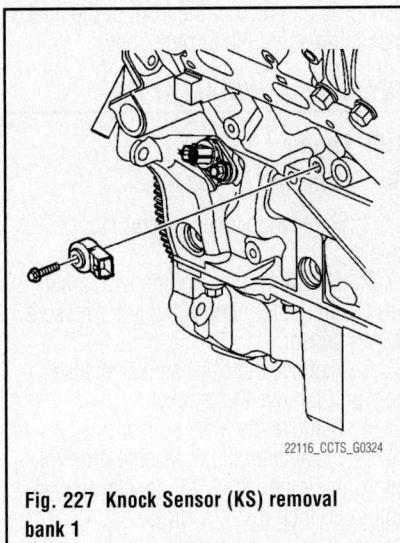

Fig. 227 Knock Sensor (KS) removal bank 1

Bank 2

See Figure 228.

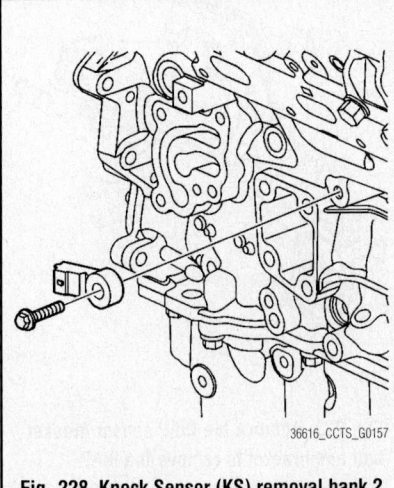

Fig. 228 Knock Sensor (KS) removal bank 2

1. Turn the ignition OFF.
2. Raise and safely support the vehicle.
3. Remove the wiring harness heat shield from the oil level indicator tube to gain access.
4. Remove the Knock Sensor (KS) electrical connector.
5. Remove the KS bolt.
6. Remove the KS.
7. Installation is the reverse order of removal. Tighten the sensor bolt to 17 ft. lbs. (23 Nm).

4.6L Engine

See Figure 229.

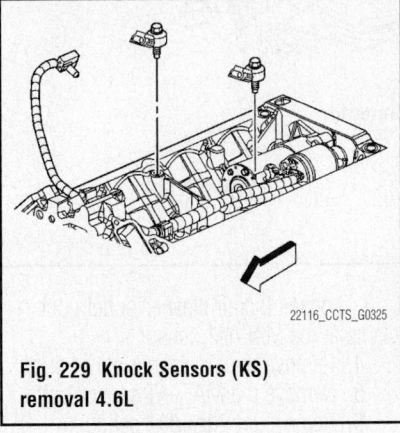

Fig. 229 Knock Sensors (KS) removal 4.6L

1. Before servicing the vehicle, refer to the Precautions Section.
2. Remove the intake manifold.
3. Disconnect the electrical connector from the right knock sensor, if required.
4. Disconnect the electrical connector from the left knock sensor, if required.
5. Remove the appropriate knock sensor.

To install:

6. Install the appropriate knock sensor.
7. Tighten the sensor to 18 ft. lbs. (25 Nm).
8. Connect the electrical connector to the left knock sensor, if required.
9. Connect the electrical connector to the right knock sensor, if required.
10. Install the intake manifold.

6.2L Engine

Sensor 1

See Figure 230.

1. Disconnect the negative battery cable.
2. Remove the left catalytic convertor.
3. Remove the left exhaust manifold.
4. Remove the mounting bolt for the Knock Sensor (KS) 1.
5. Disconnect the electrical connector of the KS from the engine harness.

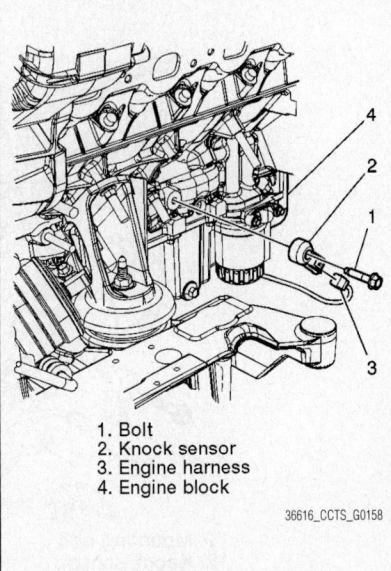

1. Bolt
2. Knock sensor
3. Engine harness
4. Engine block

Fig. 230 Knock Sensor (KS) removal—Sensor 1

6. Remove the KS from the engine block.
7. Installation is the reverse order of removal. Tighten the sensor mounting bolt to 15 ft. lbs. (20 Nm).

Sensor 2

See Figure 231.

1. Remove the right exhaust manifold.
2. Remove the right catalytic convertor.

➡ **It may be necessary to remove the starter assembly to gain enough clearance to remove the knock sensor.**

3. Remove the starter assembly, if necessary.
4. Remove the knock sensor mounting.
5. Remove the knock sensor from the engine block.
6. Disconnect the engine electrical connector from the knock sensor.
7. Remove the knock sensor.
8. Installation is the reverse order of removal. Tighten the sensor mounting bolt to 15 ft. lbs. (20 Nm).

MALFUNCTION INDICATOR LIGHT (MIL)

RESET PROCEDURE

Manual resetting of the MIL and any DTC stored in the system, requires the use of an OBD 2 scan tool connected to the data link connector for communication with the vehicle. Follow the instructions of the scan tool for both retrieval and resetting of DTC's.

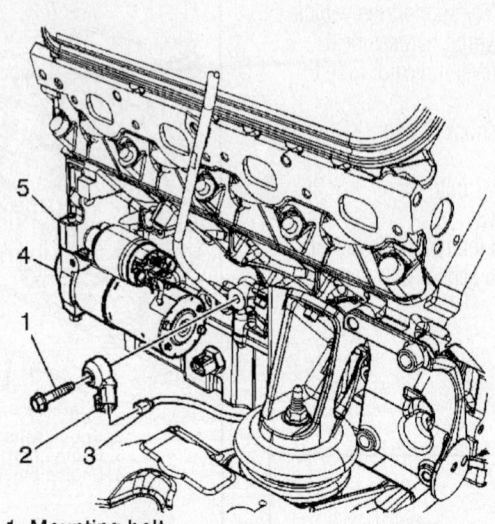

1. Mounting bolt
2. Knock sensor
3. Knock sensor harness connector
4. Starter motor
5. Engine block

22116_CCTS_G0327

Fig. 231 Knock Sensors (KS) removal bank 2

MASS AIR FLOW (MAF) SENSOR

LOCATION

The Mass Air Flow (MAF) Sensor is mounted to the air cleaner housing.

REMOVAL & INSTALLATION

3.6L & 4.6L Engines

See Figure 232.

1. Disconnect the engine harness electrical connector from the Mass Air Flow/Intake Air Temperature (MAF/IAT) sensor.
2. Loosen the air cleaner outlet duct clamp at the throttle body.

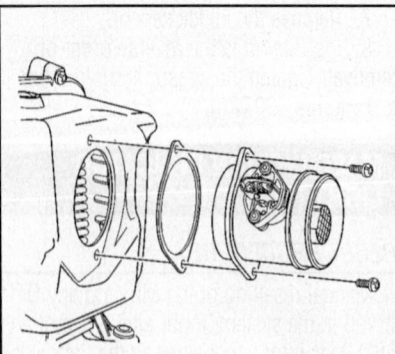

22116_CCTS_G0328

Fig. 232 Mass Air Flow (MAF) Sensor removal

3. Loosen the air cleaner outlet duct clamp at the MAF/IAT sensor.
4. Remove the air cleaner outlet duct.
5. Remove the MAF/IAT sensor bolts.
6. Remove the MAF/IAT sensor.

To install:

7. Install the MAF/IAT sensor and tighten the mounting bolts to 35 inch lbs. (4 Nm).
8. Install the air cleaner outlet duct and tighten the clamp at the MAF/IAT sensor to 35 inch lbs. (4 Nm).
9. Install the air cleaner outlet duct and tighten the clamp at the throttle body to 35 inch lbs. (4 Nm).
10. Connect the MAF/IAT electrical connector.

6.2L Engine

1. Before servicing the vehicle, refer to the Precautions Section.
2. Remove the fuel injector sight shield.
3. Disconnect the MAF/IAT sensor electrical connector.
4. Remove the air cleaner outlet duct assembly.
5. Loosen the MAF/IAT clamp.
6. Remove the MAF/IAT sensor from the air cleaner outlet duct. Note the position of the MAF/IAT sensor.

To install:

7. Carefully install the MAF/IAT sensor to the air cleaner outlet duct. Ensure that sensor is clocked properly.

8. Tighten the air cleaner outlet duct clamp.
9. Tighten the air cleaner outlet duct clamp to 27 inch lbs. (3 Nm)
10. Loosely install the air cleaner outlet duct assembly to the vehicle.
11. Connect the MAF/IAT sensor electrical connector.
12. Install the air cleaner outlet duct assembly.
13. Install the fuel injector sight shield.

MANIFOLD ABSOLUTE PRESSURE (MAP) SENSOR

LOCATION

4.6L Engine

The Manifold Absolute Pressure (MAP) Sensor is mounted in the front of the intake manifold behind the throttle body.

REMOVAL & INSTALLATION

4.6L Engine

See Figure 233.

1. Remove the fuel injector sight shield.
2. Disconnect the engine wiring harness from the Manifold Absolute Pressure (MAP) sensor.
3. Remove the MAP sensor bracket bolt, and remove the bracket.
4. Remove the MAP sensor.
5. Installation is the reverse order of removal. Tighten the MAP sensor bracket bolt to 89 inch lbs. (10 Nm).

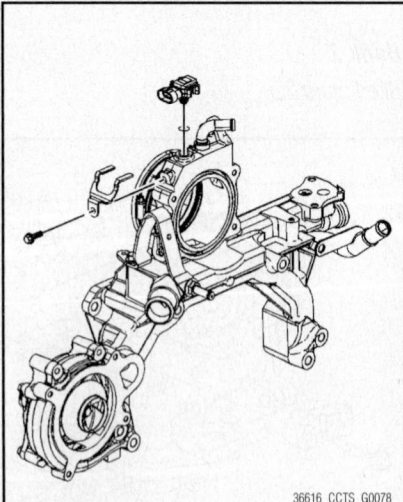

36616_CCTS_G0078

Fig. 233 Remove the MAP sensor bracket bolt and bracket to remove the MAP sensor—4.6L engine

6.2L Engine

See Figure 234.

1. Remove the components necessary to access the supercharger assembly. For additional information, refer to the following section, "Supercharger, Removal & Installation."

2. Remove the Manifold Absolute Pressure (MAP) sensor bolt and MAP sensor, and sensor seal.

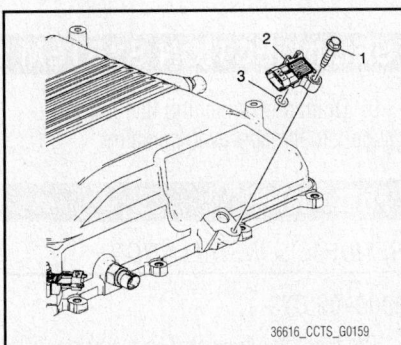

Fig. 234 Remove the MAP sensor bolt (1), MAP sensor (2) and seal (3)—6.2L engine

To install:

3. Install a NEW MAP sensor seal.
4. Install the MAP sensor and tighten the bolt to 89 inch lbs. (10 Nm).
5. Install any components removed to access the supercharger.

POSITIVE CRANKCASE VENTILATION (PCV) VALVE

REMOVAL & INSTALLATION

3.6L Engine

1. Remove the fuel injector sight shield.
2. Remove the positive crankcase ventilation (PCV) fresh air tube from the left camshaft cover.
3. Remove the PCV fresh air tube from the air inlet.
4. Remove the PCV tube bracket bolts.
5. Remove the PCV dirty air tube from the right camshaft cover.
6. Remove the PCV dirty air tube from the intake manifold.

To install:

7. Install the PCV dirty air tube to the intake manifold.
8. Install the PCV dirty air tube to the right camshaft cover.
9. Install the PCV tube bracket bolts and tighten to 89 inch lbs. (10 Nm).
10. Install the PCV fresh air tube to the air inlet.

11. Install the PCV fresh air tube to the left camshaft cover.
12. Install the fuel injector sight shield.

4.6L Engine

See Figure 235.

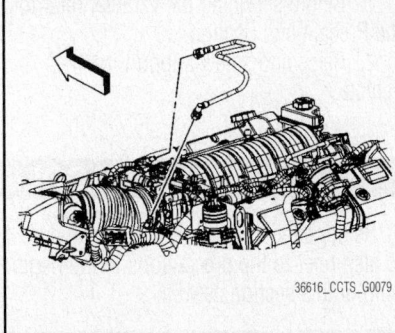

Fig. 235 Remove the PCV fresh air tube—4.6L engine

1. Remove the fuel injector sight shield.
2. Disconnect the Positive Crankcase Ventilation (PCV) fresh air tube quick connect fitting at the left camshaft cover.
3. Disconnect the PCV fresh air tube quick connect fitting at the air cleaner outlet duct.
4. Remove the PCV fresh air tube from under the brake booster vacuum hose and evaporative emission (EVAP) purge solenoid.
5. Installation is the reverse order of removal.

6.2L Engine

See Figure 236.

1. Remove the intake manifold cover.
2. Disconnect any electrical connectors necessary for access.
3. Disconnect and remove the Positive Crankcase Ventilation (PCV) hose assembly.
4. Installation is the reverse order of removal.

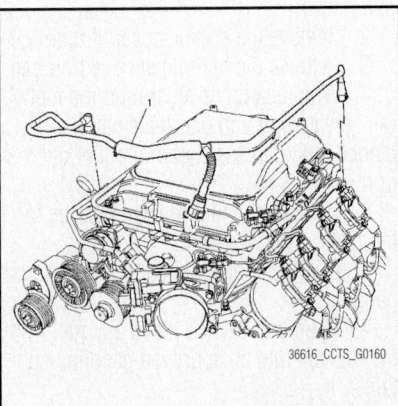

Fig. 236 PCV Removal—6.2L engine

THROTTLE POSITION SENSOR (TPS)

LOCATION

The Throttle Position Sensors (TPS) 1 and 2 are located within the throttle body assembly.

REMOVAL & INSTALLATION

The throttle position are an integral part of the throttle body. For additional information, refer to the following section, "Throttle Body, Removal & Installation."

VEHICLE SPEED SENSOR (VSS)

LOCATION

DTS

See Figure 237.

The Vehicle Speed Sensor (VSS) is located on the right side of the transmission near the output shaft.

REMOVAL & INSTALLATION

2008–09 CTS

Manual Transmission

1. Raise and safely support the vehicle.
2. Remove the transmission support.
3. Lower the rear of the transmission.
4. Remove the speed sensor mounting bolt and remove the Vehicle Speed Sensor (VSS).
5. Installation is the reverse order of removal. Tighten the mounting bolt to 71 inch lbs. (8 Nm).

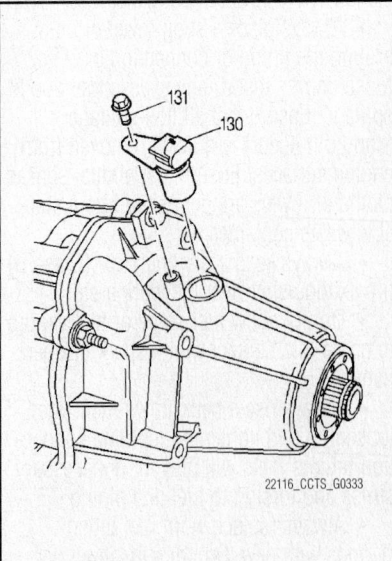

Fig. 237 Vehicle Speed Sensor (VSS) location view automatic transmission

Automatic Transmission

1. Raise and safely support the vehicle.
2. Remove the transmission fluid pan and filter.
3. Remove the upper and lower valve body assembly.
4. Disconnect the speed sensor electrical connector from the control solenoid valve assembly.
5. Remove the speed sensor

assembly bolt and remove the speed sensor.
6. Installation is the reverse order of removal. Tighten the sensor mounting bolt to 106 inch lbs. (12 Nm).

DTS

1. Before servicing the vehicle, refer to the Precautions Section.
2. Raise and safely support the vehicle.

3. Remove the bolts securing the front transaxle brace and right cylinder head.
4. Remove the electrical connector at the Vehicle Speed Sensor (VSS).
5. Remove the retaining bolt and VSS. Twisting the sensor will assist with the removal.
6. Installation is reverse order of removal. Tighten the sensor retaining bolt to 89 inch lbs. (10 Nm).

FUEL   GASOLINE FUEL INJECTION SYSTEM

FUEL SYSTEM SERVICE PRECAUTIONS

Safety is the most important factor when performing not only fuel system maintenance but any type of maintenance. Failure to conduct maintenance and repairs in a safe manner may result in serious personal injury or death. Maintenance and testing of the vehicle's fuel system components can be accomplished safely and effectively by adhering to the following rules and guidelines.

• To avoid the possibility of fire and personal injury, always disconnect the negative battery cable unless the repair or test procedure requires that battery voltage be applied.

• Always relieve the fuel system pressure prior to disconnecting any fuel system component (injector, fuel rail, pressure regulator, etc.), fitting or fuel line connection. Exercise extreme caution whenever relieving fuel system pressure to avoid exposing skin, face and eyes to fuel spray. Please be advised that fuel under pressure may penetrate the skin or any part of the body that it contacts.

• Always place a shop towel or cloth around the fitting or connection prior to loosening to absorb any excess fuel due to spillage. Ensure that all fuel spillage (should it occur) is quickly removed from engine surfaces. Ensure that all fuel soaked cloths or towels are deposited into a suitable waste container.

• Always keep a dry chemical (Class B) fire extinguisher near the work area.

• Do not allow fuel spray or fuel vapors to come into contact with a spark or open flame.

• Always use a back-up wrench when loosening and tightening fuel line connection fittings. This will prevent unnecessary stress and torsion to fuel line piping.

• Always replace worn fuel fitting O-rings with new. Do not substitute fuel hose or equivalent where fuel pipe is installed.

Before servicing the vehicle, make sure to also refer to the precautions in the beginning of this section as well.

RELIEVING FUEL SYSTEM PRESSURE

WITHOUT THE USE OF A FUEL GAUGE

1. If the fuel system requires repair, prevent fuel spillage by removing the fuel pump fuse.
2. Loosen the fuel fill cap in order to relieve the fuel tank vapor pressure.
3. Remove the engine cover, if required.
4. Remove the fuel rail service port cap.
5. Wrap a shop towel around the fuel rail service port and using a small flat-bladed tool, depress (open) the fuel rail test port valve.
6. Remove the shop towel from around the fuel rail service port, and place in an approved gasoline container.
7. Install the fuel rail service port cap.
8. Install the engine cover, if required.
9. Tighten the fuel fill cap.

WITH THE USE OF A FUEL GAUGE

1. If the fuel system requires repair, prevent fuel spillage by removing the fuel pump fuse.
2. Remove the engine cover, if required.
3. Remove the fuel rail service port cap.
4. Wrap a shop towel around the fuel rail service port and using a small flat-bladed tool, depress (open) the fuel rail test port valve.
5. Connect the fuel pressure gauge to the fuel rail service port.
6. Connect a bleed hose to the pressure gauge.
7. Open the valve to bleed any fuel from the fuel rail into an approved gasoline container.
8. Close the valve and disconnect the fuel gauge.

9. Drain any remaining fuel from the gauge into the approved container.

FUEL FILTER

REMOVAL & INSTALLATION

2008–09 CTS

The fuel filter is located in the primary fuel tank module. It is designed to last the life of the vehicle and is not serviceable. For additional information, "Fuel Sender Assembly, Removal & Installation."

FUEL SENDER ASSEMBLY

REMOVAL & INSTALLATION

CTS & CTS-V
See Figures 238 and 239.

✳✳ CAUTION

Gasoline or gasoline vapors are highly flammable. A fire could occur if an ignition source is present. Never drain or store gasoline or diesel fuel in an open container, due to the possibility of fire or explosion. Have a dry chemical (Class B) fire extinguisher nearby.

1. Before servicing the vehicle, refer to the Precautions Section.
2. Relieve the fuel system pressure.
3. Remove the fuel tank in order to gain access to the primary fuel tank module. For additional information, refer to the following section, "Fuel Tank, Removal & Installation."
4. Disconnect the fuel feed hose quick connect fitting from the primary fuel tank module.
5. Remove the fuel feed hose from the retainer on the fuel tank and position the hose aside.
6. Release the interlock and disconnect the electrical connector from the primary fuel tank module.

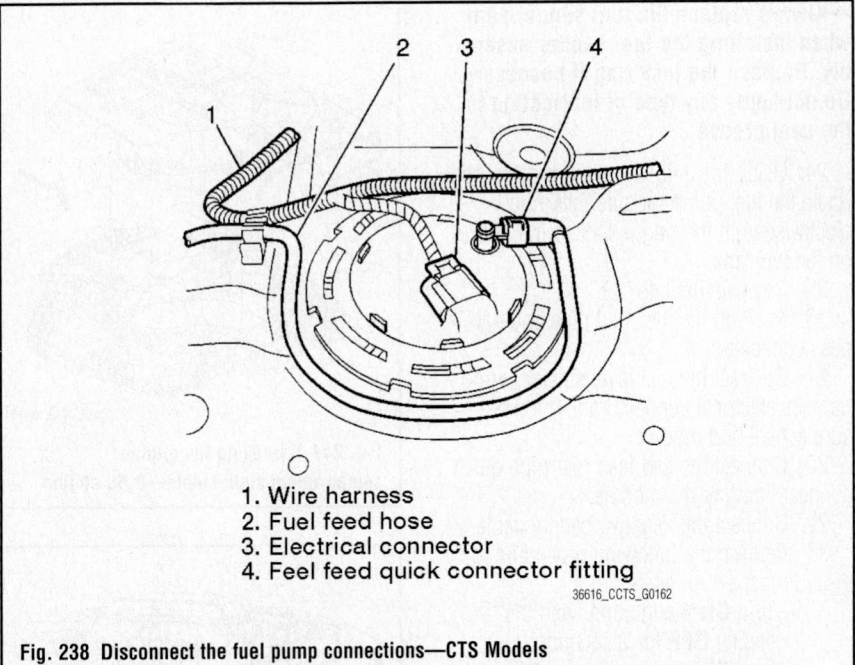

1. Wire harness
2. Fuel feed hose
3. Electrical connector
4. Feel feed quick connector fitting

36616_CCTS_G0162

Fig. 238 Disconnect the fuel pump connections—CTS Models

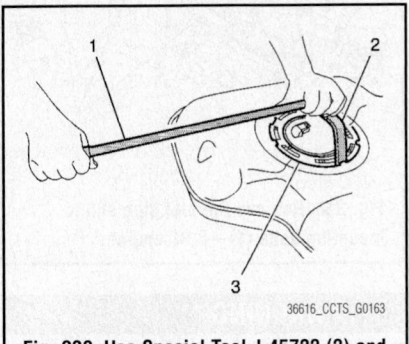

36616_CCTS_G0163

Fig. 239 Use Special Tool J-45722 (2) and a breaker bar (1) to unlock the fuel tank module lock ring (3)—CTS Models

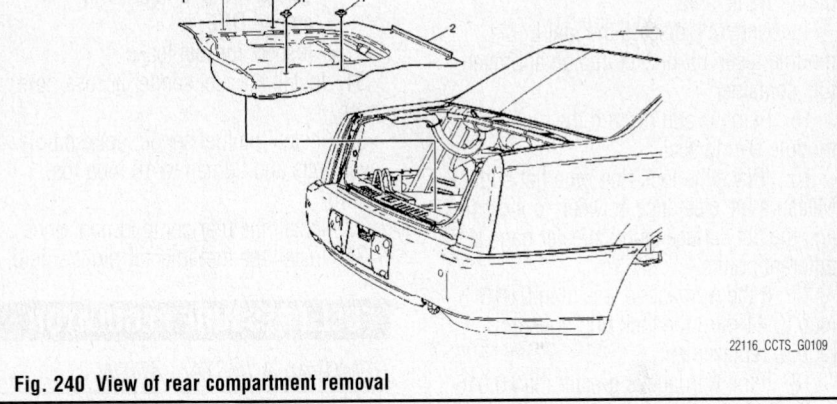

22116_CCTS_G0109

Fig. 240 View of rear compartment removal

7. Remove the wire harness from the retainer on the fuel tank and position the harness aside.

8. Using Special Tool J-45722 and a long breaker bar, unlock the fuel tank module lock ring by turning counterclockwise.

9. Remove the cam lock ring.

10. Partially remove the primary fuel tank module in order to gain access to the fuel transfer hose quick connect fitting. Use care not to damage the float arm.

11. Disconnect the fuel transfer hose quick connect fitting.

12. Remove the primary fuel tank module from the fuel tank and discard the fuel tank module seal.

To install:

13. Install a NEW fuel tank module seal.

14. Grasp the fuel transfer hose from inside the fuel tank.

15. Partially install the primary fuel tank module to the fuel tank.

16. Connect the fuel transfer hose quick connect fitting to the port on the fuel tank module.

17. Press the primary fuel tank module downward, aligning the module to the encapsulated ring.

18. Position the cam lock ring to the fuel tank.

19. Use the Special Tool J-45722 and a long breaker-bar to install the fuel tank module lock ring, by turning clockwise, until fully seated.

20. Connect the electrical connector to the primary fuel tank module and engage the connector interlock.

21. Install the wire harness to the retainer on the fuel tank.

22. Connect the fuel feed hose quick connect fitting to the primary fuel tank module.

23. Install the fuel feed hose to the retainer on the fuel tank.

24. Install the fuel tank

DTS

See Figures 240 and 241.

✲✲ CAUTION

Gasoline or gasoline vapors are highly flammable. A fire could occur if an ignition source is present. Never drain or store gasoline or diesel fuel in an open container, due to the possibility of fire or explosion. Have a dry chemical (Class B) fire extinguisher nearby.

1. Before servicing the vehicle, refer to the Precautions Section.

2. Relieve the fuel system pressure.

3. Remove the rear compartment liner.

4. Remove the fuel sender access hole cover bolts.

5. Remove the fuel sender access hole cover.

6. Disconnect the fuel feed rear pipe quick connect fitting from the module.

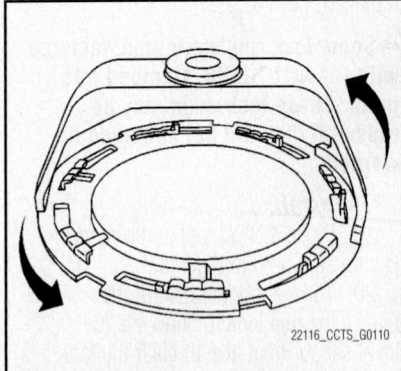

22116_CCTS_G0110

Fig. 241 J 45722 Fuel sender lock ring wrench

7. Disconnect the fuel level sensor wiring harness electrical connectors from the pressure sensor and module.

8. Reposition the fuel feed pipe and harness connectors out of the way.

9. Install the J 45722 wrench to the lock ring.

✳✳ WARNING

When removing the fuel module assembly from the fuel tank, be aware that the reservoir bucket is full of fuel. It must be tipped slightly during removal to avoid damage to the float. Discard the fuel module assembly O-ring seal and replace it with a new one.

10. Use the J 45722 and a long breaker-bar in order to unlock the fuel module lock ring. Rotate the lock ring in a counterclockwise direction.

11. Remove the J 45722 and the fuel module lock ring.

12. Slowly raise the module until the fuel level sensor float arm is just visible.

13. Tilt the module toward the rear of the fuel tank to allow the level sensor float arm to clear the tank opening. Remove the module from the tank.

14. Carefully discard the fuel in the module reservoir bucket into an approved fuel container.

15. Remove and discard the fuel pump module O-ring seal.

16. Place the lock ring on a flat surface. Measure the clearance between to lock ring and the flat surface using a feeler gage at 7 different points.

17. If the warpage is less than 0.016 inch (0.41 mm) the lock ring does not require replacement.

18. If the warpage is greater than 0.016 inch (0.41 mm), the lock ring must be replaced.

➡ Some lock ring were manufactured with **DO NOT REUSE** stamped into them. These lock rings may be reused if they are not damaged or warped.

To install:

19. Place a NEW fuel pump module O-ring seal onto the fuel tank.

20. Tilt the module toward the rear of the fuel tank to allow the fuel level sensor float arm to clear the tank opening. Install the module into the fuel tank.

21. Lower the module assembly into the tank.

22. Install the module lock ring, and move it into position on the top of the module.

23. Install the J 45722 to the lock ring.

➡ Always replace the fuel sender seal when installing the fuel sender assembly. Replace the lock ring if necessary. Do not apply any type of lubrication in the seal groove.

24. Using the J 45722 and a breaker bar, rotate the fuel pump module lock ring clockwise until the ring is locked into place on the fuel tank.

25. Remove the J 45722.

26. Position the fuel feed pipe and harness connectors.

27. Connect the fuel level sensor wiring harness electrical connectors to the pressure sensor and module.

28. Connect the fuel feed rear pipe quick connect fitting to the module.

29. Connect the negative battery cable.

30. Perform the following procedure in order to inspect for leaks:

- Turn **ON** the ignition, with the engine **OFF** for 2 seconds.
- Turn **OFF** the ignition for 10 seconds.
- Turn **ON** the ignition, with the engine **OFF**.
- Inspect for fuel leaks.

31. Install the fuel sender access hole cover.

32. Install the fuel sender access hole cover bolts and tighten to 18 inch lbs. (2 Nm).

33. Install the rear compartment liner.

34. Install the fuel injector sight shield.

FUEL PRESSURE REGULATOR

REMOVAL & INSTALLATION

DTS

The fuel pressure regulator is integral to the fuel pump module assembly.

FUEL RAIL & INJECTORS

REMOVAL & INSTALLATION

2008–09 CTS

See Figures 242 through 245.

✳✳ CAUTION

Gasoline or gasoline vapors are highly flammable. A fire could occur if an ignition source is present. Never drain or store gasoline or diesel fuel in an open container, due to the possibility of fire or explosion. Have a dry chemical (Class B) fire extinguisher nearby.

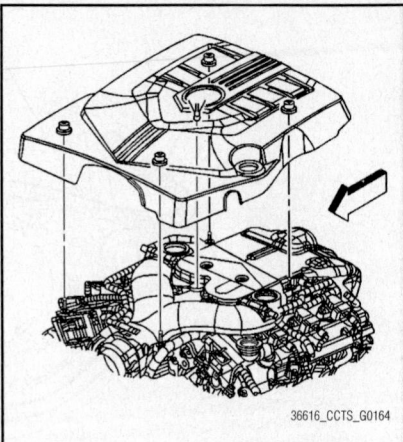

36616_CCTS_G0164

Fig. 242 Removing the engine compartment sight shield—3.6L engine

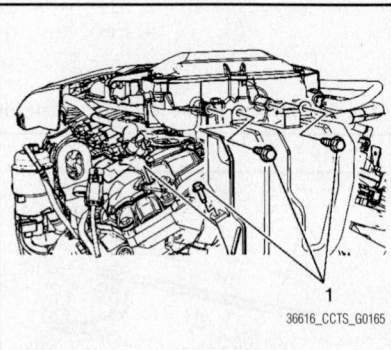

36616_CCTS_G0165

Fig. 243 Remove the fuel pipe shield mounting bolts (1)—3.6L engine

✳✳ WARNING

Remove the fuel rail assembly carefully to prevent damage to the injector electrical connector terminals and spray tips. Support the fuel rail after it is removed in order to avoid damaging the fuel rail components. Cap the fittings and plug the holes when servicing the fuel system to prevent debris from entering open ports.

1. Before servicing the vehicle, refer to the Precautions Section.

2. Properly relieve the fuel system pressure.

3. Remove the cross vehicle brace.

4. Remove the oil fill cap.

5. Disengage the cover/shield from the ball studs by pulling up firmly on the right rear and left front of the engine cover.

6. Remove the engine cover/sight shield.

7. Remove the front compartment sight shield.

8. Remove the intake manifold insulator.

9. Remove the wiper transmission.

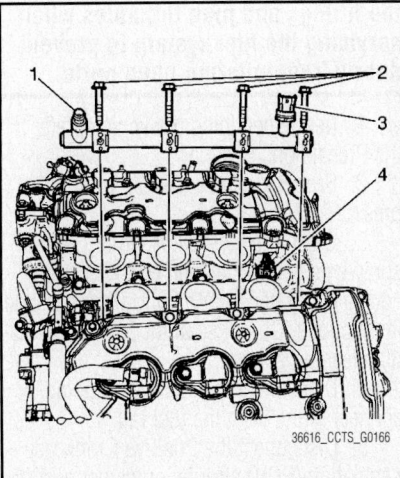

Fig. 244 Remove the fuel rail bolts (2) to remove the fuel rail (1)—3.6L engine

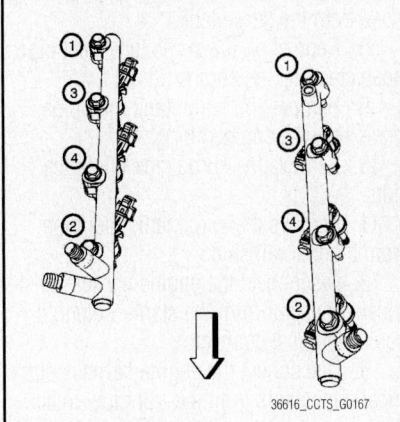

Fig. 245 Fuel rail bolt tightening sequence—3.6L engine

10. Remove the fuel pipe shield to intake manifold bolts.

11. Remove the fuel pipe shield to cylinder bolt.

12. Carefully remove the fuel pipe shield from the vehicle

13. Remove the intake manifold.

14. Remove the high pressure fuel pipe. Discard the pipe.

15. Remove the fuel rail crossover pipe. Discard the pipe.

16. Remove the foam insulator from the fuel rails.

17. Disconnect the fuel pressure sensor electrical connector and cut the wire harness tie straps.

18. Remove the fuel rail bolts and fuel rail.

19. Remove the hold down clamps and fuel injectors.

To install:

20. Install the fuel injectors to the cylinder head. Install NEW hold down clamps to each injector.

21. Carefully place the fuel rail into position, placing the front into the fuel rail over the front injector and rotating the rear downward.

22. Install the 2 outer fuel rail bolts first, then the 2 inner bolts, and hand tighten.

23. Tighten the fuel rail bolts in the sequence shown as follows:

a. Tighten in the first pass to 106 inch lbs. (12 Nm).

b. Tighten in a second pass to 17 ft. lbs. (23 Nm).

24. Ensure that the fuel rail crossover pipe, right fuel rails fittings and left fuel rail fittings are clean and dry prior to assembly.

25. Lubricate the pipes with silicon free engine oil or equivalent.

26. Position the fuel rail crossover pipe to the right fuel rails fitting and left fuel rail fitting.

27. Tighten the fuel rail crossover pipe fittings as follows:

a. Tighten the fittings first pass to 12 ft. lbs. (16 Nm).

b. Tighten the fittings final pass to 24 ft. lbs. (32 Nm).

28. Ensure that the high pressure fuel pipe, fuel rail fitting and fuel pump fitting are clean and dry prior to assembly.

29. Lubricate the pipes with silicon free engine oil or equivalent.

30. Position the NEW high pressure fuel pipe to the high pressure fuel pump fitting and left fuel rail. Hand tighten the fitting.

31. Tighten the high pressure fuel pipe fitting as follows:

a. Tighten the fittings first pass to 12 ft. lbs. (16 Nm).

b. Tighten the fittings final pass to 24 ft. lbs. (32 Nm).

32. Inspect for fuel leaks using the following procedure:

a. Turn ON the ignition, with the engine OFF for 2 seconds.

b. Turn OFF the ignition, for 10 seconds.

c. Turn ON the ignition, with the engine OFF.

d. Inspect for fuel leaks.

33. The remainder of the installation is the reverse order of removal.

2009 CTS-V

See Figure 246.

❈❈ CAUTION

Gasoline or gasoline vapors are highly flammable. A fire could occur if an ignition source is present. Never drain or store gasoline or diesel fuel in an open container, due to the possibility of fire or explosion. Have a dry chemical (Class B) fire extinguisher nearby.

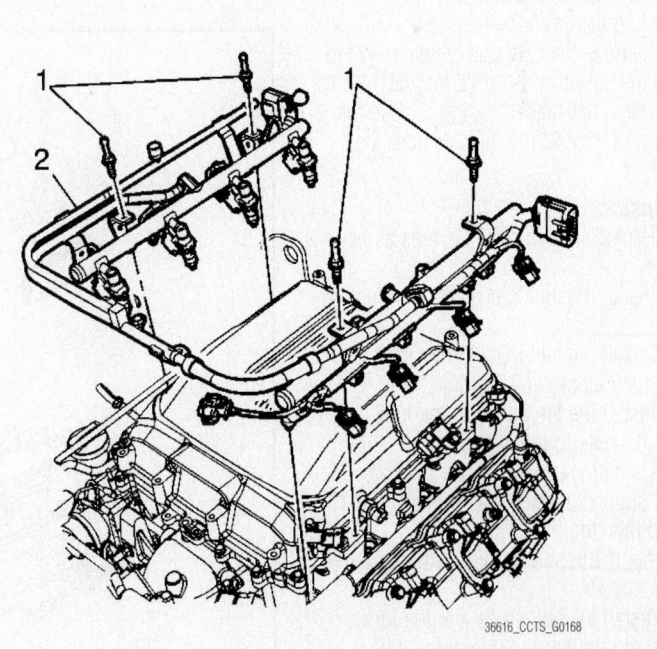

Fig. 246 Remove the ball stud fasteners (1) to remove the fail rail (2)—6.2L engine

⁂ WARNING

Remove the fuel rail assembly carefully to prevent damage to the injector electrical connector terminals and spray tips. Support the fuel rail after it is removed in order to avoid damaging the fuel rail components. Cap the fittings and plug the holes when servicing the fuel system to prevent debris from entering open ports.

1. Before servicing the vehicle, refer to the Precautions Section.

2. Properly relieve the fuel system pressure.

3. Disconnect the negative battery cable.

4. Remove the intake manifold covers.

5. Disconnect the fuel pipe from the fuel rail.

6. Disconnect the fuel injection harness connectors.

7. Disconnect the BARO sensor harness connector.

8. Disconnect the intake temperature sensor harness connector.

9. Disconnect the supercharger air outlet pressure sensor harness connector.

10. Disconnect all 8 ignition coil harness connectors.

11. Remove the front fuel rail fastener.

12. Remove the fuel rail ball stud fasteners.

13. Carefully disengage the fuel injectors from the supercharger.

14. Remove the fuel rail with the fuel injector harness from the engine.

15. Remove the ball stud fasteners (1) to remove the fail rail (2)—6.2L engine

16. Use a flat-bladed tool to release the retainer and remove the injector from the fuel rail.

To install:

17. Replace any injector O-rings as necessary.

18. Install the fuel injectors to the fuel rail.

19. Install the fuel injection wiring harness to the fuel rail and fuel injectors.

20. Install the fuel rail with the fuel injector harness to the engine.

21. Carefully locate the fuel injectors into the supercharger. Install the left side first and then the right side.

22. Apply threadlock to the ball stud and fastener threads.

23. Install the ball studs and the forward fastener and tighten to 89 inch lbs. (10 Nm).

24. Connect all 8 ignition coil harness connectors.

25. Connect the fuel injection Harness connectors.

26. Connect the barometric pressure sensor harness connector.

27. Connect the supercharger air output sensor harness connector.

28. Connect the intake temperature sensor harness connector.

29. Connect the fuel pipe to the fuel rail.

30. Connect the negative battery cable.

31. Pressure the fuel system and check for fuel leaks.

32. Install the front and rear intake manifold covers.

DTS

See Figure 247.

⁂ CAUTION

Gasoline or gasoline vapors are highly flammable. A fire could occur if an ignition source is present. Never drain or store gasoline or diesel fuel in an open container, due to the possibility of fire or explosion. Have a dry chemical (Class B) fire extinguisher nearby.

⁂ WARNING

Remove the fuel rail assembly carefully to prevent damage to the injector electrical connector terminals and spray tips. Support the fuel rail after it is removed in order to avoid damaging the fuel rail components. Cap the fittings and plug the holes when servicing the fuel system to prevent debris from entering open ports.

1. Before servicing the vehicle, refer to the Precautions Section.

2. Properly relieve the fuel system pressure.

3. Clean the fuel rail assembly with a spray type engine cleaner, GM X-30A or equivalent, if necessary. Follow the package instructions. Do not soak the fuel rail in liquid cleaning solvent.

4. Disconnect the fuel feed pipe quick connect fitting from the fuel rail.

5. Disconnect the Positive Crankcase Ventilation (PCV) air tube quick connect fitting from the camshaft cover.

6. Reposition the surge tank inlet pipe hose clamp at the surge tank.

7. Remove the surge tank inlet pipe hose from the surge tank.

8. Reposition the surge tank inlet pipe hose clamp at the engine fitting.

9. Remove the surge tank inlet pipe hose from the engine fitting.

10. Remove the surge tank inlet pipe nuts.

11. Remove the surge tank inlet pipe from the fuel rail studs.

12. Disconnect the engine harness electrical connector from the starter solenoid cable electrical connector.

13. Disconnect the engine harness electrical connectors from the front fuel injectors.

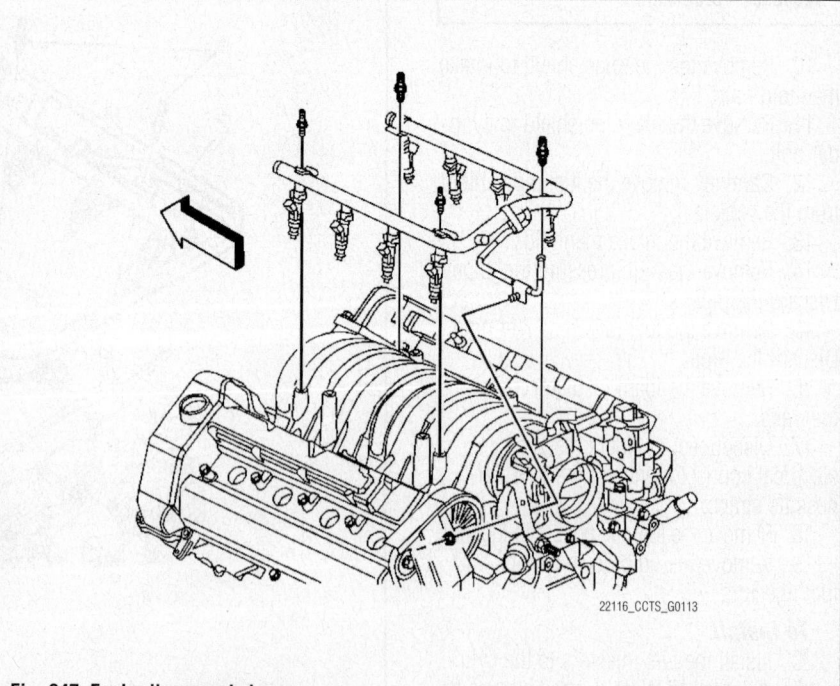

Fig. 247 Fuel rail removal shown

22116_CCTS_G0113

14. Disconnect the engine harness electrical connectors (1) from the rear fuel injectors.

15. Remove the engine harness clip from the fuel rail stud.

16. Lay the harness aside.

17. Remove the fuel rail bracket retainer nut.

18. Remove the fuel rail studs.

19. Remove the fuel rail.

20. Remove and discard the O-ring seals from the spray tip end of each fuel injector.

21. If replacing the fuel rail, remove the fuel injectors.

To install:

22. If the fuel rail was replaced, install the fuel injectors.

23. Install new O-ring seals to the spray tip end of each fuel injector.

24. Lubricate the new lower injector O-ring seals with clean engine oil.

25. Install the fuel rail.

26. Install the fuel rail studs and tighten to 89 inch lbs. (10 Nm).

27. Install the fuel rail bracket retainer nut and tighten to 89 inch lbs. (10 Nm).

28. Position the harness over the engine.

29. Install the engine harness clip to the fuel rail stud.

30. Connect the engine harness electrical connectors to the rear fuel injectors.

31. Connect the engine harness electrical connectors to the front fuel injectors.

32. Connect the engine harness electrical connector to the starter solenoid cable electrical connector.

33. Install the surge tank inlet pipe to the fuel rail studs.

34. Install the surge tank inlet pipe nuts.

35. Install the surge tank inlet pipe hose to the engine fitting.

36. Position the surge tank inlet pipe hose clamp at the engine fitting.

37. Install the surge tank inlet pipe hose to the surge tank.

38. Position the surge tank inlet pipe hose clamp at the surge tank.

39. Connect the PCV air tube quick connect fitting to the camshaft cover.

40. Connect the fuel feed pipe quick connect fitting to the fuel rail.

41. Connect the negative battery cable.

42. Perform the following procedure in order to inspect for leaks:

- Turn **ON** the ignition, with the engine **OFF** for 2 seconds.
- Turn **OFF** the ignition for 10 seconds.

- Turn **ON** the ignition, with the engine **OFF**.
- Inspect for fuel leaks.

43. Install the fuel injector sight shield.

FUEL TANK

REMOVAL & INSTALLATION

CTS & CTS-V

❋❋ CAUTION

Gasoline or gasoline vapors are highly flammable. A fire could occur if an ignition source is present. Never drain or store gasoline or diesel fuel in an open container, due to the possibility of fire or explosion. Have a dry chemical (Class B) fire extinguisher nearby.

1. Before servicing the vehicle, refer to the Precautions Section.

2. Properly relieve the fuel system pressure.

3. Drain any remaining fuel from the fuel tank using an air operated pump.

4. Raise and safely support the vehicle.

5. Remove the bolts securing the floor panel tunnel brace to the floor panel.

6. Remove the floor panel tunnel brace from the floor panel.

7. Suitably support the exhaust system.

8. Remove the exhaust pipe nuts securing the exhaust pipes to the catalytic converters.

9. Pry the front exhaust hangers free from the rear suspension hanger rods.

10. Apply a suitable lubricant to the tail pipe hanger rods in order to ease the removal of the tail pipe hanger insulators.

11. Pry the tail pipe hangers free from the tail pipe insulators.

12. With the aid of an assistant, lower the exhaust system and remove the muffler assembly from the hanger rods.

13. Remove the rear driveshaft.

14. Install the support fixture, in order to raise the lower control arm to relieve the tension from the shock.

15. Remove the shocks lower mounting bolt.

16. Remove the support fixture.

17. Disconnect the electrical connectors for the rear wheel speed sensors (WSS).

18. Disconnect the WSS wiring harness retainer clips from the upper control arms.

19. Disconnect the rear brake pipe lines forward of the rear wheelhouse.

20. Remove the fastener for the brake pipe bracket.

21. Remove the brake pipe bracket from the studs in the body.

22. Disconnect the intermediate park brake cable from the front park brake cable connector.

23. Remove the intermediate park brake cable from body bracket.

24. Position the frame support table J-39580 .

25. Remove the frame to body mounting bolts and washers.

26. Carefully raise the vehicle from the rear frame assembly.

27. Disconnect the filler hose from the fuel tank.

28. Disconnect the filler vent tube from the evaporative emission (EVAP) hose.

29. Disconnect the fuel feed pipe and fuel EVAP hose from the chassis bundle.

30. Release the electrical connector interlock and disconnect the fuel tank electrical connector.

31. Remove the fuel tank electrical connector retainer from the chassis.

32. Remove the fuel tank electrical harness from the chassis mounted retainer.

33. Disconnect the EVAP hoses from the EVAP canister.

34. Pull outward on the retainer tab in order to disengage the retainer from the chassis.

35. Disconnect the electrical connector from the fuel tank pressure sensor.

36. Disconnect the electrical connector from the EVAP canister vent valve.

37. Support the fuel tank with a suitable jack.

38. Remove the fuel tank strap bolts.

39. Remove the fuel tank straps.

40. With the aid of an assistant, carefully lower the fuel tank from the vehicle.

41. Installation is the reverse order of removal. Tighten the fuel strap bolts to 37 ft. lbs. (50 Nm).

DTS

See Figures 248 and 249.

❋❋ CAUTION

Gasoline or gasoline vapors are highly flammable. A fire could occur if an ignition source is present. Never drain or store gasoline or diesel fuel in an open container, due to the possibility of fire or explosion. Have a dry chemical (Class B) fire extinguisher nearby.

1. Before servicing the vehicle, refer to the Precautions Section.

2. Properly relieve the fuel system pressure.

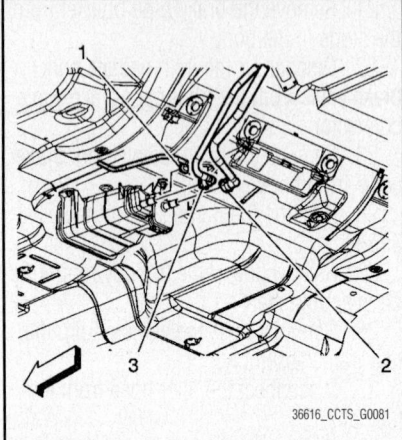

Fig. 248 Disconnect the fill pipe vent line (2) and the fuel tank vapor line (3) quick connect fittings from the EVAP canister—2008–09 DTS

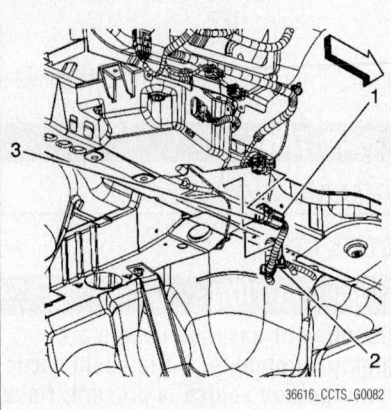

Fig. 249 Disconnect the body harness electrical connector (1) and remove the fuel tank harness clips (2,3)—2008–09 DTS

3. Drain any remaining fuel from the fuel tank using an air operated pump.

4. Remove the left rear wheel house liner.

5. Using compressed air, blow any dirt and/or debris from around the fuel fill pipe and evaporative emission (EVAP) line connections.

6. Loosen the fuel fill hose clamp at the fill pipe.

7. Disconnect the fuel fill hose from the fuel fill pipe.

8. Disconnect the fuel tank EVAP recirculation line quick connect fitting from the fill pipe line.

9. Disconnect the automatic level control sensor link from the left rear suspension control arm, if equipped.

10. Disconnect the left and right electronic position sensor links from the ball studs.

11. Disconnect the fill pipe vent line and the fuel tank vapor line quick connect fittings from the EVAP canister.

12. Disconnect the fuel feed line quick connect fitting from the chassis line.

13. Remove the fuel and EVAP line retainer from the side rail.

14. Disconnect the body harness electrical connector from the fuel tank harness electrical connector.

15. Remove the fuel tank harness clips from the rear compartment side rail.

16. Remove the exhaust system.

17. Loosen the left and right rear brake hose bracket nut and slide the stud out of the keyhole slot in the side rail.

18. Remove the rear shock bolts.

19. Support the front of the vehicle with a jack stand at the engine cradle.

20. Support the rear suspension crossmember with a suitable adjustable jack.

21. Remove the rear suspension crossmember bolts.

22. Using the adjustable jack, slowly lower the rear suspension crossmember allowing the crossmember to pivot at the front bolts, until the rear springs can be removed.

23. Remove the rear coil springs.

24. Remove the fuel tank strap bolts.

25. Remove the fuel tank straps.

26. Remove the fuel tank and disconnect the electrical harness connectors.

To install:

27. Connect the electrical harness connector and place the fuel tank onto the rear suspension crossmember.

28. Install the fuel tank straps and tighten the bolts to 34 ft. lbs. (46 Nm).

29. Install the rear coil springs while slowly raising the rear suspension crossmember using the adjustable jack. Install the rear suspension crossmember bolts and tighten the bolts to 141 ft. lbs. (191 Nm).

30. Remove the adjustable jack from the rear suspension crossmember.

31. Remove the jack stand from the front of the vehicle.

32. Install the rear shock bolts and tighten the bolts to 18 ft. lbs. (25 Nm).

33. Connect the body harness electrical connector to the fuel tank harness electrical connector.

34. Install the fuel tank harness clips to the rear compartment side rail.

35. Install the fuel and EVAP line retainer to the side rail.

36. Connect the fuel feed line quick connect fitting (1) to the chassis line.

37. Connect the fill pipe vent line and the fuel tank vapor line quick connect fittings to the EVAP canister.

38. Install the left and right rear brake hose bracket studs into the keyhole slots. Tighten the nuts to 89 inch lbs. (10 Nm).

39. Install the exhaust system.

40. Connect the left and right electronic position sensor links to the ball studs.

41. Connect the automatic level control sensor link to the left rear suspension control arm, if equipped.

➡ **Clean the fill pipe or any dirt or debris. Ensure the fill pipe is installed to the original depth to the fill hose. The fill pipe bead must be inserted into the hose past the clamp position.**

42. Connect the fuel tank EVAP recirculation line quick connect fitting to the fill pipe line.

43. Connect the fuel fill hose to the fuel fill pipe.

44. Tighten the fuel fill hose clamp at the fill pipe to 35 inch lbs. (4 Nm).

45. Install the left rear wheel house liner.

46. Fill the fuel tank.

47. Connect the negative battery cable.

48. Perform the following procedure in order to inspect for leaks:

   a. Turn ON the ignition, with the engine OFF for 2 seconds.

   b. Turn OFF the ignition for 10 seconds.

   c. Turn ON the ignition, with the engine OFF.

   d. Inspect for fuel leaks.

49. Install the fuel injector sight shield.

IDLE SPEED

ADJUSTMENT

Idle speed is maintained by the Engine Control Module (ECM). No adjustment is necessary or possible.

THROTTLE BODY

REMOVAL & INSTALLATION

3.6L Engine

See Figure 250.

1. Before servicing the vehicle, refer to the Precautions Section.

2. Turn the ignition to the OFF position

3. Remove the fuel injector sight shield.

4. Remove the air cleaner outlet duct.

5. Remove the throttle body mounting bolts.

6. Disconnect the electrical connector and remove the throttle assembly and gasket.

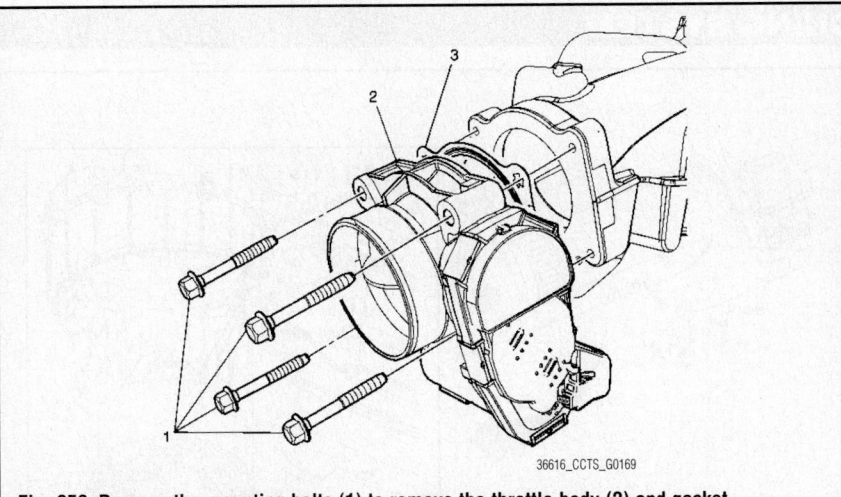

Fig. 250 Remove the mounting bolts (1) to remove the throttle body (2) and gasket (3)—3.6L engine

7. Installation is the reverse order of removal. Tighten the mounting bolts to 89 inch lbs. (10 Nm).

4.6L Engine

See Figure 253.

1. Before servicing the vehicle, refer to the Precautions Section.
2. Remove the fuel injector sight shield.
3. Remove the air cleaner outlet duct.
4. Disconnect the Positive Crankcase Ventilation (PCV) fresh air tube quick connect fittings at the camshaft cover and the air cleaner outlet duct.
5. Remove the PCV fresh air tube.
6. Disconnect the engine harness electrical connector from the throttle actuator.
7. Remove the transaxle vent hose clip from the shift cable bracket.
8. Remove the transaxle shift cable clip from the shift cable bracket.
9. Remove the throttle body bolts.
10. Remove the shift cable bracket.
11. Remove the throttle body.

12. Remove and discard the throttle body seal.

To install:

13. Install a new throttle body seal.
14. Position the throttle body.
15. Position the shift cable bracket.
16. Install the throttle body bolts and tighten to 89 inch. lbs. (10 Nm).
17. Install the transaxle shift cable clip to the shift cable bracket.
18. Install the transaxle vent hose clip to the shift cable bracket.
19. Connect the engine harness electrical connector to the throttle actuator.

➡Route the PCV fresh air tube under the vacuum brake booster hose and the

Evaporative Emission (EVAP) purge valve.

20. Install the PCV fresh air tube.
21. Connect the PCV fresh air tube quick connect fittings at the camshaft cover and the air cleaner outlet duct.
22. Install the air cleaner outlet duct.
23. Install the fuel injector sight shield.

6.2L Engine

See Figure 252.

1. Before servicing the vehicle, refer to the Precautions Section.
2. Remove the air cleaner outlet duct.
3. Remove the throttle body bolts.
4. Disconnect the throttle body harness connector.
5. Remove the throttle body assembly.
6. Installation is the reverse order of removal. Tighten the mounting bolts to 89 inch lbs. (10 Nm).
7. Perform the throttle body learn procedure:
   a. Ignition ON, engine OFF, perform the Idle Learn Reset in Module Setup with a scan tool.
   b. Start the engine and monitor the TB Idle Airflow Compensation parameter. The TB Idle Airflow
   c. Compensation value should equal 0 percent and the engine should be idling at a normal idle speed.
   d. Clear the DTCs and return to the diagnostic that referred you here.

Fig. 251 View of 4.6L throttle body removal

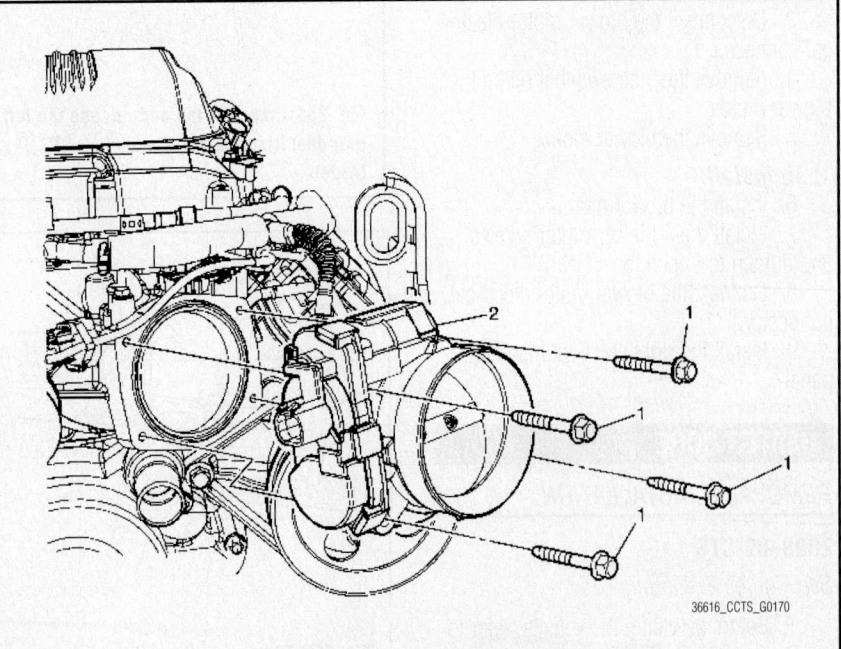

Fig. 252 Remove the mounting bolts (1) to remove the throttle body (2)—6.2L engine

HEATING & AIR CONDITIONING SYSTEM

BLOWER MOTOR

REMOVAL & INSTALLATION

CTS & CTS-V

1. Before servicing the vehicle, refer to the Precautions Section.
2. Remove the right closeout insulator panel.
3. Remove the glove box.
4. Disconnect the blower motor electrical connector.
5. Remove the screws that retain the blower motor.
6. Remove the air inlet housing bolts to gain clearance for the blower motor.
7. Remove the blower motor.

To Install:

8. Install the blower motor.
9. Install the blower motor screws and tighten to 13 inch lbs. (1.5 Nm).
10. Install the air inlet housing bolts and tighten to 53 ft. lbs. (6 Nm).
11. Connect the blower motor electrical connector.
12. Install the glove box.
13. Install the right closeout insulator panel.

2008–09 DTS

See Figure 253.

1. Before servicing the vehicle, refer to the Precautions Section.
2. Remove the right hand closeout insulator panel.
3. Disconnect the blower motor electrical connector.
4. Remove the 3 screws that retain the blower motor.
5. Remove the blower motor.

To install:

6. Install the blower motor.
7. Install the 3 blower motor screws and tighten to 9 inch lbs. (1 Nm).
8. Connect the blower motor electrical connector.
9. Install the right closeout insulator panel.

HEATER CORE

REMOVAL & INSTALLATION

2008–09 CTS

See Figures 254 through 257.

1. Before servicing the vehicle, refer to the Precautions Section.
2. Disable the SIR system.

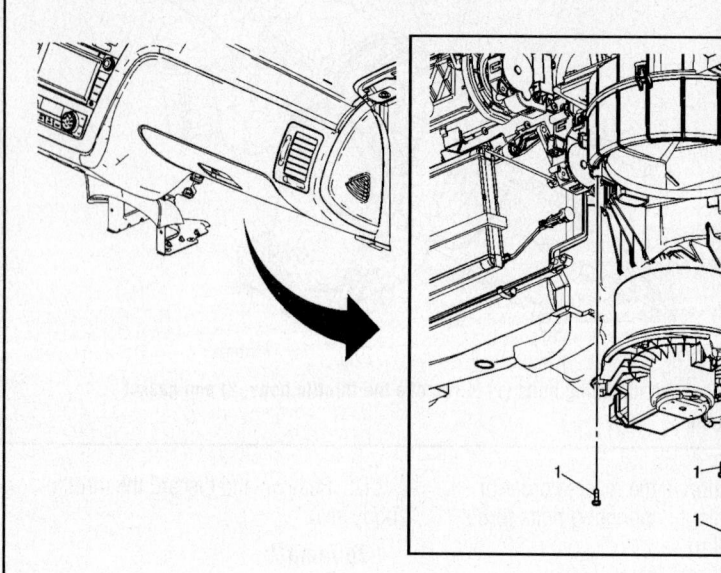

22116_CCTS_G0224

Fig. 253 Blower motor location and removal view

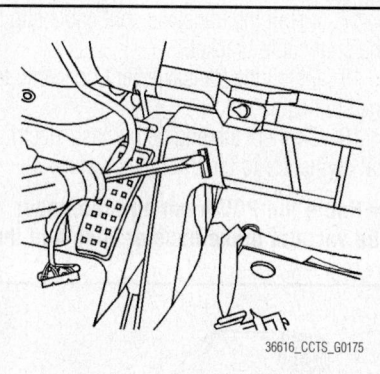

36616_CCTS_G0175

Fig. 254 Press the tab and release the left rear duct from the HVAC module—CTS Models

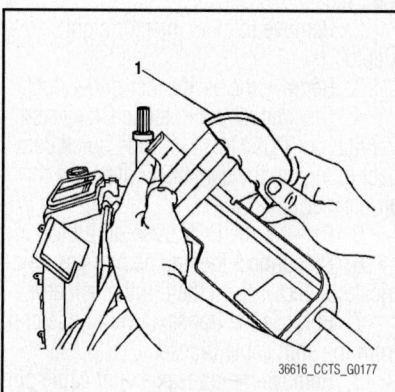

36616_CCTS_G0177

Fig. 256 Remove the heater hose bracket—CTS Models

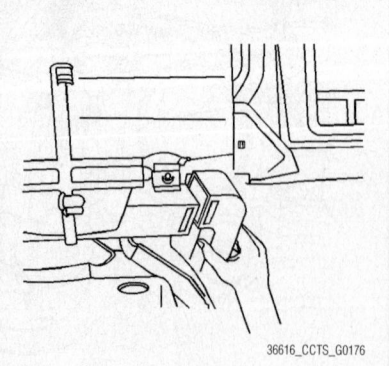

36616_CCTS_G0176

Fig. 255 Disconnect the right rear heater ducts from the HVAC module—CTS Models

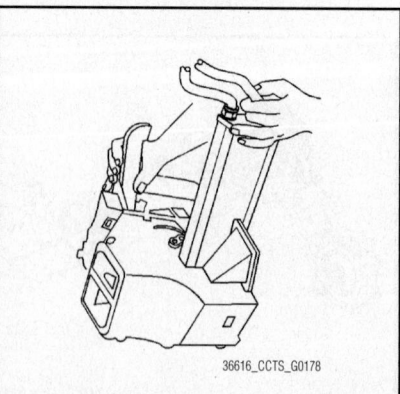

36616_CCTS_G0178

Fig. 257 Slide the heater core out of the HVAC module—CTS Models

3. Disconnect the negative battery cable.

4. Drain the cooling system.

5. Recover the refrigerant.

6. Disconnect the heater inlet and outlet hoses.

7. Disconnect both A/C lines at the cowl.

8. Using Special Tool J-45689 insert the probe end into the two small openings of the plastic quick joint.

9. Remove both quick joint clamps and disconnect both A/C lines.

10. Remove the instrument panel assembly. For additional information, refer to the following section, "Instrument Panel, Removal & Installation."

11. Remove the air inlet assembly.

12. Disconnect the HVAC module electrical connector.

13. Disconnect the HVAC module drain tube from the floor.

14. Press the tab and release the left rear duct from the HVAC module.

15. Disconnect the left rear heater duct from the HVAC module.

16. Press the tab and release the right rear duct from the HVAC module.

17. Disconnect the right rear heater ducts from the HVAC module.

18. Remove the lower left HVAC module mounting nut.

19. Remove the upper left HVAC module mounting nut.

20. Remove the HVAC module from the vehicle.

21. Remove the heater hose bracket screw and remove the heater hose bracket.

22. Slide the heater core out of the HVAC module.

23. Installation is the reverse order of removal.

24. Leak test the fitting of the reinstalled component using a halogen leak detector.

25. Refill the engine cooling system to the correct level.

2008–09 DTS

See Figures 258 through 263.

1. Before servicing the vehicle, refer to the Precautions Section.

2. Disable the SIR system.

3. Disconnect the negative battery cable.

4. Drain the cooling system.

5. Recover the refrigerant.

6. Remove the evaporator tube from the thermal expansion valve.

7. Remove the heater hoses from the heater core.

8. Remove the driver knee bolster.

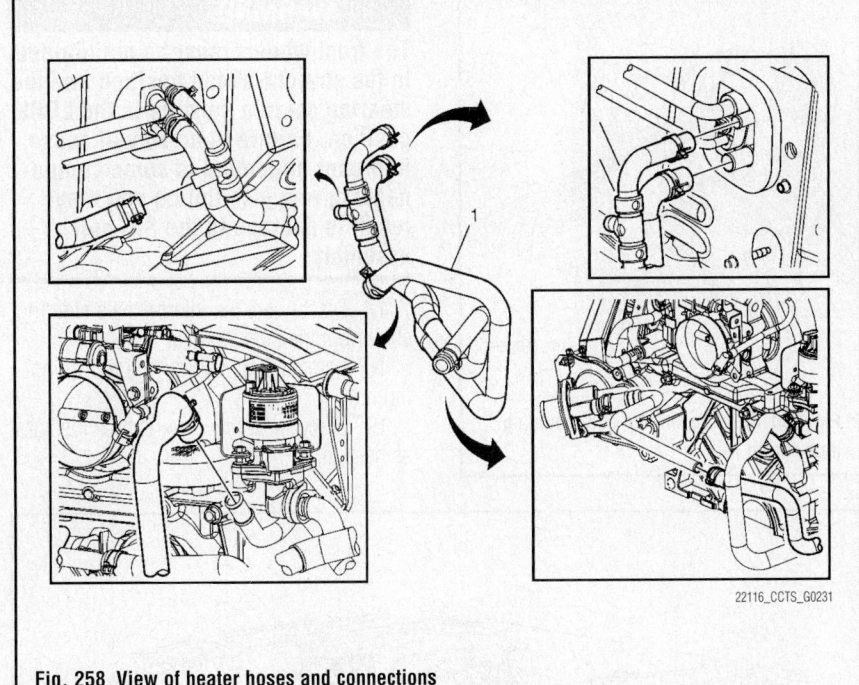

Fig. 258 View of heater hoses and connections

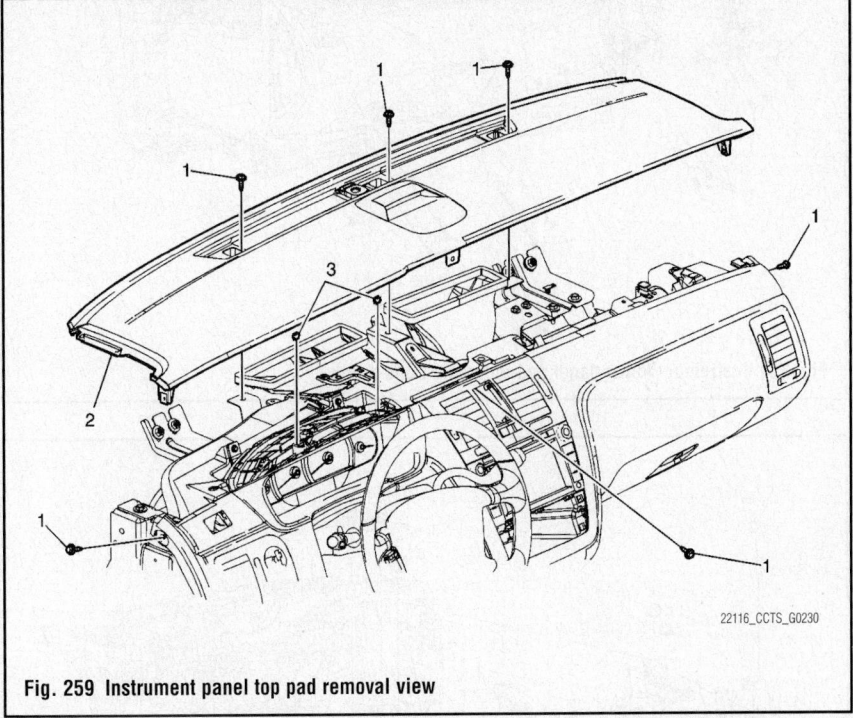

Fig. 259 Instrument panel top pad removal view

9. Remove the brake pedal bracket assembly as follows:

a. Disconnect the electrical connector for the brake pedal position sensor.

b. Accelerator pedal assembly nuts.

c. Accelerator pedal assembly.

d. Brake pedal push rod retainer clip.

e. Brake pedal assembly nuts.

10. Pull back and reposition the carpet.

11. Remove the lower Instrument Panel (I/P) support brace.

12. Reposition the auxiliary air distribution duct.

13. Remove the instrument panel top pad.

14. Remove the instrument panel center trim panel.

15. Remove the left instrument panel accessory trim plate.

16. Remove the instrument the panel cluster assembly.

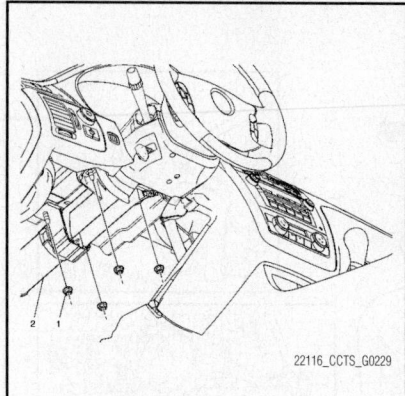

Fig. 260 Steering column and mounting nuts shown

22116_CCTS_G0229

❊❊ WARNING

The front wheels must be maintained in the straight-ahead position and the steering column must be in the LOCK position. Failure to do so will cause improper alignment of some components during installation and may result to damage to the SIR coil assembly.

17. Disconnect the intermediate steering shaft from the steering gear.

18. Remove the steering column mounting nuts.

19. Disconnect any electrical connectors as needed.

20. If equipped with AN3. disconnect the automatic transmission range selector cable.

21. Remove the steering column.

22. Remove glove box.

23. Remove the instrument panel ashtray assembly, if equipped.

24. Remove the center console, if equipped.

25. Remove the radio.

26. Remove the HVAC control assembly.

27. Remove the instrument panel left air outlet.

28. Remove the right and left side window air outlet ducts.

29. Remove the instrument panel right air outlet.

30. Remove the instrument panel lower panel bolts.

31. Disconnect the electrical harness connections.

32. Remove the instrument lower panel.

33. Remove the left and right air distribution duct.

34. Remove the center air outlet duct.

35. Remove the floor air outlet duct.

36. Remove the left and right side window defroster outlet duct.

37. Remove the screws securing the windshield defroster nozzle duct to the carrier.

38. Remove the instrument panel carrier assembly nuts.

39. Remove the instrument panel carrier assembly bolts.

40. With the aid of an assistant, remove the instrument panel carrier assembly.

41. Disconnect the HVAC module assembly electrical connectors.

42. Remove the HVAC module assembly mounting nuts.

43. Remove the left hand floor duct.

44. With the aid of an assistant, remove the HVAC module assembly and place on work bench.

45. Remove the TXV pass through seal.

46. Remove the heater and A/C pipe cover screws.

47. Remove the heater and A/C pipe cover.

48. Remove the heater core tube clamp screw.

49. Remove the heater core tube clamp

50. Remove the heater core.

To install:

51. Install heater core.

52. Install the heater core tube clamp and screw, tighten the screw to 9 inch lbs. (1 Nm).

53. Install the heater and A/C pipe cover and screws, tighten the screws to 9 inch lbs. (1 Nm).

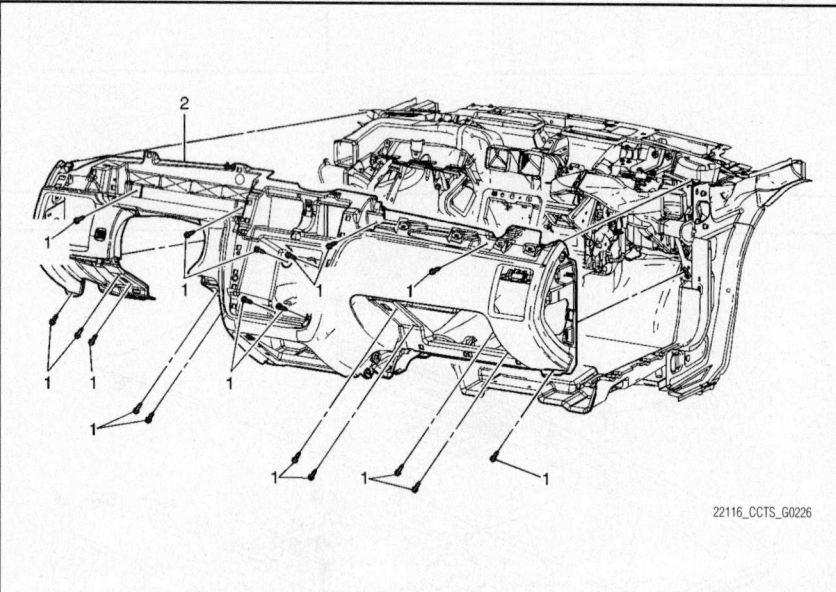

22116_CCTS_G0226

Fig. 261 Instrument lower panel and mounting bolts shown

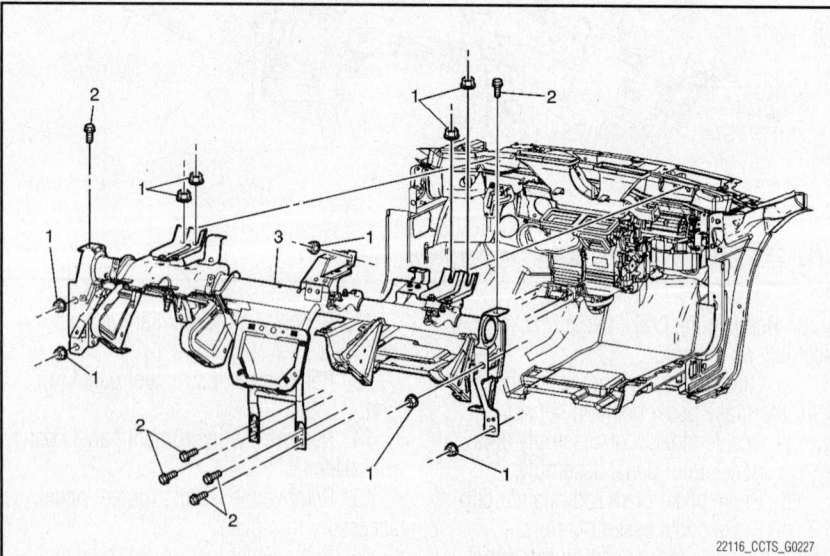

22116_CCTS_G0227

Fig. 262 Instrument panel carrier assembly and mounting hardware

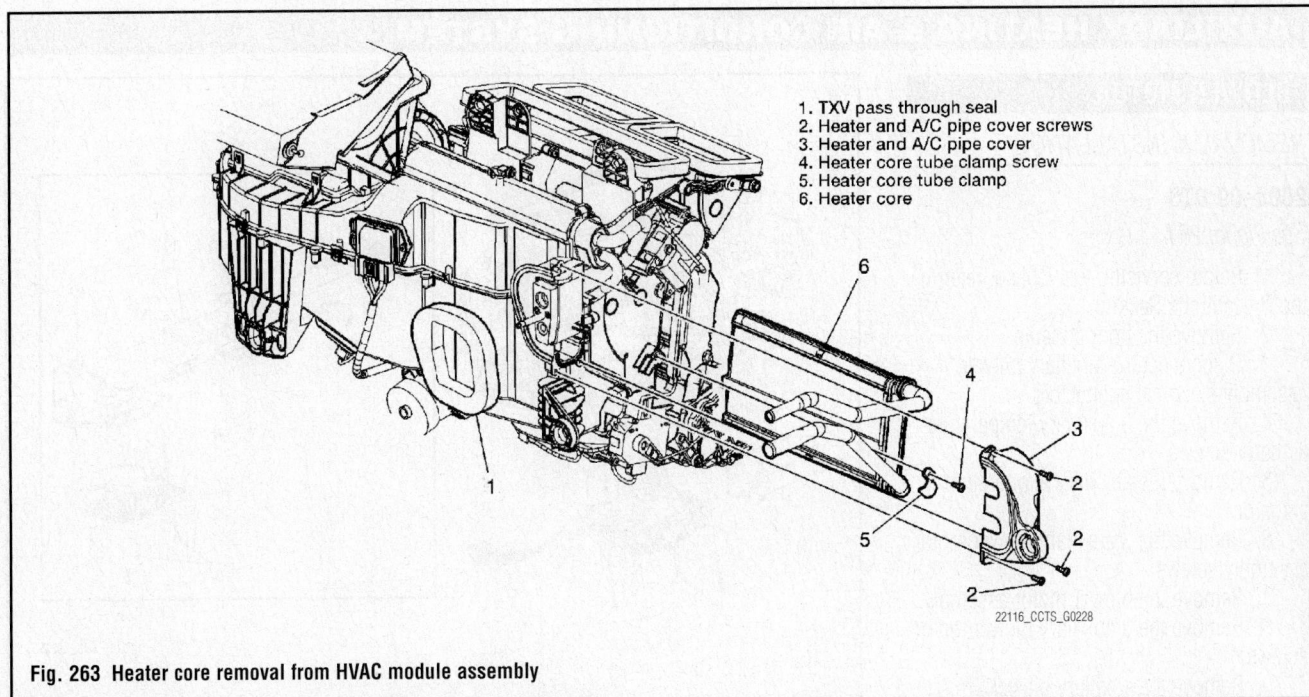

1. TXV pass through seal
2. Heater and A/C pipe cover screws
3. Heater and A/C pipe cover
4. Heater core tube clamp screw
5. Heater core tube clamp
6. Heater core

22116_CCTS_G0228

Fig. 263 Heater core removal from HVAC module assembly

54. Install the TXV pass through seal.

55. With the aid of an assistant, carefully install the HVAC assembly into the vehicle.

56. Install the left hand floor duct.

57. Install the HVAC module assembly mounting nuts. Tighten the mounting nuts to 80 inch lbs. (9 Nm).

58. Reconnect the HVAC module assembly electrical connectors.

59. With the aid of an assistant, install the instrument panel carrier assembly.

60. Install the instrument panel carrier assembly nuts and bolts. Tighten the nuts and bolts to 18 ft. lbs. (25 Nm).

61. Install the screws securing the windshield defroster nozzle duct to the carrier. Tighten the screws to 9 inch lbs. (1 Nm).

62. Install the left and right side window defroster outlet duct. Tighten the screws to 14 inch lbs. (1.5 Nm).

63. Install the floor air outlet duct, tighten the screws to 14 inch lbs. (1.5 Nm).

64. Install the center air outlet duct, tighten the screws to 9 inch lbs. (1 Nm).

65. Install the left and right air distribution duct, tighten the screws to 9 inch lbs. (1 Nm).

66. With the aid of an assistant, install the instrument panel lower panel.

67. Install the instrument panel lower panel bolts. Tighten the bolts to 80 inch lbs. (9 Nm).

68. Install the instrument panel right air outlet.

69. Install the right and left side window air outlet ducts.

70. Install the HVAC control Assembly.

71. Install the radio.

72. Install the center console, if equipped.

73. Install the instrument panel ashtray assembly, if equipped.

74. Install the glove box. Tighten the mounting screws to 18 inch lbs. (2 Nm).

75. Install the steering column.

76. If equipped with AN3. reconnect the automatic transmission range selector cable.

77. Install any electrical connectors as needed.

78. Reconnect the intermediate steering shaft to the steering gear.

79. Install the steering column mounting bolts. Tighten the nuts to 18 ft. lbs. (25 Nm).

80. Install the instrument panel cluster assembly. Tighten screws to 18 inch lbs. (2 Nm).

81. Install the left instrument panel accessory trim plate. Snap into place.

82. Install the instrument panel top pad. Tighten the bolts to 80 inch lbs. (9 Nm).

83. Reposition the auxiliary air distribution duct.

84. Install the lower Instrument Panel (I/P) support brace. Tighten the bolts to 18 ft. lbs. (25 Nm).

85. Reposition the carpet.

86. Install the brake pedal bracket assembly as follows:

    a. Reconnect the electrical connector for the brake pedal position sensor.

    b. Accelerator pedal assembly nuts.

    c. Accelerator pedal assembly.

    d. Brake pedal push rod retainer clip.

    e. Brake pedal assembly nuts.

87. Install the driver knee bolster. Tighten the mounting screws to 18 inch lbs. (2 Nm).

88. Install the heater hoses to the heater core.

89. Install the evaporator tube to the thermal expansion valve.

90. Evacuate and recharge A/C system.

91. Leak test the fitting of the reinstalled component using a halogen leak detector.

92. Refill cooling system and the bleed system as follows:

    a. Add a 50/50 mixture of water and DEX-COOL® antifreeze to the KALT/COLD mark (seam) on the surge tank.

    b. Start the engine and allow it to idle for 1 min.

    c. Add more coolant to the surge tank as necessary.

    d. Install the radiator sure tank cap.

    e. Cycle the engine, from idle to 3000 rpm, in 30 second intervals, until the engine reaches normal operating temperatures.

    f. Turn the engine OFF and recheck the coolant level when the engine is cool.

93. Connect the negative battery cable.

94. Enable the SIR system.

95. Reprogram the necessary accessories.

AUXILIARY HEATING & AIR CONDITIONING SYSTEM

BLOWER MOTOR

REMOVAL & INSTALLATION

2008–09 DTS

See Figure 264.

1. Before servicing the vehicle, refer to the Precautions Section.
2. Remove the floor console.
3. Disconnect the auxiliary blower assembly electrical connectors.
4. Remove the 3 auxiliary temperature actuator screws.
5. Remove the auxiliary temperature actuator.
6. Remove the 3 auxiliary blower motor assembly screws.
7. Remove the blower motor assembly.
8. Remove the 3 auxiliary blower motor screws.
9. Remove the auxiliary blower motor.
10. Remove the auxiliary temperature actuator mode cam screw.
11. Remove the auxiliary temperature actuator mode cam.
12. Remove the 2 auxiliary temperature actuator mode cam Levers
13. Remove the left and right blower housing.
14. Remove the blower housing temperature door.

To install:

15. Install the blower housing temperature door.

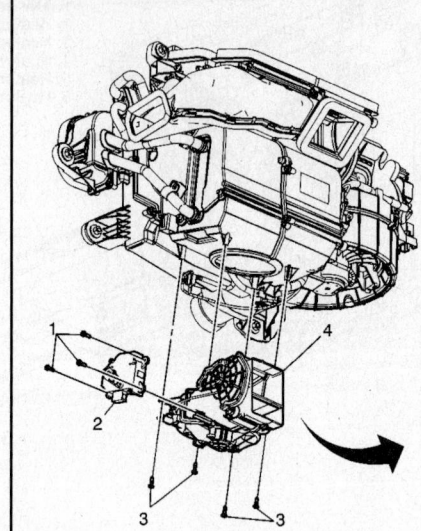
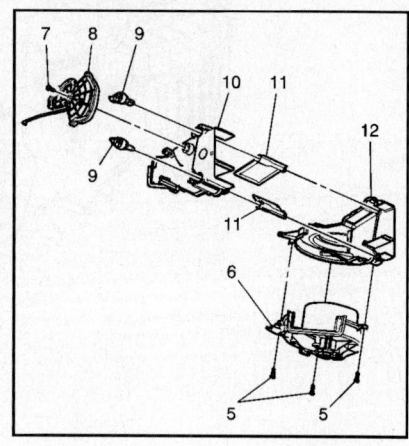

22116_CCTS_G0225

Fig. 264 Location and removal of auxiliary blower motor

16. Install the left and right blower housing.
17. Install the 2 auxiliary temperature actuator mode cam Levers
18. Install the auxiliary temperature actuator mode cam.
19. Install the auxiliary temperature actuator mode cam screw. Tighten to 9 inch lbs. (1 Nm).
20. Install the auxiliary blower motor.
21. Install the 3 auxiliary blower motor screws. Tighten to 9 inch lbs. (1 Nm).

22. Install the blower motor assembly.
23. Install the 3 auxiliary blower motor assembly screws. Tighten to 9 inch lbs. (1 Nm).
24. Install the auxiliary temperature actuator.
25. Install the 3 auxiliary temperature actuator screws. Tighten to 9 inch lbs. (1 Nm).
26. Reconnect the auxiliary blower assembly electrical connectors.
27. Install the floor console.

STEERING

POWER RACK & PINION STEERING GEAR

REMOVAL & INSTALLATION

2008–09 CTS

See Figures 265 through 269.

1. Install the engine support fixture to the engine as follows:
2. Remove the engine appearance covers and cross vehicle brace.
   a. Use a grade 10.9, M10 X 1.5 X 35 bolt, GM P/N 11519182, or equivalent, in order to install Special Tool J-36857 lift bracket, or equivalent, to the front of the left cylinder head in the location shown. Tighten the bolt to 48 ft. lbs. (65 Nm).

   b. Remove the shock module mounting stud and bolt from the left and right shock tower.
   c. Install the Engine Support Beam Adapters in the location shown on the left and right shock towers.
   d. Ensure the strut tower support assemblies are secured to the engine support beam adapters with wing nuts.
   e. Secure the strut tower tube to the strut tower support with quick release pins.
   f. Secure the strut tower tube to the radiator shelf tube with the cross bracket assembly.
   g. Tighten the cross bracket wing nuts.
   h. Assemble the lift hook wing nut and the lift hook bracket to the lift hook.

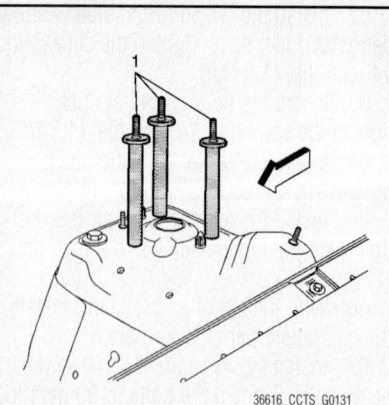

36616_CCTS_G0131

Fig. 265 Install Special Tool J-28467-550 Engine Support Beam Adapters in the location shown on the left and right shock towers—CTS 3.6L Engines

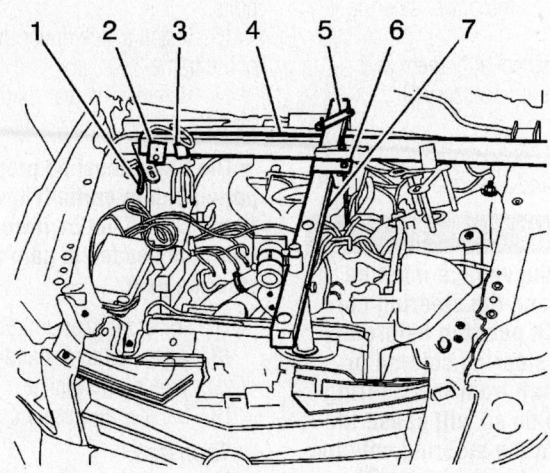

1. Engine support beam adapters
2. Strut tower support assemblies
3. Lift hook
4. Strut tower tube
5. Cross bracket assembly
6. Lift hook
7. Radiator shelf tube

36616_CCTS_G0132

Fig. 266 Engine support fixture—CTS 3.6L Engine

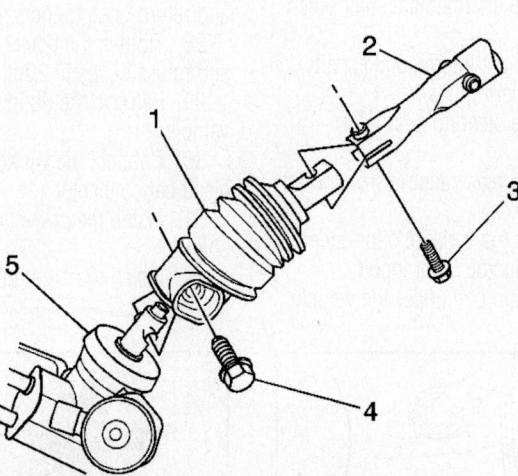

1. Lower intermediate steering shaft
2. Intermediate steering shaft
3. Intermediate steering shaft bolt
4. Lower intermediate steering shaft bolt
5. Steering gear

36616_CCTS_G0180

Fig. 267 Lower intermediate steering shaft—CTS Models

i. Install lift hook assembly to the radiator shelf tube.

j. Install lift hook assembly to left side engine lift hook bracket.

k. Assemble the lift hook wing nut and the lift hook bracket to the lift hook.

l. Install lift hook assembly to the strut tower tube.

m. Hand tighten the lift hooks in order to remove all slack from the engine support fixture.

3. Remove the front air deflector.

4. Remove the front compartment lower noise shield, if equipped.

5. Place drain pans under the vehicle.

6. Remove the intermediate steering shaft bolt.

➡**Place scribe marks on the lower intermediate steering shaft and the steering gear prior to removal.**

7. These marks will be used for the correct alignment during installation.

8. Remove the lower intermediate steering shaft bolt.

9. Disconnect the lower intermediate steering shaft from the steering gear and the intermediate steering shaft.

10. Remove the lower intermediate steering shaft from the vehicle.

11. Separate the steering linkage outer tie rods from the steering knuckles.

12. Separate the lower control arms from the steering knuckles.

13. Separate the power steering gear inlet and outlet hoses from the steering gear and the frame.

14. Support the front frame with jack stands as necessary.

15. Remove the left and right side engine mount bolts from the front frame.

16. Disconnect any electrical harnesses from the front frame as necessary.

17. Disconnect the power steering gear solenoid electrical connector.

18. Remove the front frame bolts.

19. Slowly lift the vehicle on the hoist until there is enough room to remove the steering gear from the vehicle.

20. Remove the steering gear nuts and bolts.

21. Remove the steering gear from the front frame.

To install:

22. Position the steering gear to the front frame.

23. Install the steering gear nuts and bolts and tighten to 63 ft. lbs. (85 Nm).

24. Slowly lower the vehicle on the hoist while keeping the front frame aligned with the left and right side engine mounts.

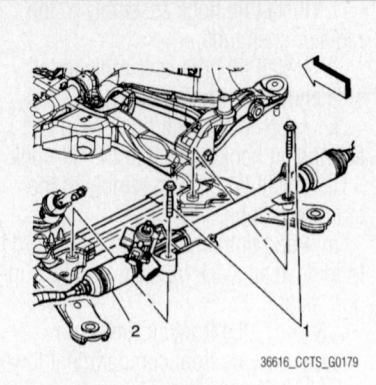

Fig. 268 Remove the bolts (1) and nuts to remove the steering gear (2)—CTS Models

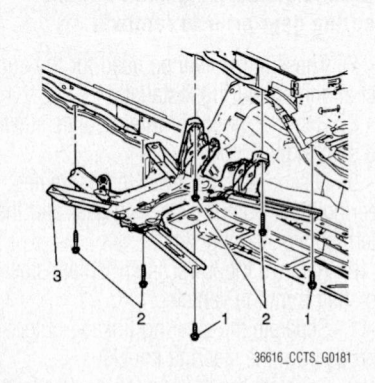

Fig. 269 Front frame (3) and frame mount bolts (2) and frame-to-body bolts (1)—CTS Models

25. Start the engine mount bolts by hand.

26. Tighten the frame mount bolts to 141 ft. lbs. (191 Nm) and frame-to-body bolts to 180 ft. lbs. (250 Nm).

27. Tighten the engine mount bolts to 59 ft. lbs. (80 Nm).

28. Connect the power steering gear solenoid electrical connector.

29. Connect any electrical harnesses to the front frame as necessary.

30. Remove the jack stands from underneath the vehicle.

31. Install the power steering gear inlet and outlet hoses to the steering gear and the frame.

32. Connect the lower control arms to the steering knuckles.

33. Connect the steering linkage outer tie rods to the steering knuckles.

34. Connect the lower intermediate steering shaft to the steering gear.

35. Clean any excess fluid from the vehicle and remove the drain pans.

36. Install the front compartment lower noise shield, if equipped.

37. Install the front air deflector.

38. Remove the engine support fixture.

39. Fill and bleed the power steering system.

40. Check the wheel alignment and adjust the front toe if necessary.

2008–09 DTS

See Figures 270 and 271.

❊❊ WARNING

The wheels of the vehicle must be straight ahead and the steering column in the LOCK position before disconnecting the steering column or intermediate shaft from the steering gear. Failure to do so will cause the coil assembly in the steering column to become uncentered which will cause damage to the coil assembly.

1. Before servicing the vehicle, refer to the Precautions Section.

2. Install J 42640 into the steering column access hole in order to lock the steering column. This will maintain the correct steering orientation.

3. Raise and support the vehicle.

4. Remove the tires and wheels.

5. Remove the outer tie rods retaining nuts.

6. Using J 24319-B remove the outer tie rod from the steering knuckle.

7. Remove the intermediate shaft pinch bolt.

8. Disconnect the intermediate shaft from the power steering gear.

9. Remove the steering gear heat shield.

10. Remove the rear transmission mount upper mounting nuts.

11. Disconnect the variable effort steering electrical connector, if equipped.

12. Install a drain pan under the vehicle.

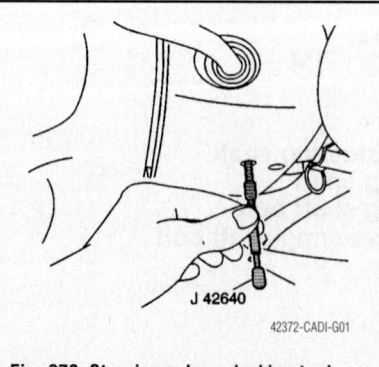

Fig. 270 Steering column locking tool J 42640

13. Remove the power steering pressure and return hose from the power steering gear.

14. Remove the steering gear mounting bolts.

15. Install a jack under the rear portion of the frame.

16. Remove the rear mounting bolts from the frame.

➡**The frame must be properly supported before partially lowering. The frame should not be lowered any further than needed to gain access to the steering gear.**

17. Lower the rear portion of the frame.

18. Remove the rack and pinion from the driver's side of the vehicle.

19. Transfer necessary components.

To install:

20. Install the rack and pinion to the vehicle.

21. Raise the rear portion of the frame.

22. Install the frame mounting bolts. Tighten the frame mounting bolts to 142 ft. lbs. (192 Nm).

23. Install the transmission mount mounting nuts.

24. Tighten the transmission mounting nuts to 30 ft. lbs. (40 Nm).

25. Install the rack and pinion mounting bolts.

26. Tighten the rack and pinion mounting bolts to 70 ft. lbs. (95 Nm).

27. Install the power steering pressure and return hose to the power steering gear.

28. Tighten the power steering pressure and return hoses to 20 ft. lbs. (27 Nm).

29. Remove the drain pan from under the vehicle.

30. Connect the variable effort steering electrical connector.

31. Install the power steering gear heat shield.

32. Install the outer tie rods to the steering knuckles.

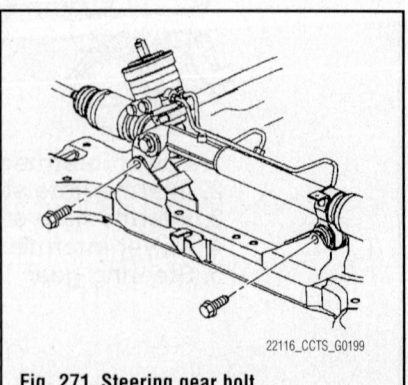

Fig. 271 Steering gear bolt removal shown

33. Install the outer tie rods retaining nuts.

34. Tighten the outer tie rod retaining nut to 35 ft. lbs. (47 Nm).

35. Tighten the outer tie rod retaining nut up to 1⁄6 additional turn, or 52 ft. lbs. (70 Nm) maximum.

36. Install the intermediate shaft to the steering gear.

37. Install the intermediate shaft pinch bolt. Tighten the intermediate shaft pinch bolt to 33 ft. lbs. (45 Nm).

38. Install the tires and wheels.

39. Lower the vehicle.

40. Remove J 42640 from the steering column access hole.

41. Bleed the power steering system.

42. Adjust front toe.

POWER STEERING PUMP

REMOVAL & INSTALLATION

2009–09 CTS

See Figures 272 and 273.

1. Before servicing the vehicle, refer to the Precautions Section.

2. Remove the front air deflector.

3. Place drain pans under the vehicle.

4. Remove as much power steering fluid from the power steering fluid reservoir as possible.

5. Remove the air cleaner outlet duct.

6. If equipped, remove the power brake booster auxiliary pump.

7. Remove the air conditioning compressor and power steering pump belt from the power steering pump pulley.

8. Using Special Tool J-25034-C, remove the power steering pump pulley.

9. Disconnect the power steering fluid reservoir outlet hose from the power steering pump.

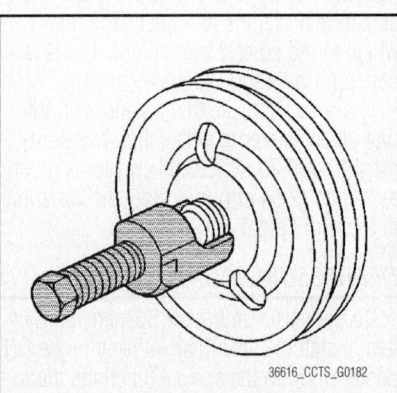

Fig. 272 Using Special Tool J-25034-C, remove the power steering pump pulley— 3.6L engine

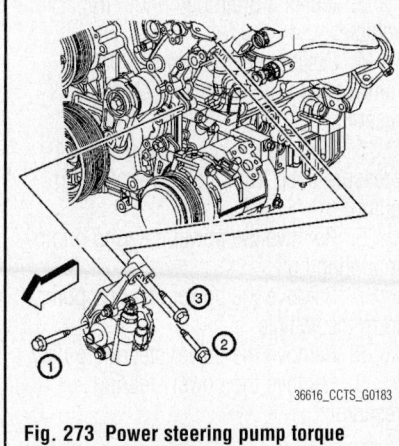

Fig. 273 Power steering pump torque sequence—3.6L engine

10. Disconnect the power steering gear inlet hose fitting from the power steering pump.

11. Remove the power steering pump bracket bolts.

12. Remove the power steering pump and bracket from the vehicle.

To install:

13. Position the power steering pump and bracket in the vehicle.

14. Install the power steering pump bracket bolts in sequence shown to 37 ft. lbs. (50 Nm).

15. Connect the power steering gear inlet hose fitting to the power steering pump and tighten the fitting to 25 ft. lbs. (34 Nm).

16. Connect the power steering fluid reservoir outlet hose to the power steering pump.

17. Clean any excess fluid from the vehicle.

18. Remove the drain pans.

19. Using Special Tool J-25033-C Installation, install the power steering pump pulley.

20. Ensure that the axial tolerance of the power steering pump pulley on the power steering pump is within 0.25 mm (0.010 in).

21. Install the air conditioning compressor and power steering pump belt to the power steering pump pulley

22. If equipped, install the power brake booster auxiliary pump.

23. Install the air cleaner outlet duct.

24. Install the front air deflector.

25. Fill and bleed the power steering system.

2009 CTS-V

See Figure 274.

1. Before servicing the vehicle, refer to the Precautions Section.

2. Remove the air intake assembly.

3. Remove the air cleaner resonator outlet duct.

4. Remove the power steering belt from the power steering pulley only.

5. Using Special Tool J-25034-C Puller Remover, remove the power steering pump pulley.

6. Place a drain pan under the vehicle.

7. Remove the remote power steering fluid reservoir.

8. Remove the power steering gear inlet hose fitting.

9. Remove the power steering pump mounting bolts and remove the pump.

To install:

10. Install the power steering pump and tighten the mounting bolts to 18 ft. lbs. (25 Nm).

11. Connect the power steering gear inlet hose fitting and tighten to 28 ft. lbs. (38 Nm).

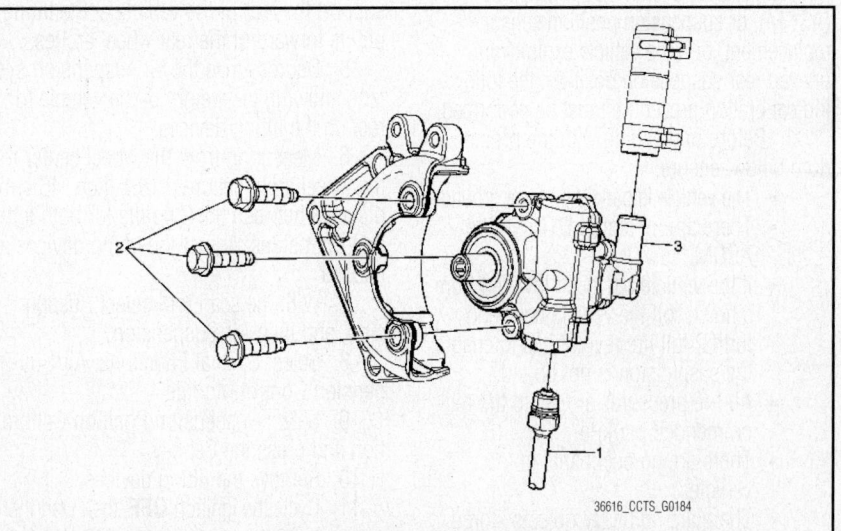

Fig. 274 Remove the inlet hose fitting (1) and bolts (2) to remove the power steering pump (3)—6.2L engines

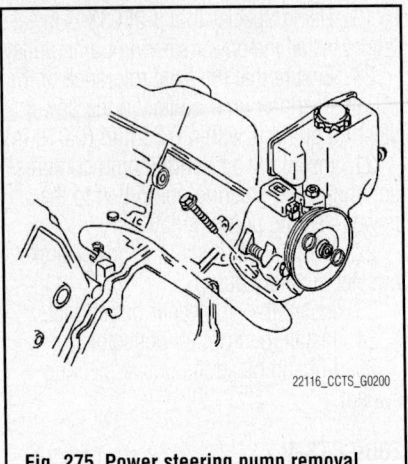

Fig. 275 Power steering pump removal

12. Install the remote reservoir.

13. Using Special Tool J-25033-C Pulley Installer, install the power steering pump pulley.

➡**Ensure the axial tolerance of the pulley on the pump shaft is within 0.25 mm (0.010 in).**

14. Install the accessory drive belt to the power steering pump pulley.

15. Install the air intake assembly.

DTS

See Figure 275.

1. Before servicing the vehicle, refer to the Precautions Section.

2. Remove the drive belt.

3. Install a drain pan under the vehicle.

4. Disconnect the power steering return hose from the power steering reservoir.

5. Remove the power steering pressure hose from the power steering pump.

6. Remove the power steering pump mounting bolt.

7. Remove the power steering pump from the vehicle.

8. Remove the power steering pulley.

9. Remove the power steering reservoir.

To install:

10. Install the power steering reservoir.

11. Install the power steering pulley.

12. Install the power steering pump to the vehicle.

13. Install the power steering pump mounting bolt.

14. Tighten the power steering pump mounting bolt to 37 ft. lbs. (50 Nm).

15. Install the power steering pressure hose to the power steering pump.

16. Tighten the power steering pressure hose to 20 ft. lbs. (27 Nm).

17. Install the power steering return hose to the power steering reservoir.

18. Remove the drain pan from under vehicle.

19. Install the drive belt.

20. Bleed the power steering system.

BLEEDING

1. Fill pump reservoir with fluid to minimum system level, FULL COLD level, or middle of hash mark on cap stick fluid level indicator.

➡**With hydro-boost only, the oil level will appear falsely high if the hydro-boost accumulator is not fully charged. Do not apply the brake pedal with the engine OFF. This will discharge the hydro-boost accumulator.**

2. If equipped with hydro-boost, fully charge the hydro-boost accumulator using the following procedure:
   a. Start the engine.
   b. Firmly apply the brake pedal 10-15 times.
   c. Turn the engine OFF.

3. Raise the vehicle until the front wheels are off the ground.

4. With the key on engine OFF, turn the steering wheel from stop to stop 12 times. Vehicles equipped with hydro-boost systems or longer length power steering hoses may require turns up to 15 to 20 stop to stops.

5. Verify power steering fluid level.

6. Start the engine. Rotate steering wheel from left to right. Check for sign of cavitation or fluid aeration (pump noise/whining).

7. Verify the fluid level. Repeat the bleed procedure, if necessary.

SUSPENSION

SUSPENSION POSITION CALIBRATION

After Air Suspension Control Module (ASCM), or suspension position sensor replacement, or if the vehicle exhibits an uneven rear suspension position, the following calibration procedure must be performed.

1. Before proceeding with the procedure below, ensure:
   - The vehicle is parked on level ground.
   - There are no stored DTCs in the ASCM.
   - If the vehicle has been lowered from a hoist, roll the vehicle back and forth 2 full tire revolutions to ensure the suspension is not bound.
   - All tire pressures are set to the recommended psi/kPa.
   - There are no occupants in the vehicle.
   - There are no heavy objects stored in the luggage compartment.

2. Install a scan tool.

3. Turn **ON** the ignition, with the engine **OFF**.

4. Using 2 adjustable lifting devices, support the rear of the vehicle at the lifting points forward of the rear wheel arches.

5. Depressurize the air suspension system, allowing the weight of the vehicle to rest on the lifting devices.

6. Measuring from the wheel center to the wheel arch, ensure a 18.1 inch (46 cm) distance between the 2 points for both left and right sides. Adjust the lifting devices as needed.

7. With the scan tool select Suspension, and then Air Suspension.

8. Select Special Functions, Air Suspension Control Module.

9. Select Suspension Position Calibration and press the Set key.

10. Remove the lifting devices.

11. Cycle the ignition **OFF**, then start the engine and allow to run for 1 minute. Verify the air suspension system is functioning properly.

AIR SUSPENSION

12. If additional adjustments are required for slight variation in the trim height after completing the Suspension Position Calibration, use the Suspension Calibration Adjustment procedure under Special Functions and follow the Tech2 on-screen instructions to adjust each rear wheel to the correct trim height. The Suspension Calibration Adjustment will increase or decrease the left and/or right rear wheel center to wheel arch measurement from 0.25 inch (0.64 cm) to as much as 1 inch (2.54 cm) to correct the variation in the trim height.

DEPRESSURIZING THE SYSTEM

To depressurize the Air Suspension System, install the scan tool with key in the ON position. Go to the special functions menu of the air suspension section and follow the on screen directions. The suspension will deflate the air springs until the suspension is on the jounce bumpers.

SUSPENSION PRESSURIZATION

1. While the vehicle is raised, ensure that the lower end of the air springs are completely engaged in the spring supports on the lower control arm.

2. Lower the vehicle but do not allow the vehicles tires to contact the ground.

3. Turn the ignition ON, with the engine OFF.

4. Install a scan tool.

5. With the scan tool in hand, raise the vehicle.

6. With the scan tool select Special Functions.

7. Select Pressurize System.

8. Press the ON soft key and visually observe the springs as their air pressures inflate.

9. When the air spring inflation pressures have reached a pressure where there are no visible wrinkles, or folds in the air springs, press the OFF soft key. This function will also stop after 40 seconds.

10. Press the Exit key.

11. Lower the vehicle.

12. Cycle the ignition OFF, then back ON, with the engine ON to allow the air suspension system to regain the desired rear suspension position.

AIR COMPRESSOR

REMOVAL & INSTALLATION

DTS

See Figures 276 and 277.

1. Raise and safely support the vehicle.
2. Depressurize the air suspension system.

➡ **Before disconnecting the air hoses from the intake air filter or the air compressor note the location of each hose. Clean the components and the surrounding area to prevent dirt and other**

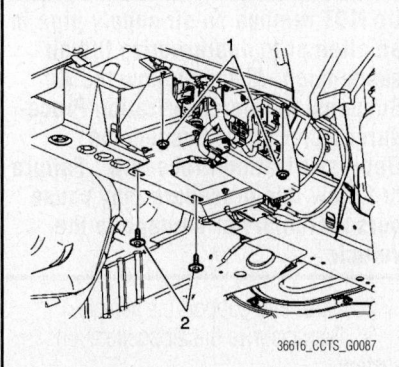

Fig. 276 Remove the compressor nuts (1) and bolts (2)

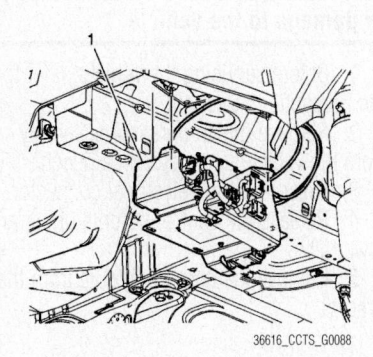

36616_CCTS_G0088

Fig. 277 Removing the air compressor assembly (1) from the vehicle.

foreign material from entering the ECAS (Electronically Controlled Air Suspension) system.

3. Disconnect the right and left air tubes from the control solenoids.

4. Disconnect the electrical connectors from the compressor assembly.

5. Remove the air intake filter from the frame.

➡ **Support the air compressor assembly before remove the mounting nuts and bolts.**

6. Remove the air compressor assembly nuts and bolts.

7. Remove the air compressor assembly from the vehicle.

8. Installation is the reverse order of removal. Tighten the mounting nuts and bolts to 80 inch lbs. (9 Nm).

AIR SPRING

REMOVAL & INSTALLATION

DTS

See Figure 278.

1. Before servicing the vehicle, refer to the Precautions Section.

2. Depressurize the air suspension.

3. Raise and support the vehicle.

4. Remove the rear tire and wheel assembly.

5. Remove the rear leveling sensor link from the control arm.

6. Disconnect the air supply line at the air spring.

7. Remove lower shock bolts.

8. Remove the rear adjusting link mounting nut.

9. Use the J 24319-B to remove the adjusting link from the control arm.

10. Place a suitable support under the control arm.

11. Lower the control arm and remove the air spring.

To install:

12. Carefully install the air spring into the seat.

13. Connect the air supply line at the air spring.

14. Use support jack to raise the control arm into position.

15. Tighten the lower shock mounting bolts to 18 ft. lbs. (25 Nm).

16. Remove the support jack.

17. Install the rear adjusting link and tighten the nut to 22 ft. lbs. (30 Nm).

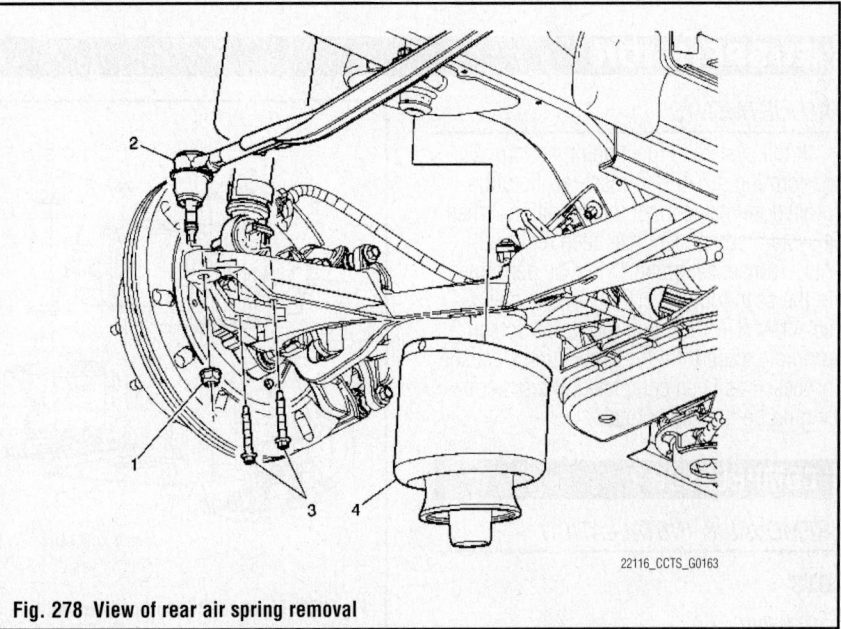

22116_CCTS_G0163

Fig. 278 View of rear air spring removal

18. Install the rear leveling sensor link from the control arm.

19. Tighten the air spring leveling sensor nut to 80 inch lbs. (9 Nm).

20. Install the rear tire and wheel assembly.

21. Lower the vehicle.

22. Pressurize the air suspension system after the repair has been completed.

CONTROL MODULE

REMOVAL & INSTALLATION

See Figure 279.

⁂ WARNING

Do NOT remove an air supply pipe in an attempt to depressurize the air suspension. Always follow the Air Suspension Depressurization Procedure in Air Suspension. Failure to follow this

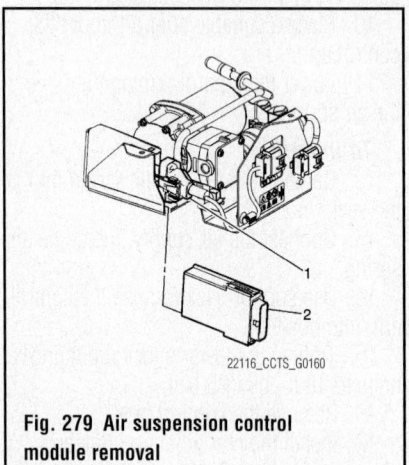

Fig. 279 Air suspension control module removal

procedure may cause personal injury or damage to the vehicle.

1. Before servicing the vehicle, refer to the Precautions Section.

2. Remove the compressor assembly from the vehicle and place on a bench.

3. Disconnect the electrical connector.

4. Release the control module upper and lower tabs.

5. Remove the control module from the bracket.

To install:

6. Install the control module to the bracket. Ensure the upper and lower locking tabs are engaged.

7. Connect the electrical connector.

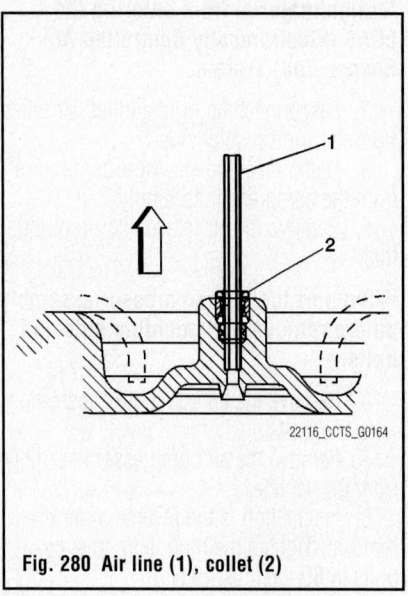

Fig. 280 Air line (1), collet (2)

8. Install the compressor assembly to the vehicle.

9. Perform the suspension position calibration procedure.

AIR LINE

REMOVAL & INSTALLATION

See Figure 280.

1. Before servicing the vehicle, refer to the Precautions Section.

2. Depressurize the air suspension system.

3. Raise and support the vehicle.

4. Disconnect all air lines using the following procedure. Air spring connection shown. All others are similar.

   a. Push the air supply line into the air spring connection and hold in place.

   b. Depress and hold the air supply line collet (2) down.

   c. Remove the air supply line (1) from the air spring.

To install:

➡ **Inspect the ends of all air supply pipes for deep scoring and sharp edges before reinstalling the pipe to the fitting. Replace any pipe that exhibits any of the above conditions.**

5. Install air line to the appropriate fitting until the line bottoms.

6. Pressurize the air springs. Refer to Air Suspension Pressurization Procedure.

7. Lower vehicle.

8. Start the vehicle and run for approximately 2 minutes to verify that the air suspension system is functioning properly.

SUSPENSION

ADJUSTMENTS

If the system is functioning abnormally, performing the ALC Trimset recalibration procedure may correct the condition. When a system component has been replaced, ALC Trimset calibration must be performed. In the scan tool Special Functions menu, select ALC Trimset and follow the screen prompts to perform the procedure. Once the process has been completed, the system should be fully functional.

COMPRESSOR

REMOVAL & INSTALLATION

DTS

See Figure 281.

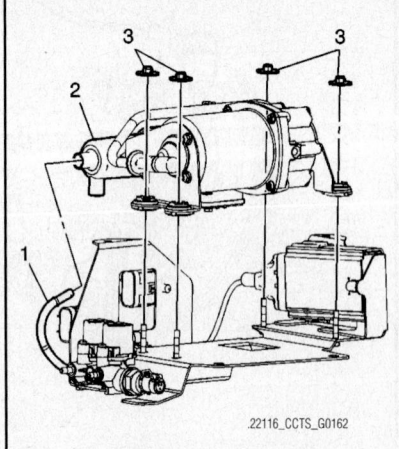

Fig. 281 Air hose (1), compressor with the dryer (2), washer and nuts (3)

AUTOMATIC LEVEL CONTROL

1. Before servicing the vehicle, refer to the Precautions Section.

⁂ CAUTION

Do NOT remove an air supply pipe in an attempt to depressurize the air suspension. Always follow the Air Suspension Depressurization Procedure. Refer to Air Suspension Depressurization Procedure . Failure to follow this procedure may cause personal injury or damage to the vehicle.

2. Raise and support the vehicle.

3. Depressurize the air suspension system.

➡ **Before disconnecting the air hoses from the intake air filter or the air** compressor note the location of each hose. Clean the components and the surrounding area to prevent dirt and other foreign material from entering the Electronically Controlled Air Suspension (ECAS) system.

4. Remove the air compressor assembly.

5. Disconnect the air hose from the air dryer.

6. Remove the air compressor nuts and washers.

7. Remove the air compressor with the dryer from the bracket.

8. Install the air compressor with the dryer to the bracket.

9. Install the air compressor nuts and washers.

10. Connect the air hose to the air dryer. Ensure the air hose is fully seated into the air dryer.

11. Install the air compressor assembly.

12. Pressurize the air springs. Refer to Air Suspension Pressurization Procedure.

13. Lower the vehicle.

SENSOR

REMOVAL & INSTALLATION

DTS

See Figure 282.

1. Before servicing the vehicle, refer to the Precautions Section.

2. Raise and support the vehicle.

3. Remove the rear wheel and tire.

4. Support the rear suspension at the proper D trim height

5. Disconnect the air spring leveling sensor arm from the trailing arm.

6. Disconnect the air spring leveling sensor electrical connector.

7. Remove the air spring leveling sensor nut and remove the sensor.

To install:

8.Position the air spring leveling sensor and install the nut.

9. Tighten the air spring leveling sensor nut to 80 inch lbs. (9 Nm).

10. Connect the air spring leveling sensor electrical connector.

11. Connect the air spring leveling sensor to the trailing arm.

12. Remove the rear suspension support.

13. Install the rear wheel and tire.

14. Lower the vehicle.

15. Perform the suspension position calibration procedure.

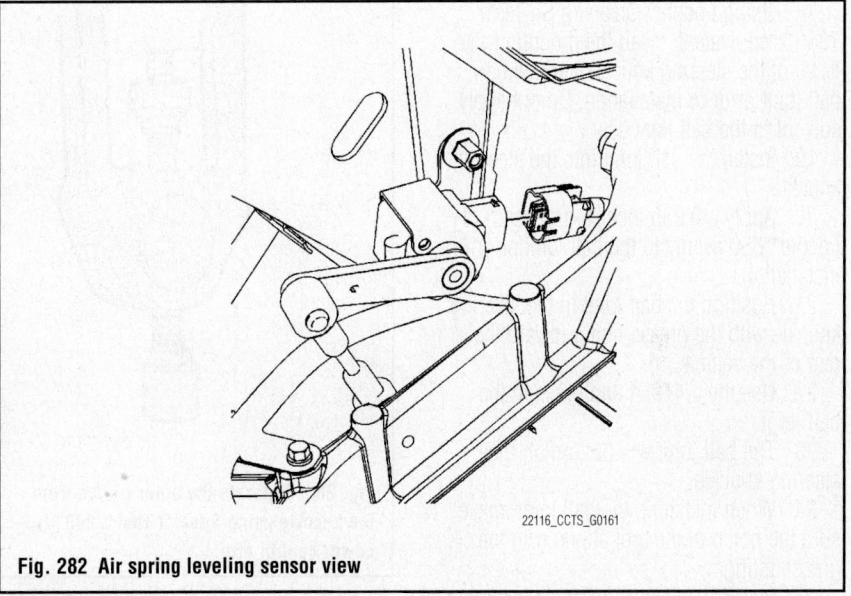

Fig. 282 Air spring leveling sensor view

SUSPENSION

FRONT SUSPENSION

LOWER BALL JOINT

REMOVAL & INSTALLATION

2008–09 CTS

The lower control arm must be replaced. The ball joint is not serviced separately.

2008–09 DTS

FE1 & FE3 Suspensions

The lower control arm must be replaced. The ball joint is not serviced separately.

FE7 Suspension

See Figures 283 and 284.

1. Before servicing the vehicle, refer to the Precautions Section.

2. Raise the vehicle.

3. Remove the tire and wheel.

4. Remove the wheel drive shaft nut.

5. Remove the brake caliper bolts.

6. Support and hang the caliper away from the brake rotor.

7. Remove the brake rotor.

8. Disconnect the wheel speed sensor connector.

9. Use the J 24319-B and separate the tie rod from the knuckle.

10. Remove the nut from the ball joint stud.

11. Use J 39549 to separate the ball joint from the lower control arm.

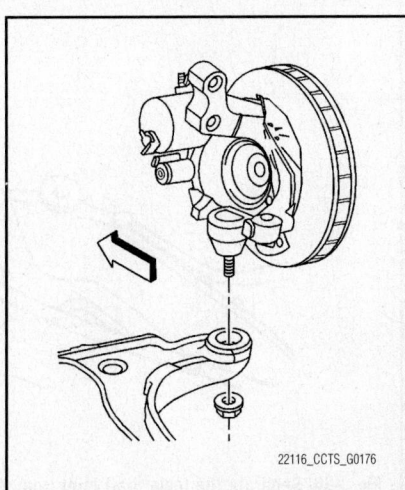

Fig. 283 Steering knuckle removal shown

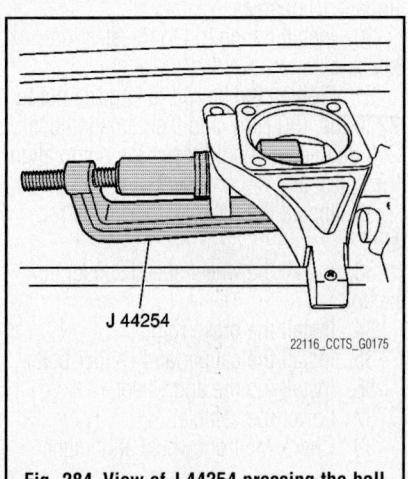

Fig. 284 View of J 44254 pressing the ball joint out of the knuckle

12. Remove the strut to knuckle attaching nuts and bolts.

13. Remove the steering knuckle from the vehicle.

14. Remove the snap ring from the steering knuckle.

15. Place the knuckle in a vise.

16. Install the J 44254 and press the ball joint out of the knuckle.

17. Inspect the tapered hole in the lower control arm and remove any dirt. If this hole is out of round, deformed, or damaged, replace the control arm.

To install:

18. Using Loctite® Cleaning Solvent 755, or equivalent, clean the mounting surfaces of the steering knuckle and the new ball joint prior to installation. Do not apply solvent to the ball joint seal.

19. Install the ball joint into the steering knuckle.

20. Apply a 0.236 inch (6 mm bead) of Loctite® 680 evenly to the ball joint prior to installation.

21. Position the ball joint in the steering knuckle with the grease fitting toward the rear of the vehicle.

22. Use the J 44254 and press in the ball joint.

23. The ball joint will bottom on the steering knuckle.

24. When installing the ball joint, make sure the notch in the tool aligns with the grease fitting.

25. Install the snap ring into the steering knuckle.

26. Install the steering knuckle to the strut.

27. Tighten the strut to knuckle nuts to 131 ft. lbs. (177 Nm).

28. Install the ball joint nut.

29. Tighten the ball joint nut to 22 ft. lbs. (30 Nm). Then tighten the nut an additional 210 degrees.

30. Install the tie rod to the steering knuckle.

31. Tighten the tie rod to knuckle nut to 22 ft. lbs. (30 Nm). and then an additional 200 degrees. Do not loosen the nut to align the cotter pin.

32. Install the cotter pin to the tie rod stud.

33. Install the wheel speed sensor connector.

34. Install the brake rotor.

35. Install the caliper and caliper bolts.

36. Install the tire and wheel.

37. Lower the vehicle.

38. Check the front wheel alignment.

LOWER CONTROL ARM

REMOVAL & INSTALLATION

CTS & CTS-V

See Figures 285 and 286.

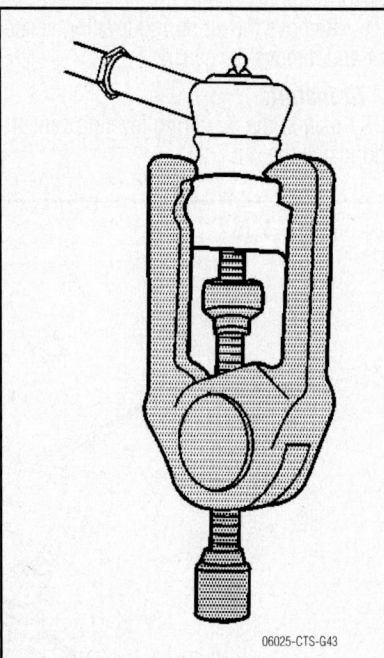

06025-CTS-G43

Fig. 285 Separate the outer tie rod from the knuckle using Special Tool J-24319-B– Lower control arm.

1. Before servicing the vehicle, refer to the Precautions Section.

2. Remove or disconnect the following:
   - Front wheel
   - Stabilizer shaft link
   - Shock assembly lower mounting bolts
   - Outer tie rod from the steering knuckle using Puller J-24319-B
   - ABS wire harness from the lower control arm
   - Lower control arm mounting bolts

3. Lower and support the lower control arm to gain access to the lower ball joint.

4. Separate the lower ball joint from the steering knuckle using Special Tool J-43631 or equivalent Ball Joint Remover.

5. Remove the lower control arm.

To install:

6. Install or connect the following:
   - Lower control arm. Tighten the mounting bolts to 100 ft. lbs. (135 Nm).
   - ABS wiring harness
   - Lower ball joint to the steering knuckle. Tighten the nut to 15 ft. lbs. (20 Nm) plus 210 degrees.
   - Outer tie rod to the steering knuckle. Tighten the retaining nut to 55 ft. lbs. (75 Nm).
   - Shock assembly lower mounting bolts. Tighten to 18 ft. lbs. (25 Nm).

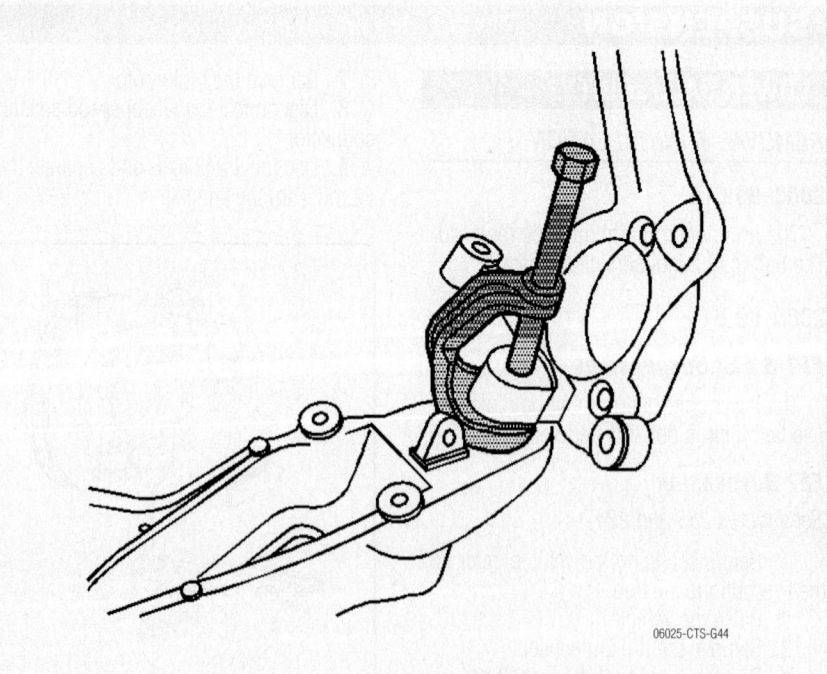

06025-CTS-G44

Fig. 286 Separate the lower ball joint from the knuckle using Special Tool J-43631–Lower control arm.

- Stabilizer shaft link to the lower control arm. Tighten the retaining nut to 37 ft. lbs. (50 Nm).
  - Front wheel.
7. Check and/or adjust the front wheel alignment.

2008–09 DTS

See Figure 287.

1. Before servicing the vehicle, refer to the Precautions Section.
2. Raise and support the vehicle.
3. Remove the front tire and wheel assembly.
4. Remove the front stabilizer shaft link.
5. Remove the ball joint retaining nut.
6. Use the J 36226 ball joint separator to separate the ball joint from the control arm.
7. Remove the front control arm nuts and bolts.
8. Remove rear control arm nut and bolt.
9. Remove the control arm from the vehicle

To install:

10. Install the control arm to the vehicle.
11. Install the front control arm nuts and bolts. Tighten the nut to 111 ft. lbs. (150 Nm).
12. Install the rear control arm nut and bolt. Do not tighten the control arm bolt until the weight of the vehicle is supported by the control arm. The vehicle needs to be sitting at normal trim height, the tighten the bolt.
13. For (FE1) and (FE3) suspensions tighten the rear control arm nut and bolt to 116 ft. lbs. (157 Nm).
14. For the (FE7) suspension, tighten the nut and bolt to 108 ft. lbs. (146 Nm).
15. Install a new ball joint retaining nut. Tighten to 22 ft. lbs. (30 Nm) plus an additional 210 degrees.
16. Install the front stabilizer shaft link. Tighten the stabilizer link nut to 13 ft. lbs. (17 Nm).
17. Install the front tire and wheel assembly.
18. Lower the vehicle.

STABILIZER BAR

REMOVAL & INSTALLATION

CTS & CTS-V

1. Before servicing the vehicle, refer to the Precautions Section.
2. Raise and support the vehicle.
3. Remove the tire and wheel.

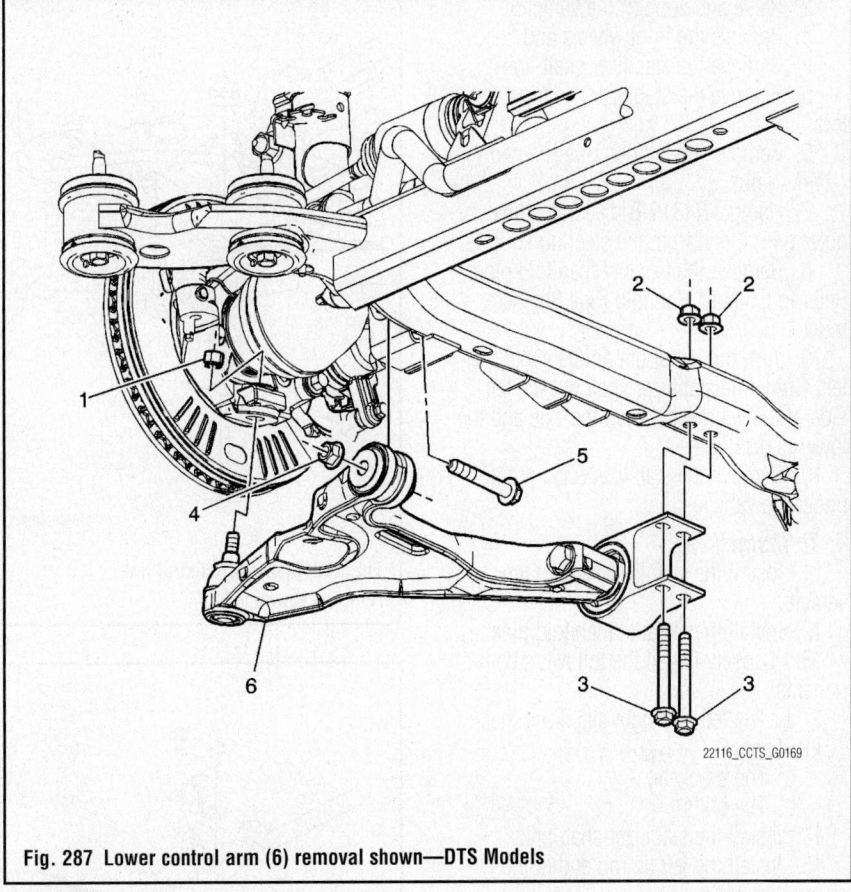

Fig. 287 Lower control arm (6) removal shown—DTS Models

4. Disconnect the ABS sensor wiring harness from the stabilizer shaft links.
5. Remove the stabilizer shaft link to stabilizer shaft retaining nuts.
6. Disconnect the stabilizer shaft links from the stabilizer shaft.
7. Remove the stabilizer shaft mounting bolts and brackets.
8. Remove the stabilizer shaft from the vehicle.
9. Remove the stabilizer shaft insulators from the stabilizer shaft.

To install:

10. Install the stabilizer shaft insulators to the stabilizer shaft. Install the insulator to the stabilizer shaft with the slit facing rearward.
11. Install the stabilizer shaft to the vehicle.
12. Do not tighten the bolts at this time.
13. Install the stabilizer shaft brackets and mounting bolts.
14. Apply threadlocker 242 or equivalent to the threads of the stabilizer shaft link.
15. Connect the stabilizer shaft links to the stabilizer shaft.
16. Install the stabilizer shaft link retaining nuts.
17. Tighten the link nuts to 37 ft. lbs. (50 Nm).

18. Tighten the bracket bolts to 44 ft. lbs. (60 Nm).
19. Connect the ABS sensor wiring harness to the stabilizer links.
20. Install the tire and wheel.
21. Lower the vehicle.

2008–09 DTS

FE1 & FE3 Suspensions

See Figure 288.

1. Before servicing the vehicle, refer to the Precautions Section.

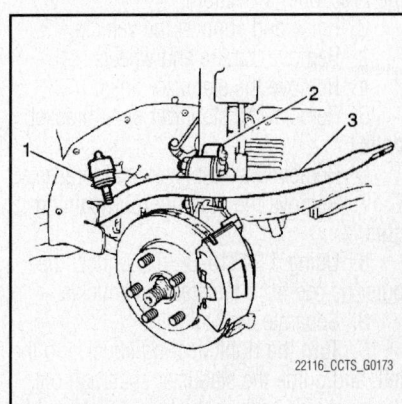

Fig. 288 Guiding the stabilizer shaft out the left side of vehicle

2. Raise and support the vehicle.

3. Remove the front wheels and tires.

4. Remove the stabilizer shaft links.

5. Remove the stabilizer shaft insulators.

6. Remove the left outer tie rod end retaining nut.

7. Using J 24319-B disconnect the outer tie rod end from the steering knuckle.

8. Remove the exhaust manifold pipe. Refer to Exhaust Manifold Pipe Replacement.

9. Turn the left strut completely to the left. Guide the stabilizer shaft out the left side of the vehicle between the axle and the lower control arm.

10. Remove the stabilizer shaft out from under the vehicle.

To install:

11. Install the stabilizer shaft to the vehicle.

12. Install the exhaust manifold pipe.

13. Loosely install the following components:

   a. The left and right stabilizer shaft insulators.

   b. The brackets.

   c. The bolts.

14. Install the stabilizer shaft links

15. Install the left tie rod end to the steering knuckle.

16. Install the left outer tie rod retaining nut.

17. Tighten the stabilizer shaft insulator bracket bolts to 24 ft. lbs. (33 Nm).

18. Tighten the outer tie rod end to steering knuckle to 22 ft. lbs. (30 Nm). Plus an additional 200 degrees.

19. Install the front wheels and tires

20. Lower the vehicle.

FE7 Suspension

See Figures 289 and 290.

1. Before servicing the vehicle, refer to the Precautions Section.

2. Raise and support the vehicle.

3. Remove the tire and wheels.

4. Remove the stabilizer links.

5. Remove the stabilizer shaft bracket bolts.

6. Remove the stabilizer shaft brackets.

7. Remove the outer tie rod retaining nuts.

8. Using J 24319-B , disconnect the outer tie rod from the steering knuckle.

9. Separate the ball joint.

10. Turn the right steering knuckle to the left, and guide the stabilizer shaft half out the right side of the vehicle in an upward direction, then remove the stabilizer shaft out the bottom center of the vehicle.

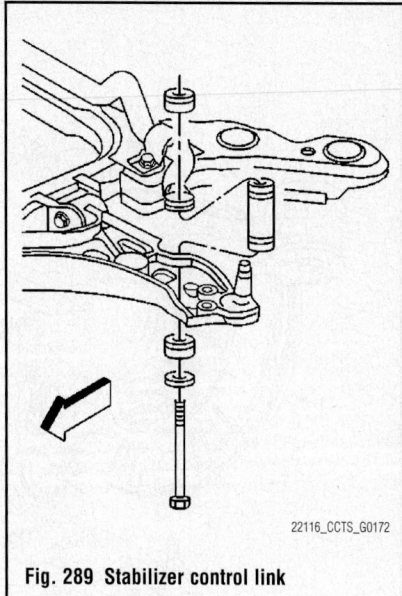

Fig. 289 Stabilizer control link removal shown

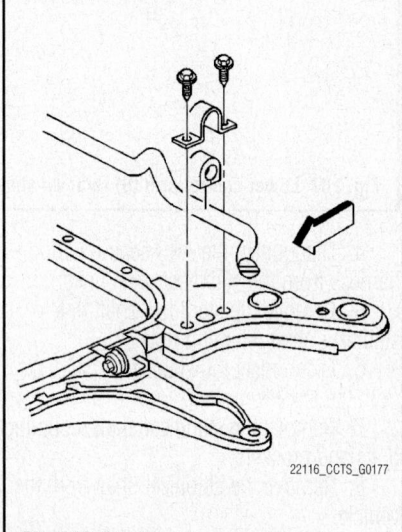

Fig. 290 Stabilizer bar, bracket and bushing shown

To install:

11. Install the stabilizer shaft to the vehicle.

12. Install the ball joint to steering knuckle.

13. Install the ball joint retaining nut.

14. Tighten the ball joint retaining nut to 22 ft. lbs. (30 Nm) plus an additional 210 degrees.

15. Loosely install the right and left stabilizer shaft insulators, brackets, and bolts.

16. Loosely install the stabilizer link insulators, washers, nut, and bolt.

17. Install the tie rod to steering knuckle.

18. Tighten the stabilizer bracket bolts to 37 ft. lbs. (50 Nm).

19. Tighten the stabilizer link nut to 17 ft. lbs. (23 Nm).

20. Tighten the tie rod end to knuckle nut to 22 inch lbs. 30 Nm plus an additional 200 degrees.

21. Install the cotter pin in tie rod ends.

22. Install the front wheels and tires.

23. Lower the vehicle.

STEERING KNUCKLE

REMOVAL & INSTALLATION

CTS & CTS-V

See Figure 291.

1. Before servicing the vehicle, refer to the Precautions Section.

2. Raise and support the vehicle.

3. Remove the tire and wheel.

4. Disconnect the wheel speed electrical connector, if equipped.

5. Remove the wheel bearing/hub.

6. Remove the outer tie rod to steering knuckle retaining nut.

7. Use a steering puller and disconnect the tie rod from the steering knuckle.

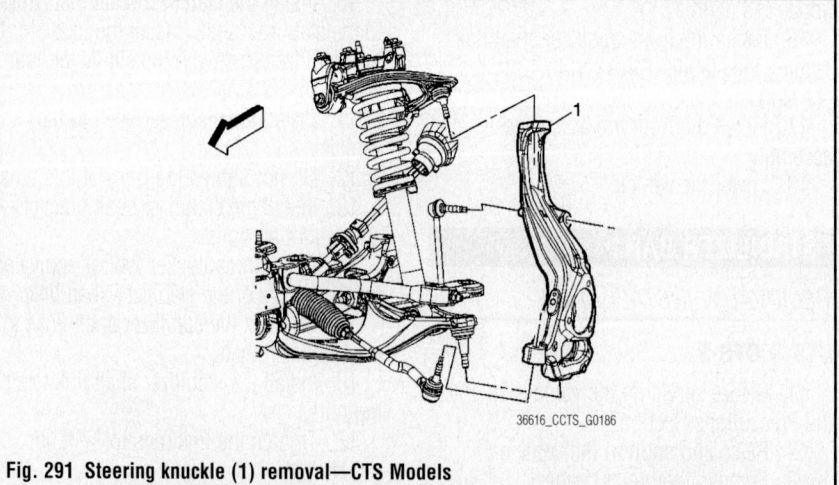

Fig. 291 Steering knuckle (1) removal—CTS Models

8. Remove the lower stabilizer shaft link retaining nut.

9. Remove the stabilizer shaft link from the lower control arm.

10. Remove the upper control arm to steering knuckle pinch bolt.

11. Separate the upper control arm from steering knuckle .

12. Remove the lower ball joint retaining nut and discard.

13. Use a ball joint remover and disconnect the lower ball joint from the steering knuckle.

14. Remove the steering knuckle from the lower ball joint stud.

To install:

15. Install the steering knuckle to the lower ball joint stud.

16. Install a new lower ball joint retaining nut.

17. Tighten the nut in the following order: Tighten the nut to 15 ft. lbs. (20 Nm), tighten the nut to an additional 210 degree turn.

18. Install the upper control arm to steering knuckle.

19. Install the upper control arm to steering knuckle pinch bolt and nut.

20. Tighten the nut to 44 ft. lbs. (60 Nm).

21. Apply threadlocker 242 or equivalent to the threads of the stabilizer shaft link.

22. Connect the stabilizer shaft link to the lower control arm.

23. Install the stabilizer shaft link retaining nut and tighten to 37 ft. lbs. (50 Nm).

24. Connect the outer tie rod to the steering knuckle.

25. Install the outer tie rod retaining nut and tighten to 55 ft. lbs. (75 Nm).

26. Install the wheel bearing/hub.

27. Reconnect the wheel speed electrical connector, if equipped.

28. Install the tire and wheel.

29. Lower the vehicle.

2008–09 DTS

FE1 & FE3 Suspensions

See Figure 292.

1. Before servicing the vehicle, refer to the Precautions Section.

2. Raise and support the vehicle.

3. Remove the front tire and wheel assembly.

4. Remove the axle shaft nut. Use a suitable tool to prevent the wheel hub/bearing from rotating while removing the axle nut.

5. Remove the front brake caliper.

6. Remove the brake rotor from the wheel hub/bearing.

7. Disconnect the wheel speed electrical connector, if equipped.

8. Remove the wheel bearing/hub.

9. Remove the outer tie rod to steering knuckle retaining nut.

10. Use the J 24319-B puller to separate the tie rod end from the steering knuckle.

11. Remove the strut to steering knuckle nuts and bolts.

12. Remove the lower ball joint retaining nut and discard.

13. Use the J 43828 to separate the ball joint from the lower control arm.

14. Remove the steering knuckle from the vehicle.

To install:

15. Install the steering knuckle to the vehicle.

16. Install the new lower ball joint retaining nut and tighten to 22 ft. lbs. (30 Nm) plus an additional 210 degrees.

17. Install the strut to steering knuckle nuts and bolts. Tighten to 131 ft. lbs. (177 Nm).

18. Install the new outer tie rod to steering knuckle retaining nut. Tighten to 22 ft.

lbs. (30 Nm) plus an additional 200 degrees.

19. Install the wheel bearing/hub. Tighten the bolts to 96 ft. lbs. (130 Nm).

20. Reconnect the wheel speed electrical connector, if equipped.

21. Install the brake rotor to the wheel hub/bearing.

22. Install the brake caliper.

23. Install the axle shaft nut. Use a suitable tool to prevent the wheel hub/bearing from rotating while installing the axle nut. Tighten the axle nut to 118ft. lbs. (160 Nm).

24. Install the front tire and wheel assembly.

25. Lower the vehicle.

FE7 Suspension

See Figure 293.

1. Before servicing the vehicle, refer to the Precautions Section.

2. Raise and support the vehicle.

3. Remove the front tire and wheel assembly.

4. Remove the axle shaft nut. Use a suitable tool to prevent the wheel hub/

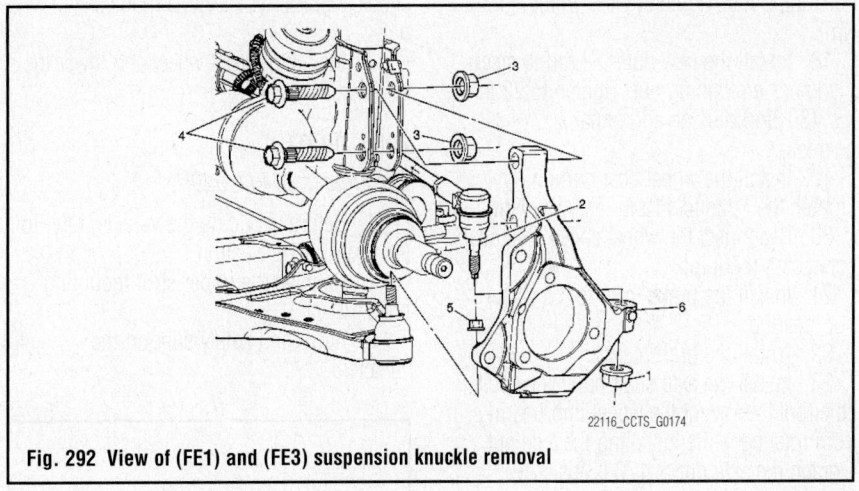

Fig. 292 View of (FE1) and (FE3) suspension knuckle removal

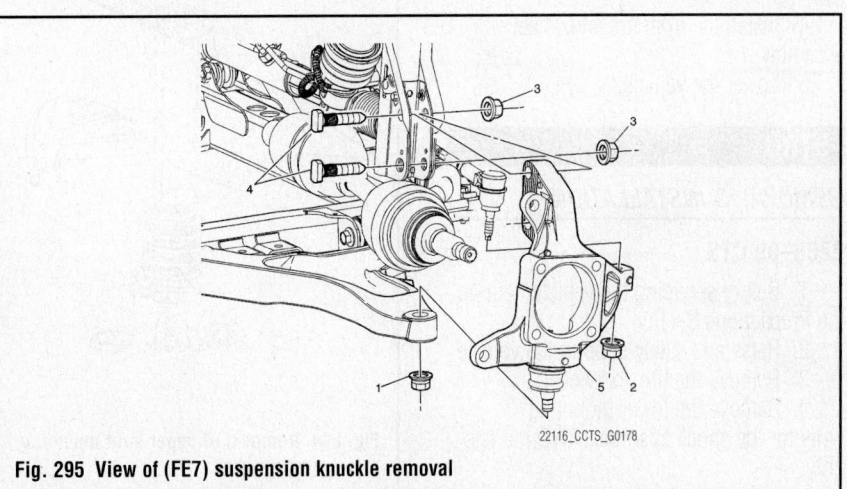

Fig. 295 View of (FE7) suspension knuckle removal

bearing from rotating while removing the axle nut.

5. Remove the front brake caliper.

6. Remove the brake rotor from the wheel hub/bearing.

7. Disconnect the wheel speed electrical connector, if equipped.

8. Remove the wheel bearing/hub.

9. Remove the outer tie rod to steering knuckle retaining nut.

10. Use the J 24319-B puller to separate the tie rod end from the steering knuckle.

11. Remove the strut to steering knuckle nuts and bolts.

12. Remove the lower ball joint retaining nut and discard.

13. Use the J 39549 to separate the ball joint from the lower control arm.

14. Remove the steering knuckle from the vehicle.

To install:

15. Install the steering knuckle to the vehicle.

16. Install the new lower ball joint retaining nut and tighten to 22 ft. lbs. (30 Nm) plus an additional 190 degrees.

17. Install the strut to steering knuckle nuts and bolts. Tighten to 131 ft. lbs. (177 Nm).

18. Install the new outer tie rod to steering knuckle retaining nut. Tighten to 22 ft. lbs. (30 Nm) plus an additional 200 degrees.

19. Install the wheel bearing/hub. Tighten the bolts to 112 ft. lbs. (152 Nm).

20. Reconnect the wheel speed electrical connector, if equipped.

21. Install the brake rotor to the wheel hub/bearing.

22. Install the brake caliper.

23. Install the axle shaft nut. Use a suitable tool to prevent the wheel hub/bearing from rotating while installing the axle nut. Tighten the axle nut to 170 ft. lbs. (230 Nm).

24. Install the front tire and wheel assembly.

25. Lower the vehicle.

STRUT

REMOVAL & INSTALLATION

2008–09 CTS

1. Before servicing the vehicle, refer to the Precautions Section.

2. Raise and safely support the vehicle.

3. Remove the tire and wheel.

4. Remove the lower mounting bolts for the shock absorber, RWD models only.

5. Remove the front shock yoke, AWD models only.

6. Remove the upper control arm to steering knuckle nut.

7. Using Special Tool J-24319-B puller, remove the upper control arm from the steering knuckle.

8. Lower the vehicle.

9. Remove the strut assembly upper mounting bolts.

10. Remove the strut assembly from the vehicle

To install:

11. Install the strut assembly into the vehicle. Tighten the upper mounting bolts to 83 ft. lbs. (112 Nm).

12. Raise and safely support the vehicle.

13. Install the upper control arm to the steering knuckle.

14. Install the upper control arm to steering knuckle retaining nut and tighten to 44 ft. lbs. (60 Nm).

15. Install the lower mounting bolts for the shock absorber and tighten to 18 ft. lbs. (25 Nm), RWD models only.

16. Install the shock to the shock absorber yoke, AWD models only.

17. Install the front wheel and lower the vehicle.

2008–09 DTS

See Figures 294 and 295.

1. Before servicing the vehicle, refer to the Precautions Section.

2. Remove the upper strut mounting bolts.

3. Raise and safely support the vehicle.

4. Remove the tire and wheel.

5. Disconnect the wheel speed sensor wiring harness.

6. Remove the wheel speed sensor bracket from the strut.

7. Remove the brake line bracket mounting bolt and bracket from the strut.

8. Remove the strut to steering knuckle bolts and nuts.

9. Remove the strut from the vehicle.

To install:

10. Lower the vehicle

11. Install the strut to the vehicle.

12. Install the upper strut mounting bolts. Tighten the upper strut mounting bolts to 44 ft. lbs. (60 Nm). For (FE7) suspension tighten to 49 ft. lbs. (66 Nm).

13. Raise the vehicle.

14. Install new strut to steering knuckle bolts and nuts. Tighten the strut to steering knuckle bolts and nuts to 108 ft. lbs. (147 Nm). For (FE7) suspension tighten to 131 ft. lbs. (177 Nm).

15. Install the brake line bracket and mounting bolt to the strut. Tighten the bolts and nuts to 17 ft. lbs. (23 Nm).

16. Install the wheel speed sensor bracket and mounting bolt to strut. Tighten the bolt to 13 ft. lbs. (17 Nm).

17. Install the wheel speed sensor bracket to strut.

18. Install the wheel speed sensor wiring harness to the bracket.

19. Install the wheel and tire.

20. Lower the vehicle.

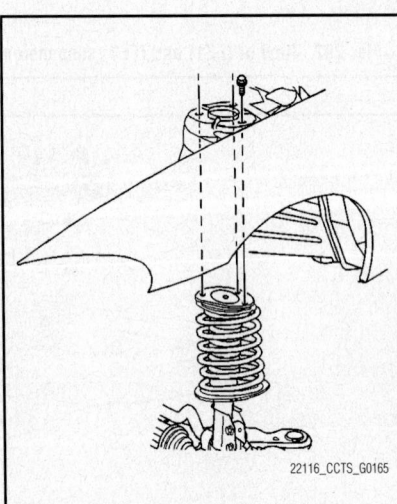

Fig. 294 Removal of upper strut mounting bolts—DTS Models

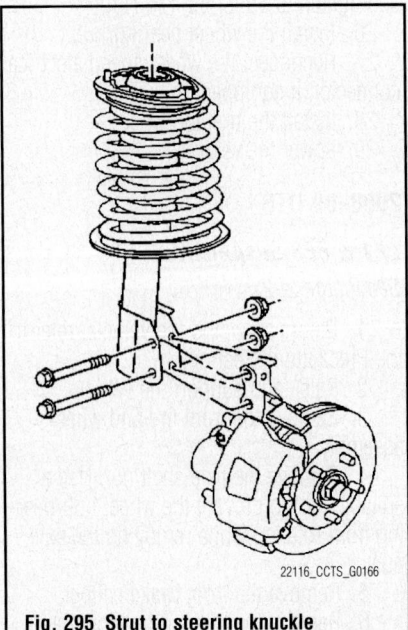

Fig. 295 Strut to steering knuckle removal—DTS Models

WHEEL BEARINGS

REMOVAL & INSTALLATION

CTS & CTS-V

See Figure 296.

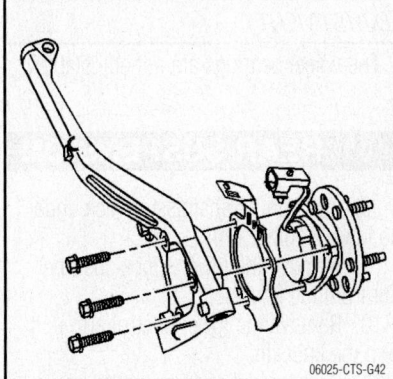

Fig. 296 Location of the bearing hub mounting bolts—Front

1. Before servicing the vehicle, refer to the Precautions Section.
2. Remove or disconnect the following:
   - Front wheel
   - Brake rotor
   - ABS wheel sensor
   - Wheel bearing mounting bolts
   - Wheel bearing

To install:
3. Install or connect the following:
   - Wheel bearing. Tighten the bolts to 100 ft. lbs. (135 Nm).
   - ABS wheel sensor
   - Brake rotor
   - Front wheel

2008–09 DTS

FE1 & FE3 Suspensions

See Figure 297.

1. Before servicing the vehicle, refer to the Precautions Section.
2. Raise and support the vehicle.
3. Remove the front tire and wheel assembly.
4. Remove the axle nut. Use a suitable tool to prevent the wheel hub/bearing from rotating while removing the axle nut.
5. Remove the brake caliper and the caliper mounting bracket as an assembly from the suspension knuckle and support the assembly with heavy mechanic's wire, or equivalent. Ensure that there is no tension on the hydraulic brake flexible hose.
6. Mark the relationship of the rotor to the hub.
7. Remove the brake rotor.

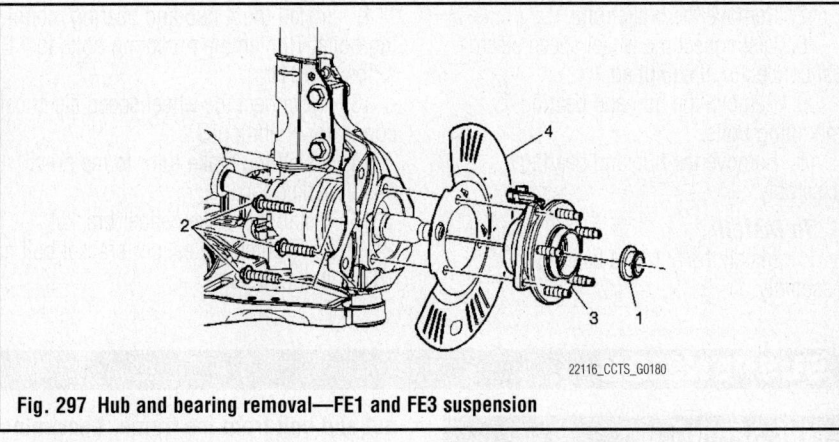

Fig. 297 Hub and bearing removal—FE1 and FE3 suspension

8. Disconnect the wheel speed electrical connector, if equipped.
9. Remove the hub and bearing 4 mounting bolts.
10. Remove the hub and bearing assembly.

To install:
11. Install the hub and bearing assembly.
12. Install the 3 hub and bearing mounting bolts. Tighten the mounting bolts to 96 ft. lbs. (130 Nm).
13. Reconnect the wheel speed electrical connector, if equipped.
14. Install the brake rotor to the previously marked location.
15. Install the brake caliper bracket assembly. Tighten the caliper bracket bolt to 133 ft. lbs. (180 Nm).
16. Install the axle nut. Use a suitable tool to prevent the wheel hub/bearing from rotating while installing the axle nut. Tighten the axle nut to 118 ft. lbs. (160 Nm).

17. Install the front tire and wheel assembly.
18. Lower the vehicle.

FE7 Suspension

See Figure 298.

1. Before servicing the vehicle, refer to the Precautions Section.
2. Raise and support the vehicle.
3. Remove the front tire and wheel assembly.
4. Remove the axle nut. Use a suitable tool to prevent the wheel hub/bearing from rotating while removing the axle nut.
5. Remove the brake caliper and the caliper mounting bracket as an assembly from the suspension knuckle and support the assembly with heavy mechanic's wire, or equivalent. Ensure that there is no tension on the hydraulic brake flexible hose.
6. Mark the relationship of the rotor to the hub.

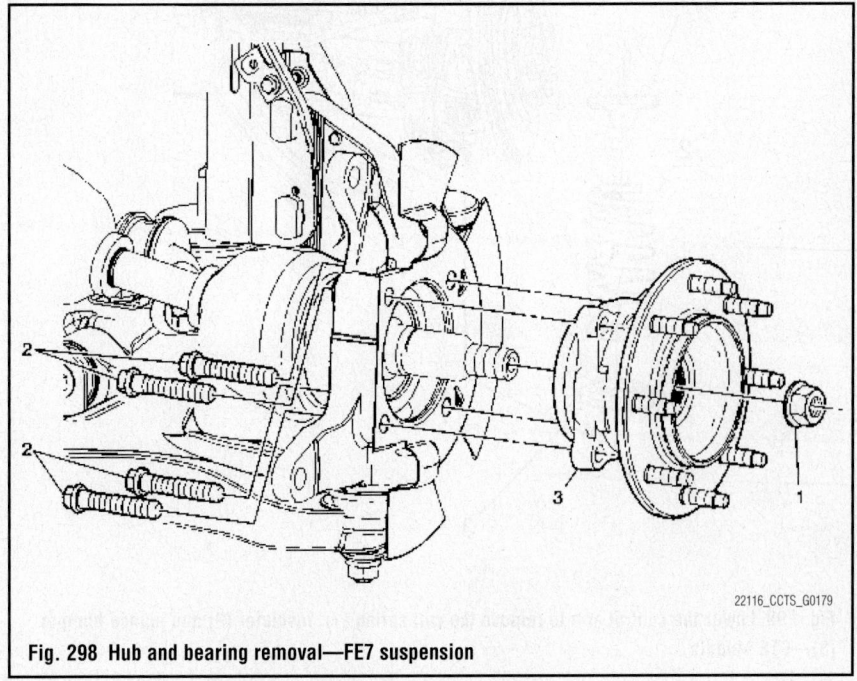

Fig. 298 Hub and bearing removal—FE7 suspension

7. Remove the brake rotor.

8. Disconnect the wheel speed electrical connector, if equipped.

9. Remove the hub and bearing 4 mounting bolts.

10. Remove the hub and bearing assembly.

To install:

11. Install the hub and bearing assembly.

12. Install the 4 hub and bearing mounting bolts. Tighten the mounting bolts to 112 ft. lbs. (152 Nm).

13. Reconnect the wheel speed electrical connector, if equipped.

14. Install the brake rotor to the previously marked location.

15. Install the brake caliper bracket assembly. Tighten the caliper bracket bolt to 181 ft. lbs. (246 Nm).

16. Install the axle nut. Use a suitable tool to prevent the wheel hub/bearing from rotating while installing the axle nut. Tighten the axle nut to 170 ft. lbs. (230 Nm).

17. Install the front tire and wheel assembly.

ADJUSTMENT

The wheel bearings are not adjustable.

SUSPENSION

COIL SPRING

REMOVAL & INSTALLATION

2008–09 CTS

See Figure 299.

1. Raise and safely support the vehicle.

2. Remove the rear tire.

3. Remove the stabilizer shaft link from the lower control arm.

4. Remove the trailing arm bolt at the knuckle.

5. Remove the adjustable link bolt from the knuckle.

➡**In the following service procedure, DO NOT remove the lower control arm** nut and bolt from the frame. Loosening the lower control arm nut and bolt will allow the lower control arm to have enough movement to remove the coil spring and other related components.

6. Loosen the lower control arm nut and bolt at the frame.

➡**In the following service procedure, it is NOT necessary to completely remove the wheel drive shaft. The wheel drive shaft can remain in the knuckle, but must be able to move freely in the knuckle.**

7. Separate the wheel drive shaft from the knuckle.

REAR SUSPENSION

8. Position a transmission jack under the lower control arm.

9. Remove the lower shock absorber bolt from the knuckle.

10. Remove the lower control arm bolt from the knuckle.

11. With the aid of an assistant, move the knuckle outward and up.

12. Slowly lower the transmission jack stand.

13. Lower the control arm and remove the coil spring, insulator and the jounce bumper.

14. Install the coil spring, insulator and the jounce bumper.

15. Using the transmission jack stand, lift the lower control arm.

➡**Leave all the bolts loose to aide in the alignment of all the suspension components prior to tightening to the final torque specifications.**

16. With the aid of an assistant, install the lower control arm on the knuckle.

17. Install the lower control arm bolt.

18. Install the trailing arm bolt in the knuckle.

19. Install the adjustable link bolt in the knuckle.

20. Install the lower shock absorber bolt in the knuckle.

21. Install the stabilizer shaft link to the lower control arm.

22. Tighten the wheel drive shaft nut to 158 ft. lbs. (215 Nm).

23. Install the rear wheel.

24. Remove the support and lower the vehicle.

25. Align the rear suspension and tighten the remaining suspension bolts.

2008–09 DTS

FE1 & FE3 SUSPENSIONS

See Figures 300 and 301.

1. Before servicing the vehicle, refer to the Precautions Section.

2. Raise and support the vehicle.

3. Remove the tire and the wheel

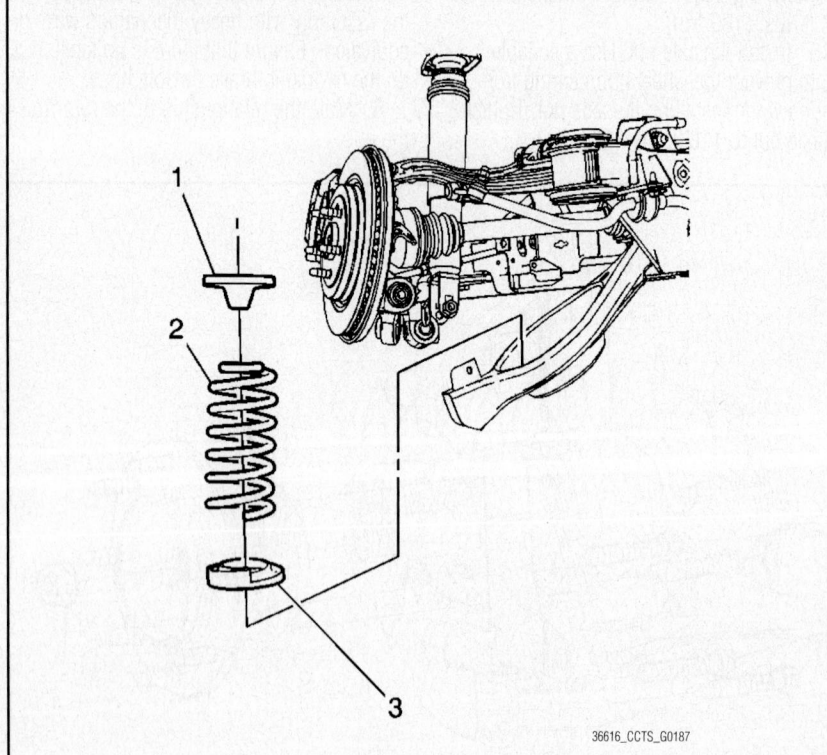

36616_CCTS_G0187

Fig. 299 Lower the control arm to remove the coil spring (1), insulator (2) and jounce bumper (3)—CTS Models

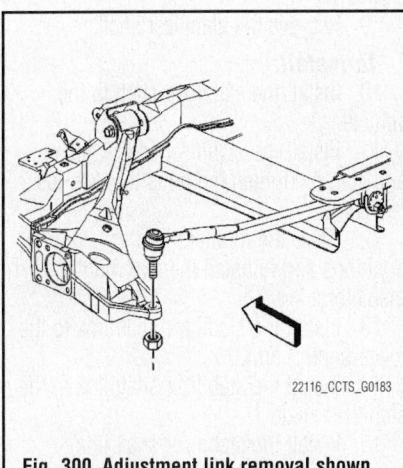

Fig. 300 Adjustment link removal shown

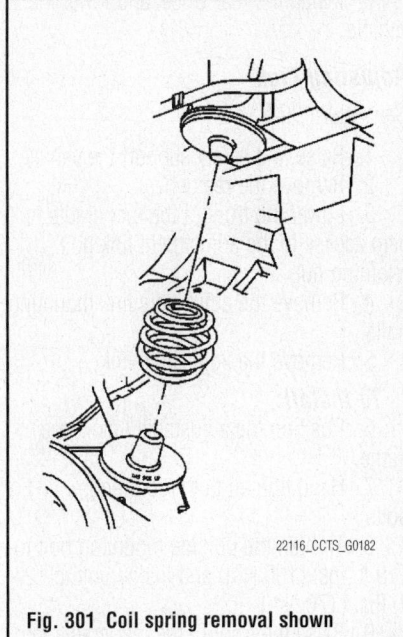

Fig. 301 Coil spring removal shown

4. Support the lower control arm with a suitable jack.

5. Remove the automatic level control link from the lower control arm.

6. Remove the shock absorber lower retaining bolts.

7. Remove the adjustment link retaining nut and use a puller to remove adjustment link.

8. Slowly lower the lower control arm until it bottoms on the support assembly.

9. Remove the coil spring.

To install:

10. Install the coil spring ensuring the insulator is seated in the lower control arm.

11. Raise the lower control arm and install the shock absorber lower retaining bolts.

12. Tighten the shock absorber lower retaining bolts to 18 ft. lbs. (25 Nm).

---

13. Install the adjustment link to the control arm.

14. Install the adjustment link retaining nut.

15. Tighten the adjustment link nut to 22 ft. lbs. (30 Nm), then tighten an additional 180 degrees.

16. Connect the automatic level control link to the lower control arm.

17. Install the tire and wheel.

18. Lower the vehicle.

FE7 SUSPENSION

1. Before servicing the vehicle, refer to the Precautions Section.

2. Raise the vehicle and support.

3. Remove the tires and the wheels.

4. Support the control arm with a suitable jack.

5. Remove the electronic level control air tube from the shock.

6. Remove the 2 bolts securing the shock to the control arm.

7. Remove the hex nut from the adjustment link.

8. Use the J 24319-B to remove the adjustment link from the control arm.

9. Install the J 44255 coil spring compressor.

10. Slowly lower the control arm until it bottoms on the support assembly.

11. Remove the coil spring.

To install:

12. Install the coil spring in the J 44255 coil spring compressor.

13. Install the spring ensuring the insulator is seated in the control arm.

14. Raise the lower control arm and install the 2 shock bolts in the control arm.

15. Tighten the shock bolts to 18 ft. lbs. (25 Nm).

16. Install the adjustment link to the control arm.

17. Tighten the adjustment link nut to 22 ft. lbs. (30 Nm), then tighten an additional 180 degrees.

18. Connect the electronic level control air tube to the shock.

19. Install the tires and the wheels.

20. Lower the vehicle.

21. Check the toe and adjust if necessary.

CONTROL ARMS/LINKS

REMOVAL & INSTALLATION

CTS & CTS-V

Lower Control Arm

See Figures 302 and 303.

1. Raise and safely support the vehicle.

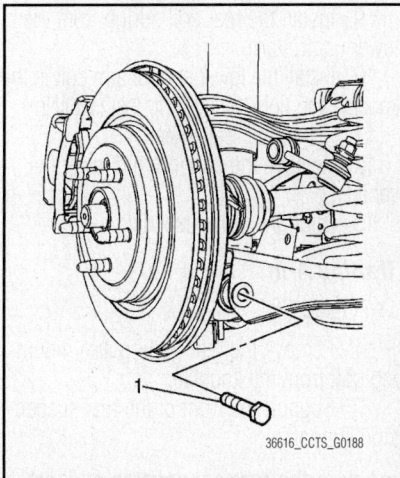

Fig. 302 Remove the lower control arm bolt (1) from the knuckle—CTS Models

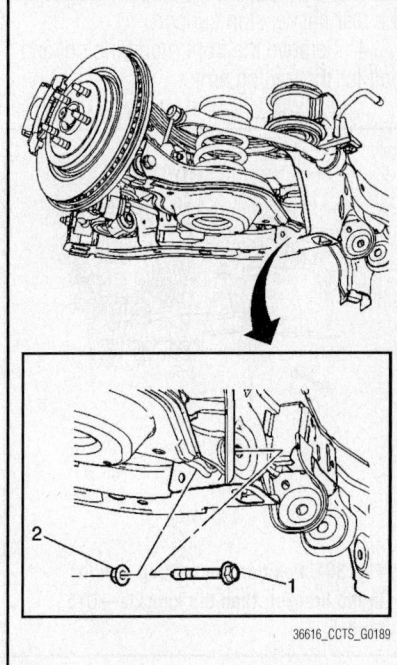

Fig. 303 Remove the retaining nut (2) and mounting bolt (1)—CTS Models

2. Remove the rear wheel.

3. Remove the lower control arm bolt from the knuckle.

4. Remove the rear coil spring from the lower control arm.

5. Remove the lower control arm retaining nut and mounting bolt.

6. Remove the lower control arm from the vehicle.

To install:

7. Position the lower control arm to the vehicle.

8. Install the lower control arm to the frame mounting bolt and nut, and tighten to 122 ft. lbs. (165 Nm).

9. Install the rear coil spring from the lower control arm.

10. Install the lower control arm bolt in the knuckle and tighten to 118 ft. lbs. (160 Nm).

11. Install the rear wheel.

12. Remove the support and lower the vehicle.

13. Align the rear suspension.

Trailing Arm

See Figure 304.

1. Remove the rear trailing arm mounting bolt from the knuckle.

2. Support the front of the rear suspension support.

➡**Lower the rear suspension support enough to gain access to the front trailing arm mounting bole and nut.**

3. Remove the front mounting bolts for the rear suspension support.

4. Remove the front mounting nut and bolt for the trailing arm.

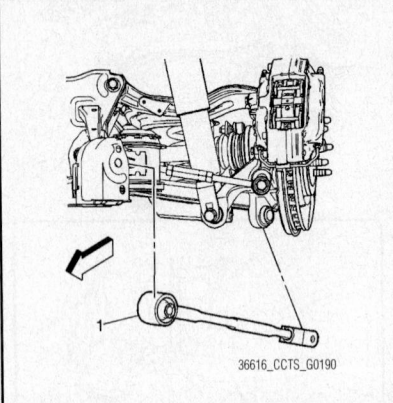

Fig. 304 Position the trailing arm (1) in the bracket, then the knuckle—CTS Models

To install:

5. Position the trailing arm in the mounting bracket first. Then position the trailing arm on the knuckle.

6. Install the trailing arm bolt and tighten the nut to 111 ft. lbs. (150 Nm).

7. Install the front mounting bolts for the rear suspension support.

8. Install the rear trailing arm mounting bolt and tighten to 125 ft. lbs. (170 Nm).

9. Install the rear wheel.

10. Remove the support from the vehicle and lower the vehicle.

11. Check and adjust the alignment of the rear suspension.

Stabilizer Shaft

See Figures 305 and 306.

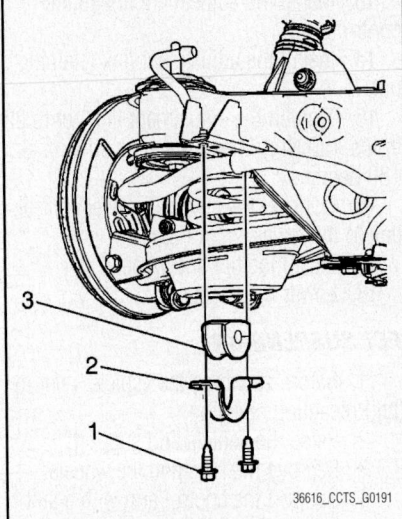

Fig. 305 Remove the stabilizer shaft insulator clamp bolts (1), clamp (2) and insulator (3)—CTS Models

1. Raise and safely support the vehicle.

2. Remove the rear wheel.

➡**Hold the shaft link stud with a hex tool to prevent damage to the link seal.**

3. Remove the stabilizer shaft link retaining nuts.

4. Remove the stabilizer shaft link from the stabilizer shaft.

5. Remove the stabilizer shaft link from the lower control arm.

6. Remove the bolts and stabilizer shaft insulator clamp and insulator.

7. Remove the rear muffler insulators.

8. Lower the rear muffler enough to remove the rear stabilizer shaft. Support the rear mufflers with jack stands.

9. Remove the stabilizer shaft.

To install:

10. Install the stabilizer shaft to the vehicle.

11. Install the stabilizer shaft insulator and clamp. Tighten the bolts to 44 ft. lbs. (60 Nm).

12. Raise the mufflers into positions and reinstall the rear muffler insulators.

13. Install the stabilizer shaft link to the lower control arm.

14. Install the stabilizer shaft link to the stabilizer shaft.

15. Install the stabilizer shaft link retaining nuts and tighten to 49 ft. lbs. (66 Nm).

16. Install the rear wheel and lower the vehicle.

Adjusting Link

See Figure 307.

1. Raise and safely support the vehicle.

2. Remove the rear wheel.

3. Lower the front of the rear cradle to gain access to the adjustment link bolt retaining nut.

4. Remove the adjustable link mounting bolts.

5. Remove the adjustable link.

To install:

6. Position the adjustable link in the frame.

7. Hand tighten both mounting bolts.

8. Tighten the outside mounting bolt to 118 ft. lbs. (160 Nm) and inside bolt to 125 ft. lbs. (170 Nm).

9. Raise the front of the rear cradle into position.

10. Install the rear wheel and lower the vehicle.

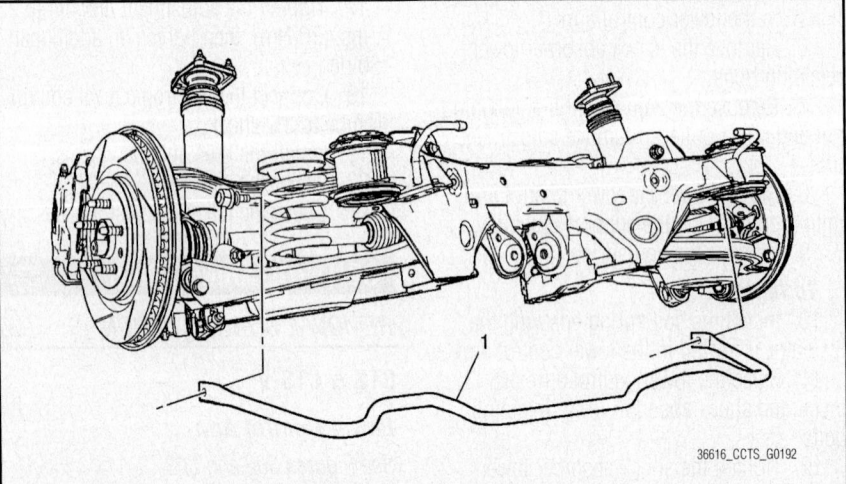

Fig. 306 Removing the rear stabilizer shaft (1)—CTS Models

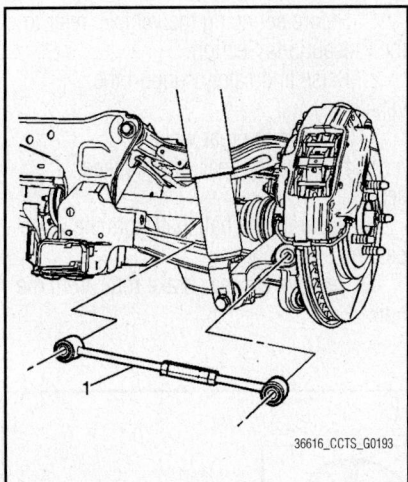

Fig. 307 Remove the adjustable link (1)— CTS Models

11. Check and adjust the rear toe as necessary.

2008–09 DTS

FE1 & FE3 Suspensions

See Figure 308.

1. Before servicing the vehicle, refer to the Precautions Section.
2. Remove the rear suspension support assembly.
3. Remove the stabilizer shaft link bolt.
4. Remove the stabilizer shaft insulators and spacer.
5. Remove the hub and bearing, if necessary.
6. Remove the nuts and the bolts securing the control arm to the rear suspension support assembly.
7. Remove the lower control arm.

To install:

➡**The control arm nuts should be tightened with the vehicle unsupported and**

resting on the wheels at the normal trim height.

8. Install the lower control arm to the rear suspension support assembly.
9. Install the wheel bearing and hub, if necessary.
10. Install stabilizer shaft link bolt, spacer, insulator, and nut.
11. Tighten the stabilizer shaft link nut to 11 ft. lbs. (15 Nm).
12. Install the rear suspension support assembly.
13. Tighten the control arm nuts and bolts with the vehicle at normal ride height.
14. Tighten the control arm nuts to 78 ft. lbs. (106 Nm).
15. Lower the vehicle.

FE7 Suspension

See Figure 309.

1. Before servicing the vehicle, refer to the Precautions Section.
2. Remove the rear suspension support assembly
3. Remove the stabilizer link bolt.
4. Remove the hub and bearing, if necessary.
5. Remove the support bracket bolts.
6. Remove the nuts and bolts securing the control arm to the rear suspension support assembly.
7. Remove the control arm.

To install:

➡**The control arm nuts should be tightened with the vehicle unsupported and resting on the wheels at the normal trim height.**

8. Install the control arm to the rear suspension support assembly.
9. Install the hub and bearing, if necessary.
10. Install a new stabilizer link bolt and nut.

11. Tighten the new stabilizer link bolt nut to 11ft. lbs. (15 Nm).
12. Install the rear suspension support assembly.
13. Install the support bracket bolts.
14. Lower the vehicle to obtain trim height.
15. Tighten the control arm nuts.
16. Tighten the control arm nuts to 110 ft. lbs. (149 Nm).
17. Lower the vehicle.

SHOCK ABSORBER

REMOVAL & INSTALLATION

CTS & CTS-V

1. Before servicing the vehicle, refer to the Precautions Section.
2. Remove the rear seat back.
3. Remove the rear compartment sill plate.
4. Remove the rear compartment side trim by removing the trim retainers.
5. Remove the upper shock mounting nuts.
6. Raise and safely support the vehicle.
7. Remove the lower shock mounting bolt.
8. Remove the shock from the vehicle.

To install:

9. Install the shock to the vehicle. Tighten the lower shock mounting bolt to 111 ft. lbs. (150 Nm).
10. Guide the shock to the body while carefully lowering the vehicle.
11. Install the upper shock mounting nuts and tighten to 18 ft. lbs. (25 Nm).
12. Install the rear compartment sill trim.

2008–09 DTS

See Figures 310 and 311.

1. Before servicing the vehicle, refer to the Precautions Section.
2. Raise and safely support the vehicle.
3. Remove the wheel and tire.
4. Support the lower control arm with a jack.
5. Disconnect the electronic level control air tube from the shock.
6. Disconnect the shock electrical connector and remove the wiring from the control arm.
7. Remove the 2 bolts securing the shock to the control arm.
8. Pull the trunk trim back to gain access to the upper shock.
9. Remove the upper shock dust cover.

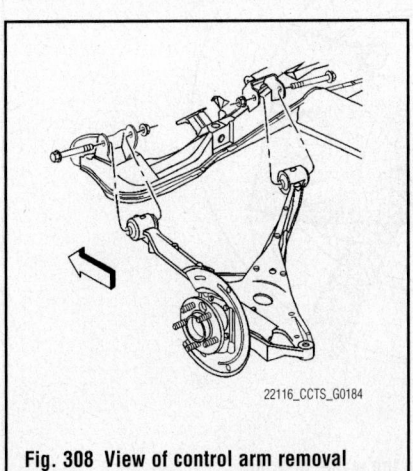

Fig. 308 View of control arm removal

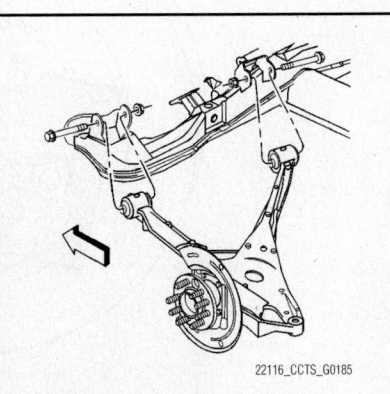

Fig. 309 View of control arm removal (FE7) suspension

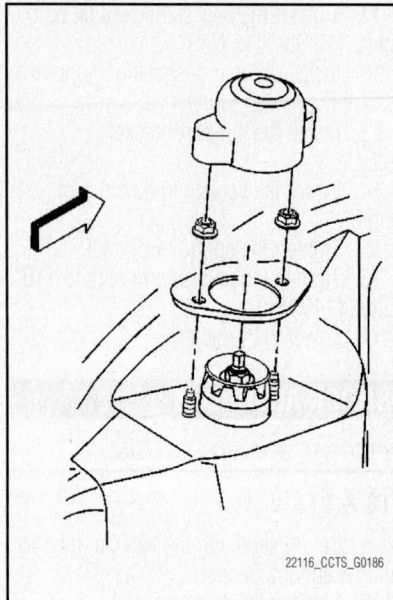

Fig. 310 Upper shock mount nuts, and cover shown

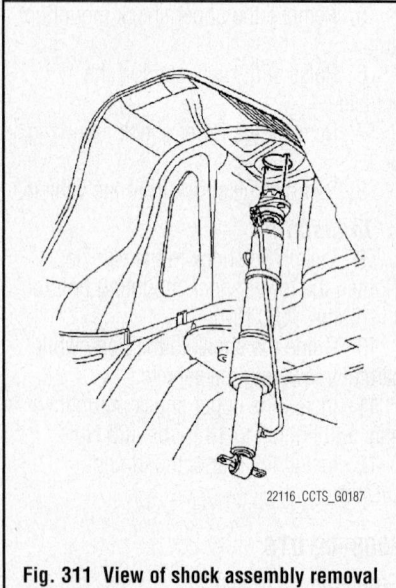

Fig. 311 View of shock assembly removal

10. Remove the 2 nuts and the reinforcement from the shock.

11. Remove the shock from the vehicle.

To install:

12. Install the shock on the vehicle.

13. Install the shock upper mount.

14. Install the shock reinforcement and the two nuts. Tighten the nuts to 18 ft. lbs. (25 Nm).

15. Install the shock cover.

16. Position the trunk trim in the proper location.

17. Install the lower shock bolts. Tighten the nuts to 18 ft. lbs. (25 Nm).

18. Connect the electronic air control air tube to the shock.

19. Connect the electrical connector and route the wiring on the control arm (FE3 and FE45).

20. Install the wheel and the tire.

21. Lower the vehicle.

WHEEL BEARINGS

REMOVAL & INSTALLATION

CTS & CTS-V

See Figures 312 and 313.

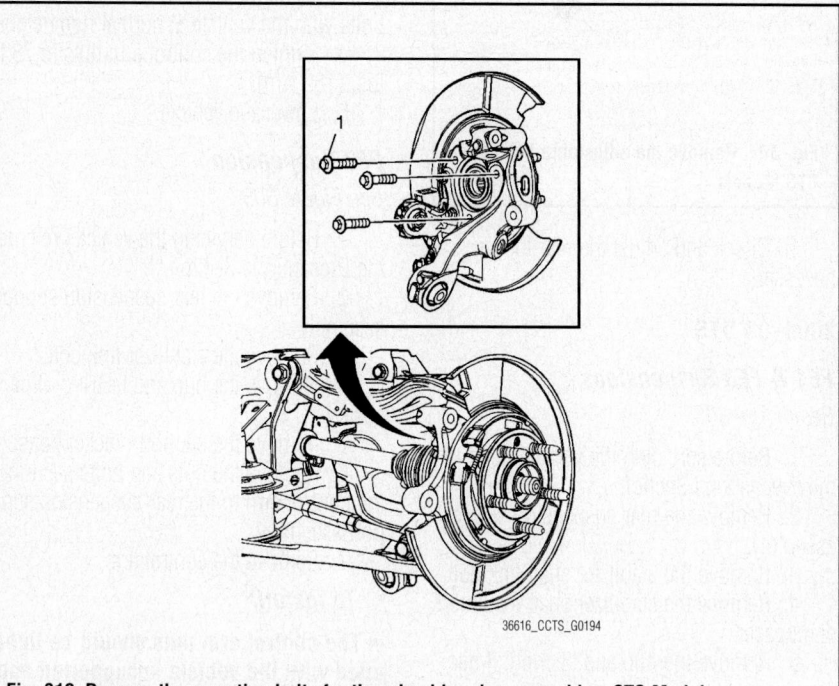

Fig. 312 Remove the mounting bolts for the wheel bearing assembly—CTS Models

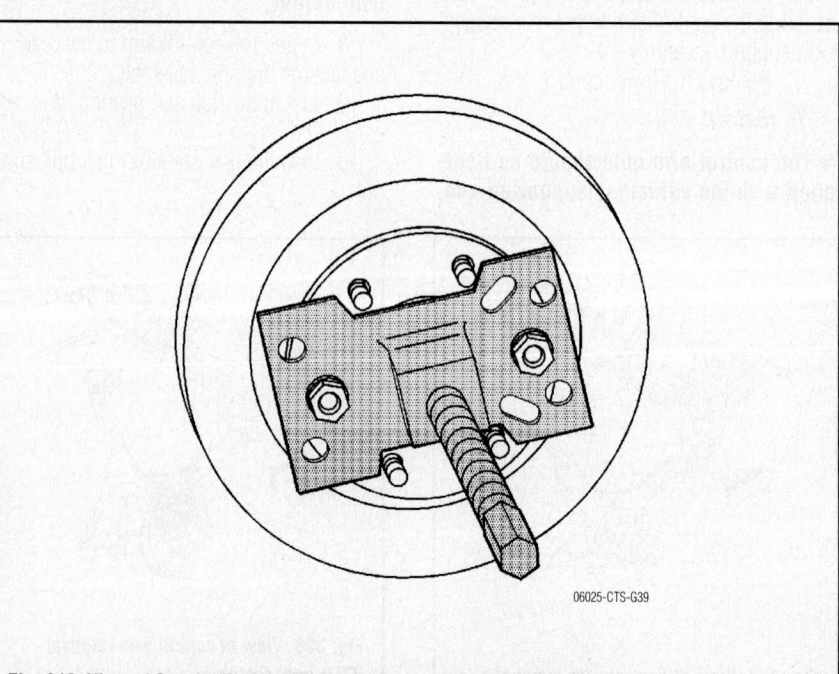

Fig. 313 View of Special Tool J-45859 installed on the wheel bearing.

1. Before servicing the vehicle, refer to the Precautions Section.

2. Raise and safely support the vehicle.

3. Remove the rear wheel.

4. Remove the rear wheel speed sensor.

5. Separate the halfshaft from the wheel bearing assembly.

6. Remove the rear brake rotor from the hub.

7. Remove the mounting bolts for the wheel bearing/hub assembly.

8. Using Special Tool J-45859, remove the wheel bearing assembly from the vehicle.

To install:

9. Position the rear wheel bearing assembly in the knuckle.

10. Insert the wheel drive axle into the wheel bearing assembly.

11. Install the wheel bearing mounting bolts to 103 ft. lbs. (140 Nm).

12. The remainder of the installation is the reverse order of removal.

2008–09 DTS

FE1 & FE3 Suspensions

See Figure 314.

1. Before servicing the vehicle, refer to the Precautions Section.

2. Raise and support the vehicle.

3. Remove the tire and wheel.

4. Remove the brake caliper with bracket.

5. Remove the brake rotor.

6. Disconnect the ABS sensor wire connector.

7. Remove the wheel bearing/hub bolts.

8. Remove the wheel bearing/hub and brake shield.

To install:

9. Clean the lower control arm face and bore before installing the wheel bearing and hub.

10. Install the wheel bearing and hub and brake shield to the lower control arm.

11. Install the wheel bearing and hub retaining bolts. Tighten the wheel bearing and hub retaining bolts to 50 ft. lbs. (68 Nm).

12. Install the brake rotor.

13. Install the brake caliper with bracket. Tighten the bracket bolts to 94 ft. lbs. (128 Nm).

14. Install the ABS sensor wire connector.

15. Install the tire and wheel.

16. Lower the vehicle.

FE7 Suspension

See Figures 315 and 316.

1. Before servicing the vehicle, refer to the Precautions Section.

2. Raise and support the vehicle.

3. Remove the rear tire and wheel assembly.

4. Remove the brake caliper with bracket.

5. Remove the brake rotor.

6. Disconnect the ABS sensor connector.

7. Remove the ABS sensor.

8. Remove and the wheel speed sensor reluctor ring (1).

9. Disconnect the park brake cable from the backing plate.

10. Remove the hub and bearing mounting bolts.

11. Remove the rear wheel bearing nut.

12. Remove the washer from the hub.

13. Remove the hub from the bearing.

14. Press the wheel bearing out the rear of the backing plate.

To install:

15. Carefully press the wheel bearing into the rear of the backing plate.

16. Install the hub into the sealed bearing.

17. Install the washer and the retaining nut to the hub. Tighten the nut to 147 ft. lbs. (200 Nm).

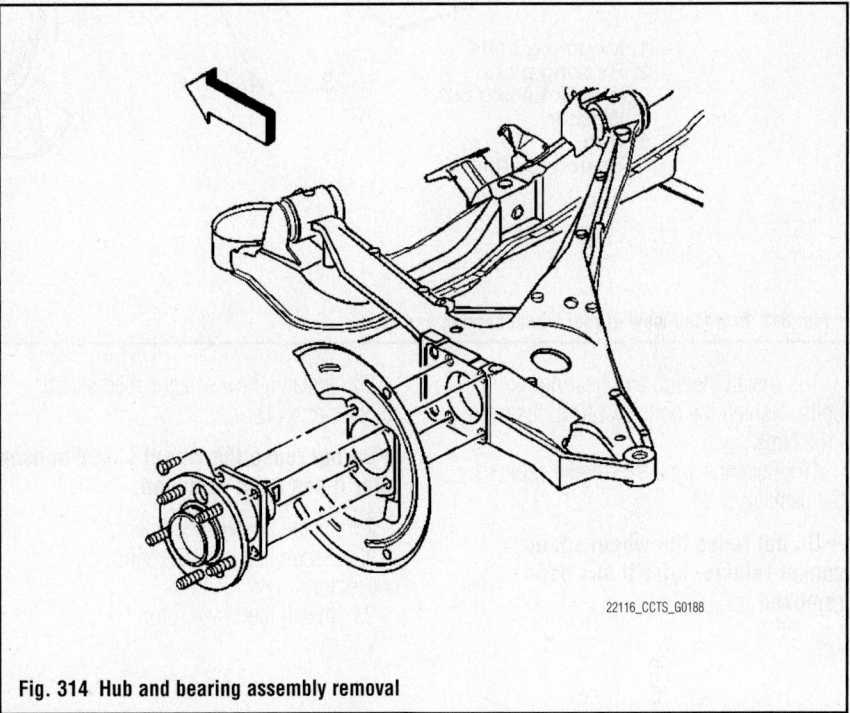

Fig. 314 Hub and bearing assembly removal

22116_CCTS_G0188

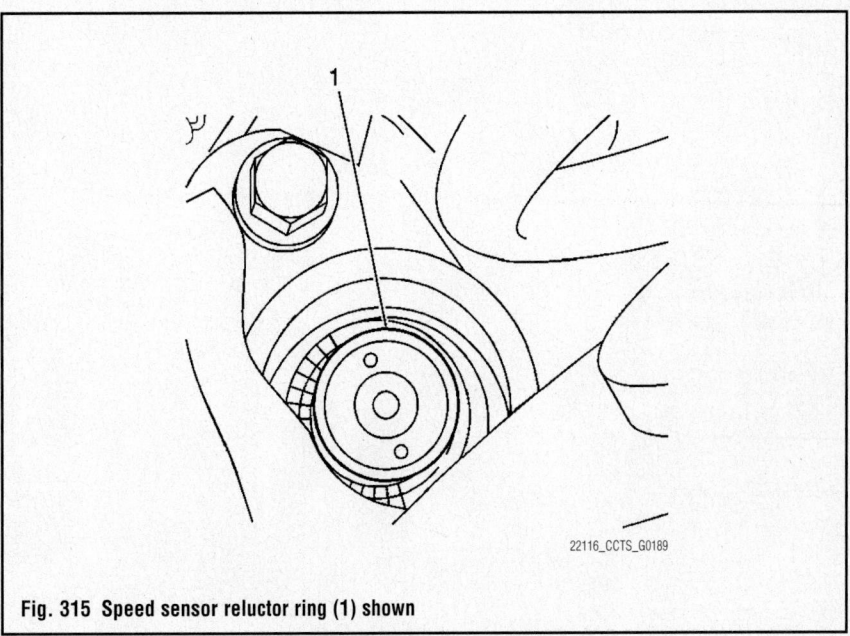

Fig. 315 Speed sensor reluctor ring (1) shown

22116_CCTS_G0189

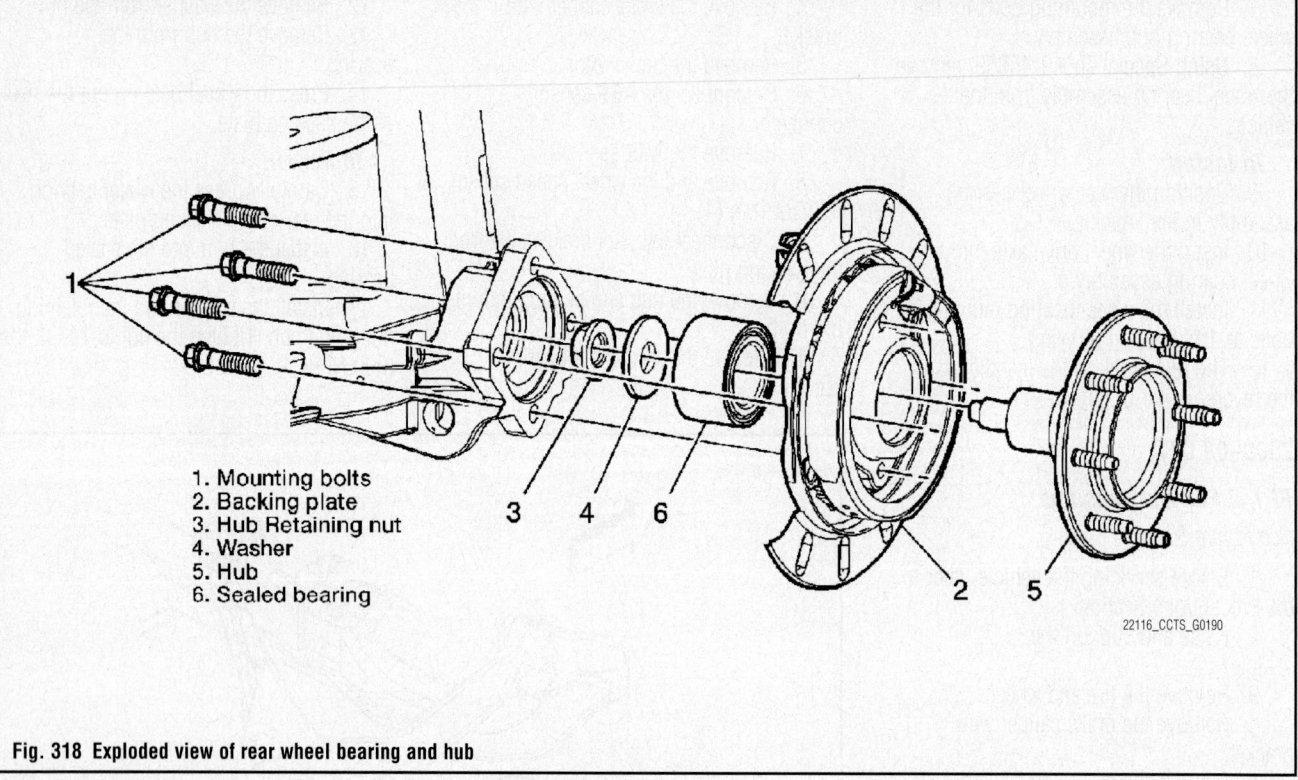

1. Mounting bolts
2. Backing plate
3. Hub Retaining nut
4. Washer
5. Hub
6. Sealed bearing

22116_CCTS_G0190

Fig. 318 Exploded view of rear wheel bearing and hub

18. Install the hub and bearing mounting bolts. Tighten the bolts to 112 ft. lbs. (152 Nm).

19. Reconnect the park brake cable to the backing plate.

➡**Do not reuse the wheel speed sensor reluctor after it has been removed.**

20. Install a new wheel speed sensor reluctor ring (1).

➡**Do not reuse the wheel speed sensor after it has been removed.**

21. Install a new speed sensor.

22. Reconnect the ABS sensor connector.

23. Install the brake rotor.

24. Install the brake caliper with bracket. Tighten the bracket bolts to 120 ft. lbs.(163 Nm).

25. Install the rear tire and wheel assembly.

26. Lower the vehicle.

ADJUSTMENT

The wheel bearings are not adjustable.

CHEVROLET AND GMC

Envoy • TrailBlazer

13

SPECIFICATIONS AND MAINTENANCE CHARTS

ENGINE AND VEHICLE IDENTIFICATION

		Engine						Model Year	
Code ①	Liters (cc)	Cu. In.	Cyl.	Fuel Sys.	Engine Type	Eng. Mfg.	Code ②		Year
S	4.2 (4200)	256	6	MFI	DOHC	CPC	8		2008
M	5.3 (5326)	325	8	SFI	OHV	CPC	9		2009
H	6.0 (5967)	364	8	SFI	OHV	CPC			

CPC: Chevrolet/Pontiac/Canada

MFI: Multi-port Fuel Injection

SFI: Sequential Fuel Injection

① 8th position of VIN

② 10th position of VIN

36616_ENVO_C0001

GENERAL ENGINE SPECIFICATIONS

All measurements are given in inches.

Year	Model	Engine Displacement Liters	Engine Series (ID/VIN)	Net Horsepower @ rpm	Net Torque @ rpm (ft. lbs.)	Bore x Stroke (in.)	Compression Ratio	Oil Pressure @ rpm
2008	Envoy	4.2	S	291@6000	277@4800	3.66x4.02	10.3:1	12@1200
		5.3	M	300@5200	330@4000	3.78x3.62	9.95:1	18@2000
	TrailBlazer	4.2	S	291@6000	277@4800	3.66x4.02	10.3:1	12@1200
		5.3	M	300@5200	330@4000	3.78x3.62	9.95:1	18@2000
		6.0	H	395@6000	400@4000	4.00x3.62	10.86:1	18@2000
2009	Envoy	4.2	S	291@6000	277@4800	3.66x4.02	10.3:1	12@1200
		5.3	M	302@5200	330@4000	3.78x3.62	9.95:1	18@2000
	TrailBlazer	4.2	S	291@6000	277@4800	3.66x4.02	10.3:1	12@1200
		6.0	H	395@6000	400@4000	4.00x3.62	10.86:1	18@2000

36616_ENVO_C0002

GASOLINE ENGINE TUNE-UP SPECIFICATIONS

Year	Engine Displacement Liters	Engine ID/VIN	Spark Plugs Gap (in.)	Ignition Timing (deg.) MT	Ignition Timing (deg.) AT	Fuel Pump (psi)	Idle Speed (rpm) MT	Idle Speed (rpm) AT	Valve Clearance In.	Valve Clearance Ex.
2008	4.2	S	0.042	—	①	50-57 ②	—	③	HYD	HYD
	5.3	M	0.040	—	①	50-60 ②	—	③	HYD	HYD
	6.0	H	0.040	—	①	50-60 ②	—	③	HYD	HYD
2009	4.2	S	0.042	—	①	50-57 ②	—	③	HYD	HYD
	5.3	M	0.040	—	①	50-60 ②	—	③	HYD	HYD
	6.0	H	0.040	—	①	50-60 ②	—	③	HYD	HYD

NOTE: The Vehicle Emission Control Information label often reflects specification changes made during production.

The label figures must be used if they differ from those in this chart.

HYD: Hydraulic

① Distributorless ignition, cannot be adjusted

② With key ON and engine OFF

③ Distributorless ignition, cannot be adjusted

36616_ENVO_C0003

CAPACITIES

Year	Model	Engine Displacement Liters	Engine ID/VIN	Engine Oil with Filter (qts.)	Transmission (pts.)		Transfer Case (pts.)	Drive Axle		Fuel Tank (gal.)	Cooling System (qts.)
					5-Spd	Auto.		Front (pts.)	Rear (pts.)		
2008	Envoy	4.2	S	7.0	NA	12.0 ①	2.0	1.7	3.6 ②	22	9.7
		5.3	M	6.0	NA	12.0 ①	2.0	1.7	4.3	22	11.2
	TrailBlazer	4.2	S	7.0	NA	12.0 ①	2.0	1.7	3.6 ②	22	9.7
		5.3	M	6.0	NA	12.0 ①	2.0	1.7	4.3	22	11.2
		6.0	H	6.0	NA	12.0 ①	2.0	1.7	4.3	22	12.2
2009	Envoy	4.2	S	7.0	NA	12.0 ①	2.0	1.7	3.6 ②	22	9.7
		5.3	M	6.0	NA	12.0 ①	2.0	1.7	4.3	22	11.2
	TrailBlazer	4.2	S	7.0	NA	12.0 ①	2.0	1.7	3.6 ②	22	9.7
		6.0	H	6.0	NA	12.0 ①	2.0	1.7	4.3	22	11.2

NOTE: All capacities are approximate. Add fluid gradually and check to be sure a proper fluid level is obtained.

NA: Not Available

① Dry fill (Pan removal 5 qts.)

② 4.2L L6 w/ opt. 18 inch wheels: 4.3 pts.

36616_ENVO_C0005

FLUID SPECIFICATIONS

Year	Model	Engine Displacement Liters	Engine ID/VIN	Engine Oil	Auto. Trans.	Drive Axles ②	Transfer Case	Power Steering Fluid	Brake Master Cylinder
2008	Envoy	4.2	S	5W-30	Dexron-VI	75W-90	Auto-Trak II	GM PS Fluid	DOT 3
		5.3	M	5W-30	Dexron-VI	75W-90	Auto-Trak II	GM PS Fluid	DOT 3
	TrailBlazer	4.2	S	5W-30	Dexron-VI	75W-90	Auto-Trak II	GM PS Fluid	DOT 3
		5.3	M	5W-30	Dexron-VI	75W-90	Auto-Trak II	GM PS Fluid	DOT 3
		6.0	H	5W-30 ①	Dexron-VI	75W-90 ③	Auto-Trak II	GM PS Fluid	DOT 3
2009	Envoy	4.2	S	5W-30	Dexron-VI	75W-90	Auto-Trak II	GM PS Fluid	DOT 3
		5.3	M	5W-30	Dexron-VI	75W-90	Auto-Trak II	GM PS Fluid	DOT 3
	TrailBlazer	4.2	S	5W-30	Dexron-VI	75W-90	Auto-Trak II	GM PS Fluid	DOT 3
		5.3	M	5W-30	Dexron-VI	75W-90	Auto-Trak II	GM PS Fluid	DOT 3
		6.0	H	5W-30 ①	Dexron-VI	75W-90 ③	Auto-Trak II	GM PS Fluid	DOT 3

DOT: Department Of Transpotation

① Mobil 1 synthetic oil

② Synthetic fluid is recomended

③ Plus a limited slip axle additive (SS Models)

36616_ENVO_C0004

VALVE SPECIFICATIONS

Year	Engine Displacement Liters	Engine ID/VIN	Seat Angle (deg.)	Face Angle (deg.)	Spring Test Pressure (lbs. @ in.)	Spring Installed Height (in.)	Stem-to-Guide Clearance (in.)		Stem Diameter (in.)	
							Intake	Exhaust	Intake	Exhaust
2008	4.2	S	NA	NA	130-142@1.26	NA	0.0011-0.0025	0.0015-0.0030	NA	NA
	5.3	M	46	45	220@1.32	1.80	0.0010-0.0026	0.0010-0.0026	0.313-0.314	0.313-0.314
	6.0	H	46	45	220@1.32	1.80	0.0010-0.0026	0.0010-0.0026	0.313-0.314	0.313-0.314
2009	4.2	S	NA	NA	130-142@1.26	NA	0.0011-0.0025	0.0015-0.0030	NA	NA
	5.3	M	46	45	220@1.32	1.80	0.0010-0.0026	0.0010-0.0026	0.313-0.314	0.313-0.314
	6.0	H	46	45	220@1.32	1.80	0.0010-0.0026	0.0010-0.0026	0.313-0.314	0.313-0.314

NA: Not Available

36616_ENVO_C0006

CAMSHAFT AND BEARING SPECIFICATIONS CHART
All measurements are given in inches.

Year	Engine Displ. Liters	Engine ID/VIN	Journal Dia.	Brg. Oil Clearance	Shaft End-play	Runout	Journal Bore	Lobe Height	
								Intake	Exhaust
2008	4.2	S	①	NA	②	NA	0.0015-0.0033	1.635 ③	1.615 ③
	5.3	M	2.164-2.1660	0.0009-0.0038	0.001-0.0120	0.002-④	NA	NA	NA
	6.0	H	2.164-2.1660	0.0009-0.0038	0.001-0.0120	0.002-④	NA	N/L	N/L
2009	4.2	S	①	NA	②	N/L	0.0015-0.0033	1.635 ③	1.615 ③
	5.3	M	2.164-2.1660	0.0009-0.0038	0.001-0.0120	0.002-④	NA	NA	NA
	6.0	H	2.164-2.1660	0.0009-0.0038	0.001-0.0120	0.002-④	NA	NA	NA

NA: Not Available

① All intake and Exhaust 2 through 7: 1.0612-1.0622 in.

Exhaust 1: 1.1794 - 1.1804 in.

② Exhaust: 0.0017-0.0084 in.

Intake: 0.0020 - 0.0079 in.

③ Minimum reading

④ Measured at the intermediate journals.

36616_ENVO_C0007

CRANKSHAFT AND CONNECTING ROD SPECIFICATIONS

All measurements are given in inches.

Year	Engine Displacement Liters	Engine ID/VIN	Crankshaft				Connecting Rod		
			Main Brg. Journal Dia.	Main Brg. Oil Clearance	Shaft End-play	Thrust on No.	Journal Diameter	Oil Clearance	Side Clearance
2008	4.2	S	2.7567-2.7574	0.0004-0.0025	0.0044-0.0153	4	2.2337-2.2342	0.0008-0.0025	0.0019-0.0137
	5.3	M	2.5587-2.5593	0.0008-0.0021	0.0015-0.0078	4	2.0991-2.0999	0.0009-0.0025	0.0043-0.0200
	6.0	H	2.5587-2.5593	0.0008-0.0025	0.0015-0.0078	4	2.0991-2.0999	0.0009-0.0025	0.0043-0.0200
2009	4.2	S	2.7567-2.7574	0.0004-0.0025	0.0044-0.0153	4	2.2337-2.2342	0.0008-0.0025	0.0019-0.0137
	5.3	M	2.5587-2.5593	0.0008-0.0021	0.0015-0.0078	4	2.0991-2.0999	0.0009-0.0025	0.0043-0.0200
	6.0	H	2.5587-2.5593	0.0008-0.0025	0.0015-0.0078	4	2.0991-2.0999	0.0009-0.0025	0.0043-0.0200

36616_ENVO_C0008

PISTON AND RING SPECIFICATIONS

All measurements are given in inches.

Year	Engine Displ. Liters	Engine ID/VIN	Piston Clearance	Ring Gap			Ring Side Clearance		
				Top Compression	Bottom Compression	Oil Control	Top Compression	Bottom Compression	Oil Control
2008	4.2	S	-0.0006 0.0014	0.0059-0.0118	0.0142-0.0201	0.0098-0.0299	0.0017-0.0037	0.0017-0.0037	0.0023-0.0085
	5.3	M	-0.0014 0.0006	0.0090-0.0173	0.0173-0.0275	0.0070-0.0295	0.0015-0.0033	0.0015-0.0031	0.0005-0.0078
	6.0	H	-0.0009 0.0012	0.0080-0.0160	0.0150-0.0270	0.0090-0.0310	0.0012-0.0040	0.0014-0.0031	0.0005-0.0079
2009	4.2	S	-0.0006 0.0014	0.0059-0.0118	0.0142-0.0201	0.0098-0.0299	0.0017-0.0037	0.0017-0.0037	0.0023-0.0085
	5.3	M	-0.0014 0.0006	0.0090-0.0173	0.0173-0.0275	0.0070-0.0295	0.0015-0.0033	0.0015-0.0031	0.0005-0.0078
	6.0	H	-0.0009 0.0012	0.0080-0.0160	0.0150-0.0270	0.0090-0.0310	0.0012-0.0040	0.0014-0.0031	0.0005-0.0079

36616_ENVO_C0009

TORQUE SPECIFICATIONS
All readings in ft. lbs.

Year	Engine Displacement Liters	Engine ID/VIN	Cylinder Head Bolts	Main Bearing Bolts	Rod Bearing Bolts	Crankshaft Damper Bolts	Flywheel Bolts	Manifold		Spark Plugs	Oil Pan Drain Plug
								Intake *	Exhaust		
2008	4.2	S	①	②	③	④	⑤	⑥	⑦	13	19
	5.3	M	⑧	⑨	⑩	⑪	⑫	⑬	⑭	11	18
	6.0	H	⑧	⑨	⑩	⑪	⑫	⑬	⑭	11	18
2009	4.2	S	①	②	③	④	⑤	⑥	⑦	13	19
	5.3	M	⑧	⑨	⑩	⑪	⑫	⑬	⑭	11	18
	6.0	H	⑧	⑨	⑩	⑪	⑫	⑬	⑭	11	18

* NOTE: Applies to Lower Manifold only.

① Cylinder head bolts (14)
  1st pass: 22 ft. lbs.
  2nd pass: Plus 155 degrees
  2 short end bolts: 62 INCH lbs.
  2nd pass: plus 60 degrees
  1 long end bolt: 62 INCH lbs.
  2nd pass: plus 120 degrees

② 18 ft. lbs., plus 180 depress

③ 18 ft. lbs., plus 110 degrees

④ 110 ft. lbs., plus 180 degrees

⑤ 30 ft. lbs., plus 45 degrees

⑥ 89 inch lbs.

⑦ 1st pass: 15 ft. lbs.
  2nd pass: 15 ft. lbs.
  3rd pass: 15 ft. lbs.

⑧ M11 bolts: 22 ft. lbs.
  2nd pass: Plus 90 degrees
  3rd pass: Plus 70 degrees
  M8 bolts: 22 ft. lbs.

⑨ Inner bolts:
  1st pass: 15 ft. lbs.
  Final pass: Plus 80 degrees
  Outer bolts:
  1st pass: 15 ft. lbs.
  Final pass: Plus 51 degrees
  M8 bolts: 18 ft. lbs.

⑩ 15 ft. lbs. plus 85 degrees

⑪ Installation pass: 240 ft. lbs. (discard bolt)
  First pass: 37 ft. lbs. (new bolt)
  Final pass: Plus 140 degrees

⑫ 1st pass: 15 ft. lbs.
  2nd pass: 37 ft. lbs.
  3rd pass: 74 ft. lbs.

⑬ 1st pass: 44 inch lbs.
  2nd pass: 89 inch lbs.

⑭ 1st pass: 11 ft. lbs.
  2nd pass: 18 ft. lbs.

36616_ENVO_C0010

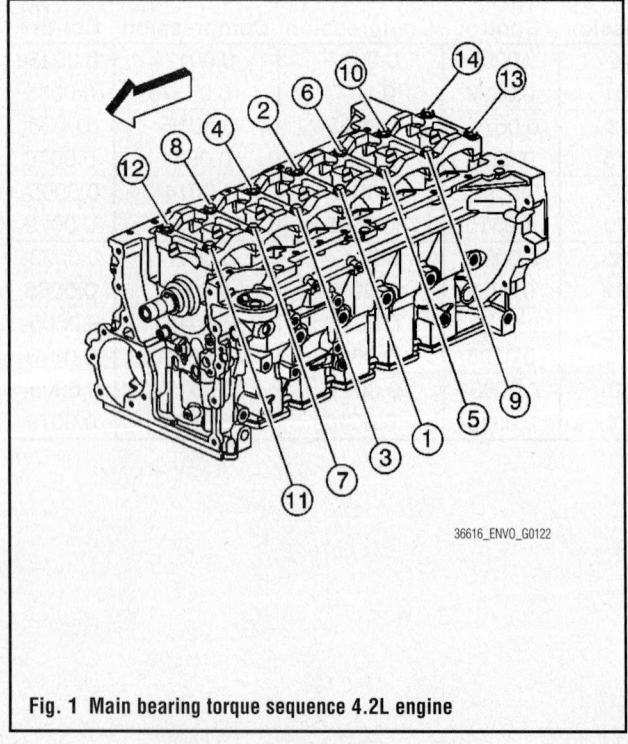

Fig. 1 Main bearing torque sequence 4.2L engine

36616_ENVO_G0122

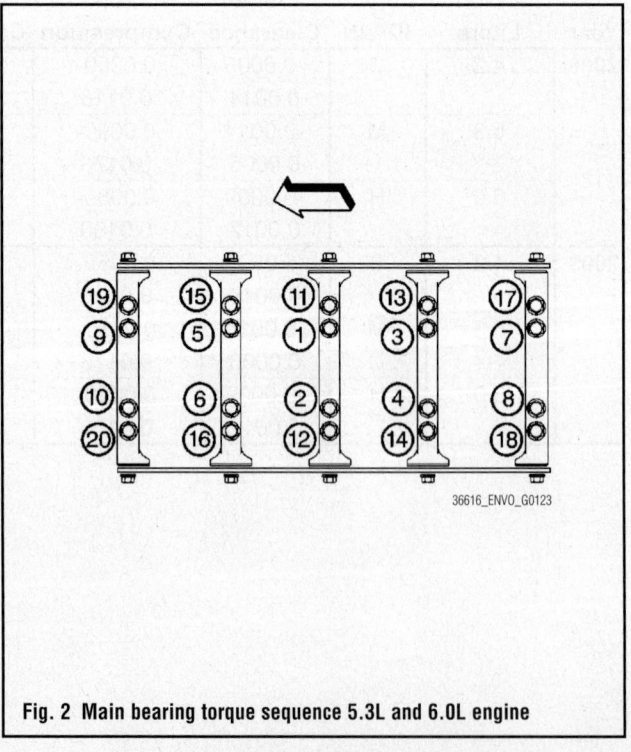

Fig. 2 Main bearing torque sequence 5.3L and 6.0L engine

36616_ENVO_G0123

WHEEL ALIGNMENT

| Year | Model | | Caster | | Camber | | Toe-in |
			Range (+/-Deg.)	Preferred Setting (Deg.)	Range (+/-Deg.)	Preferred Setting (Deg.)	(in.)
2008	Envoy/	①	0.60	+4.00	0.60	0.00	-0.10+/-0.20
	TrailBlazer	②	0.60	+4.25	0.60	0.00	-0.10+/-0.20
2009	Envoy/	①	0.60	+4.00	0.60	0.00	-0.10+/-0.20
	TrailBlazer	②	0.60	+4.25	0.60	0.00	-0.10+/-0.20

① With rear coil spring suspension.

② With rear air spring suspension.

36616_ENVO_C0011

TIRE, WHEEL AND BALL JOINT SPECIFICATIONS

| Year | Model | OEM Tires | | Tire Pressures (psi) | | Wheel Size | Ball Joint Inspection | Lug Nut (ft. lbs.) |
		Standard	Optional	Front	Rear			
2008	Envoy/ TrailBlazer	P245/65R17	②	36	36	7-JJ	L ①	103
2009	Envoy/ TrailBlazer	P245/65R17	②	36	36	7-JJ	L ①	103

OEM: Original Equipment Manufacturer

PSI: Pounds Per Square Inch

L: Lower (ball joint)

① Do not lift truck. Inspect the boss into which the grease fitting is threaded. Replace if the boss is flush or receded below the surface of the ball joint

② GMC Denali model: P245/60R18

TrailBlazer SS model: P255/50VR20

36616_ENVO_C0012

BRAKE SPECIFICATIONS
All measurements in inches unless noted

| Year | Model | Front Brake Disc | | | Rear Brake Disc | | | Brake Caliper | |
		Original Thickness	Minimum Thickness	Maximum Runout	Original Thickness	Minimum Thickness	Maximum Runout	Bracket Bolts (ft. lbs.)	Mounting Bolts (ft. lbs.)
2008	Envoy	1.140	1.080	0.002	0.787	0.728	0.002	①	②
	TrailBlazer	1.140	1.080	0.002	0.787	0.728	0.002	①	②
2009	Envoy	1.140	1.080	0.002	0.787	0.728	0.002	①	②
	TrailBlazer	1.140	1.080	0.002	0.787	0.728	0.002	①	②

① Front: 118 ft. lbs.

Rear: 148 ft. lbs.

② Front: 31 ft. lbs.

Rear: 23 ft. lbs.

36616_ENVO_C0013

MAINTENANCE I AND II SERVICE SCHEDULES
2008-09 Envoy & TrailBlazer

When the CHANGE ENGINE OIL light appears, certain services and inspections are required.
Required services are described as Maintenance I and Maintenance II.
The first service on a vehicle should be Maintenance I, and the second service should be Maintenance II.
Alternate between the 2 thereafter. However, in some cases, Maintenance II may be required more often.
Maintenance I: Use Maintenance I if the CHANGE ENGINE OIL light comes on within 10 months
since vehicle was purchased or, if Maintenance II was performed.
Maintenance II: Use Maintenance II if the previous service performed was Maintenance I.
Always use Maintenance II whenever the CHANGE ENGINE OIL light comes on 10 months or more since the last
service, or, if the CHANGE ENGINE OIL light has not come on at all for one year.

Service	Maintenance I	Maintenance II
Change the engine oil and filter. Reset the oil life system.	✓	✓
Visually inspect the vehicle for leaks or damage. A fluid loss in the vehicle system could indicate a problem. Inspected, repair and add fluid to the system if necessary.	✓	✓
Inspect the engine air cleaner filter. If necessary, replace the filter.	✓	✓
Rotate the tires. Inspect the tire inflation pressures and the tire wear.	✓	✓
Visually inspect the brake lines and hoses for proper hook-up, binding, leaks, cracks, chafing, etc. Inspect the disc brake pads for wear and the rotors for surface condition. Inspect the drum brake linings for wear or cracks. Inspect other brake parts, including drums, wheel cylinders, calipers, parking brake, etc. Inspect the parking brake adjustment.	✓	✓
Inspect the engine coolant and the windshield washer fluid levels. Add fluid as needed.	✓	✓
Inspect the suspension and steering components. Inspect the front and rear suspension and the steering system for damaged, loose or missing parts, or signs of wear. Inspect the power steering lines and the hoses for proper hook-up, binding, leaks, cracks, chafing, etc.	--	✓
Visually inspect the coolant hoses and replace the hoses if they are cracked, swollen or deteriorated. Inspect all pipes, fittings and clamps; replace with GM parts as needed. To help ensure proper operation, a pressure test of the cooling system and pressure cap and cleaning the outside of the radiator and air conditioning condenser is recommended at least once a year.		✓
Inspect the wiper blades.	--	✓
Inspect the restraint system components.Ensure the safety belt reminder light and all the belts, buckles, latch plates, retractors and anchorages are working properly. Look for any other loose or damaged safety belt system parts. If you see anything that might keep a safety belt system from working correctly, repair or replaced the damaged part. Replace torn or frayed safety belts, refer to Operational and Functional Checks in Seat Belts. Inspect for any opened or broken air bag coverings, and repair or replace as needed. The air bag system does require regular maintenance.	--	✓

36616_ENVO_C0014

MAINTENANCE I AND II SERVICE SCHEDULES (cont.)
Envoy & TrailBlazer

When the CHANGE ENGINE OIL light appears, certain services and inspections are required.
Required services are described as Maintenance I and Maintenance II.
The first service on a vehicle should be Maintenance I, and the second service should be Maintenance II.
Alternate between the 2 thereafter. However, in some cases, Maintenance II may be required more often.
Maintenance I: Use Maintenance I if the CHANGE ENGINE OIL light comes on within 10 months
since vehicle was purchased or, if Maintenance II was performed.
Maintenance II: Use Maintenance II if the previous service performed was Maintenance I.
Always use Maintenance II whenever the CHANGE ENGINE OIL light comes on 10 months or more since the last
service, or, if the CHANGE ENGINE OIL light has not come on at all for one year.

Service	Maintenance I	Maintenance II
Lubricate the body components.Lubricate all key lock cylinders, hood latch assemblies, secondary latches, pivots, spring anchor and release pawl, hood and door hinges, rear folding seats and liftgate hinges. Frequent lubrication may be required when exposed to a corrosive environment, refer to Fluid and Lubricant Recommendations . Applying dielectric silicone grease GM P/N 12345579 (Canadian P/N 1974984) or equivalent on the weatherstrips with a clean cloth.	--	✓
Inspect the transaxle fluid level and add fluid as needed.	--	✓
Inspect the suspension and steering components.Inspect the front and rear suspension and the steering system for damaged, loose or missing parts, or signs of wear. Inspect power steering lines and hoses for proper hook-up, binding, leaks, cracks, chafing, etc.	--	✓
Inspect the throttle system for interference or binding and for damaged or missing parts. Replace the parts as needed. Replace any components that have high effort or excessive wear. Do not lubricate the accelerator or the cruise control cables.	--	✓
Replace the passenger compartment air filter.	--	✓

36616_ENVO_C0015

PRECAUTIONS

Before servicing any vehicle, please be sure to read all of the following precautions, which deal with personal safety, prevention of component damage, and important points to take into consideration when servicing a motor vehicle:

• Never open, service or drain the radiator or cooling system when the engine is hot; serious burns can occur from the steam and hot coolant.

• Observe all applicable safety precautions when working around fuel. Whenever servicing the fuel system, always work in a well-ventilated area. Do not allow fuel spray or vapors to come in contact with a spark, open flame, or excessive heat (a hot drop light, for example). Keep a dry chemical fire extinguisher near the work area. Always keep fuel in a container specifically designed for fuel storage; also, always properly seal fuel containers to avoid the possibility of fire or explosion. Refer to the additional fuel system precautions later in this section.

• Fuel injection systems often remain pressurized, even after the engine has been turned **OFF**. The fuel system pressure must be relieved before disconnecting any fuel lines. Failure to do so may result in fire and/or personal injury.

• Brake fluid often contains polyglycol ethers and polyglycols. Avoid contact with the eyes and wash your hands thoroughly after handling brake fluid. If you do get brake fluid in your eyes, flush your eyes with clean, running water for 15 minutes. If eye irritation persists, or if you have taken

brake fluid internally, IMMEDIATELY seek medical assistance.

• The EPA warns that prolonged contact with used engine oil may cause a number of skin disorders, including cancer. You should make every effort to minimize your exposure to used engine oil. Protective gloves should be worn when changing oil. Wash your hands and any other exposed skin areas as soon as possible after exposure to used engine oil. Soap and water, or waterless hand cleaner should be used.

• All new vehicles are now equipped with an air bag system, often referred to as a Supplemental Restraint System (SRS) or Supplemental Inflatable Restraint (SIR) system. The system must be disabled before performing service on or around system components, steering column, instrument panel components, wiring and sensors. Failure to follow safety and disabling procedures could result in accidental air bag deployment, possible personal injury and unnecessary system repairs.

• Always wear safety goggles when working with, or around, the air bag system. When carrying a non-deployed air bag, be sure the bag and trim cover are pointed away from your body. When placing a non-deployed air bag on a work surface, always face the bag and trim cover upward, away from the surface. This will reduce the motion of the module if it is accidentally deployed. Refer to the additional air bag system precautions later in this section.

• Clean, high quality brake fluid from a

sealed container is essential to the safe and proper operation of the brake system. You should always buy the correct type of brake fluid for your vehicle. If the brake fluid becomes contaminated, completely flush the system with new fluid. Never reuse any brake fluid. Any brake fluid that is removed from the system should be discarded. Also, do not allow any brake fluid to come in contact with a painted surface; it will damage the paint.

• Never operate the engine without the proper amount and type of engine oil; doing so WILL result in severe engine damage.

• Timing belt maintenance is extremely important. Many models utilize an interference-type, non-freewheeling engine. If the timing belt breaks, the valves in the cylinder head may strike the pistons, causing potentially serious (also time-consuming and expensive) engine damage. Refer to the maintenance interval charts for the recommended replacement interval for the timing belt, and to the timing belt section for belt replacement and inspection.

• Disconnecting the negative battery cable on some vehicles may interfere with the functions of the on-board computer system(s) and may require the computer to undergo a relearning process once the negative battery cable is reconnected.

• When servicing drum brakes, only disassemble and assemble one side at a time, leaving the remaining side intact for reference.

• Only an MVAC-trained, EPA-certified automotive technician should service the air conditioning system or its components.

BRAKES

ANTI-LOCK BRAKE SYSTEM (ABS)

GENERAL INFORMATION

PRECAUTIONS

• Certain components within the ABS system are not intended to be serviced or repaired individually.

• Do not use rubber hoses or other parts not specifically specified for and ABS system. When using repair kits, replace all parts included in the kit. Partial or incorrect repair may lead to functional problems and require the replacement of components.

• Lubricate rubber parts with clean, fresh brake fluid to ease assembly. Do not use shop air to clean parts; damage to rubber components may result.

• Use only DOT 3 brake fluid from an unopened container.

• If any hydraulic component or line is

removed or replaced, it may be necessary to bleed the entire system.

• A clean repair area is essential. Always clean the reservoir and cap thoroughly before removing the cap. The slightest amount of dirt in the fluid may plug an orifice and impair the system function. Perform repairs after components have been thoroughly cleaned; use only denatured alcohol to clean components. Do not allow ABS components to come into contact with any substance containing mineral oil; this includes used shop rags.

• The Anti-Lock control unit is a microprocessor similar to other computer units in the vehicle. Ensure that the ignition switch is **OFF** before removing or installing controller harnesses. Avoid static electricity discharge at or near the controller.

• If any arc welding is to be done on the vehicle, the control unit should be

unplugged before welding operations begin.

WHEEL SPEED SENSORS

REMOVAL & INSTALLATION

Front Speed Sensor

See Figures 3 and 4.

1. Before servicing the vehicle, refer to the precautions section.
2. Disconnect the negative battery cable.
3. Raise and safely support the vehicle.
4. Remove tire and wheel assembly.
5. Remove brake caliper.
6. Remove the brake rotor.
7. Remove the wheel speed sensor wiring harness retainers.
8. Disconnect the wheel speed sensor electrical connector.

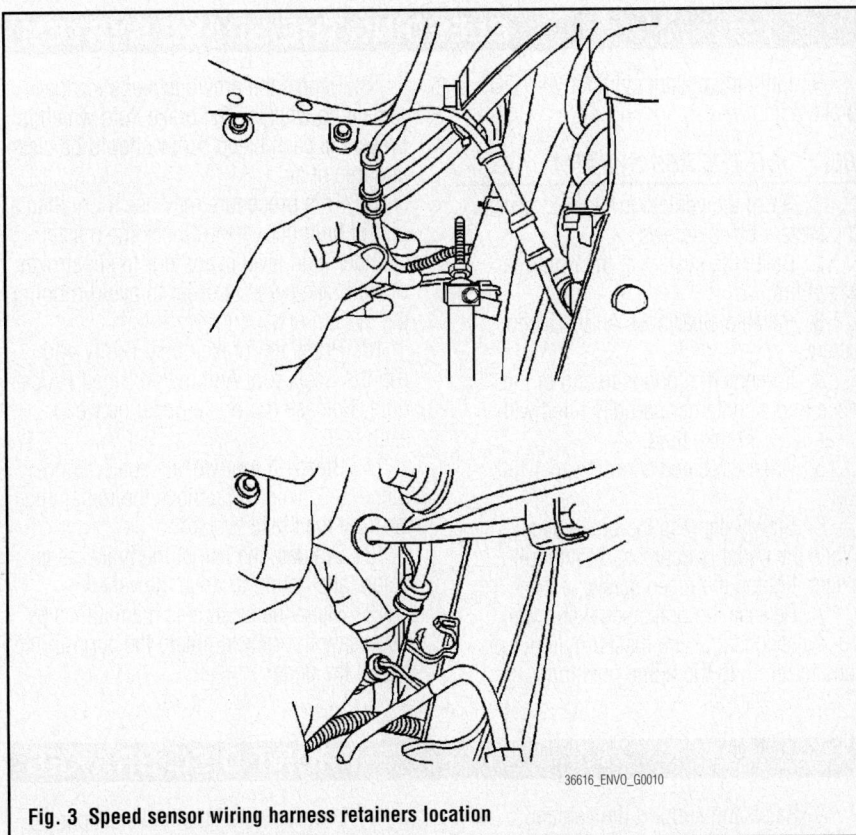

Fig. 3 Speed sensor wiring harness retainers location

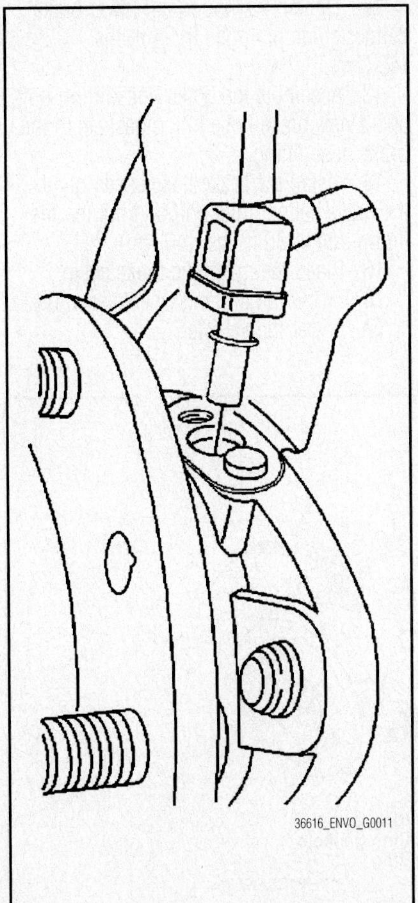

1. Before servicing the vehicle, refer to the precautions section.
2. Disconnect the negative battery cable.
3. Raise and support the vehicle.
4. Disconnect the wheel speed sensor electrical connector.
5. Remove the wheel speed sensor bolt.
6. Remove the wheel speed sensor.

To install:

7. Ensure the sensor and sensor boss (face and inner diameter) are clean and free of any debris or metal chips.
8. Place a small amount of axle lube inside the sensor boss inner diameter to ensure the seal is properly lubricated and does not roll over when installed.
9. Insert the wheel speed sensor into the hole using equal pressure to seat the sensor squarely on the sensor boss face.
10. Align the sensor with the bolt hole and install the wheel speed sensor bolt and tighten to 13 ft. lbs. (18 Nm).
11. Connect the wheel speed sensor electrical connector.
12. Lower the vehicle.
13. Connect the negative battery cable.
14. Perform a low speed test to ensure the wheel speed sensor is functioning properly:
   - Start the engine and allow it to idle.
   - Verify the ABS indicator or the traction assist indicator remains illuminated.
   - If the ABS indicator or the traction assist indicator remains illuminated, DO NOT proceed to drive the vehicle until it is diagnosed and repaired. Check the wheel speed sensor electrical connector to ensure it is not damaged and is installed properly.
   - Select a smooth, dry, clean, and level road or large lot that is as free of traffic and obstacles as possible.
   - Drive the vehicle and maintain a speed of at least 10 mph (16 km/h) for at least 5 seconds.
   - Stop the vehicle and check to see if the ABS indicator or the traction assist indicator is illuminated.

9. Remove the wheel speed sensor bolt.
10. Carefully remove the sensor by pulling it straight out of the bore. DO NOT use a screwdriver, or other device to pry the sensor out of the bore. Prying will cause the sensor body to break off in the bore.

To install:

➡The new speed sensor will have a new O-ring. Dispose of the old O-ring. Lubricate the new O-ring lightly with bearing grease prior to installation. You may also lubricate the sensor just above and below the new O-ring. DO NOT lubricate the bore.

11. Install the wheel speed sensor into the hub and bearing assembly.
12. Install the wheel speed sensor bolt and tighten to 13 ft. lbs. (18 Nm).
13. Connect the wheel speed sensor electrical connector.
14. Install the wheel speed sensor wiring harness to the frame and control arm.
15. Install the brake rotor.
16. Install brake caliper.
17. Install tire and wheel assembly.
18. Lower the vehicle.
19. Connect the negative battery cable.

Rear Speed Sensor

See Figure 5.

Fig. 4 Front wheel speed sensor removal

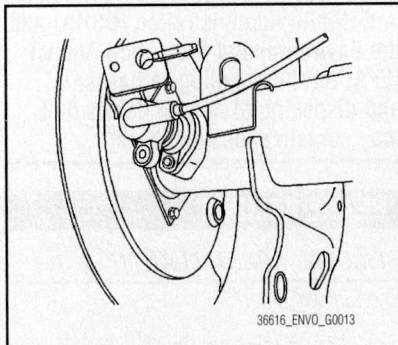

Fig. 5 Rear speed sensor location view

BRAKES

BLEEDING THE BRAKE SYSTEM

BLEEDING PROCEDURE

1. Raise the vehicle in order to access the system bleed screws.
2. Bleed the system at the right rear wheel first.
3. Install a clear hose on the bleed screw.
4. Immerse the opposite end of the hose into a container partially filled with clean DOT 3 brake fluid.
5. Open the bleed screw ½ to 1 full turn.
6. Slowly depress the brake pedal. While the pedal is depressed to its full extent, tighten the bleed screw.
7. Release the brake pedal and wait 10–15 seconds for the master cylinder pistons to return to the home position.
8. Repeat the previous steps for the remaining wheels. The brake fluid which is present at each bleed screw should be clean and free of air.

9. Refill the master cylinder with DOT 3 brake fluid.

BLEEDING THE ABS SYSTEM

1. Raise the vehicle in order to access the system bleed screws.
2. Bleed the system at the right rear wheel first.
3. Install a clear hose on the bleed screw.
4. Immerse the opposite end of the hose into a container partially filled with clean DOT 3 brake fluid.
5. Open the bleed screw ½ to 1 full turn.
6. Slowly depress the brake pedal. While the pedal is depressed to its full extent, tighten the bleed screw.
7. Release the brake pedal and wait 10–15 seconds for the master cylinder pistons to return to the home position.

8. Repeat the previous steps for the remaining wheels. The brake fluid which is present at each bleed screw should be clean and free of air.
9. This procedure may use more than a pint of fluid per wheel. Check the master cylinder fluid level every four to six strokes of the brake pedal in order to avoid running the system dry.
10. Press the brake pedal firmly and run the Scan Tool Automated Bleed Procedure. Release the brake pedal between each test.
11. Bleed all four wheels again using Steps 3–9. This will remove the remaining air from the brake system.
12. Evaluate the feel of the brake pedal before attempting to drive the vehicle.
13. Bleed the system as many times as necessary in order to obtain the appropriate feel of the pedal.

BRAKES

FRONT DISC BRAKES

✳✳ CAUTION

Dust and dirt accumulating on brake parts during normal use may contain asbestos fibers from production or aftermarket brake linings. Breathing excessive concentrations of asbestos fibers can cause serious bodily harm. Exercise care when servicing brake parts. Do not sand or grind brake lining unless equipment used is designed to contain the dust residue. Do not clean brake parts with compressed air or by dry brushing. Cleaning should be done by dampening the brake components with a fine mist of water, then wiping the brake components clean with a dampened cloth. Dispose of cloth and all residue containing asbestos fibers in an impermeable container with the appropriate label. Follow practices prescribed by the Occupational Safety and Health Administration (OSHA) and the Environmental Protection Agency (EPA) for the handling, processing, and disposing of dust or debris that may contain asbestos fibers.

BRAKE CALIPER

REMOVAL & INSTALLATION

See Figures 6 and 7.

1. Before servicing the vehicle, refer to the precautions section.

2. Raise and support the vehicle.
3. Remove the tire and wheel assembly.
4. Remove the brake hose fitting bolt.
5. Remove and discard the brake hose fitting gaskets from the brake hose fitting.
6. Cap the brake hose fitting to prevent brake fluid loss and contamination.
7. Remove the upper and lower brake caliper guide pin bolts.
8. Remove the brake caliper.

To install:

9. Clean and lubricate the guide sleeves and bushings with silicon grease.
10. Install the brake caliper.

11. Loosely install the brake caliper guide pin bolts.
12. Tighten the upper and lower brake caliper guide pin bolts to 31 ft. lbs. (42 Nm)
13. Assemble the brake hose fitting bolt and 2 new brake hose fitting gaskets to the brake hose fitting.
14. Install the brake hose assembly to the brake caliper inlet port and tighten the fitting bolt to 30 ft. lbs. (40 Nm)
15. Bleed the hydraulic brake system.
16. Install the tire and wheel assembly.
17. Lower the vehicle.

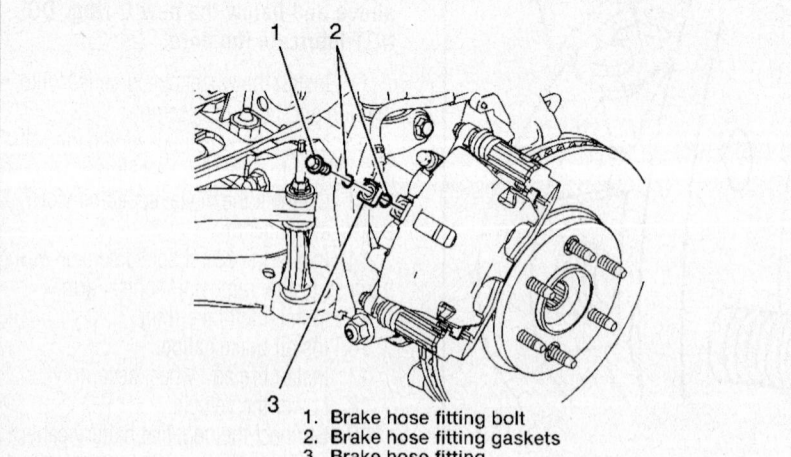

1. Brake hose fitting bolt
2. Brake hose fitting gaskets
3. Brake hose fitting

36616_ENVO_G0016

Fig. 6 Front brake hose fitting bolt removal

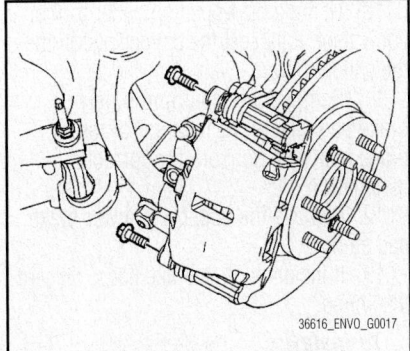

Fig. 7 Front brake caliper guide pin bolt removal

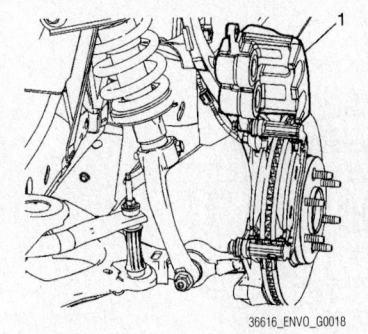

Fig. 8 Pivot the brake caliper in the upward position

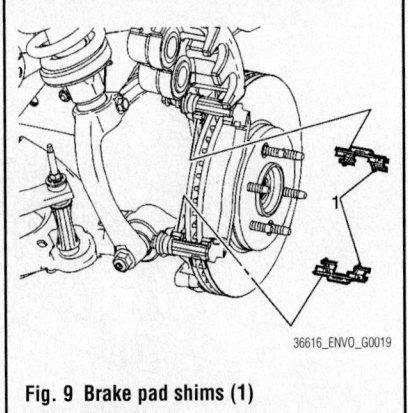

Fig. 9 Brake pad shims (1)

18. Refill the master cylinder to the correct level.

DISC BRAKE PADS

REMOVAL & INSTALLATION

See Figures 8 and 9.

1. Before servicing the vehicle, refer to the precautions in the beginning of this section.

2. Inspect the fluid level in the brake master cylinder reservoir.

3. If the brake fluid level is midway between the maximum-full point and the minimum allowable level, no brake fluid needs to be removed before proceeding.

4. If the brake fluid level is higher than midway between the maximum-full point and the minimum allowable level, remove brake fluid to the midway point before proceeding.

5. Raise and support the vehicle.

6. Remove the tire and wheel assembly.

7. Remove the lower brake caliper guide pin bolt.

8. Pivot the brake caliper upward and support with heavy mechanics wire or equivalent.

9. Place a block of wood or an old brake pad against the brake caliper pistons.

10. Using a brake pad spreader tool or equivalent, fully seat the caliper pistons in the caliper bores.

11. Remove the inner and outer brake pads. Note the location of the brake pad wear sensors for correct installation.

12. Remove the brake pad shims.

13. If installing new brake pads, discard the shims.

To install:

14. Install the brake pad shims.

15. Install the inner and outer brake pads with the warning sensors in the correct position.

16. Pivot the brake caliper into position, install the lower brake caliper guide pin bolt and tighten the bolt to 31 ft. lbs. (42 Nm).

17. Install the tire and wheel assembly. Tighten to 130 ft. lbs. (140 Nm).

18. Lower the vehicle.

19. With the engine OFF, gradually apply the brake pedal to approximately 2/3 of its travel distance.

20. Slowly release the brake pedal.

21. Wait 15 seconds, then repeat steps 6–7 until a firm brake pedal is obtained. This will properly seat the brake caliper pistons and brake pads.

22. Fill the master cylinder reservoir to the proper level.

23. Burnish the pads and rotors.

BRAKES

✳✳ CAUTION

Dust and dirt accumulating on brake parts during normal use may contain asbestos fibers from production or aftermarket brake linings. Breathing excessive concentrations of asbestos fibers can cause serious bodily harm. Exercise care when servicing brake parts. Do not sand or grind brake lining unless equipment used is designed to contain the dust residue. Do not clean brake parts with compressed air or by dry brushing. Cleaning should be done by dampening the brake components with a fine mist of water, then wiping the brake components clean with a dampened cloth. Dispose of cloth and all residue containing asbestos fibers in an impermeable container with the appropriate label. Follow practices prescribed by the Occupational Safety and Health Administration (OSHA) and the Environmental Protection Agency (EPA) for the handling, processing, and disposing of dust or debris that may contain asbestos fibers.

BRAKE CALIPER

REMOVAL & INSTALLATION

See Figures 10 and 11.

1. Before servicing the vehicle, refer to the precautions section.

2. Raise and safely support the vehicle.

3. Remove the brake hose fitting bolt.

4. Remove and discard the brake hose fitting gaskets from the brake hose fitting.

5. Cap the brake hose fitting to prevent brake fluid loss and contamination.

REAR DISC BRAKES

6. Remove the brake caliper guide pin bolts.

7. Remove the brake caliper.

To install:

8. Install the brake caliper.

9. Install the brake caliper guide pin bolts and tighten the bolts to 23 ft. lbs. (31 Nm).

➡**Install new brake hose fitting gaskets.**

10. Assemble the brake hose fitting bolt and 2 new brake hose fitting gaskets to the brake hose fitting.

11. Install the brake hose assembly to the brake caliper inlet port and tighten the fitting bolt to 40 ft. lbs. (54 Nm).

12. Bleed the hydraulic brake system.

13. Install the tire and wheel assembly. Tighten to 130 ft. lbs. (140 Nm).

14. Lower the vehicle.

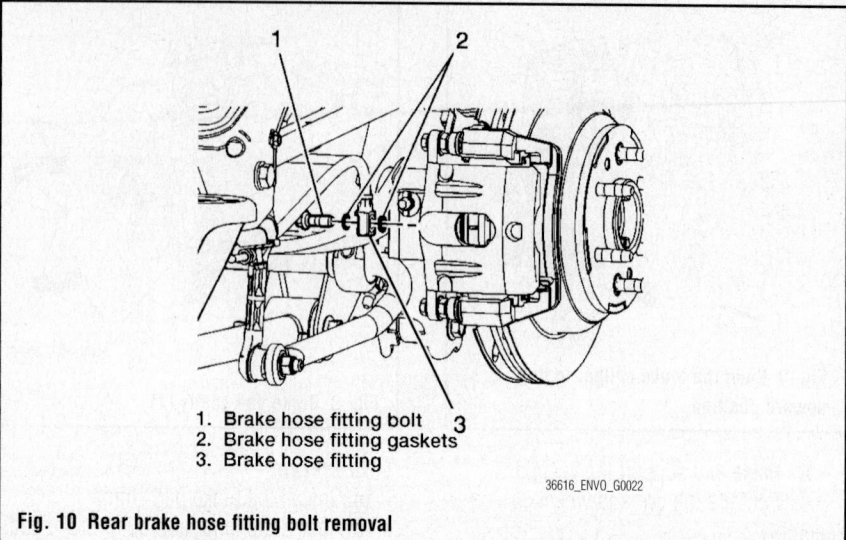

1. Brake hose fitting bolt
2. Brake hose fitting gaskets
3. Brake hose fitting

36616_ENVO_G0022

Fig. 10 Rear brake hose fitting bolt removal

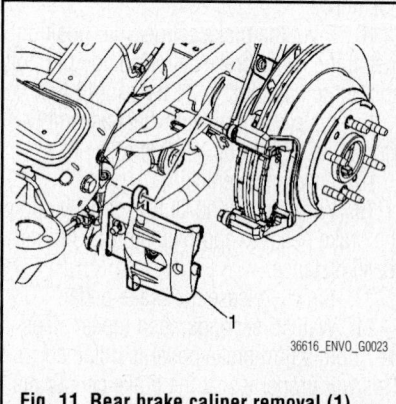

36616_ENVO_G0023

Fig. 11 Rear brake caliper removal (1)

DISC BRAKE PADS

REMOVAL & INSTALLATION

See Figures 12 and 13.

1. Before servicing the vehicle, refer to the precautions section.

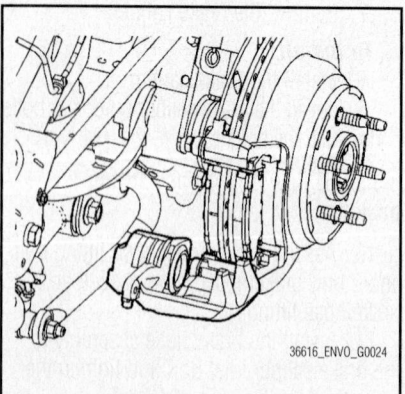

36616_ENVO_G0024

Fig. 12 Pivot the brake caliper downward

2. Inspect the fluid level in the brake master cylinder reservoir.

3. If the brake fluid level is midway between the maximum-full point and the minimum allowable level, no brake fluid needs to be removed before proceeding.

4. If the brake fluid level is higher than midway between the maximum-full point and the minimum allowable level, remove brake fluid to the midway point before proceeding.

5. Raise and support the vehicle.

6. Remove the tire and wheel assembly.

7. Remove the upper brake caliper guide pin bolt.

8. Pivot the brake caliper downward and support with heavy mechanics wire or equivalent.

9. Place a block of wood or an old brake pad against the brake caliper pistons.

10. Using a brake pad spreader tool or equivalent, fully seat the caliper piston in the caliper bore.

11. Remove the inner and outer brake pads. Note the location of the brake pad wear sensors for correct installation.

12. Remove the upper and lower brake pad shims.

13. If installing new brake pads, discard the shims.

To install:

14. Install the upper and lower brake pad shims.

➡**If installing new brake pads, install new shims.**

15. Install the inner and outer brake pads with the warning sensors in the correct position.

16. Pivot the brake caliper into position and install the upper brake caliper guide pin bolt and tighten the bolt to 23 ft. lbs. (31 Nm).

17. Install the tire and wheel assembly. Tighten to 130 ft. lbs. (140 Nm).

18. Lower the vehicle.

19. With the engine OFF, gradually apply the brake pedal to approximately ⅔ of its travel distance.

20. Slowly release the brake pedal.

21. Wait 15 seconds, then repeat steps 6–7 until a firm brake pedal is obtained. This will properly seat the brake caliper pistons and brake pads.

22. Fill the master cylinder reservoir to the proper level.

23. Burnish the pads and rotors.

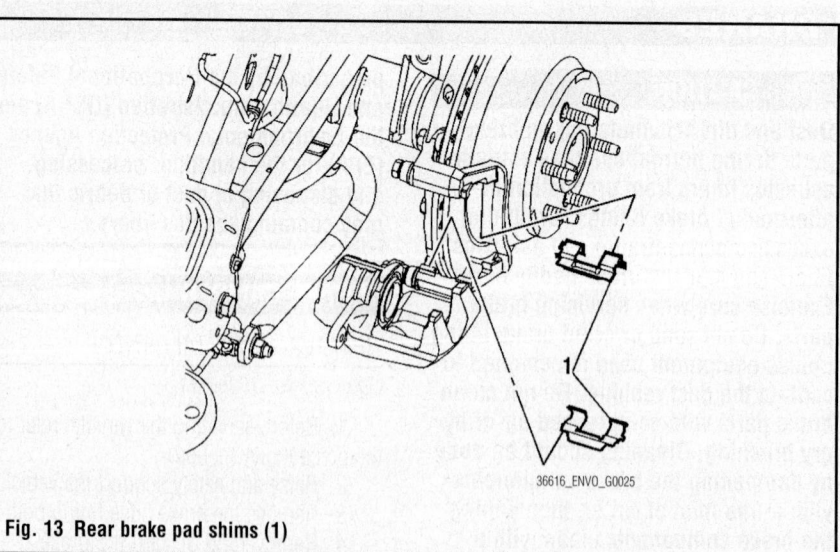

36616_ENVO_G0025

Fig. 13 Rear brake pad shims (1)

Park brake apply input force is received by the park brake lever assembly being depressed, transferred and evenly distributed, through the park brake cables and the park brake cable equalizer, to the left and right park brake apply levers. The park brake apply levers multiply and transfer the apply input force to the park brake actuators which expand the park brake shoe toward the friction surface of the drum-in-hat portion of the rear brake rotor in order to prevent the rotation of the rear tire and wheel assemblies. The park brake lever assembly releases an applied park brake system when it is returned to the at-rest (lowered) position.

The park brake system consists of the following:

• Park Brake Lever Assembly: Receives and transfers park brake system apply input force from driver to park brake cable system. Releases applied park brake system when lever is returned to at-rest (lowered) position.

• Park Brake Cables: Transfers input force received from park brake lever, through park brake cable equalizer, to park brake apply lever.

• Park Brake Cable Equalizer: Evenly distributes input force to both the left and right park brake units. Threaded park brake cable equalizers are also used to remove slack in park brake cables.

• Park Brake Apply Lever: Multiplies and transfers input force to park brake actuator.

• Park Brake Actuator: Uses multiplied input force from apply lever to expand park brake shoe toward the friction surface of the drum-in-hat portion of the rear brake rotor. Threaded park brake actuators are also used to control clearance between the park brake shoe and the friction surface of the drum-in-hat portion of the rear brake rotor.

• Park Brake Shoe: Applies mechanical output force from park brake actuator to friction surface of the drum-in-hat portion of the rear brake rotor.

PARKING BRAKE CABLES

ADJUSTMENT

This vehicle uses an automatic adjusting brake lever assembly, No cable adjustment

is possible, refer to parking brake shoe adjustment.

PARKING BRAKE SHOES

REMOVAL & INSTALLATION

See Figures 14 and 15.

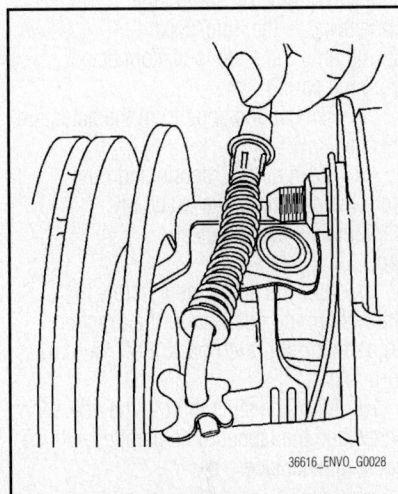

36616_ENVO_G0028

Fig. 14 Disconnecting the parking brake cable

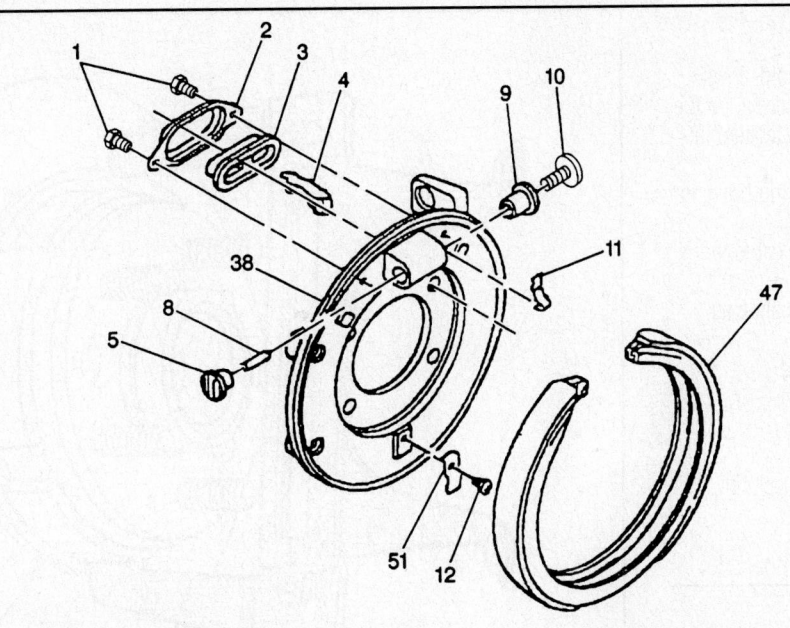

(1) Bolt/Screw, Retainer
(2) Retainer, Boot
(3) Boot
(4) Lever
(8) Tappet
(9) Pushrod
(10) Nut/Adjuster

(11) Pawl, Adjuster
(12) Bolt/Screw
(38) Mounting Plate
(47) Shoe and Lining
(49) Actuator
(51) Clip

91119G03

Fig. 15 Exploded view of the rear parking brake assembly components

1. Before servicing the vehicle, refer to the precautions section.

2. Raise and support the vehicle.

3. Remove the rear tire and wheel assembly.

4. Remove the caliper and rotor.

5. Disconnect the parking brake cable from the parking brake lever.

6. Remove the parking brake shoes assembly by sliding the shoe towards the hold-down spring until the shoe is disconnected from the spring.

7. Remove the shoe from the actuation mechanism.

8. Clean all dirt, debris and dust from the parking brake assembly components using a clean rag.

9. Turn the adjustment screw to the fully home position in the notched adjustment nut, then back it off ¼ of a turn.

10. Align the slots in both the adjusting screw and the tappet to be parallel with the backing plate face.

To install:

11. Install a new parking brake shoe.

12. Position the shoe on the inboard side of the actuation mechanism.

13. Clip the shoe onto the hold-down spring. Make sure the shoe is central on the backing plate and has both tips located in the slots.

14. Manually check the parking brake for proper operation.

15. Attach the parking brake cable to the lever.

16. Adjust the parking brake shoe as outlined later in this section.

17. Install the caliper and the rotor.

18. Install the wheel and tire assembly.

19. Lower the vehicle and check for proper operation.

ADJUSTMENT

See Figures 16 through 18.

1. Raise and support the vehicle.

2. Remove the rear tire and wheel assembly.

3. Remove the caliper and rotor.

4. Remove the parking brake lever.

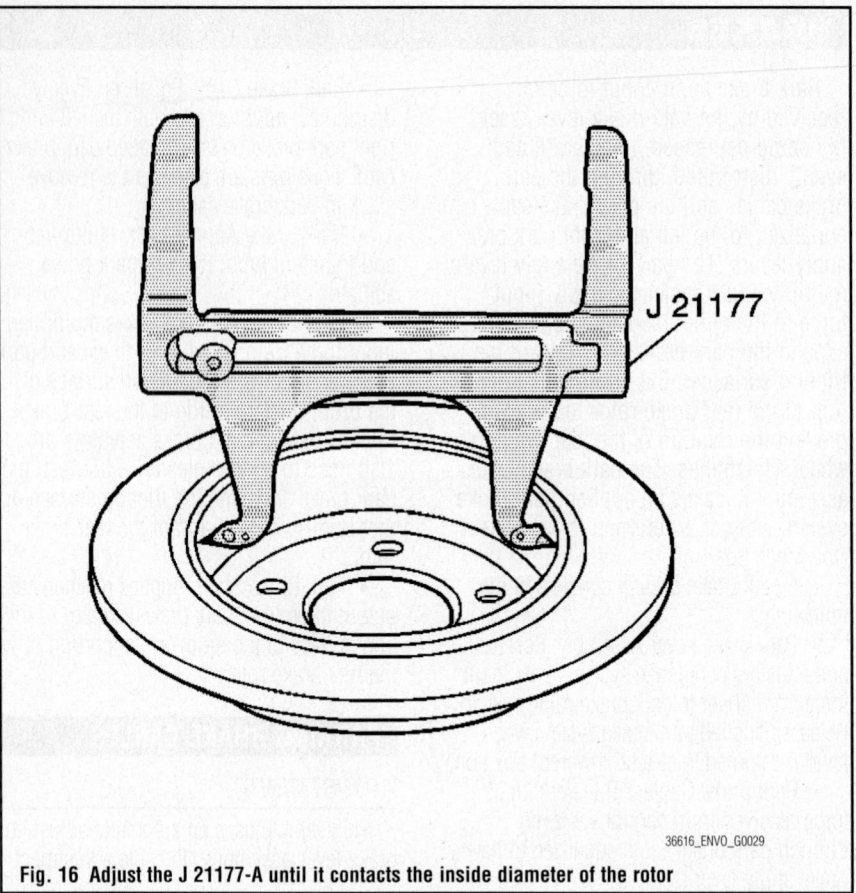

36616_ENVO_G0029

Fig. 16 Adjust the J 21177-A until it contacts the inside diameter of the rotor

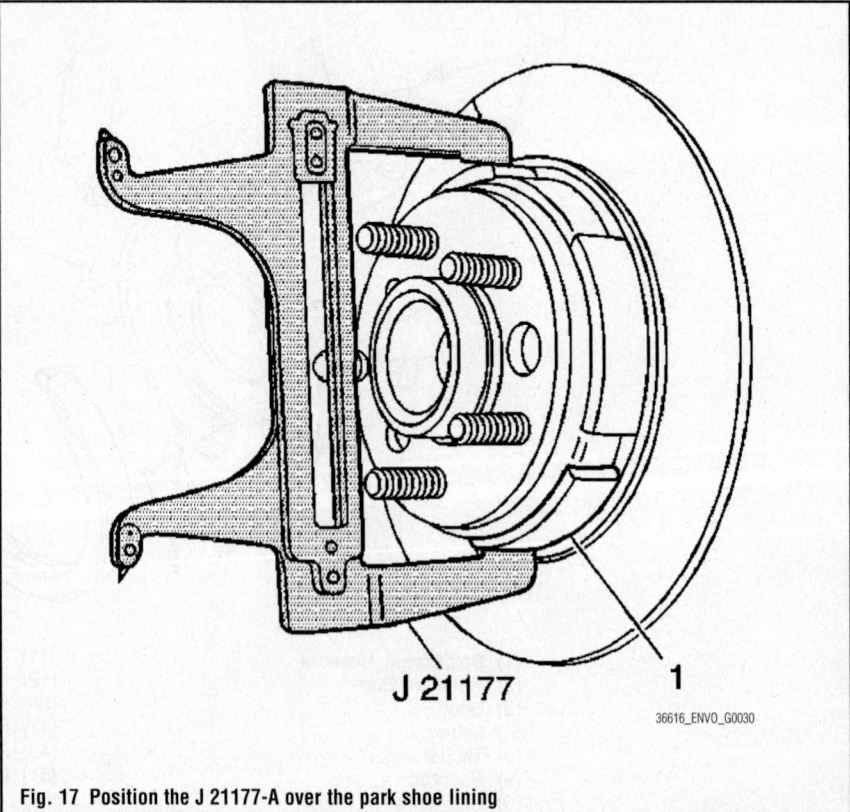

36616_ENVO_G0030

Fig. 17 Position the J 21177-A over the park shoe lining

5. Adjust the J 21177-A until it contacts the inside diameter of the rotor.

6. Position the J 21177-A over the park shoe lining, left side shown, at the widest point.

7. Turn the adjuster nut until the lining just contacts the J 21177-A.

8. Repeat steps 4 through 6 to adjust the right rear park brake.

9. The clearance between the rear park brake shoe lining and the rotor should be 0.010 inch. (0.25 mm) or .020 inch. (0.50 mm) total.

10. Attach the parking brake cable to the lever.

11. Install the caliper and the rotor.

12. Install the wheel and tire assembly.

13. Lower the vehicle and check for proper operation.

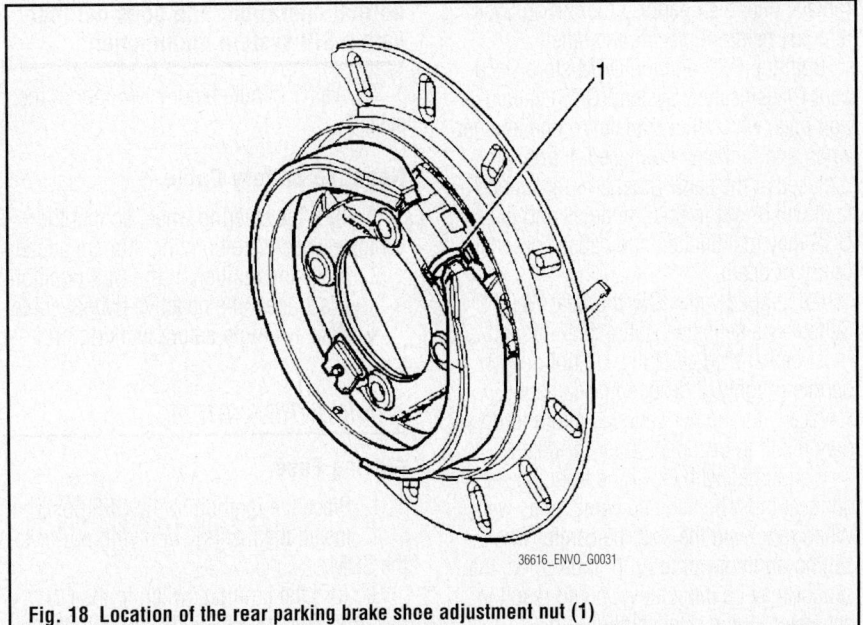

36616_ENVO_G0031

Fig. 18 Location of the rear parking brake shoe adjustment nut (1)

CHASSIS ELECTRICAL AIR BAG (SUPPLEMENTAL RESTRAINT SYSTEM)

GENERAL INFORMATION

✳✳ CAUTION

These vehicles are equipped with an air bag system. The system must be disarmed before performing service on, or around, system components, the steering column, instrument panel components, wiring and sensors. Failure to follow the safety precautions and the disarming procedure could result in accidental air bag deployment, possible injury and unnecessary system repairs.

SERVICE PRECAUTIONS

Disconnect and isolate the battery negative cable before beginning any airbag system component diagnosis, testing, removal, or installation procedures. Allow system capacitor to discharge for two minutes before beginning any component service. This will disable the airbag system. Failure to disable the airbag system may result in accidental airbag deployment, personal injury, or death.

Do not place an intact undeployed airbag face down on a solid surface. The airbag will propel into the air if accidentally deployed and may result in personal injury or death.

When carrying or handling an undeployed airbag, the trim side (face) of the airbag should be pointing towards the body to minimize possibility of injury if accidental deployment occurs. Failure to do this may result in personal injury or death.

Replace airbag system components with OEM replacement parts. Substitute parts may appear interchangeable, but internal differences may result in inferior occupant protection. Failure to do so may result in occupant personal injury or death.

Wear safety glasses, rubber gloves, and long sleeved clothing when cleaning powder residue from vehicle after an airbag deployment. Powder residue emitted from a deployed airbag can cause skin irritation. Flush affected area with cool water if irritation is experienced. If nasal or throat irritation is experienced, exit the vehicle for fresh air until the irritation ceases. If irritation continues, see a physician.

Do not use a replacement airbag that is not in the original packaging. This may result in improper deployment, personal injury, or death.

The factory installed fasteners, screws and bolts used to fasten airbag components have a special coating and are specifically designed for the airbag system. Do not use substitute fasteners. Use only original equipment fasteners listed in the parts catalog when fastener replacement is required.

During, and following, any child restraint anchor service, due to impact event or vehicle repair, carefully inspect all mounting hardware, tether straps, and anchors for proper installation, operation, or damage. If a child restraint anchor is found damaged in any way, the anchor must be replaced. Failure to do this may result in personal injury or death.

Deployed and non-deployed airbags may or may not have live pyrotechnic material within the airbag inflator.

Do not dispose of driver/passenger/curtain airbags or seat belt tensioners unless you are sure of complete deployment. Refer to the Hazardous Substance Control System for proper disposal.

Dispose of deployed airbags and tensioners consistent with state, provincial, local, and federal regulations.

After any airbag component testing or service, do not connect the battery negative cable. Personal injury or death may result if the system test is not performed first.

If the vehicle is equipped with the Occupant Classification System (OCS), do not connect the battery negative cable before performing the OCS Verification Test using the scan tool and the appropriate diagnostic information. Personal injury or death may result if the system test is not performed properly.

Never replace both the Occupant Restraint Controller (ORC) and the Occupant Classification Module (OCM) at the same time. If both require replacement, replace one, then perform the Airbag System test before replacing the other.

Both the ORC and the OCM store Occupant Classification System (OCS) calibration data, which they transfer to one another when one of them is replaced. If both are replaced at the same time, an irreversible fault will be set in both modules and the OCS may malfunction and cause personal injury or death.

If equipped with OCS, the Seat Weight Sensor is a sensitive, calibrated unit and must be handled carefully. Do not drop or handle roughly. If dropped or damaged, replace with another sensor. Failure to do so may result in occupant injury or death.

If equipped with OCS, the front passenger seat must be handled carefully as well. When removing the seat, be careful when setting on floor not to drop. If dropped, the sensor may be inoperative, could result in occupant injury, or possibly death.

If equipped with OCS, when the passenger front seat is on the floor, no one should sit in the front passenger seat. This uneven force may damage the sensing ability of the seat weight sensors. If sat on and damaged, the sensor may be inoperative, could result in occupant injury, or possibly death.

DISARMING THE SYSTEM

Air Bag Fuse

1. Turn the steering wheel so that the vehicles wheels are pointing straight ahead.
2. Place the ignition in the OFF position.

➡The sensing and diagnostic module (SDM) may have more than one fused power input. To ensure there is no unwanted SIR deployment, personal injury, or unnecessary SIR system repairs, remove all fuses supplying power to the SDM. With all SDM fuses removed and the ignition switch in the ON position, the AIR BAG warning indicator illuminates. This is normal operation, and does not indicate a SIR system malfunction.

3. Locate and remove the fuse(s) supplying power to the SDM.

✳✳ CAUTION

The SDM may have more than one fused power input. To ensure there is no unwanted SIR deployment, personal injury, or unnecessary SIR system repairs, remove all fuses supplying power to the SDM. With all SDM fuses removed and the ignition switch in the ON position, the AIR BAG warning indicator illuminates. This is

normal operation, and does not indicate a SIR system malfunction.

4. Wait 1 minute before working on the system.

Negative Battery Cable

1. Turn the steering wheel so that the vehicles wheels are pointing straight ahead.
2. Place the ignition in the OFF position.
3. Disconnect the negative battery cable.
4. Wait 1 minute before working on system.

ARMING THE SYSTEM

Air Bag Fuse

1. Place the ignition in the OFF position.
2. Install the fuse(s) supplying power to the SDM.
3. Turn the ignition switch to the ON position. The AIR BAG indicator will flash then turn OFF.
4. Perform the diagnostic system check if the AIR BAG warning indicator does not operate as described.

Negative Battery Cable

1. Place the ignition in the OFF position.
2. Connect the negative battery cable.
3. Turn the ignition switch to the ON position. The AIR BAG indicator will flash then turn OFF.
4. Perform the diagnostic system check if the AIR BAG warning indicator does not operate as described.

CLOCKSPRING CENTERING

See Figures 19 through 23.

✳✳ CAUTION

Disconnect and isolate the battery negative cable before beginning any

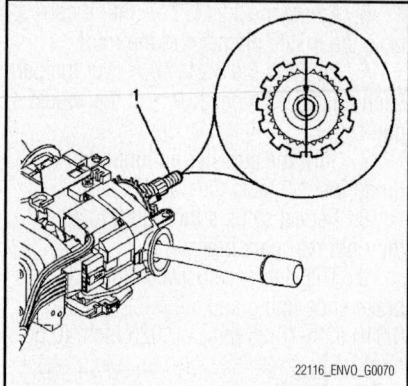

Fig. 19 Verify that the block tooth (1) of the steering shaft assembly is in the 12 o'clock position

airbag system component diagnosis, testing, removal, or installation procedures. Allow system capacitor to discharge for two minutes before beginning any component service. This will disable the airbag system. Failure to disable the airbag system may result in accidental airbag deployment, personal injury, or death.

✳✳ WARNING

A new inflatable restraint steering wheel module coil is pre-centered. Do not remove the centering tab from the new inflatable restraint steering wheel module coil until installation is complete.

➡The new SIR coil assembly will be centered. Improper alignment of the SIR coil assembly may damage the unit, causing an inflatable restraint malfunction.

1. Verify the following conditions before centering the SIR coil:

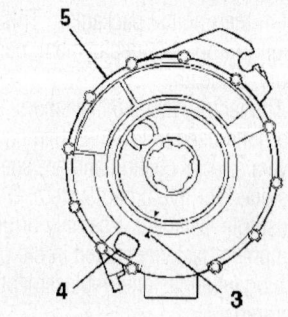
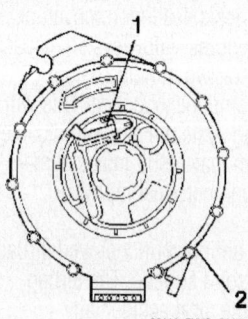

Fig. 20 Spring service lock (1), back side (2), alignment arrows (3), centering window (4) and front (5) of the SIR coil

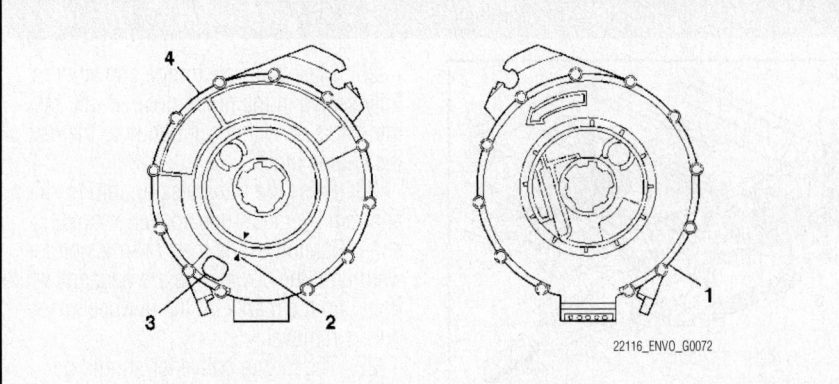

Fig. 21 Back side (1), alignment arrows (2), centering window (3) and front (4) of the SIR coil

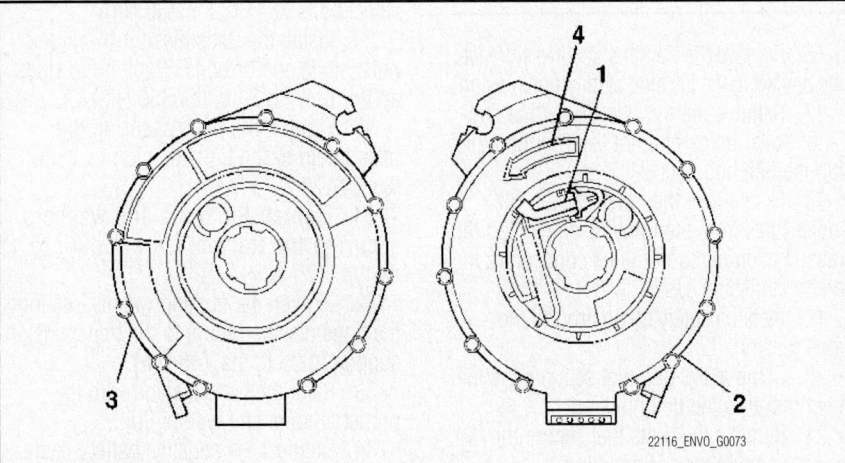

Fig. 22 Spring service lock (1), back side (2), front side (3) and directional arrow (4) of the SIR coil

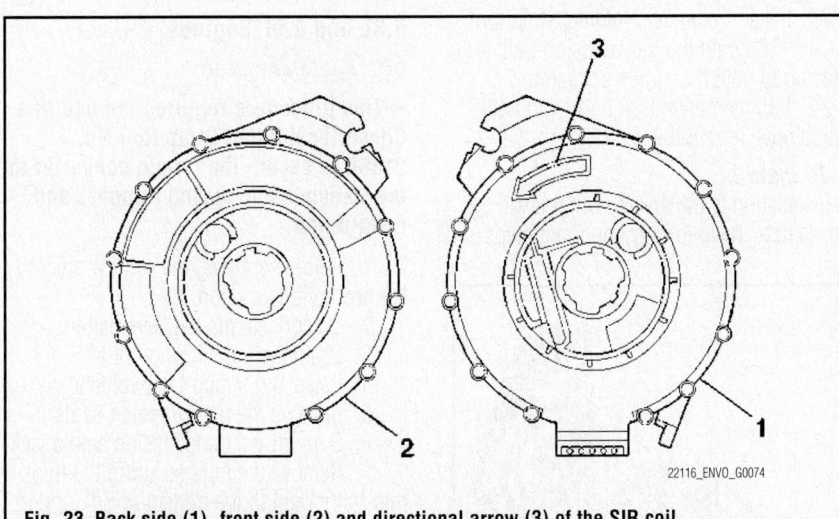

Fig. 23 Back side (1), front side (2) and directional arrow (3) of the SIR coil

- The wheels on the vehicle are straight ahead
- The block tooth (1) of the steering shaft assembly is in the 12 o'clock position
- The ignition switch assembly is in the LOCK position

2. If the front (5) of the SIR coil has a centering window (4), and the back side (2) has a spring service lock (1), perform the following steps:

   a. Hold the coil with the face up.

   b. While depressing the spring service lock, rotate the coil hub clockwise until the coil ribbon stops.

   c. Rotate the coil hub slowly, counterclockwise, until the centering window appears yellow and both arrows (3) line up.

   d. Release the spring service lock between the locking tab. The SIR coil is now centered.

   e. Align the centered SIR coil with the horn tower and slide onto the steering shaft assembly.

3. If the front (4) of the SIR coil has a centering window (3) and the back side (1) has NO spring service lock, perform the following steps:

   a. Hold the coil with the face up.

   b. Rotate the coil hub clockwise until the coil ribbon stops.

   c. Rotate the coil hub slowly, counterclockwise until the centering window appears yellow and both arrows (2) line up. This is the CENTER position.

   d. While holding the coil hub in the CENTER position, align the coil with the horn tower and slide the coil onto the steering shaft assembly.

4. If no centering window is present on the front side (3) of the SIR coil, but a spring service lock (1) is on the back side (2), perform the following steps:

   a. Hold the coil with the back side up.

   b. While depressing the spring service lock, rotate the coil hub in the direction of the arrow (4) until the coil ribbon stops.

   c. Still pressing the spring service lock, rotate the coil hub in the opposite direction 21/2 revolutions.

   d. Release the spring service lock between the locking tabs. The SIR coil is now centered.

   e. Align the centered coil with the horn tower and slide the coil onto the steering shaft assembly.

5. If no centering window appears on the front side (2) of the SIR coil and no spring service lock exists on the back side (1), perform the following steps:

   a. Hold the coil with the face up.

   b. Rotate the coil hub in the direction of the arrow until the coil ribbon stops.

   c. Rotate the coil hub, slowly, counterclockwise, for 2½ revolutions. This is the CENTER position.

   d. While maintaining the coil hub in the CENTER position, align the centered coil with the horn tower and slide the coil onto the steering shaft assembly.

DRIVE TRAIN

AUTOMATIC TRANSMISSION ASSEMBLY

REMOVAL & INSTALLATION

4.2L Engine

See Figures 24 through 26.

➡ **This procedure requires the use of a Converter Holding Strap tool No. J 21366 to secure the torque converter to the transmission during removal and installation.**

1. Before servicing the vehicle, refer to the precautions section.
2. Disconnect the negative battery.
3. Drain the transmission fluid.
4. Remove the filler tube nut and stud located on the right side of the engine.
5. Raise the vehicle.
6. If equipped with 2 wheel drive (2WD), remove the rear propeller shaft.
7. If equipped with 4 wheel drive (4WD), remove the transfer case.
8. Support the transmission with a transmission jack.
9. Remove the fuel tank shield if equipped.
10. Remove the transmission support.
11. Remove the transmission mount bolts and mount.
12. Remove the catalytic converter assembly.
13. Lower the transmission for access to the top and sides of the transmission.
14. Remove the range selector cable end from the transmission range selector lever ball stud and bracket.
15. Remove the transmission heat shield, transmission vent hose park/neutral position switch connector, and main connector from the transmission.

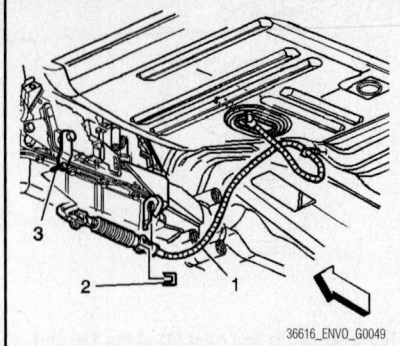

Fig. 25 Cable (1) bracket clip (2) ball stud (3)

16. Remove the bolt that secures the fuel line bracket to the left side of the transmission.
17. Remove the flywheel-to-torque converter bolts. Be careful not to drop the bolts into the bell housing.
18. Disconnect the transmission oil cooler lines from the transmission. Plug the transmission oil cooler lines connectors in the transmission case.
19. Install a safety chain around the transmission.
20. Remove the bolt that secures the fuel line bracket to the bell housing.
21. Remove the bolts that secure the coolant pipe to the bell housing.
22. Remove the remaining nuts, studs and/or bolts that secure the transmission to the engine.
23. Install Converter Holding Strap tool No. J 21366 onto the transmission bell housing to hold the torque converter.
24. Pull the transmission straight back and remove it from the vehicle.

To install:

Installation is the reverse of removal, but please note the following important steps.

25. Make sure the torque converter is fully seated in the pump drive. If not, the transmission will not fit tightly to the rear of the engine block.
26. Raise the transmission into position and remove the torque converter holding strap. Carefully slide the transmission forward until the dowel pins are engaged while lining up the marks on the flywheel made during removal.
27. The torque converter should be flush with the flywheel and turn freely by hand.
28. Tighten the torque converter-to-flywheel bolts to 44 ft. lbs. (66 Nm).
29. Install the transmission-to-engine nuts, studs and or bolts. Tighten the studs and/or bolts to 37 ft. lbs. (50 Nm).
30. Tighten the bolts securing the heat shield to the transmission to 13 ft. lbs. (17 Nm).
31. Tighten the bolts and washers securing the transmission mount to 18 ft. lbs. (25 Nm).
32. Tighten the nut and washer securing the transmission mount to the transmission support to 35 ft. lbs. (46 Nm).
33. Refill the transmission with the proper amount and type of fluid.
34. Connect the negative battery cable. Start the vehicle and allow to warm while checking for leaks. Road test the vehicle to check for shift quality.

5.3L and 6.0L Engines

See Figures 27 and 28.

➡ **This procedure requires the use of a Converter Holding Strap tool No. J 21366 to secure the torque converter to the transmission during removal and installation.**

1. Before servicing the vehicle, refer to the precautions section.
2. Disconnect the negative battery.
3. Drain the transmission fluid.
4. Raise and support the vehicle.
5. Remove the rear propeller shaft.
6. Support the transmission with a jack.
7. Remove the nuts securing the transmission mount to the transmission support.
8. Remove the transmission support from the vehicle.
9. Remove the transmission mount.
10. Remove the front exhaust pipe assembly.
11. Lower the transmission to gain access to the top and sides of the transmission.
12. Remove the transfer case, if equipped.

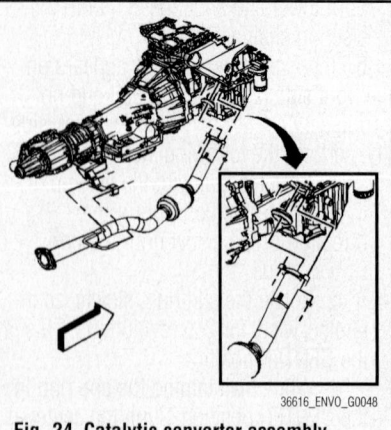

Fig. 24 Catalytic chevertor assembly removal

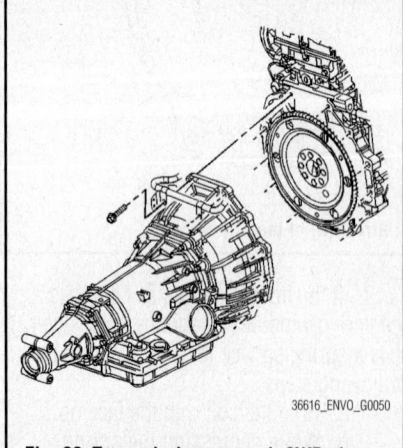

Fig. 26 Transmission removal, 2WD shown

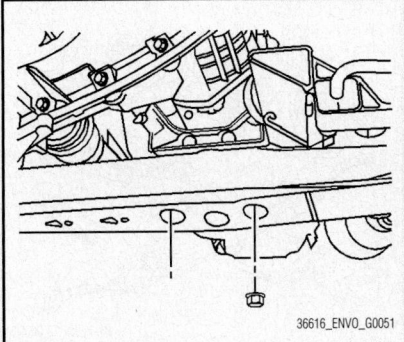

Fig. 27 Remove the nuts securing the transmission mount

13. Remove the range selector cable end from the transmission range selector lever ball stud and the bracket.

14. Remove the transmission heat shield.

15. Disconnect the transmission vent hose, the park/neutral position switch connectors, and the main electrical connector from the transmission.

16. Remove the transmission harness from the retainers.

17. Remove the bolt that secures the fuel line bracket to the left side of the transmission.

18. Remove the torque converter access plug.

19. Mark the flywheel and torque converter orientation for reassembly.

20. Remove the flywheel to torque converter bolts. Use care not to drop the bolts into the bell housing.

21. Disconnect the transmission oil cooler lines from the transmission.

22. Plug the transmission oil cooler line connectors in the transmission case.

23. Install a safety chain around the transmission.

24. Remove the nut that secures the filler tube to the bell housing.

25. Remove the transmission filler tube.

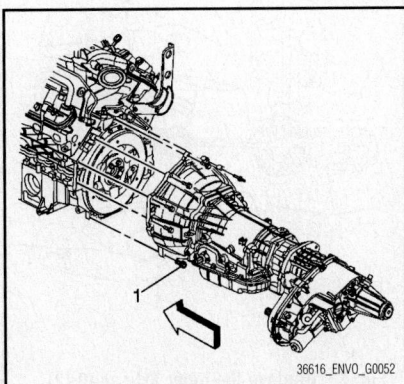

Fig. 28 Transmission removal, 4WD shown

26. Remove the remaining nuts, studs and/or bolts that secure the transmission to the engine.

27. Install the J-21366 onto the transmission bell housing to retain the torque converter.

28. Pull the transmission straight back.

29. Remove the transmission from the vehicle.

To install:

30. Raise the transmission into place and remove the torque converter holding tool.

31. Slide the transmission straight onto the locating pins while lining up the marks on the flywheel and the torque converter made during removal. The torque converter must be flush onto the flywheel and rotate freely by hand.

32. Install nuts, studs and/or bolts securing the transmission to the engine and tighten to 37 ft. lbs. (50 Nm).

33. Install the fuel line retaining bracket to the transmission.

34. Install the flywheel-to-torque converter bolts and tighten to 44 ft. lbs. (66 Nm).

35. Install the torque converter access plug.

36. Remove the safety chain from the transmission.

37. Install the transmission filler tube.

38. Install the filler tube nut.

39. Install the transmission vent hose, fuel lines, and the wiring harness to the transmission.

40. Install the transmission harness to the retainers.

41. Install the heat shield to the transmission.

42. Install the bolts securing the heat shield to the transmission and tighten to 13 ft. lbs. (17 Nm).

43. Install the shift cable end to the transmission shift lever ball stud and bracket.

44. Install the transfer case, if equipped.

45. Install the front exhaust pipe assembly.

46. Install the transmission mount to the vehicle.

47. Install the bolts securing the transmission mount to the transmission and tighten to 18 ft. lbs. (25 Nm).

48. Install the transmission support to the vehicle.

49. Lower the transmission and remove the transmission jack.

50. Install the nuts securing the transmission mount to the transmission support and tighten to 35 ft. lbs. (46 Nm).

51. Install the rear propeller shaft.

52. Flush the transmission oil cooler and cooling lines at this time, if necessary.

53. Connect the transmission oil cooler lines to the transmission.

54. Lower the vehicle.

55. Connect the battery cable.

56. Fill the transmission to the proper level with DEXRON® III transmission fluid and check for leaks.

57. Road test the vehicle and check for proper operation.

TRANSFER CASE ASSEMBLY

REMOVAL & INSTALLATION

NVG 120–NR9

See Figure 29.

1. Before servicing the vehicle, refer to the precautions section.

2. Raise the vehicle.

3. Drain the transfer case.

4. Remove the rear and front propeller shaft.

5. Remove the electrical harness from the retainer.

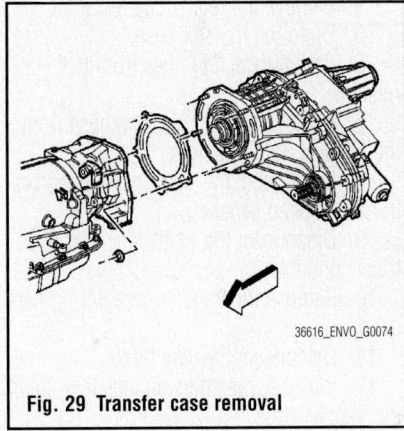

Fig. 29 Transfer case removal

6. Disconnect the electrical connector from the speed sensor.

7. Disconnect the vent hose.

8. Install a transmission jack to support the transfer case.

9. Remove the transfer case adapter to transfer case nuts.

10. Lower the transfer case.

11. Disconnect the electrical harness from the top of the transfer case.

12. Remove the transfer case.

13. Remove the transfer case gasket

To install:

➡**If the transfer case gasket is damaged, replace it. DO NOT use silicone sealant in place or with the transfer case gasket.**

14. Install or replace the transfer case gasket.

15. Raise the transfer case and install the electrical harness.

16. Install the transfer case in the vehicle

17. Install the transfer case adapter to transfer case nuts. Ensure the fuel line retainer is in place. Tighten the nuts to 35 ft. lbs, (47 Nm).

18. Remove the transmission jack stand.

19. Connect the electrical connector to the speed sensor.

20. Connect the vent hose.

21. Install the transfer case harness to the transfer case.

22. Install the rear and front propeller shaft.

23. Fill the transfer case with fluid.

24. Lower the vehicle.

NVG 226–NP8

See Figure 29.

1. Before servicing the vehicle, refer to the precautions section.

2. Raise the vehicle.

3. Remove the fuel tank shield, if equipped.

4. Remove the rear propeller Shaft.

5. Drain the transfer case.

6. Remove the fuel lines from the retainer.

7. Remove the electrical harness from the left and right retainers.

8. Disconnect the electrical connectors from the speed sensors.

9. Disconnect the motor/encoder electrical connector.

10. Remove the transfer case wiring harness.

11. Disconnect the vent hose.

12. Install a transmission jack to support the transfer case.

13. Remove the transfer case adapter to transfer case nuts.

➡**While removing the transfer case the front propeller shaft must be disconnected from the transfer case.**

14. Remove the transfer case from the vehicle.

15. Remove the transfer case gasket.

To install:

➡**If the transfer case gasket is damaged, replace it. DO NOT use silicone sealant in place or with the transfer case gasket.**

16. Install or replace the transfer case gasket

➡**While installing the transfer case the front propeller shaft must be connected to the transfer case.**

17. Install the transfer case in the vehicle.

18. Install the transfer case adapter to transfer case nuts. Ensure the fuel line retainer is in place. Tighten the nuts to 35 ft. lbs. (47 Nm).

19. Remove the transmission jack stand.

20. Connect the electrical connectors to the speed sensors.

21. Connect the vent hose.

22. Connect the motor/encoder electrical connector.

23. Install the transfer case harness to the transfer case.

24. Install the transfer case wiring harness to the left and right retainers.

25. Install the fuel lines to the retainer.

26. Install the rear propeller shaft.

27. Fill the transfer case with fluid.

28. Install the fuel tank shield, if equipped.

29. Lower the vehicle.

FRONT AXLE SHAFT, BEARING & SEAL

REMOVAL & INSTALLATION

For the Axle Shaft, Bearing and Seal, Removal and Installation, please refer to Wheel Bearing procedure located in the Suspension & Steering Section.

FRONT DIFFERENTIAL CARRIER

REMOVAL & INSTALLATION

See Figures 30 through 32.

1. Before servicing the vehicle, refer to the precautions section.

2. Disconnect the negative battery cable.

3. Raise and secure the vehicle.

4. Remove the front tires and wheels.

5. Remove the engine protection shield.

6. Drain the engine of oil.

7. Drain the front drive axle.

8. Remove the front propeller shaft from the front axle. Wrap the bearing caps with tape in order to prevent the loss of the roller bearings.

9. Remove the Antilock Brake System (ABS) wiring harness from the retainers.

10. Remove the brake hose retaining bolts.

11. Remove the front drive axle vent hose.

12. Remove the left and right upper ball pinch bolt and nut.

13. Remove the left and right upper shock module retaining nuts.

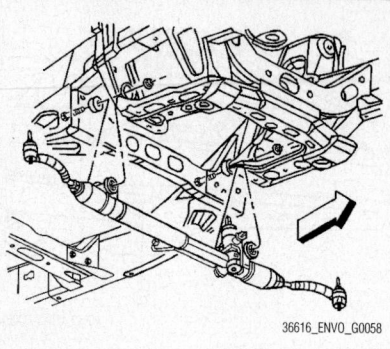

Fig. 30 Remove the power steering gear assembly

36616_ENVO_G0058

14. Remove the front stabilizer bar links from the frame.

15. Remove the shock module from the frame.

16. Remove the steering knuckle from the upper control arm.

17. Remove the left and right front wheel drive shafts from the front drive axle.

18. Relocate and secure the left and right front wheel drive shafts to the frame.

19. Using mechanics wire or hook, support the front shock modules and steering knuckle.

20. Remove the power steering gear assembly. Refer to Power Rack & Pinion Removal & Installation.

21. Support the inner axle shaft as necessary in order to pull the inner axle shaft from the differential carrier assembly and evenly through the oil pan.

22. Remove the front drive axle carrier from the oil pan.

23. Secure the front drive axle carrier to the frame.

24. Remove the oil pan. Refer to Oil pan Removal & Installation.

25. Remove the front drive axle carrier.

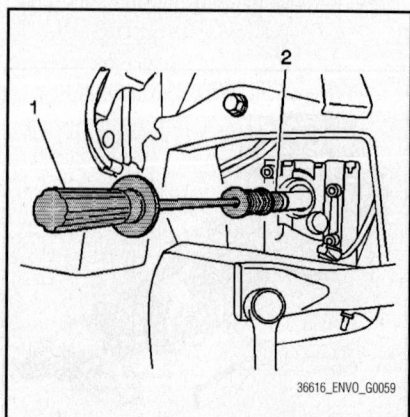

Fig. 31 Remove the inner axle shaft (2) with the puller (1)

36616_ENVO_G0059

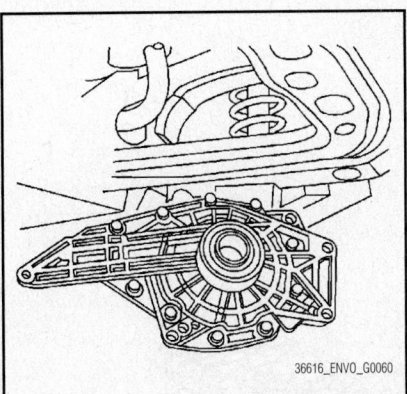

Fig. 32 Remove the front drive axle carrier

To install:

26. Install the front drive axle to the frame.

27. Secure the front drive axle to the frame.

28. Install the oil pan. Refer to Oil pan Removal & Installation.

29. Remove the front drive axle from the frame.

30. Install the front drive axle to the oil pan.

31. Install the front drive axle mounting bolts and tighten to 63 ft. lbs. (85 Nm).

32. Install the inner axle to the front drive axle. Using the J 6125-B , push the inner axle shaft into the differential side gear until the retaining ring snaps the inner axle shaft into place.

33. Install the power steering gear. Refer to Power Rack & Pinion Removal & Installation.

34. Remove the left and right front wheel drive shafts from the frame.

35. Remove the left and right shock module and steering knuckles from their supports.

36. Install the right and left front wheel drive shafts to the front drive axle.

37. Install the vent hose to the front drive axle.

38. Install the left and right shock modules to the frame.

39. Install the upper shock module retaining nuts.

40. Tighten the lower shock module mounting bolts to 74 ft. lbs. (100 Nm).

41. Install the steering knuckle to the upper control arm.

42. Install the upper ball joint pinch bolt and nut.

43. Tighten the upper shock module mounting nuts to 30 ft. lbs. (40 Nm).

44. Install the front stabilizer bar links to the frame.

45. Install the brake hose retaining bolts and tighten to 18 ft. lbs. (25 Nm).

46. Install the right and left ABS wiring harness in the retainers.

47. Install the front propeller shaft from the front axle.

48. Fill the front drive axle with the proper fluid. Install 1.7 pints of 75W-90 Synthetic gear oil.

49. Install the engine protection shield.

50. Install the tires and wheel assemblies and tighten to 103 ft. lbs. (140 Nm).

51. Lower the vehicle.

52. Fill the engine with oil.

FRONT HALFSHAFTS

REMOVAL & INSTALLATION

See Figures 33 through 35.

1. Before servicing the vehicle, refer to the precautions section.

2. Remove or disconnect the following:
   • Front wheel

➡**Place a drift through the caliper into the edge of the rotor to keep the rotor from turning when the nut is removed**

   • Wheel center cap, if equipped
   • Halfshaft nut and discard. A new nut must be used for installation.
   • Drift from the rotor
   • Brake caliper and support it with a piece of wire to avoid damaging the brake hose
   • Brake rotor

3. To remove the steering knuckle, remove or disconnect the following:
   • Wheel hub and bearing

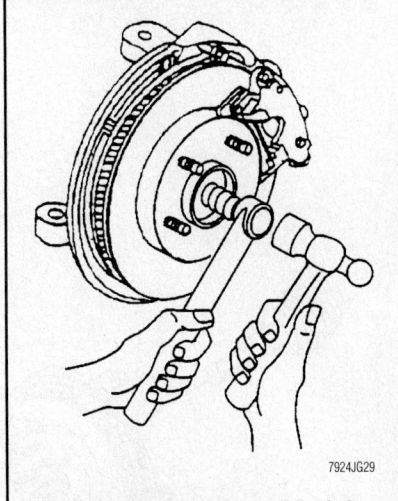

Fig. 33 Tap the halfshaft out of the hub without damaging the threads

   • Outer tie rod retaining nut
   • Outer tie rod end from the steering knuckle using a puller
   • Brake hose bracket retaining bolts
   • Brake hose bracket
   • Anti-lock Brake System (ABS) wheel speed sensor wiring harness bracket, if necessary
   • Upper control arm-to-steering knuckle pinch bolt and nut
   • Upper control arm from the steering knuckle
   • Lower ball joint retaining nut
   • Steering knuckle from the control arm using a puller
   • Steering knuckle

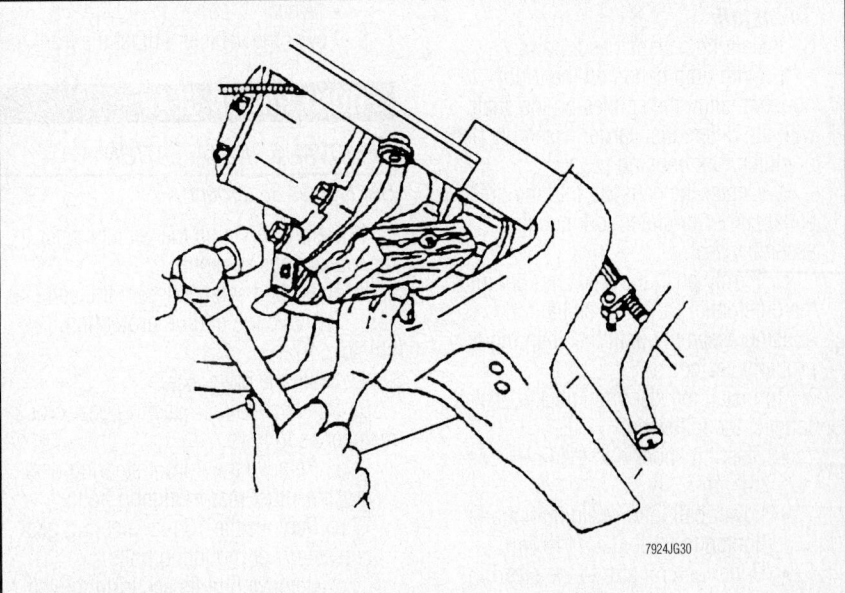

Fig. 34 Using a block of wood and a mallet, disengage the halfshaft from the differential assembly

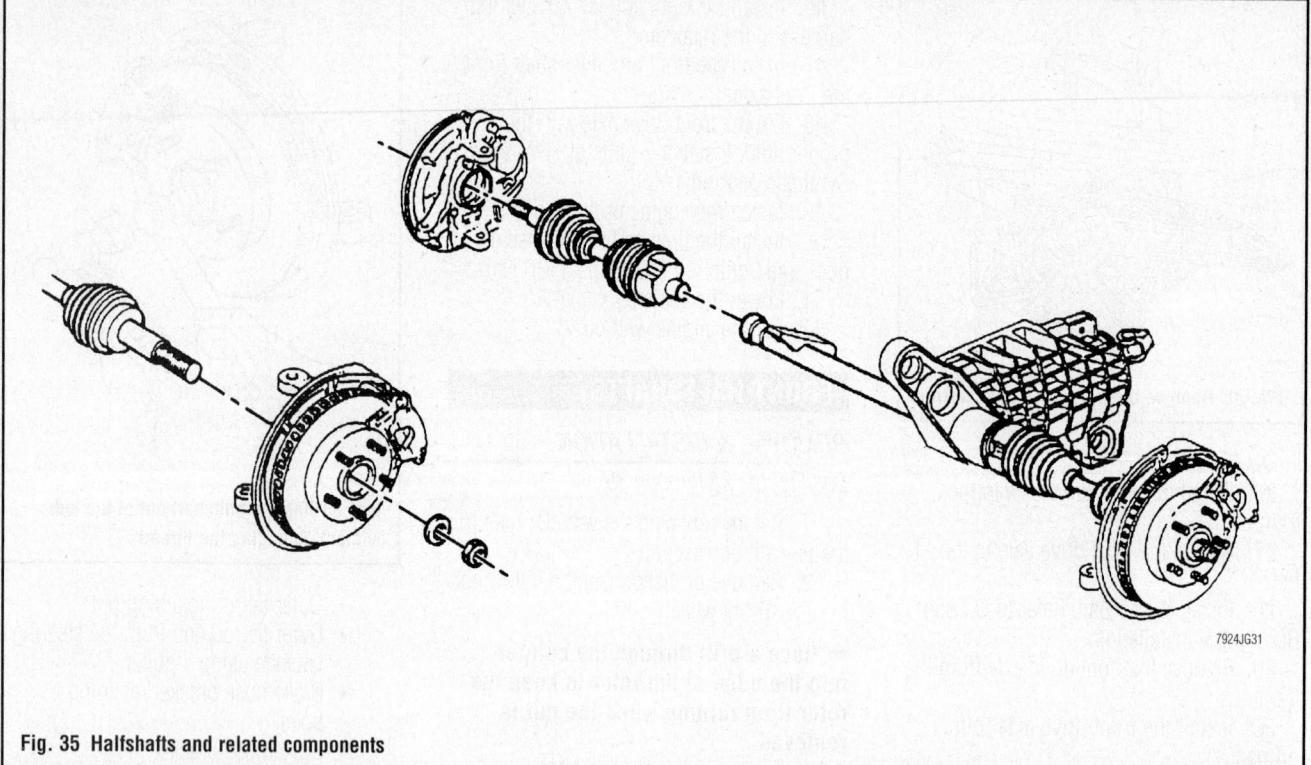

Fig. 35 Halfshafts and related components

4. Remove the left side halfshaft from differential carrier, or right halfshaft from the clutch fork housing as follows:

a. Place a brass drift against the tripot housing.

b. Use a hammer to strike the drift outward from the case, striking hard enough to overcome the snapring tension holding the halfshaft.

5. Pull the halfshaft straight out of the differential carrier or clutch fork housing.

To install:

6. Install the halfshaft as follows:

a. With both hands on the tripot housing, align the splines on the shaft with the differential carrier assembly (left) or clutch fork housing (right).

b. Center the halfshaft into the differential carrier or clutch fork housing assembly seal.

c. Firmly push the shaft straight into the differential carrier or clutch fork housing assembly until the snapring is properly seated.

7. To install the steering knuckle, install or connect the following:

- Steering knuckle to the lower control arm
- Lower ball joint retaining nut and tighten to 81 ft. lbs. (110 Nm)
- Upper control arm to the steering knuckle
- Upper control arm pinch bolt and nut and tighten to 30 ft. lbs. (40 Nm)

- ABS wheel speed sensor harness bracket
- Brake hose bracket. Tighten the bolts to 7 ft. lbs. (10 Nm).
- Outer tie rod to the steering knuckle and tighten the nut to 33 ft. lbs. (45 Nm)
- Hub and bearing

8. Install or connect the following:

- New halfshaft nut and tighten to 103 ft. lbs. (140 Nm)
- Wheel

9. Lower the vehicle. Adjust the front toe.

FRONT PINION SEAL

REMOVAL & INSTALLATION

See Figures 36 through 40.

1. Before servicing the vehicle, refer to the precautions section.

2. Raise and safely support the vehicle.

3. Remove the engine protection shield.

4. Drain the drive axle.

5. Remove the rear steering gear crossmember as follows:

a. Remove the 4 front steering gear crossmember rear mounting bolts.

b. Remove the 10 rear steering gear crossmember mounting bolts.

c. Remove 5 bolts securing the left converter heat shield to the floor panel studs and remove from the vehicle.

d. Remove the rear steering gear crossmember from the vehicle.

6. Remove the front propeller shaft as follows:

a. Reference mark the relationship of the propeller shaft to the front axle pinion yoke.

b. Remove the yoke retainer bolts and yoke retainers from the front axle pinion yoke.

✳✳ WARNING

When removing the propeller shaft, do not attempt to remove the shaft by pounding on the yoke ears or using a tool between the yoke and the universal joint. If the propeller shaft is removed by using such means, the injection joints may fracture and lead to premature failure of the joint.

c. Disconnect the propeller shaft from the front axle pinion yoke.

d. Wrap the bearing caps with tape in order to prevent the loss of bearing rollers.

e. Remove the front propeller shaft from the transfer case.

7. Measure the torque required in order to rotate the pinion. Use an inch-pound torque wrench. Record the torque value for reassembly. This will give the combined preload for the following components:

- The pinion bearings
- The pinion seal

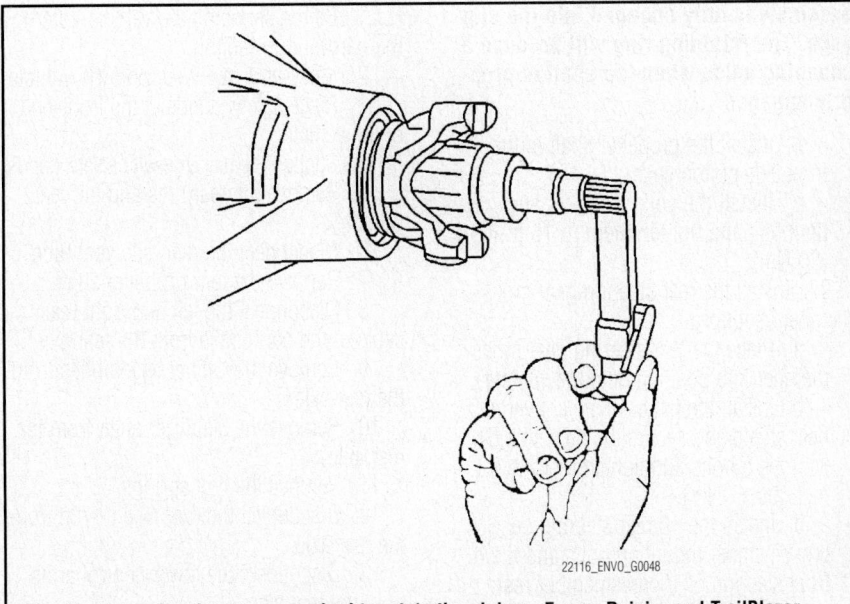

Fig. 36 Measuring the torque required to rotate the pinion—Envoy, Rainier and TrailBlazer

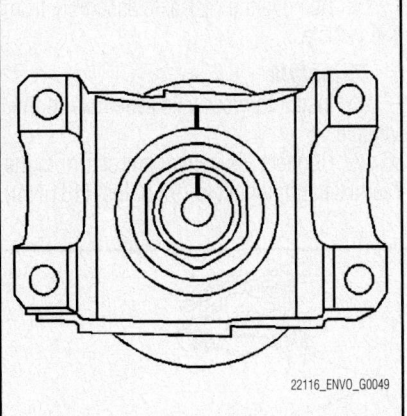

Fig. 37 Scribe an alignment line between the pinion shaft and the pinion yoke—Envoy, Rainier and TrailBlazer

- The carrier bearings
- The axle bearings
- The axle seals

8. Scribe an alignment line between the pinion shaft and the pinion yoke.

9. Install the J-8614-01 onto the pinion as shown.

10. Remove the pinion nut while holding the J-8614-01.

11. Install the J-8614-2 (2) and the J-8614-3 (3) into the J-8614-01 (1) as shown.

12. Remove the pinion yoke by turning the J-8614-3 (3) clockwise while holding the J-8614-01 (1).

13. Carefully remove the oil seal from the bore using a suitable seal removal tool. Do not distort or scratch the aluminum case.

14. Remove the dust deflector from the pinion yoke using a soft-faced hammer.

To install:

15. Install the new deflector onto the pinion yoke using a soft-faced hammer.

✳✳ WARNING

Drive the seal in straight, not at an angle, as this will damage the aluminum housing.

16. Install the new oil seal by doing the following:
   a. Position the oil seal in the bore.
   b. Install the J-33782 over the oil seal.
   c. Strike the J-33782 with a hammer until the seal flange seats on the axle housing surface.

17. Apply sealant GM P/N 12346004 (Canadian P/N 10953480) or equivalent to the splines of the drive pinion yoke.

18. Install the pinion yoke. Align the reference marks made during removal.

✳✳ WARNING

Do not hammer the pinion flange/yoke onto the pinion shaft. Pinion components may be damaged if the pinion flange/yoke is hammered onto the pinion shaft.

19. Seat the pinion yoke onto the pinion shaft by tapping it with a soft-faced hammer until a few pinion shaft threads show through the yoke.

20. Install the washer and a new pinion nut.

21. Install the J-8614-01 onto the pinion yoke as shown.

✳✳ WARNING

If the rotating torque is exceeded, the pinion will have to be removed and a new collapsible spacer installed.

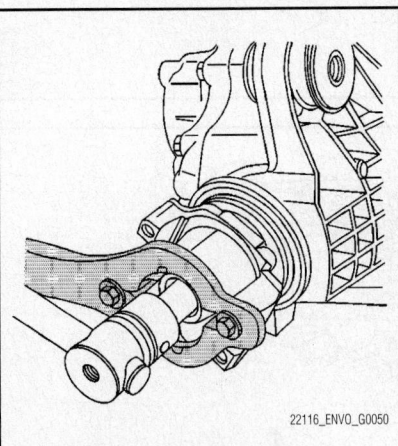

Fig. 38 Installation of special tool J-8614-01 onto the pinion—Envoy, Rainier and TrailBlazer

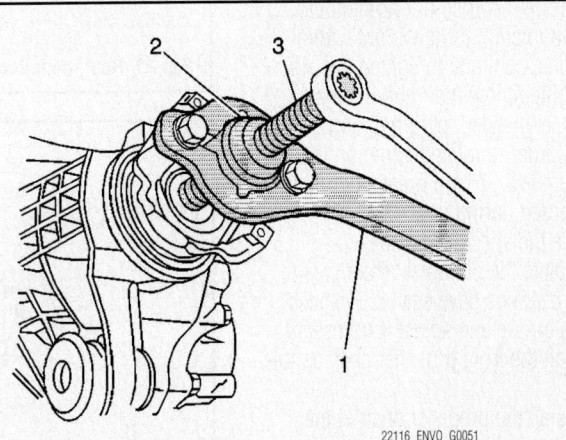

Fig. 39 Installation of J-8614-2 (2) and J-8614-3 (3) into the J-8614-01 (1)—Envoy, Rainier and TrailBlazer

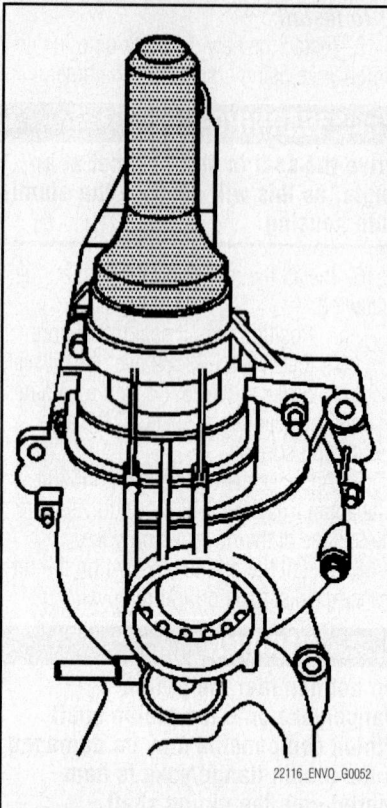

Fig. 40 Installation of the new oil seal using special tool J-33782—Envoy, Rainier and TrailBlazer

22. Tighten the pinion nut while holding the J-8614-01. Tighten the pinion nut until the pinion end play is just taken up. Rotate the pinion while tightening the nut to seat the bearings.

23. Measure the rotating torque of the pinion using an inch-pound torque wrench. Compare the measurement of the rotating torque to the measurement recorded earlier. The rotating torque of the pinion nut should be 3–5 inch lbs. (0.40–0.57 Nm) greater than the torque recorded during removal.

24. If the rotating torque is not within specifications, continue to tighten the pinion nut. Tighten the pinion nut, in small increments, as needed, until the torque required in order to rotate the pinion is 3–5 inch lbs. (0.40–0.57 Nm) greater than the torque recorded during removal.

25. Once the specified torque is obtained, rotate the pinion several times to ensure the bearings have seated. Recheck the rotating torque and adjust if necessary.

26. Install the front propeller shaft as follows:

a. Install the propeller shaft in the transfer case, aligning the reference marks made during removal.

➡**Ensure that the propeller shaft**

assembly is fully engaged into the slip yoke. The retaining ring will produce a snapping noise when the shaft is properly engaged.

b. Install the propeller shaft to the front axle pinion yoke.

c. Install the yoke retainers and the bolts and tighten them to 15 ft. lbs. (20 Nm).

27. Install the rear steering gear crossmember as follows:

a. Place the rear steering gear crossmember into position onto the vehicle.

b. Install the left catalytic converter heat shield and secure the heat shield with the 5 bolts and tighten them to 62 inch lbs. (7 Nm).

c. Install the 10 rear steering gear crossmember mounting bolts and the 4 front steering gear crossmember rear mounting bolts and tighten them to 37 ft. lbs. (50 Nm).

28. Install the engine protection shield.

29. Fill the drive axle.

30. Lower the vehicle.

REAR AXLE HOUSING

REMOVAL & INSTALLATION
See Figures 41 and 42.

1. Before servicing the vehicle, refer to the precautions section.

2. Raise and safely support the vehicle.

3. Place safety stands at the front-end of the vehicle.

4. Support the rear axle with safety stands.

5. Remove the rear tires and the rear wheels.

6. Disconnect the rear axle vent tube.

7. Remove the rear propeller shaft.

8. Disconnect the left and right rear cable of the park brake from the rear axle.

9. Remove the caliper assemblies from the rear axle.

10. Remove the stabilizer shaft from the rear axle.

11. Remove the coil springs.

12. Disconnect the rear axle tie rod from the rear axle.

13. Disconnect the lower control arms from the rear axle.

14. Disconnect the upper control arms from the rear axle.

15. Remove the rear-axle assembly from the vehicle.

To install:

16. Install the rear-axle assembly to the vehicle.

17. Connect the upper control arm to the rear axle and tighten to (97 ft. lbs. (131 Nm).

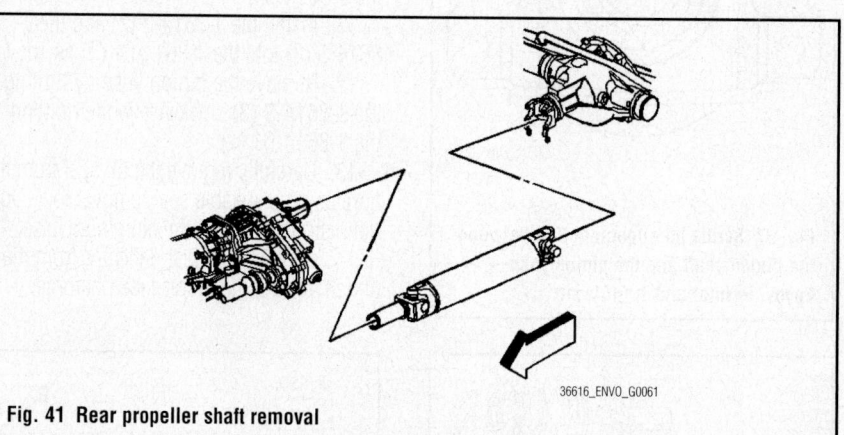

Fig. 41 Rear propeller shaft removal

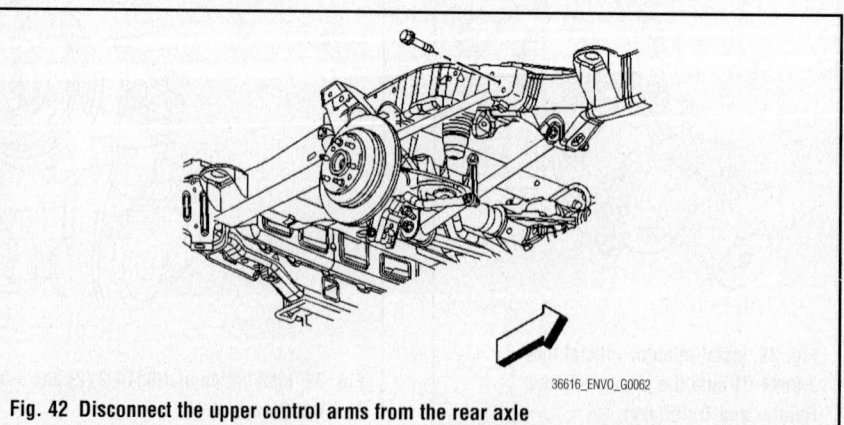

Fig. 42 Disconnect the upper control arms from the rear axle

18. Connect the lower control arm to the rear axle and tighten to 74 ft. lbs. (100 Nm).

19. Connect the rear axle tie rod to the rear axle and tighten to 140 ft. lbs. (190 Nm).

20. Install the coil springs.

21. Install the stabilizer shaft to the rear axle. Tighten the stabilizer shaft insulator clamp mounting nuts to 55 ft. lbs. (75 Nm). Tighten the stabilizer shaft links to stabilizer shaft retaining nuts to 66 ft. lbs. (90 Nm).

22. Install the caliper assemblies to the rear axle.

23. Connect the right and left rear cable of the park brake to the rear axle.

24. Install the propeller

25. Connect the rear axle vent tube.

26. Install the rear tire assemblies and tighten to 103 ft. lbs. (140 Nm).

27. Fill the axle with lubricant. Use the proper fluid.

28. Remove the safety stands.

29. Lower the vehicle.

REAR AXLE SHAFT, BEARING & SEAL

REMOVAL & INSTALLATION

See Figures 43 through 48.

1. Before servicing the vehicle, refer to the precautions section.

2. Raise and safely support the vehicle.

3. Remove the tire and wheel assembly.

4. Remove the brake caliper.

5. Remove the rear wheel speed sensor.

6. Remove the rear axle housing cover and the gasket.

7. Remove the pinion shaft locking bolt.

8. On axles without a locking differential, remove the pinion shaft.

9. On axles with a locking differential, remove the shaft part way. Rotate the case until the pinion shaft touches the housing.

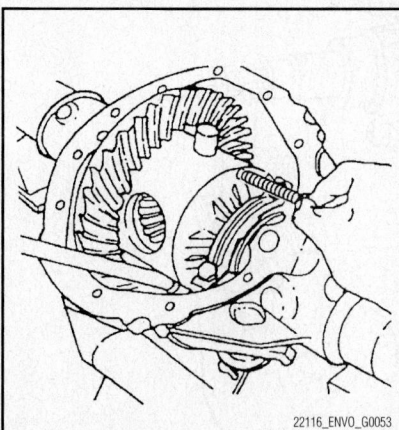

Fig. 43 Removal of the pinion shaft locking bolt

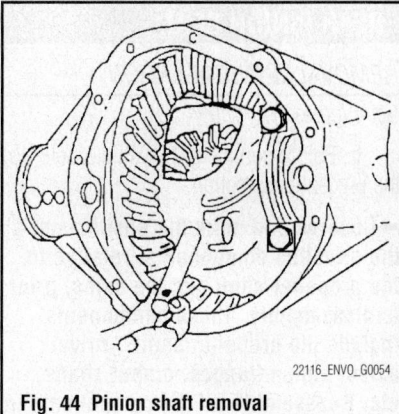

Fig. 44 Pinion shaft removal

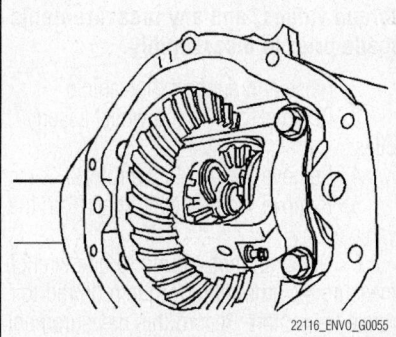

Fig. 45 Removal of the C-lock from the button end of the axle shaft

10. On axles with a locking differential, use a screwdriver, or a similar tool, in order to enter the differential case and rotate the C-lock until the C-lock aligns with the thrust block.

11. Push the flange of the axle shaft toward the differential.

12. Remove the C-lock from the button end of the axle shaft.

→When removing the axle shaft, do not rotate the shaft. Rotating the shaft will misalign the gears. Misaligning the gears will make the installing of the axle shaft difficult.

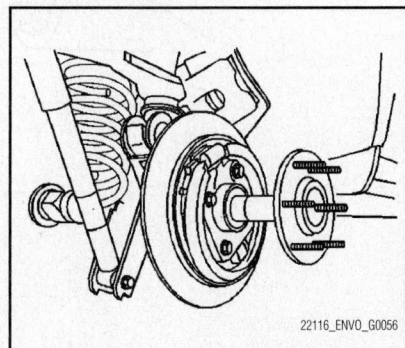

Fig. 46 Removal of the axle shaft from the housing

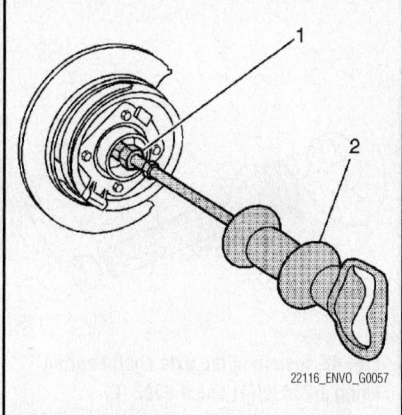

Fig. 47 Removal of the axle shaft seal and bearing together using special tools J-45857 (1) and J-2619-01 (2)

13. Remove the axle shaft from the housing. If the axle is difficult to remove, use the J-45859 (1) and the J-2619-01 (2) to remove the axle shaft from the housing.

14. To remove the seal only, use a suitable seal remover.

15. To remove the axle shaft seal and the bearing together from the axle housing, use special tools J-45857 (1) and J-2619-01 (2).

To install:

16. Using the J-23690 (1) and the J-8092 (2), install the axle shaft bearing.

17. Drive the axle shaft bearing into the axle housing until the tool bottoms against the tube.

18. Using the J-21128, install the axle shaft seal.

19. Drive the tool into the bore until the axle shaft seal bottoms flush with the tube.

✶✶ WARNING

Carefully insert the axle shaft in order to not damage the seal.

20. Install the axle shaft into the rear axle housing.

21. Slide the axle shaft into place allowing the splines to engage the differential side gear.

22. On axles without a locking differential, place the C-lock on the button end of the axle shaft.

23. On axles with a locking differential, keep the pinion shaft partially withdrawn.

24. On axles with a locking differential, place the C-lock on the axle shaft so that the ends are flush with the thrust block.

25. Pull the shaft flange outward in order to seat the C-lock in the differential gear.

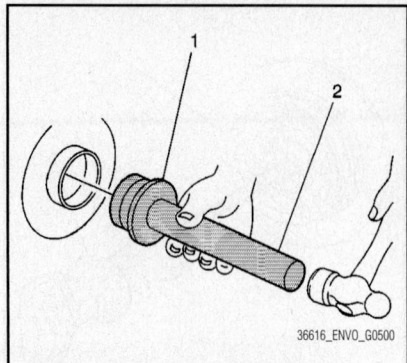

Fig. 48 Installing the axle shaft bearing using J-23690 (1) and J-8092 (2)

26. Align the hole in the pinion shaft with the bolt hole in the differential case.

27. Install the new pinion shaft locking bolt:

- For the 8.0/8.6 inch axle, tighten the pinion shaft locking bolt to 27 ft. lbs. (36 Nm).
- For the 9.5 LD inch axle, tighten the pinion shaft locking bolt to 37 ft. lbs. (50 Nm).

➡ **The axle housing gasket is reusable. Replace only if damaged.**

28. Install the axle housing cover gasket and axle housing cover.

29. Install the mounting bolts:

- For the 9.5 inch axle, tighten the rear axle housing cover bolts in a crosswise pattern to 30 ft. lbs. (40 Nm).
- For the 8.0 inch axle, tighten the rear axle housing cover bolts in a crosswise pattern to 20 ft. lbs. (30 Nm).
- For the 8.6 inch axle, tighten the rear axle housing cover bolts in a crosswise pattern to 18 ft. lbs. (25 Nm).

30. Install the drain plug and tighten to 24 inch lbs. (33 Nm).

31. Fill the rear axle with the proper axle lubricant as follows:

- For the 8.0 and 8.6 inch axles, the lubricant level should be between 0–0.4 inch (0–10mm) below the fill plug opening.
- For the 9.5 inch axle, the lubricant level should be between 0–0.5 inch (0–13mm) below the fill plug opening.

32. Install the brake caliper.

33. Install the rear wheel speed sensor.

34. Install the tire and wheel assembly.

35. Fill the rear axle with axle lubricant. Use the proper fluid.

36. Lower the vehicle.

REAR PINION SEAL

REMOVAL & INSTALLATION

See Figures 49 through 53.

1. Before servicing the vehicle, refer to the precautions section.

➡**Observe and mark the positions of all the driveline components, relative to the propeller shaft and the axles, prior to disassembly. These components include the propeller shafts, drive axles, pinion flanges, output shafts, etc. Reassemble all the components in the exact places in which you removed the parts. Follow any specifications, torque values, and any measurements made prior to disassembly.**

2. Raise and support the vehicle.

3. Remove the tire and wheel assemblies.

4. Remove the rear brake rotors.

5. Remove the propeller shaft from the vehicle.

6. Using an inch-pound torque wrench, measure the amount of torque required to rotate the pinion. Record this measurement for reassembly.

7. Place an alignment mark between the pinion and the pinion yoke.

8. Using the J 8614-01 holder/remover and holding it, remove the pinion nut. 9. Remove the washer.

10. Using the J 8614-2 (2) and the J 8614-3 (3), remove the pinion yoke. Rotate the J 8614-3 clockwise to remove the yoke.

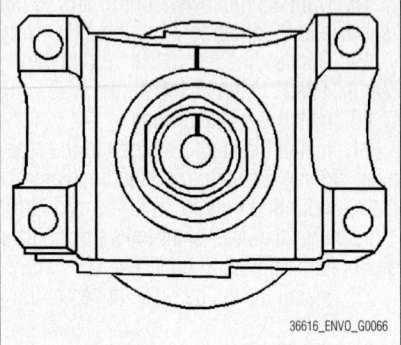

Fig. 50 Alignment mark shown between the pinion and the pinion yoke

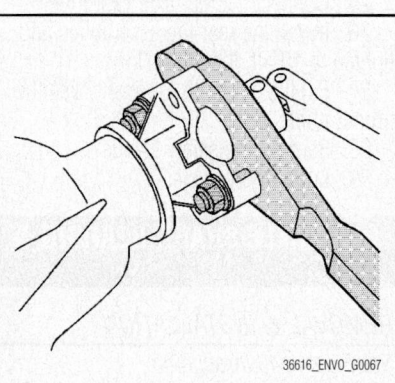

Fig. 51 Install the yoke holding tool J 8614-01 and remove pinion nut

11. Using a suitable tool, remove the drive pinion seal.

To install:

12. Using a seal installer, install a new pinion oil seal.

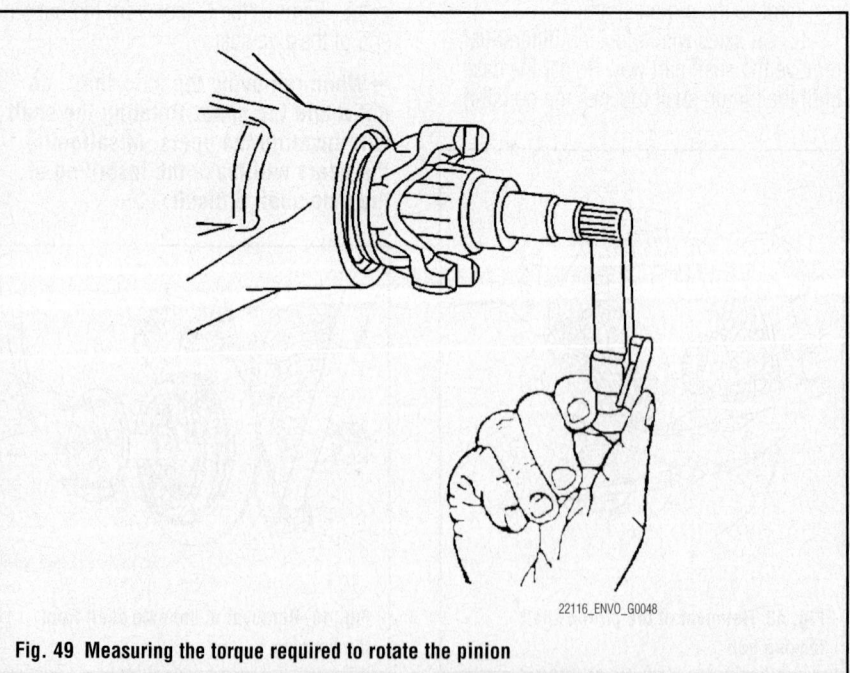

Fig. 49 Measuring the torque required to rotate the pinion

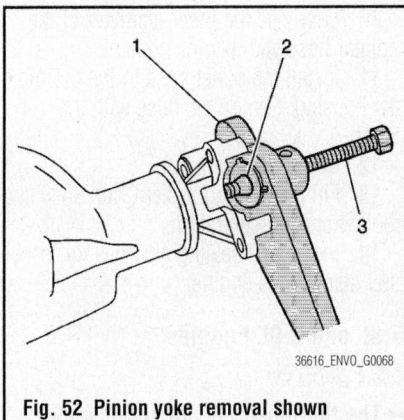

Fig. 52 Pinion yoke removal shown

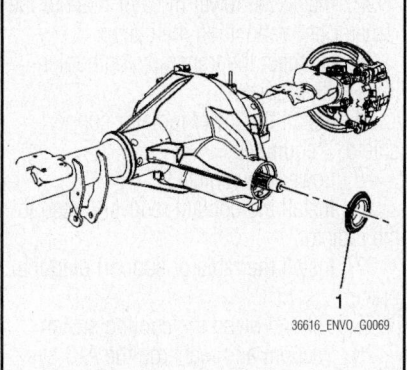

Fig. 53 Pinion seal (1) removal shown

13. Apply sealant to the splines of the pinion yoke.

14. Align the reference marks and using a soft faced hammer, install the drive pinion yoke.

15. Using and holding the J 8614-01 holder/remover , tighten the pinion nut until the pinion end play is just taken up. Rotate the pinion while tightening the nut to seat the bearing.

➡️**If the rotating torque is exceeded, the pinion will have to be removed and a new collapsible spacer installed.**

16. Using an inch-pound torque wrench, tighten the nut in small increments, as needed, until the rotating torque is 3–5 inch. lbs. (0.40–0.57 Nm) greater than the rotating torque recorded during removal.

17. Once the specified torque is obtained, rotate the pinion several times to ensure the bearings have seated.

18. Install the propeller shaft assembly.

19. Install the rear brake rotors.

20. Install the tire and wheel assemblies and tighten to 103 ft. lbs. (140 Nm).

21. Inspect and add axle lubricant to the axle housing, if necessary.

22. Remove the support and lower the vehicle.

ENGINE COOLING

ENGINE FAN

REMOVAL & INSTALLATION

See Figures 54 and 55.

1. Before servicing the vehicle, refer to the precautions section.

2. Drain the cooling system.

3. Remove the air cleaner assembly.

4. Remove the air resonator assembly.

5. Remove the inlet radiator hose.

6. Remove the transmission oil cooler lines from the fan shroud.

7. Using J 46406 remove the fan clutch from the water pump.

8. Remove the mounting bolts from the upper fan shroud.

9. Lift and push the fan shroud inward to clear the filler neck on the radiator.

10. Remove the fan and the shroud.

To install:

11. Install the fan and the shroud.

12. Install the mounting bolts to the upper fan shroud and tighten to 21 ft. lbs. (28 Nm).

13. Using J 46406 install the fan clutch to the water pump.

14. Install the transmission oil cooler lines to the fan shroud.

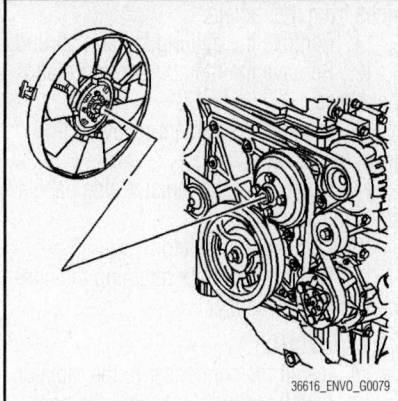

Fig. 55 remove the fan clutch from the water pump

15. Install the inlet radiator hose.

16. Install the air resonator assembly.

17. Install the air cleaner assembly.

18. Fill and bleed the cooling system.

19. Check transmission fluid and add as needed.

RADIATOR

REMOVAL & INSTALLATION

See Figures 56 and 57.

1. Before servicing the vehicle, refer to the precautions section.

2. Drain the cooling system.

3. Recover the refrigerant.

4. Raise the vehicle.

5. Remove the lower radiator support shield, if equipped.

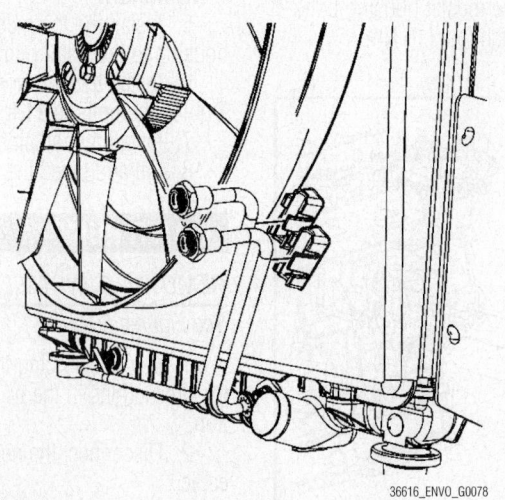

Fig. 54 Transmission oil cooler lines shown

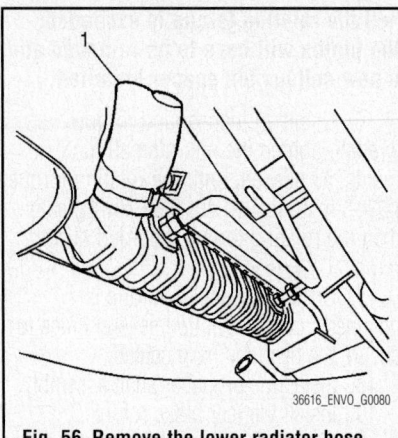

Fig. 56 Remove the lower radiator hose

6. Reposition the lower radiator hose clamp from the lower radiator hose.

7. Remove the lower radiator hose from the radiator

8. Lower the vehicle.

9. Reposition the upper radiator hose clamp and remove the upper radiator hose.

10. Remove the transmission cooler lines from the radiator.

11. Remove the cooling fan and shroud.

12. Remove the radiator support diagonal brace.

13. Remove the coolant recovery line from the radiator.

14. Disconnect the radiator side panels from the shroud.

15. Remove the radiator.

16. Remove the bolts retaining the condenser to the radiator.

To install:

17. Install the condenser to the radiator.

18. Install the bolts retaining the condenser to the radiator and tighten to 21 ft. lbs. (28 Nm).

19. Install the radiator.

20. Install the cooling fan and shroud.

21. Raise the vehicle.

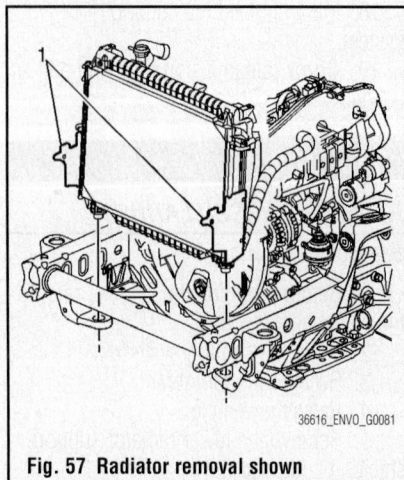

Fig. 57 Radiator removal shown

22. Install the lower radiator hose to the radiator and reposition the clamp.

23. Connect the transmission cooler lines to the radiator.

24. Install the lower radiator support shield, if equipped.

25. Lower the vehicle.

26. Install the coolant recovery hose to the radiator.

27. Install the radiator support diagonal brace.

28. Fill and bleed the cooling system.

29. Vacuum and recharge the A/C system.

30. Check transmission fluid and add as needed.

THERMOSTAT

REMOVAL & INSTALLATION

4.2L Engine

See Figure 58.

1. Remove the necessary coolant from the radiator.

2. Remove the alternator, as outlined in the Engine Electrical Section.

3. Loosen the outlet hose clamp at the thermostat housing. Remove the outlet hose from the thermostat housing.

4. Remove the thermostat housing bolts.

5. Remove the thermostat housing from the engine block.

6. Clean all of the surfaces of the thermostat housing.

7. Clean the sealing surface of the engine block.

To install:

8. Install the thermostat housing to the engine block.

9. Install the thermostat housing bolts and tighten to 89 inch lbs. (10 Nm).

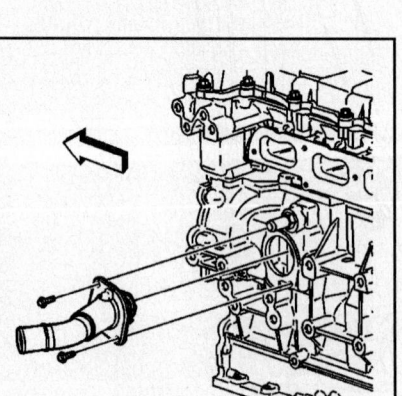

Fig. 58 Thermostat mounting—4.2L engine

10. Lubricate the inner diameter of the radiator hose with engine coolant.

11. Install the outlet hose to the thermostat housing. Secure the hose with the clamp.

12. Install the alternator.

13. Fill the cooling system with specified coolant and concentration.

14. Inspect all sealing surfaces for leaks after starting the engine.

5.3L and 6.0L Engines

See Figure 59.

➡**The thermostat is not serviceable separately. The water pump inlet and thermostat must be replaced as an assembly.**

1. Drain the cooling system to a level below the thermostat.

2. Remove the radiator lower hose.

3. Remove the water pump inlet bolts.

4. Remove the water pump inlet and thermostat from the water pump.

Fig. 59 Remove the water pump inlet and thermostat from the water pump

To install:

5. Install the thermostat and thermostat housing to the water pump.

6. Install the thermostat housing bolts. Tighten the bolts to 11 ft. lbs. (15 Nm).

7. Install the radiator lower hose.

8. Fill and bleed the cooling system.

WATER PUMP

REMOVAL & INSTALLATION

See Figures 60 and 61.

1. Before servicing the vehicle, refer to the precautions in the beginning of this section.

2. Disconnect the negative battery cable.

3. Drain the engine cooling system.

4. For 5.3L and 6.0L engines, loosen the air cleaner outlet duct clamps at the

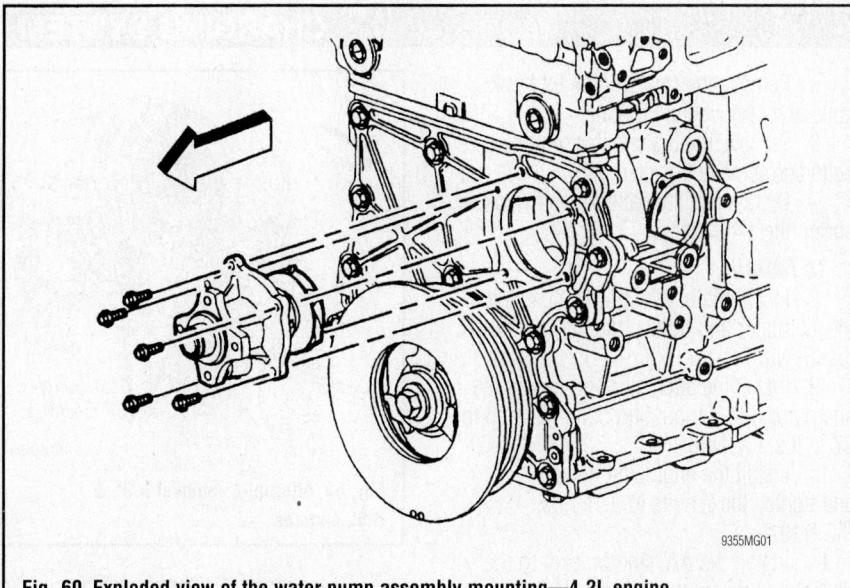

Fig. 60 Exploded view of the water pump assembly mounting—4.2L engine

throttle body and Mass Airflow/Intake Air Temperature (MAF/IAT) sensor. Remove the bolt and air cleaner outlet duct.

5. Relieve the belt tension and remove the accessory drive belts or the serpentine drive belt, as applicable.

6. Remove or disconnect the following:
- Upper fan shroud
- Fan or fan and clutch assembly, as applicable

- Water pump pulley; use a suitable tool to hold the pulley while removing the bolts
- Coolant hose(s) from the water pump

➡For the hoses on some engines, removal may be easier if the hose is left attached until the pump is free from the block. Once the pump is removed from the engine, the pump

may be pulled (giving a better grip and greater leverage) from the tight hose connection.

- Water pump retainers
- Water pump from the engine

✳✳ WARNING

Note the positions of all retainers as some engines will utilize different length fasteners in different locations and/or bolts and studs in different locations.

To install:

7. Clean the gasket mounting surfaces.

➡The water pumps on some of the engines covered may have been installed using sealer only, no gasket, at the factory. If a gasket is supplied with the replacement part, it should be used. Otherwise, a 1/8 in. (3mm) bead of RTV sealer should be used around the sealing surface of the pump.

8. Apply sealant to the water pump retainer threads.

9. Install or connect the following:
- Water pump using a new gasket. Tighten the water pump retainers to 89 inch lbs. (10 Nm) for 4.2L engines. For 5.3L and 6.0L engines, tighten the bolts to 11 ft. lbs. (15 Nm), then to 22 ft. lbs. (30 Nm).
- Coolant hose(s)
- Water pump pulley. Tighten the pulley bolts to 18 ft. lbs. (25 Nm).
- Fan or fan and clutch assembly
- Serpentine drive belt (if equipped) by positioning the belt over the pulleys and carefully allow the tensioner back into contact with the belt.
- V-belts (if equipped) and adjust the tension
- Upper fan shroud
- Negative battery cable

10. Refill the engine cooling system.

11. Run the engine and check for leaks.

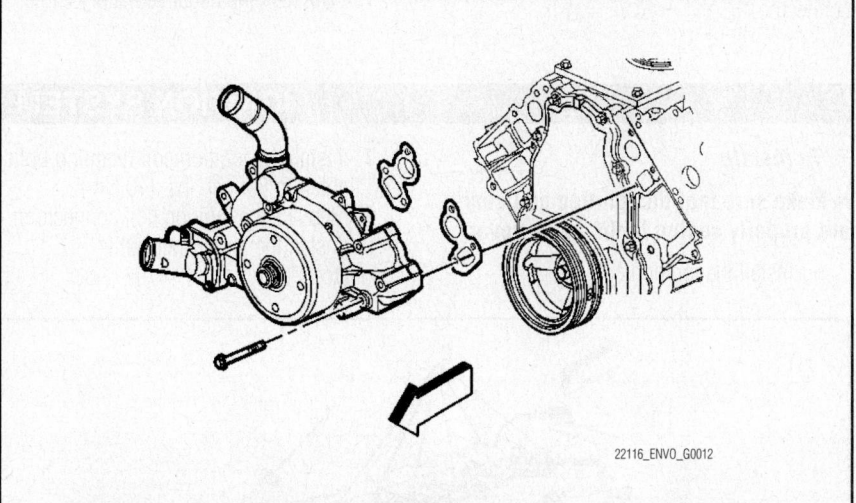

Fig. 61 Exploded view of the water pump assembly mounting—5.3L and 6.0L engines

ENGINE ELECTRICAL   CHARGING SYSTEM

ALTERNATOR

REMOVAL & INSTALLATION

4.2L Engine

See Figure 62.

1. Before servicing the vehicle, refer to the precautions section.
2. Disconnect the negative battery cable.
3. Remove the drive belt.
4. Remove the Air Conditioning (A/C) line mounting bracket bolt at the engine lift hook.

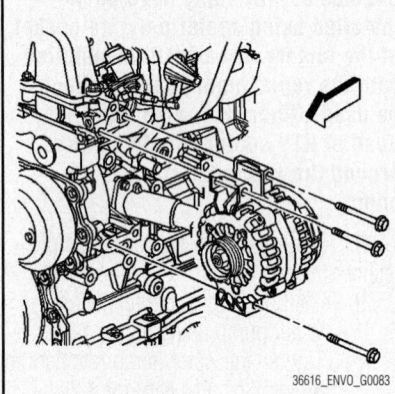

Fig. 62 Alternator and mounting bolt removal 4.2L engine

36616_ENVO_G0083

5. Remove the right engine lift hook bolts and remove the lift hook.
6. Remove the 3 alternator mounting bolts and remove the alternator.
7. Disconnect the battery positive cable nut on the alternator.

To install:

8. Install the battery positive cable to the alternator and tighten the nut to 80 inch. lbs. (9 Nm).
9. Install the alternator and secure the alternator with 3 mounting bolts. Tighten to 37 ft. lbs. (50 Nm).
10. Install the engine lift hook and tighten the 2 bolts to 37 ft. lbs. (50 Nm).
11. Install the A/C line bracket to the lift hook and secure the bracket with the bolt and tighten to 89 inch. lbs. (10 Nm).
12. Install the drive belt.
13. Connect the battery negative cable.

5.3L and 6.0L Engines

See Figure 63.

1. Before servicing the vehicle, refer to the precautions section.
2. Disconnect the negative battery cable.
3. Remove the drive belt.
4. Disconnect the alternator electrical connector.

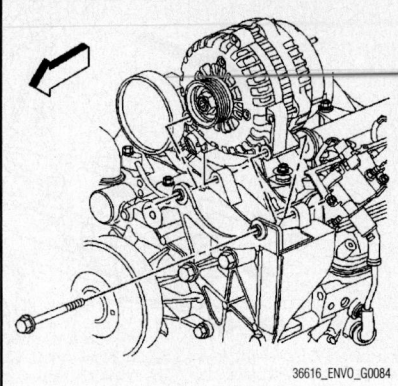

Fig. 63 Alternator removal 5.3L & 6.0L engines

36616_ENVO_G0084

5. Disconnect the battery positive cable nut on the alternator.
6. Remove the alternator bolts.
7. Remove the alternator.

To install:

8. Install the alternator.
9. Install the alternator bolts and tighten to 37 ft. lbs. (50 Nm).
10. Install the battery positive cable to the alternator and tighten the nut to 80 inch. lbs. (9 Nm).
11. Connect the alternator electrical connector.
12. Install the accessory drive belt.
13. Connect the negative battery cable.

ENGINE ELECTRICAL   IGNITION SYSTEM

FIRING ORDERS

The firing order for the 4.2L engine is 1-5-3-6-2-4.

The firing order for the 5.3L and 6.0L engines is 1-8-7-2-6-5-4-3.

IGNITION COIL

REMOVAL & INSTALLATION

4.2L Engine

See Figure 64.

1. Before servicing the vehicle, refer to the precautions section.
2. Remove the air cleaner outlet resonator.
3. Disconnect the ignition coil connectors from the ignition coils.
4. Remove the retaining bolts from the ignition coils.
5. Remove the ignition coils from the engine.

To install:

➡ **Make sure that the ignition coil seals are properly seated to the valve cover.**

6. Install the ignition coil.

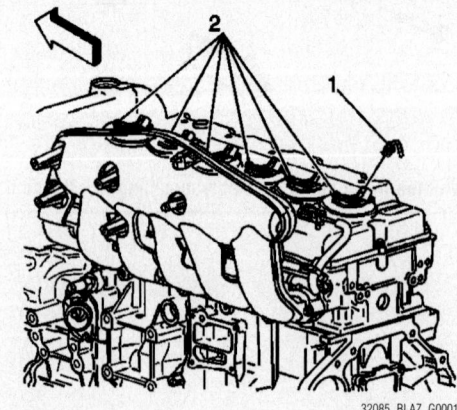

Fig. 64 Detach the connectors (1) and remove the bolts (2) from the ignition coils

32085_BLAZ_G0001

7. Install the ignition coil retaining bolts and tighten to 89 inch lbs. (10 Nm).
8. Replace the ignition coil connectors.
9. Install the air cleaner outlet resonator.

5.3L & 6.0L Engines

See Figure 65.

1. Before servicing the vehicle, refer to the precautions section.
2. Disconnect the negative battery cable.
3. Remove the spark plug wire from the ignition coil.
4. Disconnect the ignition coil electrical connector.
5. Remove the ignition coil bolts.
6. Remove the ignition coil.

To install:

7. Install the ignition coil.
8. Install the ignition coil bolts and tighten to 71 inch lbs. (8 Nm).
9. Connect the ignition coil electrical connector.
10. Connect the spark plug wire to the ignition coil.
11. Connect the negative battery cable.

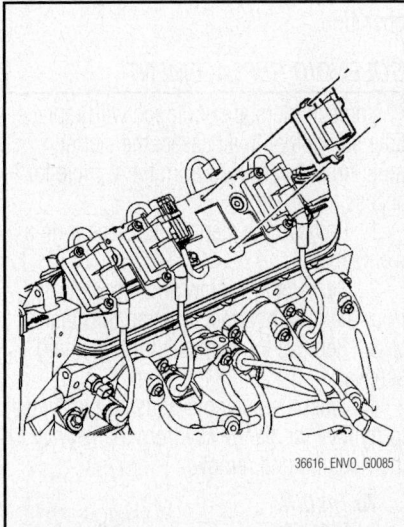

Fig. 65 Ignition coil removal 5.3L and 6.0L engines

IGNITION TIMING

ADJUSTMENT

The ignition timing is controlled by the Powertrain Control Module (PCM). No adjustment is necessary or possible

SPARK PLUGS

REMOVAL & INSTALLATION

4.2L Engine

See Figure 66.

1. Before servicing the vehicle, refer to the precautions section.
2. Disconnect the negative battery cable.
3. Turn OFF the ignition switch.
4. Remove the ignition coils.

⁂ WARNING

Allow the engine to cool before removing the spark plugs. Attempting to remove the spark plugs from a hot engine may cause the plug threads to seize, causing damage to cylinder head threads. Clean the spark plug recess area before removing the spark plug. Failure to do so could result in engine damage because of dirt or foreign material entering the cylinder head, or by the contamination of the cylinder head threads. The contaminated threads may prevent the proper seating of the new plug. Use a thread chaser to clean the threads of any contamination.

5. Remove the spark plugs from the engine.

To install:

➡ Check the gap of all new and reconditioned spark plugs before installation. The pre-set gaps may have changed during handling. Use a round feeler gage to ensure an accurate check. Installing the spark plugs with the wrong gap can cause poor engine performance and may even damage the engine.

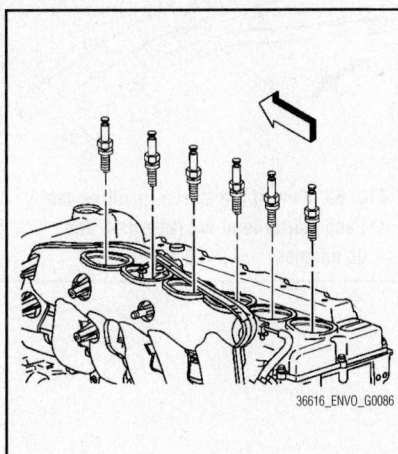

Fig. 66 4.2L engine spark plug removal

6. Measure the spark plug gap on the spark plugs to be installed. Compare the measurement to the gap specifications 0.040 inch. Correct as necessary.
7. Install the spark plugs to the engine and tighten to 13 ft. lbs. (18 Nm).
8. Install the ignition coils.

5.3L & 6.0L Engines

See Figure 67.

1. Before servicing the vehicle, refer to the precautions section.
2. Disconnect the negative battery cable.
3. Remove the spark plug wire.
4. Remove the washer solvent container to gain access to the number 2 spark plug.
5. Loosen the spark plug 1–2 turns.
6. Brush or using compressed air, blow away any dirt from around the spark plug.
7. If removing more than one plug, place each plug in a tray marked with the corresponding cylinder number.

To install:

8. Correctly position the spark plug washer.
9. Inspect the spark plug gap. Adjust the gap as needed. 0.060 inch.
10. Hand start the spark plug in the corresponding cylinder.
11. Tighten the spark plug as follows:
    - For used heads, tighten the plug to 11 ft. lbs. (15 Nm).
    - For NEW heads, tighten the plug to 15 ft. lbs. (20 Nm).
12. Install the spark plug wire.
13. If removed, install the washer solvent container.

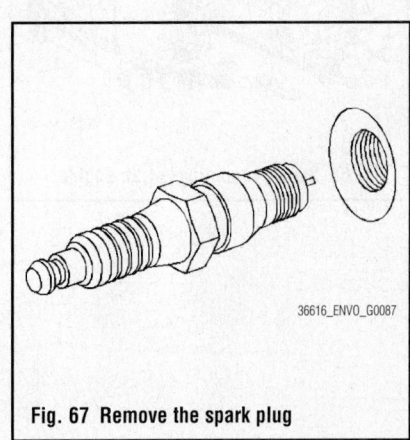

Fig. 67 Remove the spark plug

STARTER

REMOVAL & INSTALLATION

4.2L Engine

See Figure 68.

1. Before servicing the vehicle, refer to the precautions in the beginning of this section.
2. Disconnect the negative battery cable.
3. Raise and safely support the vehicle.
4. Remove the left front tire and wheel assembly.
5. Working in the left fender area, disconnect the positive battery lead from the solenoid.
6. Remove or disconnect the following:
   • Starter mount bolt and nut
   • Starter motor

To install:

7. Install or connect the following:
   • Starter motor
   • Starter mounting bolt and nut. Tighten to 37 ft. lbs. (50 Nm).
   • Positive battery cable to the starter. Tighten the nut to 80 inch lbs. (9 Nm).
   • Left front tire and wheel assembly

Fig. 68 Starter mounting—4.2L engine

8. Carefully lower the vehicle, then connect the negative battery cable.

5.3L and 6.0L Engines

See Figure 69.

1. Before servicing the vehicle, refer to the precautions section.
2. Remove or disconnect the following:
   • Negative battery cable
   • Catalytic converter
   • Engine shield bolts and shield
   • Right transmission cover bolt
   • Starter bolts
   • Transmission cover and shield, after repositioning the starter
3. Position the starter down, with the terminals facing toward the front of the vehicle.
   • Starter solenoid nut
   • Starter lead from the solenoid stud
   • Starter lead nut
   • Positive cable from the starter stud
   • Starter

To install:

4. Install or connect the following:

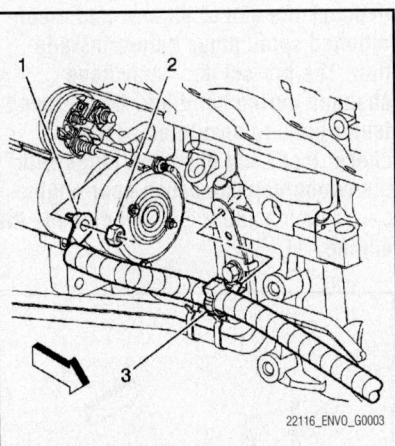

Fig. 69 View of the starter, positive cable (1) and starter lead nut (2)—5.3L and 6.0L engines

   • Starter in the vehicle. Position the starter down , with the terminals facing toward the front of the vehicle.
   • Positive cable to the starter stud.
   • Starter lead nut and tighten to 80 inch lbs. (9 Nm)
   • Starter solenoid lead to the stud
   • Starter solenoid nut and tighten to 30 inch lbs. (3.4 Nm)
   • Install the shield and transmission cover, after repositioning the starter
5. Slide the starter rearward.
   • Starter bolts and tighten to 37 ft. lbs. (50 Nm)
   • Right transmission cover bolt and tighten to 80 inch lbs. (9 Nm)
   • Catalytic converter
   • Negative battery cable
6. Start the vehicle to check for proper operation.

SOLENOID REPLACEMENT

Some starters are equipped with replaceable solenoids. In all cases, the starter must first be removed from the vehicle for access.

1. Remove the starter and place it on a workbench.
2. Remove the screw and the washer from the motor connector strap terminal.
3. Remove the two solenoid retaining screws.
4. Twist the solenoid housing clockwise to remove the flange key from the keyway in the housing and remove.

To install:

5. Place the return spring on the plunger and place the solenoid body on the drive housing.
6. Turn solenoid counterclockwise to engage the flange key.
7. Install the two retaining screws, then install the screw and washer which secures the strap terminal.
8. Install the starter on the vehicle.

ENGINE MECHANICAL

ACCESSORY DRIVE BELTS

ACCESSORY BELT ROUTING

See Figures 70 and 71.

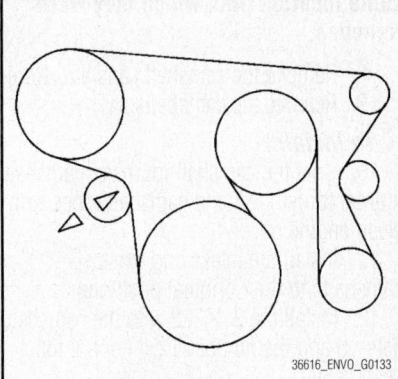

Fig. 70 Accessory serpentine belt routing—4.2L engines

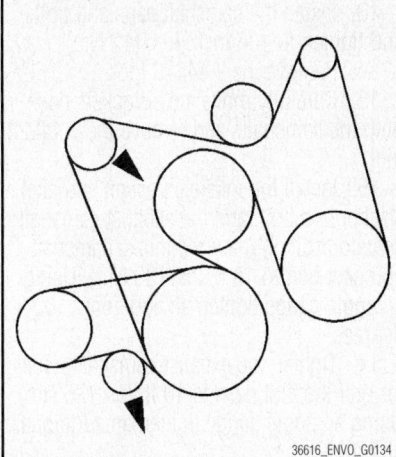

Fig. 71 Accessory drive belt and A/C belt routing—5.3L and 6.0L engines

INSPECTION

Inspect the drive belt for signs of glazing or cracking. A glazed belt will be perfectly smooth from slippage, while a good belt will have a slight texture of fabric visible. Cracks will usually start at the inner edge of the belt and run outward. All worn or damaged drive belts should be replaced immediately.

ADJUSTMENT

See Figure 72.

Serpentine belts are automatically tensioned by a system of idler and tensioner

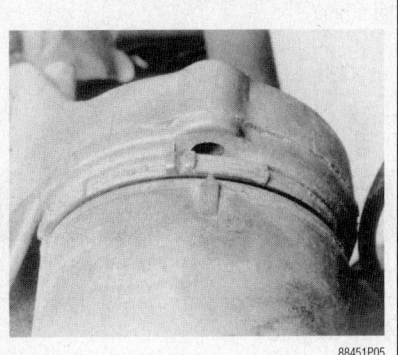

Fig. 72 Check the belt tension by simply observing the range indicator located on the tensioner spindle

pulleys, thus require no adjustment. The serpentine belt tension can be checked by simply observing the belt acceptable belt wear range indicator located on the tensioner spindle. If the belt does not meet the specified range, it must be replaced.

➡A belt is considered "used" after 15 minutes of operation.

REMOVAL & INSTALLATION

4.2L Engine

See Figure 73.

1. Install ⅜ inch breaker bar on the drive belt tensioner arm and turn the breaker bar clockwise enough to relieve the tension on the drive belt.
2. Remove the drive belt.
3. Release the tension on the tensioner arm.

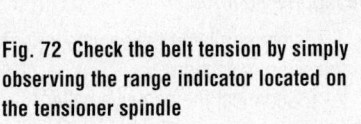

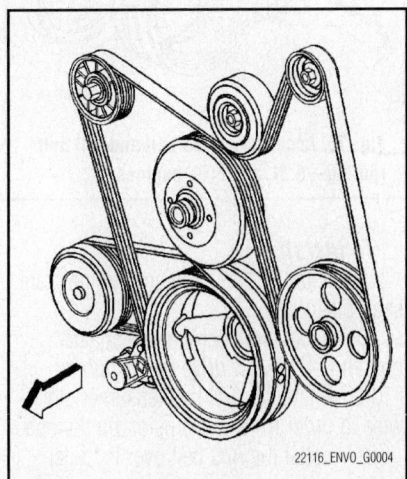

Fig. 73 Accessory serpentine belt routing—4.2L engines

To install:

4. Route the drive belt over all the pulleys except the drive belt tensioner pulley.
5. Install the ⅜ inch breaker bar on the drive belt tensioner arm and turn the breaker bar clockwise.
6. Install the drive belt over the drive belt tensioner pulley.
7. Slowly release the tension to the drive belt tensioner arm.
8. Inspect for proper installation of the drive belt on the pulleys.

5.3L and 6.0L Engines

Accessory Drive Belt

See Figure 74.

1. Remove the air cleaner outlet duct.
2. Install a breaker bar with hex-head socket to the drive belt tensioner bolt.
3. Rotate the drive belt tensioner clockwise in order to relieve tension on the belt.
4. Remove the belt from the generator pulley.
5. Slowly release the tension on the drive belt tensioner.
6. Remove the breaker bar and socket and from the drive belt tensioner bolt.
7. Remove the belt from the remaining pulleys.
8. Clean and inspect the belt surfaces of all the pulleys.

To install:

9. Route the drive belt around all the pulleys except the generator pulley.
10. Install the breaker bar with hex-head socket to the belt tensioner bolt.

Fig. 74 Accessory drive belt and A/C belt routing—5.3L and 6.0L engines

11. Rotate the belt tensioner clockwise in order to relieve the tension on the belt.

12. Install the drive belt on the generator pulley.

13. Slowly release the tension on the belt tensioner.

14. Remove the breaker bar and socket from the belt tensioner bolt.

15. Inspect the drive belt for proper installation and alignment.

16. Install the air cleaner outlet duct.

A/C Compressor Belt

See Figure 75.

1. Remove the accessory drive belt.
2. Raise the vehicle.
3. Install a ratchet into the square opening of the air conditioning (A/C) belt tensioner.
4. Rotate the A/C belt tensioner clockwise in order to relieve tension on the belt.
5. Remove the A/C belt from the pulleys.
6. Slowly release the tension on the A/C belt tensioner.
7. Remove the ratchet from the A/C belt tensioner.
8. Clean and inspect the belt surfaces of all the pulleys.

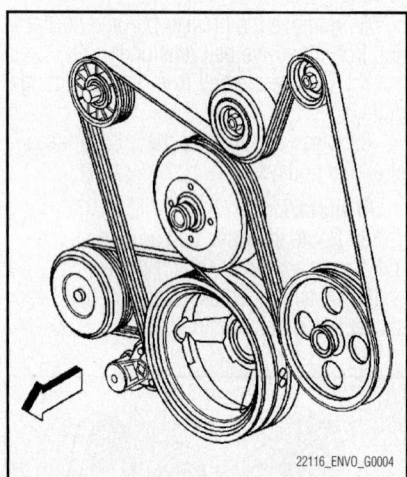

22116_ENVO_G0004

Fig. 75 Accessory drive belt and A/C belt routing—5.3L and 6.0L engines

To install:

9. Install the A/C belt around the crankshaft balancer.
10. Install a ratchet into the square opening of the A/C drive belt tensioner.
11. Rotate the A/C belt tensioner clockwise in order to relieve tension on the belt.
12. Install the A/C belt over the idler pulley.
13. Install the A/C belt around the A/C compressor pulley.

14. Slowly release the tension on the A/C belt tensioner.

15. Remove the ratchet from the A/C belt tensioner.

16. Inspect the A/C belt for proper installation and alignment.

17. Lower the vehicle.

18. Install the accessory drive belt.

CAMSHAFT AND VALVE LIFTERS

REMOVAL & INSTALLATION

4.2L Engine

See Figures 76 through 78.

1. Before servicing the vehicle, refer to the precautions section.
2. Disconnect the negative battery cable.
3. Remove the valve cover.
4. Remove the intake and the exhaust camshaft sprocket bolts.
5. Install the J 44222 onto the cylinder head and adjust the horizontal bolts into the camshaft sprockets in order to maintain

36616_ENVO_G0089

Fig. 76 J 44222 tool shown installed

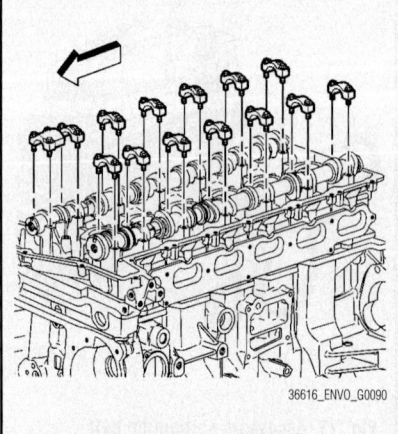

36616_ENVO_G0090

Fig. 77 Remove the camshaft caps

chain tension and keep from disturbing the timing chain components.

6. Carefully move the sprockets with the timing chain, off of the camshafts.

7. Remove the camshaft cap bolts.

➡ **Place the camshaft caps in a rack to ensure the caps are installed in the same location from which they were removed.**

8. Remove the camshaft caps and store.

9. Remove the camshafts.

To install:

10. Coat the camshaft journals, camshaft journal thrust face, and camshaft lobes with clean engine oil.

11. Install the intake and exhaust camshafts to their original positions.

12. Install the J 44222 with the camshaft flats up and the number 1 cylinder at top dead center.

➡ **Install the camshaft caps onto their original locations. The camshaft caps are pin stamped for direction and numerical order.**

13. Install the camshaft caps and bolts and tighten to 106 inch. lbs. (12 Nm).

14. Remove the J 44222 tool.

15. Carefully move the sprockets back onto the camshafts and remove the J 44222 tool.

16. Install the intake camshaft sprocket washer and bolt, and the exhaust camshaft actuator bolt. Tighten the intake camshaft sprocket bolt to 15 ft. lbs. (20 Nm). Using an angle gauge tighten an additional 100 degrees.

17. Tighten the exhaust camshaft actuator bolt the first pass to 18 ft. lbs. (25 Nm). Using an angle gauge tighten an additional 135 degrees.

18. Install the camshaft cover.

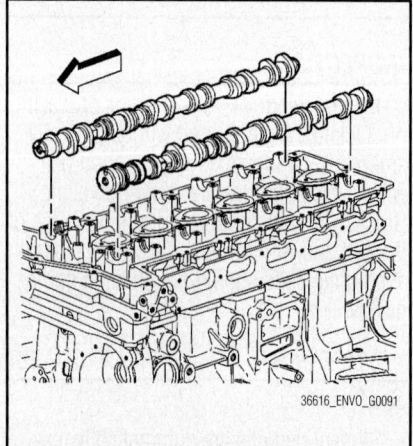

36616_ENVO_G0091

Fig. 78 Camshaft removal shown

5.3L and 6.0L Engines

See Figures 79 through 81.

1. Before servicing the vehicle, refer to the precautions section.
2. Disconnect the negative battery cable.
3. Discharge and recover the refrigerant from the air conditioning system, using the proper equipment.
4. Drain the cooling system.
5. Remove or disconnect the following:
   - Radiator and condenser
   - Cylinder heads and gaskets
   - Valve lifter guide bolts
   - Valve lifters and guide

➡️**If the lifters are stuck in the bores due to built up deposits, use Valve Lifter Remover tool No. J 3049-A or equivalent to remove the lifters**

   - Valve lifters from the guide

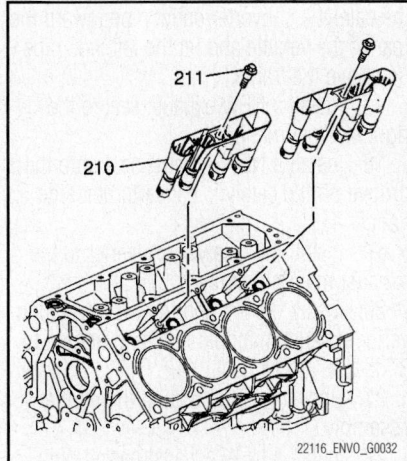

Fig. 79 Valve lifters and guides—5.3L and 6.0L engines

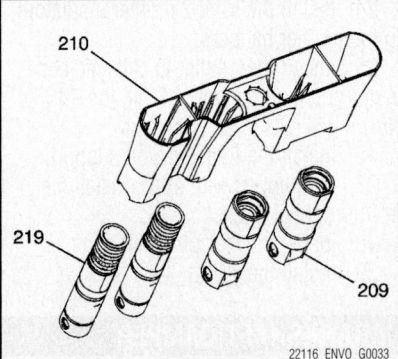

Fig. 80 Remove the lifters from the guides, making sure to keep them in order—5.3L and 6.0L engines

➡️**Make sure to keep the lifters in order as you are removing them. They must be installed in their original locations.**

6. Clean and inspect the lifters for damage.
   - Camshaft sensor bolt and sensor
7. Rotate the crankshaft until the timing marks on the crankshaft and camshaft sprockets are aligned.
   - Camshaft sprocket bolts

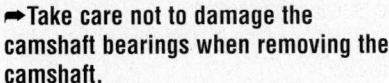

✳✳ WARNING

Do NOT turn the crankshaft after the timing chain has been removed to avoid damaging the pistons or valves!

   - Camshaft sprocket and reposition the timing chain
   - Camshaft retaining bolts and retainer
   - Camshaft by installing three M8-1.25 x 4.0 in. (M8-1.25 x 1.00mm) bolts in the front of the camshaft to act as a handle; then, remove the camshaft while turning slightly from side to side, as necessary. Remove the bolts from the camshaft.

➡️**Take care not to damage the camshaft bearings when removing the camshaft.**

8. Clean and inspect the camshaft and bearings.

To install:

➡️**If the camshaft must be replaced, you must also replace the lifters.**

9. Lubricate the camshaft journals with clean engine oil.
10. Install or connect the following:
    - Three bolts used during removal into the bolt hold in the front of the camshaft
    - Camshaft carefully into the engine block, using the bolts as a handle. Remove the bolts.
    - Camshaft retainer and bolts. Make sure the retaining plate is installed with the sealing gasket facing the engine block. Tighten the bolts to 18 ft. lbs. (25 Nm).
11. Properly locate the camshaft sprocket locating pin with the cam sprocket alignment hole. The sprocket teeth and timing chain must mesh. The camshaft and crankshaft sprocket alignment marks MUST be aligned properly. Locate the camshaft sprocket alignment mark in the 6 o'clock position. It may be necessary to rotate

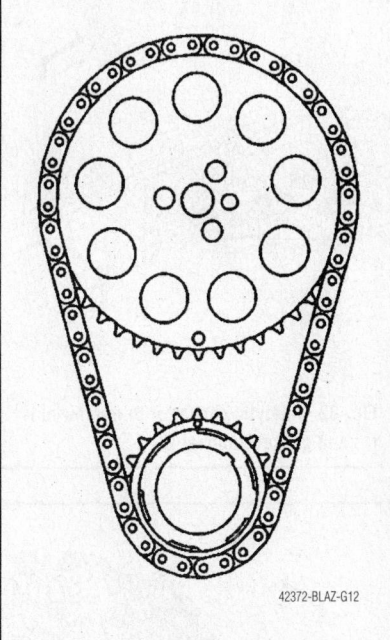

Fig. 81 Make sure the crankshaft and camshaft timing marks are aligned

the camshaft or crankshaft to align the marks.
    - Camshaft sprocket and timing chain
    - Camshaft sprocket bolts and tighten to 26 ft. lbs. (35 Nm)
    - Camshaft sensor O-ring, after making sure it is not damaged and lubricating it with clean engine oil
    - Camshaft sensor and bolt. Torque the bolt to 18 ft. lbs. (25 Nm).
12. Lubricate the valve lifters and engine block lifter bores with clean engine oil.
13. Install or connect the following:
    - Lifters into the lifter guides. Align the area on top of the lifter with the flat area in the lifter guide bore. Push the lifter completely into the guide bore.
    - Valve lifters and guide to the engine block
    - Valve lifter guide bolt and tighten to 106 inch lbs. (12 Nm)
    - Cylinder heads and gaskets
    - Condenser and radiator
14. Connect the negative battery cable.
15. Refill and bleed the cooling system.
16. Using the proper equipment, recharge the A/C system.

CATALYTIC CONVERTER

REMOVAL & INSTALLATION

4.2L Engine

See Figures 82 and 83.

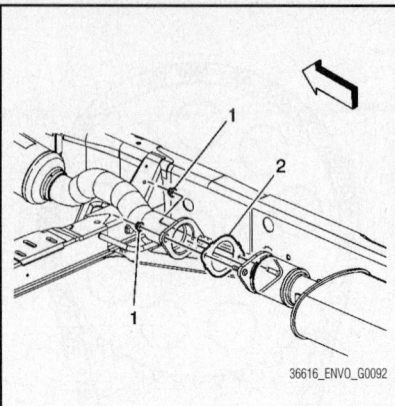

Fig. 82 Catalytic converter to muffler nuts (1) and gasket removal (2)

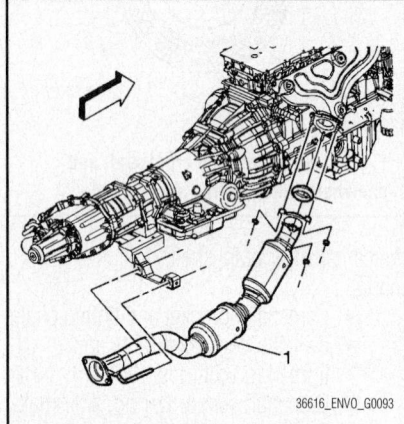

Fig. 83 Catalytic converter removal (1) 4.2L engine

1. Before servicing the vehicle, refer to the precautions section.

2. Remove the Heated Oxygen Sensors (H2OS).

3. Remove the transmission mount to the exhaust hanger mounting bolt.

4. Remove the catalytic converter to muffler nuts.

5. Remove the front 2 muffler insulators from the muffler hangers.

6. Pull back and separate the muffler flange studs from the catalytic converter flange.

7. Reposition and secure the muffler end out of the way.

8. Remove and discard the old exhaust gasket.

9. Remove the catalytic converter to exhaust manifold nuts.

10. Remove the catalytic converter from the vehicle.

11. Remove and discard the old exhaust seal.

12. Remove the catalytic converter hanger from the catalytic converter.

To install:

13. Install the catalytic converter hanger to the catalytic converter.

14. Install a NEW exhaust seal into the exhaust manifold.

15. Install the catalytic converter to the vehicle.

16. Install the catalytic converter to exhaust manifold nuts. Tighten the nuts to 33 ft. lbs. (45 Nm).

17. Unsecure and position the muffler assembly.

18. Install a NEW exhaust gasket onto the muffler studs.

19. Pull back and install the muffler flange studs to the catalytic converter flange.

20. Install the front 2 muffler insulators to the muffler hangers.

21. Install the catalytic converter to muffler nuts and tighten to 33 ft. lbs. (45 Nm).

22. Install the bolt that secures the transmission mount to the exhaust hanger bracket and tighten to 22 ft. lbs. (30 Nm).

23. Install the H2OS.

5.3L & 6.0L Engine

See Figure 84.

1. Before servicing the vehicle, refer to the precautions section.

2. Remove the Heated Oxygen Sensors (HO2S).

3. Remove the rear propeller shaft.

4. If equipped with Four Wheel Drive (4WD), remove the front propeller shaft.

5. Support the transmission with a transmission jack and remove the transmission support.

6. Remove the muffler to catalytic converter nuts.

7. Remove the front 2 muffler insulators from the muffler hangers.

8. Pull back and separate the muffler flange from the catalytic converter flange studs.

9. Reposition and secure the muffler end out of the way.

10. Remove and discard the old exhaust gasket.

11. Remove the catalytic converter to right and left exhaust manifold nuts.

12. Raise the transmission using the transmission jack for additional catalytic converter pipe clearance.

13. Tilt the catalytic converter in order to lower the left side pipe below the vehicle frame. Rotate the catalytic converter outlet pipe toward the left side of the vehicle to gain the necessary clearance for the right side pipe to clear the vehicle frame.

14. Remove the catalytic converter from the vehicle.

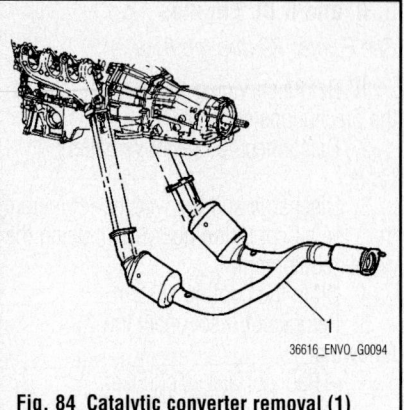

Fig. 84 Catalytic converter removal (1) 5.3L and 6.0L engines

15. Remove and discard the catalytic converter to exhaust manifold seals.

To install:

16. Install the catalytic converter in reverse order of removal by starting with the catalytic converter outlet pipe angled toward the left side of the vehicle and positioning the right side pipe above the frame. Rotate the catalytic converter outlet pipe toward the rear of the vehicle and lift the left side pipe up above the frame.

17. Install a NEW exhaust seal to the right exhaust manifold.

18. Install a NEW exhaust seal onto the groove on the catalytic converter left side flange.

19. Install the catalytic converter to the exhaust manifold studs.

20. Install the left and right catalytic converter exhaust manifold nuts and tighten to 37 ft. lbs. (50 Nm).

21. Unsecure and position the muffler assembly.

22. Install a NEW exhaust gasket onto the catalytic converter studs.

23. Pull back and install the muffler flange onto the catalytic converter flange studs.

24. Install the front 2 muffler insulators to the muffler hangers.

25. Install the muffler to catalytic converter nuts and tighten to 33 ft. lbs. (45 Nm).

26. Install the transmission support.

27. If equipped with 4WD, install the front propeller shaft.

28. Install the rear propeller shaft.

29. Install the HO2S.

CRANKSHAFT DAMPER

REMOVAL & INSTALLATION

4.2L Engine

See Figures 85 and 86.

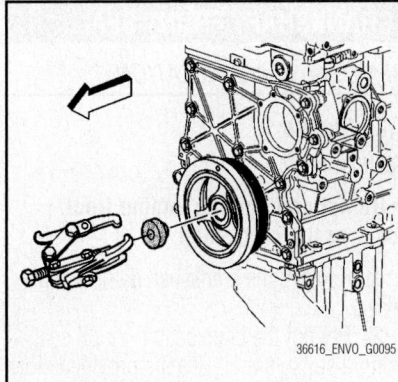

Fig. 85 Install a three jaw puller to the balancer

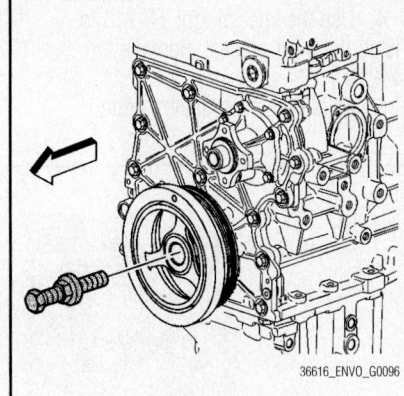

Fig. 86 EN-48034 used for proper installation

1. Drain the cooling system.
2. Recover the refrigerant.
3. Remove the lower radiator support shield, if equipped.
4. Reposition the lower radiator hose clamp from the lower radiator hose.
5. Remove the lower radiator hose from the radiator.
6. Reposition the upper radiator hose clamp and remove the upper radiator hose.
7. Remove the transmission cooler lines from the radiator.
8. Remove the cooling fan and shroud.
9. Remove the radiator support diagonal brace.
10. Remove the coolant recovery line from the radiator.
11. Disconnect the radiator side panels from the shroud.
12. Remove the radiator.
13. Carefully loosen and remove the balancer bolt. Discard the bolt.
14. Remove the flywheel service slot plug.
15. Install the EN 46547 into the flywheel teeth.

16. Install a three jaw puller to the balancer.
17. Remove the crankshaft balancer.
18. Remove the three jaw puller.
19. Remove the crankshaft balancer shim from the crankshaft snout.
20. Clean and inspect the crankshaft balancer.

To install:

21. Install a new crankshaft balancer shim GM P/N 12578073 over the crankshaft snout, against the crankshaft gear.(A new balance will include a shim.)

➡The crankshaft balancer does not have a key-way; so the crankshaft could turn when tightening, causing an improper torque. Make sure to follow the installation procedure to prevent damage.

22. Using the EN-48034, install and seat the crankshaft balancer.
23. Remove the EN-48034.
24. While still holding the flywheel, install the balancer washer and a new bolt and tighten to 110 ft. lbs. (150 Nm). Use a torque angle meter in order to tighten the balancer bolt an additional 180 degrees.
25. Remove the flywheel holding tool.
26. Install the torque converter access plug.
27. Install the condenser to the radiator.
28. Install the bolts retaining the condenser to the radiator and tighten to 21 ft. lbs. (28 Nm).
29. Install the radiator.
30. Install the cooling fan and shroud.
31. Raise the vehicle.
32. Install the lower radiator hose to the radiator and reposition the clamp.
33. Connect the transmission cooler lines to the radiator.
34. Install the lower radiator support shield, if equipped.
35. Lower the vehicle.
36. Install the coolant recovery hose to the radiator.
37. Install the radiator support diagonal brace.
38. Fill and bleed the cooling system.
39. Vacuum and recharge the A/C system.
40. Check transmission fluid and add as needed.

5.3L and 6.0L Engines

See Figures 87 through 90.

1. Before servicing the vehicle, refer to the precautions section.
2. Disconnect the negative battery cable.

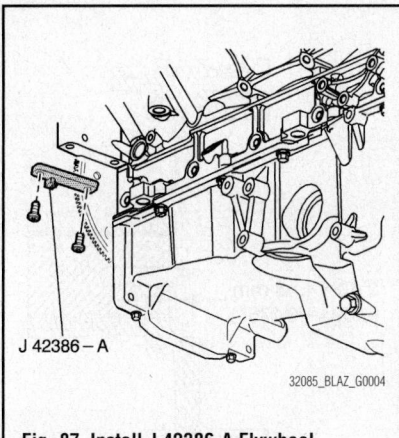

Fig. 87 Install J 42386-A Flywheel Holding Tool

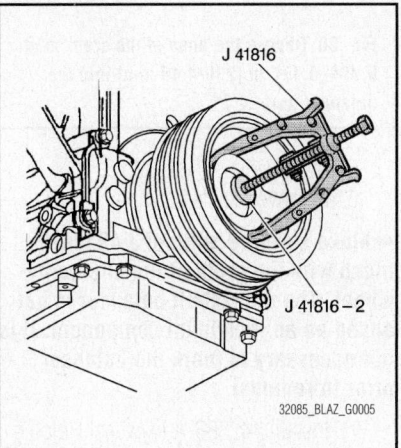

Fig. 88 Install the J 41816 Crankshaft Balancer Remover and J 41816-2 Crankshaft End Protector tools

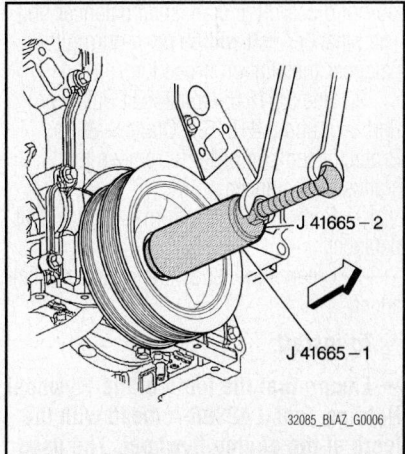

Fig. 89 Install the J 41665 Crankshaft Balancer and Sprocket Installer tool

3. Remove the accessory drive belt, as outlined in this section.
4. Remove the air conditioning (A/C) drive belt, if equipped, as outlined in this section.

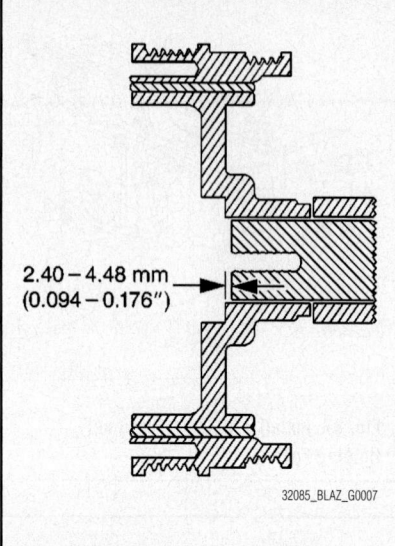

Fig. 90 Recess the nose of the crankshaft 0.094–0.176 in (2.4–4.48 mm) into the balancer bore

2.40 – 4.48 mm (0.094 – 0.176")

32085_BLAZ_G0007

5. Remove the fan shroud.
6. Remove the starter motor.

➡Make sure the teeth of J 42386-A mesh with the teeth of the engine flywheel. The crankshaft balancer is balanced as an individual component. It is not necessary to mark the balancer prior to removal

7. Install J 42386-A Flywheel Holding Tool and bolts. Use one M10-1.5 x 120 mm and one M10-1.5 x 45 mm bolt for proper tool operation. Tighten the tool bolts to 37 ft. lbs. (50 Nm).
8. Remove the crankshaft balancer bolt. Do not discard the crankshaft balancer bolt. The balancer bolt will be used during the balancer installation procedure.
9. Use J 41816 Crankshaft Balancer Remover and J 41816-2 Crankshaft End Protector tools in order to remove the crankshaft balancer.
10. Remove to tools from the crankshaft balancer.
11. Clean and inspect the crankshaft balancer.

To install:

➡ Ensure that the teeth of the Flywheel Holding Tool J 42386-A mesh with the teeth of the engine flywheel. The used crankshaft balancer bolt will be used only during the first pass of the balancer installation procedure. Install a NEW bolt and tighten as described in the second pass of the balancer bolt tightening procedure. The crankshaft balancer installation and bolt tightening involves a four stage tightening

process. The first pass ensures that the balancer is installed completely onto the crankshaft. The second, third, and forth passes tighten the new bolt to the proper torque.

➡Position the balancer onto the end of the crankshaft as straight as possible prior to tool installation.

12. Install the crankshaft balancer onto the end of the crankshaft.
13. Use J 41665 Crankshaft Balancer and Sprocket Installer tool in order to install the crankshaft balancer.
14. Assemble the threaded rod, nut, washer and installer. Insert the smaller end of the installer into the front of the balancer.
15. Use a wrench and hold the hex end of the threaded rod.
16. Use a second wrench and rotate the installation tool nut clockwise until the balancer is started onto the crankshaft.
17. Remove the tool and reverse the installation tool. Position the larger end of the installer against the front of the balancer.
18. Use a wrench and hold the hex end of the threaded rod.
19. Use a second wrench and rotate the installation tool nut clockwise until the balancer is installed onto the crankshaft.
20. Remove the balancer installation tool.
21. Install the used crankshaft balancer bolt. Tighten the USED bolt to 240 ft. lbs. (330 Nm).
22. Remove the used crankshaft balancer bolt.

➡Recess the nose of the crankshaft 0.094–0.176 in (2.4–4.48mm) into the balancer bore.

23. Measure for a correctly installed balancer. If the balancer is not installed to the proper dimensions, install the Crankshaft Balancer and Sprocket Installer tool and repeat the installation procedure.
24. Install a NEW crankshaft balancer bolt. Tighten the bolt as follows:
    a. First pass: 37 ft. lbs. (50 Nm).
    b. Final pass to 140 degrees using Torque Angle Meter J 36660-A or equivalent.
25. Remove the flywheel holding tool and bolts.
26. Install the starter motor.
27. Install the fan shroud.
28. Install the A/C drive belt, if equipped.
29. Install the accessory drive belt.
30. Connect the negative battery cable.
31. Use an OBD-II compliant scan tool to perform the Crankshaft Position (CKP) system variation learn procedure.

CRANKSHAFT FRONT SEAL

REMOVAL & INSTALLATION

4.2L Engine
See Figure 91.

➡Do not damage the engine front cover or the crankshaft.

1. Remove the crankshaft damper (balancer).
2. Pry out the crankshaft front oil seal using a suitable tool. Use the provided slots for prying out the seal.

To install:
3. Apply the engine oil to the outside diameter of the crankshaft front oil seal.
4. Use the special tool J44218 to install the front oil seal. Remove the J44218.
5. Install the crankshaft damper.

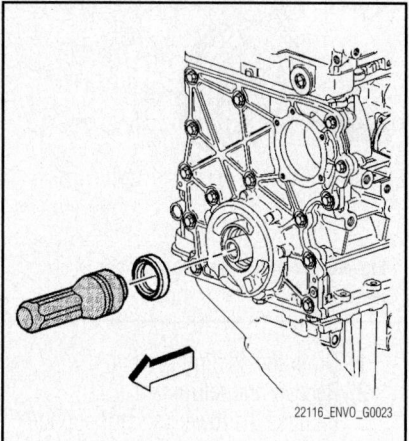

22116_ENVO_G0023

Fig. 91 Using the proper tool to install the crankshaft front oil seal—4.2L engine

5.3L and 6.0L Engines
See Figure 92.

1. Remove the radiator.
2. Remove the crankshaft damper (balancer).
3. Remove the crankshaft oil seal from the front cover.

To install:

➡Do not lubricate the oil seal sealing surface. Do not reuse the crankshaft oil seal.

4. Lubricate the outer edge of the oil seal (1) with clean engine oil.
5. Lubricate the front cover oil seal bore with clean engine oil.
6. Install the crankshaft front oil seal onto the J41478 guide.
7. Install J41478 threaded rod with nut,

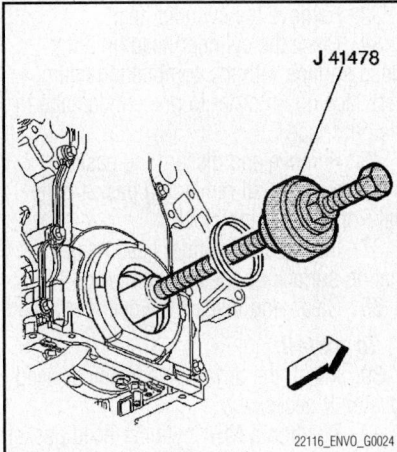

Fig. 92 Using the proper tool to install the crankshaft front oil seal—5.3L and 6.0L engines

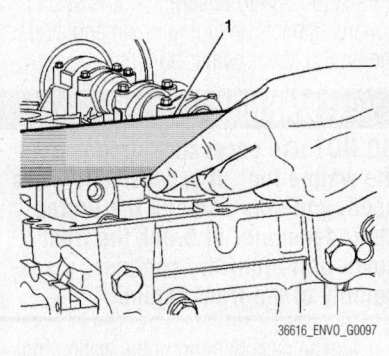

Fig. 93 Flats of cam shown level with a straight edge (1)

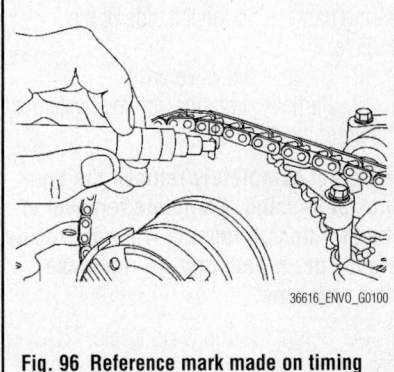

Fig. 96 Reference mark made on timing gear sprocket at 12 o'clock position

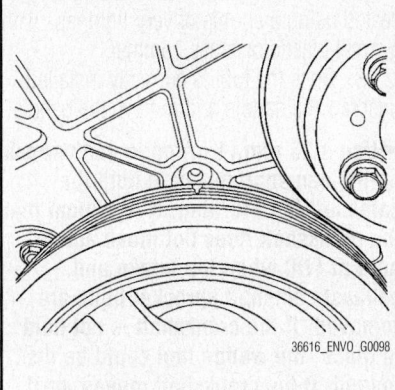

Fig. 94 Place a reference mark on the harmonic balancer

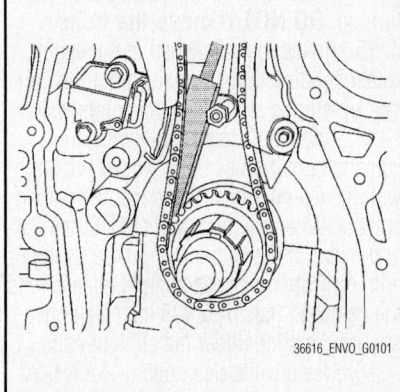

Fig. 97 Correct timing chain holding wedge installation

washer, guide, and oil seal into the end of the crankshaft.

8. Use J41478 in order to install the oil seal into the cover bore as follows:
- Use a wrench and hold the hex on the installer bolt.
- Use a second wrench and rotate the installer nut clockwise until the seal bottoms in the cover bore.
- Remove J41478.
- Inspect the oil seal for proper installation.

9. The oil seal should be installed evenly and completely into the front cover bore.

10. Install the crankshaft damper.
11. Install the radiator.

CYLINDER HEAD

REMOVAL & INSTALLATION

4.2L Engine

See Figures 93 through 99.

1. Before servicing the vehicle, refer to the precautions section.
2. Disconnect the negative battery cable.
3. Remove the air cleaner element.
4. Remove the air cleaner outlet resonator.
5. Remove the Powertrain Control Module (PCM) and engine wire harness bracket and related hoses and connections.
6. Remove the alternator.
7. Remove the intake manifold.
8. Remove the exhaust manifold. Do not remove the exhaust pipe from the manifold. Only have the manifold pushed off to the side of the engine.

Fig. 95 Special tool J 44221 (1) installed to the back of the camshafts

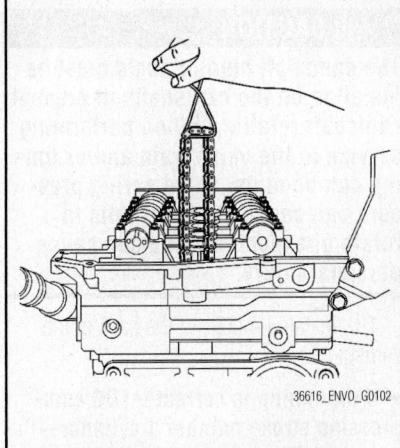

Fig. 98 Mechanics wire secured to the timing chain

9. Position the A/C line out of the way towards the front of the vehicle.
10. Disconnect the following cross-vehicle engine wiring harness connectors:
- Engine coolant temperature sensor
- Manifold Absolute Pressure (MAP) sensor
- Ignition coils

- Harness clamps at power steering pump
- Wiring harness fastener at the right front inner fender
- Throttle body
- Camshaft sensors
- Camshaft actuators
- Fuel rail
- Heated Oxygen Sensor (HO2S)

11. Set aside the cross-vehicle engine wiring harness on the left side of the vehicle.

12. Remove the valve cover.

13. Partially drain the cooling system at the thermostat housing.

➡Do not completely remove the thermostat housing. Complete removal of the thermostat housing will not provide steady drain path and will increase clean up time.

14. Before the Top Dead Center (TDC) procedures, break loose both the exhaust and intake camshaft sprocket bolts. Use a 1 inch. (25 mm) open end wrench on the camshaft hexes to hold the camshaft from turning. **DO NOT remove the bolts.**

15. Rotate the crankshaft in the engine rotational direction clockwise until the number 1 piston is at TDC on the compression stroke. The word Delphi on the exhaust camshaft position actuator will be parallel with the cylinder head to cam cover mating surface. When the piston is at TDC, the flats at the rear of the camshafts will be facing up and level when using a straight edge across the camshaft flats. A 0.005 inch feeler gage should not slide under the straight edge.

16. Use a white paint pen or equivalent to place a reference mark on the harmonic balancer to the front cover for alignment purposes.

17. Lower the vehicle.

✲✲ CAUTION

The camshaft holding tools must be installed on the camshafts to prevent camshaft rotation. When performing service to the valve train and/or timing components, valve spring pressure can cause the camshafts to rotate unexpectedly and can cause personal injury.

18. Install J 44221 to the back of the camshafts.

➡If the timing is correct—TDC compression stroke number 1 cylinder—the camshaft flats will be in the up position.

19. Clean the timing chain and gears with brake cleaner or suitable solvent. Use a white paint pen or equivalent to place a reference mark on both timing gear sprockets and the timing chain to mark location prior to disassembly. It is recommended that the paint marks be in the 12 o'clock position.

20. Install EN-48464 wedge tool. It is important to install the tool with the proper orientation and to ensure that it is seated square against the timing chain and against the timing cover center bolt.

✲✲ WARNING

DO NOT use excessive force to seat the wedge tool. If excessive force is used, you may damage the timing chain tensioner or break the front cover bolt requiring complete disassembly of the front engine.

21. The narrow ramp of the wedge tool needs to be placed so that it faces the timing chain. The front cover is removed for illustration purposes.

22. The wedge tool should be lightly seated using a couple of very light taps with a small plastic or brass hammer.

23. Once the tool is correctly installed, unscrew the handle and remove the handle.

➡Use a 25 mm (1 in) open end wrench on the camshaft hexes to hold the camshaft from turning. It is critical that the crankshaft does not move and is held at TDC when the intake and exhaust camshaft sprocket bolts are removed. If the crankshaft is not held in place, the wedge tool could be dislodged. If the crankshaft moves, or if the tool is not seated properly allowing the timing chain tensioner to extend, the repair will have to be completed by removing the front cover to release the timing chain tensioner.

24. Remove both upper cylinder head access hole plugs from the front of the cylinder head.

25. Remove the 1 long and 2 short cylinder head bolts next to the exhaust and intake timing chain tensioner shoes and discard the bolts.

26. Remove upper timing chain tensioner shoe bolt.

27. Remove upper timing chain tensioner guide bolt.

28. Remove the exhaust and the intake camshaft sprocket bolts. Discard the bolts.

29. Carefully remove the exhaust and intake camshaft sprockets from the exhaust and intake camshafts.

30. After sprockets are removed from the chain, tie a piece of mechanics wire on the timing chain and let it drop.

31. Before removing the cylinder head bolts, use a drift punch and hammer to shock the bolts. This will ensure that the cylinder head bolts will not strip out the threads in the engine block or break.

32. Remove the cylinder head bolts. Discard the bolts.

33. Remove the cylinder head.

34. Place the cylinder head on a flat, clean surface with the combustion chambers face up, in order to prevent damage to the deck face.

35. Remove and discard the gasket.

36. Remove all remaining gasket material from the engine block.

37. Inspect the cylinder head gasket mating surface on the engine block.

38. Clean and inspect the cylinder head.

To install:

39. Install the dowel pins, cylinder head locator, if necessary.

40. Position a NEW cylinder head gasket to the engine block.

41. Install the cylinder head and ensure all wires, components, etc. are out of the way when installing the cylinder head.

42. Install NEW cylinder head bolts.

✲✲ WARNING

This component uses torque-to-yield bolts. When servicing this component do not reuse the bolts, New torque-to-yield bolts must be installed. Reusing used torque-to-yield bolts will not provide proper bolt torque and clamp load. Failure to install NEW torque-to-yield bolts may lead to engine damage.

43. Install NEW cylinder head bolts.

44. Tighten the NEW cylinder head bolts in the following sequence:

- Tighten the cylinder head bolts (1–14) in sequence to 22 ft. lbs. (30 Nm).
- Use the J 45059 torque angle meter to rotate the cylinder head bolts (1–14) in sequence an additional 155 degrees.
- Tighten the 2 short end bolts to 62 inch. lbs. (7 Nm).

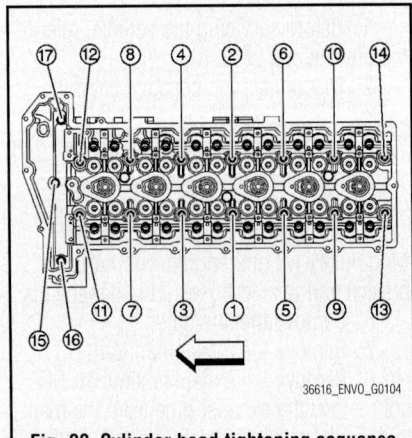

36616_ENVO_G0104

Fig. 99 Cylinder head tightening sequence 4.2L engine

- Use the J 45059 torque angle meter to rotate the short cylinder head end bolts an additional 60 degrees.
- Tighten the 1 long end bolt to 62 inch. lbs. (7 Nm).
- Use the J 45059 torque angle meter to rotate the long cylinder head end bolt an additional 120 degrees.

45. Install the exhaust camshaft actuator/sprocket and chain onto the exhaust camshaft. Use the paint marks as an alignment guide.

46. Install the intake camshaft sprocket and chain onto the intake camshaft. Use paint marks as alignment guide.

47. Tighten the new intake camshaft sprocket bolt to 15 ft. lbs. (20 Nm) plus 100 degrees.

48. Tighten the new exhaust camshaft actuator sprocket bolt to 18 ft. lbs. (25 Nm) plus 135 degrees.

49. Remove the J 44221 holding tool from the back of the camshafts.

50. Install the handle of EN-48464 and remove the wedge portion of the tool from the engine.

✳✳ WARNING

Ensure that the wedge tool is removed from engine prior to rotation. If the wedge tool is not removed, engine damage will result.

51. Install a new seal and tighten the thermostat housing.

52. Clean and inspect the valve cover.

53. Install a NEW camshaft cover seal and NEW ignition control module seals to the cam cover. Position the camshaft cover to the cylinder head. Install the camshaft cover bolts and tighten to 89 inch. lbs. (10 Nm).

54. Check the gap on all of the spark plugs. The gap should be 0.042 inch. (1.08 mm). Tighten all of the spark plugs to 13 ft. lbs. (18 Nm).

55. Install the ignition coils into the camshaft cover, tighten the mounting bolts to 89 inch. lbs. (10 Nm).

56. Install the exhaust manifold to the cylinder head.

57. Install the intake manifold to the cylinder head.

58. Install the engine wiring harness bracket.

59. Install the cross-vehicle wiring harness connectors to the following components:

- ECM
- Map sensor
- Ignition coils
- Ignition coils

- Harness clamps at power steering pump
- Wiring harness fastener at right front inner fender
- Throttle body
- Camshaft sensors
- Exhaust camshaft actuator
- Fuel injectors
- HO2S
- AIR valve and connectors

60. Install the PCV pipes to the intake manifold.

61. Reposition the Fuel/EVAP lines to the intake manifold retainer.

62. Install the alternator.

63. Install the drive belt.

64. Install the air cleaner element and resonator.

65. Install new engine oil.

66. Refill and bleed the cooling system.

67. Connect the negative battery cable.

68. Install a scan tool and start the engine. Check for any DTCs.

69. Road test the vehicle and check for leaks.

5.3L and 6.0L Engines

Left Side

See Figures 100 through 102.

1. Before servicing the vehicle, refer to the precautions section.

2. Drain the engine cooling system.

3. Remove or disconnect the following:

- Negative battery cable
- Alternator bracket
- Coolant air bleed pipe
- Left exhaust manifold
- Pushrods
- Auxiliary A/C bracket bolt, if equipped

- Cylinder head bolts. Discard the bolts
- Cylinder head
- Cylinder head gasket and discard

To install:

4. Carefully clean and inspect the cylinder head and the gasket mounting surfaces.

➡**The gasket surfaces on both the head and block must be clean of any foreign matter and free of nicks or heavy scratches. The cylinder bolt threads in the block and thread on the bolts must be cleaned (dirt will affect the bolt torque).**

➡**DO NOT apply any type sealer to the cylinder head gasket, unless otherwise specified.**

5. Check the cylinder head locating pins for proper installation, location 0.236 in. (6.0mm), as shown.

6. Place a new gasket over the dowel pins. Inspect the displacement markings on the gasket for proper usage. When installed properly, the word "FRONT" on the left side, the tab on the gasket should be left of center or closer to the front of the engine.

7. Install or connect the following:

- Cylinder head

➡**You must use new cylinder head bolts during reassembly. Do NOT reuse the old head bolts.**

- NEW cylinder head bolts.

8. Tighten the cylinder head bolts in sequence as follows:

   a. Tighten the M11 bolts to 22 ft. lbs. (30 Nm).

   b. Tighten the M11 an additional 90 degrees.

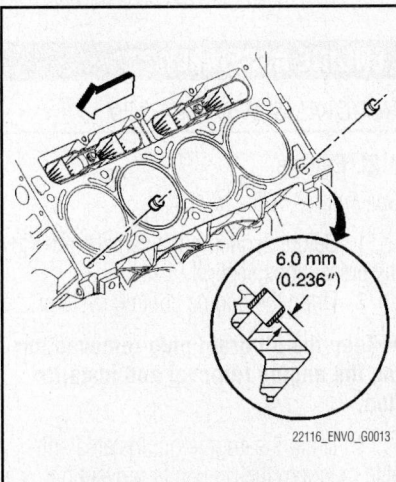

Fig. 100 Make sure the cylinder head locating pins are properly installed—5.3L and 6.0L engines

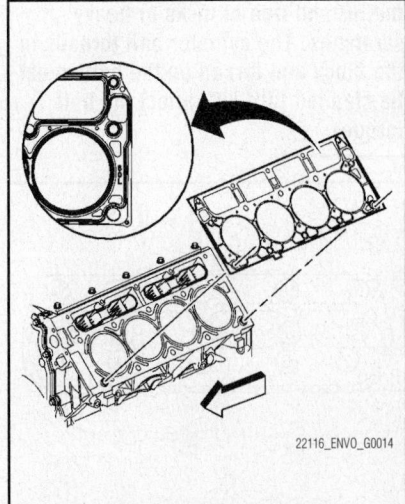

Fig. 101 Proper cylinder head gasket installation—5.3L and 6.0L engines

c. Tighten M11 bolts, an additional 70 degrees.

d. Tighten the M8 bolts to 22 ft. lbs. (30 Nm). Tighten all the bolts beginning with the center bolt and working outward, alternating sides

9. Install or connect the following:
- Auxiliary A/C bracket, if equipped. Torque the bolt to 15 ft. lbs. (20 Nm).
- Pushrods
- Left exhaust manifold
- Coolant air bleed pipe
- Alternator bracket

10. Properly refill the engine cooling system.

11. Run the engine to check for leaks.

Right Side

See Figure 102.

1. Before servicing the vehicle, refer to the precautions in the beginning of this section.

2. Drain the engine cooling system.

3. Remove or disconnect the following:
- Negative battery cable
- Oil level dipstick
- Coolant air bleed pipe
- Right exhaust manifold
- Pushrods
- Auxiliary A/C bracket nut, if equipped
- Cylinder head bolts 1, 2 and 3. Discard the bolts
- Cylinder head
- Cylinder head gasket and discard

To install:

4. Carefully clean and inspect the cylinder head and the gasket mounting surfaces.

➡The gasket surfaces on both the head and block must be clean of any foreign matter and free of nicks or heavy scratches. The cylinder bolt threads in the block and thread on the bolts must be cleaned (dirt will affect the bolt torque).

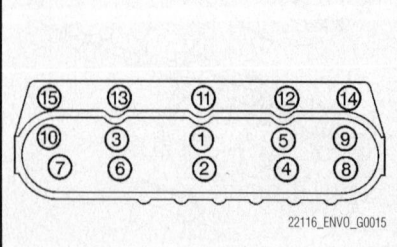

Fig. 102 Cylinder head bolt torque sequence—5.3L and 6.0L engines

➡DO NOT apply any type sealer to the cylinder head gasket, unless otherwise specified.

5. Check the cylinder head locating pins for proper installation, location (a) 0.327 in. (8.3mm), as shown.

6. Place a new gasket over the dowel pins. When installed properly, the word "FRONT" on the right side, the tab on the gasket should be right of center or closer.

7. Install or connect the following:
- Cylinder head

➡You must use new cylinder head bolts during reassembly. Do NOT reuse the old head bolts.

- NEW cylinder head bolts 1, 2 and 3.

8. Tighten the cylinder head bolts in sequence as follows:
- Tighten the M11 bolts to 22 ft. lbs. (30 Nm).
- Tighten the M11 an additional 90 degrees.
- Tighten M11 bolts, an additional 70 degrees.
- Tighten the M8 bolts to 22 ft. lbs. (30 Nm). Tighten all the bolts beginning with the center bolt and working outward, alternating sides

9. Install or connect the following:
- Auxiliary A/C bracket, if equipped. Torque the nut to 15 ft. lbs. (20 Nm).
- Pushrods
- Right exhaust manifold
- Coolant air bleed pipe
- Oil level dipstick

10. Properly refill the engine cooling system.

11. Run the engine to check for leaks.

ENGINE ASSEMBLY

REMOVAL & INSTALLATION

4.2L Engine

See Figures 103 and 104.

1. Before servicing the vehicle, refer to the precautions section.

2. Drain the engine cooling system

➡Keep the oil drain plug removed during the engine removal and installation.

3. Drain the engine oil. Install a suitable plug into the oil pan to prevent oil leakage during the remainder of the procedure.

4. Using the proper equipment, dis-

charge and recover the refrigerant from the A/C system, if equipped.

5. Remove or disconnect the following:
- Hood
- Negative battery cable
- Fuel system pressure
- Air cleaner assembly
- Throttle body
- Manifold Absolute Pressure (MAP) sensor
- Windshield washer solvent container
- Air intake baffle
- Grille
- Headlight housing
- Radiator support brace
- Hood latch
- A/C lines from the condenser
- Transmission cooler lines from the engine, not the radiator

6. Remove the cooling fan and shroud, tilting the radiator forward, and the cooling fan and shroud rearward for clearance.

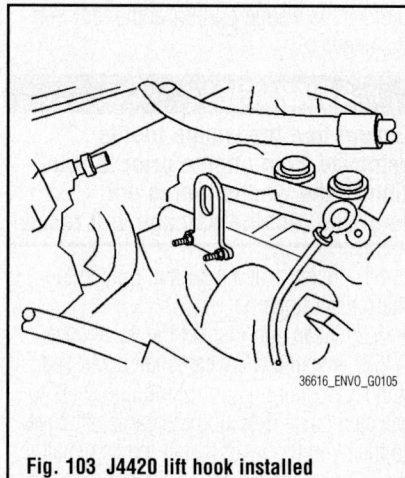

Fig. 103 J4420 lift hook installed 4.2L engine

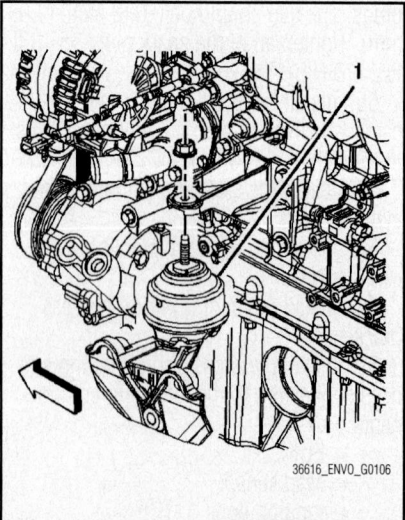

Fig. 104 Left engine mount shown (1)

- Accessory belt
- Power steering pump bolts; position the pump aside
- Heater hoses from the heater core
- Transmission filler tube bracket nut from the Air Injector Reactor (AIR) adapter
- AIR adapter

7. Install a suitable lift hook to the AIR adapter

8. Remove or disconnect the following:
- Oxygen (O₂) sensor connector
- A/C line from the accumulator
- Front axle actuator electrical connector
- Camshaft phaser actuator valve electrical connector
- Transmission cooler lines from the clips on the right side of the engine block
- Ignition coil harness connectors
- Harness retainer from the clips
- Power brake hose from the booster
- Powertrain Control Module (PCM)
- Fuel lines from the fuel pressure regulator. Cap the lines to avoid excessive fuel leakage.
- All harnesses from the engine harness bracket
- Engine harness bracket bolt and bracket
- Starter electrical connections
- A/C pressure sensor and clutch electrical connector
- Alternator electrical connector and battery lead
- Knock Sensor (KS), Crankshaft Position (CKP) and Camshaft Position (CMP) sensor electrical connectors
- 4 ground on the left side of the block

9. Raise and safely support the vehicle.
- Left and right side driveshafts
- Propeller shaft from the front axle pinion yoke
- Engine protection shield
- Exhaust pipe from the exhaust manifold. Slide the exhaust pipe backward slightly.
- Fuel tank shield, if equipped
- Torque converter access cover and bolts

10. Place a jack on the transmission fluid pan for support.

11. Remove the transmission support.

12. Lower the transmission enough to reach the top bell housing bolts.

13. Remove the top 4 bell housing bolts, there may be 2 harness clips that will need to be removed in order to have access to 2 of the top bolts.

14. Raise the transmission.

15. Reinstall the transmission support using only 2 through bolts.

16. Remove or disconnect the following:
- Remaining bell housing bolts (11 total)
- Left and right engine lower mount nuts
- Oil level sensor electrical connector
- Oil pressure switch electrical connector

17. Carefully lower the vehicle.

18. Remove the left, then the right upper engine mount nut.

19. Install the J4420 lift hook to the air port on the engine head.

20. Install a suitable engine hoist.

21. Raise the engine out of the compartment slowly, keeping the transmission supported.

22. Remove both engine mounts for clearance.

23. Continue raising the engine out of the vehicle.

24. Place the engine on a suitable engine stand.

To install:

25. Remove the engine from the engine stand.

26. Slowly install the engine into the engine compartment, aligning the engine mounts with the brackets.

27. When the engine mounts are aligned, install the engine mounts, putting the mount up through the engine mount brackets before inserting into the chassis mount brackets.

28. Lower the engine onto the mounts and install the upper engine mounting nuts. Tighten the nuts to 51 ft. lbs. (71 Nm).

29. Remove the engine hoist.

30. Lay the radiator into the radiator support, but do not install the radiator completely.

31. Raise and safely support the vehicle.

32. Install the lower bell housing bolts, except the top four.

33. Remove the 2 through bolts secure the transmission support, then lower the transmission.

34. Install the top 4 bell housing bolts and tighten all 11 bolts to 37 ft. lbs. (50 Nm).

35. Raise the transmission.

36. Install or connect the following:
- Transmission support
- 3 torque converter bolts and tighten to 44 ft. lbs. (60 Nm)
- Torque converter bolt cover
- Fuel tank shield, if equipped
- Engine protection shield

- Propeller shaft to the front axle pinion yoke
- Exhaust pipe to the manifold and tighten the bolts to 37 ft. lbs. (50 Nm)
- Oil level switch and oil pressure sender electrical connectors
- Oil pan drain plug and tighten to 19 ft. lbs. (26 Nm)
- Lower radiator hose
- Left and right wheel driveshafts

37. Lower the vehicle.
- 4 grounds on the left side of the block
- CMP, CKP and knock sensor electrical connectors
- Alternator and starter electrical connectors and battery leads. Torque the nuts to 80 inch lbs. (9 Nm)
- Fuel lines at the fuel pressure regulator
- Engine harness bracket and bolt. Torque the bolt to 37 ft. lbs. (50 Nm).
- Front differential vent hose, to the engine harness bracket
- PCM
- Power brake hose to the booster
- Harness retainer to its original location
- Ignition coil harness connectors
- Transmission cooler lines to clips on right side of engine block
- Camshaft phaser actuator valve electrical connector
- Front axle actuator electrical connector
- A/C line at the accumulator

38. Remove the lift hook.

39. Install or connect the following:
- AIR adapter and secure with the studs. Tighten to 18 ft. lbs. (25 Nm).
- Transmission filler tube bracket to AIR adapter stud and secure the bracket with the nut. Torque the nut to 89 inch lbs. (10 Nm).
- Heater hoses to the heater core
- Power steering pump and tighten the bolts to 18 ft. lbs. (25 Nm).

40. The remainder of installation is the reverse of removal, but please note the following important steps:

41. Connect the negative battery cable

42. Check all powertrain fluid levels and add, as necessary.

43. Refill the engine crankcase.

44. Refill the engine cooling system.

45. Perform the CKP System Variation Learn Procedure, as follows:
- Install a suitable scan tool and check for Diagnostic Trouble Codes

(DTCs). If any DTCs, other than P1336 are set, resolve those codes first, before proceeding with this procedure.

- With the scan tool, select the crankshaft position variation learn procedure.
- Observe the fuel cut-off for the 4.2L engine.
- The scan tool will instruct you to perform certain steps, make sure you follow all directions given by the scan tool exactly.
- Enable the crankshaft position system variation learn procedure.

➡ **While the learn procedure is in progress, release the throttle immediately when the engine started to decelerate. The engine control is returned to the operator and the engine responds to throttle position after the learn procedure is complete.**

- Slowly increase the engine speed to the RPM that you observed.
- Immediately release the throttle when fuel cut-out is reached.
- The scan tool displays: Learn Status: Learned this ignition. If the scan tool does NOT display this message and not other DTCs set, you must perform further troubleshooting.
- Turn the ignition **OFF** for 30 seconds after the learn procedure has been completed successfully.

46. Start and run the engine, then check for leaks.

5.3L and 6.0L Engines

See Figure 105.

1. Before servicing the vehicle, refer to the precautions in the beginning of this section.
2. Drain the engine cooling system
3. Drain the engine oil.
4. Remove and recover the refrigerant, if equipped with A/C.
5. Remove or disconnect the following:
   - Negative battery cable
   - Hood
   - Radiator
   - Radiator support brace
   - Front axle, if 4WD
   - Drive shafts
   - Intake manifold
   - Oil pressure sensor connector
   - Oxygen (O_2) sensor connector
   - Camshaft Position (CMP) sensor connector
   - A/C compressor hose

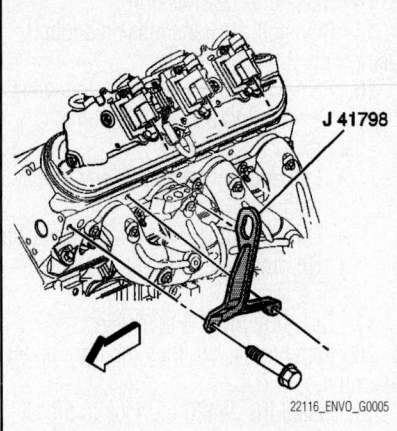

Fig. 105 If necessary, remove ignition coil(s) to install the engine lifting brackets—5.3L and 6.0L engines

22116_ENVO_G0005

J 41798

- Rear auxiliary A/C compressor pipe fitting
- Rear auxiliary A/C compressor pipe nut and bolt. Tie the pipe out of the way.
- Engine Coolant Temperature (ECT) sensor
- Ground terminal bolt
- Retaining clips from the brackets
- A/C pressure switch electrical connector
- Retaining clip from the cylinder head
- Ground terminal bolts
- Starter
- Battery cable channel bolt
- Battery cable channel from the oil pan
- A/C compressor electrical connector

6. Collect all branches of the engine wiring harness, then position the harness out of the way.
   - Alternator cable from the alternator
   - Alternator bracket bolts, then position the bracket and alternator assembly aside
   - Inlet and outlet hoses from the water outlet, using J 38185 to move the hose clamps
   - Auxiliary heater inlet and outlet hose/pipe assembly from the heater water shutoff valve pipes
   - Auxiliary heater inlet and outlet hoses/pipes from the water pump, using Hose Clamp Pliers J 38185
   - Remove ignition coils, if necessary, to install Engine Lifting Brackets J 41798 to the cylinder heads

7. Install Engine Lifting Brackets J 41798 to the cylinder heads. Tighten the M8

bolts to 18 ft. lbs. (25 Nm) and the M10 bolts to 37 ft. lbs. (50 Nm).
   - Catalytic converter
   - 3 frame engine mount bracket bolts from the right and left sides
   - Torque converter bolts
   - Transmission oil level dipstick tube nut and tube
   - Transmission bolt and stud on the right side
   - Lower transmission bolt/studs
   - 3 upper transmission bolts/studs

8. Install a suitable engine hoist to the engine lifting brackets.
9. Place a floor jack under the transmission for support.
10. Separate the engine from the transmission.
11. Remove the engine from the vehicle and place on a suitable engine stand.
12. Install Converter Holding Strap J 21366 to the transmission to hold the torque converter.

To install:

13. Remove Converter Holding Strap J 21366 from the transmission.
14. Attach the engine to a hoist and remove it from the engine stand
15. Install or connect the following:
   - Engine into the vehicle. Match the transmission up to the engine, then remove the floor jack.
   - 3 upper transmission bolts/studs and tighten to 37 ft. lbs. (50 Nm)
   - Lower transmission bolts/studs and tighten to 37 ft. lbs. (50 Nm)
   - Transmission bolt and stud on the right side and tighten to 37 ft. lbs. (50 Nm)
   - Transmission oil level dipstick tube and nut. Torque to 89 inch lbs. (10 Nm).
   - Torque converter bolts and tighten to 44 ft. lbs. (60 Nm)
   - 3 frame engine mount bracket bolts to both the right and left sides. Torque the bolts to 37 ft. lbs. (50 Nm).
   - Catalytic converter

16. Remove the engine lifting brackets from the cylinder heads
   - Ignition coils, if removed, and tighten the bolts to 71 inch lbs. (8 Nm)
   - Auxiliary heater inlet and outlet hoses
   - Auxiliary heater inlet and outlet hose/pipe assembly to the heater water shutoff valve pipes
   - Outlet and inlet hoses to the water outlet

- Bracket and alternator assembly. Tighten the bolts to 37 ft. lbs. (50 Nm).
- Cable to the alternator
- Position the engine wiring harness back over the engine
- A/C compressor electrical connector
- Battery cable channel to the oil pan and secure with the bolt. Torque to 106 inch lbs. (12 Nm).
- Starter
- Ground terminal bolts and tighten to 18 ft. lbs. (25 Nm)
- Retaining clip to the cylinder head
- A/C pressure switch electrical connector
- Retaining clips to the brackets
- Ground terminal bolt and tighten to 18 ft. lbs. (25 Nm)
- ECT sensor connector
- Rear auxiliary A/C compressor pipe nut and bolt. Torque to 15 ft. lbs. (20 Nm).
- A/C compressor hose
- Oil pressure sensor connector
- O_2 sensor connector
- CMP sensor connector
- Intake manifold
- Drive shafts
- Front axle, if removed
- Radiator support brace
- Radiator

17. Recharge the A/C system
- Negative battery cable
- Hood

18. Check all powertrain fluid levels and add, as necessary.
19. Refill the engine crankcase.
20. Refill the engine cooling system.
21. Start and run the engine, then check for leaks.

EXHAUST MANIFOLD

REMOVAL & INSTALLATION

4.2L Engine

See Figures 106 through 108.

1. Before servicing the vehicle, refer to the precautions section.
2. Disconnect the negative battery cable.
3. Raise and suitably support the vehicle.
4. Remove the catalytic converter to exhaust manifold nuts.
5. Lower the vehicle.
6. Remove the 4 manifold heat shield nuts and remove the heat shield.
7. Remove the exhaust manifold bolts.

8. Remove the exhaust manifold.
9. Remove the exhaust manifold gasket.

To install:

10. Position a NEW exhaust manifold gasket to the cylinder head.
11. Position the exhaust manifold to the cylinder head and install the studs to the catalytic converter.

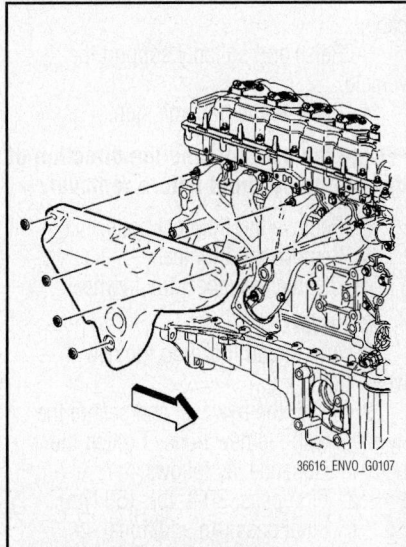

Fig. 106 Heat shield removal

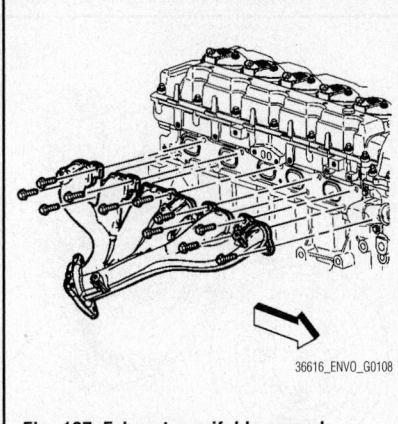

Fig. 107 Exhaust manifold removal

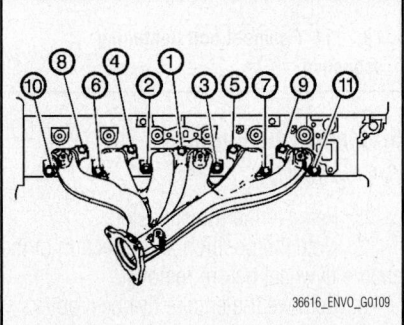

Fig. 108 Exhaust manifold tightening sequence 4.2L engine

12. Apply thread locker to the exhaust manifold bolt threads.
13. Install the exhaust manifold bolts.
14. Tighten the exhaust manifold bolts in the sequence shown as follows:
- Tighten the bolts first pass in sequence to 15 ft. lbs. (20 Nm).
- Tighten the bolts second pass in sequence to 15 ft. lbs. (20 Nm).
- Tighten the bolts final pass in sequence to 15 ft. lbs. (20 Nm).

15. Install the exhaust manifold heat shield.
16. Raise the suitably support the vehicle.
17. Install the catalytic converter to exhaust manifold. Tighten the mounting nuts to 37 ft. lbs. (50 Nm).
18. Lower the vehicle.
19. Connect the negative battery cable.
20. Check for exhaust leaks.

5.3L and 6.0L Engines

See Figures 109 and 110.

1. Before servicing the vehicle, refer to the precautions section.
2. Disconnect the negative battery cable.
3. Raise and suitably support the vehicle.
4. Remove the catalytic converter to exhaust manifold nuts.
5. Lower the vehicle.
6. Remove the spark plugs.
7. Remove the exhaust manifold bolts.

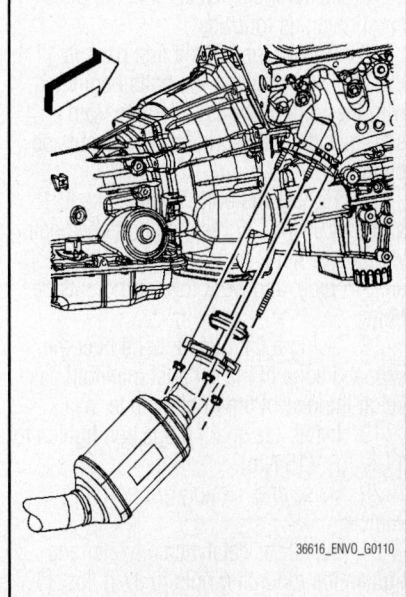

Fig. 109 Right side catalytic converter removal 5.3L and 6.0L engines (Left similar)

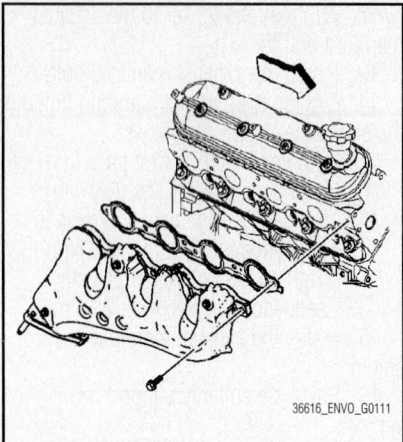

Fig. 110 Right side exhaust manifold removal 5.3L and 6.0L engines

8. Remove the exhaust manifold.

9. Remove and discard the exhaust manifold gasket.

10. Remove the exhaust manifold heat shield, if required.

To install:

11. Position the exhaust manifold heat shield to the manifold and install the bolts, if required. Tighten to 80 inch. lbs. (9 Nm).

12. Apply a 0.2 inch. (5 mm) wide band of thread locker to the threads of the exhaust manifold bolts.

13. Position a NEW exhaust manifold gasket to the cylinder head.

14. Position the exhaust manifold to the cylinder head and install the studs to the catalytic converter.

15. Install the exhaust manifold bolts and tighten as follows:

16. Tighten the bolts a first pass to 11 ft. lbs. (15 Nm). Tighten the bolts beginning with the center 2 bolts. Alternate from side-to-side, and work toward the outside bolts.

17. Tighten the bolts a final pass to 15 ft. lbs. (20 Nm). Tighten the bolts beginning with the center 2 bolts. Alternate from side-to-side, and work toward the outside bolts.

18. Using a flat punch, bend over the exposed edge of the exhaust manifold gasket at the rear of the right cylinder head.

19. Install the spark plugs and tighten to 11 ft. lbs. (15 Nm).

20. Raise and suitably support the vehicle.

21. Install the catalytic converter and tighten the mounting nuts to 37 ft. lbs. (50 Nm).

22. Lower the vehicle.

23. Connect the negative battery cable.

24. Check for exhaust leaks.

FLYWHEEL

REMOVAL & INSTALLATION

4.2L Engine

See Figure 111.

1. Before servicing the vehicle, refer to the precautions section.

2. Disconnect the negative battery cable.

3. Raise and suitably support the vehicle.

4. Remove the transmission.

➡**Note the position and the direction of the engine flywheel before removal.**

5. Remove the flywheel bolts.

6. Remove the flywheel.

7. Clean and Inspect the flywheel.

To install:

8. Add thread locker to the new flywheel bolts.

9. Install the flywheel and secure the flywheel with the new bolts. Tighten the bolts in sequence, as follows:

   a. First pass: 30 ft. lbs. (50 Nm)

   b. Final pass: An additional 45 degrees, with a torque angle meter

10. Install the transmission.

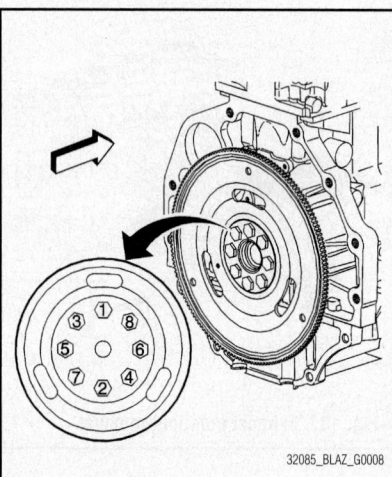

Fig. 111 Flywheel bolt tightening sequence

5.3L and 6.0L Engines

See Figure 112.

1. Remove the transmission.

2. Note the position and direction of the engine flywheel before removal.

3. Remove the engine flywheel bolts.

4. Remove the engine flywheel.

5. Clean and inspect the engine flywheel.

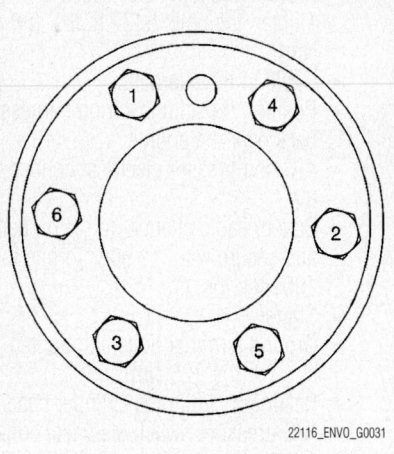

Fig. 112 Flywheel bolt tightening sequence—5.3L and 6.0L engines

To install:

➡**The flywheel does not use a locating pin for alignment and will not initially seat against the crankshaft flange, but will be pulled onto the crankshaft by the engine flywheel bolts. This procedure requires a three stage tightening process.**

6. Install the engine flywheel to the crankshaft.

7. Apply thread locker GM P/N 12345382 (Canadian P/N 10953489) or equivalent to the threads of the flywheel bolts.

8. Install the engine flywheel bolts. Tighten, in sequence, as follows:

   a. First pass: 15 ft. lbs. (20 Nm)

   b. Second pass: 37 ft. lbs. (50 Nm)

   c. Final pass: 74 ft. lbs. (100 Nm)

9. Install the transmission.

10. Lower the vehicle.

11. Connect the negative battery cable.

INTAKE MANIFOLD

REMOVAL & INSTALLATION

4.2L Engine

See Figure 113.

1. Before servicing the vehicle, refer to the precautions in the beginning of this section.

2. Properly relieve the fuel system pressure.

3. Disconnect the negative battery cable.

4. Drain the engine cooling system.

5. Remove or disconnect the following:

  • Throttle body

  • Engine Control Module (ECM)

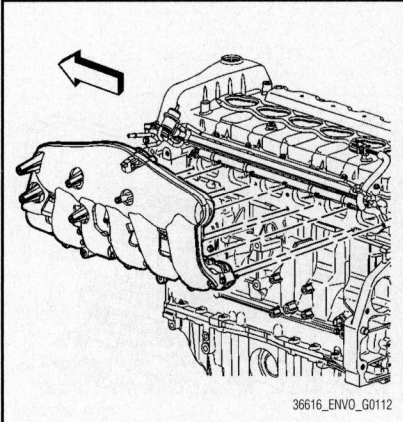

Fig. 113 Intake manifold removal 4.2L engine

- All electrical harnesses from the engine harness bracket
- Front differential vent hose from the bracket clip
- Engine harness bracket bolt and bracket
- Manifold Absolute Pressure (MAP) sensor connector
- Crankcase ventilation hose
- Brake hose from the booster
- Alternator
- Intake manifold bolts and manifold.
- Manifold gasket

To install:

6. Clean the gasket mounting surfaces. Be sure to inspect the manifold for warpage and/or cracks. If necessary, replace it.

7. Properly position a new intake manifold gasket.

8. Install or connect the following:
- Intake manifold and bolts. Torque the bolts to 16 ft. lbs. (22 Nm).
- Alternator
- Brake hose to the booster
- Crankcase ventilation hose, lubricating the inner diameter first with 12345884, or equivalent lubricant
- MAP sensor electrical connector
- Engine harness bracket. Tighten the retaining bolt to 37 ft. lbs. (50 Nm).
- Front differential vent hose to the engine harness bracket clip
- All harnesses to their original locations onto the engine harness bracket
- PCM
- Throttle body
- Negative battery cable

9. Refill the engine cooling system.

10. Inspect for fuel leaks.

5.3L Engine

See Figures 114 through 116.

➡The intake manifold, throttle body, fuel rail and injectors can be removed as an assembly. If you are not servicing these components individually, remove the intake manifold as a complete assembly.

1. Before servicing the vehicle, refer to the precautions section.

2. Properly relieve the fuel system pressure.

3. Disconnect the negative battery cable.

4. Drain the engine cooling system.

5. Remove or disconnect the following:
- Air cleaner outlet duct
- A/C compressor pressure switch electrical connector
- Harness clip from the cylinder head and fuel rail
- Mass Airflow/Intake Air Temperature sensor connector

6. Disconnect the electrical connectors from the following:
a. Main coil
b. Electronic Throttle Control (ETC)
c. Fuel injectors. Matchmark the connectors, pull the Connector Position Assurance (CPA) retainer up 1 click. Push the tab on the connector in, then detach the injector connector.
- Alternator connector
- Evaporative emission (EVAP) purge solenoid electrical connector
- Knock Sensor (KS) electrical connector
- Main coil
- Fuel injector electrical connector
- Electrical harness clips from the fuel rail
- KS harness electrical connector from the intake manifold
- Positive Crankcase Ventilation (PCV) valve hose and valve
- Heater water shutoff valve actuator inlet hose from the intake manifold
- EVAP purge solenoid vent tube
- Vacuum brake booster hose from the rear of the intake manifold
- Upper engine wire harness retainer nut. Position the wire harness aside.
- Intake manifold bolts
- Intake manifold and gaskets. Discard the gaskets.

To install:

7. Clean the gasket mounting surfaces. Be sure to inspect the manifold for warpage and/or cracks. If necessary, replace it.

8. Properly position a new intake manifold gasket.

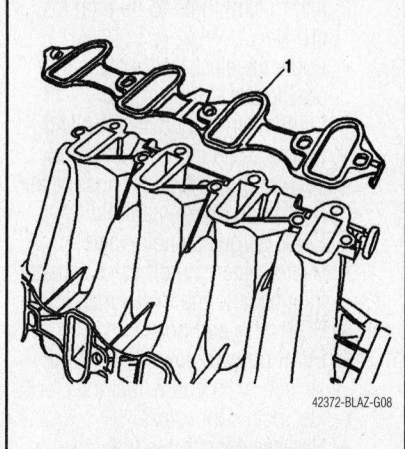

Fig. 114 Make sure to use NEW intake manifold gaskets (1)—5.3L engine

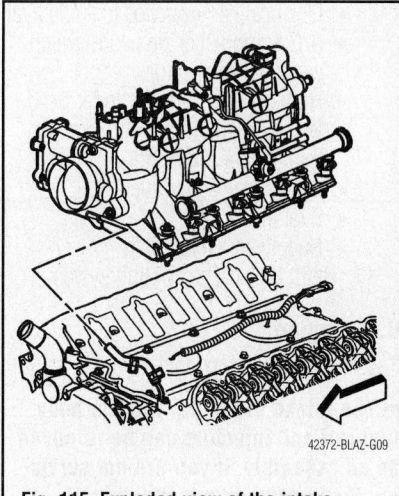

Fig. 115 Exploded view of the intake manifold—5.3L engine

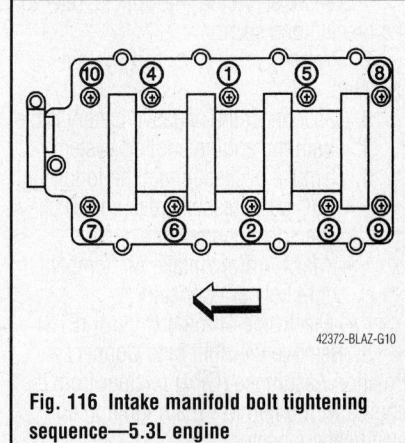

Fig. 116 Intake manifold bolt tightening sequence—5.3L engine

9. Apply a 0.20 in. (5mm) band of a suitable thread locking material to the intake manifold bolt threads.

10. Install or connect the following:
- Intake manifold and bolts. Torque the bolts, in sequence to 44 inch

lbs. (5 Nm), then to 89 inch lbs. (10 Nm).
- Route the electrical harness into position over the engine.
- Engine harness bracket nut and tighten to 89 inch lbs. (10 Nm)
- Vacuum brake booster hose to the rear of the intake manifold
- EVAP purge solenoid valve
- Heater water shutoff valve actuator inlet hose to the intake manifold
- PCV valve and hose
- EVAP purge solenoid, KS, MAP sensor, main coil & fuel injector electrical connectors
- Harness clips to the fuel rail
- Alternator electrical connector
- Main coil, ETC, fuel injector electrical connectors
- Electrical harness clips to the fuel rail
- A/C compressor pressure switch electrical connector
- Harness clip to the cylinder head
- Mass Airflow/Intake Air Temperature sensor connector
- Air cleaner outlet duct
- Fuel fill cap
- Negative battery cable

11. Refill the engine cooling system.

6.0L Engine

See Figures 117 through 119.

➡**The intake manifold, throttle body, fuel rail and injectors can be removed as an assembly. If you are not servicing these components individually, remove the intake manifold as a complete assembly.**

1. Before servicing the vehicle, refer to the precautions section.
2.. Properly relieve the fuel system pressure.
3. Disconnect the negative battery cable.
4. Drain the engine cooling system.
5. Remove or disconnect the following:
- A/C compressor pressure switch electrical connector
- Mass Airflow/Intake Air Temperature sensor connector
- Electronic Throttle Control (ETC)

6. Remove the right side Connector Position Assurance (CPA) retainer from the engine wiring harness main ignition coil electrical connector.
7. Disconnect the right side engine wiring harness electrical connector from the main ignition coil electrical connector.
8. Disconnect the right side engine wiring harness electrical connectors from the fuel injectors.
9. Perform the following steps (for the

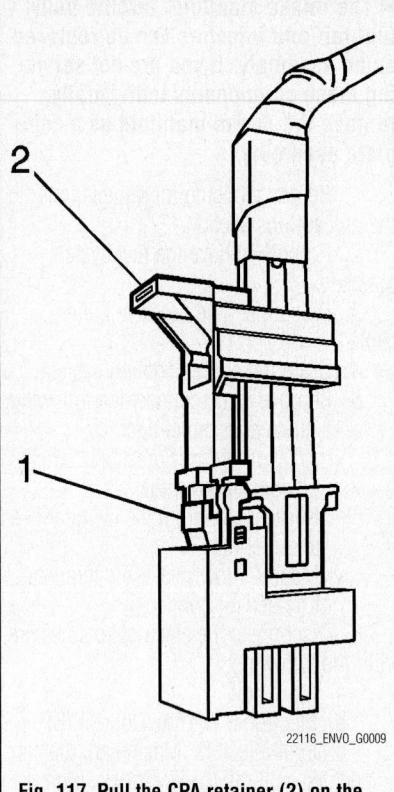

Fig. 117 Pull the CPA retainer (2) on the connector up one click, then push the tab (1) on the connector in to disconnect the fuel injector electrical connector—6.0L engine

left and right sides) in order to disconnect the fuel injector electrical connectors.

a. Mark the connectors to their corresponding injectors to ensure correct reassembly.

b. Pull the Connector Position Assurance (CPA) retainer (2) on the connector up one click.

c. Push the tab (1) on the connector in.

d. Disconnect the fuel injector electrical connector.

e. Repeat the steps for each injector electrical connector.

10. Remove the left side CPA retainer from the engine wiring harness main ignition coil electrical connector.

11. Disconnect the left side engine wiring harness electrical connector from the main ignition coil electrical connector.

12. Disconnect the left side engine wiring harness electrical connectors from the fuel injectors.

13. Disconnect the engine wiring harness electrical connector from the alternator.

14. Disconnect the engine wiring harness electrical connector from the Manifold Absolute Pressure (MAP) sensor.

15. Disconnect the engine wiring harness electrical connector from the Evapora-

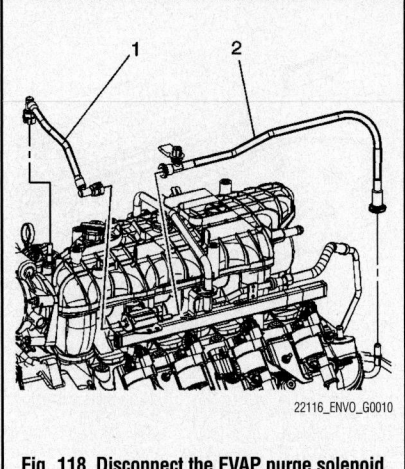

Fig. 118 Disconnect the EVAP purge solenoid vent tubes (1 and 2)—6.0L engine

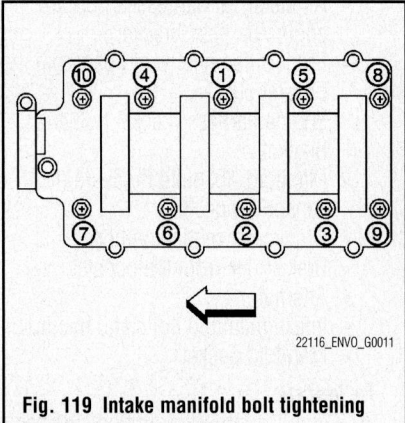

Fig. 119 Intake manifold bolt tightening sequence—6.0L engine

tive Emission (EVAP) canister purge solenoid valve.

16. Disconnect the Positive Crankcase Ventilation (PCV) hose.

17. Disconnect the EVAP purge solenoid vent tubes (1, 2).

18. Disconnect the fuel feed pipe from the fuel rail.

19. Reposition the vacuum brake booster hose clamp at the brake booster and disconnect the vacuum brake booster hose from the brake booster.

20. Remove the engine wire harness retainer nut and reposition the upper engine wire harness aside.

21. Remove the drive belt.

22. Remove the right alternator bolt, then loosen the left alternator bolt and reposition the alternator to the left.

23. Remove the intake manifold bolts.

24. Remove the intake manifold and gaskets. Discard the gaskets.

To install:

25. Clean the gasket mounting surfaces. Be sure to inspect the manifold for warpage and/or cracks. If necessary, replace it.

26. Install NEW intake manifold gaskets to the intake manifold.

27. Install the intake manifold.

28. Apply a 0.2 inch (5mm) bead thread locker to the threads of the intake manifold bolts.

29. Install the intake manifold bolts. Torque the bolts, in sequence to 44 inch lbs. (5 Nm), then to 89 inch lbs. (10 Nm).

30. Position the alternator and install the right alternator bolt and tighten the left alternator bolt to 37 ft. lbs. (50 Nm).

31. Install the drive belt.

32. Route the electrical harness into position over the engine. Install the engine harness bracket nut and tighten to 89 inch lbs. (10 Nm).

33. Connect the vacuum brake booster hose to the brake booster and position the vacuum brake booster hose clamp at the brake booster.

34. Connect the fuel feed pipe to the fuel rail.

35. Install the EVAP purge solenoid vent tubes (1, 2).

36. Install the PCV hose.

37. Connect the engine wiring harness electrical connector to the MAP sensor.

38. Connect the engine wiring harness electrical connector to the EVAP canister purge solenoid valve.

39. Connect the engine wiring harness electrical connector to the alternator.

40. Connect the left side engine wiring harness electrical connector to the main ignition coil electrical connector.

41. Install the left side CPA retainer to the engine wiring harness main ignition coil electrical connector.

42. Connect the left side engine wiring harness electrical connectors to the fuel injectors.

43. Perform the following steps (for the left and right sides) in order to connect the fuel injector electrical connectors:

- Install the connectors to their corresponding injectors to ensure correct reassembly.
- Connect the fuel injector electrical connector.
- Push the CPA retainer (2) on the connector in one click.
- Repeat the steps for each injector electrical connector.

44. Connect the engine wiring harness electrical connector to the ETC.

45. Connect the right side engine wiring harness electrical connector to the main ignition coil electrical connector.

46. Install the right side CPA retainer to the engine wiring harness main ignition coil electrical connector.

47. Connect the right side engine wiring harness electrical connectors to the fuel injectors.

48. Connect the engine harness wiring harness electrical connector to the MAF/IAT sensor.

49. Connect the engine wiring harness electrical connector to the A/C compressor pressure switch.

50. Install the fuel fill cap.

51. Connect the negative battery cable.

52. Use the following procedure in order to inspect for leaks:

- Turn the ignition ON, with the engine OFF, for 2 seconds.
- Turn the ignition OFF for 10 seconds.
- Turn the ignition ON, with the engine OFF.
- Inspect for fuel leaks.

OIL PAN

REMOVAL & INSTALLATION

4.2L Engine

See Figures 120 through 122.

1. Before servicing the vehicle, refer to the precautions section.

2. Disconnect the negative battery cable.

3. Remove the A/C compressor bottom bolts and loosen the top bolts (2, 3).

4. Remove the oil level indicator and tube.

5. Remove the stabilizer shaft.

6. Remove the front differential and secure to the frame.

7. Remove the front drive axle intermediate shaft bearing assembly.

8. Drain the engine oil.

9. Unclip the transmission cooler lines from the engine block.

10. Remove 4 transmission bell housing bolts that are attached to the oil pan.

11. Remove the remaining oil pan bolts.

12. Place 2 oil pan bolts in the jack screws on the oil pan and tighten evenly to release the oil pan from the engine.

13. Clean and inspect the oil pan.

To install:

14. Apply a 0.12 inch. (3 mm) bead of sealer to the block, rather than the oil pan.

➡ **The oil pan must be installed within 10 minutes from when sealer was applied. When you install the oil pan, it could be shifted front or back a little which could cause a transmission alignment problem. The back of the oil pan needs to be flush with the block.**

15. Install the oil pan, maneuvering the oil pan to clear the oil pump and screen assembly.

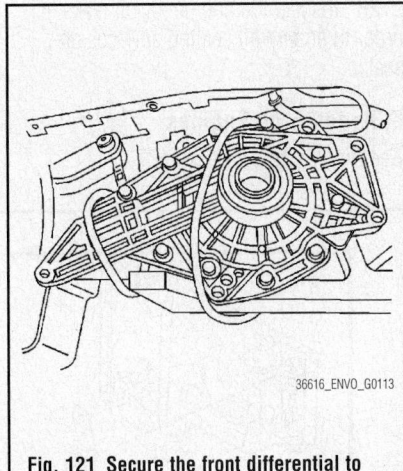

36616_ENVO_G0113

Fig. 121 Secure the front differential to the frame

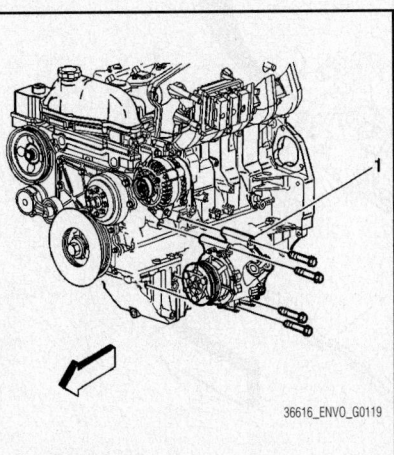

36616_ENVO_G0119

Fig. 120 A/C compressor (1) and mounting bolt view 4.2L engine

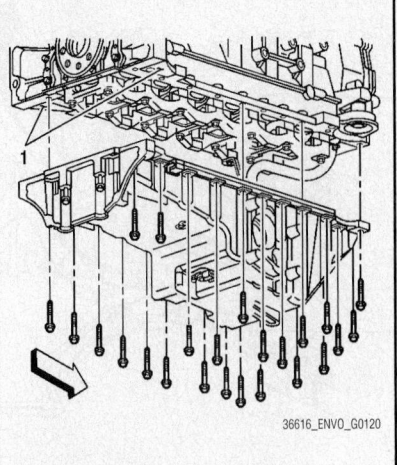

36616_ENVO_G0120

Fig. 122 Oil pan removal 4.2L engine

16. Install the oil pan bolts.

17. Inspect the oil pan alignment. Use a straight edge on the back of the block and the oil pan transmission mounting surface.

18. Tighten the oil pan bolts as follows:

- Tighten the oil pan side bolts to 18 ft. lbs. (25 Nm).
- Tighten the oil pan end bolts to 89 inch. lbs. (10 Nm).

19. Install the 4 transmission bell housing bolts that attach to the oil pan. Tighten the bolts to 35 ft. lbs. (47 Nm).

20. Clip transmission cooler lines to the engine block.

21. Install the front drive axle intermediate shaft bearing assembly.

22. Install the front differential to the engine.

23. Install the stabilizer shaft.

24. Install the A/C compressor 2 bottom bolts. Tighten all 4 bolts (2, 3, and 4) to 37 ft. lbs. (50 Nm).

25. Install the oil level indicator and tube.

26. Connect the negative battery cable

27. Fill the engine with oil.

28. Inspect the engine for oil leaks in order to ensure all sealing surfaces are sealed.

5.3L and 6.0L Engines

See Figures 123 through 127.

1. Before servicing the vehicle, refer to the precautions section.

2. Disconnect the negative battery cable.

3. Remove the oil level indicator tube.

4. If equipped with Four-Wheel Drive (4WD), remove the front differential and secure to the frame.

5. If equipped with Two-Wheel Drive (2WD), remove the steering gear.

6. Drain the engine oil.

7. Remove the transmission oil cooler lines from the retainer.

8. Remove the transmission oil cooler line retaining bracket bolt and bracket.

9. Remove the starter motor.

10. Remove the flywheel inspection cover from the left side of the transmission.

11. Remove the battery cable channel bolt from the front of the oil pan.

12. Remove the battery cable channel from the oil pan.

13. Loosen the 2 upper Air Conditioning (A/C) compressor bracket bolts.

14. Remove the 2 lower A/C compressor bracket bolts.

15. Remove the 2 lower bellhousing bolts.

16. Remove the oil pan bolts.

17. Remove the oil pan by tilting the rear of the oil pan down to clear the transmission, pull the oil pan rearward past the front wire harness, then lower the oil pan clear of the vehicle.

➡The oil pan gasket is reusable. It is NOT necessary to remove the oil pan gasket unless damaged. DO NOT allow foreign material to enter the oil passages of the oil pan, cap or cover the openings as required.

18. Drill out the oil pan gasket retaining rivets, if required.

19. Remove the gasket from the pan.

20. Discard the gasket and rivets.

21. Clean and inspect the oil pan.

To install:

➡The alignment of the structural oil pan is critical. The rear bolt hole locations of the oil pan provide mounting points for the transmission bellhousing. To ensure the rigidity of the

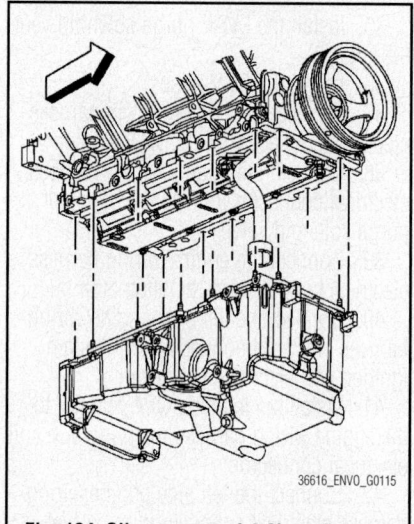

36616_ENVO_G0115

Fig. 124 Oil pan removal 4.2L engine

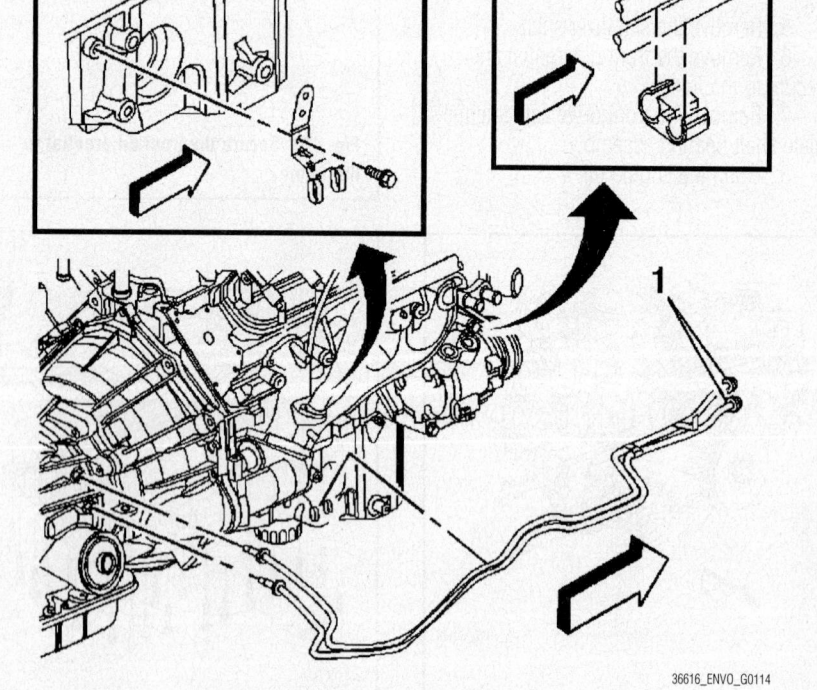

36616_ENVO_G0114

Fig. 123 Remove the transmission oil cooler lines

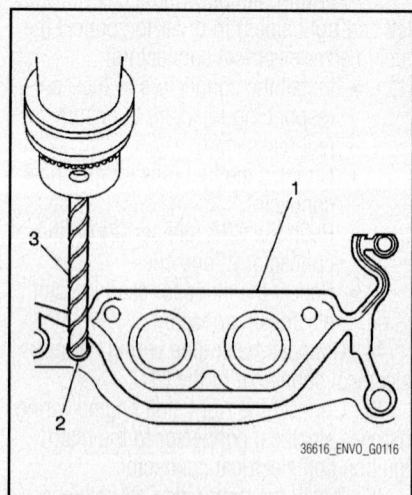

36616_ENVO_G0116

Fig. 125 Drill out the oil pan gasket retaining rivets (2)

powertrain and correct transmission alignment, it is important that the rear of the block and the rear of the oil pan must NEVER protrude beyond the engine block and transmission bellhousing plane. If replacing the oil pan gasket it is not necessary to rivet the NEW gasket to the oil pan.

22. Apply a 0.20 inch. (5 mm) bead of 0.80 inch. (20 mm) long to the engine block.

23. Apply the sealant directly onto the tabs of the front cover gasket that protrudes into the oil pan surface.

24. Apply a 0.20 inch. (5 mm) bead of 0.80 inch. (20 mm) long to the engine block

25. Apply the sealant directly onto the tabs of the rear cover gasket that protrudes into the oil pan surface.

26. Pre-assemble the oil pan gasket and bolts to the pan.

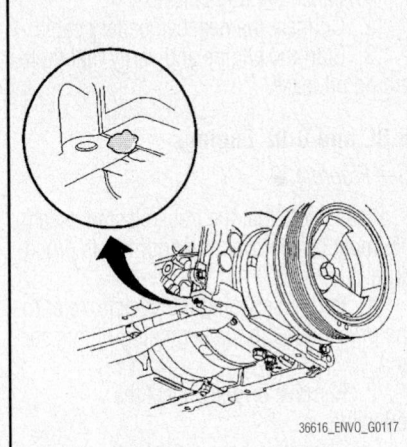

Fig. 126 Applied sealant front location view 4.2L engine

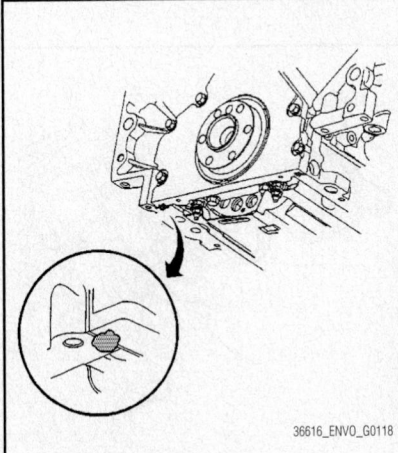

Fig. 127 Applied sealant rear location view 4.2L engine

27. Install the oil pan, oil pan gasket, and bolts to the engine block as an assembly.

28. Hand thread the oil pan bolts into the engine block until snug. Do not tighten at this time.

29. Install and tighten the lower bellhousing bolts to 37 ft. lbs. (50 Nm).

30. Install and tighten the 2 rear oil pan to rear cover bolts to 106 inch. lbs. (12 Nm).

31. Tighten the remaining oil pan bolts to 18 ft. lbs. (25 Nm).

32. Install the 2 lower A/C compressor bracket bolts and tighten to 37 ft. lbs. (50 Nm).

33. Tighten the 2 upper A/C compressor bracket bolts (4) to 37 ft. lbs. (50 Nm).

34. Install the battery cable channel to the oil pan.

35. Install the battery cable channel bolt to the oil pan and tighten to 106 inch. lbs. (12 Nm).

36. Install the flywheel inspection cover to the left side of the transmission.

37. Install the starter motor.

38. If equipped with 4WD, install the inner axle shaft.

39. If equipped with 2WD, install the steering gear.

40. Install the transmission oil cooler line retaining bracket and bolt. Tighten the bolt to 80 inch. lbs. (9 Nm).

41. Install the transmission oil cooler lines to the retainer.

42. Install the oil level indicator tube.

43. Fill the engine with oil.

44. If equipped with 4WD, install the front differential.

45. Connect the negative battery cable.

OIL PUMP

REMOVAL & INSTALLATION

4.2L Engine

See Figure 128.

1. Before servicing the vehicle, refer to the precautions section.

2. Remove the engine front cover.

3. Remove the oil pump cover bolts.

4. Remove the oil pump cover.

5. Mark the inner and the outer gears in relation to the oil pump housing.

6. Remove the inner and the outer oil pump gears.

7. Remove the oil pump pressure relief valve plug.

8. Remove the oil pump pressure relief valve and the spring.

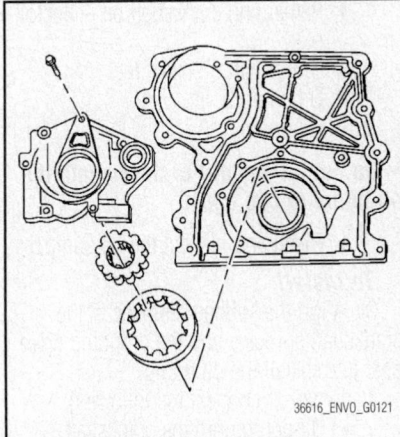

Fig. 128 Front cover and oil pump view 4.2L engine

To install:

9. Install the oil pump pressure relief valve plug and tighten to 124 inch. lbs. (14 Nm).

10. Install the oil pump outer and inner gears as removed.

11. Install the oil pump cover.

12. Install the oil pump cover bolts 89 inch. lbs. (10 Nm).

13. Install the front cover.

5.3L and 6.0L Engines

See Figure 129.

1. Before servicing the vehicle, refer to the precautions in the beginning of this section.

2. Remove or disconnect the following:

• Oil pan
• Engine front cover
• Oil pump screen bolt and nuts
• Oil pump screen with O-ring seal
• O-ring seal from the pump screen. Discard the O-ring seal.

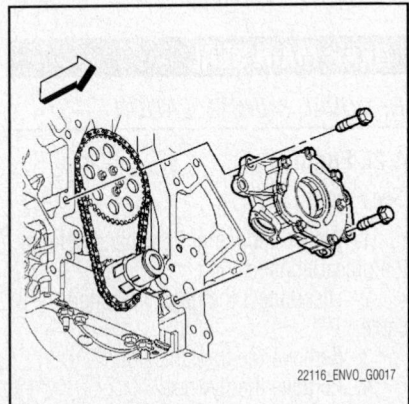

Fig. 129 Exploded view of the oil pump mounting—5.3L and 6.0L engines

- Remaining crankshaft oil deflector nuts
- Crankshaft oil deflector
- Oil pump bolts
- Oil pump

➡ **Do not let any dirt or debris into the oil pump or cap end.**

- Clean and inspect the oil pump.

To install:

3. Align the splined surfaces of the crankshaft sprocket and the oil pump drive gear and install the oil pump.

4. Install or connect the following:
- Oil pump onto the crankshaft sprocket until the pump housing contacts the face of the engine block
- Oil pump bolts and tighten to 18 ft. lbs. (25 Nm)
- Crankshaft oil deflector and nuts until snug
- New oil pump screen O-ring seal into the oil pump screen, after lubricating with clean engine oil

➡ **Push the oil pump screen tube completely into the oil pump prior to tightening the bolt. Do not let the bolt pull the tube into the pump.**

5. Align the oil pump screen mounting brackets with the correct crankshaft bearing cap studs.
- Oil pump screen
- Oil pump screen bolts and nuts. Tighten the bolts to 106 inch lbs. (12 Nm) and the nuts to 18 ft. lbs. (25 Nm).
- Engine front cover
- Oil pan

PISTON AND RING

POSITIONING

See Figures 130 and 131.

REAR MAIN SEAL

REMOVAL & INSTALLATION

4.2L Engine

See Figure 132.

1. Before servicing the vehicle, refer to the precautions section.
2. Disconnect the negative battery cable.
3. Remove the transmission.
4. Remove the flywheel.
5. Carefully pry the crankshaft rear oil seal out of the rear oil seal housing using a suitable tool.

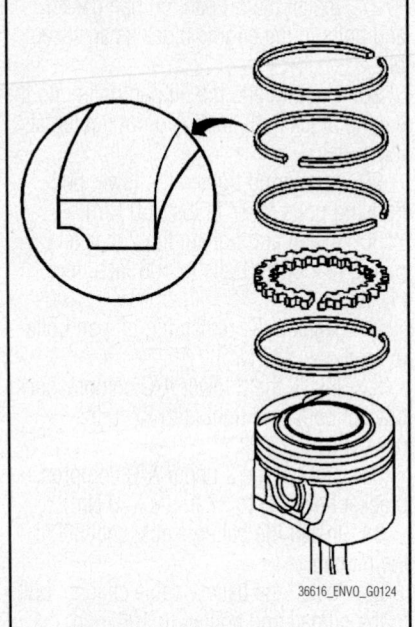

Fig. 130 Piston ring positioning— 4.2L engine

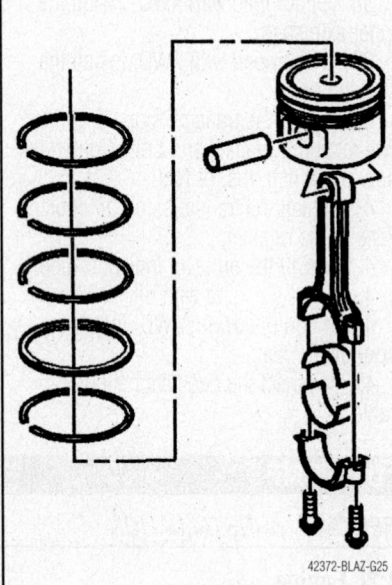

Fig. 131 Piston ring positioning— 5.3L engine

➡ **Do not damage the crankshaft or seal bore.**

To install:

6. Use the plastic installation sleeve supplied with the new seal when installing a new seal.
7. Use J 44227 seal installer to install the crankshaft rear oil seal.
8. Remove the J 44227.
9. Remove the seal installation sleeve

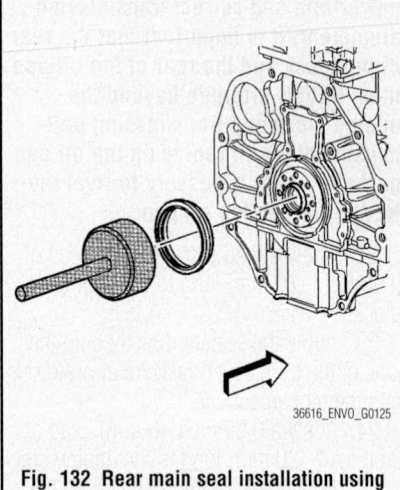

Fig. 132 Rear main seal installation using the J 44227 seal installer—4.2L engine

after the seal is installed. Discard the sleeve.
10. Install the flywheel.
11. Install the transmission.
12. Connect the negative battery cable.
13. Start the engine and verify that there are no oil leaks.

5.3L and 6.0L Engines

See Figure 133.

Please note that the transmission assembly must be removed to perform this procedure.

1. Before servicing the vehicle, refer to the precautions in the beginning of this section.
2. Remove or disconnect the following:
- Negative battery cable
- Transmission
- Flywheel
- Crankshaft rear main oil seal from the rear cover

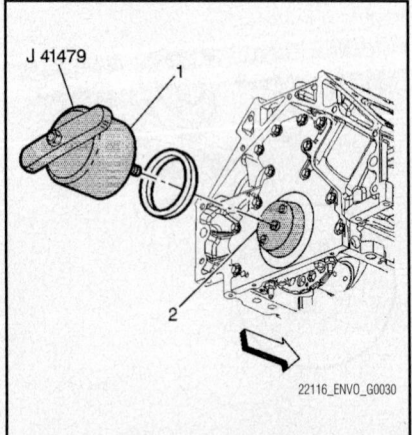

Fig. 133 View of the rear main seal installation—5.3L and 6.0L engines

To install:

➡The flywheel spacer (if applicable) must be removed prior to oil seal installation. Do not lubricate the oil seal Inside Diameter (ID) or crankshaft surface. Never reuse the rear main seal. Once it is removed, it must be replaced with a new seal.

3. Lubricate the Outside Diameter (OD) of the rear main seal and the rear cover oil seal bore with clean engine oil. Do NOT let oil contact the seal surface or the crankshaft surface.

4. Install or connect the following:
- Crankshaft Rear Oil Seal Installer Tool No. J 41479 tapered cone and bolts onto the rear of the crankshaft. Tighten the bolts until just snug, being careful not to over tighten.
- Rear oil seal onto the tapered cone until the tool contacts the oil seal

5. Align the oil seal into the tool, Rotate the handle of the tool clockwise until the seal enters the rear cover and bottoms into the cover bore. Remove the tool.
- Flywheel
- Transmission
- Negative battery cable

6. Start the engine and verify that there are no oil leaks.

ROCKER ARMS/SHAFTS

REMOVAL & INSTALLATION

4.2L Engine

See Figure 134.

1. Before servicing the vehicle, refer to the precautions section.
2. Disconnect the negative battery cable.
3. Remove the valve cover.
4. Rotate the crankshaft until the affected cylinder valve is fully open (cam lobe fully depressing the spring.

➡Engine design and packaging does not allow all cylinder locations to use both fasteners for holding the tool to the cylinder head. One fastener is sufficient in these locations.

5. Install the EN-47945 on the engine cylinder head using either one or two of the supplied fasteners installed in the coil fastener hole.

➡If valve train components, such as the rocker arms, pushrods or pivot supports, are to be reused, they must be tagged or arranged to insure installation in their original locations.

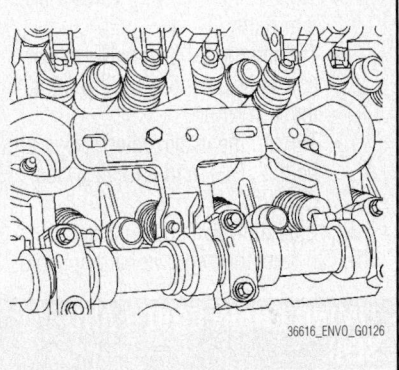

Fig. 134 EN-47945 installed to help remove rocker arm and valve lash adjuster

36616_ENVO_G0126

✳✳ WARNING

DO NOT rotate the engine with the tool installed. It is possible to damage the valves if they contact the piston. Rotate the engine enough to come back to the base circle of the cam.

6. Rotate the engine clockwise enough to ensure the cam is on the base circle (spring will stay compressed by the tool). This will allow the lash adjuster and rocker to be removed
7. Remove the valve rocker arm and valve lash adjuster.
8. Clean, inspect or replace the valve rocker arm and valve lash adjuster.

To install:

9. Lubricate the valve rocker arm and fill the valve lash adjuster with oil.
10. Install the valve rocker arm and valve lash adjuster.
11. When the valve rocker arm and valve lash adjuster are in place, slowly rotate the engine counterclockwise enough that the cam lobe fully depresses the spring again.
12. Remove the EN-47945 from the cylinder head and repeat as required.
13. Install the valve cover.
14. Connect the negative battery cable.

5.3L and 6.0L Engines

See Figures 135 through 138.

1. Before servicing the vehicle, refer to the precautions in the beginning of this section.
2. Disconnect the negative battery cable.
3. Remove the valve cover.

➡If valve train components, such as the rocker arms, pushrods or pivot supports, are to be reused, they must be tagged or arranged to insure installation in their original locations.

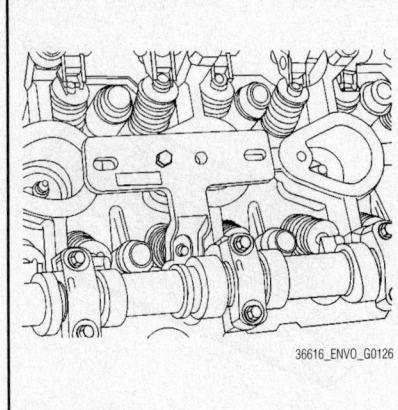

Fig. 135 Rocker arms and mounting bolt

36616_ENVO_G0126

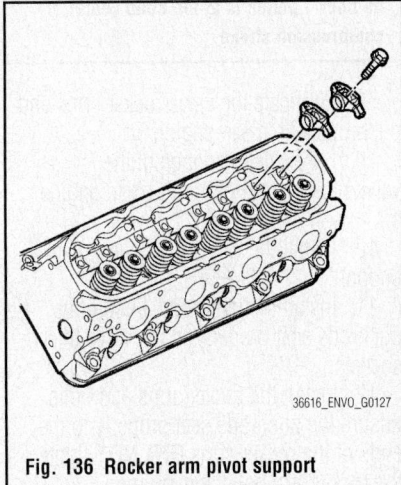

Fig. 136 Rocker arm pivot support

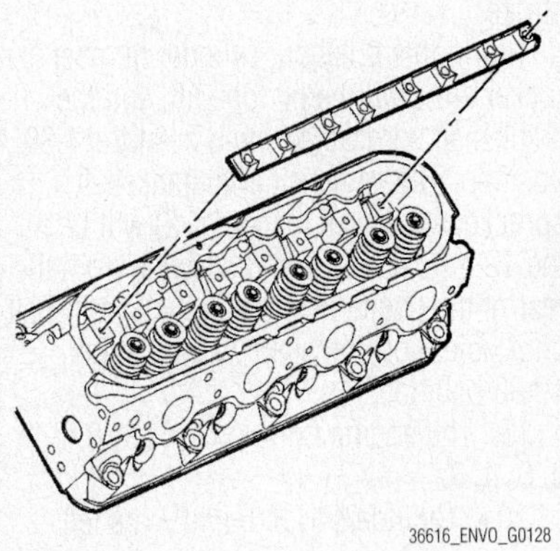

36616_ENVO_G0127

Fig. 137 Pushrods

36616_ENVO_G0128

4. Remove the valve rocker arm bolts.
5. Remove the valve rocker arms.
6. Remove the valve rocker arm pivot support.
7. Remove the pushrods.

To install:

➡Valve lash is net build. No valve adjustment is required.

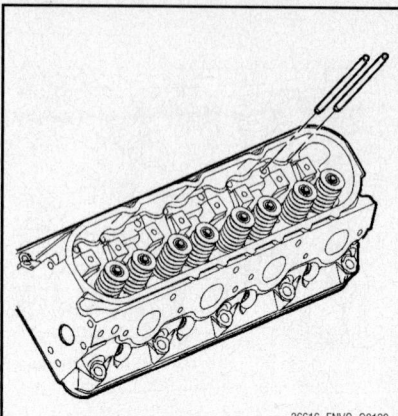

Fig. 138 Rotate the crankshaft until number 1 piston is at top dead center of compression stroke

8. Lubricate the valve rocker arms and pushrods with clean engine oil.

9. Lubricate the flange of the valve rocker arm bolts with clean engine oil.

10. Install the valve rocker arm pivot support.

11. Install the pushrods. Ensure the pushrods seat properly to the valve lifter sockets.

12. Install the rocker arms and bolts. Ensure the pushrods seat properly to the ends of the rocker arms.(**DO NOT** tighten the rocker arm bolts at this time.)

13. Rotate the crankshaft until number 1 piston is at top dead center of compression stroke.

14. In this position, cylinder number 1 rocker arms will be off lobe lift, and the crankshaft sprocket key will be at the 1:30 position. The camshaft and crankshaft sprocket alignment marks (1, 2) will be in the 12 o'clock position. If viewing from the rear of the engine, the additional crankshaft pilot hole, non-threaded, will be in the 10:30 position.

15. The engine firing order is 1, 8, 7, 2, 6, 5, 4, 3:
- Cylinders 1, 3, 5 and 7 are left bank.
- Cylinders 2, 4, 6, and 8 are right bank.

16. With the engine in the number 1 firing position, tighten the following valve rocker arm bolts:
- Tighten the exhaust valve rocker arm bolts 1, 2, 7, and 8 to 22 ft. lbs. (30 Nm).
- Tighten the intake valve rocker arm bolts 1, 3, 4, and 5 to 22 ft. lbs. (30 Nm).

17. Rotate the crankshaft 360 degrees.

- Tighten the following valve rocker arm bolts:
- Tighten the exhaust valve rocker arm bolts 3, 4, 5, and 6 to 22 ft. lbs. (30 Nm).
- Tighten the intake valve rocker arm bolts 2, 6, 7, and 8 to 22 ft. lbs. (30 Nm).

18. Install the valve cover gasket.

19. Connect the negative battery cable.

TIMING CHAIN COVER AND SEAL

REMOVAL & INSTALLATION

4.2L Engine

See Figures 139 through 141.

1. Before servicing the vehicle, refer to the precautions in the beginning of this section.

2. Remove or disconnect the following:
- Negative battery cable
- Drain the engine cooling system.

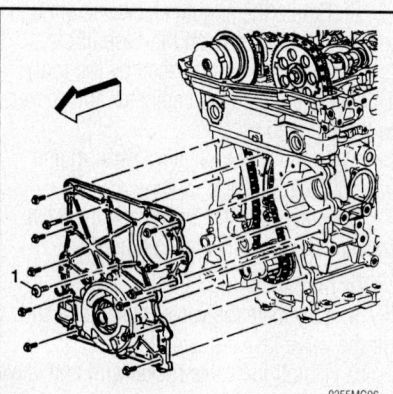

Fig. 139 Place 2 front cover bolts in the jackscrew holes on the cover and tighten to push the cover off of the engine

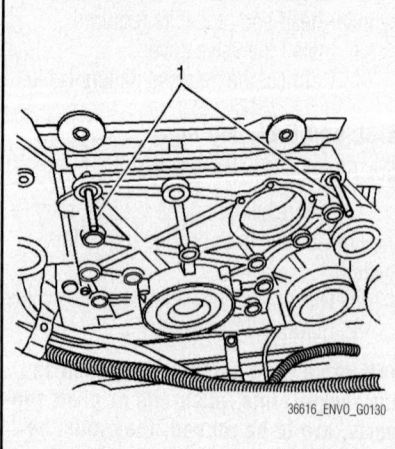

Fig. 140 J 44219 cover alignment pins (1)

- Cooling fan and shroud
- Accessory belt
- Water pump
- Crankshaft balancer

✴✴ WARNING

When removing the seal, be careful not to damage the front cover or crankshaft.

- Seal from the front cover, using a suitable prytool in the slots provided
- Power steering pump

3. Raise and safely support the vehicle.
- Oil pan, then carefully lower the vehicle
- 7mm center bolt
- Remaining front cover bolts. Place two of the front cover bolts in the jackscrew holes on the front cover and tighten the bolts evenly to release the front cover from the engine.
- 2 bolts from the front cover
- Oil pump

To install:

4. Clean the gasket mating surfaces of the engine and cover of all remaining gasket or sealer material. Be careful not to score or damage the surfaces.

5. Install or connect the following:
- Suitable cover alignment pins, onto the engine

➡**The front cover MUST be installed within 10 minutes of applying the sealant.**

- Apply a 0.12 in. (3mm) beat of 12378521 or equivalent sealant to the trace grooves on the back side of the engine front cover. Apply sealant on the inside 3 bolt hole bosses on the cover also.

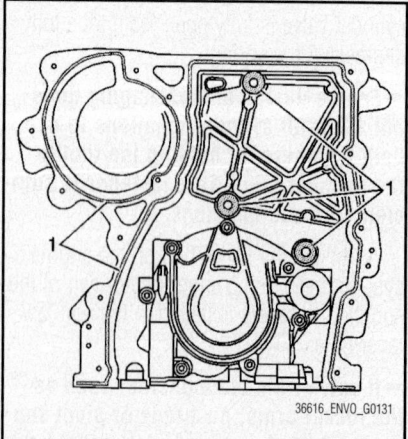

Fig. 141 Back side view of the front engine cover—4.2L engine

- Oil pump to the crankshaft splines
- Front cover and bolts, tighten the center bolt last. Tighten to 89 inch lbs. (10 Nm).

6. Remove the alignment pins and raise and safely support the vehicle. Install the oil pan, then lower the vehicle.

- Power steering pump
- Crankshaft balancer
- Water pump
- Accessory belt
- Cooling fan and shroud
- Negative battery cable

7. Properly refill and bleed the engine cooling system.

8. Run the engine until normal operating temperature has been reached, then check for leaks.

5.3L & 6.0L Engines

See Figures 142 and 143.

1. Before servicing the vehicle, refer to the precautions in the beginning of this section.

2. Properly discharge the A/C system.

3. Drain the engine cooling system.

4. Remove or disconnect the following:

- Negative battery cable
- A/C compressor and bracket
- Water pump
- Crankshaft balancer
- Oil pan-to-front cover bolts
- Front cover bolts
- Front cover and gasket. Discard the gasket.

5. Clean and inspect the front cover.

To install:

6. Apply a 0.20 in. (5mm) bead of

sealant 0.80 in. (20mm) long to the oil pan-to-engine block junction.

7. Install or connect the following:

- New front cover gasket and cover
- Front cover bolts, finger-tight
- Oil pan-to-front cover bolts, finger-tight
- Front and Rear Cover Alignment Tool No. J 41476 to the front cover. Align the tapered legs of the tool with the machined alignment surfaces on the front cover
- Crankshaft balancer bolt, finger-tight
- Oil pan-to-front cover bolts to 18 ft. lbs. (25 Nm)
- Front cover bolts to 18 ft. lbs. (25 Nm)

8. Remove the tool.

9. Install a NEW crankshaft front oil seal as follows:

a. Remove the radiator for access.

b. Remove the crankshaft balancer.

c. Remove the crankshaft oil seal.

d. Lubricate the outer edge ONLY of the NEW crankshaft oil seal with clean engine oil.

e. Install the crankshaft front oil seal into the Crankshaft Front Seal Installation Tool No. J 41478 guide.

f. Install the J 41478 threaded rod (with nut, washer, guide and oil seal) into the end of the crankshaft.

g. Use J 41478 to install the oil seal into the cover bore. Use a wrench and hold the hex on the installer bolt. Use a second wrench to rotate the installer nut clockwise until the seal bottoms in the cover bore. Remove the tool.

h. Check the seal for proper installa-

tion. It should be installed evenly and completely into the front cover bore.

i. Install the crankshaft balancer. Tighten the bolt to 37 ft. lbs. (50 Nm), plus an additional 140 degrees using a torque angle meter.

j. Install the radiator.

10. Install or connect the following:

- Water pump
- A/C compressor and bracket
- Cooling system with coolant
- Negative battery cable

11. Properly recharge the A/C system

TIMING CHAIN AND SPROCKETS

REMOVAL & INSTALLATION

4.2L Engine

See Figures 144 through 146.

➡**The following procedure requires the use of the Crankshaft Holding tool No. J-44221 and a suitable torque angle meter.**

1. Before servicing the vehicle, refer to the precautions section.

2. Remove or disconnect the following:

- Camshaft cover
- Timing chain (front) cover
- Tension on the timing chain by moving the tensioner shoe in. Place a tee into the tension to hold the shoe in place.
- Top chain guide bolts and guide
- Exhaust camshaft position actuator bolt and actuator
- Intake camshaft sprocket bolt and sprocket
- Timing chain

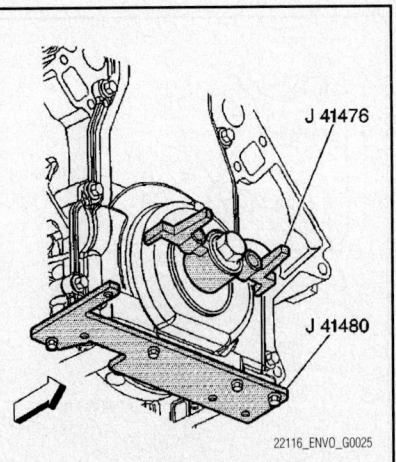

Fig. 142 Align the tapered legs of the tool with the machined alignment surfaces on the front cover—5.3L and 6.0L engines

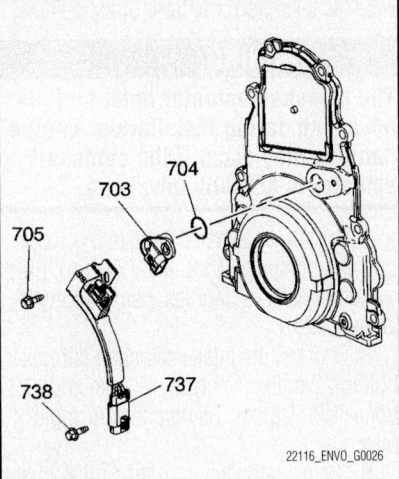

Fig. 143 Front cover—5.3L and 6.0L engines

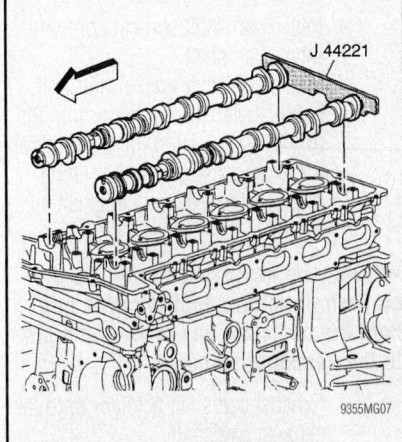

Fig. 144 Proper installation of the crankshaft holding tool with the No. 1 cylinder at TDC

- Crankshaft sprocket
- Cylinder head access hole plugs
- Timing chain tensioner shoe bolt and shoe
- Timing chain tensioner guide bolts and guide
- Timing chain tensioner bolts and tensioner

To install:

➡️ **Every seventh link of the timing chain is darkened to help in aligning the timing marks.**

3. Install or connect the following:
- Timing chain tensioner and bolts. Tighten to 18 ft. lbs. (25 Nm).
- Timing chain guide and bolts. Tighten to 89 inch lbs. (10 Nm).
- Timing chain tensioner shoe and bolt. Tighten to 19 ft. lbs. (26 Nm).
- Cylinder head access hole plugs and tighten to 44 inch lbs. (5 Nm)
- Crankshaft Holding tool No. J-44221, or equivalent with the camshaft flats up and the No. 1 cylinder at Top Dead Center (TDC)
- Crankshaft sprocket
- Intake camshaft sprocket into the timing chain

4. Align the dark link of the timing chain with the timing mark on the intake camshaft sprocket.

5. Feed the timing chain down through the opening in the head.
- Timing chain onto the crankshaft sprocket. Align the dark link of the timing chain with the timing mark on the crankshaft sprocket.

➡️ **It may be necessary to remove the crankshaft holding tool to rotate and hold the camshaft hex to align the pin to the camshaft sprocket**

- Intake camshaft sprocket onto the intake camshaft
- Intake camshaft washer and bolt
- Exhaust camshaft actuator into the timing chain. Align the dark link of the timing chain with the timing mark on the exhaust camshaft actuator.

➡️ **It may be necessary to remove the crankshaft holding tool to rotate and hold the camshaft hex to align the pin to the camshaft sprocket**

- Exhaust camshaft actuator onto the exhaust camshaft

➡️ **Rotate the camshaft actuator clockwise relative to the camshaft prior to tightening the bolt.**

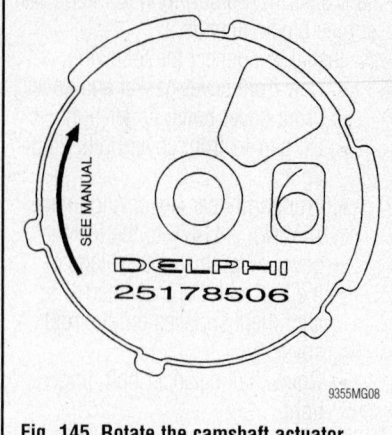

Fig. 145 Rotate the camshaft actuator clockwise

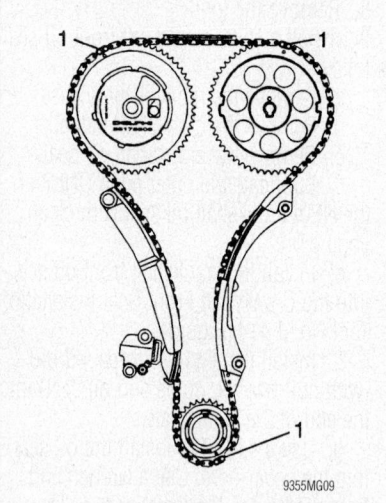

Fig. 146 The dark lines on the timing chain should be aligned with the marks on the sprockets

6. Rotate the camshaft actuator clockwise (as seen from the front of the vehicle).

✳️ WARNING

The camshaft actuator must be fully advanced during installation. Engine damage may occur if the camshaft actuator is not fully advanced.

7. Install the exhaust camshaft actuator bolt and tighten to 18 ft. lbs. (25 Nm), plus an additional 135 degrees, using a torque angle meter.

8. Tighten the intake camshaft sprocket bolt to 22 ft. lbs. (30 Nm), plus an additional 135 degrees, using a torque angle meter.

9. Remove the tee from the timing chain tensioner to regain tension on the timing chain.

10. Remove the crankshaft holding tool. The dark lines on the timing chain should be aligned with the marks on the sprockets.

11. Install or connect the following:
- Top chain guide
- Suitable thread locker to the top chain guide bolt threads, then install and tighten to 89 inch lbs. (10 Nm)
- Engine front cover
- Camshaft cover

5.3L & 6.0L Engines

See Figures 147 through 149.

1. Before servicing the vehicle, refer to the precautions section.

2. Remove the oil pump.

3. Rotate the crankshaft until the timing marks on the crankshaft and the camshaft sprockets are aligned.

✳️ WARNING

Do NOT turn the crankshaft after the timing chain has been removed to prevent damage to the pistons and valves.

4. Remove or disconnect the following:
- Camshaft sprocket bolts
- Camshaft sprocket and timing chain
- Crankshaft sprocket using Pulley Puller No. J 8433, Crankshaft End Protector Tool No. J 41816-2 and Crankshaft Sprocket Removal Tool No. J 41558
- Crankshaft sprocket key, if necessary

5. Clean and inspect the timing chain and sprockets.

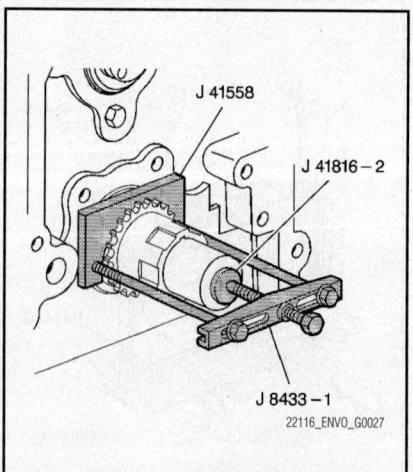

Fig. 147 Use the proper tools to remove the crankshaft sprocket—5.3L and 6.0L engines

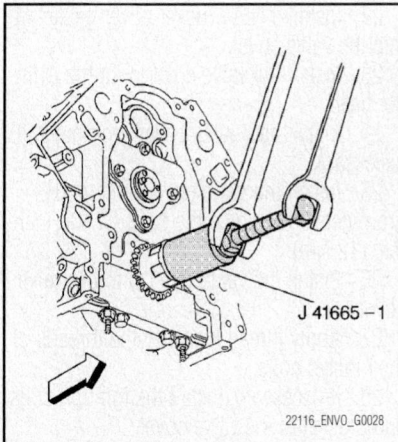

Fig. 148 Crankshaft sprocket installation—5.3L and 6.0L engines

To install:

6. Install or connect the following:
- Key into the crankshaft keyway, if removed. Tap the key into the keyway until both ends of the key bottom into the crankshaft.
- Crankshaft sprocket onto the front of the crankshaft. Align the crankshaft key with the sprocket keyway.
- Crankshaft sprocket using Sprocket Installation Tool No. J 41665. Install the sprocket onto the crankshaft until fully seated against the crankshaft flange. Rotate the crankshaft sprocket until the alignment mark is in the 12 o'clock position.

➡**Properly locate the camshaft sprocket**

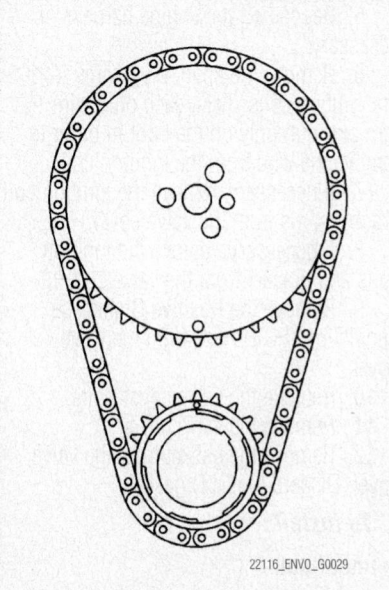

Fig. 149 Proper alignment of the timing marks for timing chain installation—5.3L and 6.0L engines

locating pin with the cam sprocket alignment hole. The sprocket teeth and timing chain must mesh. The camshaft and crankshaft sprocket alignment marks MUST be aligned properly. Locate the camshaft sprocket alignment mark in the 6 o'clock position. It may be necessary to rotate the camshaft or crankshaft to align the marks.

- Camshaft sprocket and timing chain
- Camshaft sprocket bolts and tighten to 26 ft. lbs. (35 Nm)
- Oil pump

VALVE COVERS

REMOVAL & INSTALLATION

4.2L Engine

See Figure 150.

1. Before servicing the vehicle, refer to the precautions section.
2. Remove the intake manifold, as outlined in this section.
3. Remove the A/C line at the oil level indicator tube bracket nut.
4. Remove the A/C bracket bolt from the engine lift hook.
5. Position the A/C line out of the way.
6. Remove the engine lift bracket.
7. Disconnect the ignition control module electrical connectors.
8. Loosen the ignition control module bolts.

9. Remove the ignition control module.
10. Disconnect the engine electrical harness housing from the camshaft cover (1) taking care not to damage the clips that hold the housing in place.
11. Disconnect the fuel injection harness electrical connector.
12. Loosen and remove the valve cover bolts.
13. Remove the valve cover.
14. Clean and inspect the camshaft cover.

To install:

15. Install a new valve cover seal.
16. Install new rubber ignition control module seals.
17. Install the valve cover and secure with the valve cover bolts. Tighten the bolts to 89 inch lbs. (10 Nm).
18. Install the ignition control modules and secure the modules with bolts. Tighten to 89 inch lbs. (10 Nm).
19. Connect the ignition control module electrical connectors.
20. Install the fuel injector electrical connectors.
21. Install the engine electrical harness housing.
22. Install the A/C line bracket to the oil level indicator tube stud and secure the bracket with the nut. Tighten the A/C line bracket nut to 62 inch lbs. (7 Nm).
23. Install the engine lift bracket and secure the lift hook with the bolts. Tighten the lift bracket bolts to 37 ft. lbs. (50 Nm).
24. Install the A/C line bracket to the

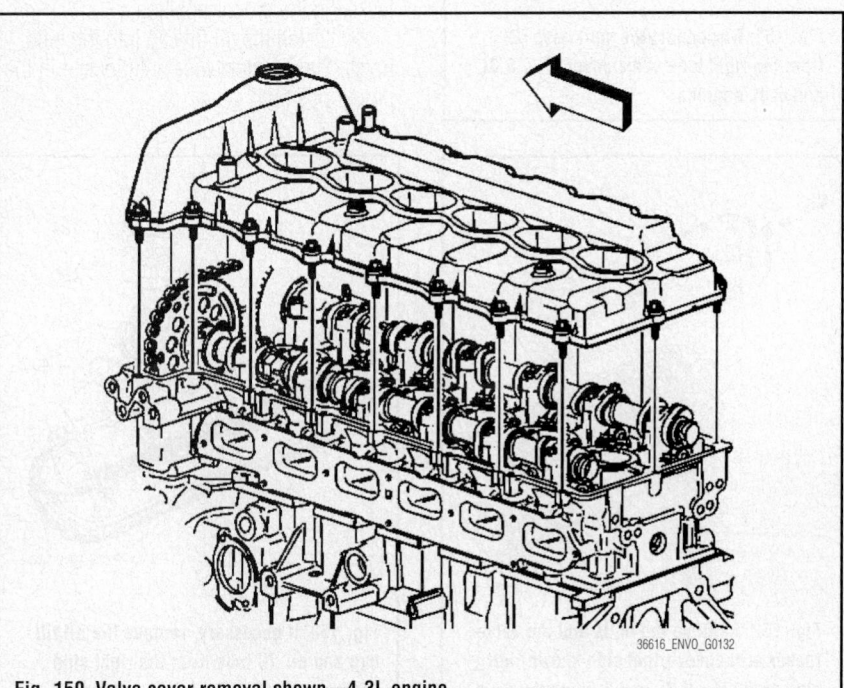

Fig. 150 Valve cover removal shown—4.3L engine

engine lift bracket and secure the A/C bracket with the bolt. Tighten the A/C bracket bolt to 89 inch lbs. (10 Nm).

25. Install the intake manifold.

5.3L and 6.0L Engines

Right Side

See Figures 151 through 153.

1. Before servicing the vehicle, refer to the precautions section.
2. Remove the intake manifold sight shield.
3. Remove the air conditioning (A/C) compressor hose.
4. Remove the connector position assurance (CPA) lock.
5. Disconnect the main electrical connector to the ignition coil wire harness.
6. Remove the harness clips.
7. Reposition the engine harness, if necessary.

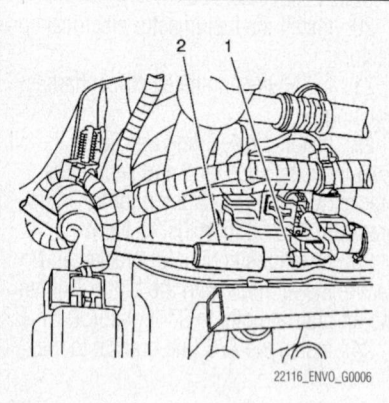

Fig. 151 Disconnect the vent hose (2) from the right side valve cover (1)—5.3L and 6.0L engines

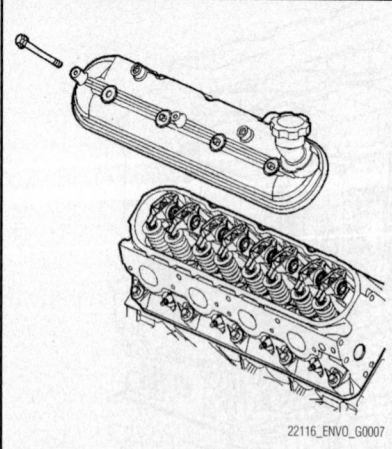

Fig. 152 Remove the bolts and the valve rocker arm cover (right side shown, left side similar)—5.3L and 6.0L engines

8. Remove the spark plug wires from the ignition coils.
9. If necessary, remove the ignition coil bracket studs from the valve cover.
10. If necessary, remove the ignition coils and bracket from the valve cover.
11. Remove the vent hose (2) from the valve rocker arm cover (1).
12. Remove the valve rocker arm cover bolts.
13. Remove the valve cover.
14. Remove the gasket from the valve cover.
15. Discard the OLD gasket.
16. Remove the oil fill cap from the oil fill tube.
17. Remove the oil fill tube from the valve cover, if required.
18. Discard the oil fill tube.

To install:

➡ **Important information is as follows:**

- All gasket surfaces should be free of oil and/or other foreign material during assembly.
- DO NOT reuse the valve cover gasket.
- The valve cover bolt grommets may be reused.
- If the oil fill tube has been removed from the valve cover, install a NEW fill tube during assembly.

19. Lubricate the O-ring seal of the NEW oil fill tube with clean engine oil.
20. Insert the NEW oil fill tube into the valve cover. Rotate the tube clockwise until locked in the proper position.
21. Install the oil fill cap into the tube. Rotate the cap clockwise until locked in the proper position.

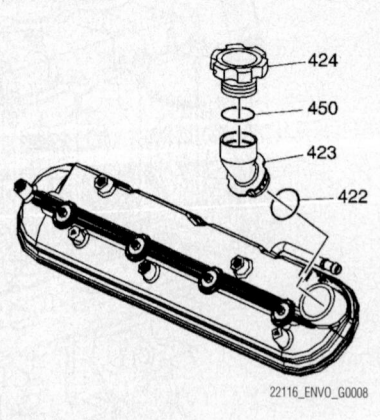

Fig. 153 If necessary, remove the oil fill cap and oil fill tube from the right side valve cover—5.3L and 6.0L engines

22. Install a NEW rocker cover gasket (1) into the valve cover.
23. Install the valve cover onto the cylinder head.
24. Install new valve cover grommets, if necessary.
25. Install the valve cover bolts and grommets and tighten the bolts to 106 inch lbs. (12 Nm).
26. Install the vent hose (2) to the valve cover (1).
27. Apply thread locker to the threads of the bracket bolts.
28. If necessary, install the ignition coils and bracket to the valve cover.
29. If necessary, install the ignition coil bracket studs to the valve cover and tighten to 106 inch lbs. (12 Nm).
30. Install the spark plug wires to the ignition coils.
31. Position the engine harness, if necessary.
32. Install the harness clips.
33. Connect the main electrical connector (1) feeding the ignition coils.
34. Install the CPA lock.
35. Install the A/C compressor hose.
36. Install the intake manifold sight shield.

Left Side

1. Before servicing the vehicle, refer to the precautions section.
2. Remove the connector position assurance (CPA) lock.
3. Disconnect the main electrical connector to the ignition coil wire harness.
4. Remove the harness clips.
5. Reposition the engine harness, if necessary.
6. Remove the spark plug wires from the ignition coils. Twist each plug wire ½ turn and pull only on the boot in order to remove the wire from the ignition coil.
7. If necessary, remove the ignition coil bracket studs from the valve cover.
8. If necessary, remove the ignition coils and bracket from the valve cover.
9. Remove the Positive Crankcase Ventilation (PCV) hose from the valve cover.
10. Remove the valve cover bolts.
11. Remove the valve cover.
12. Remove the gasket from the valve cover. Discard the OLD gasket.

To install:

➡ **Important:**

- All gasket surfaces should be free of oil and/or other foreign material during assembly.

- DO NOT reuse the valve cover gasket.
- The valve cover bolt grommets may be reused.
- If the PCV valve grommet has been removed from the rocker cover, install a NEW grommet during assembly.

13. Install a NEW valve cover gasket into the groove of the valve rocker arm cover.

14. Install the valve cover onto the cylinder head.

15. Install new rocker arm cover grommets, if necessary.

16. Install the valve cover bolts and tighten to 106 inch lbs. (12 Nm).

17. Install the PCV hose to the valve cover.

18. Apply thread locker GM P/N 12345382 (Canadian P/N 10953489) or equivalent to the threads of the bracket bolts.

19. If necessary, install the ignition coils and bracket to the rocker arm cover.

20. If necessary, install the ignition coil bracket studs to the rocker arm cover. Tighten the studs to 106 inch lbs. (12 Nm).

21. Install the spark plug wires to the ignition coils.

22. Position the engine harness, if necessary.

23. Install the harness clips.

24. Connect the main electrical connector to the ignition coil wire harness.

25. Install the CPA lock.

VALVE LASH

ADJUSTMENT

The 4.2L, 5.3L and 6.0L engines do not require a periodic valve lash adjustment.

ENGINE PERFORMANCE & EMISSION CONTROLS

ACCELERATOR PEDAL POSITION (APP) SENSOR

LOCATION

The Accelerator Pedal Position (APP) sensor is mounted on the accelerator pedal assembly.

REMOVAL & INSTALLATION

See Figure 154.

1. Disconnect the negative battery cable.
2. Disconnect the accelerator pedal position (APP) sensor electrical connector.
3. Remove the APP sensor retaining fasteners.
4. Remove the APP sensor from the vehicle.

To install:

5. Install the APP sensor to vehicle.
6. Install the APP sensor retaining fasteners and tighten to 15 ft. lbs. (18 Nm).
7. Connect the APP sensor electrical connector.
8. Connect the negative battery cable.

AIR INJECTION (AIR) PUMP

LOCATION

4.2L Engine

The Air Injection pump is located at the right front side of the frame.

REMOVAL & INSTALLATION

4.2L Engine

See Figure 155.

1. Before servicing the vehicle, refer to the precautions section.
2. Raise the vehicle.
3. Disconnect both the air inlet and air outlet pipes from the secondary air injection pump.
4. Remove the electrical relay from the air pump bracket.
5. Disconnect the electrical connector from the air pump.
6. Remove the 3 bolts securing the air pump bracket to the vehicle frame.

7. Remove the air pump from the vehicle.

To install:

8. Install the air pump to the vehicle.
9. Install the 3 bolts securing the air pump bracket to the vehicle frame and tighten to 15 ft. lbs. (20 Nm).
10. Connect the electrical connector to the air pump.
11. Install the electrical relay to the air pump bracket.
12. Connect both the air inlet and air outlet pipe to the air pump.
13. Lower the vehicle.

CAMSHAFT POSITION (CMP) SENSOR

LOCATION

4.2L Engine

The Camshaft Position (CMP) sensor is located on the front right corner of the engine cylinder head.

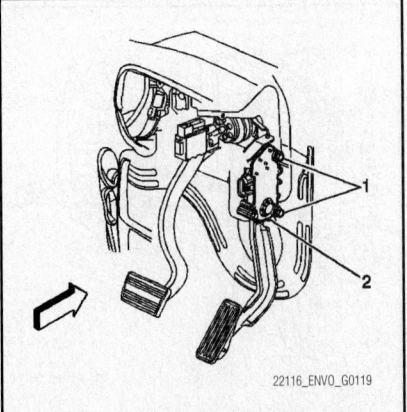

22116_ENVO_G0119

Fig. 154 Location of the accelerator pedal position (APP) sensor (2)

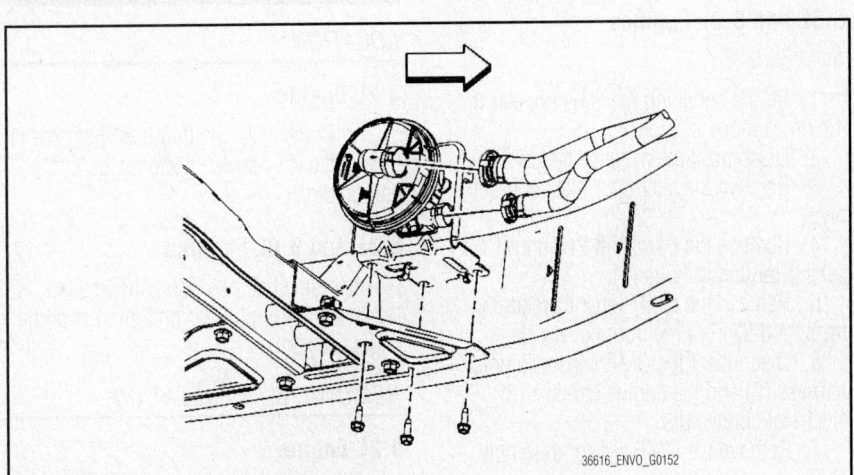

36616_ENVO_G0152

Fig. 155 Air pump removal—4.2L engine

5.3L and 6.0L Engines

The Camshaft Position (CMP) sensor is located on the front of the engine block, just above the crankshaft.

REMOVAL & INSTALLATION

4.2L Engine

See Figure 156.

1. Before servicing the vehicle, refer to the precautions section.
2. Disconnect the negative battery cable.
3. Remove the Camshaft Position (CMP) sensor electrical connector.
4. Remove the CMP sensor retaining bolt.

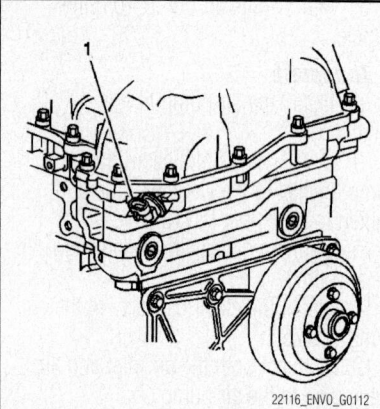

Fig. 156 Location of the Camshaft Position (CMP) sensor (1)—4.2L engine

To install:

5. Install the CMP sensor and tighten the CMP sensor bolt to 89 inch lbs. (10 Nm).
6. Install the CMP sensor electrical connector .
7. Connect the negative battery cable.

5.3L and 6.0L Engines

See Figure 157.

1. Before servicing the vehicle, refer to the precautions section.
2. Disconnect the negative battery cable.
3. Remove the alternator bracket assembly.
4. Remove the Camshaft Position (CMP) sensor mounting bolts (1).
5. Remove the CMP sensor assembly (4, 5, and 6) from the front cover (7).
6. Disconnect the CMP sensor jumper harness (2) and the engine harness (3) electrical connectors.
7. Remove the CMP sensor assembly (4, 5, 6).

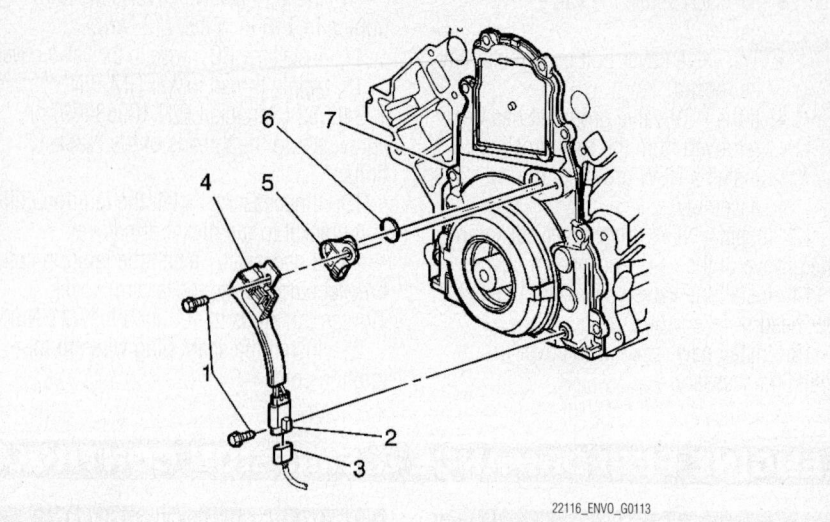

Fig. 157 Location of the Camshaft Position (CMP) sensor (5) and related components—5.3L and 6.0L engines

8. Disconnect CMP sensor (5) from the jumper harness (4).

To install:

9. Reconnect the CMP sensor (5) and the jumper harness (4).
10. Install the O-ring (6) on the CMP sensor assembly (4, 5).
11. Reconnect the CMP sensor assembly (4, 5, and 6) and the engine harness connector (3).
12. Install the CMP sensor assembly (4, 5, and 6) in the front cover (7). Apply a small amount of clean motor oil to the O-ring (6).
13. Install the CMP sensor mounting bolts and tighten them to 18 ft. lbs. (25 Nm).
14. Install the alternator assembly.
15. Connect the negative battery cable.

CRANKSHAFT POSITION (CKP) SENSOR

LOCATION

4.2L Engine

The Crankshaft Position (CKP) sensor is located on the rear left bottom side of the engine block.

5.3L and 6.0L Engines

The crankshaft position (CKP) sensor is located on the right rear bottom side of the engine block.

REMOVAL & INSTALLATION

4.2L Engine

See Figure 158.

1. Before servicing the vehicle, refer to the precautions section.
2. Disconnect the negative battery cable.
3. Raise and safely support the front of the vehicle securely on jackstands.
4. Disconnect the CKP sensor harness connector.
5. Remove the CKP sensor retaining bolt.
6. Remove the CKP sensor from the engine block.

To install:

7. Inspect the sensor O-ring for wear cracks or leakage and replace if necessary. Lubricate the new O-ring with engine oil before installation.
8. Install the CKP sensor into the engine block and tighten the bolt to 89 inch lbs. (10 Nm).
9. Install the CKP sensor retaining bolt.
10. Connect the CKP sensor harness connector.

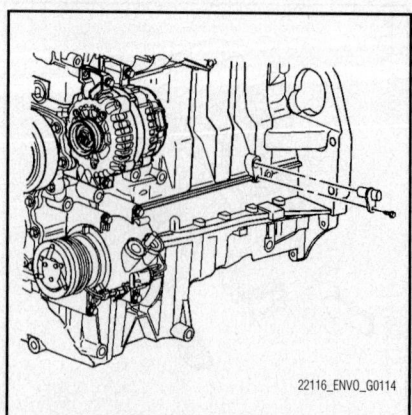

Fig. 158 Location of the Crankshaft Position (CKP) sensor—4.2L engine

11. Lower the vehicle.

12. Connect the negative battery cable.

5.3L and 6.0L Engines

See Figure 159.

1. Before servicing the vehicle, refer to the precautions section.

2. Disconnect the negative battery cable.

3. Remove the starter.

4. Disconnect the electrical connector (2) from the CKP sensor (1).

5. Clean the area around the CKP sensor before removal in order to avoid debris from entering the engine.

6. Remove the CKP sensor bolt.

7. Remove the CKP sensor.

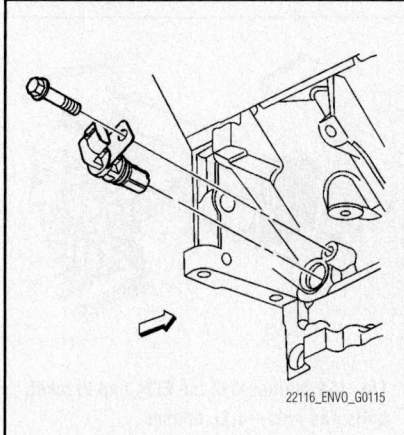

Fig. 159 Location CKP sensor—5.3L and 6.0L engines

To install:

8. Install the CKP sensor.

9. Install the CKP sensor bolt and tighten to 18 ft. lbs. (25 Nm).

10. Connect the electrical connector (2) to the CKP sensor (1).

11. Install the starter.

12. Connect the negative battery cable.

RELEARN PROCEDURE

1. Perform the crankshaft position system variation learn procedure as follows:

2. Install a scan tool.

3. Monitor the ECM for DTCs with a scan tool. If other DTCs are set, except DTC P0315, refer to Diagnostic Trouble Code (DTC) List - Vehicle for the applicable DTC that set.

4. With a scan tool, select the CKP system variation learn procedure and perform the following:
   - Observe the fuel cut-off for the applicable engine
   - Block the drive wheels

- Set the parking brake
- Place the vehicle's transmission in Park or Neutral
- Turn the A/C OFF
- Cycle the ignition from OFF to ON
- Apply and hold the brake pedal for the duration of the procedure
- Start and idle the engine
- Accelerate to Wide Open Throttle (WOT). The engine should not accelerate beyond the calibrated fuel cut-off RPM value noted earlier. Release the throttle immediately if the value is exceeded.
- While the learn procedure is in progress, release the throttle immediately when the engine starts to decelerate. The engine control is returned to the operator and the engine responds to throttle position after the learn procedure is complete.
- Release the throttle when fuel cut-off occurs

5. The scan tool displays Learn Status: Learned this Ignition. If the scan tool indicates that DTC P0315 ran and passed, the CKP variation learn procedure is complete. If the scan tool indicates DTC P0315 failed or did not run, refer to DTC P0315. If any other DTCs set, refer to Diagnostic Trouble Code (DTC) List - Vehicle for the applicable DTC that set.

6. Turn OFF the ignition for 30 seconds after the learn procedure is completed successfully.

EVAPORATIVE EMISSION (EVAP) CANISTER

LOCATION

The Evaporative Emission (EVAP) Canister is located at the rear of the vehicle, behind the fuel tank.

REMOVAL & INSTALLATION

See Figures 160 and 161.

1. Before servicing the vehicle, refer to the precautions section.

2. Remove the spare tire. Reference the owner's manual for additional information if needed.

3. Raise the vehicle.

4. Disconnect the Evaporative Emission (EVAP) vapor pipe from the EVAP canister.

5. Disconnect the EVAP purge pipe from the EVAP canister.

6. Disconnect the EVAP vent pipe from the EVAP canister.

7. Remove the bolts from the EVAP mounting bracket.

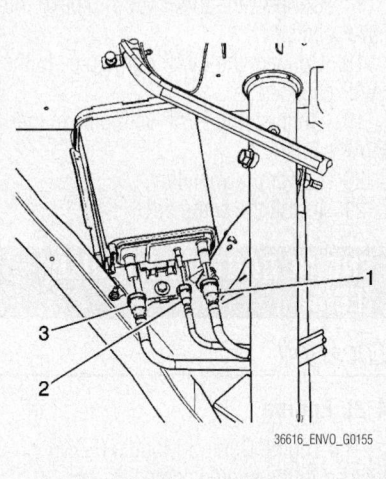

Fig. 160 Disconnect the vapor (1) purge (2) and vent pipe (3)

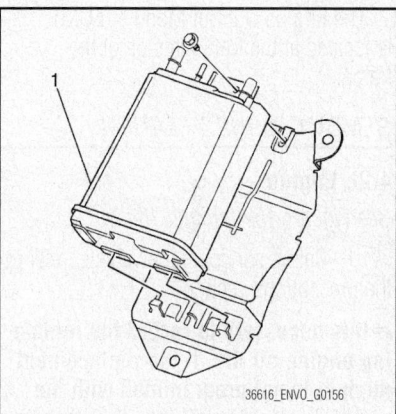

Fig. 161 Remove the EVAP canister (1) from the mounting bracket.

8. Remove the EVAP canister and bracket assembly from the vehicle.

9. Remove the bolt attaching the EVAP canister to the mounting bracket.

10. Remove the EVAP canister from the mounting bracket.

11. Remove the EVAP retaining bracket from the EVAP canister by releasing the retaining bracket clip from the EVAP canister.

To install:

12. Install the EVAP retaining bracket to the EVAP canister ensuring the retaining bracket clip is fully engaged.

13. Install the EVAP canister to the mounting bracket.

14. Install the bolt attaching the EVAP canister to the mounting bracket and tighten to 15 ft. lbs. (20 Nm).

15. Install the EVAP canister and bracket assembly to the vehicle.

16. Install the bolts to the EVAP mounting bracket and tighten to 15 ft. lbs. (20 Nm).

17. Connect the EVAP vapor pipe to the EVAP canister.

18. Connect the EVAP purge pipe to the EVAP canister.

19. Connect the EVAP vent pipe to the EVAP canister.

20. Lower the vehicle.

21. Install the spare tire.

ENGINE CONTROL MODULE (ECM)

LOCATION

4.2L Engine

The Engine Control Module (ECM) is located in the engine compartment, mounted to the intake manifold.

5.3L and 6.0L Engines

The Engine Control Module (ECM) is located at the front left side of the frame.

REMOVAL & INSTALLATION

4.2L Engine

See Figures 162 through 164.

1. Before servicing the vehicle, refer to the precautions section.

➡ It is necessary to record the remaining engine oil life. If the replacement module is not programmed with the remaining engine oil life, the engine oil life will default to 100%. If the replacement module is not programmed with the remaining engine oil life, the engine oil will need to be changed at 5000 km (3,000 mi) from the last engine oil change.

2. Using a scan tool, retrieve the percentage of remaining engine oil. Record the remaining engine oil life.

3. Disconnect the negative battery cable.

✳✳ WARNING

In order to prevent internal damage to the Electronic Control Module (ECM), the ignition must be OFF when disconnecting or reconnecting the ECM connector.

4. Disconnect the engine wiring harness electrical connectors from the ECM.

✳✳ WARNING

Do not touch the connector pins or soldered components on the circuit board in order to prevent possible Electrostatic Discharge (ESD) damage to the ECM.

5. Disengage the top 2 retainers and remove the ECM from the bracket.

6. If the ECM and bracket require removal, perform the following steps:
- Remove the ECM bracket bolts and nuts.
- Remove the ECM bracket w/ECM from the studs.

To install:

7. If the ECM and bracket were removed, perform the following steps:
- Install the ECM bracket w/ECM to the studs.
- Install the PCM bracket bolts and nuts and tighten to 80 inch lbs. (9 Nm).

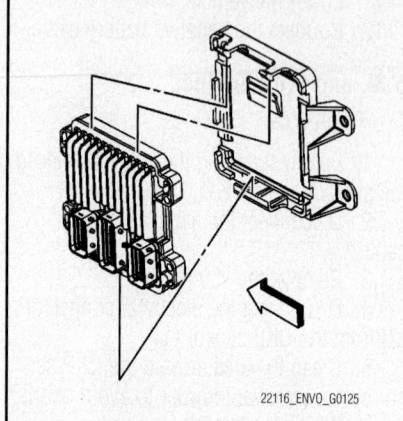

Fig. 163 Disengage the top retainers and remove the ECM from the bracket—4.2L engine

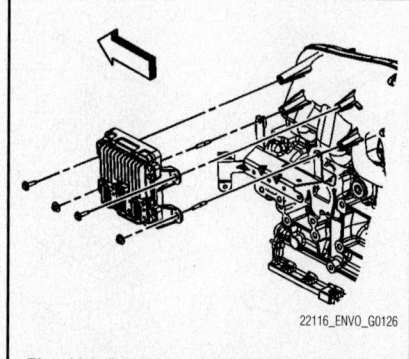

Fig. 164 Removal of the ECM and bracket, bolts and nuts—4.2L engine

8. Set the ECM into the bottom retainer on the bracket and push the ECM rearward, engaging the 2 top retainers.

9. Connect the engine wiring harness electrical connectors to the ECM.

10. Connect the I/P wiring harness electrical connector to the ECM.

11. Connect the negative battery cable.

12. If a new ECM was installed, program the ECM.

13. Using a scan tool, set the remaining engine oil life.

5.3L and 6.0L Engines

See Figure 165.

➡ It is necessary to record the remaining engine oil life. If the replacement module is not programmed with the remaining engine oil life, the engine oil life will default to 100%. If the replacement module is not programmed with the remaining engine oil life, the engine oil will need to be changed at 5000 km (3,000 mi) from the last engine oil change.

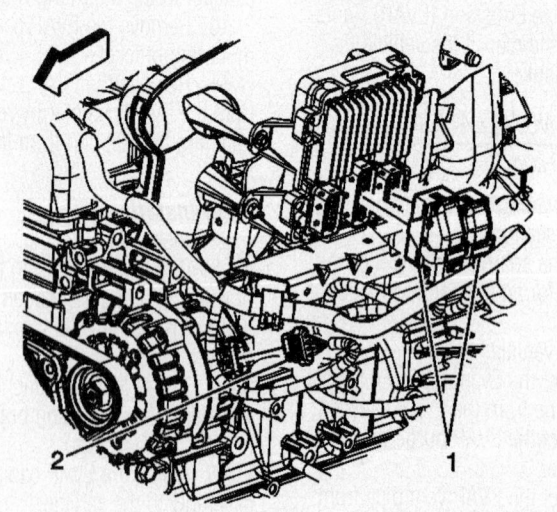

Fig. 162 Disconnect the wiring harness electrical connectors (1) from the ECM—4.2L engine

1. Using a scan tool, retrieve the percentage of remaining engine oil. Record the remaining engine oil life.

2. Disconnect the negative battery cable.

3. Disconnect the cooling fan electrical connector for additional clearance while removing the ECM.

4. Depress the ECM/Transmission Control Module (TCM) cover retainers.

5. Remove the ECM/TCM cover from the ECM/TCM bracket.

✳✳ WARNING

Do not touch the connector pins or soldered components on the circuit board in order to prevent possible Electrostatic Discharge (ESD) damage to the ECM.

→ It is not necessary to disconnect the ECM electrical connectors in order to remove the ECM from the ECM/TCM bracket. Only disconnect the electrical connectors if servicing of component requires disconnecting of the electrical connectors.

✳✳ WARNING

Remove any debris from around the ECM connector surfaces before servicing the ECM. Inspect the ECM module connector gaskets when diagnosing or replacing the ECM. Ensure that the gaskets are installed correctly. The gaskets prevent contaminant intrusion into the ECM.

6. Disconnect the ECM electrical connectors from the ECM.

7. Release the bracket ECM retainers.

8. Tilt the ECM away from the ECM/TCM bracket.

9. Remove the ECM from the ECM bracket.

10. Only when replacement of the ECM/TCM bracket is necessary, remove the TCM.

11. Remove the ECM/TCM bracket retaining bolts.

12. Remove the ECM/TCM bracket from the vehicle frame.

To install:

13. If the ECM/TCM bracket was previously removed, install the ECM/TCM bracket to the vehicle frame.

14. Install the ECM/TCM bracket retaining bolts.

15. Tighten the ECM/TCM bracket bolts to 89 inch lbs. (10 Nm).

16. If the TCM was previously removed from the ECM/TCM bracket, install the TCM.

17. Insert the ECM into the retaining slots of the ECM/TCM bracket.

18. Secure the ECM to the ECM/TCM mounting bracket ensuring the ECM retaining tabs are fully engaged.

19. Connect the ECM electrical connectors to the ECM if previously removed.

20. Install the ECM/TCM cover to the ECM/TCM bracket.

21. Ensure the ECM/TCM cover retainers are fully engaged with the ECM/TCM bracket.

22. Connect the cooling fan electrical connector.

23. Connect the negative battery cable.

24. If the ECM was replaced the replacement ECM must be programmed.

ENGINE COOLANT TEMPERATURE (ECT) SENSOR

LOCATION

4.2L Engine

The Engine Coolant Temperature (ECT) sensor is located at the rear of the cylinder head, just above the exhaust manifold.

5.3L and 6.0L Engines

The Engine Coolant Temperature (ECT) sensor is mounted on the top front of the engine's left cylinder head.

REMOVAL & INSTALLATION

4.2L Engine

See Figure 166.

1. Before servicing the vehicle, refer to the precautions section.

2. Turn the engine OFF.

3. Disconnect the negative battery terminal.

4. Drain coolant below the level of the Engine Coolant Temperature (ECT) sensor.

5. Disconnect the ECT sensor electrical connector.

6. Carefully remove the ECT sensor.

To install:

7. If installing the original sensor or a new sensor without sealant, apply thread sealer P/N 12346004 or equivalent.

8. Install the ECT sensor and tighten to 12 ft. lbs. (16 Nm).

9. Connect the ECT electrical connector.

10. Connect the negative battery terminal.

11. Refill and bleed the cooling system.

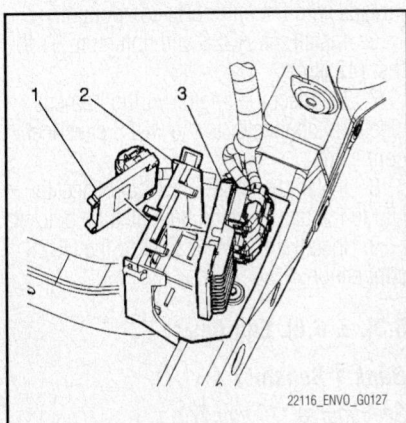

Fig. 165 Transmission Control Module (TCM) (1), ECM/TCM bracket (2) and Engine Control Module (3)—5.3L and 6.0L engines

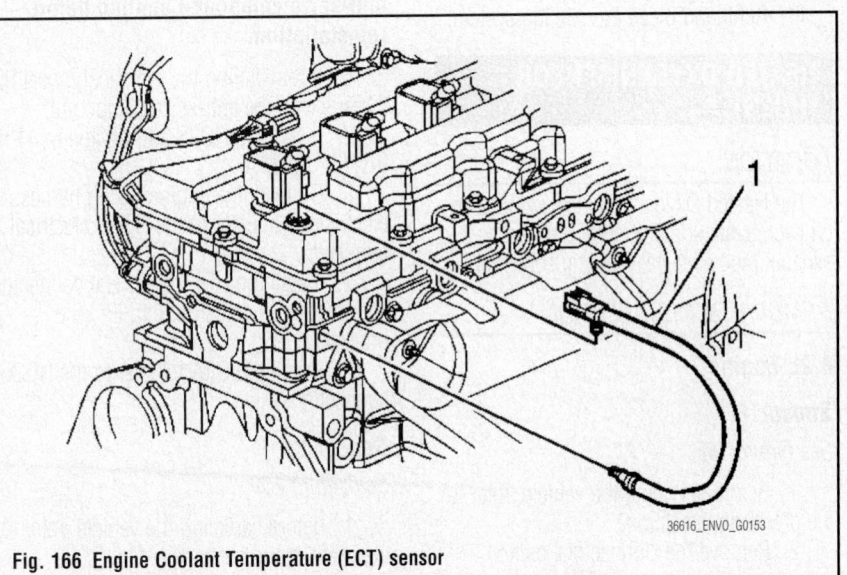

Fig. 166 Engine Coolant Temperature (ECT) sensor

5.3L and 6.0L Engines

See Figure 167.

1. Before servicing the vehicle, refer to the precautions section.
2. Turn OFF the ignition.
3. Raise and suitably support the vehicle.
4. Drain the cooling system below the level of the ECT sensor
5. Lower the vehicle.
6. Disconnect the Engine Coolant Temperature (ECT) sensor electrical connector.
7. Remove the ECT sensor.

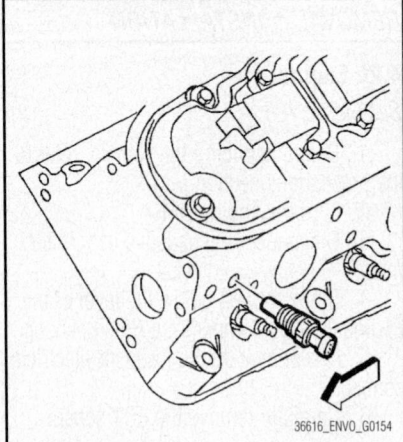

Fig. 167 Engine Coolant Temperature (ECT) sensor removal

To install:

8. Coat the ECT sensor threads with sealer.
9. Install the ECT sensor and tighten to 15 ft. lbs. (20 Nm).
10. Connect the ECT sensor electrical connector.
11. Refill and bleed the cooling system.

HEATED OXYGEN SENSOR (HO2S)

LOCATION

The Heated Oxygen Sensors are located on each exhaust manifold and on each exhaust pipe after the catalytic converter.

REMOVAL & INSTALLATION

4.2L Engine

Sensor 1

See Figure 168.

1. Before servicing the vehicle, refer to the precautions section.
2. Remove the Connector Position

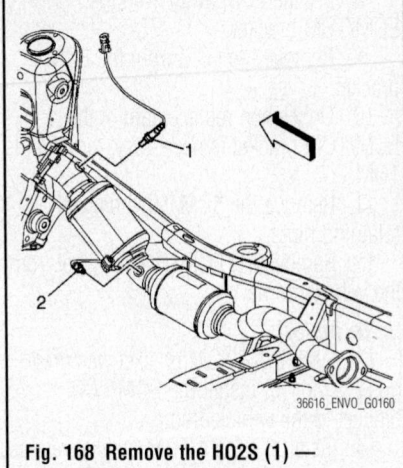

Fig. 168 Remove the HO2S (1) — 4.2L engine

Assurance (CPA) retainer from the Heated Oxygen Sensor (HO2S) connection.

3. Disconnect the engine wiring harness electrical connector from the HO2S electrical connector.
4. Remove the HO2S electrical connector clip from the transmission fluid fill tube bracket.
5. Remove the HO2S.

To install:

➡A special anti-seize compound is used on the HO2S threads. The compound consists of liquid graphite and glass beads. The graphite tends to burns away, but the glass beads remain, making the sensor easier to remove. New, or service replacement sensors already have the compound applied to the threads. If the sensor is removed from an exhaust component and if for any reason the sensor is to be reinstalled, the threads must have anti-seize compound applied before reinstallation.

6. If reinstalling the old sensor, coat the threads with the anti-seize compound.
7. Install the HO2S and tighten to 31 ft. lbs. (42 Nm).
8. Connect the engine wiring harness electrical connector to the HO2S electrical connector.
9. Install the HO2S electrical connector clip to the transmission fluid fill tube bracket.
10. Install the CPA retainer to the HO2S connection.

Sensor 2

See Figure 169.

1. Before servicing the vehicle, refer to the precautions section.

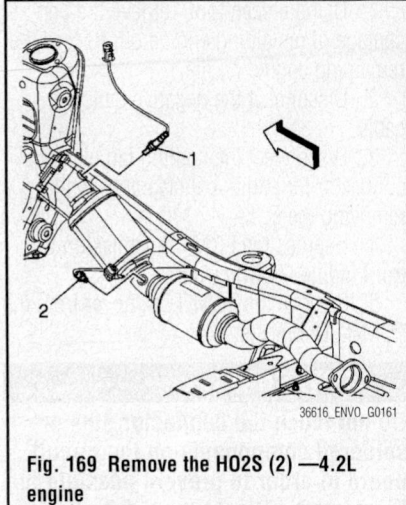

Fig. 169 Remove the HO2S (2) —4.2L engine

2. Raise and suitably support the vehicle.
3. Disconnect the Heated Oxygen Sensor (HO2S) electrical connector from the engine wiring harness electrical connector.
4. Remove the HO2S.

To install:

➡A special anti-seize compound is used on the HO2S threads. The compound consists of liquid graphite and glass beads. The graphite tends to burns away, but the glass beads remain, making the sensor easier to remove. New, or service replacement sensors already have the compound applied to the threads. If the sensor is removed from an exhaust component and if for any reason the sensor is to be reinstalled, the threads must have anti-seize compound applied before reinstallation.

5. If reinstalling the old sensor, coat the threads with the anti-seize compound.
6. Install the HO2S and tighten to 31 ft. lbs. (42 Nm).
7. Connect the engine wiring harness electrical connector to the HO2S electrical connector.
8. Install the HO2S electrical connector clip to the transmission fluid fill tube bracket.
9. Install the CPA retainer to the HO2S connection.

5.3L & 6.0L Engines

Bank 1 Sensor 1

See Figures 170 and 171.

1. Before servicing the vehicle, refer to the precautions section.
2. Raise and suitably support the vehicle.

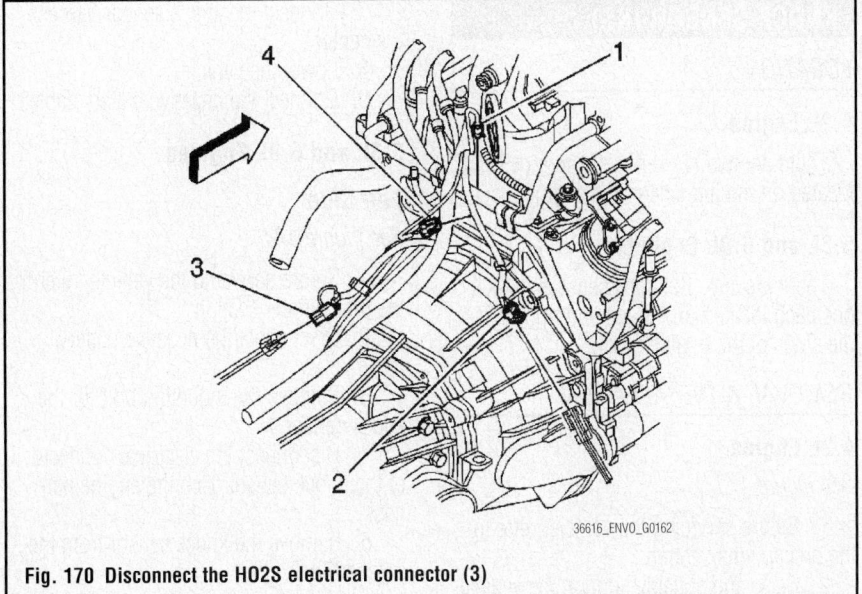

Fig. 170 Disconnect the HO2S electrical connector (3)

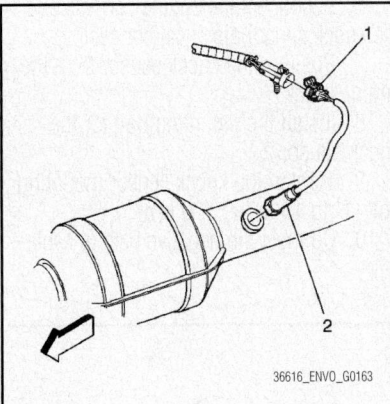

Fig. 171 Install the HO2S—5.3L and 6.0L engines

3. Unscrew the Heated Oxygen Sensor (HO2S) sensor from the catalytic converter.
4. Remove the Connector Position Assurance (CPA) retainer.
5. Disconnect the HO2S electrical connector.

To install:
6. Connect the HO2S electrical connector.
7. Install the CPA retainer.
8. If reinstalling the old sensor, coat the threads with anti-seize compound.

➡A special anti-seize compound is used on the HO2S threads. The compound consists of liquid graphite and glass beads. The graphite tends to burn away, but the glass beads remain, making the sensor easier to remove. New, or service replacement sensors already have the compound applied to the threads. If the sensor is removed

from an exhaust component and if for any reason the sensor is to be reinstalled, the threads must have anti-seize compound applied before the reinstallation.

9. Install the HO2S and tighten to 31 ft. lbs. (42 Nm).

➡If the HO2S sensor is connected to the main wiring harness during installation. Rotate the HO2S sensor several turns counterclockwise before threading the HO2S sensor into the catalytic converter. This action of initially reverse winding of the pigtail wires will prevent a condition where the HO2S sensor pigtail wires become severely twisted or binding once the HO2S sensor is installed into the catalytic converter.

10. Lower the vehicle.

Bank 1 Sensor 2
See Figure 172.

1. Before servicing the vehicle, refer to the precautions section.
2. Raise and suitably support the vehicle.
3. Remove the Connector Position Assurance (CPA) retainer.
4. Disconnect the Heated Oxygen Sensor (HO2S) electrical connector.
5. Remove the HO2S (2).

To install:

➡A special anti-seize compound is used on the HO2S threads. The compound consists of liquid graphite and glass beads. The graphite tends to burn away, but the glass beads remain,

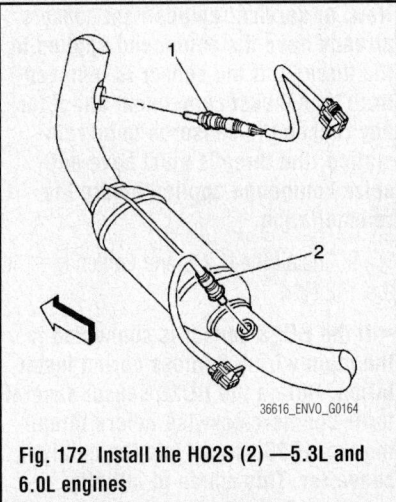

Fig. 172 Install the HO2S (2) —5.3L and 6.0L engines

making the sensor easier to remove. New, or service replacement sensors already have the compound applied to the threads. If the sensor is removed from an exhaust component and if for any reason the sensor is to be reinstalled, the threads must have anti-seize compound applied before the reinstallation.

6. If reinstalling the old sensor, coat the threads with anti-seize compound.
7. Install the HO2S and tighten to 31 ft. lbs. (42 Nm).
8. Connect the HO2S electrical connector.
9. Install the CPA retainer.
10. Lower the vehicle.

Bank 2 Sensor 1
See Figures 170 and 171.

1. Before servicing the vehicle, refer to the precautions section.
2. Raise and suitably support the vehicle.
3. Unscrew the Heated Oxygen Sensor (HO2S) sensor from the catalytic converter.
4. Remove the Connector Position Assurance (CPA) retainer.
5. Disconnect the HO2S electrical connector.

To install:
6. Connect the HO2S electrical connector.
7. Install the CPA retainer.
8. If reinstalling the old sensor, coat the threads with anti-seize compound.

➡A special anti-seize compound is used on the HO2S threads. The compound consists of liquid graphite and glass beads. The graphite tends to burn away, but the glass beads remain, making the sensor easier to remove.

New, or service replacement sensors already have the compound applied to the threads. If the sensor is removed from an exhaust component and if for any reason the sensor is to be reinstalled, the threads must have anti-seize compound applied before the reinstallation.

9. Install the HO2S and tighten to 31 ft. lbs. (42 Nm).

→If the HO2S sensor is connected to the main wiring harness during installation. Rotate the HO2S sensor several turns counterclockwise before threading the HO2S sensor into the catalytic converter. This action of initially reverse winding of the pigtail wires will prevent a condition where the HO2S sensor pigtail wires become severely twisted or binding once the HO2S sensor is installed into the catalytic converter.

10. Lower the vehicle.

Bank 2 Sensor 2

See Figure 172.

1. Before servicing the vehicle, refer to the precautions section.
2. Raise and suitably support the vehicle.
3. Remove the Connector Position Assurance (CPA) retainer.
4. Disconnect the Heated Oxygen Sensor (HO2S) electrical connector.
5. Remove the HO2S (2).

To install:

→A special anti-seize compound is used on the HO2S threads. The compound consists of liquid graphite and glass beads. The graphite tends to burn away, but the glass beads remain, making the sensor easier to remove. New, or service replacement sensors already have the compound applied to the threads. If the sensor is removed from an exhaust component and if for any reason the sensor is to be reinstalled, the threads must have anti-seize compound applied before the reinstallation.

6. If reinstalling the old sensor, coat the threads with anti-seize compound.
7. Install the HO2S and tighten to 31 ft. lbs. (42 Nm).
8. Connect the HO2S electrical connector.
9. Install the CPA retainer.
10. Lower the vehicle.

KNOCK SENSOR (KS)

LOCATION

4.2L Engine

There are two (2) knock sensors (KS) are located on the left side of the engine block.

5.3L and 6.0L Engines

There are two (2) knock sensors (KS), one each located on the left and right middle sides of the engine block.

REMOVAL & INSTALLATION

4.2L Engine

See Figure 173.

1. Before servicing the vehicle, refer to the precautions section.
2. Raise and suitably support the vehicle.
3. Remove the knock sensor harness connector.
4. Remove the knock sensor retaining bolt.
5. Remove the appropriate knock sensor (1 or 2).

To install:

6. Install the knock sensor (1 or 2) and the bolt, then tighten the sensor to 18 ft. lbs. (25 Nm).

7. Connect the knock sensor harness connector .
8. Lower the vehicle.
9. Connect the negative battery cable.

5.3L and 6.0L Engines

Left Side

See Figure 174.

1. Before servicing the vehicle, refer to the precautions section.
2. Disconnect the negative battery cable.
3. Remove the mounting bolt for the knock sensor 1.
4. Disconnect the electrical connector of the knock sensor from the engine harness.
5. Remove the knock sensor from the engine block.

To install:

6. Reconnect the engine harness and the knock sensor electrical connectors.
7. Position the knock sensor 2 on the engine block.
8. Install the mounting bolt for the knock sensor 2.
9. Tighten the knock sensor mounting bolt (1) to 15 ft. lbs. (20 Nm).
10. Connect the negative battery cable.

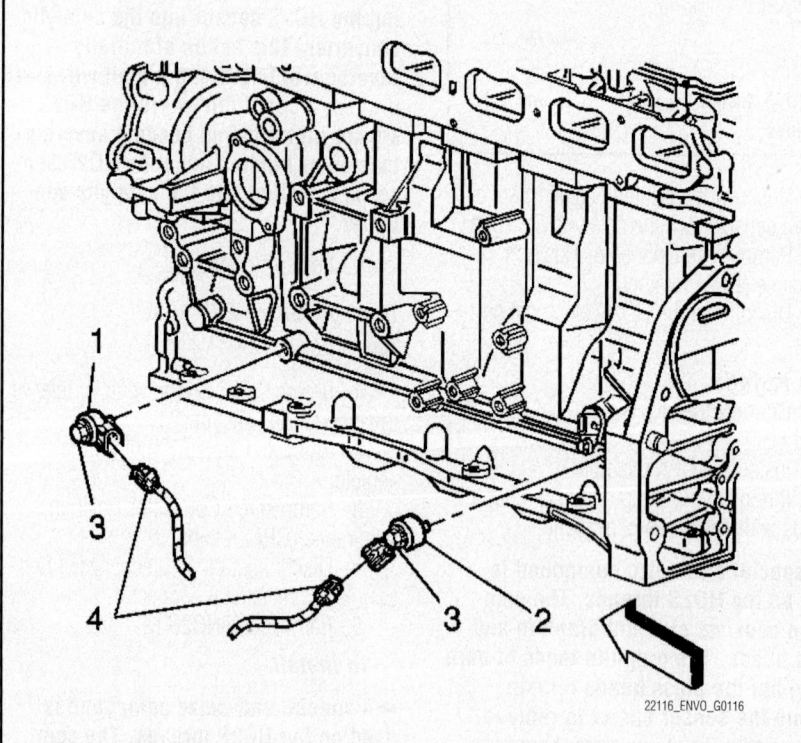

Fig. 173 Location of the knock sensors (1 and 2)—4.2L engine

22116_ENVO_G0116

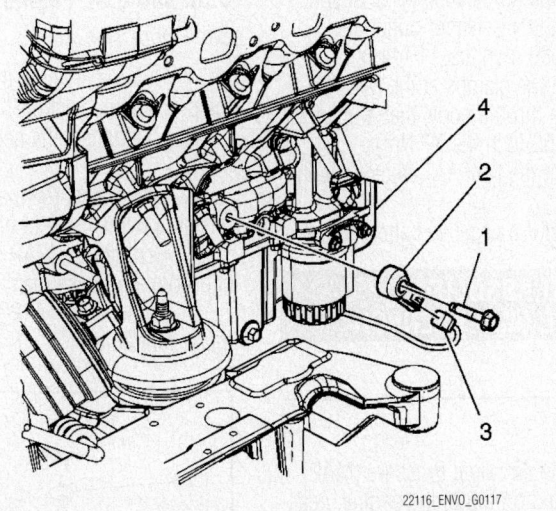

Fig. 174 Location of the left side knock sensor (2)—5.3L and 6.0L engines

Right Side

See Figure 175.

1. Before servicing the vehicle, refer to the precautions section.
2. Disconnect the negative battery cable.
3. Disconnect the electrical connector from the knock sensor.
4. Remove the knock sensor bolt.
5. Remove the knock sensor (2) from the engine block.

To install:

6. Position the knock sensor on the engine block.
7. Install the knock sensor bolt and tighten to 15 ft. lbs. (20 Nm).
8. Connect the electrical connector to the knock sensor.

9. Connect the negative battery cable.

MALFUNCTION INDICATOR LIGHT (MIL)

RESET PROCEDURES

1. Install any components or connectors that may have been removed.
2. Perform any adjustment, programming or setup procedures that are required when a component or module is removed or replaced.

➡ **The DLC is located inside the drivers compartment, underneath the dash.**

3. Using a suitable scan tool connect to the Data Link Connector (DLC), clear any Diagnostic Trouble Codes (DTC).

4. Turn OFF the ignition for 60 seconds.

MASS AIR FLOW (MAF) SENSOR

LOCATION

The Mass Air Flow/Intake Air Temperature (MAF/IAT) sensor is mounted ahead of the throttle body on the air cleaner assembly.

REMOVAL & INSTALLATION

4.2L Engine

See Figure 176.

➡**Use care when handling the Mass Air Flow/Intake Air Temperature (MAF/IAT) sensor. Do not dent, puncture, or otherwise damage the honeycell located at the air inlet end of the MAF/IAT. Do not touch the sensing elements or allow anything including cleaning solvents and lubricants to come in contact with them. Use a small amount of a non-silicone based lubricant, on the air duct only, to aid in installation.**

1. Disconnect the negative battery cable.
2. Disconnect the engine harness electrical connector (5) from the MAF/IAT sensor.
3. Remove the MAF/IAT sensor screws.
4. Remove the MAF/IAT sensor .

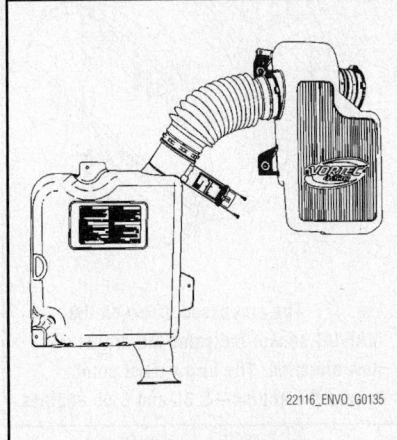

Fig. 176 Location of the Mass Air Flow/Intake Air Temperature (MAF/IAT) sensor—4.2L engine

To install:

5. Install the MAF/IAT sensor.
6. Install the MAF/IAT sensor screws and tighten to 5 inch lbs. (0.6 Nm).
7. Connect the engine harness electrical connector (5) to the MAF/IAT sensor.
8. Connect the negative battery cable.

5.3L and 6.0L Engines

See Figure 177.

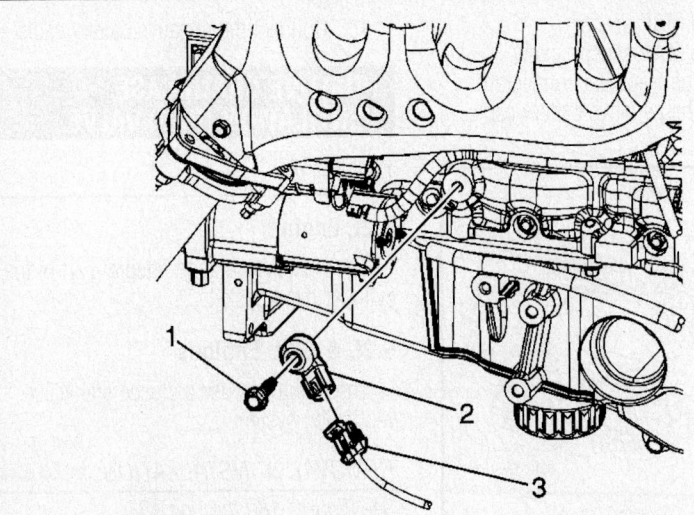

Fig. 175 Location of the right side knock sensor (2)—5.3L and 6.0L engines

→Use care when handling the Mass Air Flow/Intake Air Temperature (MAF/IAT) sensor. Do not dent, puncture, or otherwise damage the honeycell located at the air inlet end of the MAF/IAT. Do not touch the sensing elements or allow anything including cleaning solvents and lubricants to come in contact with them. Use a small amount of a non-silicone based lubricant, on the air duct only, to aid in installation.

1. Disconnect the negative battery cable.
2. Disconnect the MAF/IAT sensor electrical connector.
3. Loosen the clamps at the MAF/IAT sensor and the throttle body.
4. Remove the air cleaner outlet duct bolt.
5. Remove the air cleaner outlet duct.
6. Loosen the clamp attaching the MAF/IAT sensor to the air cleaner housing.
7. Remove the MAF/IAT sensor from the air cleaner housing.

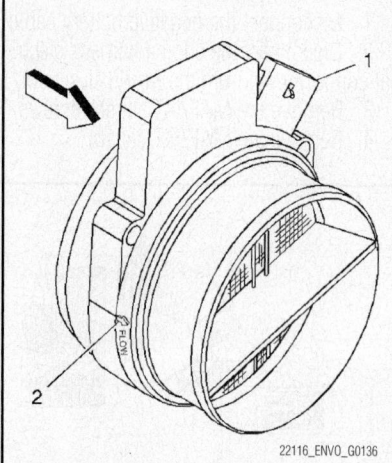

Fig. 177 The embossed arrow on the MAF/IAT sensor indicates the proper air flow direction. The arrow must point toward the engine—5.3L and 6.0L engines

To install:

→The embossed arrow on the MAF/IAT sensor indicates the proper air flow direction. The arrow must point toward the engine.

8. Locate the air flow direction arrow (2) on the MAF/IAT sensor.
9. Install the MAF/IAT sensor on to the air cleaner housing.
10. Tighten the clamp securing the MAF/IAT sensor to the air cleaner housing and tighten the clamp to 62 inch lbs. (7 Nm).

11. Install the air cleaner outlet duct.
12. Install the air cleaner outlet duct bolt and tighten to 89 inch lbs. (10 Nm).
13. Tighten the clamps at the MAF/IAT sensor and the throttle body, then tighten the clamps to 62 inch lbs. (7 Nm).
14. Connect the MAF/IAT electrical connector.
15. Connect the negative battery cable.

MANIFOLD ABSOLUTE PRESSURE (MAP) SENSOR

LOCATION

4.2L Engine

The Manifold Absolute Pressure (MAP) sensor is located on top of the engine, near the firewall.

5.3L and 6.0L Engines

The Manifold Absolute Pressure (MAP) sensor is located on top of the engine, on top of the intake manifold plenum.

REMOVAL & INSTALLATION

4.2L Engine

See Figure 178.

1. Before servicing the vehicle, refer to the precautions section.
2. Disconnect the negative battery cable.
3. Turn OFF the ignition.
4. Disconnect the Manifold Absolute Pressure (MAP) sensor electrical connector.
5. Remove the MAP sensor screw.
6. Remove the MAP sensor.
7. Inspect the MAP sensor seal for damage, and replace as necessary.

To install:

8. Install the MAP sensor.
9. Install the MAP sensor screw
10. Connect the electrical connector.
11. Connect the negative battery cable.

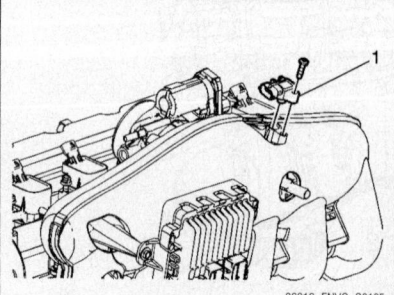

Fig. 178 Manifold Absolute Pressure (MAP) sensor (1)—4.2L engine

5.3L and 6.0L Engines

See Figure 179.

1. Before servicing the vehicle, refer to the precautions section.
2. Disconnect the negative battery cable.
3. Disconnect the manifold absolute pressure (MAP) sensor electrical connector.
4. Remove the MAP sensor retaining clip from the intake manifold.
5. Remove the MAP sensor from the intake manifold.

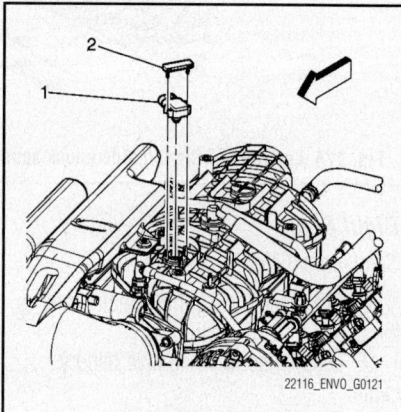

Fig. 179 Location of the Manifold Absolute Pressure (MAP) sensor (1) and retaining clip (2)—5.3L and 6.0L engines

To install:

6. Lightly coat the MAP sensor seal with clean engine oil before installing the sensor.
7. Install the MAP sensor. Push the MAP sensor into the intake manifold.
8. Install the MAP sensor retainer to the intake manifold.
9. Connect the MAP sensor electrical connector.
10. Connect the negative battery cable.

POSITIVE CRANKCASE VENTILATION (PCV) VALVE

LOCATION

4.2L Engine

The PCV orifice is an integral part of the cylinder head gasket.

5.3L & 6.0L Engines

These engines use a closed crankcase ventilation system.

REMOVAL & INSTALLATION

See Figures 180 through 183.

1. Before servicing the vehicle, refer to the precautions section.

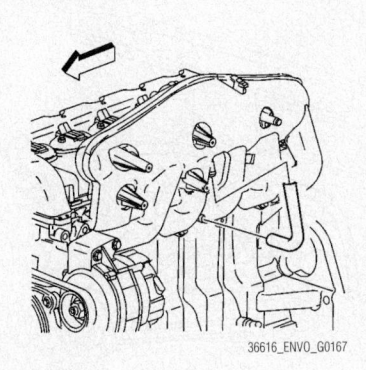

Fig. 180 Disconnect the crankcase dirty air hose from the PCV orifice tube— 4.2L engine

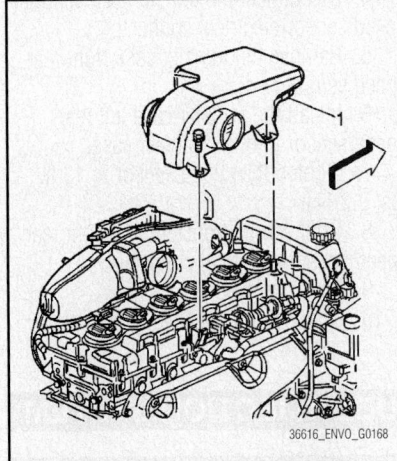

Fig. 181 Air cleaner outlet resonator (1) removal—4.2L engine

2. Disconnect the crankcase dirty air hose from the intake manifold.

3. Disconnect the crankcase dirty air hose from the Positive Crankcase Ventilation (PCV) orifice tube.

4. Loosen the throttle body clamps.

5. Disconnect the fuel pressure regulator vacuum supply hose from the air cleaner outlet resonator.

6. Remove the 2 resonator to engine bolts from the air cleaner outlet resonator.

7. Lift up the front of the air cleaner outlet resonator.

8. Disconnect the crankcase clean air hose from the valve cover port.

9. Disconnect the crankcase clean air hose from the air cleaner outlet resonator.

To install:

10. Connect the crankcase clean air hose to the air cleaner outlet resonator.

11. Connect the crankcase clean air hose to the valve cover port.

12. Install the 2 resonator to engine bolts to the air cleaner outlet resonator and tighten to 53 inch. lbs. (6 Nm).

13. Tighten the throttle body clamps to 35 inch. lbs. (4 Nm).

14. Connect the fuel pressure regulator vacuum supply hose to the air cleaner outlet resonator.

15. Lubricate the inner diameter of the crankcase ventilation hose.

16. Connect the crankcase dirty air hose to the intake manifold.

17. Connect the crankcase dirty air hose to the PCV orifice tube.

5.3L & 6.0L Engines

1. Before servicing the vehicle, refer to the precautions section.

2. Remove the intake manifold sight shield.

3. Remove the Positive Crankcase Ventilation (PCV) foul air hose from the intake manifold and valve rocker arm cover.

4. Remove the PCV fresh air hose from the valve rocker arm cover.

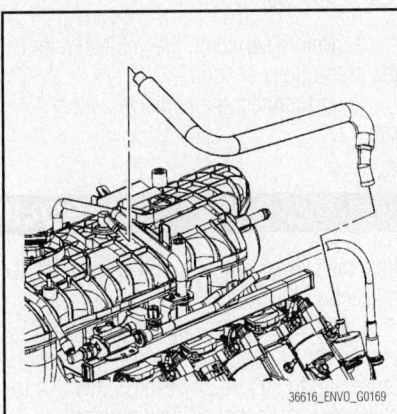

Fig. 182 PCV foul air hose removal 5.3L and 6.0L engines

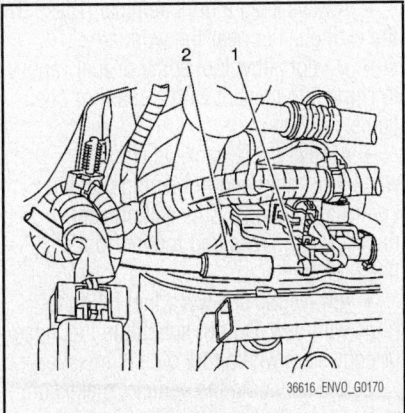

Fig. 183 PCV fresh air hose (2) removal 5.3L and 6.0L engines

To install:

5. Install the PCV fresh air hose to the valve rocker arm cover.

6. Install the PCV foul air hose to the intake manifold and valve rocker arm cover.

7. Install the intake manifold sight shield.

THROTTLE POSITION SENSOR (TPS)

LOCATION

The Throttle Position Sensor (TPS) is an integral component of the throttle body assembly and cannot be serviced separately.

REMOVAL & INSTALLATION

Refer to the Throttle Body Removal & Installation procedure.

VEHICLE SPEED SENSOR (VSS)

LOCATION

2WD Models

The Vehicle Speed Sensor (VSS) is located on the right rear side of the transmission case.

REMOVAL & INSTALLATION

2WD Models

See Figure 184.

1. Before servicing the vehicle, refer to the precautions section.

2. Disconnect the negative battery cable.

3. Raise the vehicle.

4. Remove the harness connector.

5. Remove the bolt.

6. Remove the vehicle speed sensor.

7. Remove the O-ring seal.

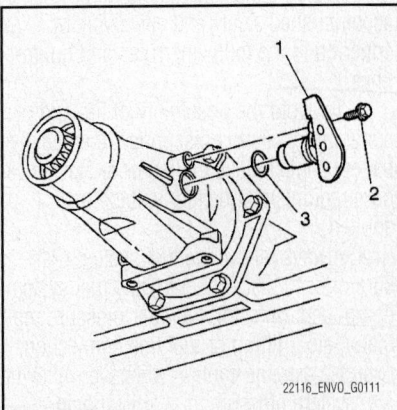

Fig. 184 Location of the vehicle speed sensor (1), bolt (2) and O-ring seal (3)

To install:

8. Install the O-ring seal on the vehicle speed sensor.

9. Coat the O-ring seal with a thin film of transmission fluid.

10. Install the vehicle speed sensor into the transmission case.

11. Install the bolt and tighten to 97 inch lbs. (11 Nm).

12. Connect the wiring harness electrical connector to the vehicle speed sensor.

13. Refill the fluid as required.

14. Lower the vehicle.

15. Connect the negative battery cable.

4WD Models

Left Sensor

See Figure 185.

1. Before servicing the vehicle, refer to the precautions section.

2. Disconnect the negative battery cable.

3. Raise the vehicle.

4. Disconnect the transfer case left rear speed sensor electrical connector.

5. Remove the transfer case left rear speed sensor.

6. Install the transfer case left rear speed sensor into the transfer case.

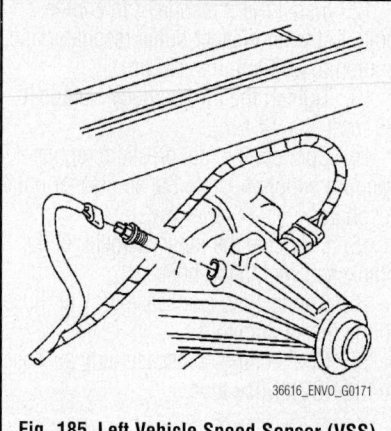

Fig. 185 Left Vehicle Speed Sensor (VSS) removal

36616_ENVO_G0171

7. Tighten the speed sensor to 13 ft. lbs. (17 Nm).

8. Connect the transfer case left rear speed sensor electrical connector.

9. Lower the vehicle.

10. Connect the negative battery cable.

Right Sensor

See Figure 186.

1. Before servicing the vehicle, refer to the precautions section.

2. Disconnect the negative battery cable.

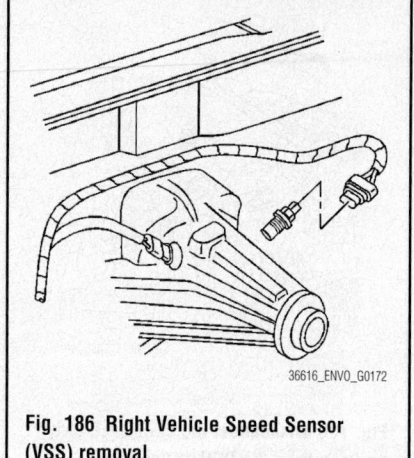

Fig. 186 Right Vehicle Speed Sensor (VSS) removal

36616_ENVO_G0172

3. Raise the vehicle.

4. Disconnect the transfer case left rear speed sensor electrical connector.

5. Remove the transfer case right rear speed sensor.

6. Install the transfer case left rear speed sensor into the transfer case.

7. Tighten the speed sensor to 13 ft. lbs. (17 Nm).

8. Connect the transfer case right rear speed sensor electrical connector.

9. Lower the vehicle.

10. Connect the negative battery cable.

FUEL
GASOLINE FUEL INJECTION SYSTEM

FUEL SYSTEM SERVICE PRECAUTIONS

Safety is the most important factor when performing not only fuel system maintenance but any type of maintenance. Failure to conduct maintenance and repairs in a safe manner may result in serious personal injury or death. Maintenance and testing of the vehicle's fuel system components can be accomplished safely and effectively by adhering to the following rules and guidelines.

• To avoid the possibility of fire and personal injury, always disconnect the negative battery cable unless the repair or test procedure requires that battery voltage be applied.

• Always relieve the fuel system pressure prior to disconnecting any fuel system component (injector, fuel rail, pressure regulator, etc.), fitting or fuel line connection. Exercise extreme caution whenever relieving fuel system pressure to avoid exposing skin, face and eyes to fuel spray. Please be advised that fuel under pressure may penetrate the skin or any part of the body that it contacts.

• Always place a shop towel or cloth around the fitting or connection prior to loosening to absorb any excess fuel due to spillage. Ensure that all fuel spillage (should it occur) is quickly removed from engine surfaces. Ensure that all fuel soaked cloths or towels are deposited into a suitable waste container.

• Always keep a dry chemical (Class B) fire extinguisher near the work area.

• Do not allow fuel spray or fuel vapors to come into contact with a spark or open flame.

• Always use a back-up wrench when loosening and tightening fuel line connection fittings. This will prevent unnecessary stress and torsion to fuel line piping.

• Always replace worn fuel fitting O-rings with new. Do not substitute fuel hose or equivalent where fuel pipe is installed.

Before servicing the vehicle, make sure to also refer to the precautions in the beginning of this section as well.

RELIEVING FUEL SYSTEM PRESSURE

4.2L Engine

1. Before servicing the vehicle, refer to the precautions in the beginning of this section.

✳✳ WARNING

Do not perform this procedure for more than 2 minutes to avoid damaging the catalytic converter.

2. Loosen the fuel filler cap to release the fuel tank pressure.

3. Remove the fuel pump relay from the junction block.

4. Crank the engine, allowing it to start and stall.

5. Crank the engine for an additional 3 seconds to relieve any remaining fuel pressure.

6. Disconnect the negative battery cable to avoid repressurizing the fuel system.

7. Install the fuel pump relay in the junction block.

8. Tighten the fuel filler cap.

9. After you are finished working on the fuel system, connect the negative battery cable.

5.3L and 6.0L Engines

1. Disconnect the negative battery cable.

2. Install Fuel Pressure Gauge J 34730-1A or equivalent to the fuel pressure connection.

3. Loosen the fuel fill cap to relieve the fuel tank vapor pressure.

4. Open the valve on the fuel pressure gauge to bleed the system pressure. The fuel connections are now safe for servicing. Drain any fuel remaining in the gauge into an approved container. Once the system pressure is completely relieved, remove the fuel pressure gauge.

FUEL FILTER

REMOVAL & INSTALLATION

The fuel filter is contained in the fuel sender assembly inside the fuel tank. The paper filter element traps particles in the fuel that may damage the fuel injection system. The filter housing is made to withstand maximum fuel system pressure, exposure to fuel additives, and changes in temperature.

1. Before servicing the vehicle, refer to the precautions in the beginning of this section.

2. Properly relieve the fuel system pressure.

3. Disconnect the negative battery cable.

4. Remove the fuel filler cap, if not already done.

5. Remove the fuel pump assembly.

6. Remove the fuel filter from the fuel pump assembly. Replace the seals or O-rings.

To install:

7. Install the new fuel filter to the fuel pump assembly along with new seals or O-rings.

8. Install the fuel pump assembly.

9. Install the fuel filler cap.

10. Connect the negative battery cable.

11. Start the engine and check for leaks.

FUEL PUMP

REMOVAL & INSTALLATION

See Figures 187 and 188.

1. Before servicing the vehicle, refer to the precautions in the beginning of this section.

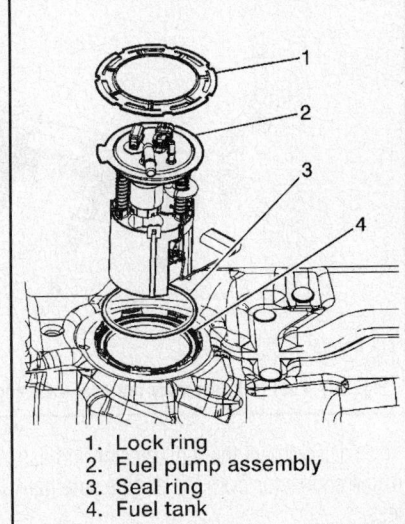

1. Lock ring
2. Fuel pump assembly
3. Seal ring
4. Fuel tank

36616_ENVO_G0174

Fig. 187 Fuel pump assembly removal

2. Properly relieve the fuel system pressure.

3. Drain the fuel tank.

4. Remove the fuel tank.

➡ **Do NOT use impact tools. Significant force will be required to release the lock ring. The use of a hammer and screwdriver is not recommended. Secure the fuel tank in order to prevent fuel tank rotation. Use the J 45722 spanner wrench and a long breaker-bar in order to unlock the fuel sender lock ring. Turn the fuel sender lock ring in a counterclockwise direction.**

5. Remove the fuel pump assembly and the seal. Discard the seal.

6. Clean the fuel sender sealing surfaces.

7. Place the lock ring on a flat surface. Measure the clearance between to lock ring

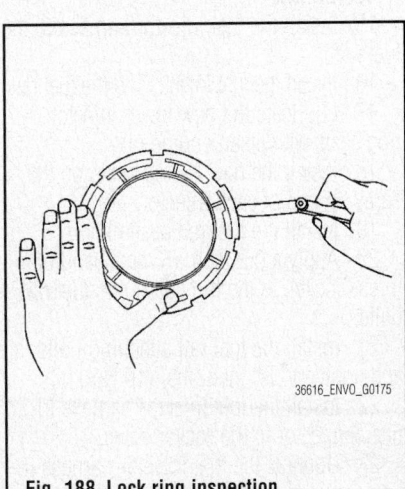

36616_ENVO_G0175

Fig. 188 Lock ring inspection

and the flat surface using a feeler gage at 7 points.

8. If the warpage is less than 0.016 inch. (0.41 mm), the lock ring does not require replacement.

9. If the warpage is greater than 0.016 inch. (0.41 mm), the lock ring must be replaced

10. Install the new seal on the fuel tank.

11. Install the fuel sender assembly into the fuel tank.

➡ **The fuel pump strainer must be in a horizontal position when the fuel sender is installed in the tank. When installing the fuel sender assembly, assure that the fuel pump strainer does not block full travel of the float arm.**

12. Use the J 45722 in order to install the fuel sender lock ring. Turn the fuel sender lock ring in a clockwise direction.

13. Install the fuel tank.

14. Install the fuel and check for leaks.

FUEL PRESSURE REGULATOR

REMOVAL & INSTALLATION

See Figure 189.

The fuel system is a returnless, on-demand design. The fuel pressure regulator is contained in the fuel sender assembly inside the fuel tank.

1. Before servicing the vehicle, refer to the precautions in the beginning of this section.

2. Properly relieve the fuel system pressure.

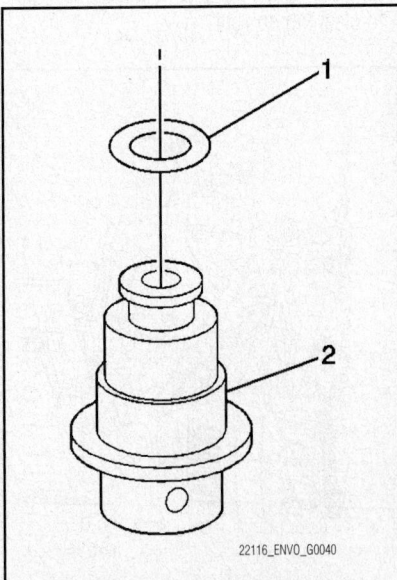

22116_ENVO_G0040

Fig. 189 Fuel pressure regulator (2) and O-ring assembly (1)—4.2L engine shown, others similar

3. Disconnect the negative battery cable.

4. Remove the fuel filler cap, if not already done.

5. Remove the fuel pump assembly.

6. Remove the fuel pressure regulator from the fuel pump assembly. Replace the seal(s) or O-ring(s).

To install:

7. Install the new fuel pressure regulator to the fuel pump assembly along with new seal(s) or O-ring(s).

8. Install the fuel pump assembly.

9. Install the fuel filler cap.

10. Connect the negative battery cable.

11. Start the engine and check for leaks.

FUEL RAIL & INJECTORS

REMOVAL & INSTALLATION

4.2L Engine

See Figures 190 and 191.

1. Before servicing the vehicle, refer to the precautions in the beginning of this section.

2. Relieve the fuel system pressure. Refer to the fuel system relief procedure in this section.

3. Disconnect the negative battery cable.

4. Disconnect the fuel feed pipe from the fuel rail.

5. Remove the intake manifold.

6. Before removal, clean the fuel rail assembly and the cylinder head with a spray type engine cleaner, GM X-30A or equivalent, if necessary. Follow the package instructions. Do not soak the fuel rail in liquid cleaning solvent.

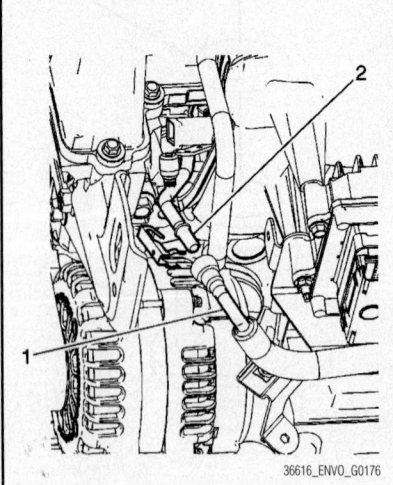

Fig. 190 Disconnect the fuel feed pipe (1) from the fuel rail (2)

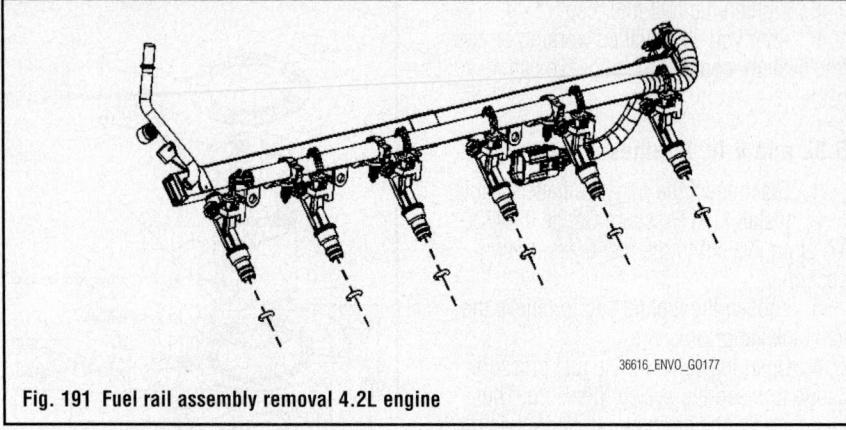

Fig. 191 Fuel rail assembly removal 4.2L engine

7. Disconnect the fuel injector harness in-line connector from the engine wire harness.

8. Remove the fuel injector harness in-line connector from the rocker cover.

9. Remove the fuel rail attaching bolts.

✳✳ WARNING

Remove the fuel rail assembly carefully in order to prevent damage to the injector electrical connector terminals and the injector spray tips. Support the fuel rail after the fuel rail is removed in order to avoid damaging the fuel rail components. Cap the fittings and plug the holes when servicing the fuel system in order to prevent dirt and other contaminants from entering open pipes and passages.

10. Remove the fuel rail assembly.

11. Remove the injector lower O-ring seal from the spray tip end of each injector.

12. Discard the O-ring seals.

13. Remove the fuel injector wire harness from the fuel rail.

14. Remove the fuel injectors from the fuel rail.

To install:

15. Install the fuel injector harness to the fuel rail.

16. Install the fuel injectors to the fuel rail.

17. Lubricate the new lower injector O-ring seals with clean engine oil.

18. Install the new O-ring seals on the spray tip end of each injector.

19. Install the fuel rail assembly

20. Apply a 0.2 inch. (5 mm) band of thread locker, to the threads of the fuel rail bolts.

21. Install the fuel rail attaching bolts and tighten to 89 inch. lbs. (10 Nm).

22. Install the fuel injector harness in-line connector to the rocker cover.

23. Connect the fuel injector harness in-line connector to the engine wire harness.

24. Connect the fuel feed pipe to the fuel rail.

25. Connect the fuel injector electrical connectors.

26. Install the intake manifold.

27. Connect the negative battery cable.

28. Inspect for leaks.

5.3L and 6.0L Engines

See Figures 192 and 193.

1. Before servicing the vehicle, refer to the precautions in the beginning of this section.

2. Relieve the fuel system pressure. Refer to the fuel system relief procedure in this section.

3. Remove or disconnect the following:

- Negative battery cable, if not done already
- A/C compressor pressure switch electrical connector
- Wire harness from the clip on the cylinder head
- Mass Airflow/Intake Air Temperature (MAF/IAT) sensor connector
- Alternator electrical connector
- Right side electrical connectors from the coil main electrical harness, Electronic Throttle Control (ETC) and fuel injectors.

4. To detach the injector connector: Matchmark the connectors, pull the Connector Position Assurance (CPA) retainer up 1 click. Push the tab on the connector in, then detach the injector connector.

- Electrical harness from the clips on the ignition coil bracket
- Evaporative emission (EVAP) purge solenoid electrical connector
- Knock Sensor (KS) electrical connector
- Manifold Absolute Pressure (MAP) electrical connector
- Main coil
- Fuel injector electrical connector (right side)

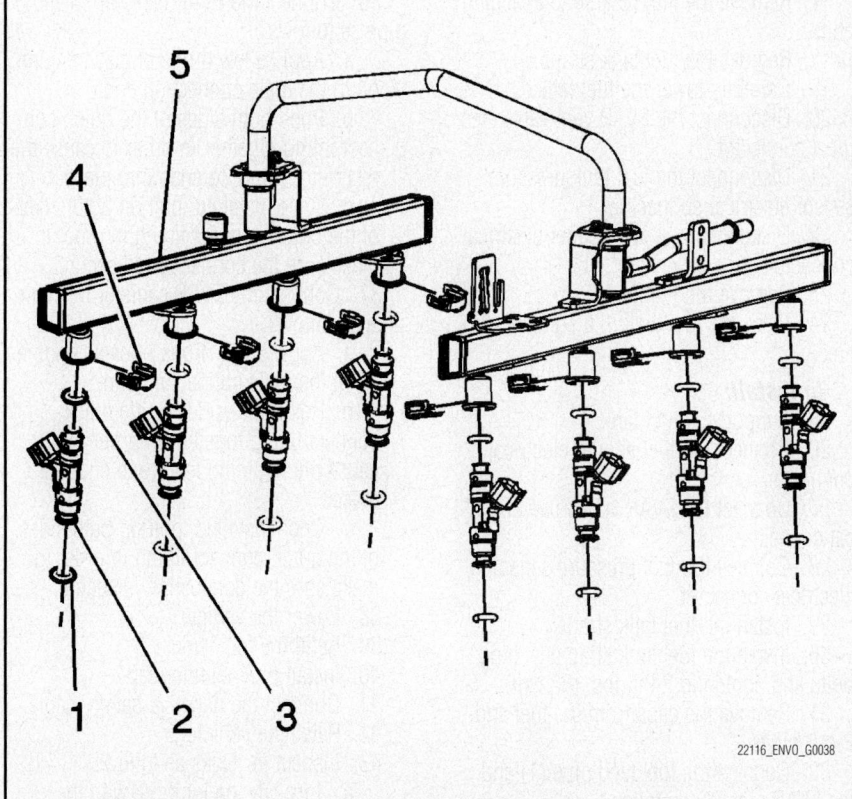

Fig. 192 Exploded view of the fuel rail mounting—5.3L and 6.0L engines

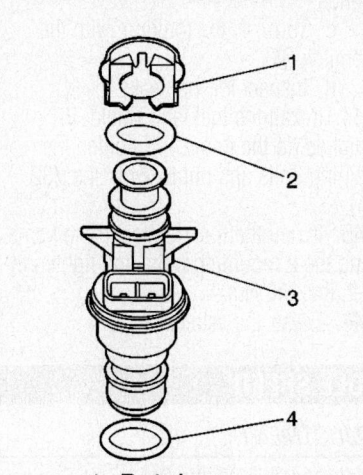

1. Retainer
2. O-ring seal
3. Fuel injector
4. O-ring seal

Fig. 193 Exploded view of the fuel injector (3), retainer (1) and O-ring seals (2, 4)—5.3L and 6.0L engines

- Electrical harness from the clips on the ignition coil bracket
- Upper engine wire harness retainer nut. Position the wire harness aside.

- Fuel feed and return pipes from the rail
- Fuel pressure regulator vacuum line
- Fuel rail bolts
- Fuel rail, after cleaning with a spray-type cleaner

✳✳ WARNING

Be very careful when removing the fuel rail and injectors not to damage the connector terminals or injector spray tips

- Fuel injector from the fuel rail
- Fuel injector retainer clip and discard
- Fuel injector lower O-ring seals and discard

To install:

5. Install or connect the following:
   - New O-ring seals on the injectors, after lubricating with clean engine oil
   - New retainer clip on the injector
   - Fuel injector by pushing it into the fuel rail socket
   - Fuel rail
   - Apply 0.20 (5mm) band of thread locker to the threads of the fuel rail bolts

- Fuel rail bolts and tighten to 89 inch lbs. (10 Nm)
- Fuel pressure regulator vacuum line
- Fuel feel and return pipes
- Route the upper electrical harness into position over the engine.
- Engine harness bracket nut and tighten to 89 inch lbs. (10 Nm)
- PCV valve and hose
- EVAP purge solenoid, KS, MAP sensor, main coil & fuel injector electrical connectors
- Harness to the clips on the ignition coil bracket
- Main coil, ETC, fuel injector electrical connectors
- Harness to the clips on the ignition coil bracket
- Alternator electrical connector
- MAF/IAT sensor connector
- Wire harness to the clip on the cylinder head
- A/C compressor switch electrical connector
- Air cleaner outlet duct
- Fuel fill cap
- Negative battery cable
6. Refill the engine cooling system.

FUEL TANK

REMOVAL & INSTALLATION

See Figures 194 through 196.

1. Before servicing the vehicle, refer to the precautions in the beginning of this section.
2. Relieve the fuel system pressure.
3. Disconnect the negative battery cable.
4. Raise and safely support the vehicle securely on jackstands.
5. Remove the 2 mounting bolts from

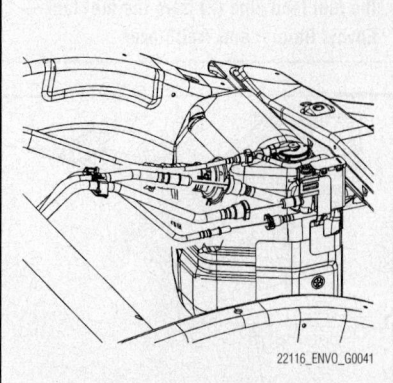

Fig. 194 Disconnect the EVAP canister fresh air pipe, EVAP canister solenoid pipe and EVAP purge pipe from the fuel tank

the frame brace and remove the frame brace from the frame.

6. Remove the fuel tank shield to the frame retaining bolts and nut, then remove the fuel tank shield from the frame.

7. Drain the fuel tank as follows:

   a. Loosen the fuel fill hose clamp.

   b. Disconnect the fuel fill hose from the fuel tank.

   c. Use a hand or air operated pump device in order to drain as much fuel from the fuel tank as possible.

8. Disconnect the evaporative emission (EVAP) canister fresh air pipe.

9. Disconnect the EVAP canister solenoid pipe.

10. Disconnect the EVAP purge pipe.

11. Disconnect the fuel filler pipe recirculation hose from the fuel tank.

12. Loosen the clamp securing the fuel fill pipe to the fuel tank.

13. Disconnect the fuel fill pipe from the fuel tank.

14. Disconnect the fuel feed pipe (2) and EVAP pipe (1) from the fuel tank.

15. Cap the fuel and EVAP pipes in order to prevent possible fuel system contamination.

16. Support the fuel tank.

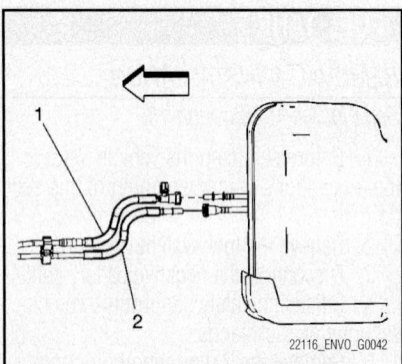

Fig. 195 Disconnect the EVAP pipe (1) and the fuel feed pipe (2) from the fuel tank—Envoy, Rainier and TrailBlazer

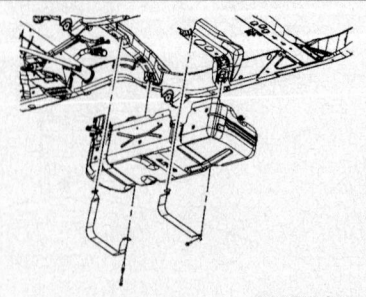

Fig. 196 Remove the fuel tank straps and carefully lower the fuel tank—Envoy, Rainier and TrailBlazer

17. Remove the fuel tank strap attaching bolts.

18. Remove the fuel tank straps.

19. Carefully lower the fuel tank.

20. Disconnect the EVAP vent valve electrical connector.

21. Disconnect the fuel tank pressure sensor electrical connector.

22. Disconnect the fuel sender electrical connector.

23. Remove the fuel tank.

24. Place the fuel tank in a suitable work area.

To install:

25. Support the fuel tank.

26. Connect the fuel sender electrical connector.

27. Connect the EVAP vent valve electrical connector.

28. Connect the fuel pressure sensor electrical connector.

29. Install the fuel tank straps.

30. Install the fuel tank strap attaching bolts and tighten to 24 ft. lbs. (32 Nm).

31. Remove the caps from the fuel and EVAP pipes.

32. Connect the fuel feed pipe (1) and the EVAP pipe (2) as follows:

   a. Apply a few drops of clean engine oil to the male connection end.

   b. Push both sides of the quick-connect fitting together in order to cause the retaining feature to snap into place.

   c. Once installed, pull on both sides of the quick-connect fitting in order to make sure the connection is secure.

33. Connect the fuel fill pipe to the fuel tank and tighten the fuel fill hose clamp to 22 inch lbs. (2.5 Nm).

34. Connect the fuel filler pipe recirculation hose to the fuel tank as follows:

   a. Apply a few drops of clean engine oil to the male connection end.

   b. Push both sides of the quick-connect fitting together in order to cause the retaining feature to snap into place.

   c. Once installed, pull on both sides of the quick-connect fitting in order to make sure the connection is secure.

35. Connect the EVAP purge pipe as follows:

   a. Apply a few drops of clean engine oil to the male connection end.

   b. Push both sides of the quick-connect fitting together in order to cause the retaining feature to snap into place.

   c. Once installed, pull on both sides of the quick-connect fitting in order to make sure the connection is secure.

36. Connect the EVAP canister solenoid pipe as follows:

   a. Apply a few drops of clean engine oil to the male connection end.

   b. Push both sides of the quick-connect fitting together in order to cause the retaining feature to snap into place.

   c. Once installed, pull on both sides of the quick-connect fitting in order to make sure the connection is secure.

37. Connect the EVAP canister fresh air pipe as follows:

   a. Apply a few drops of clean engine oil to the male connection end.

   b. Push both sides of the quick-connect fitting together in order to cause the retaining feature to snap into place.

   c. Once installed, pull on both sides of the quick-connect fitting in order to make sure the connection is secure.

38. Lower the vehicle.

39. Refill the fuel tank.

40. Install the fuel filler cap.

41. Connect the negative battery cable.

42. Raise the vehicle.

43. Inspect for leaks as follows:

   a. Turn ON the ignition, with the engine OFF for 10 seconds.

   b. Turn OFF the ignition for 10 seconds.

   c. Turn ON the ignition, with the engine OFF.

   d. Inspect for fuel leaks.

44. Install the fuel tank shield, if equipped, to the frame and tighten the retaining bolts and nut to 24 ft. lbs. (32 Nm).

45. Install the frame brace to the frame using the 2 mounting bolts and tighten to 37 ft. lbs. (50 Nm).

46. Lower the vehicle.

IDLE SPEED

ADJUSTMENT

Idle speed is maintained by the Engine Control Module (ECM). No adjustment is necessary or possible.

THROTTLE BODY

REMOVAL & INSTALLATION

4.2L Engine

See Figure 197.

1. Before servicing the vehicle, refer to the precautions in the beginning of this section.

2. Remove the resonator assembly.

3. Remove the evaporative emission

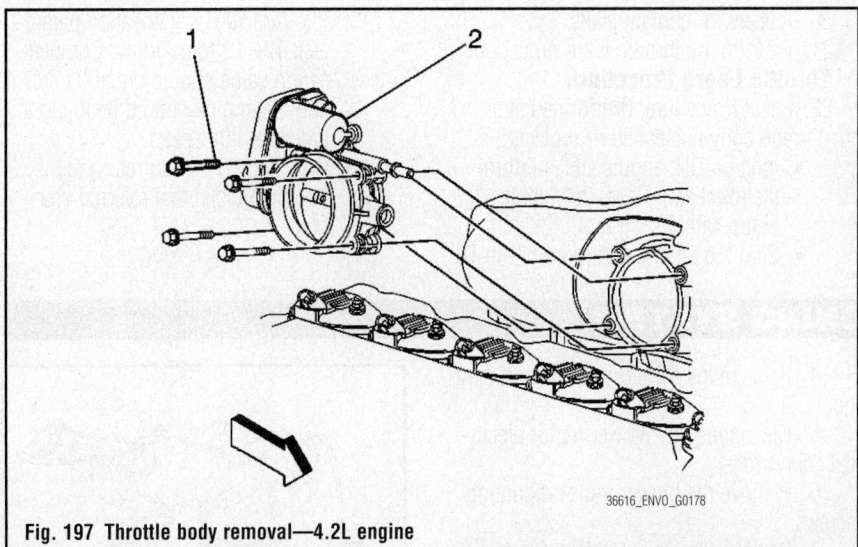

Fig. 197 Throttle body removal—4.2L engine

(EVAP) canister purge line from the throttle body.

4. Disconnect the throttle body electrical connector.

5. Remove the throttle body assembly retaining bolts.

6. Remove the throttle body assembly and the gasket from the intake manifold.

To install:

7. Clean the gasket surface.

8. Install the throttle body assembly to the intake manifold with the gasket.

9. Add sealer GM P/N 12346004 (Canadian P/N 10953480) to the throttle control module bolt threads.

10. Install the throttle body assembly retaining bolts and tighten to 89 inch. lbs. (10 Nm).

11. Connect the throttle body electrical connector.

12. Install the EVAP canister purge line to the throttle body.

13. Install the resonator assembly.

To install:

14. Install the throttle body assembly to the intake manifold with the gasket.

15. Add sealer GM P/N 12346004 (Canadian P/N 10953480) to the throttle control module bolt threads.

16. Install the throttle body assembly retaining bolts. Tighten the bolts to 89 inch lbs. (10 Nm).

17. Connect the throttle body electrical connector.

18. Install the EVAP canister purge line to the throttle body.

19. Install the resonator assembly.

5.3L and 6.0L Engines

See Figure 198.

> ❉❉ **WARNING**
>
> **Handle the electronic throttle control components carefully. Use cleanliness in order to prevent damage. Do not drop the electronic throttle control components. Do not roughly handle the electronic throttle control components. Do not immerse the electronic throttle control components in cleaning solvents of any type.**

> ❉❉ **WARNING**
>
> **DO NOT for any reason, insert a screwdriver or other small hand tools into the throttle body to hold open the throttle plate, as the throttle body could be damaged.**

➡An eight digit part identification number is stamped on the throttle body casting. Refer to this number if servicing, or part replacement is required.

1. Partially drain the cooling system in order to allow the hose at the throttle body to be removed.

2. Remove the air cleaner outlet duct.

3. Disconnect the throttle actuator motor electrical connector.

4. Reposition the throttle body hose clamp.

5. Remove both of the throttle body engine coolant hoses from the throttle body.

6. Remove the throttle body bolts and nuts.

➡Do not reuse the throttle body gasket. Install a new gasket during assembly.

7. Remove the throttle body and gasket. Discard the gasket.

To install:

8. Install a NEW throttle body gasket.

9. Install the throttle body.

10. Install the throttle body bolts and nuts. Tighten the bolts and nuts to 53 inch lbs. (6 Nm).

11. Connect the 2 throttle body engine coolant hoses to the throttle body.

12. Position the throttle body hose clamps.

13. Connect the throttle actuator motor electrical connector.

14. Install the air cleaner outlet duct.

15. Refill the cooling system.

16. Verify that the vehicle meets the following conditions:

a. The vehicle is not in a reduced engine power mode.

b. The ignition is **ON**.

c. The engine is OFF.

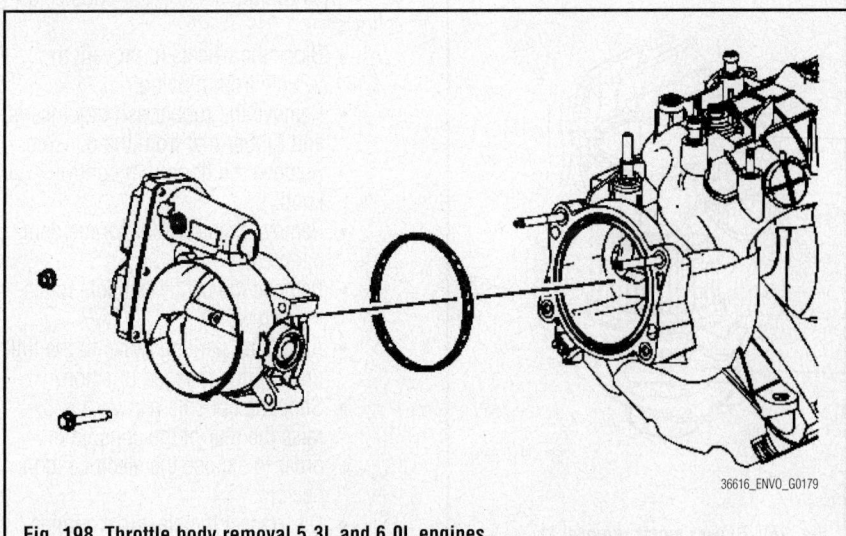

Fig. 198 Throttle body removal 5.3L and 6.0L engines

17. Connect a scan tool in order to test for a proper throttle-opening and throttle-closing range.

18. Operate the accelerator pedal and monitor the throttle angles. The accelerator pedal should operate freely, without binding, between a closed throttle, and a wide open throttle (WOT).

19. Start the engine.

20. Inspect for coolant leaks.
21. Perform the throttle learn procedure.

Throttle Learn Procedure

22. Reset Procedure: (Performed after the throttle body is cleaned or replaced)
 • Ignition ON, engine OFF, perform the Idle Learn Reset in Module Setup with a scan tool.
 • Start the engine and monitor the TB

Idle Airflow Compensation parameter. The TB Idle Airflow Compensation value should equal 0 percent and the engine should be idling at a normal idle speed.
 • Clear the DTCs and return to the diagnostic that referred you here.

HEATING & AIR CONDITIONING SYSTEM

BLOWER MOTOR

REMOVAL & INSTALLATION

See Figures 199 and 200.

1. Before servicing the vehicle, refer to the precautions section.
2. Disconnect the negative battery cable.
3. Remove the right closeout/insulator panel.

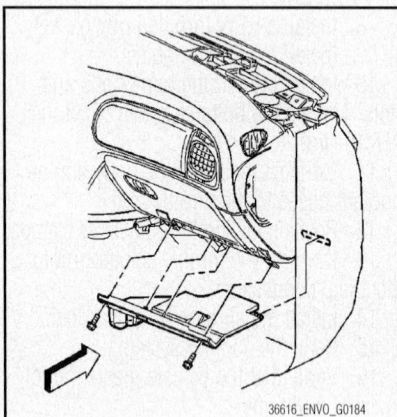

Fig. 199 Right closeout/insulator panel removal

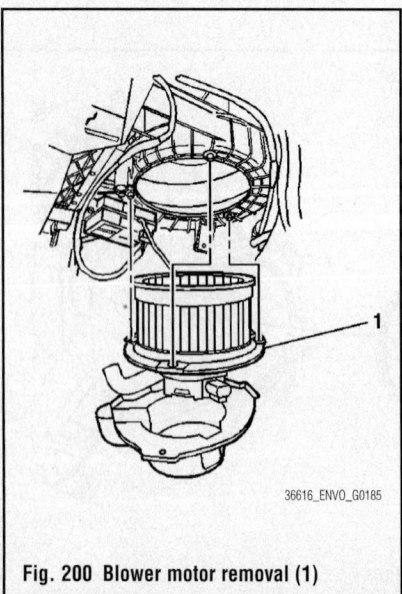

Fig. 200 Blower motor removal (1)

4. Remove the I/P storage compartment door.
5. Disconnect the blower motor electrical connector.
6. Remove the blower motor mounting screws.
7. Remove the blower motor cooling tube.
8. Remove the blower motor.

To install:

9. Install the blower motor.
10. Install the blower motor cooling tube.
11. Install the blower motor mounting screws and tighten to 18 inch lbs. (2 Nm).
12. Connect the blower motor electrical connector.
13. Install the right closeout/insulator panel.
14. Connect the negative battery cable.

HEATER CORE

REMOVAL & INSTALLATION

See Figures 201 through 209.

1. Before servicing the vehicle, refer to the precautions section.
2. Drain the engine coolant.
3. Recover the refrigerant.
4. Remove the center floor console as follows:
 • Block the wheels to prevent the vehicle from moving.
 • Remove the rubber ash tray inserts and rubber mat from the console.
 • Remove the floor shift control knob.
 • Remove the console storage compartment.
 • Remove the center console retaining screws.
 • Adjust the parking brake to the full-up, or fully engaged position.
 • Slide the console rearward and raise the rear of the console in order to expose the electrical connectors.
 • Disconnect the electrical connectors, as necessary.

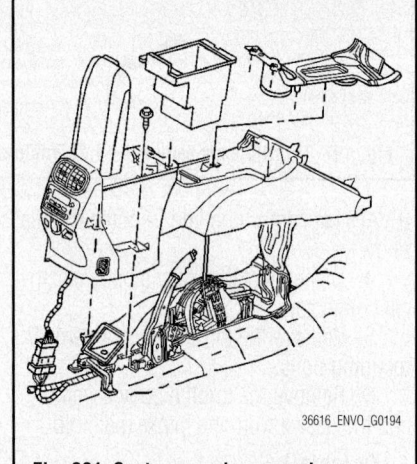

Fig. 201 Center console removal

 • Adjust the parking brake to approximately the halfway position.
 • Remove the center console from the vehicle.

✳✳ CAUTION

When performing service on or near the SIR components or the SIR wiring, the SIR system must be disabled. Failure to observe the correct procedure could cause deployment of the SIR components. Serious injury can occur. Failure to observe the correct procedure could also result in unnecessary SIR system repairs.

5. Remove the instrument panel assembly as follows:
 • Disable the SIR system.
 • Remove the left closeout/insulator panel.
 • Remove the knee bolster trim panel.
 • Remove the knee bolster.
 • Remove the left HVAC push pin.
 • Remove the left HVAC floor duct.
 • Fully lower the steering column.
 • Remove the instrument panel (I/P) lower sound insulator panel, GMC or Chevrolet only.
 • Remove the I/P accessory trim plate, GMC only.

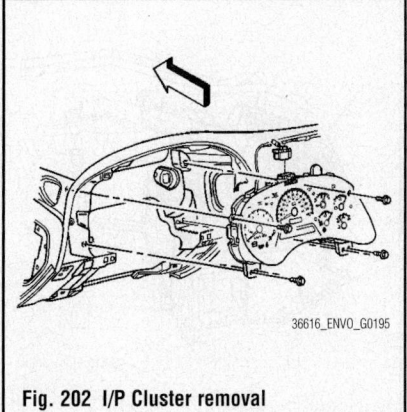

Fig. 202 I/P Cluster removal

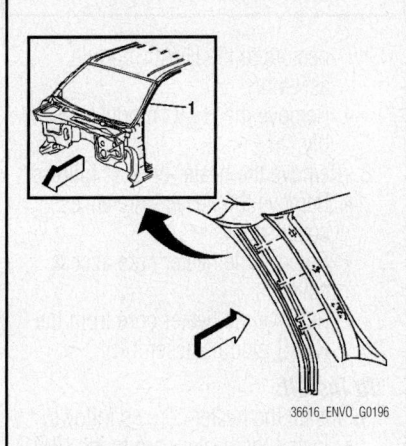

Fig. 203 Windshield garnish molding removal

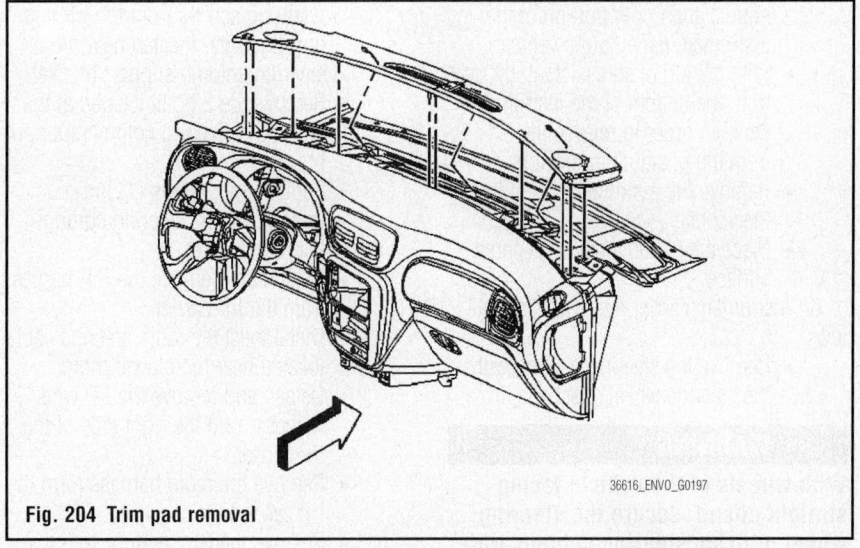

Fig. 204 Trim pad removal

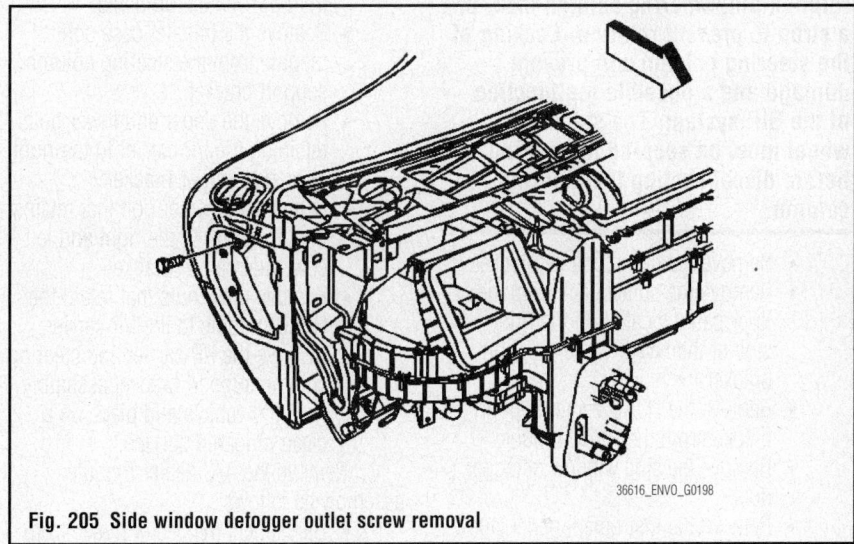

Fig. 205 Side window defogger outlet screw removal

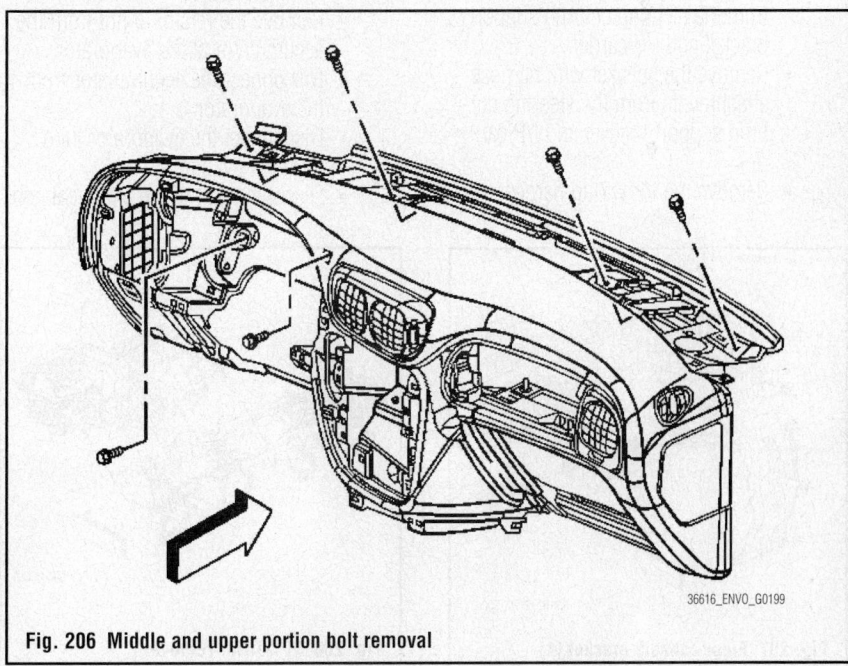

Fig. 206 Middle and upper portion bolt removal

- Remove the I/P cluster bezel, Chevrolet only.
- Remove the I/P cluster.
- Remove the right closeout/insulator panel.
- Remove the I/P storage compartment door.
- Remove the radio.
- Remove the HVAC control module.
- Remove the HVAC control module wire harness attachment from the I/P substrate.
- Remove the left I/P access cover.
- Remove the headlamp switch.
- Remove the windshield garnish moldings.
- Remove the trim pad.
- Remove the front upper speakers, if equipped.
- Remove the right I/P access cover.
- Remove the side window defogger outlet screw.
- Remove the bolts securing the lower portion of the instrument panel to the vehicle.
- Remove the bolts that secure the

middle and upper portion of the instrument panel to the vehicle.
- With the aid of an assistant, lift up from the bottom of the instrument panel in order to release the I/P from the positioning locators.
- Remove the instrument panel from the vehicle.
- Place the I/P on a clean prepared surface.

6. Instrument carrier removal is as follows:
- Remove the steering column with the steering wheel attached.

✳✳ WARNING

With wheels of the vehicle facing straight ahead, secure the steering wheel utilizing steering column anti-rotation pin, steering column lock, or a strap to prevent rotation. Locking of the steering column will prevent damage and a possible malfunction of the SIR system. The steering wheel must be secured in position before disconnecting the steering column.

- Remove the floor console bracket.
- Remove the splice pack from the floor panel located on the right side of the HVAC center support bracket.
- Remove the HVAC center support bracket from the HVAC module.
- Remove the side window defogger duct.
- Remove the instrument panel cluster (IPC) wire harness attachments from the steering column support bracket and I/P carrier.
- Remove the speaker wire harness attachments from the steering column support bracket and I/P carrier.
- Remove the I/P wiring harness

retaining screws from the I/P support brackets, located near the steering column support bracket.
- Remove the 2 bolts located at the top of the steering column support bracket.
- Remove the 2 bolts (1) located underneath the steering column support bracket.
- Detach and remove the SIR harness from the I/P carrier.
- Disconnect the radio antenna cable located near the blower motor.
- Detach and remove the I/P wire harness from the right side of the I/P carrier.
- Remove the radio harness form the I/P carrier.
- Remove the temperature sensors from the ventilation ducts.
- Remove the transfer case control module from the steering column support bracket.
- Remove the upper and lower bolts retaining the I/P carrier to the right cowl side carrier bracket.
- Remove the center bolt that retains the I/P carrier to the right and left cowl side carrier bracket.
- Remove the 6 nuts that retain the HVAC module to the I/P carrier.
- Remove the I/P carrier and steering column support bracket assembly from the vehicle and place on a clean prepared surface.

7. Remove the A/C heater module assembly as follows:
- Disconnect the heater hoses from the heater core.
- Remove the retaining nut from the accumulator at the evaporator.
- Disconnect the accumulator from the evaporator.
- Disconnect the evaporator tube from the evaporator.
- Disconnect all of the electrical con-

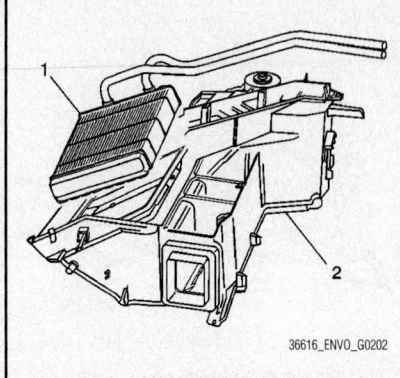

Fig. 209 Heater core (1) removal from the HVAC module assembly (2)

nectors to the HVAC module assembly.
- Remove the HVAC module assembly.

8. Remove the heater core as follows:
- Remove the heater core access cover screws.
- Remove the heater core access cover.
- Remove the heater core from the HVAC module assembly.

To install:

9. Install the heater core as follows:
- Install the heater core to the HVAC module assembly.
- Install the heater core access cover and tighten the screws to 17 inch. lbs. (2 Nm).

10. Install the HVAC module assembly as follows:
- With the help of an assistant, install the HVAC module assembly.
- Connect all of the electrical connectors to the HVAC module assembly.
- Connect the heater hoses to the heater core.
- Connect the evaporator tube to the evaporator.
- Install the accumulator to the evaporator. Tighten the accumulator retaining nut to 40 inch. lbs. (4.5 Nm).

11. Install the instrument panel carrier as follows:
- Install the I/P carrier and steering column support bracket assembly to the vehicle.
- Install the 6 nuts that retain the HVAC module to the I/P carrier. Tighten to 89 inch. lbs. (10 Nm).
- Install the center bolt retaining the steering column support bracket to the left cowl side carrier bracket.

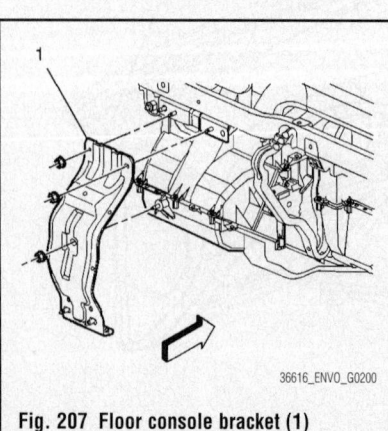

Fig. 207 Floor console bracket (1)

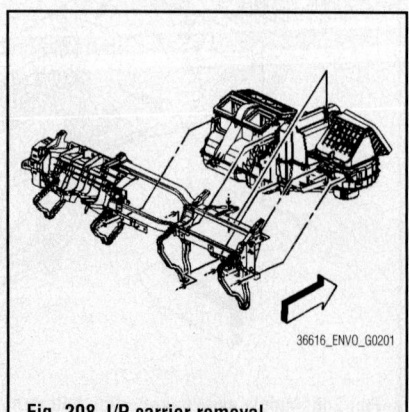

Fig. 208 I/P carrier removal

- Install the upper and lower bolts retaining the steering column support bracket to the left and right cowl side carrier bracket. Tighten the bolts to 36 ft. lbs. (50 Nm).
- Install and attach the I/P wire harness to the I/P carrier.
- Connect the radio antenna cable located near the blower motor.
- Install the SIR harness to the I/P carrier.
- Install the radio harness to the I/P carrier.
- Install the temperature sensors to the ventilation ducts.
- Install the transfer case control module to the steering column support bracket.
- Install the 2 bolts located at the top of the steering column support bracket. Tighten the bolts to 36 ft. lbs. (50 Nm).
- Install the 2 bolts located underneath the steering column support bracket. Tighten the bolts to 36 ft. lbs. (50 Nm).
- Install the I/P wire harness retaining screws to the I/P support bracket located near the steering column support bracket. Tighten the I/P wire harness screws to 22 inch. lbs. (2.5 Nm).
- Install the IPC wire harness attachments to the steering column support bracket and I/P carrier.
- Install the speaker wire harness attachments to the steering column support bracket and I/P carrier.
- Install the side window defogger duct and tighten the retaining screw to 22 inch. lbs. (2.5 Nm).
- Install the HVAC center support bracket to the HVAC module.
- Install the nuts retaining the HVAC center support bracket to the HVAC

module and tighten to 89 inch. lbs. (10 Nm).
- Install the splice pack to the floor panel. Tighten the bolts to 89 inch. lbs. (10 Nm).
- Install the steering column.

12. Install the instrument panel assembly as follows:
- With the aid of an assistant, install the instrument panel to the vehicle.

➡**Ensure the wiring harnesses and electrical connectors are not pinched behind the instrument panel and are positioned for proper connection.**

- Fully seat the instrument panel to the positioning locators.
- Install the bolts securing the middle and upper portion of the instrument panel to the vehicle. Do not tighten the I/P retaining bolts until all of the bolts have been loosely installed.
- Install the bolts that secure the lower portion of the instrument panel to the vehicle.
- Complete the installation of all of the bolts that retain the I/P to the vehicle and tighten to 62 inch. lbs. (7 Nm).
- Install the side window defogger outlet screw and tighten to 22 inch. lbs. (2.5 Nm).
- Install the right I/P access cover.
- Install the front upper speakers, if equipped.
- Install the trim pad.
- Install the windshield garnish moldings.
- Install the headlamp switch to the bezel.
- Install the left I/P access cover.
- Install the HVAC control module wire harness attachment to the I/P substrate.

- Install the HVAC control module.
- Install the radio.
- Install the I/P cluster.
- Install the I/P cluster bezel, Chevrolet only.
- Install the I/P accessory trim plate, GMC only.
- Install the I/P lower sound insulator, GMC or Chevrolet only.
- Install the I/P compartment door.
- Install the right closeout/insulator panel.
- Raise the steering column.
- Install the steering column mounting nuts and tighten to 20 ft. lbs. (27 Nm).
- Install the center console as follows:
- Position the center console to the vehicle.
- Adjust the parking brake to the full-up, or fully engaged position.
- Connect the electrical connectors, as necessary.
- Lower the rear of the console and slide the console forward into position.
- Install the center console retaining screws and tighten to 22 inch. lbs. (2.5 Nm).
- Install the console storage compartment.
- Install the floor shift control knob.
- Install the rubber ash tray inserts and rubber mat to the console.
- Remove the blocks from the vehicle.

13. Refill and bleed the cooling system.
14. Evacuate and recharge the A/C system.
15. Connect the negative battery cable.
16. Leak test the fittings.
17. Check the HVAC system for proper operation.

AUXILIARY HEATING & AIR CONDITIONING SYSTEM

BLOWER MOTOR

REMOVAL & INSTALLATION

See Figure 210.

1. Before servicing the vehicle, refer to the precautions section.
2. Disconnect the negative battery cable.
3. Remove the floor console.
4. Remove the instrument panel assembly.
5. Disconnect the electrical connectors from the blower motor-auxiliary.
6. Remove the air outlet duct from the auxiliary blower motor.

7. Remove the screws from the auxiliary blower motor.
8. Remove the auxiliary blower motor.

To install:

9. Install the auxiliary blower motor.
10. Install the retaining screws to the auxiliary blower motor and tighten to 89 inch. lbs. (10 Nm).
11. Install the air outlet duct to the auxiliary blower motor.
12. Connect the electrical connectors to the auxiliary blower motor.
13. Install the instrument panel assembly.
14. Install the floor console.
15. Connect the negative battery cable.

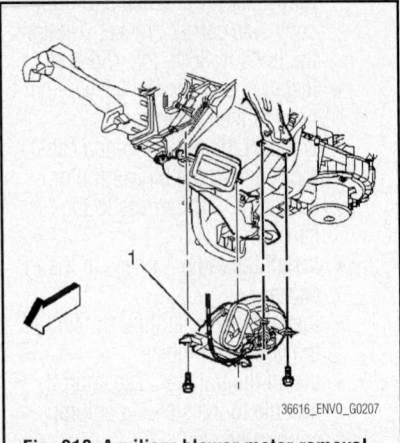

36616_ENVO_G0207

Fig. 210 Auxiliary blower motor removal

STEERING

POWER RACK & PINION STEERING GEAR

REMOVAL & INSTALLATION

See Figure 211.

1. Before servicing the vehicle, refer to the precautions section.
2. Raise and support the vehicle.
3. Position a fluid catch pan under the power steering gear.
4. Remove or disconnect the following:
   - Front tire and wheel assemblies
   - Outer tie rod retaining nuts

⁑ WARNING

Do not try to separate a steering linkage joint by driving a wedge between the joint and the attached part. Doing this can cause seal damage and premature failure of the part.

   - Outer tie rods from the steering knuckles using a suitable steering linkage and tie rod puller
   - Lower intermediate shaft retaining bolt and shaft from the power steering gear
   - Steering gear crossmember
   - Feed and return fluid hoses from the steering gear. Immediately cap or plug all openings to prevent system contamination or excessive fluid loss.
5. Support the power steering gear.
   - Power steering gear mounting bolts, then remove the gear from the vehicle
6. Loosen the outer tie rod jam nuts,

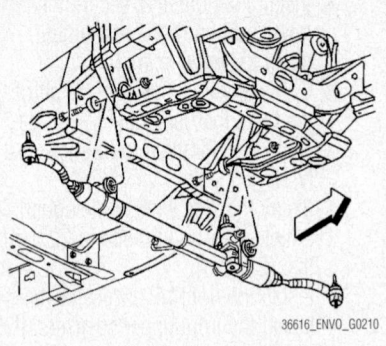

36616_ENVO_G0210

Fig. 211 Power steering gear removal

then remove the outer tie rods from the inner tie rods and discard the jam nut.

To install:

7. Lubricate the inner tie rod threads with a suitable lubricant before installing the outer tie rod.
8. Install or connect the following:
   - New jam nuts to the outer tie rods
   - Outer tie rods to the inner tie rods
   - Power steering gear to the vehicle. Tighten the retaining bolts to 81 ft. lbs. (110 Nm).
9. Remove the support from the power steering gear.
   - Power steering hose(s) to the gear. Tighten the retaining bolt to 9 ft. lbs. (12 Nm).
   - Steering gear crossmember
   - Lower intermediate shaft to the power steering gear. Tighten the retaining bolt to 30 ft. lbs. (40 Nm).
   - Outer tie rod ends to the steering

knuckles. Tighten the retaining nuts to 33 ft. lbs. (45 Nm).
   - Front tire and wheel assemblies
10. Remove the drain pan, then lower the vehicle.
11. Bleed the power steering system and adjust the front toe as necessary.

POWER STEERING PUMP

REMOVAL & INSTALLATION

4.2L Engine

See Figures 212 through 215.

1. Before servicing the vehicle, refer to the precautions section.
2. Remove the air cleaner assembly.
3. Remove the drive belt.
4. Install a drain pan under the vehicle.

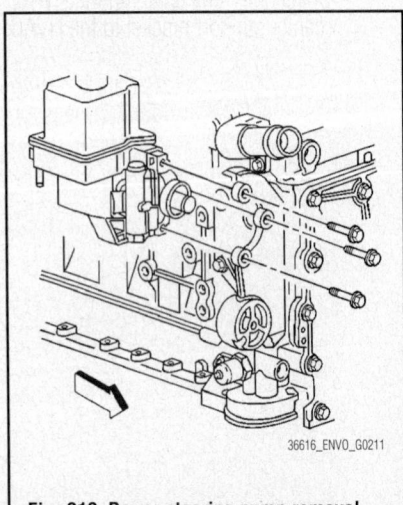

36616_ENVO_G0211

Fig. 212 Power steering pump removal

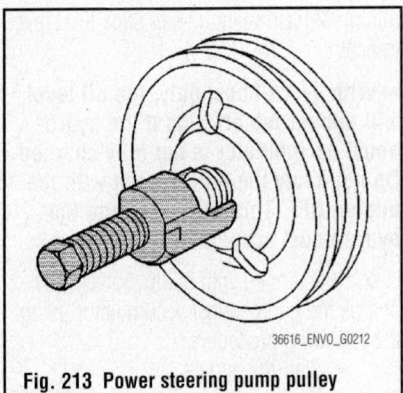

Fig. 213 Power steering pump pulley removal

5. Disconnect the power steering pressure hose from the power steering pump.

6. Disconnect the power steering cooler hose from the power steering pump.

7. Disconnect the wiring harness from the wiring loom on the power steering pump.

8. Remove the power steering pump mounting bolts.

9. Remove the power steering pump.

10. Remove the power steering pump pulley.

11. Remove the power steering pump pulley using Power Steering Pump Pulley Remover tool no. J 25034-C, or equivalent.

To install:

12. Install the power steering pump pulley, as follows:
- Install the power steering pump pulley to the end of the power steering pump shaft.
- Install the power steering pump pulley to the power steering pump using Power Steering Pump Pulley Installer tool no. J 25033-C, or equivalent.
- Install the power steering pump

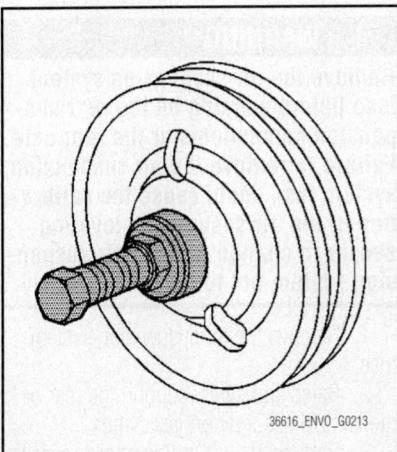

Fig. 214 Installer tool no. J 25033-C

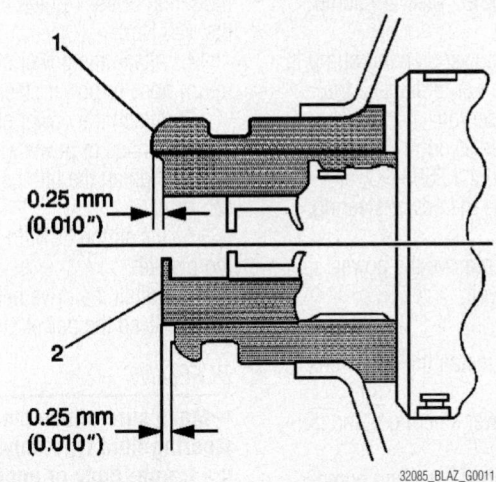

Fig. 215 Install the power steering pump pulley (1) flush against the end of the power steering pump shaft (2), with an allowable variance of 0.010 in. (0.25mm)

pulley (1) flush against the end of the power steering pump shaft (2), with an allowable variance of 0.010 in. (0.25mm).

13. Install the power steering pump.

14. Install the power steering pump mounting bolts. Tighten the power steering pump mounting bolts to 18 ft. lbs. (25 Nm).

15. Install the power steering cooler hose to the power steering pump.

16. Install the power steering pressure hose to the power steering pump. Tighten the power steering pressure hose to 18 ft. lbs. (25 Nm).

17. Remove the drain pan from under the vehicle.

18. Install the drive belt.

19. Install the air cleaner assembly.

20. Bleed the power steering system.

21. Inspect the power steering system for leaks and the hoses for clearance away from the frame and other components.

5.3L and 6.0L Engines

See Figure 215 and 216.

1. Before servicing the vehicle, refer to the precautions section.

2. Remove the drive belt.

3. Remove the Engine Control Module (ECM) from the ECM mounting bracket and move to the side.

4. Remove the power steering pressure hose from power steering pump.

5. Remove the power steering pump return hose from power steering pump.

6. Remove the power steering pump mounting bolts.

7. Remove the power steering pump.

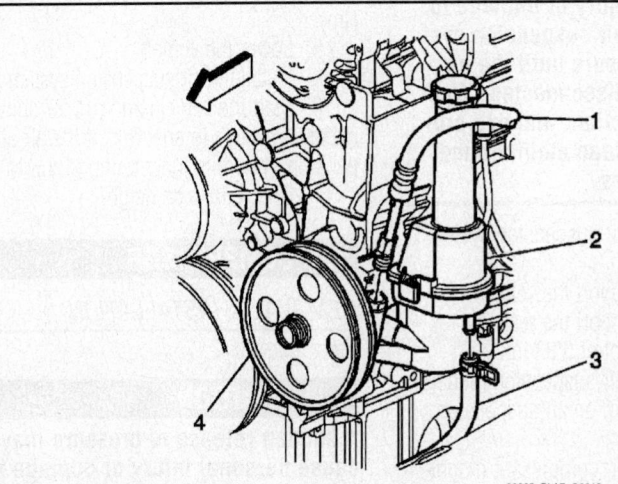

Fig. 216 Remove the power steering pressure hose (1) and return hose (3) from power steering pump (2)

8. Remove the power steering pump pulley, as follows:

a. Secure the power steering pump in a vise, taking care not to damage the power steering reservoir.

b. Using Power Steering Pump Pulley Removal Tool J 25034-C, or equivalent, remove the power steering pump pulley.

9. If applicable, remove the power steering pump reservoir.

To install:

10. If applicable, install the power steering pump reservoir.

11. Install the power steering pump pulley, as follows:

a. Install the power steering pump pulley to the end of the power steering pump shaft.

b. Install the power steering pump pulley to the power steering pump using Power Steering Pump Pulley Installer tool no. J 25033-C, or equivalent.

c. Install the power steering pump pulley (1) flush against the end of the power steering pump shaft (2), with an allowable variance of 0.010 in. (0.25mm).

12. Align the power steering pump with mounting bolt holes on engine block.

13. Install the power steering pump mounting bolts. Tighten the bolts to 18 ft. lbs. (25 Nm).

14. Attach the power steering pump return hose to power steering pump.

15. Attach the power steering pump pressure hose to power steering pump.

16. Tighten the fittings to 18 ft. lbs. (25 Nm).

17. Install the ECM to the ECM mounting bracket.

18. Install the drive belt.

19. Bleed the power steering system.

BLEEDING

➡Make sure to use clean, new power steering fluid type only. Hoses touching the frame, body or engine may cause system noise. Verify that the hoses do not touch any other part of the vehicle. Loose connections may not leak, but could allow air into the steering system. Verify that all hose connections are tight.

✻✻ WARNING

Power steering fluid level must be maintained throughout bleed procedure.

1. Fill pump reservoir with fluid to minimum system level, FULL COLD level, or middle of hash mark on cap stick fluid level indicator.

➡With hydro-boost only, the oil level will appear falsely high if the hydro-boost accumulator is not fully charged. Do not apply the brake pedal with the engine OFF. This will discharge the hydro-boost accumulator.

2. If equipped with hydro-boost, fully charge the hydro-boost accumulator using the following procedure:
   - Start the engine.
   - Firmly apply the brake pedal 10-15 times.
   - Turn the engine OFF.

3. Raise the vehicle until the front wheels are off the ground.

4. Key on engine OFF, turn the steering wheel from stop to stop 12 times. Vehicles equipped with hydro-boost systems or longer length power steering hoses may require turns up to 15 to 20 stop to stops.

5. Verify power steering fluid level per operating specification.

6. Start the engine. Rotate steering wheel from left to right. Check for sign of cavitation or fluid aeration (pump noise/whining).

7. Verify the fluid level. Repeat the bleed procedure, if necessary.

SUSPENSION

DEPRESSURIZING

PROCEDURE

✻✻ CAUTION

A sudden release of pressure may cause personal injury or damage to the vehicle. The air suspension system is under pressure until the air supply lines are disconnected. Wear gloves, ear protection, and eye protection. Wrap a clean cloth around the air supply lines.

1. Remove the air suspension system fuse.

2. Raise and support the vehicle.

3. Raise and support the rear axle at the designed height of 5.33 in. (135.4mm) on non-air suspension models or 6.12 in. (155.4mm) on air suspension models.

4. Remove the air compressor mounting bolts from the frame and support air compressor.

5. Loosen both of the air supply line connections at the air compressor in order to depressurize the air springs.

6. To pressurize the system, tighten the air supply lines to the air compressor to 20 inch lbs. (2.25 Nm).

7. Install the air compressor to frame mounting bolts and tighten to 15 ft. lbs. (20 Nm).

8. Lower the vehicle.

9. Install the air suspension system fuse.

10. Start the vehicle and run for approximately 1 minute to ensure that the air suspension system is functioning properly.

11. Check the axle height.

AIR COMPRESSOR

REMOVAL & INSTALLATION
See Figure 217.

✻✻ CAUTION

A sudden release of pressure may cause personal injury or damage to the vehicle. The air suspension system is under pressure until the air supply lines are disconnected. Use

AIR SUSPENSION

the following precautions when servicing the air suspension system: Wear gloves, ear protection, and eye protection. Wrap a clean cloth around the air supply lines.

➡Depressurize the air suspension system only after the rear axle is supported and is set between D- Height and Full Jounce.

✻✻ WARNING

Remove the air suspension system fuse before working on the rear suspension components or the rear axle. Failure to remove the air suspension system fuse could cause the calibration of the air suspension leveling sensor to change and the air suspension system not to function properly.

1. Remove the air suspension system fuse.

2. Raise and safely support the rear of the vehicle securely on jackstands.

3. Remove the air spring compressor to the frame mounting bolts.

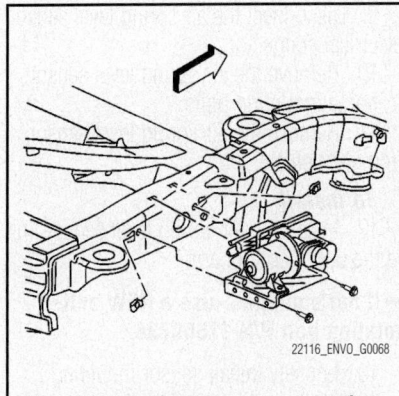

Fig. 217 Air spring compressor mounting

4. Disconnect the air inflator switch electrical connection, air supply lines, and air spring compressor vent hose from the air spring compressor.

5. Disconnect the air spring compressor electrical connection.

➡Ensure the color on air supply lines match the color on the air spring compressor for reassembly.

6. Disconnect the air supply lines from the air spring compressor.

7. Remove the air spring compressor from the vehicle.

To install:

✷✷ WARNING

Inspect the air supply lines for deep scores or cuts. If the air supply lines are damaged, the lines must be replaced. Ensure the color on the air supply lines match the color on the air spring compressor for reassembly.

8. If no damage to the air supply pipes is evident, then remove the fittings from the new compressor and use existing fittings that are already attached to air supply lines. Install the air supply lines with existing fittings to the air spring compressor and tighten the fittings to 20 inch lbs. (2.25 Nm).

9. If damage is evident to the air supply lines, then replace the air supply lines.

10. Connect the air spring compressor electrical connection.

11. Connect the air inflator switch electrical connection, air supply line, and air spring compressor vent hose to the air spring compressor.

12. Install the air spring compressor to the frame mounting bolts and tighten the bolts to 15 ft. lbs. (20 Nm).

13. Lower the vehicle.

14. Install the air suspension system fuse.

15. Start the vehicle and run for approximately 1 minute to ensure that the air spring leveling system is functioning properly.

16. Inspect the designed D - height to measure 5.17–5.49 inches (131.4–139.4mm).

17. Inspect for leaks. If a leak is found at the air supply lines connections at the air spring compressor, replace the air supply lines.

AIR SPRING

REMOVAL & INSTALLATION
See Figures 218 and 219.

✷✷ CAUTION

A sudden release of pressure may cause personal injury or damage to the vehicle. The air suspension system is under pressure until the air supply lines are disconnected. Use the following precautions when servicing the air suspension system: Wear gloves, ear protection, and eye protection. Wrap a clean cloth around the air supply lines.

1. Before servicing the vehicle, refer to the precautions section.

2. Depressurize the air suspension system.

➡There is a raised feature on the outer rim of the air spring top plate that denotes the anti-rotation peg position.

3. Depress the anti-rotation peg in the air spring top plate located in the upper spring seat.

4. With the anti rotation peg depressed, rotate the air spring counterclockwise and remove the air spring from the upper spring seat.

5. Disconnect the air supply line from the air spring in the following way:
   - Push the air supply line into the air spring connection and hold in place.
   - Depress and hold the air supply line collet down.
   - Remove the air supply line from the air spring.

6. Remove the air spring.

To install:

7. Install the air supply line to the air spring. Ensure the air supply line is fully seated.

✷✷ CAUTION

Ensure that the air spring is fully seated and properly positioned on the axle pilot. Failure to properly position the air spring may cause the air spring to break apart, possibly resulting in personal injury or damage to the vehicle.

8. Install the air spring (2) to the frame by aligning the mounting tabs (3) with the keyhole slots (1) in the upper spring seat.

9. Apply upward pressure to the air spring and rotate clockwise until the anti-rotation peg snaps into place.

10. Lower the vehicle slightly below the correct D-height position.

11. Install the air suspension system fuse.

12. Turn ON the ignition, engine OFF. Allow the air suspension compressor to run for approximately 1 minute to ensure that the air suspension is functioning properly.

➡When the air springs are completely deflated, an additional ignition cycle may be required to allow the compressor to completely inflate the air springs.

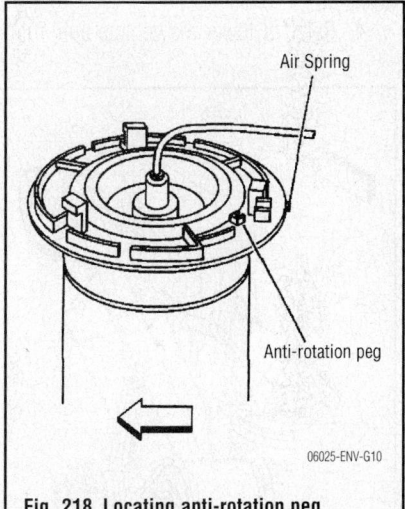

Fig. 218 Locating anti-rotation peg in air spring

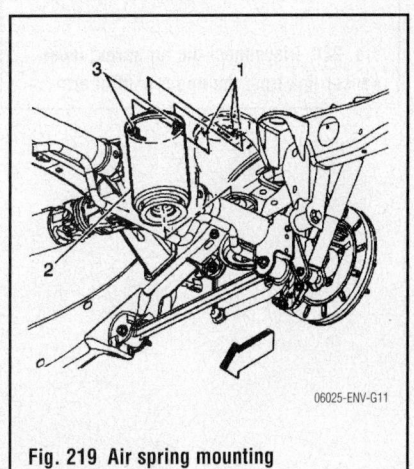

Fig. 219 Air spring mounting

13. Inspect the D—height to measure 5.17–5.49 inches (131.4–139.4mm).

AIR SPRING LEVELING SENSOR

REMOVAL & INSTALLATION

See Figures 220 through 222.

✳✳ CAUTION

A sudden release of pressure may cause personal injury or damage to the vehicle. The air suspension system is under pressure until the air supply lines are disconnected. Use the following precautions when servicing the air suspension system: Wear gloves, ear protection, and eye protection. Wrap a clean cloth around the air supply lines.

1. Before servicing the vehicle, refer to the precautions section.
2. Raise and support the vehicle.
3. Remove the rear wheels and lower the vehicle with the rear axle supported by jackstands.
4. Raise or lower the vehicle until the

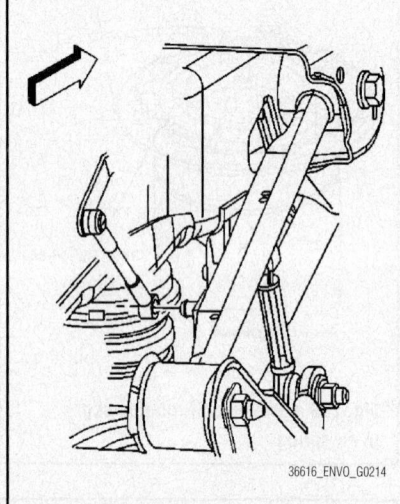

Fig. 220 Disconnect the air spring level sensor link from the upper control arm

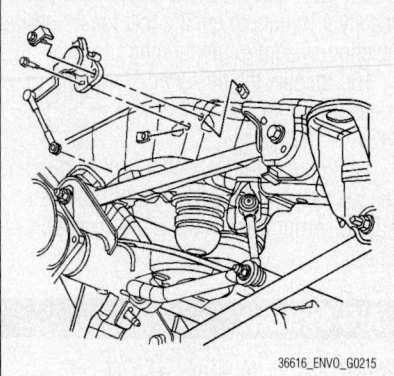

36616_ENVO_G0215

Fig. 221 Air spring level sensor removal

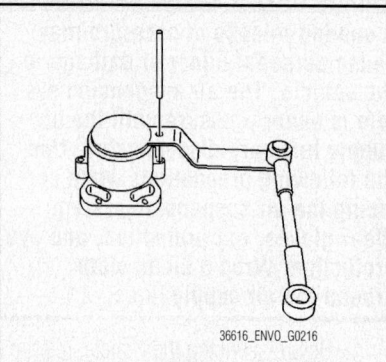

36616_ENVO_G0216

Fig. 222 Verify the pin can be removed and installed with ease

D-height measurement is 1 inch. (25 mm) above the published D-height specification, 5.33 inch. (135 mm) for Trailblazer SS or 6.33 inch. (160 mm) for all other vehicles.

5. Turn the ignition key to the ON position. This will partially deflate the air spring.
6. After two minutes, turn the ignition key to the OFF position and remove the air suspension fuse.
7. Raise or lower the vehicle so that the D-height is at published specification 4.33 inch. (110 mm) for Trailblazer SS or 5.33 inch. (135 mm) for all other vehicles.
8. Disconnect the air spring level sensor link from the upper control arm.

9. Disconnect the air spring level sensor electrical connector.
10. Remove the air spring level sensor-to-frame mounting bolts.
11. Remove the air spring level sensor from the vehicle.

To install:

12. Install the air spring level sensor link to the upper control arm.

➡If not equipped, use a NEW anti-rotation bolt P/N 11569736.

13. Loosely install sensor mounting bolts with the anti-rotation bolt in the right hand mounting hole. Do not remove the air spring level sensor locating pin until the air spring level sensor has been properly mounted and aligned.
14. While holding the body of the sensor, tighten the anti-rotation bolt first.
15. Tighten the air spring level sensor frame mounting bolts to 71 inch. lbs. (8 Nm).
16. Connect the air spring level sensor electrical connector.
17. Verify the pin can be removed and installed with ease to ensure the correct sensor installation.
18. If the pin cannot be inserted with ease, loosen the sensor fasteners, adjust the sensor, and retighten the sensor fasteners so that the pin can be removed and installed with ease.
19. Remove the air spring level sensor locating pin.
20. Raise the vehicle off the jackstands and remove the stands from under the vehicle.
21. Install the rear wheels.
22. Lower the vehicle.
23. Install the air suspension fuse.
24. Turn the ignition key to the ON position to inflate the rear air springs.
25. After two minutes, turn the ignition key to the OFF position.
26. Recycle the ignition, if needed.
27. Inspect the D—height to measure 5.17–5.49 inches (131.4–139.4mm).

SUSPENSION   **FRONT SUSPENSION**

COIL SPRING

REMOVAL & INSTALLATION

See Figure 223.

➡ **This procedure requires the use of a suitable spring compressor.**

1. Before servicing the vehicle, refer to the precautions section.
2. Remove or disconnect the following:
   • Wheel
   • Shock module
   • Shock module yoke-to-shock absorber pinch bolt and nut
3. Spread the shock module yoke at the pinch bolt using a suitable flat-bladed tool.
   • Shock module yoke from the shock absorber
4. Install pieces of heater hose or equivalent material to the shock module spring where the spring compressor contacts the lower part of the spring.
5. Install the shock module into the spring compressor.

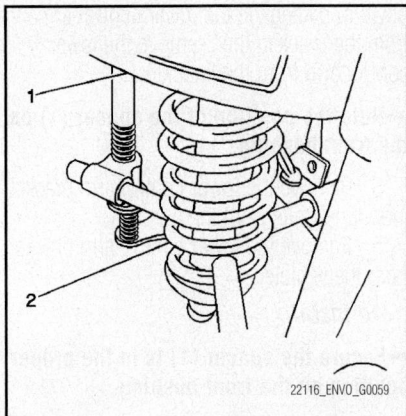

Fig. 223 Place pieces of heater hose to the spring where the compressor contacts the lower part of the spring

➡ **The spring is compressed when the shock absorber moves freely.**

6. Turn the spring compressor forcing screw until the coil spring is compressed.
7. Remove or disconnect the following:
   • Shock absorber upper retaining nut
   • Shock absorber from the shock module
8. Loosen the compressor forcing screw until the upper mounting plate and coil spring can be removed.
   • Upper mounting plate and coil spring from the spring compressor

To install:

9. Install or connect the following:
   • Coil spring and upper mounting plate to the spring compressor
10. Turn the compressor forcing screw until the coil spring is compressed.
    • Shock absorber to the shock module. Tighten the retaining nut to 33 ft. lbs. (45 Nm)
11. Remove the shock module from the spring compressor. Remove the pieces of heater hose from the spring..
    • Shock module yoke to the shock absorber
    • Shock module yoke-to-shock pinch bolt and nut and tighten to 52 ft. lbs. (70 Nm)
    • Shock module to the vehicle
    • Tire and wheel
12. Lower the vehicle

LOWER BALL JOINT

REMOVAL & INSTALLATION

See Figures 224 through 226.

Ball joint removal and installation tools are as follows:
• J 9519-E Ball joint remover and installer set
• J 34874 Booster seal remover/installer
• J 41435 Ball joint installer
• J 45105-1 Ball joint flaring adapter
• J 45105-2 Receiver

1. Before servicing the vehicle, refer to the precautions section.
2. Raise and support the vehicle.
3. Remove the tire and wheel assembly.
4. Remove the steering knuckle with wheel hub and bearing attached.
5. Remove the lower ball joint flange with a chisel.

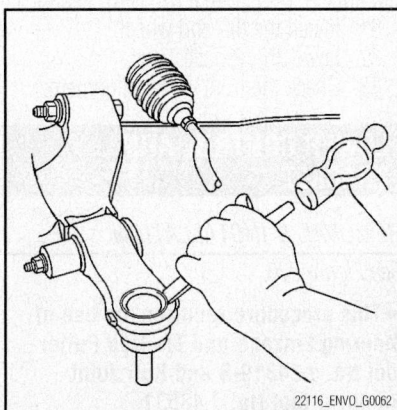

Fig. 224 Remove the lower ball joint flange with a chisel

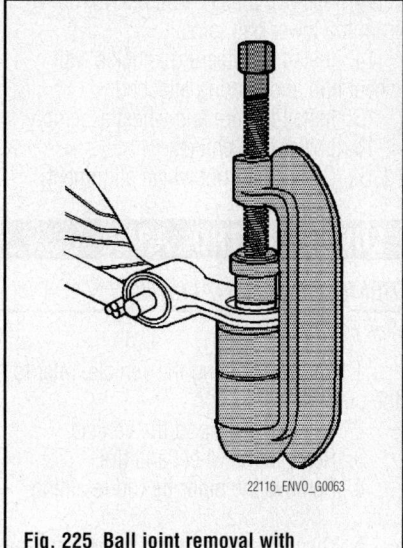

Fig. 225 Ball joint removal with tools shown

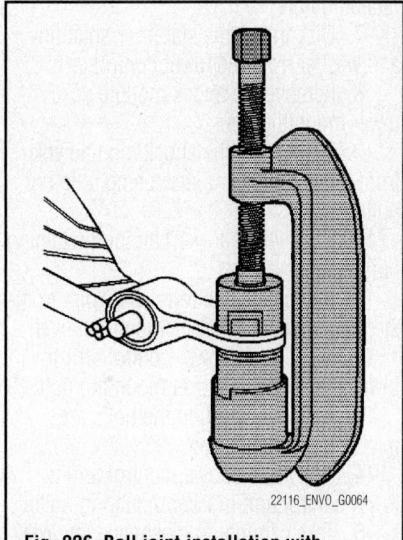

Fig. 226 Ball joint installation with tools shown

6. Install J 9519-E and J 34874 to the lower ball joint.
7. Remove the lower ball joint from the lower control arm using J 9519-E and J 34874 .

To install:

8. Install the lower ball joint and J 9519-E, J 41435, and J 45105-2 to the lower control arm.
9. Install the lower ball joint to the lower control arm using J 9519-E, J 41435, and J 45105-2.
10. Remove J 9519-E, J 41435, and J 45105-2 from the lower control arm.
11. Install J 9519-E and J 45105-1 to the lower ball joint.

12. Flare the lower ball joint flange using J 9519-E and J 45105-1.

13. Remove J 9519-E and J 45105-1 from the lower ball joint.

14. Install the steering knuckle with wheel hub and bearing attached.

15. Install the tire and wheel assembly.

16. Lower the vehicle.

17. Check the front wheel alignment.

LOWER CONTROL ARM

REMOVAL & INSTALLATION

See Figure 227.

1. Before servicing the vehicle, refer to the precautions section

2. Raise and support the vehicle.

3. Remove the wheel and tire.

4. Remove the outer tie rod retaining nut.

5. Disconnect the outer tie rod from the steering knuckle using a tie rod puller.

6. Remove the stabilizer shaft link lower retaining nut.

7. Disconnect the stabilizer shaft link and washer from the lower control arm.

8. Remove the shock module yoke lower mounting nut.

9. Disconnect the shock module yoke from the lower control arm using a tie rod puller.

10. Remove the lower ball joint retaining nut.

11. Disconnect the lower ball joint from steering knuckle using ball joint remover.

12. Remove the lower control arm-to-lower control arm bracket mounting nuts.

13. Note the direction the bolts are removed for installation.

14. Remove the lower control arm to lower control arm bracket mounting bolts.

15. Take care not to disengage the axle shaft from the transmission (4WD only).

16. Pivot the lower control arm outward and downward in order to disconnect the lower control arm from the lower control arm bracket.

17. Ensure that the spacer stays in position on the front control arm bracket front bushing.

18. Remove the lower control arm from the vehicle.

To install:

19. Position the lower control arm ball joint stud to the steering knuckle.

20. Ensure that the spacer stays in position on the front control arm bracket front bushing.

21. Pivot the lower control arm outward and upward in order to connect the lower control arm to the lower control arm bracket.

22. Install the lower control arm to lower control arm bracket mounting bolts.

➡**Ensure that the lower control arm is parallel to the lower control arm bracket during the installation and tightening of the lower control arm mounting bolts and nuts. This will ensure correct alignment of the lower control arm bushings.**

23. Install the lower control arm to lower control arm bracket mounting nuts and tighten to 96 ft. lbs. (130 Nm).

24. Connect the shock module yoke to the lower control arm.

25. Install the shock module yoke lower mounting nut and tighten to 81 ft. lbs. (110 Nm).

26. Install the lower ball joint retaining nut and tighten to 81 ft. lbs. (110 Nm).

27. Install the stabilizer shaft link and washer to the lower control arm.

28. Install the stabilizer shaft link retaining nut and tighten to 17 ft. lbs. (23 Nm).

29. Install the outer tie rod to the steering knuckle.

30. Install the outer tie rod retaining nut and tighten to 42 ft. lbs. (57 Nm).

31. Install the tire and wheel.

32. Lower the vehicle.

33. Check the front wheel alignment.

LOWER CONTROL ARM BRACKET

REMOVAL & INSTALLATION

See Figure 228.

➡**This procedure requires the use of Steering Linkage and Tie Rod Puller tool No. J 24319-B and Ball Joint Remover tool No. J 43631.**

1. Before servicing the vehicle, refer to the precautions section.

2. Raise the vehicle.

3. Remove or disconnect the following:
   • Tire and wheel
   • Outer tie rod retaining nut
   • Outer tie rod from the steering knuckle using Ball Joint Removal tool No. J 43631
   • Stabilizer shaft link lower nut, link and washer
   • Shock module yoke lower nut and shock module using Steering Linkage and Tie Rod Puller tool No. J 24319-B
   • Lower control arm-to-lower control arm bracket mounting bolts

➡**Make sure to note the direction that the bolts are removed for installation.**

   • Lower control arm-to-lower control arm bracket mounting bolts
   • Lower ball joint retaining nut
   • Lower ball joint from the steering knuckle using Ball Joint Removal tool No. J 43631

➡**On 4WD vehicles, make sure not to disengage the axle shaft from the transmission.**

4. Pivot the lower control arm out and down to disengage the lower control arm from the bracket, then remove the lower control arm from the knuckle.

➡**Note the position of the spacer (1) on the front bushing.**

5. Remove the lower control arm bracket mounting bolts from the frame.

6. Remove the lower control arm bracket from the vehicle.

To install:

➡**Ensure the spacer (1) is in the proper position on the front bushing.**

06025-ENV-G09

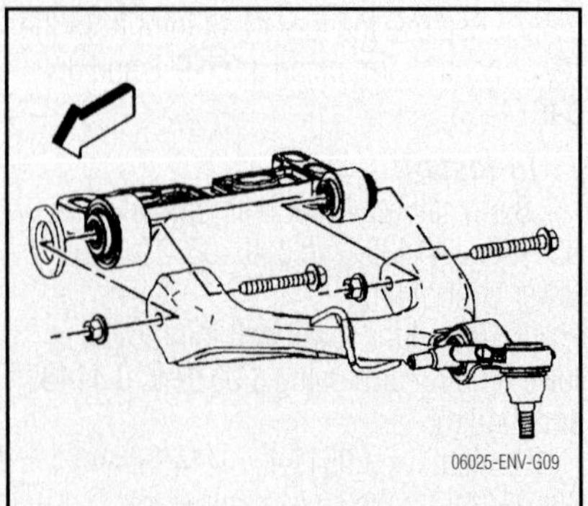

Fig. 227 Front lower control arm mounting

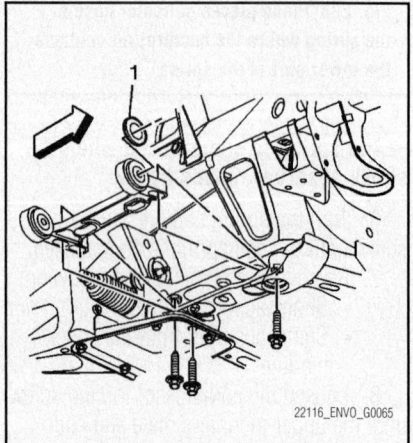

22116_ENVO_G0065

Fig. 228 Remove the lower control arm bracket from the vehicle

7. Install the lower control arm bracket to the vehicle.

8. Install the lower control arm bracket mounting bolts to the frame.
  - Tighten the front lower control arm bracket mounting bolt to 192 ft. lbs. (260 Nm).
  - Tighten the rear lower control arm bracket mounting bolts to 170 ft. lbs. (230 Nm).

9. Install or connect the following:
  - Lower control arm to the steering knuckle
  - Lower control to the bracket by pivoting it out and up

→During installation and tightening of the bolts and nuts, make sure that the lower control arm is parallel to the bracket. This is to maintain proper alignment of the lower control arm bushings.

  - Lower control arm-to-bracket mounting bolts and tighten to 81 ft. lbs. (111 Nm)
  - Shock module yoke to the lower control arm
  - Shock module yoke lower mounting nut

→If it becomes necessary to replace the washer, use only an identical hardened steel, felt lined washer. Standard washers must not be used.

  - Stabilizer shaft link and washer to the lower control arm
  - Stabilizer shaft link retaining bolt and tighten to 74 ft. lbs. (100 Nm)
  - Outer tie rod to the steering knuckle. Tighten the nuts to 33 ft. lbs. (45 Nm).
  - Tire and wheel

10. Lower the vehicle and check the front end alignment.

SHOCK ABSORBERS

REMOVAL & INSTALLATION

See Figures 229 and 230.

1. Before servicing the vehicle, refer to the precautions section.

2. Remove or disconnect the following:
  - Shock module upper retaining nuts
  - Tire and wheel
  - Shock module-to-lower control arm retaining nut
  - Shock module yoke from the lower control arm using a suitable puller
  - Shock module from the shock tower and lower control arm

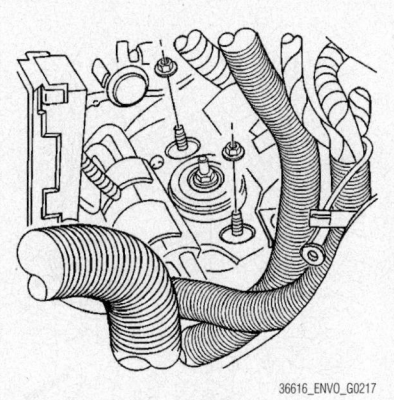

Fig. 229 View of the shock module upper retaining nuts

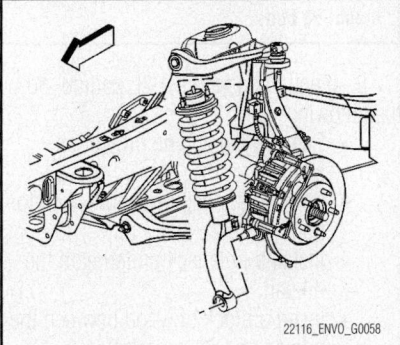

Fig. 230 View of the shock module used on the front suspension

To install:

3. Install or connect the following:
  - Shock module to the shock tower and lower control arm
  - Shock module yoke to the lower control arm
  - Shock module upper retaining nuts and tighten to 33 ft. lbs. (45 Nm)
  - Shock module-to-lower control arm retaining nut and tighten to 81 ft. lbs. (110 Nm)
  - Tire and wheel

STEERING KNUCKLE

REMOVAL & INSTALLATION

See Figures 231 through 233.

1. Before servicing the vehicle, refer to the precautions section.

2. Raise and support the vehicle.

3. Remove the tire and wheel.

4. On 4WD vehicles, remove wheel center cap, if equipped, and the drive axle nut and washer.

5. Remove the brake caliper and rotor.

6. Remove the wheel hub and bearing.

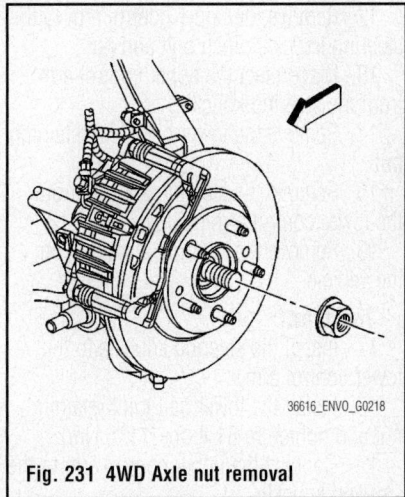

Fig. 231 4WD Axle nut removal

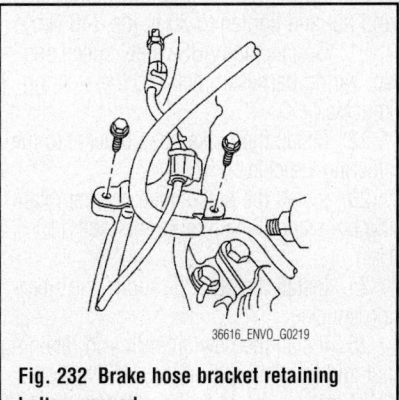

Fig. 232 Brake hose bracket retaining bolts removed

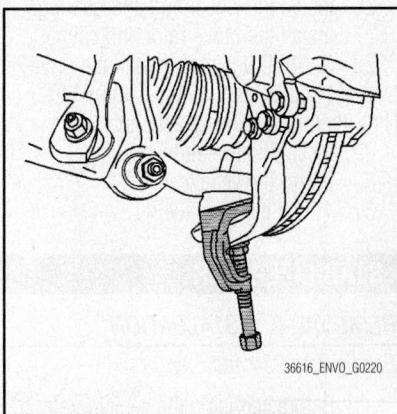

Fig. 233 Steering knuckle removal from the lower control arm using J 43631

7. Remove the outer tie rod retaining nut.

8. Disconnect the outer tie rod from the steering knuckle using a tie rod puller.

9. Remove the brake hose bracket retaining bolts.

10. Remove the brake hose bracket from the steering knuckle.

11. Disconnect the ABS wheel speed sensor wiring harness bracket from the steering knuckle.

12. Remove the upper control arm to the steering knuckle pinch bolt and nut.

13. Disconnect the upper control arm from the steering knuckle.

14. Remove the lower ball joint retaining nut.

15. Remove the steering knuckle from the lower control arm using J 43631.

16. Remove the steering knuckle from the vehicle.

To install:

17. Install the steering knuckle to the lower control arm.

18. Install the lower ball joint retaining nut and tighten to 81 ft. lbs. (110 Nm).

19. Connect the upper control arm to the steering knuckle.

20. Install upper control arm pinch bolt and nut and tighten to 30 ft. lbs. (40 Nm).

21. Connect the ABS wheel speed sensor wiring harness bracket to the steering knuckle.

22. Install the brake hose bracket to the steering knuckle.

23. Install the brake hose bracket retaining bolts and tighten to 89 inch lbs. (10 Nm).

24. Install the outer tie rod to the steering knuckle.

25. Install the new outer tie rod retaining nut and tighten to 33 ft. lbs. (45 Nm) on 2WD models, or 44 ft. lbs. (60 Nm) on 4WD models.

26. Install the wheel hub and bearing.

27. Install the brake rotor and caliper.

28. On 4WD vehicles, install the drive axle nut and tighten to 103 ft. lbs. (140 Nm), then install the center cap.

29. Install the tire and wheel.

30. Lower the vehicle.

31. Adjust the front toe.

STABILIZER BAR

REMOVAL & INSTALLATION

See Figures 234 and 235.

1. Before servicing the vehicle, refer to the precautions section.

2. Raise and support the vehicle.

3. Remove the tire and wheel assembly.

4. Remove the stabilizer shaft links to the stabilizer shaft retaining nuts.

5. Remove the stabilizer shaft insulator clamp mounting bolts.

6. Remove the stabilizer shaft insulator clamp from the stabilizer shaft insulator.

➡**Note the position of the bend in the stabilizer shaft.**

7. Remove the stabilizer shaft insulators from the stabilizer shaft.

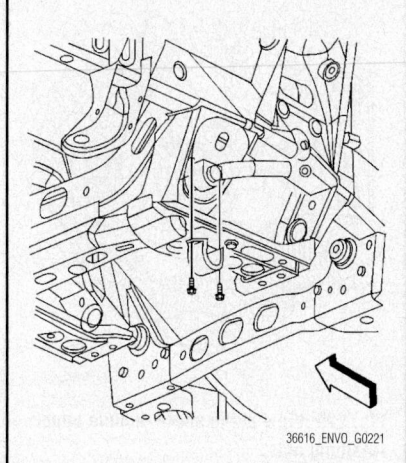

Fig. 234 Stabilizer shaft insulator clamp mounting bolts

8. If equipped with a 4.2L engine, do the following:

• Remove the engine protection shield.

• Remove the engine mount nuts-to-frame bracket.

• Install a pole jack underneath the oil pan.

• Insert a block of wood between the oil pan and the pole jack.

• Raise the engine 10 mm measuring from the bottom of the oil pan to the rear edge of the front suspension crossmember.

➡**The jack stand should only be used to support the weight of the powertrain. DO NOT lift the entire weight of the front end of the vehicle by the jack stand.**

• Remove the stabilizer shaft from the vehicle.

To install:

9. Install the stabilizer shaft to the vehicle, with the bend down and away from the engine. There may be a label on the shaft. If so, it should be on the LH side.

If equipped with a 4.2L engine, do the following:

• Lower the engine.

• Install the engine mounting nuts-to-frame bracket and tighten to 52 ft. lbs. (70 Nm).

• Remove the block of wood between the oil pan and the pole jack.

• Remove the jack stand from underneath the oil pan

• Install the engine protection shield.

10. Install the stabilizer shaft insulators to the stabilizer shaft.

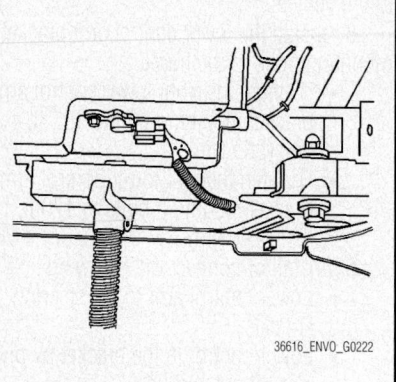

Fig. 235 Raise the engine 10 mm measuring from the bottom of the oil pan to the rear edge of the front suspension crossmember—4.2L engines only

11. Install the stabilizer shaft insulator clamp to the stabilizer shaft insulator.

12. Install the stabilizer shaft insulator clamp mounting bolts and tighten to 41 ft. lbs. (55 Nm).

13. Install the stabilizer shaft links to the stabilizer shaft and tighten to 17 ft. lbs. (23 Nm).

14. Install the tire and wheel assembly.

15. Lower the vehicle.

STABILIZER LINK

REMOVAL & INSTALLATION

See Figure 236.

1. Before servicing the vehicle, refer to the precautions section.

2. Raise and support the vehicle.

3. Remove the tire and wheel assembly.

4. Remove any dirt or debris from the threads of the stabilizer link bolt.

5. Use the proper size wrench or socket to hold the stabilizer bolt while removing the stabilizer shaft nut.

6. Remove the washer and the insulator from the stabilizer shaft link bolt.

7. Remove the stabilizer shaft link bolt, washer and the insulator.

8. Remove the insulators, and spacer.

To install:

9. Install the washer and the insulator on the stabilizer shaft link bolt.

10. Position the insulators, and spacer between the stabilizer shaft and the lower control arm.

11. Install the stabilizer shaft link bolt, washer and the insulator.

12. Install the insulator and the washer.

13. Install the stabilizer shaft link nut and tighten to 17 ft. lbs. (23 Nm).

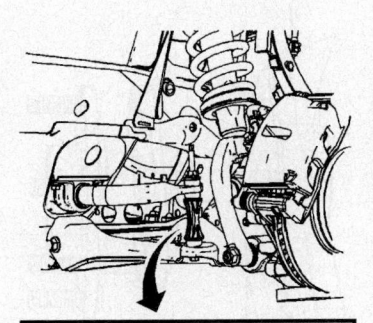

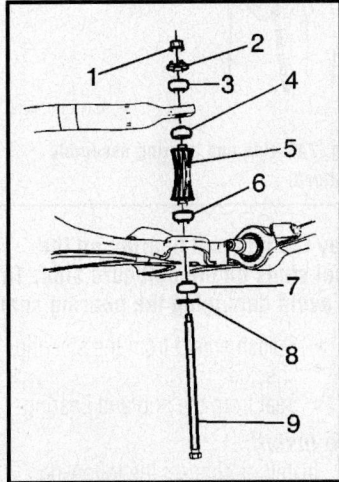

1. Stabilizer shaft nut
2. Washer
3. Insulator
4. Insulator
5. Spacer
6. Insulator
7. Insulator
8. Washer
9. Stabilizer shaft link bolt

36616_ENVO_G0223

Fig. 236 Stabilizer link component view

14. Install the tire and wheel assembly.
15. Remove the support and lower the vehicle.

UPPER BALL JOINT

REMOVAL & INSTALLATION
See Figures 237 and 238.

➡This procedure requires the use of the following special tools: J 9519-E Lower Ball Joint Remover and Installer, J 21474-01 Control Arm Bushing Set and J 45117 Ball Joint Installation Spacer.

1. Raise and safely support the front of the vehicle securely on jackstands.
2. Remove the tire and wheel assembly.
3. Remove the steering knuckle with wheel hub attached.

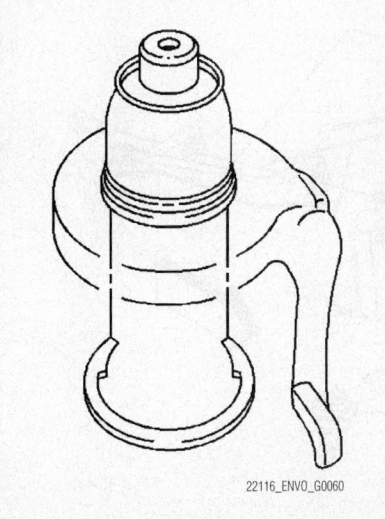

22116_ENVO_G0060

Fig. 237 Remove the upper ball joint boot

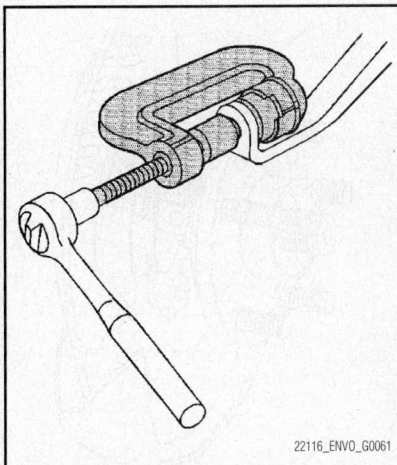

22116_ENVO_G0061

Fig. 238 Remove the upper ball joint from the steering knuckle using J-9519-E

4. Remove the upper ball joint retaining clip.
5. Remove the upper ball joint boot.
6. Remove the upper ball joint from the steering knuckle using J-9519-E.

To install:
7. Install the upper ball joint to steering knuckle using J-9519-E, J-21474-01, and J-45117 .
8. Install the upper ball joint retaining clip.
9. Install the steering knuckle with wheel hub attached.
10. Install the tire and wheel assembly.
11. Lower the vehicle.
12. Check the front wheel alignment.

UPPER CONTROL ARM

REMOVAL & INSTALLATION
See Figures 239 through 241.

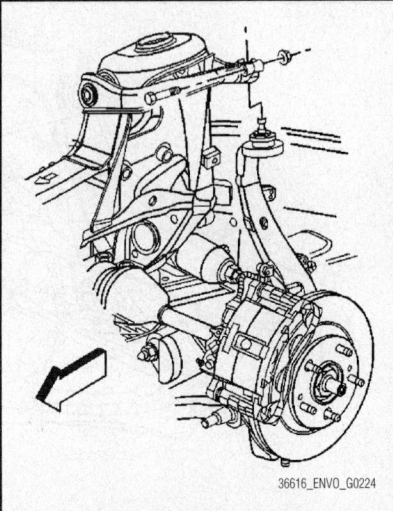

36616_ENVO_G0224

Fig. 239 Separate the upper control arm from the steering knuckle

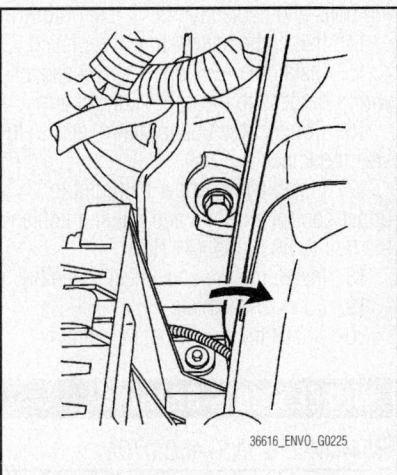

36616_ENVO_G0225

Fig. 240 Gently pry out on inner fender body panel to access forward facing bolt

1. Before servicing the vehicle, refer to the precautions section.
2. Raise and support the vehicle.
3. Remove the tire and wheel assembly.
4. Remove and discard the upper ball joint to upper control arm bolt and nut.
5. Separate the upper control arm from the steering knuckle.
6. Remove the wheel speed sensor wiring harness from the upper control arm.
7. If servicing the left upper control arm, remove the battery tray.
8. Gently pry out on inner fender body panel to access forward facing bolt.
9. Remove the upper control arm mounting bolts.
10. Remove the upper control arm.

To install:
11. Install the upper control arm.
12. Gently pry out on inner fender to access the forward facing bolt.

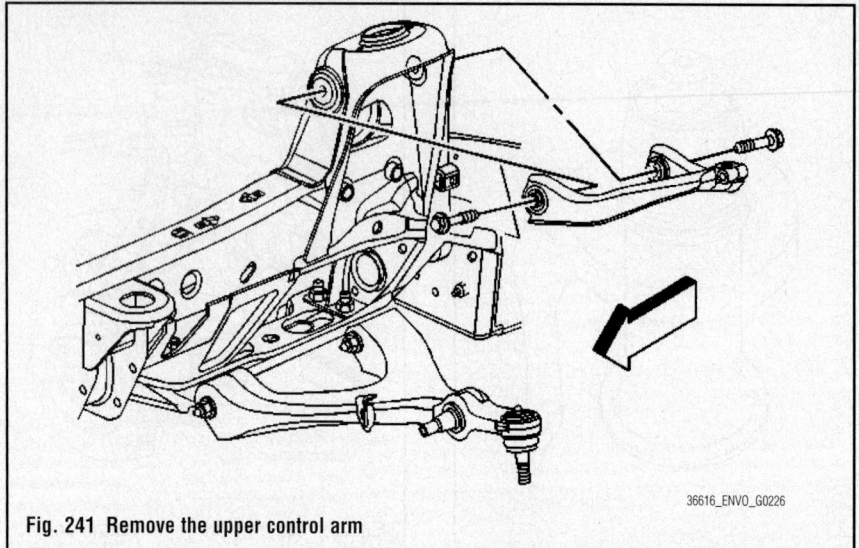

Fig. 241 Remove the upper control arm

36616_ENVO_G0226

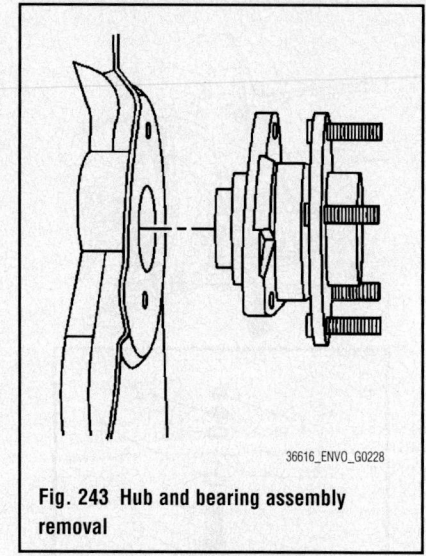

36616_ENVO_G0228

Fig. 243 Hub and bearing assembly removal

13. Install the upper control arm mounting bolts and tighten to 108 ft. lbs. (146 Nm).

14. Install the battery tray, if removed.

15. Install the ABS wheel speed sensor wiring harness to the upper control arm

16. Connect the upper control arm to the steering knuckle.

17. Install a new upper ball joint to upper control arm bolt and nut and tighten the bolt to 30 ft. lbs. (41 Nm).

18. Install the tire and wheel assembly.

19. Lower the vehicle.

20. Check the front wheel alignment.

WHEEL HUB & BEARING

REMOVAL & INSTALLATION

See Figures 242 and 243.

1. Before servicing the vehicle, refer to the precautions in the beginning of this section.

2. On 4WD vehicles, remove wheel center cap, if equipped, and the drive axle nut and washer

3. Raise and support the vehicle.

4. Remove or disconnect the following:
- Tire and wheel
- Caliper, leaving the fluid lines connected
- Brake rotor
- Halfshaft from the hub and bearing

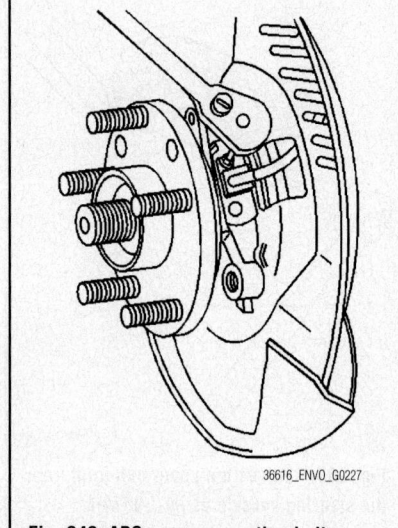

36616_ENVO_G0227

Fig. 242 ABS sensor mounting bolt removal

on 4WD vehicles. Place a brass drift against the outer edge of the halfshaft to protect the shaft threads. Use a hammer to sharply strike the brass drift, but to do not remove the halfshaft at this time.
- Wheel speed sensor
- Wheel hub and bearing-to-steering knuckle bolts and hub and bearing

➡ Lay the hub and bearing on the wheel studs on the outboard side. This will avoid damaging the bearing seal.

- Splash shield from the steering knuckle
- Seal from the hub and bearing

To install:

5. Install or connect the following:
- Wheel hub and bearing seal
- Splash shield to the steering knuckle, making sure it's properly aligned
- Hub and bearing to the steering knuckle, aligning the threaded holes
- Hub and bearing bolts and tighten to 77 ft. lbs. (105 Nm)
- Wheel speed sensor. Tighten the bolt to 13 ft. lbs. (18 Nm).
- Rotor and brake caliper
- Tire and wheel

6. Lower the vehicle

7. On 4WD vehicles, install the drive axle nut and tighten to 103 ft. lbs. (140 Nm), then install the center cap.

ADJUSTMENT

The wheel bearings on these vehicles are not adjustable. If the bearings become loose or make noise, they must be replaced.

SUSPENSION

REAR SUSPENSION

COIL SPRING

REMOVAL & INSTALLATION

See Figures 244 and 245.

1. Before servicing the vehicle, refer to the precautions section.
2. Raise and support the vehicle.
3. Support the rear axle.
4. Remove the shock absorber lower mounting bolts.

➡ **Do not lower the rear axle so the upper control arms contact the frame. This will damage the upper control arms.**

5. Lower the rear axle, then remove the coil spring.

➡ **Be careful not to chip or scratch the coating of the coil springs when removing and installing the springs. Damaging the coating will cause premature failure of the coil springs.**

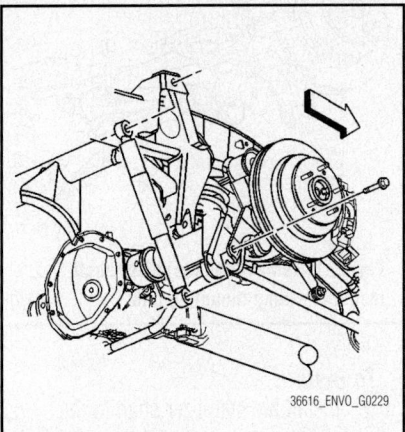

Fig. 244 Remove the shock absorber lower mounting bolts

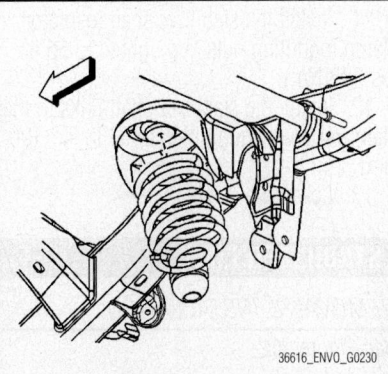

Fig. 245 Lower the rear axle, then remove the coil spring

To install:

6. Install the coil springs, then raise the rear axle.
7. Install the shock absorber lower mounting bolts and tighten to 59 ft. lbs. (80 Nm).
8. Remove the rear axle support.
9. Lower the vehicle.

CONTROL ARMS/LINKS

REMOVAL & INSTALLATION

Upper Control Arm

See Figure 246.

1. Before servicing the vehicle, refer to the precautions section.
2. Raise and safely support the rear of the vehicle securely on jackstands.
3. Remove the tire and wheel.
4. Remove the wheelhouse panel.
5. Raise and support the rear axle at the designed D - height, which are as follows:
   - Except Air Suspension; 5.88–6.35 inches (149.4–161.4mm)
   - Trailblazer SS; 4.17–4.49 inches (106–114mm)
6. Remove the rear axle upper control arm to axle mounting bolt and nut.
7. Remove the rear axle upper control arm to frame mounting bolt.
8. Remove the rear axle upper control arm.

To install:

9. Install the rear axle upper control arm.
10. Install the rear axle upper control arm to frame mounting bolt.
11. Install the rear axle upper control arm to axle mounting nut and bolt and tighten the bolts to 97 ft. lbs. (131 Nm).

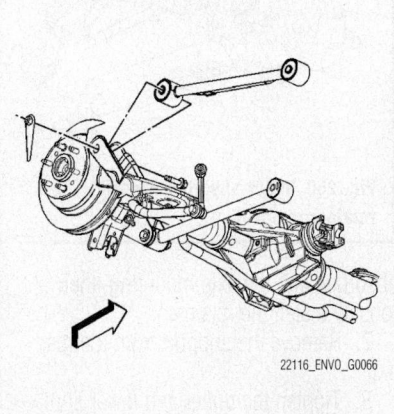

Fig. 246 Upper control arm mounting

12. Remove the rear axle support.
13. Install the wheelhouse panel.
14. Install the tire and wheel.
15. Lower the vehicle.

Rear Axle Brace

See Figure 247.

1. Before servicing the vehicle, refer to the precautions section.
2. Raise and safely support the rear of the vehicle securely on jackstands.
3. Raise and support the rear axle at the designed D - height, which are as follows:
   - Except Air Suspension; 5.88–6.35 inches (149.4–161.4mm)
   - Trailblazer SS; 4.17–4.49 inches (106–114mm)
4. Remove the rear axle brace and rear axle tie rod to the rear axle mounting bolt.
5. Remove the rear axle brace to frame mounting nut.
6. Remove the rear axle brace from the vehicle.

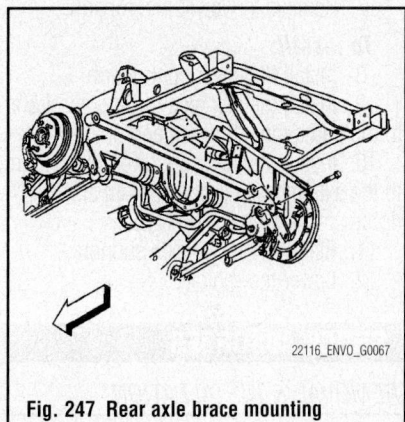

Fig. 247 Rear axle brace mounting

To install:

7. Install the rear axle brace to the vehicle.
8. Install the rear axle brace to frame mounting nut and tighten to 70 ft. lbs. (95 Nm).
9. Install the rear axle brace and rear axle tie rod to the rear axle mounting bolt and tighten to 140 ft. lbs. (190 Nm).
10. Remove the rear axle support.
11. Lower the vehicle.

Lower Control Arm

See Figure 248.

1. Before servicing the vehicle, refer to the precautions section.
2. Raise and support the vehicle.
3. Remove the wheel and tire.

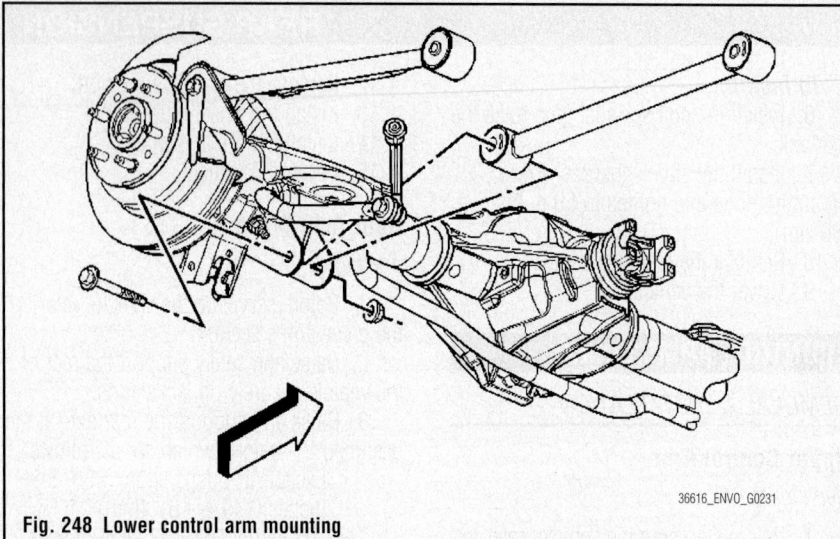

Fig. 248 Lower control arm mounting

4. Raise and support the rear axle at the designed height of 5.33 in. (135.4mm).

5. Remove the rear axle lower control arm to the axle mounting nut and bolt.

6. Remove the rear axle lower control arm to the frame mounting nut and bolt.

7. Remove the lower control arm.

To install:

8. Install the lower control arm.

9. Install the rear axle lower control arm to the frame mounting nut and bolt.

10. Install the rear axle lower control arm to the axle mounting bolt and nut and tighten to 74 ft. lbs. (100 Nm).

11. Remove the rear axle support.

12. Lower the vehicle.

SHOCK ABSORBER

REMOVAL & INSTALLATION

See Figures 249 and 250.

1. Before servicing the vehicle, refer to the precautions section.

2. Raise and support the vehicle.

3. Properly support the rear axle assembly.

4. Remove or disconnect the following:
- Automatic level control air lines from the shock absorber, if equipped
- Shock absorber-to-frame retainer(s) at the top of the shock
- Shock-to-axle retainer(s) at the bottom of the shock
- Shock absorber

To install:

5. Install the shock in the vehicle and loosely install the upper mounting fasteners to retain it.

6. Align the lower-end of the shock

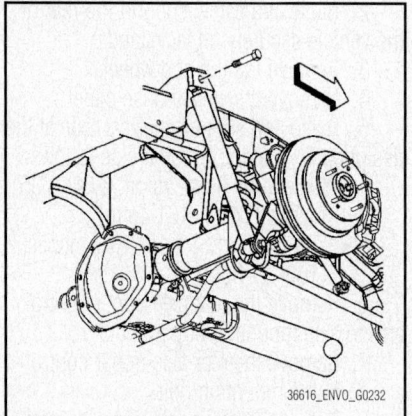

Fig. 249 Shock absorber top retainer removal

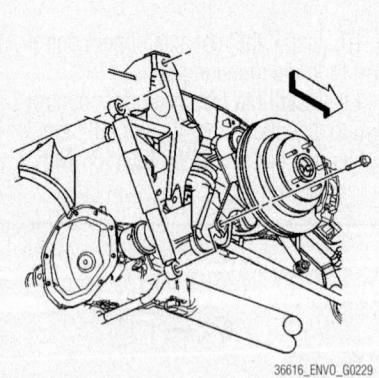

Fig. 250 Shock absorber lower retainer removal

absorber with the axle mounting, then loosely install the retainers.

7. Remove the support from the rear axle.

8. Tighten the upper and lower shock retainers to 63 ft. lbs. (85 Nm).

9. If equipped, attach the automatic level control air lines to the shock absorber.

10. Lower the vehicle.

STABILIZER BAR

REMOVAL & INSTALLATION

See Figure 251.

1. Before servicing the vehicle, refer to the precautions section.

2. Raise and support the vehicle.

3. Remove the stabilizer shaft links to the stabilizer shaft retaining nuts.

4. Remove the stabilizer shaft insulator clamp mounting nuts.

5. Remove the stabilizer shaft insulator clamp from the stabilizer shaft insulator.

6. Remove the stabilizer shaft insulators from the stabilizer shaft.

7. Remove the stabilizer shaft from the vehicle.

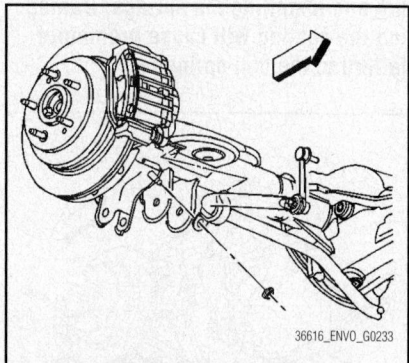

Fig. 251 Remove the stabilizer shaft insulator clamp mounting nuts

To install:

8. Install the stabilizer shaft to the vehicle.

9. Install the stabilizer shaft insulators to the stabilizer shaft.

10. Install the stabilizer shaft insulator clamp to the stabilizer shaft insulator.

11. Install the stabilizer shaft insulator clamp mounting nuts and tighten to 55 ft. lbs. (75 Nm).

12. Install the stabilizer shaft links to the stabilizer shaft and tighten to 66 ft. lbs. (90 Nm).

13. Lower the vehicle.

STABILIZER LINK

REMOVAL & INSTALLATION

See Figure 252.

1. Before servicing the vehicle, refer to the precautions section.

2. Raise and support the vehicle.

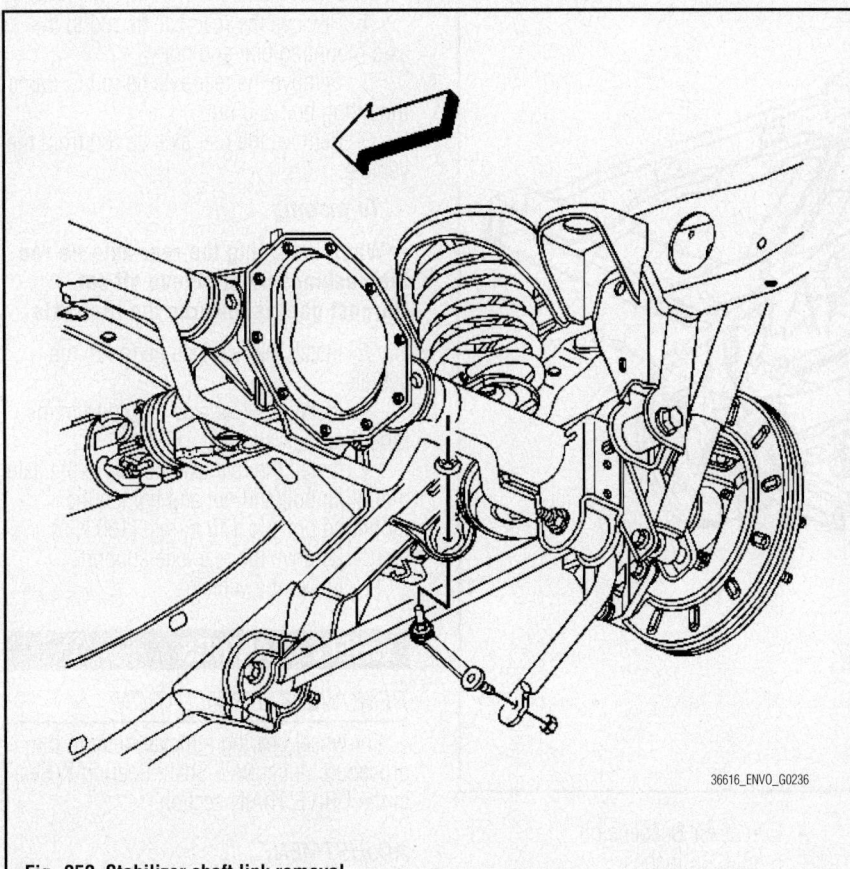

Fig. 252 Stabilizer shaft link removal

3. Remove the stabilizer shaft link retaining nuts

✻✻ WARNING

Do not pry on the stabilizer shaft link. Use care when removing or installing the stabilizer shaft link in order to avoid tearing or puncturing the stabilizer shaft link boot. Damage to the stabilizer shaft link boot will lead to damage to the stabilizer shaft link.

4. Disconnect the stabilizer shaft link from the frame.
5. Disconnect the stabilizer shaft link from the stabilizer shaft and remove the stabilizer shaft link.

To install:

6. Connect the stabilizer shaft link to the stabilizer shaft and to the frame.
7. Install the stabilizer shaft link retaining nuts.
8. Tighten the stabilizer shaft nuts to 66 ft. lbs. (90 Nm).
9. Lower the vehicle.

TIE ROD

REMOVAL & INSTALLATION

See Figures 253 and 254.

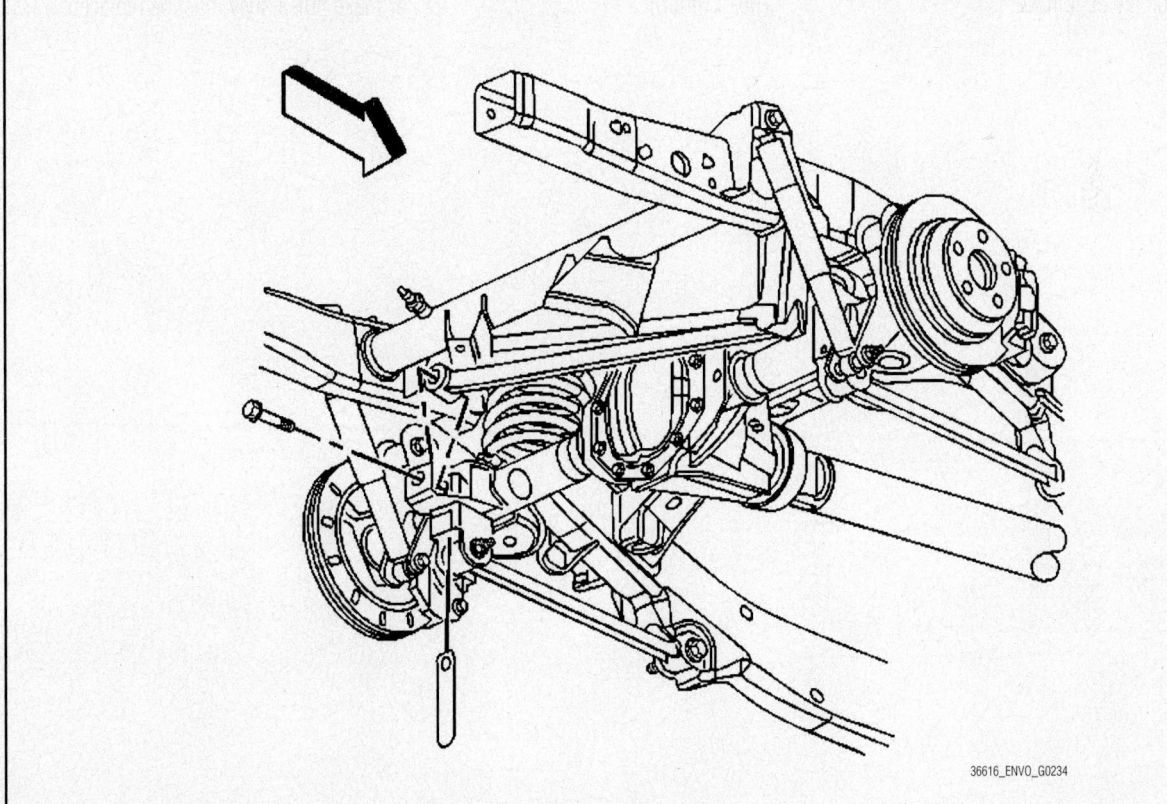

Fig. 253 Remove the rear axle tie rod to the axle mounting bolt and nut

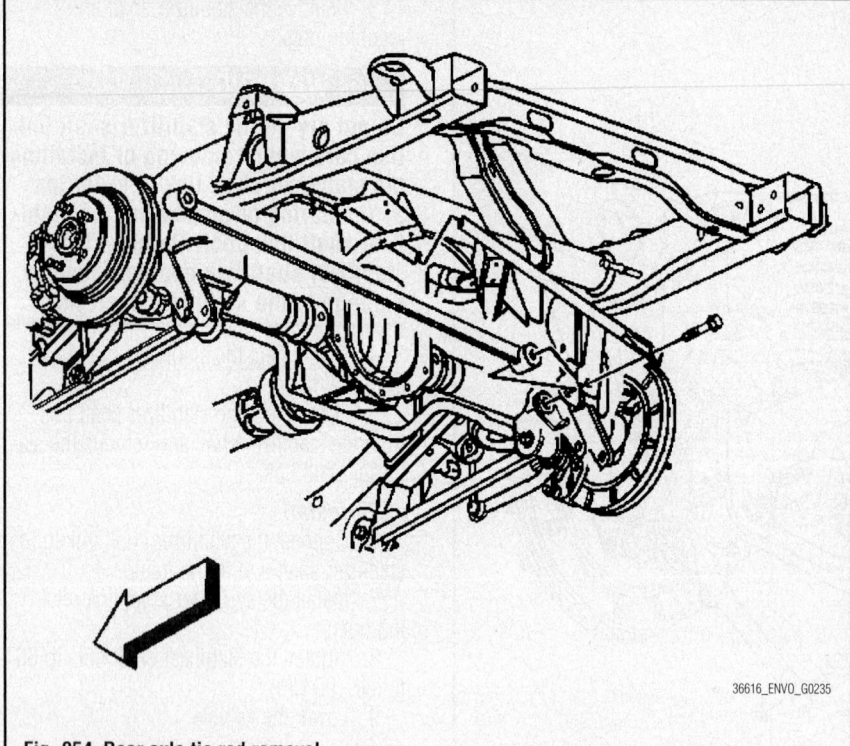

Fig. 254 Rear axle tie rod removal

36616_ENVO_G0235

1. Before servicing the vehicle, refer to the precautions section.
2. Raise and support the vehicle.
3. Support the rear axle at the designed D - height, which are as follows:

- Except Air Suspension; 5.88–6.35 inches (149.4–161.4mm)
- Trailblazer SS; 4.17–4.49 inches (106–114mm)

4. Remove the rear axle tie rod to the axle mounting bolt and nut.
5. Remove the rear axle tie rod to frame mounting bolt and nut.
6. Remove the rear axle tie rod from the vehicle.

To install:

➡**When installing the rear axle tie rod the bushings inner sleeve off set (largest gap) is towards the rear axle.**

7. Install the rear axle tie rod to the vehicle.
8. Install the rear axle tie rod to frame mounting bolt and nut.
9. Install the rear axle tie rod to the axle mounting bolt and nut and tighten the mounting bolts to 140 ft. lbs. (190 Nm).
10. Remove the rear axle support.
11. Lower the vehicle.

WHEEL BEARINGS

REMOVAL & INSTALLATION

For wheel bearing removal, refer to the procedure under Axle Shaft, Bearing & Seal in the DRIVE TRAIN section.

ADJUSTMENT

The wheel bearings on these vehicles are not adjustable. If the bearings become loose or make noise, they must be replaced.

CHEVROLET AND PONTIAC

Equinox • Torrent

SPECIFICATIONS AND MAINTENANCE CHARTS

ENGINE AND VEHICLE IDENTIFICATION

Engine							Model Year	
Code ①	Liters	Cu. In.	Cyl.	Fuel Sys.	Engine Type	Eng. Mfg.	Code ②	Year
F	3.4	204	6	SFI	OHV	Chev.	8	2008
7	3.6	217	6	SFI	DOHC	Chev.	9	2009

MFI: Multi-port Fuel Injection

OHV: Overhead valves

① 8th digit of VIN

② 10th digit of VIN

36616_EQUI_C0001

GENERAL ENGINE SPECIFICATIONS

Year	Engine Displacement Liters	Engine VIN	Net Horsepower @ rpm	Net Torque @ rpm (ft. lbs.)	Bore x Stroke (in.)	Compression Ratio	Oil Pressure @ rpm
2008	3.4	F	185@5200	210@3800	3.62x3.31	9.6:1	30-35@1850
	3.6	7	264@6500	250@2300	3.70x3.37	10.2:1	20@2000
2009	3.4	F	185@5200	210@3800	3.62x3.31	9.6:1	30-35@1850
	3.6	7	264@6500	250@2300	3.70x3.37	10.2:1	20@2000

36616_EQUI_C0002

GASOLINE ENGINE TUNE-UP SPECIFICATIONS

Year	Engine Displacement Liters	Engine VIN	Spark Plug Gap (in.)	Ignition Timing (deg.)	Fuel Pump (psi)	Idle Speed (rpm)	Valve Clearance In.	Valve Clearance Ex.
2008	3.4	F	0.060	①	50-60	N/A	HYD	HYD
	3.6	7	0.044	①	50-60	②	HYD	HYD
2009	3.4	F	0.060	①	50-60	N/A	HYD	HYD
	3.6	7	0.044	①	50-60	②	HYD	HYD

NOTE: The Vehicle Emission Control Information label often reflects specification changes changes made during production. The label figures must be used if they differ from those in this chart.

N/A: Not Available

HYD: Hydraulic

① Controlled by the Powertrain Control Module (PCM) and cannot be manually adjusted.

② 600 A/C-Off and 700 A/C-On

36616_EQUI_C0003

CAPACITIES

Year	Model	Engine Displacement Liters	Engine ID/VIN	Engine Oil with Filter (qts.)	Transmission (pts.)	Transfer Case (pts.)	Rear Drive Axle (pts.)	Fuel Tank (gal.)	Cooling System (qts.)
2008	Equinox	3.4	F	4.5	16.5 ①	1.69 ②	1.59	③	10.5
		3.6	7	5.5	16.5 ①	1.69 ②	1.59	③	11.0
	Torrent	3.4	F	4.0	16.5 ①	1.69 ②	1.59	③	10.5
		3.6	7	5.5	16.5 ①	1.69 ②	1.59	③	11.0
2009	Equinox	3.4	F	4.5	16.5 ①	1.69 ②	1.59	③	10.5
		3.6	7	5.5	16.5 ①	1.69 ②	1.59	③	11.0
	Torrent	3.4	F	4.0	16.5 ①	1.69 ②	1.59	③	10.5
		3.6	7	5.5	16.5 ①	1.69 ②	1.59	③	11.0

NOTE: All capacities are approximate. Add fluid gradually and check to be sure a proper fluid level is obtained.

① FWD: 4.1 pts

② Or to bottom of the fill hole.

③ FWD: 20.5 gal
    AWD: 16.6 gal

36616_EQUI_C0004

FLUID SPECIFICATIONS

Year	Model	Engine Displacement Liters (VIN)	Engine Oil	Automatic Transmission	Rear Drive Axle ②	Transfer Case ③	Power Steering Fluid	Brake Master Cylinder	Engine Coolant
2008	Equinox	3.4 (F)	5W-30	Dexron-VI ①	75W-90	VERSATRAK®	GM PS Fluid	DOT 3	DEXCOOL®
		3.6 (7)	5W-30	Dexron-VI ①	75W-90	VERSATRAK®	GM PS Fluid	DOT 3	DEXCOOL®
	Torrent	3.4 (F)	5W-30	Dexron-VI ①	75W-90	VERSATRAK®	GM PS Fluid	DOT 3	DEXCOOL®
		3.6 (7)	5W-30	Dexron-VI ①	75W-90	VERSATRAK®	GM PS Fluid	DOT 3	DEXCOOL®
2009	Equinox	3.4 (F)	5W-30	Dexron-VI ①	75W-90	VERSATRAK®	GM PS Fluid	DOT 3	DEXCOOL®
		3.6 (7)	5W-30	Dexron-VI ①	75W-90	VERSATRAK®	GM PS Fluid	DOT 3	DEXCOOL®
	Torrent	3.4 (F)	5W-30	Dexron-VI ①	75W-90	VERSATRAK®	GM PS Fluid	DOT 3	DEXCOOL®
		3.6 (7)	5W-30	Dexron-VI ①	75W-90	VERSATRAK®	GM PS Fluid	DOT 3	DEXCOOL®

DOT: Department Of Transpotation

① 5-speed Automatic Transmission (3.4L engine) T-IV Fluid only.

② Synthetic fluid is recomended

③ With a 3.6L Engine 75W-90 Synthetic lubricant (Getrag 760 transfer case)

36616_EQUI_C0005

VALVE SPECIFICATIONS

Year	Engine VIN	Engine Displacement Liters	Seat Angle (deg.)	Face Angle (deg.)	Spring Test Pressure (lbs. @ in.)	Spring Installed Height (in.)	Stem-to-Guide Clearance (in.) Intake	Stem-to-Guide Clearance (in.) Exhaust	Stem Diameter (in.) Intake	Stem Diameter (in.) Exhaust
2008	F	3.4	46	45	230@1.260	1.701	0.0010-0.0027	0.0010-0.0027	N/A	N/A
	7	3.6	45	44.25	N/A	1.3779	0.0010-0.0026	0.0014-0.0030	0.2344-0.2352	0.2341-0.2348
2009	F	3.4	46	45	230@1.260	1.701	0.0010-0.0027	0.0010-0.0027	N/A	N/A
	7	3.6	45	44.25	N/A	1.3779	0.0010-0.0026	0.0014-0.0030	0.2344-0.2352	0.2341-0.2348

N/A: Not Available

36616_EQUI_C0008

CAMSHAFT AND BEARING SPECIFICATIONS CHART
All measurements are given in inches.

Year	Engine Displacement Liters	Engine VIN	Journal Diameter	Brg. Oil Clearance	Shaft End-play	Runout	Journal Bore	Lobe Lift Intake	Lobe Lift Exhaust
2008	3.4	F	1.8680-1.8690	N/A	0.0039-0.0079	0.001	1.8710-1.8720	0.2727	0.2727
	3.6	7	①	N/A	0.0018-0.0085	②	③	1.6687-1.6805	1.6703-1.6821
2009	3.4	F	1.8680-1.8690	N/A	0.0039-0.0079	0.001	1.8710-1.8720	0.2727	0.2727
	3.6	7	①	N/A	0.0018-0.0085	②	③	1.6687-1.6805	1.6703-1.6821

N/A: Not Applicable

① Front Number 1: 1.3754-1.3764
  Middle and Rear number 2-4: 1.0605-1.0614

② Front and Rear number 1 and 4: 0.0010
  Middle 2 and 3: 0.0020

③ Front number 1: 1.3779-1.3787
  Middle and Rear number 2-4: 1.0630-1.0638

36616_EQUI_C0007

CRANKSHAFT AND CONNECTING ROD SPECIFICATIONS

All measurements are given in inches.

Year	Engine Displ. Liters	Engine VIN	Crankshaft				Connecting Rod		
			Main Brg. Journal Dia.	Main Brg. Oil Clearance	Shaft End-play	Thrust on No.	Journal Diameter	Oil Clearance	Side Clearance
2008	3.4	F	2.6473-2.6483	①	0.0024-0.0083	3	1.9987-1.9994	0.0007-0.0017	0.0100-0.0150
	3.6	7	2.6768-2.6775	0.0004-0.0024	0.0039-0.0130	3	2.2044-2.5050	0.0004-0.0028	0.0374-0.0140
2009	3.4	F	2.6473-2.6483	①	0.0024-0.0083	3	1.9987-1.9994	0.0007-0.0017	0.0100-0.0150
	3.6	7	2.6768-2.6775	0.0004-0.0024	0.0039-0.0130	3	2.2044-2.5050	0.0004-0.0028	0.0374-0.0140

① Except No.3: 0.0008-0.0025 in.
No.3: 0.0012-0.0030 in.

36616_EQUI_C0006

PISTON AND RING SPECIFICATIONS

All measurements are given in inches.

Year	Engine Displacement Liters	Engine VIN	Piston Clearance	Ring Gap			Ring Side Clearance		
				Top Comp.	Bottom Comp.	Oil Control	Top Comp.	Bottom Comp.	Oil Control
2008	3.4	F	0.0036	0.0060-0.0140	0.019-0.029	0.0098-0.0303	0.002-0.003	0.002-0.003	0.003-0.004
	3.6	7	0.0010-0.0021	0.0059-0.0118	0.0110-0.0189	0.0059-0.0236	0.0012-0.0026	0.0006-0.0024	0.0012-0.0067
2009	3.4	F	0.0036	0.0060-0.0140	0.019-0.029	0.0098-0.0303	0.002-0.003	0.002-0.003	0.003-0.004
	3.6	7	0.0010-0.0021	0.0059-0.0118	0.0110-0.0189	0.0059-0.0236	0.0012-0.0026	0.0006-0.0024	0.0012-0.0067

36616_EQUI_C0009

TORQUE SPECIFICATIONS
All readings in ft. lbs.

Year	Engine VIN	Engine Displacement Liters	Cylinder Head Bolts	Main Bearing Bolts	Rod Bearing Bolts	Crankshaft Damper Bolts	Flywheel Bolts	Manifold Intake	Manifold Exhaust	Spark Plugs	Oil Pan Drain Plug
2008	F	3.4	①	②	③	④	52	⑤	12	11	18
	7	3.6	⑥	⑦	⑧	⑨	52	18	15	15	15
2009	F	3.4	①	②	③	④	52	⑤	12	11	18
	7	3.6	⑥	⑦	⑧	⑨	52	18	15	15	15

① Step 1: 44 ft. lbs.
　Step 2: plus 95 degrees
② Step 1: 37 ft. lbs.
　Step 2: plus 77 degrees
③ Step 1: 15 ft. lbs.
　Step 2: plus 75 degrees
④ Step 1: 92 ft. lbs.
　Step 2: plus 130 degrees

⑤ Upper intake.
　Step 1: 18 ft. lbs.
　Lower intake corber
　Step 1: (Bolts 1-4) 115 inch lbs.
　Step 2: (Bolts 5-8) 18 ft. lbs.
⑥ Step 1: Tighten the M 11 bolts to 22 ft. lbs.
　Step 2: plus 150 degrees
　Step 3: Tighten the M 8 bolts to 11 ft. lbs.
　Step 4: plus 75 degrees

⑦ Step 1: Tighten the Inboard bolts (1-8) to 15 ft. lbs.
　Step 2: plus 80 degrees
　Step 3: Tighten the Outboard bolts (9-16) to 11 ft. lbs.
　Step 4: plus 110 degrees
　Step 5: Tighten the side bolts to 22 ft. lbs.
　Step 6: plus 60 degrees
⑧ Step 1: Tighten to 22 ft. lbs.
　Step 2: Loosen bolts to zero
　Step 3: 18 ft. lbs.
　Step 4: plus 110 degrees
⑨ Step 1: 74 ft. lbs.
　Step 2: plus 150 degrees

36616_EQUI_C0010

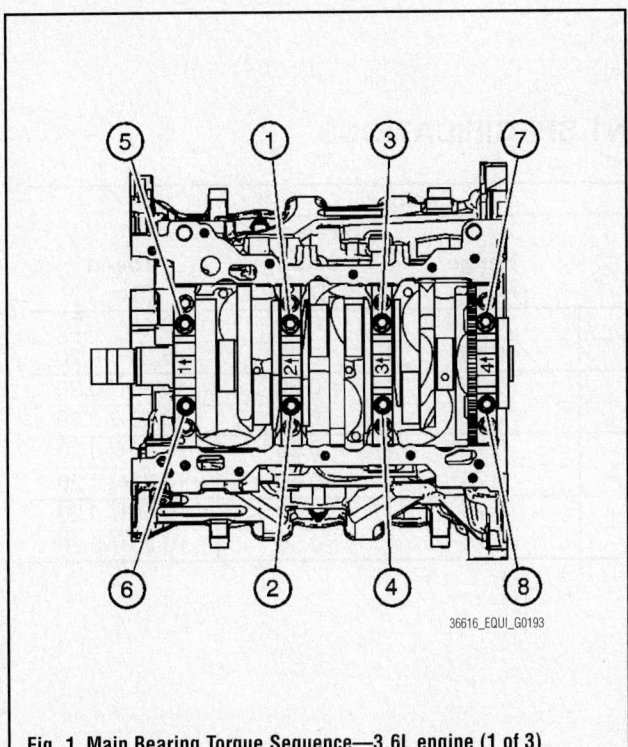

Fig. 1 Main Bearing Torque Sequence—3.6L engine (1 of 3)

36616_EQUI_G0193

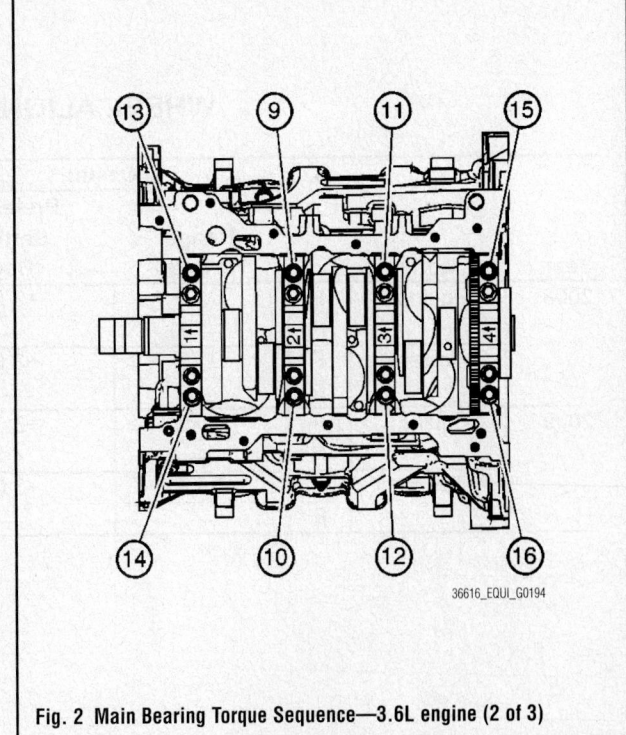

Fig. 2 Main Bearing Torque Sequence—3.6L engine (2 of 3)

36616_EQUI_G0194

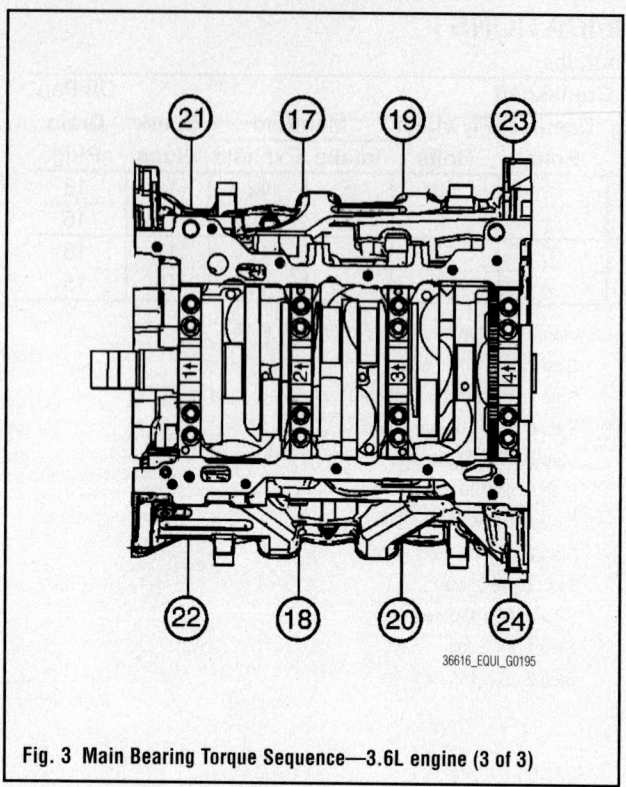

Fig. 3 Main Bearing Torque Sequence—3.6L engine (3 of 3)

36616_EQUI_G0195

WHEEL ALIGNMENT SPECIFICATIONS

Year	Model		Caster Range (+/-Deg.)	Caster Preferred Setting (Deg.)	Camber Range (+/-Deg.)	Camber Preferred Setting (Deg.)	Toe-in (Deg.)
2008	Equinox	F	0.75	+3.00	0.75	-0.60	+0.15+/-0.20
		R	—	—	0.75	-0.50	+0.20+/-0.20
	Torrent	F	0.75	+3.00	0.75	-0.60	+0.15+/-0.20
		R	—	—	0.75	-0.50	+0.20+/-0.20
2009	Equinox	F	0.75	+3.00	0.75	-0.60	+0.15+/-0.20
		R	—	—	0.75	-0.50	+0.20+/-0.20
	Torrent	F	0.75	+3.00	0.75	-0.60	+0.15+/-0.20
		R	—	—	0.75	-0.50	+0.20+/-0.20

36616_EQUI_C0011

TIRE AND WHEEL SPECIFICATIONS

| Year | Model | OEM Tires | | Tire Pressures (psi) | | Wheel Size | Ball Joint Inspection | Lug Nut (ft. lbs.) |
		Standard	Optional	Front	Rear			
2008	Equinox	P235/65R16	P235/60R17 P235/50R18	①	①	①	②	100
	Torrent	P235/65R16	P235/60R17 P235/50R18	①	①	①	②	100
2009	Equinox	P235/65R16	P235/60R17 P235/50R18	①	①	①	②	100
	Torrent	P235/65R16	P235/60R17 P235/50R18	①	①	①	②	100

OEM: Original Equipment Manufacturer

PSI: Pounds Per Square Inch

① See placard on vehicle

② If the reading is greater than 0.5 mm (0.02 in), replace the ball joint

36616_EQUI_C0013

BRAKE SPECIFICATIONS

All measurements in inches unless noted

| Year | Model | | Brake Disc | | | Brake Drum Diameter | | | Minimum Lining Thickness | Brake Caliper | |
			Original Thickness	Minimum Thickness	Maximum Runout	Original Inside Diameter	Max. Wear Limit	Maximum Machine Diameter		Bracket Bolts (ft. lbs.)	Mounting Bolts (ft. lbs.)
2008	Equinox	F	NA	1.079	0.002	N/A	N/A	N/A	0.080	136	20
		R	NA	0.724	0.002	N/A	N/A	N/A	0.080	89	20
	Torrent	F	NA	1.079	0.002	N/A	N/A	N/A	0.080	137	20
		R	NA	0.724	0.002	N/A	N/A	N/A	0.080	89	20
2009	Equinox	F	NA	1.079	0.002	N/A	N/A	N/A	0.080	137	20
		R	NA	0.724	0.002	N/A	N/A	N/A	0.080	89	20
	Torrent	F	NA	1.079	0.002	N/A	N/A	N/A	0.080	137	20
		R	NA	0.724	0.002	N/A	N/A	N/A	0.080	89	20

N/A: Not Applicable

36616_EQUI_C0012

MAINTENANCE I AND II SERVICE SCHEDULES
Chevrolet Equinox, Pontiac Torrent

When the CHANGE ENGINE OIL light appears, certain services and inspections are required.
Required services are described as Maintenance I and Maintenance II.
The first service on a vehicle should be Maintenance I, and the second service should be Maintenance II.
Alternate between the 2 thereafter. However, in some cases, Maintenance II may be required more often.
Maintenance I: Use Maintenance I if the CHANGE ENGINE OIL light comes on within 10 months since vehicle was purchased or, if Maintenance II was performed.
Maintenance II: Use Maintenance II if the previous service performed was Maintenance I. Always use Maintenance II whenever the CHANGE ENGINE OIL light comes on 10 months or more since the last service, or, if the CHANGE ENGINE OIL light has not come on at all for one year.

Service	Maintenance I	Maintenance II
Change the engine oil and filter. Reset the oil life system.	✓	✓
Visually inspect the vehicle for leaks or damage. A fluid loss in the vehicle system could indicate a problem. Inspected, repair and add fluid to the system if necessary.	✓	✓
Inspect the engine air cleaner filter. If necessary, replace the filter.	✓	✓
Rotate the tires. Inspect the tire inflation pressures and the tire wear.	✓	✓
Visually inspect the brake lines and hoses for proper hook-up, binding, leaks, cracks, chafing, etc. Inspect the disc brake pads for wear and the rotors for surface condition. Inspect the drum brake linings for wear or cracks. Inspect other brake parts, including drums, wheel cylinders, calipers, parking brake, etc. Inspect the parking brake adjustment.	✓	✓
needed.	✓	✓
Inspect the suspension and steering components. Inspect the front and rear suspension and the steering system for damaged, loose or missing parts, or signs of wear. Inspect the power steering lines and the hoses for proper hook-up, binding, leaks, cracks, chafing, etc.		✓
Visually inspect the coolant hoses and replace the hoses if they are cracked, swollen or deteriorated. Inspect all pipes, fittings and clamps; replace with GM parts as needed. To help ensure proper operation, a pressure test of the cooling system and pressure cap and cleaning the outside of the radiator and air conditioning condenser is recommended at least once a year.		✓
Inspect the front and rear suspension and the steering system for damaged, loose or missing parts, or signs of wear. Inspect power steering lines and hoses for proper hook-up, binding, leaks, cracks, chafing, etc.		✓
Inspect the throttle system for interference or binding and for damaged or missing parts. Replace the parts as needed. Replace any components that have high effort or excessive wear. Do not lubricate the accelerator or the cruise control cables.		✓
Replace the passenger compartment air filter.		✓

To reset the CHANGE ENGINE OIL LIGHT:
1. Turn the ignition key to RUN with the engine off.
2. Fully press and release the accelerator pedal three times within five seconds. The change engine oil light will flash while the system is resetting
3. Turn the key to LOCK.

If the change engine oil light comes back on and stays on when you start your vehicle, the engine oil life system has not reset, repeat the procedure

ADDITIONAL MAINTENANCE SERVICES
Chevrolet Equinox, Pontiac Torrent

TO BE SERVICED	TYPE OF SERVICE	VEHICLE MILEAGE INTERVAL (x1000)					
		25	50	75	100	125	150
Air cleaner filter	R		✓		✓		✓
Accessory drive belt	I						✓
Auto. Trans. Fluid ①	R				✓		✓
Cooling system service	S/I		✓		✓		✓
Engine coolant	R						✓
Fuel system	I	✓	✓	✓	✓	✓	✓
Exhaust system & heat shields	S/I	✓	✓	✓	✓	✓	✓
Spark plugs	R				✓		
Transfer case ①	R				✓		✓

R: Replace   S/I: Inspect and service, if necessary

① Replace if any of the following conditions are met:

Heavy city traffic where the outside temperature regularly reaches 32°C (90°F) or higher

Hilly or mountainous terrain

Frequent trailer towing

Taxi, police or delivery service

Otherwise, change every 100,000 miles

36616_EQUI_C0015

PRECAUTIONS

Before servicing any vehicle, please be sure to read all of the following precautions, which deal with personal safety, prevention of component damage, and important points to take into consideration when servicing a motor vehicle:

• Never open, service or drain the radiator or cooling system when the engine is hot; serious burns can occur from the steam and hot coolant.

• Observe all applicable safety precautions when working around fuel. Whenever servicing the fuel system, always work in a well-ventilated area. Do not allow fuel spray or vapors to come in contact with a spark, open flame, or excessive heat (a hot drop light, for example). Keep a dry chemical fire extinguisher near the work area. Always keep fuel in a container specifically designed for fuel storage; also, always properly seal fuel containers to avoid the possibility of fire or explosion. Refer to the additional fuel system precautions later in this section.

• Fuel injection systems often remain pressurized, even after the engine has been turned **OFF**. The fuel system pressure must be relieved before disconnecting any fuel lines. Failure to do so may result in fire and/or personal injury.

• Brake fluid often contains polyglycol ethers and polyglycols. Avoid contact with the eyes and wash your hands thoroughly after handling brake fluid. If you do get brake fluid in your eyes, flush your eyes with clean, running water for 15 minutes. If eye irritation persists, or if you have taken brake fluid internally, IMMEDIATELY seek medical assistance.

• The EPA warns that prolonged contact with used engine oil may cause a number of skin disorders, including cancer. You should make every effort to minimize your exposure to used engine oil. Protective gloves should be worn when changing oil. Wash your hands and any other exposed skin areas as soon as possible after exposure to used engine oil. Soap and water, or waterless hand cleaner should be used.

• All new vehicles are now equipped with an air bag system, often referred to as a Supplemental Restraint System (SRS) or Supplemental Inflatable Restraint (SIR) system. The system must be disabled before performing service on or around system components, steering column, instrument panel components, wiring and sensors. Failure to follow safety and disabling procedures could result in accidental air bag deployment, possible personal injury and unnecessary system repairs.

• Always wear safety goggles when working with, or around, the air bag system. When carrying a non-deployed air bag, be sure the bag and trim cover are pointed away from your body. When placing a non-deployed air bag on a work surface, always face the bag and trim cover upward, away from the surface. This will reduce the motion of the module if it is accidentally deployed. Refer to the additional air bag system precautions later in this section.

• Clean, high quality brake fluid from a sealed container is essential to the safe and proper operation of the brake system. You should always buy the correct type of brake fluid for your vehicle. If the brake fluid becomes contaminated, completely flush the system with new fluid. Never reuse any brake fluid. Any brake fluid that is removed from the system should be discarded. Also, do not allow any brake fluid to come in contact with a painted surface; it will damage the paint.

• Never operate the engine without the proper amount and type of engine oil; doing so WILL result in severe engine damage.

• Timing belt maintenance is extremely important. Many models utilize an interference-type, non-freewheeling engine. If the timing belt breaks, the valves in the cylinder head may strike the pistons, causing potentially serious (also time-consuming and expensive) engine damage. Refer to the maintenance interval charts for the recommended replacement interval for the timing belt, and to the timing belt section for belt replacement and inspection.

• Disconnecting the negative battery cable on some vehicles may interfere with the functions of the on-board computer system(s) and may require the computer to undergo a relearning process once the negative battery cable is reconnected.

• When servicing drum brakes, only disassemble and assemble one side at a time, leaving the remaining side intact for reference.

• Only an MVAC-trained, EPA-certified automotive technician should service the air conditioning system or its components.

BRAKES

GENERAL INFORMATION

PRECAUTIONS

• Certain components within the ABS system are not intended to be serviced or repaired individually.

• Do not use rubber hoses or other parts not specifically specified for and ABS system. When using repair kits, replace all parts included in the kit. Partial or incorrect repair may lead to functional problems and require the replacement of components.

• Lubricate rubber parts with clean, fresh brake fluid to ease assembly. Do not use shop air to clean parts; damage to rubber components may result.

• Use only DOT 3 brake fluid from an unopened container.

• If any hydraulic component or line is removed or replaced, it may be necessary to bleed the entire system.

• A clean repair area is essential. Always clean the reservoir and cap thoroughly before removing the cap. The slightest amount of dirt in the fluid may plug an orifice and impair the system function. Perform repairs after components have been thoroughly cleaned; use only denatured alcohol to clean components. Do not allow ABS components to come into contact with any substance containing mineral oil; this includes used shop rags.

• The Anti-Lock control unit is a microprocessor similar to other computer units in the vehicle. Ensure that the ignition switch is **OFF** before removing or installing controller harnesses. Avoid static electricity discharge at or near the controller.

ANTI-LOCK BRAKE SYSTEM (ABS)

• If any arc welding is to be done on the vehicle, the control unit should be unplugged before welding operations begin.

WHEEL SPEED SENSORS

REMOVAL & INSTALLATION

Front Sensor

See Figure 4.

1. Before servicing the vehicle, refer to the precautions section.
2. Raise and support the vehicle.
3. Remove the tire and wheel assembly.
4. Remove the brake rotor.
5. Disconnect the wheel speed sensor electrical connector.
6. Remove the wheel speed sensor bolt.
7. Remove the wheel speed sensor.

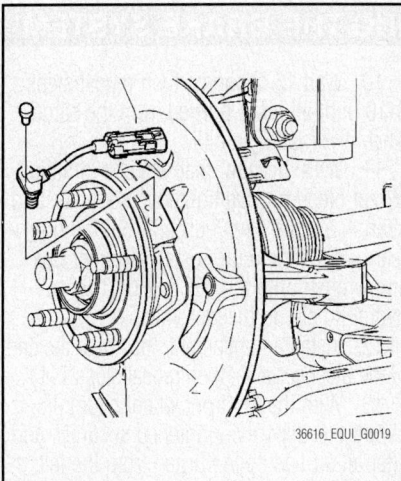

Fig. 4 Front wheel speed sensor removal shown

To install:

8. Install the wheel speed sensor to the wheel bearing/hub assembly.

9. Install the wheel speed sensor mounting bolt and tighten to 71 inch lbs. (8 Nm).

10. Connect the wheel speed sensor electrical connector.

11. Install the brake rotor.

12. Install the tire and wheel assembly.

13. Lower the vehicle.

Rear Sensor

See Figure 5.

1. Before servicing the vehicle, refer to the precautions section.

2. Raise and support the vehicle.

3. Remove the tire and wheel assembly.

4. Remove the parking brake shoes.

5. Disconnect the wheel speed sensor electrical connector.

6. Remove the wheel speed sensor bolt.

7. Remove the wheel speed sensor through the backing plate.

To install:

8. Install the wheel speed sensor through the drum brake backing plate to the wheel bearing/hub assembly.

9. Seat the wheel speed sensor harness grommet into the backing plate.

10. Install the wheel speed sensor mounting bolt and tighten to 71 inch lbs. (8 Nm).

11. Connect the wheel speed sensor electrical connector.

12. Install the parking brake shoes.

13. Install the tire and wheel assembly.

14. Lower the vehicle.

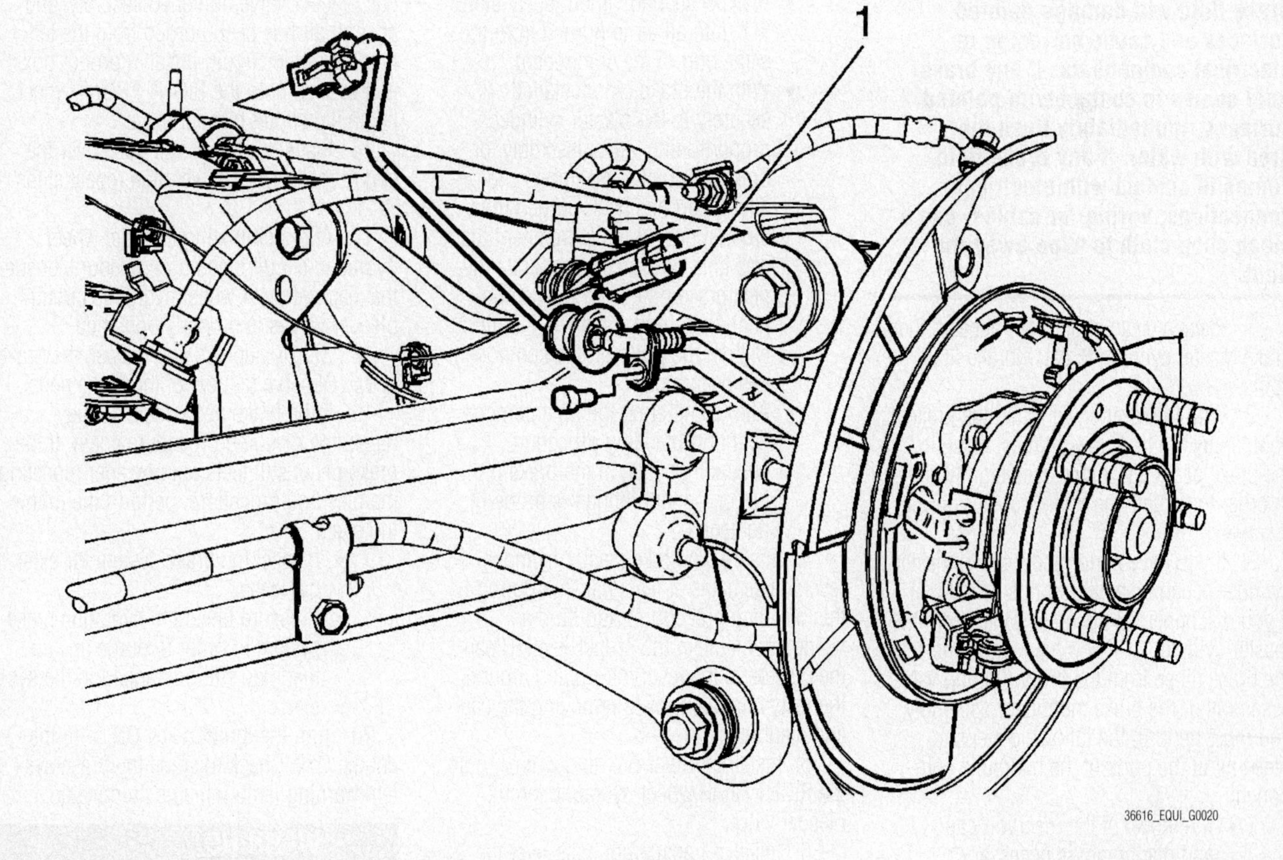

Fig. 5 Rear wheel speed sensor (1) removal shown

BRAKES   **BLEEDING THE BRAKE SYSTEM**

BLEEDING PROCEDURE

❋❋ WARNING

When adding fluid to the brake master cylinder reservoir, use only GM approved or equivalent DOT-3 brake fluid from a clean, sealed brake fluid container. The use of any type of fluid other than the recommended type of brake fluid may cause contamination which could result in damage to the internal rubber seals and/or rubber linings of hydraulic brake system components.

❋❋ WARNING

Avoid spilling brake fluid onto painted surfaces, electrical connections, wiring, or cables. Brake fluid will damage painted surfaces and cause corrosion to electrical components. If any brake fluid comes in contact with painted surfaces, immediately flush the area with water. If any brake fluid comes in contact with electrical connections, wiring, or cables, use a clean shop cloth to wipe away the fluid.

1. Place a clean shop cloth beneath the brake master cylinder to catch brake fluid spills.

2. With the ignition OFF and the brakes cool, apply the brakes 3-5 times, or until the brake pedal effort increases significantly, in order to deplete the brake booster power reserve.

3. If you have performed a brake master cylinder bench bleeding on this vehicle, or if you disconnected the brake pipes from the master cylinder, or if you have disconnected the brake pipes from the proportioning valve assembly or the brake modulator assembly, you must perform the following steps to bleed air at the ports of the hydraulic component:

- If removal of the reservoir cap and diaphragm is necessary, clean the outside of the reservoir on and around the cap prior to removal.
- With the brake pipes installed securely to the master cylinder, proportioning valve assembly, or brake modulator assembly, loosen and separate one of the brake pipes from the port of the component. For

the proportioning valve assembly or the brake modulator assembly, perform these steps in the sequence of system flow; begin with the fluid feed pipes from the master cylinder.

- Allow a small amount of brake fluid to gravity bleed from the open port of the component.
- Reconnect the brake pipe to the component and tighten securely.
- Have an assistant slowly depress the brake pedal fully and maintain steady pressure on the pedal.
- Loosen the same brake pipe to purge air from the open port of the component.
- Tighten the brake pipe, then have the assistant slowly release the brake pedal.
- Wait 15 seconds, then repeat steps 3-7 until all air is purged from the same port of the component.
- With the brake pipe installed securely to the master cylinder, proportioning valve assembly, or brake modulator assembly, and after all air has been purged from the first port of the component that was bled, loosen and separate the next brake pipe from the component, then repeat steps 3-8 until each of the ports on the component has been bled.
- After completing the final component port bleeding procedure, ensure that each of the brake pipe-to-component fittings is properly tightened.

4. Ensure the brake master cylinder reservoir remains at least half-full during this bleeding procedure. Add fluid as needed to maintain the proper level. Clean the outside of the reservoir on and around the reservoir cap prior to removing the cap and diaphragm.

5. Install a proper box-end wrench onto the RIGHT REAR wheel hydraulic circuit bleeder valve.

6. Install a transparent hose over the end of the bleeder valve.

7. Have an assistant slowly depress the brake pedal fully and maintain steady pressure on the pedal.

8. Loosen the bleeder valve to purge air from the wheel hydraulic circuit.

9. Tighten the bleeder valve, then have the assistant slowly release the brake pedal.

10. Wait 15 seconds, then repeat steps 8-10 until all air is purged from the same wheel hydraulic circuit.

11. With the right rear wheel hydraulic circuit bleeder valve tightened securely, and after all air has been purged from the right rear hydraulic circuit, install a proper box-end wrench onto the LEFT FRONT wheel hydraulic circuit bleeder valve.

12. Install a transparent hose over the end of the bleeder valve, then repeat steps 7-11.

13. With the left front wheel hydraulic circuit bleeder valve tightened securely, and after all air has been purged from the left front hydraulic circuit, install a proper box-end wrench onto the LEFT REAR wheel hydraulic circuit bleeder valve.

14. Install a transparent hose over the end of the bleeder valve, then repeat steps 7-11.

15. With the left rear wheel hydraulic circuit bleeder valve tightened securely, and after all air has been purged from the left rear hydraulic circuit, install a proper box-end wrench onto the RIGHT FRONT wheel hydraulic circuit bleeder valve.

16. Install a transparent hose over the end of the bleeder valve, then repeat steps 7-11.

17. After completing the final wheel hydraulic circuit bleeding procedure, ensure that each of the 4 wheel hydraulic circuit bleeder valves is properly tightened.

18. Slowly depress and release the brake pedal. Observe the feel of the brake pedal.

19. If the brake pedal feels spongy, repeat the bleeding procedure again. If the brake pedal still feels spongy after repeating the bleeding procedure, perform the following steps:

- Inspect the brake system for external leaks.
- Pressure bleed the hydraulic brake system in order to purge any air that may still be trapped in the system.

20. Turn the ignition key ON, with the engine OFF. Check to see if the brake system warning lamp remains illuminated.

❋❋ WARNING

DO NOT allow the vehicle to be driven until it is diagnosed and repaired.

BLEEDING THE ABS SYSTEM

The ABS Automated Bleed Procedure uses a scan tool to cycle the system solenoid valves and run the pump in order to purge any air from the secondary circuits. These circuits are normally closed off, and are only opened during system initialization at vehicle start up and during ABS operation. The automated bleed procedure opens these secondary circuits and allows any air trapped in these circuits to flow out toward the brake corners.

➡ **The Auto Bleed Procedure may be terminated at any time during the process by pressing the EXIT button. No further Scan Tool prompts pertaining to the Auto Bleed procedure will be given. After exiting the bleed procedure, relieve bleed pressure and disconnect bleed equipment per manufacturer's instructions. Failure to properly relieve pressure may result in spilled brake fluid causing damage to components and painted surfaces.**

1. Raise and support the vehicle.
2. Remove all 4 tire and wheel assemblies.
3. Inspect the brake system for leaks and visual damage.
4. Lower the vehicle.
5. Inspect the battery state of charge.
6. Install a scan tool.
7. Turn the ignition ON, with the engine OFF.
8. With the scan tool, establish communications with the ABS system. Select Special Functions. Select Automated Bleed from the Special Functions menu.
9. Raise and support the vehicle.
10. Following the directions given on the scan tool, pressure bleed the base brake system.
11. Follow the scan tool directions until the desired brake pedal height is achieved.

12. If the bleed procedure is aborted, a malfunction exists. Perform the following steps before resuming the bleed procedure:
- If a DTC is detected, diagnose the appropriate DTC.
- If the brake pedal feels spongy, perform the conventional brake bleed procedure again.

13. When the desired pedal height is achieved, press the brake pedal to inspect for firmness.
14. Lower the vehicle.
15. Remove the scan tool.
16. Install the tire and wheel assemblies.
17. Inspect the brake fluid level.
18. Road test the vehicle while inspecting that the pedal remains high and firm.

BRAKES   FRONT DISC BRAKES

✳ CAUTION

Dust and dirt accumulating on brake parts during normal use may contain asbestos fibers from production or aftermarket brake linings. Breathing excessive concentrations of asbestos fibers can cause serious bodily harm. Exercise care when servicing brake parts. Do not sand or grind brake lining unless equipment used is designed to contain the dust residue. Do not clean brake parts with compressed air or by dry brushing. Cleaning should be done by dampening the brake components with a fine mist of water, then wiping the brake components clean with a dampened cloth. Dispose of cloth and all residue containing asbestos fibers in an impermeable container with the appropriate label. Follow practices prescribed by the Occupational Safety and Health Administration (OSHA) and the Environmental Protection Agency (EPA) for the handling, processing, and disposing of dust or debris that may contain asbestos fibers.

BRAKE CALIPER

REMOVAL & INSTALLATION

See Figure 6.

1. Before servicing the vehicle, refer to the precautions section.
2. Inspect the fluid level in the brake master cylinder reservoir.

3. If the brake fluid level is midway between the maximum-full point and the minimum allowable level, no brake fluid needs to be removed from the reservoir before proceeding.
4. If the brake fluid level is higher than midway between the maximum-full point and the minimum allowable level, remove brake fluid to the midway point before proceeding.
5. Raise and safely support the vehicle.
6. Remove the tire and wheel assembly.
7. Install and firmly hand tighten 2 wheel nuts to opposite wheel studs in order to retain the rotor to the hub.
8. Install a large C-clamp over the body of the brake caliper with the C-clamp ends against the rear of the caliper body and against the outer brake pad.
9. Tighten the C-clamp until the caliper piston is compressed into the caliper bore

Fig. 6 Caliper mounting

06025-EQUI-G108

enough to allow the caliper to slide past the brake rotor.
10. Remove the C-clamp from the caliper.
11. Remove the brake hose-to-caliper bolt from the brake caliper.
12. Remove the brake hose from the brake caliper.
13. Remove and discard the 2 copper brake hose gaskets. These gaskets may be stuck to the brake caliper and/or the brake hose end.
14. Cap or plug the opening in the brake caliper and the brake hose to prevent fluid loss and contamination.
15. Remove the brake caliper guide pin bolts.
16. Remove the brake caliper from the caliper bracket.
17. Inspect the brake caliper guide pins for freedom of movement, and inspect the condition of the guide pin boots. Move the guide pins inboard and outboard within the bracket bores, without disengaging the slides from the boots, and observe for the following:
- Restricted caliper guide pin movement
- Looseness in the brake caliper mounting bracket
- Seized or binding caliper guide pins
- Split or torn boots

If any of the conditions listed are found, the brake caliper guide pins and/or boots require replacement.

To install:

18. Apply a light, thin coat of high temperature silicone brake lubricant to the caliper guide pins.

19. Install the guide pins to the brake caliper bracket.

20. Install the brake caliper to the brake caliper bracket.

21. Thoroughly clean the thread locker residue from the guide pin bolt threads with denatured alcohol or equivalent and allow to dry.

22. Apply high-temperature, high-strength thread locker to ⅔ of the threaded length of the brake caliper guide pin bolt.

23. Install the brake caliper guide pin bolts. Tighten the bolts to 20 ft. lbs. (27 Nm).

24. Remove the caps or plugs from the brake caliper opening and the brake hose.

❋❋ WARNING

Do not reuse the copper brake hose gaskets.

25. Install NEW copper brake hose gaskets to the brake hose-to-caliper bolt and to the brake hose.

26. Install the brake hose and the brake hose-to-brake caliper bolt to the brake caliper. Tighten the bolt to 38 ft. lbs. (52 Nm).

27. Bleed the hydraulic brake system.

28. Remove the wheel nuts retaining the brake rotor to the wheel hub.

29. Install the tire and wheel assembly.

30. Lower the vehicle.

31. With the engine OFF, gradually apply the brake pedal to approximately ⅔ of its travel distance.

32. Slowly release the brake pedal.

33. Wait 15 seconds, then gradually apply the brake pedal approximately ⅔ of its travel distance again until a firm brake pedal apply is obtained. This will properly seat the brake caliper pistons and brake pads.

34. Fill the master cylinder reservoir to the proper level.

DISC BRAKE PADS

REMOVAL & INSTALLATION

See Figures 7 and 8.

1. Before servicing the vehicle, refer to the precautions section.

2. Inspect the fluid level in the brake master cylinder auxiliary reservoir.

3. If the brake fluid level is midway between the maximum-full point and the minimum allowable level, no brake fluid

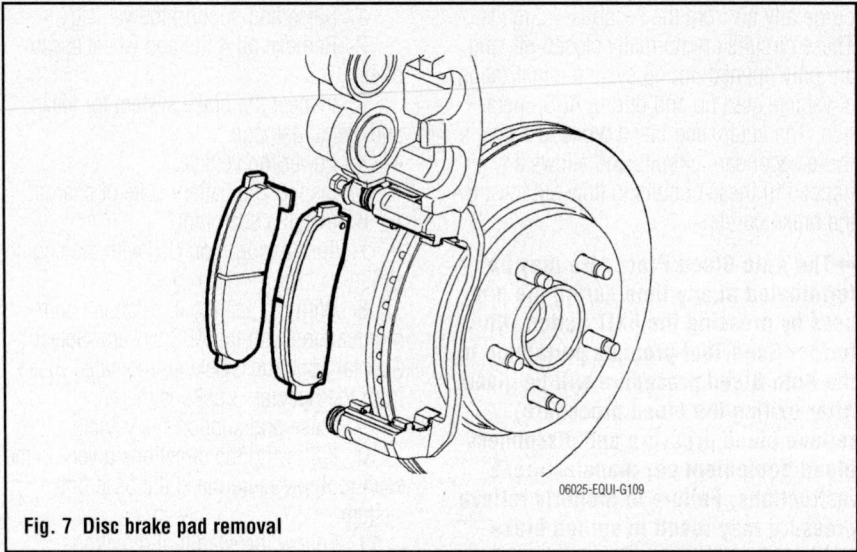
Fig. 7 Disc brake pad removal

06025-EQUI-G109

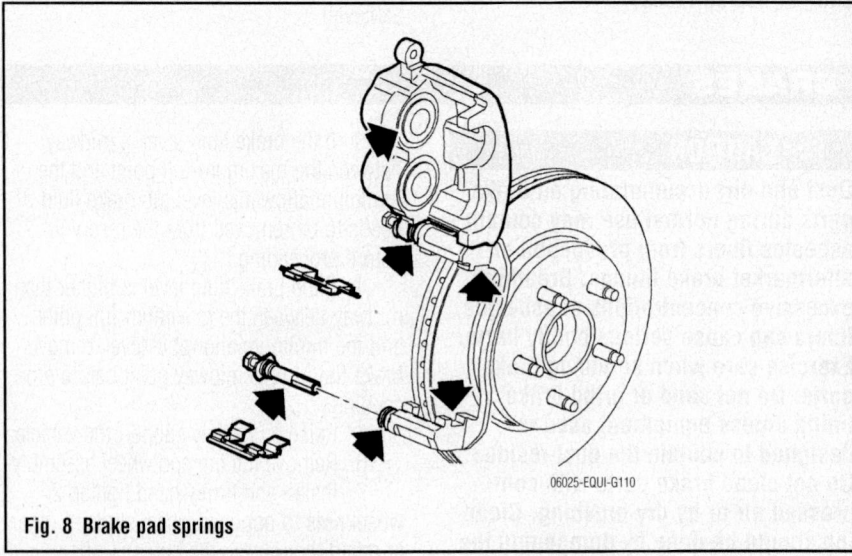
Fig. 8 Brake pad springs

06025-EQUI-G110

needs to be removed from the reservoir before proceeding.

4. If the brake fluid level is higher than midway between the maximum-full point and the minimum allowable level, remove brake fluid to the midway point before proceeding.

5. Raise and safely support the vehicle.

6. Remove the tire and wheel assembly.

7. Install and firmly hand tighten 2 wheel nuts to opposite wheel studs in order to retain the rotor to the hub.

8. Install a large C-clamp over the body of the brake caliper with the C-clamp ends against the rear of the caliper body and against the outboard brake pad.

9. Tighten the C-clamp evenly until the caliper piston is compressed into the caliper bore enough to allow the caliper to slide past the brake rotor.

10. Remove the C-clamp from the caliper.

11. Remove the brake caliper lower guide pin bolt.

❋❋ WARNING

Support the brake caliper with heavy mechanic's wire, or equivalent, whenever it is separated from its mount and the hydraulic flexible brake hose is still connected. Failure to support the caliper in this manner will cause the flexible brake hose to bear the weight of the caliper, which may cause damage to the brake hose and in turn may cause a brake fluid leak.

12. Without disconnecting the hydraulic brake flexible hose, pivot the caliper upward and secure the caliper with heavy mechanics wire, or equivalent.

13. Remove the brake pads from the caliper mounting bracket.

14. Remove the brake pad springs from the caliper bracket.

15. Thoroughly clean the brake pad hardware mating surfaces of the caliper bracket, of any debris and corrosion.

16. Inspect the brake caliper guide pins for freedom of movement, and inspect the condition of the guide pin boots. Move the guide pins inboard and outboard within the bracket bores, without disengaging the slides from the boots, and observe for the following:
- Restricted caliper guide pin movement
- Looseness in the brake caliper mounting bracket
- Seized or binding caliper guide pins
- Split or torn boots

If any of the conditions listed are found, the brake caliper guide pins and/or boots require replacement.

To install:

17. Install a large C-clamp over the body of the brake caliper, with the C-clamp ends against the rear of the caliper body and against an old inboard brake pad or a wood block installed against the caliper piston.

18. Tighten the C-clamp evenly until the caliper piston is compressed completely into the caliper bore.

19. Remove the C-clamp and the old brake pad or wood block from the caliper.

20. Apply a very thin coating of high temperature silicone brake lubricant to the pad hardware mating surfaces of the caliper bracket only.

21. Install new springs to the brake caliper bracket. **DO NOT** reuse the springs.

✳✳ WARNING

The wear sensor equipped disc brake pad must be mounted inboard of the rotor with the leading edge of the sensor facing the brake rotor during forward wheel rotation, or at the top of the pad when installed in vehicle position.

22. Install the brake pads to the caliper bracket.

23. Remove the support, and rotate the brake caliper into position over the disc brake pads and to the caliper mounting bracket.

24. Install the lower brake caliper guide pin bolt. Tighten the bolt to 20 ft. lbs. (27 Nm).

25. Remove the wheel nuts retaining the brake rotor to the hub.

26. Install the tire and wheel assembly.

27. Lower the vehicle.

28. With the engine OFF, gradually apply the brake pedal approximately ⅔ of its travel distance.

29. Slowly release the brake pedal.

30. Wait 15 seconds, then gradually apply the brake pedal approximately ⅔ of its travel distance again until a firm brake pedal apply is obtained. This will properly seat the brake caliper pistons and brake pads.

31. Fill the master cylinder auxiliary reservoir to the proper level.

32. Burnish the pads and rotors.

BRAKES

REAR DISC BRAKES

✳✳ CAUTION

Dust and dirt accumulating on brake parts during normal use may contain asbestos fibers from production or aftermarket brake linings. Breathing excessive concentrations of asbestos fibers can cause serious bodily harm. Exercise care when servicing brake parts. Do not sand or grind brake lining unless equipment used is designed to contain the dust residue. Do not clean brake parts with compressed air or by dry brushing. Cleaning should be done by dampening the brake components with a fine mist of water, then wiping the brake components clean with a dampened cloth. Dispose of cloth and all residue containing asbestos fibers in an impermeable container with the appropriate label. Follow practices prescribed by the Occupational Safety and Health Administration (OSHA) and the Environmental Protection Agency (EPA) for the handling, processing, and disposing of dust or debris that may contain asbestos fibers.

BRAKE CALIPER

REMOVAL & INSTALLATION

See Figure 9.

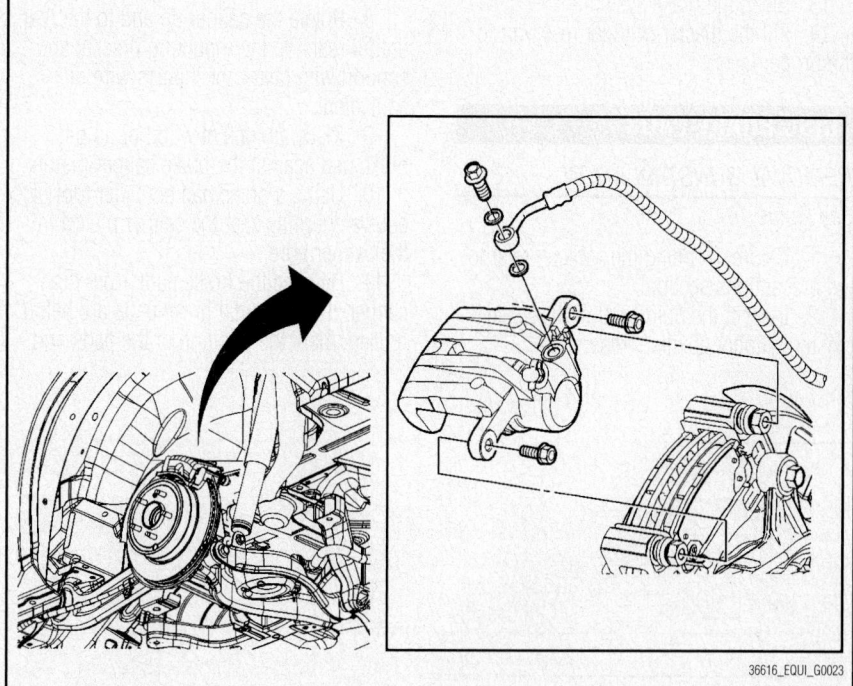

36616_EQUI_G0023

Fig. 9 Rear brake caliper removal shown

1. Before servicing the vehicle, refer to the precautions section.

2. Raise and safely support the vehicle.

3. Remove the rear wheel.

4. Remove the brake hose fitting bolt ,and discard the gasket.

✳✳ WARNING

Cap the brake hose to prevent any contamination to the brake fluid.

5. Remove the brake caliper guide pin bolts.

6. Remove the brake caliper from the caliper bracket.

To install:

7. Thoroughly clean the thread locker residue from the guide pin bolt threads with denatured alcohol or equivalent and allow to dry.

8. Apply high-temperature, high-strength thread locker to ⅔ of the threaded length of the brake caliper guide pin bolt.

9. Install the brake caliper guide pin bolts to the caliper mounting bracket. Tighten the guide pin bolts to 20 ft. lbs. (27 Nm).

10. Install the brake hoses with NEW gaskets. Tighten the brake hose fitting bolt to 38 ft. lbs. (52 Nm).

11. Install the rear wheel.

12. Lower the vehicle.

13. Bleed the brake system.

14. Fill the master cylinder reservoir to the proper level.

DISC BRAKE PADS

REMOVAL & INSTALLATION

See Figure 10.

1. Before servicing the vehicle, refer to the precautions section.

2. Inspect the fluid level in the brake master cylinder auxiliary reservoir.

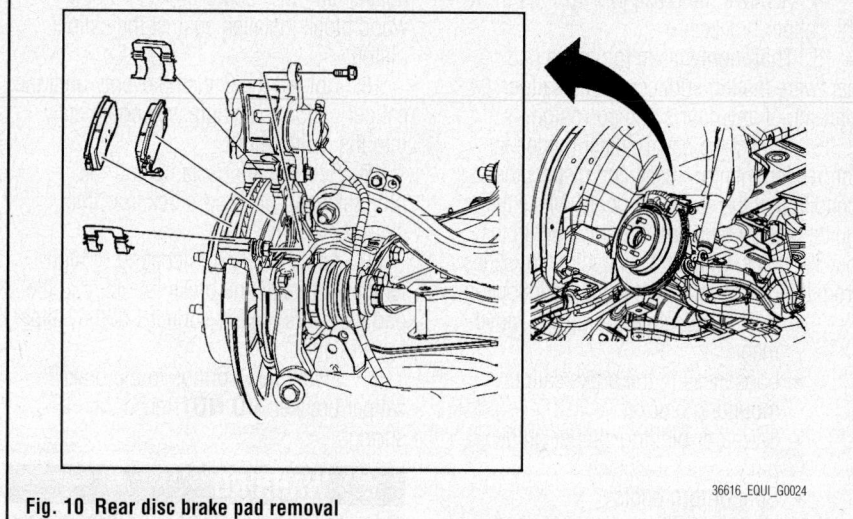

Fig. 10 Rear disc brake pad removal

36616_EQUI_G0024

3. If the brake fluid level is midway between the maximum-full point and the minimum allowable level, no brake fluid needs to be removed from the reservoir before proceeding.

4. If the brake fluid level is higher than midway between the maximum-full point and the minimum allowable level, remove brake fluid to the midway point before proceeding.

5. Raise and safely support the vehicle.

6. Remove the rear wheel.

7. Remove one caliper guide pin bolt.

8. Rotate the caliper up and to the rear until it rests on the mounting bracket and support with heavy mechanics wire or equivalent.

9. Place a block of wood or an old brake pad against the brake caliper piston.

10. Using a brake pad spreader tool or equivalent, fully seat the caliper piston in the caliper bore.

11. Remove the brake pads from the caliper. If the original brake pads are being reused, mark the position of the pads and springs. If the brake pads are being replaced, discard the springs.

To install:

12. Install the brake pads with new springs to the caliper. **DO NOT** reuse the springs.

13. Rotate the caliper down and tighten the guide pin bolt to 20 ft. lbs. (27 Nm).

14. Install the tire and wheel assembly.

15. Lower the vehicle.

16. With the engine OFF, gradually apply the brake pedal approximately ⅔ of its travel distance.

17. Slowly release the brake pedal.

18. Wait 15 seconds, then gradually apply the brake pedal approximately ⅔ of its travel distance again until a firm brake pedal apply is obtained. This will properly seat the brake caliper pistons and brake pads.

19. Fill the master cylinder reservoir to the proper level.

20. Burnish the pads and rotors.

BRAKES   **PARKING BRAKE**

PARKING BRAKE CABLES

ADJUSTMENT

See Figures 11 and 12.

1. Before servicing the vehicle, refer to the precautions section.

2. Remove the front floor console.

3. With the park brake lever in the fully released position, using **ONLY** hand tools, loosen the adjusting nut completely to the end of the front cable threaded rod.

4. Raise the park brake lever 1 detent position.

5. Using **ONLY** hand tools, tighten the park brake cable adjusting nut until light to moderate drag is exhibited while rotating the rear wheels.

6. Attempt to rotate the rear wheels. There should be no rotation forward or rearward.

7. Fully release the park brake lever.

8. Verify the park brake is released by rotating the rear wheels. The wheels should rotate freely and exhibit no park brake shoe drag.

9. If the wheels do not rotate freely, repeat the park brake cable adjustment procedure.

10. Raise the park brake lever 3 detent positions and attempt to rotate the rear wheels as follows:
   - One of the wheels should not rotate forward or rearward.
   - The other wheel should not rotate forward or rearward, or should require substantial effort to rotate.

11. Install the front floor console.

12. Release the park brake lever.

PARKING BRAKE SHOES

REMOVAL & INSTALLATION

See Figure 13.

1. Before servicing the vehicle, refer to the precautions section.

2. Raise and safely support the vehicle.

3. Remove the rear wheel.

4. Remove the rear brake rotor.

5. Use denatured alcohol to clean brake dust or grease from the park brake shoes and hardware

6. Compress the parking brake shoe hold spring and rotate ¼ turn to release.

7. Using a Brake Spring Remover, remove the parking brake shoe adjuster spring.

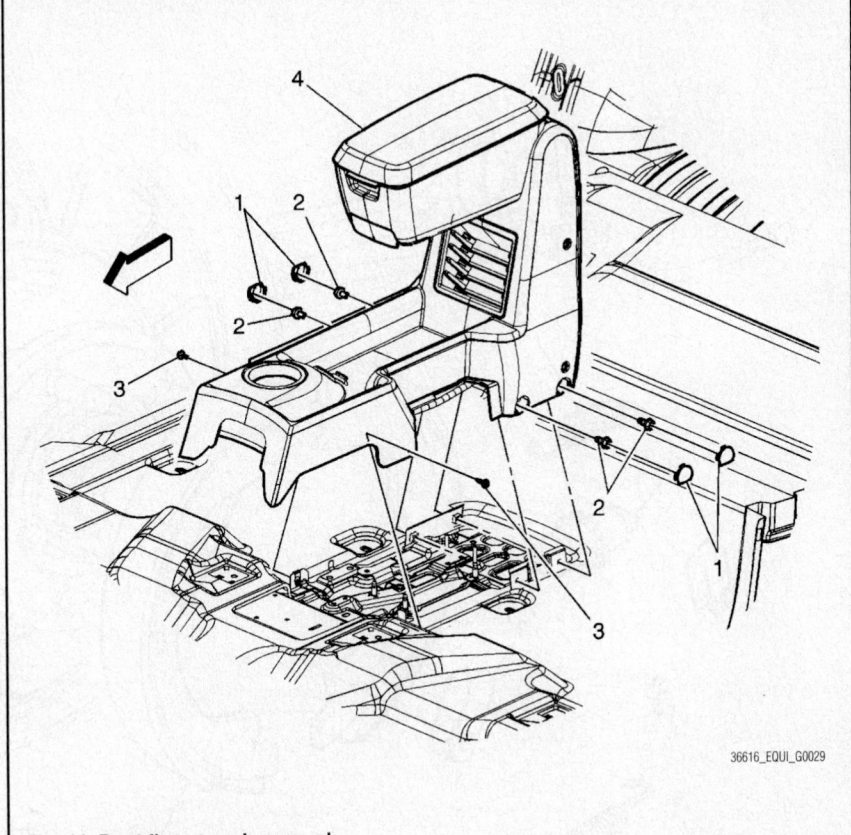

Fig. 11 Front floor console removal.

36616_EQUI_G0029

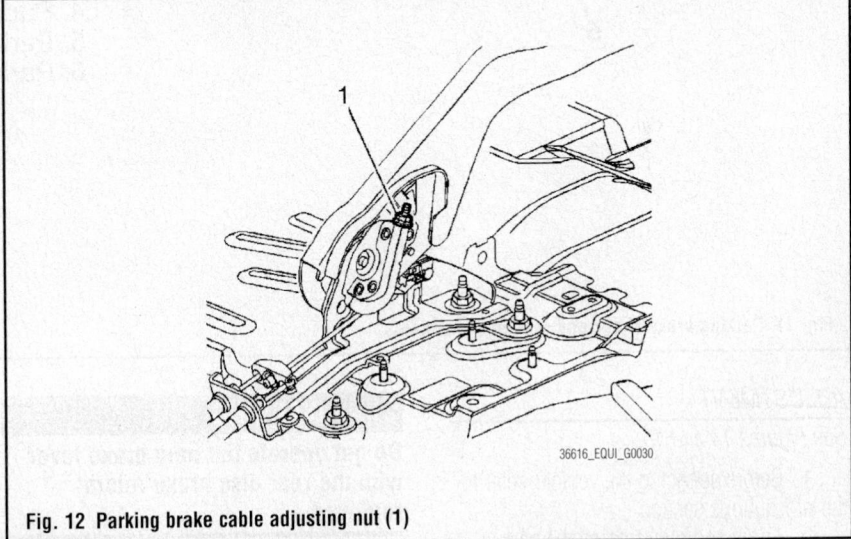

36616_EQUI_G0030

Fig. 12 Parking brake cable adjusting nut (1)

8. Remove the parking brake shoe adjuster screw.

9. Using a Brake Spring Remover, remove the parking brake shoe return spring.

10. Remove the parking brake shoes.

To install:

11. Clean the threads and apply high temperature grease to the adjuster screw

12. Apply a small amount of high temperature silicone grease to the brake shoe and backing plate contact points.

13. Reverse the removal procedure to install the parking brake shoes.

14. Adjust the parking brake shoes.

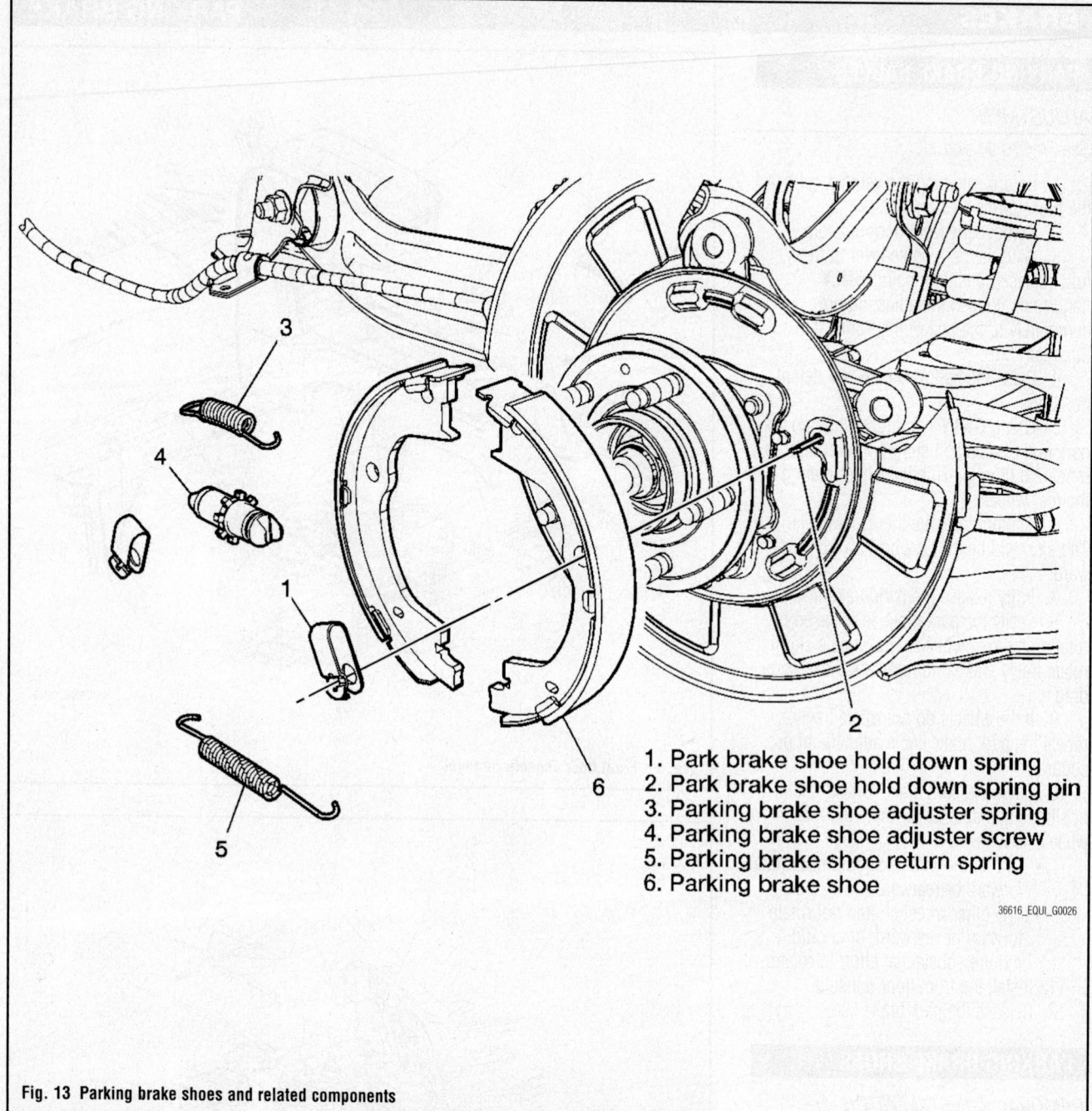

1. Park brake shoe hold down spring
2. Park brake shoe hold down spring pin
3. Parking brake shoe adjuster spring
4. Parking brake shoe adjuster screw
5. Parking brake shoe return spring
6. Parking brake shoe

36616_EQUI_G0026

Fig. 13 Parking brake shoes and related components

ADJUSTMENT

See Figures 14 and 15.

1. Before servicing the vehicle, refer to the precautions section.

2. Apply and fully release the park brake lever.

3. Verify that the park brake lever releases completely.

4. Turn ON the ignition. Verify that the red BRAKE warning indicator lamp is off.

5. Turn OFF the ignition.

6. Raise and safely support the vehicle.

7. Remove the rear wheel assemblies.

✱✱ WARNING

Do not operate the park brake lever with the rear disc brake rotors removed.

8. Remove the rear disc brake rotors.

9. Place the inside measurement contacts of the Special Tool J 21177-A Drum to Brake Shoe Clearance Gauge at the widest point of the drum portion of the brake rotor.

10. Tighten the set screw on the tool in order to ensure the proper measurement

when removing the tool from the drum.

11. Position the outside measurement contacts of Special Tool J 21177-A over the park brake shoe at the widest point.

✱✱ WARNING

If the gap between the adjuster nut and the adjuster screw exceeds 5 mm (0.25 in) during the adjustment procedure, the park brake shoe must be replaced.

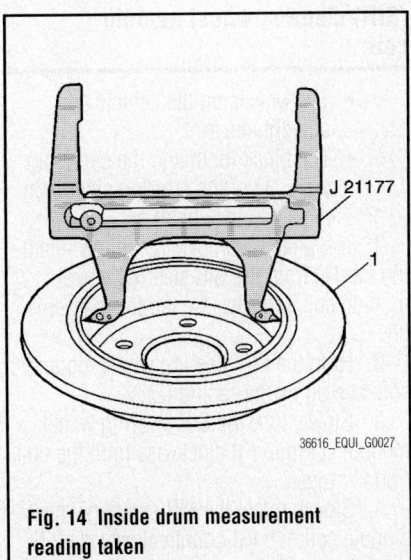

Fig. 14 Inside drum measurement reading taken

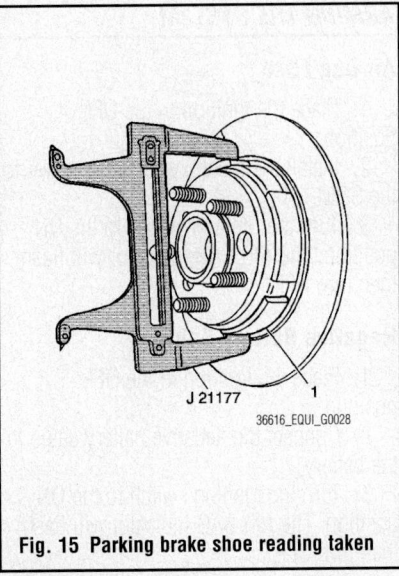

Fig. 15 Parking brake shoe reading taken

12. Adjust the park brake shoe-to-drum clearance by rotating the adjustment nut on the park brake actuator. Clearance should be 0.015 in (0.38 mm).

13. Install the rear brake rotors.

14. Install the rear wheel.

15. Apply the park brake lever. Inspect the rotation of the rear wheels:

- The wheels should not rotate forward.
- The wheels should drag or not rotate rearward.

16. If the rear tire and wheel assemblies rotate forward or do not exhibit drag rearward, proceed to the park brake cable adjustment.

17. Release the park brake lever. Verify that the wheels rotate freely.

CHASSIS ELECTRICAL · AIR BAG (SUPPLEMENTAL RESTRAINT SYSTEM)

GENERAL INFORMATION

✷✷ CAUTION

These vehicles are equipped with an air bag system. The system must be disarmed before performing service on, or around, system components, the steering column, instrument panel components, wiring and sensors. Failure to follow the safety precautions and the disarming procedure could result in accidental air bag deployment, possible injury and unnecessary system repairs.

SERVICE PRECAUTIONS

Disconnect and isolate the battery negative cable before beginning any airbag system component diagnosis, testing, removal, or installation procedures. Allow system capacitor to discharge for two minutes before beginning any component service. This will disable the airbag system. Failure to disable the airbag system may result in accidental airbag deployment, personal injury, or death.

Do not place an intact undeployed airbag face down on a solid surface. The airbag will propel into the air if accidentally deployed and may result in personal injury or death.

When carrying or handling an undeployed airbag, the trim side (face) of the airbag should be pointing towards the body to minimize possibility of injury if accidental deployment occurs. Failure to do this may result in personal injury or death.

Replace airbag system components with OEM replacement parts. Substitute parts may appear interchangeable, but internal differences may result in inferior occupant protection. Failure to do so may result in occupant personal injury or death.

Wear safety glasses, rubber gloves, and long sleeved clothing when cleaning powder residue from vehicle after an airbag deployment. Powder residue emitted from a deployed airbag can cause skin irritation. Flush affected area with cool water if irritation is experienced. If nasal or throat irritation is experienced, exit the vehicle for fresh air until the irritation ceases. If irritation continues, see a physician.

Do not use a replacement airbag that is not in the original packaging. This may result in improper deployment, personal injury, or death.

The factory installed fasteners, screws and bolts used to fasten airbag components have a special coating and are specifically designed for the airbag system. Do not use substitute fasteners. Use only original equipment fasteners listed in the parts catalog when fastener replacement is required.

During, and following, any child restraint anchor service, due to impact event or vehicle repair, carefully inspect all mounting hardware, tether straps, and anchors for proper installation, operation, or damage. If a child restraint anchor is found damaged in any way, the anchor must be replaced. Failure to do this may result in personal injury or death.

Deployed and non-deployed airbags may or may not have live pyrotechnic material within the airbag inflator.

Do not dispose of driver/passenger/curtain airbags or seat belt tensioners unless you are sure of complete deployment. Refer to the Hazardous Substance Control System for proper disposal.

Dispose of deployed airbags and tensioners consistent with state, provincial, local, and federal regulations.

After any airbag component testing or service, do not connect the battery negative cable. Personal injury or death may result if the system test is not performed first.

If the vehicle is equipped with the Occupant Classification System (OCS), do not connect the battery negative cable before performing the OCS Verification Test using the scan tool and the appropriate diagnostic information. Personal injury or death may result if the system test is not performed properly.

Never replace both the Occupant Restraint Controller (ORC) and the Occupant Classification Module (OCM) at the same time. If both require replacement, replace one, then perform the Airbag System test before replacing the other.

Both the ORC and the OCM store Occupant Classification System (OCS) calibration data, which they transfer to one another when one of them is replaced. If both are replaced at the same time, an irreversible fault will be set in both modules and the OCS may malfunction and cause personal injury or death.

If equipped with OCS, the Seat Weight Sensor is a sensitive, calibrated unit and must be handled carefully. Do not drop or handle roughly. If dropped or damaged, replace with another sensor. Failure to do so may result in occupant injury or death.

If equipped with OCS, the front passenger seat must be handled carefully as well. When removing the seat, be careful when setting on floor not to drop. If dropped, the sensor may be inoperative, could result in occupant injury, or possibly death.

If equipped with OCS, when the passenger front seat is on the floor, no one should sit in the front passenger seat. This uneven force may damage the sensing ability of the seat weight sensors. If sat on and damaged, the sensor may be inoperative, could result in occupant injury, or possibly death.

DISARMING THE SYSTEM

Air Bag Fuse

1. Turn the steering wheel so that the vehicles wheels are pointing straight ahead.
2. Place the ignition in the OFF position.

✴✴ CAUTION

The Sensing and Diagnostic Module (SDM) may have more than one fused power input. To ensure there is no unwanted Supplemental Inflatable Restraint (SIR) deployment, personal injury, or unnecessary SIR system repairs, remove all fuses supplying power to the SDM. With all SDM fuses removed and the ignition switch in the ON position, the AIR BAG warning indicator illuminates. This is normal operation, and does not indicate a SIR system malfunction.

3. Locate and remove the fuse(s) supplying power to the SDM.
4. Wait 1 minute before working on the system

Negative Battery Cable

1. Turn the steering wheel so that the vehicles wheels are pointing straight ahead.
2. Place the ignition in the OFF position.
3. Disconnect the negative battery cable from the battery.
4. Wait 1 minute before working on system.

ARMING THE SYSTEM

Air Bag Fuse

1. Place the ignition in the OFF position.
2. Install the fuse(s) supplying power to the SDM.
3. Turn the ignition switch to the ON position. The AIR BAG indicator will flash then turn OFF.

Negative Battery Cable

1. Place the ignition in the OFF position.
2. Connect the negative battery cable to the battery.
3. Turn the ignition switch to the ON position. The AIR BAG indicator will flash then turn OFF.

CLOCKSPRING CENTERING

See Figure 16.

✴✴ WARNING

The new SIR coil assembly will be centered. Improper alignment of the SIR coil assembly may damage the unit, causing an inflatable restraint malfunction. Verify the following conditions before centering the Supplemental Inflatable Restraint

(SIR) steering wheel module coil:

- The wheels on the vehicle are straight ahead.
- The block tooth and the centering mark (1) of the steering shaft is in the 12 o'clock position.

1. If available, remove the yellow retaining tab (1) from the SIR steering wheel module coil and save the tab for reassembly.
2. Hold the SIR steering wheel module coil face up by the casing (2).
3. Slowly turn the SIR steering wheel module coil hub (3) clockwise until the coil ribbon stops.
4. Slowly rotate the SIR steering wheel module coil hub (3) counterclockwise 2.5 revolutions until the centering window (4) turns yellow. This indicates the CENTER position.

→If the retaining tab is not available, the use of tape to secure the SIR steering wheel module coil is recommended for installation to the steering column.

5. Install the yellow retaining tab (1) to the SIR steering wheel module coil.
6. Slide the centered SIR steering wheel module coil onto the steering shaft.

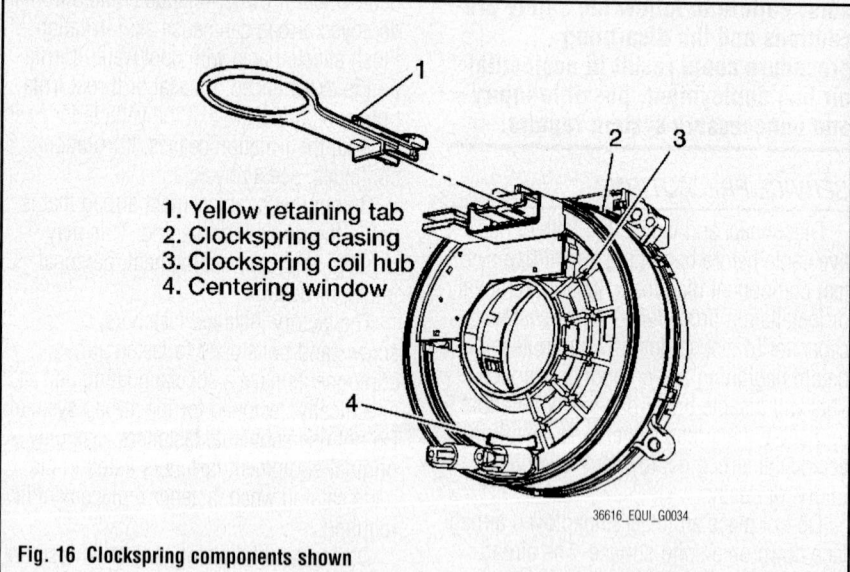

1. Yellow retaining tab
2. Clockspring casing
3. Clockspring coil hub
4. Centering window

36616_EQUI_G0034

Fig. 16 Clockspring components shown

DRIVE TRAIN

AUTOMATIC TRANSAXLE ASSEMBLY

REMOVAL & INSTALLATION

6T70/6T75 Transaxles

See Figures 17 and 18.

1. Before servicing the vehicle, refer to the precautions section.

2. Disconnect the battery terminals and remove the battery.

3. Remove the battery tray.

4. Raise the vehicle.

5. Remove the tire and wheel assemblies.

6. Remove the engine splash shields.

7. Disconnect the control valve body Transaxle Control Module (TCM) electrical connector.

8. Remove the transaxle fluid cooler pipe retainer nut.

9. Remove the transaxle fluid cooler inlet hose and seal from the transaxle.

10. Plug the hose and transaxle to prevent contamination.

11. Remove the transaxle fluid cooler pipe retainer nut.

12. Remove the transaxle fluid cooler outlet hose and seal from the transaxle.

13. Plug the hose and transaxle to prevent contamination.

14. Remove the frame. Refer to Frame Removal & Installation in the Front Suspension section.

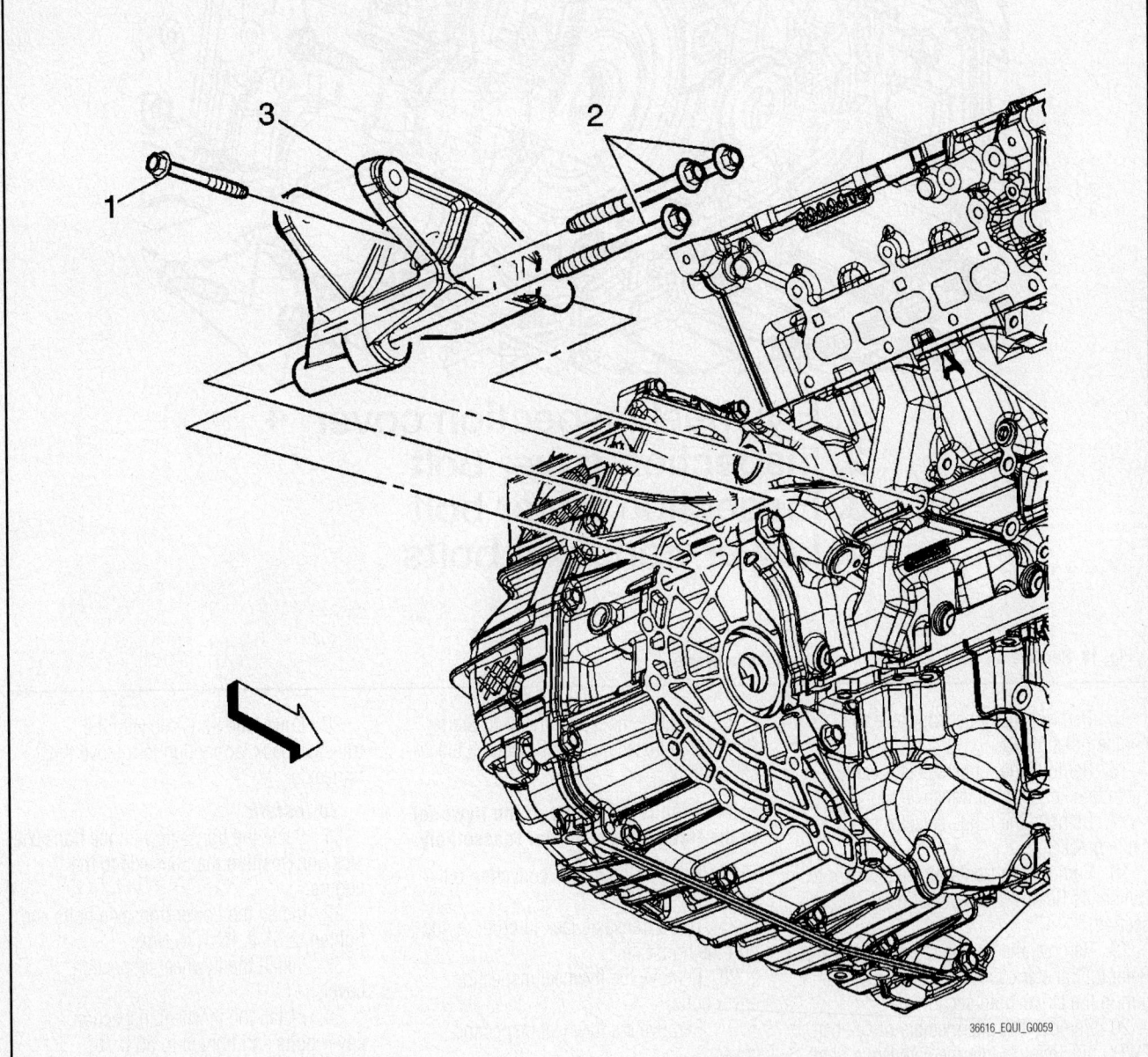

36616_EQUI_G0059

Fig. 17 Rear transaxle mount bracket removal—2WD

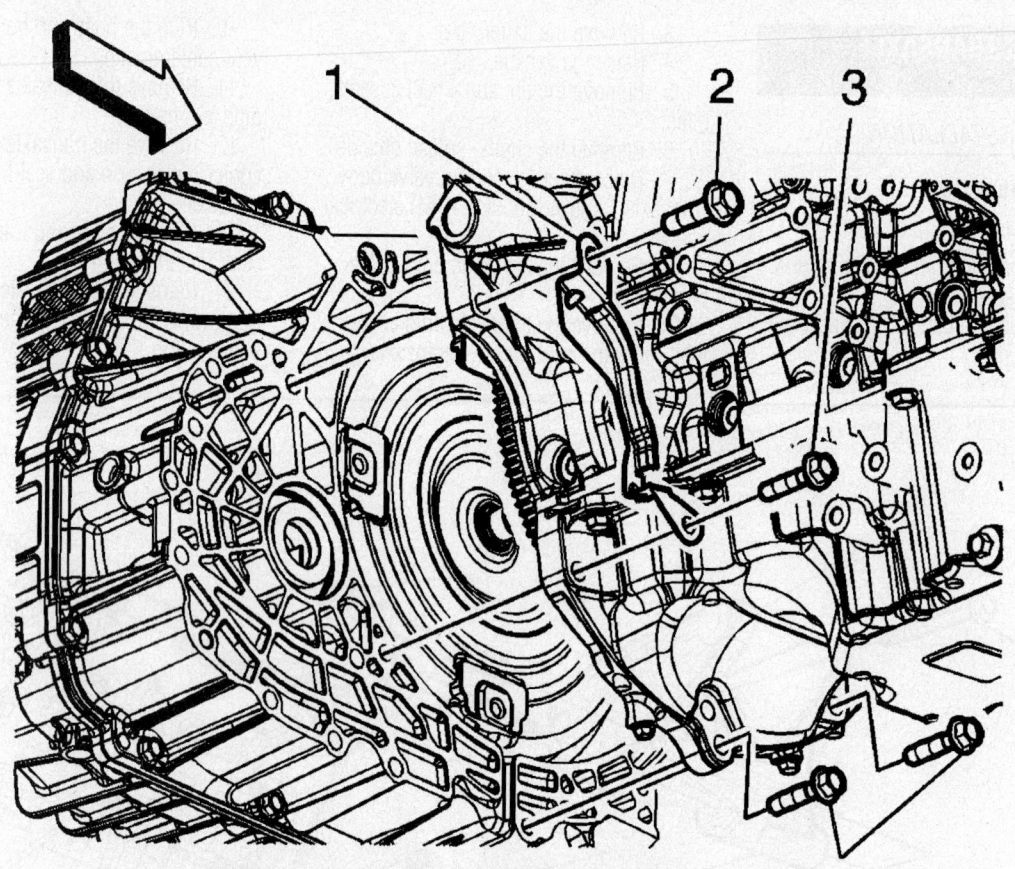

1. Flywheel inspection cover
2. Inspection cover bolt
3. Inspection cover bolt
4. Lower transaxle bolts

36616_EQUI_G0060

Fig. 18 Remove the bolts, separate and remove the transaxle

15. Remove the upper transaxle to engine bolts (1, 2).

16. Remove the range selector cable, cable bracket, and left transaxle mount.

17. Remove the range selector cable, cable bracket.

18. Remove the front halfshafts. Refer to Halfshafts Removal & Installation in this section.

19. Remove the transfer case, AWD only. Refer to Transfer case Removal & Installation in the Drive Train section

20. Remove the intermediate drive shaft, 2WD only. Refer to Intermediate Drive Shaft Removal & Installation.

21. Remove the rear transaxle mount bracket, 2WD only.

22. Remove the front transaxle mount.

23. Remove the starter. Refer to Starter Removal & Installation in the Engine Electrical section.

→ **Mark the relationship of the flywheel to the torque converter for reassembly.**

24. Remove the torque converter to flywheel bolts.

25. Use a transaxle jack in order to support the transaxle.

26. Remove the flywheel inspection cover bolts.

27. Remove the flywheel inspection cover.

28. Remove the remaining transaxle bolts.

29. Separate the transaxle from the engine.

30. Lower the transaxle with the transaxle jack far enough to remove the transaxle.

To install:

31. Raise the transaxle with the transaxle jack and position the transaxle to the engine.

32. Install the Lower transaxle bolts and tighten to 55 ft. lbs. (75 Nm).

33. Install the flywheel inspection cover.

34. Install the flywheel inspection cover bolts and tighten to 55 ft. lbs. (75 Nm).

35. Remove the transaxle jack.

36. Install the torque converter to flywheel bolts and tighten to 46 ft. lbs. (62 Nm).

37. Install the starter. Refer to Starter Removal & Installation in the Engine Electrical section.

38. Install the front transaxle mount.

39. Install the rear transaxle mount bracket and mount, 2WD only.

40. Install the intermediate drive shaft, 2WD only. Refer to Intermediate Drive Shaft Removal & Installation in the Drive Train section.

41. Install the transfer case, AWD only. Refer to Transfer case Removal & Installation in the Drive Train section.

42. Install the wheel halfshafts. Refer to Halfshaft Removal & Installation in this section.

43. Lower the vehicle.

44. Install the left transaxle mount, range selector cable bracket, and cable.

45. Install the upper transaxle to engine bolt (1, 2) and tighten to 55 ft. lbs. (75 Nm).

46. Install the frame.

47. Install the transaxle fluid cooler outlet and inlet hoses and seals to the transaxle.

48. Install the transaxle fluid cooler pipe retainer nuts and tighten to 16 ft. lbs. (22 Nm).

49. Connect the control valve body TCM electrical connector.

50. Install the side splash shield-to-frame fasteners.

51. Install the front wheels.

52. Lower the vehicle.

53. Install the battery tray.

54. Adjust the automatic transaxle range selector lever cable, if needed.

55. Verify the proper fluid level of the transaxle. Use Dexron VI transaxle fluid only. Failure to use the proper fluid may result in transaxle internal damage.

56. Check the vehicles wheel alignment.

57. For transaxle control module programming, this will require specialized GM equipment. For step-by-step programming instructions, please refer to the Techline Information System (TIS) terminal.

➡**After an internal transaxle repair or internal part replacement the service fast learn adapt procedure should be performed.**

58. Road test the vehicle for proper transaxle operation and recheck the fluid level.

AF33-5 Transaxle

See Figures 19 through 24.

1. Before servicing the vehicle, refer to the precautions section.

2. Disconnect and remove the battery.

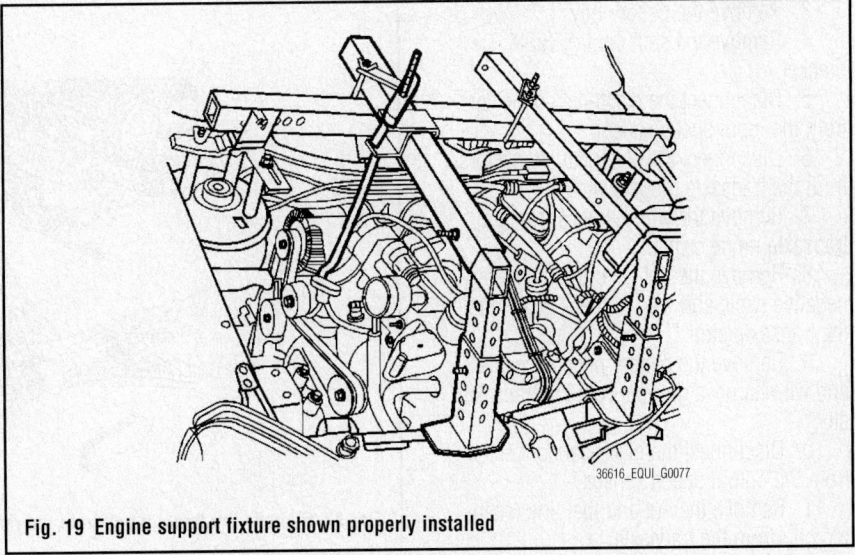

Fig. 19 Engine support fixture shown properly installed

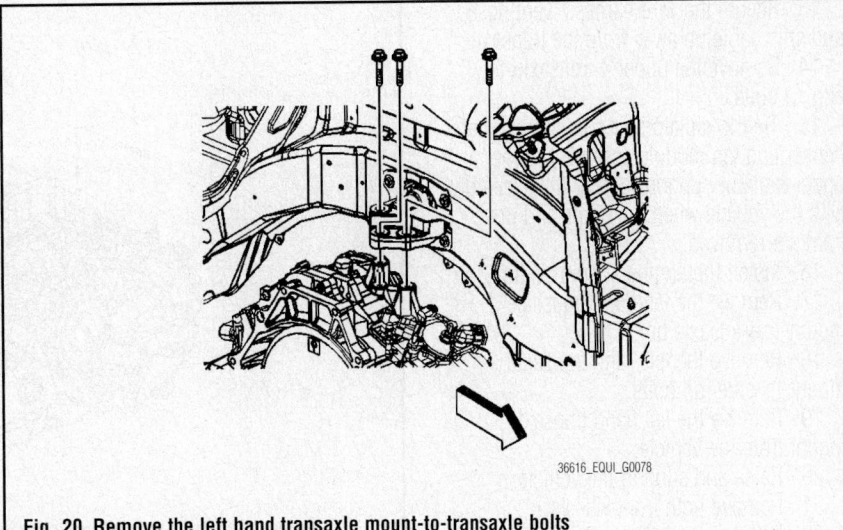

Fig. 20 Remove the left hand transaxle mount-to-transaxle bolts

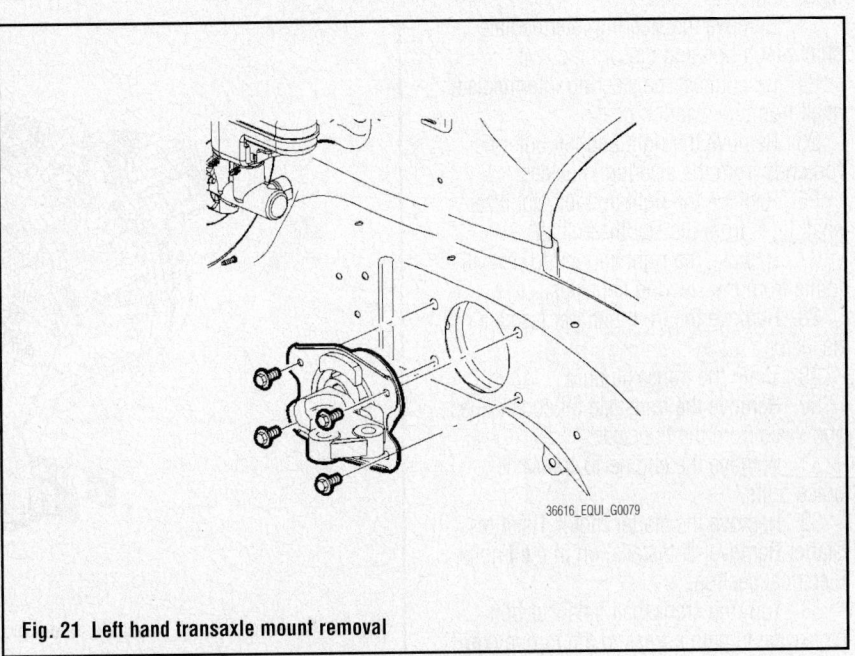

Fig. 21 Left hand transaxle mount removal

3. Remove the battery tray.

4. Remove the shift control cable bracket.

5. Disconnect the electrical connector from the input speed sensor.

6. Disconnect the electrical connectors from the transaxle range switch.

7. Remove the wire harness from the transaxle range switch.

8. Remove the nut securing the battery negative cable and wire harness ground to the transaxle stud.

9. Remove the battery negative cable and wire harness ground from the transaxle stud.

10. Disconnect the electrical connector from the output speed sensor.

11. Remove the nut and fuel line retaining clip from the transaxle.

12. Disconnect the transaxle vent tube.

13. Secure the wire harness, vent hose, and shift cable up away from the transaxle.

14. Remove the upper 4 transaxle-to-engine bolts.

15. Tie the radiator, air conditioning condenser and fan module assembly to the upper radiator support to keep the assembly with the vehicle when the frame and drive train are removed.

16. Install the engine support fixture.

17. Remove the left hand transaxle mount-to-transaxle bolts.

18. Remove the left hand transaxle mount-to-side rail bolts.

19. Remove the left hand transaxle mount from the vehicle.

20. Raise and support the vehicle.

21. Remove both front wheels.

22. Remove the left and right side engine splash shields.

23. Remove the steering intermediate shaft pinch bolt and discard the bolt.

24. Disconnect the steering intermediate shaft from the steering gear.

25. Remove the right and left outer tie rod ends from the steering knuckles.

26. Remove the right and left stabilizer shaft links from the stabilizer shaft.

27. Remove the right and left lower ball joints from the steering knuckles.

28. Remove the front bumper fascia air deflector.

29. Drain the transaxle fluid.

30. Remove the transaxle oil cooler lines and seals from the transaxle.

31. Remove the engine-to-transaxle brace bolts.

32. Remove the starter motor. Refer to Starter Removal & Installation in the Engine Electrical section.

33. Turn the crankshaft balancer bolt clockwise to gain access to the torque con-

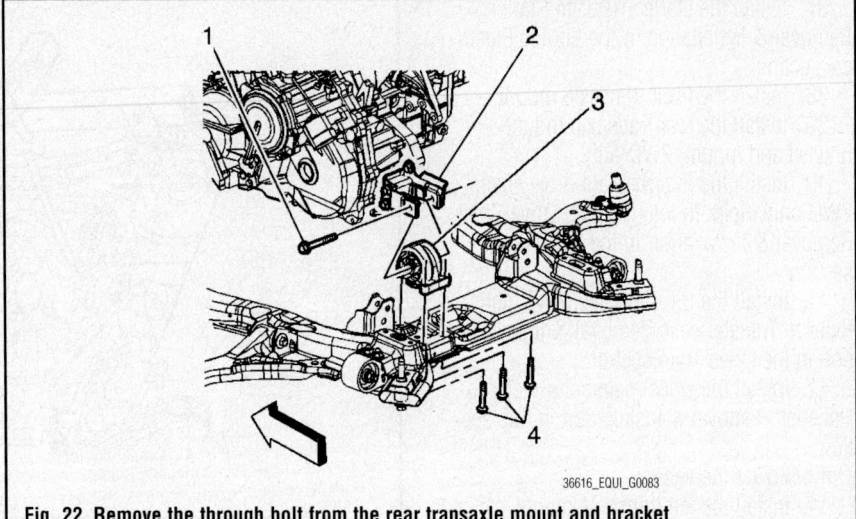

36616_EQUI_G0083

Fig. 22 Remove the through bolt from the rear transaxle mount and bracket

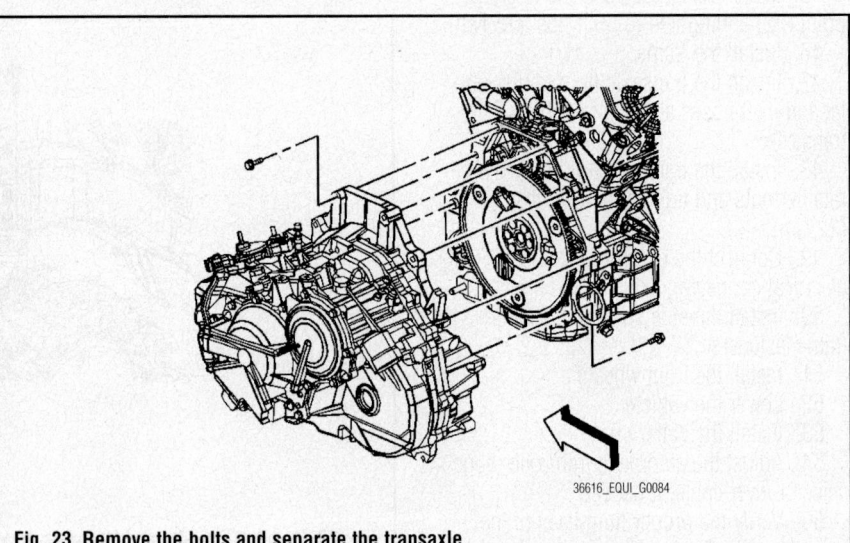

36616_EQUI_G0084

Fig. 23 Remove the bolts and separate the transaxle

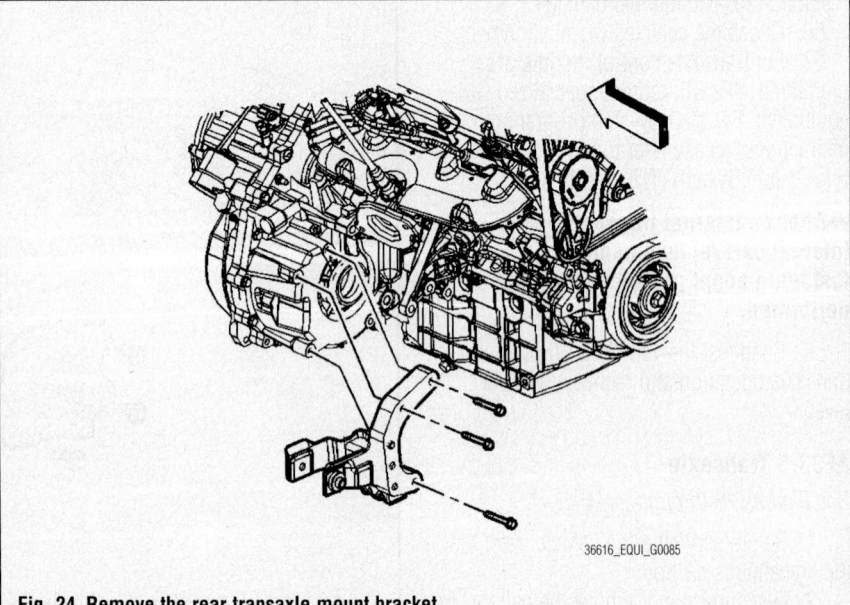

36616_EQUI_G0085

Fig. 24 Remove the rear transaxle mount bracket

verter-to-flywheel bolts through the starter motor hole.

➡ **Mark the relation of the flywheel to torque converter for reassembly.**

34. Remove the torque converter-to-flywheel bolts.

35. Remove the front engine mount.

36. Remove the through bolt from the rear transaxle mount and bracket.

37. Place a universal frame support fixture under the frame.

38. Lower the vehicle until the frame contacts the frame support fixture.

39. Remove the frame-to-body bolts. Discard the bolts.

40. Raise the vehicle up away from the frame and remove the frame from under the vehicle.

41. Disconnect the right and left halfshafts from the intermediate shaft and transaxle. Secure both drive shafts out of the way.

42. Remove the intermediate shaft. Refer to Intermediate Shaft Removal & Installation in the Drive Train section.

43. If vehicle is equipped with AWD complete the following steps:
- Remove the driveshaft. Refer to Driveshaft Removal & Installation in the Drive Train section.
- Remove the transfer case mounting bracket.
- Disconnect the vent hose from the top of the transfer case.

44. Support the transaxle with a suitable transaxle jack.

45. Remove the 4 lower transaxle-to-engine bolts.

46. Slide the transaxle away from the engine until the transaxle torque-converter clears the flywheel.

47. If equipped with a drive axle seal dust cover, discard it and do not replace it.

48. Lower the transaxle away from the vehicle.

49. If the vehicle is equipped with AWD complete the following steps:
- Remove the retaining ring from the stub shaft for tool installation. Discard the retainer ring.
- Remove the stub shaft from the transfer case.
- Remove the bolts securing the transfer case to the transaxle.
- Remove the transfer case from the transaxle

50. If the vehicle is equipped with 2WD complete the following steps:
- Remove the bolts securing the rear transaxle mount bracket to the transaxle.

- Remove the rear transaxle mount bracket from the transaxle

To install:

51. If the vehicle is equipped with 2WD complete the following steps:
- Install the rear transaxle mount bracket to the transaxle.
- Install the bolts securing the rear transaxle mount bracket to the transaxle and tighten the bolts to 41 ft. lbs. (55 Nm).

52. If the vehicle is equipped with AWD complete the following steps:
- Install the transfer case to the transaxle.
- Install the bolts securing the transfer case to the transaxle and tighten the bolts to 44 ft. lbs. (60 Nm).
- Install the stub shaft using a slide hammer and the adapter J 38868.
- Install a NEW retaining ring on the stub shaft.

53. Raise the transaxle up into the vehicle engine compartment.

54. Align and install the transaxle to the engine.

55. Install the 4 lower transaxle-to-engine bolts and tighten to 55 ft. lbs. (75 Nm).

56. If the vehicle is equipped with AWD complete the following steps:
- Connect the vent hose to the top of the transfer case.
- Install the transfer case mounting bracket.

57. Install the drive shaft, AWD only. Refer to Intermediate Drive Shaft Removal & Installation in the Drive Train section.

58. Install the intermediate drive shaft, 2WD only. Refer to Intermediate Drive Shaft Removal & Installation in the Drive Train section.

59. Install the wheel halfshafts. Refer to Halfshaft Removal & Installation in the Drive Train section.

60. Install the frame to the vehicle. Install NEW frame-to-body bolts and tighten to 114 ft. lbs. (155 Nm).

61. Install the bolt through the rear transaxle mount and transaxle mount bracket. Tighten the through bolt to 80 ft. lbs. (110 Nm).

62. Install the front engine mount and tighten the mounting bolts to 37 ft. lbs. (50 Nm).

63. Install the engine mount through bolt and tighten to 80 ft. lbs. (110 Nm).

64. Turn the crankshaft balancer bolt clockwise to gain access to the torque converter-to-flywheel bolts through the starter motor hole.

65. Align the reference marks made earlier on the flywheel and torque converter.

66. Install the torque converter to flywheel bolts and tighten to 44 ft. lbs. (60 Nm).

67. Install the starter motor. Refer to Starter Removal & Installation in the Engine Electrical section.

68. Install the engine-to-transaxle brace.

69. Install the engine-to-transaxle brace bolts and tighten to 37 ft. lbs. (50 Nm).

70. Install the transaxle oil cooler lines and seals to the transaxle.

71. Install the front bumper fascia air deflector.

72. Install the right and left lower ball joints to the steering knuckles. Tighten the lower nuts to 30 ft. lbs. (40 Nm) and install the cotter pin.

73. Install the right and left stabilizer shaft links to the stabilizer shaft. Tighten the lower nut to 63 ft. lbs. (85 Nm).

74. Install the right and left outer tie rod ends to the steering knuckles. Tighten the retention nuts to 18 ft. lbs. (25 Nm) plus 90 degrees.

75. Connect the steering intermediate shaft to the steering gear.

76. Install a NEW pinch bolt to the steering intermediate shaft and tighten the bolt to 25 ft. lbs. (34 Nm).

77. Install the right and left side engine splash shields.

78. Install the front tire assemblies and tighten to 100 ft. lbs. (140 Nm).

79. Lower the vehicle.

80. Install the left hand transaxle mount to the vehicle.

81. Install the left hand transaxle mount-to-side rail bolts and tighten to (27 ft. lbs. (37 Nm).

82. Install the left hand transaxle mount to transaxle bolts and tighten to 37 ft. lbs. (50 Nm).

83. Remove the engine support fixture.

84. Untie the radiator, air conditioning condenser and fan module assembly from the upper radiator support

85. Install the upper 4 transaxle-to-engine bolts and tighten to 55 ft. lbs. (75 Nm).

86. Connect the transaxle vent tube.

87. Connect the electrical connector to the output speed sensor.

88. Install the nut and fuel line retaining clip to the transaxle and tighten to 18 inch lbs. (25 Nm).

89. Install the battery negative cable and wire harness ground to the transaxle stud. Tighten the retaining nut to 33 ft. lbs. (45 Nm).

90. Connect the electrical connectors to the transaxle range switch.

91. Connect the electrical connector from the input speed sensor.

92. Install the shift control cable bracket.

93. Install the battery tray.

94. Install the battery and cables.

95. Add GM T-IV transmission fluid to the transaxle.

✳✳ WARNING

Dexron®III automatic transmission fluid is not compatible with this transaxle. If Dexron®III ATF is used, transaxle failure will result.

96. Perform the transmission adaptive learn and neutral learn procedure.

ADAPTIVE LEARN AND TRANSMISSION NEUTRAL LEARN

See Figure 25.

Perform the transmission adaptive learn and transmission neutral learn procedure after any of the following service procedures:

- Transmission Control Module (TCM) replacement
- TCM calibration change
- Control valve body replacement
- Transaxle overhaul
- Transaxle replacement

1. With the vehicle in park "P" and ignition "OFF" set the parking brake and block the tires.

2. Turn the ignition switch to the "ACC" position.

3. Release the shift lock and place the transmission shift lever in the neutral "N" position.

4. Turn the ignition to the "OFF" position.

5. Remove the shift cable from the transaxle range switch lever.

6. Verify the two arrows on the TCM are aligned.

7. Install the shift cable on the transaxle range switch lever.

8. Turn the ignition to "ON", do not start the vehicle.

9. Using a scan tool implement the N-position adaptive learn.

10. If N-position adaptation is okay go to step 14.

11. If N-position adaptation does not learn go back to step 5.

12. If N-position adaptation sets a DTC, clear DTC and go to step 5.

13. If still cannot learn N-position after three times replace the TCM.

14. Shift the transmission to park "P".

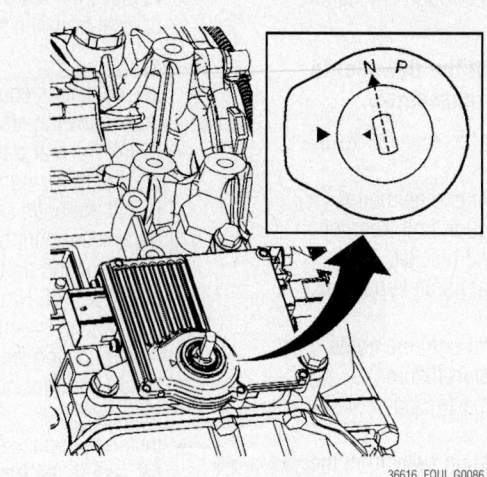

Fig. 25 Verify the two arrows on the TCM are aligned

15. Turn ignition "OFF".

16. Wait 10 seconds.

17. Turn ignition "ON".

18. Verify the shift lever indicator aligns in all gear positions.

19. If they do not align check for DTC.

20. Road test vehicle to confirm gear shift positions.

➡**Perform all steps of the adaptive learn procedure. Repeat the steps as many times as indicated. Engine flare during shifting or harsh shifts will occur if not done correctly. When performing the up/down shifting during 2–3 and 3–4 up-shifts, small shift flare may occur the first or second time depending on transaxle internal tolerances.**

21. Drive the vehicle to warm the transaxle fluid until 150–230°F (65–110°C). The adaptive learn procedure will not work unless transaxle fluid is the correct temperature.

22. Reset the transaxle adaptive learns using a scan tool. Go to the Transmission Special Functions then Trans. Output Controls menu and select Reset Transmission Adapts.

23. Perform the following steps for the garage shifts adaptive learn:

- Apply the parking brake and the foot brake.
- Shift from NEUTRAL to REVERSE and keep in REVERSE for 3 seconds.
- Shift from REVERSE to NEUTRAL.
- Repeat the above two steps five times.
- Shift from NEUTRAL to DRIVE and keep in DRIVE for 3 seconds.
- Shift from DRIVE to NEUTRAL.

- Repeat the above two steps five times.

24. Perform the following steps for the Up/Down shifting adaptive learn:

- Drive the vehicle in DRIVE with light (15–20 percent) throttle until above 31 mph (50 km/h) in 4th gear.
- If vehicle is not connected to a scan tool and throttle percentage cannot be observed, take 30 seconds for reaching the 50 km/h (31 mph).
- Decelerate and apply the brakes until vehicle comes to a stop. Brake the vehicle so that it takes at least 14 seconds.
- Repeat the above steps five times.

25. Perform the following steps for 2-1 Manual down shift adaptive learn:

- Drive the vehicle in I until over 16 mph (25 km/h) in 2nd with any throttle position.
- Decelerate, shift from I to L manually and stop the vehicle.
- Repeat the above two steps ten times.

26. Confirm shift quality.

➡**If shift quality does not improve, ensure the TCM has the correct transmission calibration.**

SERVICE FAST LEARN ADAPTIVE PROCEDURE

1. Ensure the following conditions are met before performing the Service Fast Learn Adapts procedure:

- Drive wheels are blocked
- Parking brake is applied
- Service brake is applied
- Zero percent throttle and no external engine RPM control

- Transaxle Fluid Temperature (TFT) is between 158–212°F (70–100°C)
- Transaxle gear selector has been cycled from Park to Reverse 3 times in order to purge air from the reverse clutches.

2. Use the scan tool to navigate to Service Fast Learn Adapts by selecting the following commands:
- F1: Transaxle Control Module
- F5: Module Setup
- F0: Fast Learn Adapts Process

➡️**If at any time during the procedure, required conditions are not met, Service Fast Learn Adapts may abort and the process may need to be started again from the beginning.**

3. Use the scan tool to perform the Service Fast Learn Adapts procedure. As the procedure is being performed, the scan tool data display will provide operator instructions. Follow the scan tool instructions as required.

4. Once the procedure is complete, shut OFF the engine and power down the TCM. You will lose communication to the scan tool.

5. Restart the engine. This will complete the Service Fast Learn Adapts procedure.

➡️**When the Service Fast Learn Adapts procedure is completed, the transaxle will remain in a neutral state.**

TRANSFER CASE ASSEMBLY

REMOVAL & INSTALLATION

NVG 900 Transfer Case

See Figures 26 and 27.

1. Before servicing the vehicle, refer to the precautions section.
2. Raise and support the vehicle.
3. Drain the transfer case fluid.
4. Remove the driveshaft. Refer to Driveshaft Removal & Installation in the Drive Train section.
5. Remove the right wheel halfshaft. Refer to Halfshaft Removal & Installation in the Drive Train section.
6. Remove the intermediate shaft.
7. Remove the retainer ring from the stub shaft for tool installation. Discard the used retainer ring.
8. Remove the stub shaft using a slide hammer and adapter.
9. Remove the transfer case mounting bracket.
10. Disconnect the transfer case vent hose.

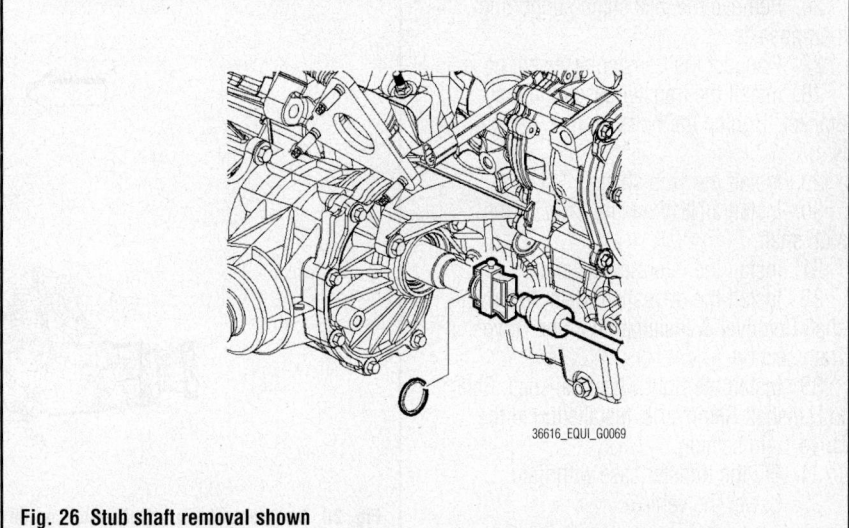
Fig. 26 Stub shaft removal shown

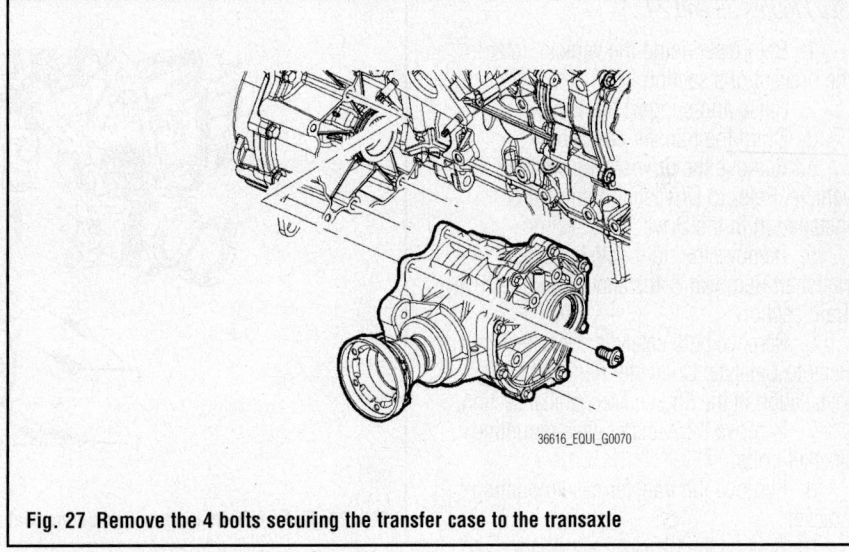
Fig. 27 Remove the 4 bolts securing the transfer case to the transaxle

11. Support the transaxle with a jack stand.
12. Remove the 4 bolts securing the transfer case to the transaxle.

➡️**Remove the rear transaxle mount from the transfer case after the transfer case has been removed from the vehicle.**

13. Remove the 3 bolts securing the rear transaxle mount to the vehicle frame.
14. Slide the transfer case away from the transaxle.
15. Rotate the transfer case so that the driveshaft drive flange faces the transaxle.
16. Lift and rotate the transfer case so that the driveshaft drive flange is pointing down toward the floor.
17. Lower the transfer case through the opening between the engine oil pan and the vehicle frame.

18. Remove the 3 bolts and rear transaxle mount from the transfer case.

To install:

19. Install the rear transaxle mount to the transfer case.
20. Install the 3 bolts securing the rear transaxle mount to the transfer case. Tighten the bolts to 81 ft. lbs. (110 Nm).
21. Ensure the torque converter cover is in the proper location.
22. With the transfer case driveshaft drive flange pointing down toward the floor, lift the transfer case up between the engine oil pan and the vehicle frame.
23. Rotate and align the transfer case with the transaxle.
24. Install the 4 bolts securing the transfer case to the transaxle. Tighten the bolts to 44 ft. lbs. (60 Nm).
25. Install the 3 bolts securing the rear transaxle mount to the vehicle frame. Tighten the bolts to 37 ft. lbs. (50 Nm).

26. Remove the jack stand supporting the transaxle.

27. Connect the transfer case vent hose.

28. Install the transfer case mounting bracket. Tighten the bolts to 37 ft. lbs. (50 Nm).

29. Install the stub shaft.

30. Install a NEW retainer ring on the stub shaft.

31. Install the intermediate shaft.

32. Install the driveshaft. Refer to Driveshaft Removal & Installation in the Drive Train section

33. Install the right wheel halfshaft. Refer to Halfshaft Removal & Installation in the Drive Train section.

34. Fill the transfer case with fluid.

35. Lower the vehicle.

Getrag 760 Transfer Case

See Figures 28 and 29.

1. Before servicing the vehicle, refer to the precautions section.

2. Raise and support the vehicle.

3. Drain the transfer case fluid.

4. Remove the driveshaft from the vehicle. Refer to Driveshaft Removal & Installation in the Drive Train section

5. Remove the right halfshaft. Refer to Halfshaft Removal & Installation in the Drive Train section.

6. Remove both catalytic converters. Refer to Catalytic Converter Removal & Installation in the Engine Mechanical section.

7. Remove the transfer case mounting bracket bolts.

8. Remove the transfer case mounting bracket.

9. Support the transaxle with a jack stand.

10. Remove the rear transmission mount and bracket.

11. Remove the bolts securing the transfer case to the transaxle.

12. Remove the transfer case from the transaxle.

13. If replacing the transfer case, complete the following steps:
   • Remove the transfer case heat shield bolts
   • Remove the transfer case heat shield

To install:

14. If the transfer case heat shield was previously removed, complete the following steps:
   • Install the transfer case heat shield
   • Install the transfer case heat shield bolts and tighten to 89 inch lbs. (10 Nm).

15. Install the transfer case to the transaxle. Install a jack stand for support.

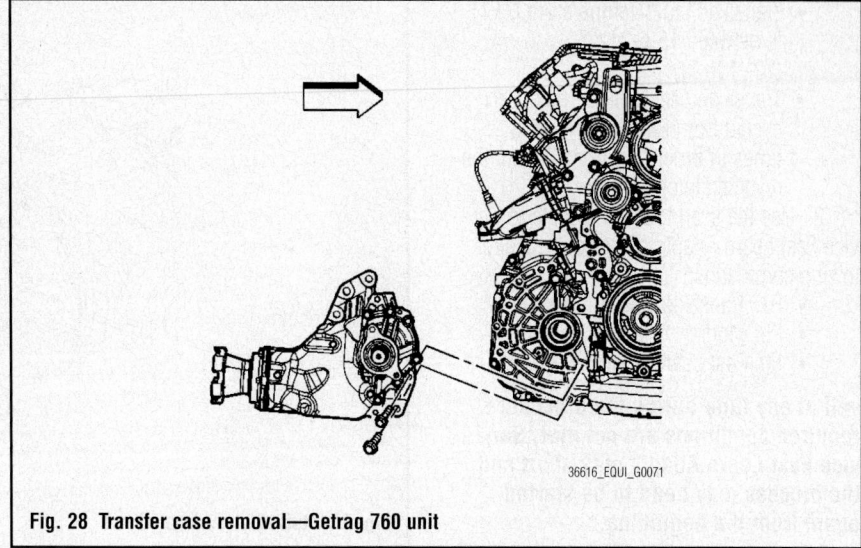

Fig. 28 Transfer case removal—Getrag 760 unit

36616_EQUI_G0071

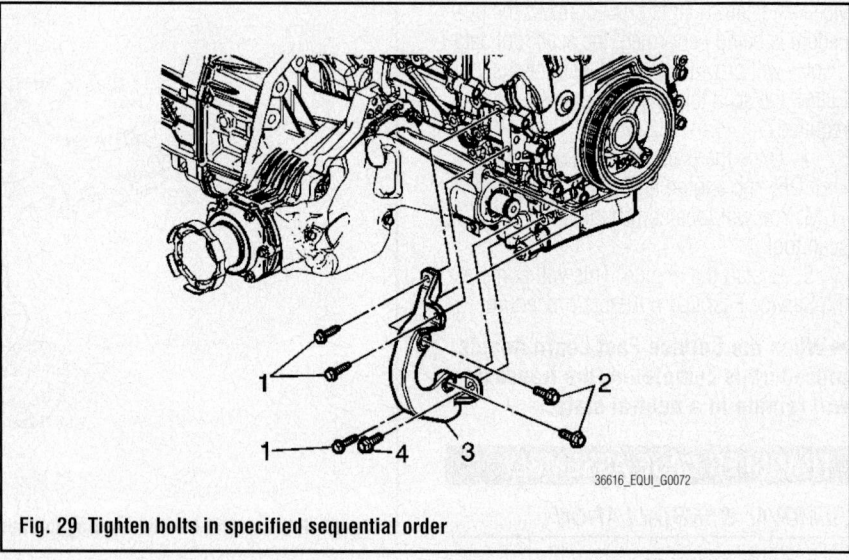

Fig. 29 Tighten bolts in specified sequential order

36616_EQUI_G0072

16. Install the bolts securing the transfer case to the transaxle and tighten the bolts to 37 ft. lbs. (50 Nm).

17. Install the rear transmission mount and bracket.

18. Remove the jack stand supporting the transaxle.

➡**Tighten bolts in specified sequential order.**

19. Install the transfer case mounting bracket (3).

20. Install the transfer case mounting bracket bolts (1) and tighten to 17 ft. lbs. (23 Nm).

21. Install the transfer case mounting bracket bolt (4) and tighten to 37 ft. lbs. (50 Nm).

22. Install the transfer case mounting bracket bolts (2) and tighten to 37 ft. lbs. (50 Nm).

23. Install both catalytic converters.

Refer to Catalytic Converter Removal & Installation in the Engine Mechanical section.

24. Install the right wheel halfshaft. Refer to Halfshaft Removal & Installation in the Drive Train section.

25. Install the driveshaft to the vehicle. Refer to Driveshaft Removal & Installation the Drive Train section.

26. Fill the transfer case with fluid.

27. Lower the vehicle.

FRONT HALFSHAFTS

REMOVAL & INSTALLATION

See Figures 30 and 31.

1. Before servicing the vehicle, refer to the Precautions Section.

2. Raise and support the vehicle.

3. Remove the tire and wheel assembly.

4. Remove and discard the halfshaft spindle nut.

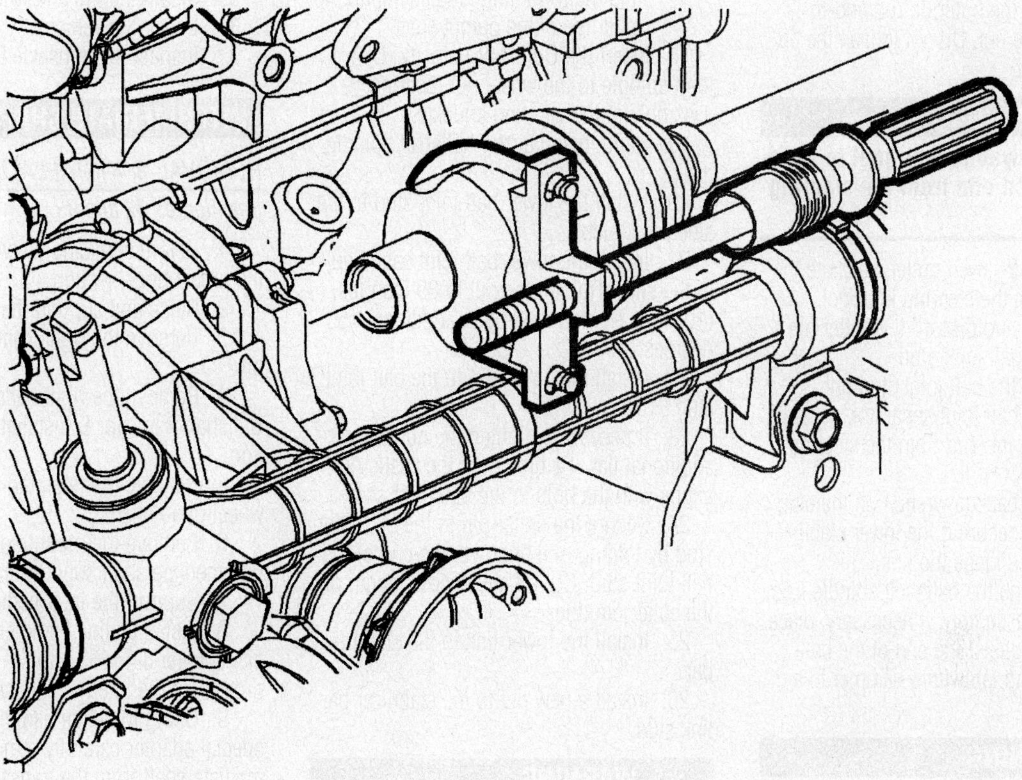

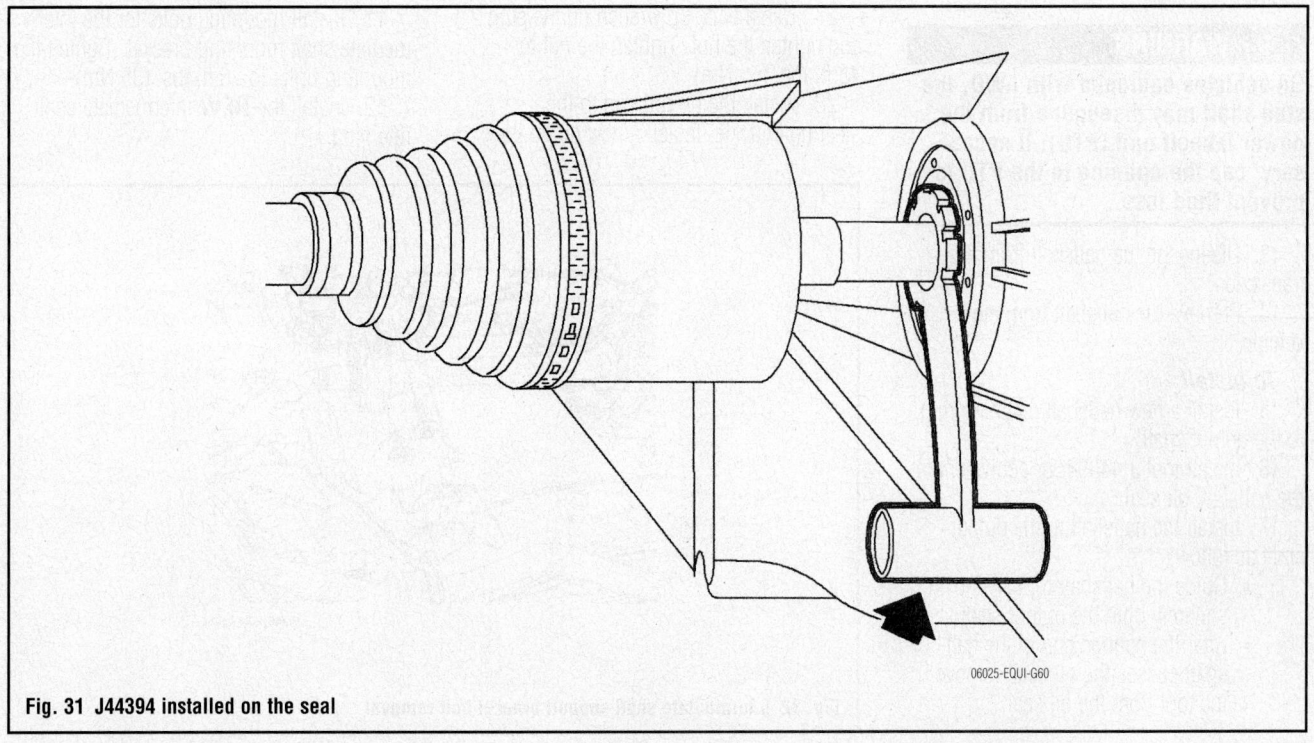

Fig. 30 J45341 and J2619-01 assembled on the halfshaft.

06025-EQUI-G59

06025-EQUI-G60

Fig. 31 J44394 installed on the seal

➡ **Hold the ball stud from turning when removing/installing the nut. The boot can become torn and damaged if the ball stud turns.**

5. Remove the outer tie rod end-to-steering knuckle nut. Do not loosen the tie rod end jam nut.

❋❋ WARNING

Do not use a wedge type tool to separate the tie rod end from the steering knuckle.

6. Using a 2-jawed puller, separate the tie rod end from the steering knuckle.

7. Remove and discard the cotter pin from the lower ball joint stud.

8. Remove the ball joint stud nut.

9. Using a ball joint separator, separate the lower ball joint stud from the steering knuckle.

10. Using a backup wrench on the stud, remove the nut securing the lower stabilizer bar link and disengage the link.

11. Disengage the halfshaft spindle from the wheel hub assembly. If necessary, place a wood block against the end of the halfshaft spindle and tap with a hammer to aid removal.

❋❋ WARNING

Use care not to damage the joint seal when removing the halfshaft.

12. Assemble tools J 45341 and J 2619-01, or equivalent to the halfshaft inner tripot joint.

❋❋ WARNING

On vehicles equipped with AWD, the stub shaft may disengage from the power takeoff unit (PTU). If necessary, cap the opening in the PTU to prevent fluid loss.

13. Disengage the halfshaft from the transaxle.

14. Remove the halfshaft from the vehicle.

To install:

15. Install a new halfshaft retaining ring to the output shaft.

16. Install tool J 44394, or equivalent to the halfshaft oil seal.

17. Install the halfshaft to the output shaft as follows:

- Guide the halfshaft tripot joint squarely onto the output shaft.
- After the splined end of the halfshaft passes the oil seal, remove the tool from the oil seal.

- Firmly engage the halfshaft to the output shaft.
- Ensure that the tripot joint is fully seated on the output shaft by grasping the tripot joint and attempting to pull free of the output shaft.

18. Insert the Constant Velocity (CV) joint spindle to the wheel hub/bearing assembly of the steering knuckle.

19. Hand install a new halfshaft spindle nut.

20. Install the lower ball joint stud to the steering knuckle.

21. Install the lower ball joint castle nut to the stud. Tighten the nut to 89 inch lbs. (10 Nm). Tighten the nut an additional 150 degrees.

22. Install the cotter pin to the ball joint stud.

23. If necessary, tighten the nut one additional flat at a time until the castle nut aligns with the hole in the ball joint stud.

24. Secure the cotter pin to the ball joint stud by folding one tine over the end of the ball joint stud. Cut off any excess length of the cotter pin tines.

25. Install the lower link to the stabilizer bar.

26. Install a new nut to the stabilizer bar link stud.

❋❋ WARNING

In order to prevent damaging the stabilizer bar link stud seal, do not allow the stud to rotate while tightening the nut.

27. Use a back up wrench on the stud and tighten the nut. Tighten the nut to 48 ft. lbs. (65 Nm).

28. Install the tie rod end to the steering knuckle. Install a new nut to the

tie rod end stud. Tighten the nut to 37 ft. lbs. (50 Nm).

29. Tighten the halfshaft spindle nut. Tighten the nut to 151 ft. lbs. (205 Nm).

30. Install the tire and wheel assembly.

31. Lower the vehicle.

32. Inspect the transaxle fluid level.

INTERMEDIATE SHAFT

REMOVAL & INSTALLATION

See Figures 32 and 33.

1. Before servicing the vehicle, refer to the precautions section.

2. Raise and support the vehicle.

3. Remove the right front wheel assembly.

4. Remove the right halfshaft. Refer to Halfshaft Removal & Installation in this section.

5. Remove the retaining clip for the wheel drive shaft.

6. Remove the mounting bolts for the intermediate shaft support bracket.

7. Support the intermediate shaft.

8. Install a slide hammer with the special adapter J 44467 into the retaining ring groove on the intermediate shaft.

9. Using the slide hammer with the special adapter carefully remove the intermediate shaft from the transaxle.

To install:

10. Carefully install the intermediate shaft in the transmission. Move the intermediate shaft back and forth to ensure that the intermediate shaft is properly seated.

11. Install mounting bolts for the intermediate shaft mounting bracket. Tighten the mounting bolts to 26 ft. lbs. (35 Nm).

12. Install the **NEW** intermediate shaft retaining.

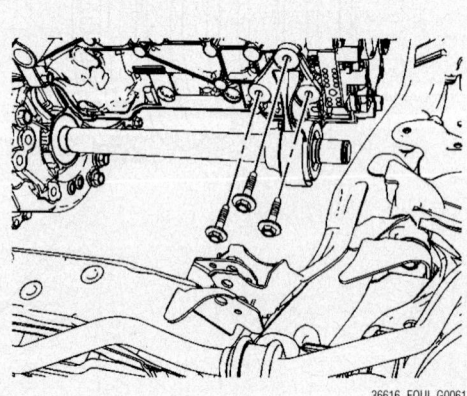

36616_EQUI_G0061

Fig. 32 Intermediate shaft support bracket bolt removal

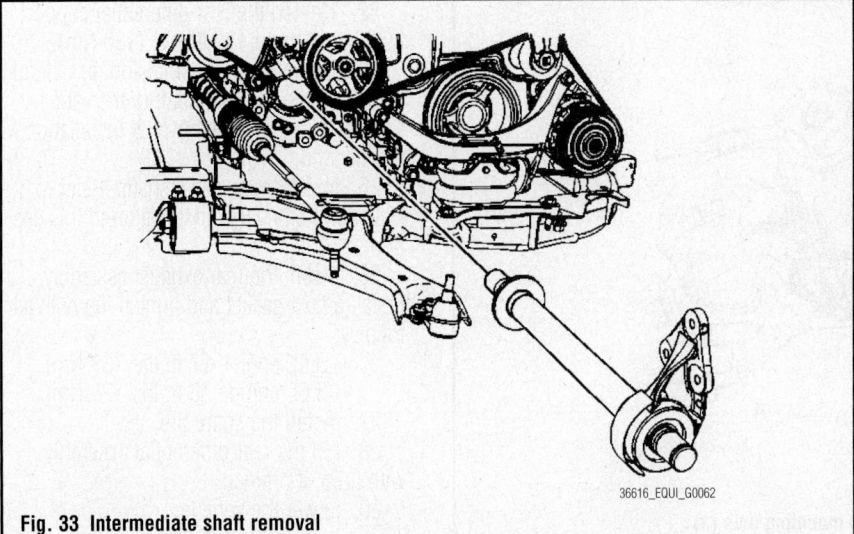

Fig. 33 Intermediate shaft removal

13. Install the halfshaft. Refer to Half-shaft Removal & Installation in this section.

14. Lower the vehicle.

15. Check transaxle fluid.

REAR AXLE SHAFT SEAL

REMOVAL & INSTALLATION

See Figure 34.

1. Raise and support the vehicle.
2. Drain the rear differential.
3. Remove the exhaust system.
4. Remove the spare tire.

➡**In the following service procedure, it is not necessary to completely remove the drive shaft. Relocate the propeller shaft to the side and secure with mechanics wire or equivalent.**

5. Remove the drive shaft.
6. Remove the rear halfshaft.
7. Support rear differential with a transaxle jack stand.
8. Remove the rear differential support bushing bolt.
9. Remove the differential mount.
10. Remove the differential support bushing nut.
11. Lower the differential to gain access to the axle shaft seal.
12. Using a suitable pry tool, remove the axle shaft seal.

To install:

13. Install the new output shaft seal using a seal installer.
14. Raise and position the differential in the rear cradle.
15. Install the rear support bolt.
16. Install the differential support bushing nut.
17. Install the differential mount.

18. The transaxle jack stand may be removed at this time.
19. Install the rear halfshaft.
20. Install the drive shaft.
21. Install the exhaust system.
22. Install the spare tire.
23. Inspect the rear differential fluid level.
24. Lower the vehicle.

REAR DIFFERENTIAL

REMOVAL & INSTALLATION

See Figures 35 through 37.

1. Before servicing the vehicle, refer to the precautions section.
2. Raise and support the vehicle.
3. Drain the rear differential, if needed.

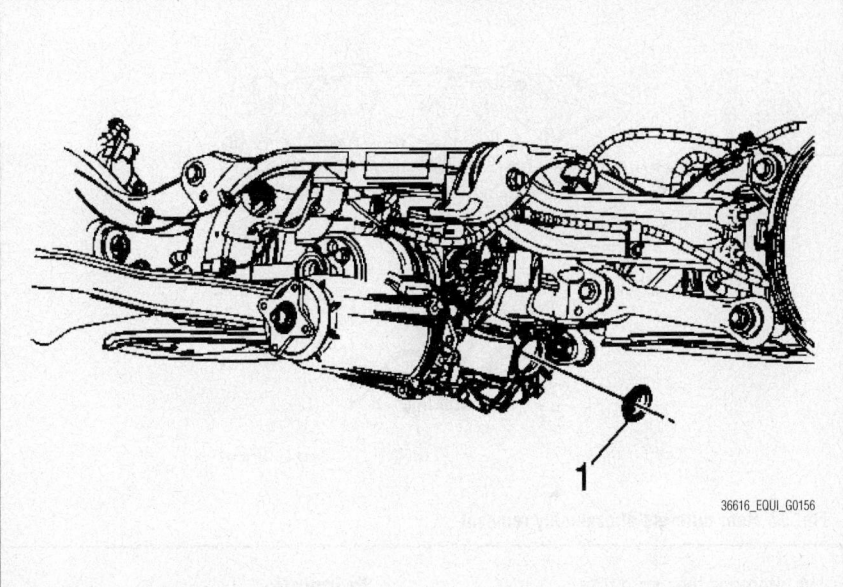

Fig. 34 Axle shaft seal (1) removal

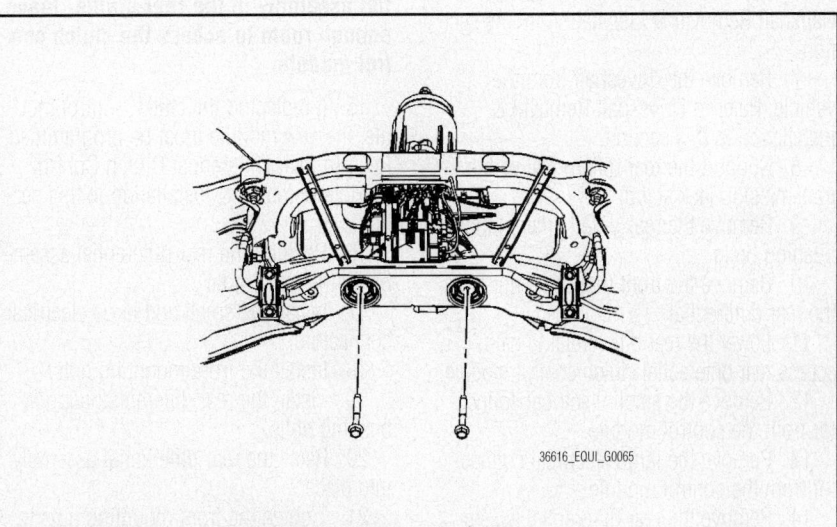

Fig. 35 Remove the rear differential support bushing bolts

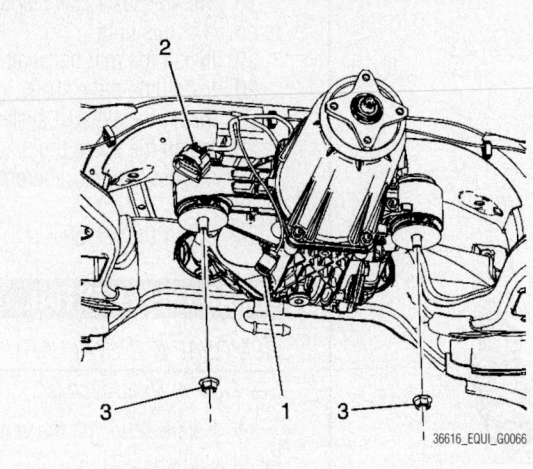

Fig. 36 Remove the electrical connectors (1,2) and mounting nuts (3)

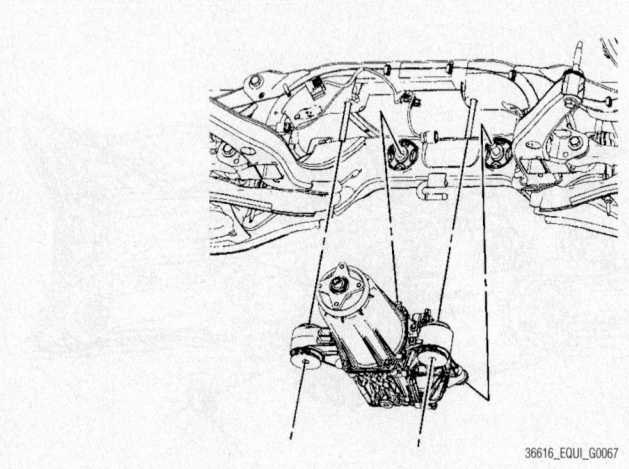

Fig. 37 Rear differential assembly removal

4. Remove the spare tire.

5. Remove the rear exhaust assembly.

6. Remove the rear halfshafts. Refer to Halfshaft Removal & Installation in this section.

7. Remove the driveshaft from the vehicle. Refer to Driveshaft Removal & Installation in this section.

8. Support the rear differential with a transmission jack stand.

9. Remove the rear differential support bushing bolts.

10. Remove the front mounting nuts for the rear differential.

11. Lower the rear differential to gain access rear differential clutch control module.

12. Remove the small electrical connector from the control module.

13. Remove the large electrical connector from the control module.

14. Remove the rear differential assembly from the vehicle.

To install:

➡When positioning the rear differential assembly in the rear cradle, leave enough room to access the clutch control module.

15. If replacing the clutch control module, the new module must be programmed. Refer to Rear Differential Clutch Control Module Removal & Installation in this section.

16. Position the rear differential assembly in the rear cradle.

17. Install the small and large electrical connectors.

18. Install the front mounting nuts.

19. Install the rear differential support bushing bolts.

20. Raise the rear differential assembly into place.

21. Tighten the front mounting nuts to 90 ft. lbs. (122 Nm).

22. Tighten the rear differential support bushing bolts to 139 ft. lbs. (188 Nm).

23. Remove the transmission jack stand.

24. Install the driveshaft to the vehicle. Refer to Driveshaft Removal & Installation in this section.

25. Install the rear halfshafts. Refer to Halfshaft Removal & Installation in this section.

26. Install the rear exhaust assembly. Install a new gasket and tighten the nuts as follows:

- 3.4L engine 27 ft. lbs. (37 Nm).
- 3.6L engine 18 ft. lbs. (25 Nm).

27. Install the spare tire.

28. Fill the rear differential assembly with fluid, if drained.

29. Lower the vehicle.

REAR DRIVESHAFT

REMOVAL & INSTALLATION

See Figures 38 through 40.

1. Before servicing the vehicle, refer to the precautions section.

2. Place the transaxle in neutral.

3. Raise and support the vehicle.

4. Index mark the relationship of the driveshaft to the rear drive module flange.

5. Support the driveshaft at the rear differential.

6. Remove the mounting bolts for the driveshaft at the rear differential drive flange.

7. Support driveshaft at the transfer case.

8. Remove the mounting bolts for the driveshaft at the transfer case.

9. Place a support under the driveshaft at the center support bearing.

10. Remove the bolts securing the driveshaft support bearing to the vehicle underbody.

11. With the aid of an assistant, remove the driveshaft from the vehicle.

To install

12. Thoroughly clean the driveshaft flange mounting bolts and apply thread locker, GM P/N 89021297 (Canadian P/N 10953488), to the bolt threads.

13. With the aid of an assistant, position the driveshaft on the supports.

14. Align the reference marks on the front and rear of the driveshaft to the transfer case and rear differential.

15. Position the driveshaft on the transfer case output flange.

16. Finger tighten the mounting bolts for the driveshaft at the transfer case output flange.

17. Position the center support bearing of the driveshaft on the vehicle.

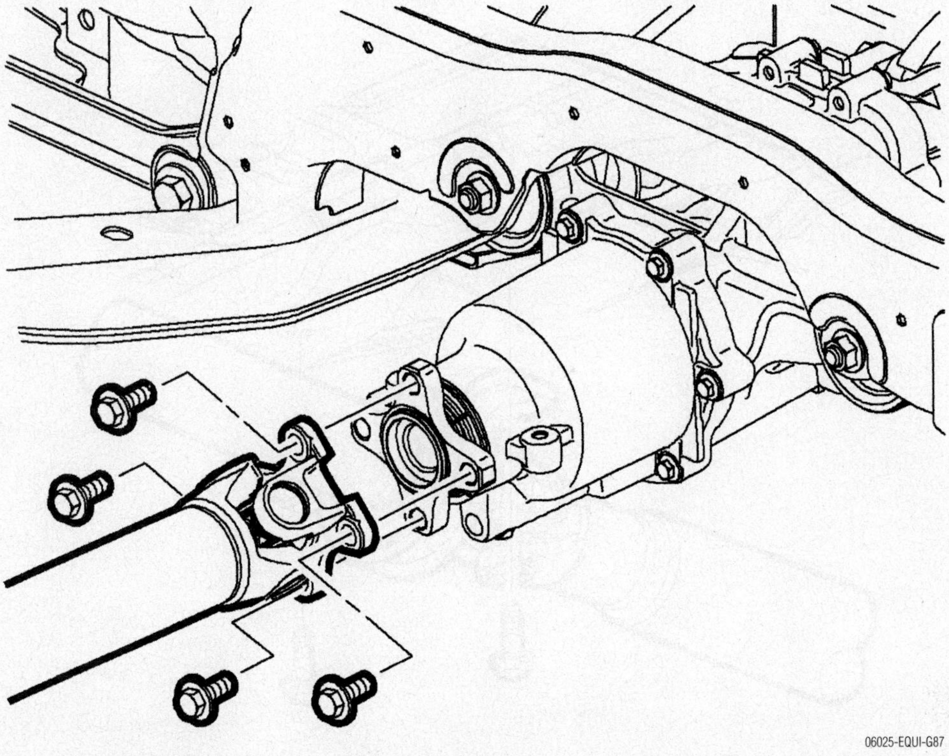

06025-EQUI-G87

Fig. 38 Bolts securing the driveshaft yoke flange to the rear drive module flange

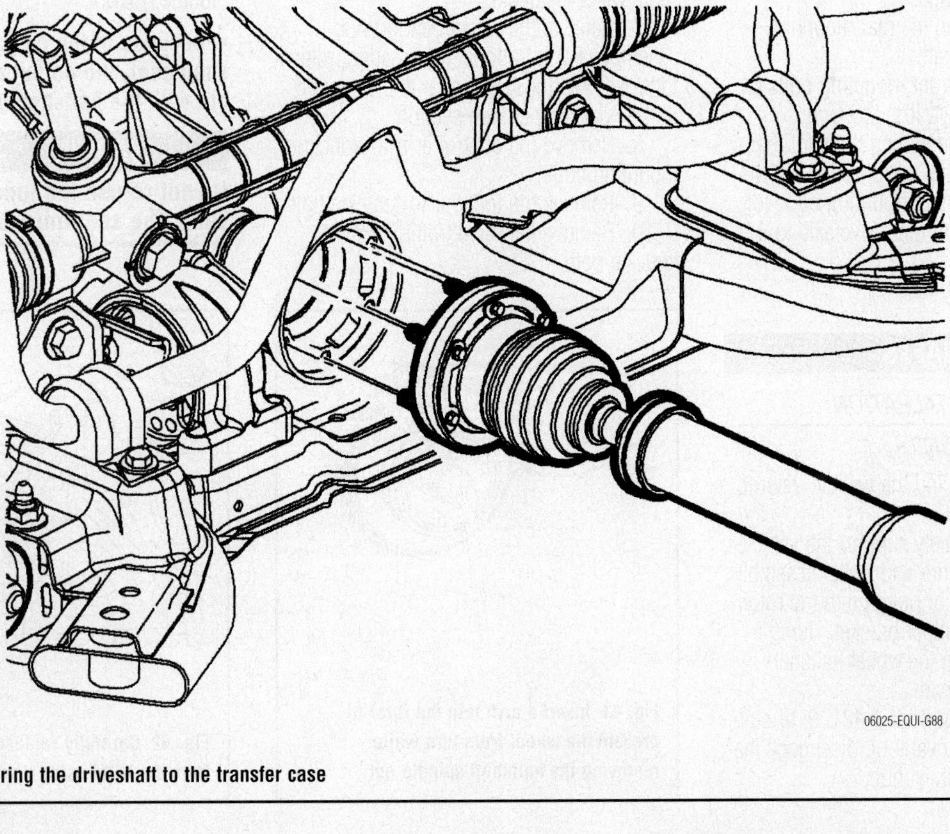

06025-EQUI-G88

Fig. 39 Bolts securing the driveshaft to the transfer case

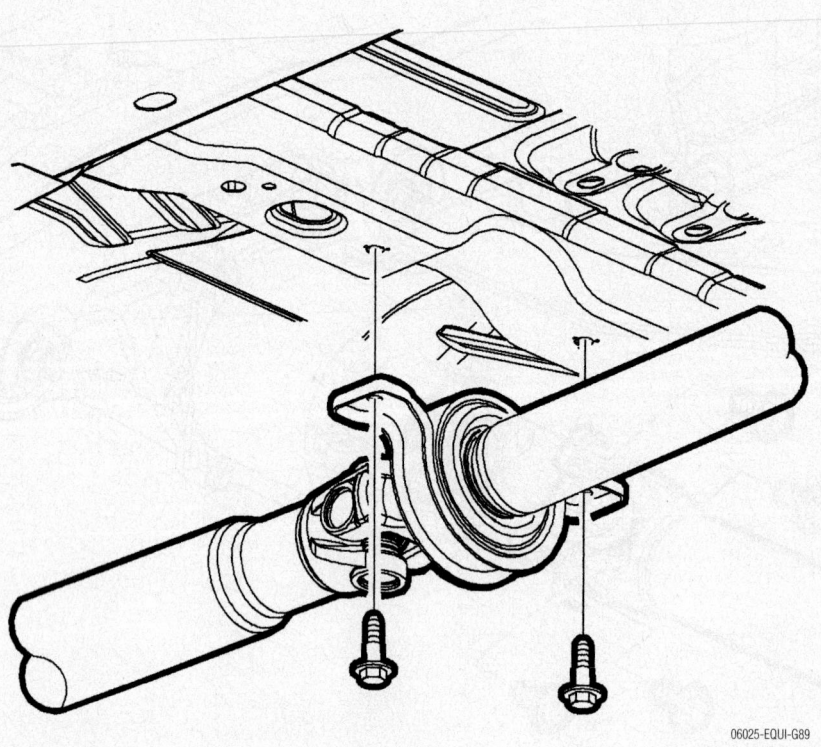

Fig. 40 Bolts securing the driveshaft support bearing to the vehicle underbody

18. Finger tighten the mounting bolts for the center support bearing.

19. Position the driveshaft on the rear differential drive flange.

20. Finger tighten the rear mounting bolts for the driveshaft.

21. Tighten the front mounting bolts for the driveshaft to 25 ft. lbs. (35 Nm).

22. Tighten the mounting bolts for the center support bearing to 18 ft. lbs. (25 Nm).

23. Tighten the rear mounting bolts for the driveshaft yoke to rear drive axle to 37 ft. lbs. (50 Nm).

24. Lower the vehicle.

REAR HALFSHAFTS

REMOVAL & INSTALLATION

See Figures 41 through 43.

1. Before servicing the vehicle, refer to the precautions section.

2. Raise and safely support the vehicle.

3. Remove the tire and wheel assembly.

4. Insert a drift or punch into the rotor, against the brake caliper bracket. Using a suitable tool, loosen the wheel halfshaft spindle nut and discard.

5. Using Special Tool J-42129, or suitable wheel hub removal tool, disengage the halfshaft from the wheel hub.

6. Remove the rear brake caliper. For additional information, refer to the following section, "Rear Disc Brakes, Brake Caliper, Removal & Installation."

7. Remove the wheel bearing/hub assembly. For additional information, refer to Wheel Bearings, Removal & Installation in the Rear Suspension section

8. Remove the control arm-to-knuckle mounting bolts.

9. Remove the toe link-to-knuckle bolt.

10. Remove the three trailing arm-to-knuckle bolts.

11. Remove the rear suspension knuckle.

12. Using a suitable pry tool, carefully release the halfshaft from the rear drive module (RDM).

➡ Because of the design of the halfshaft seal, the output seal will come out with the halfshaft when removed.

❈❈ WARNING

Do not re-use the inner halfshaft seal. The seal must be replaced.

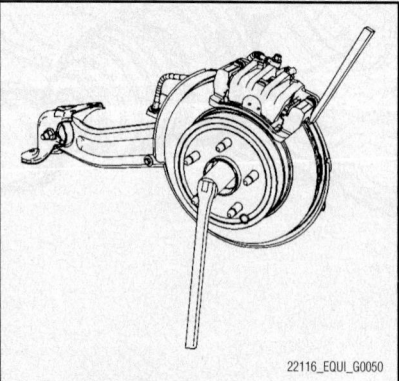

Fig. 41 Insert a drift into the rotor to prevent the wheel from turn while removing the halfshaft spindle nut

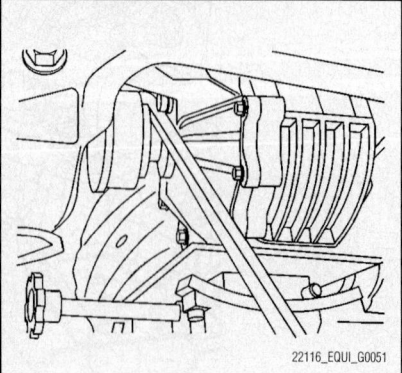

Fig. 42 Carefully release the halfshaft from the RDM using a pry tool

Fig. 43 Before reinstalling the halfshaft, the tripod joint retaining clip must be replaced

To install:

13. Replace the retaining clip on the tripod joint.

14. Install a new halfshaft seal. For additional information, refer to the following section, "Rear Drive Axle, Halfshaft, Bearing & Seal, Removal & Installation."

➡**When installing the wheel drive shaft, you will notice a slight resistance. This is the wheel drive shaft seal. A snap or click should be heard when the wheel drive shaft is fully seated.**

15. Install the halfshaft.

16. Install the rear suspension knuckle. Install all of the bolts loosely at first. Then tighten the bolts in sequence as follows:
   - Tighten the knuckle-to-lower control arm bolt and nut to 118 ft. lbs. (160 Nm).
   - Tighten the knuckle-to-upper control arm bolt and nut to 118 ft. lbs. (160 Nm).
   - Tighten the knuckle-to-toe link bolt and nut to 118 ft. lbs. (160 Nm).
   - Tighten the three trailing arm-to-knuckle bolts to 81 ft. lbs. (110 Nm).

17. Install the bearing/hub assembly.

18. Install the brake caliper assembly.

19. Install the a new halfshaft spindle nut. Hand tighten at this time.

20. Insert a drift or punch into the rotor, against the brake caliper bracket. Tighten the wheel halfshaft spindle nut to 151 ft. lbs. (205 Nm).

21. Install the tire/wheel assembly.

22. Lower the vehicle.

REAR PINION SEAL

REMOVAL & INSTALLATION

See Figures 44 and 45.

1. Before servicing the vehicle, refer to the precautions section.

2. Raise and support the vehicle.

3. Remove the differential clutch drum assembly as follows:
   - Remove the driveshaft from the differential clutch drum assembly. Relocate the rear portion of the driveshaft to the side and support it with mechanics wire.
   - Remove the electrical clutch control connector and wire retaining clips.
   - Remove the 4 differential clutch drum bolts.
   - Remove the differential clutch drum.

➡**The pinion flange, dust cover and pinion nut are serviced with the differential clutch drum assembly.**

4. Install a sheet metal screw into the seal.

5. Attach a pair of pliers or a slider hammer to the screw and remove the seal.

6. Using the slide hammer or pliers, remove the seal.

To install:

7. Using the seal installation tool J 44636-1, install the pinion seal.

8. Install the differential clutch drum assembly as follows:
   - Install the differential clutch drum gasket.
   - Install the clutch drum assembly and hand tighten the 4 mounting bolts.

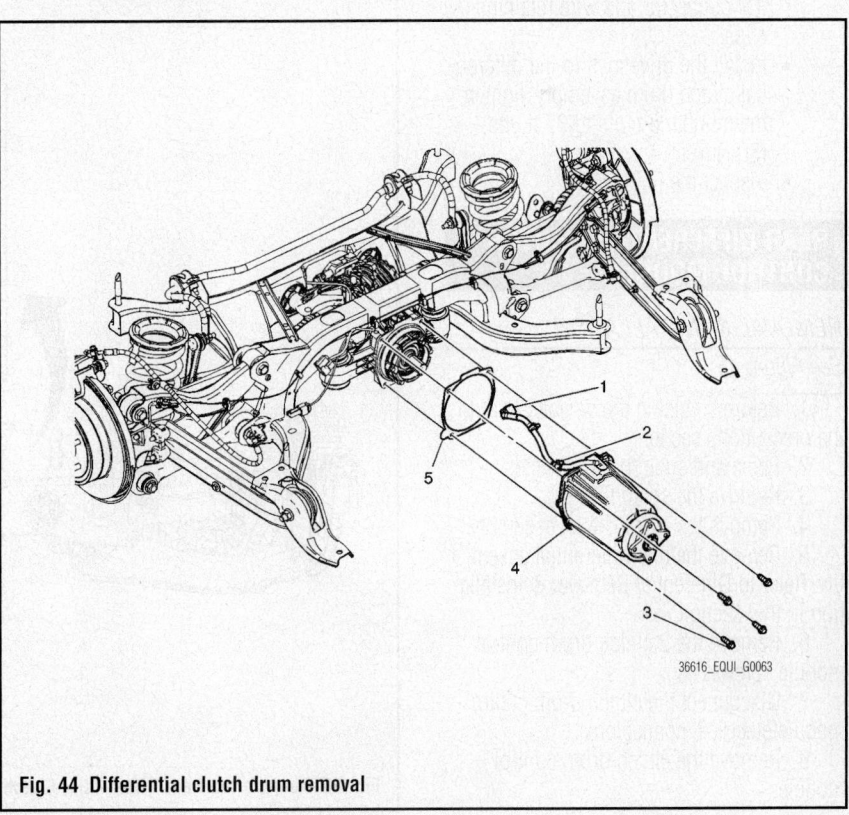

Fig. 44 Differential clutch drum removal

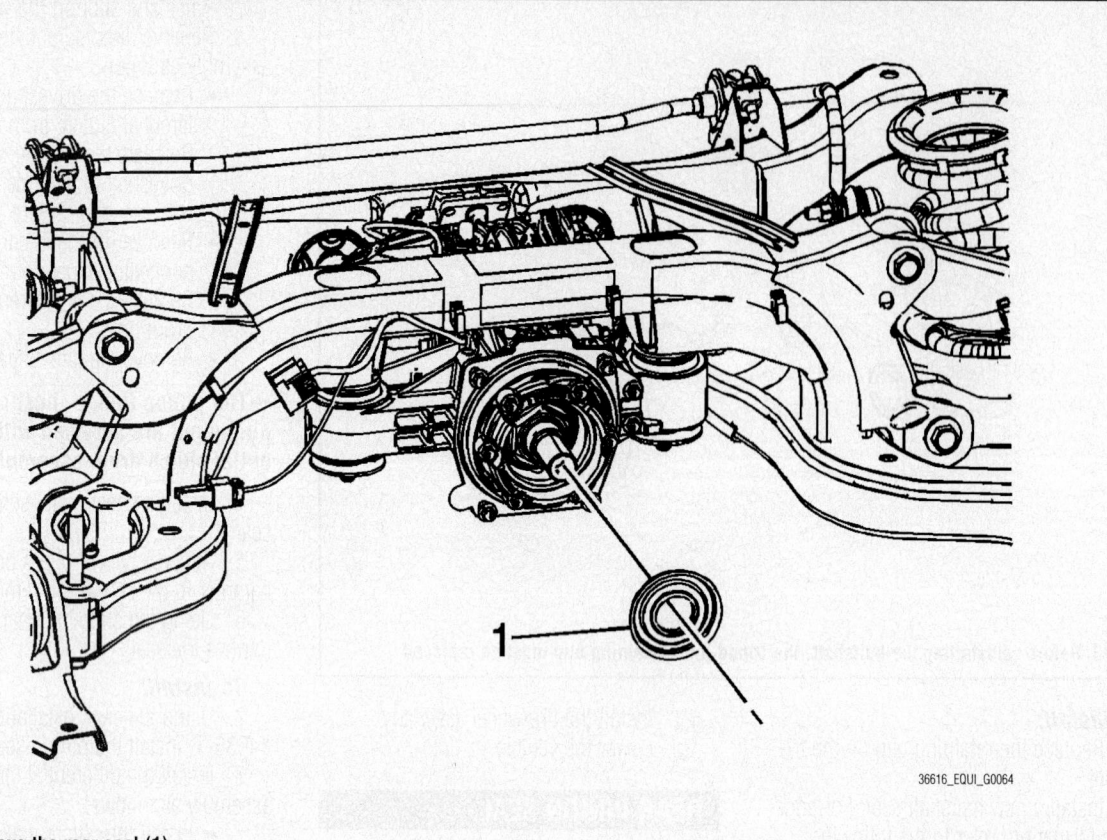

Fig. 45 Remove the rear seal (1)

36616_EQUI_G0064

- Tighten the bolts to 21 ft. lbs. (29 Nm). in a crisscross pattern.
- Connect the electrical clutch control connector and wire retaining clips.
- Install the driveshaft to the differential clutch drum assembly, tighten the mounting bolts to 37 ft. lbs. (50 Nm).
- Inspect the fluid level.

REAR DIFFERENTIAL CLUTCH CONTROL MODULE

REMOVAL & INSTALLATION

See Figure 46.

1. Before servicing the vehicle, refer to the precautions section.
2. Raise and support the vehicle.
3. Remove the spare tire.
4. Remove the rear exhaust assembly.
5. Remove the rear differential assembly. Refer to Differential Removal & Installation in this section.
6. Remove the 2 clutch drum control module screws.
7. Disconnect the clutch drum control module electrical connectors.
8. Remove the clutch drum control module.

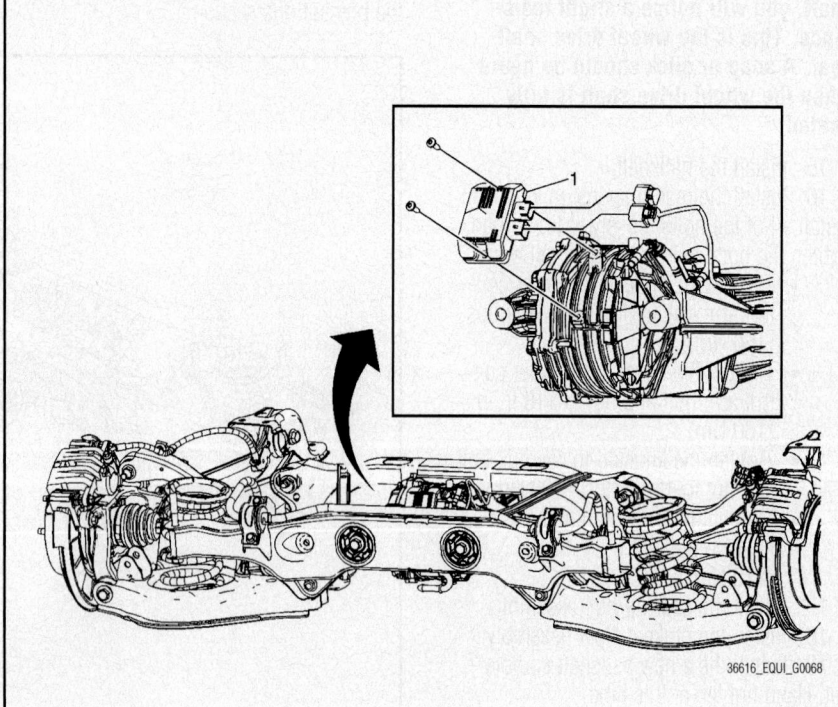

Fig. 46 Remove the Rear Differential Clutch Control Module (1)

36616_EQUI_G0068

9. Install the clutch drum control module and tighten the screws to 133 inch lbs. (15 Nm).

10. Connect the clutch drum control module electrical connectors.

11. Install the rear differential assembly. Refer to Differential Removal & Installation in this section.

12. Install the rear exhaust assembly. Install a new gasket and tighten the nuts as follows:

- 3.4L engine 27 ft. lbs. (37 Nm).
- 3.6L engine 18 ft. lbs. (25 Nm).

13. Install the spare tire.

14. Lower the vehicle.

15. Program the Rear Differential Clutch Control Module

REAR DIFFERENTIAL CLUTCH CONTROL MODULE PROGRAMMING

❋❋ WARNING

Specialized GM equipment is required for programming. For step-by-step programming instructions, please refer to the Techline Information System (TIS) terminal.

1. If the Rear Differential Clutch Control Module is replaced, the following procedures must be performed:

- Install a scan tool.
- Turn ON the ignition, with the engine OFF.
- Select Special Functions, Rear Drive System, CCM RDS Matching ID, follow instruction on the Tech 2. The CCM RDS Matching ID number can be found on the CCM harness connector.
- Cycle the ignition OFF, then start the engine and allow to run for 1 minute. Verify the rear differential system is functioning properly.
- After the calibration procedure, clear all DTCs and road test the vehicle.

ENGINE COOLING

ENGINE FAN

REMOVAL & INSTALLATION

See Figures 47 and 48.

1. Before servicing the vehicle, refer to the precautions section.

2. Remove the front fascia by removing all of the push-in retainers and screws.

3. Drain the cooling system.

4. Disconnect the electrical connectors from the fan motors.

5. Unclip the wire harness from the fan assembly.

6. Remove the Condenser Radiator Fan Module (CRFM) closeout panel retainers from the condenser.

7. Remove the CRFM closeout panel from the condenser.

8. Remove the front impact bar.

9. Remove the CRFM mounting bracket bolts from the radiator support.

10. Remove the CRFM mounting brackets from the radiator support.

11. Remove the radiator inlet hose clamp from the radiator.

12. Remove the radiator inlet hose from the radiator.

13. Disconnect the upper transaxle cooler line from the radiator.

14. Unclip the transaxle cooler lines from the fan assembly.

15. Lift the CRFM assembly from the lower mounts and carefully move the bottom of the assembly rearward while tilting the top forward.

16. Remove the fan assembly bolts from the radiator.

17. Remove the fan assembly from the radiator.

To install:

18. Install the fan to the motor.

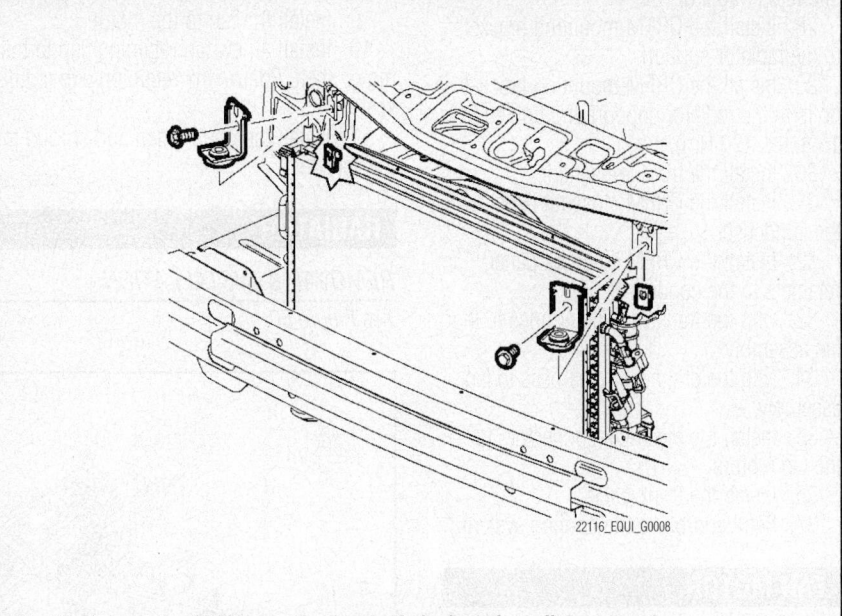

Fig. 47 Remove the CRFM mounting bracket bolts from the radiator support

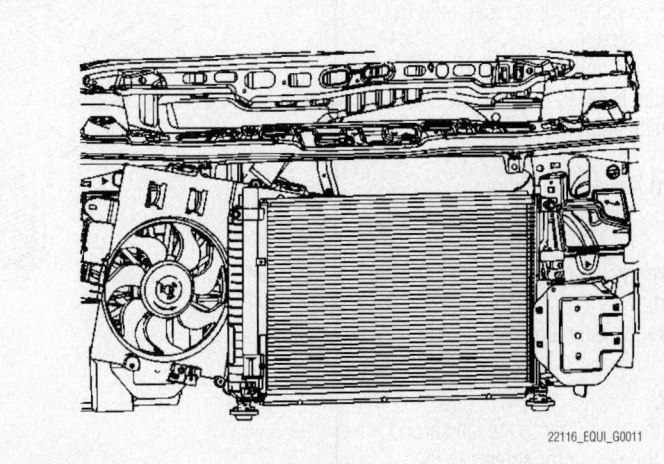

Fig. 48 Removing the fan assembly from the radiator

19. Align the scribe marks previously made on the fan hub and the motor shaft.

20. Install a new fan retaining clip to the motor shaft. Ensure the retaining clip is fully seated.

21. Install the fan assembly to the radiator by guiding the lower tabs into the corresponding hooks on the radiator.

22. Install the fan assembly bolts to the radiator and tighten to 80 inch lbs. (9 Nm).

23. Position the CRFM assembly onto the lower mounts.

24. Install the radiator inlet hose to the radiator.

25. Install the radiator inlet hose clamp to the radiator.

26. Clip the transaxle cooler lines to the fan assembly.

27. Connect the upper transaxle cooler line to the radiator.

28. Install the CRFM mounting brackets to the radiator support.

29. Install the CRFM mounting bracket bolts to the radiator support and tighten to 15 ft. lbs. (20 Nm).

30. Install the front impact bar.

31. Install the CRFM closeout panel to the condenser.

32. Install the CRFM closeout panel retainers to the condenser.

33. Clip the transaxle cooler lines to the fan assembly.

34. Clip the engine wire harness to fan assembly.

35. Install the electrical connectors to the fan motors.

36. Install the front fascia.

37. Refill and bleed the cooling system.

FAN MOTOR

REMOVAL & INSTALLATION

See Figure 49.

1. Before servicing the vehicle, refer to the precautions section.

2. Remove the cooling fan and shroud from the vehicle. Refer to Engine Fan Removal & Installation in the Engine Cooling section.

3. Discard fan retaining clip.

4. Carefully remove the fan from the motor.

5. Remove the fan motor screws from the fan shroud.

6. Remove the fan motor from the fan shroud.

To install:

7. Install the fan motor to the fan shroud.

8. Install the fan motor screws to the fan shroud and tighten to 71 inch lbs. (8 Nm)

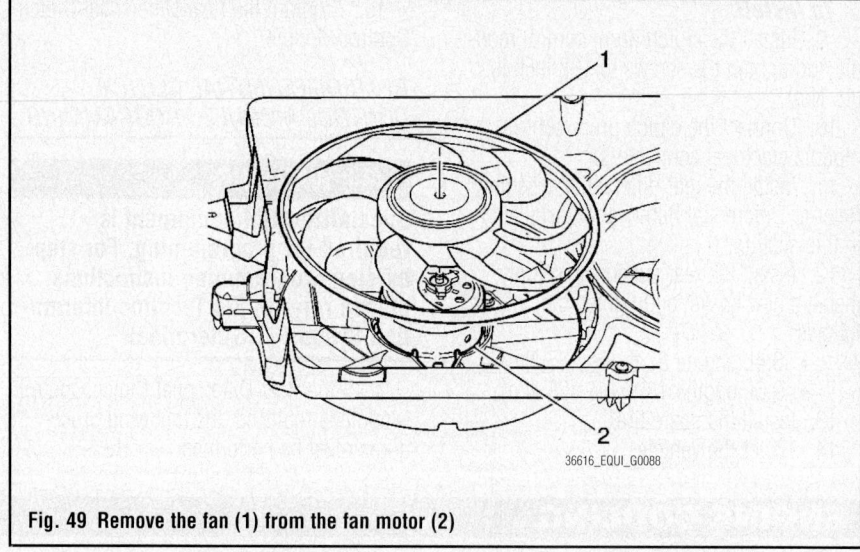

Fig. 49 Remove the fan (1) from the fan motor (2)

36616_EQUI_G0088

9. Install the fan to the motor.

10. Install a new fan retaining clip to the motor shaft. Ensure the retaining clip is fully seated.

11. Install the cooling fan and shroud to the vehicle.

RADIATOR

REMOVAL & INSTALLATION

See Figure 50.

1. Before servicing the vehicle, refer to the precautions section.

2. Drain the cooling system.

3. Raise and support the vehicle.

4. Remove the front bumper air deflector, if equipped.

5. Remove the front fascia.

6. Remove the front energy absorber.

7. Remove the front bumper impact bar.

8. Remove radiator closeout panel.

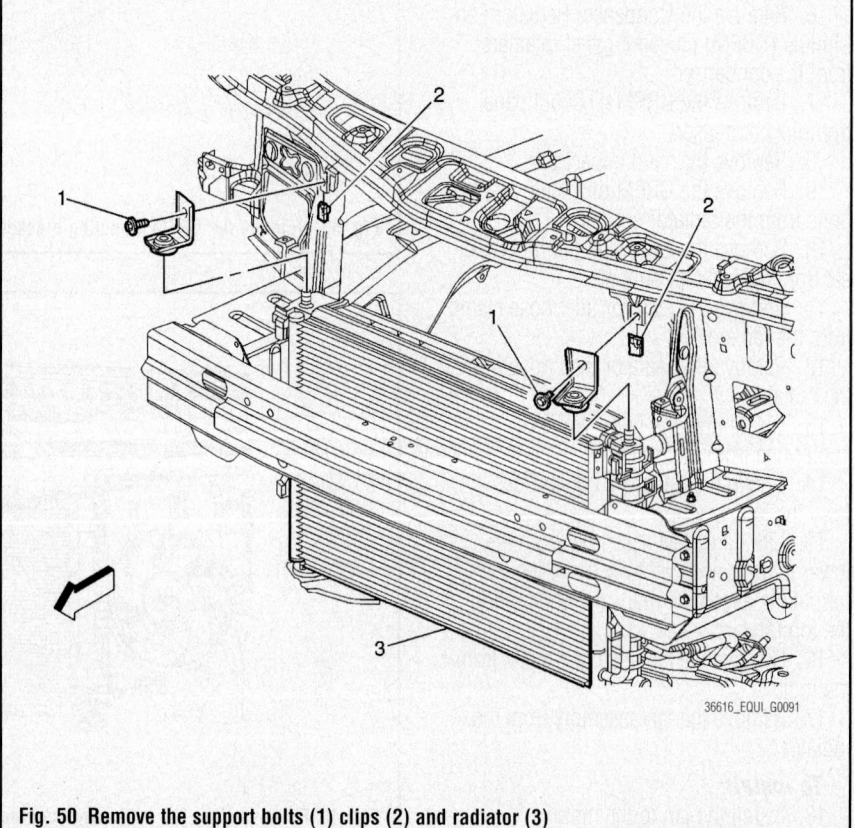

Fig. 50 Remove the support bolts (1) clips (2) and radiator (3)

36616_EQUI_G0091

9. Disconnect the compressor hose/pipe clip at bottom of fan shroud.

10. Remove mounting bolts from condenser using care with the upper left bolt to clear the compressor hose/pipe, reposition and support the condenser.

11. Remove the inlet and outlet radiator hoses.

12. Disconnect the transmission oil cooler lines from the attaching clips on radiator.

13. Remove the 2 fan shroud bolts and reposition the fan shroud.

14. Remove the 2 radiator support bolts.

15. Remove the 2 radiator support clips.

16. Remove the radiator from the vehicle.

To install:

17. Install the radiator to the vehicle.

18. Remove the 2 radiator support clips.

19. Install the 2 radiator support bolts and tighten to 15 ft. lbs. (20 Nm).

20. Reposition the fan shroud, install the bolts and tighten to 80 inch lbs. (9 Nm).

21. Connect the transmission oil cooler lines to the radiator.

22. Install the inlet and outlet radiator hoses and clamps

23. Connect the compressor hose/pipe clip at bottom of fan shroud.

24. Install the front bumper impact bar and tighten the mounting bolts to 18 ft. lbs. (25 Nm).

25. Install the front energy absorber.

26. Install the front fascia.

27. Install the front bumper air deflector, if equipped.

28. Lower the vehicle.

29. Refill and bleed the cooling system.

THERMOSTAT

REMOVAL & INSTALLATION

3.4L Engine

See Figure 51.

1. Before servicing the vehicle, refer to the precautions section.

2. Remove the fuel injector sight shield.

3. Drain the coolant until the coolant level is below the thermostat.

4. Remove the crossover exhaust pipe.

5. Remove the radiator hose from the thermostat housing.

6. Remove the thermostat housing bolts and clean any sealer from the bolt threads.

7. Remove the thermostat housing.

8. Remove the thermostat.

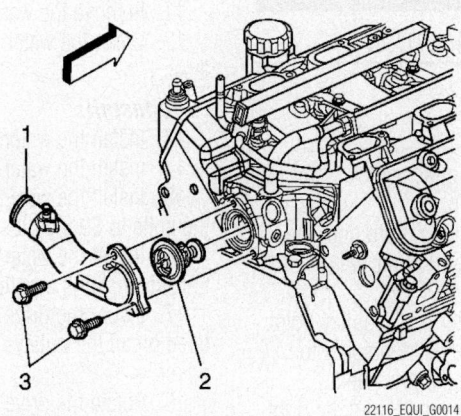

Fig. 51 Remove the housing bolts (3) and thermostat housing (1) to remove the thermostat (2).

To install:

9. Clean the mating surfaces.

10. Install the thermostat.

11. Install the thermostat housing.

12. Install RTV sealer to the thermostat housing bolt threads.

13. Install the thermostat housing bolts and tighten to 18 ft. lbs. (25 Nm).

14. Install the radiator hose to the thermostat housing.

15. Install the crossover exhaust pipe.

16. Install the fuel injector sight shield.

17. Fill the cooling system.

18. Inspect the cooling system for leaks.

3.6L Engine

See Figure 52.

1. Before servicing the vehicle, refer to the precautions section.

2. Partially drain the cooling system.

3. Remove the heater inlet and outlet pipes.

4. Remove the thermostat housing bolts.

5. Remove the housing.

6. Remove the thermostat and discard the thermostat seal.

7. Clean the mating surfaces.

8. Install the thermostat with a NEW thermostat seal.

9. Install the thermostat housing and bolts, tighten to 89 inch lbs. (10 Nm).

10. Install the heater inlet and outlet pipes.

11. Refill and bleed the cooling system.

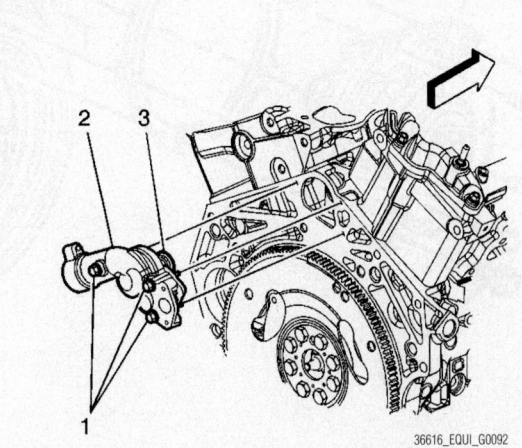

Fig. 52 Remove the housing bolts (1) housing (2) and the thermostat (3)

WATER PUMP

REMOVAL & INSTALLATION

3.4L Engine

See Figure 53.

1. Before servicing the vehicle, refer to the precautions section.

2. Drain the cooling system until the coolant is below the level of the water pump.

3. Loosen the water pump pulley bolts.

4. Rotate the drive belt tensioner to release the tension on the drive belt.

5. Remove the drive belt from the right idler pulley.

6. Carefully release the drive belt tensioner spring tension.

7. Remove the water pump pulley bolts.

8. Remove the water pump pulley.

9. Remove the water pump bolts.

10. Remove the water pump.

11. Remove the water pump gasket.

12. Clean the water pump mating surfaces.

To install:

13. Install the water pump gasket.

14. Install the water pump.

15. Install the water pump bolts. Tighten the bolts to 89 inch lbs. (10 Nm)

16. Install the water pump pulley. Loosely install the pulley bolts.

17. Insure the drive belt is properly centered on all the pulleys except the right idler puller.

18. Rotate the drive belt tensioner away from the drive belt.

19. Install the drive belt to the right idler pulley.

20. Release the tensioner allowing the drive belt tensioner to come in contact with the drive belt.

21. Inspect the drive belt to insure the belt is properly centered on all the pulleys.

22. Tighten the water pump pulley bolts. Tighten the bolts to 18 ft. lbs. (25 Nm).

23. Fill and bleed the cooling system.

24. Inspect the cooling system for leaks.

3.6L Engine

See Figures 54 and 55.

1. Before servicing the vehicle, refer to the precautions section.

2. Drain the cooling system until the coolant is below the level of the water pump.

3. Remove the drive belt.

4. Use the EN 46104 holding tool in order to retain the water pump pulley.

5. Remove the water pump pulley bolts.

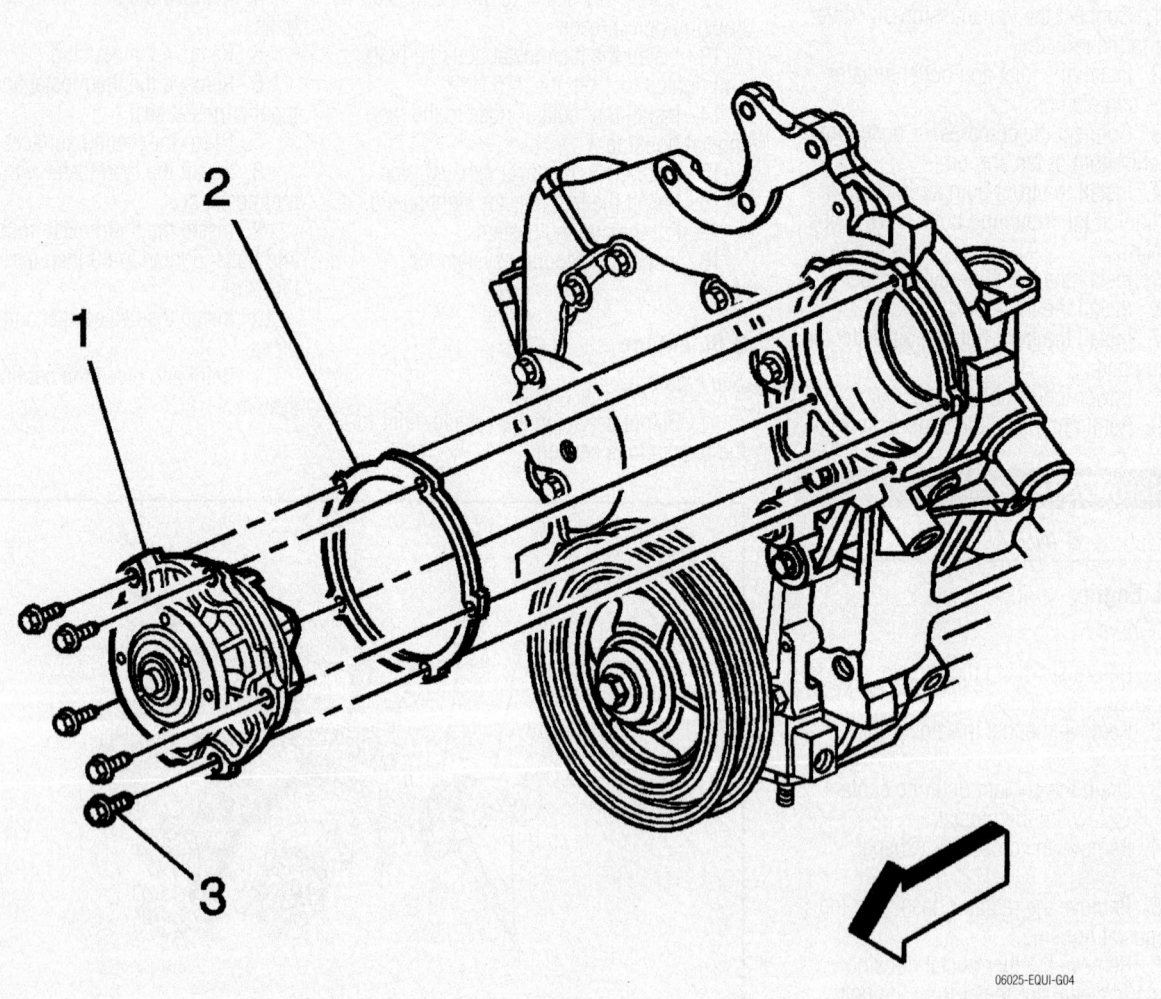

Fig. 53 Remove the mounting bolts (3) to remove the water pump (1) and gasket (2).

06025-EQUI-G04

Fig. 54 EN 46104 holding tool shown retaining the water pump pulley

36616_EQUI_G0093

Fig. 55 Water pump removal— 3.6L engine

36616_EQUI_G0094

6. Remove the water pump pulley.
7. Remove the water pump bolts.
8. Remove the water pump.
9. Remove and discard the water pump seal.
10. Carefully clean the water pump sealing surfaces.

To install:
11. Install a NEW water pump seal.
12. Install the water pump.
13. Install the water pump bolts and tighten to 89 inch lbs. (10 Nm)
14. Install the drive belt
15. Fill and bleed the cooling system.
16. Inspect the cooling system for leaks.

ENGINE ELECTRICAL

CHARGING SYSTEM

ALTERNATOR

REMOVAL & INSTALLATION

3.4L Engine

See Figure 56.

1. Before servicing the vehicle, refer to the precautions section.
2. Disconnect the negative battery cable.
3. Remove the accessory drive belt.
4. Disconnect the engine wiring harness electrical connector from the alternator.
5. Reposition the engine wiring harness boot.
6. Remove the alternator terminal nut.
7. Remove the engine wiring harness terminal lead from the alternator.
8. Remove the alternator bolts.
9. Remove the alternator.

To install:
10. Position the alternator to the engine.
11. Loosely install the engine bolts.
12. Tighten the alternating mounting bolts to 37 ft. lbs. (50 Nm).
13. Connect the engine wiring harness electrical connector to the generator.
14. Install the engine wiring harness terminal lead to the generator.
15. Install the generator terminal nut and tighten to 15 ft. lbs. (20 Nm).
16. Reposition the engine wiring harness boot.
17. Install the accessory drive belt.
18. Connect the negative battery cable.

3.6L Engine

See Figure 57.

1. Before servicing the vehicle, refer to the precautions section.

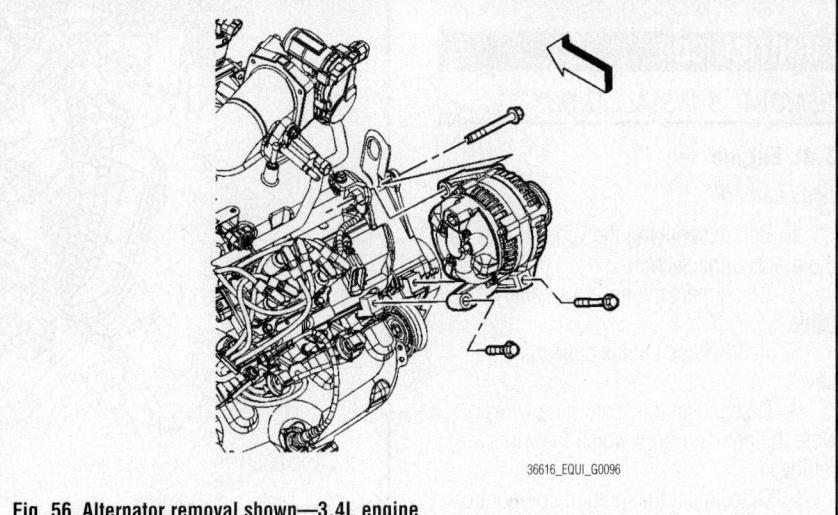

36616_EQUI_G0096

Fig. 56 Alternator removal shown—3.4L engine

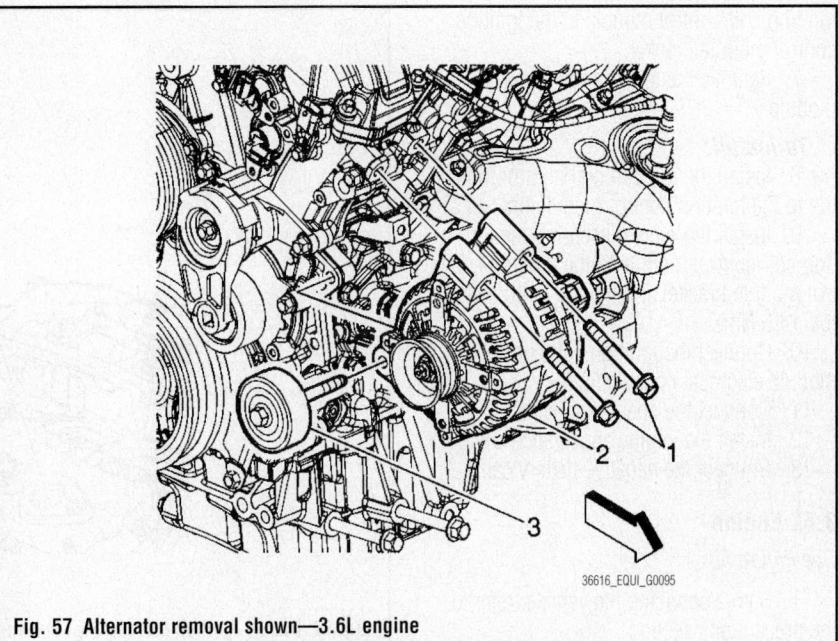

36616_EQUI_G0095

Fig. 57 Alternator removal shown—3.6L engine

2. Disconnect the negative battery cable.

3. Remove the accessory drive belt.

4. Reposition the engine wiring harness boot.

5. Remove the alternator terminal nut.

6. Remove the engine wiring harness terminal lead from the alternator.

7. Disconnect the engine wiring harness electrical connector from the alternator.

8. Remove the idler pulley mounting bolt.

9. Remove the idler pulley.

10. Remove the alternator mounting bolts.

11. Remove the alternator

To install:

12. Position the alternator to the engine.

13. Loosely install the engine bolts.

14. Install the idler pulley and tighten the mounting bolt to 37 ft. lbs. (50 Nm).

15. Tighten the alternating mounting bolts to 37 ft. lbs. (50 Nm).

16. Connect the engine wiring harness electrical connector to the generator.

17. Install the engine wiring harness terminal lead to the generator.

18. Install the generator terminal nut and tighten to 15 ft. lbs. (20 Nm).

19. Reposition the engine wiring harness boot.

20. Install the accessory drive belt.

21. Connect the negative battery cable.

ENGINE ELECTRICAL

IGNITION SYSTEM

FIRING ORDERS

Firing order for the 3.4L and 3.6L engine are as follows:

- 1-2-3-4-5-6

IGNITION COIL

REMOVAL & INSTALLATION

3.4L Engine

See Figure 58.

1. Before servicing the vehicle, refer to the precautions section.

2. Disconnect the negative battery cable.

3. Remove the engine appearance cover.

4. Disconnect the spark plug wires. Note the position from which the wires are removed.

5. Disconnect the ignition coil/control module electrical connectors.

6. Remove the 4 bolts securing the ignition coil/control module to the ignition control module bracket.

7. Remove the ignition coil/control module.

To install:

8. Install the ignition coil/control module to the ignition control module bracket.

9. Install the 4 bolts securing the ignition coil/control module to the ignition control module bracket and tighten to 40 inch lbs. (4.5 Nm).

10. Connect the ignition coil/control module electrical connectors.

11. Connect the spark plug wires.

12. Install the engine appearance cover.

13. Connect the negative battery cable.

3.6L Engine

See Figure 59.

1. Before servicing the vehicle, refer to the precautions section.

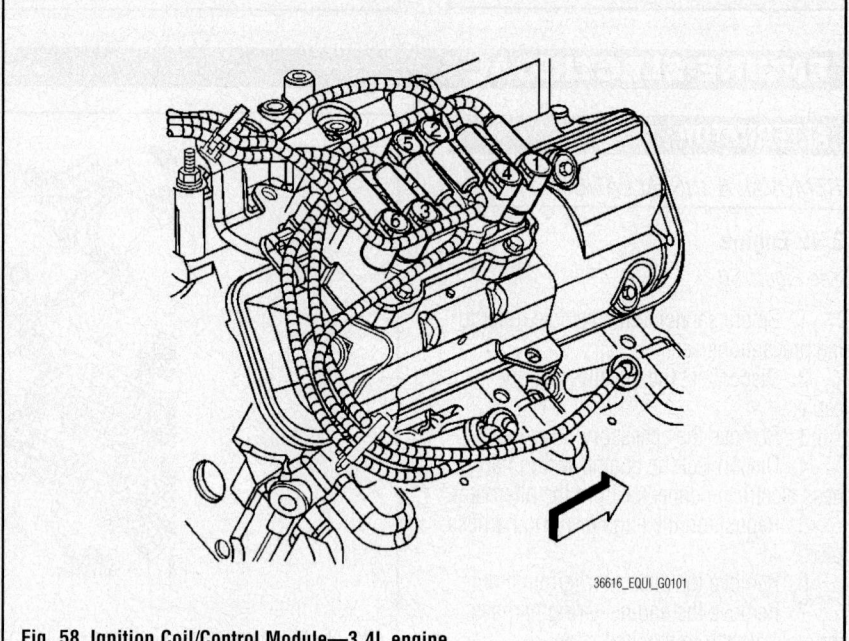

Fig. 58 Ignition Coil/Control Module—3.4L engine

36616_EQUI_G0101

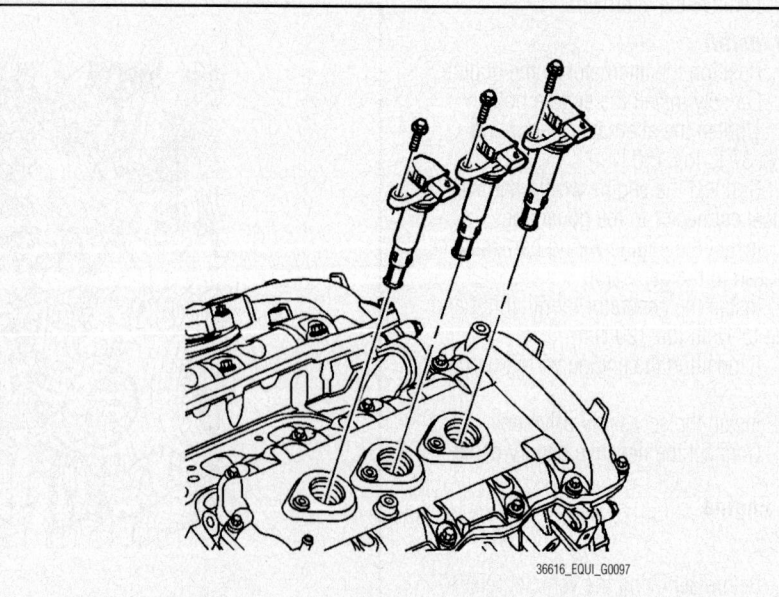

Fig. 59 Bank 1 ignition coil removal shown—3.6L engine

36616_EQUI_G0097

2. Remove the fuel injector sight shield.

3. Remove the air cleaner outlet duct for (Bank 2) coil removal.

4. Disconnect the negative battery cable.

5. Disconnect the engine wiring harness electrical connectors from the ignition coils.

6. Remove the ignition coil bolts.

7. Remove the ignition coils.

To install:

8. Install the ignition coils and tighten the bolts to 89 inch lbs. (10 Nm).

9. Connect the engine wiring harness electrical connectors to the ignition coils.

10. Install the fuel injector sight shield.

11. Install the air cleaner outlet duct for (Bank 2) coils.

12. Connect the negative battery cable.

IGNITION TIMING

ADJUSTMENT

The ignition timing is controlled by the Engine Control Module (ECM). No adjustment is necessary or possible.

SPARK PLUGS

REMOVAL & INSTALLATION

3.4L Engine

See Figure 60.

1. Before servicing the vehicle, refer to the precautions section.

2. Remove the spark plug wires from the spark plugs.

3. Remove the spark plugs from the cylinder head.

To install:

> ❋❋ **WARNING**
>
> **Installing plugs with the wrong gap can cause poor engine performance and may even damage the engine.**

4. Gap the spark plugs to the 0.060 inch

5. Install the spark plugs to the cylinder head. Tighten the plugs to 11 ft. lbs. (15 Nm).

6. Install the spark plug wires to the spark plugs.

3.6L Engine

See Figure 61.

1. Before servicing the vehicle, refer to the precautions section.

2. Remove the ignition coils. Refer to Ignition Coil Removal & Installation in the Engine Electrical section.

Fig. 60 Remove the spark plugs (1) from the cylinder head.

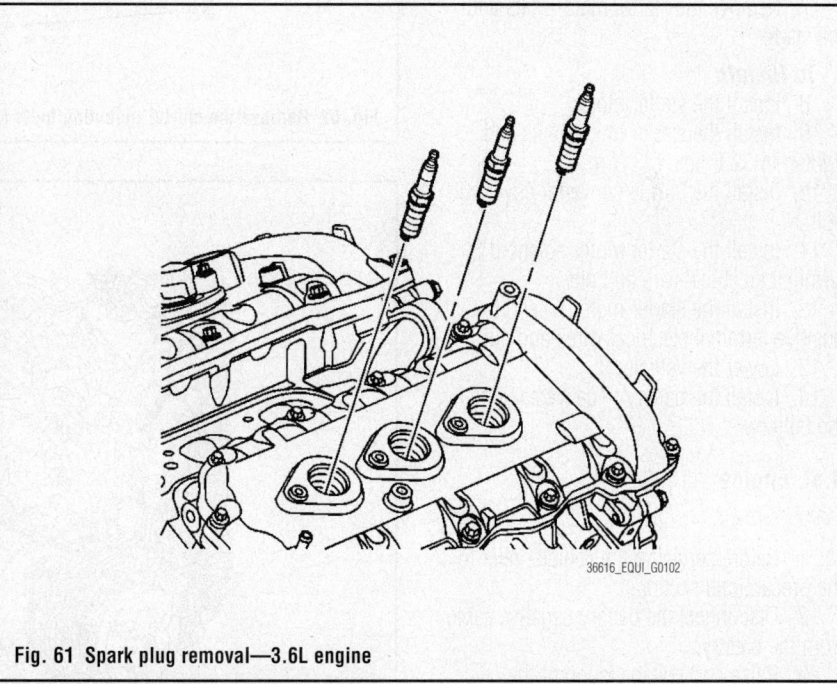

Fig. 61 Spark plug removal—3.6L engine

> ❋❋ **WARNING**
>
> **Clean the spark plug recess area before removing the spark plug. Failure to do so could result in engine damage because of dirt or foreign material entering the cylinder head, or by the contamination of the cylinder head threads. The contaminated threads may prevent the proper seating of the new plug. Use a thread chaser to clean the threads of any contamination.**

3. Use compressed air in order to remove debris from the spark plug cavity

4. Remove the spark plugs.

To install:

> ❋❋ **WARNING**
>
> **Use only the spark plugs specified for use in the vehicle. Do not install spark plugs that are either hotter or colder than those specified for the vehicle. Installing spark plugs of another type can severely damage the engine.**

5. Ensure that the spark plug gap is equivalent to the spark plug gap specification: 0.044 inch.

6. Install the spark plug and tighten to 15 ft. lbs. (20 Nm).

7. Install the ignition coil and tighten the retaining bolt to 89 inch lbs. (10 Nm).

STARTER

REMOVAL & INSTALLATION

3.4L Engine

See Figure 62.

1. Before servicing the vehicle, refer to the precautions section.

2. Disconnect the battery negative cable from the battery.

3. Raise and suitably support the vehicle.

4. Remove the starter motor solenoid positive terminal nut and electrical wires.

5. Remove the starter motor solenoid S terminal nut and electrical wire.

6. Remove the torque converter cover bolt and cover.

7. Remove the starter motor bolts and the starter.

To install:

8. Install the starter motor.

9. Install the starter motor bolts and tighten to 32 ft. lbs. (43 Nm).

10. Install the torque converter cover and bolt.

11. Install the starter motor solenoid S terminal electrical wire and nut.

12. Install the starter motor solenoid positive terminal electrical wires and nut.

13. Lower the vehicle.

14. Install the battery negative cable to the battery.

3.6L Engine

See Figure 63.

1. Before servicing the vehicle, refer to the precautions section.

2. Disconnect the battery negative cable from the battery.

3. Raise and suitably support the vehicle.

4. Remove the front catalytic converter. Refer to Catalytic Converter Removal & Installation in the Engine Mechanical section.

5. Remove the positive battery cable terminal to starter solenoid nut.

6. Remove the generator wiring lead from the starter solenoid.

7. Remove the positive battery cable lead from the starter solenoid.

8. Disconnect the engine wiring harness electrical connector from the starter.

9. Remove the starter bolts and starter.

To install:

10. Position the starter motor in the engine block.

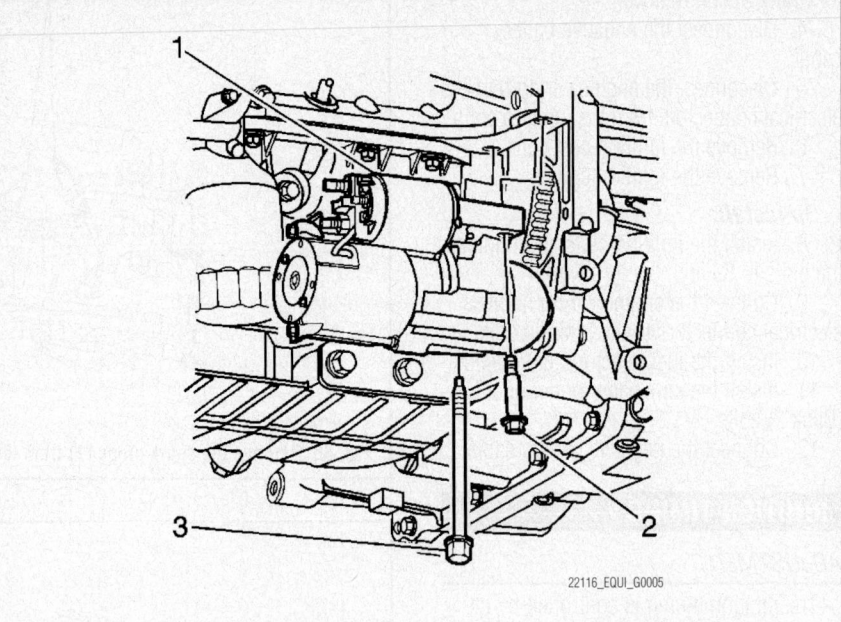

Fig. 62 Remove the starter mounting bolts (2, 3) to remove the starter (1)—Torrent shown

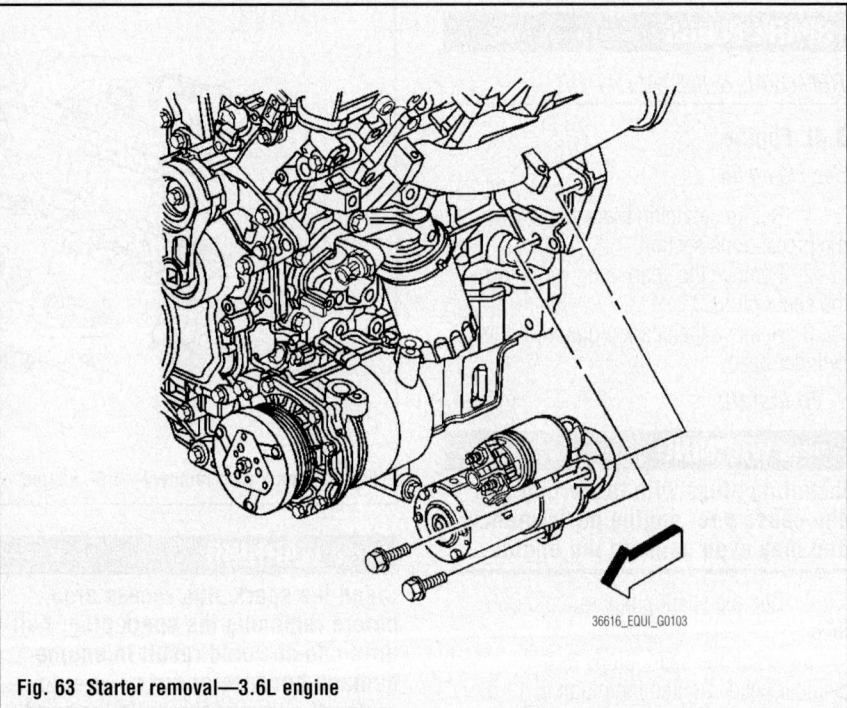

Fig. 63 Starter removal—3.6L engine

11. Install the starter bolts and tighten to 37 ft. lbs. (50 Nm).

12. Connect the engine wiring harness electrical connector to the starter.

13. Install the positive battery cable lead to the starter solenoid.

14. Install the generator wiring lead to the starter solenoid.

15. Install the positive battery cable terminal to starter solenoid nut and tighten to 89 inch lbs. (10 Nm).

16. Install the front catalytic converter.

17. Lower the vehicle.

18. Connect the negative battery cable.

19. Check starter for the correct operation.

ENGINE MECHANICAL

ACCESSORY DRIVE BELTS

ACCESSORY BELT ROUTING

See Figures 64 and 65.

INSPECTION

Inspect the drive belt for signs of glazing or cracking. A glazed belt will be perfectly smooth from slippage, while a good belt will have a slight texture of fabric visible. Cracks will usually start at the inner edge of the belt and run outward. All worn or damaged drive belts should be replaced immediately.

ADJUSTMENT

The engine accessory drive belt uses an auto-tensioner. No adjustment is necessary.

REMOVAL & INSTALLATION

3.4L Engine

See Figure 64.

1. Before servicing the vehicle, refer to the precautions section.
2. Remove the air cleaner assembly.
3. Using Special Tool J-39914, or a suitable belt tensioner unloader, rotate the drive belt tensioner to release the tension on the drive belt.
4. Remove the drive belt from the right idler pulley.
5. Carefully release the unloader to relieve the drive belt tensioner spring tension.
6. Remove the unloader from the drive belt tensioner .
7. Provided the vehicle will not be raised or lifted to perform additional work. Utilizing a floor jack and a wood block, support the front of the engine unlock between the lift point of the floor jack and the bottom of the engine oil pan.
8. Raise the jack until the wood block comes into contact with the engine oil pan and is capable of supporting the weight of the engine.
9. If the vehicle is to be raised or lifted in order to perform additional work. Support the engine using the engine support fixture.
10. Remove the right engine mount.
11. Remove the drive belt from the remaining pulleys.

To install:

12. Install the drive belt to all the pulleys except the right idler pulley.

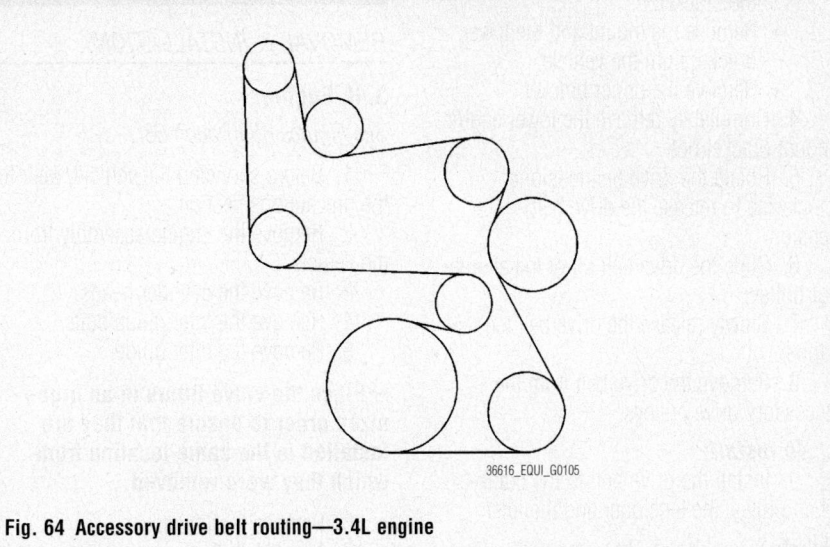

Fig. 64 Accessory drive belt routing—3.4L engine

13. Install the right engine mount. Tighten the nuts to 81 ft. lbs. (110 Nm).
14. Remove the floor jack from under the engine oil pan or remove the engine support fixture.
15. Using tensioner tool and rotate the drive belt tensioner away from the drive belt.
16. Install the drive belt to the right idler pulley.
17. Carefully release the tool allowing the drive belt tensioner to come in contact with the drive belt.
18. Remove the tool.
19. Inspect the drive belt to insure the belt is properly centered on all pulleys.
20. Install the air cleaner assembly.

3.6L Engine

See Figure 65.

1. Before servicing the vehicle, refer to the precautions section.
2. Remove the engine splash shield.
3. Remove the right side engine mount bracket as follows:
   - Remove the air cleaner assembly.
   - Support the engine.
   - Raise and support the vehicle.
   - Remove 3 upper engine mount bracket bolts.
   - Loosen right upper front bolt.
   - Remove the ABS connector clip from the frame.
   - Remove the upper engine mount bracket nuts.

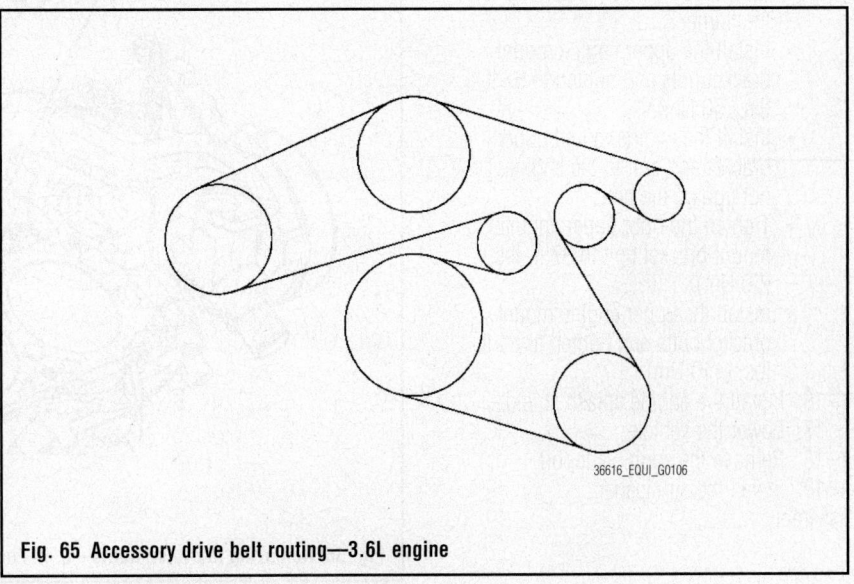

Fig. 65 Accessory drive belt routing—3.6L engine

- Remove the lower bracket bolts.
- Remove the upper bracket bolt from the bracket.
- Remove the mount and the lower bracket from the vehicle.
- Remove the upper bracket.

4. Completely remove the lower engine mount bracket bolt.

5. Rotate the drive belt tensioner clockwise to release the drive belt tension.

6. Slide the drive belt off of the alternator pulley.

7. Slowly release the drive belt tensioner.

8. Remove the drive belt from the accessory drive pulleys.

To install:

9. Install the drive belt to the crankshaft pulley, the tensioner and the idler pulley.

10. Rotate the drive belt tensioner clockwise.

11. Install the drive belt to the alternator.

➥ **Ensure the drive belt is properly aligned and seated into the grooves of the accessory drive pulleys.**

12. Slowly release the drive belt tensioner.

13. Raise the vehicle.

14. Partially thread the lower right side engine mount bracket bolt in place.

15. Install the right side engine mount bracket as follows:
- Install the engine mount and the lower bracket to the vehicle. Tighten the lower bracket bolts to 37 ft. lbs. (50 Nm).
- Install the ABS connector clip to the frame.
- Install the upper engine mount bracket nuts and tighten to 37 ft. lbs. (50 Nm).
- Install the engine mount upper bracket and bolt to the engine. Do not tighten the bolt.
- Tighten the right upper engine mount bracket bolt to 37 ft. lbs. (50 Nm).
- Install the upper engine mount bracket bolts and tighten to 81 ft. lbs. (110 Nm).

16. Install the engine splash shield.

17. Lower the vehicle.

18. Remove the engine support.

19. Install the air cleaner assembly.

CAMSHAFT AND VALVE LIFTERS

REMOVAL & INSTALLATION

3.4L Engine

See Figures 66 through 68.

1. Before servicing the vehicle, refer to the precautions section.

2. Remove the engine assembly from the vehicle.

3. Remove the cylinder heads.

4. Remove the lifter guide bolts.

5. Remove the lifter guide.

➥ **Place the valve lifters in an organized order to ensure that they are installed in the same location from which they were removed.**

6. Remove the lifters.

7. Remove the oil pan.

8. Remove the camshaft position sensor bolt.

9. Remove the camshaft position sensor.

10. Remove the camshaft thrust plate screws.

11. Remove the camshaft thrust plate.

➥ **All camshaft journals are the same diameter, so care must be used in removing or installing the camshaft to avoid damage to the camshaft bearings.**

12. Complete the following steps in order to remove the camshaft.
- Install the camshaft sprocket bolt into the camshaft. Tighten finger tight only.
- Carefully rotate and remove the camshaft from the engine block.

To install:

13. Coat the camshaft journals with clean engine oil.

14. Coat the camshaft lobes with prelube GM P/N 12345501 (Canadian P/N 992704) or the equivalent.

15. Install the camshaft using the following procedure:
- Install the camshaft sprocket bolt into the camshaft. Tighten finger tight only.
- Carefully rotate the camshaft while installing the camshaft into the camshaft bearings.

16. Install the camshaft thrust plate.

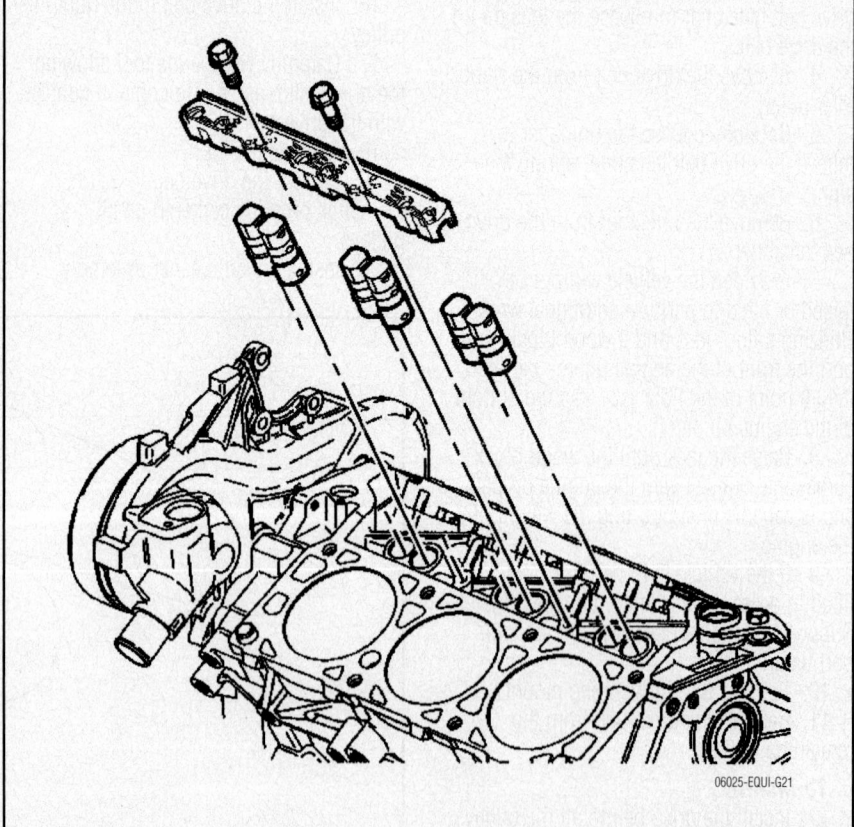

06025-EQUI-G21

Fig. 66 Removing the valve lifters—3.4L Engine

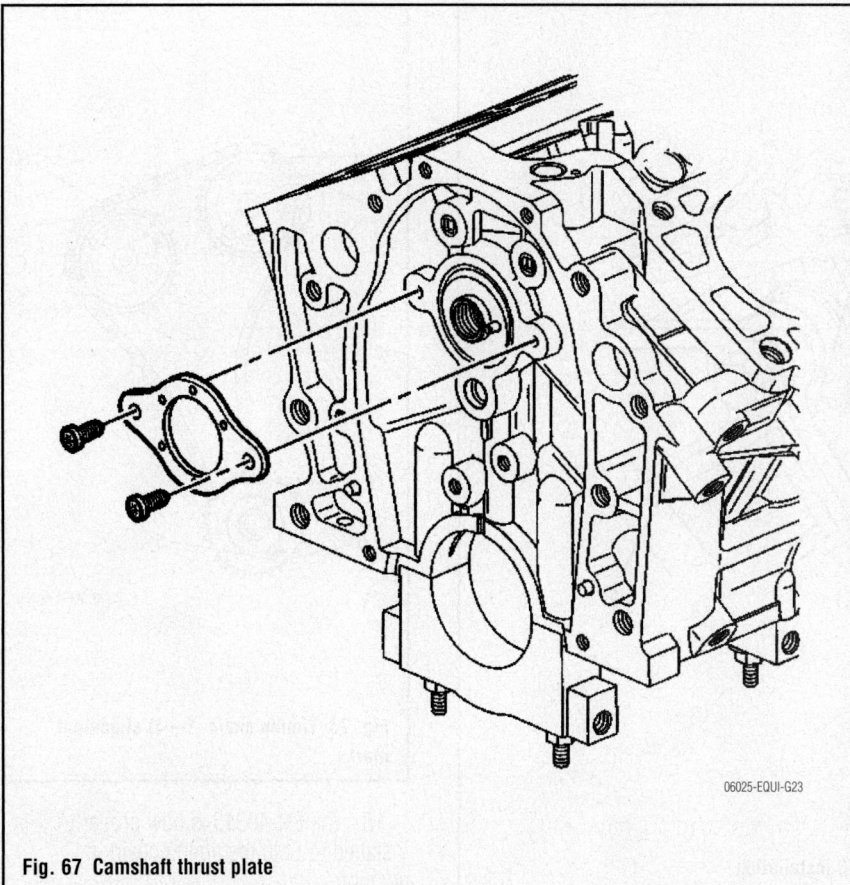

06025-EQUI-G23

Fig. 67 Camshaft thrust plate

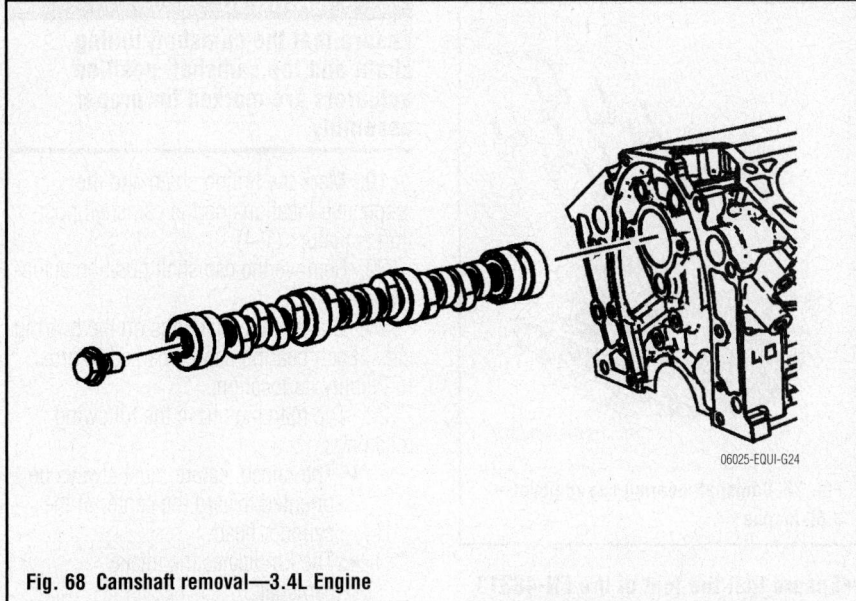

06025-EQUI-G24

Fig. 68 Camshaft removal—3.4L Engine

17. Install the camshaft thrust plate screws. Tighten the camshaft thrust plate screws to 89 inch lbs. (10 Nm).

18. Install the camshaft position sensor.

19. Install the camshaft position sensor bolt. Tighten the camshaft position sensor bolt to 89 inch lbs. (10 Nm).

20. Install the oil pan.

21. Coat the valve lifters using pre-lube GM P/N 1052367 (Canadian P/N 992869) or the equivalent.

22. Install the valve lifters in their original locations.

23. Install the lifter guide.

24. Apply thread lock GM P/N 12345382 (Canadian P/N 10953489) or the equivalent

to the lifter guide bolt threads and install the bolts. Tighten the bolts to 89 inch lbs. (10 Nm).

25. Install the cylinder heads.

26. Install the engine assembly into the vehicle.

27. Start the engine and check for leaks.

3.6L Engine

Left Camshaft & Lifters

See Figures 69 through 75.

1. Before servicing the vehicle, refer to the precautions section.

2. Disconnect the negative battery cable.

3. Remove the lower intake manifold.

4. Remove the left bank camshaft cover.

5. Remove the camshaft sensors.

6. Remove the camshaft position actuator solenoid.

7. Remove the crankshaft balancer

8. Rotate the crankshaft with the EN 46111 until the camshafts are in a neutral (low tension) position.

9. The camshaft flats will be parallel with the camshaft cover rail .

☀ WARNING

Use an open-end wrench at the camshaft hex to prevent camshaft/engine rotation. DO NOT remove the camshaft position actuator bolt at this time.

10. Unscrew the EN-48313 timing chain holding tool so that the legs of the tool are retracted.

11. Insert the EN-48313 between the camshaft actuators, rearward of the timing chain until the bottom line that is scribed in the body of the tool is adjacent to the top surface of the cylinder head. This is the approximate installed position.

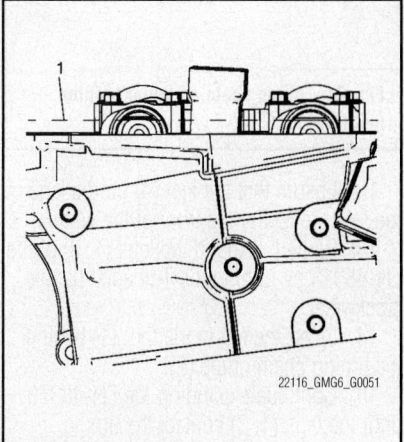

22116_GMG6_G0051

Fig. 69 Camshaft flats shown

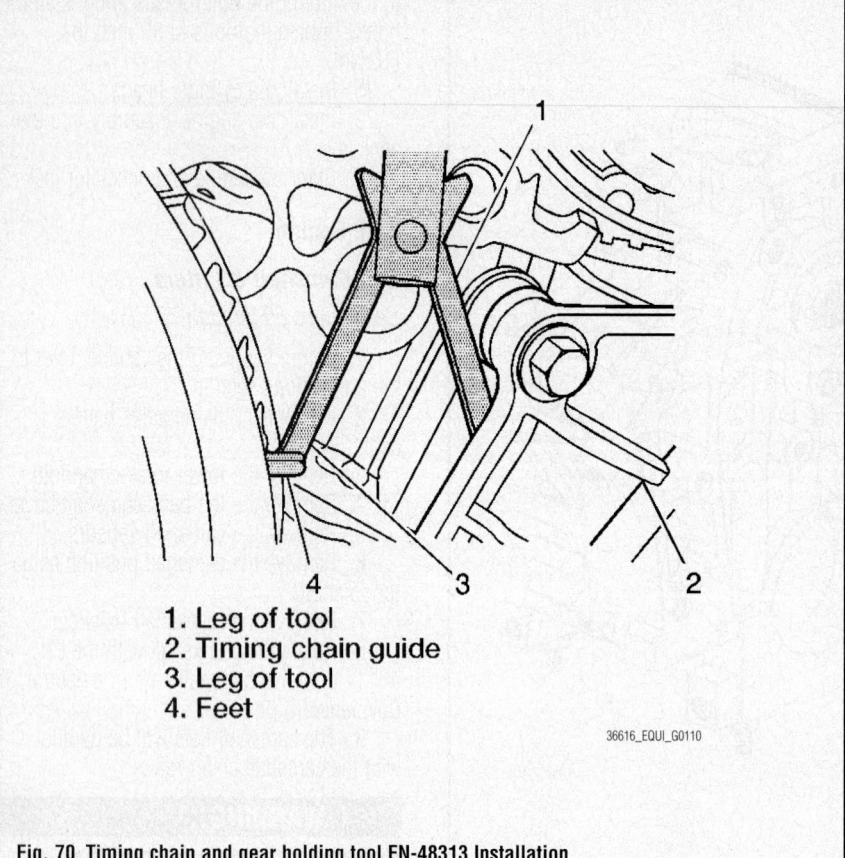

1. Leg of tool
2. Timing chain guide
3. Leg of tool
4. Feet

36616_EQUI_G0110

Fig. 70 Timing chain and gear holding tool EN-48313 Installation

36616_EQUI_G0111

Fig. 71 Timing chain and gear holding tool EN-48313

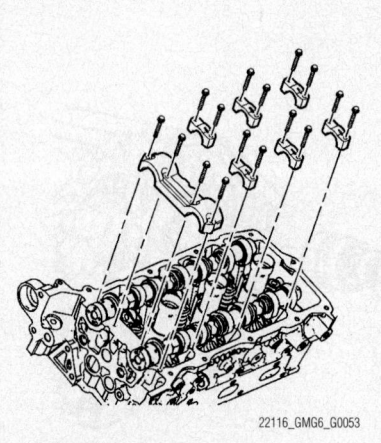

22116_GMG6_G0053

Fig. 72 Camshaft bearing cap removal— 3.6L engine

12. Ensure that the feet (4) on the legs of the tool are facing the front of the engine.

13. Partially expand the legs (1, 3) of the EN-48313 by turning the T-shaped handle clockwise.

14. Insert the leg of the tool (1) behind the timing chain guide (2).

15. Continue expanding the EN-48313 until the legs (1, 3) contact the timing chain. Do not tighten at this time.

➥Ensure that the foot of the EN-48313 is engaged into one of the link pockets to prevent tool slippage during tightening of the EN-48313.

16. Hand tighten the EN-48313.

17. Use an open end wrench on the hex cast into the left intake and exhaust camshafts and rotate the camshafts toward each other in order to create slack in the chain between the actuators.

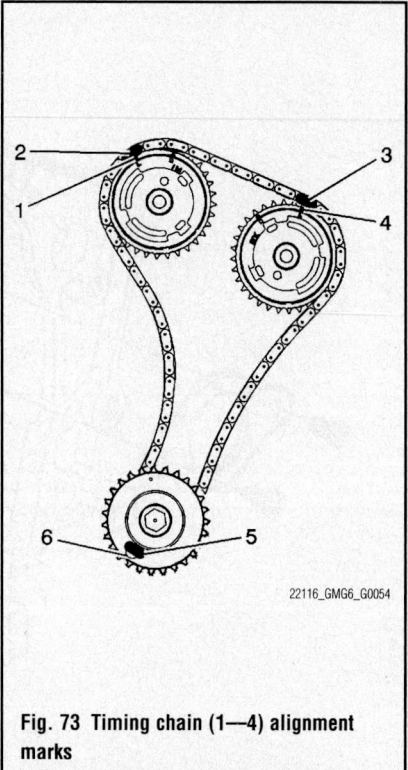

22116_GMG6_G0054

Fig. 73 Timing chain (1—4) alignment marks

18. The EN-48313 is now properly installed to hold the timing chain in position.

❋❋ WARNING

Ensure that the camshaft timing chain and the camshaft position actuators are marked for proper assembly.

19. Mark the timing chain and the respective locations on the camshaft position actuators (1-4).

20. Remove the camshaft position actuator bolt.

21. Observe the markings on the bearing caps. Each bearing cap is marked in order to identify its location.

22. The markings have the following meanings:

- The raised feature must always be oriented toward the center of the cylinder head.
- The I indicates the intake camshaft.
- The E indicates the exhaust camshaft
- The number indicates the journal position from the front of the engine

23. Remove the camshaft bearing cap bolts.

24. Remove the camshaft bearing caps.

25. Remove the camshafts.

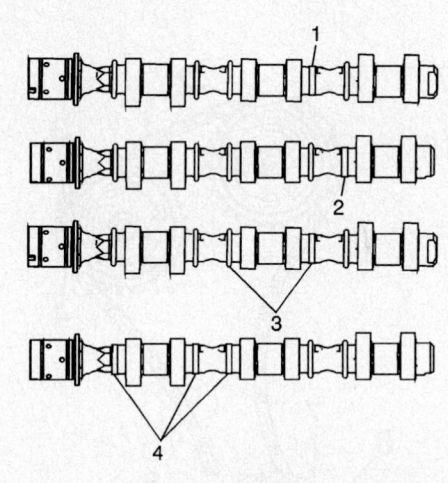

1. The number 4 identification ring for the left intake camshaft is machined off (1) - Third Design, Camshaft Timing Drive System.

2. The number 5 identification ring for the left exhaust camshaft is machined off (2) - Third Design and Fourth, except High Output, Camshaft Timing Drive System.

3. The number 3 and 4 identification rings for the left intake camshaft is machined off (3) - Fourth Design, Camshaft Timing Drive System.

4. The number 1, 2 and 3 identification rings for the left exhaust camshaft is machined off (4) - Fourth Design High Output, Camshaft Timing Drive System.

22116_GMG6_G0055

Fig. 74 Camshaft design identification—3.6L engine

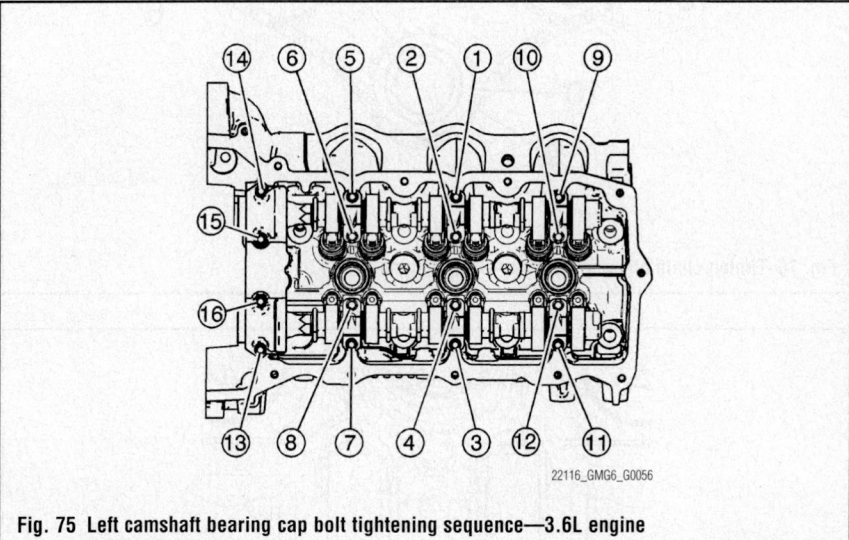

22116_GMG6_G0056

Fig. 75 Left camshaft bearing cap bolt tightening sequence—3.6L engine

26. Remove the rocker arms.

27. Remove lifters.

28. Replace the camshaft bearing caps and bolts.

To install:

★✕ **WARNING**

Ensure that the marks on the camshaft position actuator and the timing chain (1—4) are aligned. DO NOT tighten the camshaft position actuator bolt at this time.

29. Locate the camshafts to the cylinder head and assemble the camshaft actuators to the camshafts.

30. Ensure that the crankshaft is in the stage one timing drive assembly position using the EN 46111.

31. Ensure that the camshaft sealing rings are in place in the camshaft grooves. Camshaft sealing rings must be in place below the surface of the camshaft journal in order to avoid being pinched between the cylinder head and the camshaft caps.

➥**Ensure each valve lifter is filled with clean engine oil and the valve lifter does not tip over (plunger down) before the installation of the valve lifters. The loss of oil in the valve lifter lower pressure chamber or the dry stroking/ cycling of the valve lifter plunger will allow air to travel into the high pressure chamber of the valve lifter. Air in the high pressure chamber of the valve lifter may not be purged causing extensive engine component damage.**

32. Install valve lifters.

33. Install rocker arms.

34. Apply a liberal amount of lubricant to the camshaft journals and the left cylinder head camshaft carriers.

35. Place the left intake and left exhaust camshafts in position in the left cylinder head.

36. Position the camshaft lobes in a neutral position with the flats on the back of the camshafts up and parallel with the left cylinder head camshaft cover rail.

37. Observe the markings on the left cylinder head camshaft bearing caps. Each bearing cap is marked in order to identify its location.

38. The markings have the following meanings:

- The raised feature must always be oriented toward the center of the cylinder head.
- The I indicates the intake camshaft.
- The E indicates the exhaust camshaft
- The number indicates the journal position from the front of the engine

39. Apply a liberal amount of lubricant to the camshaft bearing caps.

40. Install the camshaft bearing thrust cap in the first journal of the left cylinder head.

41. Install the remaining bearing caps with their orientation mark toward the center of the cylinder head.

42. Hand start all the camshaft bearing cap bolts.

43. Tighten the bearing cap bolts by following the next few steps:

- Tighten the camshaft bearing cap bolts in sequence to 89 inch lbs.(10 Nm).
- Loosen the center intake camshaft bearing cap bolts 1, 2 and the center exhaust camshaft bearing cap bolts.
- Retighten the center camshaft bearing cap bolts 1, 2, 3, and 4.
- Retighten the camshaft bearing cap bolts to 89 inch lbs.(10 Nm).

44. Remove the EN-48313 timing chain holding tool

45. Install and tighten the camshaft position actuators.

46. Install the intake camshaft position actuator solenoid.

47. Install the camshaft sensors.

48. Install the crankshaft balancer.

49. Install the camshaft cover.

50. Install the lower intake manifold.

51. Connect the negative battery cable.

52. Drain crankcase and install recommended motor oil.

53. Start the vehicle, check for leaks and repair if necessary.

Right Camshaft & Lifters

See Figures 76 through 78.

1. Disconnect the negative battery cable.
2. Remove the lower intake manifold.
3. Remove the camshaft cover.
4. Remove the camshaft sensors.
5. Remove the intake camshaft position actuator solenoid.
6. Rotate the crankshaft with the EN 46111 until the camshafts are in a neutral (low tension) position. The camshaft flats will be parallel with the camshaft cover rail.

❋❋ WARNING

Use an open-end wrench at the camshaft hex to prevent camshaft/engine rotation. DO NOT remove the camshaft position actuator bolt at this time.

7. Loosen the camshaft position actuator bolt.
8. Unscrew the EN-48313 timing chain holding tool so that the legs of the tool are retracted.
9. Insert the EN-48313 between the camshaft actuators, rearward of the timing chain until the bottom line that is scribed in the body of the tool is adjacent to the top surface of the cylinder head. This is the approximate installed position.
10. Ensure that the feet (4) on the legs of the tool are facing the front of the engine.
11. Partially expand the legs (1, 3) of the EN-48313 by turning the T-shaped handle clockwise.
12. Insert the leg of the tool (1) behind the timing chain guide (2).
13. Continue expanding the EN-48313 until the legs (1, 3) contact the timing chain. Do not tighten at this time.

➡**Ensure that the foot of the EN-48313 is engaged into one of the link pockets to prevent tool slippage during tightening of the EN-48313.**

14. Hand tighten the EN-48313.
15. Use an open end wrench on the hex cast into the left intake and exhaust camshafts and rotate the camshafts toward each other in order to create slack in the chain between the actuators.
16. The EN-48313 is now properly installed to hold the timing chain in position.

❋❋ WARNING

Ensure that the camshaft timing chain and the camshaft position actuators are marked for proper assembly.

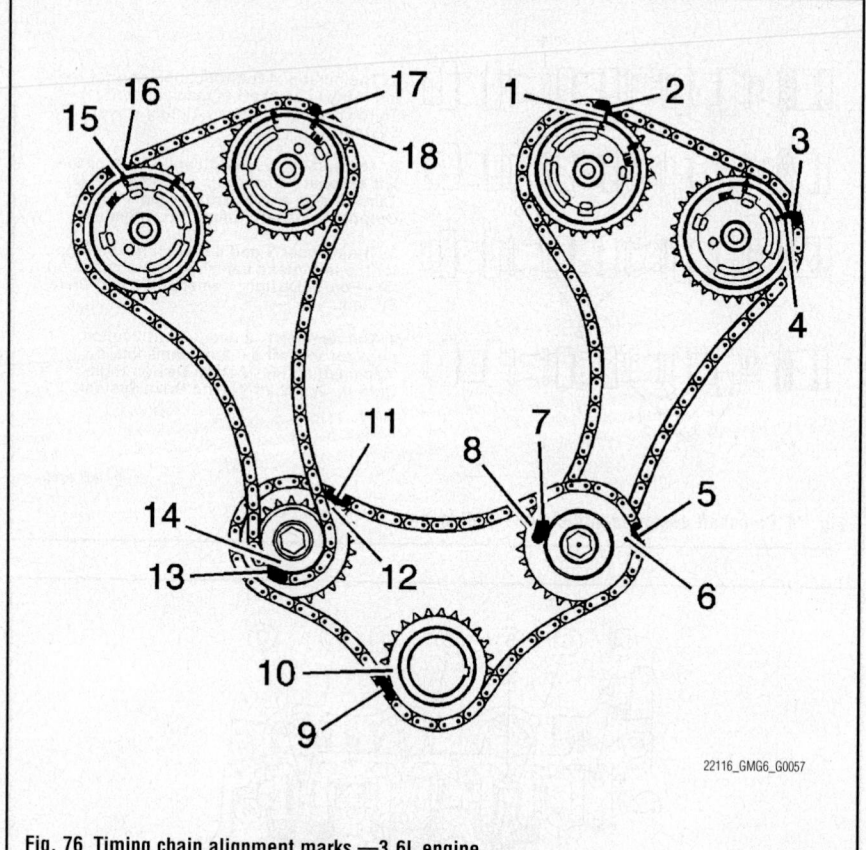

Fig. 76 Timing chain alignment marks —3.6L engine

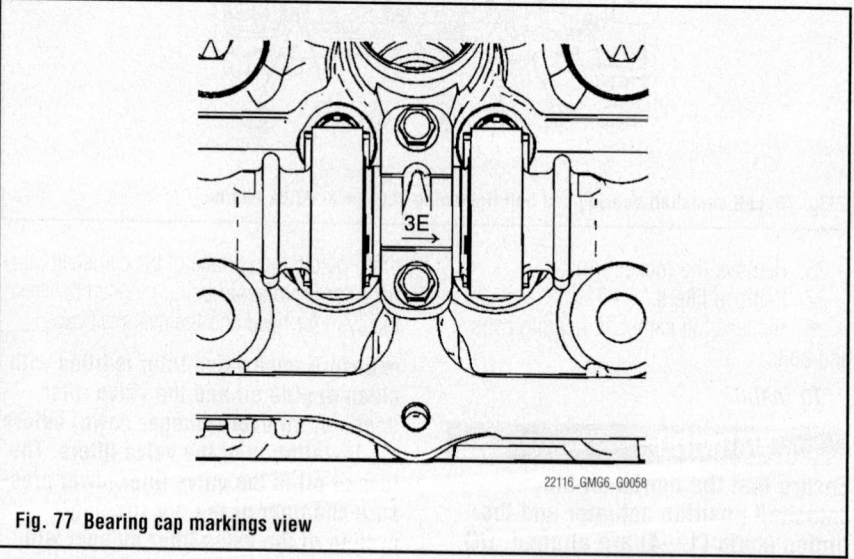

Fig. 77 Bearing cap markings view

17. Mark the timing chain and the respective locations on camshaft position actuators (15-18).
18. Remove the camshaft position actuator bolt.
19. Observe the markings on the right cylinder head camshaft bearing caps. Each bearing cap is marked in order to identify its location.
20. The markings have the following meanings:

- The raised feature must always be oriented toward the center of the cylinder head.
- The I indicates the intake camshaft.
- The E indicates the exhaust camshaft
- The number indicates the journal position from the front of the engine

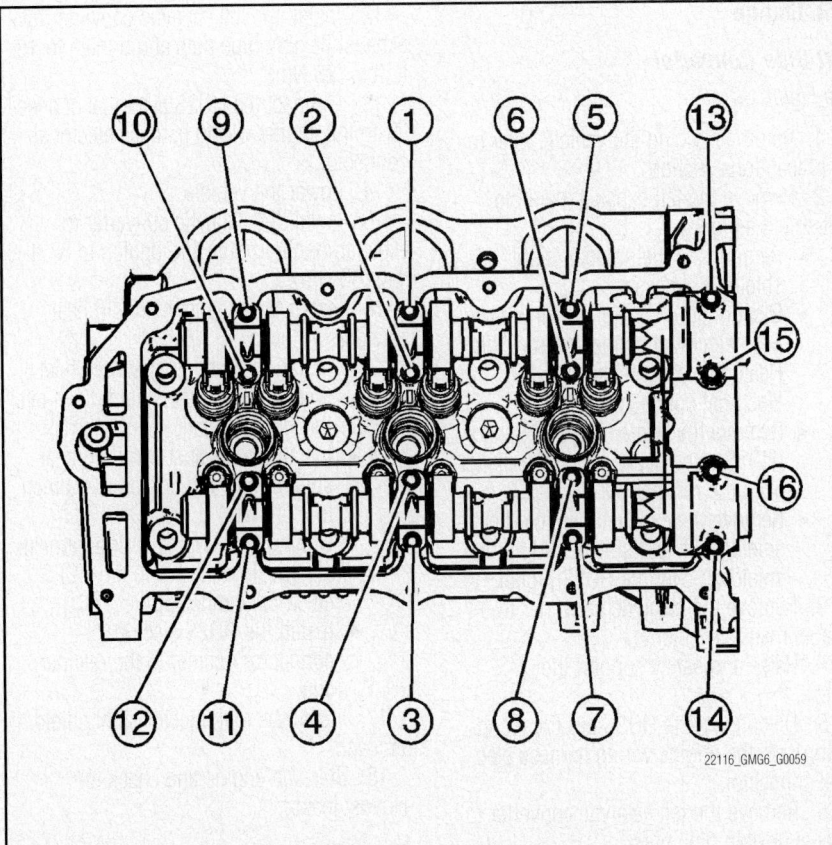

Fig. 78 Right camshaft bearing cap bolt tightening sequence—3.6L engine

21. Remove the camshaft bearing cap bolts.
22. Remove the camshaft bearing caps.
23. Remove the camshafts.
24. Remove the rocker arms.
25. Remove lifters.
26. Replace the camshaft bearing caps and bolts.

To install:

✳✳ WARNING

Ensure that the marks on the camshaft position actuator and the timing chain (1—4) are aligned. DO NOT tighten the camshaft position actuator bolt at this time.

27. Locate the camshafts to the cylinder head and assemble the camshaft actuators to the camshafts.
28. Ensure that the crankshaft is in the stage one timing drive assembly position using the EN 46111.
29. Ensure that the camshaft sealing rings (1) are in place in the camshaft grooves. Camshaft sealing rings must be in place below the surface of the camshaft journal in order to avoid being pinched between the cylinder head and the camshaft caps.

➡Ensure each valve lifter is filled with clean engine oil and the valve lifter does not tip over (plunger down) before the installation of the valve lifters. The loss of oil in the valve lifter lower pressure chamber or the dry stroking/cycling of the valve lifter plunger will allow air to travel into the high pressure chamber of the valve lifter. Air in the high pressure chamber of the valve lifter may not be purged causing extensive engine component damage.

30. Install valve lifters.
31. Install rocker arms.
32. Apply a liberal amount of lubricant to the camshaft journals and the right cylinder head camshaft carriers.
33. Place the right intake and right exhaust camshafts in position in the right cylinder head.
34. Position the camshaft lobes in a neutral position with the flats on the back of the camshafts up and parallel (1) with the right cylinder head camshaft cover rail.
35. Observe the markings on the right cylinder head camshaft bearing caps. Each bearing cap is marked in order to identify its location.

36. The markings have the following meanings:
- The raised feature must always be oriented toward the center of the cylinder head.
- The I indicates the intake camshaft.
- The E indicates the exhaust camshaft
- The number indicates the journal position from the front of the engine

37. Apply a liberal amount of lubricant to the camshaft bearing caps.
38. Install the camshaft bearing thrust cap in the first journal of the right cylinder head.
39. Install the remaining bearing caps with their orientation mark toward the center of the cylinder head.
40. Hand start all the camshaft bearing cap bolts.
41. Tighten the bearing cap bolts by following the next few steps:
- Tighten the camshaft bearing cap bolts in sequence to 89 inch lbs.(10 Nm).
- Loosen the center intake camshaft bearing cap bolts (1, 2) and the center exhaust camshaft bearing cap bolts (3, 4).
- Retighten the center camshaft bearing cap bolts 1, 2, 3, and 4.
- Retighten the camshaft bearing cap bolts to 89 inch lbs.(10 Nm).

42. Install and tighten the camshaft position actuators.
43. Install the intake camshaft position actuator solenoid.
44. Install the camshaft sensors.
45. Install the crankshaft balancer.
46. Install the camshaft cover.
47. Install the lower intake manifold.
48. Connect the negative battery cable.
49. Drain crankcase and install recommended motor oil.
50. Start the vehicle, check for leaks and repair if necessary.

CATALYTIC CONVERTER

REMOVAL & INSTALLATION

3.4L Engine

See Figure 79.

1. Before servicing the vehicle, refer to the precautions section.
2. Raise and support the vehicle.
3. Disconnect the Heated Oxygen Sensor (HO2S) connector from the wiring harness.
4. Remove the catalytic converter pipe flange to exhaust system pipe flange nuts.

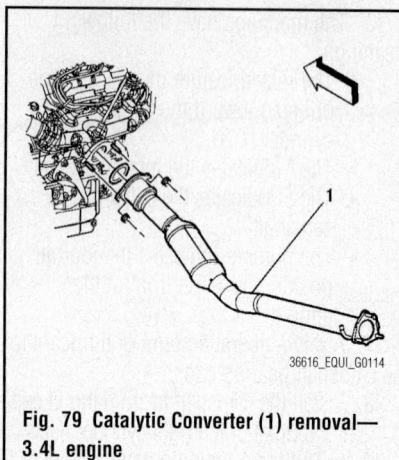

Fig. 79 Catalytic Converter (1) removal—3.4L engine

5. Separate the pipes and discard the gasket.

6. Remove the nuts securing the catalytic converter to the exhaust manifold.

7. Separate the catalytic converter flange from the exhaust manifold and discard the gasket.

➡ **Catalytic converter flex coupler must NEVER be deflected more than 6 degrees or failure of flex coupler could result.**

8. Separate the catalytic converter hanger from the rubber isolator and remove the catalytic converter from the vehicle.

9. Remove the exhaust manifold studs if worn or damaged.

To install:

10. Install the exhaust manifold studs if previously removed and tighten to 53 inch lbs. (6 Nm).

11. Install the rubber isolator and to the catalytic converter hanger.

12. Install a new gasket and attach the catalytic converter to the exhaust manifold.

13. Install the catalytic converter to the exhaust manifold nuts and tighten the nuts to 27 ft. lbs. (37 Nm).

14. Install a new exhaust pipe flange gasket to the catalytic converter flange.

15. Install the exhaust pipe to the catalytic converter pipe. with the catalytic converter nuts.

16. Install the exhaust pipe to the catalytic converter pipe. Tighten the nuts to 27 ft. lbs. (37 Nm).

17. Connect the HO2S connector to the wiring harness.

18. Lower the vehicle.

19. Start the engine and check for exhaust leaks.

3.6L Engine

Left Side Converter

See Figure 80.

1. Before servicing the vehicle, refer to the precautions section.

2. Remove the left exhaust manifold heat shield as follows:

- Remove the fuel injector sight shield, if necessary.
- Disconnect the engine wiring harness electrical connector from the Heated Oxygen sensor (HO2S) electrical connector.
- Remove the Heated Oxygen Sensor (HO2S) electrical connector retainer from the retainer clip.
- Remove the exhaust manifold heat shield bolts and shield, sliding the shield up over the HO2S pigtail.

3. Remove the catalytic converter to exhaust manifold nuts.

4. Raise and safely support the vehicle.

5. Disconnect the HO2S electrical connector from the engine wiring harness electrical connector.

6. Remove the left catalytic converter to exhaust flexible pipe nuts.

7. Remove the catalytic converter from the vehicle.

8. Remove and discard the catalytic converter to exhaust manifold and flexible pipe gaskets.

To install:

9. Install a NEW catalytic converter to exhaust manifold gasket onto the catalytic converter.

10. Install the catalytic converter to the vehicle.

11. Install a NEW catalytic converter to exhaust flexible pipe gasket between the converter and the flexible pipe.

12. Install the left catalytic converter to exhaust flexible pipe nuts and tighten to 18 ft. lbs. (25 Nm).

13. Connect the HO2S electrical connector to the engine wiring harness electrical connector.

14. Lower the vehicle

15. Install the catalytic converter to exhaust manifold nuts and tighten to 37 ft. lbs. (50 Nm).

16. Install the exhaust manifold heat shield as follows:

- Install the exhaust manifold heat shield, sliding the shield down over the HO2S pigtail.
- Install the exhaust manifold heat shield bolts and tighten to 89 inch lbs. (10 Nm).
- Connect the engine wiring harness electrical connector to the HO2S electrical connector.
- Install the HO2S electrical connector retainer to the retainer clip.

17. Install the fuel injector sight shield, if removed.

18. Start the engine and check for exhaust leaks.

Right Side Converter

See Figure 81.

1. Before servicing the vehicle, refer to the precautions section.

2. Remove the right exhaust manifold heat shield as follows:

- Remove the fuel injector sight shield, if necessary.
- Disconnect the engine wiring harness electrical connector from the Heated Oxygen sensor (HO2S) electrical connector.
- Remove the HO2S electrical connector retainer from the valve cover.

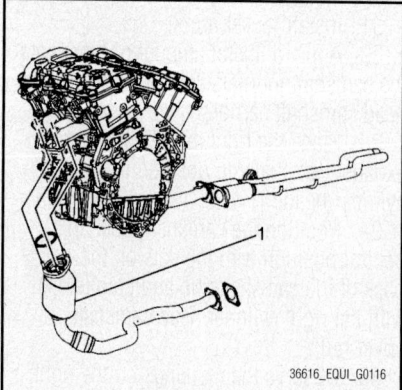

Fig. 80 Left side catalytic converter (1) removal—3.6L engine

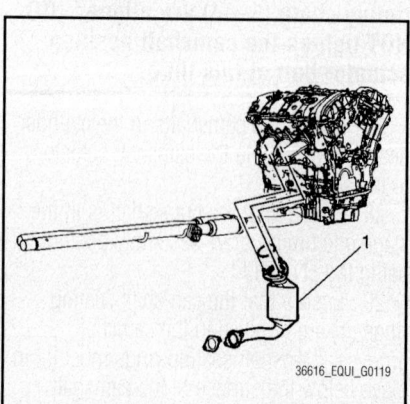

Fig. 81 Right side catalytic converter (1) removal—3.6L engine

- Remove the exhaust manifold heat shield bolts and shield, sliding the shield up over the HO2S pigtail.

3. Remove the catalytic converter to exhaust manifold nuts.

4. Raise and safely support the vehicle.

5. Disconnect the heated Oxygen Sensor (HO2S) electrical connector from the engine wiring harness electrical connector.

6. Remove the catalytic converter to exhaust flexible pipe nuts.

7. Remove the catalytic converter from the vehicle.

8. Remove and discard the catalytic converter to exhaust manifold and flexible pipe gaskets.

To install:

9. Install a NEW catalytic converter to exhaust manifold gasket onto the catalytic converter.

10. Install the right catalytic converter to the vehicle.

11. Install a NEW catalytic converter to exhaust flexible pipe gasket between the converter and the flexible pipe.

12. Install the catalytic converter to exhaust flexible pipe nuts and tighten to 18 ft. lbs. (25 Nm).

13. Connect the HO2S electrical connector to the engine wiring harness electrical connector.

14. Lower the vehicle

15. Install the catalytic converter to exhaust manifold nuts and tighten to 37 ft. lbs. (50 Nm).

16. Install the exhaust manifold heat shield as follows:

- Install the exhaust manifold heat shield, sliding the shield down over the HO2S pigtail.
- Install the exhaust manifold heat shield bolts and tighten to 89 inch lbs. (10 Nm).
- Connect the engine wiring harness electrical connector to the HO2S electrical connector.
- Install the HO2S electrical connector retainer to the retainer clip.

17. Install the fuel injector sight shield, if removed.

18. Start the engine and check for exhaust leaks.

CRANKSHAFT DAMPER

REMOVAL & INSTALLATION

3.4L Engine

See Figures 82 through 84.

1. Before servicing the vehicle, refer to the precautions section.

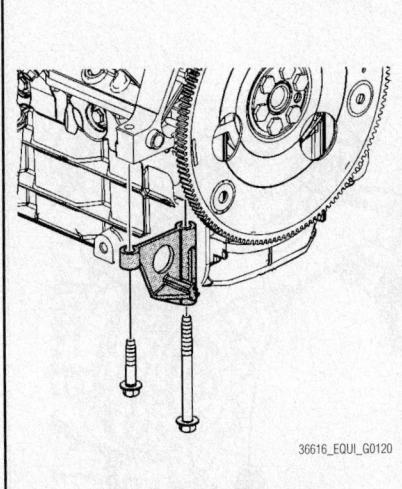

Fig. 82 Install the EN-49010 flywheel holding

36616_EQUI_G0120

2. Disconnect the negative battery cable.

3. Rotate the drive belt tensioner to release the tension on the drive belt.

4. Remove the drive belt from the right idler pulley.

5. Carefully release the drive belt tensioner spring tension.

6. Raise and safely support the vehicle.

7. Remove the right front wheel.

8. Remove the wheelhouse liner.

9. Remove the starter. Refer to Starter Removal & Installation in the Engine Electrical section.

10. Install the EN-49010 flywheel holding tool to the starter mounting holes.

11. Remove the crankshaft damper bolt and washer.

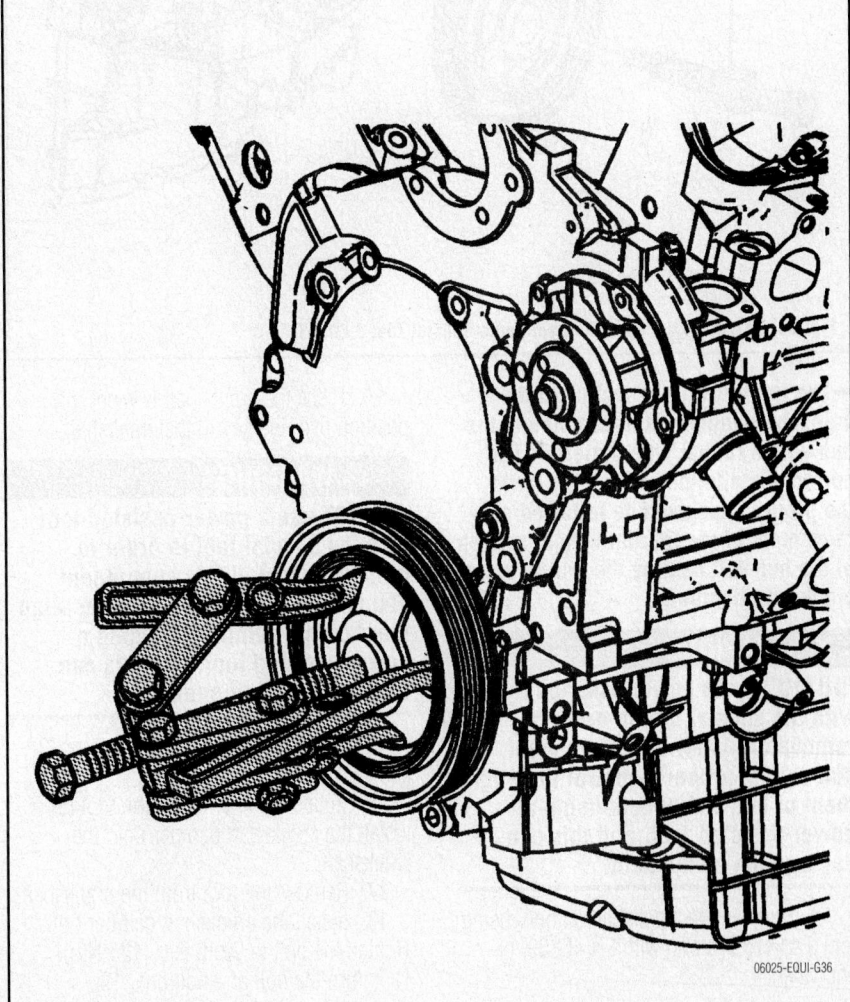

06025-EQUI-G36

Fig. 83 Remove the crankshaft damper with Special Tool J 41816-A and EN-46359

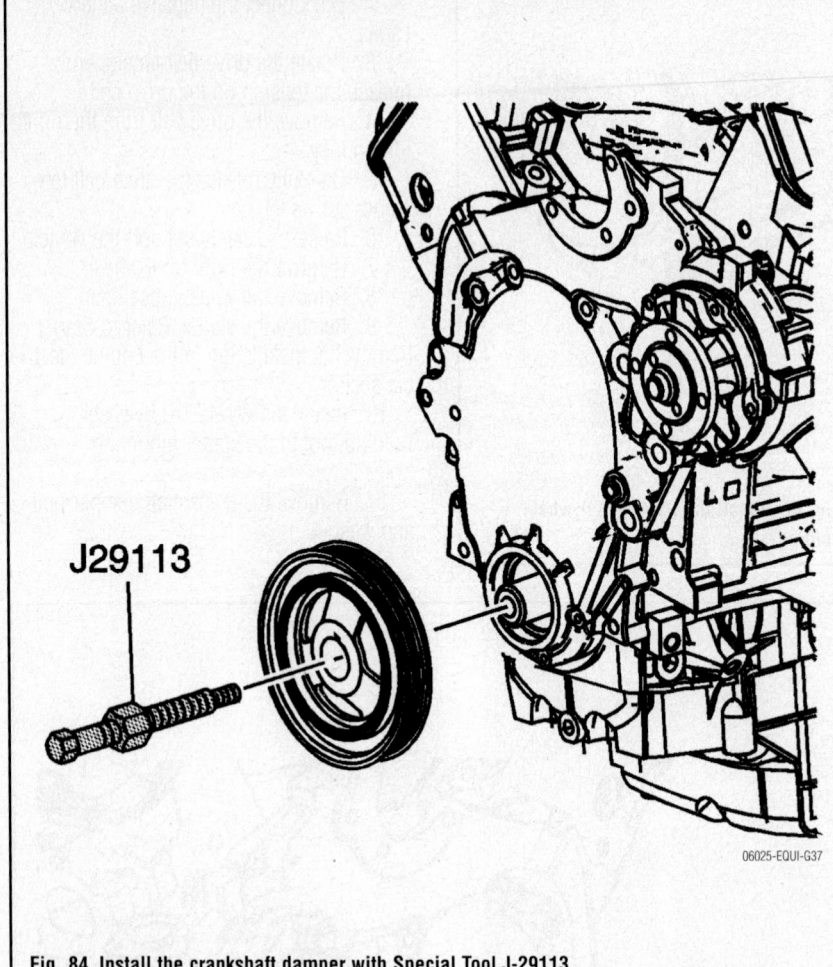

J29113

06025-EQUI-G37

Fig. 84 Install the crankshaft damper with Special Tool J-29113

➡The inertial weight section of the crankshaft damper is assembled to the hub with a rubber type material. The correct installation procedures (with the proper tool) must be followed or movement of the inertial weight section of the hub will destroy the tuning of the crankshaft damper.

✳✳ WARNING

DO NOT use a power-assisted tool with the special tool in order to remove or install this component. You cannot properly control the alignment of this component using a power-assisted tool, and this can damage the component.

12. Remove the crankshaft damper using tool J 41816-A along with EN 46359, or equivalent.

To install:

13. Apply sealer GM P/N 12378521 (Canadian P/N 88901148) or the equivalent, to the keyway of the crankshaft damper.

14. Place the crankshaft damper into position over the key in the crankshaft.

✳✳ WARNING

DO NOT use a power-assisted tool with the special tool in order to remove or install this component. You cannot properly control the alignment of this component using a power-assisted tool, and this can damage the component.

15. Install Special Tool J 29113, or equivalent onto the crankshaft.

16. Rotate the hex nut on the tool to install the crankshaft damper onto the crankshaft.

17. Remove the tool from the crankshaft.

18. Install the crankshaft damper bolt. Tighten the bolt to 92 ft. lbs. (125 Nm). Then turn the bolt an additional 130 degrees.

19. Remove the flywheel holding tool EN-49010.

20. Install the starter motor.

21. Install the wheelhouse liner.

22. Install the right front wheel.

23. Lower the vehicle.

24. Insure the drive belt is properly centered on all the pulleys except the right idler pulley.

25. Rotate the drive belt tensioner away from the drive belt.

26. Install the drive belt to the right idler pulley.

27. Carefully release the drive belt tensioner to come in contact with the drive belt.

28. Inspect the drive belt to insure the belt is properly centered on all the pulleys.

29. Connect the negative battery cable.

3.6L Engine

See Figures 85 through 88.

1. Before servicing the vehicle, refer to the precautions section.

2. Disconnect the negative battery cable.

3. Remove the drive belt.

4. Install the engine support fixture, securing the engine to the fixture.

5. Remove the engine mount.

6. Remove the right side engine mount bracket as follows:

- Remove the air cleaner assembly.
- Raise and support the vehicle.
- Remove 3 upper engine mount bracket bolts.
- Loosen right upper front bolt.
- Remove the ABS connector clip from the frame.
- Remove the upper engine mount bracket nuts.
- Remove the lower bracket bolts.
- Remove the upper bracket bolt from the bracket.
- Remove the mount and the lower bracket from the vehicle.
- Remove the upper bracket.

7. Remove the starter motor.

8. Install the EN-46106 flywheel holder through the starter mounting hole.

9. Using the engine support fixture, lower the engine approximately two inches.

10. Remove the crankshaft balancer bolt.

11. Install the J-38416-2 in the nose of the crankshaft.

12. Install the in order to remove the crankshaft balancer.

13. Tighten the center bolt of the J-41816 in order to pull the crankshaft balancer off of the crankshaft.

14. Remove the J-41816 from the crankshaft balancer.

To install:

➡DO NOT lubricate the crankshaft front oil seal or crankshaft balancer sealing surfaces. The crankshaft balancer is installed into a dry seal.

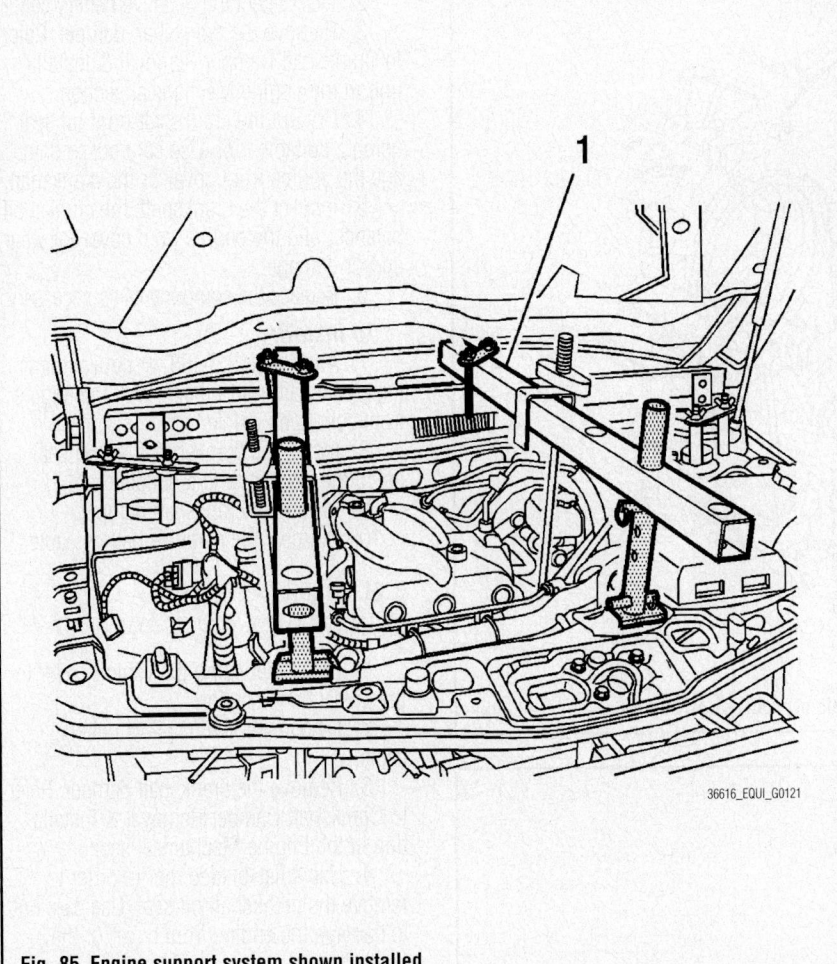

Fig. 85 Engine support system shown installed

Fig. 88 Use the J 41998-B, nut, bearing and washer to install the crankshaft balancer

- Tighten the crankshaft balancer bolt to 74 ft. lbs. (100 Nm).
- Tighten the crankshaft balancer bolt an additional 150 degrees using an angle meter.

22. Remove the EN-46106 flywheel holding tool from the flywheel.

23. Install the starter motor.

24. Using engine support fixture, raise the engine into position.

25. Install the engine mount as follows:
- Install the engine mount and the lower bracket to the vehicle. Tighten the lower bracket bolts to 37 ft. lbs. (50 Nm).
- Install the ABS connector clip to the frame.
- Install the upper engine mount bracket nuts and tighten to 37 ft. lbs. (50 Nm).
- Install the engine mount upper bracket and bolt to the engine. Do not tighten the bolt.
- Tighten the right upper engine mount bracket bolt to 37 ft. lbs. (50 Nm).
- Install the upper engine mount bracket bolts and tighten to 81 ft. lbs. (110 Nm).

26. Install the drive belt.

27. Remove the engine support system.

28. Connect the negative battery cable.

CRANKSHAFT FRONT SEAL

REMOVAL & INSTALLATION

3.4L Engine

See Figures 89 and 90.

1. Before servicing the vehicle, refer to the precautions section.

15. Apply lubricant to the inside of the crankshaft balancer hub bore.

16. Place the crankshaft balancer in position on the crankshaft.

17. Thread the J 41998-B in the crankshaft. Ensure you engage at least 10 threads of the J 41998-B before pressing the crankshaft balancer in place.

18. Push the crankshaft balancer into position by tightening the nut on the J 41998-B until the large washer bottoms out on the crankshaft end.

19. Remove the J 41998-B installation tool.

20. Install the crankshaft balancer bolt.

21. Tighten the crankshaft bolt as follow:

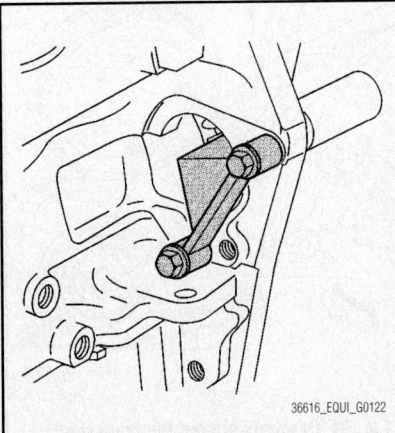

Fig. 86 Flywheel holding tool EN-46106 installed

Fig. 87 Three jaw removal tool J-41816 and adapter J-38416-2

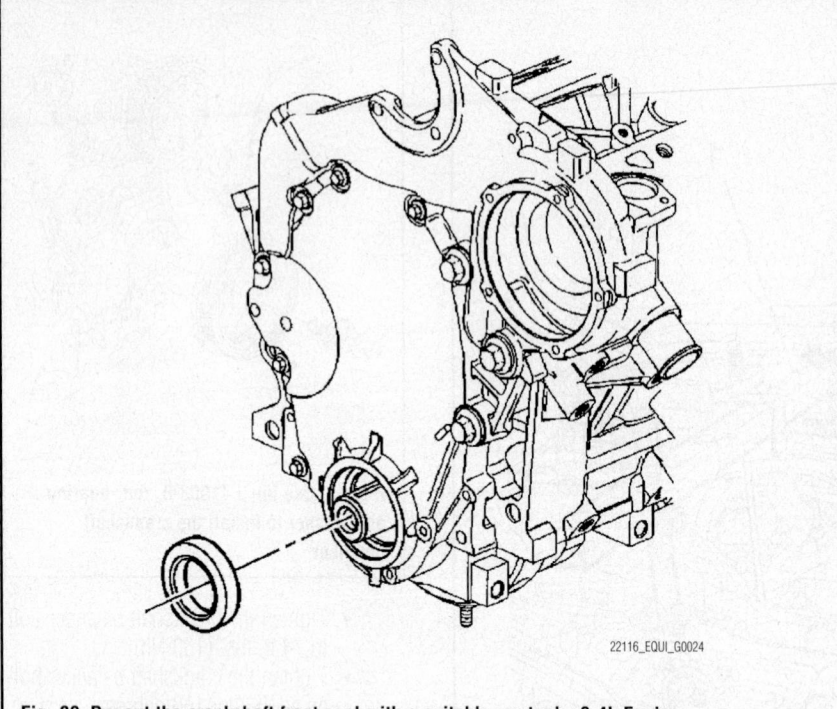

Fig. 89 Pry out the crankshaft front seal with a suitable pry tool—3.4L Engine

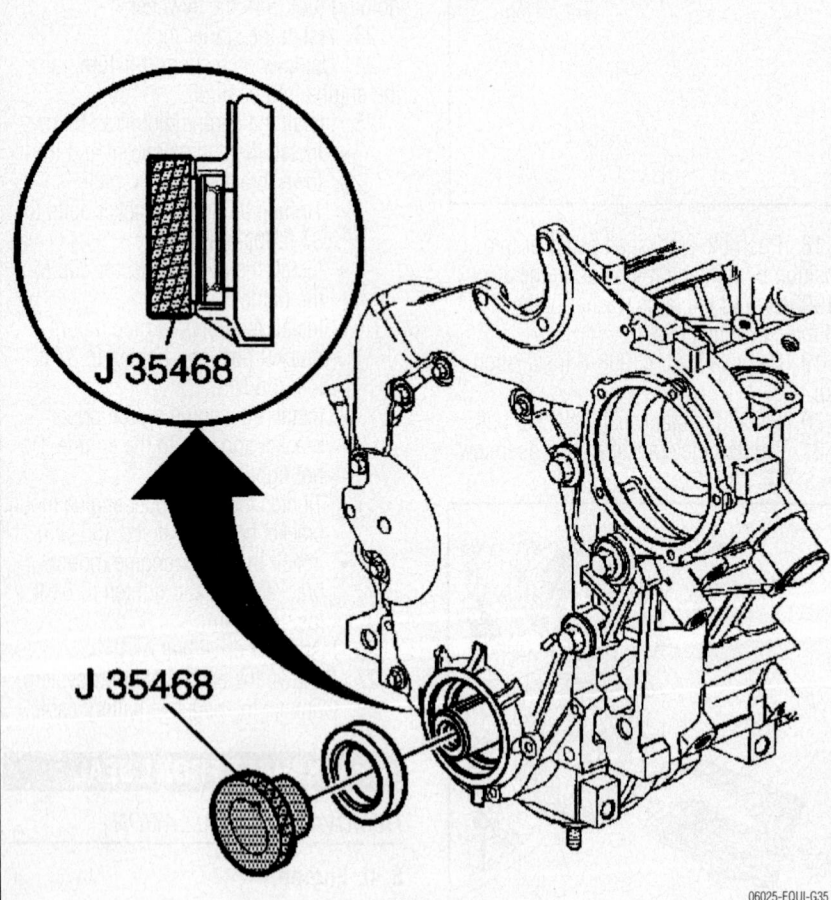

Fig. 90 Install the front seal using Special Tool J 35468 installation tool—3.4L Engine

2. Disconnect the negative battery cable.

3. Remove the crankshaft damper. Refer to Crankshaft Damper Removal & Installation in the Engine Mechanical section.

4. Pry out the crankshaft front oil seal using a suitable tool. Use care not to damage the engine front cover or the crankshaft.

5. Inspect the crankshaft, the crankshaft balancer and the engine front cover for wear and/or damage.

6. Replace the components as necessary.

To install:

7. Align tool J 35468, or equivalent and the crankshaft front oil seal with the engine front cover and crankshaft.

8. Install the crankshaft front oil seal using the installer and a suitable tool.

9. Install the crankshaft damper.

10. Connect the negative battery cable.

3.6L Engine

See Figures 91 and 92.

1. Before servicing the vehicle, refer to the precautions section.

2. Disconnect the negative battery cable.

3. Remove the crankshaft damper. Refer to Crankshaft Damper Removal & Installation in the Engine Mechanical section.

4. Use a flat-bladed tool in order to remove the crankshaft oil seal. Use care not to damage the engine front cover or the crankshaft

To install:

➡**Do not lubricate the crankshaft front oil seal or the crankshaft balancer sealing surfaces.**

5. Use the J-29184 installation tool or equivalent to install the crankshaft front oil seal.

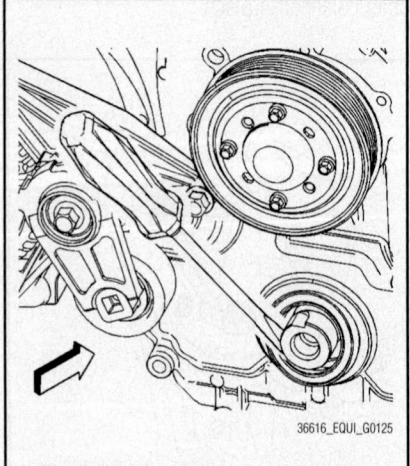

Fig. 91 Carefully pry out the crankshaft front seal with a flat-bladed tool —3.6L Engine

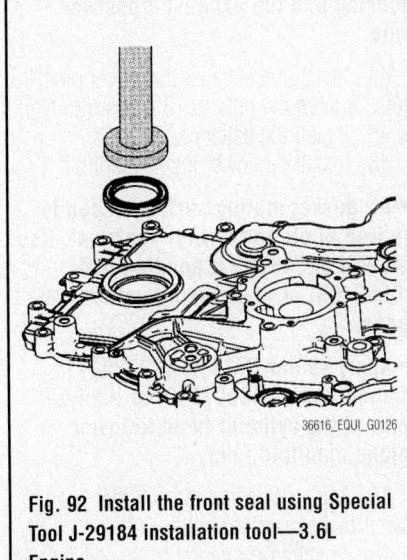

Fig. 92 Install the front seal using Special Tool J-29184 installation tool—3.6L Engine

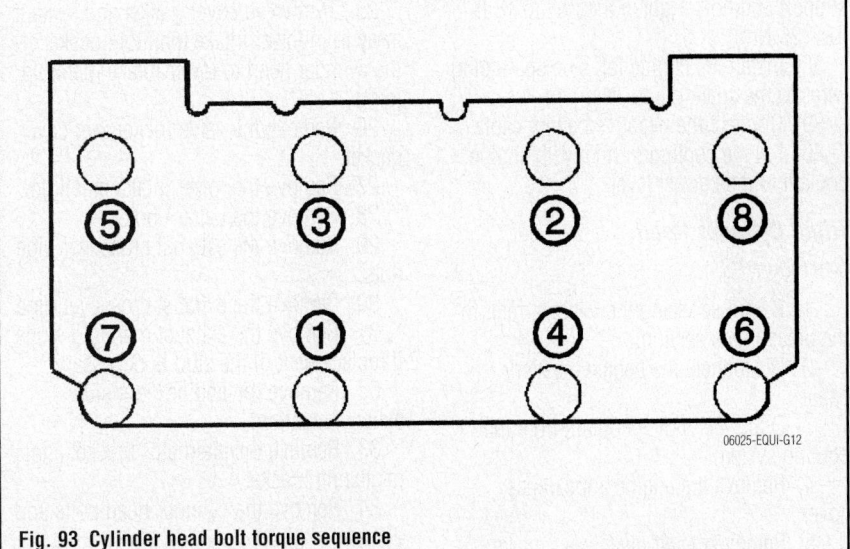

Fig. 93 Cylinder head bolt torque sequence

6. Install the crankshaft balancer.
7. Connect the negative battery cable.

CYLINDER HEAD

REMOVAL & INSTALLATION

3.4L Engine

Left Cylinder Head

See Figure 93.

1. Before servicing the vehicle, refer to the precautions section.
2. Disconnect the negative battery cable.
3. Drain the engine coolant from the cooling system.
4. Remove the engine left side spark plug wires from the spark plugs.
5. Remove the spark plug wire retainer support bolt and support.
6. Remove the engine left side spark plugs.
7. Remove the valve rocker arm cover.
8. Trim valve cover gasket and sealant away from lower intake manifold gasket at the cylinder head to lower intake manifold joints.
9. Remove the valve rocker arm cover gasket.
10. Remove the lower intake manifold.
11. Remove the oil level indicator tube.
12. Remove the battery box.
13. Remove the exhaust crossover pipe nuts.
14. Remove the exhaust crossover pipe.
15. Remove the exhaust manifold studs, if replacement of the stud is necessary.
16. Remove the engine left side exhaust manifold.

17. Remove the cylinder head bolts and discard.
18. Remove the cylinder head.
19. Remove the cylinder head gasket.

➡All gasket mating surfaces must remain free of oil and foreign material. Use GM P/N 12346139 (Canadian P/N 10953463) or equivalent to clean surfaces.

20. Clean the following areas:
   • The gasket sealing surfaces on the cylinder head, cylinder block, intake manifold, and exhaust manifold
   • The cylinder block bolt threads

To install:
21. Clean the following areas:
   • The gasket sealing surfaces on the cylinder head, cylinder block, intake manifold, and exhaust manifold
   • The cylinder block bolt threads
22. Install the cylinder head gasket.
23. Install the cylinder head.

➡This component uses torque-to-yield bolts. When servicing this component do not reuse the bolts, New torque-to-yield bolts must be installed. Reusing used torque-to-yield bolts will not provide proper bolt torque and clamp load. Failure to install NEW torque-to-yield bolts may lead to engine damage.

24. Install the NEW cylinder head bolts. Tighten the bolts as follows:
   • Tighten the bolts in sequence to 44 ft. lbs. (60 Nm).
   • Turn the bolts in sequence an additional 95 degrees.

25. Install the engine left side exhaust manifold.
26. Install any previously removed exhaust manifold studs. Tighten the studs to 18 ft. lbs. (25 Nm).
27. Install the exhaust crossover pipe.

➡Maintain approximately 0.25 inches (6.35 mm) between the thermostat housing and the exhaust crossover pipe.

28. Install the exhaust crossover pipe nuts. Tighten the nuts to 18 ft. lbs. (25 Nm).
29. Install the battery box.
30. Install the oil level indicator tube.
31. Install the lower intake manifold.

➡All gasket mating surfaces need to be free of oil and foreign material. Use GM P/N 12346139 (Canadian P/N 10953463) or equivalent to clean surfaces.

➡Apply sealant GM P/N 12378521 (Canadian P/N 88901148) or equivalent, at the cylinder head to lower intake manifold joint.

32. Apply sealant at the cylinder head to lower intake manifold joints.
33. Install a new gasket to the valve rocker arm cover. Ensure the gasket is properly seated in the groove of the valve rocker arm cover.
34. Install the valve rocker arm cover. Tighten the bolts to 89 inch lbs. (10 Nm).
35. Install the spark plug wire support and bolt. Tighten the bolt to 18 ft. lbs. (25 Nm).
36. Install the engine left side spark plugs.

37. Install the spark plug wire retainer support and bolt. Tighten the bolt to 18 ft. lbs. (25 Nm).

38. Install the engine left side spark plug wires to the spark plugs.

39. Connect the negative battery cable.

40. Fill the cooling system with engine coolant to the correct level.

Right Cylinder Head

See Figure 93.

1. Before servicing the vehicle, refer to the precautions section.

2. Disconnect the negative battery cable.

3. Drain the engine coolant from the cooling system.

4. Remove the engine appearance cover.

5. Remove the air cleaner air intake duct.

6. Remove the Manifold Absolute Pressure (MAP) sensor bolt and bracket.

7. Rotate the MAP sensor out of the way of the heater outlet pipe.

8. Disconnect the Evaporative Emissions (EVAP) pipe from the EVAP canister purge solenoid.

9. Disconnect the electrical connector from the EVAP canister purge solenoid.

10. Disconnect the Exhaust Gas Recirculation (EGR) valve electrical connector.

11. Release and slide the heater outlet hose clamp away from the heater outlet pipe connection.

12. Disconnect the heater outlet hose from the heater outlet pipe.

13. Release and slide the heater core outlet hose clamp away from the heater outlet pipe connection.

14. Disconnect the heater core outlet hose from the heater outlet pipe.

15. Remove the heater outlet pipe nut securing the heater outlet pipe to the intake manifold.

16. Remove the two nuts and bolt securing the heater outlet pipe to the throttle body.

17. Remove the heater outlet pipe from the engine.

18. Remove the nut securing the hose/pipe retainer to the right cylinder head.

19. Remove the engine coolant temperature sensor.

20. Remove the ignition control module and bracket.

21. Remove the ignition control module bracket studs.

22. Remove the engine right side spark plug wires from the spark plugs.

23. Remove the engine right side spark plugs.

24. Remove the valve rocker arm cover.

25. Trim valve cover gasket and sealant away from lower intake manifold gasket at the cylinder head to lower intake manifold joints.

26. Remove the valve rocker arm cover gasket.

27. Remove the lower intake manifold..

28. Remove the battery box.

29. Remove the exhaust crossover pipe nuts.

30. Remove the exhaust crossover pipe.

31. Remove the exhaust manifold studs, if replacement of the stud is necessary.

32. Remove the engine right side exhaust manifold.

33. Remove the alternator bracket and engine lift bracket.

34. Remove the cylinder head bolts and discard.

35. Remove the cylinder head.

36. Remove the cylinder head gasket.

➡**All gasket mating surfaces must remain free of oil and foreign material. Use GM P/N 12346139 (Canadian P/N 10953463) or equivalent to clean surfaces.**

To install:

37. Clean the following areas:
   - The gasket sealing surfaces on the cylinder head, cylinder block, intake manifold, and exhaust manifold
   - The cylinder block bolt threads

38. Install the cylinder head gasket.

39. Install the cylinder head.

➡**This component uses torque-to-yield bolts. When servicing this component do not reuse the bolts, New torque-to-yield bolts must be installed. Reusing used torque-to-yield bolts will not provide proper bolt torque and clamp load. Failure to install NEW torque-to-yield bolts may lead to engine damage.**

40. Install the NEW cylinder head bolts. Tighten the bolts as follows:
   - Tighten the bolts in sequence to 44 ft. lbs. (60 Nm).
   - Turn the bolts in sequence an additional 95 degrees.

41. Install the alternator bracket and engine lift bracket. Torque to 37 ft. lbs. (50 Nm). Install the engine right side exhaust manifold.

42. Install any previously removed exhaust manifold studs. Tighten the studs to 18 ft. lbs. (25 Nm).

43. Install the exhaust crossover pipe.

➡**Maintain approximately 0.25 inches (6.35 mm) between the thermostat**

housing and the exhaust crossover pipe.

44. Install the exhaust crossover pipe nuts. Tighten the nuts to 18 ft. lbs. (25 Nm).

45. Install the battery box.

46. Install the lower intake manifold.

➡**All gasket mating surfaces need to be free of oil and foreign material. Use GM P/N 12346139 (Canadian P/N 10953463) or equivalent to clean surfaces.**

➡**Apply sealer GM P/N 12378521 (Canadian P/N 88901148) or equivalent, at the cylinder head to lower intake manifold joint.**

47. Apply sealant at the cylinder head to lower intake manifold joints.

48. Install a new gasket to the valve rocker arm cover. Ensure the gasket is properly seated in the groove of the valve rocker arm cover.

49. Install the valve rocker arm cover. Tighten the bolts to 89 inch lbs. (10 Nm).

50. Connect the PCV fresh air pipe to the right valve rocker arm cover.

51. Install the ignition control module bracket with the ignition control module and spark plug wired still attached.

52. Install the alternator bracket. Torque to 37 ft. lbs. (50 Nm).

53. Install the engine left side spark plugs.

54. Install the engine left side spark plug wires to the spark plugs.

55. Install the ignition module bracket studs. Tighten the studs to 18 ft. lbs. (25 Nm).

56. Install the ignition control module and bracket.

57. Install the engine coolant temperature sensor.

58. Install the nut securing the hose/pipe retainer to the right cylinder head. Tighten the nut to 18 ft. lbs. (25 Nm).

59. Install the heater outlet pipe to the engine.

60. Install the heater outlet pipe nut securing the heater outlet pipe to the intake manifold. Tighten the nut to 18 ft. lbs. (25 Nm).

61. Install the heater outlet pipe to the throttle body nuts and bolt. Tighten the nuts and bolt to 89 inch lbs. (10 Nm).

62. Connect the heater core outlet hose to the heater outlet pipe.

63. Position the heater core outlet hose clamp over the heater outlet pipe connection.

64. Connect the heater outlet hose to the heater outlet pipe.

65. Position the heater outlet hose clamp over the heater outlet pipe connection.

66. Connect the electrical connector to the EGR valve.

67. Connect the electrical connector to the EVAP canister purge solenoid.

68. Connect the EVAP pipe to the EVAP canister purge solenoid.

69. Reposition the MAP sensor.

70. Install the MAP sensor bracket and bolt. Tighten the bolt to 89 inch lbs. (10 Nm).

71. Install the air cleaner air intake duct.

72. Install the engine appearance cover.

73. Connect the negative battery cable.

74. Fill the cooling system with engine coolant to the correct level.

3.6L Engine

Left Cylinder Head

See Figures 94 and 95.

1. Before servicing the vehicle, refer to the precautions section.

2. Disconnect the negative battery cable.

3. Relieve the fuel system pressure.

4. Drain the cooling system.

5. Drain engine oil.

6. Remove the upper and lower intake manifolds.

7. Remove the valve covers.

8. Remove the spark plugs in order to ease crankshaft/engine rotation.

9. Remove the engine front cover.

10. Remove the right bank secondary camshaft drive chain.

11. Remove the primary camshaft drive chain.

12. Remove the left bank secondary camshaft drive chain tensioner.

13. Remove the left bank secondary camshaft drive chain shoe.

14. Remove the left bank secondary camshaft drive chain guide.

15. Remove the left bank camshaft intermediate drive chain idler.

16. Remove the left bank secondary camshaft drive chain.

17. Remove the oil level indicator

18. Disconnect the coolant temperature sensor electrical connector.

19. Remove the wiring harness ground from the cylinder head.

20. Remove the catalytic converter.

21. Remove the two front M8 left cylinder head bolts.

22. Remove the left cylinder head bolts.

23. Remove the cylinder head with the exhaust manifold.

24. Remove and discard the cylinder head gasket.

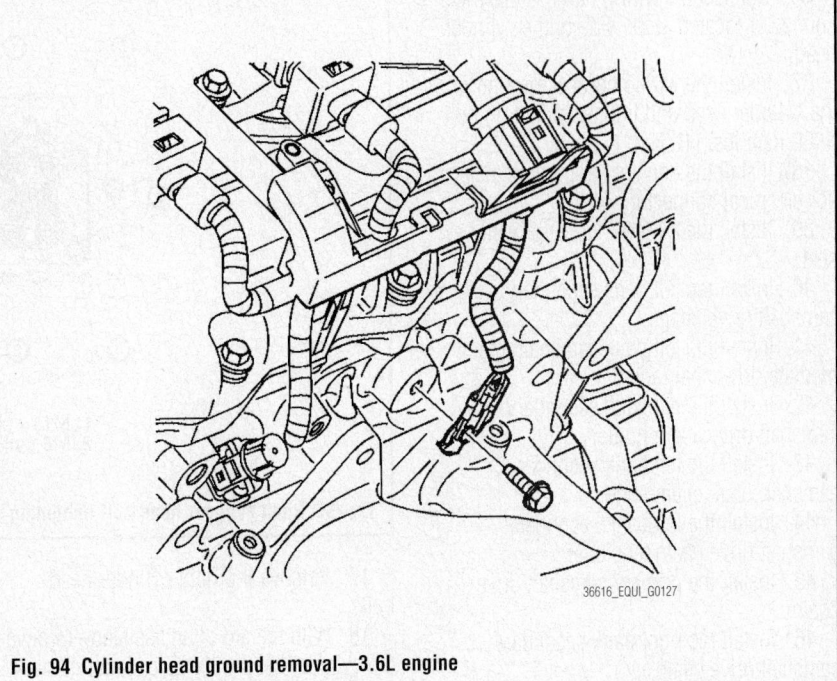

Fig. 94 Cylinder head ground removal—3.6L engine

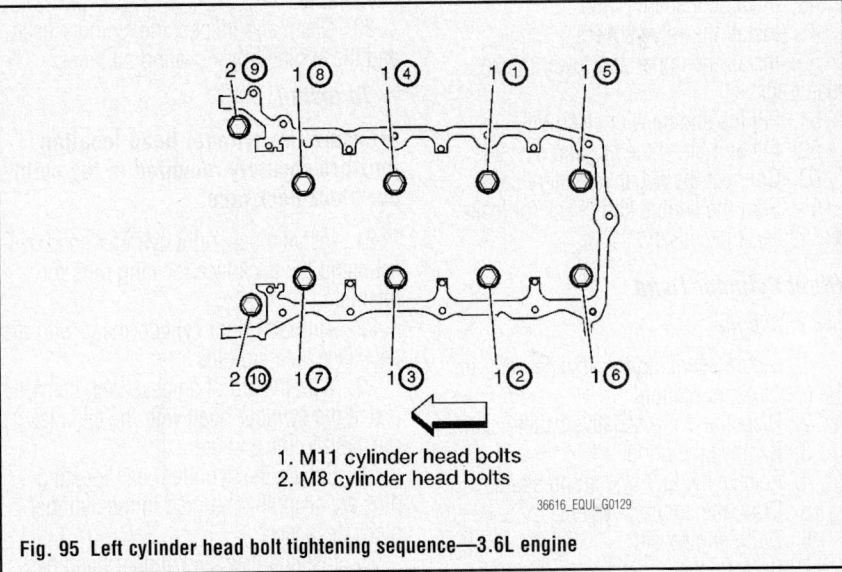

1. M11 cylinder head bolts
2. M8 cylinder head bolts

Fig. 95 Left cylinder head bolt tightening sequence—3.6L engine

25. Clean and inspect the cylinder head and the engine block sealing surfaces.

To install:

26. Ensure the cylinder head locating pins are securely mounted in the cylinder block deck face.

27. Install a new left cylinder head gasket using the deck face locating pins for retention.

28. Carefully install and align the left cylinder head with the deck face locating pins.

※※ WARNING

DO NOT allow oil on the cylinder head bolt bosses or reuse the old M11 cylinder head bolts.

29. Install new M11 cylinder head bolts.

30. Tighten the M11 cylinder head bolts a first pass in sequence to 22 ft. lbs. (30 Nm).

31. Tighten the M11 cylinder head bolts a second pass in sequence an additional 150 degrees using a angel meter.

32. Install the 2 front M8 left cylinder head bolts.

33. Tighten the M8 cylinder head bolts a first pass to 11ft. lbs. (15 Nm).

34. Tighten the M8 cylinder head bolts a second pass in sequence an additional 75 degrees using a angel meter.

35. Install the catalytic converter to the exhaust manifold.

36. Connect the wiring harness electrical connector located at the side of the cylinder head.

37. Install the wiring harness ground to the cylinder head and tighten mounting bolt to 89 inch lbs. (10 Nm).

38. Install the coolant temperature sensor electrical connector.

39. Install the oil level indicator with new seal.

40. Install the left bank secondary camshaft drive chain

41. Install the left bank camshaft intermediate drive chain idler.

42. Install the left bank secondary camshaft drive chain guide.

43. Install the left bank secondary camshaft drive chain shoe.

44. Install the left bank secondary camshaft drive chain tensioner.

45. Install the primary camshaft drive chain.

46. Install the right bank secondary camshaft drive chain.

47. Install the engine front cover.

48. Install the spark plugs.

49. Install the valve covers.

50. Install the upper and lower intake manifolds.

51. Fill the engine with clean oil.

52. Fill and bleed the cooling system.

53. Connect the negative battery cable.

54. Start the engine and check for leaks and repair if necessary.

Right Cylinder Head

See Figure 96.

1. Before servicing the vehicle, refer to the precautions section.

2. Disconnect the negative battery cable.

3. Remove the hood.

4. Relieve the fuel system pressure.

5. Drain the cooling system.

6. Drain engine oil.

7. Remove the upper and lower intake manifolds.

8. Remove the valve covers.

9. Remove the spark plugs in order to ease crankshaft/engine rotation.

10. Remove the ground wires from the cylinder head.

11. Remove the catalytic converter.

12. Remove the engine front cover.

13. Remove the right bank secondary camshaft drive chain tensioner.

14. Remove the right bank secondary camshaft drive chain shoe.

15. Remove the right bank secondary camshaft drive chain guide.

16. Remove the right bank secondary camshaft drive chain.

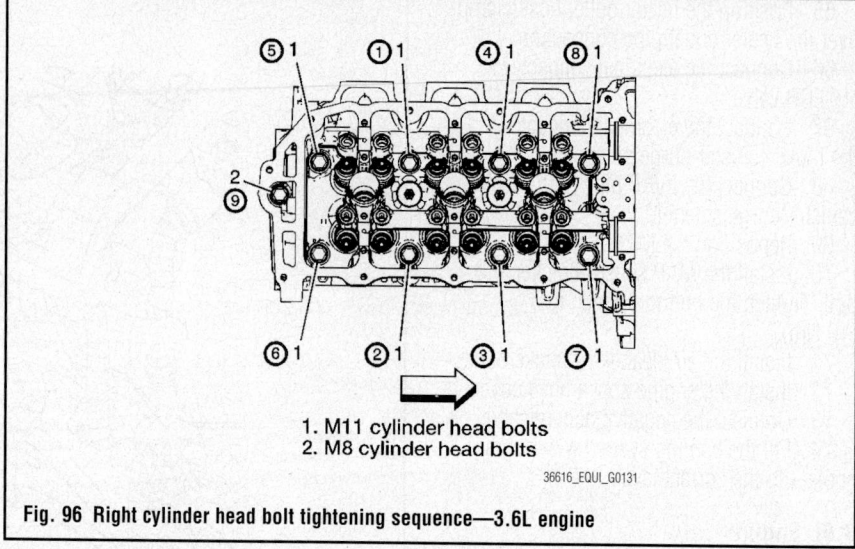

1. M11 cylinder head bolts
2. M8 cylinder head bolts

36616_EQUI_G0131

Fig. 96 Right cylinder head bolt tightening sequence—3.6L engine

17. Remove the right cylinder head bolts.

18. With the aid of an assistant, remove the cylinder head with the exhaust manifold.

19. Remove and discard the cylinder head gasket.

20. Clean and inspect the cylinder head and the engine block sealing surfaces.

To install:

➡ Ensure the cylinder head locating pins are securely mounted in the cylinder block deck face.

21. Install a new right cylinder head gasket using the deck face locating pins for retention.

22. Align the right cylinder head with the deck face locating pins.

23. With the aid of an assistant, carefully install the cylinder head with the exhaust manifold to the engine.

24. Ensure the cylinder head locating pins are securely mounted in the cylinder block deck face.

25. Install a new left cylinder head gasket using the deck face locating pins for retention.

26. Carefully install and align the left cylinder head with the deck face locating pins.

✱✱ WARNING

DO NOT allow oil on the cylinder head bolt bosses or reuse the old M11 cylinder head bolts.

27. Install new M11 cylinder head bolts.

28. Tighten the M11 cylinder head bolts a first pass in sequence to 22 ft. lbs. (30 Nm).

29. Tighten the M11 cylinder head bolts a second pass in sequence an additional 150 degrees using a angel meter.

30. Install the 2 front M8 left cylinder head bolts.

31. Tighten the M8 cylinder head bolts a first pass to 11 ft. lbs. (15 Nm).

32. Tighten the M8 cylinder head bolts a second pass in sequence an additional 75 degrees using a angel meter.

33. Install the catalytic converter to the exhaust manifold.

34. Connect the wiring harness electrical connector located at the side of the cylinder head.

35. Install the wiring harness ground to the cylinder head and tighten mounting bolt to 89 inch lbs. (10 Nm).

36. Install the right bank secondary camshaft drive chain

37. Install the right bank camshaft intermediate drive chain idler.

38. Install the right bank secondary camshaft drive chain guide.

39. Install the right bank secondary camshaft drive chain shoe.

40. Install the right bank secondary camshaft drive chain tensioner.

41. Install the engine front cover.

42. Install the spark plugs.

43. Install the valve covers.

44. Install the upper and lower intake manifolds.

45. Fill the engine with clean oil.

46. Fill and bleed the cooling system.

47. Connect the negative battery cable.

48. Start the engine and check for leaks and repair if necessary.

ENGINE ASSEMBLY

REMOVAL & INSTALLATION

3.4L Engine

See Figures 97 through 100.

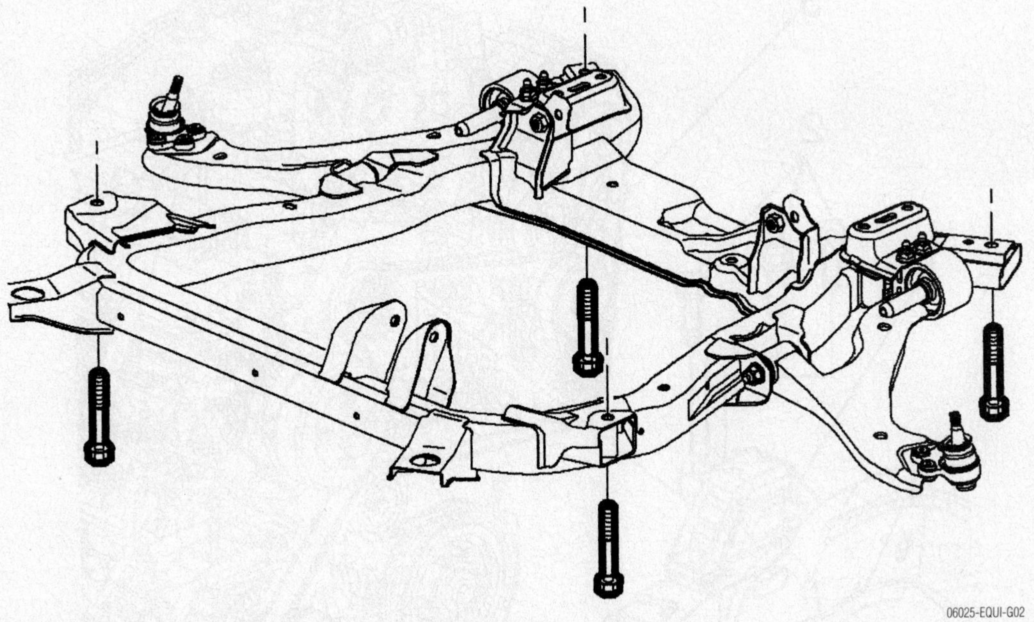

06025-EQUI-G02

Fig. 97 Frame-to-body bolts

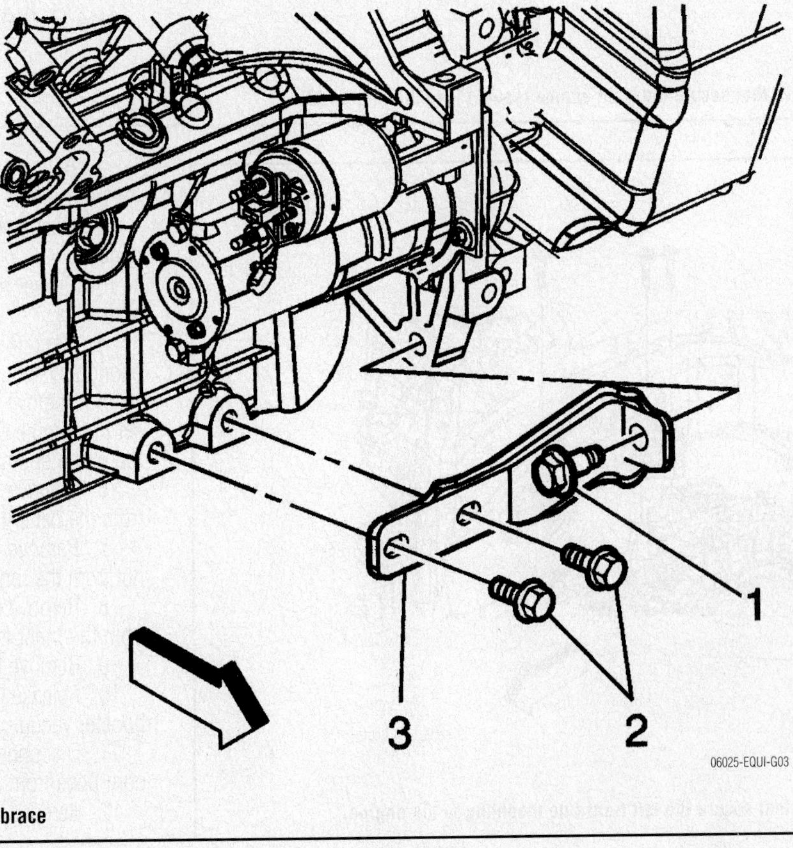

06025-EQUI-G03

Fig. 98 Engine-to-transaxle brace

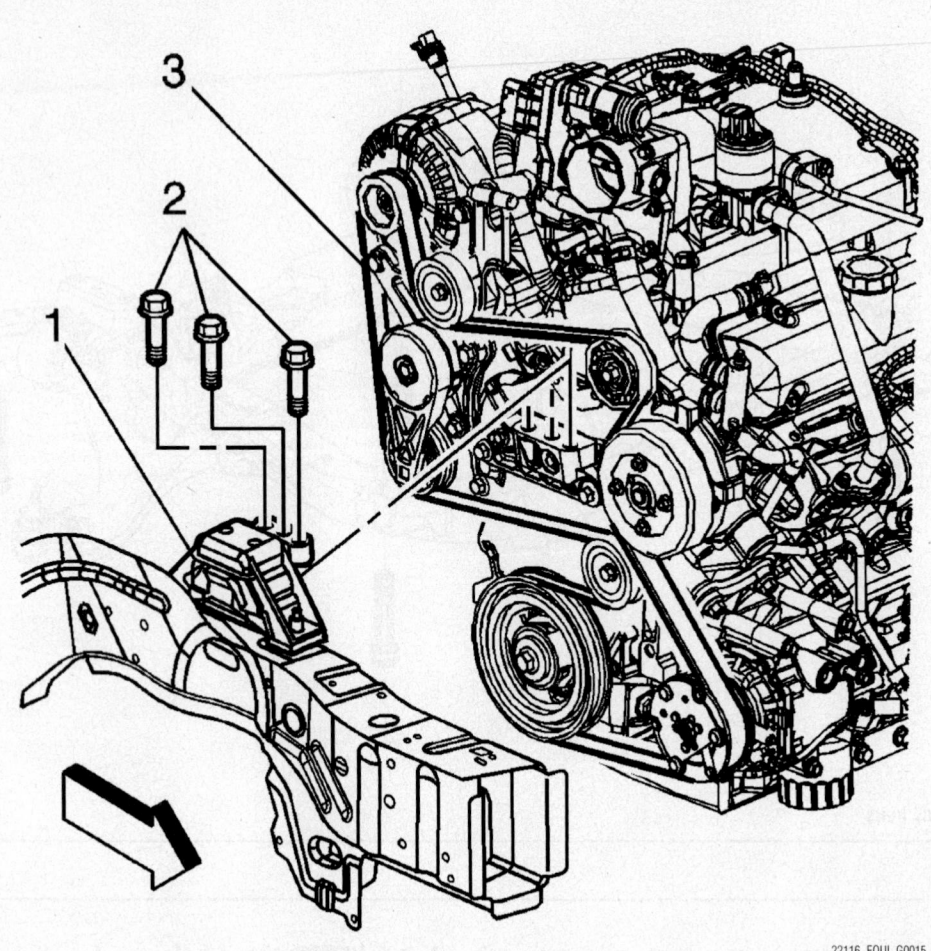

Fig. 99 Remove the bolts (2) that secure the right engine mount (1) to the engine (2).

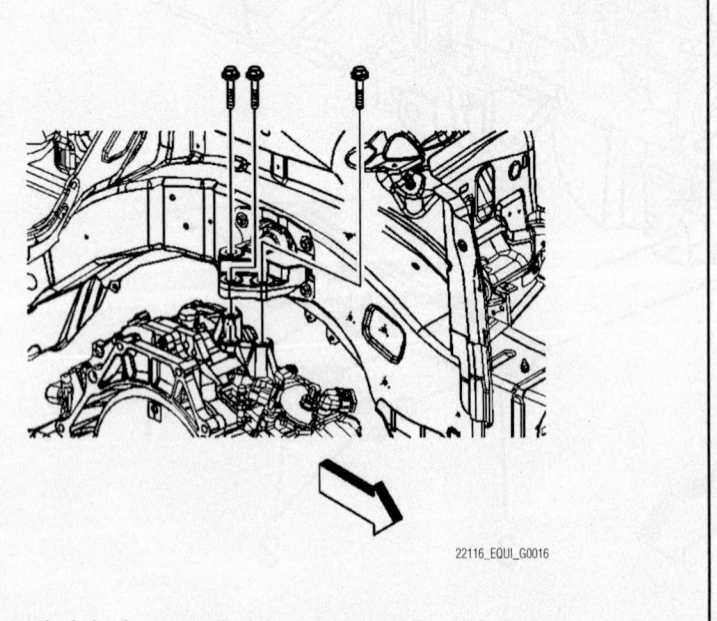

Fig. 100 Remove the bolts that secure the left transaxle mounting to the engine.

1. Before servicing the vehicle, refer to the precautions section.

2. Disconnect the negative battery cable.

3. Proper relieve the fuel system pressure.

4. Drain the engine coolant from the cooling system.

5. Remove the battery box and carefully set the Engine Control Module (ECM) on top of the engine.

6. Remove the battery cable retainers from the battery tray.

7. Remove the negative battery cable nut from the inner fender body ground stud.

8. Remove the negative battery cable from the inner fender body ground stud.

9. Remove the fuel injector sight shield.

10. Release the clamp from the brake booster vacuum hose connection.

11. Disconnect the brake booster vacuum hose from the intake manifold.

12. Remove the Transaxle Control Mod-

ule (TCM) from the bracket and set the TCM on top of the engine.

13. Remove the air cleaner assembly and air intake duct.

14. Disconnect the Evaporative Emission (EVAP) hose/pipe from the EVAP canister purge solenoid valve.

15. Disconnect the engine fuel hose/pipe from the chassis fuel hose/pipe.

16. Properly discharge the Air Conditioning (A/C) system.

17. Remove the A/C compressor hose assembly from the compressor. Cap or plug the hoses and compressor to prevent contamination.

18. Disconnect the transaxle shift control cable from the transaxle.

19. Disconnect engine to body inline connector C102.

20. Tie the radiator, A/C condenser, and fan module assembly to the upper radiator support to keep the assembly with the vehicle when the frame and drive train is removed.

21. Remove the coolant surge tank.

22. Disconnect the heater hoses from the engine.

23. Remove the radiator inlet hose.

24. Raise and support the vehicle.

25. Remove the radiator outlet hose.

26. Disconnect the transaxle oil cooler lines from the transaxle and remove the seals.

27. Cap the transaxle oil cooler lines and plug the transaxle oil cooler line fittings to prevent loss of transaxle fluid.

28. Remove the front bumper fascia air deflector.

29. Disconnect the heated oxygen sensor (HO2S) wiring harness.

30. Remove the HO2S wiring harness retainers from the vehicle underbody.

31. Remove the catalytic converter and secure the rear half of the exhaust system to the vehicle underbody.

32. If equipped with All Wheel Drive (AWD), disconnect the transfer case vent hose from the transfer case.

33. Remove the front tires.

34. Remove the right and left engine splash shields.

35. Remove the steering intermediate shaft pinch bolt and discard the bolt.

36. Disconnect the steering intermediate shaft from the steering gear.

37. Remove the right and left outer tie rod ends from the steering knuckles.

38. Remove the right and left stabilizer shaft links from the stabilizer shaft.

39. Remove the right and left lower ball joints from the steering knuckles.

40. Remove the right and left front half-shafts.

41. If equipped with AWD, remove the rear driveshaft.

42. Place a block of wood between the frame and the engine oil pan in order to support the engine once the bolts are removed from the right engine mount.

43. Place a block of wood between the frame and the transaxle in order to support the transaxle once the bolts are removed from the left transaxle mount.

44. Lower the vehicle.

45. Remove the bolts that secure the right engine mount to the engine.

46. Remove the bolts that secure the left transaxle mount to the transaxle.

➡ **Insure the vehicle body is secured to the hoist.**

47. Raise the vehicle.

48. Place a universal frame support fixture or jack stands under the frame.

49. Lower the vehicle until the frame contacts the frame support fixture or jack stands.

50. Remove the frame-to-body bolts. Discard the bolts.

➡ **Inspect for areas of body to power train contact or entanglement of wires and hoses while separating the vehicle body and power train.**

51. Carefully raise the vehicle body up away from the power train.

52. Disconnect the engine electrical wiring harness from the following components:

- Exhaust Gas Recirculation (EGR) valve
- Throttle body EVAP purge solenoid
- Remove nut and alternator B+ lead
- Generator regulator
- Fuel injector inline connector
- Heated oxygen sensor (HO2S)
- Ignition coil/control module. Remove wire harness from retainers

53. Disconnect the engine electrical wiring harness from the following components:

- Knock Sensor (KS)
- Crankshaft Position (CKP) sensor
- Remove bolt and ground lead
- Remove the wire harness from retainers

54. If equipped with an engine coolant heater, disconnect the coolant heater cord.

55. Disconnect the engine electrical wiring harness from the following components:

- Air Conditioning (AC) compressor clutch
- AC refrigerant pressure sensor
- Remove wire harness from retainer

56. Disconnect the engine electrical wiring harness from the following components:

- Knock Sensor (KS)
- Oil pressure indicator switch

57. Remove the throttle body assembly.

58. Remove the nut securing the fuel pipe to the transaxle.

59. Remove the fuel pipe retainer from the threaded stud on the transaxle.

60. If equipped with AWD, remove the transfer case mounting bracket bolts and bracket.

61. If equipped with front wheel drive, remove the intermediate shaft.

62. Remove the negative battery cable-to-transaxle nut from the transaxle stud

63. Remove the negative battery cable from the transaxle stud.

64. Remove the engine-to-transaxle brace bolts and brace.

65. Remove the starter motor.

66. Remove the torque converter bolts.

67. Install an engine lift chain to the engine lift brackets.

68. Support the engine weight with an engine hoist.

69. Remove the automatic transaxle bolts.

70. Separate the automatic transaxle from the engine.

71. Lift the engine away from the frame and the automatic transaxle.

72. Secure the engine to an engine stand.

73. Remove any additional engine components as necessary. Refer to appropriate component sections, if needed.

To install:

74. Remove the engine from the engine stand.

75. Align the engine to the frame and automatic transaxle.

76. Install the automatic transaxle bolts. Tighten the bolts to 55 ft. lbs. (75 Nm).

77. Place a block of wood between the frame and the engine oil pan in order to support the engine on the frame once the engine hoist is removed.

78. Remove the engine hoist and lift chain.

79. Install the torque converter bolts. Tighten the bolts to 44 ft. lbs. (60 Nm).

80. Install the starter motor.

81. Install the engine to transaxle brace and bolts. Tighten the bolts to 37 ft. lbs. (50 Nm).

82. Install the negative battery cable to the transaxle stud.

83. Install the negative battery cable-to-transaxle nut to the transaxle stud. Tighten the nut to 33 ft. lbs. (45 Nm).

84. If equipped with AWD, install the transfer case mounting bracket and bolts. Tighten the bolts to 44 ft. lbs. (60 Nm).

85. If equipped with front wheel drive, install the intermediate shaft.

86. Install the fuel pipe retainer to the threaded stud on the transaxle.

87. Install the nut securing the fuel pipe to the transaxle. Tighten the nut to 21 ft. lbs. (28 Nm).

88. Install the throttle body assembly.

89. Connect the engine electrical wiring harness to the following components:
   - Oil pressure indicator switch
   - Knock Sensor (KS)

90. Connect the engine electrical wiring harness to the following components:
   - Install wire harness to retainer
   - AC refrigerant pressure sensor
   - Air Conditioning (AC) compressor clutch

91. If equipped with an engine coolant heater, connect the coolant heater cord.

92. Connect the engine electrical wiring harness to the following components:
   - Install the wire harness to retainers
   - Install ground lead and bolt. Tighten the bolt to 18 ft. lbs. (25 Nm)
   - CKP sensor
   - KS

93. Connect the engine electrical wiring harness to the following components:
   - Install wire harness to retainers
   - Ignition coil/control module HO2S 1
   - Fuel injector inline connector
   - Generator regulator
   - Install alternator B+ lead and nut. Tighten the nut to 115 inch lbs. (13 Nm).
   - EVAP purge solenoid
   - Throttle body EGR valve

➡ **Inspect for areas of body to power train contact or entanglement of wires and hoses while joining the vehicle body to the power train.**

94. Carefully lower the vehicle body down to the power train.

95. Install NEW frame-to-body bolts. Tighten the bolts to 114 ft. lbs. (155 Nm).

96. Raise the vehicle up away from the frame support fixture or jack stands and remove the support fixture or jack stands from under the vehicle.

97. Lower the vehicle.

98. Install the bolts that secure the left transaxle mount to the transaxle. Tighten the bolts to 37 ft. lbs. (50 Nm).

99. Install the bolts that secure the right engine mount to the engine. Tighten the bolts to 37 ft. lbs. (50 Nm).

100. Raise the vehicle.

101. Remove the block of wood between the frame and the transaxle used to support the transaxle while the bolts were removed from the left transaxle mount.

102. Remove the block of wood between the frame and the engine oil pan used to support the engine while the bolts were removed from the right engine mount.

103. If equipped with AWD, install the rear driveshaft.

104. Install the right and left front half-shafts.

105. Install the right and left lower ball joints to the steering knuckles.

106. Install the right and left stabilizer shaft links to the stabilizer shaft.

107. Install the right and left tie rod ends to the steering knuckles.

108. Connect the steering intermediate shaft to the steering gear.

109. Install a NEW pinch bolt to the steering intermediate shaft. Tighten the bolt to 25 ft. lbs. (34 Nm).

110. Install the right and left engine splash shields.

111. Install the front tires.

112. If equipped with AWD, connect the transfer case vent hose to the transfer case.

113. Install the catalytic converter.

114. Install the HO2S 2 wiring harness retainers to the vehicle underbody.

115. Connect the HO2S 2 wiring harness.

116. Install the front bumper fascia air deflector.

117. Install new seals and then connect the transaxle oil cooler lines to the transaxle.

118. Install the radiator outlet hose.

119. Lower the vehicle.

120. Install the radiator inlet hose.

121. Connect the heater hoses to the engine.

122. Install the coolant surge tank.

123. Untie the radiator, AC condenser, and fan module assembly from the upper radiator support.

124. Connect engine to body inline connector C102.

125. Connect the transaxle shift control cable to the transaxle.

126. Install the AC compressor hose assembly to the compressor.

127. Connect the engine fuel hose/pipe to the chassis fuel hose/pipe.

128. Connect the EVAP hose/pipe to the EVAP canister purge solenoid valve.

129. Install the air cleaner assembly and air intake duct.

130. Install the TCM to the TCM bracket.

131. Connect the brake booster vacuum hose to the intake manifold.

132. Position the clamp on the brake booster vacuum hose connection.

133. Install the fuel injector sight shield.

134. Install the negative battery cable from the inner fender body ground stud.

135. Install the negative battery cable nut to the inner fender body ground stud. Tighten the nut to 106 inch lbs. (12 Nm).

136. Install the battery cable retainers to the battery tray.

137. Install the battery box, battery and ECM.

138. Fill the engine with oil to the correct level.

139. Fill the engine with coolant to the correct level.

140. Check the transaxle fluid level.

141. Charge the AC system.

142. Prime the fuel system.

143. Cycle the ignition ON for 5 seconds then OFF for 10 seconds. Repeat cycling twice.

144. Crank the engine until it starts. The maximum starter motor cranking time is 20 seconds.

145. If the engine does not start, repeat the steps.

146. Install a scan tool.

147. Monitor the Engine Control Module (ECM) for DTCs with a scan tool. If other DTCs are set, except DTC P0315, refer to Diagnostic Trouble Code (DTC) List.

3.6L Engine

See Figures 101 through 106.

1. Before servicing the vehicle, refer to the precautions section.

2. Disconnect the negative battery cable.

3. Disconnect the negative battery cable.

4. Disconnect the ECM connector from the under-hood fuse block.

5. Disconnect ground wire from frame, near battery box.

6. Remove the fuel injector sight shield.

7. Release the clamp from the brake booster vacuum hose connection.

8. Disconnect the brake booster vacuum hose from the intake manifold.

9. Remove the air cleaner assembly.

10. Discharge the fuel system. Refer to Relieving Fuel System Pressure in the Fuel Systems section

11. Disconnect the Evaporative Emission (EVAP) hose/pipe from the EVAP canister purge solenoid valve.

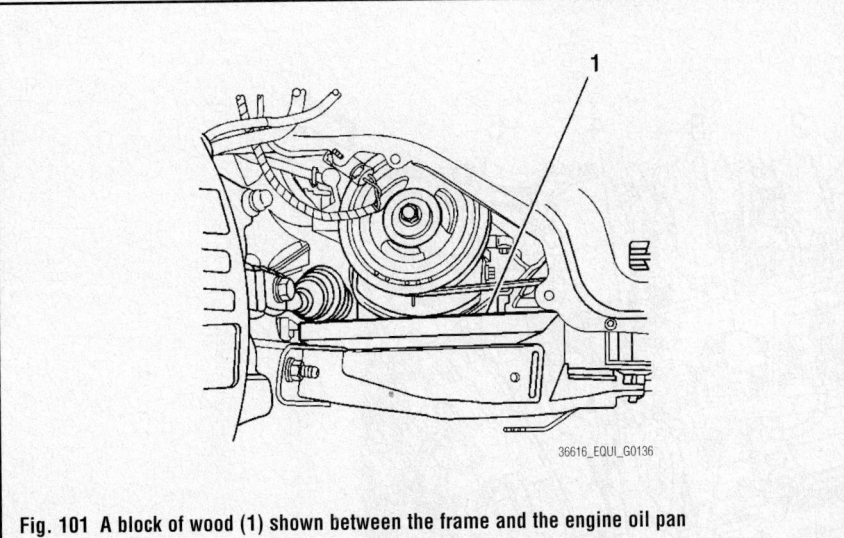

36616_EQUI_G0136

Fig. 101 A block of wood (1) shown between the frame and the engine oil pan

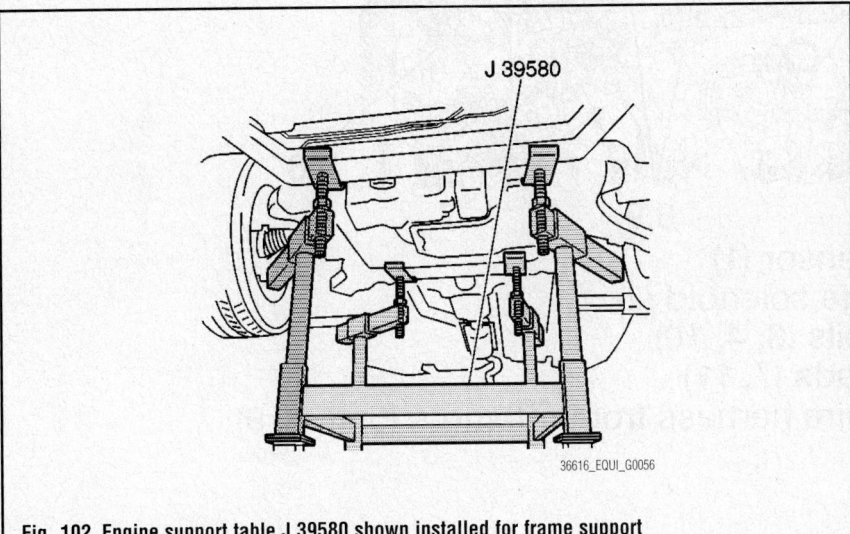

J 39580

36616_EQUI_G0056

Fig. 102 Engine support table J 39580 shown installed for frame support

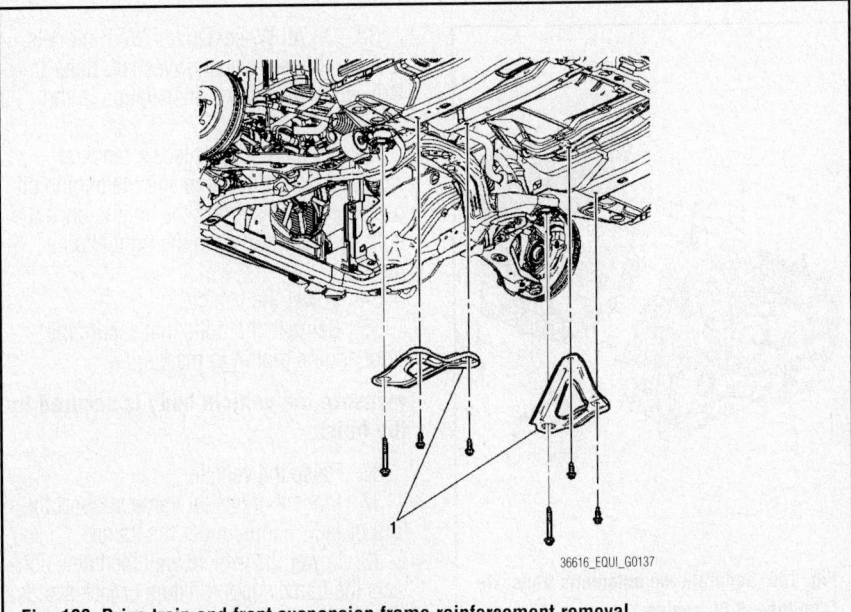

36616_EQUI_G0137

Fig. 103 Drive train and front suspension frame reinforcement removal

12. Disconnect the engine fuel hose/pipe from the chassis fuel hose/pipe.

13. Discharge the Air Conditioning (A/C) system.

14. Remove the A/C compressor hose assembly from the compressor. Cap or plug the hoses and compressor to prevent contamination.

15. Disconnect the transaxle shift control cable from the transaxle.

16. Drain the engine coolant from the cooling system.

17. Tie the radiator, A/C condenser, and fan module assembly to the upper radiator support to keep the assembly with the vehicle when the frame and drive train is removed.

18. Disconnect the heater hoses from the engine.

19. Remove the radiator inlet hose.

20. Raise and support the vehicle.

21. Remove the radiator outlet hose.

22. Disconnect the transaxle oil cooler lines from the transaxle and remove the seals.

➡ **Cap the transaxle oil cooler lines and plug the transaxle oil cooler line fittings to prevent loss of transmission fluid.**

23. Remove the catalytic converters and secure the rear half of the exhaust system to the vehicle underbody. Refer to Catalytic Converter Removal & Installation in the Engine Mechanical section.

24. Remove the front tire and wheel assemblies.

25. Remove the right and left engine splash shields.

26. Remove the steering intermediate shaft pinch bolt and discard the bolt.

27. Disconnect the steering intermediate shaft from the steering gear. Refer to Power Rack & Pinion Steering Gear Removal & Installation in the Steering section. Refer to Steering Linkage Removal & Installation in the Steering section.

28. Remove the right and left outer tie rod ends from the steering knuckles.

29. Remove the right and left stabilizer shaft links from the stabilizer shaft. Refer to Stabilizer Links Removal & Installation in the Suspension section.

30. Remove the right and left lower ball joints from the steering knuckles. Refer to Lower Ball joint Removal & Installation in the Suspension section.

31. On Front Wheel Drive (FWD) models, place a drain pan under the transaxle then separate the right and left front wheel halfshafts from the transaxle. Refer to Halfshaft Removal & Installation in the Drive Train section.

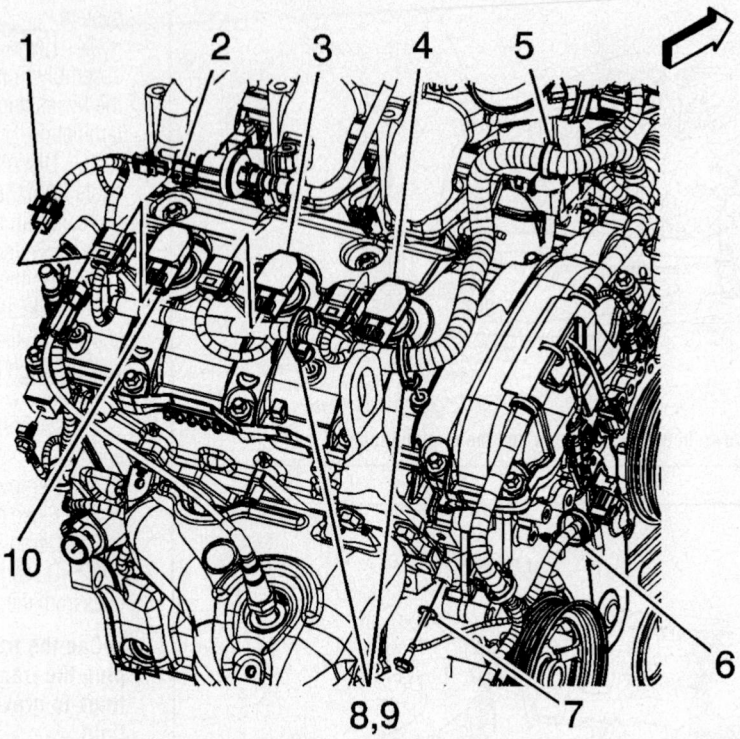

1. Oxygen Sensor (1)
2. EVAP purge solenoid (2)
3. Ignition coils (3, 4, 10)
4. Ground leads (7, 11)
5. Remove wire harness from retainers (5, 6, 8, 9)

36616_EQUI_G0138

Fig. 104 Disconnect the engine electrical wiring harness from the following components

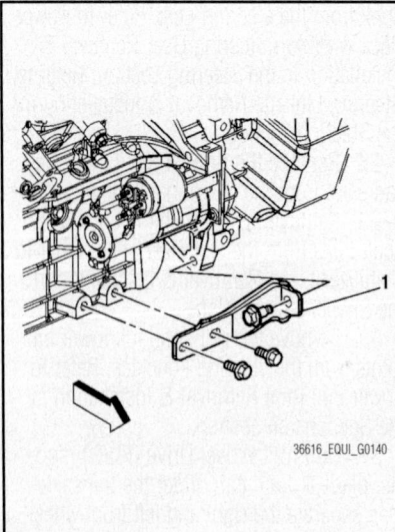

36616_EQUI_G0140

Fig. 105 Remove the engine-to-transaxle brace (1)

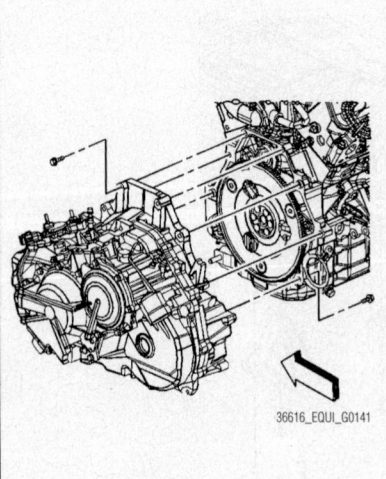

36616_EQUI_G0141

Fig. 106 Separate the automatic transaxle from the—3.6L engine

32. On All Wheel Drive (AWD) models, remove the rear wheel driveshaft. Refer to Driveshaft Removal & Installation in the Drive Train section.

33. On all models, place a block of wood between the frame and the engine oil pan in order to support the engine once the bolts are removed from the right engine mount.

34. Lower the vehicle.

35. Remove the bolts that secure the right engine mount to the engine.

➡ **Insure the vehicle body is secured to the hoist.**

36. Raise the vehicle.

37. Place a universal frame support fixture or jack stands under the frame.

38. Lower the vehicle until the frame contacts the frame support fixture or jack stands.

39. Disconnect the wiring harness

retaining clips near the right and left shock towers.

40. Remove the drive train and front suspension frame reinforcement.

41. Remove the frame-to-body bolts. Discard the bolts.

☀☀ WARNING

Inspect for areas of body to power train contact or entanglement of wires and hoses while separating the vehicle body and power train.

42. Carefully raise the vehicle body up away from the power train.

43. Disconnect the engine electrical wiring harness from the following components:

  - Oxygen sensor (1)
  - EVAP purge solenoid (2
  - Ignition coils (3, 4, 10)
  - Ground leads (7, 11)
  - Remove wire harness from retainers (5, 6, 8, 9)

44. Disconnect the left and right camshaft position sensors and actuators.

45. Disconnect the engine electrical wiring harness from the following components:

  - Alternator
  - A/C compressor hose
  - Oil pressure switch
  - A/C compressor
  - Disconnect retaining clips
  - Battery cable
  - Transmission module

46. If equipped with an engine coolant heater, disconnect the coolant heater cord.

47. Remove the throttle body assembly. Refer to Throttle Body Removal & Installation in the Fuel System section.

48. Remove the engine-to-transaxle brace bolts and brace.

49. Remove the starter motor. Refer to Starter Removal & Installation in the Engine Electrical section.

50. Remove the torque converter bolts.

51. Install the engine support adapters to the engine.

52. Raise the engine with an engine hoist.

53. Remove the automatic transaxle bolts.

54. Separate the automatic transaxle from the engine.

55. Lift the engine away from the frame and the automatic transaxle.

56. Secure the engine to an engine stand.

57. Remove any additional engine components as necessary. Refer to appropriate component sections, if needed.

To install:

58. Remove the engine from the engine stand.

59. Align the engine to the frame and automatic transaxle.

60. Install the automatic transaxle bolts and tighten to 55 ft. lbs. (75 Nm).

61. Place a block of wood between the frame and the engine oil pan in order to support the engine on the frame once the engine hoist is removed.

62. Remove the engine hoist and lift chain.

63. Remove the engine support adapters from the engine.

64. Install the torque converter bolts and tighten to 44 ft. lbs. (60 Nm).

65. Install the starter motor.

66. Install the engine to transaxle brace and bolts and tighten the bolts to 37 ft. lbs. (50 Nm).

67. Install the throttle body assembly.

68. If equipped with an engine coolant heater, connect the coolant heater cord.

69. Connect the engine electrical wiring harness to the following components:

  - Transmission module
  - Battery cable, Tighten the bolt to 18 ft. lbs. (25 Nm).
  - A/C compressor
  - Oil pressure switch
  - A/C compressor hose
  - Alternator, Tighten the nut to 115 inch lbs. (15 Nm).
  - All retainer clips

70. Connect the left and right camshaft position sensors and actuators.

71. Connect the engine electrical wiring harness to the following components:

  - Install wire harness to retainers
  - Ground leads
  - Ignition coils
  - EVAP purge solenoid
  - Oxygen Sensor

72. Connect the wiring harness retaining clips near the right and left shock towers.

73. Install NEW frame-to-body bolts and tighten to 114 ft. lbs. (155 Nm).

74. Install the drive train and front suspension frame reinforcement. Tighten the 4 short bolts to 74 ft. lbs. (100 Nm). and the 2 long bolts to 114 ft. lbs. (155 Nm).

75. Raise the vehicle up away from the frame support fixture or jack stands and remove the support fixture or jack stands from under the vehicle.

76. Lower the vehicle.

77. Install the bolts that secure the right engine mount to the engine. Tighten the bolts to 37 ft. lbs. (50 Nm).

78. Remove the block of wood between the frame and the engine oil pan used to support the engine while the bolts were removed from the right engine mount.

79. On AWD models, install the rear wheel driveshaft.

80. On FWD models, install the right and left front wheel drive shafts into the transaxle.

81. On all models, install the right and left lower ball joints to the steering knuckles.

82. Install the right and left stabilizer shaft links to the stabilizer shaft.

83. Install the right and left tie rod ends to the steering knuckles. Install a new tie rod retention nut and tighten to 18 ft. lbs. (25 Nm) plus 90 degrees.

84. Connect the steering intermediate shaft to the steering gear.

85. Install a NEW pinch bolt to the steering intermediate shaft and tighten the bolt to 25 ft. lbs. (34 Nm).

86. Install the right and left engine splash shields.

87. Install the front tire and wheel assemblies.

88. Install the catalytic converters.

89. Install new seals and connect the transaxle oil cooler lines to the transaxle.

90. Install the radiator outlet hose.

91. Lower the vehicle.

92. Install the radiator inlet hose.

93. Connect the heater hoses to the engine.

94. Untie the radiator, AC condenser, and fan module assembly from the upper radiator support.

95. Connect the transaxle shift control cable to the transaxle.

96. Install the AC compressor hose assembly to the compressor.

97. Connect the engine fuel hose/pipe to the chassis fuel hose/pipe.

98. Connect the EVAP hose/pipe to the EVAP canister purge solenoid valve.

99. Install the air cleaner assembly.

100. Connect the brake booster vacuum hose to the intake manifold.

101. Position the clamp on the brake booster vacuum hose connection.

102. Connect ground wire from frame, near battery box.

103. Connect the ECM connector to the under-hood fuse block.

104. Install the fuel injector sight shield.

105. Connect the negative battery cable.

106. Fill the engine with engine oil.

107. Fill and bleed the engine cooling system.

108. Check the transaxle fluid level.

109. Vacuum and recharge the A/C system.

110. Prime the fuel system. Cycle the ignition ON for 5 seconds then OFF for 10

seconds. Repeat cycling twice. Crank the engine until it starts.

111. Road test and check the vehicle for leaks.

EXHAUST MANIFOLD

REMOVAL & INSTALLATION

3.4L Engine

Left Exhaust Manifold

See Figure 107.

1. Before servicing the vehicle, refer to the precautions section.

2. Remove the three nuts attaching the exhaust crossover pipe to the left exhaust manifold.

3. Remove the EGR pipe bolts and gasket from the left exhaust manifold.

4. Remove the EGR valve bolts, EGR valve, and gasket from the upper intake manifold and remove the assembly from the engine.

5. Remove the spark plug wires from the spark plugs.

6. Remove the spark plugs.

7. Remove the exhaust manifold heat shield bolts.

8. Remove the exhaust manifold heat shield.

9. Remove the exhaust manifold nuts.

10. Remove the exhaust manifold.

11. Remove the exhaust manifold gasket.

12. Remove the exhaust studs, if required.

To install:

13. Clean the exhaust manifold and the cylinder head sealing surfaces.

14. Install the exhaust manifold studs. Tighten the exhaust manifold studs to 13 ft. lbs. (18 Nm).

15. Install the exhaust manifold gasket.

16. Install the exhaust manifold.

17. Install the exhaust manifold nuts, working from the center out to 12 ft. lbs. (16 Nm).

18. Install the exhaust manifold heat shield.

19. Install the exhaust manifold heat shield bolts. Tighten the exhaust manifold heat shield bolts to 89 inch lbs. (10 Nm).

20. Install the exhaust gas recirculation (EGR) valve gasket and the EGR assembly to the upper intake manifold.

21. Install the EGR valve bolts. Tighten the EGR valve bolts to 22 ft. lbs. (30 Nm).

22. Install the EGR pipe gasket and pipe to the left exhaust manifold.

23. Install the EGR pipe bolts. Tighten the EGR pipe bolts to 22 ft. lbs. (30 Nm).

24. Install the three nuts that attach the exhaust crossover pipe to the left exhaust manifold and tighten to 18 ft. lbs. (25 Nm).

Right Exhaust Manifold

See Figures 108 and 109.

1. Before servicing the vehicle, refer to the precautions section.

2. Disconnect the Heated Oxygen Sensor (HO2S) electrical connector.

3. Remove the three nuts attaching the exhaust crossover pipe to the right exhaust manifold.

4. Raise and safely support the vehicle.

5. Remove the three nuts securing the catalytic converter to the exhaust manifold. Position the catalytic converter out of the way.

6. Remove the exhaust manifold heat shield bolts.

7. Remove the exhaust manifold heat shields.

8. Remove the exhaust manifold nuts.

9. Remove the exhaust manifold.

10. Remove the exhaust manifold gasket.

11. Remove the exhaust studs, if required.

To install:

➡ **If you are replacing the exhaust manifold, the heated oxygen sensor must be transferred to the new manifold.**

12. Install the exhaust manifold studs. Tighten the exhaust manifold studs to 13 ft. lbs. (18 Nm).

13. Install the exhaust manifold gasket.

14. Install the exhaust manifold.

15. Install the exhaust manifold nuts. Tighten the exhaust manifold nuts working from the center out to 12 ft. lbs. (16 Nm).

16. Install the lower exhaust manifold heat shield.

17. Install the upper exhaust manifold heat shield.

18. Install the exhaust manifold heat shield bolts. Tighten the exhaust manifold heat shield bolts to 89 inch lbs. (10 Nm).

19. Install the catalytic converter to the exhaust manifold and tighten the three nuts to 27 ft. lbs. (37 Nm).

20. Lower the vehicle.

21. Install the three nuts that attach the exhaust crossover pipe to the left exhaust manifold and tighten to 18 ft. lbs. (25 Nm).

22. Connect the HO2S electrical connector.

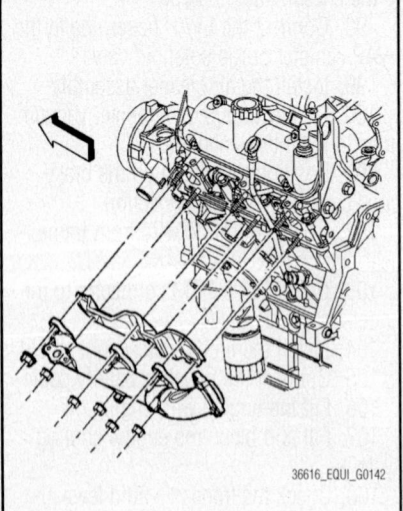

36616_EQUI_G0142

Fig. 107 Exploded view of the left side exhaust manifold

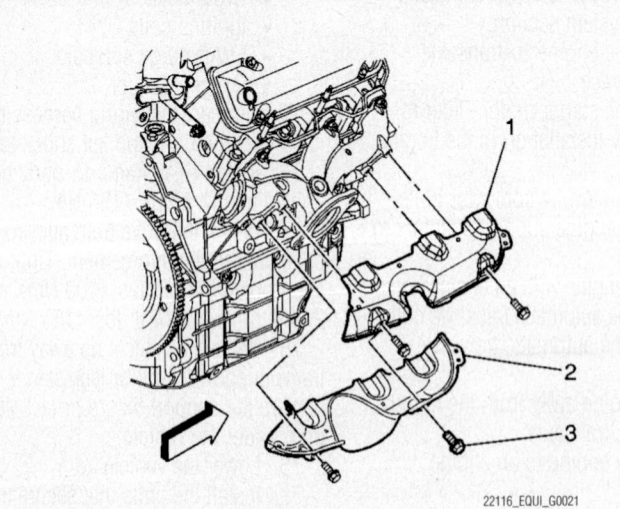

22116_EQUI_G0021

Fig. 108 Remove the mounting bolts (3) to remove the exhaust manifold heat shields (1,2)

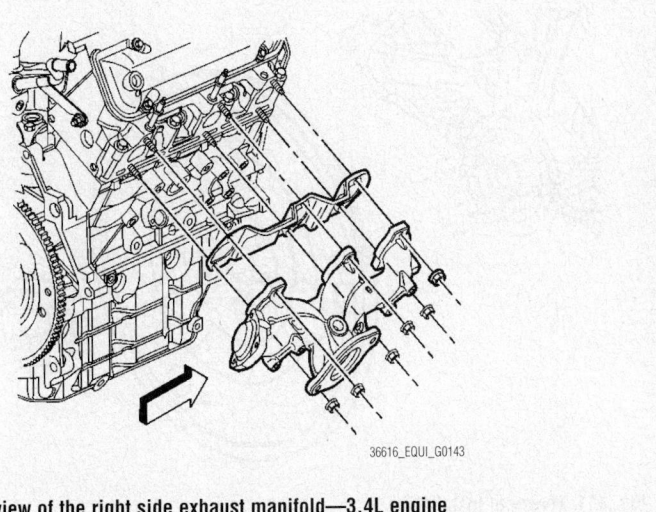

Fig. 109 Exploded view of the right side exhaust manifold—3.4L engine

3.6L Engine

Left Side Exhaust Manifold

See Figure 110.

1. Before servicing the vehicle, refer to the precautions section.

2. Remove the fuel injector sight shield, if necessary.

3. Disconnect the engine wiring harness electrical connector from the Heated Oxygen Sensor (HO2S) electrical connector.

4. Remove the HO2S electrical connector retainer from the retainer clip.

5. Remove the exhaust manifold heat shield bolts.

6. Remove the exhaust manifold heat shield, sliding the shield up over the HO2S pigtail.

7. Remove the oil level indicator.

8. Remove the catalytic converter to exhaust manifold nuts.

9. Remove the exhaust manifold bolts.

10. Remove the exhaust manifold and gasket. Discard the gasket.

To install:

11. Install one exhaust manifold bolt to the exhaust manifold.

12. Install the **NEW** exhaust manifold gasket onto the cylinder head and bolt.

13. Install the exhaust manifold (with gasket) to the catalytic converter and the cylinder head.

14. Install the remaining exhaust manifold bolts and tighten to 15 ft. lbs. (20 Nm).

15. Install the oil level indicator.

16. Install the exhaust manifold heat shield, sliding the shield down over the HO2S pigtail.

17. Install the exhaust manifold heat shield bolts and tighten to 89 inch lbs. (10 Nm).

18. Connect the engine wiring harness

electrical connector to the HO2S electrical connector.

19. Install the HO2S electrical connector retainer to the retainer clip.

20. Install the fuel injector sight shield, if necessary.

Right Side Exhaust Manifold

1. Before servicing the vehicle, refer to the precautions section.

2. Remove the fuel injector sight shield, if necessary.

3. Disconnect the engine wiring harness electrical connector from the Heated Oxygen Sensor (HO2S) electrical connector.

4. Remove the HO2S electrical connector retainer from the camshaft cover.

5. Remove the exhaust manifold heat shield bolts.

6. Remove the exhaust manifold heat shield, sliding the shield up over the HO2S pigtail.

7. Remove the catalytic converter to exhaust manifold nuts.

8. Remove the exhaust manifold bolts.

9. Remove the exhaust manifold and gasket. Discard the gasket.

10. Remove the right catalytic converter. Refer to Catalytic Converter Removal & Installation in the Engine Mechanical section.

11. Remove the exhaust manifold bolts.

12. Remove the exhaust manifold and gasket out from the vehicle. Discard the gasket.

To install:

13. Install one exhaust manifold bolt to the exhaust manifold.

14. Install the NEW exhaust manifold gasket onto the cylinder head and bolt.

15. Install the exhaust manifold (with gasket) to the catalytic converter and the cylinder head.

16. Install the exhaust manifold bolts and tighten to 15 ft. lbs. (20 Nm).

17. Install the right catalytic converter.

18. Install the catalytic converter nuts and tighten to 37 ft. lbs. (50 Nm).

19. Install the exhaust manifold heat shield, sliding the shield down over the HO2S pigtail.

20. Install the exhaust manifold heat shield bolts and tighten to 89 inc lbs. (10 Nm).

21. Connect the engine wiring harness electrical connector to the HO2S electrical connector.

22. Install the HO2S electrical connector retainer to the camshaft cover.

23. Install the fuel injector sight shield, if necessary

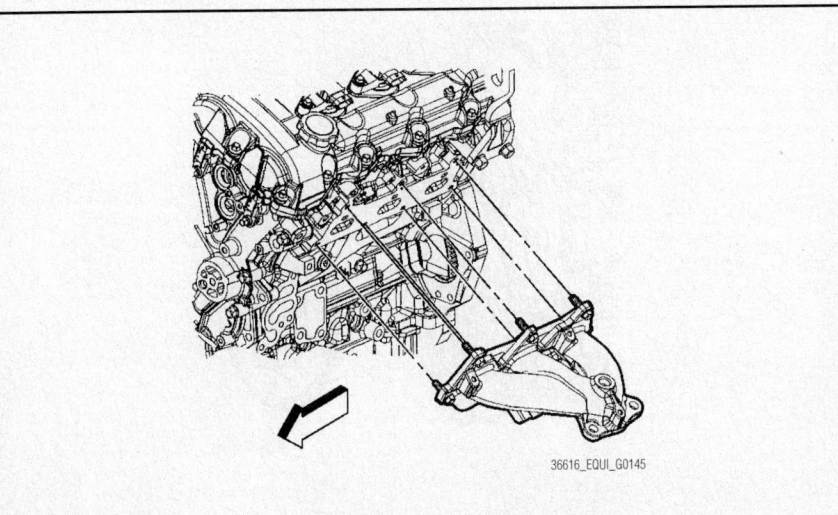

Fig. 110 Exploded view of the left side exhaust manifold—3.6L engine

FLYWHEEL

REMOVAL & INSTALLATION

3.4L Engine

See Figure 111.

1. Before servicing the vehicle, refer to the precautions section.
2. Remove the transaxle assembly.
3. Remove the engine flywheel bolts and flywheel.
4. Clean the engine flywheel bolt threads and bolt holes.
5. Clean and inspect the engine flywheel.

To install:

6. Install the engine flywheel and bolts. Tighten bolts to 52 ft. lbs. (71 Nm).
7. Install the automatic transaxle.

3.6L Engine

See Figures 112 and 113.

1. Before servicing the vehicle, refer to the precautions section.
2. Disconnect the negative battery cable.
3. Remove the transaxle assembly.
4. Install the EN 46106 flywheel holding tool through the starter mounting hole.
5. Remove the engine flywheel bolts and discard.
6. Remove the engine flywheel from the crankshaft.
7. Remove the flywheel holding tool EN 46106.

To install:

8. Place the engine flywheel in position on the crankshaft.
9. Install 2 NEW bolts in location at the top and bottom of the engine flywheel bolt pattern allowing the engine flywheel to hang in position.
10. Install the EN 46106 flywheel holding tool.
11. Install the remaining **NEW** engine flywheel bolts and tighten to 22 ft. lbs. (30 Nm) and an additional 45 degrees using an angle meter.
12. Remove the flywheel holding tool EN 46106.
13. Install the transaxle assembly.
14. Connect the negative battery cable.

INTAKE MANIFOLD

REMOVAL & INSTALLATION

3.4L Engine

Upper Intake Manifold

See Figure 114.

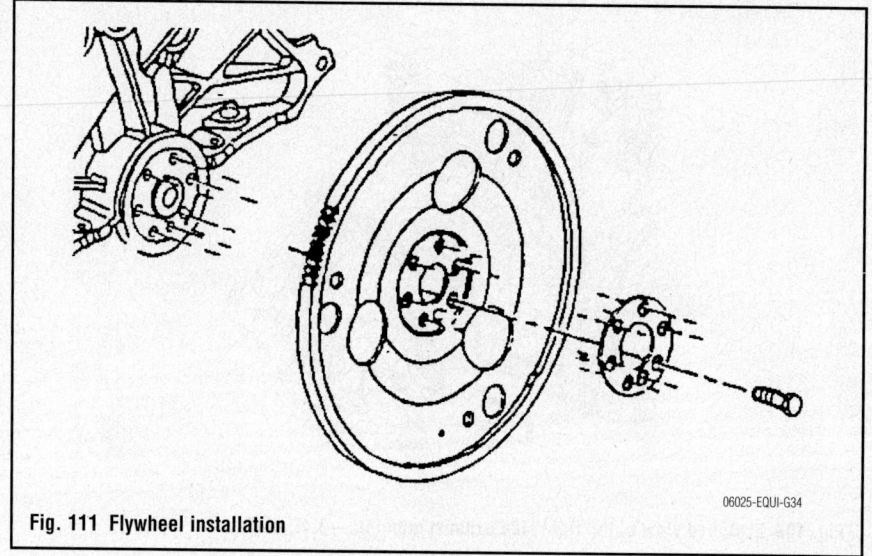

Fig. 111 Flywheel installation

06025-EQUI-G34

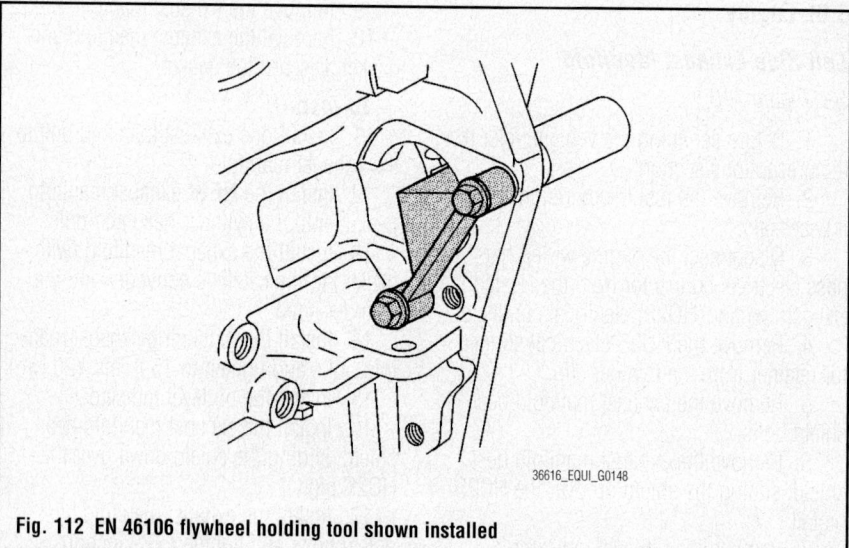

Fig. 112 EN 46106 flywheel holding tool shown installed

36616_EQUI_G0148

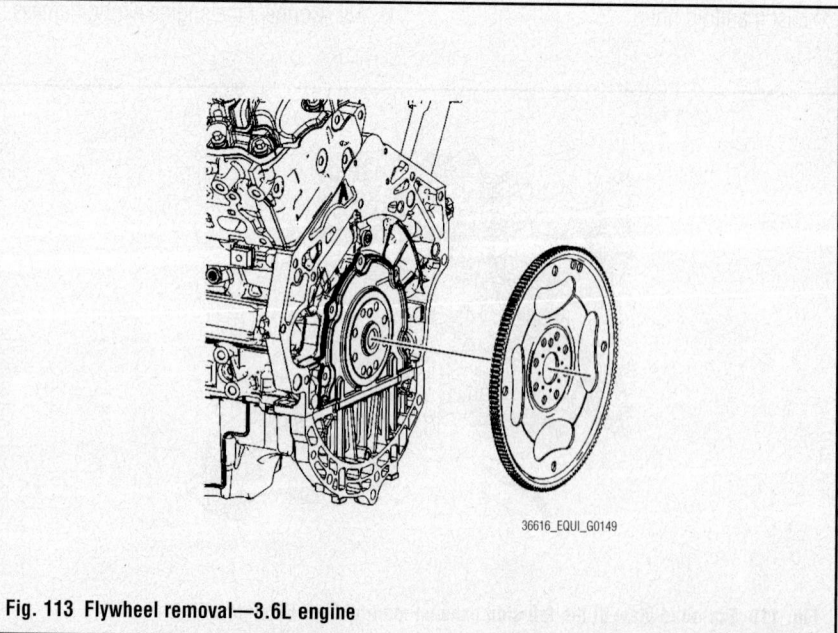

Fig. 113 Flywheel removal—3.6L engine

36616_EQUI_G0149

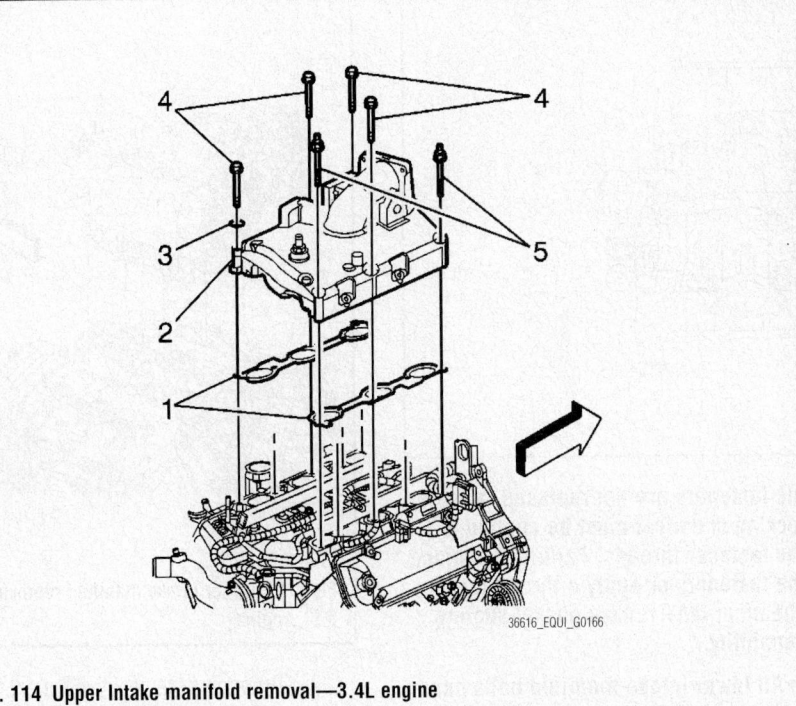

Fig. 114 Upper Intake manifold removal—3.4L engine

1. Before servicing the vehicle, refer to the precautions section.

2. Disconnect the negative battery cable.

3. Remove the fuel injector sight shield.

4. Release the clamp from the brake booster vacuum hose connection.

5. Disconnect the brake booster vacuum hose from the intake manifold.

6. Disconnect the left side spark plug wires from the retainers and from the spark plugs.

7. Remove the ignition control module bracket from the engine with the ignition control module and spark plug wires still attached.

8. Remove the air cleaner intake duct.

9. Remove the heater outlet pipe nut from the upper intake manifold.

10. Remove the heater outlet pipe nuts and bolt from the throttle body.

11. Position the heater outlet pipe out of the way without disconnecting the heater hoses.

12. Remove the EGR pipe.

13. Remove the PCV foul air hose.

14. Loosen but do not completely remove the alternator attachment bolt most near the intake manifold.

15. Remove the alternator brace nut.

16. Remove the alternator brace.

17. Remove the upper intake manifold bolts.

18. Remove the spark plug wire retainer.

19. Remove the upper intake manifold.

20. Remove the upper intake manifold gaskets.

To install:

21. Install the **NEW** upper intake manifold gaskets to the lower intake manifold and install the fir tree retainers to retain the upper intake manifold gasket position.

22. Install the upper intake manifold.

23. Install the spark plug wire retainer.

24. Apply thread lock GM P/N 12345382 (Canadian P/N 10953489) to the bolt threads. Install the upper intake manifold bolts. Tighten the bolts to 18 ft. lbs. (25 Nm).

25. Install the alternator brace. Tighten the nut to 18 ft. lbs. (25 Nm).

26. Fully insert the alternator attachment bolt most near the intake manifold. Tighten the bolt to 18 ft. lbs. (25 Nm).

27. Install the PCV foul air hose.

28. Install the EGR pipe.

29. Position the heater outlet pipe to the throttle body and the upper intake manifold.

30. Install the heater outlet pipe nuts to the throttle body. Tighten the nut to 89 inch lbs. (10 Nm).

31. Install the heater outlet pipe bolt to the throttle body. Tighten the bolt to 89 inch lbs. (10 Nm).

32. Install the heater outlet pipe nut to the upper intake manifold. Tighten the nut to 18 ft. lbs. (25 Nm).

33. Install the air cleaner intake duct.

34. Install the ignition control module bracket.

35. Connect the left side spark plug wires to the spark plugs and to the spark plug wire retainers.

36. Connect the brake booster vacuum hose to the intake manifold.

37. Install the clamp to the brake booster vacuum hose connection.

38. Install the fuel injector sight shield.

39. Connect the negative battery cable.

Lower Intake Manifold

See Figures 115 and 116.

1. Before servicing the vehicle, refer to the precautions section.

2. Disconnect the negative battery cable.

3. Drain the cooling system.

4. Remove the upper intake manifold.

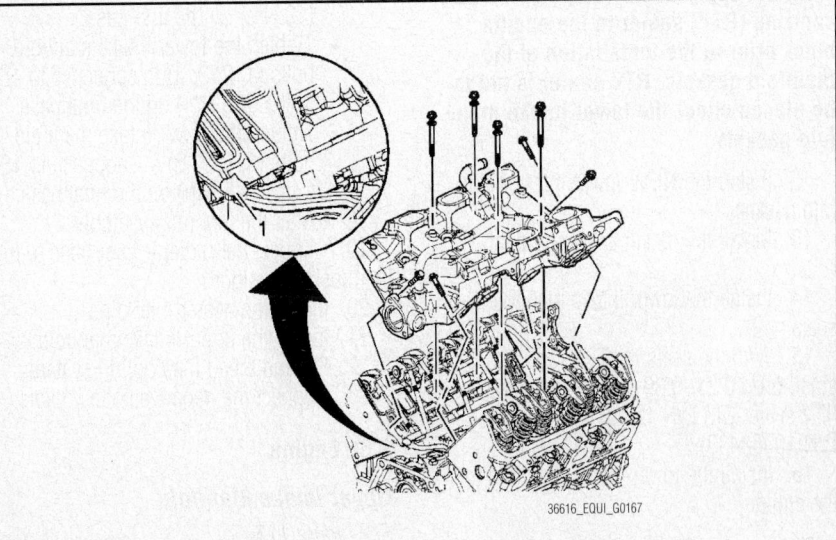

Fig. 115 With the seals in place, apply a small drop 0.31–0.39 inch (8–10 mm) of RTV sealer as shown

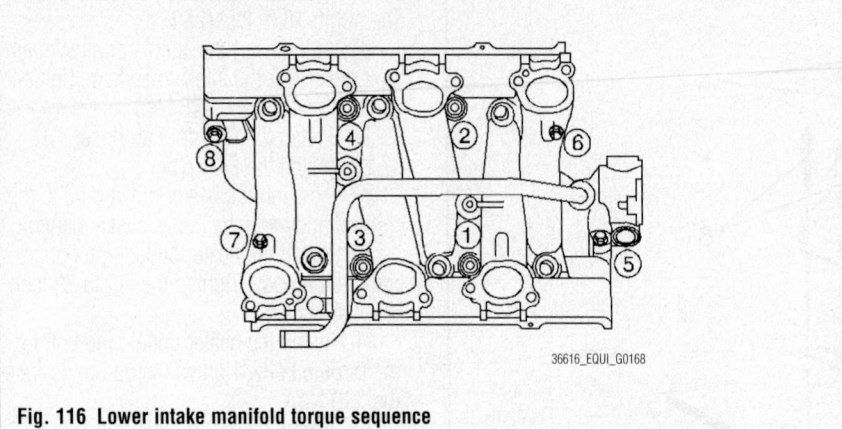

Fig. 116 Lower intake manifold torque sequence

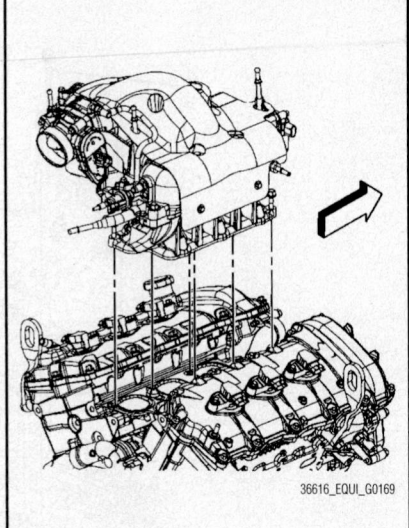

Fig. 117 Upper intake manifold removal—3.6L engine

Refer to Upper Intake Manifold Removal & Installation in the Engine Mechanical section.

5. Remove the heater inlet pipe.

6. Disconnect the radiator inlet hose from the thermostat housing.

7. Remove the fuel rail assembly.

8. Remove the lower intake manifold bolts.

9. Remove the lower intake manifold from the engine.

10. Remove the rocker arms and push rods. Refer to Rocker Arms/Shafts Removal & Installation in the Engine Mechanical section.

11. Remove the lower intake manifold gaskets.

To install:

➡All gasket mating surfaces must remain free of oil and foreign material. Use GM P/N 12346139 (Canadian P/N 10953463) or equivalent to clean surfaces.

➡Do not apply Room Temperature Vulcanizing (RTV) sealer to the engine block prior to the installation of the manifold gaskets. RTV sealer is not to be placed under the lower intake manifold gaskets.

12. Install the **NEW** lower intake manifold gaskets.

13. Install the rocker arms and push rods.

14. Install the lower intake manifold seals.

15. With the seals in place, apply a small drop 0.31–0.39 inch (8–10 mm) of RTV sealer GM P/N 12346141 (Canadian P/N 10953433).

16. Install the lower intake manifold to the engine.

➡Maximum gasket performance is achieved when using new fasteners, which contain a thread-locking patch. If the fasteners are not replaced, a thread locking chemical must be applied to the fastener threads. Failure to replace the fasteners or apply a thread-locking chemical MAY reduce gasket sealing capability.

➡All lower intake manifold bolts need to be clean, free of foreign materials, and reused only if new bolts are unavailable. Use GM P/N 1234382 (Canadian P/N 10953489) or equivalent and apply to the old intake manifold bolt threads. Manufacturer recommends the center bolts be fully torqued before the diagonal bolts to assure proper torque distribution. Lower intake manifold bolts in locations (6) and (7) should be torqued to specification using a crow's foot type tool.

17. Install the lower intake manifold bolts as follows:
- Tighten the lower intake manifold bolts in sequence to 115 inch lbs. (13 Nm) on the first pass.
- Tighten the lower intake manifold bolts (1, 2, 3, 4) in sequence to 15 ft. lbs. (20 Nm) on the final pass.
- Tighten the lower intake manifold bolts (5, 6, 7, 8) in sequence to 18 ft. lbs. (25 Nm) on the final pass.

18. Install the fuel rail assembly.

19. Connect the radiator inlet hose to the thermostat housing.

20. Install the heater inlet pipe.

21. Install the upper intake manifold.

22. Fill and bleed the cooling system.

23. Connect the negative battery cable.

3.6L Engine

Upper Intake Manifold

See Figure 117.

1. Before servicing the vehicle, refer to the precautions section.

2. Disconnect the negative battery cable.

3. Remove the engine cover.

4. Remove the air cleaner outlet duct.

5. Reposition the fresh air Positive Crankcase Ventilation (PCV) line from the air cleaner inlet tube.

6. Disconnect the Electronic Throttle Control (ETC) electrical connector.

7. Disconnect the PCV line from the top of the intake manifold and reposition aside.

8. Disconnect the Evaporative Emissions (EVAP) canister purge line and reposition aside.

9. Remove the bleed pipe bolts.

10. Remove the bleed pipe hose clamp.

11. Reposition the bleed pipe.

12. Remove the brake booster vacuum hose from the intake manifold.

13. Remove the engine harness retaining clips.

14. Remove the upper intake retaining bolts.

15. Remove the upper intake manifold and gasket. Discard gasket.

To install:

16. Clean and inspect the intake manifold and the sealing surfaces.

17. Install a **NEW** upper intake manifold gaskets.

18. Carefully install the intake manifold.

19. Install the intake manifold mounting bolts and tighten in sequence to 17 ft. (23 Nm).

20. Install the engine harness retaining clips.

21. Install the brake booster vacuum hose to the intake manifold.

22. Position the bleed pipe.

23. Install the bleed pipe hose clamp.

24. Install the bleed pipe bolts and tighten to 89 inch lbs. (10 Nm).

25. Connect the coolant hose bleed pipe.

26. Connect the EVAP canister purge line.

27. Connect the PCV line to the top of the intake manifold.

28. Connect the ETC electrical connector.

29. Install the air cleaner outlet duct.

30. Install the fresh air PCV line to the air cleaner inlet duct.

31. Install the engine cover.

32. Connect the negative battery cable.

Lower Intake Manifold

See Figure 118.

1. Before servicing the vehicle, refer to the precautions section.

2. Disconnect the negative battery cable.

3. Remove the fuel injectors and fuel rail. Refer to Fuel Rail & Injectors, Removal & Installation in the Fuel System section.

4. Remove the lower intake manifold bolts.

5. Remove the lower intake manifold and gasket from engine. Discard the gasket.

6. Clean and inspect the intake manifold and the sealing surfaces.

To install:

7. Install the **NEW** lower intake manifold gasket.

8. Install the lower intake manifold bolts

9. Install the fuel injectors and fuel rail and tighten the bolts to 17 ft. lbs. (23 Nm).

10. Tighten the remaining intake manifold bolts to 17 ft. lbs. (23 Nm).

11. Connect the negative battery cable.

OIL PAN

REMOVAL & INSTALLATION

3.4L Engine

See Figures 119 through 121.

1. Before servicing the vehicle, refer to the precautions section.

2. Disconnect the negative battery cable.

3. Remove the fuel injector sight shield.

4. Install the engine support fixture.

5. Raise and support the vehicle.

6. Remove the Air Conditioning (A/C) compressor. Refer to A/C Compressor, Removal & Installation in the Heating & Air Conditioning section.

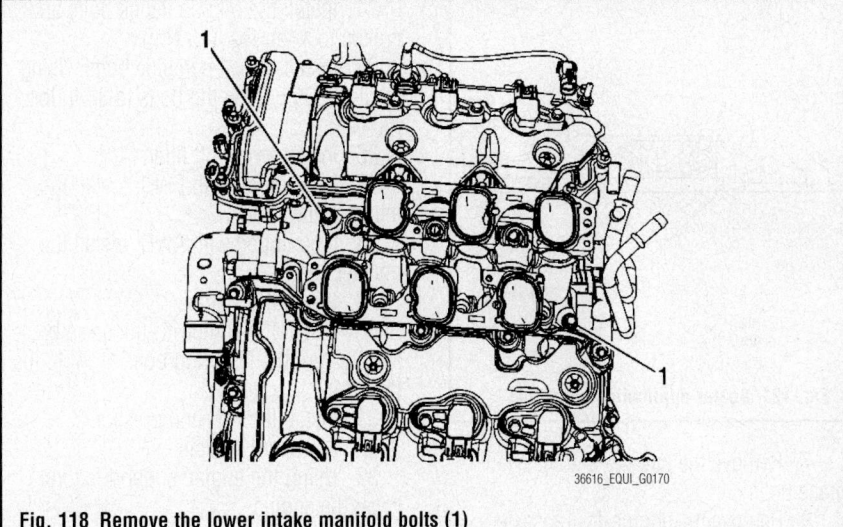

Fig. 118 Remove the lower intake manifold bolts (1)

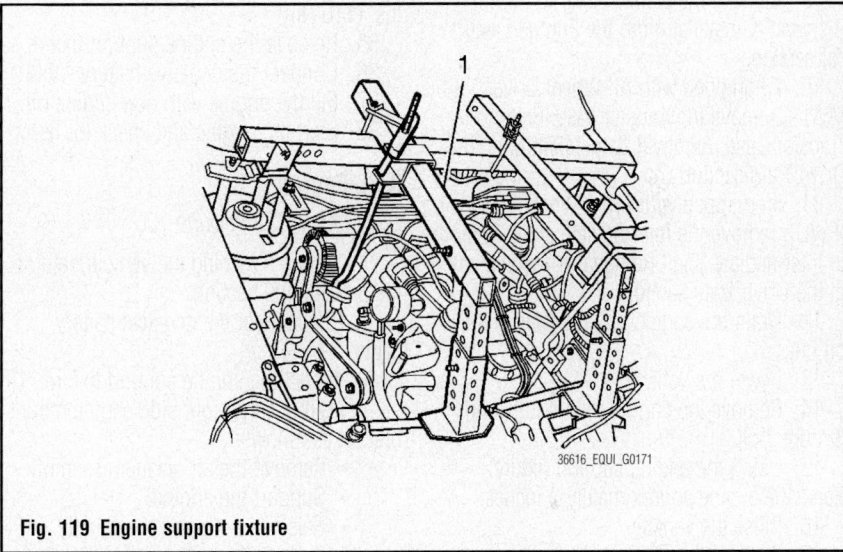

Fig. 119 Engine support fixture

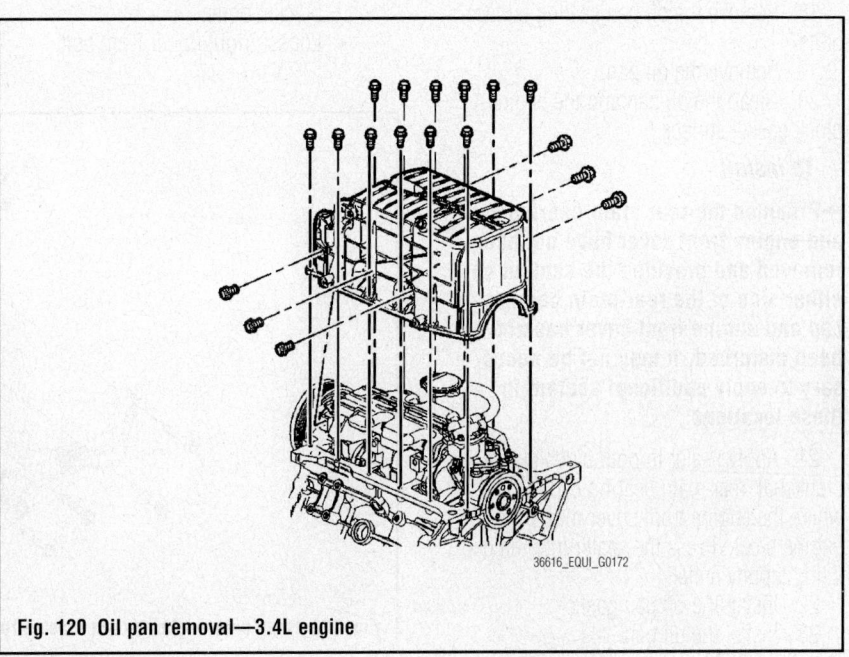

Fig. 120 Oil pan removal—3.4L engine

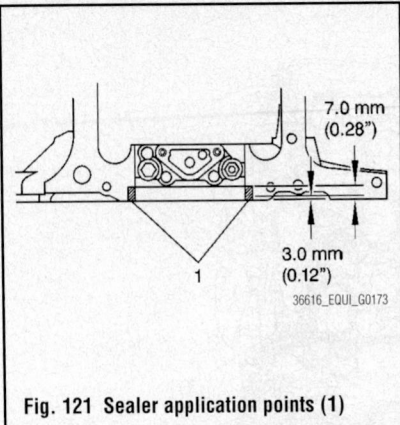

Fig. 121 Sealer application points (1)

7. Remove the engine-to-transaxle brace bolts.

8. Remove the engine-to-transaxle brace.

9. Remove the starter. Refer to Starter, Removal & Installation in the Engine Electrical section.

10. If equipped with All Wheel Drive (AWD), remove the transfer case. Refer to Transfer Case, Removal & Installation in the Drive Train section.

11. If equipped with Front Wheel Drive (FWD), remove the intermediate shaft. Refer to Intermediate Shaft Removal & Installation in the Drive Train section.

12. Drain the engine oil and remove the oil filter.

13. Lower the vehicle.

14. Remove the engine mount nuts and through bolt.

15. Using the engine support fixture. Raise the engine approximately 2 inches.

16. Raise the vehicle.

17. Remove the oil pan side bolts.

18. Remove the oil pan sealing surface bolts.

19. Remove the oil pan.

20. Clean the oil pan and the engine block gasket surface.

To install:

➥Provided the rear main bearing cap and engine front cover have not been removed and provided the sealant on either side of the rear main bearing cap and engine front cover has not been disturbed, it may not be necessary to apply additional sealant in these locations.

21. Apply sealer to both sides of the crankshaft rear main bearing cap (1) and where the engine front cover meets the engine block. Press the sealer into the gap using a putty knife.

22. Install the oil pan gasket.

23. Install the oil pan.

24. Install the oil pan flange bolts and tighten to 18 ft. lbs. (25 Nm).

25. Install the oil pan side bolts. Using the J-39505 tighten the bolts to 37 ft. lbs. (50 Nm).

26. Install a new oil filter.

27. If equipped with FWD, install the intermediate shaft.

28. If equipped with AWD, install the transfer case.

29. Install the starter.

30. Install the engine-to-transaxle brace and tighten the mounting bolts to 37 ft. lbs. (50 Nm).

31. Install the A/C compressor.

32. Lower the vehicle.

33. Using the engine support fixture, lower the engine.

34. Install the engine mount through bolt and nuts tighten the retaining nuts to 81 ft. lbs. (110 Nm).

35. Remove the engine support fixture.

36. Connect the negative battery cable.

37. Fill the engine with new engine oil.

38. Start the engine and check for leaks.

3.6L Engine

See Figures 122 through 126.

1. Before servicing the vehicle, refer to the precautions section.

2. Disconnect the negative battery cable.

3. Install the engine support fixture.

4. Remove the right side engine mount bracket as follows:
- Remove the air cleaner assembly.
- Support the engine.
- Raise and support the vehicle.
- Remove 3 upper engine mount bracket bolts.
- Loosen right upper front bolt.
- Remove the ABS connector clip from the frame.
- Remove the upper engine mount bracket nuts.
- Remove the lower bracket bolts.
- Remove the upper bracket bolt from the bracket.
- Remove the mount and the lower bracket from the vehicle.
- Remove the upper bracket.
- Remove the engine mount.

5. Raise and support the vehicle.

6. Drain the engine oil and remove the oil filter.

7. Remove the catalytic converter. Refer to Catalytic Converter, Removal & Installation in the Engine Mechanical section.

8. Remove the Air Conditioning (A/C) compressor. Refer to A/C Compressor, Removal & Installation in the Heating & Air Conditioning section.

9. Remove the oil pan bolts.

10. Remove the oil pan.

11. Clean the oil pan and the engine block gasket surface.

To install:

12. Install the 0.315 inch (8 mm) oil pan guides EN 46109 into the center oil pan rail bolt hole on each side of the engine block.

13. Place a 0.118 inch (3 mm) bead of RTV sealant, GM P/N 12378521 (Canadian P/N 88901148) or equivalent, on the block pan rail and the crankshaft rear oil seal housing.

14. Position the oil pan onto the block.

15. Remove the EN 46109 guides from the engine block.

16. Loosely install the oil pan bolts.

17. Tighten the oil pan bolts in sequence as shown:
- Tighten the 8 mm bolts (1–11) to 17 ft. lbs. (23 Nm).

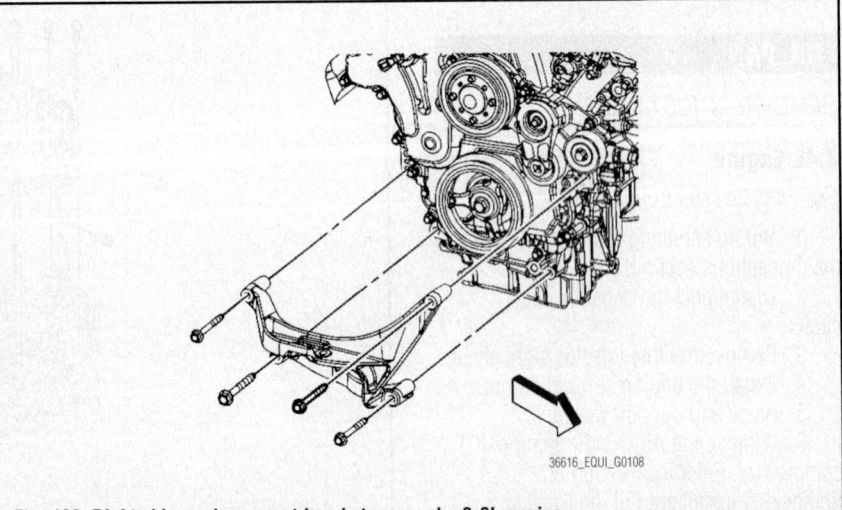

Fig. 122 Right side engine mount bracket removal—3.6L engine

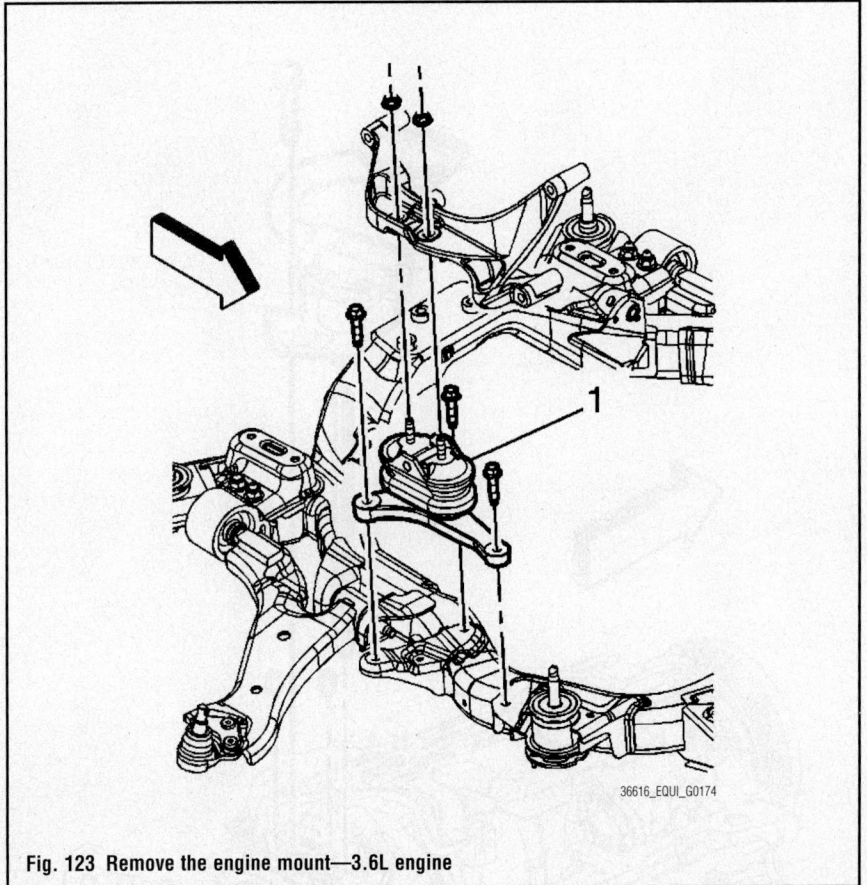

Fig. 123 Remove the engine mount—3.6L engine

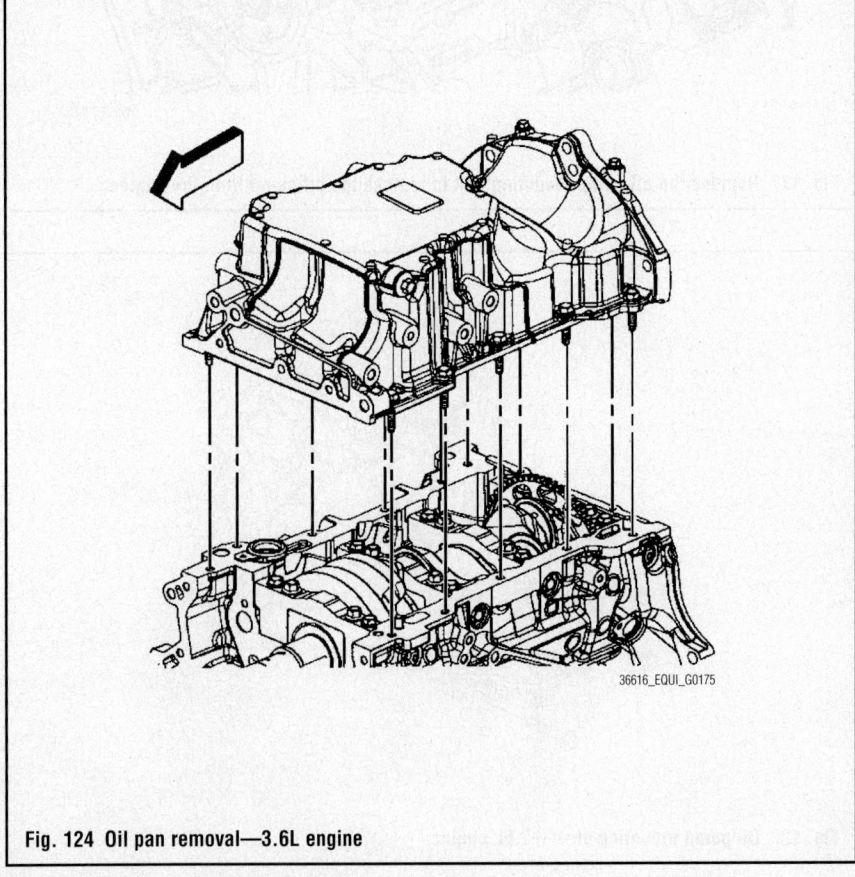

Fig. 124 Oil pan removal—3.6L engine

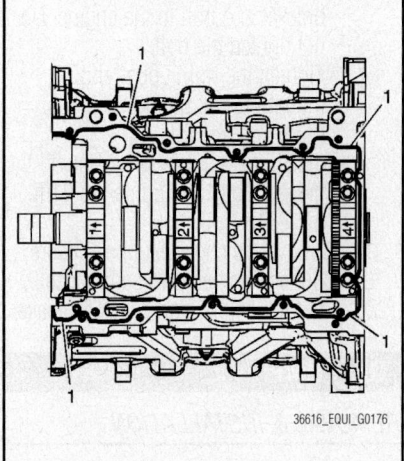

Fig. 125 Place a 0.118 inch (3 mm) bead (1) of RTV sealant on the block pan rail and the crankshaft rear oil seal housing

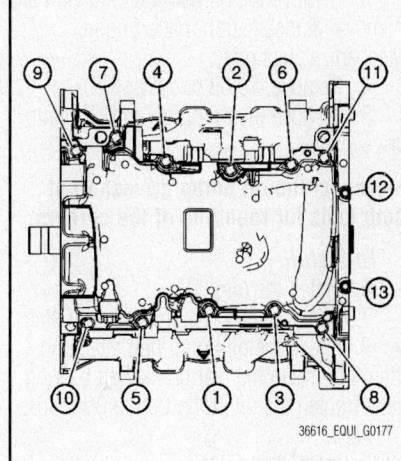

Fig. 126 Oil pan tightening sequence—3.6L engine

- Tighten the 6 mm bolts (12, 13) to 89 inch lbs. (10 Nm).
18. Install the A/C compressor.
19. Install the catalytic converter.
20. Install a new oil filter.
21. Lower the vehicle.
22. Refill the engine with oil.
23. Install the right side engine mount bracket as follows:
- Install the engine mount and the lower bracket to the vehicle. Tighten the lower bracket bolts to 37 ft. lbs. (50 Nm).
- Install the ABS connector clip to the frame.
- Install the upper engine mount bracket nuts and tighten to 37 ft. lbs. (50 Nm).

- Install the engine mount upper bracket and bolt to the engine. Do not tighten the bolt.
- Tighten the right upper engine mount bracket bolt to 37 ft. lbs. (50 Nm).
- Install the upper engine mount bracket bolts and tighten to 81 ft. lbs. (110 Nm).

24. Remove the engine support fixture.
25. Connect the negative battery cable.
26. Start the engine and check for leaks.

OIL PUMP

REMOVAL & INSTALLATION

3.4L Engine

See Figure 127.

1. Before servicing the vehicle, refer to the precautions section.
2. Disconnect the negative battery cable.
3. Remove the oil pan. Refer to Oil Pan, Removal & Installation in the Engine Mechanical section.
4. Remove the oil pump bolt.
5. Remove the oil pump and oil pump drive shaft.

➡**Inspect the oil pump driveshaft at both ends for rounding of the corners.**

To install:

6. Install the oil pump.
7. Position the oil pump onto the pins.
8. Install the oil pump bolt attaching the oil pump to the rear crankshaft bearing cap. Tighten the oil pump bolt to 30 ft. lbs. (41 Nm).
9. Install the oil pan.
10. Connect the negative battery cable.

3.6L Engine

See Figure 128.

1. Remove the front timing cover. Refer to Front Timing Cover and Seal, Removal & Installation in the Engine Mechanical section.
2. Remove the primary timing chain. Refer to Timing Chain and Sprockets, Removal & Installation in the Engine Mechanical section.
3. Remove the oil pump bolts and the oil pump.

To install:

4. Align the oil pump generator with the crankshaft flats and install the oil pump to the engine block.
5. Align the pump body with the mounting holes in the cylinder block.

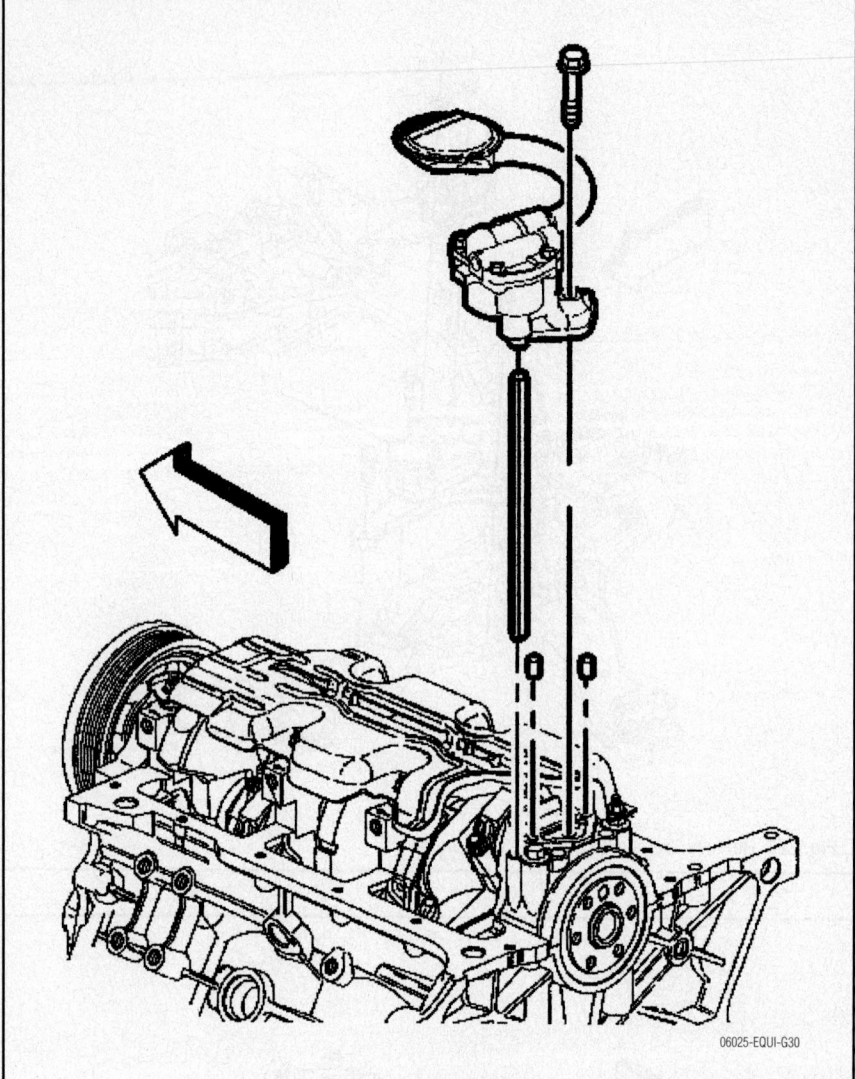

06025-EQUI-G30

Fig. 127 Remove the oil pump mounting bolt to remove the oil pump from the engine.

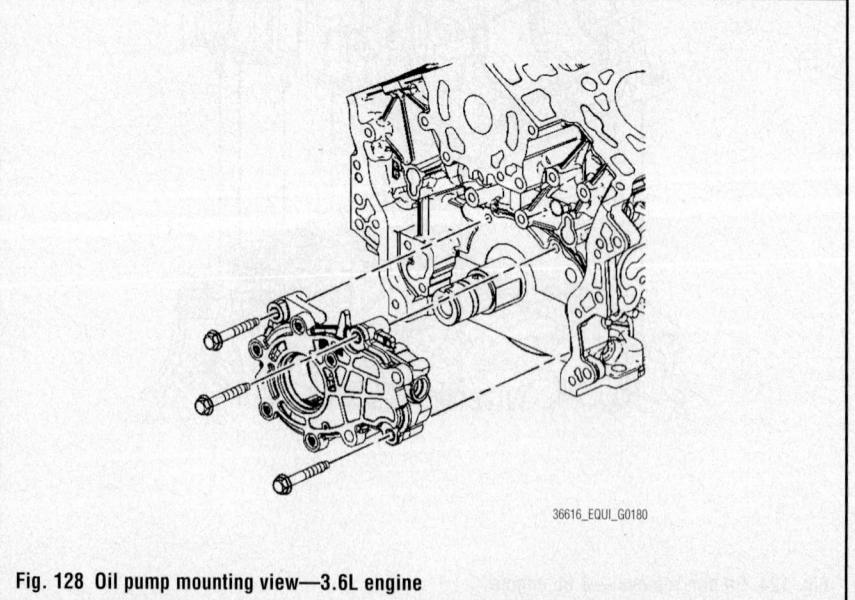

36616_EQUI_G0180

Fig. 128 Oil pump mounting view—3.6L engine

6. Install the oil pump bolts and tighten to 17 ft. lbs. (23 Nm).

7. Install the primary timing chain.

8. Install the front timing cover.

9. Connect the negative battery cable.

PISTON AND RING

POSITIONING

See Figures 129 and 130.

REAR MAIN SEAL

REMOVAL & INSTALLATION

3.4L Engine

See Figures 131 through 137.

➡**A Rear Main Oil Seal Remover Kit is required to remove the rear seal. The use of this kit allows the seal to be easily removed without nicking the crankshaft sealing surface. The kit includes a removal plate, adjustment pins and nuts, a force screw, self-tapping screws and lubricant.**

1. Before servicing the vehicle, refer to the precautions section.

2. Disconnect the negative battery cable.

3. Remove the transaxle assembly. Refer to Transaxle, Removal & Installation in the Drive Train section.

4. Remove the engine flywheel bolts and flywheel. Refer to Flywheel, Removal & Installation in the Engine Mechanical section.

5. Clean the engine flywheel bolt threads and bolt holes.

6. Clean and inspect the engine flywheel.

➡**Do not damage the crankshaft or seal bore.**

7. Remove the engine flywheel.

8. Install the removal plate and both threaded adjustment pins and jam nuts into the back of the crankshaft flange. Secure the plate with the adjustment pins and jam nuts.

9. Install the self-tapping screws into perimeter holes on the removal plate and tighten them so they are flush to the plate.

10. Apply a small amount of the kit-supplied lubricant to the force screw.

11. Install the force screw and back off both jam nuts. Continue to turn the force screw into the removal plate in order to remove the seal from the crankshaft.

12. Once removed, back out and save all of the self-tapping screws and discard the old seal.

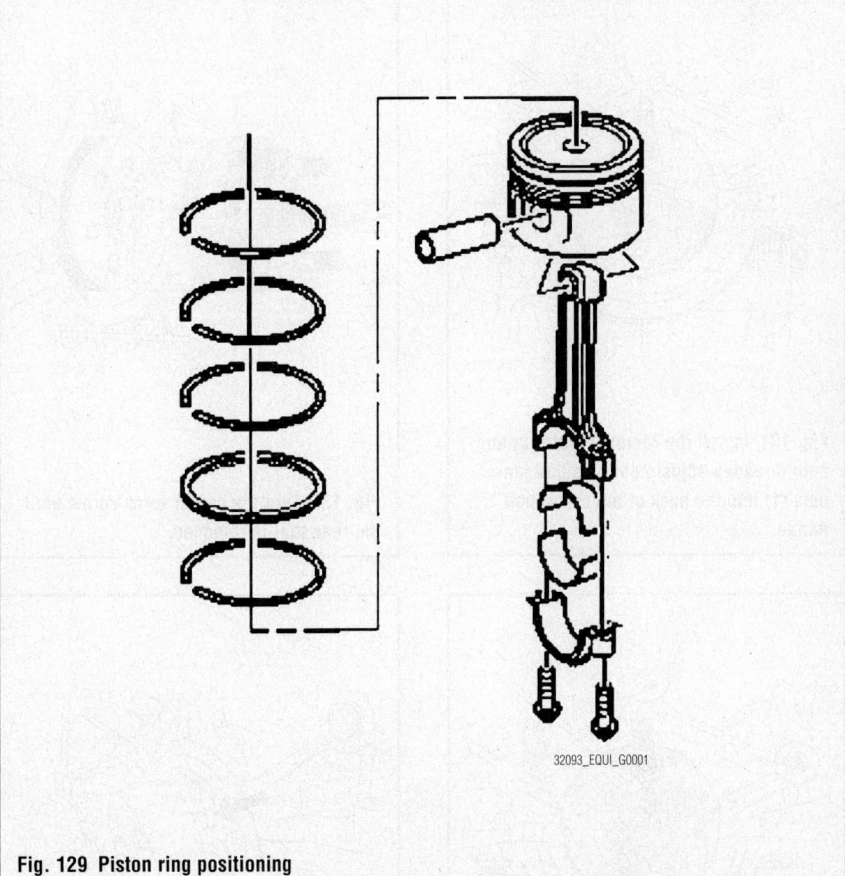

32093_EQUI_G0001

Fig. 129 Piston ring positioning

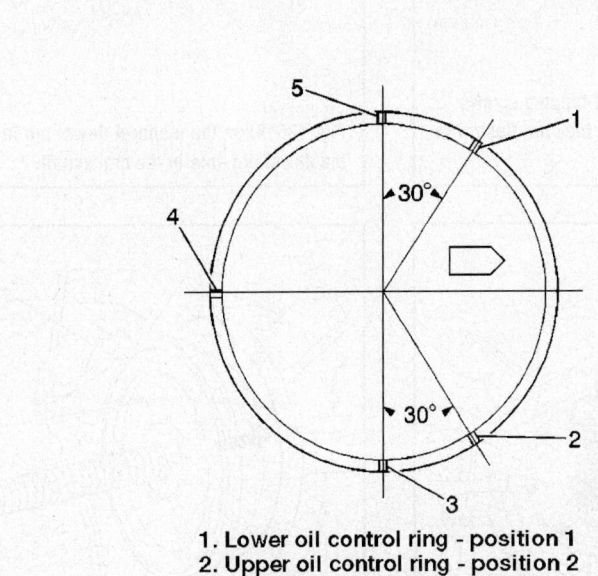

1. Lower oil control ring - position 1
2. Upper oil control ring - position 2
3. Top Ring - position 3
4. Oil control ring expander - position 4
5. Second ring - position 5

36616_EQUI_G0196

Fig. 130 Piston ring gap positioning

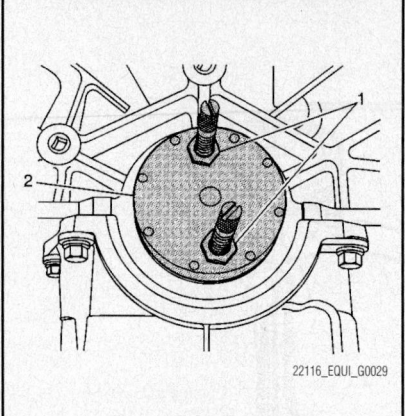

22116_EQUI_G0029

Fig. 131 Install the removal plate (2) and both threaded adjustment pins and jam nuts (1) into the back of the crankshaft flange.

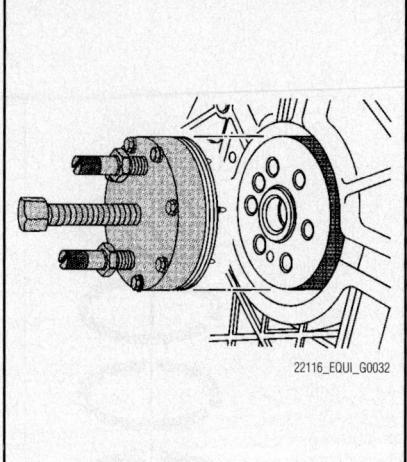

22116_EQUI_G0032

Fig. 134 Turn the center force screw until the rear seal is removed.

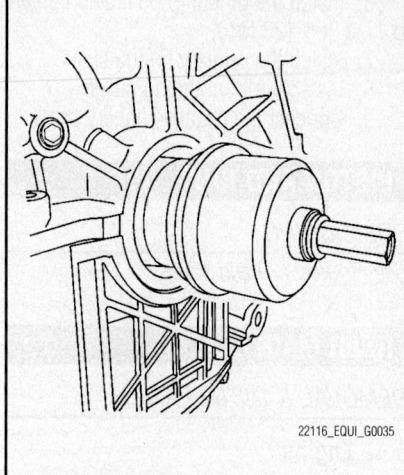

22116_EQUI_G0035

Fig. 137 Install the outer drive drum onto the mandrel.

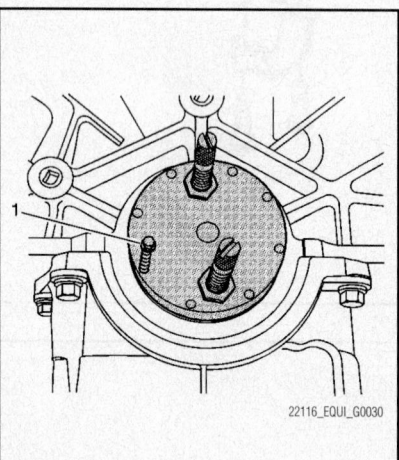

22116_EQUI_G0030

Fig. 132 Install the self-tapping screws (1) and tighten them so they are flush with the removal plate.

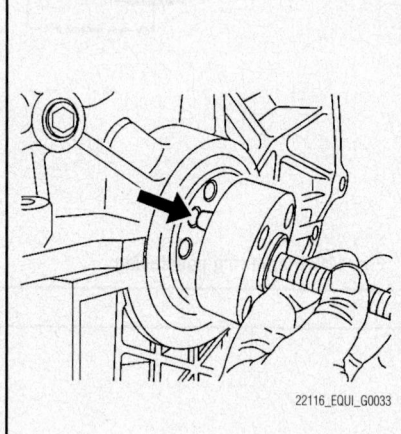

22116_EQUI_G0033

Fig. 135 Align the mandrel dowel pin to the dowel pin hole in the crankshaft.

To install:

➡ A Rear Main Oil Seal Installer Kit is used to install the rear oil seal. The kit includes a mandrel, drive drum, drive nut, washer and bearing.

13. Align the mandrel dowel pin to the dowel pin hole in the crankshaft.

14. Using a large flat-blade screwdriver, tighten the 2 mandrel screws to the crankshaft. Ensure the mandrel is snug to the crankshaft hub.

15. Install the rear main seal, with the protective nylon sleeve attached, onto the mandrel. The seal, if properly installed, will center on a step that protrudes from the center of the mandrel.

❊❊ WARNING

Before installing the outer drive drum, bearing, washer, and drive nut onto the threaded shaft, apply a small amount of the extreme pressure lubricant provided in the tool kit.

16. Install the outer drive drum onto the mandrel.

17. Install the bearing, washer, and drive nut onto the threaded shaft.

18. Using a wrench, turn the drive nut on the mandrel, which will push the seal into the engine block bore. Turn the wrench until the drive drum is snug and flush against the engine block.

19. Loosen and remove the drive nut, washer, bearing, and drive drum. Discard the protective nylon sleeve.

20. Verify that the seal has seated properly.

21. Use a flat-blade screwdriver in order to remove the 2 attachment screws from the

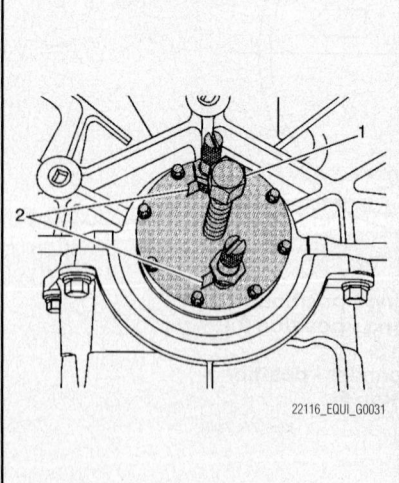

22116_EQUI_G0031

Fig. 133 Install the force screw (1) and then back off the jam nuts (2).

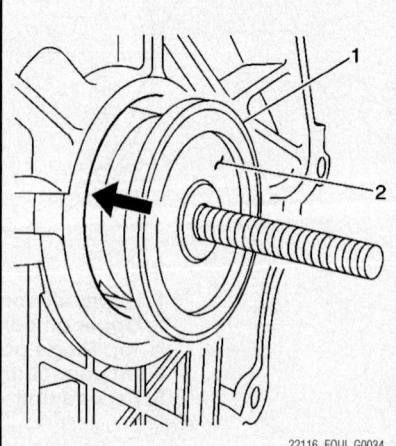

22116_EQUI_G0034

Fig. 136 Install the rear main seal (1), with the protective nylon sleeve attached (2), onto the mandrel.

mandrel and remove the mandrel from the crankshaft hub.

22. Install the flywheel and tighten the bolts to 52 ft. lbs. (71 Nm).

23. Install the transaxle assembly.

24. Connect the negative battery cable.

25. Start the engine and check for leaks.

3.6L Engine

See Figures 138 through 143.

1. Before servicing the vehicle, refer to the precautions section.

2. Disconnect the negative battery cable.

3. Remove the transaxle assembly. Refer to Transaxle, Removal & Installation in the Drive Train section.

4. Remove the oil pan. Refer to Oil Pan Removal & Installation

5. Remove the engine flywheel bolts and flywheel. Refer to Flywheel, Removal & Installation in the Engine Mechanical section.

6. Remove the crankshaft rear oil seal housing bolts.

7. Use the pry points located at the edge of the crankshaft rear oil seal housing to separate the RTV sealant.

8. Remove and discard the crankshaft rear oil seal housing.

To install:

9. Install the 0.236 inch (6 mm) guides from the EN-46109 pin set into the 2 crankshaft rear oil seal housing corner bolt holes of the engine block.

10. Install the EN-47839 tool with the J-42183 handle onto the rear of the crankshaft flange.

11. Place a 0.118 inch (3 mm) bead of RTV sealant, GM P/N 12378521 (Canadian P/N 88901148) or equivalent, to the NEW crankshaft rear oil seal housing as shown.

➡**DO NOT allow any engine oil on the area where the crankshaft rear oil seal housing is to be installed.**

12. Install the crankshaft rear oil seal housing to the engine block.

13. Remove the guide pins from the engine block.

14. Install the crankshaft rear oil seal housing bolts.

15. Tighten the crankshaft rear oil seal housing bolts in sequence to 89 inch lbs. (10 Nm).

16. Remove the EN-47839 tool and J-42183 handle (1, 2) from the crankshaft flange.

17. Install the oil pan.

18. Install the flywheel and tighten the retaining bolts to 22 ft. lbs. (30 Nm) then an additional 45 degrees.

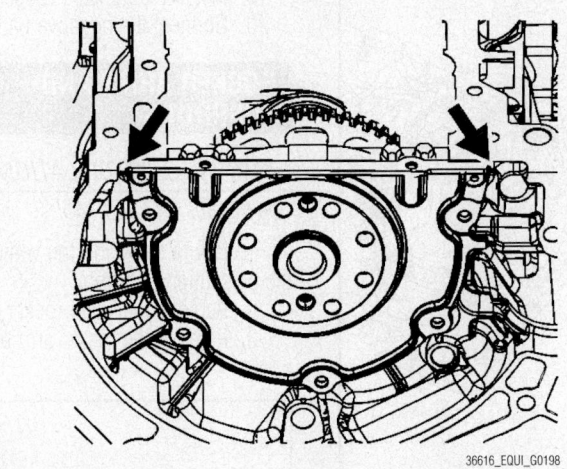

36616_EQUI_G0198

Fig. 138 Crankshaft rear oil seal housing pry points—3.6L engine

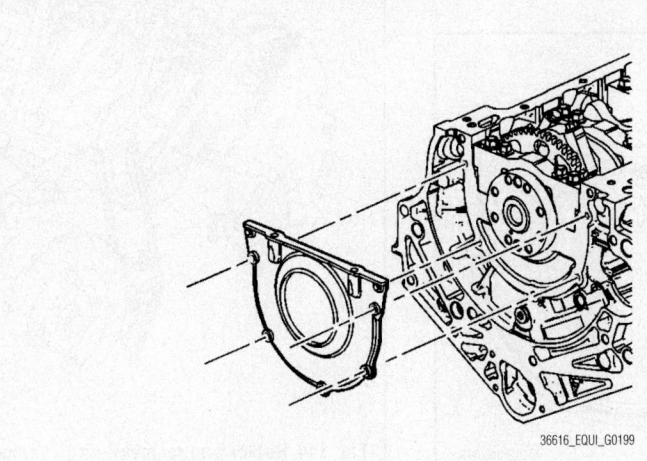

36616_EQUI_G0199

Fig. 139 Remove the crankshaft rear oil seal housing—3.6L engine

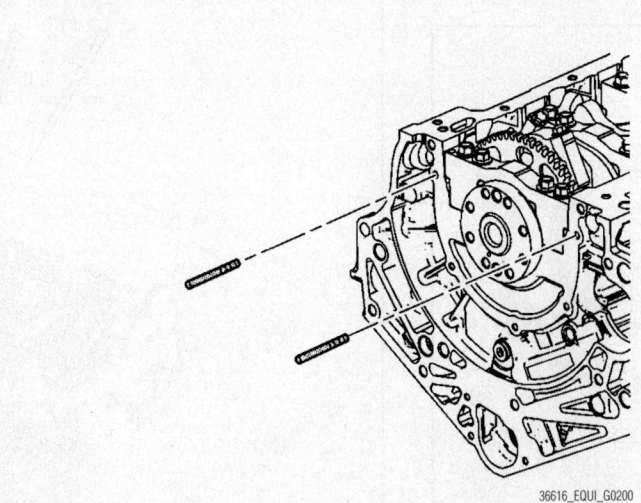

36616_EQUI_G0200

Fig. 140 Install the guide pins into the 2 crankshaft rear oil seal housing corner bolt holes of the engine block

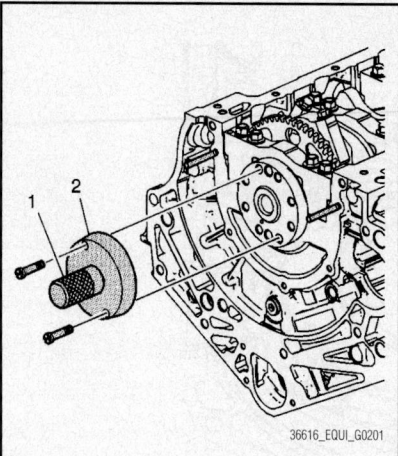

Fig. 141 Install the EN-47839 tool (1) with the J-42183 handle (2) onto the rear of the crankshaft flange.

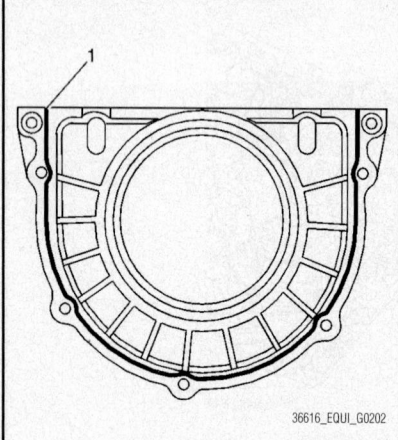

Fig. 142 Place a 0.118 inch (3 mm) bead of RTV sealant on seal housing

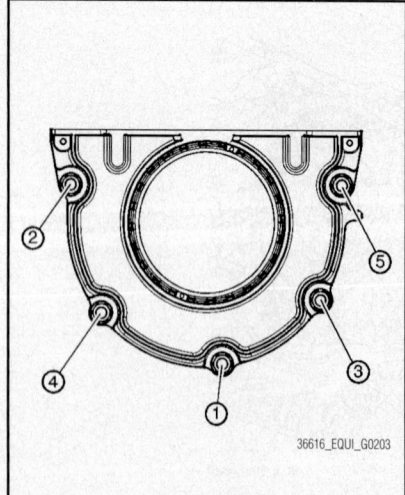

Fig. 143 Rear oil seal housing tightening sequence

19. Install the transaxle assembly.
20. Connect the negative battery cable.

ROCKER ARMS AND PUSHRODS

REMOVAL & INSTALLATION

See Figures 144 and 145.

1. Before servicing the vehicle, refer to the precautions section.
2. Remove the valve rocker arm cover.
3. Remove the rocker arm bolt(s).

4. Remove the valve rocker arm(s) and the pushrod(s).

To install:

5. Coat the ends of the push rods using prelube GM P/N 1052367 (Canadian P/N 992869) or the equivalent.

➡The intake valve push rods measure 5.75 inch (146.0 mm) in length. The exhaust valve push rods measure 6.0 inch (152.5 mm) in length.

6. Install the push rods in their original location.

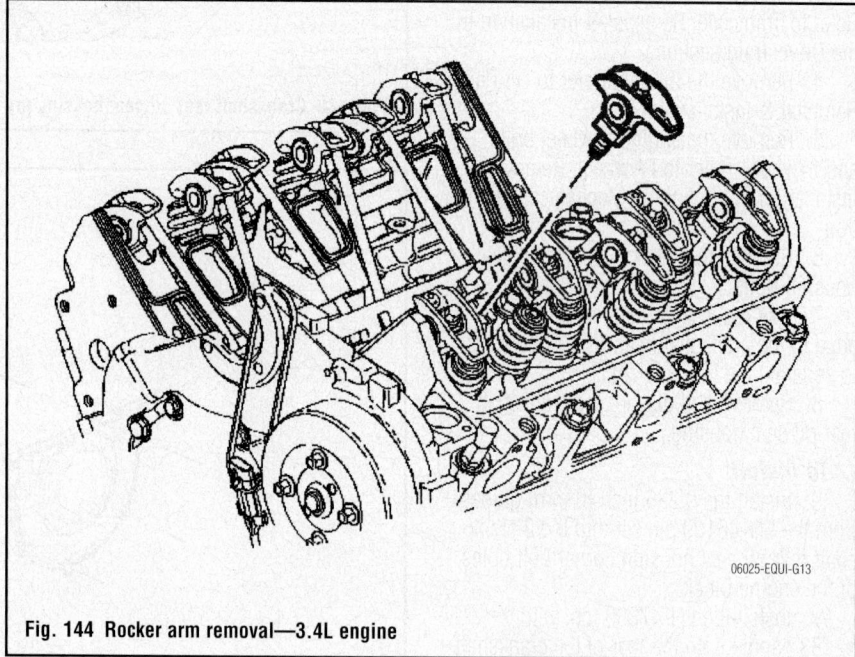

Fig. 144 Rocker arm removal—3.4L engine

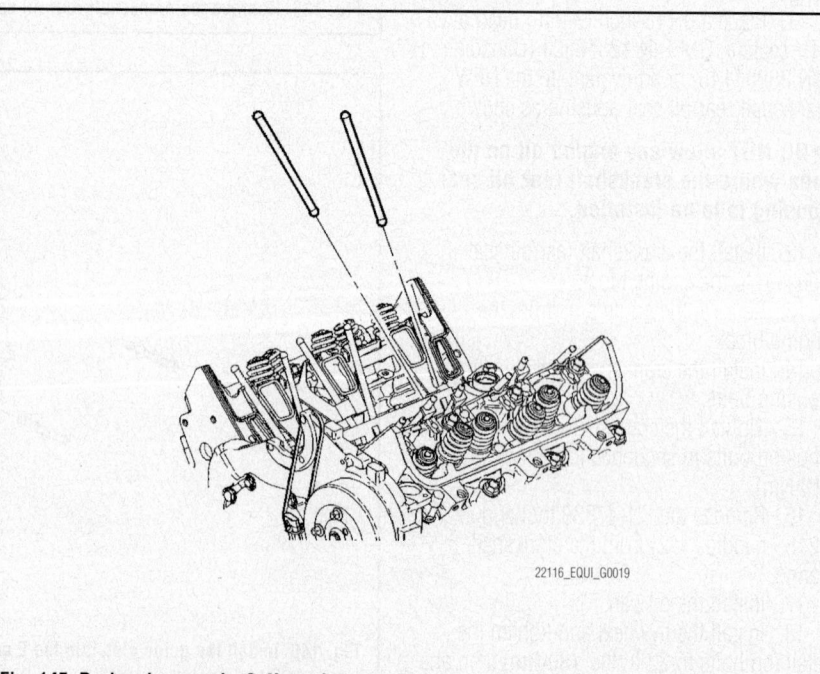

Fig. 145 Push rod removal—3.4L engine

7. Coat the rocker arm friction surfaces using prelube GM P/N 1052367 (Canadian P/N 992869) or the equivalent.

➡**Shims may be required under the valve rocker arm pedestals if reconditioning has been performed on the cylinder head or its components.**

8. Install the valve rocker arms in their original positions.

9. Install the valve rocker arm bolts. Tighten the bolts to 31 ft. lbs. (42 Nm) .

10. Install the valve rocker arm cover.

3.6L Engine

See Figure 146.

1. Before servicing the vehicle, refer to the precautions section.

2. Remove the applicable camshaft(s). Refer to Camshaft and Valve Lifters Removal and Installation, in the Engine Mechanical section.

3. Remove the rocker arms.

4. Clean and inspect the camshaft(s) and the rocker arm(s). Repair or replace as necessary.

To install:

5. Install the rocker arms.

6. Install the applicable camshaft(s).

TIMING CHAIN COVER

REMOVAL & INSTALLATION

3.4L Engine

See Figures 147 through 157.

1. Before servicing the vehicle, refer to the precautions section.

2. Disconnect the negative battery cable.

3. Remove the air cleaner assembly.

4. Remove the engine appearance cover.

5. Pull each end of the hood rear seal away from the cowl panel flange near both strut towers.

6. Replace 2 strut bolts with studs GM P/N 11519137 on right and left sides of the vehicle for installation of support fixture. Tighten the studs to 18 ft. lbs. (25 Nm).

7. Install tool J-28467-13 and J 28467-5 strut tower adapter to the top of the right strut tower.

8. Install tool J-28467-13 and J 28467-5 strut tower adapter to the top of the left strut tower.

9. Install a 50 inch (127 cm) engine support fixture cross bar (2) transversely across the vehicle between both J 28467-5 strut tower adapters.

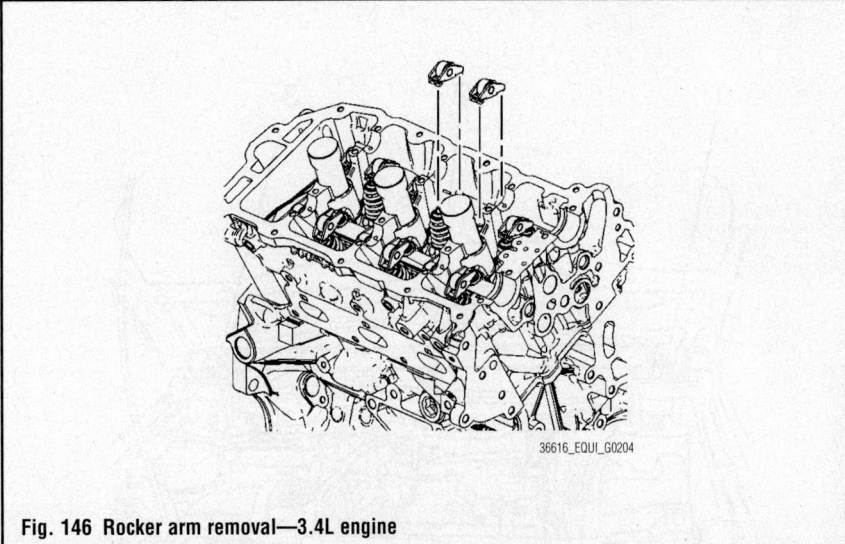

Fig. 146 Rocker arm removal—3.4L engine

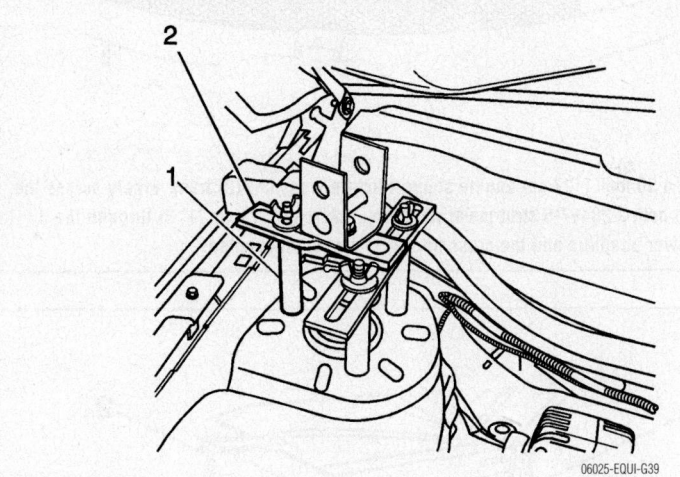

Fig. 147 Install tool J-28467-13 (1) and J 28467-5 strut tower adapter (2) to the top of the right strut tower

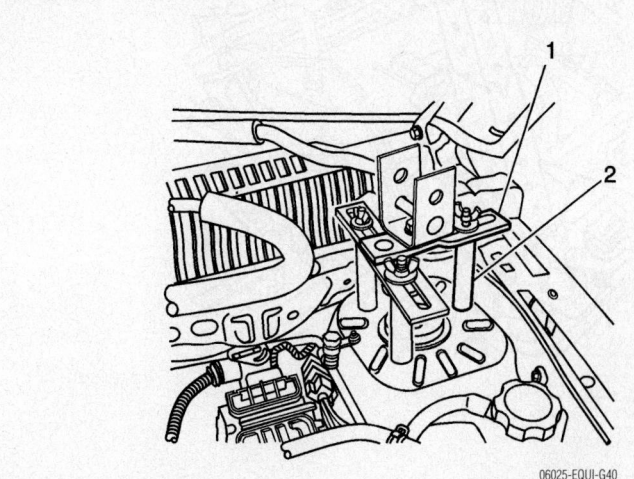

Fig. 148 Install tool J-28467-13 (2) and J 28467-5 strut tower adapter (1) to the top of the left strut tower

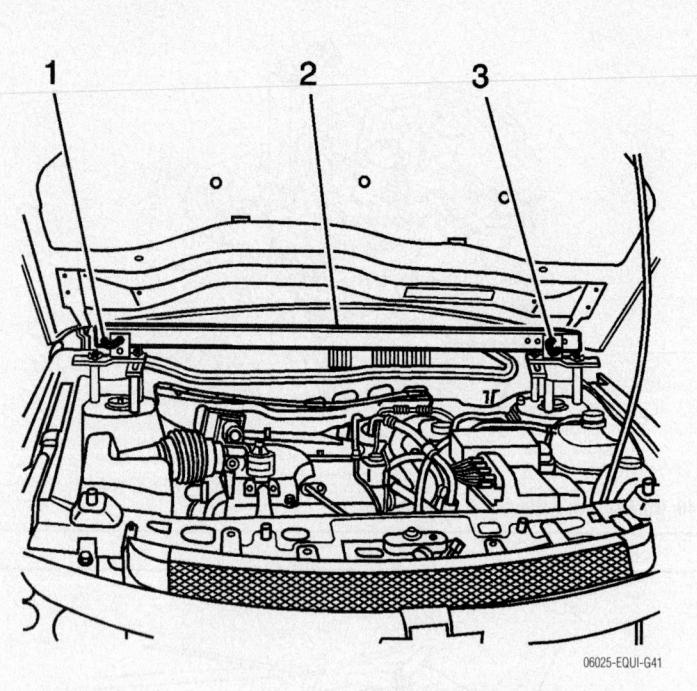

06025-EQUI-G41

Fig. 149 Install a 50 inch (127 cm engine support fixture cross bar (2) transversely across the vehicle between both J 28467-5 strut tower adapters. Insert safety pins (1, 3) through the J 28467-5 strut tower adapters and the cross bar (2) to prevent movement

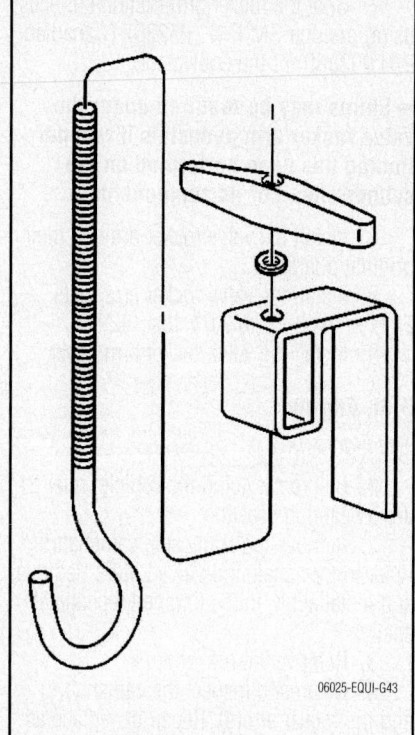

06025-EQUI-G43

Fig. 151 Insert a J 28467-7A lift hook through a J 28467-6 bracket and install a J 28467-34 wing nut

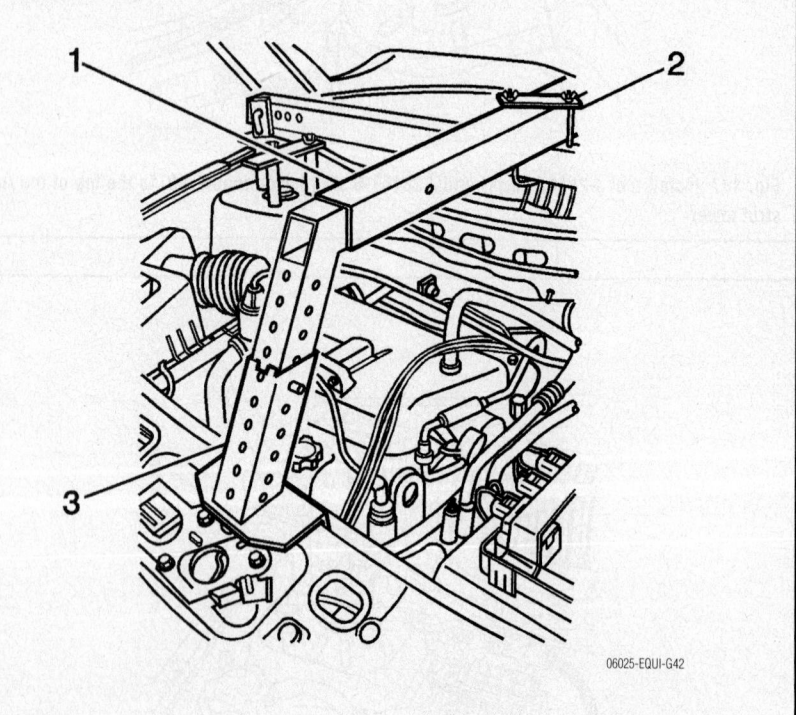

06025-EQUI-G42

Fig. 150 Position a 23 inch (58 cm) engine support fixture cross bar (1) longitudinally with J 36462-A leg assembly (3) next to the rear engine lift bracket. Install a J 28467-1A clamp (2) to secure the longitudinal mounted cross bar to the transverse mounted cross bar

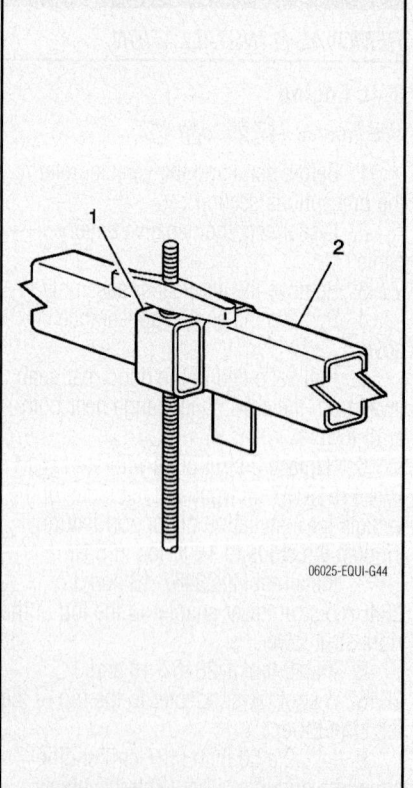

06025-EQUI-G44

Fig. 152 Install the lift hook and bracket assembly (1) to the longitudinal mounted cross bar (2)

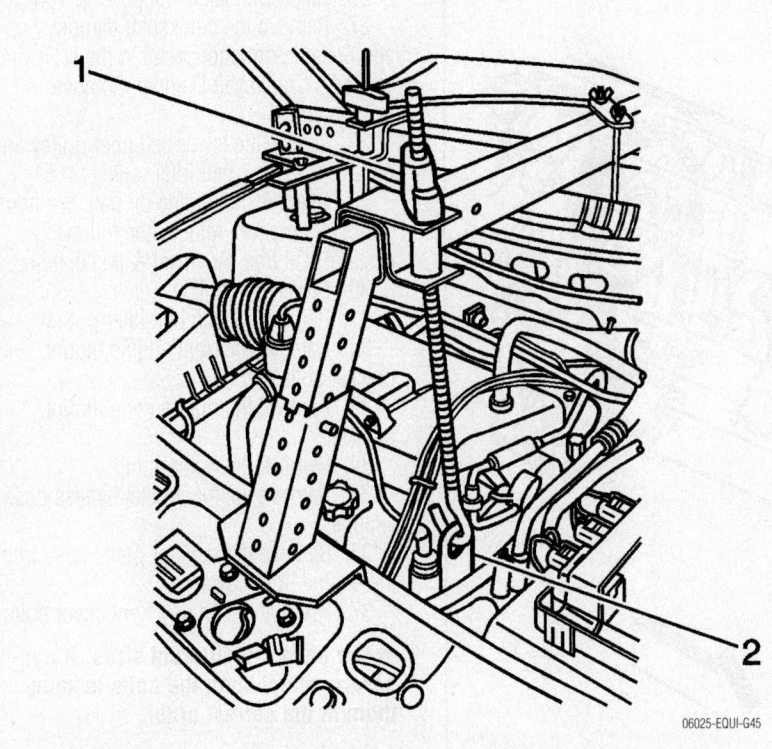

06025-EQUI-G45

Fig. 153 Position the J 28467-7A lift hook to the rear engine lift bracket (2). Tighten the J 28467-34 wing nut (1) until all free slack is removed from the J 28467-7A bolt hook

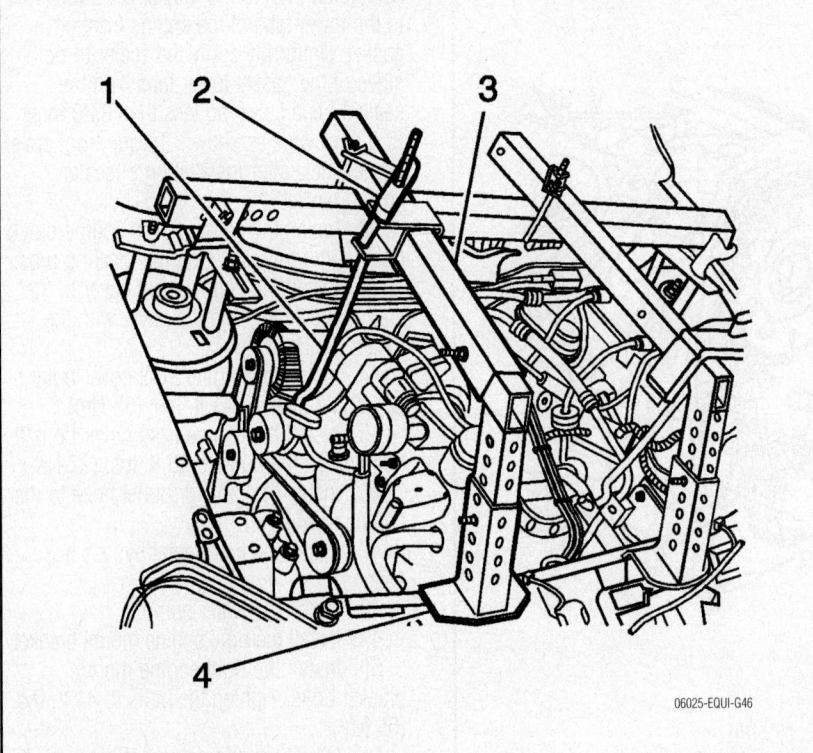

06025-EQUI-G46

Fig. 154 Engine support fixture installed

10. Insert safety pins through the J 28467-5 strut tower adapters and the cross bar to prevent movement.

➡ **If 23 inch (58 cm) length engine support cross bar is not available it may be necessary to remove the vehicle hood for additional clearance if a longer cross bar is to be substituted.**

11. Position a 23 inch (58 cm) engine support fixture cross bar longitudinally with J 36462-A leg assembly next to the rear engine lift bracket.

12. Install a J 28467-1A clamp to secure the longitudinal mounted cross bar to the transverse mounted cross bar.

13. Insert a J 28467-7A lift hook through a J 28467-6 bracket and install a J 28467-34 wing nut.

14. Install the lift hook and bracket assembly to the longitudinal mounted cross bar.

15. Position the J 28467-7A lift hook to the rear engine lift bracket.

16. Tighten the J 28467-34 wing nut until all free slack is removed from the J 28467-7A bolt hook.

➡ **If 23 inch (58 cm) length engine support cross bar is not available it may be necessary to remove the vehicle hood for additional clearance if a longer cross bar is to be substituted.**

17. Position a 23 inch (58 cm) engine support fixture cross bar longitudinally with J 36462-A leg assembly next to the front engine lift bracket.

18. Install a J 28467-1A clamp to secure the longitudinal mounted cross bar to the transverse mounted cross bar.

19. Insert a J 28467-7A lift hook through a J 28467-6 bracket and install a J 28467-34 wing nut.

20. Install the lift hook and bracket assembly to the longitudinal mounted cross bar.

21. Position the J 28467-7A bolt hook to the front engine lift bracket.

22. Tighten the J 28467-34 wing nut until all free slack is removed from the J 28467-7A lift hook.

23. Evenly tighten both wing nuts until the engine weight is supported by the engine support fixture and no longer carried by the engine mounts.

➡ **After removing the engine support fixture, replace the temporary strut studs with the original strut bolts. Tighten the studs to 18 ft. lbs. (25 Nm).**

24. Remove the accessory drive belt.
25. Drain the cooling system.

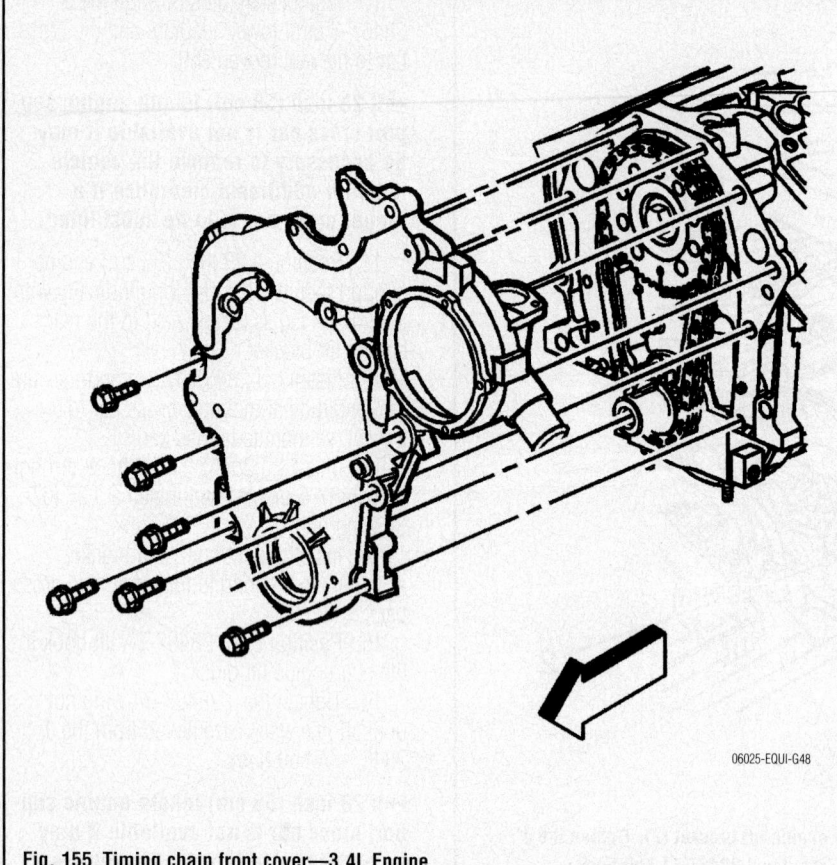

06025-EQUI-G48

Fig. 155 Timing chain front cover—3.4L Engine

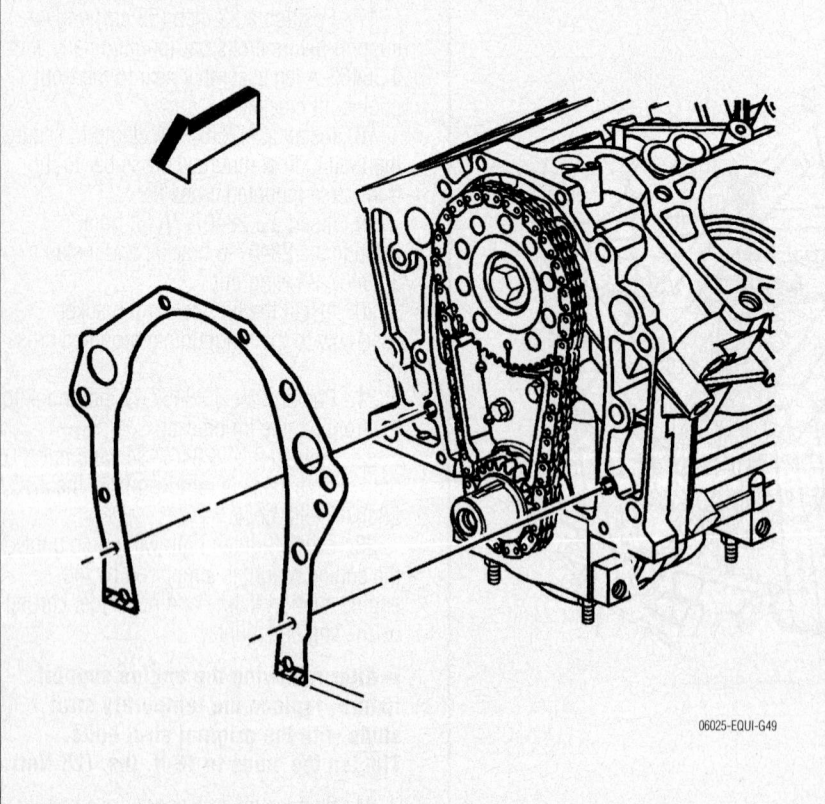

06025-EQUI-G49

Fig. 156 Timing chain front cover gasket—3.4L Engine

26. Raise and safely support the vehicle.

27. Remove the crankshaft damper. For additional information, refer to the following section, "Crankshaft Damper, Removal & Installation."

28. Looser the lower belt idler pulley and remove the lower belt idler pulley.

29. Remove the engine oil pan. For additional information, refer to the following section, "Oil Pan, Removal & Installation."

30. Lower the vehicle.

31. Remove the left belt idler pulley.

32. Remove the right engine mount bracket bolts.

33. Remove the right engine mount bracket.

34. Remove the water pump.

35. Remove the thermostat bypass hose adapter.

36. Remove the radiator outlet hose from the engine front cover.

37. Remove the engine front cover bolts.

➡**The bolts are different sizes. If necessary, matchmark the bolts to keep them in the correct order.**

38. Remove the engine front cover.

39. Remove the engine front cover gasket.

40. Clean the engine block and front cover gasket sealing surfaces.

To install:

41. Apply sealer GM P/N 12346004 (Canadian P/N 10953480) or the equivalent, to the lower tabs of the engine front cover gasket. Uniformly apply the sealer to both sides of the gasket lower tabs with the sealant bead being no less than 0.20 inch (5.0 mm) wide as shown. Torque front cover immediately after installation of sealer coated gasket.

42. Install the gasket to the engine block positioning the gasket on the locating pins.

43. Install the engine front cover to the engine block aligning the cover with the locating pins.

44. Install the engine front cover bolts 3 & 4 and tighten to 41 ft. lbs. (55 Nm).

45. Install the engine front cover bolts 2 and tighten the bolts to 20 ft. lbs. (27 Nm).

46. Install the radiator outlet hose to the engine front cover.

47. Install the thermostat bypass hose adapter.

48. Install the water pump.

49. Install the right engine mount bracket.

50. Install the right engine mount bracket bolts. Tighten the bolts to 41 ft. lbs. (55 Nm).

51. Install the engine mount bracket bolts. Tighten the bolts to 18 ft. lbs. (25 Nm).

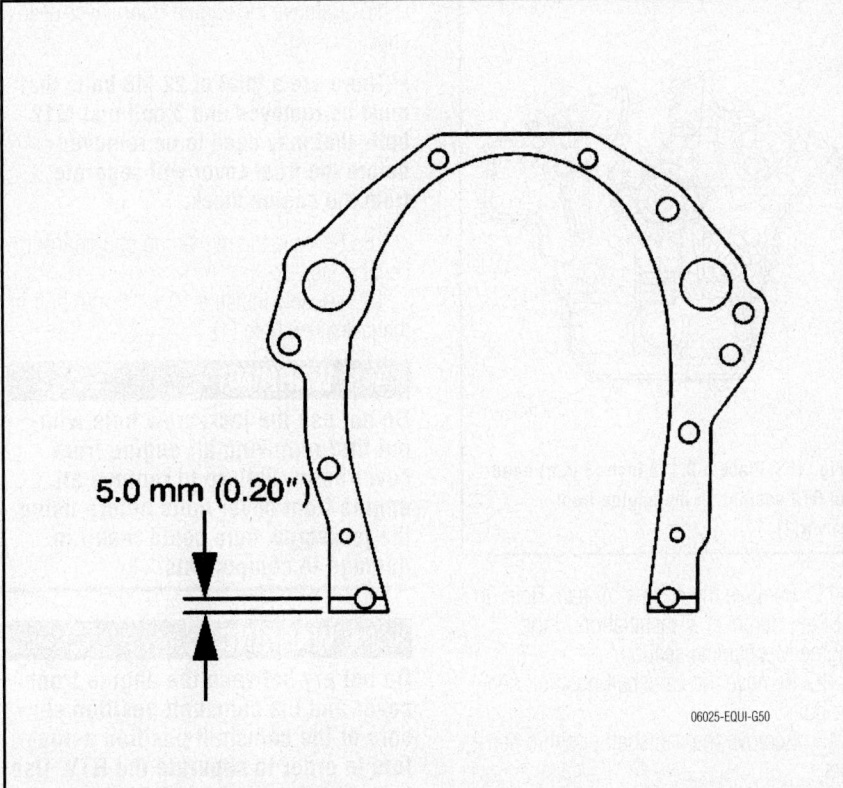

5.0 mm (0.20″)

06025-EQUI-G50

Fig. 157 Apply sealer GM P/N 12346004 (Canadian P/N 10953480) or the equivalent, to the lower tabs of the engine front cover gasket

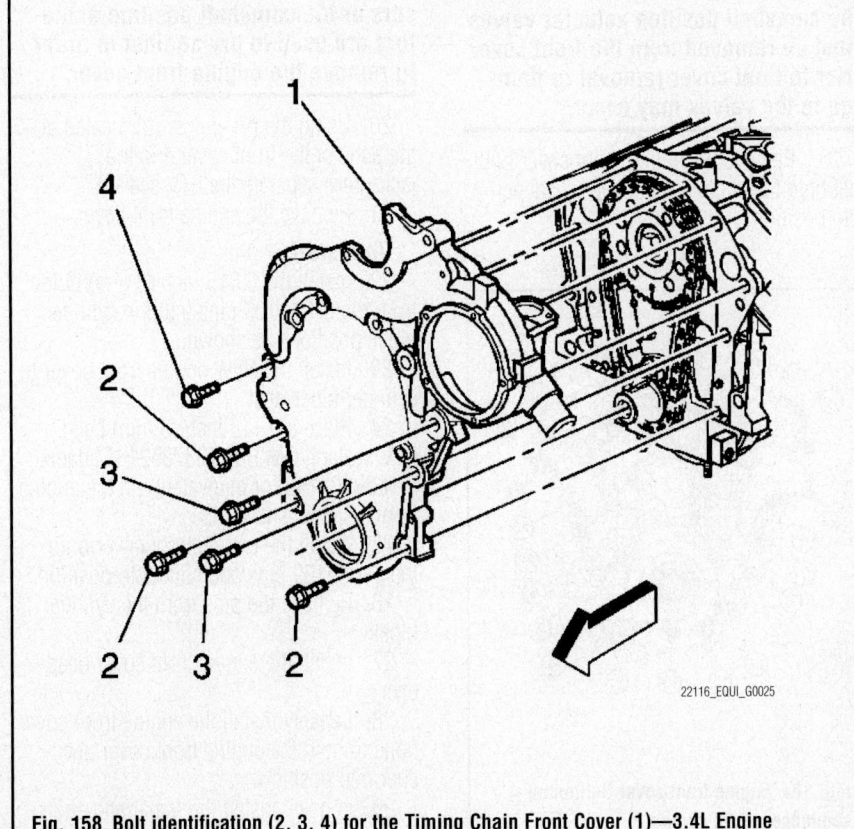

1
4
2
3
2   3   2

22116_EQUI_G0025

Fig. 158 Bolt identification (2, 3, 4) for the Timing Chain Front Cover (1)—3.4L Engine

52. Install the left belt idler pulley.
53. Raise and support the vehicle.
54. Install the engine oil pan.
55. Install the lower belt idler pulley.
56. Install the crankshaft balancer.
57. Lower the vehicle.
58. Install the drive belt.
59. Remove the engine support fixture.
60. Install the air cleaner assembly.
61. Connect the negative battery cable.
62. Fill the cooling system with coolant to the correct level.

3.6L Engine

See Figures 159 through 164.

1. Before servicing the vehicle, refer to the precautions section.
2. Disconnect the negative battery cable.
3. Remove the lower intake manifold. Refer to Intake Manifold, Removal & Installation in the Engine Mechanical Section.
4. Remove the valve covers. Refer to Valve covers, Removal & Installation in the Engine Mechanical Section.
5. Drain the engine coolant.
6. Remove the water outlet housing assembly.
7. Remove the drive belt tensioner.
8. Remove the water pump. Refer to Water Pump, Removal & Installation in the Engine Cooling Section.
9. Remove the power steering pump and position aside. Refer to Power Steering Pump, Removal & Installation in the Steering Section.
10. Remove the crankshaft balancer. Refer to Crankshaft Damper, Removal & Installation in the Engine Mechanical Section.

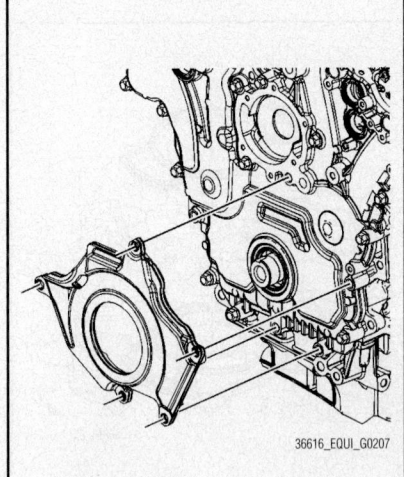

36616_EQUI_G0207

Fig. 159 Engine front cover deadener removal—3.6L engine

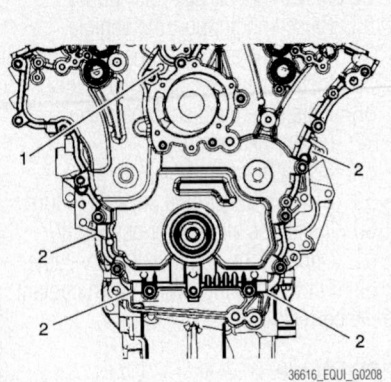

Fig. 160 Using the pry points (2) located at the edge of the front cover and the jackscrew, separate the RTV sealant—3.6L engine

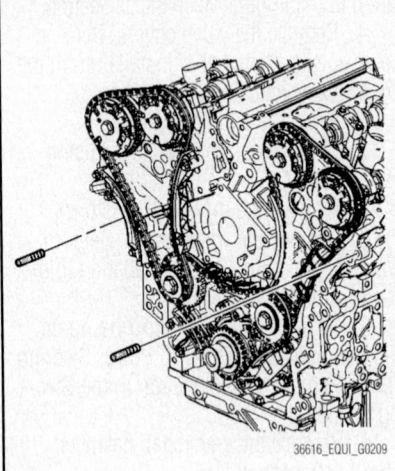

Fig. 161 Guide pin installation shown on the —3.6L engine

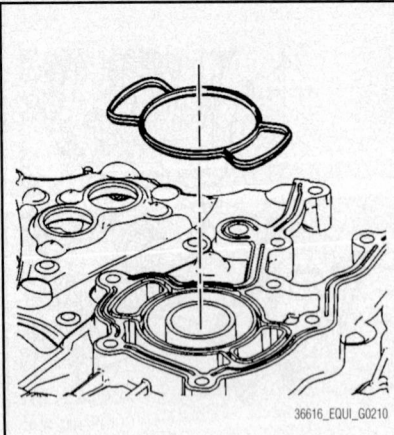

Fig. 162 Engine front cover to cylinder block seal

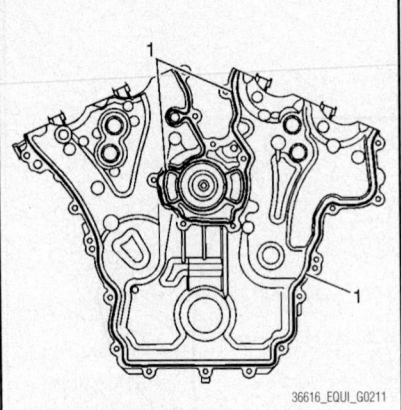

Fig. 163 Place a 0.118 inch (3 mm) bead of RTV sealant on the engine front cover(1)

11. Remove the engine oil pan. Refer to Oil Pan, Removal & Installation in the Engine Mechanical section.

12. Remove the camshaft position sensor bolts.

13. Remove the camshaft position sensors.

14. Remove the camshaft position actuator valve bolts.

15. Remove the camshaft position actuator valves from the front cover.

✳✳ WARNING

The camshaft position actuator valves must be removed from the front cover prior to front cover removal or damage to the valves may occur.

16. Remove the engine front cover bolts that hold the engine front cover deadener into position.

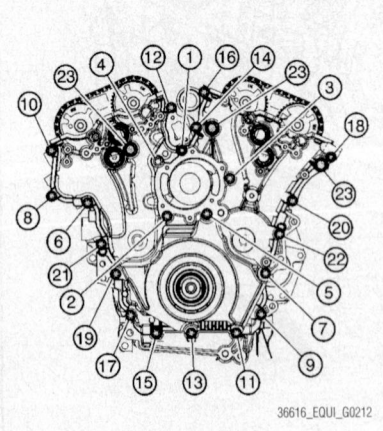

Fig. 164 Engine front cover tightening sequence—3.6L engine

17. Remove the engine front cover deadener.

➡There are a total of 22 M8 bolts that must be removed and 3 optional M12 bolts that may need to be removed before the front cover will separate from the engine block.

18. Remove the remaining engine front cover bolts.

19. Loosely install a 10 x 1.5 mm bolt in the jackscrew hole (1).

✳✳ WARNING

Do not use the jackscrew hole without first removing all engine front cover bolts. Failure to remove all engine front cover bolts before using the jackscrew hole could result in damage to components.

✳✳ WARNING

Do not pry between the engine front cover and the camshaft position sensors or the camshaft position actuators in order to separate the RTV. Use the pry points and a bolt in the jackscrew hole in order to remove the engine front cover. Damage to the camshaft position sensors or the camshaft position actuators may occur if the camshaft position sensors or the camshaft position actuators are used to pry against in order to remove the engine front cover.

20. Using the pry points (2) located at the edge of the front cover and the jackscrew, separate the RTV sealant.

21. Remove the engine front cover.

To install:

22. Install the 0.315 inch (8 mm) guide from the EN-46109 pins into the cylinder block positions as shown.

23. Install the NEW engine front cover to cylinder block seal.

24. Place a 0.118 inch (3 mm) bead of RTV sealant, GM P/N 12378521 (Canadian P/N 88901148) or equivalent, on the engine front cover as shown.

25. Install the engine front cover onto the EN-46109 pins and slide into position.

26. Remove the pins from the cylinder block.

27. Install the engine front cover deadener.

28. Loosely install the engine front cover bolts to hold the engine front cover deadener into position.

29. Loosely install the remaining engine front cover bolts.

30. Tighten the engine front cover bolts in sequence as follows:
- Step 1: Tighten the bolts (1–22) to 14 ft. lbs. (20 Nm).
- Step 2: Tighten the bolts (1–22) an additional 60 degrees.
- Step 3: Tighten the bolts (23) to 48 ft. lbs. (65 Nm).

➡**Engine front cover bolts in the number (23) location are model dependent and may not apply.**

31. Install the camshaft position actuator valves and tighten the bolts to 89 inch lbs. (10 Nm).

32. Install NEW O-rings on the camshaft position sensor.

33. Install the camshaft position sensors and tighten the mounting bolts to 89 inch lbs. (10 Nm).

34. Install the engine oil pan.

35. Install the crankshaft balancer.

36. Install the power steering pump.

37. Install the water pump.

38. Install the water outlet housing assembly.

39. Install the drive belt tensioner.

40. Install the valve covers.

41. Install the lower intake manifold.

42. Connect the negative battery cable.

43. Refill and bleed the cooling system.

44. Start the engine and check for leaks.

TIMING CHAIN AND SPROCKETS

REMOVAL & INSTALLATION

3.4L Engine

See Figures 165 through 168.

1. Before servicing the vehicle, refer to the precautions section.

2. Disconnect the negative battery cable.

3. Remove the timing chain front cover.

4. Remove the camshaft sprocket bolt.

5. Remove the camshaft sprocket and timing chain.

6. Remove the crankshaft sprocket.

7. Remove the timing chain dampener bolts.

8. Remove the timing chain dampener.

To install:

9. Install the crankshaft sprocket.

10. Apply prelube GM P/N 12345501 (Canadian P/N 992704) or the equivalent to the crankshaft sprocket thrust surface.

11. Install the timing chain dampener.

12. Install the timing chain dampener bolts. Tighten the bolt to 15 ft. lbs. (20 Nm).

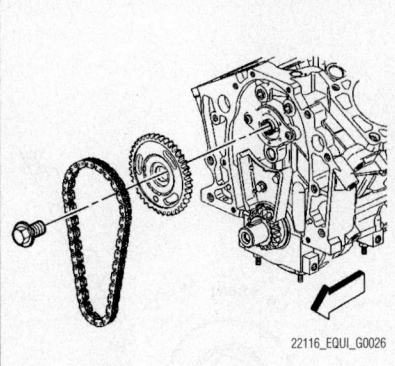

Fig. 165 Removing the camshaft sprocket bolt, timing chain and camshaft sprocket—3.4L Engine

Fig. 166 Removing the crankshaft sprocket—3.4L Engine

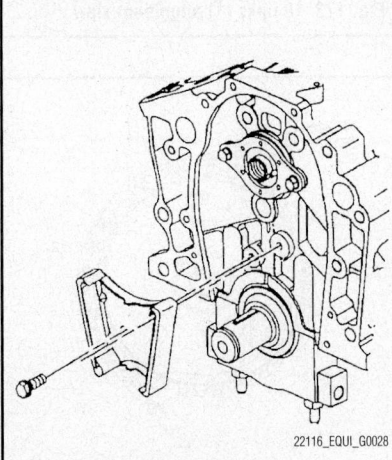

Fig. 167 Removing the timing chain dampener—3.4L Engine

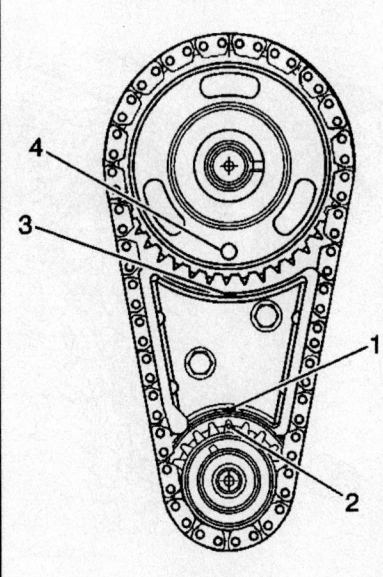

1. Dampener timing mark
2. Crankshaft sprocket timing mark
3. Dampener upper mark
4. Camshaft sprocket timing mark

06025-EQUI-G51

Fig. 168 Aligning the timing marks when installing the timing chain—3.4L Engine

13. Align the crankshaft timing mark to the timing mark on the bottom of the timing chain dampener.

14. Hold the camshaft sprocket with the timing chain hanging down and install the timing chain to the crankshaft gear.

15. Align the timing mark on the camshaft gear with the timing mark on top of the timing chain dampener.

16. Align the dowel in the camshaft with the dowel hole in the camshaft sprocket.

17. Draw the camshaft sprocket onto the camshaft using the mounting bolt.

18. Coat the crankshaft and camshaft sprocket with engine oil. Tighten the bolt to 103 ft. lbs. (140 Nm).

19. Install the timing chain front cover.

20. Connect the negative battery cable.

3.6L Engine

See Figures 169 through 180.

1. Before servicing the vehicle, refer to the precautions section.

2. Disconnect the negative battery cable.

3. Remove the timing chain front cover.

4. Using the special camshaft locking tool EN 46111 , rotate the crankshaft until the left cylinder head camshafts align with

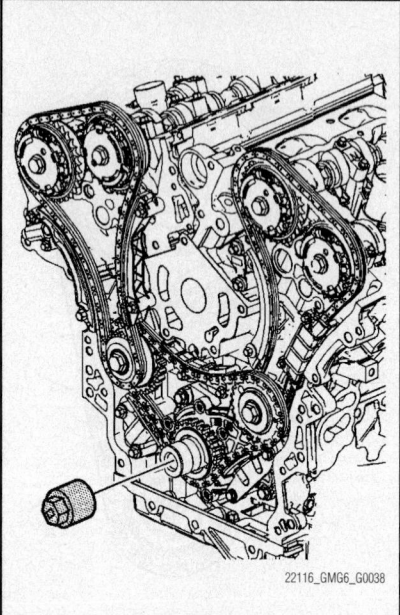

Fig. 169 Rotating crankshaft with tool EN 46111for camshaft alignment—3.6L engine

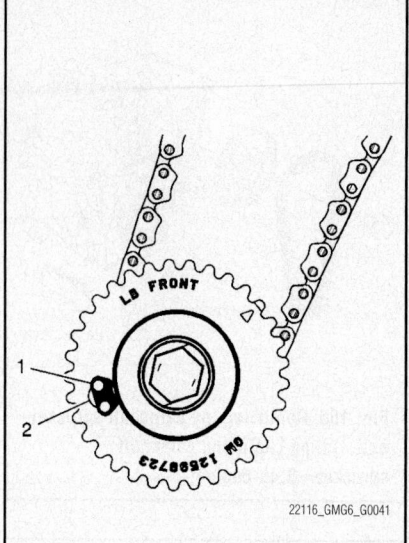

Fig. 172 Left camshaft intermediate drive chain idler outer sprocket and chain alignment.

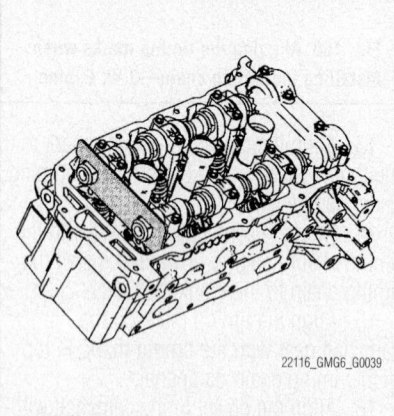

Fig. 170 Right camshaft alignment shown with tool EN 46105—1 left similar

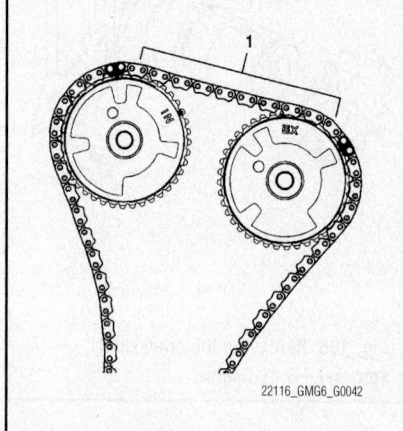

Fig. 173 10 links (1) alignment view

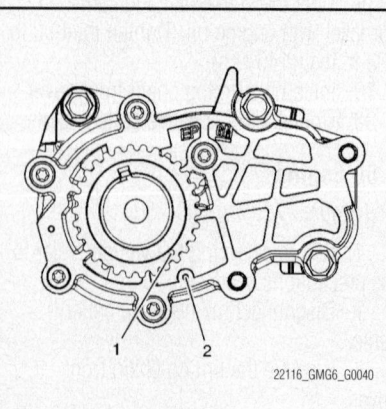

Fig. 171 Crankshaft sprocket (1) and oil pump (2) alignment marks

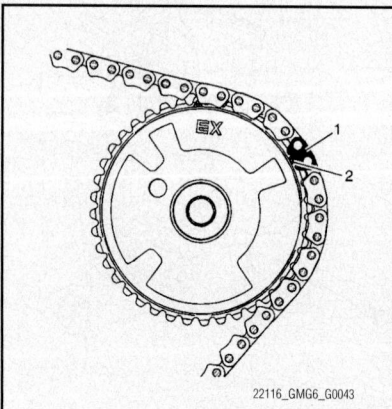

Fig. 174 Exhaust camshaft alignment marks

the EN 46105-2 tool and the right cylinder head camshafts align with the EN 46105-1.

5. Install the EN 46105-1 to the right camshafts.

6. Install the EN 46105-2 to the left camshafts.

7. Remove the right secondary camshaft drive chain from the right camshaft position actuators and the right camshaft intermediate drive chain idler sprocket.

8. Remove the primary camshaft drive chain.

9. Remove the left secondary camshaft drive chain tensioner bolts.

10. Remove the left secondary camshaft drive chain tensioner.

11. Remove and discard the left secondary camshaft drive chain tensioner gasket.

➡**Inspect the left secondary camshaft drive chain tensioner mounting surface on the left cylinder head for burrs or any defects that would degrade the sealing of the new left secondary camshaft drive chain tensioner gasket.**

12. Remove the left secondary camshaft drive chain shoe bolt.

13. Remove the left secondary camshaft drive chain shoe.

14. Remove the left secondary camshaft drive chain guide bolts.

15. Remove the left secondary camshaft drive chain guide.

16. Remove the left camshaft intermediate drive chain idler bolt

17. Remove the left camshaft intermediate drive chain idler.

18. Remove the left secondary camshaft drive chain from the left camshaft position actuators and the left camshaft intermediate drive chain idler sprocket.

19. Clean and inspect all of the camshaft timing drive components.

To install:

✳✳ WARNING

All camshafts must be locked in place before installation of any camshaft drive chains.

20. Ensure that the EN 46105-1 is fully seated onto the camshafts.

21. Ensure the crankshaft is in the stage one timing position with the crankshaft sprocket timing mark (1) aligned to the stage one timing mark on the oil pump cover (2) using the EN-48589.

22. Install the left secondary camshaft drive chain.

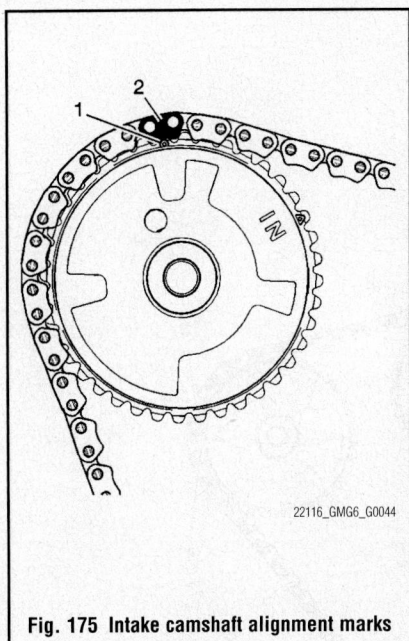

Fig. 175 Intake camshaft alignment marks

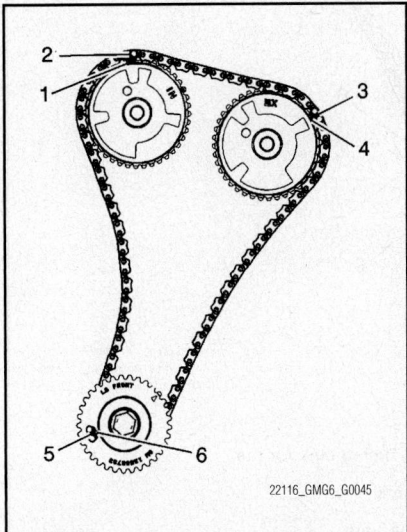

Fig. 176 Left secondary camshaft drive chain timing mark alignments (1—6)

23. Place the left secondary camshaft drive chain around the inner sprocket of the left camshaft intermediate drive chain idler with the timing camshaft drive chain link (1) aligned to the alignment access hole (2) made in the left camshaft intermediate drive chain idler outer sprocket.

24. Wrap the secondary camshaft drive chain around both left actuator drive sprockets.

25. Ensure there are 10 links (1) between the timing camshaft drive chain links for the camshaft position actuator sprockets.

26. Align the left exhaust camshaft position actuator sprocket alignment circle mark (2) with the timing camshaft drive chain link (1).

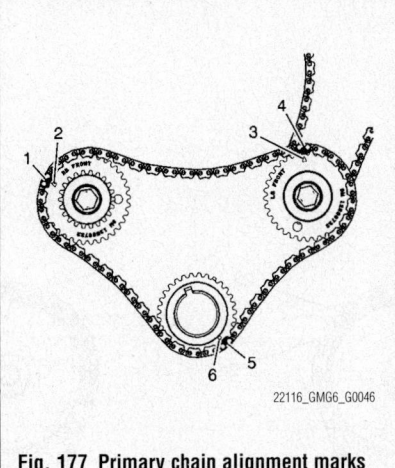

Fig. 177 Primary chain alignment marks

27. Align the left intake camshaft position actuator sprocket alignment circle mark (1) with the timing camshaft drive chain link (2).

28. Ensure that the left camshaft intermediate drive chain idler is being installed. The recessed hub and the larger sprocket of the left camshaft intermediate drive chain idler is installed outward. The raised hub and the smaller sprocket of the left camshaft intermediate drive chain idler is installed towards the block.

29. Place the left camshaft intermediate drive chain idler to the cylinder block.

30. Install the camshaft intermediate drive chain idler bolt and tighten to 43 ft. lbs. (58 Nm).

31. Position the left secondary camshaft drive chain guide.

32. Install the secondary camshaft drive chain guide bolts and tighten to 17 ft. lbs. (23 Nm).

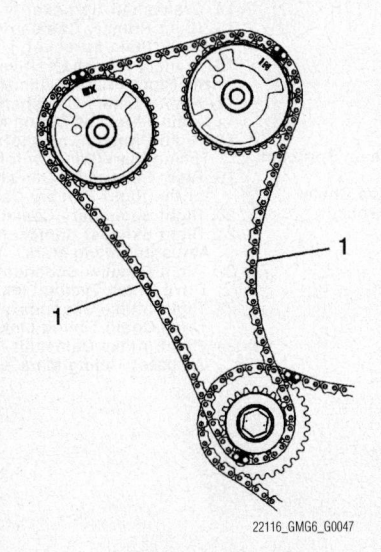

Fig. 178 Secondary drive chain alignment marks

33. Position the left secondary camshaft drive chain shoe.

34. Install the secondary camshaft drive chain shoe bolt and tighten to 17 ft. lbs. (23 Nm).

35. Using the J 45027 , reset the left secondary camshaft drive chain tensioner plunger.

36. Install the plunger into the left secondary camshaft drive chain tensioner body.

37. Compress the plunger into the body and lock the left secondary camshaft drive chain tensioner by inserting the EN 46112 into the access hole in the side of the left secondary camshaft drive chain tensioner body.

38. Slowly release pressure on the left secondary camshaft drive chain tensioner. The left secondary camshaft drive chain tensioner should remain compressed.

39. Install a NEW left secondary camshaft drive chain tensioner gasket to the left secondary camshaft drive chain tensioner.

40. Install the left secondary camshaft drive chain tensioner bolts through the left secondary camshaft drive chain tensioner and gasket.

41. Ensure the left secondary camshaft drive chain tensioner mounting surface on the left cylinder head does not have any burrs or defects that would degrade the sealing of the NEW left secondary camshaft drive chain tensioner gasket.

42. Place the left secondary camshaft drive chain tensioner into position and loosely install the bolts to the block.

43. Verify the proper placement of the left secondary camshaft drive chain tensioner gasket tab.

44. Tighten the left secondary camshaft drive chain tensioner bolts in two steps:

    a. Tighten tensioner bolts to 44 inch lbs. (5 Nm).

    b. Tighten tensioner bots an additional 17 ft. lbs. (23 Nm).

45. Release the left secondary camshaft drive chain tensioner by pulling out the EN 46112 pin and unlocking the tensioner plunger.

46. Verify the left secondary camshaft drive chain timing mark alignments.

✳✳ WARNING

Ensure that the crankshaft is in the stage one timing drive assembly position.

47. Install the primary camshaft drive chain.

48. Wrap the primary camshaft drive chain around the large sprockets of each

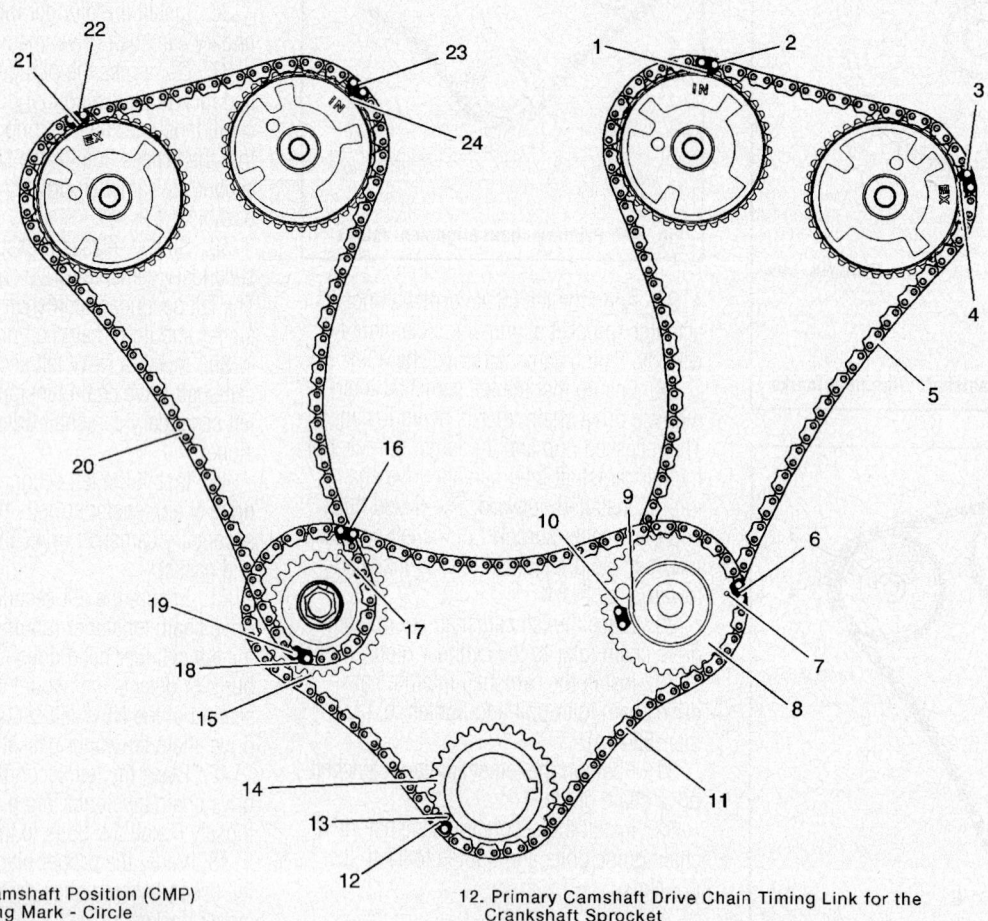

1. Left Intake Camshaft Position (CMP)
   Actuator Timing Mark - Circle
2. Left Intake Secondary Camshaft
   Timing Drive Chain Timing Link
3. Left Exhaust Secondary Camshaft
   Timing Drive Chain Timing Link
4. Left Exhaust Camshaft Position (CMP)
   Actuator Timing Mark - Circle
5. Left Secondary Camshaft Timing
   Drive Chain
6. Primary Camshaft Drive Chain Timing Link
   for the Left Primary Camshaft Intermediate Drive Chain Sprocket
7. Left Primary Camshaft Intermediate Drive Chain
   Sprocket Timing Mark for the Primary Camshaft Drive Chain
8. Left Primary Camshaft Intermediate Drive Chain Sprocket
9. Left Secondary Camshaft Timing Drive Chain
   Timing Link for the Left Primary Camshaft
   Intermediate Drive Chain Sprocket
10. Left Primary Camshaft Intermediate
    Drive Chain Sprocket Timing Window
11. Primary Camshaft Drive Chain

12. Primary Camshaft Drive Chain Timing Link for the
    Crankshaft Sprocket
13. Crankshaft Sprocket Timing Mark
14. Crankshaft Sprocket
15. Right Primary Camshaft Intermediate
    Drive Chain Sprocket
16. Primary Camshaft Drive Chain Timing Link for
    the Right Primary Camshaft Intermediate Drive Chain Sprocket
17. Right Primary Camshaft Intermediate Drive
    Chain Sprocket Timing Mark for the Primary Camshaft Drive Chain
18. Right Primary Camshaft Intermediate Drive Chain Sprocket
    Timing Mark/Window for the Right Secondary Camshaft Timing Drive Chain
19. Right Secondary Camshaft Timing Drive Chain Timing Link
    for the Right Primary Camshaft Intermediate Drive Chain Sprocket
20. Right Secondary Camshaft Timing Drive Chain
21. Right Exhaust Camshaft Position (CMP)
    Actuator Timing Mark - Triangle
22. Right Exhaust Secondary Camshaft Timing
    Drive Chain Timing Link
23. Right Intake Secondary Camshaft Timing
    Drive Chain Timing Link
24. Right Intake Camshaft Position (CMP)
    Actuator Timing Mark - Triangle

22116_GMG6_G0048

Fig. 179 Timing drive chain alignment diagram (Fourth Design)—3.6L engine

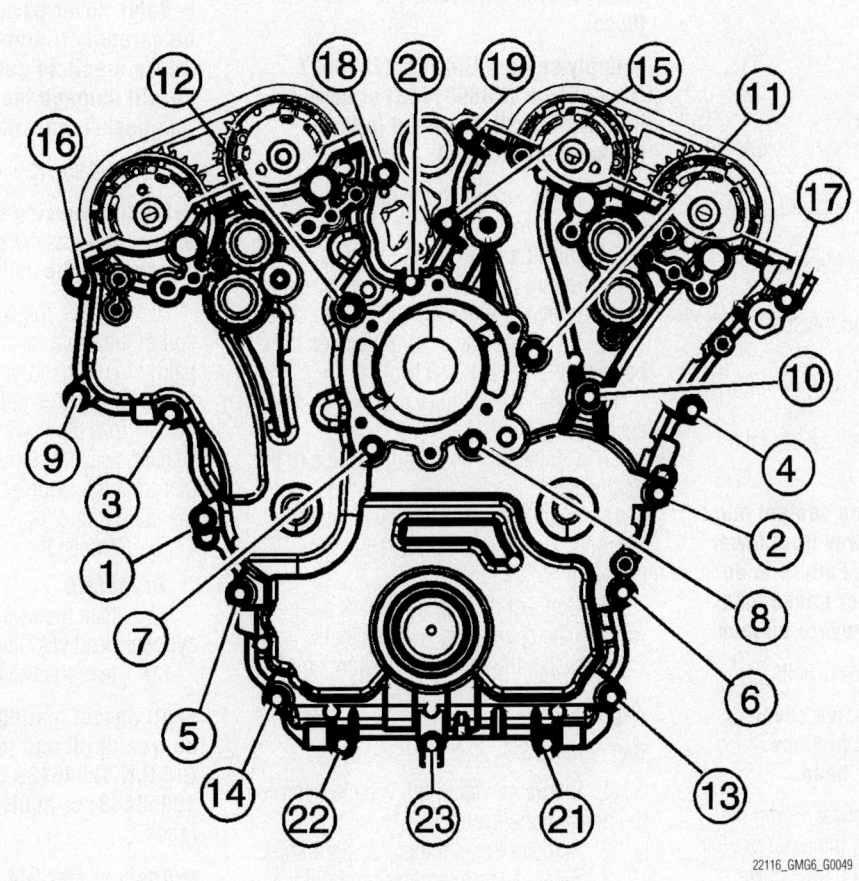

22116_GMG6_G0049

Fig. 180 Engine front cover tightening sequence—3.6L engine

camshaft intermediate drive chain idler and the crankshaft sprocket.

49. The left camshaft intermediate drive chain idler timing mark (1) will align with a timing camshaft drive chain link (2).

50. The right camshaft intermediate drive chain idler timing mark (2) will align with a timing camshaft drive chain link (1).

51. The crankshaft sprocket timing mark (2) will align with a timing camshaft drive chain link (1).

52. Ensure all the timing marks (2, 3, and 6) are properly aligned with the timing camshaft drive chain links (1, 4, and 5).

53. Ensure that the crankshaft is in the stage 2 timing drive assembly position (1).

54. Install the right secondary camshaft drive chain.

55. Place the secondary camshaft drive chain around the right camshaft intermediate drive chain idler outer sprocket, aligning

the timing camshaft drive chain link (1) with the alignment access hole (2) made in the right camshaft intermediate drive chain idler inner sprocket.

56. Wrap the secondary camshaft drive chain around both right actuator drive sprockets.

57. Ensure there are 10 links (1) between the timing camshaft drive chain links for the camshaft position actuator sprockets

58. Align the right exhaust camshaft position actuator sprocket alignment triangle mark (1) with the timing camshaft drive chain link (2).

59. Align the right intake camshaft position actuator sprocket alignment triangle mark (2) with the timing camshaft drive chain link (1).

60. There will be 22 links (1) between the right camshaft intermediate drive chain

idler timing camshaft drive chain link and each right camshaft position actuator sprocket timing camshaft drive chain link.

61. Install the 0.315 inch. (8 mm) guide pins from the EN 46109 into the cylinder block.

62. Install the engine front cover to cylinder block seal.

63. Place a 3 mm (0.118 in) bead of RTV sealant, or equivalent, on the engine front cover.

64. Place the engine front cover onto the guide pins EN 46109 and slide into position.

65. Remove the EN 46109 guide pins.

66. Hand start all the front cover bolts.

67. Tighten the engine front cover bolts in sequence to 17 ft. lbs. (23 Nm).

68. Fill and bleed the cooling system.

69. Start the engine and check for leaks.

VALVE COVERS

REMOVAL & INSTALLATION

3.4L Engine

Left Side

See Figure 181.

1. Before servicing the vehicle, refer to the precautions section.
2. Remove the engine appearance cover.
3. Disconnect the left side spark plug wires from the retainers.
4. Remove the bolt and the spark plug wire support.
5. Disconnect the PCV foul air pipe from the PCV valve.
6. Remove the oil filler cap from the valve rocker arm cover.

➡ **Valve cover gasket and sealant must be carefully trimmed away from lower intake manifold gasket. Failure to do so will damage the lower intake manifold gasket, causing a severe oil leak.**

7. Loosen the valve cover bolts.

➡ **When removing the valve cover, ensure the gasket stays in place attached to the cylinder head.**

8. Remove the valve cover. Bump the end of the valve cover with the palm of your hand or a soft rubber mallet if the cover adheres to the cylinder head.
9. Trim the valve cover gasket and sealant away from the lower intake manifold gasket at the cylinder head to the lower intake manifold joints.
10. Remove the rocker arm cover gasket.

To install:

11. Clean the sealing surface on the cylinder head with degreaser.
12. Clean the valve cover.

➡ **All gasket mating surfaces need to be free of oil and foreign material. Use GM P/N 12346139 (Canadian P/N 10953463) or equivalent to clean surfaces.**

➡ **Apply sealant GM P/N 12378521 (Canadian P/N 88901148) or equivalent, at the cylinder head to lower intake manifold joint.**

13. Apply sealant at the cylinder head to lower intake manifold joints.
14. Install a new gasket to the valve cover. Ensure the gasket is properly seated in the groove of the valve rocker arm cover.
15. Install the valve cover. Tighten the bolts to 89 inch lbs. (10 Nm).
16. Install the oil filler cap to the valve cover.
17. Connect the PCV foul air pipe to the PCV valve.
18. Install the spark plug wire support and bolt. Tighten the bolt to 18 ft. lbs. (25 Nm).
19. Connect the left side spark plug wires to the spark plug wire retainers.
20. Install the fuel injector sight shield.

Right Side

See Figure 182.

1. Before servicing the vehicle, refer to the precautions section.
2. Remove the fuel injector sight shield.
3. Remove the alternator mounting bracket.
4. Remove the ignition control module bracket from the engine with the ignition control module and spark plug wires still attached. Position out of the way.

5. Disconnect the Positive Crankcase Ventilation (PCV) fresh air pipe from the right valve cover.

➡ **Valve cover gasket and sealant must be carefully trimmed away from lower intake manifold gasket. Failure to do so will damage the lower intake manifold gasket, causing a severe oil leak.**

6. Loosen the valve cover bolts.

➡ **When removing the valve cover, ensure the gasket stays in place attached to the cylinder head.**

7. Remove the valve cover. Bump the end of the valve rocker arm cover with the palm of your hand or a soft rubber mallet if the cover adheres to the cylinder head.
8. Trim the valve cover gasket and sealant away from the lower intake manifold gasket at the cylinder head to lower intake manifold joints.
9. Remove the valve cover gasket.

To install:

10. Clean the sealing surface on the cylinder head with degreaser.
11. Clean the valve cover.

➡ **All gasket mating surfaces need to be free of oil and foreign material. Use GM P/N 12346139 (Canadian P/N 10953463) or equivalent to clean surfaces.**

➡ **Apply sealer GM P/N 12378521 (Canadian P/N 88901148) or equivalent, at the cylinder head to lower intake manifold joint.**

12. Apply sealant at the cylinder head to lower intake manifold joints.
13. Install a new gasket to the valve cover. Ensure the gasket is properly seated in the groove of the valve cover.
14. Install the valve cover. Tighten the bolts to 89 inch lbs. (10 Nm).
15. Connect the PCV fresh air pipe to the right valve rocker arm cover.
16. Install the ignition control module bracket with the ignition control module and spark plug wired still attached.
17. Install the alternator bracket. Torque to 37 ft. lbs. (50 Nm).
18. Install the fuel injector sight shield.

3.6L Engine

Left Side

See Figures 183 through 185.

1. Before servicing the vehicle, refer to the precautions section.
2. Disconnect the negative battery cable.

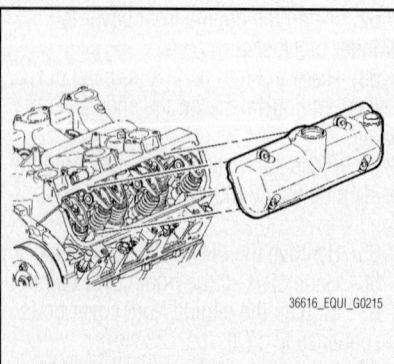

Fig. 181 Valve cover removal—3.4L engine

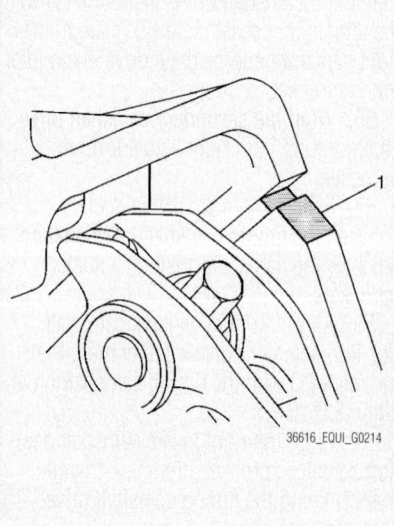

Fig. 182 Apply sealant at the cylinder head to lower intake manifold joints (1)

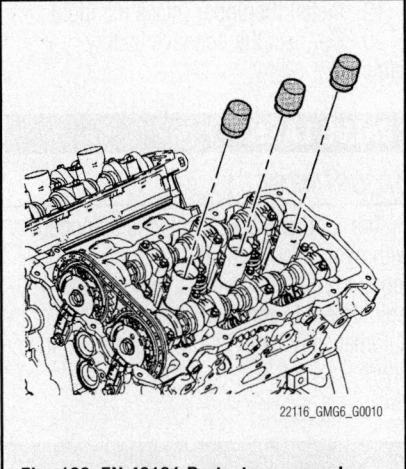

Fig. 183 EN 46101 Protectors —spark plug tubes

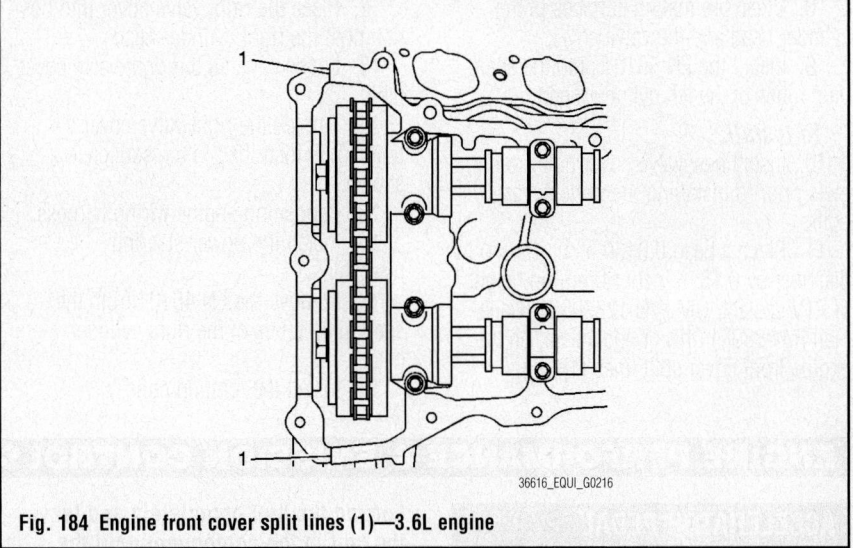

Fig. 184 Engine front cover split lines (1)—3.6L engine

3. Remove the ignition coils.

4. Remove the left valve cover bolts.

5. Remove the left valve cover from the left cylinder head.

6. Clean the mating surfaces of the cylinder head and the camshaft cover.

7. Install the EN 46101 onto the spark plug tubes of the left cylinder head.

To install:

8. Install new valve cover bolt grommets prior to installing the valve cover bolts.

9. Place a bead 0.3150 inch. (8 mm) in diameter by 0.1575 inch. (4 mm) in height of RTV sealant, GM P/N 12378521 (Canadian P/N 88901148) or equivalent, on the engine front cover split lines.

10. Place the left valve cover into position onto the left cylinder head.

11. Loosely install the left valve cover bolts.

12. Tighten the left cover bolts to 89 inch lbs., in the sequence shown.

13. Remove the EN 46101 from the spark plug tubes of the left cylinder head.

14. Install the ignition coils.

15. Connect the negative battery cable.

Right Side

See Figure 186.

1. Before servicing the vehicle, refer to the precautions section.

2. Remove the upper intake manifold.

3. Remove the ignition coils.

4. Unbolt the power steering reservoir and position aside. Refer to Power Steering Pump, Removal & Installation in the Steering section.

5. Reposition engine wiring harness aside.

6. Remove the right valve cover bolts.

7. Remove the right valve cover from the right cylinder head.

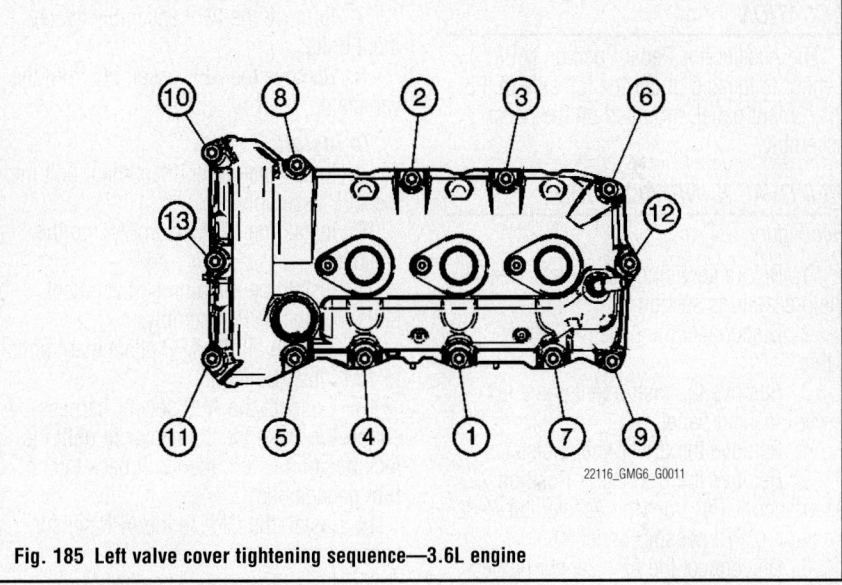

Fig. 185 Left valve cover tightening sequence—3.6L engine

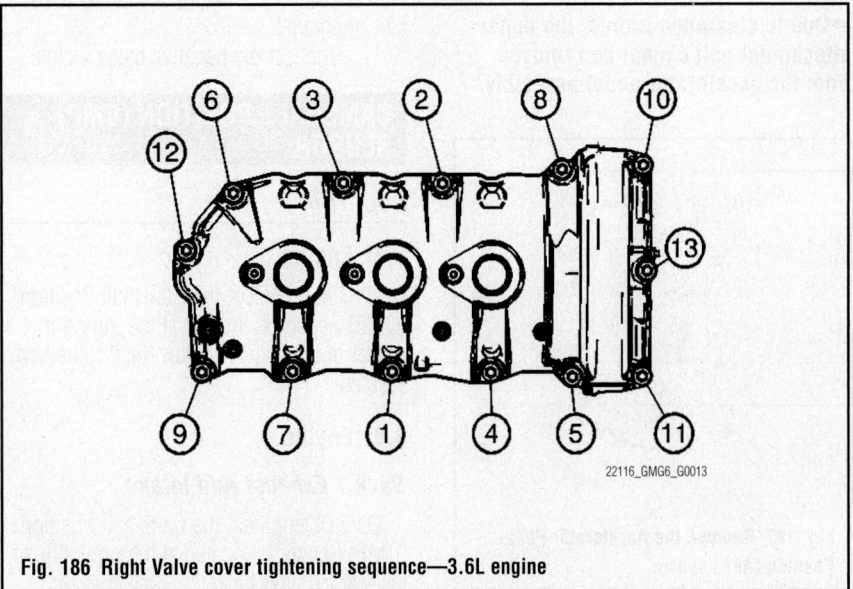

Fig. 186 Right Valve cover tightening sequence—3.6L engine

8. Clean the mating surfaces of the cylinder head and the valve cover.

9. Install the EN 46101 onto the spark plug tubes of the left cylinder head.

To install:

10. Install new valve cover bolt grommets prior to installing the valve cover bolts.

11. Place a bead 0.3150 inch. (8 mm) in diameter by 0.1575 inch. (4 mm) in height of RTV sealant, GM P/N 12378521 (Canadian P/N 88901148) or equivalent, on the engine front cover split lines (1).

12. Place the right valve cover into position onto the right cylinder head.

13. Loosely install the right valve cover bolts.

14. Tighten the right valve cover bolts to 89 inch lbs., in the sequence shown.

15. Reposition engine wiring harness.

16. Install the power steering reservoir.

17. Remove the EN 46101 from the spark plug tubes of the right cylinder head.

18. Install the ignition coils.

19. Install the upper intake manifold.

20. Connect the negative battery cable.

VALVE LASH

ADJUSTMENT

The 3.4L and 3.6L engine is equipped with hydraulic valve lifters that do not require periodic valve lash adjustment. Adjustment to zero lash is maintained automatically by hydraulic pressure in the lifters.

ENGINE PERFORMANCE & EMISSION CONTROLS

ACCELERATOR PEDAL POSITION (APP) SENSOR

LOCATION

The Accelerator Pedal Position (APP) Sensor is located under the left side of the instrument panel, mounted on the pedal assembly.

REMOVAL & INSTALLATION

See Figure 187.

1. Before servicing the vehicle, refer to the precautions section.

2. Disconnect the negative battery cable.

3. Remove the instrument panel left lower closeout panel.

4. Remove the driver knee bolster.

5. Remove the Connector Position Assurance (CPA) from the Accelerator Pedal Position (APP) sensor connector.

6. Disconnect the APP sensor harness connector.

➡ Due to clearance issues, the upper attachment bolt cannot be removed from the accelerator pedal assembly.

Loosen the bolt completely and leave the bolt in the component until the assembly is removed from the vehicle.

7. Remove the APP assembly attachment bolts.

8. Remove the APP assembly from the vehicle.

To install:

9. Install the upper attachment bolt into the APP assembly.

10. Install the APP assembly into the vehicle.

11. Install the remaining attachment bolts into the APP assembly.

12. Tighten all the APP attachment bolts to 18 ft. lbs. (25 Nm).

13. Connect the APP sensor harness connector. Push the connector in until the lock position is felt, then pull back to confirm engagement.

14. Install the CPA to the APP sensor harness connector.

15. Install the driver knee bolster.

16. Install the instrument panel left lower closeout panel.

17. Connect the negative battery cable.

CAMSHAFT POSITION (CMP) SENSOR

LOCATION

3.4L Engine

On 3.4L engines, the Camshaft Position (CMP) Sensor is located at the top right corner of the engine, below the throttle body assembly.

3.6L Engine

Bank 1 Exhaust And Intake

On 3.6L engines, the Camshaft Position (CMP) Sensor is located at the right side of the rear cylinder head.

Bank 2 Exhaust And Intake

On 3.6L engines, the Camshaft Position (CMP) Sensor is located at the right side of the front cylinder head.

REMOVAL & INSTALLATION

3.4L Engine

See Figure 188.

1. Before servicing the vehicle, refer to the precautions section.

2. Disconnect the negative battery cable.

3. Remove the air cleaner inlet duct.

4. Disconnect the engine wiring harness electrical connector from the Camshaft Position (CMP) Sensor.

5. Remove the CMP sensor bolt.

6. Remove the CMP sensor.

7. Inspect the CMP sensor O-rings for wear, cracks, or leakage if the sensor is being reused. Replace the O-rings if damaged.

To install:

8. Lubricate the CMP sensor O-rings with clean engine oil.

9. Install the CMP sensor and tighten the mounting bolt to 89 inch lbs. (10 Nm.).

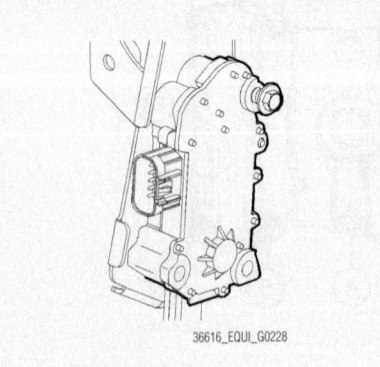

36616_EQUI_G0228

Fig. 187 Remove the Accelerator Pedal Position (APP) sensor

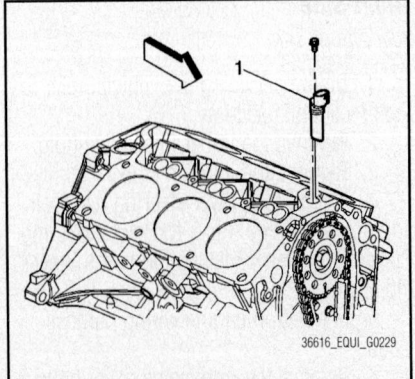

36616_EQUI_G0229

Fig. 188 Camshaft Position (CMP) Sensor (1) removal—3.4L engine

10. Connect the engine wiring harness electrical connector to the CMP sensor.

11. Install the air cleaner inlet duct.

12. Connect the negative battery cable.

3.6L Engine

Bank 1 Exhaust

See Figure 189.

1. Before servicing the vehicle, refer to the precautions section.

2. Remove the air cleaner assembly.

3. Disconnect the engine wiring harness electrical connector from the bank 1 exhaust Camshaft Position (CMP) Sensor.

4. Remove the CMP sensor bolt.

5. Remove the bank 1 exhaust CMP sensor.

To install:

6. Install the CMP sensor.

7. Install the CMP sensor bolt and tighten to 89 inch lbs. (10 Nm.).

8. Connect the engine wiring harness electrical connector to the bank 1 exhaust CMP sensor.

9. Install the air cleaner assembly.

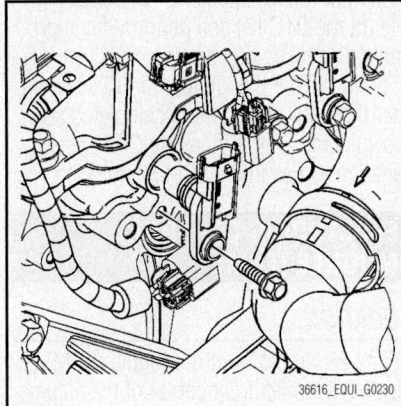

Fig. 189 Bank 1 exhaust Camshaft Position (CMP) Sensor removal

Bank 1 Intake

See Figure 190.

1. Before servicing the vehicle, refer to the precautions section.

2. Remove the air cleaner assembly.

3. Disconnect the engine wiring harness electrical connector from the bank 1 intake Camshaft Position (CMP) Sensor.

4. Remove the CMP sensor bolt.

5. Remove the bank 1 intake CMP sensor.

To install:

6. Install the CMP sensor.

7. Install the CMP sensor bolt and tighten to 89 inch lbs. (10 Nm.).

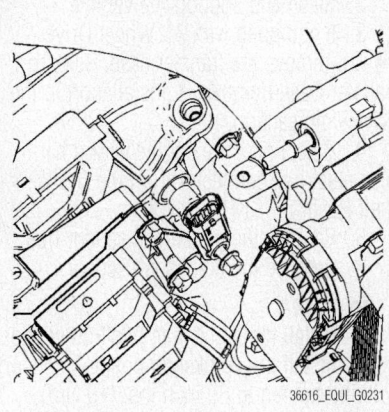

Fig. 190 Bank 1 intake Camshaft Position (CMP) Sensor removal

8. Connect the engine wiring harness electrical connector to the bank 1 intake CMP sensor.

9. Install the air cleaner assembly.

Bank 2 Exhaust

See Figure 191.

1. Before servicing the vehicle, refer to the precautions section.

2. Remove the air cleaner assembly.

3. Disconnect the engine wiring harness electrical connector from the bank 2 exhaust Camshaft Position (CMP) Sensor.

4. Remove the CMP sensor bolt.

5. Remove the bank 2 exhaust CMP sensor.

To install:

6. Install the CMP sensor.

7. Install the CMP sensor bolt and tighten to 89 inch lbs. (10 Nm.).

8. Connect the engine wiring harness electrical connector to the bank 2 exhaust CMP sensor.

9. Install the air cleaner assembly.

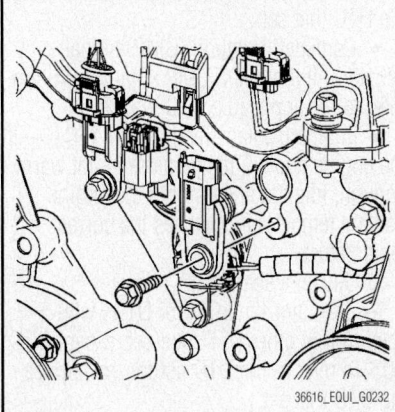

Fig. 191 Bank 2 exhaust Camshaft Position (CMP) Sensor removal

Bank 2 Intake

See Figure 192.

1. Before servicing the vehicle, refer to the precautions section.

2. Remove the air cleaner assembly.

3. Disconnect the engine wiring harness electrical connector from the bank 2 intake Camshaft Position (CMP) Sensor.

4. Remove the CMP sensor bolt.

5. Remove the bank 2 intake CMP sensor.

To install:

6. Install the CMP sensor.

7. Install the CMP sensor bolt and tighten to 89 inch lbs. (10 Nm.).

8. Connect the engine wiring harness electrical connector to the bank 2 intake CMP sensor.

9. Install the air cleaner assembly.

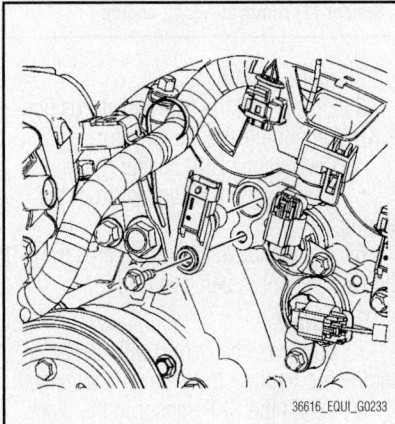

Fig. 192 Bank 2 intake Camshaft Position (CMP) Sensor removal

CRANKSHAFT POSITION (CKP) SENSOR

LOCATION

3.4L Engine

The Crankshaft Position (CMP) Sensor—3.4L engine is located at the rear of the engine, on the lower back side.

3.6L Engine

The Crankshaft Position (CMP) Sensor—3.6L engine is located at the rear of the engine, on the lower back side.

REMOVAL & INSTALLATION

3.4L Engine

See Figure 193.

1. Before servicing the vehicle, refer to the precautions section.

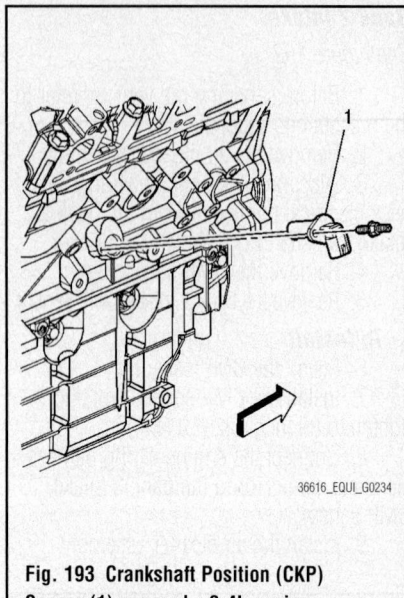

Fig. 193 Crankshaft Position (CKP) Sensor (1) removal—3.4L engine

2. Raise the vehicle.

3. Disconnect the Crankshaft Position (CKP) Sensor electrical connector.

4. Remove the CKP sensor nut.

5. Remove the CKP sensor from the engine.

6. Inspect for wear, cracks, or leakage if the CKP sensor is being reused.

To install:

7. Lubricate the O-ring with clean engine oil. Replace the O-rings if damaged.

8. Install the CKP sensor to the block tighten the retainer to 97 inch lbs. (11 Nm).

9. Connect the CKP sensor electrical connector.

10. Lower the vehicle.

3.6L Engine

See Figure 194.

1. Before servicing the vehicle, refer to the precautions section.

Fig. 194 Crankshaft Position (CKP) Sensor removal—3.6L engine

2. Raise and support the vehicle.

3. If equipped with All Wheel Drive (AWD), remove the transfer case. Refer to Transfer Case Removal & Installation in the Drive Train section.

4. Disconnect the engine wiring harness electrical connector from the Crankshaft Position (CKP) Sensor.

5. Remove the crankshaft sensor bolt.

6. Remove the crankshaft sensor.

To install:

7. Install the crankshaft position sensor.

8. Install the crankshaft position sensor bolt and tighten to 89 inch lbs. (10 Nm).

9. Connect the engine wiring harness electrical connector to the CKP sensor.

10. If equipped with all AWD, install the transfer case.

11. Lower the vehicle.

CRANKSHAFT POSITION SYSTEM VARIATION LEARN—3.4L ENGINE

The Crankshaft Position (CKP) system variation learn procedure is also required when the following service procedures have been performed, regardless of whether DTC P0315 is set:

- An engine replacement
- A Engine Control Module (ECM) replacement
- A crankshaft balancer replacement
- A crankshaft replacement
- A CKP sensor replacement
- Any engine repairs which disturb the crankshaft to CKP sensor relationship.

The ECM monitors certain component signals to determine if all the conditions are met to continue with the CKP System Variation Learn Procedure. The scan tool only displays the condition that inhibits the procedure. The scan tool displays the signals of the following components:

- CKP sensors activity—If there is a CKP sensor condition, refer to the applicable DTC that set.
- Camshaft Position (CMP) signal activity—If there is a CMP signal condition, refer to the applicable DTC that set.
- Engine Coolant Temperature (ECT)—If the engine coolant temperature is not warm enough, idle the engine until the engine coolant temperature reaches the correct temperature.

1. Install a scan tool.

2. Monitor the ECM for DTCs with a scan tool. If other DTCs are set, except DTC P0315, refer to the DTC list for the applicable DTC that set.

3. With a scan tool, select the CKP System Variation Learn Procedure and perform the following:

- Block drive wheels.
- Set parking brake.
- **DO NOT** apply brake pedal.
- Cycle ignition from OFF to ON.
- Apply and hold brake pedal for the duration of the procedure.
- Start and idle engine.
- Turn the Air Conditioning (A/C) OFF.
- The vehicle must remain in Park or Neutral.
- Accelerate to Wide Open Throttle (WOT) and release when the fuel cut-off occurs.

➡**While the learn procedure is in progress, release the throttle immediately when the engine starts to decelerate. The engine control is returned to the operator and the engine responds to throttle position after the learn procedure is complete.**

4. The scan tool displays Learn Status: Learned this Ignition. If the scan tool indicates that DTC P0315 ran and passed, the CKP variation learn procedure is complete. If the scan tool indicates DTC P0315 failed or did not run, or another DTC is present, refer to the DTC list and perform the appropriate diagnostic procedure.

5. Turn OFF the ignition for 30 seconds after the learn procedure is completed successfully in order to store the CKP system variation values in the ECM memory.

ELECTRONIC CONTROL MODULE (ECM)

LOCATION

The Electronic Control Module (ECM) is located at the left front corner of the engine compartment, mounted on top of the battery cover.

The Electronic Control Module (ECM) is located at the left front corner of the engine compartment, mounted on top of the battery cover.

REMOVAL & INSTALLATION

3.4L Engine

See Figures 195 and 196.

✳✳ WARNING

Turn the ignition OFF when installing or removing the control module connectors and disconnecting or reconnecting the power to the control module (battery cable, Engine Control Module (ECM)/Transaxle Control Module (TCM) pigtail, control

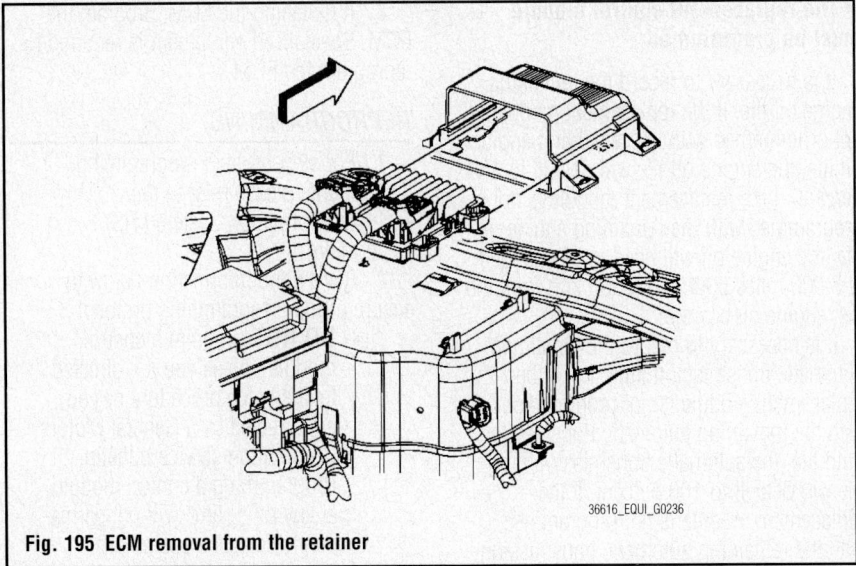

Fig. 195 ECM removal from the retainer

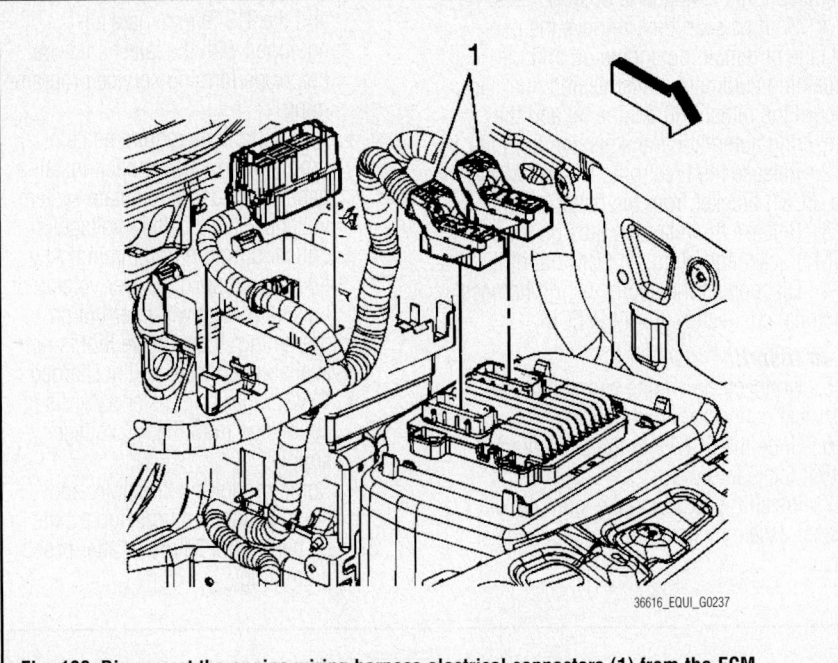

Fig. 196 Disconnect the engine wiring harness electrical connectors (1) from the ECM

➡ **The replacement control module must be programmed.**

It is necessary to record the remaining engine oil life. If the replacement module is not programmed with the remaining engine oil life, the engine oil life will default to 100 percent. If the replacement module is not programmed with the remaining engine oil life, the engine oil will need to be changed at 3,000 miles 5000 km (5000 km) from the last engine oil change.

It is necessary to record the remaining automatic transmission fluid life. If the replacement module is not programmed with the remaining automatic transmission fluid life, the automatic transmission fluid life will default to 100 percent. If the replacement module is not programmed with the remaining automatic transmission fluid life, the automatic transmission fluid will need to be changed at 50,000 miles. (83000 km) from the last automatic transmission fluid change.

1. Using a scan tool, retrieve the percentage of remaining engine oil and the remaining automatic transmission fluid life. Record the remaining engine oil and the remaining automatic transmission fluid life.

2. Slide the ECM retainer rearward, disengaging the retainer from the battery shield.

3. Remove the ECM retainer from the top of the battery shield.

4. Remove the ECM from the retainer. Reposition the ECM out of the way.

5. Disconnect the negative battery cable.

6. Place the battery shield over the battery.

7. Place the ECM on top of the battery shield.

8. Disconnect the engine wiring harness electrical connectors from the ECM.

9. Remove the ECM from the vehicle.

To install:

10. Install the ECM to the vehicle.

11. Connect the engine wiring harness electrical connectors to the ECM. Reposition the ECM out of the way.

12. Remove the battery shield from over the battery.

13. Connect the negative battery cable.

14. Install the ECM to the retainer.

15. Position the ECM and retainer to the top of the battery shield.

16. Slide the ECM retainer rearward, engaging the retainer to the battery shield.

17. If replacing the ECM, program the ECM. Specialized equipment is required to reprogram the ECM.

module fuse, jumper cables, etc.) in order to prevent internal control module damage.

module, do not touch the connector pins or the soldered components on the circuit board.

⁂ WARNING

Control module damage may result when the metal case contacts battery voltage. DO NOT contact the control module metal case with battery voltage when servicing a control module, using battery booster cables, or when charging the vehicle battery. In order to prevent any possible electrostatic discharge damage to the control

⁂ WARNING

Remove any debris from around the control module connector surfaces before servicing the control module. Inspect the control module connector gaskets when diagnosing or replacing the control module. Ensure that the gaskets are installed correctly. The gaskets prevent contaminant intrusion into the control module.

3.4L Engine

See Figures 197 and 198.

> ※※ **WARNING**
>
> **Turn the ignition OFF when installing or removing the control module connectors and disconnecting or reconnecting the power to the control module (battery cable, Engine Control Module (ECM)/Transaxle Control Module (TCM) pigtail, control module fuse, jumper cables, etc.) in order to prevent internal control module damage.**

> ※※ **WARNING**
>
> **Control module damage may result when the metal case contacts battery voltage. DO NOT contact the control module metal case with battery voltage when servicing a control module, using battery booster cables, or when charging the vehicle battery. In order to prevent any possible electrostatic discharge damage to the control module, do not touch the connector pins or the soldered components on the circuit board.**

> ※※ **WARNING**
>
> **Remove any debris from around the control module connector surfaces before servicing the control module. Inspect the control module connector gaskets when diagnosing or replacing the control module. Ensure that the gaskets are installed correctly. The gaskets prevent contaminant intrusion into the control module.**

➡**The replacement control module must be programmed.**

It is necessary to record the remaining engine oil life. If the replacement module is not programmed with the remaining engine oil life, the engine oil life will default to 100 percent. If the replacement module is not programmed with the remaining engine oil life, the engine oil will need to be changed at 3,000 miles 5000 km (5000 km) from the last engine oil change.

It is necessary to record the remaining automatic transmission fluid life. If the replacement module is not programmed with the remaining automatic transmission fluid life, the automatic transmission fluid life will default to 100 percent. If the replacement module is not programmed with the remaining automatic transmission fluid life, the automatic transmission fluid will need to be changed at 50,000 miles.

1. Using a scan tool, retrieve the percentage of remaining engine oil and the remaining automatic transmission fluid life. Record the remaining engine oil and the remaining automatic transmission fluid life.

2. Release the Electronic Control Module (ECM) bracket from the battery cover.

3. Release the retaining tabs on the ECM bracket and slide the ECM out of it.

4. Disconnect the engine wiring harness electrical connectors from the ECM.

To install:

5. Connect the engine wiring harness electrical connectors to the ECM.

6. Slide the ECM into the ECM bracket until it locks into place.

7. Install the ECM bracket onto the air cleaner assembly cover until it locks in place.

8. If replacing the ECM, program the ECM. Specialized equipment is required to reprogram the ECM.

REPROGRAMMING

1. For step-by-step programming instructions, please refer to the Techline Information System (TIS) terminal.

2. Review the information below to ensure proper programming protocol.

- **DO NOT** program a control module unless you are directed by a service procedure or you are directed by a General Motors Corporation service bulletin. Programming a control module at any other time will not permanently correct a customer's concern.

- It is essential that the Tech 2, MDI and the TIS terminal are all equipped with the latest software before performing service programming.

- Due to the time requirements of programming a controller, install a battery charger to maintain system voltage. Stable battery voltage is critical during programming. Any fluctuation, spiking, over voltage or loss of voltage will interrupt programming. If the above tool is not available, connect a fully charged 12V jumper or booster pack disconnected from the AC voltage supply.

- Some modules will require additional programming/setup events to be performed before or after programming

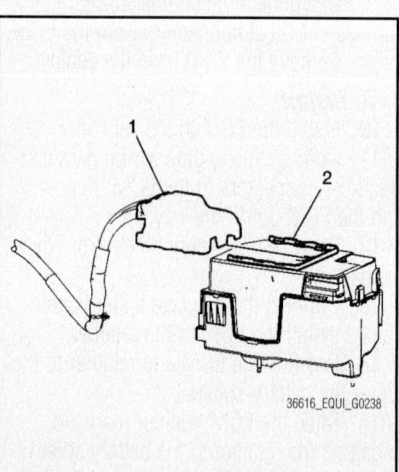

Fig. 197 Release the Electronic Control Module (ECM) bracket (1) from the battery cover (2)

36616_EQUI_G0238

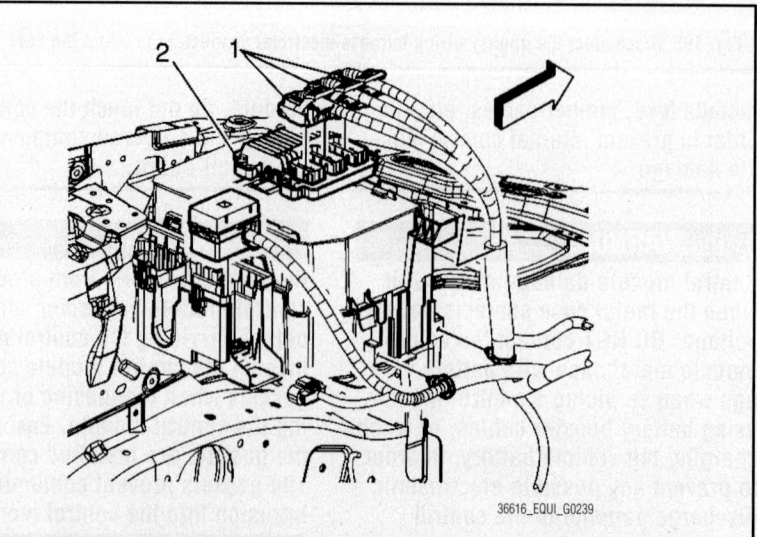

36616_EQUI_G0239

Fig. 198 Disconnect the engine wiring harness electrical connectors (1) from the ECM (2)

- Some vehicles may require the use of a CANDi or MDI module for programming.
- Review the appropriate service information for these procedures.
- DTCs may set during programming. Clear DTCs after programming is complete.
- Clearing power train DTCs will set the Inspection/Maintenance (I/M) system status indicators to NO.

3. Ensure the following conditions are met before programming a control module:

- There is not a charging system concern. All charging system concerns must be repaired before programming a control module.
- Battery voltage is greater than 12 volts but less than 16 volts. The battery must be fully charged before programming the control module.

4. Turn **OFF** or disable any system that may put a load on the vehicles battery, such as the following components:

- Twilight sentinel
- Interior lights
- Daytime running lights (DRL)— Applying the parking brake, on most vehicles, disables the DRL system
- Heating, ventilation, and air conditioning (HVAC) systems
- Engine cooling fans, radio, etc.

5. The ignition switch must be in the proper position. SPS prompts you to turn ON the ignition, with the engine OFF. **DO NOT** change the position of the ignition switch during the programming procedure, unless instructed to do so.

6. Make certain all tool connections are secure, including the following components and circuits:

- 1: Tech 2
- The RS-232 communication cable port
- The connection at the Data Link Connector (DLC)
- The voltage supply circuits
- 2: MDI
- The USB, Ethernet or Wireless communication port
- The connection at the Data Link Connector (DLC)

7. **DO NOT** disturb the tool harnesses while programming. If an interruption occurs during the programming procedure, programming failure or control module damage may occur.

8. **DO NOT** turn OFF the ignition if the programming procedure is interrupted or unsuccessful. Ensure that all control module and DLC connections are secure and the TIS terminal operating software is up to date. Attempt to reprogram the control module. If the control module cannot be programmed, replace the control module.

ENGINE COOLANT TEMPERATURE (ECT) SENSOR

LOCATION

3.4L Engine

The Engine Coolant Temperature (ECT) Sensor is located at the rear of the engine cylinder head, below the brake master cylinder—3.4L engine.

3.6L Engine

The Engine Coolant Temperature (ECT) Sensor is located at the right front of the cylinder head between cylinder 2 and 4 exhaust ports—3.6L engine.

REMOVAL & INSTALLATION

3.4L Engine

See Figure 199.

1. Before servicing the vehicle, refer to the precautions section.
2. Drain the engine coolant to a level below the Engine Coolant Temperature (ECT) sensor.
3. Remove the fuel injector sight shield.
4. Disconnect the ECT sensor harness connector.

5. Remove the ECT sensor.

To install:

➡ Tap out sensor mounting hole in engine head to remove any thread sealant residue. Clean any sealant residue from old sensor if the sensor is going to be reused.

6. If the sensor is being reused, apply thread sealant GM P/N 12345382 (Canadian P/N 10953489) or equivalent, to sensor threads.
7. Install the ECT sensor and tighten to 17 ft. lbs. (23 Nm).
8. Connect the ECT sensor harness connector. Push in the connector until a click is heard, then pull back to confirm a positive engagement.
9. Install the fuel injector sight shield.
10. Refill and bleed the cooling system.

3.6L Engine

See Figure 200.

1. Before servicing the vehicle, refer to the precautions section.
2. Partially drain the cooling system.
3. Disconnect the engine wiring harness electrical connector from the Engine Coolant Temperature (ECT) sensor.
4. Remove the ECT sensor.

To install:

5. Install the ECT sensor and tighten to 16 ft. lbs. (22 Nm).
6. Connect the engine wiring harness electrical connector to the ECT sensor.
7. Refill and bleed the cooling system.

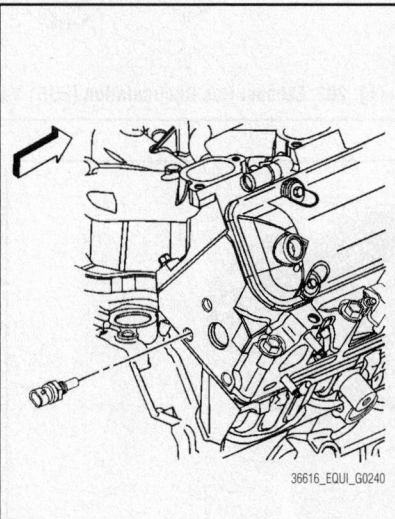

Fig. 199 Engine Coolant Temperature (ECT) sensor removal—3.4L engine

Fig. 200 Engine Coolant Temperature (ECT) sensor removal—3.6L engine

EVAPORATIVE EMISSIONS (EVAP) CANISTER

LOCATION

The Evaporative Emissions (EVAP) Canister is located under the center of the vehicle, in front of the fuel tank.

REMOVAL & INSTALLATION

See Figure 201.

1. Before servicing the vehicle, refer to the precautions section.
2. Raise and support the vehicle.
3. Disconnect the EVAP canister fresh air hose/pipe from the fuel tank fresh air hose/pipe.
4. Disconnect the fuel tank vent pipe from the EVAP canister.
5. Disconnect the chassis EVAP pipe from the EVAP canister.
6. Remove the EVAP canister-to-underbody nuts.
7. Lower the EVAP canister.
8. Disconnect the EVAP vent solenoid electrical connector.
9. Remove the EVAP canister from the vehicle.

To install:

10. Connect the EVAP vent solenoid electrical connector.
11. Install the EVAP canister to the underbody of the vehicle.
12. Install the EVAP canister-to-underbody nuts and tighten to 80 inch lbs. (9 Nm).
13. Connect the chassis EVAP pipe to the EVAP canister.
14. Connect the fuel tank vent pipe to the EVAP canister.
15. Connect the EVAP canister fresh air hose/pipe to the fuel tank fresh air hose/pipe.
16. Lower the vehicle.

EXHAUST GAS RECIRCULATION (EGR) VALVE

LOCATION

3.4L Engine

The Exhaust Gas Recirculation (EGR) Valve is located on the top right side of the engine, near the throttle body assembly.

REMOVAL & INSTALLATION

3.4L Engine

See Figure 202.

1. Before servicing the vehicle, refer to the precautions section.
2. Remove the injector sight shield.
3. Remove the Exhaust Gas Recirculation (EGR) pipe.
4. Disconnect the EGR valve electrical connector.
5. Remove the EGR valve bolts.
6. Remove the EGR valve.
7. Remove the EGR valve gasket.

To install:

8. Clean the EGR valve mating surface.
9. Install the EGR valve with a new gasket to the intake manifold.
10. Install the EGR valve bolts and tighten to 22 ft. lbs. (30 Nm).
11. Connect the EGR valve electrical connector.
12. Install the 2 bolts that secure the EGR pipe to exhaust manifold. Tighten the bolts to 89 inch lbs. (10 Nm).
13. Install the bolt the secures the EGR pipe bolt to the EGR valve. Tighten to 22 ft. lbs. (30 Nm).
14. Install the injector sight shield.

HEATED OXYGEN SENSOR (HO2S)

LOCATION

3.4L Engine

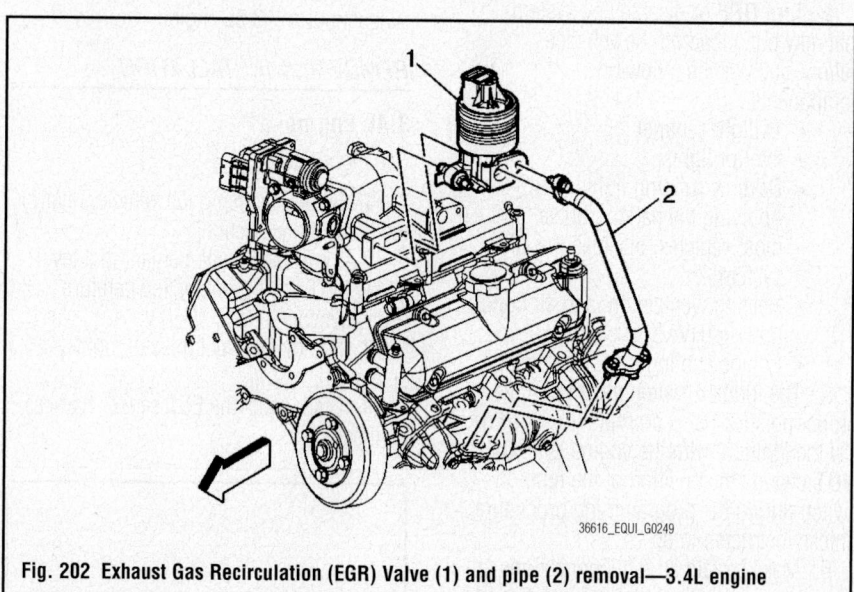

Fig. 202 Exhaust Gas Recirculation (EGR) Valve (1) and pipe (2) removal—3.4L engine

36616_EQUI_G0249

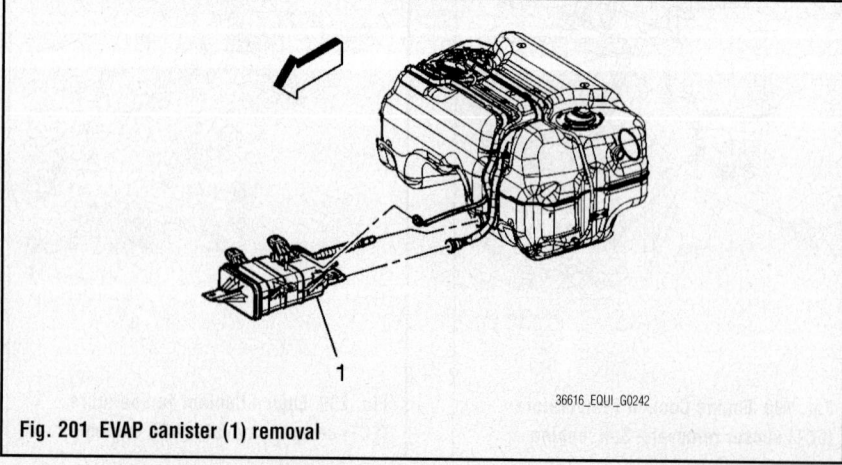

Fig. 201 EVAP canister (1) removal

36616_EQUI_G0242

The Heated Oxygen Sensor (HO2S) (1) is attached to the exhaust manifold, at the lower rear of the engine.

The Heated Oxygen Sensor (HO2S) (2) is attached to the exhaust pipe, behind the catalytic converter.

3.6L Engine

The Heated Oxygen Sensor (HO2S) (Bank 1 Sensor 1) is attached to the rear exhaust bank, above the catalytic converter.

The Heated Oxygen Sensor (HO2S) (Bank 1 Sensor 2) is attached to the rear exhaust bank, below the catalytic converter.

The Heated Oxygen Sensor (HO2S)

(Bank 2 Sensor 1) is attached to the front exhaust bank, above the catalytic converter.

The Heated Oxygen Sensor (HO2S) (Bank 2 Sensor 2) is attached to the front exhaust bank, below the catalytic converter.

REMOVAL & INSTALLATION

3.4L Engine

Sensor 1

See Figure 203.

1. Before servicing the vehicle, refer to the precautions section.
2. Raise and support the vehicle.
3. Disconnect the engine wiring harness electrical connector from the Heated Oxygen Sensor (HO2S).
4. Use a liquid penetrate before removing the sensor.
5. Remove the HO2S from the exhaust manifold.

To install:

✱✱ WARNING

Silicone based products will contaminate the HO2S. Use only a nickel based anti-seize compound that does not contain silicone.

6. Apply a small amount of anti-seize compound to the threads of the HO2S.
7. Install the HO2S to the exhaust manifold and tighten to 31 ft. lbs. (42 Nm).
8. Connect the engine wiring harness electrical connector to the HO2S. Push in the connector until a click is heard and pull back to confirm a positive engagement.
9. Lower the vehicle.

Sensor 2

See Figure 204.

1. Before servicing the vehicle, refer to the precautions section.
2. Raise and support the vehicle.
3. Disconnect the Heated Oxygen Sensor (HO2S) from the harness connector.
4. Use a liquid penetrate before removing the sensor.
5. Remove the HO2S 2 (2) from the exhaust pipe.

To install:

✱✱ WARNING

Silicone based products will contaminate the HO2S. Use only a nickel based anti-seize compound that does not contain silicone.

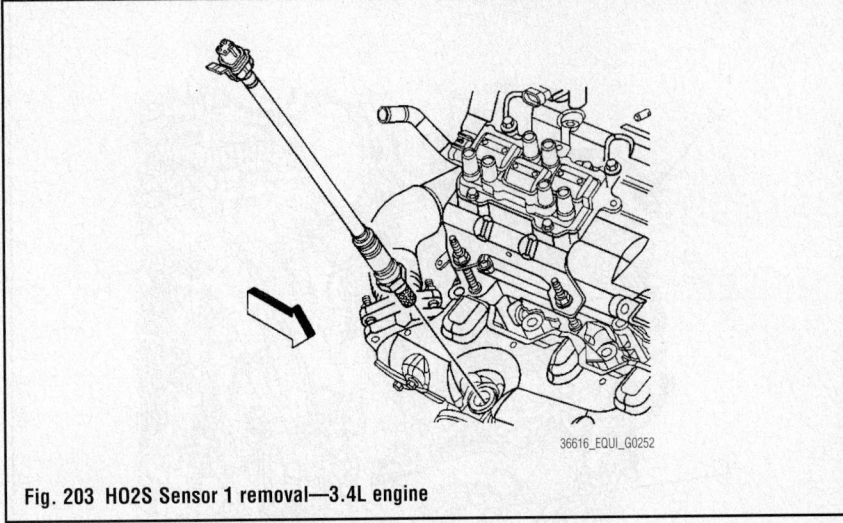

36616_EQUI_G0252

Fig. 203 HO2S Sensor 1 removal—3.4L engine

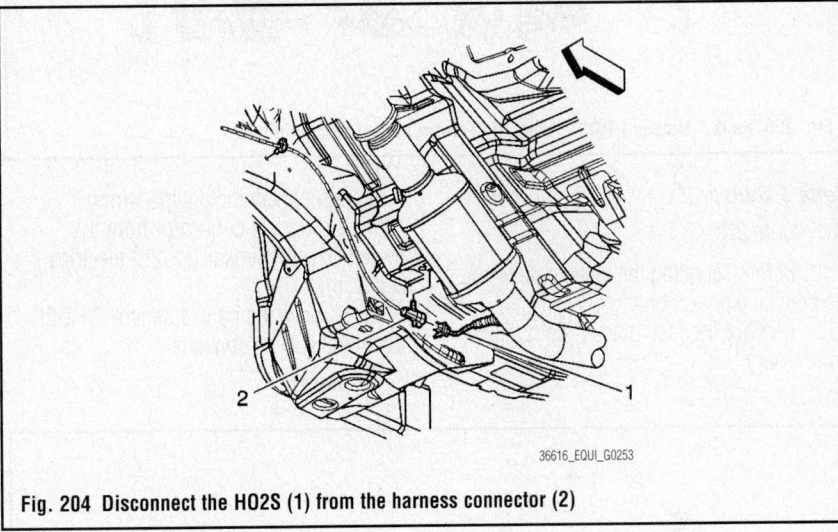

36616_EQUI_G0253

Fig. 204 Disconnect the HO2S (1) from the harness connector (2)

6. Apply a small amount of anti-seize compound to the threads of the HO2S.
7. Install the HO2S (2) to the exhaust pipe and tighten to 31 ft. lbs. (42 Nm).
8. Connect the HO2S 2 harness connector. Push in the connector until a click is heard, then pull back to confirm a positive engagement.
9. Ensure the HO2S 2 harness pigtail connector is secure to the chassis.

3.6L Engine

Bank 1 Sensor 1

See Figure 205.

1. Before servicing the vehicle, refer to the precautions section.
2. Remove the fuel injector sight shield, if necessary.
3. Disconnect the engine wiring harness electrical connector from the heated Oxygen Sensor (HO2S) electrical connector. Remove

the HO2S electrical connector retainer from the camshaft cover.

To install:

✱✱ WARNING

Silicone based products will contaminate the HO2S. Use only a nickel based anti-seize compound that does not contain silicone.

4. Apply a small amount of anti-seize compound to the threads of the HO2S.
5. Install the HO2S to the exhaust manifold and tighten to 31 ft. lbs. (42 Nm).
6. Connect the engine wiring harness electrical connector to the HO2S electrical connector.
7. Install the HO2S electrical connector retainer to the camshaft cover.
8. Install the fuel injector sight shield, if necessary.

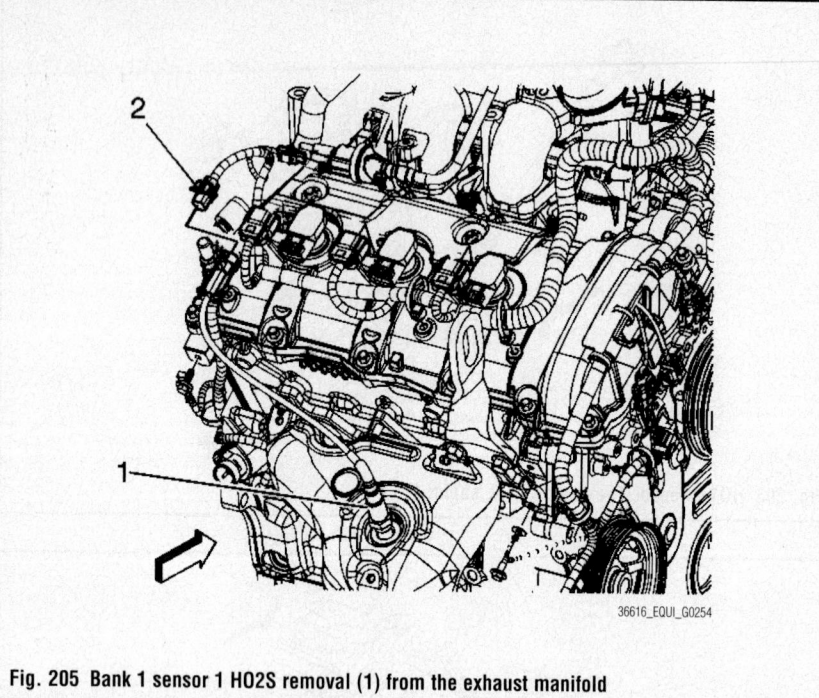

Fig. 205 Bank 1 sensor 1 HO2S removal (1) from the exhaust manifold

Bank 1 Sensor 2

See Figure 206.

1. Before servicing the vehicle, refer to the precautions section.
2. Remove the fuel injector sight shield, if necessary.
3. Disconnect the engine wiring harness electrical connector from the heated Oxygen Sensor (HO2S) electrical connector.
4. Remove the bank 1 sensor 2 HO2S from the catalytic converter.

To install:

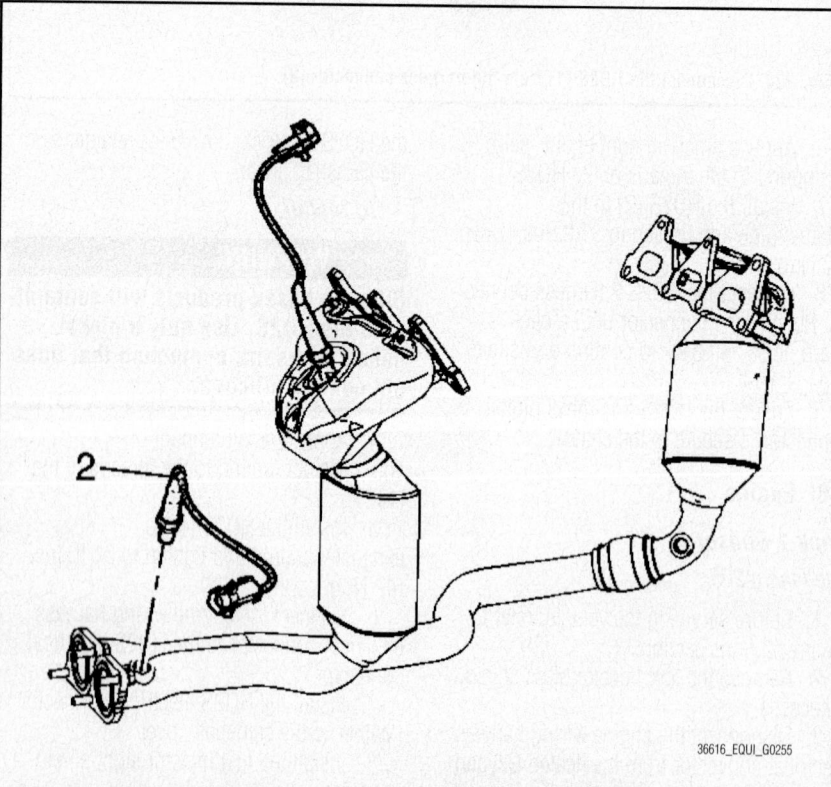

Fig. 206 Remove the bank 1 sensor 2 HO2S from the catalytic converter

✳✳ WARNING

Silicone based products will contaminate the HO2S. Use only a nickel based anti-seize compound that does not contain silicone.

5. Apply a small amount of anti-seize compound to the threads of the HO2S.
6. Install the HO2S to the exhaust manifold and tighten to 31 ft. lbs. (42 Nm).
7. Connect the engine wiring harness electrical connector to the HO2S electrical connector.
8. Install the fuel injector sight shield, if necessary.

Bank 2 Sensor 1

See Figure 207.

1. Before servicing the vehicle, refer to the precautions section.
2. Remove the fuel injector sight shield, if necessary.
3. Disconnect the engine wiring harness electrical connector from the heated Oxygen Sensor (HO2S) electrical connector.
4. Remove the HO2S electrical connector retainer from the retainer clip.
5. Remove the bank 2 sensor 1 HO2S from the exhaust manifold.

To install:

✳✳ WARNING

Silicone based products will contaminate the HO2S. Use only a nickel based anti-seize compound that does not contain silicone.

6. Apply a small amount of anti-seize compound to the threads of the HO2S.
7. Install the HO2S to the exhaust manifold and tighten to 31 ft. lbs. (42 Nm).
8. Connect the engine wiring harness electrical connector to the HO2S electrical connector.
9. Install the HO2S electrical connector retainer to the retainer clip.
10. Install the fuel injector sight shield, if necessary.

Bank 2 Sensor 2

See Figure 208.

1. Before servicing the vehicle, refer to the precautions section.
2. Remove the fuel injector sight shield, if necessary.
3. Disconnect the engine wiring harness electrical connector from the heated Oxygen Sensor (HO2S) electrical connector.
4. Remove the bank 2 sensor 2 HO2S from the exhaust manifold.

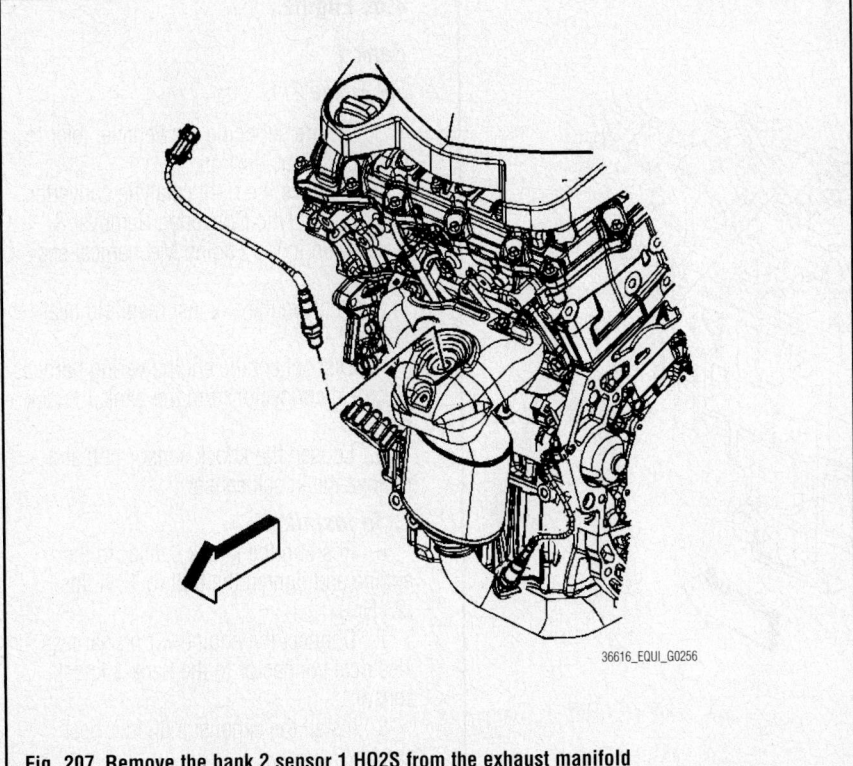

Fig. 207 Remove the bank 2 sensor 1 HO2S from the exhaust manifold

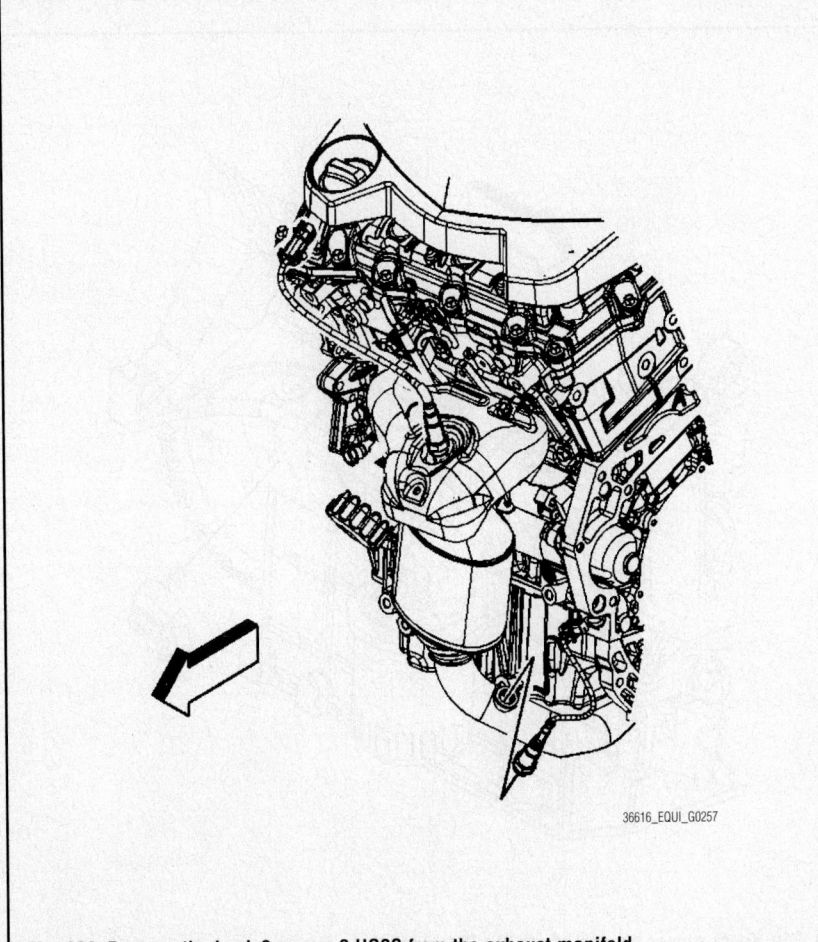

Fig. 208 Remove the bank 2 sensor 2 HO2S from the exhaust manifold

To install:

✳✳ WARNING

Silicone based products will contaminate the HO2S. Use only a nickel based anti-seize compound that does not contain silicone.

5. Apply a small amount of anti-seize compound to the threads of the HO2S.

6. Install the HO2S to the exhaust manifold and tighten to 31 ft. lbs. (42 Nm).

7. Connect the engine wiring harness electrical connector to the HO2S electrical connector.

8. Install the fuel injector sight shield, if necessary.

INTAKE AIR TEMPERATURE (IAT) SENSOR

LOCATION

The IAT Sensor is integrated with the Mass Air Flow (MAF) Sensor as a physical component. It is located on the right side of the engine compartment, to the right side of the throttle body, in the cold air duct.

REMOVAL & INSTALLATION

Refer to Mass Air Flow (MAF) Sensor in this section.

KNOCK SENSOR (KS)

LOCATION

The Knock Sensor (KS) bank 1 is located on the lower rear side of the engine, near the CKP sensor.

The Knock Sensor (KS) bank 2 is located on the lower front side of the engine.

REMOVAL & INSTALLATION

3.4L Engine

Bank 1

See Figure 209.

1. Before servicing the vehicle, refer to the precautions section.

2. Raise and support the vehicle.

3. Disconnect the engine wiring harness electrical connector from the Knock Sensor (KS).

4. Loosen the knock sensor bolt and remove the knock sensor.

To install:

➡DO NOT apply thread locker to the sensor threads. The sensor threads are coated at the factory and applying additional thread locker affects the sensor's ability to detect detonation.

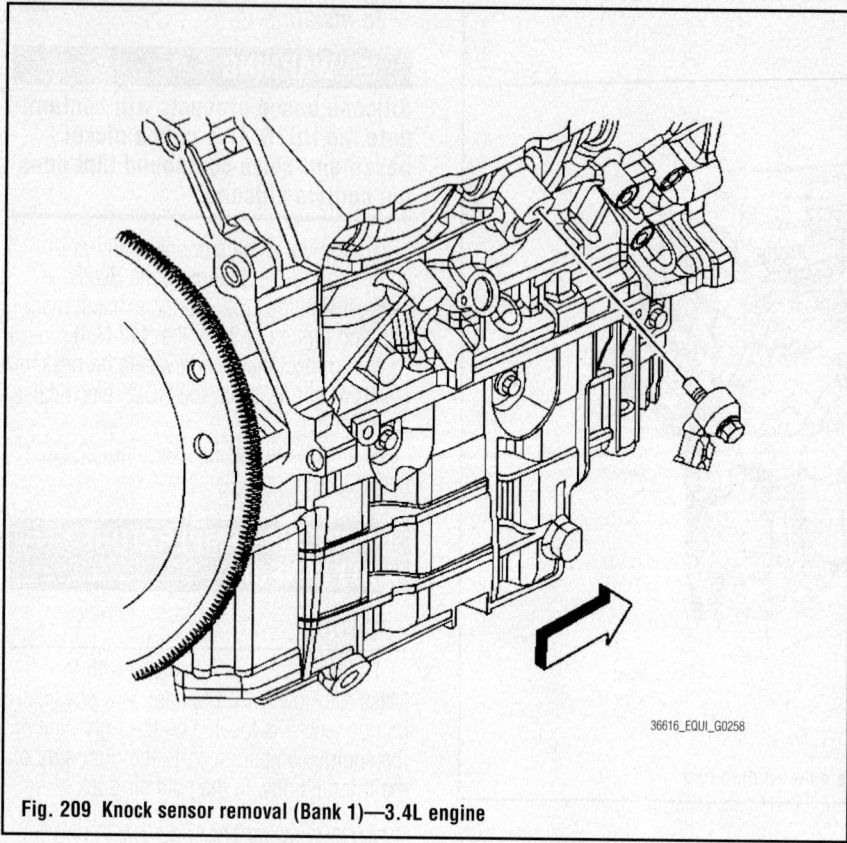

Fig. 209 Knock sensor removal (Bank 1)—3.4L engine

5. Position the knock sensor to the engine and tighten the bolt to 18 ft. lbs. (25 Nm).

6. Connect the engine wiring harness electrical connector to the knock sensor.

7. Lower the vehicle.

Bank 2

See Figure 210.

1. Before servicing the vehicle, refer to the precautions section.

2. Raise and support the vehicle.

3. Disconnect the engine wiring harness electrical connector from the Knock Sensor (KS).

4. Loosen the knock sensor bolt and remove the knock sensor.

To install:

➡DO NOT apply thread locker to the sensor threads. The sensor threads are coated at the factory and applying additional thread locker affects the sensor's ability to detect detonation.

5. Position the knock sensor to the engine and tighten the bolt to 18 ft. lbs. (25 Nm).

6. Connect the engine wiring harness electrical connector to the knock sensor.

7. Lower the vehicle.

3.6L Engine

Bank 1

See Figure 211.

1. Before servicing the vehicle, refer to the precautions section.

2. Remove the right catalytic converter. Refer to Catalytic Converter, Removal & Installation in the Engine Mechanical section.

3. Remove the exhaust manifold heat shield.

4. Disconnect the engine wiring harness electrical connector from the bank 1 knock sensor.

5. Loosen the knock sensor bolt and remove the knock sensor.

To install:

6. Position the knock sensor to the engine and tighten the bolt to 17 ft. lbs. (23 Nm).

7. Connect the engine wiring harness electrical connector to the bank 1 knock sensor.

8. Install the exhaust manifold heat shield.

9. Install the right catalytic converter.

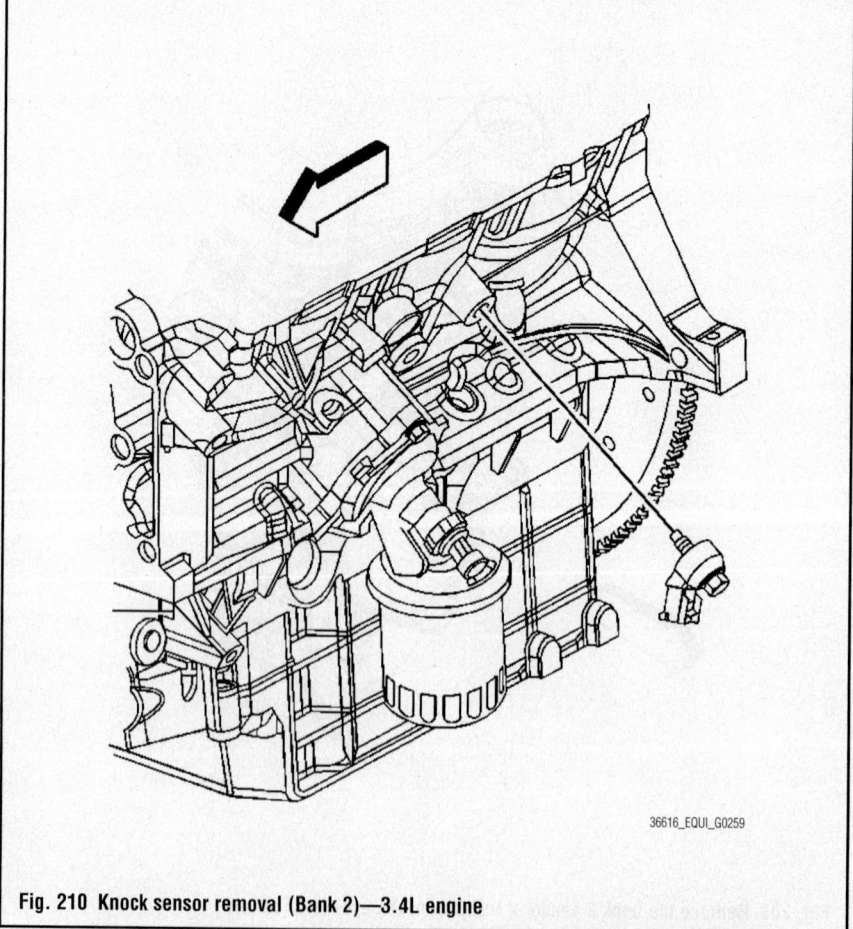

Fig. 210 Knock sensor removal (Bank 2)—3.4L engine

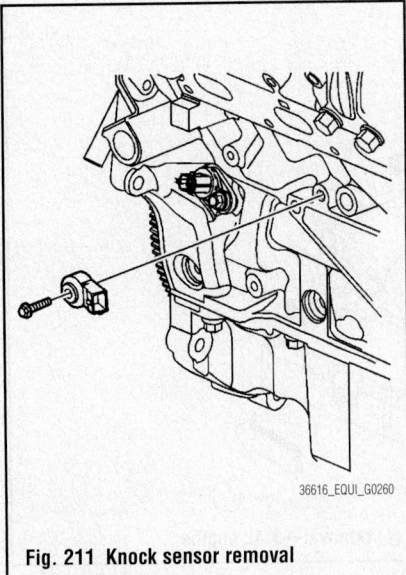

Fig. 211 Knock sensor removal (Bank 1)—3.6L engine

Bank 2

See Figure 212.

1. Before servicing the vehicle, refer to the precautions section.
2. Raise and suitably support the vehicle.
3. Disconnect the engine wiring harness electrical connector from the bank 1 knock sensor.
4. Loosen the knock sensor bolt and remove the knock sensor.

To install:

5. Position the knock sensor to the engine and tighten the bolt to 17 ft. lbs. (23 Nm).
6. Connect the engine wiring harness electrical connector to the bank 2 knock sensor.
7. Install the right catalytic converter.

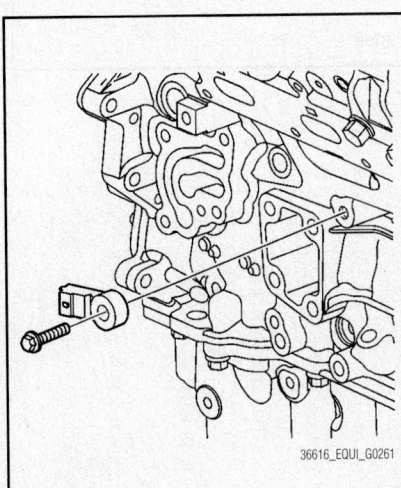

Fig. 212 Knock sensor removal (Bank 2)—3.6L engine

MALFUNCTION INDICATOR LIGHT (MIL)

RESET PROCEDURE

1. Install any components or connectors that may have been removed.
2. Perform any adjustment, programming or setup procedures that are required when a component or module is removed or replaced.
3. Using a suitable scan tool, clear any Diagnostic Trouble Codes (DTC).
4. Turn OFF the ignition for 30 seconds.

MASS AIR FLOW (MAF) SENSOR

LOCATION

The Mass Air Flow (MAF) Sensor is located on the right side of the engine compartment, to the right side of the throttle body, in the cold air duct.

REMOVAL & INSTALLATION

See Figures 213 and 214.

1. Before servicing the vehicle, refer to the precautions section.
2. Remove the air cleaner outlet duct.
3. Disconnect the engine wiring harness electrical connector from the Mass Air Flow (MAF)/Intake Air Temperature (IAT) sensor.
4. Remove the MAF/IAT sensor screws.
5. Remove the MAF/IAT sensor from the air cleaner assembly.
6. Remove the MAF/IAT sensor seal.

To install:

7. Install the MAF/IAT sensor seal to the MAF/IAT sensor.

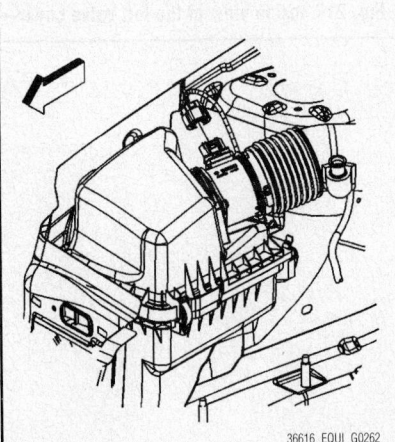

Fig. 213 Disconnect the MAF/IAT sensor connector

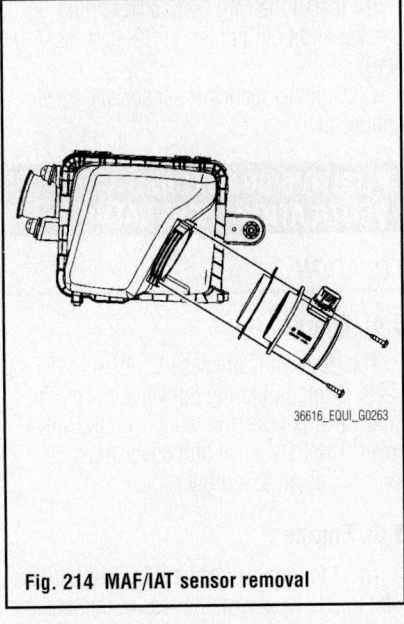

Fig. 214 MAF/IAT sensor removal

8. Install the MAF/IAT sensor to the air cleaner assembly.
9. Install the MAF/IAT sensor screws and tighten to 35 inch lbs. (4 Nm).
10. Connect the engine wiring harness electrical connector to the MAF/IAT sensor.
11. Install the air cleaner outlet duct.

MANIFOLD ABSOLUTE PRESSURE (MAP) SENSOR

LOCATION

3.4L Engine

The Manifold Absolute Pressure (MAP) Sensor is located on the top rear side of the engine, on top of the intake manifold.

REMOVAL & INSTALLATION

3.4L Engine

See Figure 215.

1. Before servicing the vehicle, refer to the precautions section.
2. Disconnect the Manifold Absolute Pressure (MAP) sensor electrical connector.
3. Remove the MAP sensor retaining bolt and bracket.
4. Remove the MAP sensor and the MAP sensor port seal if it is still retained in the intake manifold.

To install:

5. Install the MAP sensor to the intake manifold.

6. Install the MAP sensor retaining bracket and bolt, tighten to 89 inch lbs. (10 Nm).

7. Connect the MAP sensor electrical connector.

POSITIVE CRANKCASE VENTILATION (PCV) VALVE

LOCATION

3.4L Engine

The Positive Crankcase Ventilation (PCV) Valve is integral to the left valve cover. The PCV valve is not removable from the valve cover. The PCV valve and cover must be replaced as an assembly.

3.6L Engine

The 3.6L engine uses a PCV fixed orifice tube that is located at the rear of the intake manifold.

REMOVAL & INSTALLATION

3.4L Engine

See Figure 216.

1. Before servicing the vehicle, refer to the precautions section.

2. Remove the left valve cover. Refer to Valve Cover Removal & Installation in the Engine Mechanical section.

3. Remove the screws from the PCV baffle.

4. Remove the PCV baffle.

5. Clean the PCV valve or replace the valve cover.

To install:

6. Install the PCV baffle.

7. Install the PCV baffle screws and tighten to 53 inch lbs. (6 Nm).

8. Install the left valve rocker arm cover.

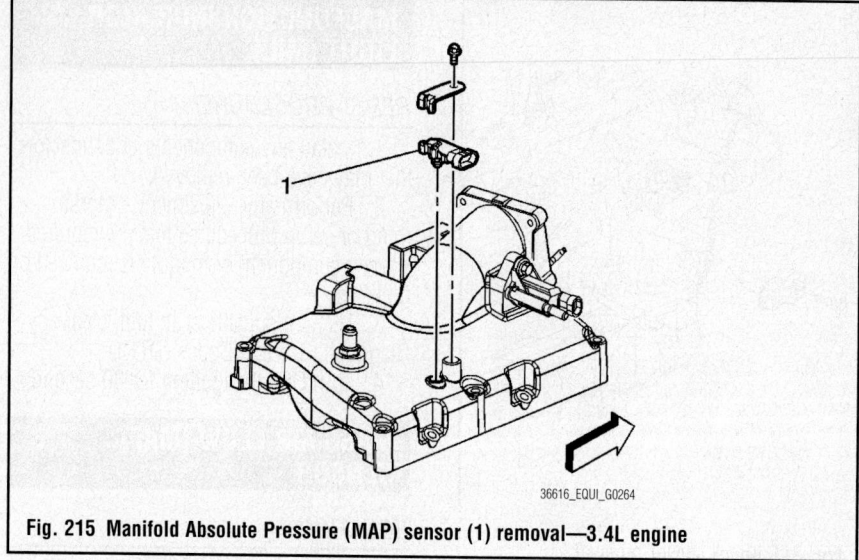

36616_EQUI_G0264

Fig. 215 Manifold Absolute Pressure (MAP) sensor (1) removal—3.4L engine

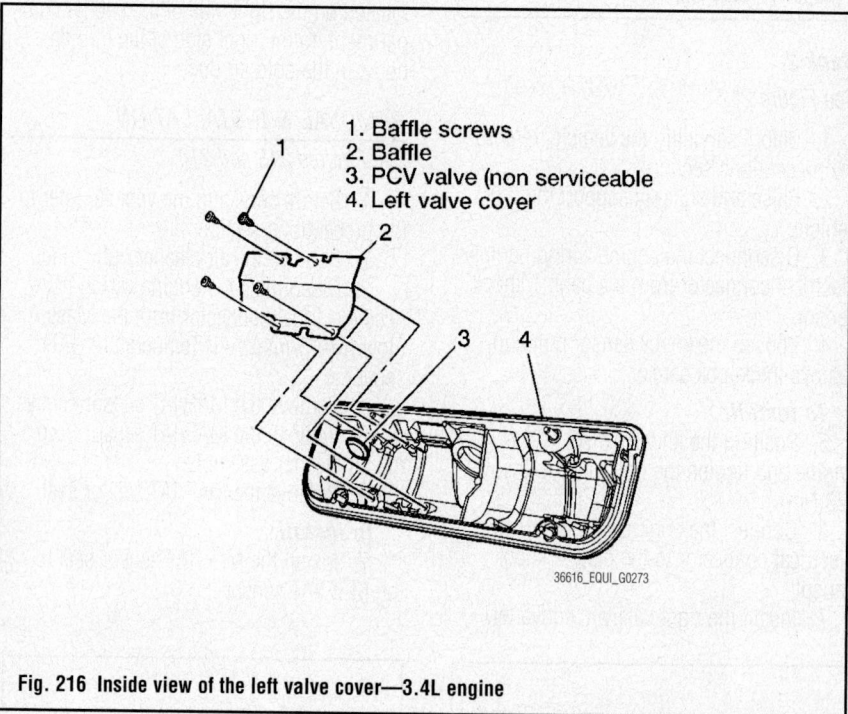

1. Baffle screws
2. Baffle
3. PCV valve (non serviceable)
4. Left valve cover

36616_EQUI_G0273

Fig. 216 Inside view of the left valve cover—3.4L engine

FUEL SYSTEM SERVICE PRECAUTIONS

Safety is the most important factor when performing not only fuel system maintenance but any type of maintenance. Failure to conduct maintenance and repairs in a safe manner may result in serious personal injury or death. Maintenance and testing of the vehicle's fuel system components can be accomplished safely and effectively by adhering to the following rules and guidelines.

• To avoid the possibility of fire and personal injury, always disconnect the negative battery cable unless the repair or test procedure requires that battery voltage be applied.

• Always relieve the fuel system pressure prior to disconnecting any fuel system component (injector, fuel rail, pressure regulator, etc.), fitting or fuel line connection. Exercise extreme caution whenever relieving fuel system pressure to avoid exposing skin, face and eyes to fuel spray. Please be advised that fuel under pressure may penetrate the skin or any part of the body that it contacts.

• Always place a shop towel or cloth around the fitting or connection prior to loosening to absorb any excess fuel due to spillage. Ensure that all fuel spillage (should it occur) is quickly removed from engine surfaces. Ensure that all fuel soaked cloths or towels are deposited into a suitable waste container.

• Always keep a dry chemical (Class B) fire extinguisher near the work area.

• Do not allow fuel spray or fuel vapors to come into contact with a spark or open flame.

• Always use a back-up wrench when loosening and tightening fuel line connection fittings. This will prevent unnecessary stress and torsion to fuel line piping.

• Always replace worn fuel fitting O-rings with new. Do not substitute fuel hose or equivalent where fuel pipe is installed.

Before servicing the vehicle, make sure to also refer to the precautions in the beginning of this section as well.

RELIEVING FUEL SYSTEM PRESSURE

FUEL PRESSURE RELIEF WITH OUT A FUEL PRESSURE GAUGE

✳✳ CAUTION

Always keep a dry chemical (Class B) fire extinguisher near the work area.

1. Before servicing the vehicle, refer to the precautions section.
2. If the fuel system requires repair, prevent fuel spillage by removing the fuel pump fuse.
3. Loosen the fuel fill cap in order to relieve the fuel tank vapor pressure.
4. Remove the engine cover, if required.
5. Remove the fuel rail service port cap.
6. Wrap a shop towel around the fuel rail service port and using a small flat-bladed tool, depress (open) the fuel rail test port valve.
7. Remove the shop towel from around the fuel rail service port, and place in an approved gasoline container.
8. Install the fuel rail service port cap.
9. Install the engine cover, if required.
10. Tighten the fuel fill cap.

FUEL PRESSURE RELIEF WITH A FUEL PRESSURE GAUGE

✳✳ CAUTION

Always keep a dry chemical (Class B) fire extinguisher near the work area.

1. Before servicing the vehicle, refer to the precautions section.
2. If the fuel system requires repair, prevent fuel spillage by removing the fuel pump fuse.
3. Remove the engine cover, if required.
4. Loosen the fuel fill cap in order to relieve the fuel tank vapor pressure.
5. Remove the fuel rail service port cap.

✳✳ CAUTION

Wrap a shop towel around the fuel pressure connection in order to reduce the risk of fire and personal injury. The towel will absorb any fuel leakage that occurs during the connection of the fuel pressure gage. Place the towel in an approved container when the connection of the fuel pressure gage is complete.

6. Wrap a shop towel around the fuel rail service port.
7. Connect the fuel pressure gauge to the fuel rail service port.
8. Place the hose on the fuel pressure gauge into an approved gasoline container.
9. Open the valve on the fuel pressure gauge in order to bleed any fuel from the fuel rail.
10. Close the valve on the fuel pressure gauge

11. Remove the hose on the fuel pressure gauge from the approved gasoline container.
12. Disconnect the fuel pressure gauge from the fuel rail service port.
13. Remove the shop towel from around the fuel rail service port, and place in an approved gasoline container.
14. Install the fuel rail service port cap.
15. Install the engine cover, if required.
16. Tighten the fuel fill cap.

FUEL FILTER

REMOVAL & INSTALLATION

The fuel filter is located in the primary fuel tank module.

FUEL LEVEL SENDING UNIT

LOCATION

The Primary Fuel Level Sending Unit is located inside of the right side of the fuel tank.

The Secondary Fuel Level Sending Unit is located inside of the left side of the fuel tank.

REMOVAL & INSTALLATION

Primary Sending Unit
See Figure 217.

✳✳ CAUTION

Always keep a dry chemical (Class B) fire extinguisher near the work area.

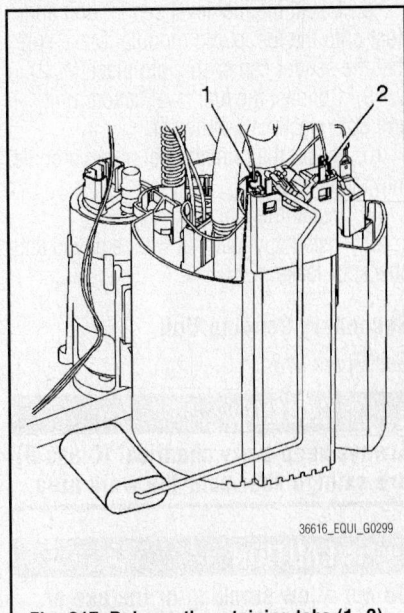

36616_EQUI_G0299

Fig. 217 Release the retaining tabs (1, 2)

⁜ **CAUTION**

Do not allow smoking or the use of open flames in the area where work on the fuel or EVAP system is taking place. Anytime work is being done on the fuel system, disconnect the negative battery cable, except for those tests where battery voltage is required.

⁜ **WARNING**

NEW fuel tank module seals are necessary each time the fuel tank module is serviced or removed. Obtain NEW seals for both the primary and secondary modules prior to beginning this service procedure.

1. Before servicing the vehicle, refer to the precautions section.
2. Relieve the fuel system pressure. Refer to Relieving Fuel System Pressure in the Fuel System section.
3. Ensure that the fuel level in the tank is less than ¼ full. If necessary, drain the fuel tank to at least this level.
4. Remove the fuel tank. Refer to Fuel Tank, Removal & Installation in the Fuel System section.
5. Remove the primary fuel pump module. Refer to Fuel Pump Module, Removal & Installation in the Fuel System section.
6. Disconnect the fuel level sender unit and float electrical connector from the underside of the top of the pump module.
7. Release the retaining tabs (1, 2) and remove the level sensor by sliding up.

To install:
8. Install the fuel level sender unit and float onto the fuel pump module. Make sure that the sender cap snaps into place (1, 2).
9. Connect the fuel level sender unit and float electrical connector.
10. Install the primary fuel pump module into the fuel tank.
11. Install the fuel tank.
12. Install any fuel that was removed and check for leaks.

Secondary Sending Unit
See Figure 218.

⁜ **CAUTION**

Always keep a dry chemical (Class B) fire extinguisher near the work area.

⁜ **CAUTION**

Do not allow smoking or the use of open flames in the area where work

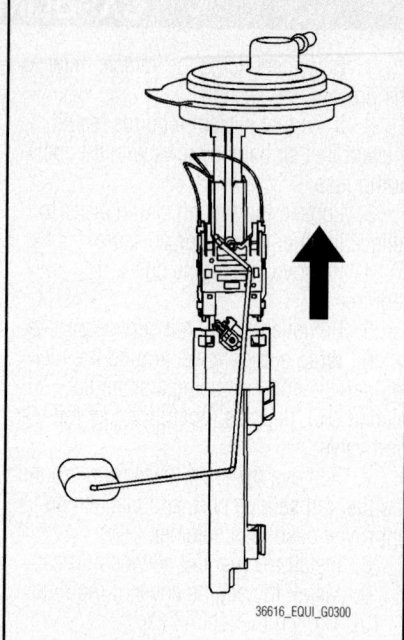

Fig. 218 Release the retaining tabs and remove the level sensor by sliding up

on the fuel or EVAP system is taking place. Anytime work is being done on the fuel system, disconnect the negative battery cable, except for those tests where battery voltage is required.

⁜ **WARNING**

NEW fuel tank module seals are necessary each time the fuel tank module is serviced or removed. Obtain NEW seals for both the primary and secondary modules prior to beginning this service procedure.

1. Before servicing the vehicle, refer to the precautions section.
2. Relieve the fuel system pressure. Refer to Relieving Fuel System Pressure in the Fuel System section.
3. Ensure that the fuel level in the tank is less than ¼ full. If necessary, drain the fuel tank to at least this level.
4. Remove the fuel tank. Refer to Fuel Tank, Removal & Installation in the Fuel System section.
5. Remove the secondary fuel pump module. Refer to Fuel Pump Module, Removal & Installation in the Fuel System section.
6. Disconnect the fuel level sender unit and float electrical connector from the underside of the top of the pump module.
7. Release the retaining tabs and remove the level sensor by sliding up.

To install:
8. Install the fuel level sender unit and float onto the fuel pump module. Make sure that the sender cap snaps into place.
9. Connect the fuel level sender unit and float electrical connector.
10. Install the secondary fuel pump module into the fuel tank.
11. Install the fuel tank.
12. Install any fuel that was removed and check for leaks.

FUEL PUMP MODULE

REMOVAL & INSTALLATION

Primary Module
See Figures 219 and 220.

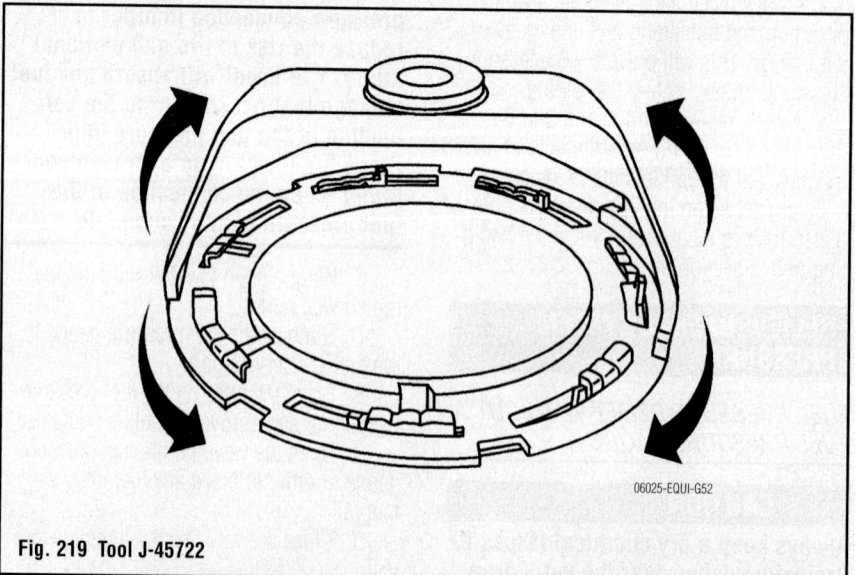

Fig. 219 Tool J-45722

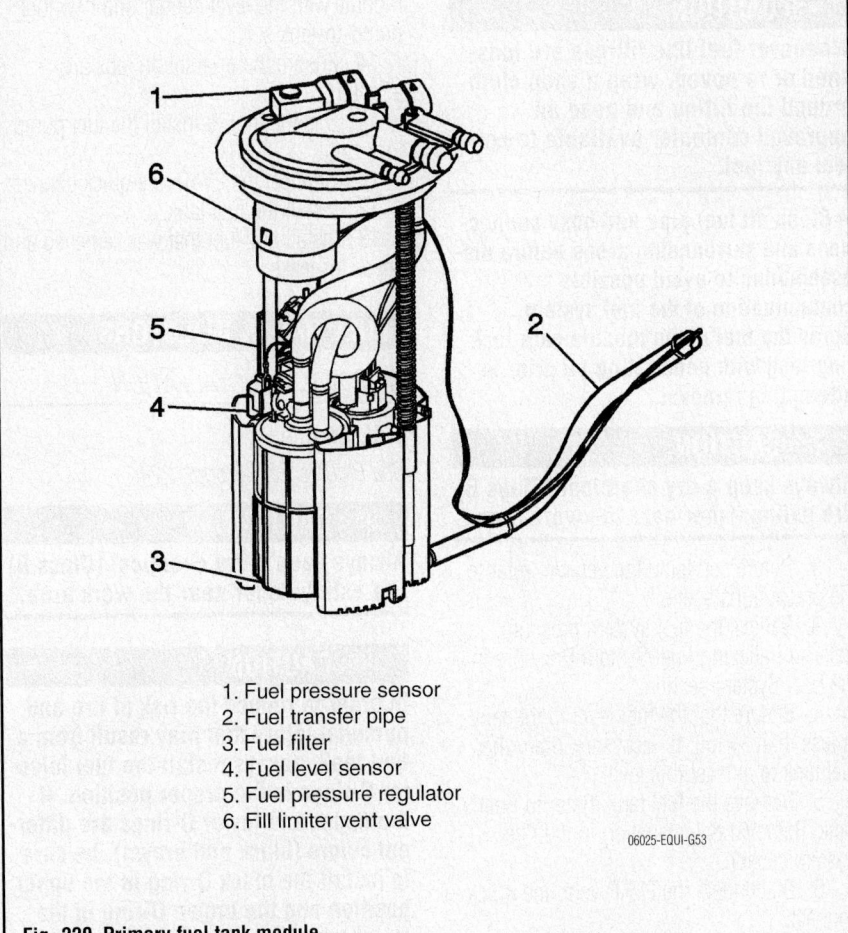

1. Fuel pressure sensor
2. Fuel transfer pipe
3. Fuel filter
4. Fuel level sensor
5. Fuel pressure regulator
6. Fill limiter vent valve

06025-EQUI-G53

Fig. 220 Primary fuel tank module

❋❋ **WARNING**

NEW fuel tank module seals are necessary each time the fuel tank module is serviced. Obtain NEW seals for both the primary and secondary modules prior to beginning this service procedure.

❋❋ **CAUTION**

Whenever fuel line fittings are loosened or removed, wrap a shop cloth around the fitting and have an approved container available to collect any fuel.

➡Clean all fuel pipe and hose connections and surrounding areas before disassembling to avoid possible contamination of the fuel system. Spray the fuel pump module cam-lock ring tang with penetrating oil prior to attempting removal.

❋❋ **CAUTION**

Always keep a dry chemical (Class B) fire extinguisher near the work area.

1. Before servicing the vehicle, refer to the precautions section.
2. Relieve the fuel system pressure. Refer to Relieving Fuel System Pressure in the Fuel System section.
3. Ensure that the fuel level in the tank is less than ¼ full. If necessary, drain the fuel tank to at least this level.
4. Remove the fuel tank. Refer to Fuel Tank, Removal & Installation in the Fuel System section.
5. Remove the secondary fuel pump module.
6. Disconnect the electrical connectors from the primary fuel pump module and fuel tank pressure sensor.

➡Avoid damaging the lock ring. Use only tool J-45722 to prevent damage to the lock ring.

➡Do not handle the fuel sender assembly by the fuel pipes. The amount of leverage generated by handling the fuel pipes could damage the joints.

❋❋ **WARNING**

Do NOT use impact tools. Significant force will be required to release the lock ring. The use of a hammer and screwdriver is not recommended. Secure the fuel tank in order to prevent fuel tank rotation.

7. Use tool J 45722, or equivalent and a long breaker-bar in order to unlock the fuel sender lock ring. Turn the fuel sender lock ring in a counterclockwise direction.
8. Disconnect the fuel feed and vent lines from the fuel tank.

➡To prevent bending of the sending unit float arm during removal, lift the pump module up slightly to disengage the orientation tabs in the tank and rotate the module 45 degrees.

9. Remove the primary fuel pump module assembly.

❋❋ **WARNING**

Always replace the fuel pump module-to-tank seal, O-ring, when the fuel pump module is removed.

10. Discard the fuel pump module-to-tank seal.

❋❋ **WARNING**

Some lock ring were manufactured with **DO NOT REUSE** stamped into them. These lock rings may be reused if they are not damaged or warped.

❋❋ **WARNING**

Inspect the lock ring for damage due to improper removal or installation procedures. If damage is found, install a NEW lock ring.

❋❋ **WARNING**

Check the lock ring for flatness.

11. Place the lock ring on a flat surface. Measure the clearance between to lock ring and the flat surface using a feeler gage at 7 points. If the warpage is less than 0.016 inch (0.41 mm), (the lock ring does not require replacement. If the warpage is greater than 0.016 inch (0.41 mm), the lock ring must be replaced.

To install:
12. Insert the new primary fuel pump module assembly with the level sender and the new fuel pump-to-tank seal. Ensure the orientation tabs are aligned.

✳✳ WARNING

Always replace the fuel sender seal when installing the fuel sender assembly. Replace the lock ring if necessary. Do not apply any type of lubrication in the seal groove.

13. Ensure the lock ring is installed with the correct side facing upward. A correctly installed lock ring will only turn in a clockwise direction.

14. Use tool J 45722 in order to install the fuel sender lock ring. Turn the fuel sender lock ring in a clockwise direction.

15. Connect the wiring harness to the primary fuel pump module and fuel tank pressure sensor.

16. Install the secondary fuel pump module.

17. Install the fuel tank.

18. Install any fuel that was removed and check for leaks.

Secondary Module

See Figure 221.

1. Before servicing the vehicle, refer to the Precautions Section.

✳✳ WARNING

A NEW fuel tank module seal is necessary each time the fuel tank module is serviced. Obtain a NEW seal prior to beginning this service procedure.

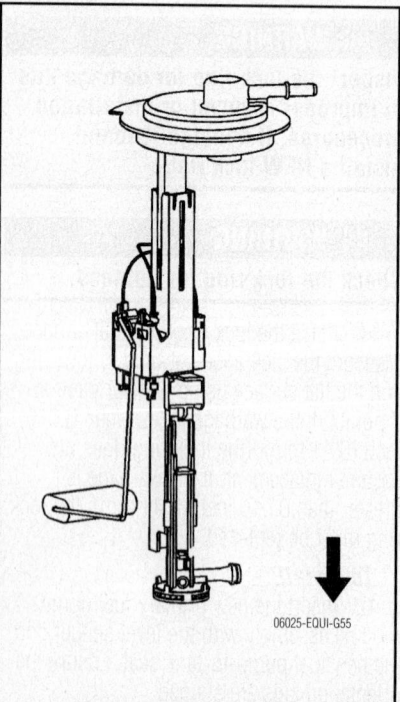

06025-EQUI-G55

Fig. 221 Secondary fuel tank module

✳✳ CAUTION

Whenever fuel line fittings are loosened or removed, wrap a shop cloth around the fitting and have an approved container available to collect any fuel.

➡ Clean all fuel pipe and hose connections and surrounding areas before disassembling to avoid possible contamination of the fuel system. Spray the fuel pump module cam-lock ring tang with penetrating oil prior to attempting removal.

✳✳ CAUTION

Always keep a dry chemical (Class B) fire extinguisher near the work area.

2. Before servicing the vehicle, refer to the precautions section.

3. Relieve the fuel system pressure. Refer to Relieving Fuel System Pressure in the Fuel System section.

4. Ensure that the fuel level in the tank is less than ¼ full. If necessary, drain the fuel tank to at least this level.

5. Remove the fuel tank. Refer to Fuel Tank, Removal & Installation in the Fuel System section.

6. Disconnect the EVAP vent line quick connect.

➡ To prevent retainer damage, do not attempt to remove the retainer with a 12 inch or shorter ratchet/breaker bar.

7. Use tool J39765-A and remove the fuel pump module retaining ring.

8. Disconnect the secondary level sensor electrical connector.

9. Disconnect the suction port attaching tube by pressing down on the tab.

➡ To prevent bending of the sending unit float arm during removal, lift the pump module up slightly to disengage the orientation tabs in the tank and rotate the module 45 degrees.

10. Remove the secondary fuel pump module.

✳✳ WARNING

Always replace the fuel pump module-to-tank seal, O-ring, when the fuel pump module is removed.

11. Discard the fuel pump module-to-tank seal.

To install:

12. Connect the suction port

13. Insert the new secondary fuel pump

module with the level sender and new fuel pump-to-tank seal.

14. Ensure the orientation tabs are aligned.

15. Use the tool to install the fuel pump lock ring.

16. Connect the EVAP line quick connect.

17. Install the fuel tank.

18. Install any fuel that was removed and check for leaks.

FUEL RAIL & INJECTORS

REMOVAL & INSTALLATION

3.4L Engine

See Figures 222 through 224.

✳✳ CAUTION

Always keep a dry chemical (Class B) fire extinguisher near the work area.

✳✳ CAUTION

In order to reduce the risk of fire and personal injury that may result from a fuel leak, always install the fuel injector O-rings in the proper position. If the upper and lower O-rings are different colors (black and brown), be sure to install the black O-ring in the upper position and the brown O-ring in the lower position on the fuel injector. The O-rings are the same size but are made of different materials.

✳✳ WARNING

When servicing the fuel rail assembly, precautions must be taken to prevent dirt and other contaminants from entering the fuel passages. It is recommended that the fittings be capped, and the holes be plugged during servicing.

1. Before servicing the vehicle, refer to the precautions section.

2. Relieve the fuel system pressure. Refer to Relieving Fuel System Pressure in the Fuel System section.

3. Remove the upper intake manifold. For additional information, refer to the following section, "Intake Manifold, Removal & Installation."

4. Disconnect the engine fuel feed pipe at the fuel rail.

5. Disconnect the main fuel injector harness electrical connector.

6. Disconnect the coolant temperature sensor and camshaft position sensor electrical connectors

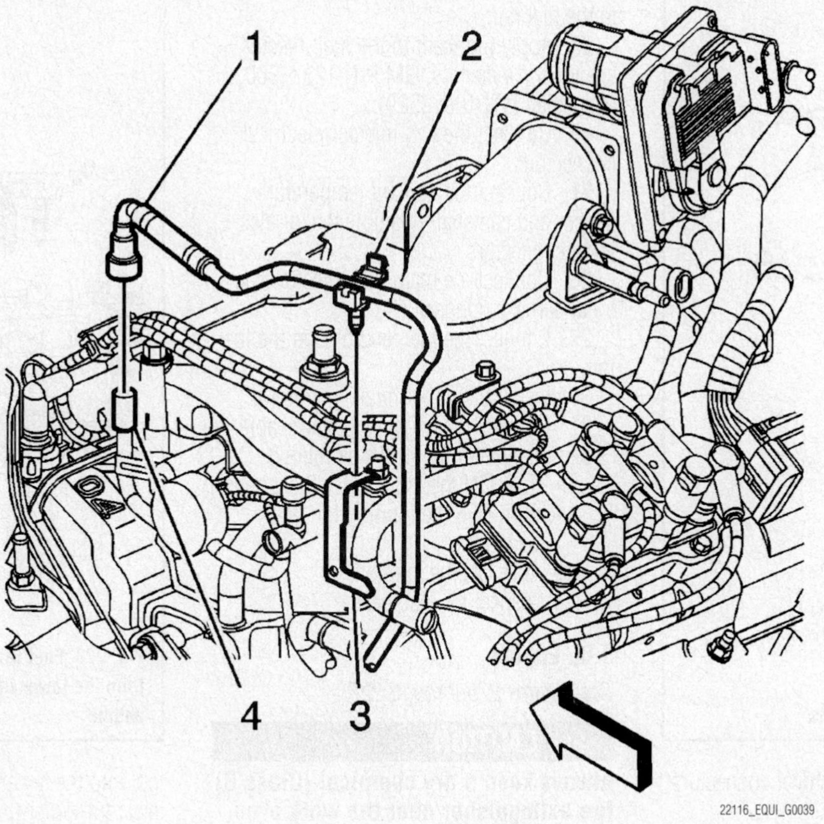
1
2
3
4
22116_EQUI_G0039

Fig. 222 Disconnect the fuel supply pipe (1) at the fuel rail (4).

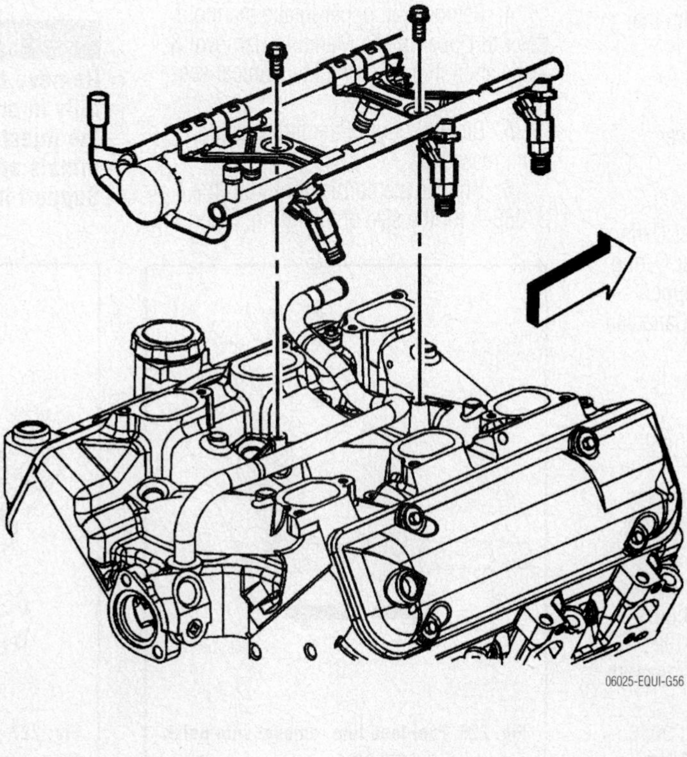
06025-EQUI-G56

Fig. 223 Fuel rail assembly

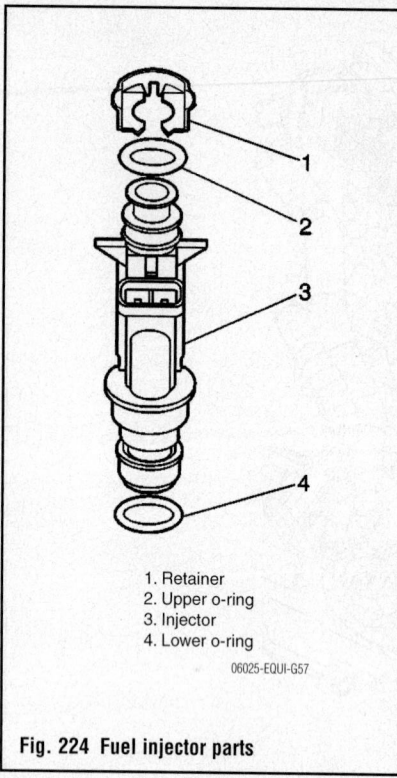

1. Retainer
2. Upper o-ring
3. Injector
4. Lower o-ring

06025-EQUI-G57

Fig. 224 Fuel injector parts

7. Disconnect the electrical connectors from the fuel injectors.

8. Remove the fuel rail retaining bolts.

9. Remove the fuel rail assembly.

10. Remove the injector O-ring seal from the spray tip end of each injector.

11. Remove the fuel injector retaining clip.

12. Remove the fuel injector from the fuel rail.

13. Remove the fuel injector upper O-ring.

14. Remove the fuel injector lower O-ring.

To install:

15. Install the fuel injector upper O-ring.

16. Install the fuel injector lower O-ring.

17. Lubricate the fuel injector upper O-ring using GM P/N 12345616 (Canadian P/N 993182).

18. Install the fuel injector to the fuel rail.

19. Install the fuel injector retaining clip.

20. Lubricate the fuel injector O-rings using GM P/N 12345616, (Canadian P/N 993182)

21. Install the fuel injector nozzles into the lower intake manifold injector bores.

22. Press on the fuel rail using the palms of both hands until the fuel injectors are fully seated.

23. Install the fuel rail attaching bolts. Tighten the bolt to 89 inch lbs. (10 Nm).

24. Install the injector electrical harness to the fuel rail.

25. Apply lubricant to the fuel injector electrical connectors; GM P/N 12377900, (Canadian P/N 10953529).

26. Connect the fuel injector electrical connectors.

27. Connect the coolant temperature sensor and camshaft position sensor electrical connectors

28. Connect the main fuel injector electrical harness connector.

29. Connect the fuel feed pipe at the fuel rail.

30. Install the upper intake manifold.

31. Connect the negative battery cable.

32. Inspect for fuel leaks as follows:
 • Turn ON the ignition for 2 seconds.
 • Turn OFF the ignition for 10 seconds.
 • Turn ON the ignition.
 • Inspect for fuel leaks.

3.6L Engine

See Figures 225 through 227.

❋❋ CAUTION

Always keep a dry chemical (Class B) fire extinguisher near the work area.

1. Before servicing the vehicle, refer to the precautions section.

2. Relieve the fuel system pressure.

3. Remove the fuel feed line quick connect fitting retainer.

4. Remove the upper intake manifold. Refer to Upper Intake Manifold Removal & Installation in the Engine Mechanical section.

5. Blow dirt out of the fitting using compressed air.

6. Choose the correct tool from the J 37088-A for the size of the fitting. Insert the

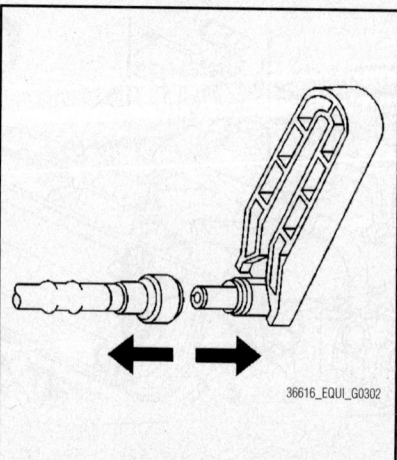

36616_EQUI_G0302

Fig. 225 Fuel feed line removal with quick connect tool J 37088-A

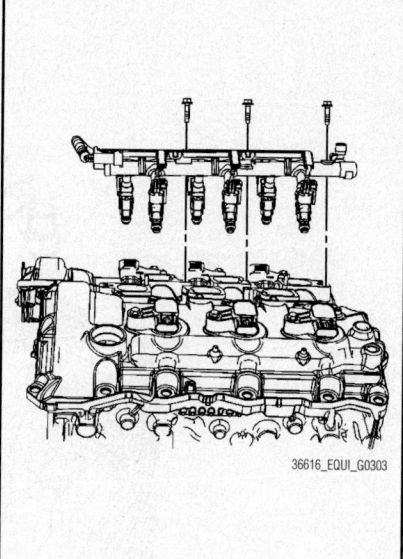

36616_EQUI_G0303

Fig. 226 Fuel rail removal with injectors from the lower intake manifold—3.6L engine

tool into the female connector, then push inward in order to release the locking tabs. Pull the connection apart.

7. Use compressed air in order to remove any debris from the around the area where the fuel injectors enter the lower intake manifold.

8. Remove the fuel rail bolts.

❋❋ WARNING

Remove the fuel rail assembly carefully in order to prevent damage to the injector electrical connector terminals and the injector spray tips. Support the fuel rail after the fuel rail

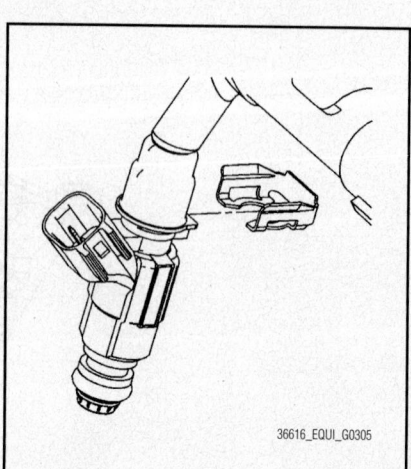

36616_EQUI_G0305

Fig. 227 Fuel injector retainer clip removal

is removed in order to avoid damaging the fuel rail components. Cap the fittings and plug the holes when servicing the fuel system in order to prevent dirt and other contaminants from entering open pipes and passages.

9. Remove the fuel rail with fuel injectors from the lower intake manifold.

10. Disengage the fuel injector electrical connector lock.

11. Remove the fuel injector electrical connector.

12. Remove the fuel injector retainer clip.

13. Remove the fuel injector.

14. Remove and discard the fuel injector seals.

To install:

15. Install new fuel injector seals.

16. Install the fuel injector.

17. Install the fuel injector retainer clip.

18. Install the fuel injector electrical connector.

19. Engage the fuel injector electrical connector lock.

20. Carefully Install the fuel rail with fuel injectors to the lower intake manifold.

➡ **Apply a little petroleum jelly to the lower injector O-rings to help with the installation.**

21. Install the fuel rail bolts and tighten to 89 inch lbs. (10 Nm).

22. Before installing the fuel feed line, use a clean shop towel in order to wipe off the male pipe end.

23. Inspect both ends of the fitting for dirt and burrs. Clean or replace the components as required.

24. Apply a few drops of clean engine oil to the male pipe end.

25. Push both sides of the fitting together in order to snap the retaining tabs into place.

26. Once installed, pull on both sides of the fitting in order to make sure the connection is secure.

27. Install the retainer to the quick-connect fitting.

28. Install the upper intake manifold.

29. Pressurize the fuel system and check for leaks as follows:

- Turn ON the ignition for 2 seconds.
- Turn OFF the ignition for 10 seconds.
- Turn ON the ignition.
- Inspect for fuel leaks.

FUEL TANK

REMOVAL & INSTALLATION
See Figures 228 and 229.

✻✻ CAUTION

Always keep a dry chemical (Class B) fire extinguisher near the work area.

✻✻ CAUTION

Do not allow smoking or the use of open flames in the area where work on the fuel or EVAP system is taking place. Anytime work is being done on the fuel system, disconnect the negative battery cable, except for those tests where battery voltage is required.

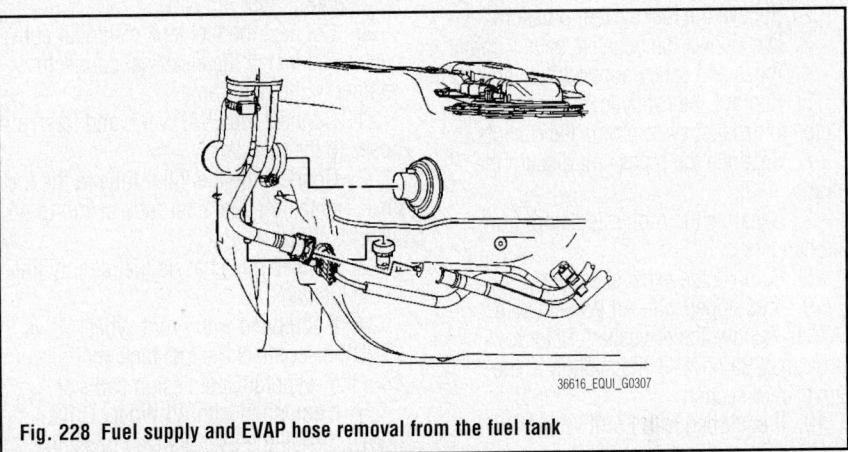

36616_EQUI_G0307

Fig. 228 Fuel supply and EVAP hose removal from the fuel tank

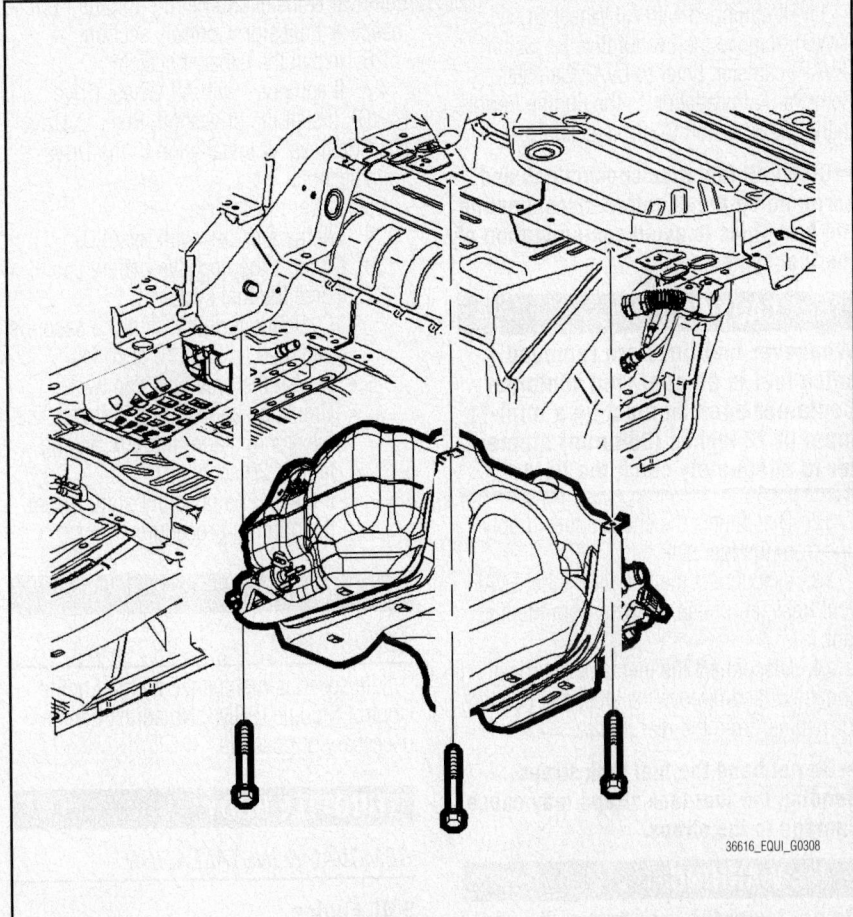

36616_EQUI_G0308

Fig. 229 Lower the fuel tank from the underbody of the vehicle

1. Ensure that the fuel level in the tank is less than ¼ full. If necessary, drain the fuel tank to at least this level.

✳✳ CAUTION

Fuel supply lines will remain pressurized for long periods of time after the engine is shutdown. This pressure must be relieved before servicing the fuel system.

2. Relieve the fuel system pressure.
3. Disconnect the negative battery cable.
4. Raise and safely support the vehicle.
5. Remove the catalytic converter pipe flange to exhaust system pipe flange nuts.
6. Separate the pipes and discard the gasket.
7. Separate the rubber isolators from the hangers.
8. Remove the exhaust system.
9. If equipped with All Wheel Drive (AWD), remove the driveshaft. Refer to Driveshaft Removal & Installation in the Drive Train section.
10. If equipped with Front Wheel Drive (FWD), disconnect the fuel tank vent pipe from the evaporative emission canister.
11. If equipped with All Wheel Drive (AWD), remove the Evaporative Emission (EVAP) canister. Refer to EVAP Canister Removal & Installation in the Engine Performance & Emission Controls section.

➡ **Clean all fuel pipe connections and surrounding areas before disconnecting the fuel pipes to avoid contamination of the fuel system.**

✳✳ CAUTION

Whenever fuel lines are removed, catch fuel in an approved container. Container opening must be a minimum of 12 inches (300 mm) diameter to adequately catch the fluid.

12. Disconnect the chassis fuel supply line from the fuel tank.
13. Disconnect the fuel filler tube, EVAP vent hose, and fresh air hose from the fuel tank.
14. Disconnect the fuel tank electrical connector and remove the electrical connector retainer from the rear frame.

➡ **Do not bend the fuel tank straps. Bending the fuel tank straps may cause damage to the straps.**

✳✳ WARNING

Do not lower the rear frame. It is not necessary to lower the rear frame for fuel tank removal.

15. Support the fuel tank.
16. Remove the fuel tank strap bolts and fuel tank straps.
17. Lower the fuel tank from the underbody of the vehicle.

To install:

18. Install the fuel tank heat shield and fuel tank assembly to the vehicle.
19. Install the fuel tank straps and the fuel tank strap-to-body bolts. Tighten the bolts to 18 ft. lbs. (25 Nm).
20. Connect the fuel tank electrical connector and install the electrical connector retainer to the rear frame.
21. Connect the EVAP vent, and fresh air hoses to the fuel tank.
22. Connect the fuel filler tube to the fuel tank. Tighten the fuel filler tube clamp to 44 inch lbs. (5 Nm).
23. Connect the chassis fuel supply line to the fuel tank.
24. If equipped with Front Wheel Drive (FWD), disconnect the fuel tank vent pipe from the evaporative emission canister.
25. If equipped with All Wheel Drive (AWD), Install the Evaporative Emission (EVAP) canister. Refer to EVAP Canister Removal & Installation in the Engine Performance & Emission Controls section.
26. Install the exhaust system.
27. If equipped with All Wheel Drive (AWD), Install the driveshaft. Refer to Driveshaft Removal & Installation in the Drive Train section.
28. Lower the vehicle.
29. Fill the fuel tank with gasoline.
30. Connect the negative battery cable.
31. Prime the fuel system:
- Cycle the ignition ON for 5 seconds and then OFF for 10 seconds.
- Repeat the previous step twice.
- Crank the engine until it starts. The maximum starter motor cranking time is 20 seconds.
- If the engine does not start, repeat the priming procedure.

IDLE SPEED

ADJUSTMENT

Idle speed is maintained by the Engine Control Module (ECM). No adjustment is necessary or possible.

THROTTLE BODY

REMOVAL & INSTALLATION

3.4L Engine

1. Before servicing the vehicle, refer to the precautions section.

2. Remove the air cleaner intake duct.
3. Remove the heater outlet pipe.
4. Cover the throttle body opening with a shop towel and use the shop air to remove any dirt at the base of the throttle body.
5. Disconnect the TAC module electrical connector by pulling up on the connector lock to release the connector from the TAC module
6. Remove the throttle body bolts.
7. Remove the throttle body from the intake manifold.
8. Block the intake manifold opening with a clean shop towel to prevent dirt from entering.
9. Remove the throttle body studs ONLY If replacement of stud is necessary.

To install:

10. Install the throttle body studs if previously removed and tighten to 53 inch lbs. (6 Nm).
11. Install the throttle body to the intake manifold.
12. Install the throttle body bolts and tighten to 89 inch lbs. (10 Nm).
13. Connect the TAC module electrical connector to the TAC module then press down the connector lock in order to secure the TAC module electrical connector.
14. Install the heater outlet pipe.
15. Install the air cleaner intake duct.

3.6L Engine

See Figure 230.

➡ **The Throttle Actuator Control (TAC) module is not replaceable separate of the throttle body assembly. If the TAC module requires replacement the entire throttle body assembly must be replaced.**

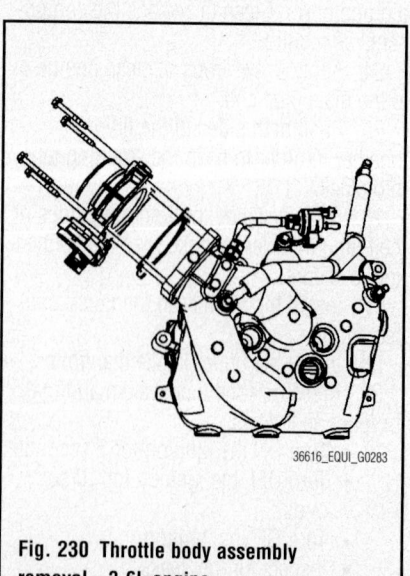

36616_EQUI_G0283

Fig. 230 Throttle body assembly removal—3.6L engine

1. Before servicing the vehicle, refer to the precautions section.
2. Remove the air cleaner outlet duct.
3. Disconnect the engine wiring harness electrical connector from the Throttle Actuator Control (TAC) module.
4. Remove the throttle body bolts.

5. Remove the throttle body and gasket. Discard the gasket.

To install:
6. Position a NEW throttle body gasket to the upper intake manifold.
7. Position the throttle body to the upper intake manifold.

8. Install the throttle body bolts and tighten to 89 inch lbs. (10 Nm).
9. Connect the engine wiring harness electrical connector to the TAC module.
10. Install the air cleaner outlet duct.

HEATING & AIR CONDITIONING SYSTEM

BLOWER MOTOR

REMOVAL & INSTALLATION

See Figure 231.

1. Before servicing the vehicle, refer to the precautions section.
2. Remove the right sound insulator panel.
3. Disconnect the electrical connector from the blower motor.
4. Remove the blower motor screws from the HVAC module.
5. Remove the blower motor from the HVAC module.

To install:
6. Install the blower motor to the HVAC module. Tighten the mounting screws to 13 inch lbs. (1.5 Nm).
7. Connect the electrical connector to the blower motor.
8. Install the right sound insulator panel.

HEATER CORE

REMOVAL & INSTALLATION

See Figures 232 and 233.

1. Before servicing the vehicle, refer to the precautions section.
2. Disable the frontal and curtain air bags.
3. Disconnect the negative battery cable.
4. Recover the refrigerant.
5. Drain the engine coolant.
6. Remove the HVAC module. Refer to HVAC Module, Removal & Installation in the Heating & Air Conditioning section.
7. Remove the heater core cover screws from the HVAC module.
8. Remove the heater core cover from the HVAC module.
9. Remove the heater core from the HVAC module.

To install:
10. Install the heater core to the HVAC module.
11. Install the heater core cover to the HVAC module.
12. Install the heater core cover screws

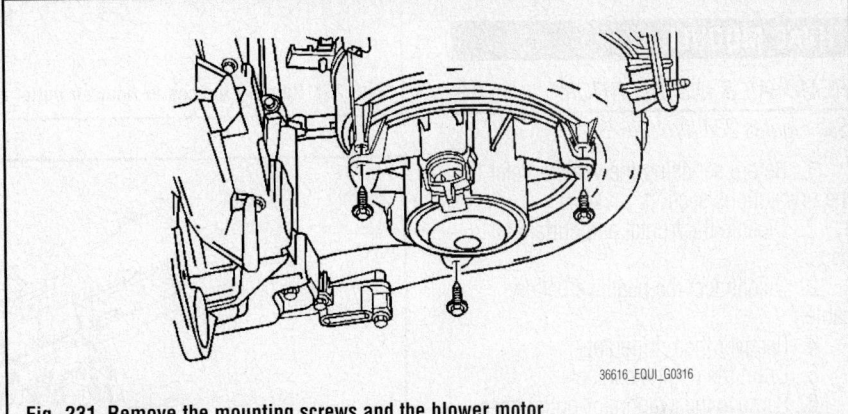

Fig. 231 Remove the mounting screws and the blower motor

36616_EQUI_G0316

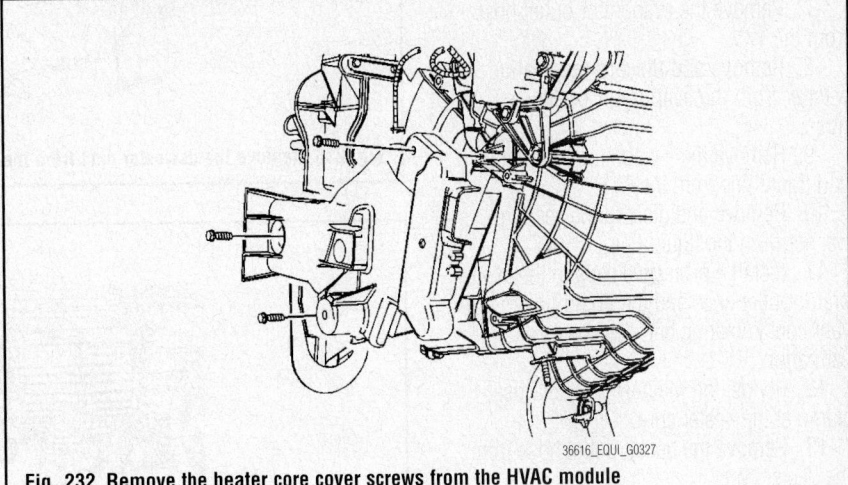

Fig. 232 Remove the heater core cover screws from the HVAC module

36616_EQUI_G0327

Fig. 233 Remove the heater core from the HVAC module

36616_EQUI_G0328

to the HVAC module. Tighten the screw to 13 inch lbs. (2 Nm)

13. Install the HVAC module to the vehicle.

14. Enable the frontal and curtain air bags.

15. Connect the negative battery cable.

16. Fill and bleed the cooling system.

17. Evacuate and charge the A/C system.

18. Test the affected A/C joints for leaks using a halogen leak detector.

HVAC MODULE

REMOVAL & INSTALLATION

See Figures 234 through 236.

1. Before servicing the vehicle, refer to the precautions section.

2. Disable the frontal and curtain air bags.

3. Disconnect the negative battery cable.

4. Recover the refrigerant.

5. Drain the engine coolant.

6. Remove the evaporator outlet hose and liquid line nut from the Thermal Expansion Valve (TXV).

7. Remove the evaporator outlet hose from the TXV.

8. Remove and discard the sealing washer from the evaporator outlet hose.

9. Remove the evaporator outlet hose and liquid line from the TXV.

10. Remove and discard the sealing washer from the liquid line.

11. Install a protective caps to the evaporator outlet hose and the liquid line to prevent contamination and desiccant saturation.

12. Reposition the heater outlet hose clamp at the heater core.

13. Remove the heater outlet hose from the heater core.

14. Reposition the heater inlet hose clamp at the heater core.

15. Remove the heater inlet hose at the heater core.

16. Plug the heater core and the evaporator core with clean towels to prevent spillage when the HVAC module is removed.

17. Remove the HVAC module seal nuts from the front of dash.

18. Remove the Instrument Panel (I/P) retainer.

19. Remove the shift control bracket as follows:
- Set parking brake.
- Place the shift control in the neutral position.

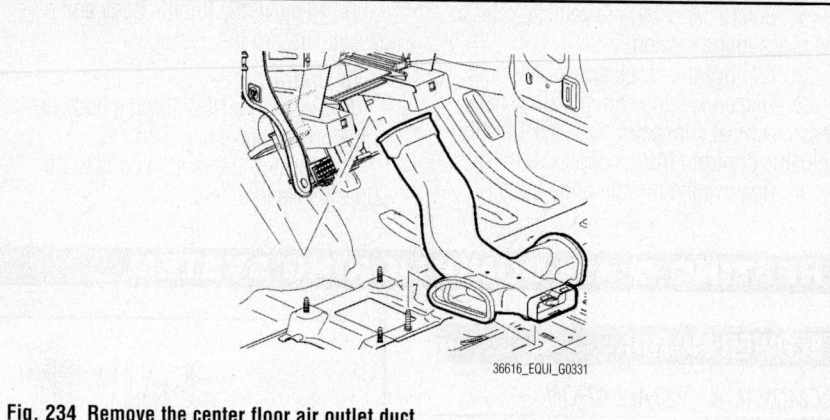

Fig. 234 Remove the center floor air outlet duct

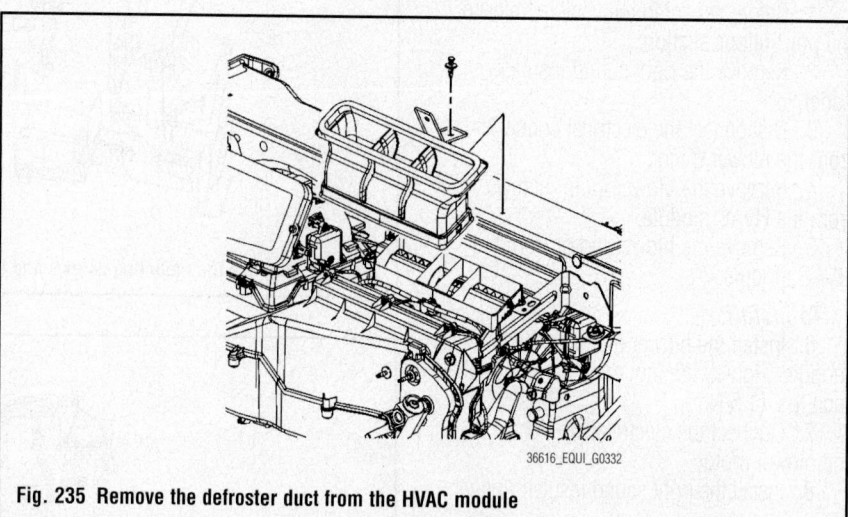

Fig. 235 Remove the defroster duct from the HVAC module

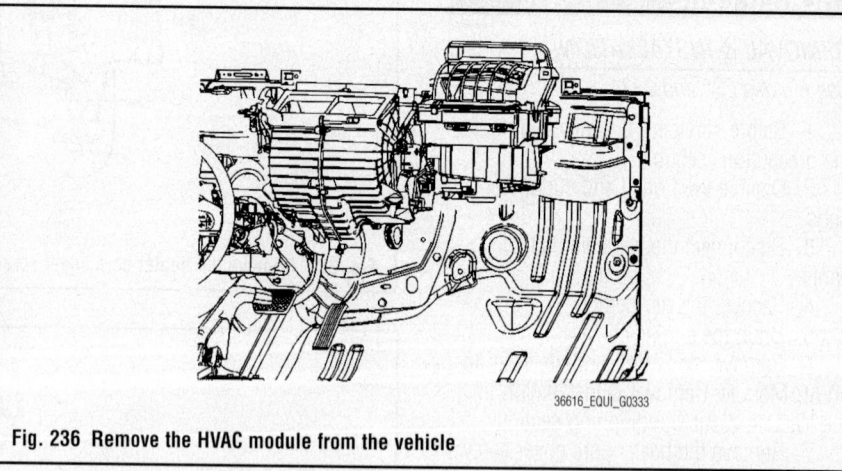

Fig. 236 Remove the HVAC module from the vehicle

- Apply careful downward pressure to the bezel to separate the bezel from the shift lever knob.
- Loosen the shift control lever knob screw approximately 4-5 turns, remove the knob. It is not necessary to fully remove the screw from the shift control lever knob.
- Remove the center trim bezel.
- Remove the console trim plate.
- Disconnect the shift control cable.
- Disconnect the shift control electrical connector.
- Remove the shift control bracket mounting nuts.
- Remove the shift control bracket.

20. Remove the center floor air outlet duct by sliding the duct forward then up at the rear

21. Remove the center I/P air outlet duct retainers from the instrument panel tie bar.

22. Remove the center I/P air outlet duct from the instrument panel tie bar.

23. Remove the instrument panel tie bar.

24. Disconnect the blower motor electrical connector from the I/P wire harness.

25. Disconnect the blower motor control module electrical connector from the I/P wire harness.

26. Disconnect the HVAC module electrical connector from the I/P wire harness.

27. Remove the defroster duct retainer from the instrument panel tie bar.

28. Remove the defroster duct from the HVAC module.

29. Disconnect the I/P wire harness clips from the HVAC module.

30. Remove the HVAC module from the vehicle.

To install:

➥Make sure the HVAC module seals are flush and even as they meet their mating surfaces. This will reduce the chance of leaks and ensure proper fit.

31. Inspect the front of dash seal for proper alignment.

32. Inspect the seal mating surfaces to ensure there are no obstructions.

33. Position the HVAC module in the vehicle.

34. Install, but do not tighten, the seal nuts to the front of dash.

35. Install the instrument panel tie bar

➥New front of dash seal nuts must be used to prevent leaks.

36. Tighten the HVAC module seal nuts to the front of dash. Draw the HVAC module to the front of dash evenly by alternating between the seal nuts. Tighten the nuts to 71 inch lbs. (8 Nm).

37. Install the defroster duct to the HVAC module.

38. Install the defroster duct retainer to the instrument panel tie bar.

39. Connect the I/P wire harness clips to the HVAC module.

40. Connect the blower motor electrical connector to the I/P wire harness.

41. Connect the blower motor control module electrical connector to the I/P wire harness.

42. Connect the HVAC module electrical connector to the I/P wire harness.

43. Install the center I/P duct to the instrument panel tie bar.

44. Install the center I/P duct retainers to the instrument panel tie bar.

45. Install the center floor air outlet by sliding forward onto the front floor air outlet then down and rearward over the rear floor air outlet.

46. Install the shift control bracket as follows:

- Install the shift control bracket and retaining nuts Tighten the nuts to 18 ft. lbs. (25 Nm).
- Connect the shift control electrical connector.

- Connect the shift control cable.
- Install the console trim plate.
- Install the center trim bezel. Push inward and down to engage the retainers.
- Install the shift control knob and tighten the set screw to 13 inch lbs. (2 Nm). Lift the bezel up to the shift lever knob until a click sound is heard.
- Place the shift control in the park position.
- Release the parking brake.

47. Install the I/P retainer.

48. Install the heater inlet and outlet hoses to the heater core.

49. Install the heater inlet and outlet hose clamp to the heater core

50. Ensure the mating surfaces are clean and free of debris, and install new seal washers to the evaporator outlet hose and the liquid line.

51. Install the evaporator outlet hose and the liquid line to the TXV.

52. Install the evaporator outlet hose and liquid line nut to the TXV. Tighten to 15 ft. lbs. (20 Nm).

53. Enable the frontal and curtain air bags.

54. Connect the negative battery cable.

55. Fill and bleed the cooling system.

56. Evacuate and charge the A/C system.

57. Test the affected A/C joints for leaks using a halogen leak detector.

STEERING

POWER RACK & PINION STEERING GEAR

REMOVAL & INSTALLATION

Electronic Power Steering (EPS)
See Figures 237 through 239.

✳✳ WARNING

With wheels of the vehicle facing straight ahead, secure the steering wheel utilizing steering column anti-rotation pin, steering column lock, or a strap to prevent rotation. Locking of the steering column will prevent damage and a possible malfunction of the SRS system.

1. Before servicing the vehicle, refer to the precautions section.

2. Disable the SRS air bag system.

3. Disconnect the negative battery cable.

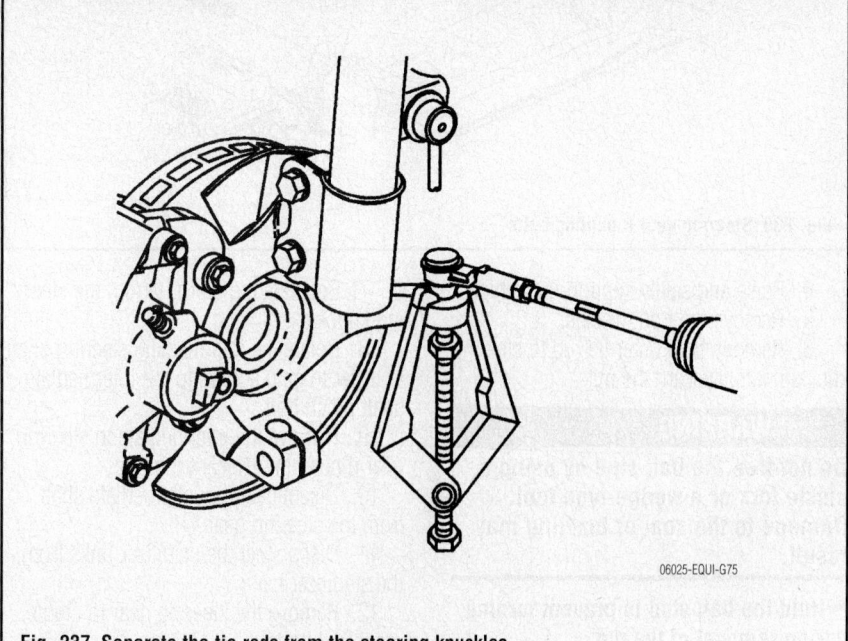

06025-EQUI-G75

Fig. 237 Separate the tie rods from the steering knuckles

06025-EQUI-G76

Fig. 238 Remove the intermediate to steering gear pinch bolt

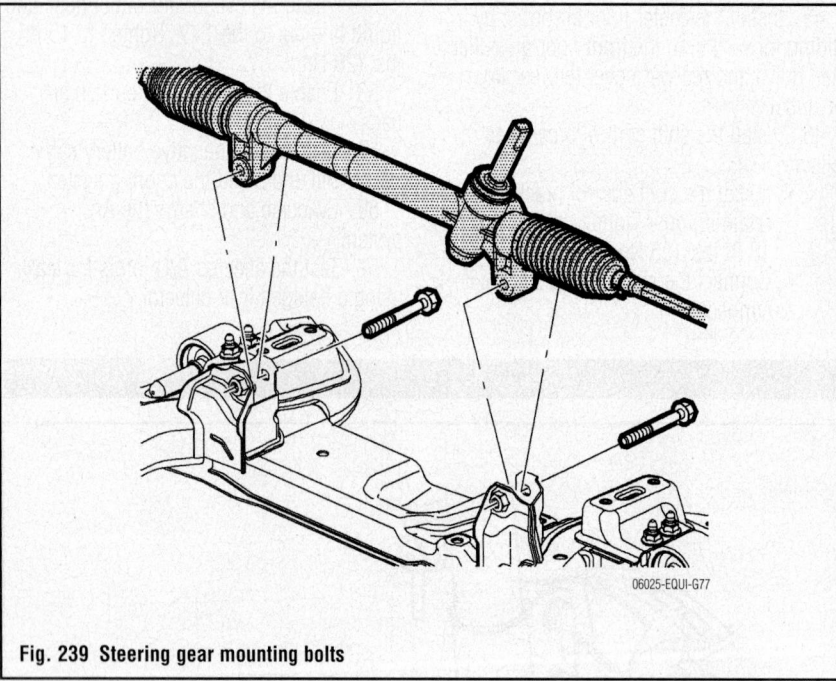

06025-EQUI-G77

Fig. 239 Steering gear mounting bolts

4. Raise and safely support the vehicle.
5. Remove the front wheels.
6. Remove both outer tie rod to steering knuckle nuts. Discard the nuts.

✳✳ WARNING

Do not free the ball stud by using a pickle fork or a wedge-type tool. Damage to the seal or bushing may result.

➡**Hold the ball stud to prevent turning during removal of the nut.**

7. Separate the tie rods from the steering knuckles.
8. Rotate the intermediate steering shaft in order to gain access to the intermediate shaft pinch bolt.
9. Remove the intermediate to steering gear pinch bolt. Discard the bolt.
10. Disconnect the intermediate shaft from the steering gear.
11. Disconnect the stabilizer links from the stabilizer bar.
12. Remove the steering gear to cradle mounting bolts.

13. Remove the steering gear through the right side of the vehicle.
14. With heat shield equipped steering gears, remove the heat shield. Save for installation.

To install:

15. If applicable, install the heat shield.

➡**Ensure the stabilizer is swung in the uppermost position for gear clearance.**

16. Install the steering gear from the right side of the vehicle.
17. Center the gear mounting bushings into the cradle supports.
18. Hand start both steering gear to cradle mounting bolts. Tighten the bolts to 81 ft. lbs. (110 Nm).
19. Connect the intermediate shaft to the steering gear and install a new pinch bolt. Tighten the intermediate pinch bolt to 25 ft. lbs. (34 Nm).
20. Connect the stabilizer links to the stabilizer bar.

➡**Hold the ball stud to prevent turning during installation of the nut.**

21. Connect the tie rod to the knuckle and install a new nut. Tighten the nut to 44 ft. lbs. (60 Nm).
22. Install the front wheels.
23. Enable the SRS air bag system.
24. Connect the negative battery cable.
25. Check the front wheel alignment and align as necessary.
26. Lower the vehicle.

Hydraulic Power Steering (EPS)

See Figures 240 through 242.

✳✳ WARNING

With wheels of the vehicle facing straight ahead, secure the steering wheel utilizing steering column anti-rotation pin, steering column lock, or a strap to prevent rotation. Locking of the steering column will prevent damage and a possible malfunction of the SRS system.

1. Before servicing the vehicle, refer to the precautions section.
2. Disable the SRS air bag system.
3. Disconnect the negative battery cable.
4. Raise and safely support the vehicle.
5. Remove the front wheels.
6. Remove both outer tie rod to steering knuckle nuts. Discard the nuts.

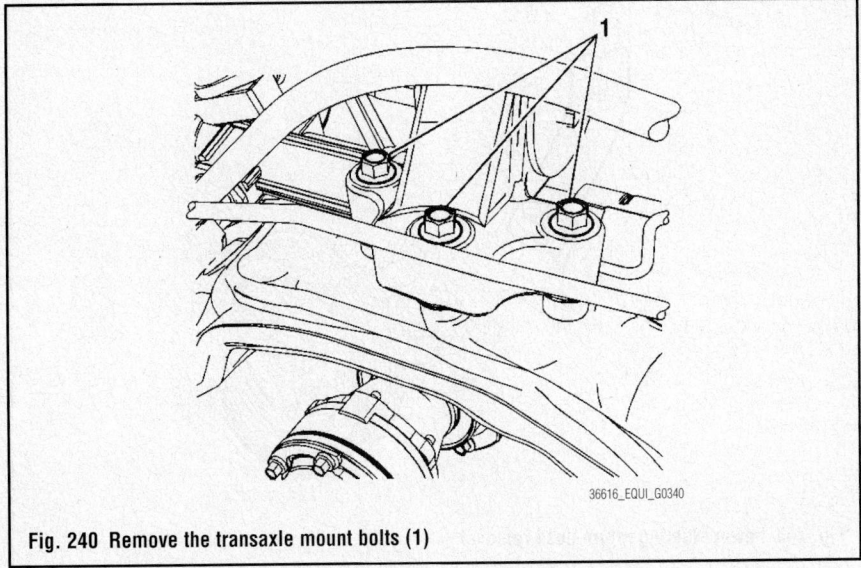

Fig. 240 Remove the transaxle mount bolts (1)

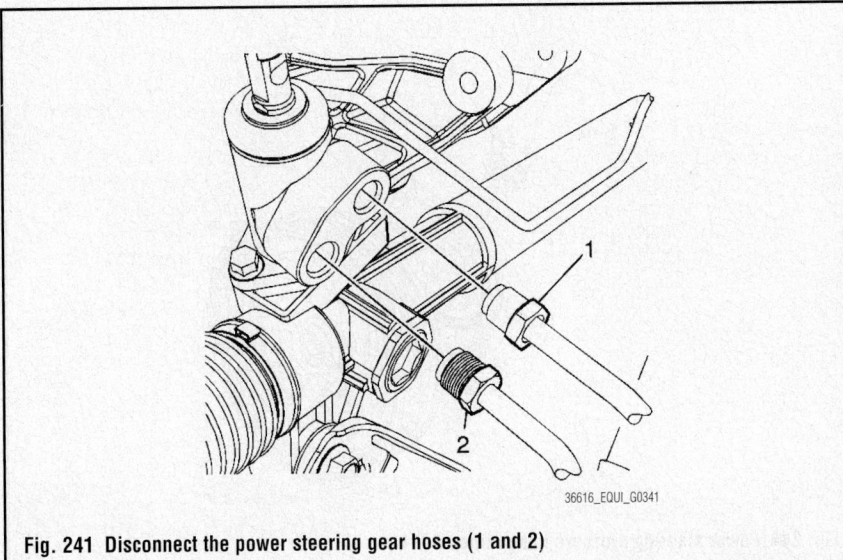

Fig. 241 Disconnect the power steering gear hoses (1 and 2)

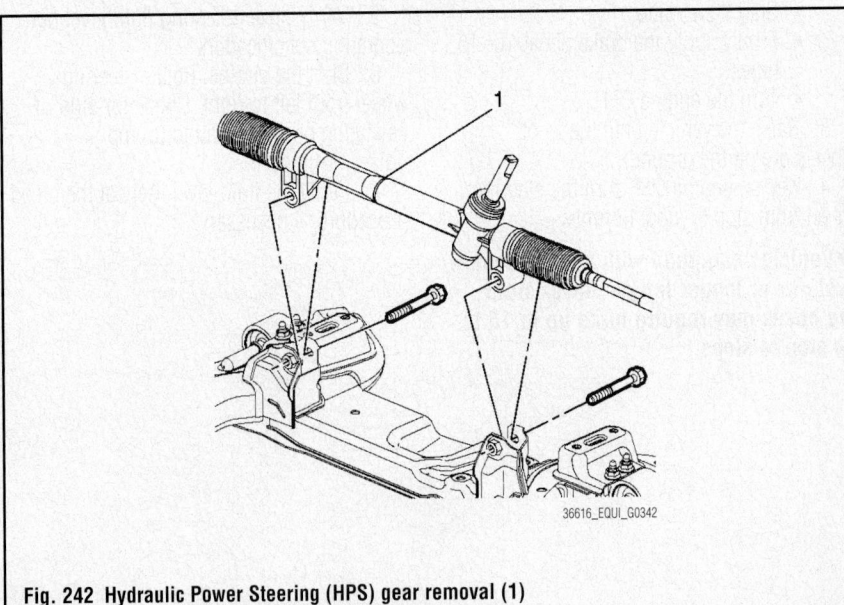

Fig. 242 Hydraulic Power Steering (HPS) gear removal (1)

✳✳ WARNING

Do not free the ball stud by using a pickle fork or a wedge-type tool. Damage to the seal or bushing may result.

→Hold the ball stud to prevent turning during removal of the nut.

7. Rotate the intermediate steering shaft in order to gain access to the intermediate shaft pinch bolt.

8. Remove the intermediate to steering gear pinch bolt. Discard the bolt.

9. Disconnect the intermediate shaft from the steering gear.

10. Place drain pans under the vehicle as needed.

11. Remove the transaxle mount through bolt.

12. Remove the transaxle mount bolts (1) and position the transaxle mount aside.

13. Disconnect the power steering gear inlet hose and the power steering cooler hose from the power steering gear.

14. If equipped, remove the power steering gear hoses bracket.

15. Remove the power steering gear bolts (1).

16. Remove the power steering gear through the left wheel house area.

17. Transfer any parts as needed.

To install:

18. Position the power steering gear into the vehicle through the left wheel house area.

19. Install the power steering gear mounting bolts and tighten to 81 ft. lbs. (110 Nm).

20. If equipped, install the power steering gear hoses bracket and tighten the mounting bolt to 80 inch lbs. (9 Nm).

21. Install the power steering hoses and tighten to 18 ft. lbs. (25 Nm).

22. Install the transaxle mount and transaxle mount bolts, tighten the bolts to 37 ft. lbs. (50 Nm).

23. Install the transaxle mount bolt through and tighten to 81 ft. lbs. (110 Nm).

24. Clean any excess fluid from the vehicle and remove the drain pans.

25. Connect the intermediate shaft to the steering gear and install a new pinch bolt. Tighten the intermediate pinch bolt to 25 ft. lbs. (34 Nm).

26. Connect the tie rod to the knuckle and install a new nut. Tighten the nut to 44 ft. lbs. (60 Nm).

27. Install the front wheels.

28. Enable the SRS air bag system.

29. Connect the negative battery cable.

30. Check the front wheel alignment and align as necessary.

31. Lower the vehicle.

POWER STEERING PUMP

REMOVAL & INSTALLATION

See Figures 243 and 244.

1. Before servicing the vehicle, refer to the precautions section.

2. Remove the drive belt.

3. Remove as much power steering fluid from the remote power steering fluid reservoir as possible.

4. Place drain pans under the vehicle as needed.

5. Remove the power steering reservoir return hose clamp and disconnect the return hose from the power steering pump.

6. Disconnect the power steering pressure hose from the power steering pump.

7. Remove the power steering pump bolts.

8. Remove the power steering pump through the right wheelhouse area.

9. Transfer the power steering pump pulley if needed.

To install:

10. Position the power steering pump to the vehicle through the right wheelhouse area.

11. Install the power steering pump bolts and tighten to 37 ft. lbs. (50 Nm).

12. Connect the power steering gear pressure hose to the power steering pump. Tighten the hose to 18 ft. lbs. (25 Nm).

13. Install the power steering return hose and reposition the clamp.

14. Install the drive belt.

15. Fill and bleed the power steering system.

16. Remove the drain pans and clean off any excess fluid.

BLEEDING

1. Fill pump reservoir with fluid to minimum system level, FULL COLD level, or middle of hash mark on cap stick fluid level indicator.

2. If equipped with hydro-boost, fully charge the hydro-boost accumulator using the following procedure:

Fig. 243 Power steering return hose removal

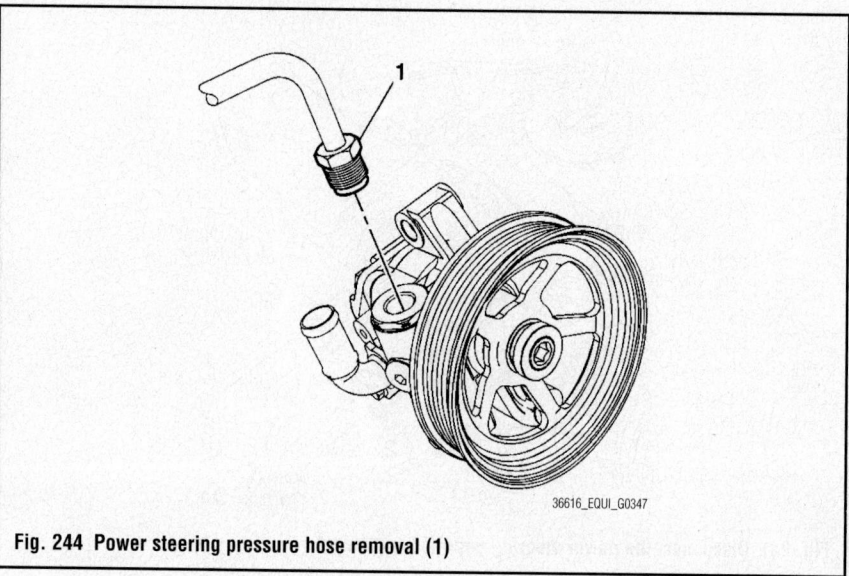

Fig. 244 Power steering pressure hose removal (1)

- Start the engine.
- Firmly apply the brake pedal 10–15 times.
- Turn the engine OFF.

3. Raise the vehicle until the front wheels are off the ground.

4. Key on engine OFF, turn the steering wheel from stop to stop 12 times.

➡**Vehicles equipped with hydro-boost systems or longer length power steering hoses may require turns up to 15 to 20 stop to stops.**

5. Verify power steering fluid level per operating specification.

6. Start the engine. Rotate steering wheel from left to right. Check for sign of cavitation or fluid aeration (pump noise/whining).

7. Verify the fluid level. Repeat the bleed procedure, if necessary.

SUSPENSION

FRAME

REMOVAL & INSTALLATION

3.4L Engine

See Figure 245.

1. Before servicing the vehicle, refer to the precautions section.
2. Secure the radiator to the upper radiator support.
3. Raise and support the vehicle.
4. Remove the front wheels.
5. Remove the side splash shield-to-frame fasteners.
6. Remove the front air dam-to-frame fasteners.
7. Remove the rear transaxle mount-to-frame bolts.
8. Remove the front transaxle mount through bolt.
9. Remove the steering gear-to-frame bolts.
10. Using mechanics wire, secure the steering gear to the exhaust.
11. Remove the stabilizer shaft clamp-to-frame bolts.
12. Remove the lower ball joint cotter pins. Discard the cotter pins.

Loosen the lower ball joint castle nut until the nut is level with the top of the ball stud. Separate the lower control arm from the steering knuckle.

13. Remove the frame-to-body bolts. Discard the bolts.
14. With the help of and assistant, carefully lower the frame from the vehicle.

To install:

15. With the help of and assistant, carefully raise the frame to the body.
16. Loosely install new frame-to-body bolts.

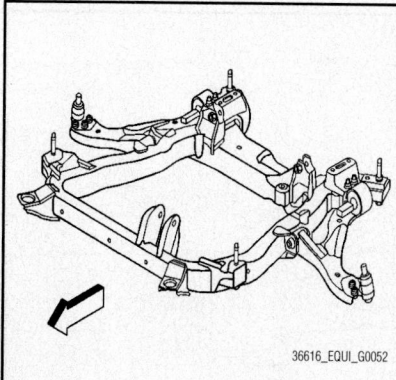

Fig. 245 Frame removal for the 3.4L engine

17. Connect the ball joint stud to the steering knuckle.
18. Install the ball stud castle nut and tighten to 30 ft. lbs. (40 Nm).

➡ **Do not loosen the castle nut in order to align the cotter pin slots. Ensure the cutter pin ends do not contact the wheel speed sensor harness.**

19. Remove the mechanics wire and install the steering gear to the frame. Tighten the bolts to 81 ft. lbs. (110 Nm).
20. Install the front transaxle mount through bolt and tighten to 81 ft. lbs. (110 Nm).
21. Install the rear transaxle mount-to-frame bolts and tighten to 37 ft. lbs. (50 Nm).
22. Install the stabilizer shaft clamp and tighten the bolts to 37 ft. lbs. (50 Nm).
23. Tighten the frame-to-body bolts to 114 ft. lbs. (155 Nm).
24. Install the front air dam fasteners.
25. Install the side splash shield-to-frame fasteners.
26. Install the front wheels.
27. Lower the vehicle.
28. Release the radiator from the upper radiator support.
29. Align the front suspension.

3.6L Engine

See Figures 246 through 249.

1. Before servicing the vehicle, refer to the precautions section.
2. Secure the radiator, air conditioning condenser, and fan module assembly to the upper tie bar to keep the assembly with the vehicle when the frame is removed.

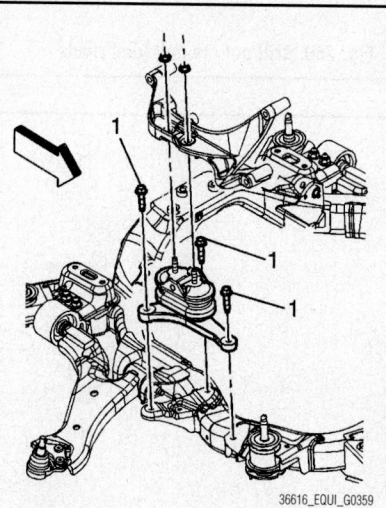

Fig. 246 Remove the lower engine mount bracket to frame bolts (1)

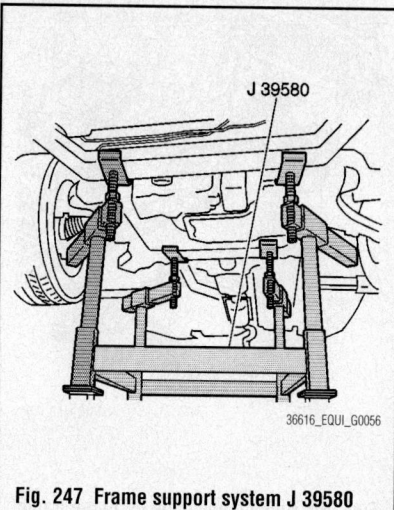

Fig. 247 Frame support system J 39580

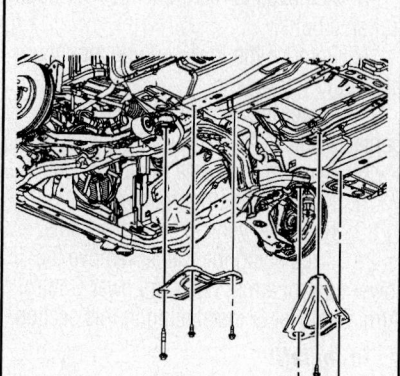

Fig. 248 Remove the frame reinforcements

3. Install the engine support fixture.
4. Raise and support the vehicle.
5. Remove the tire and wheel assemblies.
6. Remove the engine splash shields..
7. Remove the catalytic converters.
8. Remove the propeller shaft if the vehicle is equipped with AWD.
9. Remove both left and right stabilizer shaft insulator clamps. Refer
10. Remove the lower ball joints from the steering knuckles.
11. Disconnect the intermediate steering shaft from the steering gear.
12. Remove the power steering gear mounting bolts and secure the gear out of the way using mechanics wire or equivalent.
13. Remove the front transmission mount thru bolt.
14. Remove the left transmission mount lower nuts.

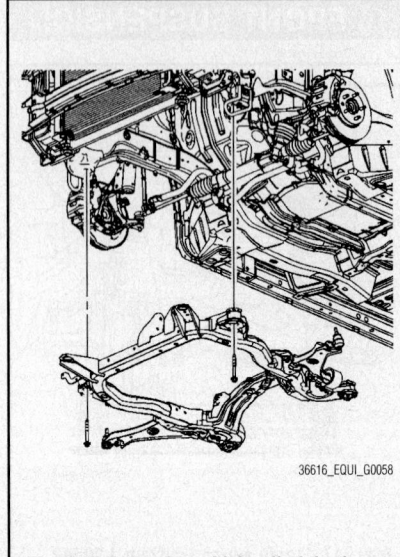

Fig. 249 Raise the vehicle off of the frame

15. Remove the rear transmission mount to frame bolts.

16. Remove the lower engine mount bracket to frame bolts

17. Lower the vehicle until the frame contacts the J 39580 support system .

18. Remove the frame reinforcements.

19. Remove the front frame bolts.

20. Raise the vehicle off of the frame.

21. If replacing the frame, remove the lower control arms. Refer to Lower Control Arm, Removal & Installation in this section.

To install:

22. If removed, install the lower control arms.

23. Carefully lower the vehicle on to the frame.

24. Install the front frame bolts and tighten to 144 ft. lbs. (155 Nm).

25. Install the frame reinforcement. Tighten the frame reinforcement bolts as follows:

- (4) Short bolts: 74 ft. lbs. (100 Nm).
- (2) Long bolts: 114 ft. lbs. (155 Nm).

26. Raise the vehicle off of the J 39580 support system .

27. Install the lower engine mount bracket to frame bolts and tighten to 37 ft. lbs. (50 Nm).

28. Install the rear transmission mount to frame bolts and tighten to 37 ft. lbs. (50 Nm).

29. Install the left transmission mount lower nuts and tighten to 37 ft. lbs. (50 Nm).

30. Install the front transmission mount thru bolt and tighten to 81 ft. lbs. (110 Nm).

31. Install the power steering gear mounting bolts and tighten to 81 ft. lbs. (110 Nm).

32. Install the intermediate steering shaft to the steering gear. Install a new lower intermediate shaft pinch bolt and tighten to 25 ft. lbs. (34 Nm).

33. Install the lower ball joints to the steering knuckles.

34. Install the propeller shaft if the vehicle is equipped with AWD.

35. Install the catalytic converters.

36. Install both left and right stabilizer shaft insulator clamps

37. Install the engine splash shields.

38. Install the tire and wheel assemblies.

39. Remove the engine support fixture.

40. Release the radiator, air conditioning condenser, and fan module assembly from the upper tie bar.

41. Perform a wheel alignment.

LOWER BALL JOINT

REMOVAL & INSTALLATION

See Figures 250 and 251.

1. Before servicing the vehicle, refer to the precautions section.

2. Remove the lower control arm. Refer to Lower Control Arm, Removal & Installation in this section.

3. Place the control arm in a vise or suitable holding device.

4. Remove the ball joint rivets using the following procedure:

- Drill through the rivets using a 5⁄16 in. (8 mm) drill bit.
- Enlarge the hole using a 31⁄64 in. (12 mm) drill bit.
- Remove any remaining burs from the control arm.

5. Remove the ball joint from the control arm. Note the position of the ball joint for reassembly.

To install:

➡The control arm must be clean and free of debris.

6. Install the ball joint to the control arm as previously noted.

※※ WARNING

Only use hardware provided with the new ball joint. The bolts must be

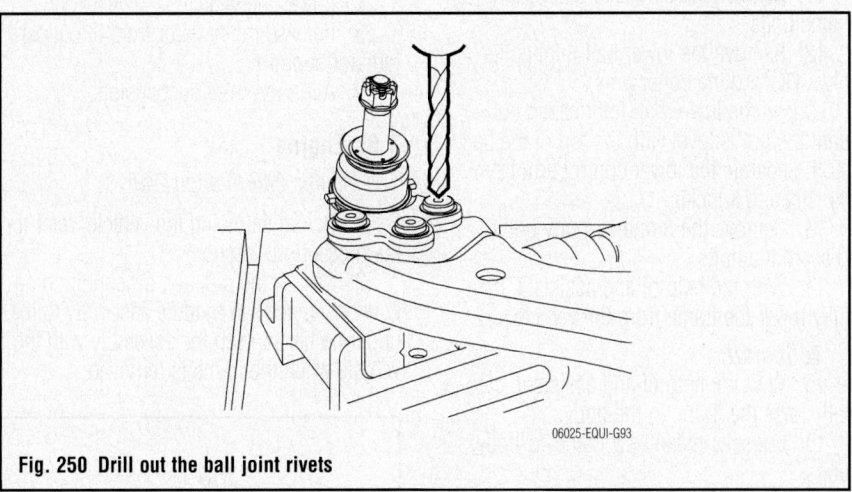

Fig. 250 Drill out the ball joint rivets

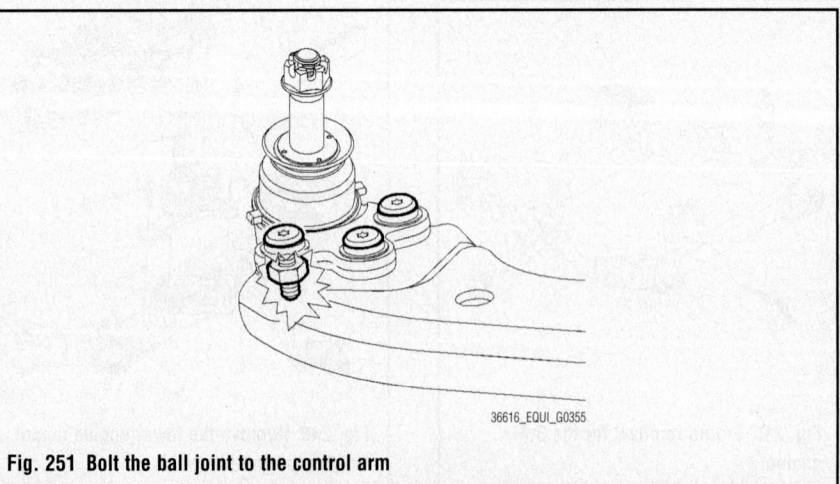

Fig. 251 Bolt the ball joint to the control arm

installed with the bolt head on top of the ball joint.

7. Install the ball joint to control arm bolts. Tighten the bolts and nuts to 50 ft. lbs. (68 Nm).

8. Install the lower control arm.

9. Perform a wheel alignment.

LOWER CONTROL ARM

REMOVAL & INSTALLATION

See Figures 252 and 253.

1. Before servicing the vehicle, refer to the precautions section.

2. Raise and support the vehicle.

3. Remove the wheel and tire assembly.

4. Remove the control arm ball stud cotter pin. Discard the cotter pin.

5. Loosen the ball stud nut until the nut is level with the top of the ball stud.

6. Separate the lower control arm from the steering knuckle.

7. Remove the ball stud nut.

8. Remove the control arm-to-frame front bolt and nut. Discard the bolt and nut.

9. Remove the control arm-to-frame rear bolts and nuts. Discard the bolts and nuts.

10. Remove the control arm.

To install:

11. Install the control arm to the frame.

12. Install new control arm-to-frame rear bolts and nuts. Tighten the nuts to 52 ft. lbs. (70 Nm).

13. Install a new arm-to-frame front bolt and nut. Tighten the bolt to 140 ft. lbs. (190 Nm) or 110 ft. lbs. (145 Nm) for the Sport or GXP models.

14. Position the control arm ball stud into the steering knuckle, tighten the nut to 30 ft. lbs. (40 Nm).

✴✴ WARNING

Do not loosen the castle nut, only tighten to align the ball stud slot. Ensure that the cotter pin ends do not contact the Antilock Brake System (ABS) sensor harness or drive axle.

15. Continue to tighten the nut only enough to align the castle nut slots with the ball stud, install the cotter pin.

16. Install the wheel and tire assembly.

17. Lower the vehicle.

18. Perform a wheel alignment.

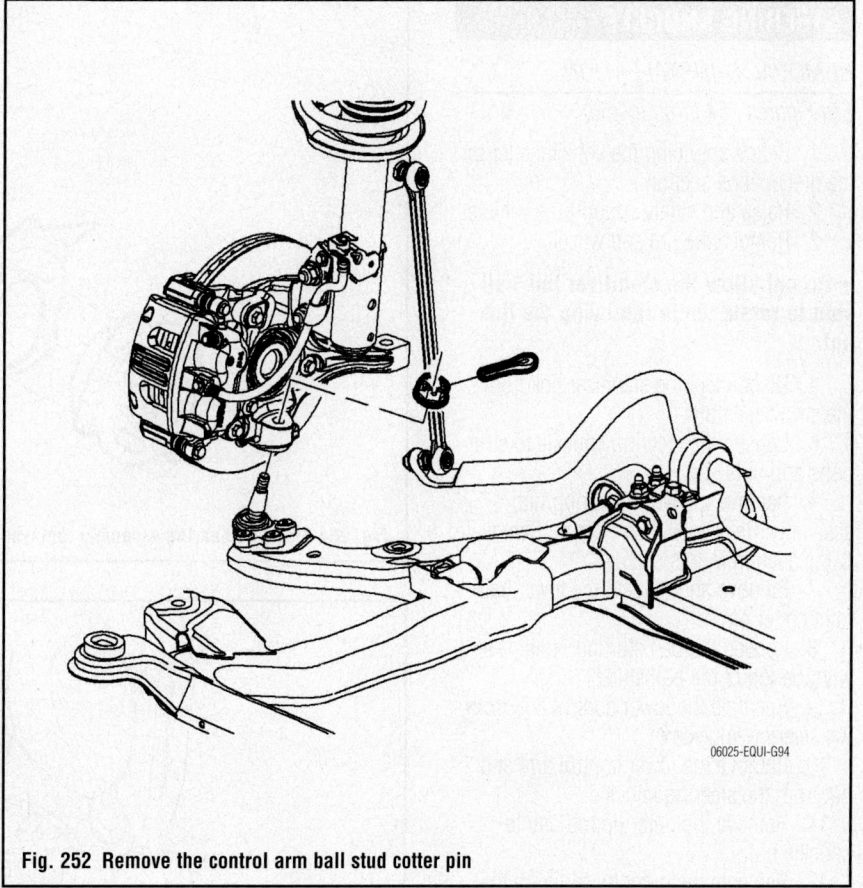

Fig. 252 Remove the control arm ball stud cotter pin

06025-EQUI-G94

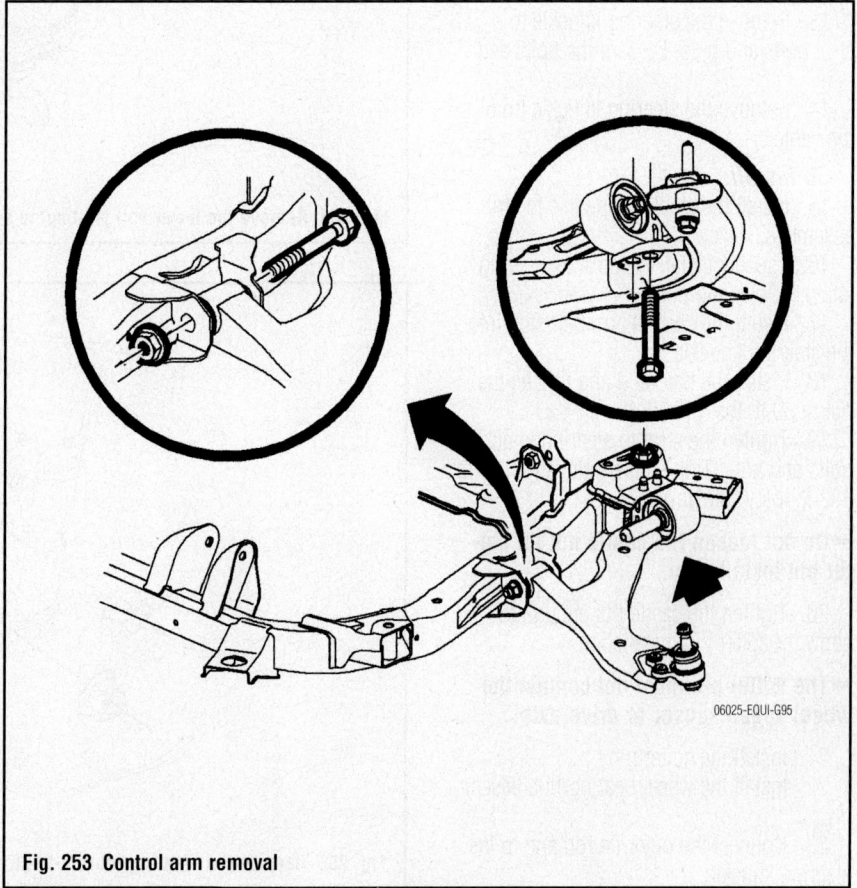

Fig. 253 Control arm removal

06025-EQUI-G95

STEERING KNUCKLE

REMOVAL & INSTALLATION

See Figures 254 through 256.

1. Before servicing the vehicle, refer to the precautions section.
2. Raise and safely support the vehicle.
3. Remove the tire and wheel.

➡ **Do not allow the stabilizer link ball stud to rotate while removing the link nut.**

4. Disconnect the stabilizer link from the strut assembly.
5. Loosen the steering knuckle to strut bolts and nuts.
6. Remove the wheel bearing/hub assembly. Refer to Hub & Bearing Removal & Installation in this section.
7. Remove and discard the lower ball joint cotter pin.
8. Loosen the ball stud nut, until level with the top of the ball stud.
9. Separate the lower control arm from the steering knuckle.
10. Remove the lower control arm and nut from the steering knuckle.
11. Remove the outer tie rod end to knuckle nut.
12. Separate the outer tie rod from the steering knuckle.
13. Remove the steering knuckle to strut bolts and nuts. Discard the bolts and nuts.
14. Remove the steering knuckle from the vehicle.

To install:

15. Install the steering knuckle to strut assembly.
16. Loosely install the strut to steering knuckle bolts and nuts.
17. Install the control arm ball stud into the steering knuckle.
18. Install the ball stud and tighten the nut to 30 ft. lbs. (40 Nm).
19. Tighten the strut to steering knuckle bolts and nuts. Tighten the bolts and nuts to 133 ft. lbs. (180 Nm).

➡ **Do not loosen the castle nut for cotter pin installation.**

20. Tighten the castle nut enough to allow for cotter pin installation.

➡ **The cotter pin must not contact the wheel speed sensor or drive axle.**

21. Install the cotter pin.
22. Install the wheel bearing/hub assembly.
23. Connect the outer tie rod end to the steering knuckle.

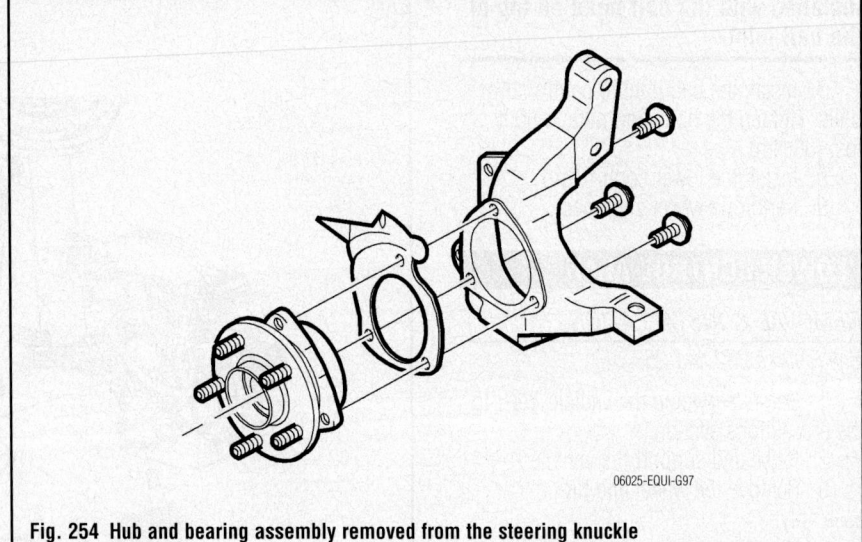

Fig. 254 Hub and bearing assembly removed from the steering knuckle

06025-EQUI-G97

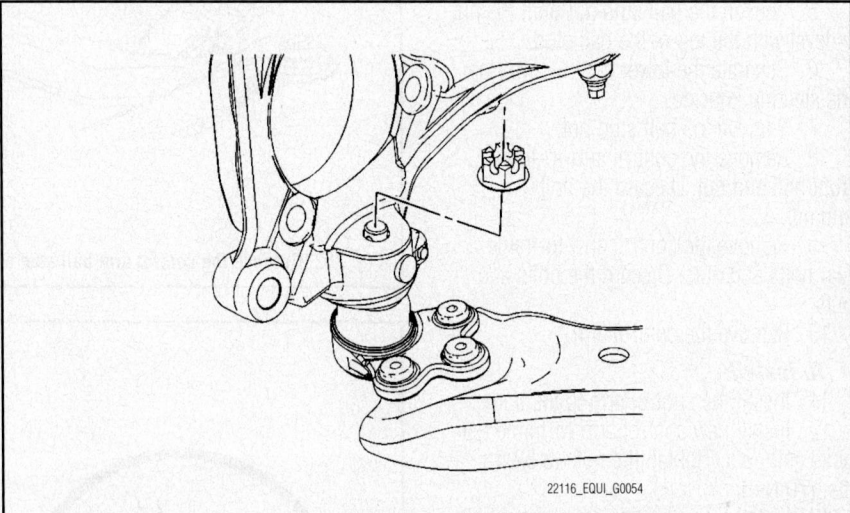

22116_EQUI_G0054

Fig. 255 Remove the lower ball joint nut to separate the lower control arm from the knuckle.

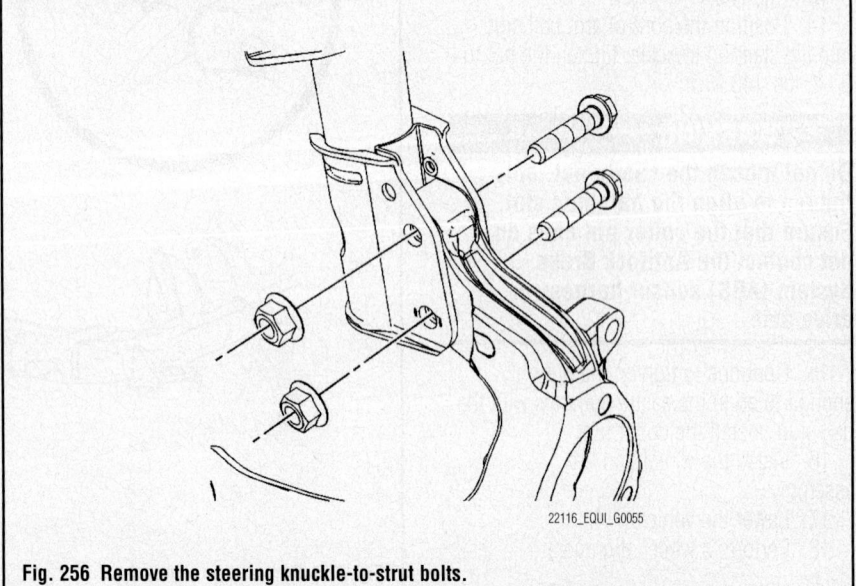

22116_EQUI_G0055

Fig. 256 Remove the steering knuckle-to-strut bolts.

24. Seat the ball stud taper. Tighten to 30 ft. lbs. (40 Nm).

25. Install a new tie rod retention nut. Tighten the nut to 37 ft. lbs. (50 Nm).

26. Connect the stabilizer link to the strut assembly. Tighten the nut to 55 ft. lbs. (75 Nm).

27. Install the tire and wheel.

28. Lower the vehicle.

29. Perform a wheel alignment.

STRUT

REMOVAL & INSTALLATION

See Figures 257 and 258.

1. Before servicing the vehicle, refer to the precautions section.

2. Remove the 3 upper strut mount bolts.

3. Raise and safely support the vehicle.

4. Remove the wheel assembly.

5. Remove the brake hose bracket from the strut assembly.

6. Disconnect the stabilizer link from the strut assembly.

7. Remove the strut to knuckle bolts and nuts.

8. Remove the strut assembly from the vehicle.

To install:

9. Position the strut assembly to the vehicle.

10. Install the 3 upper strut mount bolts and tighten to 18 ft. lbs. (25 Nm).

11. Attach the strut to the steering knuckle and install the nuts and bolts. Tighten the bolts and nuts to 133 ft. lbs. (180 Nm).

➡**Inspect the stabilizer link seals for damage and replace the link as necessary. Do not allow the stabilizer link ball stud to rotate while installing the link nut.**

12. Connect the stabilizer link to the strut. Tighten the nut to 55 ft. lbs. (75 Nm).

13. Install the brake hose bracket to the strut assembly. Tighten the brake bracket bolt to 11 ft. lbs. (15 Nm).

14. Install the wheel assembly.

15. Lower the vehicle.

16. Perform a wheel alignment.

STABILIZER BAR (SHAFT)

REMOVAL & INSTALLATION

See Figure 259.

1. Before servicing the vehicle, refer to the precautions section.

2. Position the front wheels in the straight ahead position.

3. Raise and safely support the vehicle.

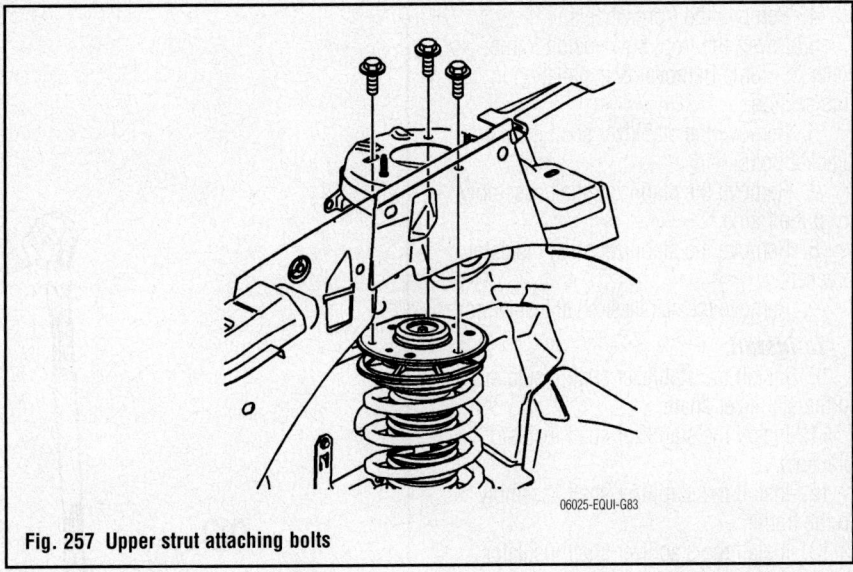

Fig. 257 Upper strut attaching bolts

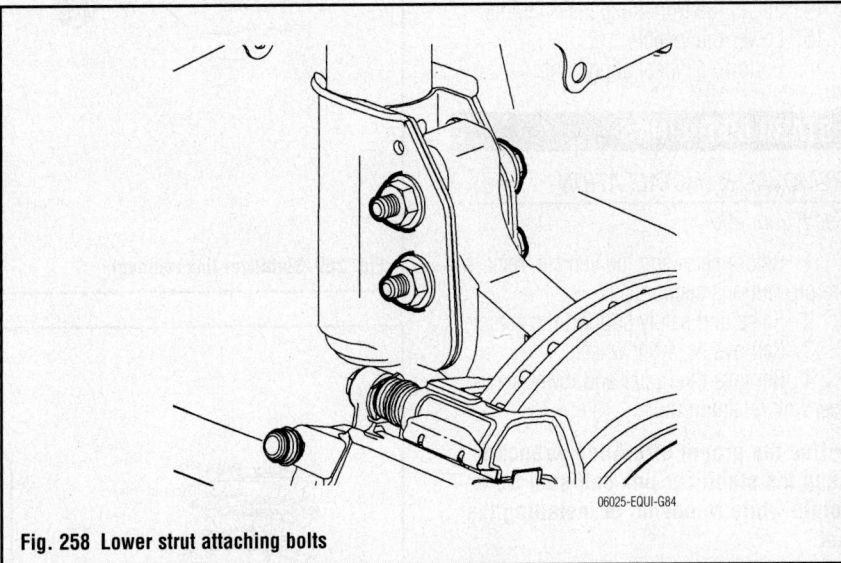

Fig. 258 Lower strut attaching bolts

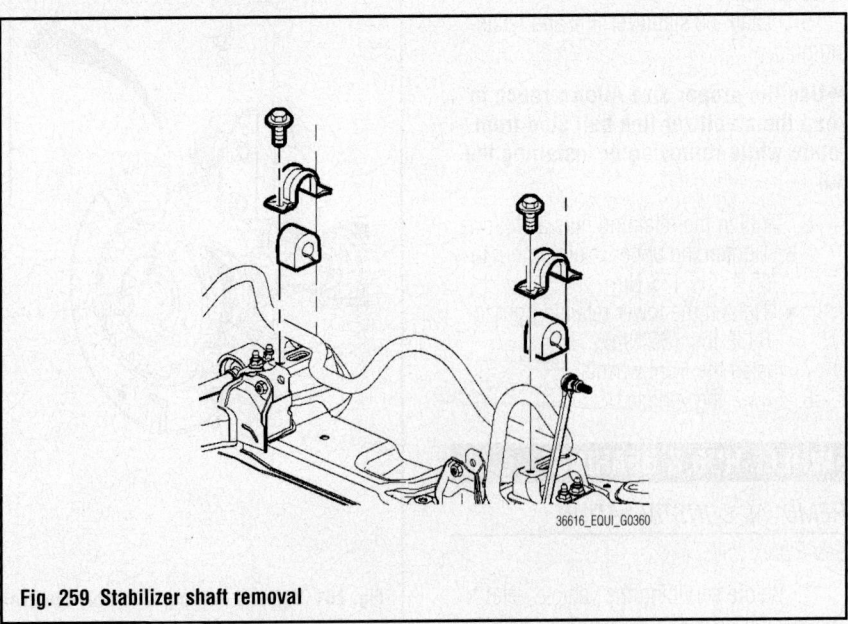

Fig. 259 Stabilizer shaft removal

4. Remove the front wheels.

5. Lower the front suspension frame. Refer to Frame Removal & Installation in this section.

6. Remove the stabilizer shaft insulator bracket bolts.

7. Remove the stabilizer shaft assembly from the frame.

8. Remove the stabilizer shaft insulator brackets.

9. Remove the stabilizer shaft insulators.

To install:

10. Install the stabilizer shaft insulators to the stabilizer shaft.

11. Install the stabilizer shaft insulator brackets.

12. Install the stabilizer shaft assembly to the frame.

13. Install the stabilizer shaft insulator bracket bolts to 37 ft. lbs. (50 Nm).

14. Install the front suspension frame.

15. Lower the vehicle.

16. Perform a wheel alignment.

STABILIZER LINKS

REMOVAL & INSTALLATION

See Figure 260.

1. Before servicing the vehicle, refer to the precautions section.

2. Raise and safely support the vehicle.

3. Remove the front wheels.

4. Remove the upper and lower stabilizer link retaining nuts.

➡**Use the proper size Allen wrench to keep the stabilizer link ball stud from rotate while removing or installing the nut.**

To install:

5. Install the stabilizer link and retaining nuts.

➡**Use the proper size Allen wrench to keep the stabilizer link ball stud from rotate while removing or installing the nut.**

6. Tighten the retaining nuts as follows:
- Tighten the upper retaining nut to 55 ft. lbs. (75 Nm).
- Tighten the lower retaining nut to 63 ft. lbs. (85 Nm).

7. Install the front wheels.

8. Lower the vehicle.

WHEEL HUB & BEARING

REMOVAL & INSTALLATION

See Figure 261.

1. Before servicing the vehicle, refer to the precautions section.

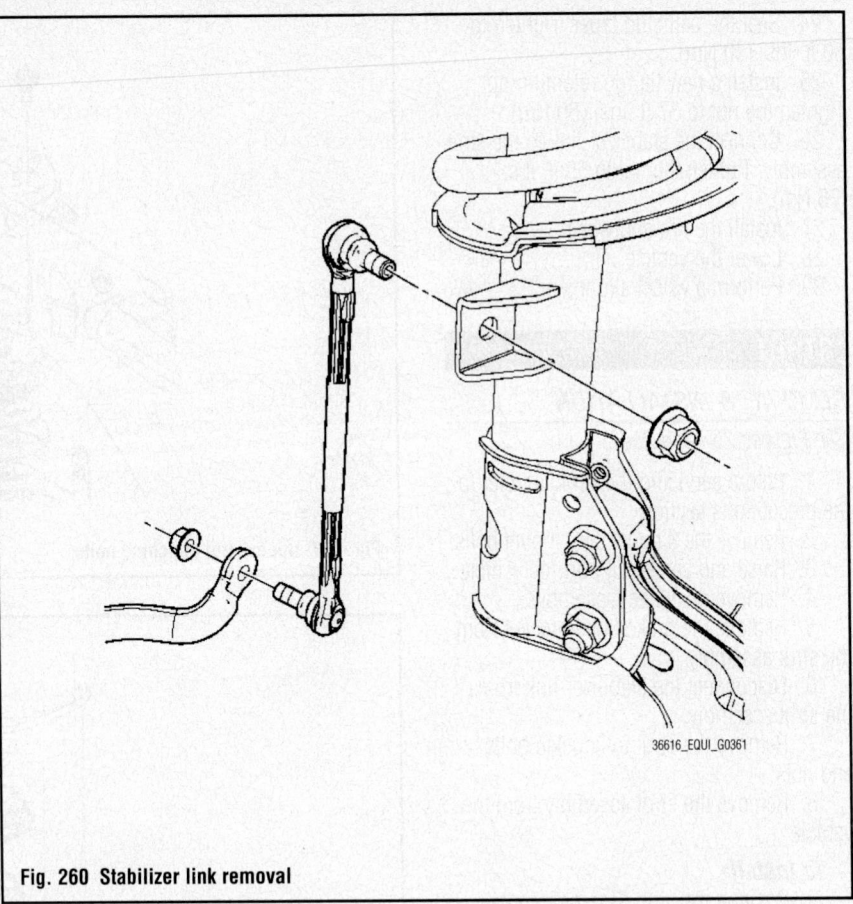

Fig. 260 Stabilizer link removal

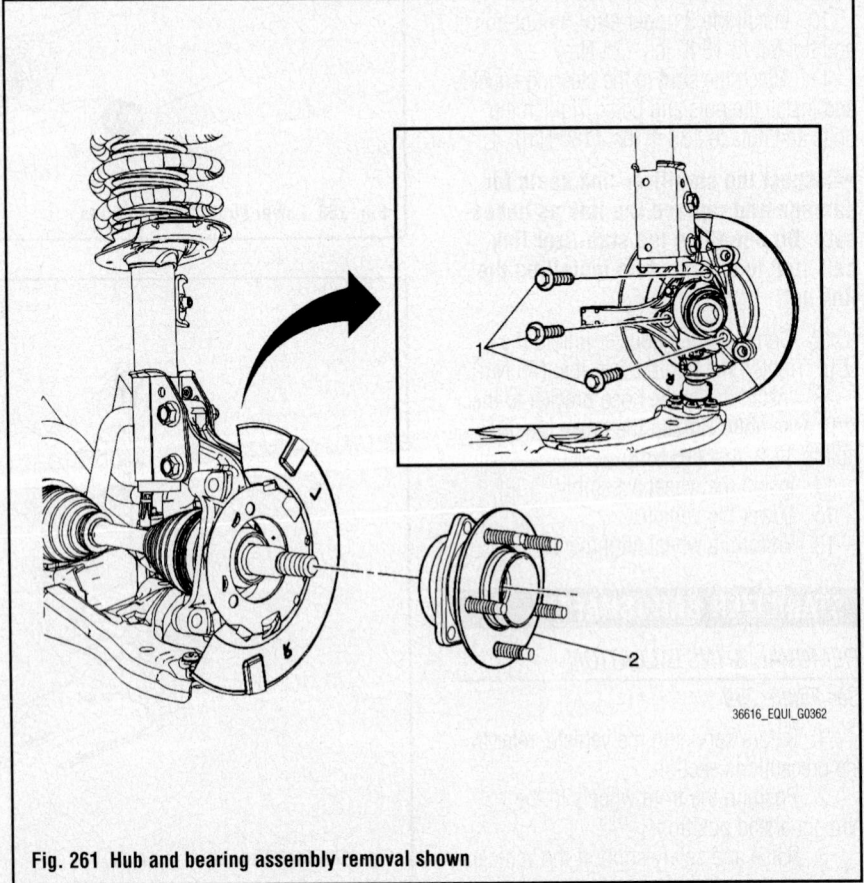

Fig. 261 Hub and bearing assembly removal shown

2. Raise and support the vehicle.

3. Remove the wheel assembly.

4. Remove the wheel drive shaft nut.

5. Remove the brake rotor.

6. Remove the wheel speed sensor. Refer to Front Speed Sensor, Removal & Installation in the Brake section.

7. Remove the hub and bearing mounting bolts.

8. Remove the hub and bearing assembly.

➡ **If removing the wheel bearing/hub assembly to service other components,** support the wheel drive shaft with mechanics wire.

To install:

9. Install the hub and bearing assembly.

10. Clean the threads on the wheel bearing/hub bolts, use the proper cleaner.

11. Apply thread locker on ⅔ of the wheel bearing/hub bolts. Allow the thread locker to set for 10 minutes before using.

12. Install the hub and bearing mounting bolts and tighten to 96 ft. lbs. (130 Nm).

13. Install the wheel speed sensor.

14. Install the brake rotor.

15. Install the wheel drive shaft nut and tighten to 151 ft. lbs. (205 Nm).

16. Install the wheel assembly.

17. Lower the vehicle.

ADJUSTMENT

The front wheel bearings are a sealed unit, and cannot be adjusted. If movement is present in the hub and bearing assembly it must be replaced.

SUSPENSION

COIL SPRING

REMOVAL & INSTALLATION

See Figures 262 through 264.

1. Before servicing the vehicle, refer to the precautions section.

2. Raise and support the vehicle.

3. Remove the wheel assembly.

➡ **Hold the link with an Allen wrench during nut removal.**

4. Remove the stabilizer link to lower control arm nut.

5. Position a jack stand underneath the lower control arm.

6. Raise the jack stand slightly to compress the coil spring.

7. Remove the lower shock bolt and nut.

8. Loosen the lower control arm to support frame bolt and nut.

9. Remove the lower control arm to knuckle nut and bolt.

10. Slowly lower the control arm in order to unload the coil spring.

11. Remove the coil spring and insulators.

To install:

12. Fully seat the top and bottom coil spring insulators to the spring.

➡ **Spray silicon lubricant on the insulators to aid in installation. Ensure that part number identification tape located on the coil spring is oriented outboard of the vehicle and at the top of the spring.**

13. Position the spring with the rubber insulators into the vehicle.

14. Raise the jack stand to compress the spring.

15. Install the knuckle to the lower control arm. Tighten the lower control arm to knuckle bolt to 118 ft. lbs. (160 Nm).

16. Tighten the lower control arm to support nut and bolt. Tighten the bolt to 81 ft. lbs. (110 Nm).

17. Install the shock to the lower control arm. Tighten the lower shock bolt to 81 ft. lbs. (110 Nm).

18. Remove the jack stand from under the vehicle.

REAR SUSPENSION

➡ **Hold the link with a wrench during nut installation.**

19. Install the stabilizer link to the lower control arm. Tighten the nut to 11 ft. lbs. (15 Nm).

20. Push the trailing arm upward to align the front bracket to body bolt.

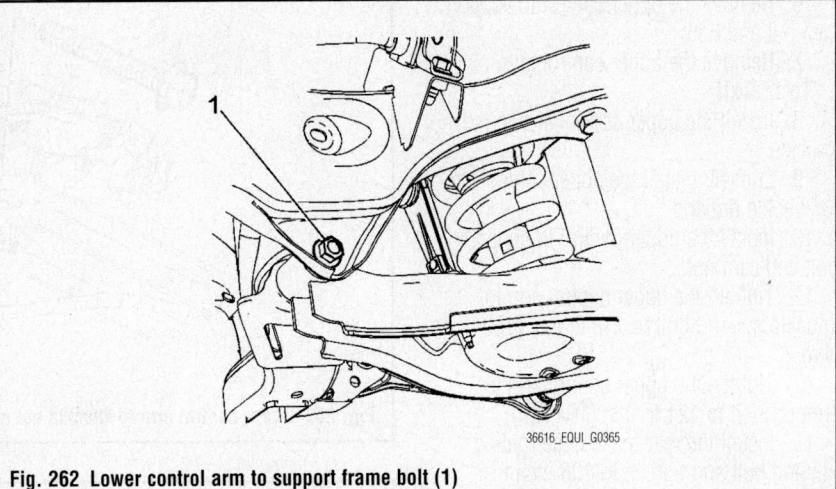

Fig. 262 Lower control arm to support frame bolt (1)

36616_EQUI_G0365

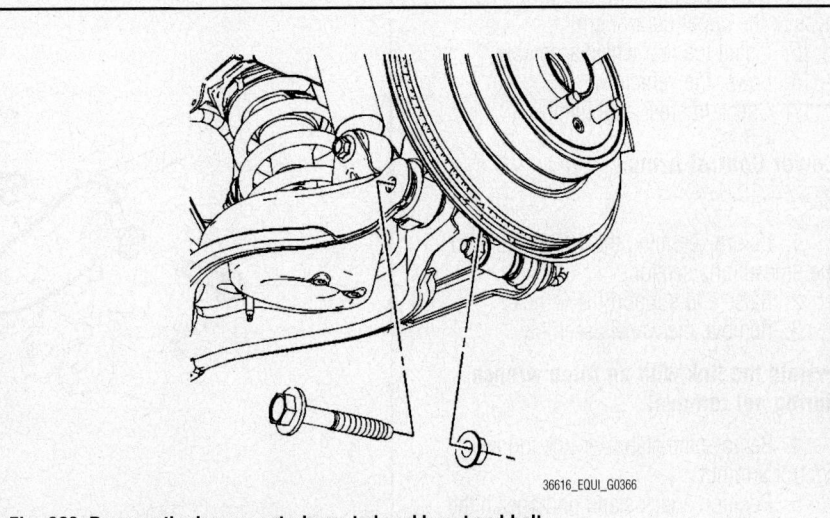

36616_EQUI_G0366

Fig. 263 Remove the lower control arm to knuckle nut and bolt

21. Use a drift to aid in bracket alignment and install the remaining bolts. Tighten the bracket to body bolts to 81 ft. lbs. (110 Nm).

22. Install the wheel assembly.

23. Lower the vehicle.

24. Check the rear alignment.

CONTROL ARMS/LINKS

REMOVAL & INSTALLATION

Upper Control Arms

See Figures 265 and 266.

1. Before servicing the vehicle, refer to the precautions section.

2. Raise and safely support the vehicle.

3. Remove the Antilock Brake System (ABS) brake harness from the upper control arm.

4. Remove the rear brake hose routing nut and bolt.

5. Remove the upper control arm to knuckle nut and bolt.

6. Remove the upper control to support cam nut and bolt.

7. Remove the upper control arm.

To install

8. Install the upper control arm to the knuckle.

9. Loosely install the upper control arm to knuckle nut and bolt.

10. Install the upper control to support bolt and cam nut.

11. Tighten the upper control arm to knuckle nut and bolt to 118 ft. lbs. (160 Nm).

12. Tighten the upper control arm to support bolt to 121 ft. lbs. (164 Nm).

13. Install the rear brake hose routing nut and bolt and tighten to 106 inch lbs. (12 Nm).

14. Connect the ABS brake wiring harness to the upper control arm.

15. Install the rear wheel assembly.

16. Lower the vehicle.

17. Check the rear alignment.

Lower Control Arms

See Figure 267.

1. Before servicing the vehicle, refer to the precautions section.

2. Raise and support the vehicle.

3. Remove the wheel assembly.

➡**Hold the link with an Allen wrench during nut removal.**

4. Remove the stabilizer link to lower control arm nut.

5. Position a jack stand underneath the lower control arm.

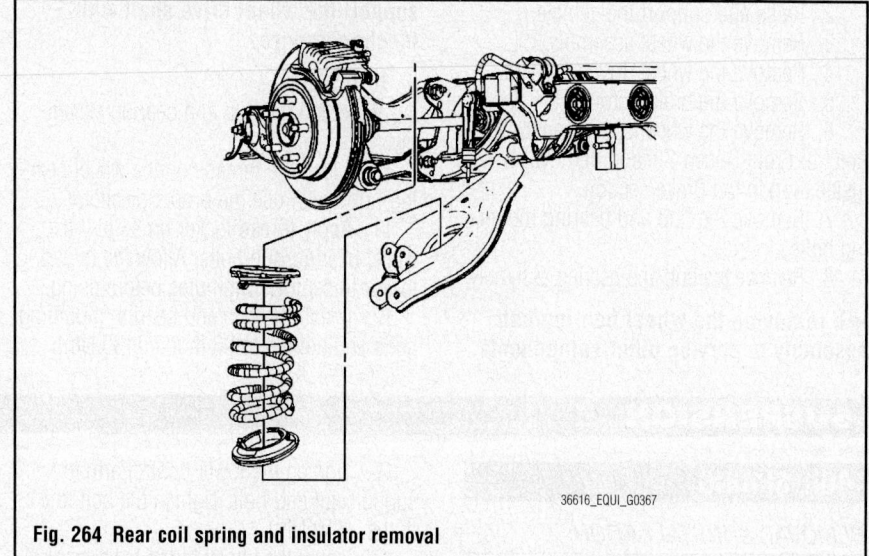

Fig. 264 Rear coil spring and insulator removal

36616_EQUI_G0367

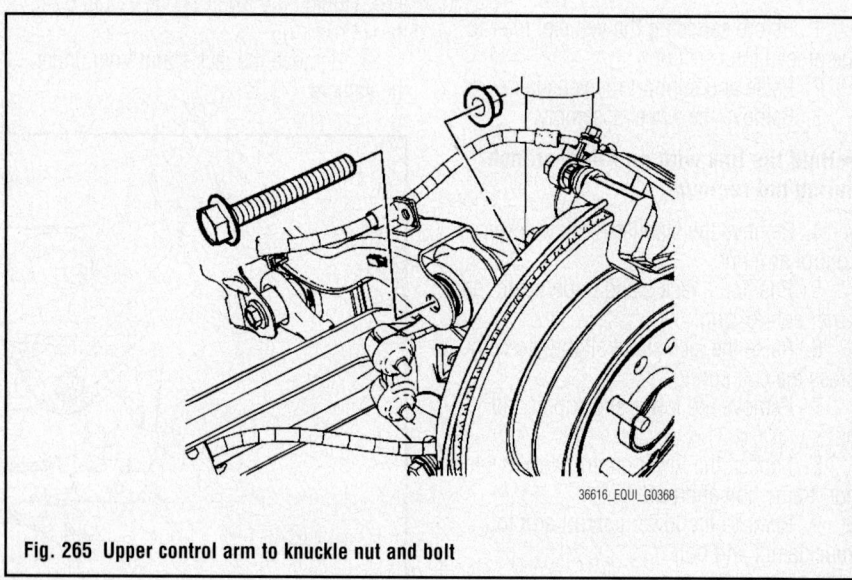

Fig. 265 Upper control arm to knuckle nut and bolt

36616_EQUI_G0368

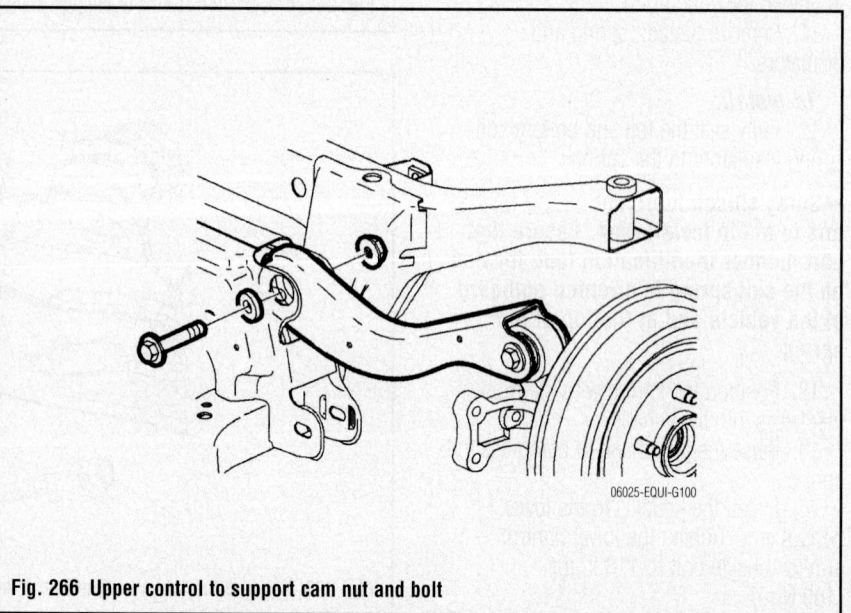

Fig. 266 Upper control to support cam nut and bolt

06025-EQUI-G100

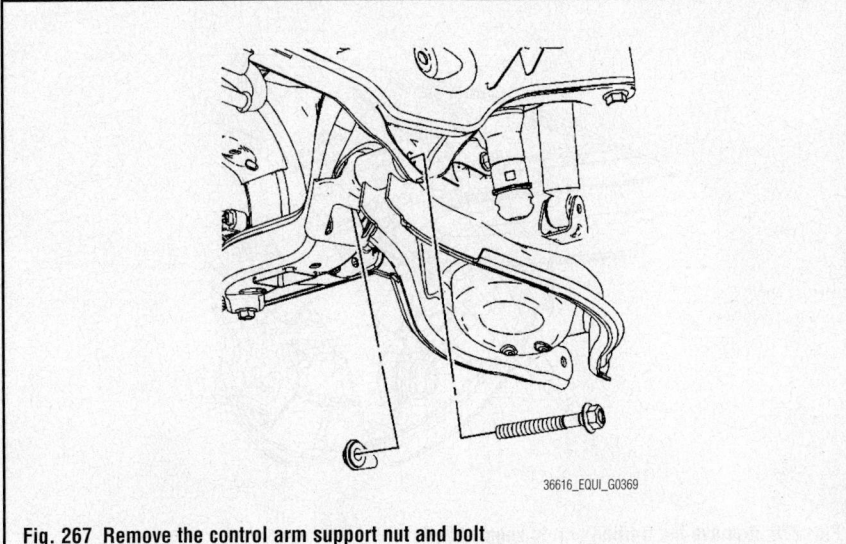

Fig. 267 Remove the control arm support nut and bolt

6. Raise the jack stand slightly to compress the coil spring.

7. Remove the lower shock bolt and nut.

8. Loosen the lower control arm to support frame bolt and nut.

9. Remove the lower control arm to knuckle nut and bolt.

10. Slowly lower the control arm in order to unload the coil spring.

11. Remove the coil spring.

12. Remove the jack stand.

13. Remove the lower control arm support nut and bolt.

14. Remove the lower control arm.

To install:

15. Inspect the coil spring upper and lower insulators, if damage exists replace the insulators.

16. Position the lower control to the support and hand tighten the bolt and nut.

➡ **Spray silicon lubricant on the insulators to aid in installation. Ensure the spring is properly seated.**

17. Position the spring with the rubber insulators into the vehicle.

18. Use a screw type jack stand to compress the spring.

19. Install the knuckle to the lower control arm. Tighten the lower control arm to knuckle nut and bolt to 118 ft. lbs. (160 Nm).

20. Tighten the lower control arm to support nut and bolt to 118 ft. lbs. (160 Nm).

21. Install the shock to the lower control arm. Tighten the lower shock bolt to 81 ft. lbs. (110 Nm).

22. Remove the jack stand.

23. Install the stabilizer link to the lower control arm. Tighten the nut to 11 ft. lbs. (15 Nm).

➡ **Hold the link with a wrench during nut installation.**

24. Install the wheel assembly.

25. Lower the vehicle.

26. Check the rear alignment.

Trailing Arm

See Figures 268 through 270.

1. Before servicing the vehicle, refer to the precautions section.

2. Raise and safely support the vehicle.

3. Remove the wheel assembly.

4. Remove the park brake cable bolt from the trailing arm and from the frame.

5. Remove the trailing arm bracket to body bolts.

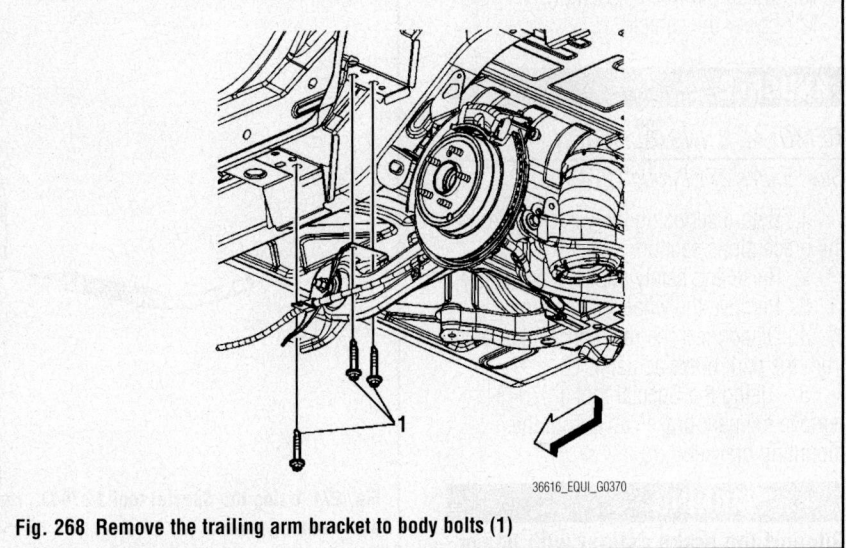

Fig. 268 Remove the trailing arm bracket to body bolts (1)

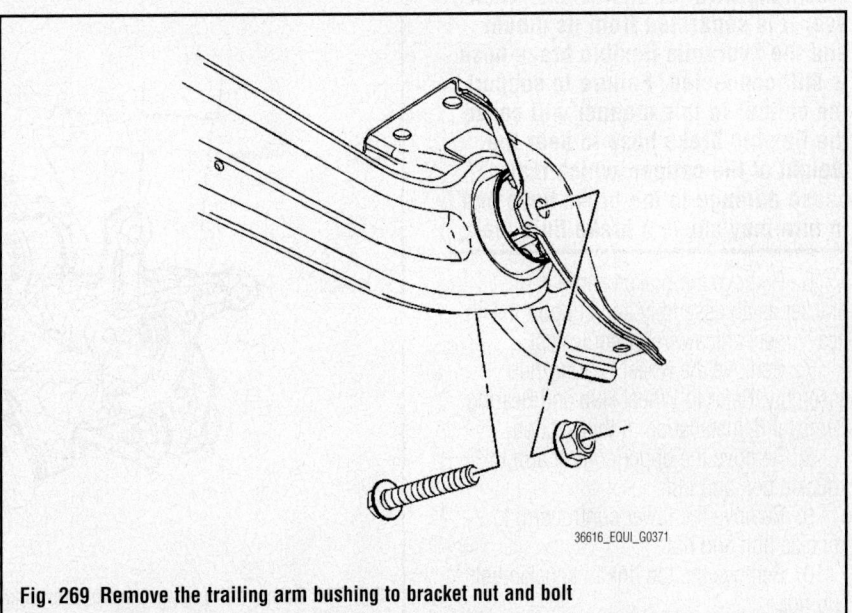

Fig. 269 Remove the trailing arm bushing to bracket nut and bolt

6. Remove the trailing arm bushing to bracket nut and bolt.

7. Remove the trailing arm to knuckle bolts.

8. Remove the trailing arm.

To install:

9. Position the trailing arm to the vehicle.

10. Install the trailing arm to knuckle bolts and tighten to 81 ft. lbs. (110 Nm).

11. Position the trailing arm bracket to the trailing arm.

12. Loosely install the trailing arm bushing to bracket nut and bolt.

13. Install the trail arm bracket.

14. Tighten the trailing arm bushing to bracket nut and bolt to 118 ft. lbs. (160 Nm).

15. Install the park brake cable bolt to trailing arm and to the frame.

16. Install the wheel assembly.

17. Lower the vehicle.

KNUCKLE

REMOVAL & INSTALLATION

See Figures 271 through 274.

1. Before servicing the vehicle, refer to the precautions section.

2. Raise and safely support the vehicle.

3. Remove the wheel assembly.

4. Disconnect the rear park brake cable from the park brake actuator.

5. Using the Special tool J 37043 , remove the park brake cable from the mounting bracket.

✴✴ WARNING

Support the brake caliper with heavy mechanic wire, or equivalent, whenever it is separated from its mount and the hydraulic flexible brake hose is still connected. Failure to support the caliper in this manner will cause the flexible brake hose to bear the weight of the caliper, which may cause damage to the brake hose and in turn may cause a brake fluid leak.

6. Remove the brake caliper and bracket as an assembly and support it with heavy mechanics wire or equivalent.

7. Remove the wheel bearing/hub assembly. Refer to Wheel Hub and Bearing Removal & Installation in this section.

8. Remove the upper control arm to knuckle bolt and nut.

9. Remove the lower control arm to knuckle bolt and nut.

10. Remove the toe link to knuckle bolt and nut.

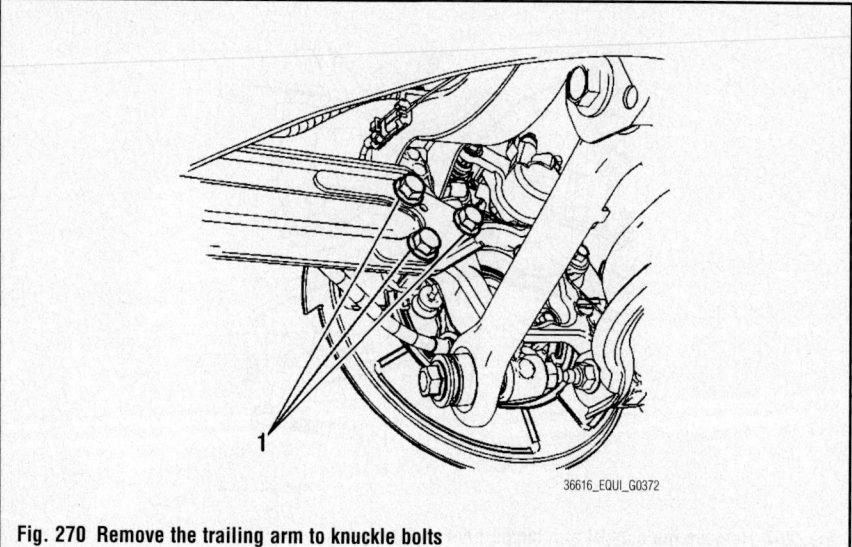

Fig. 270 Remove the trailing arm to knuckle bolts

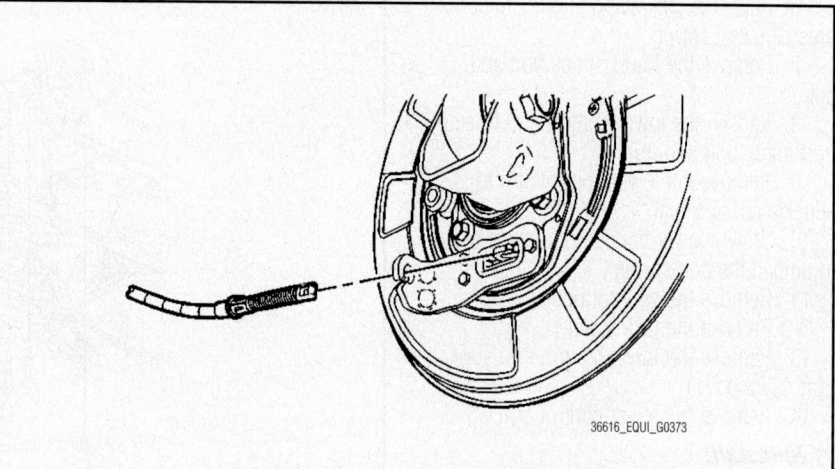

Fig. 271 Using the Special tool J 37043 , remove the park brake cable from the mounting bracket

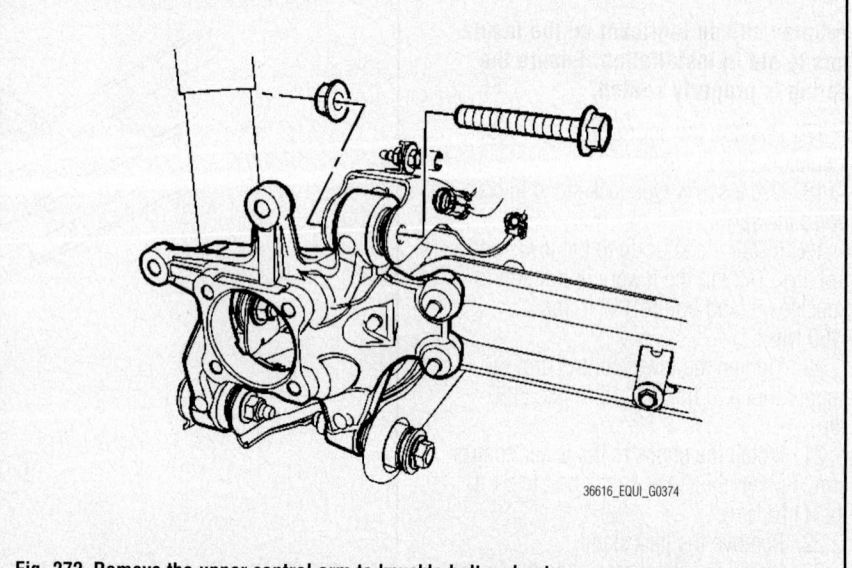

Fig. 272 Remove the upper control arm to knuckle bolt and nut

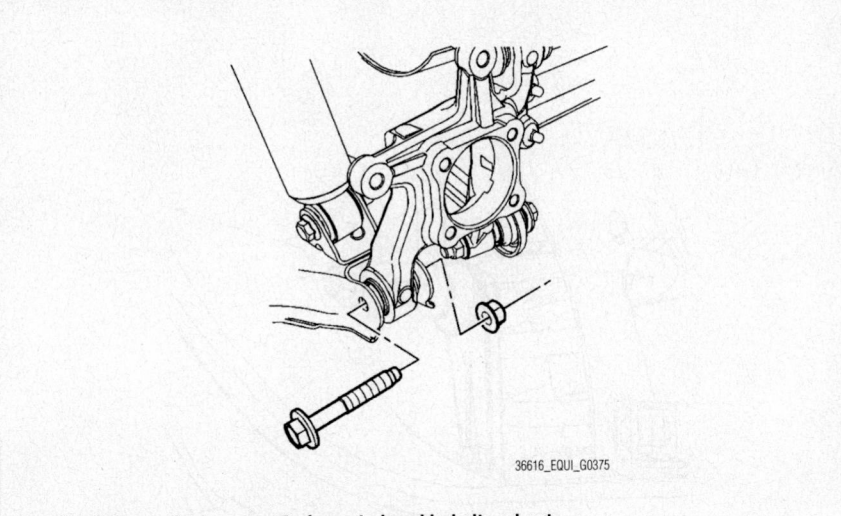

Fig. 273 Remove the lower control arm to knuckle bolt and nut.

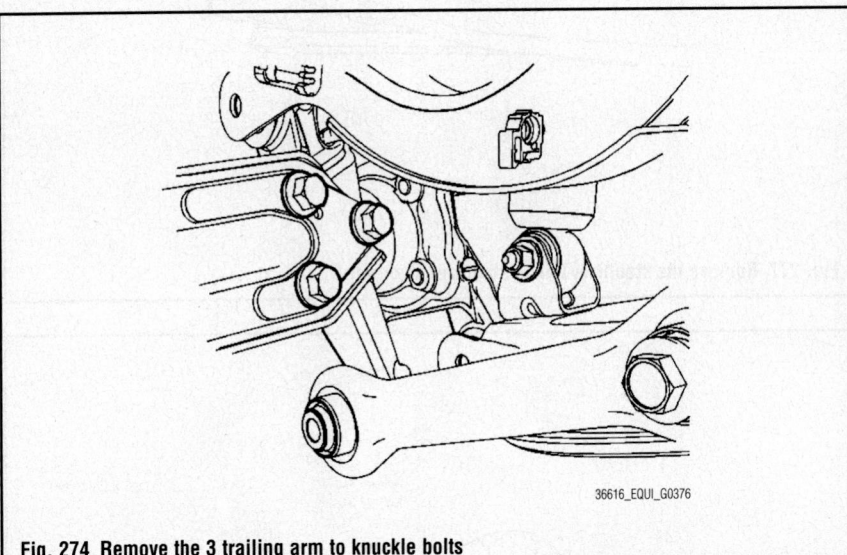

Fig. 274 Remove the 3 trailing arm to knuckle bolts

11. Remove the 3 trailing arm to knuckle bolts.

12. Remove the knuckle from the vehicle.

To install:

13. Install the knuckle to the lower control arm. Loosely install the bolt and nut.

14. Install the knuckle to the upper control arm. Loosely install the bolt and nut.

15. Install the knuckle to the toe link. Loosely install the bolt and nut.

16. Install the 3 trailing arm to knuckle bolts. Loosely install the bolt and nut.

17. Tighten the bolts and nuts in the following sequence:

- Tighten the knuckle to lower control arm bolt and nut to 118 ft. lbs. (160 Nm).

- Tighten the knuckle to upper control arm bolt and nut to 118 ft. lbs. (160 Nm).

- Tighten the knuckle to toe link bolt and nut to 118 ft. lbs. (160 Nm).

- Tighten the 3 trailing arm to knuckle bolts to 81 ft. lbs. (110 Nm).

18. Install the wheel bearing/hub assembly.

19. Remove the supporting wire and position the brake caliper and bracket assemblies back onto the knuckles.

20. Connect the rear park brake cable through the mounting bracket and onto the park brake actuator.

21. Install the tire and wheel.

22. Lower the vehicle.

23. Perform a vehicle wheel alignment.

SHOCK ABSORBER

REMOVAL & INSTALLATION

See Figures 275 and 276.

1. Before servicing the vehicle, refer to the precautions section.

2. Raise and support the vehicle.

3. Remove the wheel assembly.

4. Remove the lower shock bolt.

5. Remove the rear wheel house from the vehicle.

6. Remove the upper shock bolt.

7. Remove the shock from the vehicle.

To install:

8. Install the shock to the vehicle.

9. Install the upper shock bolt. Tighten the bolt to 81 ft. lbs. (110 Nm).

10. Install the lower shock bolt. Tighten the bolt to 81 ft. lbs. (110 Nm).

11. Install the rear wheel house in the vehicle.

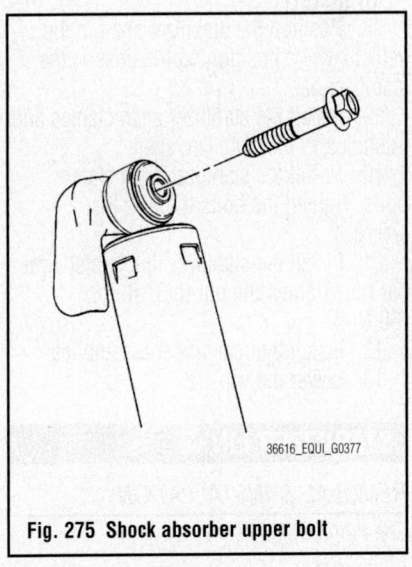

Fig. 275 Shock absorber upper bolt

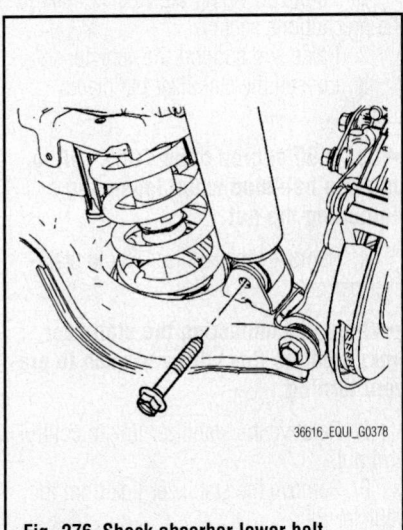

Fig. 276 Shock absorber lower bolt

12. Install the wheel assembly.
13. Lower the vehicle.

STABILIZER BAR (SHAFT)

REMOVAL & INSTALLATION

See Figures 277 and 278.

1. Before servicing the vehicle, refer to the precautions section.
2. Raise and support the vehicle.
3. Remove the rear wheel assemblies.
4. Lower the rear suspension support.

➡**Hold the ball shaft secure with a TORX® bit, when installing the nut.**

5. Remove the stabilizer link to stabilizer shaft nut.
6. Remove the stabilizer shaft clamp bolts.
7. Disengage the stabilizer shaft from the stabilizer link ball studs, while removing the stabilizer bar from the vehicle.

To install

8. Position the stabilizer shaft in the vehicle, while positioning the links to the stabilizer bar.
9. Install the stabilizer shaft clamps and bushings to the stabilizer shaft.
10. Install the stabilizer shaft clamp bolts. Tighten the bolts to 52 ft. lbs. (70 Nm).
11. Install the stabilizer link to stabilizer bar nut. Tighten the nut to 37 ft. lbs. (50 Nm).
12. Install the rear wheel assemblies.
13. Lower the vehicle.

STABILIZER LINKS

REMOVAL & INSTALLATION

See Figure 279.

1. Before servicing the vehicle, refer to the precautions section.
2. Raise and support the vehicle.
3. Loosen the stabilizer bar clamp bolts.

➡**Use a 90 degree bend TORX® bit to hold the ball stud when loosening or tightening the nut.**

4. Remove the stabilizer link to stabilizer bar nut.

➡**When disconnecting the stabilizer link, hold the link with a wrench to prevent turning.**

5. Remove the stabilizer link to control arm nut.
6. Remove the stabilizer link from the vehicle.

36616_EQUI_G0379

Fig. 277 Remove the stabilizer link to stabilizer shaft nut

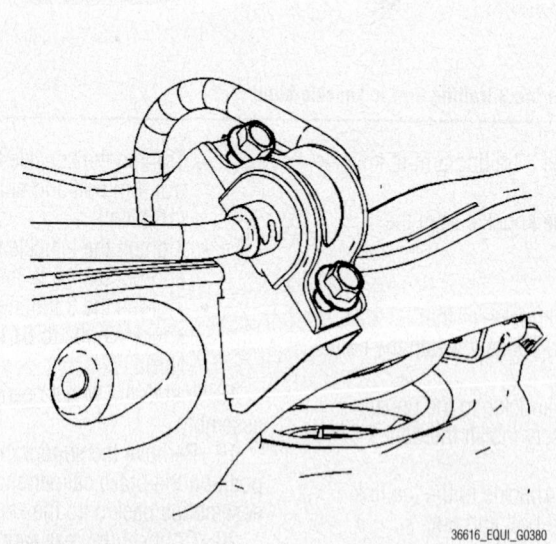

36616_EQUI_G0380

Fig. 278 Remove the stabilizer shaft clamp bolts

CHEVROLET AND PONTIAC 14-135
EQUINOX • TORRENT

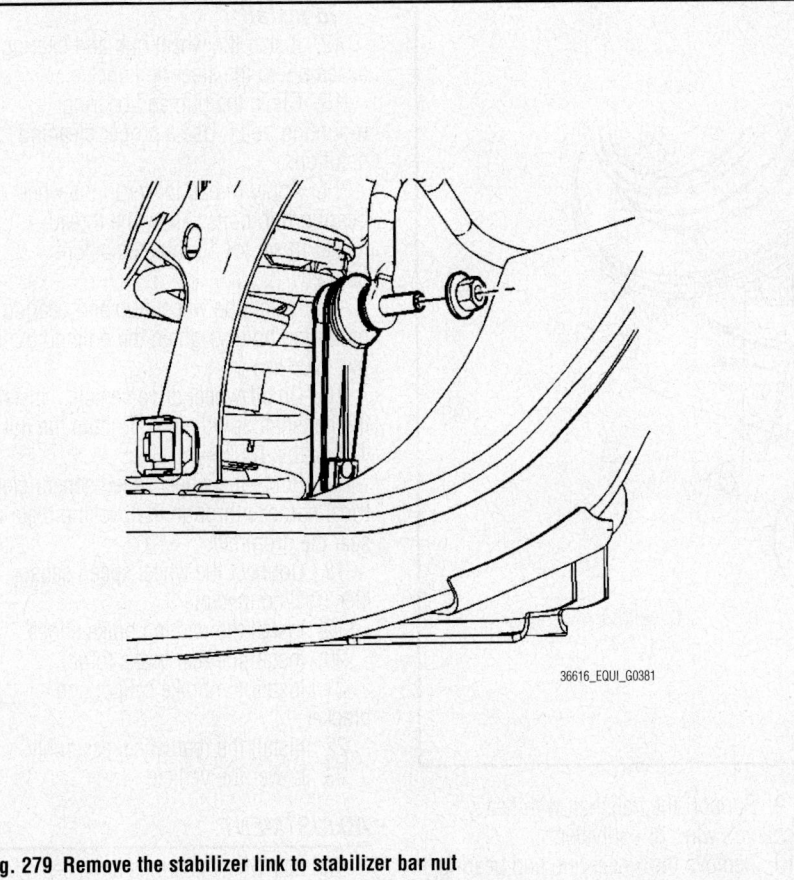

Fig. 279 Remove the stabilizer link to stabilizer bar nut

To install:

7. Position the stabilizer link through the control arm.

8. Install the stabilizer link to control arm nut. Tighten the nut to 11 ft. lbs. (15 Nm).

9. Install the stabilizer link to stabilizer bar nut. Tighten the nut to 37 ft. lbs. (50 Nm).

10. Tighten the loose stabilizer bar clamp bolts to 52 ft. lbs. (70 Nm).

11. Lower the vehicle.

TOE LINK

REMOVAL & INSTALLATION

See Figure 280.

1. Before servicing the vehicle, refer to the precautions section.

2. Raise and safely support the vehicle.

3. Remove the wheel assembly.

4. Remove the toe link to knuckle nut and bolt.

5. Remove the toe link to support nut and bolt.

6. Remove the toe link from the vehicle.

To install:

7. Install the toe link to the support assembly.

→Install the bolt with the head towards the front of the vehicle. Position the cam nut in same position as in the upper control arm.

8. Install the toe link to support nut and bolt.

9. Install the toe link to the knuckle. Tighten the bolt to 118 ft. lbs. (160 Nm).

10. Tighten the toe link to support bolt. Tighten the bolt to 118 ft. lbs. (160 Nm).

11. Install the wheel assembly.

12. Lower the vehicle.

13. Check the rear alignment.

WHEEL HUB & BEARING

REMOVAL & INSTALLATION

See Figure 281.

1. Before servicing the vehicle, refer to the precautions section.

2. Raise and support the vehicle.

3. Remove the rear wheel assembly.

4. Remove the brake caliper and bracket.

5. Remove the rear brake rotor.

6. Remove the parking brake shoes. Refer to Parking Brake Shoes Removal & Installation in the Brake section.

7. On vehicles with AWD, remove the halfshaft spindle nut.

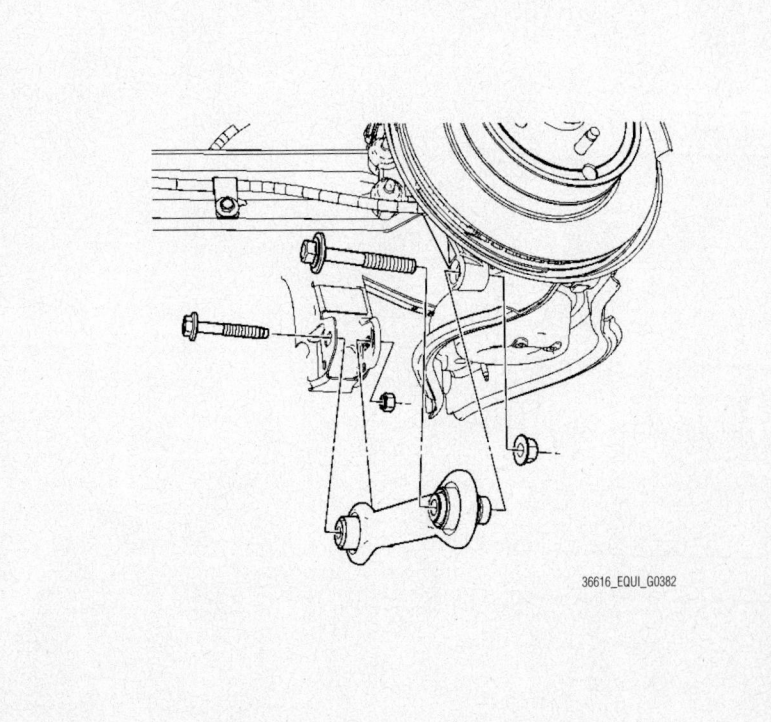

Fig. 280 Toe link removal

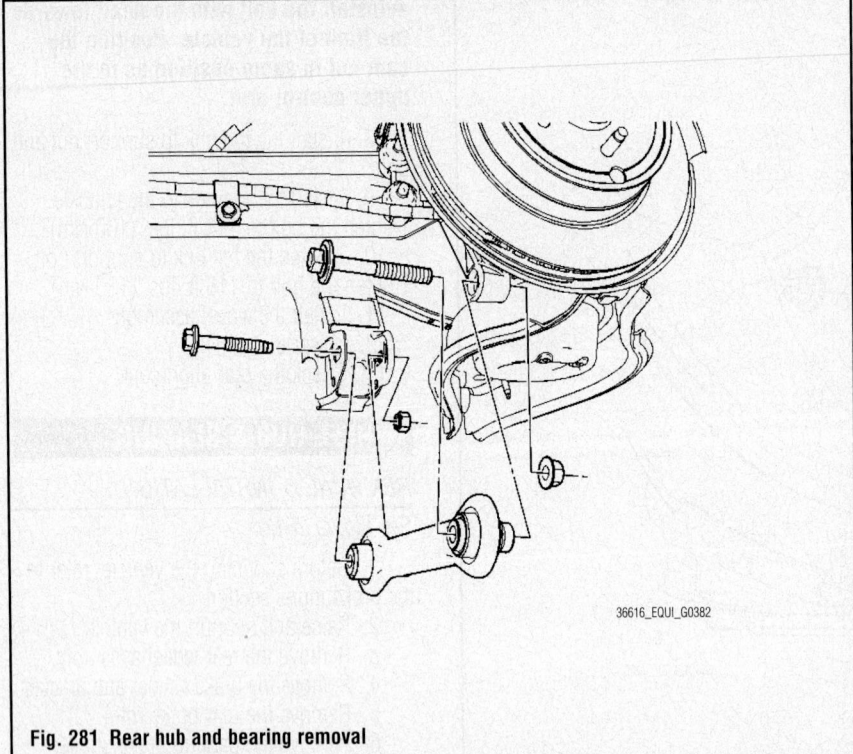

Fig. 281 Rear hub and bearing removal

8. Disconnect the wheel speed sensor electrical connector.

✳✳ WARNING

Do not damage the halfshaft joint seal.

9. Support the halfshaft with heavy mechanic's wire, or equivalent.
10. Remove the wheel hub and bearing mounting bolts.
11. Remove the wheel hub and bearing assembly from the suspension knuckle.

To install:

12. Install the wheel hub and bearing assembly to the steering knuckle.
13. Clean the hub and bearing mounting bolts. Use a proper cleaning solution.
14. Apply thread locker to the wheel bearing/hub bolts. Allow the thread locker to set for 10 minutes before using.
15. Install the wheel hub and bearing mounting bolts. Tighten the bolts to 52 ft. lbs. (70 Nm)
16. On all-wheel drive vehicles, install the halfshaft spindle nut. Tighten the nut to 151 ft. lbs. (205 Nm).
17. Route the wheel speed sensor electrical harness through the backing plate and seat the grommet.
18. Connect the wheel speed sensor electrical connector.
19. Install the parking brake shoes.
20. Install the rear brake rotor.
21. Install the brake caliper and bracket.
22. Install the rear wheel assembly.
23. Lower the vehicle

ADJUSTMENT

The rear wheel bearings are a sealed unit, and cannot be adjusted. If movement is present in the hub and bearing assembly it must be replaced.

CHEVROLET AND GMC

15

Express • Savana

SPECIFICATIONS AND MAINTENANCE CHARTS

ENGINE AND VEHICLE IDENTIFICATION

Engine								Model Year	
Code ①	Liters	Cu. In.	Cyl.	Fuel Sys.	Engine Type	Eng. Mfg.		Code ②	Year
X	4.3	262	6	MFI	OHV	CPC		8	2008
C	4.8	293	8	SFI	OHV	CPC		9	2009
4	5.3	325	8	SFI	OHV	CPC			
K	6.0	364	8	SFI	OHV	CPC			
6	6.6	402	8	DSL	OHV	CPC			

CPC: Chevrolet/Pontiac/Canada

DSL: Diesel

MFI: Multi-port Fuel Injection

SFI: Sequential Fuel Injection

① 8th position of VIN

② 10th position of VIN

36616_EXPR_C0001

GENERAL ENGINE SPECIFICATIONS

All measurements are given in inches.

Year	Model	Engine Displacement Liters	Engine Series VIN	Net Horsepower @ rpm	Net Torque @ rpm (ft. lbs.)	Bore x Stroke (in.)	Com-pression Ratio	Oil Pressure @ rpm
2008	Express	4.3	X	195@4600	260@2800	4.012x3.480	9.20:1	18@2000
		4.8	C	279@5200	294@4000	3.779x3.270	9.08:1	18@2000
		5.3	4	301@5200	325@4500	3.779x3.622	9.95:1	18@2000
		6.0	K	323@4600	373@4400	4.007x3.622	9.67:1	18@2000
		6.6	6	250@3200	460@1600	4.055x3.898	16.8:1	42@1800
	Savanna	4.3	X	195@4600	260@2800	4.012x3.480	9.20:1	18@2000
		4.8	C	279@5200	294@4000	3.779x3.270	9.08:1	18@2000
		5.3	4	301@5200	325@4500	3.779x3.622	9.95:1	18@2000
		6.0	K	323@4600	373@4400	4.007x3.622	9.67:1	18@2000
		6.6	6	250@3200	460@1600	4.055x3.898	16.8:1	42@1800
2009	Express	4.3	X	195@4600	260@2800	4.012x3.480	9.20:1	18@2000
		4.8	C	279@5200	294@4000	3.779x3.270	9.08:1	18@2000
		5.3	4	301@5200	325@4500	3.779x3.622	9.95:1	18@2000
		6.0	K	323@4600	373@4400	4.007x3.622	9.67:1	18@2000
		6.6	6	250@3200	460@1600	4.055x3.898	16.8:1	42@1800
	Savanna	4.3	X	195@4600	260@2800	4.012x3.480	9.20:1	18@2000
		4.8	C	279@5200	294@4000	3.779x3.270	9.08:1	18@2000
		5.3	4	301@5200	325@4500	3.779x3.622	9.95:1	18@2000
		6.0	K	323@4600	373@4400	4.007x3.622	9.67:1	18@2000
		6.6	6	250@3200	460@1600	4.055x3.898	16.8:1	42@1800

36616_EXPR_C0002

GASOLINE ENGINE TUNE-UP SPECIFICATIONS

Year	Engine Displacement Liters	Engine VIN	Spark Plugs Gap (in.)	Ignition Timing (deg.) MT	Ignition Timing (deg.) AT	Fuel Pump (psi)	Idle Speed (rpm) MT	Idle Speed (rpm) AT	Valve Clearance In.	Valve Clearance Ex.
2008	4.3	X	0.060	①	①	55-62 ②	③	③	HYD	HYD
	4.8	C	0.040	①	①	55-62 ②	③	③	HYD	HYD
	5.3	4	0.040	①	①	55-62 ②	③	③	HYD	HYD
	6.0	K	0.040	①	①	55-62 ②	③	③	HYD	HYD
2009	4.3	X	0.060	①	①	50-60 ②	③	③	HYD	HYD
	4.8	C	0.040	①	①	55-62 ②	③	③	HYD	HYD
	5.3	4	0.040	①	①	50-60 ②	③	③	HYD	HYD
	6.0	K	0.040	①	①	55-62 ②	③	③	HYD	HYD

NOTE: The Vehicle Emission Control Information label often reflects specification changes made during production.
The label figures must be used if they differ from those in this chart.

HYD: Hydraulic
① Ignition timing is preset and cannot be adjusted
② With key ON and engine OFF
③ Idle speed is maintained by the Powertrain Control Module (PCM)

36616_EXPR_C0004

DIESEL ENGINE TUNE-UP SPECIFICATIONS

Year	Engine Displacement Liters	Engine VIN	Valve Clearance Intake (in.)	Valve Clearance Exhaust (in.)	Intake Valve Opens (deg.)	Injection Pump Setting (deg.)	Injection Nozzle Pressure (psi) New	Injection Nozzle Pressure (psi) Used	Idle Speed (rpm)	Cranking Compression Pressure (psi)
2008	6.6	6	HYD	HYD	①	①	NA	NA	①	300
2009	6.6	6	HYD	HYD	①	①	NA	NA	①	300

NOTE: The Vehicle Emission Control Information label often reflects specification changes made during production.
The label figures must be used if they differ from those in this chart.

HYD: Hydraulic
NA: Not Available
① Refer to Vehicle Emission Control Information label

36616_EXPR_C0005

CAPACITIES

Year	Model	Engine Displacement Liters	Engine VIN	Engine Oil with Filter (qts.)	Transmission (pts.) Man.	Transmission (pts.) Auto.	Transfer Case (pts.)	Drive Axle Front (pts.)	Drive Axle Rear (pts.)	Fuel Tank (gal.)	Cooling System (qts.)
2008	Express	4.3	X	4.5	—	①	—	—	②	31.0 ③	10.0 ④
	Express	4.8	C	6.0	—	①	—	—	②	31.0 ③	12.4 ④
	Express	5.3	4	6.0	—	①	3.0	2.54	②	31.0 ③	12.4 ④
	Express	6.0	K	6.0	—	①	—	—	②	31.0 ③	13.8 ④
	Express	6.6	6	10.0	—	①	—	—	②	31.0 ③	21.6
	Savana	4.3	X	4.5	—	①	—	—	②	31.0 ③	10.0 ④
	Savana	4.8	C	6.0	—	①	—	—	②	31.0 ③	12.4 ④
	Savana	5.3	4	6.0	—	①	3.0	2.54	②	31.0 ③	12.4 ④
	Savana	6.0	K	6.0	—	①	—	—	②	31.0 ③	13.8 ④
	Savana	6.6	6	10.0	—	①	—	—	②	31.0 ③	21.6
2009	Express	4.3	X	4.5	—	①	—	—	②	31.0 ③	10.0 ④
	Express	4.8	C	6.0	—	①	—	—	②	31.0 ③	12.4 ④
	Express	5.3	4	6.0	—	①	3.0	2.54	②	31.0 ③	12.4 ④
	Express	6.0	K	6.0	—	①	—	—	②	31.0 ③	13.8 ④
	Express	6.6	6	10.0	—	①	—	—	②	31.0 ③	21.6
	Savana	4.3	X	4.5	—	①	—	—	②	31.0 ③	10.0 ④
	Savana	4.8	C	6.0	—	①	—	—	②	31.0 ③	12.4 ④
	Savana	5.3	4	6.0	—	①	3.0	2.54	②	31.0 ③	12.4 ④
	Savana	6.0	K	6.0	—	①	—	—	②	31.0 ③	13.8 ④
	Savana	6.6	6	10.0	—	①	—	—	②	31.0 ③	21.6

NOTE: All capacities are approximate. Add fluid gradually and check to be sure a proper fluid level is obtained.

① 4L60-E: 19.4 pts. With 258 converter
  4L60-E: 22.4 pts. With 298 converter
  4L60-E: 17.6 pts. With 245 converter
  4L80-E: 15.4 pts.

② 8.60 in. ring gear: 4.30 pts.
  9.50 in. ring gear: 5.50 pts.
  9.75 in. ring gear: 6.26 pts.
  10.5 in. ring gear: 6.62 pts.

③ Optional 33 and 57 gallon

④ Add three qts. with rear heater

36616_EXPR_C0003

FLUID SPECIFICATIONS

Year	Model	Engine Displacement Liters	Engine ID/VIN	Engine Oil	Auto. Trans.	Drive Axle	Power Steering Fluid	Brake Master Cylinder
2008	Express	4.3	X	5W-30	Dexron VI	①	GM PS Fluid	DOT-3
		4.8	C	5W-30	Dexron VI	①	GM PS Fluid	DOT-3
		5.3	4	5W-30	Dexron VI	①	GM PS Fluid	DOT-3
		6.0	K	5W-30	Dexron VI	①	GM PS Fluid	DOT-3
		6.6	6	②	Dexron VI	①	GM PS Fluid	DOT-3
	Savana	4.3	X	5W-30	Dexron VI	①	GM PS Fluid	DOT-3
		4.8	C	5W-30	Dexron VI	①	GM PS Fluid	DOT-3
		5.3	4	5W-30	Dexron VI	①	GM PS Fluid	DOT-3
		6.0	K	5W-30	Dexron VI	①	GM PS Fluid	DOT-3
		6.6	6	②	Dexron VI	①	GM PS Fluid	DOT-3
2009	Express	4.3	X	5W-30	Dexron VI	①	GM PS Fluid	DOT-3
		4.8	C	5W-30	Dexron VI	①	GM PS Fluid	DOT-3
		5.3	4	5W-30	Dexron VI	①	GM PS Fluid	DOT-3
		6.0	K	5W-30	Dexron VI	①	GM PS Fluid	DOT-3
		6.6	6	②	Dexron VI	①	GM PS Fluid	DOT-3
	Savana	4.3	X	5W-30	Dexron VI	①	GM PS Fluid	DOT-3
		4.8	C	5W-30	Dexron VI	①	GM PS Fluid	DOT-3
		5.3	4	5W-30	Dexron VI	①	GM PS Fluid	DOT-3
		6.0	K	5W-30	Dexron VI	①	GM PS Fluid	DOT-3
		6.6	6	②	Dexron VI	①	GM PS Fluid	DOT-3

DOT: Department Of Transpotation

① SAE 75W-90 synthetic axle lubricant part #89021677-US, 89021678-Canada or equivalent meeting GM specificarion 9986155

② 5W-40. 15-W-40 prefered above 0 degrees F

36616_EXPR_C0014

VALVE SPECIFICATIONS

Year	Engine Displacement Liters	Engine VIN	Seat Angle (deg.)	Face Angle (deg.)	Spring Test Pressure (lbs. @ in.)	Spring Installed Height (in.)	Stem-to-Guide Clearance (in.) Intake	Stem-to-Guide Clearance (in.) Exhaust	Stem Diameter (in.) Intake	Stem Diameter (in.) Exhaust
2008	4.3	X	46	45	187-203@1.27	1.67-1.70	0.0010-0.0037	0.0010-0.0037	NA	NA
	4.8	C	46	45	220@1.32	1.80	0.0010-0.0026	0.0010-0.0026	0.3132-0.3140	0.3132-0.3140
	5.3	4	46	45	220@1.32	1.80	0.0010-0.0026	0.0010-0.0026	0.3130-0.3140	0.3130-0.3140
	6.0	K	46	45	220@1.32	1.80	0.0010-0.0027	0.0010-0.0027	0.3130-0.3140	0.3130-0.3140
	6.6	6	45	45	NA	1.61	0.0012-0.0025	0.0015-0.0028	NA	NA
2009	4.3	X	46	45	187-203@1.27	1.67-1.70	0.0010-0.0037	0.0010-0.0037	NA	NA
	4.8	C	46	45	220@1.32	1.80	0.0010-0.0026	0.0010-0.0026	0.3132-0.3140	0.3132-0.3140
	5.3	4	46	45	220@1.32	1.80	0.0010-0.0026	0.0010-0.0026	0.3130-0.3140	0.3130-0.3140
	6.0	K	46	45	220@1.32	1.80	0.0010-0.0027	0.0010-0.0027	0.3130-0.3140	0.3130-0.3140
	6.6	6	45	45	NA	1.61	0.0012-0.0025	0.0015-0.0028	NA	NA

NA: Not Available

36616_EXPR_C0006

CAMSHAFT AND BEARING SPECIFICATIONS CHART
All measurements are given in inches.

Year	Engine Displacement Liters	Engine VIN	Journal Dia.	Brg. Oil Clearance	Shaft End-play	Runout	Journal Bore	Lobe Height Intake	Lobe Height Exhaust
2008	4.3	X	1.8677-1.8696	NA	0.001-0.009	0.0039	NA	0.2704	0.2793
	4.8	C	2.164-2.166	NA	0.001-0.012	0.0020	①	0.2830	0.2830
	5.3	4	2.164-2.166	NA	0.001-0.012	0.0020	①	0.2830	0.2830
	6.0	K	2.164-2.166	NA	0.001-0.012	0.0020	①	0.2740	0.2813
	6.6	6	2.3990-2.4001	NA	0.0079	0.0020	②	0.2863	0.2326
2009	4.3	X	1.8677-1.8696	NA	0.001-0.009	0.0039	NA	0.2704	0.2793
	4.8	C	2.164-2.166	NA	0.001-0.012	0.0020	①	0.2830	0.2830
	5.3	4	2.164-2.166	NA	0.001-0.012	0.0020	①	0.2830	0.2830
	6.0	K	2.164-2.166	NA	0.001-0.012	0.0020	①	0.2740	0.2813
	6.6	6	2.3990-2.4001	NA	0.0079	0.0020	②	0.2863	0.2326

NA: Not Available

① Bearing diameter: 2.1678-2.1688
   Journal to bearing: 0.0009-0.0038

② Journal diameter: 2.3984

36616_EXPR_C0008

CRANKSHAFT AND CONNECTING ROD SPECIFICATIONS

All measurements are given in inches.

Year	Engine Displacement Liters	Engine VIN	Crankshaft				Connecting Rod		
			Main Brg. Journal Dia.	Main Brg. Oil Clearance	Shaft End-play	Thrust on No.	Journal Diameter	Oil Clearance	Side Clearance
2008	4.3	X	①	②	0.0020-0.0080	4	2.2487-2.2497	0.0010-0.0025	0.0060-0.0170
	4.8	C	2.5580-2.5593	0.0008-0.0021	0.0015-0.0078	5	2.0991-2.0999	0.0009-0.0025	0.0043-0.0200
	5.3	4	2.5580-2.5593	0.0008-0.0021	0.0015-0.0078	5	2.0991-2.0999	0.0009-0.0025	0.0043-0.0200
	6.0	K	2.5580-2.5590	0.0008-0.0021	0.0015-0.0078	5	2.0991-2.0999	0.0009-0.0025	0.0043-0.2000
	6.6	6	3.1459-3.1466	0.0015-0.0028	0.0016-0.0081	NA	2.4764-2.4772	0.0014-0.0030	0.0122-0.0193
2009	4.3	X	①	②	0.0020-0.0080	4	2.2487-2.2497	0.0010-0.0025	0.0060-0.0170
	4.8	C	2.5580-2.5593	0.0008-0.0021	0.0015-0.0078	5	2.0991-2.0999	0.0009-0.0025	0.0043-0.0200
	5.3	4	2.5580-2.5593	0.0008-0.0021	0.0015-0.0078	5	2.0991-2.0999	0.0009-0.0025	0.0043-0.0200
	6.0	K	2.5580-2.5590	0.0008-0.0021	0.0015-0.0078	5	2.0991-2.0999	0.0009-0.0025	0.0043-0.2000
	6.6	6	3.1459-3.1466	0.0015-0.0028	0.0016-0.0081	NA	2.4764-2.4772	0.0014-0.0030	0.0122-0.0193

NA - Not Available

① No. 1: 2.4488 in.-2.4495 in.
   Nos. 2, 3: 2.4485 in.-2.4494 in.
   No. 4: 2.4480 in.-2.4489 in.

② No. 1: 0.0010-0.0020 in.
   No. 2, 3, 4: 0.0010-0.0025 in.

36616_EXPR_C0009

PISTON AND RING SPECIFICATIONS

All measurements are given in inches.

Year	Engine Displacement Liters	Engine VIN	Piston Clearance	Ring Gap			Ring Side Clearance		
				Top Compression	Bottom Compression	Oil Control	Top Compression	Bottom Compression	Oil Control
2008	4.3	X	0.0007-0.0024	0.0100-0.0200	0.0150-0.0310	0.0002 0.0035	0.0012 0.0033	0.0012 0.0033	0.0030-0.0079
	4.8	C	0.0014 -0.0006	0.0090-0.0196	0.0173-0.0300	0.0070-0.0320	0.0016-0.0033	0.0016-0.0031	0.0005-0.0078
	5.3	4	0.0014 -0.0006	0.0090-0.0196	0.0173-0.0300	0.007-0.0320	0.0016-0.0034	0.0016-0.0031	0.0005-0.0078
	6.0	K	0.0009 -0.0012	0.0079-0.0181	0.0146-0.0295	0.0086-0.0331	0.0016-0.0033	0.0016-0.0031	0.0005-0.0078
	6.6	6	NA	0.0118-0.0177	0.0197-0.0256	0.0059-0.0138	0.0030-0.0067	0.0004-0.0012	0.0004-0.0012
2009	4.3	X	0.0007-0.0024	0.0100-0.0200	0.0150-0.0310	0.0002 0.0035	0.0012 0.0033	0.0012 0.0033	0.0030-0.0079
	4.8	C	0.0014 -0.0006	0.0090-0.0196	0.0173-0.0300	0.007-0.0320	0.0016-0.0033	0.0016-0.0031	0.0005-0.0078
	5.3	4	0.0014 -0.0006	0.0090-0.0196	0.0173-0.0300	0.007-0.0320	0.0016-0.0034	0.0016-0.0031	0.0005-0.0078
	6.0	K	0.0009 -0.0012	0.0079-0.0181	0.0146-0.0295	0.0086-0.0331	0.0016-0.0033	0.0016-0.0031	0.0005-0.0078
	6.6	6	NA	0.0118-0.0177	0.0197-0.0256	0.0059-0.0138	0.0030-0.0067	0.0004-0.0012	0.0004-0.0012

36616_EXPR_C0010

TORQUE SPECIFICATIONS

All readings in ft. lbs.

Year	Engine Displacement Liters	Engine VIN	Cylinder Head Bolts	Main Bearing Bolts	Rod Bearing Bolts	Crankshaft Damper Bolts	Flywheel Bolts	Manifold Intake *	Exhaust	Spark Plugs	Oil Pan Drain Plug
2008	4.3	X	①	77	②	70	74	③	④	11	18
	4.8	C	⑤	⑥	⑦	⑧	⑨	⑩	⑪	11	18
	5.3	4	⑤	⑥	⑦	⑧	⑨	⑩	⑪	11	18
	6.0	K	⑤	⑥	⑦	⑧	⑨	⑩	⑪	11	18
	6.6	6	⑫	⑬	⑭	⑮	⑯	18	42	—	62
2009	4.3	X	①	77	②	70	74	③	④	11	18
	4.8	C	⑤	⑥	⑦	⑧	⑨	⑩	⑪	11	18
	5.3	4	⑤	⑥	⑦	⑧	⑨	⑩	⑪	11	18
	6.0	K	⑤	⑥	⑦	⑧	⑨	⑩	⑪	11	18
	6.6	6	⑫	⑬	⑭	⑮	⑯	18	⑰	—	62

* NOTE: Applies to Lower Manifold only.

① Step 1: 22 ft. lbs.

Step 2:

Short bolt: Plus 55 degrees

Medium bolt: Plus 65 degrees

Long bolt: Plus 75 degrees

② 15 ft. lbs. plus 100 degrees

③ Lower intake manifold:

Step 1: 27 inch lbs.

Step 2: 106 inch lbs.

Step 3: 11 ft. lbs.

Upper manifold bolts:

Step 1: 44 inch lbs.

Step 2: 80 inch lbs.

④ Tighten bolts to 12 ft. lbs.

Retorque to 22 ft. lbs.

⑤ M11 bolts Step 1: 22 ft. lbs.

M11 bolts Step 2: 90 degrees

M11 bolts Step 3: 70 degrees

M8 bolts: 22 ft. lbs.

⑥ Inner bolts:

Step 1: 15 ft. lbs.

Step 2: 80 degrees

Side Bolts: 18 ft. lbs.

Outer bolts:

Step 1: 15 ft. lbs.

Step 2: 51 degrees

⑦ Step 1: 15 ft. lbs.

Step 2: 85 degrees

⑧ First pass: 111

Second pass: loosen 360 degrees

Third pass: 37

Fourth pass: 280 degrees

⑨ Step 1: 15 ft. lbs.

Step 2: 37 ft. lbs.

Step 3: 74 ft. lbs.

⑩ Step 1: 44 inch lbs.

Step 2: 89 inch lbs.

⑪ Step 1: 11 ft. lbs.

Step 2: 15 ft. lbs.

⑫ M12 bolts: Step 1: 37 ft. lbs.

Step 2: 59 ft. lbs.

Step 3: Plus 60 degrees

Step 4: Plus 90 degrees

⑬ Step 1: 74 ft. lbs.

Step 2: Plus 90 degrees

⑭ Step 1: 47 ft. lbs.

Step 2: Plus 30 degrees

Step 3: Plus 30 degrees

⑮ 1st pass: 74 ft. lbs.

2nd pass: Plus 105 degrees

⑯ Step 1: 58 ft. lbs.

Step 2: Plus 60 degrees

Step 3: Plus 60 degrees

⑰ First pass: 42 ft. lbs.

Four center bolts an additional pass

36616_EXPR_C0011

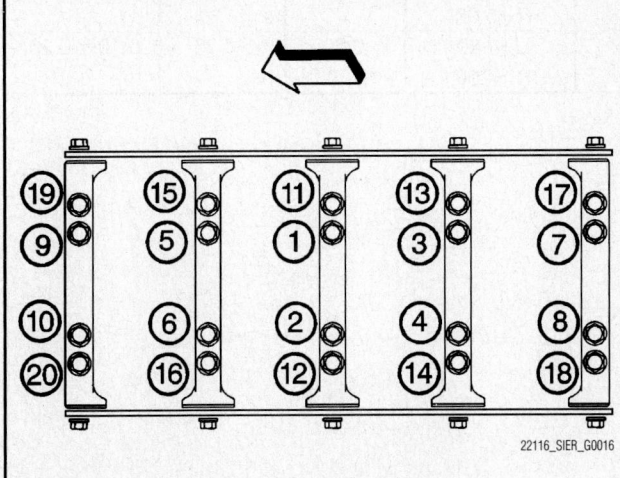

22116_SIER_G0016

Fig. 1 Main bearing bolt identification and torque sequence—4.8L, 5.3L and 6.0L engines

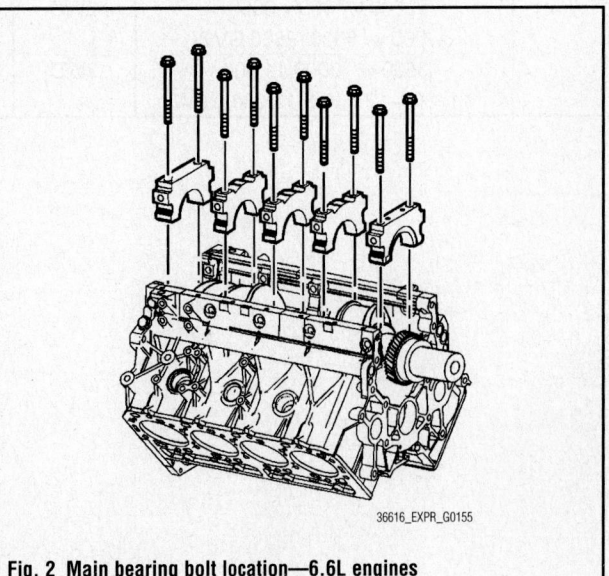

36616_EXPR_G0155

Fig. 2 Main bearing bolt location—6.6L engines

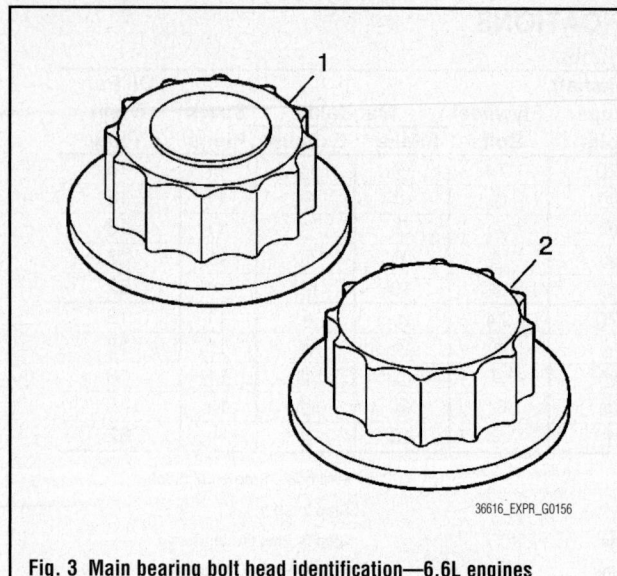

Fig. 3 Main bearing bolt head identification—6.6L engines

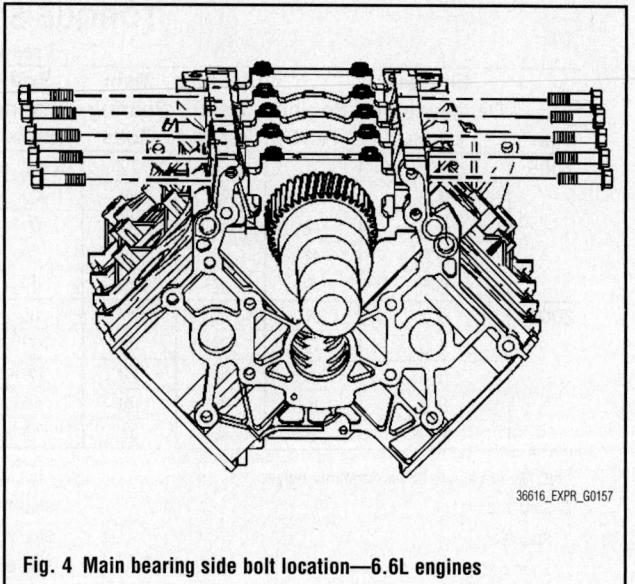

Fig. 4 Main bearing side bolt location—6.6L engines

WHEEL ALIGNMENT

Year	Series	Model	Caster Range (+/-Deg.)	Caster Preferred Setting (Deg.)	Camber Range (+/-Deg.)	Camber Preferred Setting (Deg.)	Toe-in (Deg.)
2008	1500 w/ 6200, 7200 & 2500 w/ 7300 GVW	2WD/AWD	1.00	L +4.20 R +4.50	0.50	+0.15	0.10+/-0.20
	2500 w/ 8500, 8600 &3500 w/ 8600, 9600 GVW	2WD	1.00	L +4.60 R +5.00	0.50	+0.25	0.10+/-0.20
	3500 w/10000,11,000 11, 500, 12,000 & 12,300 GVW	2WD	1.00	L +4.60 R +4.90	0.50	+0.25	0.10+/-0.20
2009	1500 w/ 6200, 7200 & 2500 w/ 7300 GVW	2WD/AWD	1.00	L +4.20 R +4.50	0.50	+0.15	0.10+/-0.20
	2500 w/ 8500, 8600 &3500 w/ 8600, 9600 GVW	2WD	1.00	L +4.60 R +5.00	0.50	+0.25	0.10+/-0.20
	3500 w/10000,11,000 11, 500, 12,000 & 12,300 GVW	2WD	1.00	L +4.60 R +4.90	0.50	+0.25	0.10+/-0.20

36616_EXPR_C0015

TIRE, WHEEL AND BALL JOINT SPECIFICATIONS

Year	Model	OEM Tires Standard	OEM Tires Optional	Tire Pressures (psi) Front	Tire Pressures (psi) Rear	Wheel Size	Ball Joint Inspection	Lug Nut (ft. lbs.)
2008	1500	P245/70R17	None	②	②	7-JJ	L ①	140
	2500	LT225/75R16E	LT245/75R16E	②	②	7-JJ	L ①	140
	3500	LT245/75R16E	None	②	②	7-JJ	0.125 in.③	140
2009	1500	P245/70R17	None	②	②	7-JJ	L ①	140
	2500	LT225/75R16E	LT245/75R16E	②	②	7-JJ	L ①	140
	3500	LT245/75R16E	None	②	②	7-JJ	0.125 in.③	140

OEM: Original Equipment Manufacturer

PSI: Pounds Per Square Inch

STD: Standard

OPT: Optional

L: Lower

U: Upper

① Do not lift truck. Inspect the boss into which the grease fitting is threaded. Replace if the boss is flush or receded below the surface of the ball joint

② Specification is listed on inside driver's side front door placard

③ Applies to both upper and lower

36616_EXPR_C0016

BRAKE SPECIFICATIONS

All measurements in inches unless noted

Year	Model		Brake Disc Original Thickness	Brake Disc Minimum Thickness	Brake Disc Maximum Runout	Brake Drum Diameter Original Inside Diameter	Brake Drum Diameter Max. Wear Limit	Brake Drum Diameter Max. Machine Diameter	Minimum Lining Thickness	Brake Caliper Bracket Bolts (ft. lbs.)	Brake Caliper Mounting Bolts (ft. lbs.)
2008	Express	F	①	②	0.005	—	—	—	—	③	④
		R	⑤	⑥	0.005	—	—	—	—	⑦	⑧
	Savana	F	①	②	0.005	—	—	—	—	③	④
		R	⑤	⑥	0.005	—	—	—	—	⑦	⑧
2009	Express	F	①	②	0.005	—	—	—	—	③	④
		R	⑤	⑥	0.005	—	—	—	—	⑦	⑧
	Savana	F	①	②	0.005	—	—	—	—	③	④
		R	⑤	⑥	0.005	—	—	—	—	⑦	⑧

NA: Not Available

① JH5: 1.142
JH6: 1.496
JH7: 1.496

② JH5: 1.102
JH6: 1.457
JH7: 1.457

③ JH5: 129
JH6, JH7: 221

④ All 80

⑤ JH5: 1.181
JH6: 1.142
JH7: 1.181

⑥ JH5: 1.142
JH6: 1.102
JH7: 1.142

⑦ JH5: 148 single rear wheel
JH6: 123 single rear wheel
JH7: 123 single rear wheel
All 221 dual rear wheel

⑧ JH5: 25 single rear wheel
JH6: 53 single rear wheel
JH7: 53 single rear wheel
All 45 dual rear wheel

36616_EXPR_C0017

MAINTENANCE I AND II SERVICE SCHEDULES
EXPRESS & SAVANA

When the CHANGE ENGINE OIL light appears, certain services and inspections are required.

Required services are described as Maintenance I and Maintenance II.

The first service on a vehicle should be Maintenance I, and the second service should be Maintenance II.

Alternate between the 2 thereafter. However, in some cases, Maintenance II may be required more often.

Maintenance I: Use Maintenance I if the CHANGE ENGINE OIL light comes on within 10 months since vehicle was purchased or, if Maintenance II was performed.

Maintenance II: Use Maintenance II if the previous service performed was Maintenance I.

Always use Maintenance II whenever the CHANGE ENGINE OIL light comes on 10 months or more since the last service, or, if the CHANGE ENGINE OIL light has not come on at all for one year.

Service	Maintenance I	Maintenance II
Change the engine oil and filter. Reset the oil life system.	✓	✓
Visually inspect the vehicle for leaks or damage. A fluid loss in the vehicle system could indicate a problem. Inspect, repair and add fluid to the system	✓	✓
Inspect the engine air cleaner filter. If necessary, replace the filter.	✓	✓
Rotate the tires. Inspect the tire inflation pressures and the tire wear.	✓	✓
Visually inspect the brake lines and hoses for proper hook-up, binding, leaks, cracks, chafing, etc. Inspect the disc brake pads for wear and the rotors for surface condition. Inspect the drum brake linings for wear or cracks. Inspect other brake parts, including drums, wheel cylinders, calipers, parking brake, etc. Inspect the parking brake adjustment.	✓	✓
Inspect the engine coolant and the windshield washer fluid levels. Add fluid as needed.	✓	✓
Inspect the suspension and steering components. Inspect the front and rear suspension and the steering system for damaged, loose or missing parts, or signs of wear. Inspect the power steering lines and the hoses for proper hook-up, binding, leaks, cracks, chafing, etc.	--	✓
Visually inspect the coolant hoses and replace the hoses if they are cracked, swollen or deteriorated. Inspect all pipes, fittings and clamps; replace with GM parts as needed. To help ensure proper operation, a pressure test of the cooling system and pressure cap and cleaning the outside of the radiator and air conditioning condenser is recommended at least once a year.	✓	✓
Inspect the wiper blades for wear or cracking.	--	✓
Inspect the restraint system components. Ensure the safety belt reminder light and all the belts, buckles, latch plates, retractors and anchorages are working properly. Look for any other loose or damaged safety belt system parts. If you see anything that might keep a safety belt system from working correctly, repair or replaced the damaged part. Replace torn or frayed safety belts, refer to Operational and Functional Checks in Seat Belts. Inspect for any opened or broken air bag coverings, and repair or replace as needed. The air bag system does require regular maintenance.	--	✓
assemblies, secondary latches, pivots, spring anchor and release pawl, hood and door hinges, rear folding seats and liftgate hinges. Frequent lubrication may be required when exposed to a corrosive environment, refer to Fluid and Lubricant Recommendations . Applying dielectric silicone grease GM P/N 12345579 (Canadian P/N 1974984) or equivalent on the weatherstrips with a clean cloth.	--	✓
Inspect the transaxle fluid level and add fluid as needed.	--	✓

36616_EXPR_C0012

MAINTENANCE I AND II SERVICE SCHEDULES (cont.)
EXPRESS & SAVANA

When the CHANGE ENGINE OIL light appears, certain services and inspections are required.

Required services are described as Maintenance I and Maintenance II.

The first service on a vehicle should be Maintenance I, and the second service should be Maintenance II.

Alternate between the 2 thereafter. However, in some cases, Maintenance II may be required more often.

Maintenance I: Use Maintenance I if the CHANGE ENGINE OIL light comes on within 10 months since vehicle was purchased or, if Maintenance II was performed.

Maintenance II: Use Maintenance II if the previous service performed was Maintenance I.

Always use Maintenance II whenever the CHANGE ENGINE OIL light comes on 10 months or more since the last service, or, if the CHANGE ENGINE OIL light has not come on at all for one year.

Service	Maintenance I	Maintenance
Inspect the suspension and steering components.Inspect the front and rear suspension and the steering system for damaged, loose or missing parts, or signs of wear. Inspect power steering lines and hoses for proper hook-up, binding, leaks, cracks, chafing, etc.	--	✓
missing parts. Replace the parts as needed. Replace any components that have high effort or excessive wear. Do not lubricate the accelerator or the cruise control cables.	--	✓
Replace the passenger compartment air filter.	--	✓

36616_EXPR_C0013

PRECAUTIONS

Before servicing any vehicle, please be sure to read all of the following precautions, which deal with personal safety, prevention of component damage, and important points to take into consideration when servicing a motor vehicle:

• Never open, service or drain the radiator or cooling system when the engine is hot; serious burns can occur from the steam and hot coolant.

• Observe all applicable safety precautions when working around fuel. Whenever servicing the fuel system, always work in a well-ventilated area. Do not allow fuel spray or vapors to come in contact with a spark, open flame, or excessive heat (a hot drop light, for example). Keep a dry chemical fire extinguisher near the work area. Always keep fuel in a container specifically designed for fuel storage; also, always properly seal fuel containers to avoid the possibility of fire or explosion. Refer to the additional fuel system precautions later in this section.

• Fuel injection systems often remain pressurized, even after the engine has been turned **OFF**. The fuel system pressure must be relieved before disconnecting any fuel lines. Failure to do so may result in fire and/or personal injury.

• Brake fluid often contains polyglycol ethers and polyglycols. Avoid contact with the eyes and wash your hands thoroughly after handling brake fluid. If you do get brake fluid in your eyes, flush your eyes with clean, running water for 15 minutes. If eye irritation persists, or if you have taken brake fluid internally, IMMEDIATELY seek medical assistance.

• The EPA warns that prolonged contact with used engine oil may cause a number of skin disorders, including cancer. You should make every effort to minimize your exposure to used engine oil. Protective gloves should be worn when changing oil. Wash your hands and any other exposed skin areas as soon as possible after exposure to used engine oil. Soap and water, or waterless hand cleaner should be used.

• All new vehicles are now equipped with an air bag system, often referred to as a Supplemental Restraint System (SRS) or Supplemental Inflatable Restraint (SIR) system. The system must be disabled before performing service on or around system components, steering column, instrument panel components, wiring and sensors. Failure to follow safety and disabling procedures could result in accidental air bag deployment, possible personal injury and unnecessary system repairs.

• Always wear safety goggles when working with, or around, the air bag system. When carrying a non-deployed air bag, be sure the bag and trim cover are pointed away from your body. When placing a non-deployed air bag on a work surface, always face the bag and trim cover upward, away from the surface. This will reduce the motion of the module if it is accidentally deployed. Refer to the additional air bag system precautions later in this section.

• Clean, high quality brake fluid from a sealed container is essential to the safe and proper operation of the brake system. You should always buy the correct type of brake fluid for your vehicle. If the brake fluid becomes contaminated, completely flush the system with new fluid. Never reuse any brake fluid. Any brake fluid that is removed from the system should be discarded. Also, do not allow any brake fluid to come in contact with a painted surface; it will damage the paint.

• Never operate the engine without the proper amount and type of engine oil; doing so WILL result in severe engine damage.

• Timing belt maintenance is extremely important. Many models utilize an interference-type, non-freewheeling engine. If the timing belt breaks, the valves in the cylinder head may strike the pistons, causing potentially serious (also time-consuming and expensive) engine damage. Refer to the maintenance interval charts for the recommended replacement interval for the timing belt, and to the timing belt section for belt replacement and inspection.

• Disconnecting the negative battery cable on some vehicles may interfere with the functions of the on-board computer system(s) and may require the computer to undergo a relearning process once the negative battery cable is reconnected.

• When servicing drum brakes, only disassemble and assemble one side at a time, leaving the remaining side intact for reference.

• Only an MVAC-trained, EPA-certified automotive technician should service the air conditioning system or its components.

BRAKES

GENERAL INFORMATION

PRECAUTIONS

• Certain components within the ABS system are not intended to be serviced or repaired individually.

• Do not use rubber hoses or other parts not specifically specified for and ABS system. When using repair kits, replace all parts included in the kit. Partial or incorrect repair may lead to functional problems and require the replacement of components.

• Lubricate rubber parts with clean, fresh brake fluid to ease assembly. Do not use shop air to clean parts; damage to rubber components may result.

• Use only DOT 3 brake fluid from an unopened container.

• If any hydraulic component or line is removed or replaced, it may be necessary to bleed the entire system.

• A clean repair area is essential. Always clean the reservoir and cap thoroughly before removing the cap. The slightest amount of dirt in the fluid may plug an orifice and impair the system function. Perform repairs after components have been thoroughly cleaned; use only denatured alcohol to clean components. Do not allow ABS components to come into contact with any substance containing mineral oil; this includes used shop rags.

• The Anti-Lock control unit is a microprocessor similar to other computer units in the vehicle. Ensure that the ignition switch is **OFF** before removing or installing controller harnesses. Avoid static electricity discharge at or near the controller.

• If any arc welding is to be done on the vehicle, the control unit should be unplugged before welding operations begin.

ANTI-LOCK BRAKE SYSTEM (ABS)

WHEEL SPEED SENSORS

REMOVAL & INSTALLATION

Front Sensor

See Figure 5.

✶✶ CAUTION

Before servicing any electrical component, the ignition key must be in the OFF or LOCK position and all electrical loads must be OFF, unless instructed otherwise in these proce-

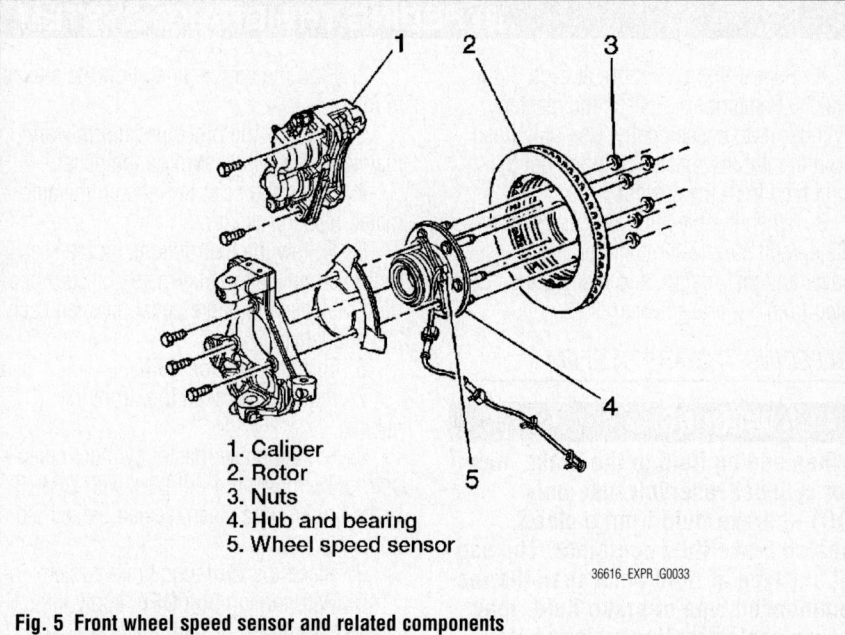

1. Caliper
2. Rotor
3. Nuts
4. Hub and bearing
5. Wheel speed sensor

36616_EXPR_G0033

Fig. 5 Front wheel speed sensor and related components

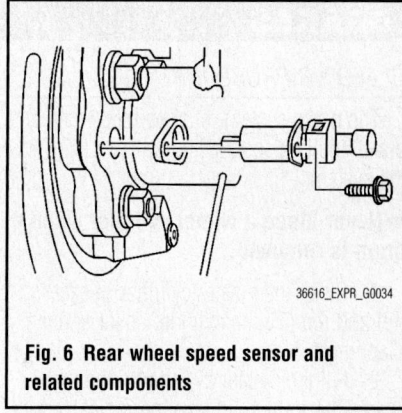

36616_EXPR_G0034

Fig. 6 Rear wheel speed sensor and related components

dures. **If a tool or equipment could easily come in contact with a live exposed electrical terminal, also disconnect the negative battery cable. Failure to follow these precautions may cause personal injury and/or damage to the vehicle or its components.**

1. Before servicing the vehicle, refer to the Precautions Section.
2. Disconnect the negative battery cable.
3. Raise and support the vehicle safely.
4. Remove the tire and wheel assembly.
5. Remove the brake rotor.
6. Remove the sensor cable mounting clip from the steering knuckle.
7. Remove the clip from the upper control arm. Remove the clip from the frame attaching point.
8. Remove the cable electrical connector.
9. Remove the sensor mounting bolt.
10. Carefully remove the sensor by pulling it straight out of the bore. Do not use a screwdriver, or other pry device to pry the sensor out of the bore. Prying will cause the sensor to break off in the bore.
11. On 2500 and 3500 remove the sensor from the hub and bearing assembly.

To install:

➡**Be sure to use new fasteners, as required.**

12. Installation is the reverse of the removal procedure.

➡**Using the GM diagnostic scan tool, or equivalent, refer to the on-screen reprogramming directions and perform the diagnostic system check procedure.**

13. Connect the negative battery cable.
14. Check for proper operation. Correct, as required.

Rear Sensor

See Figure 6.

✳✳ CAUTION

Before servicing any electrical component, the ignition key must be in the OFF or LOCKposition and all electrical loads must be OFF, unless instructed otherwise in these procedures. If a tool or equipment could easily come in contact with a live exposed electrical terminal, also disconnect the negative battery cable. Failure to follow these precautions may cause personal injury and/or damage to the vehicle or its components.

1. Before servicing the vehicle, refer to the Precautions Section.
2. Disconnect the negative battery cable.
3. Raise and support the vehicle safely.
4. Remove the tire and wheel assembly.

5. If removing the left sensor, remove the leaf spring anchor plate.
6. Disconnect the electrical connector.
7. Remove the sensor retaining bolt. Remove the sensor and spacer block

To install:

➡**Be sure to use new fasteners, as required.**

8. Install the speed sensor. Tighten the retaining bolt to 124 inch lbs. (14 Nm).
9. Continue the installation is the reverse of the removal procedure.
10. Lower the vehicle.
11. Start the engine and allow it to idle. Check to see if the ABS indicator or traction assist indicator remains illuminated.

➡**If so, do not drive the vehicle until it is diagnosed and repaired. Check the speed sensor electrical connector to be sure it is not damaged, and is properly installed. If the problem still exists use the GM diagnostic scan tool, or equivalent, and refer to the on-screen reprogramming directions to perform the diagnostic system check procedure.**

12. If the ABS indicator or traction assist indicator does not remain illuminated, select a smooth, dry, clean and level road or large lot that is free of traffic and obstacles.
13. Drive the vehicle and maintain a speed of at least 10 miles per hour for five seconds.
14. Stop the vehicle and check to see if the ABS indicator or traction assist indicator is illuminated.
15. If an indicator light is illuminated, use the GM diagnostic scan tool, or equivalent, and refer to the on-screen reprogramming directions to perform the diagnostic system check procedure.
16. Correct, as required.

BLEEDING PROCEDURE

The brake system must be bled when any brake line is disconnected or there is air in the system.

→**Never bleed a wheel cylinder when a drum is removed.**

1. Clean the master cylinder of excess dirt and remove the cylinder cover and the diaphragm.

2. Fill the master cylinder to the proper level. Check the fluid level periodically during the bleeding process and replenish it as necessary. Do not allow the master cylinder to run dry, or you will have to start over.

3. Before opening any of the bleeder screws, you may want to give each one a shot of penetrating solvent. This reduces the possibility of breakage when they are unscrewed.

4. Attach a length of vinyl hose to the bleeder screw of the brake to be bled. Insert the other end of the hose into a clear jar half full of clean brake fluid, so that the end of the hose is beneath the level of fluid. The correct sequence for bleeding is to work from the brake farthest from the master cylinder to the one closest; right rear, left rear, right front, left front.

5. Depress and release the brake pedal three or four times to exhaust any residual vacuum.

6. Have an assistant push down on the brake pedal and hold it down. Open the bleeder valve slightly. As the pedal reaches the end of its travel, close the bleeder screw and release the brake pedal. Repeat this process until no air bubbles are visible in the expelled fluid.

→**Make sure your assistant presses the brake pedal to the floor slowly. Pressing too fast will cause air bubbles to form in the fluid.**

7. Repeat this procedure at each of the brakes. Remember to check the master cylinder level occasionally. Use only fresh fluid to refill the master cylinder, not the stuff bled from the system.

8. When the bleeding process is complete, refill the master cylinder, install its cover and diaphragm, and discard the fluid bled from the brake system.

BLEEDING THE ABS SYSTEM

✳✳ WARNING

When adding fluid to the brake master cylinder reservoir, use only DOT–3 brake fluid from a clean, sealed brake fluid container. The use of any type of fluid other than the recommended type of brake fluid, may cause contamination which could result in damage to the internal rubber seals and/or rubber linings of hydraulic brake system components.

✳✳ WARNING

Avoid spilling brake fluid onto painted surfaces, electrical connections, wiring, or cables. Brake fluid will damage painted surfaces and cause corrosion to electrical components. If any brake fluid comes in contact with painted surfaces, immediately flush the area with water. If any brake fluid comes in contact with electrical connections, wiring, or cables, use a clean shop cloth to wipe away the fluid.

→**The base hydraulic brake system must be bled before performing this automated bleeding procedure.**

1. Connect a scan tool to the vehicle's Data Link Connector (DLC).

2. Start the engine and allow the engine to idle.

3. Depress the brake pedal firmly and maintain steady pressure on the pedal.

4. Using the scan tool, begin the automated bleed procedure.

5. Follow the instructions on the scan tool to complete the automated bleed procedure. Release the brake pedal between each test sequence.

6. Turn the ignition **OFF**.

7. Remove the scan tool from the vehicle.

8. Fill the brake master cylinder reservoir to the maximum–fill level with DOT–3 brake fluid from a clean, sealed brake fluid container.

9. Bleed the hydraulic brake system.

10. With the ignition **OFF**, apply the brakes 3–5 times, or until the brake pedal becomes firm, in order to deplete the brake booster power reserve.

11. Slowly depress and release the brake pedal. Observe the feel of the brake pedal.

12. If the brake pedal feels spongy, repeat the automated bleeding procedure. If the brake pedal still feels spongy after repeating the automated bleeding procedure inspect the brake system for external leaks.

13. Turn the ignition key **ON** but DO NOT start the engine; check to see if the brake system warning lamp remains illuminated.

14. If the brake system warning lamp remains illuminated, DO NOT allow the vehicle to be driven until it is diagnosed and repaired.

15. Drive the vehicle to exceed 8 mph (13 kph) to allow ABS initialization to occur. Observe brake pedal feel.

16. If the brake pedal feels spongy, repeat the automated bleeding procedure until a firm brake pedal is obtained.

✳✳ CAUTION

Dust and dirt accumulating on brake parts during normal use may contain asbestos fibers from production or aftermarket brake linings. Breathing excessive concentrations of asbestos fibers can cause serious bodily harm. Exercise care when servicing brake parts. Do not sand or grind brake lining unless equipment used is designed to contain the dust residue. Do not clean brake parts with compressed air or by dry brushing. Cleaning should be done by dampening the brake components with a fine mist of water, then wiping the brake components clean with a dampened cloth. Dispose of cloth and all residue containing asbestos fibers in an impermeable container with the appropriate label. Follow practices prescribed by the Occupational Safety and Health Administration (OSHA) and the Environmental Protection Agency (EPA) for the handling, processing, and disposing of dust or debris that may contain asbestos fibers.

BRAKE CALIPER

REMOVAL & INSTALLATION

See Figures 7 and 8.

1. Remove or disconnect the following:
   • ⅔ of the brake fluid from the master cylinder
   • Tire and wheel assembly
2. Using a C-clamp or the equivalent, compress the caliper piston until the caliper piston bottoms in the bore.
   • Brake hose at caliper by removing the inlet fitting bolt. Plug the line.
   • Caliper mounting bolts
   • Caliper
3. Inspect the caliper assembly.

To install:
4. Install or connect the following:
   • Caliper. Tighten the caliper guide pin bolts to specification.
   • Brake hose at caliper by installing the inlet fitting bolt. Tighten the inlet fitting bolt to 30 ft. lbs. (40 Nm).
5. Bleed the brakes.
   • Tire and wheel assembly

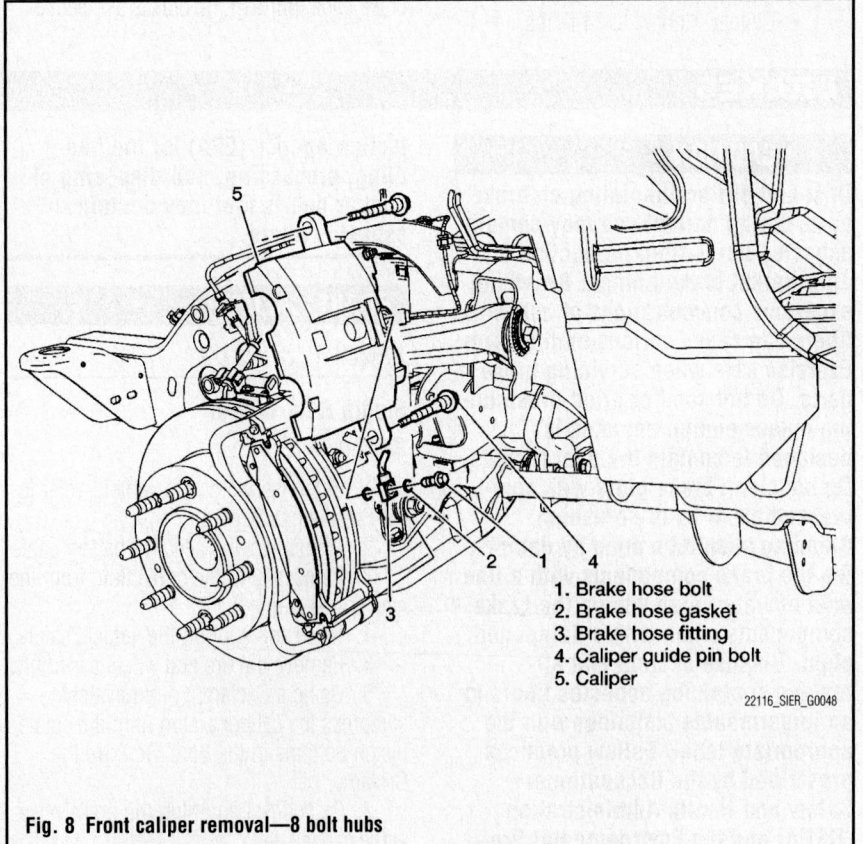

1. Brake hose bolt
2. Brake hose gasket
3. Brake hose fitting
4. Caliper guide pin bolt
5. Caliper

22116_SIER_G0047

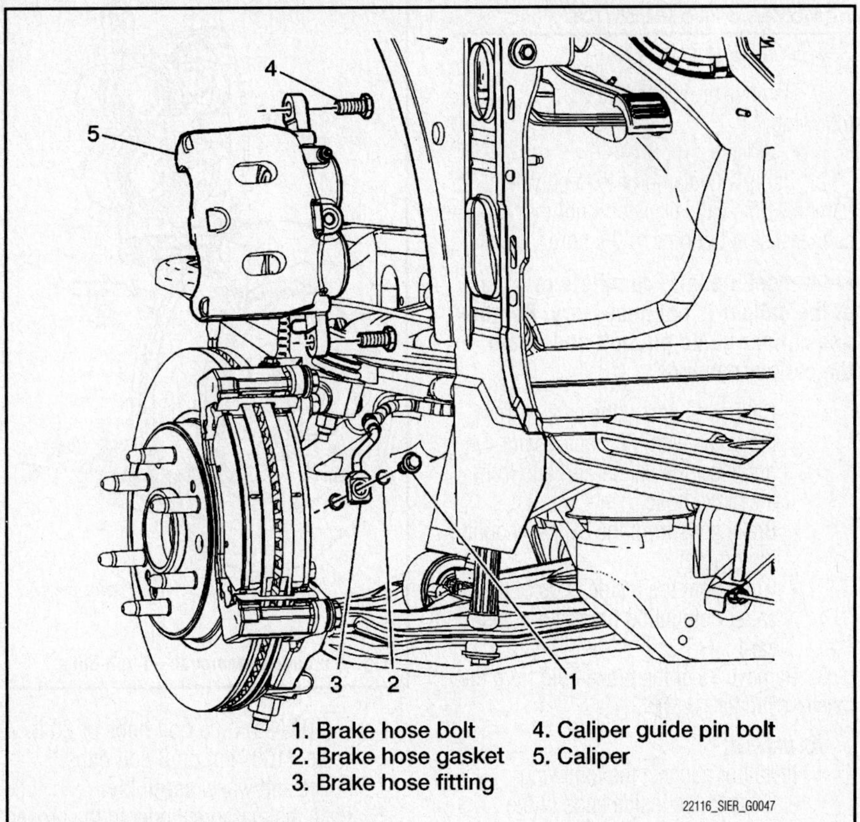

Fig. 7 Front caliper removal—6 bolt hubs

1. Brake hose bolt
2. Brake hose gasket
3. Brake hose fitting
4. Caliper guide pin bolt
5. Caliper

22116_SIER_G0048

Fig. 8 Front caliper removal—8 bolt hubs

DISC BRAKE PADS

REMOVAL & INSTALLATION

See Figures 9 through 11.

1. Remove or disconnect the following:
   • Wheel
2. Using a C-clamp or the equivalent, compress the caliper piston until the caliper piston bottoms in the bore.

➡ **On most models, complete removal of the caliper is not necessary. Remove one caliper guide pin bolt and rotate the caliper upwards.**

   • Caliper. Suspend the caliper from the frame with mechanic's wire. Do not allow the caliper to hang from the brake hose.
   • Brake pads from the caliper mounting bracket
   • Clips from the inside ends of the caliper mounting bracket and discard
3. Remove ⅔ of the brake fluid from the master cylinder.

To install:

4. Install or connect the following:
   • Clips to the inside ends of the caliper mounting bracket
   • Brake pads to the caliper mounting bracket
   • Caliper. Tighten to 74 ft. lbs.

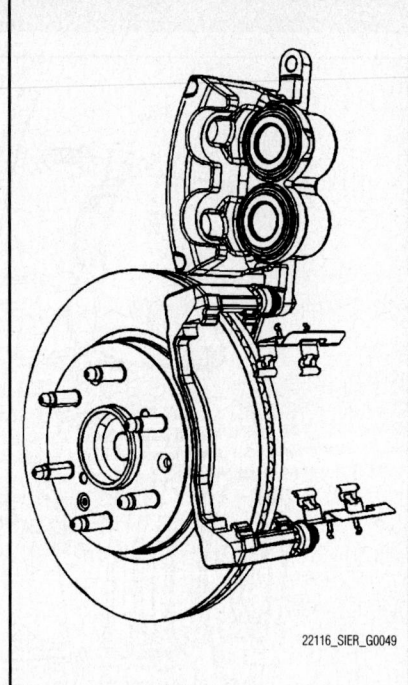

22116_SIER_G0049

Fig. 9 Front pad removal—6 bolt hubs

(100 Nm) on 6 bolt hubs or 80 ft. lbs. (108 Nm) on 8 bolt hubs.
   • Tire and wheel assembly
5. Refill the master cylinder to the proper level with fresh brake fluid. Pump the brake pedal slowly and firmly in order to seat the brake pads. Burnish the brakes as needed.

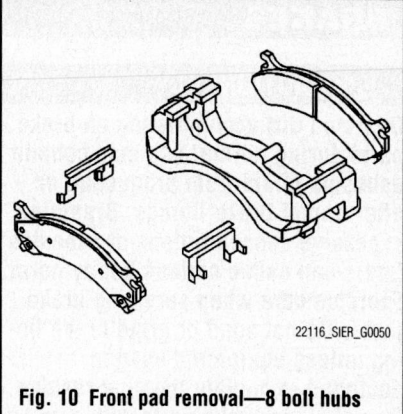

22116_SIER_G0050

Fig. 10 Front pad removal—8 bolt hubs

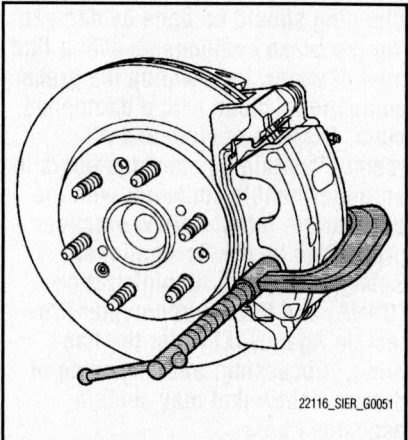

22116_SIER_G0051

Fig. 11 Use a C-clamp to compress the piston in its bore

BRAKES

✳✳ CAUTION

Dust and dirt accumulating on brake parts during normal use may contain asbestos fibers from production or aftermarket brake linings. Breathing excessive concentrations of asbestos fibers can cause serious bodily harm. Exercise care when servicing brake parts. Do not sand or grind brake lining unless equipment used is designed to contain the dust residue. Do not clean brake parts with compressed air or by dry brushing. Cleaning should be done by dampening the brake components with a fine mist of water, then wiping the brake components clean with a dampened cloth. Dispose of cloth and all residue containing asbestos fibers in an impermeable container with the appropriate label. Follow practices prescribed by the Occupational Safety and Health Administration (OSHA) and the Environmental Pro-
tection Agency (EPA) for the handling, processing, and disposing of dust or debris that may contain asbestos fibers.

BRAKE CALIPER

REMOVAL & INSTALLATION

Single Rear Wheel

See Figure 12.

1. Before servicing the vehicle, refer to the Precautions Section.
2. Disconnect the negative battery cable.
3. Remove ⅔ of the brake fluid from master cylinder.
4. Raise and support the vehicle safely.
5. Remove the tire and wheel assembly.
6. Using a C-clamp, or equivalent, compress the caliper piston until the caliper piston bottoms in the bore. Remove the C-clamp.
7. Disconnect and plug the brake hose at the caliper.

REAR DISC BRAKES

8. Remove and discard the two copper brake hose gaskets. These gaskets may be stuck to the caliper housing or brake hose end.
9. Remove the caliper guide pin bolts.
10. Remove the caliper from its mounting.

To install:

➡ **Be sure to use new fasteners, as required. Be sure to use new copper gaskets.**

11. Properly position the caliper to its mounting.
12. Apply thread locker GM part number 12345493 or equivalent to the threads of the caliper mounting bolts.
13. Install the guide pin bolts. Tighten to 25 ft. lbs. (34 Nm) for JH5 vehicles and 53 ft. lbs. (72 Nm) for JH6 and JH7 vehicles.
14. Continue the installation in the reverse order of the removal procedure.
15. Fill the master cylinder with the proper grade and type brake fluid. Bleed the brake system.

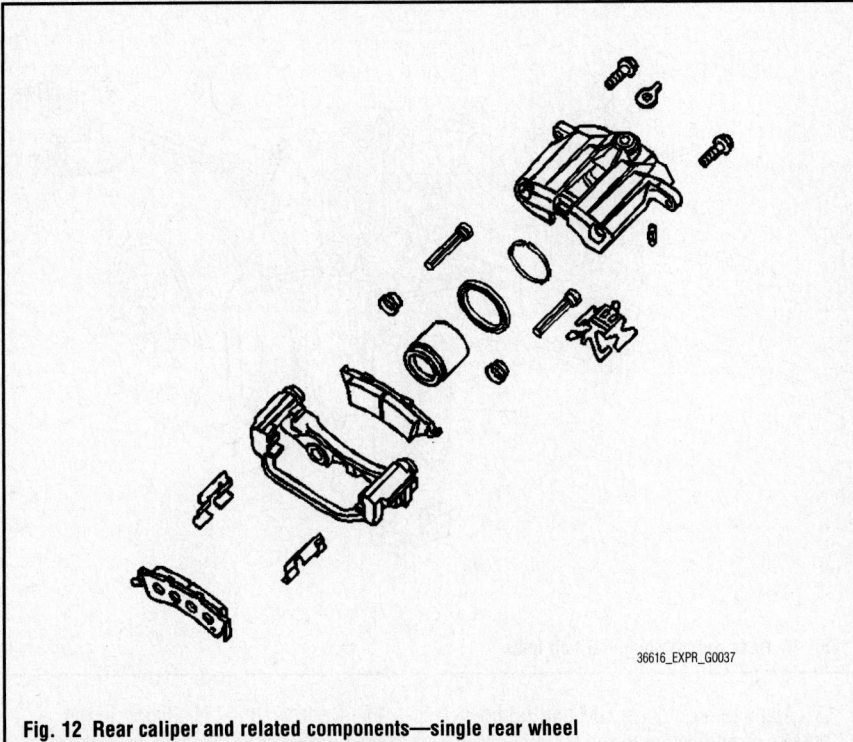

Fig. 12 Rear caliper and related components—single rear wheel

16. Connect the negative battery cable.
17. Check for proper operation. Correct, as required.

Dual Rear Wheel

See Figure 13.

1. Before servicing the vehicle, refer to the Precautions Section.

2. Disconnect the negative battery cable.
3. Remove ⅔ of the brake fluid from the master cylinder.
4. Raise and support the vehicle safely.
5. Remove the tire and wheel assembly.
6. Using a C-clamp, or equivalent, compress the caliper piston until the caliper pis-

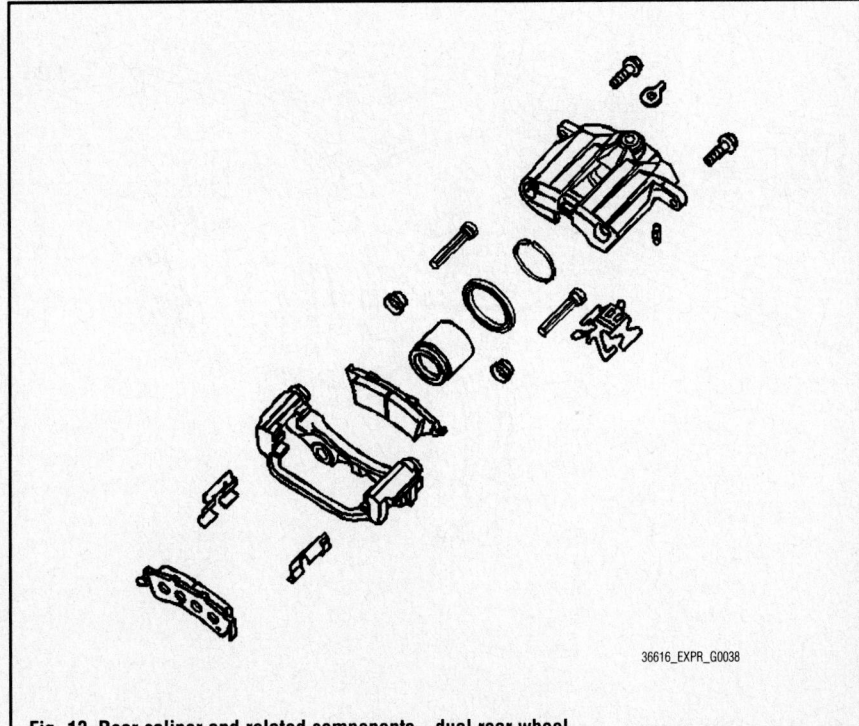

Fig. 13 Rear caliper and related components—dual rear wheel

ton bottoms in the bore. Remove the C-clamp.
7. Disconnect and plug the brake hose at the caliper.
8. Remove and discard the two copper brake hose gaskets. These gaskets may be stuck to the caliper housing or brake hose end.
9. Remove the caliper bracket bolts.
10. Remove the caliper and bracket assembly from its mounting.
11. Remove the brake pads.
12. Remove the brake pad springs.

➡**Do not remove the brake caliper guide pins unless they require replacement.**

13. Slide the caliper off of the guide pins and bracket.
14. Inspect the caliper mounting hardware for damage and wear.

To install:

➡**Be sure to use new fasteners, as required. Be sure to use new copper gaskets.**

15. Apply a light coat of high temperature silicone brake lubricant to the caliper guide pin bores.
16. Install the guide pin seals. Be sure that the seals are fully seated in the groove of the caliper housing.
17. Install the guide pin caps. Be sure that the caps are fully seated in the groove of the caliper housing.

➡**Do not remove the guide pins unless replacement is required.**

18. Slide the caliper onto the guide pins and the caliper bracket. Be sure that the guide pin seals are fully seated in the groove of the caliper bracket.
19. Install the brake pad shims.
20. Apply thread locker GM part number 89021297 or equivalent to ⅔ of the threaded length of the brake caliper bracket bolts. Allow the thread locker to cure for ten minutes before assembly.
21. Position the caliper and bracket assembly to the rear axle. Install the retaining bolts. Tighten them to 221 ft. lbs. (300 Nm).
22. Continue the installation in the reverse order of the removal procedure.
23. Tighten the brake hose fitting bolt to 30 ft. lbs. (40 Nm).
24. Fill the master cylinder with the proper grade and type brake fluid. Bleed the brake system.
25. Connect the negative battery cable.
26. Check for proper operation. Correct, as required.

DISC BRAKE PADS

REMOVAL & INSTALLATION

Single Rear Wheel

See Figures 14 through 16.

1. Before servicing the vehicle, refer to the Precautions Section.

2. Disconnect the negative battery cable.

3. Remove ⅔ of the brake fluid from the master cylinder.

4. Raise and support the vehicle safely.

5. Remove the tire and wheel assembly.

6. Using a C-clamp, or equivalent, compress the caliper piston until the caliper piston bottoms in the bore. Remove the C-clamp.

7. Remove the caliper guide pin bolts.

8. Remove the caliper from its mounting.

➡**Position the caliper to the side. Do not allow it to hang by the brake line. Support the assembly using mechanics wire. Do not disconnect the brake line from the caliper.**

9. Remove the pads from the caliper bracket. Note their orientation.

10. Remove and discard the anti-rattle clips.

To install:

➡**Be sure to use new fasteners, as required. Be sure to use new copper gaskets.**

11. Properly install the pads and shims.

12. Properly position the caliper to its mounting.

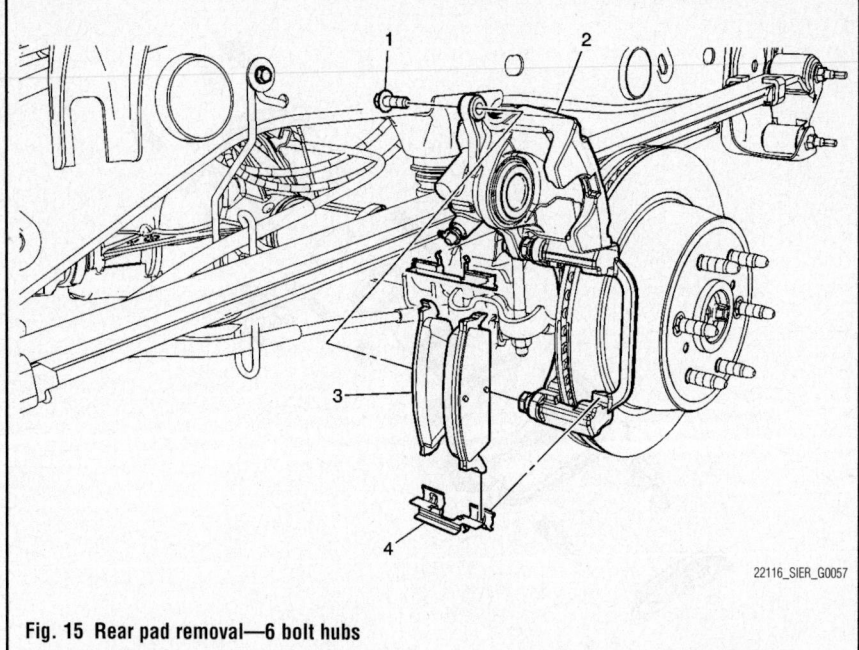

Fig. 15 Rear pad removal—6 bolt hubs

13. Apply thread locker GM part number 12345493 or equivalent to the threads of the caliper mounting bolts.

14. Install the guide pin bolts. Tighten to 25 ft. lbs. (34 Nm) for JH5 vehicles and 53 ft. lbs. (72 Nm) for JH6 and JH7 vehicles.

15. Continue the installation in the reverse order of the removal procedure.

16. Fill the master cylinder with the proper grade and type brake fluid. Bleed the brake system.

17. Connect the negative battery cable.

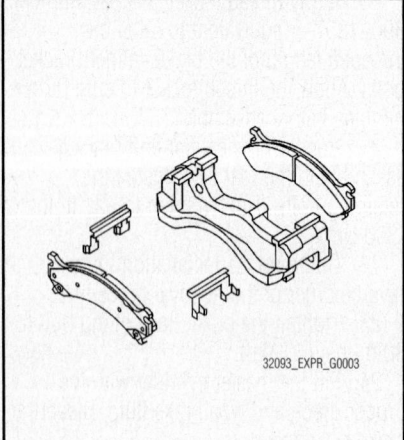

Fig. 14 Rear brake pads and related components—single rear wheel

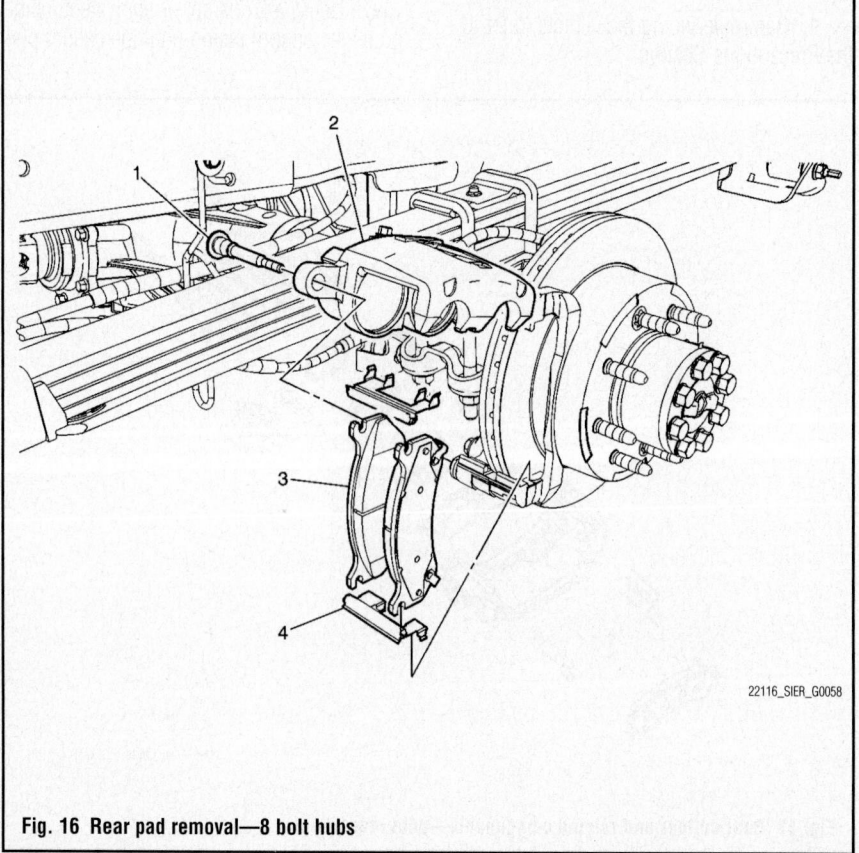

Fig. 16 Rear pad removal—8 bolt hubs

18. Check for proper operation. Correct, as required.

Dual Rear Wheel

1. Before servicing the vehicle, refer to the Precautions Section.
2. Disconnect the negative battery cable.
3. Remove ⅔ of the brake fluid from the master cylinder.
4. Raise and support the vehicle safely.
5. Remove the tire and wheel assembly.
6. Using a C-clamp, or equivalent, compress the caliper piston until the caliper piston bottoms in the bore. Remove the C-clamp.
7. Remove the caliper bracket bolts.
8. Remove the caliper and bracket assembly from its mounting.

➡ **Position the caliper to the side. Do not allow it to hang by the brake line. Support the assembly using mechanics wire. Do not disconnect the brake line from the caliper.**

9. Remove the brake pads.
10. Remove the brake pad springs.

➡ **Do not remove the brake caliper guide pins unless they require replacement.**

11. Slide the caliper off of the guide pins and bracket.
12. Inspect the caliper mounting hardware for damage and wear.

To install:

➡ **Be sure to use new fasteners, as required. Be sure to use new copper gaskets.**

13. Apply a light coat of high temperature silicone brake lubricant to the caliper guide pin bores.
14. Install the guide pin seals. Be sure that the seals are fully seated in the groove of the caliper housing.
15. Install the guide pin caps. Be sure that the caps are fully seated in the groove of the caliper housing.

➡ **Do not remove the guide pins unless replacement is required.**

16. Slide the caliper onto the guide pins and the caliper bracket. Be sure that the guide pin seals are fully seated in the groove of the caliper bracket.
17. Install the brake pad shims.
18. Apply thread locker GM part number 89021297 or equivalent to ⅔rds of the threaded length of the brake caliper bracket bolts. Allow the thread locker to cure for ten minutes before assembly.
19. Position the caliper and bracket assembly to the rear axle. Install the retaining bolts. Tighten them to 221 ft. lbs. (300 Nm).
20. Continue the installation in the reverse order of the removal procedure.
21. Tighten the brake hose fitting bolt to 30 ft. lbs. (40 Nm).
22. Fill the master cylinder with the proper grade and type brake fluid. Bleed the brake system.
23. Connect the negative battery cable.
24. Check for proper operation. Correct, as required.

BRAKES   PARKING BRAKE

PARKING BRAKE CABLES

ADJUSTMENT

The parking brake pedals are equipped with automatic adjusters. The Park Brake Cable Equalizer evenly distributes input force to both the left and right park brake units and the threaded park brake cable equalizers are also used to remove slack in park brake cables

PARKING BRAKE SHOES

REMOVAL & INSTALLATION

1500

See Figures 17 and 18.

1. Before servicing the vehicle, refer to the Precautions Section.
2. Raise and properly support the vehicle.
3. Remove the tire and the wheel assembly.
4. To disable the park brake cable automatic adjuster, hold the parking brake pedal to the full up position.
5. Pull rearward on the front parking brake cable until the pedal drum reaches its full reset position.
6. Insert a scribe or nail, on an upward angle thru the hole in the front of the pedal assembly, past the retracted pedal drum,

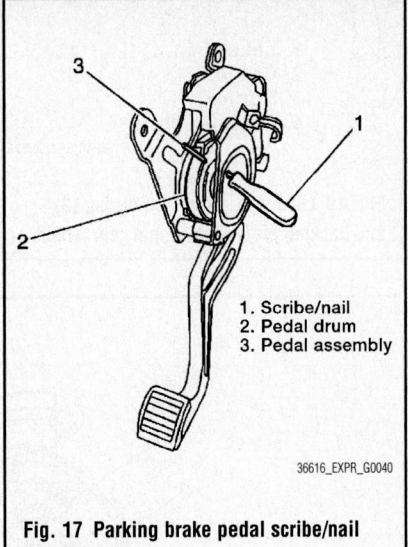

1. Scribe/nail
2. Pedal drum
3. Pedal assembly

36616_EXPR_G0040

Fig. 17 Parking brake pedal scribe/nail location point

and into the hole in the back of the pedal assembly.
7. Slowly release the cable.
8. Remove the parking brake cable from the lever.
9. Remove the rotor.
10. Turn the adjustment screw (1) to the fully home position in the notched adjustment nut.
11. Remove the park brake shoe assembly from the backing plate by removing the tips from the slots and sliding the shoe (2)

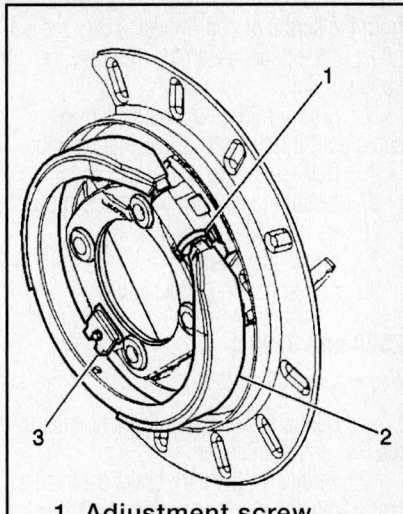

1. Adjustment screw
2. Parking brake shoe
3. Retaining spring

32085_SILV_G0067

Fig. 18 Adjustment screw (1), parking brake shoe (2) and retaining spring (3)— single rear wheel

toward the retaining spring (3) until the shoe is disengaged from the spring.
12. Remove the park brake shoe assembly from the vehicle by placing one of the open ends of the shoe over the axle flange and rotating the shoe until it has cleared the flange.

To install:

13. Clean the debris and the dust from the park brake components using a clean towel.

14. Align the slots in both the adjusting screw and tappet to be parallel with the backing plate face.

15. Install the park brake shoe assembly (2) to the vehicle by placing one of the open ends of the shoe over the axle flange and rotating the shoe until it is behind the flange.

16. Position the park brake shoe on the inboard side of the actuation.

17. Slide the parking brake shoe into position and seat into the retaining spring.

18. Inspect the shoe assembly position. The shoe must be central on the backing plate with both tips located in the slots.

19. Adjust the park brake shoe.

20. Install the rotor.

21. Install the park brake cable to the park brake lever.

22. Install the park brake cable to the park brake actuator lever.

23. To enable the park brake cable automatic adjuster, hold the parking brake pedal to the full up position.

24. Pull rearward on the front parking brake cable until the tension is released from the scribe or nail, installed thru the holes in the pedal assembly. Remove the scribe or nail.

25. Slowly release the parking brake cable until it returns to its normal position.

26. Release the parking brake pedal.

27. Install the tire and wheel assembly.

28. Remove the safety stands.

29. Lower the vehicle.

30. Adjust parking brake cable.

2500 and 3500

See Figures 19 and 20.

1. Before servicing the vehicle, refer to the Precautions Section.

2. To disable the park brake cable automatic adjuster, hold the parking brake pedal to the full up position.

3. Pull rearward on the front parking brake cable until the pedal drum reaches its full reset position.

4. Insert a scribe or nail, on an upward angle thru the hole in the front of the pedal assembly, past the retracted pedal drum, and into the hole in the back of the pedal assembly.

5. Slowly release the cable.

6. Raise and safely support the vehicle.

7. Remove the tire and the wheel.

8. Remove the rotor.

9. Perform the following procedure to remove the cable from the backing plate:

a. Compress the spring by pushing toward the lever.

b. Depress the locking tabs.

c. Pull the cable housing out of the backing plate.

d. Remove the cable through the slot in the backing plate.

10. Remove the park brake cable from the lever.

11. Remove the park brake shoe return spring.

12. Remove the park brake shoe anchor springs and pins.

13. Separate the tips of the shoes from the park brake actuator and remove the park

1. Lever
2. Cable
3. Spring
4. Backing plate

32085_SILV_G0069

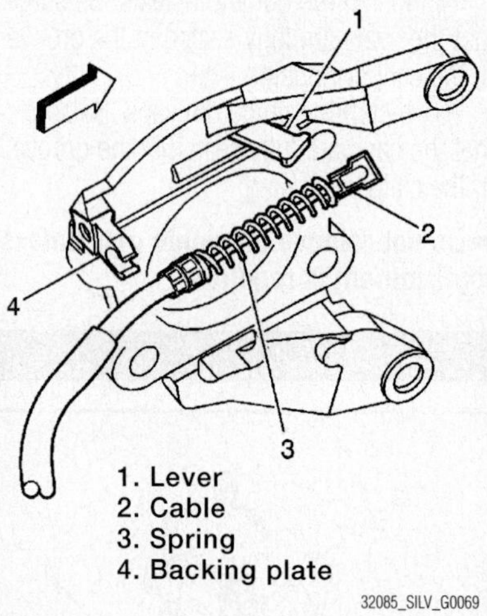

Fig. 19 Lever (1), cable (2), spring (3) and backing plate (4)—single rear wheel

brake shoes and adjuster assembly from the vehicle.

To install:

14. Clean the debris and the dust from the park brake components using a clean shop cloth.

15. Install the adjuster assembly to the park brake shoes.

16. Separate the tips of the shoes and install the park brake shoes to the park brake actuator.

17. Install the park brake shoe anchor springs and pins.

18. Install the park brake shoe return spring.

19. Adjust the park brake shoe.

20. Install the rotor.

21. Install the park brake cable to the lever.

22. Perform the following procedure to install the cable to the backing plate:

a. Compress the spring by pushing toward the lever.

b. Route the cable through the slot in the backing plate.

c. Push the cable housing into the backing plate until the locking tabs snap into place.

23. Install the tire and wheel.

24. Remove the safety stands.

25. Lower the vehicle.

26. To enable the park brake cable automatic adjuster, hold the parking brake pedal to the full up position.

27. Pull rearward on the front parking brake cable until the tension is released from the scribe or nail, installed thru the

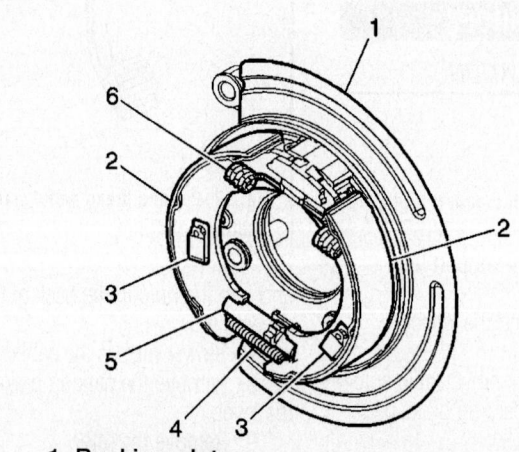

1. Backing plate
2. Parking brake shoe (qty. 2)
3. Parking brake shoe hold-down spring (qty. 2)

32085_SILV_G0070

Fig. 20 Park brake shoe assembly 1500HD, 2500 and 3500—single rear wheel

holes in the pedal assembly. Remove the scribe or nail.

28. Slowly release the parking brake cable until it returns to its normal position.

29. Release the parking brake pedal.

30. Adjust the park brake cable.

ADJUSTMENT

See Figures 21 and 22.

1. Set the J 21177–A so that the J 21177–A contacts the inside diameter of the rotor.

2. Position the J 21177–A over the shoe and the lining at the widest point.

3. Turn the adjuster nut until the lining just contacts the J 21177–A.

4. Repeat steps 1 through 3 for the opposite side.

5. The clearance between the park brake shoe and the rotor is 0.026 inch (0.66 mm) for single rear wheel vehicles.

6. The clearance between the park brake shoe and the rotor is 0.024 inch (0.62 mm) for dual rear wheel vehicles.

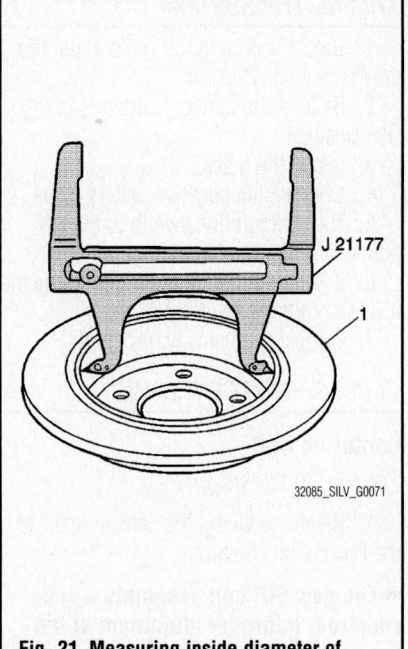

Fig. 21 Measuring inside diameter of brake rotor

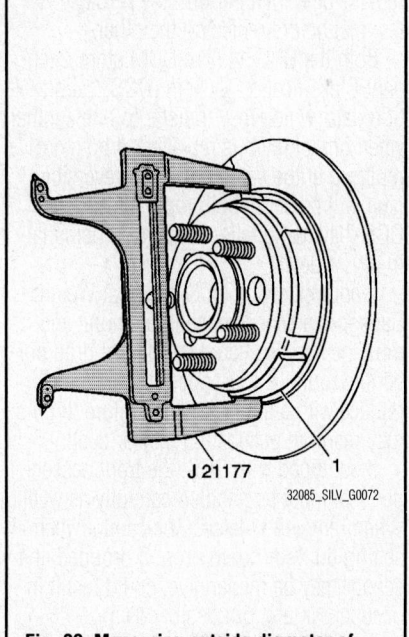

Fig. 22 Measuring outside diameter of brake rotor

CHASSIS ELECTRICAL — AIR BAG (SUPPLEMENTAL RESTRAINT SYSTEM)

GENERAL INFORMATION

☀ CAUTION

These vehicles are equipped with an air bag system. The system must be disarmed before performing service on, or around, system components, the steering column, instrument panel components, wiring and sensors. Failure to follow the safety precautions and the disarming procedure could result in accidental air bag deployment, possible injury and unnecessary system repairs.

SERVICE PRECAUTIONS

Disconnect and isolate the battery negative cable before beginning any airbag system component diagnosis, testing, removal, or installation procedures. Allow system capacitor to discharge for two minutes before beginning any component service. This will disable the airbag system. Failure to disable the airbag system may result in accidental airbag deployment, personal injury, or death.

Do not place an intact undeployed airbag face down on a solid surface. The airbag will propel into the air if accidentally deployed and may result in personal injury or death.

When carrying or handling an undeployed airbag, the trim side (face) of the airbag should be pointing toward the body to minimize possibility of injury if accidental deployment occurs. Failure to do this may result in personal injury or death.

Replace airbag system components with OEM replacement parts. Substitute parts may appear interchangeable, but internal differences may result in inferior occupant protection. Failure to do so may result in occupant personal injury or death.

Wear safety glasses, rubber gloves, and long sleeved clothing when cleaning powder residue from vehicle after an airbag deployment. Powder residue emitted from a deployed airbag can cause skin irritation. Flush affected area with cool water if irritation is experienced. If nasal or throat irritation is experienced, exit the vehicle for fresh air until the irritation ceases. If irritation continues, see a physician.

Do not use a replacement airbag that is not in the original packaging. This may result in improper deployment, personal injury, or death.

The factory installed fasteners, screws and bolts used to fasten airbag components have a special coating and are specifically designed for the airbag system. Do not use substitute fasteners. Use only original equipment fasteners listed in the parts catalog when fastener replacement is required.

During, and following, any child restraint anchor service, due to impact event or vehicle repair, carefully inspect all mounting hardware, tether straps, and anchors for proper installation, operation, or damage. If a child restraint anchor is found damaged in any way, the anchor must be replaced. Failure to do this may result in personal injury or death.

Deployed and non–deployed airbags may or may not have live pyrotechnic material within the airbag inflator.

Do not dispose of driver/passenger/curtain airbags or seat belt tensioners unless you are sure of complete deployment. Refer to the Hazardous Substance Control System for proper disposal.

Dispose of deployed airbags and tensioners consistent with state, provincial, local, and federal regulations.

After any airbag component testing or service, do not connect the battery negative cable. Personal injury or death may result if the system test is not performed first.

If the vehicle is equipped with the Occupant Classification System (OCS), do not connect the battery negative cable before performing the OCS Verification Test using the scan tool and the appropriate diagnostic information. Personal injury or death may result if the system test is not performed properly.

Never replace both the Occupant Restraint Controller (ORC) and the Occupant Classification Module (OCM) at the same time. If both require replacement, replace one, then perform the Airbag System test before replacing the other.

Both the ORC and the OCM store Occupant Classification System (OCS) calibration data, which they transfer to one another when one of them is replaced. If both are replaced at the same time, an irreversible fault will be set in both modules and the OCS may malfunction and cause personal injury or death.

If equipped with OCS, the Seat Weight Sensor is a sensitive, calibrated unit and must be handled carefully. Do not drop or handle roughly. If dropped or damaged, replace with another sensor. Failure to do so may result in occupant injury or death.

If equipped with OCS, the front passenger seat must be handled carefully as well. When removing the seat, be careful when setting on floor not to drop. If dropped, the sensor may be inoperative, could result in occupant injury, or possibly death.

If equipped with OCS, when the passenger front seat is on the floor, no one should sit in the front passenger seat. This uneven force may damage the sensing ability of the seat weight sensors. If sat on and damaged, the sensor may be inoperative, could result in occupant injury, or possibly death.

DISARMING THE SYSTEM

1. Before servicing the vehicle, refer to the Precautions Section.

➡**When performing service on or near the SRS components, or SRS wiring the SRS must be disabled. Failure to observe the correct procedure could cause deployment of the SRS components. Serious injury can occur.**

2. Position the steering wheel so the front wheels are in the straight ahead position.
3. Be sure the ignition switch is in the OFF position.
4. Disconnect the negative battery cable.

➡**The SDM may have more than one fused power input. To ensure that there is no unwanted SRS deployment, personal injury, or unnecessary SRS system repairs, remove all fuses supplying power to the SDM. With all SDM fuses removed and the ignition switch in the ON position, the AIR BAG warning indicator will illuminate. This is normal and does not indicate a SRS system malfunction.**

5. Locate and remove the fuses supplying power to the SDM.
6. Wait one minute before working on the vehicle.

ARMING THE SYSTEM

1. Before servicing the vehicle, refer to the Precautions Section.
2. Be sure the ignition switch is in the OFF position.
3. Install the fuses.
4. Connect the negative battery cable.
5. Turn the ignition switch to the ON position.
6. If the system is operating properly the AIR BAG indicator will flash
7. Correct problems as required.

CLOCKSPRING CENTERING

Centering Coil

See Figures 23 through 27.

1. Before servicing the vehicle, refer to the Precautions Section.

➡**The new SIR coil assembly will be centered. Improper alignment of the**

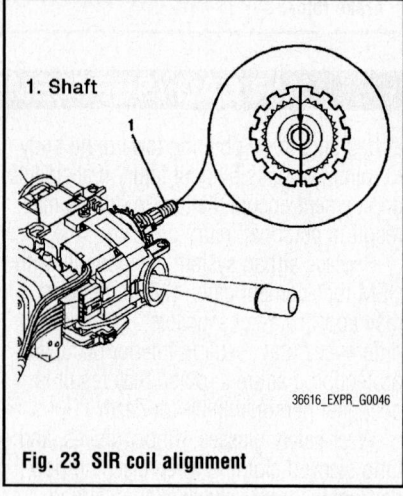

1. Shaft

36616_EXPR_G0046

Fig. 23 SIR coil alignment

SIR coil assembly may damage the unit, causing an inflatable restraint malfunction.

➡**If a double wire harness strap is installed onto the wire harness assembly and column, you must reuse the holder for the wire straps during installation. Remove the wire harness strap(s) where necessary.**

2. Verify that the front wheels are in the straight ahead position, the tooth block of the steering shaft assembly is in the 12 o'clock position and the ignition switch is in the LOCK position
3. If the front of the SIR coil has a centering window, and the back side includes a spring service lock, hold the coil face up. While depressing the spring service lock, rotate the coil hub clockwise until the coil ribbon stops. Rotate the coil hub slowly, counterclockwise, until the centering window appears yellow and the tooth arrows align. Release the spring service lock between the locking tab. The coil is now centered. Align the coil with the horn tower and slide it onto the steering shaft assembly.
4. If the front of the SIR coil has a centering window, and the back side does not include a spring service lock, hold the coil face up. Rotate the coil hub clockwise until the coil ribbon stops. Rotate the coil hub slowly, counterclockwise, until the centering window appears yellow and both arrows align. This is the center position. While holding the coil hub in the center position, align the coil with the horn tower and slide it onto the steering shaft assembly.

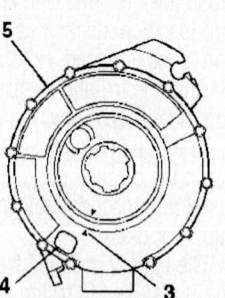
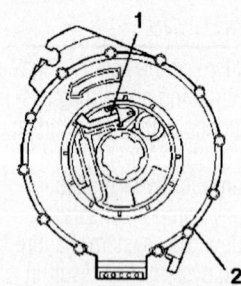

1. Tooth block
2. Back side
3. Arrows
4. Centering window
5. Front

36616_EXPR_G0047

Fig. 24 SIR coil alignment—with spring service lock setup points

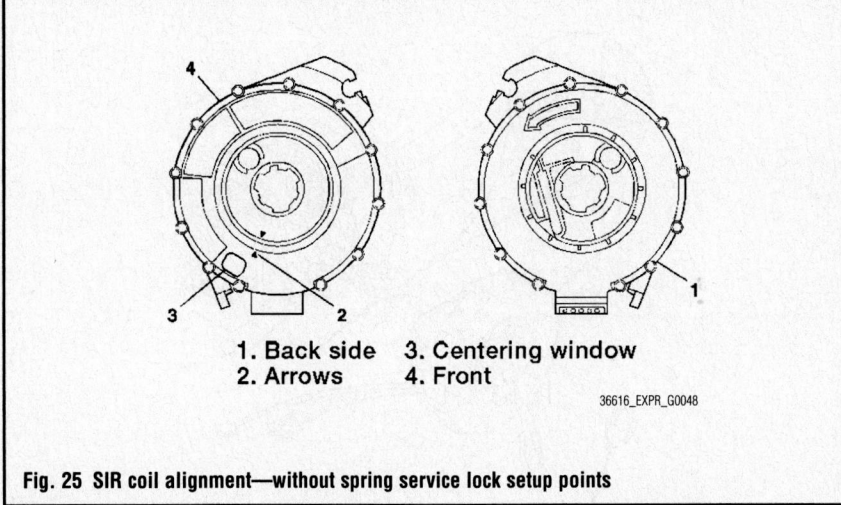

1. Back side   3. Centering window
2. Arrows   4. Front

36616_EXPR_G0048

Fig. 25 SIR coil alignment—without spring service lock setup points

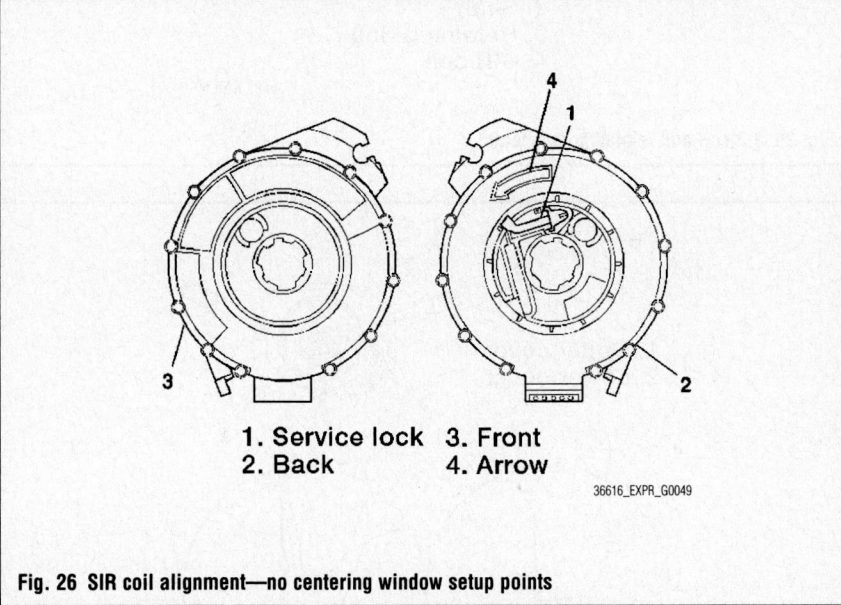

1. Service lock   3. Front
2. Back   4. Arrow

36616_EXPR_G0049

Fig. 26 SIR coil alignment—no centering window setup points

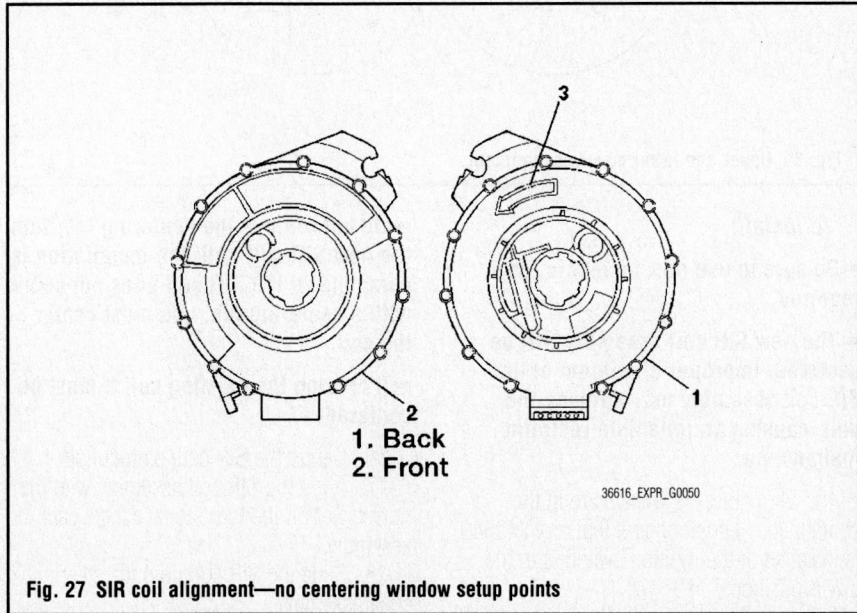

1. Back
2. Front

36616_EXPR_G0050

Fig. 27 SIR coil alignment—no centering window setup points

5. If the front of the SIR coil has no centering window, and the back side includes a spring service lock, hold the coil face up. While depressing the spring service lock, rotate the coil hub in the direction of the arrow until the coil ribbon stops. Still pressing the spring service lock, rotate the coil hub slowly, in the opposite direction 2½ revolutions. Release the spring service lock between the locking tab. The coil is now centered. Align the coil with the horn tower and slide it onto the steering shaft assembly.

6. If the front of the SIR coil has no centering window, and the back side has no spring service lock, hold the coil face up. Rotate the coil hub in the direction of the arrow until the coil ribbon stops. Rotate the coil hub slowly, counterclockwise 2½ revolutions. While maintaining the coil hub in the centered position, align the coil with the horn tower and slide it onto the steering shaft assembly.

7. If a double wire harness strap is installed onto the wire harness assembly and column, you must route the wires up against the steering column.

8. One wire harness strap will surround one lead from the coil to the steering column.

9. The other wire harness strap will surround all leads to the steering column.

Replacing Coil

See Figures 28 through 30.

1. Before servicing the vehicle, refer to the Precautions Section.

➡**When performing service on or near the SRS components, or SRS wiring the SRS must be disabled. Failure to observe the correct procedure could cause deployment of the SRS components. Serious injury can occur.**

2. Position the steering wheel so the front wheels are in the straight ahead position.

3. Be sure the ignition switch is in the OFF position.

4. Disconnect the negative battery cable.

➡**The SDM may have more than one fused power input. To ensure that there is no unwanted SRS deployment, personal injury, or unnecessary SRS system repairs, remove all fuses supplying power to the SDM. With all SDM fuses removed and the ignition switch in the ON position, the AIR BAG warning indicator will illuminate. This is normal and does not indicate a SRS system malfunction.**

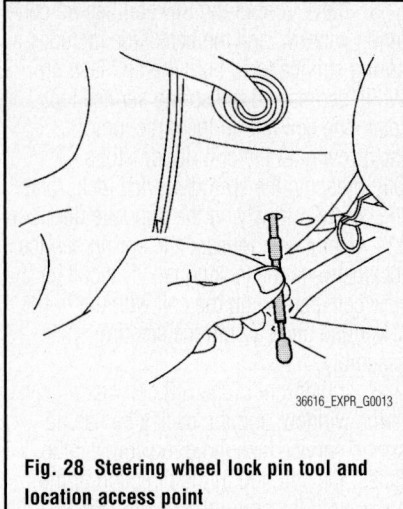

Fig. 28 Steering wheel lock pin tool and location access point

5. Locate and remove the fuses supplying power to the SDM.

6. Wait one minute before working on the vehicle.

➡**Check that the front wheels are in the straight ahead position. Secure the steering wheel using the steering column anti-rotation pin, steering column lock, or a strap to prevent rotation. Locking the steering column will prevent damage and a possible malfunction of the SRS system. The steering wheel must be secured when disconnecting the intermediate shaft and the steering gear. After disconnecting these components do not rotate the steering wheel or move the front wheels. Failure to follow this procedure may cause the SRS coil assembly to become uncentered and cause possible damage to the SRS coil.**

7. Lock the steering column through the access hole in the lower steering column trim cover using tool J-42640 or equivalent.

8. Remove the driver's side air bag module.

9. Remove the steering wheel retaining nut. Using the proper puller, carefully remove the steering wheel.

10. If equipped with tilt wheel, pull the tilt lever straight out from the steering column.

11. Remove the screws from the lower trim cover. Remove the lower trim cover.

12. Remove the screws from the upper trim cover. Remove the upper trim cover.

13. Remove the wire harness straps from the steering wheel column wire harness.

14. Remove the retaining ring. Remove the SIR coil from the steering shaft.

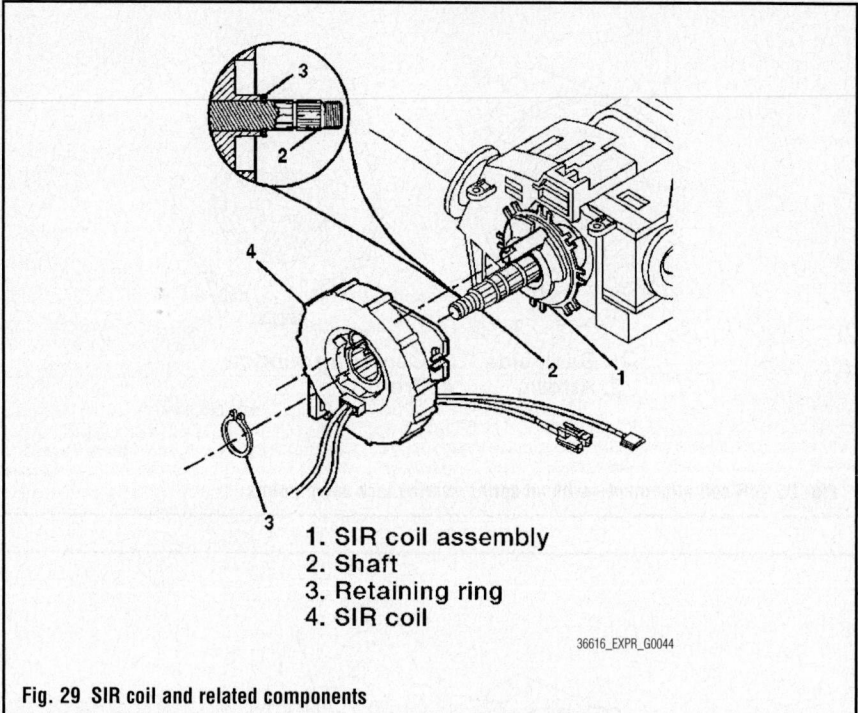

1. SIR coil assembly
2. Shaft
3. Retaining ring
4. SIR coil

Fig. 29 SIR coil and related components

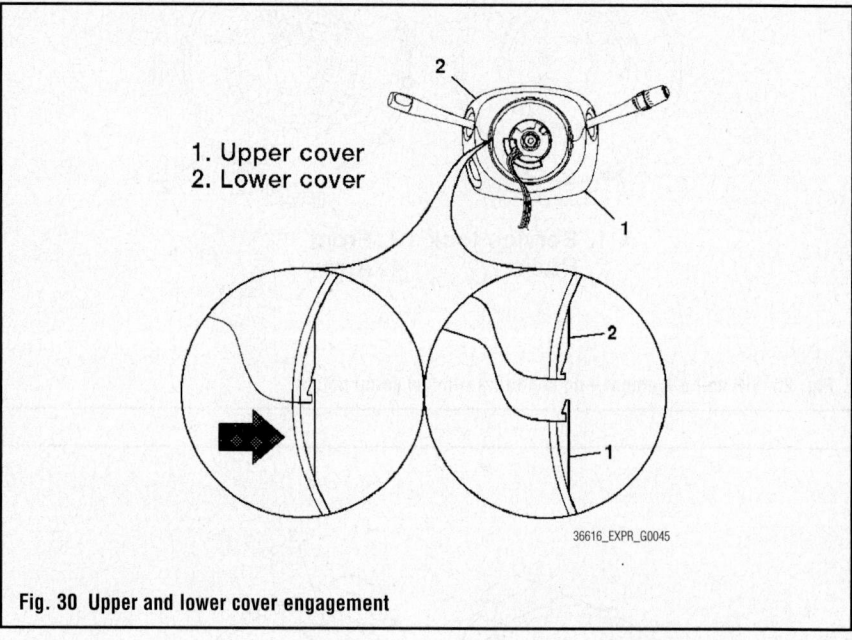

1. Upper cover
2. Lower cover

Fig. 30 Upper and lower cover engagement

To install:

➡**Be sure to use new fasteners, as required.**

➡**The new SIR coil assembly will be centered. Improper alignment of the SIR coil assembly may damage the unit, causing an inflatable restraint malfunction.**

15. Verify that the wheels are in the straight ahead position and that tool J42640 is installed or the ignition switch is in the LOCK position.

➡**Do not remove the centering tab from the new SIR coil until the installation is complete. If the SIR coil does not come with a centering tab, you must center the coil.**

➡**If reusing the existing coil it must be centered.**

16. Center the SIR coil, as required.

17. Align the SIR coil assembly with the horn tower on the turn signal cancel cam assembly.

18. Slide the SIR coil onto the steering shaft assembly.

19. Firmly seat the retaining ring into the groove on the steering shaft assembly.

➡️**If installing a new SIR coil, remove and discard the centering tab, if equipped.**

20. Install the upper trim cover. Tighten the retaining screws to 13 inch lbs.

21. Install the lower trim cover.
22. Verify the upper and lower retaining tabs engage with each other. Tighten the screws to 13 inch lbs.
23. Continue the installation in the reverse order of the removal procedure.
24. Be sure the ignition switch is in the OFF position.

25. Install the fuses.
26. Connect the negative battery cable.
27. Turn the ignition switch to the ON position.
28. If the system is operating properly the AIR BAG indicator will flash
29. Correct problems as required.

DRIVE TRAIN

AUTOMATIC TRANSMISSION ASSEMBLY

REMOVAL & INSTALLATION

4L60E, 4L65E and 4L70E Transmissions

See Figure 31.

1. Before servicing the vehicle, refer to the Precautions Section.
2. Remove or disconnect the following:
   - Transmission fluid
   - Transmission oil level indicator tube and seal from the transmission

➡️**Plug the oil level indicator tube opening in the transmission.**

   - Shift cable end from the transmission shift lever ball stud
   - Transfer case, if AWD
   - Rear driveshaft.
3. Plug the transmission oil cooler line connectors in the transmission case.
4. Remove or disconnect the following:
   - Starter motor
5. Support the transmission with a transmission jack.

6. Remove or disconnect the following:
   - Torque converter access plug
   - Mark the flywheel and the torque converter alignment
   - Flywheel-to-torque converter bolts
   - Transmission rear mount-to-transmission bolts and nut
   - Heat shield-to-transmission bolts
   - Transmission vent hose from the transmission
   - Fuel lines from the transmission
   - Wiring harness from the transmission
   - Transmission-to-engine stud and bolt
   - Studs and bolt securing the transmission to the engine.
7. Pull the transmission straight back.
8. The transmission from the vehicle
9. Flush the transmission oil cooler and cooling lines.

To install:
10. Support the transmission with a transmission jack.
11. Raise the transmission into place and remove the tool from the transmission.
12. Slide the transmission straight onto the locating pins while lining up the marks

on the flywheel and the torque converter. The torque converter must be flush onto the flywheel and rotate freely by hand.
13. Install or connect the following:
   - Studs and bolt securing the transmission to the engine. Tighten to 34 ft. lbs. (47 Nm).
   - Flywheel to torque converter bolts. Tighten to 46 ft. lbs. (63 Nm) and use Loctite 242 on the threads
   - Torque converter access plug
   - Transmission vent hose to the transmission
   - Fuel lines to the transmission
   - Wiring harness to the transmission.
   - Heat shield-to-transmission bolts and tighten to 13 ft. lbs. (17 Nm)
   - Transmission rear mount-to-transmission bolt and nut and tighten to 18 ft. lbs. (25 Nm)
14. Remove the transmission jack from the transmission.
15. Unplug the transmission oil cooler line connectors in the transmission case.
16. Install or connect the following:
   - Transmission oil cooler lines
   - Transfer case, if equipped
   - Rear driveshaft
   - Shift cable end to the transmission shift lever ball stud
17. Unplug the oil level indicator tube opening in the transmission.
18. Install the transmission oil level indicator tube and seal to the transmission.
19. Tighten the oil pan bolts and fill the transmission with transmission fluid.
20. Lower the vehicle.

4L80E and 4L85E Transmissions

See Figure 32.

1. Before servicing the vehicle, refer to the Precautions Section.
2. Remove or disconnect the following:
   - Transmission fluid
   - Transmission oil level indicator tube and seal from the transmission
3. Plug the oil level indicator tube opening in the transmission.
   - Shift cable from the transmission shift lever ball stud

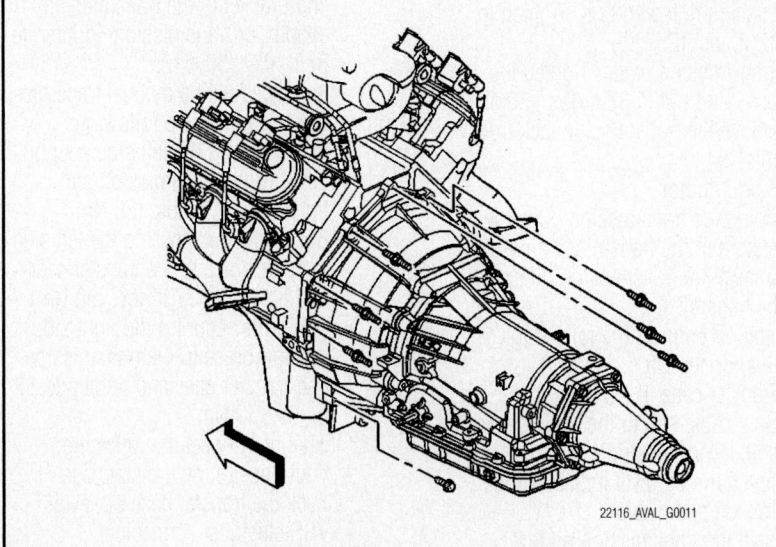

22116_AVAL_G0011

Fig. 31 Transmission mounting bolt location points—4L60E, 4L65E and 4L70E

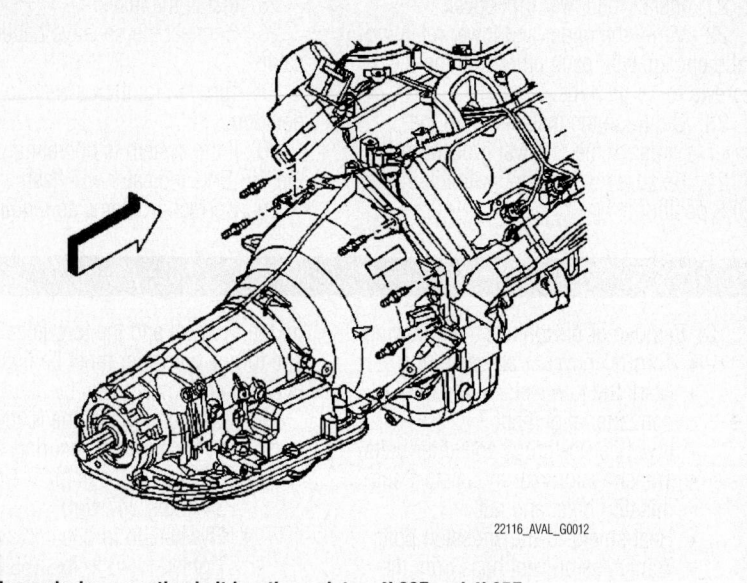

Fig. 32 Transmission mounting bolt location points—4L80E and 4L85E

- Transfer case, if AWD
- Rear driveshaft.
- Transmission oil cooler lines, then plug thee openings in the transmission case
- Starter motor

4. Support the transmission with a transmission jack.
- Heat shield
- Transmission vent hose
- Fuel lines from the transmission
- Wiring harness from the transmission
- Transmission brace-to-engine bracket and transmission nut and bolt
- Torque converter cover
- Mark the flywheel and the torque converter alignment
- Flywheel to torque converter bolts
- Transmission rear mount
- Stud and bolt on the right side securing the transmission to the engine
- Remaining six studs and the bolt securing the transmission to the engine

5. Pull the transmission straight back. Remove the transmission from the vehicle.

6. Flush the transmission oil cooler and cooling lines when you remove the transmission.

To install:

7. Support the transmission with a transmission jack.

8. Raise the transmission into place and remove the tool from the transmission.

9. Slide the transmission straight onto the locating pins while lining up the marks on the flywheel and the torque converter. The torque converter must be flush onto the flywheel and rotate freely by hand.

10. Install or connect the following:
- Six studs and bolt securing the transmission to the engine. Tighten to 34 ft. lbs. (47 Nm).
- Stud and bolt on the right side securing the transmission to the engine. Tighten to 34 ft. lbs. (47 Nm).
- Flywheel-to-torque converter bolts and tighten to 46 ft. lbs. (63 Nm).
- Transmission vent hose
- Fuel lines
- Wiring harness
- Heat shield. Tighten the bolts to 13 ft. lbs. (17 Nm).
- Transmission rear mount-to-transmission nuts and bolt. Tighten to 18 ft. lbs. (25 Nm).
- Transmission brace. Tighten the bolts and nut to 37 ft. lbs. (50 Nm).

11. Remove the transmission jack from the transmission.
- Starter motor

12. Unplug the transmission oil cooler line connectors in the transmission case.

13. Connect the transmission oil cooler lines to the transmission.

14. Install or connect the following:
- Rear driveshaft
- Transfer case, if AWD
- Shift cable end to the transmission shift lever ball stud

15. Unplug the oil level indicator tube opening in the transmission.

16. Install the transmission oil level indicator tube and seal to the transmission.

17. Tighten the oil pan bolts and fill the transmission with transmission fluid.

18. Lower the vehicle.

TRANSFER CASE ASSEMBLY

REMOVAL & INSTALLATION

See Figure 33.

1. Before servicing the vehicle, refer to the Precautions Section.

2. Disconnect the negative battery cable.

3. Raise and support the vehicle safely.

4. Remove or disconnect the following:
- Transfer case shields
- Front driveshaft
- Rear driveshaft
- Shift rod from the transfer case
- Vent hose from the transfer case
- Vehicle Speed Sensor (VSS) electrical connectors
- All necessary wiring harnesses from the transfer case

5. Support the transfer case with a transmission jack.

6. Remove or disconnect the following:
- Six nuts securing the transfer case and bracket to the transmission or transmission adapter, as applicable
- Transfer case
- Gasket, then discard

To install:

7. Install a new gasket to the transmission. Use Teflon pipe sealant GM P/N 12346004 in order to hold the gasket in place.

8. Raise and position the transfer case to the vehicle.

9. Install or connect the following:
- Six nuts securing the transfer case and bracket to the transmission adapter or transmission. Tighten to 37 ft. lbs. (50 Nm).

10. If equipped with a manual transmission, install or connect the following:
- Bolt securing the left side support brace to the transmission and tighten to 37 ft. lbs. (50 Nm)
- Bolt and stud securing the left side support brace to the transfer case and tighten to 37 ft. lbs. (50 Nm)
- Two bolts securing the right side support brace to the transmission and transfer case and tighten to 37 ft. lbs. (50 Nm)

11. Install or connect the following:
- Vent hose to the transfer case

12. Check the transfer case oil level.
- VSS electrical connectors
- Wiring harness to the transfer case
- Shift rod to the transfer case

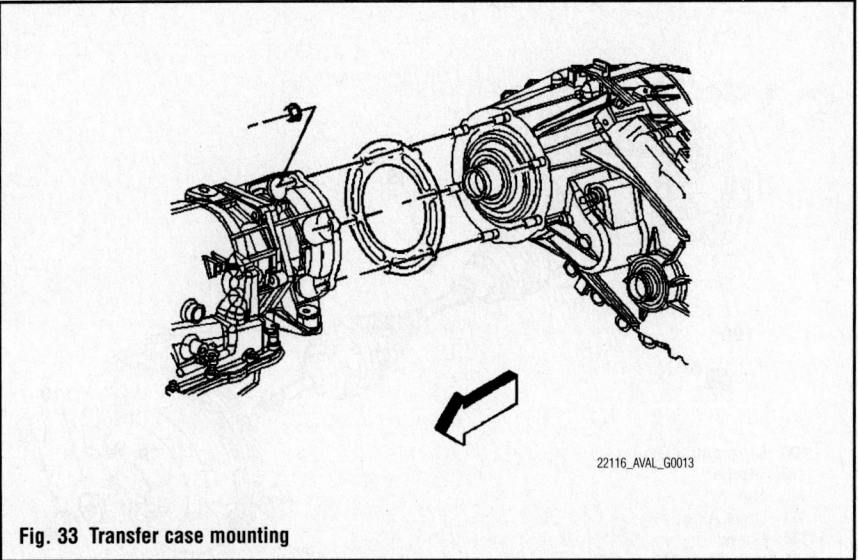

Fig. 33 Transfer case mounting

- Front and rear driveshafts
- Transfer case shields
13. Lower the vehicle.

FRONT AXLE SHAFT, BEARING & SEAL

REMOVAL & INSTALLATION

See Figures 34 and 35.

1. Before servicing the vehicle, refer to the Precautions Section.
2. Raise and support the vehicle.
3. Drain the differential carrier assembly.
4. If only replacing the right side inner shaft and/or housing, follow the steps below. If only replacing the left side inner shaft, proceed to step 16.
5. Remove the stabilizer shaft link assembly.
6. Remove the wheel drive shaft inboard flange bolts from the inner axle shaft.

7. Disconnect the wheel drive shaft from the inner axle shaft.
8. Disconnect the inner axle shaft from the differential case side gear using a hammer and brass drift. Remove the inner axle shaft housing nuts from the bracket.
9. Remove the inner axle shaft housing bolts from the differential carrier assembly.
10. Remove the inner axle shaft and inner axle shaft housing from the vehicle.
11. Remove the inner axle shaft from the inner axle shaft housing.
12. Remove the inner axle shaft seal and the bearing from the inner axle shaft housing.
13. Install the inner axle shaft housing into a vise. Clamp only on the mounting flange of the inner axle shaft housing.

14. Install the bushing and bearing removal tool J-29369–1 behind the inner axle shaft seal or the inner axle shaft bearing as necessary.
15. Install a slide hammer to the removal tool.
16. Remove the inner axle shaft seal and/or the inner axle shaft bearing using the slide hammer.
17. If only replacing the left side seal, place an alignment mark between the inner axle shaft and the wheel drive shaft.
18. Disconnect the wheel drive shaft from the inner axle shaft.
19. Remove the inner axle shaft using a hammer and a brass drift.
20. Remove the inner axle shaft seal using a suitable seal remover tool.

To install:

→Be sure to use new fasteners, as required.

21. Install the right side bearing with the square shoulder in using and axle bearing tube installer and a universal driver handle.
22. Install the new axle shaft seal using the sane tools.
23. Install the inner axle shaft into the inner axle shaft housing. Carefully tap the inner axle shaft into place with a soft–faced mallet.
24. Install the inner axle shaft and clutch fork assembly components into the inner shaft housing.
25. If only the left side inner axle shaft was removed, install the shaft by performing the following steps:
26. Install the inner axle shaft into the differential case side gear using a soft–faced mallet until the retaining ring on the inner axle shaft is fully seated within the groove in the differential case side gear.
27. Pull back on the inner axle shaft to ensure that the inner axle shaft is properly retained in the differential case side gear.
28. Connect the halfshaft to the inner axle shaft.
29. Install the halfshaft inboard flange to inner axle shaft bolts and tighten to 58 ft. lbs. (79 Nm).
30. If the right side inner axle shaft and/or housing was removed, install the shaft and/or housing using the following steps.
31. Install the new inner axle shaft bearing and the new seal to the inner axle shaft housing.
32. Install the inner axle shaft into the inner axle shaft housing. Do not install the inner axle shaft completely into the inner axle shaft housing at this time.

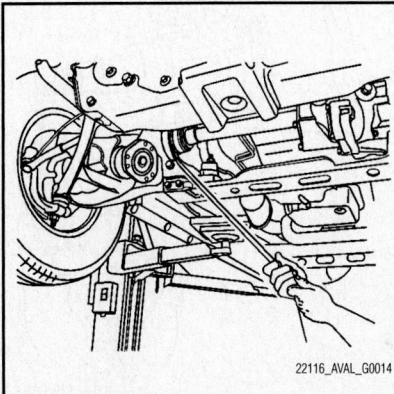

Fig. 34 Removing the halfshaft shaft from the inner axle shaft

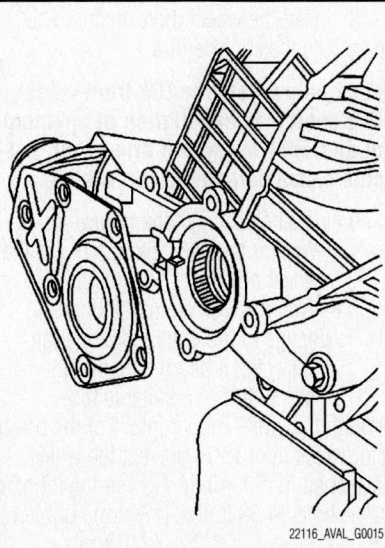

Fig. 35 Inner axle shaft seal and bearing cover

33. Apply sealant to the inner axle housing to differential carrier sealing surface.

34. Install the inner axle shaft and the inner axle shaft housing to the differential carrier assembly.

35. Install the inner axle shaft housing bolts and tighten to 30 ft. lbs. (40 Nm).

36. Install the inner axle shaft housing nuts to the bracket and tighten to 75 ft. lbs. (100 Nm).

37. Install the inner axle shaft into the differential case side gear by doing the following:

38. Turn the inner axle shaft and align the splines of the inner axle shaft with the splines on the differential side gear.

39. Install the inner axle shaft into the differential case side gear using a soft–faced mallet until the retaining ring on the inner axle shaft is fully seated within the groove in the differential case side gear.

40. Pull back on the inner axle shaft to ensure that the inner axle shaft is properly retained in the differential case side gear.

41. Install the wheel drive shaft inboard flange to the inner axle shaft.

42. Install the wheel drive shaft inboard flange to inner axle shaft bolts and tighten to 58 ft. lbs. (79 Nm).

43. Install the stabilizer shaft link assembly.

44. Fill the differential carrier assembly with axle lubricant

45. Lower the vehicle.

FRONT HALFSHAFTS

REMOVAL & INSTALLATION

See Figure 36.

1. Before servicing the vehicle, refer to the Precautions Section.

2. Remove or disconnect the following:
   • Wheels

3. Insert a drift or a suitable tool through the brake caliper into one of the brake rotor vanes in order to prevent the drive axle wheel drive shaft from turning.

4. Remove or disconnect the following:
   • Nut and the washer from the hub

➡ **Do not reuse the hub nut. A new nut must be used when installing the wheel drive shaft.**

   • Bolts (6) securing the wheel drive shaft inboard flange to the output shaft flange
   • Drift from the rotor
   • Stabilizer shaft link from the lower control arm

5. Wrap shop towels around both the inner and the outer wheel drive shaft boots

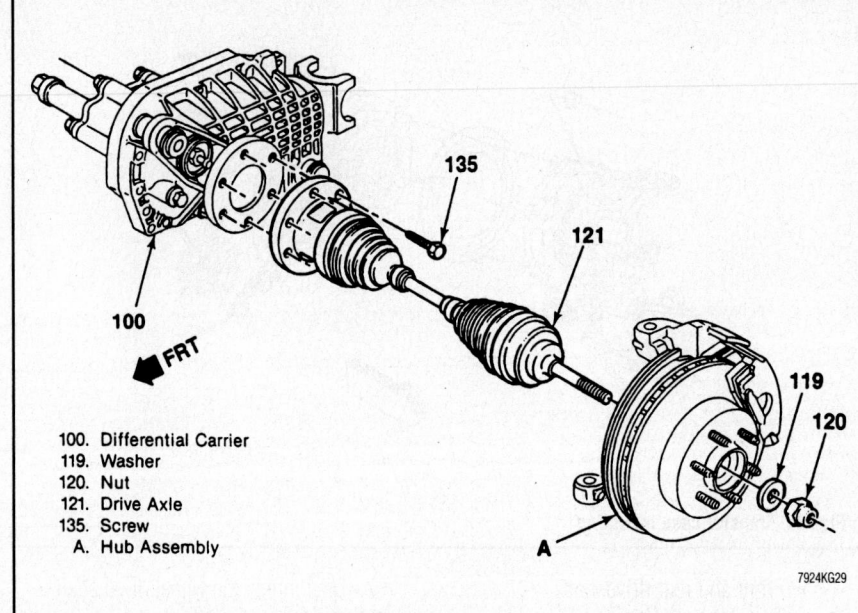

100. Differential Carrier
119. Washer
120. Nut
121. Drive Axle
135. Screw
  A. Hub Assembly

Fig. 36 The halfshaft is mounted to the flange on the differential and through the hub assembly—AWD

in order to avoid damage to the boots during removal and installation.

6. Pull the wheel drive shaft through the lower control arm opening.

To install:

7. Wrap shop towels around both the inner and the outer wheel drive shaft boots in order to avoid damage to the boots during removal and installation.

➡ **Clean the steering knuckle and the wheel drive shaft splines and threads. These areas must be dry and free of grease, dirt, and contamination.**

8. Insert the wheel drive shaft splined shank into the knuckle hub.

➡ **Use only a genuine GM front wheel drive shaft nut. Installation of anything but an OEM front wheel drive shaft nut could cause damage to the vehicle.**

9. Install or connect the following:
   • Washer and the new hub nut to the wheel driveshaft. Do not tighten.
   • The wheel drive shaft inboard flange to the output shaft flange using the inboard flange bolts

10. Insert a drift or a suitable tool through the brake caliper into 1 of the brake rotor vanes in order to prevent the wheel drive shaft from turning. Tighten the inboard flange bolts to 58 ft. lbs. (78 Nm). Tighten the hub nut to 177 ft. lbs. (240 Nm).

11. Remove the drift from the rotor.

12. Install the stabilizer shaft link.

13. Install the wheel and tire assembly.

FRONT PINION SEAL

REMOVAL & INSTALLATION

See Figure 37.

1. Before servicing the vehicle, refer to the Precautions Section.

2. Raise and support the vehicle safely.

3. Remove the tire and wheel assembly.

4. Remove the brake calipers.

5. Remove the differential carrier assembly shield, if equipped.

6. Reference mark the relationship of the driveshaft to the front axle pinion yoke.

7. Remove the driveshaft.

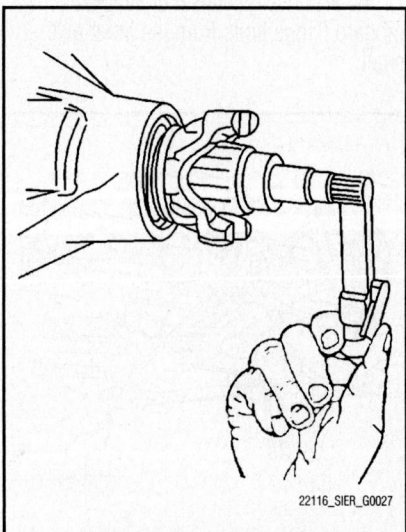

Fig. 37 Measuring the turning torque of the pinion

8. Tie the driveshaft to a frame rail or the crossmember.

9. Measure the torque required in order to rotate the pinion. Record the torque value for reassembly.

10. Scribe a line on the pinion stem, the pinion nut and the companion flange. Record the number of exposed threads on the pinion stem.

11. Remove the nut.

REAR AXLE HOUSING

REMOVAL & INSTALLATION

1. Before servicing the vehicle, refer to the Precautions Section.

2. Raise and support the vehicle safely.

3. Remove the tire and wheel assembly.

4. Properly support the rear axle assembly.

5. Remove the stabilizer shaft, if equipped.

6. As required, disconnect the electrical connector from the rear wheel speed sensor.

7. Remove the brake calipers.

8. Remove the driveshaft.

9. Remove the parking brake cables, the rear springs and rear axle housing.

10. Drain the rear lubricant. Properly dispose of used fluid.

11. Remove the rear axle vent hose from the axle.

12. Remove the lower shock absorber bolt from the rear axle.

13. Remove the rear spring U-bolts, rear spring anchor plates and rear spring spacers from the vehicle.

14. Remove the rear axle assembly from the vehicle.

To install:

➡**Be sure to use new fasteners, as required.**

15. Installation is the reverse of the removal procedure.

16. Be sure to fill the differential with the correct grade and type lubricant.

REAR AXLE SHAFT, BEARING & SEAL

REMOVAL & INSTALLATION

8.6 and 9.5 Inch Rear Axles

1. Before servicing the vehicle, refer to the Precautions Section.

2. Raise and support the vehicle on a hoist.

3. Remove the tire and wheel assembly.

4. Remove the brake caliper on disc brake models.

5. Remove the rear cover and gasket.

6. Remove the pinion shaft locking bolt.

7. On axles without a locking differential, remove the pinion shaft.

8. On axles with a locking differential, remove the shaft part way. Rotate the case until the pinion shaft touches the housing.

9. On axles with a locking differential, use a suitable tool, in order to enter the differential case and rotate the lock until the lock aligns with the thrust block.

10. Push the flange of the axle shaft in toward the differential.

11. Remove the C–lock from the button end of the axle shaft.

12. When removing the axle shaft, do not rotate the shaft. Rotating the shaft will misalign the gears. Misaligning the gears will make assembly difficult.

13. Remove the axle shaft from the housing.

To install:

14. Install the axle shaft into the rear axle housing.

15. Slide the axle shaft into place allowing the splines to engage the differential side gear.

16. On axles without a locking differential, place the C–lock on the button end of the axle shaft.

17. On axles with a locking differential, keep the pinion shaft partially withdrawn.

18. Install the brake drum on drum brake models.

19. On axles with a locking differential, place the C–lock on the axle shaft so that the ends are flush with the thrust block.

20. Pull the shaft flange outward in order to seat the lock in the differential gear.

21. Align the hole in the pinion shaft with the bolt hole in the differential case.

22. Install the new pinion shaft locking bolt and tighten to 27 ft. lbs. (36 Nm) on 8.5 inch axles or 20 ft. lbs. (27 Nm) on 9.5 inch axles.

23. Install the rear cover and the gasket.

24. Install the caliper on disc brake models.

25. Install the tire and wheel assembly.

26. Fill the rear axle, using the proper fluid.

27. Lower the vehicle.

9.75 Inch Rear Axles

See Figure 38.

1. Before servicing the vehicle, refer to the Precautions Section.

2. Release the parking brake.

3. Raise and support the vehicle.

4. Remove the tire and wheel assembly.

5. Remove the rear steering gear assembly.

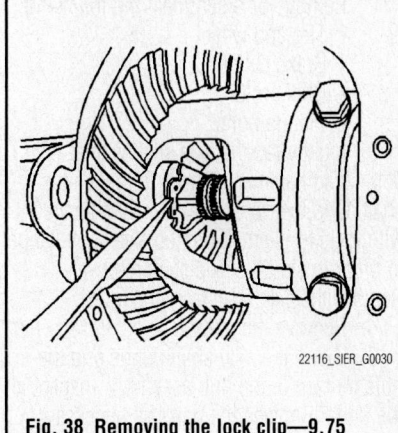

Fig. 38 Removing the lock clip—9.75 inch axles

6. Remove the steering knuckle assembly.

7. Remove the lock clip from the axle shaft end. The lock clip is spring loaded and fits securely in the axle shaft slot and may need to be push off the shaft end with a screw driver or related tool. Pushing the axle shaft inwards toward the gears my help in removal of the lock clip.

8. When removing the axle shaft do not rotate the shaft. Rotating the shaft will cause the gears to move. Misalignment of gears will make the assembly difficult.

9. Remove the axle shaft.

To install:

10. Install the axle shaft.

11. Install the spring loaded lock clip to the axle shaft end.

12. Install the steering knuckle assembly.

13. Install the rear steering gear assembly.

14. Install the tire and wheel assembly.

15. Lower the vehicle.

10.5 and 10.75 Inch Rear Axles

See Figure 39.

1. Before servicing the vehicle, refer to the Precautions Section.

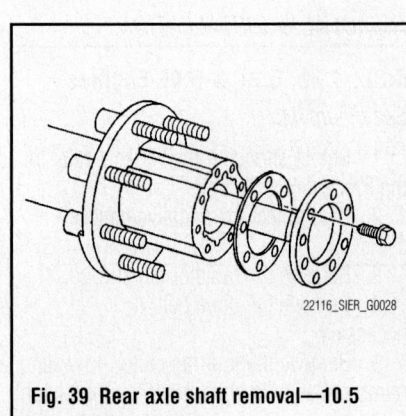

Fig. 39 Rear axle shaft removal—10.5 and 10.75 inch axles

2. Remove or disconnect the following:
- Tire and wheel
- Brake caliper
- Brake rotor
- Flange bolts

3. Lightly rap the axle shaft with a soft–faced hammer in order to loosen the shaft. Grip the rib on the axle shaft flange with locking pliers. Twist the axle shaft flange in order to start the axle shaft removal. Remove the axle shaft from the tube.

4. Remove the gasket.

5. Clean the axle shaft flange and the outside face of the hub assembly. Inspect all the parts. Replace the parts as necessary.

To install:

6. Install or connect the following:
- Gasket onto the axle shaft
- Gasket and axle shaft into the tube. Ensure the shaft splines mesh into the differential side gear. Align the holes in the axle flange and the gasket with the holes in the hub.
- Axle flange bolts and tighten to 110 ft. lbs. (150 Nm).
- Rotor
- Caliper
- Wheel and tire

REAR PINION SEAL

REMOVAL & INSTALLATION

See Figure 40.

1. Before servicing the vehicle, refer to the Precautions Section.
2. Disconnect the negative battery cable.
3. Raise and support the vehicle safely.
4. Remove the tire and wheel assembly.
5. Remove the rear brake calipers and rotors.

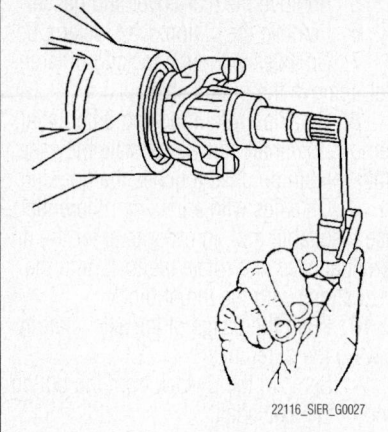

Fig. 40 Measuring the turning torque of the pinion

6. Remove the axle shafts on 10.5 inch and 11.5 inch axles.

7. Reference mark the rear driveshaft to the rear axle pinion yoke.

8. Disconnect the driveshaft from the axle.

9. Measure the torque required to turn the pinion. Record the torque number measurement which gives the combined pinion bearing, seal, carrier bearing, axle bearing and seal preload.

10. Make and accurate alignment mark on the pinion flange. Record the number of exposed threads on the pinion stem.

11. Remove the pinion flange nut and the washer. Use a container in order to catch any lubricant.

➡️Use care not to damage any of the machined surfaces.

12. Remove the pinion flange.

➡️The pinion flange has an oil seal that is part of the pinion flange assembly. The pinion flange must be inspected to ensure that the seal is not damaged.

13. Pry the oil seal from the bore.

14. Thoroughly clean any foreign material from the contact area. Replace any parts as necessary.

To install:

15. Lubricate the cavity between the lips of the oil seal with wheel bearing lubricant.

16. Install the oil seal into the bore using a driver.

➡️Do not hammer the pinion flange onto the pinion stem.

17. Install the pinion flange. Use the alignment marks in the installation of the pinion flange.

18. Install the washer and a new nut. Tighten the nut on the pinion stem as close as possible to the alignment marks without going past the marks. Use the alignment marks and the thread count as a reference. Tighten the nut a little at a time. Turn the pinion flange several times after each tightening in order to seat the rollers.

19. Measure the torque required to rotate the pinion flange. Compare this to the original torque. Tighten the pinion nut, in small increments, until the rotating torque is 3 inch lbs. (0.35 Nm) GREATER than the original torque.

20. Align the driveshaft with the alignment marks. Connect the driveshaft.

21. Install the axle shafts on 10.5 inch and 11.5 inch axle.

22. Install the rear brake calipers and rotors or drums.

23. Install the tire and wheel assemblies.

ENGINE COOLING

ENGINE FAN

REMOVAL & INSTALLATION

4.3L, 4.8L, 5.3L & 6.0L Engines

See Figure 41.

1. Before servicing the vehicle, refer to the Precautions Section.

2. Disconnect the negative battery cable.

3. Remove the radiator fan shroud.

4. Remove the drive belt, if necessary.

5. Remove the four fan clutch-to-water pump pulley nuts and lift out the fan/clutch assembly.

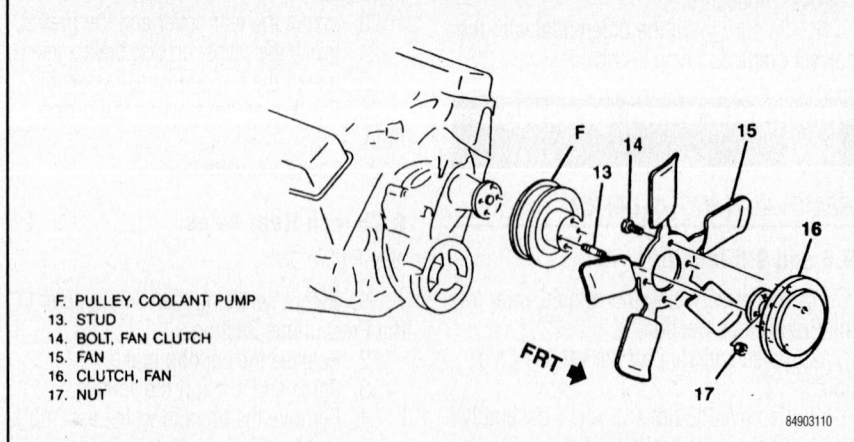

F. PULLEY, COOLANT PUMP
13. STUD
14. BOLT, FAN CLUTCH
15. FAN
16. CLUTCH, FAN
17. NUT

Fig. 41 Engine fan and clutch assembly—4.3L, 4.8L, 5.3L and 6.0L engines

6. Remove the fan clutch bolts and separate the fan from the clutch.

To install:

7. Install the fan on the fan clutch and tighten the bolts to 17 ft. lbs. (23 Nm).

8. Position the fan/clutch assembly on the water pump pulley. Tighten the nuts to 18 ft. lbs. (24 Nm).

9. Install the fan shroud.

10. Connect the battery cable.

6.6L Engines

See Figure 42.

1. Before servicing the vehicle, refer to the Precautions Section.

2. Disconnect the negative battery cable.

3. Remove the radiator shroud.

4. Locate the yellow dot on the fan clutch hub and matchmark the water pump pulley.

5. Remove the drive belt, if necessary.

6. Remove the fan clutch-to-water pump pulley nuts and lift out the fan/clutch assembly.

7. Remove the fan clutch bolts and separate the fan from the clutch.

To install:

8. Install the fan on the fan clutch and tighten the bolts to 18 ft. lbs. (24 Nm).

9. Position the fan/clutch assembly on the water pump pulley so that the reference marks on each hub align. Tighten the nuts to 18 ft. lbs. (24 Nm).

10. Install the fan shroud.

11. Connect the battery cable.

RADIATOR

REMOVAL & INSTALLATION

❋❋ CAUTION

Never open, service or drain the radiator or cooling system when hot; serious burns can occur from the steam and hot coolant. Also, when draining engine coolant, keep in mind that cats and dogs are attracted to ethylene glycol antifreeze and could drink any that is left in an uncovered container or in puddles on the ground. This will prove fatal in sufficient quantities. Always drain coolant into a sealable container. Coolant should be reused unless it is contaminated or is several years old.

4.3L, 4.8L, 5.3L & 6.0L Engines

See Figure 43.

1. Before servicing the vehicle, refer to the Precautions Section.

2. Disconnect the negative battery cable.

3. Drain the cooling system.

4. Unfasten the upper fan shroud bolts and remove the upper fan shroud.

5. If equipped, remove the upper panel fasteners and the panel.

6. If equipped, remove the upper insulators and brackets.

7. Disconnect the radiator upper and lower hoses and, if applicable, the transmission fluid lines.

8. Remove the coolant recovery system line, if so equipped.

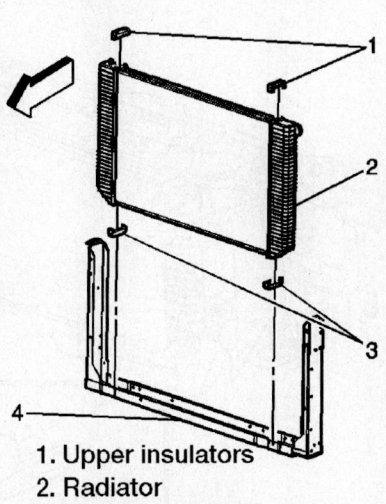

1. Upper insulators
2. Radiator
3. Lower insulators
4. Lower bracket

22116_AVAL_G0006

Fig. 43 Exploded view of the radiator mounting—4.3L, 4.8L, 5.3L and 6.0L engines

9. Remove the transmission fluid lines.

10. Remove the lower fan shroud bolts and the lower fan shroud.

11. Remove radiator from the lower brackets and insulators.

To install:

12. Install the radiator on the lower brackets and insulators.

13. Install the lower fan shroud and its retaining bolts. Tighten the shroud bolts to 71 inch lbs. (9 Nm).

14. Attach and tighten the engine oil cooler pipe bolts to 18 ft. lbs. (24 Nm) and the transmission oil cooler bolts to 19 ft. lbs. (26 Nm).

15. Attach the lower and upper radiator hoses..

16. Install the upper insulators, the upper fan shroud and fan shroud bolts. Tighten the shroud bolts to 71 inch lbs. (9 Nm).

17. Attach the coolant recovery system line, if so equipped.

18. If equipped, install the upper panel fasteners.

19. Refill the cooling system.

6.6L Engines

See Figure 44.

1. Before servicing the vehicle, refer to the Precautions Section.

2. Disconnect the negative battery cable.

3. Drain the cooling system.

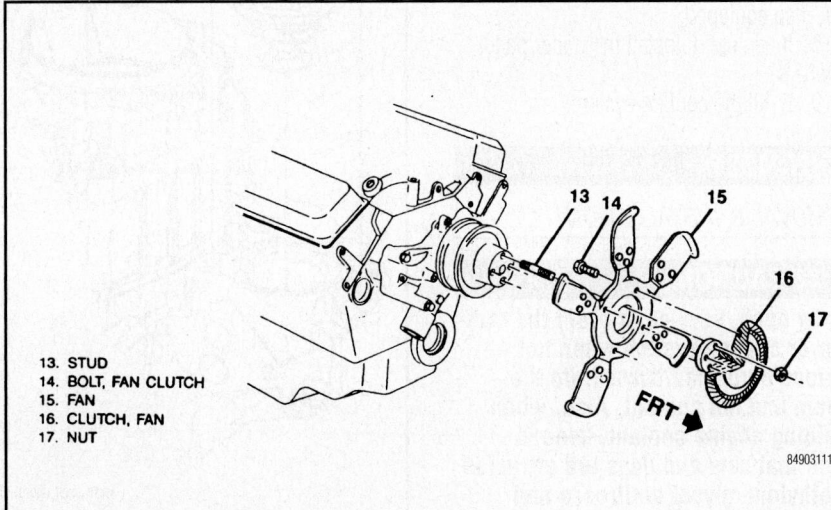

13. STUD
14. BOLT, FAN CLUTCH
15. FAN
16. CLUTCH, FAN
17. NUT

FRT

84903111

Fig. 42 Engine fan and clutch assembly—6.6L engines

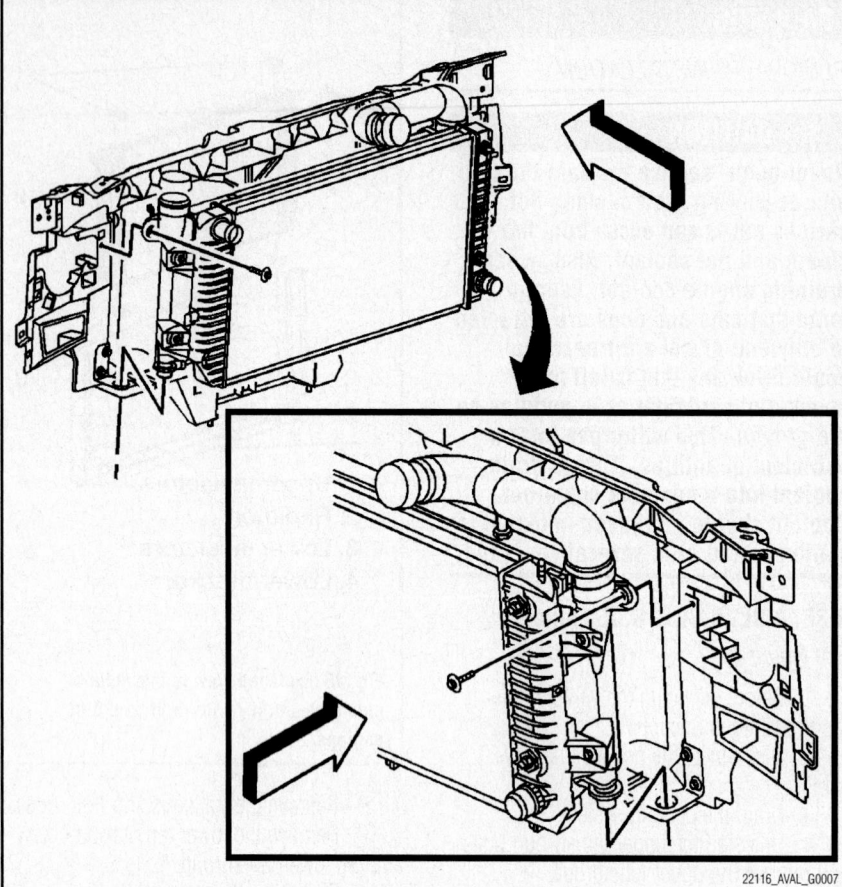

22116_AVAL_G0007

Fig. 44 Exploded view of the radiator mounting—6.6L engines

4. Unfasten the upper fan shroud bolts and remove the upper fan shroud.

5. If equipped, remove the upper panel fasteners and the panel.

6. If equipped, remove the upper insulators and brackets.

7. Disconnect the radiator upper and lower hoses and, if applicable, the transmission coolant lines.

8. Remove the coolant recovery system line, if so equipped.

9. Remove the transmission fluid lines.

10. Remove the lower fan shroud bolts and the lower fan shroud.

11. Remove radiator from the lower brackets and insulators.

To install:

12. Install the radiator on the lower brackets and insulators.

13. Install the lower fan shroud and its retaining bolts. Tighten the shroud bolts to 71 inch lbs. (9 Nm).

14. Attach and tighten the engine oil cooler pipe bolts to 18 ft. lbs. (24 Nm) and the transmission oil cooler bolts to 19 ft. lbs. (26 Nm).

15. Attach the lower and upper radiator hoses.

16. Install the upper insulators, the upper fan shroud and fan shroud bolts. Tighten the shroud bolts to 71 inch lbs. (9 Nm).

17. Attach the coolant recovery system line, if so equipped.

18. If equipped, install the upper panel fasteners.

19. Refill the cooling system.

THERMOSTAT

REMOVAL & INSTALLATION

✳✳ CAUTION

Never open, service or drain the radiator or cooling system when hot; serious burns can occur from the steam and hot coolant. Also, when draining engine coolant, keep in mind that cats and dogs are attracted to ethylene glycol antifreeze and could drink any that is left in an uncovered container or in puddles on the ground. This will prove fatal in

sufficient quantities. Always drain coolant into a sealable container. Coolant should be reused unless it is contaminated or is several years old.

4.3L Engines

See Figure 45.

1. Before servicing the vehicle, refer to the Precautions Section.

2. Disconnect the negative battery cable.

3. Drain the radiator until the coolant is below the thermostat level (below the level of the intake manifold). Properly dispose of used coolant.

4. Remove the water outlet elbow assembly from the engine. Remove the thermostat from the engine.

5. Remove the coolant recovery reservoir.

6. Remove the upper radiator hose.

7. Remove the thermostat housing retaining bolts.

8. Remove the thermostat housing.

9. Remove the thermostat from its mounting on the engine.

36616_EXPR_G0078

Fig. 45 Thermostat and related components—4.3L engines

To install:

10. Clean the gasket surfaces on the thermostat housing and engine mating surface.

11. Install the new thermostat making sure the spring side is inserted into the engine. Tighten the thermostat housing bolts to 18 ft. lbs. (25 Nm).

12. Refill the cooling system.

13. Start the engine and check for leaks. Correct as required.

4.8L, 5.3L & 6.0L Engines

See Figure 46.

1. Before servicing the vehicle, refer to the Precautions Section.

2. Disconnect the negative battery cable.

3. Remove the air inlet duct.

4. Drain the cooling system.

5. Remove the radiator outlet hose.

6. Remove the thermostat housing bolts.

7. Remove the thermostat from the water pump housing.

➡The O–ring seal is integral to the thermostat housing

To install:

8. Install the thermostat to the water pump housing making sure the spring side is inserted into the engine.

9. Install the bolts.

10. Tighten the bolts to 11 ft. lbs. (15 Nm).

11. Install the radiator outlet hose.

12. Fill the cooling system.

13. Install the air inlet duct.

14. Test the system for leaks.

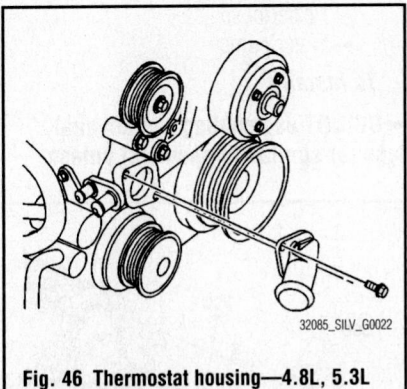

Fig. 46 Thermostat housing—4.8L, 5.3L and 6.0L engines

6.6L Engines

Thermostat

See Figures 47 and 48.

1. Before servicing the vehicle, refer to the Precautions Section.

2. Disconnect the negative battery cable.

3. Drain the engine coolant.

4. Remove the water outlet tube.

5. Remove the bolt for the fuel line bracket.

6. Remove the 4 bolts retaining the thermostat housing cover.

7. Remove the 2 thermostats with the seals.

To install:

8. Install the 2 thermostats with the seals to the thermostat housing. The rear thermostat (4) has 2 vent valves. Install with the vent valves toward the rear of engine.

9. Install the thermostat housing cover.

10. Tighten the thermostat housing cover bolts to 15 ft. lbs. (21 Nm).

11. Install the fuel line bracket bolt.

12. Tighten the fuel line bracket and bolt to 15 ft. lbs. (21 Nm).

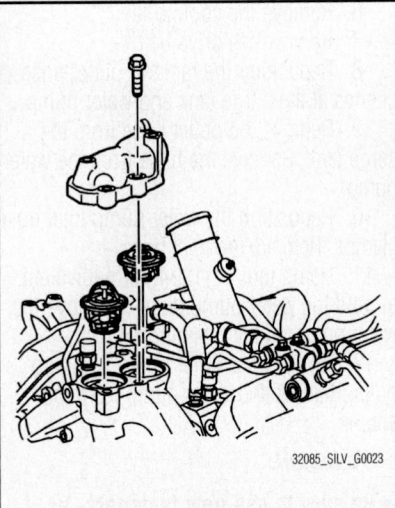

Fig. 47 Exploded view thermostat housing assembly—6.6L engines

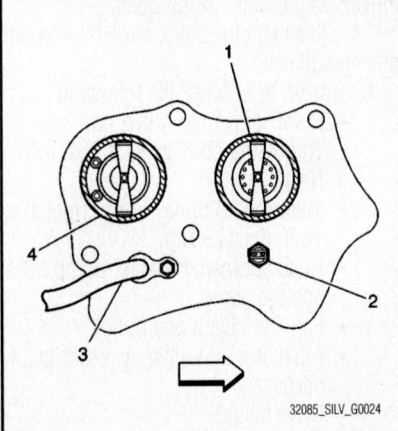

Fig. 48 View of thermostats in thermostat housing—6.6L engines

13. Install the water outlet tube.

14. Fill the engine coolant.

15. With the engine idling, add coolant to the radiator until the coolant level reaches the bottom of the filler neck.

16. Install the radiator cap to the radiator.

17. Inspect the coolant system for leaks.

Water Outlet Tube

See Figures 49 and 50.

1. Remove the upper intake manifold sight shield using the following procedure:

   a. Remove the retaining bolt in the front of the shield.

   b. Lift–up on the front of the shield.

   c. Lift the shield off the rear bracket.

2. Drain the engine coolant.

3. Remove the radiator inlet hose from the water outlet tube.

4. Remove the bolt and wiring harness bracket at the thermostat housing.

5. Disconnect the turbocharger coolant hose from the turbocharger bypass valve.

6. Remove the turbocharger bypass valve and sealing washer from the water outlet tube.

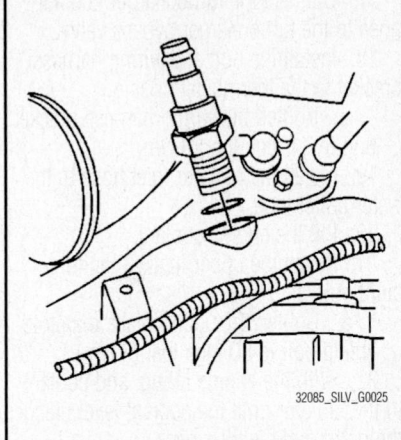

Fig. 49 Turbocharger bypass valve and sealing washer—6.6L engines

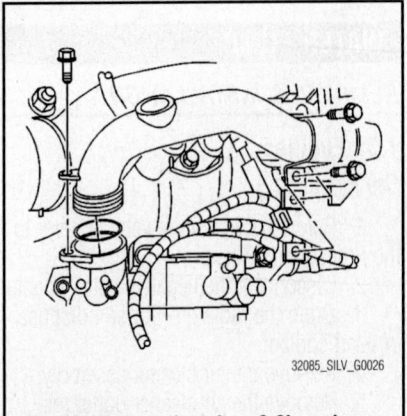

Fig. 50 Water outlet tube—6.6L engines

7. Remove the 2 bolts retaining the water outlet tube to the left valve rocker arm cover.

8. Remove the bolt retaining the water outlet tube to the thermostat housing.

9. Remove the water outlet tube.

10. Remove and discard the O–ring seal.

To install:

11. Install a new O–ring seal on the water outlet tube.

12. Lightly lubricate the O–ring seal with coolant.

13. Install the water outlet tube.

14. Install the bolt retaining the water outlet tube to the thermostat housing.

   a. Tighten the water outlet tube to thermostat housing bolt to 15 ft. lbs. (21 Nm).

15. Install the 2 bolts retaining the water outlet tube to the valve rocker arm cover.

   a. Tighten the water outlet tube to valve rocker arm cover bolts to 15 ft. lbs. (21 Nm).

16. Install the turbocharger bypass valve and sealing washer to the water outlet tube.

   a. Tighten the turbocharger bypass valve to 44 ft. lbs. (60 Nm).

17. Connect the turbocharger coolant hose to the turbocharger bypass valve.

18. Install the bolt and wiring harness bracket to the thermostat housing.

   a. Tighten the wiring harness bracket bolt to 71 inch lbs. (8 Nm).

19. Install the radiator inlet hose to the water outlet tube.

20. Fill the engine coolant.

21. Install the upper intake manifold sight shield.

   a. Tighten the upper intake manifold shield bolt to 80 inch lbs. (9 Nm).

22. With the engine idling, add coolant to the radiator until the coolant level reaches the bottom of the filler neck.

23. Install the radiator cap to the radiator.

24. Inspect the coolant system for leaks.

WATER PUMP

REMOVAL & INSTALLATION

4.3L Engines

See Figure 51.

1. Before servicing the vehicle, refer to the Precautions Section.

2. Disconnect the negative battery cable.

3. Drain the radiator. Properly dispose of used coolant.

4. Remove the air cleaner assembly.

5. Remove the air cleaner outlet resonator duct.

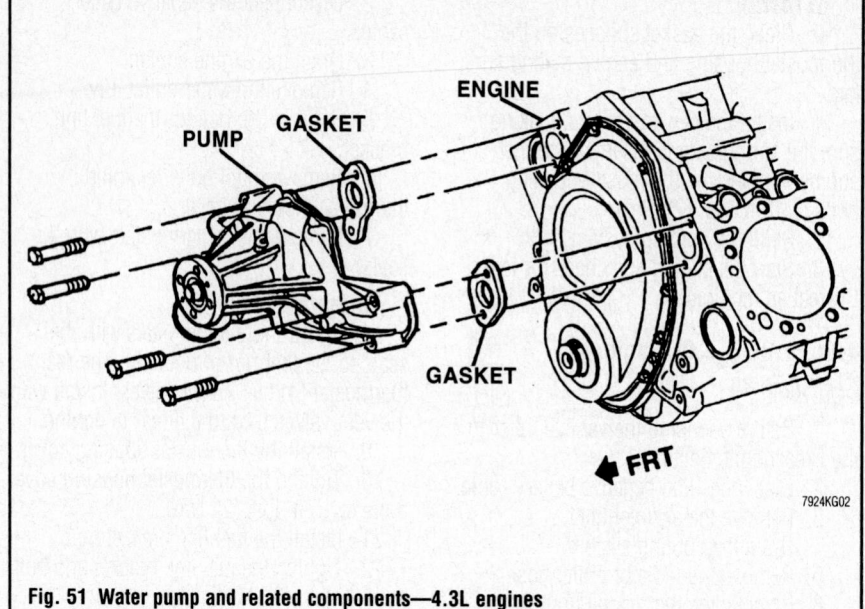

Fig. 51 Water pump and related components—4.3L engines

6. Remove the cooling fan.

7. Remove the drive belt.

8. Reposition the radiator outlet hose clamps at the surge tank and water pump.

9. Remove the outlet hose from the serge tank. Remove the hose from the water pump.

10. Reposition the water pump inlet hose clamps. Remove the inlet hose.

11. Using tool J-412240 or equivalent, to hold the water pump pulley. Remove the water pump pulley retaining bolts.

12. Remove the water pump retaining bolts. Remove the water pump from the engine.

To install:

➡**Be sure to use new fasteners, as required.**

13. If reusing the old fasteners, apply GM 12346004 sealant or equivalent to the threads of the water pump bolts.

14. Clean all old gasket material from all mating surfaces.

15. Install or connect the following:

   • Pump assembly with a new gasket. Torque the bolts to 33 ft. lbs. (45 Nm).

   • Water pump pulley bolts. Tighten to 18 ft. lbs. (25 Nm).

   • Hose between the water pump inlet and the pump

   • Fan, fan clutch and pulley

   • Alternator and other accessories, if necessary

   • Drive belt(s)

   • Upper radiator shroud

16. Refill the cooling system.

17. Connect the battery.

4.8L, 5.3L & 6.0L Engines

See Figure 52.

1. Before servicing the vehicle, refer to the Precautions Section.

2. Disconnect the negative battery cable.

3. Remove or disconnect the following:

   • Air outlet duct

   • Coolant

   • Inlet radiator hose from the water pump

   • Upper fan shroud

   • Cooling fan and clutch assembly

   • Drive belt

   • Radiator outlet hose from the coolant pump

   • Surge tank hose

   • Heater hose

   • Water pump

To install:

➡**DO NOT use cooling system seal tabs (or similar compounds) unless**

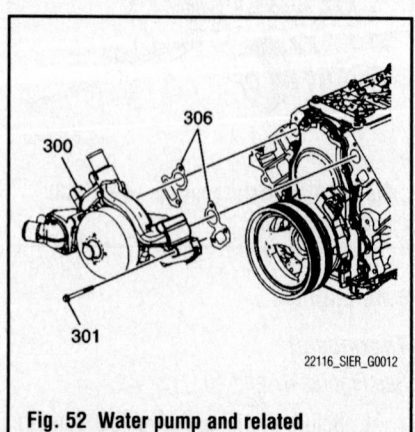

Fig. 52 Water pump and related components—4.8L, 5.3L and 6.0L engines

otherwise instructed. The use of cooling system seal tabs (or similar compounds) may restrict coolant flow through the passages of the cooling system or the engine components. Restricted coolant flow may cause engine overheating and/or damage to the cooling system or the engine components/assembly.

4. Install or connect the following:
- Water pump. Install the water pump bolts. Tighten the water pump bolts first pass to 11 ft. lbs. (15 Nm); tighten the bolts final pass to 22 ft. lbs. (30 Nm).
- Water pump drive belt pulley and bolts (if applicable). Tighten the pulley bolts first pass to 89 inch lbs. (10 Nm); tighten the bolts final pass to 18 ft. lbs. (25 Nm).
- Surge tank hose
- Heater hose
- Outlet radiator hose to the coolant pump
- Drive belt
- Cooling fan and clutch assembly
- Upper fan shroud
- Inlet radiator hose to the water pump
- Air inlet duct
- Coolant

6.6L Engines

See Figure 53.

1. Before servicing the vehicle, refer to the Precautions Section.
2. Disconnect the negative battery cable.
3. Remove the left front fender wheelhouse inner panel.
4. Drain the coolant.
5. Remove or disconnect the following:
- Thermostat housing crossover
- Fan clutch
- Crankshaft balancer
- Water pump outlet pipe-to-water pump nuts
- Engine wiring harness retainer front the inner stud
- Water pump bolts, noting their locations as they are different lengths
- Water pump and gasket

To install:

6. Lubricate the water pump O–ring with engine oil.
7. Install or connect the following:
- Water pump
- Water pump bolts and tighten to 18 ft. lbs. (25 Nm)
- Water pump-to-water pump outlet gasket

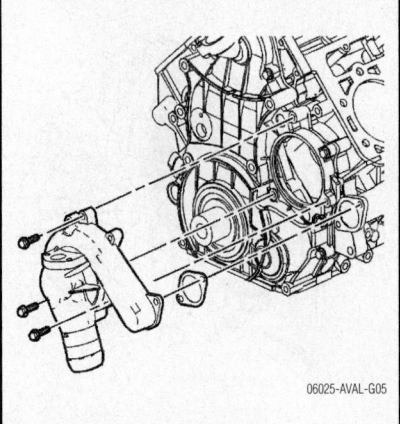

Fig. 53 Water pump and related components—6.6L engines

06025-AVAL-G05

- Engine wiring harness retainer on the water pump outlet pipe inner stud
- Water pump-to-water pump outlet pipe nuts and tighten to 18 ft. lbs. (25 Nm)
- Thermostat housing crossover
- Crankshaft balancer
- Fan clutch

8. Fill the cooling system and install the left front fender wheelhouse inner panel.

ENGINE ELECTRICAL

CHARGING SYSTEM

ALTERNATOR

REMOVAL & INSTALLATION

4.3L Engines

See Figure 54.

1. Before servicing the vehicle, refer to the Precautions Section.
2. Disconnect the negative battery cable.
3. Remove the drive belt.
4. Unbolt and reposition the oil level indicator tube. Unbolt and reposition the oil fill tube.
5. Disconnect the electrical connectors from the alternator.
6. Remove the oil fill tube bracket stud.
7. Reposition the engine wiring harness clip.
8. Reposition the positive battery cable boot at the alternator.
9. Remove the alternator nut. Remove the cable from the alternator.
10. Remove the oil fill tube bracket bolt and bracket.

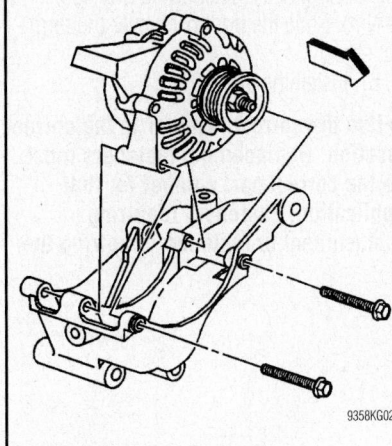

Fig. 54 Alternator and related components—4.3L engines

9358KG02

11. Remove the alternator retaining bolts. Remove the alternator from its mounting.

To install:

➡Be sure to use new fasteners, as required.

12. Position the alternator to its mounting.
13. Tighten the retaining bolts to 37 ft. lbs. (50 Nm).
14. Continue the installation in the reverse order of the removal procedure.
15. Connect the battery cable.
16. Check for proper system operation. Correct as required.

4.8L, 5.3L & 6.0L Engines

See Figure 55.

1. Before servicing the vehicle, refer to the Precautions Section.
2. Disconnect the negative battery cable.
3. Remove or disconnect the following:
- Accessory drive belt
- Engine sight shield, if necessary
- Electrical connections from the alternator
- Mounting bolts
- Alternator

To install:

➡Be sure to use new fasteners, as required.

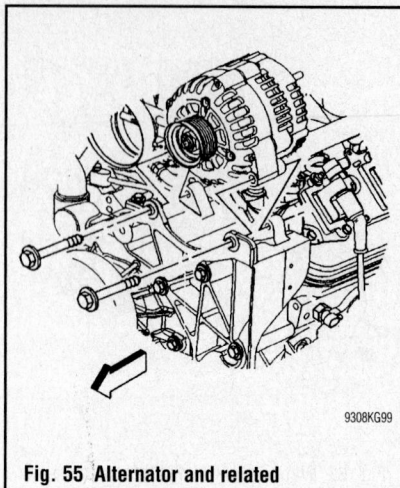

Fig. 55 Alternator and related components—4.8L, 5.3L, 6.0L engines

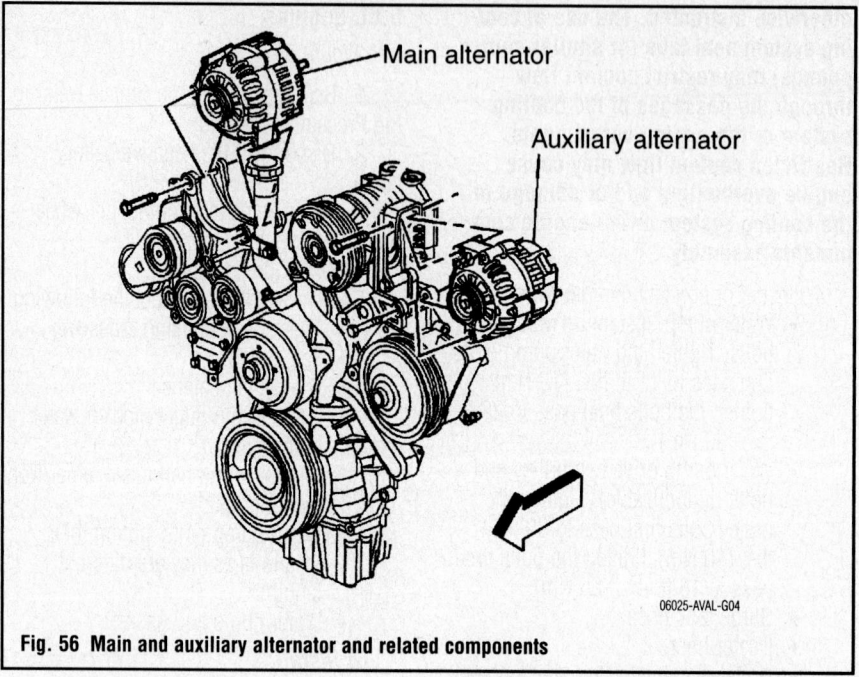

Fig. 56 Main and auxiliary alternator and related components

4. Install the alternator.
5. Install or connect the following:
   - Alternator mounting bolts. Tighten the bolts to 37 ft. lbs. (50 Nm).
   - Electrical connections to the alternator. Tighten the B+ nut to 80 inch. lbs. (9 Nm).
   - Engine sight shield, if removed
   - Accessory drive belt
6. Connect the negative battery cable.

6.6L Engines

See Figure 56.

➡**This procedure applies to both the main and auxiliary alternators.**

1. Before servicing the vehicle, refer to the Precautions Section.
2. Disconnect the negative battery cable.
3. Remove or disconnect the following:
   - Accessory drive belt
   - Engine sight shield, if necessary
   - Electrical connections from the alternator
   - Mounting bolts
   - Alternator

4. If necessary, remove the cable from the alternator as follows:
   a. Slide the boot down, to reveal the terminal stud.
   b. Unfasten the cable nut from the stud, then remove the alternator cable.

To install:

➡**Be sure to use new fasteners, as required.**

5. Connect the alternator cable, secure with the nut and tighten to 80 inch lbs. (9 Nm). Slide the boot back over the terminal stud.
6. Install the alternator.

➡**Use the correct fastener in the correct location. Replacement fasteners must be the correct part number for that application. Fasteners requiring replacement or fasteners requiring the use of thread locking compound or sealant are identified in the service procedure. Do not use paints, lubricants, or corrosion inhibitors on fasteners or fastener joint surfaces unless specified. These coatings affect fastener torque and joint clamping force and may damage the fastener. Use the correct tightening sequence and specifications when installing fasteners in order to avoid damage to parts and systems.**

7. Install or connect the following:
   - Alternator mounting bolts and tighten to 37 ft. lbs. (50 Nm)
   - Electrical connections to the alternator. Tighten the B+ nut to 13 ft. lbs. (18 Nm).
   - Engine sight shield, if removed
   - Accessory drive belt
8. Connect the negative battery cable.

ENGINE ELECTRICAL   **IGNITION SYSTEM**

FIRING ORDERS

See Figures 57 and 58.

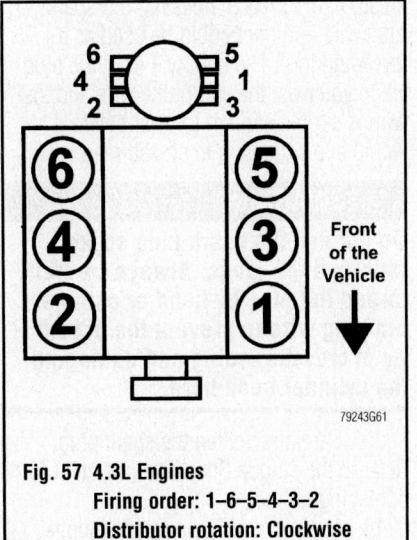

79243G61

Fig. 57 4.3L Engines
Firing order: 1–6–5–4–3–2
Distributor rotation: Clockwise

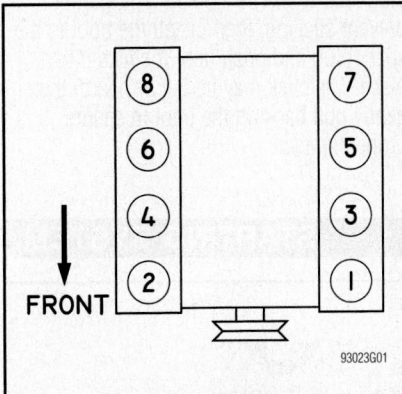

93023G01

Fig. 58 4.8L, 5.3L and 6.0L Engines
Firing order: 1–8–7–2–6–5–4–3
Distributorless ignition system
(one coil for each cylinder)

IGNITION COIL

REMOVAL & INSTALLATION

4.3L Engines
See Figure 59.

1. Before servicing the vehicle, refer to the Precautions Section.
2. Disconnect the negative battery cable.
3. Remove the engine cover.
4. Properly relieve the fuel system pressure.
5. Disconnect the fuel feed pipe quick fitting from the engine fuel feed pipe.

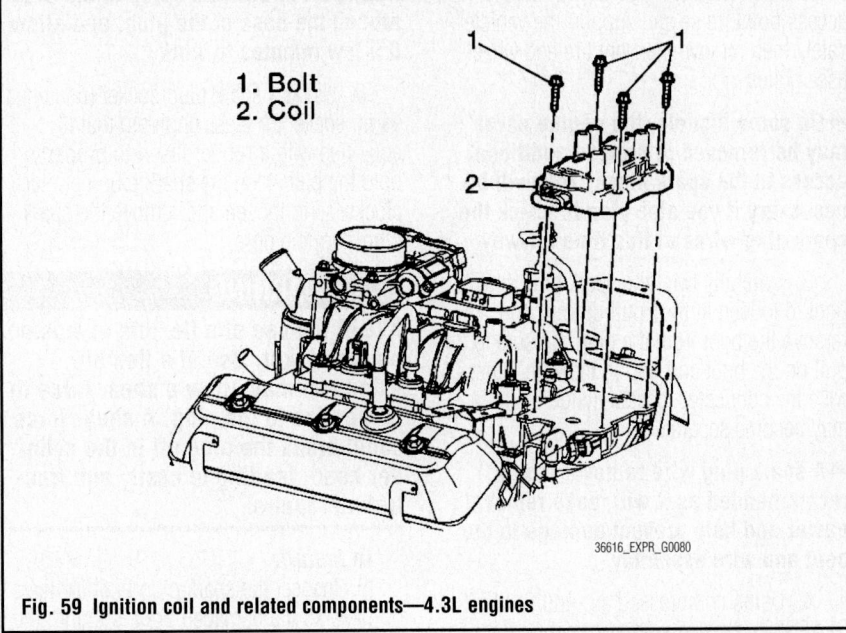

1. Bolt
2. Coil

36616_EXPR_G0080

Fig. 59 Ignition coil and related components—4.3L engines

6. Note the routing of the spark plug wires prior to disconnecting the wires from the ignition coil. Disconnect the wires.
7. Remove the spark plug wire retainer from the ignition coil bracket. Reposition the wires out of the way.
8. Disconnect the engine wiring harness electrical connector from the ignition coil.
9. Remove the ignition coil retaining bolts and ignition from the bracket.

To install:

➡**Be sure to use new fasteners, as required.**

10. Position the component on its mounting.
11. Tighten the retaining bolts to 30 ft. lbs. (40 Nm).
12. Continue the installation in the reverse order of the removal procedure.
13. Connect the negative battery cable.
14. Start the engine and check for fuel leaks. Correct as required.

IGNITION TIMING

ADJUSTMENT

The ignition timing is controlled by the Powertrain Control Module (PCM). No adjustment is necessary or possible.

SPARK PLUGS

REMOVAL & INSTALLATION

➡**All models were originally equipped with platinum–tip spark plugs which** can be used for as–long–as 100,000 miles (161,000 km). This holds true unless internal engine wear or damage and/or improperly operating emissions controls cause plug fouling. If you suspect this, you may wish to remove and inspect the platinum plugs before the recommended mileage. Most platinum plugs should not be cleaned or re–gapped. If you find their condition unsuitable, they should be replaced.

When removing the spark plugs, work on 1 at a time. Don't start by removing the plug wires all at once because unless you number them, they're going to get mixed up. On some models though, it will be more convenient for you to remove all of the wires before you start to work on the plugs. If this is necessary, take a minute before you begin and number the wires with tape before you take them off. The time you spend here will pay off later.

1. Disconnect the negative battery cable, and if the vehicle has been run recently, allow the engine to thoroughly cool. Attempting to remove plugs from a hot cylinder head could cause the plugs to seize and damage the threads in the cylinder head.
2. Check for access to the plugs on your vehicle. The wheel wells of some vehicles covered by this manual are designed to allow access to the sides of the engine. A rubber cover may be draped over the opening, and it may require removal of 1 or more plastic body snap–fasteners (which are

carefully pried loose using a special C–shaped tool) before you can move it aside for clearance. If this is your best access point, raise and support the vehicle safely then remove the front tire and wheel assemblies.

➡ On some models, the engine cover may be removed to provide additional access to the spark plugs. This will be necessary if you also plan to check the spark plug wires at this time anyway.

3. Carefully twist the spark plug wire boot to loosen it, then pull upward and remove the boot from the plug. Be sure to pull on the boot and not on the wire, otherwise the connector located inside the boot may become separated.

➡ A spark plug wire removal tool is recommended as it will make removal easier and help prevent damage to the boot and wire assembly.

4. Using compressed air (and SAFETY GLASSES), blow any water or debris from the spark plug well to assure that no harmful contaminants are allowed to enter the combustion chamber when the spark plug is removed. If compressed air is not available, use a rag or a brush to clean the area.

➡ Remove the spark plugs when the engine is cold, if possible, to prevent damage to the threads. If plug removal is difficult, apply a few drops of penetrating oil or silicone spray to the area around the base of the plug, and allow it a few minutes to work.

5. Using a spark plug socket (usually a ⅝ in. socket on these engines) that is equipped with a rubber insert to properly hold the plug, turn the spark plug counterclockwise to loosen and remove the spark plug from the bore.

❊❊ WARNING

AVOID the use of a flexible extension on the socket. Use of a flexible extension may allow a shear force to be applied to the plug. A shear force could break the plug off in the cylinder head, leading to costly and frustrating repairs.

To install:

6. Inspect the spark plug boot for tears or damage. If a damaged boot is found, the spark plug wire must be replaced. As mentioned earlier, this is an excellent time to check each of the spark plug wires for proper resistance and/or for damage.

7. Using a wire feeler gauge, check and adjust the spark plug gap. When using a gauge, the proper size should pass between the electrodes with a slight drag. The next larger size should not be able to pass while the next smaller size should pass freely.

8. Carefully thread the plug into the bore by hand. If resistance is felt before the plug is almost completely threaded, back the plug out and begin threading again. In small, hard to reach areas, an old spark plug wire and boot could be used as a threading tool. The boot will hold the plug while you twist the end of the wire and the wire is supple enough to twist before it would allow the plug to crossthread.

❊❊ WARNING

Do not use the spark plug socket to thread the plugs. Always carefully thread the plug by hand or using an old plug wire to prevent the possibility of crossthreading and damaging the cylinder head bore.

9. Carefully tighten the spark plug. Refer to the Torque Specifications chart for tightening torque.

10. Apply a small amount of silicone dielectric compound to the end of the spark plug lead or inside the spark plug boot to prevent sticking, then install the boot to the spark plug and push until it clicks into place. The click may be felt or heard, then gently pull back on the boot to assure proper contact.

ENGINE ELECTRICAL   STARTING SYSTEM

STARTER

REMOVAL & INSTALLATION

4.3L Engines

See Figure 60.

1. Before servicing the vehicle, refer to the Precautions Section.
2. Remove or disconnect the following:
   - Negative battery cable
   - Bracket and shield
   - Wires
   - Mounting bolts and shims
   - Starter

To install:

3. Install or connect the following:
   - Starter
   - Mounting bolts and shim. Torque the bolts to 37 ft lbs. (50 Nm).
   - Wires. Torque battery wire nut to 80 inch lbs. (9 Nm) and ignition nut to 18 inch lbs. (2 Nm).
   - Bracket and shield. Torque the nuts to 53 inch lbs. (6 Nm).
   - Negative battery cable

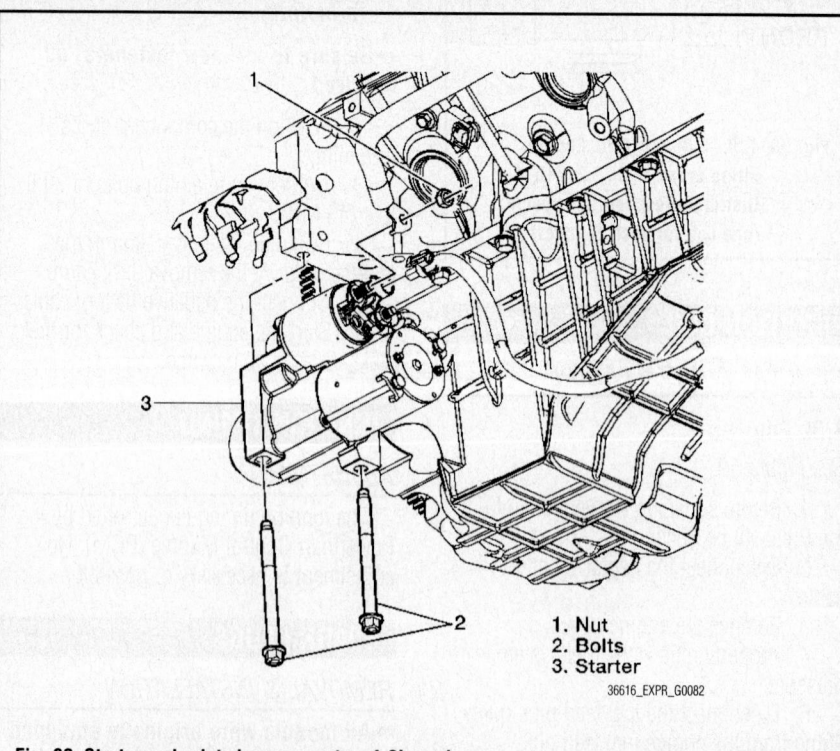

1. Nut
2. Bolts
3. Starter

36616_EXPR_G0082

Fig. 60 Starter and related components—4.3L engines

4.8L, 5.3L & 6.0L Engines

See Figure 61.

1. Before servicing the vehicle, refer to the Precautions Section.
2. Disconnect the negative battery cable.
3. Raise and support the vehicle.
4. Remove or disconnect the following:
   - Protective shields (as necessary)
   - Starter solenoid shield
   - Starter-to-transmission close out cover bolt
   - Engine oil level sensor connection
5. Slide the starter forward until the starter clears the transmission.
   - Starter transmission close out cover
   - Positive battery cable and wiring harness from the starter
   - Starter

➥**If additional clearance is necessary, remove the right front wheel and tire, then remove the starter from the wheel well.**

To install:

6. Install or connect the following:
   - Starter
   - Positive battery cable.
   - Starter transmission close out cover
   - Mounting bolts to the engine block and tighten to 37 ft. lbs. (50 Nm)

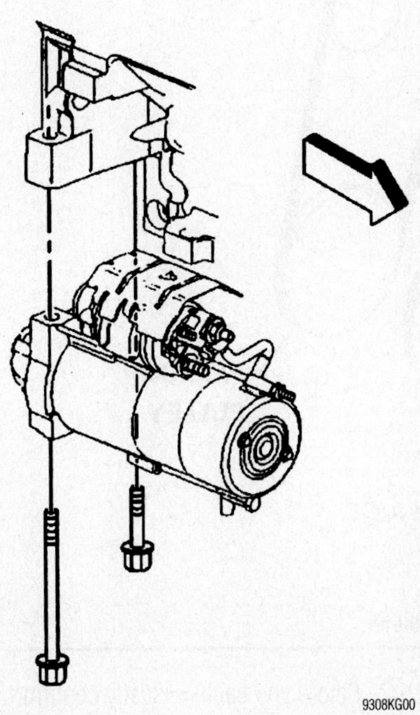

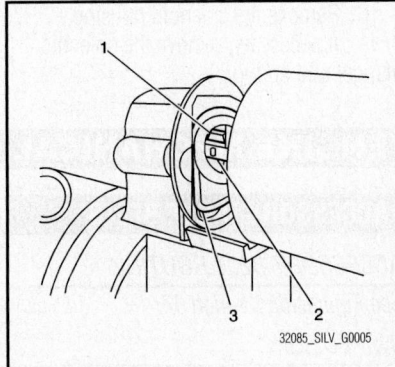

Fig. 61 Starter and related components—4.8L, 5.3L and 6.0L engines

9308KG00

   - Oil level sensor connection
   - Starter-to-transmission close out cover bolt
   - Starter solenoid shield
   - Protective shields (as necessary)
7. Remove the safety stands.
8. Lower the vehicle.
9. Connect the negative battery cable.

6.6L Engines

See Figure 62.

1. Before servicing the vehicle, refer to the Precautions Section.
2. Disconnect the negative battery cables.
3. Raise and support the vehicle safely.
4. Remove the engine wiring harness nut.
5. Remove the engine wiring harness lead from the starter.
6. Remove the positive battery cable nut. Remove the positive battery cable lead from the starter.
7. Remove the starter retaining bolts.
8. Remove the starter from its mounting.

To install:

➥**Be sure to use new fasteners, as required.**

9. Position the starter on its mounting.
10. Install the retaining bolts.
11. Tighten the bolts to 58 ft. lbs. (78 Nm).
12. Continue the installation in the reverse order of the removal procedure.

SOLENOID REPLACEMENT

See Figures 63 and 64.

1. Before servicing the vehicle, refer to the Precautions Section.
2. Remove the starter motor.
3. Reposition the M–terminal stud weather cover.
4. Clean the epoxy coating from the M–terminal stud.
5. Loosen the M–terminal stud nut.
6. Remove the cable from the M–terminal stud.
7. Remove the solenoid bolts.
8. Separate the solenoid from the housing and unhook the solenoid plunger from the drive gear lever.
9. Note that the spring (3) is positioned against the drive gear lever (1) and the drive

32085_SILV_G0005

Fig. 63 Spring (3) is positioned against the drive gear lever (1) and the drive gear lever is placed inside the solenoid plunger loop (2)

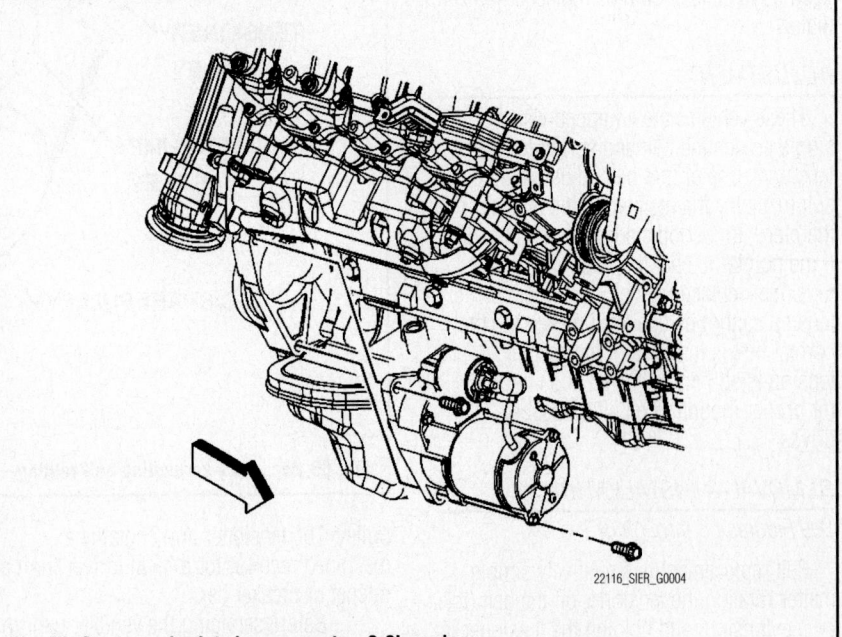

Fig. 62 Starter and related components—6.6L engines

22116_SIER_G0004

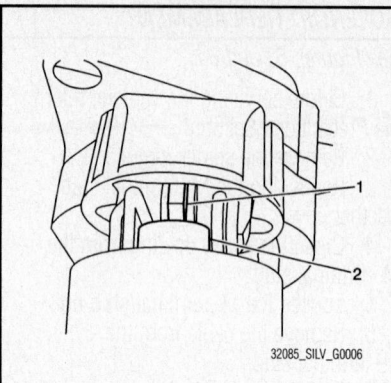

Fig. 64 Make sure that the drive gear lever (1) is properly installed into the solenoid plunger (2) loop

gear lever is placed inside the solenoid plunger loop (2).

10. Remove the solenoid housing.

11. If necessary, remove the solenoid plunger and spring.

To install:

12. If necessary, install the solenoid plunger and spring.

13. Using Three Bond silicone 1207B, GM P/N 97720043, seal the starter solenoid attachment area.

✳✳ WARNING

Make sure that the drive gear lever (1) is properly installed into the solenoid plunger (2) loop. Improper installation of the drive gear lever will cause an abnormal or no operation condition of the starter.

14. Install the solenoid, making sure to insert the drive gear lever (1) into the solenoid plunger (2) loop, perform the following:

   a. Pull the gear lever (1) out away from the starter housing and pull the plunger (2) out away from the solenoid.

   b. Tip the solenoid and insert the lever into the loop, push the solenoid against the housing.

15. Install the solenoid bolts and tighten the bolts to 89 inch lbs. (10 Nm).

16. Wipe the excess silicone pressed out during the solenoid installation from around the base of the solenoid to make a weather proof seal.

17. Install the cable to the M–terminal stud between the washers and terminal nut.

18. Tighten the M–terminal stud nut and tighten the nut to 71 inch lbs. (8 Nm).

19. Using Three Bond silicone 1207B, GM P/N 97720043, seal the M–terminal stud connection.

20. Reposition the M–terminal stud weather cover.

21. Bench test the starter in a free–run condition prior to installation.

22. Install the starter motor.

ENGINE MECHANICAL

ACCESSORY DRIVE BELTS

ACCESSORY BELT ROUTING

See Figures 65 through 67.

INSPECTION

Inspect the drive belt for signs of glazing or cracking. A glazed belt will be perfectly smooth from slippage, while a good belt will have a slight texture of fabric visible. Cracks will usually start at the inner edge of the belt and run outward. All worn or damaged drive belts should be replaced immediately.

ADJUSTMENT

These vehicles are equipped with a single serpentine belt and spring loaded tensioner. The proper belt adjustment is automatically maintained by the tensioner, therefore, no periodic adjustment is needed. If the pointer is past the scale on the tensioner replace the belt. If correct belt tension cannot be achieved make sure the correct belt is installed. If the correct tension is still not achieved and check for proper mounting off all accessory drives.

REMOVAL & INSTALLATION

See Figures 65 through 67.

Belt replacement is a relatively simple matter rotating the tensioner off the belt (to relieve tension) and holding the tensioner in this position as the belt is slipped from its

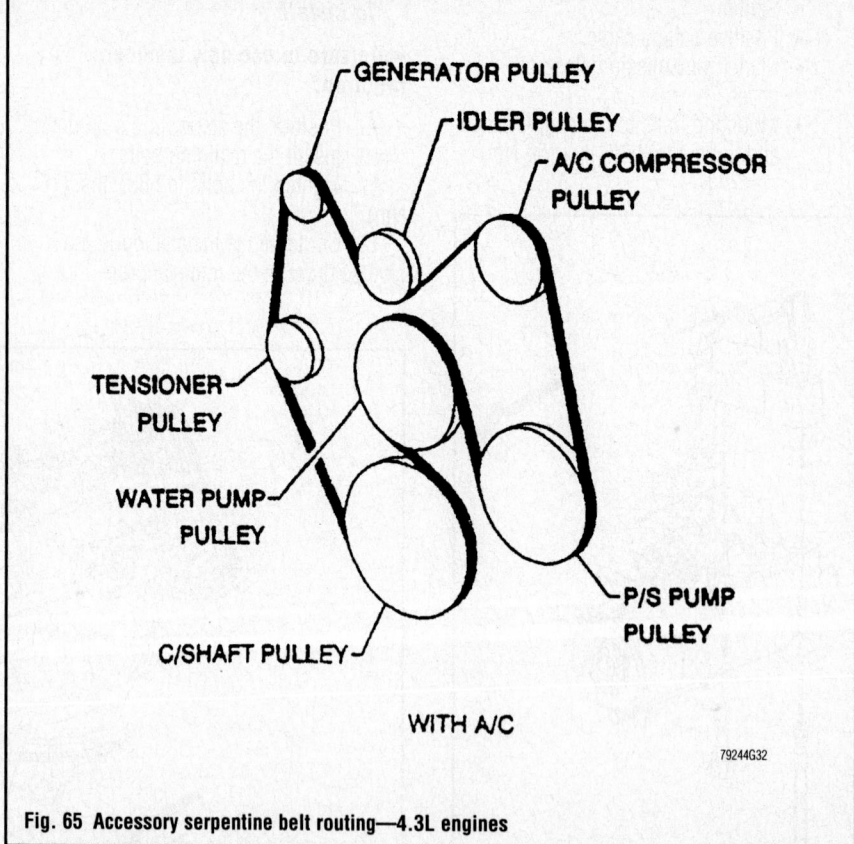

Fig. 65 Accessory serpentine belt routing—4.3L engines

pulley. The tensioner arm contains a machined receiver for a ⅜ in. driver from a ratchet or breaker bar.

1. Before servicing the vehicle, refer to the Precautions Section.

2. Before you begin, visually confirm the belt routing to the engine compartment label (if present) or to the appropriate diagram (if the label is not present). If you cannot make a match (perhaps it is not the

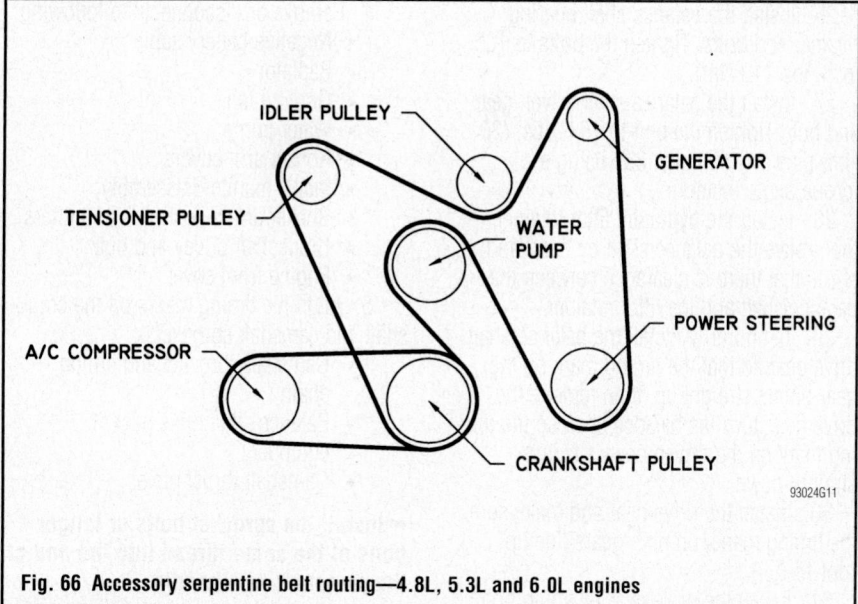

Fig. 66 Accessory serpentine belt routing—4.8L, 5.3L and 6.0L engines

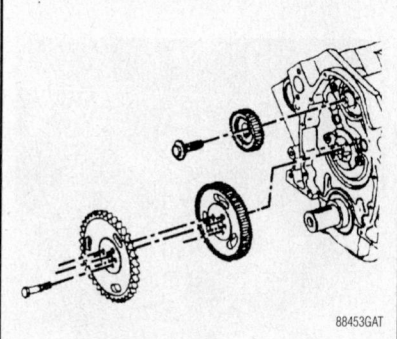

Fig. 68 View of the balance shaft drive and driven gears—4.3L engines

Fig. 69 View of the balance shaft location—4.3L engines

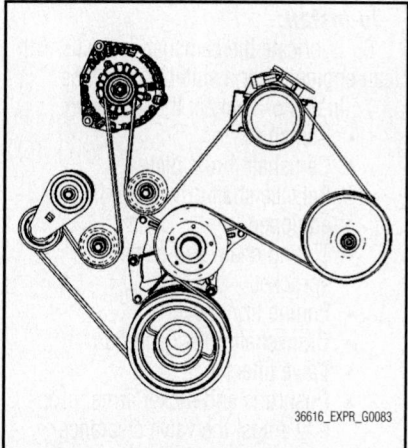

Fig. 67 Accessory serpentine belt routing—6.6L engines

7. Slip the belt from the remaining pulleys (this can get difficult is there is little room between the radiator/fan assembly and the accessory pulleys. Work slowly and be patient.

8. Once the belt is free, remove it from the engine compartment.

To install:

9. Route the belt over all the pulleys except the water pump and/or the tensioner. Refer to the routing illustration that you identified as a match before beginning.

10. Rotate the tensioner pulley to the left (counterclockwise) and hold it while you finish slipping the belt into position. Slowly allow the tensioner into contact with the belt.

11. Check to see if the correct V–groove tracking is around each pulley.

✳✳ WARNING

Improper V–groove tracking will cause the belt to fail in a short period of time.

12. Connect the negative battery cable.

BALANCE SHAFT

REMOVAL & INSTALLATION

4.3L Engines

See Figures 68 through 71.

1. Before servicing the vehicle, refer to the Precautions Section.

2. Discharge and recover the air conditioning system using a proper refrigerant recovery/recycling station.

3. Properly relieve the fuel system pressure.

Fig. 70 Unfasten the balance shaft gear bolt . . .

4. Disconnect the negative battery cable.

5. Remove the air cleaner intake duct.

6. Drain the engine cooling system.

7. Remove the A/C compressor and its brackets.

8. Remove the radiator and air conditioning condenser from the vehicle.

9. Remove the fan assembly.

original motor for this vehicle), scribble your own diagram before proceeding.

➡ **On the 4.3L engine, remove the air cleaner outlet resonator. On 4.8L, 5.3L and 6.0L engines remove the air cleaner assembly. On 6.6L engines, remove the coolant fan upper shroud.**

3. Disconnect the negative battery cable.

4. Install the appropriate sized breaker bar, wrench, or socket to the tensioner arm or pulley, as applicable.

5. Rotate the tensioner to the left (counterclockwise) and slip the belt from the tensioner pulley.

6. Once the belt is free from the tensioner, CAREFULLY rotate the tensioner back into position. DO NOT allow the tensioner to suddenly snap into place or damage could occur to the assembly.

88453P58

Fig. 71 . . . then remove the gear—
4.3L engines

10. Carefully release the belt tension, then remove the serpentine drive belt.

11. Remove the water pump.

12. Remove the crankshaft pulley and damper.

13. Drain the oil and remove the oil pan.

14. Remove the front cover.

15. Remove the timing chain and sprockets.

16. Unfasten the balance shaft gear bolt, then remove the gear.

17. Remove the balance shaft retainer.

18. Remove the intake manifold assembly.

19. Remove the hydraulic lifter retainer.

20. Remove the balance shaft and front bearing by gently driving them out using a soft faced mallet.

21. Using tool J-38834 or its equivalent, remove the balance shaft rear bearing.

➡The balance shaft and drive and driven gears are serviced only as a set, including the gear bolt. The balance shaft and front bearing are serviced as a package.

✳✳ WARNING

The front bearing must not be removed from the balance shaft

To install:

22. Inspect the balance shaft gears for damage, such as nicks and burrs.

23. Using a suitable gasket scraper, clean the gasket mounting surfaces. Using solvent, clean the oil and grease from the gasket mounting surfaces.

24. Lubricate the balance shaft rear bearing with clean engine oil, then install the bearing using tool J-38834 or its equivalent.

25. Lubricate the balance shaft with clean engine oil, then install the balance shaft into the block.

26. Install the balance shaft bearing retainer and bolts. Tighten the bolts to 106 inch. lbs. (12 Nm).

27. Install the balance shaft driven gear and bolt. Tighten the bolt to 15 ft. lbs. (20 Nm) plus an additional 35° using a torque/angle meter.

28. Install the hydraulic lifter retainer, then rotate the balance shaft by hand and check that there is clearance between the balance shaft and the lifter retainer.

29. Temporarily install the balance shaft drive gear so that the timing mark on the gear points straight up, then remove the drive gear, turn the balance shaft so the timing mark on the driven gear is facing straight down.

30. Install the drive gear and make sure the timing marks on both gears line up (dot-to-dot).

31. Install the drive gear retaining bolt and tighten to 12 ft. lbs. (16 Nm).

32. Install the intake manifold assembly.

33. Install the timing chain and sprocket assemblies.

34. Install the front cover, seal, bolts and the oil pan assembly.

35. Using tool J-39046 or its equivalent engage the crankshaft pulley and damper.

36. Install the water pump.

37. Install the serpentine drive belt.

38. Install the fan assembly.

39. Install the air conditioning condenser and the radiator assemblies. Engage all hoses removed from the radiator.

40. Install the A/C compressor.

41. Engage the oil and transmission cooler lines at the radiator, then install the radiator shroud.

42. Install the air cleaner assembly and connect the negative battery cable.

43. Fill the crankcase with the correct grade and amount of oil.

44. Fill the cooling system with coolant.

45. Start the vehicle and check for leaks.

46. Charge the air conditioning system using a proper refrigerant recovery/recycling station.

CAMSHAFT AND VALVE LIFTERS

REMOVAL & INSTALLATION

4.3L Engines

1. Before servicing the vehicle, refer to the Precautions Section.

2. Properly relieve the fuel system pressure.

3. Drain the engine cooling system.

4. Remove or disconnect the following:
- Negative battery cable
- Radiator
- Cooling fan
- Water pump
- Rocker arm covers
- Intake manifold assembly
- Rocker arms, pushrods and lifters
- Crankshaft pulley and hub
- Engine front cover

5. Align the timing marks on the crankshaft and camshaft sprockets.
- Camshaft sprocket and timing chain
- Balance shaft drive gear, if equipped
- Camshaft thrust plate

➡**Install the sprocket bolts or longer bolts of the same thread into the end of the camshaft as a handle.**

- Camshaft

To install:

6. Lubricate the camshaft journals with clean engine oil or a suitable pre-lube.

7. Install or connect the following:
- Camshaft
- Camshaft thrust plate
- Balance shaft drive gear, if equipped
- Timing chain and camshaft sprocket
- Engine front cover
- Crankshaft pulley and hub
- Valve lifters
- Pushrods and rocker arms, properly adjust the valve clearance
- Intake manifold assembly
- Rocker arm covers to the engine
- Radiator to the vehicle
- Negative battery cable

8. Refill the engine cooling system.

4.8L, 5.3L & 6.0L Engines

See Figures 72 through 74.

1. Before servicing the vehicle, refer to the Precautions Section.

2. Disconnect the negative battery cable.

3. Properly relieve the fuel system pressure.

4. Properly discharge the air conditioning system.

5. Remove the front grille.

6. Remove the radiator support.

7. Remove the engine front cover.

8. Remove the valve lifters.

9. Remove the camshaft sensor bolt and sensor.

10. Rotate the crankshaft until the timing marks are aligned. Remove the camshaft sprocket bolt.

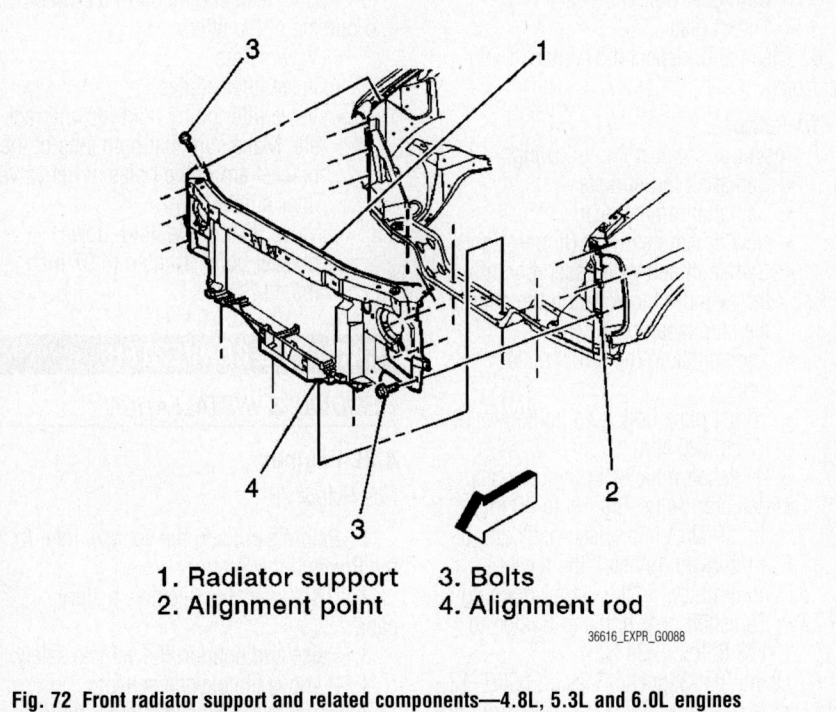

1. Radiator support   3. Bolts
2. Alignment point   4. Alignment rod

36616_EXPR_G0088

Fig. 72 Front radiator support and related components—4.8L, 5.3L and 6.0L engines

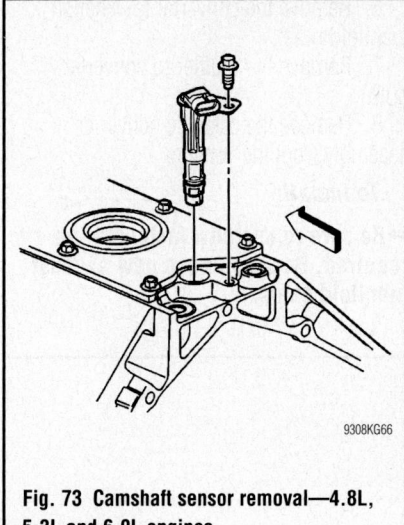

9308KG66

Fig. 73 Camshaft sensor removal—4.8L, 5.3L and 6.0L engines

11. Remove the bolts and the timing chain tensioner. Remove the camshaft sprocket and reposition the timing chain.

12. Remove the camshaft retainer bolts and retainer.

13. Install a bolt into the camshaft. Using the bolt as a handle carefully remove the camshaft from the engine.

To install:

➡**Be sure to use new fasteners, as required.**

➡**If camshaft replacement is required, the valve lifters must also be replaced.**

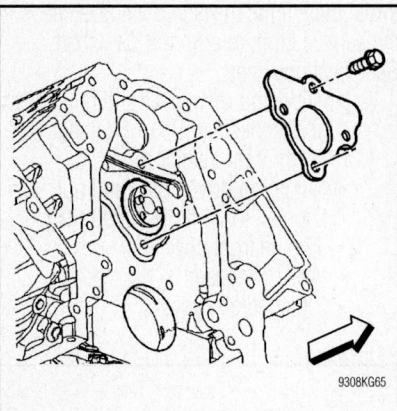

9308KG65

Fig. 74 Camshaft retainer removal—4.8L, 5.3L and 6.0L engines

14. Clean and inspect all sealing surfaces.

15. Lubricate the camshaft journals and the bearings with clean engine oil.

➡**All camshaft journals are the same diameter, so care must be used in removing or installing the camshaft to avoid damage to the camshaft bearings.**

16. Using a bolt as a handle, carefully install the camshaft into the engine block. Remove the bolt from the front of the camshaft.

17. Install the retainer plate. Tighten the retainer bolts to 18 ft lbs. (25 Nm) for first design hex head bolts and 11 ft. lbs. (15 Nm) for second design Torx head bolts.

18. Continue the installation in the reverse order of the removal procedure.

19. Start the engine and check for leaks.

20. Correct as required.

6.6L Engines

See Figures 75 through 77.

➡**This procedure requires the use of the following special tools: Flywheel Holding Tool No. J 44643, Magnetic Base J 26900–13 and Dial Indicator J 26900–12.**

1. Before servicing the vehicle, refer to the Precautions Section.

2. Properly discharge the A/C system.

3. Remove or disconnect the following:
   - Both cylinder heads
   - Valve lifter guide hold–down bracket bolts

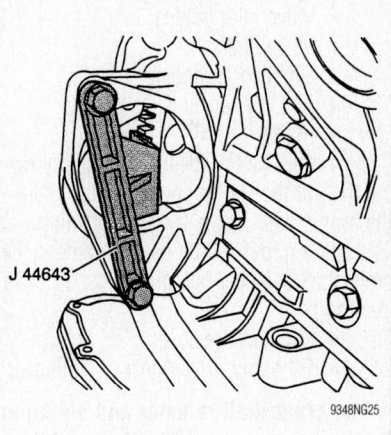

J 44643

9348NG25

Fig. 75 Proper installation of the flywheel holding tool in the starter opening—6.6L engines

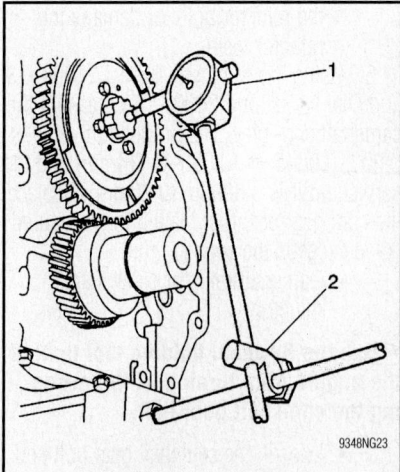

9348NG23

Fig. 76 Use the dial indicator (1) and magnetic base (2) to measure the camshaft end–play—6.6L engines

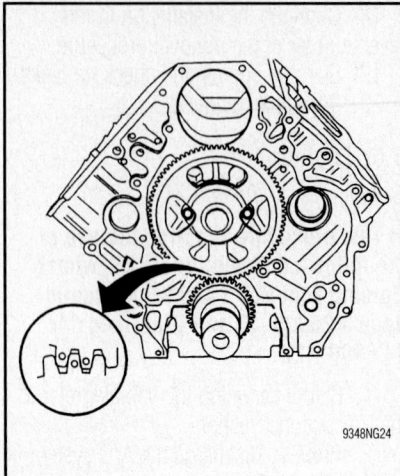

Fig. 77 Camshaft and crankshaft gear alignment—6.6L engines

- Valve lifter guide hold–down brackets
- Valve lifter guides
- Valve lifters
- Charged air cooler
- A/C condenser
- Starter

4. Install the Flywheel Holding Tool No. J 44643 in the starter opening. Make sure the tool is flush to the flywheel opening. The holding tool will be used to remove the crankshaft balancer bolt and camshaft drive gear bolt.

- Engine front cover
- Oil pump driven gear nut and gear

➡The crankshaft reluctor and oil pump drive gear are timed together at the factory. Do NOT remove the reluctor from the oil pump drive gear.

- Oil pump drive gear and crankshaft reluctor assembly. Do not remove the reluctor bolts or damage the reluctor teeth

5. Using the Magnetic Base J 26900–13 and Dial Indicator J 26900–12, measure the camshaft end–play. The production value is 0.002–0.0045 in. (0.050–0.114mm) and the service limit is 0.008 in. (0.20mm). Replace the cam gear or thrust plate if the measured value exceeds the service limit.

- Camshaft reluctor screws and reluctor

➡Use the flywheel holding tool to hold the engine from turning while loosening the camshaft gear bolt.

- Loosen the camshaft gear bolt and leave the bolt finger–tight
- Camshaft thrust plate bolts through the holes in the camshaft gear
- Camshaft with the gear attached

- Cam gear bolt and gear
- Thrust plate

6. Clean and inspect the camshaft and bearings.

To install:

7. Install or connect the following:
- Camshaft thrust plate
- Camshaft driven gear
- New driven gear bolt (finger–tight)
- Camshaft and gear assembly into the cylinder block. Align the gear to the crankshaft gear
- Threadlock to the thrust plate bolts
- Thrust plate bolts and tighten to 19 ft. lbs. (26 Nm)
- Camshaft reluctor to the cam gear
- Reluctor bolts. Tighten to 80 inch lbs. (9 Nm) in a crisscross pattern.
- If removed, reinstall the flywheel holding tool in the starter opening
- Camshaft gear bolt and tighten to 173 ft. lbs. (234 Nm)

8. Using the Magnetic Base J 26900–13 and Dial Indicator J 26900–12, measure the camshaft end–play. Replace the cam gear or thrust plate if the measured value exceeds the service limit; refer to the Camshaft Specifications chart.

- Oil pump drive gear and reluctor to the crankshaft. Do not damage the teeth of the reluctor.
- Oil pump driven gear and nut. Tighten to 74 ft. lbs. (100 Nm).
- Engine front cover
- A/C condenser
- Charged air cooler

9. Apply clean engine oil to the roller and outside of the lifters.
- Valve lifters
- Valve lifter guides
- Valve lifter guide hold–down brackets. Make sure that both tabs of the bracket are in the holes of the valve lifter guides.
- Valve lifter guide hold–down bracket bolts. Tighten to 97 inch lbs. (11 Nm).

CATALYTIC CONVERTER

REMOVAL & INSTALLATION

4.3L Engines

See Figure 78.

1. Before servicing the vehicle, refer to the Precautions Section.
2. Disconnect the negative battery cable.
3. Raise and support the vehicle safely.
4. Remove the oxygen sensors.
5. Remove the exhaust hanger bolts and hanger from the transmission.
6. Remove the converter to exhaust manifold nuts.
7. Remove the muffler to converter nuts.
8. Remove the catalytic converter assembly from the vehicle.

To install:

➡Be sure to use new fasteners, as required. Be sure to use new exhaust manifold seals.

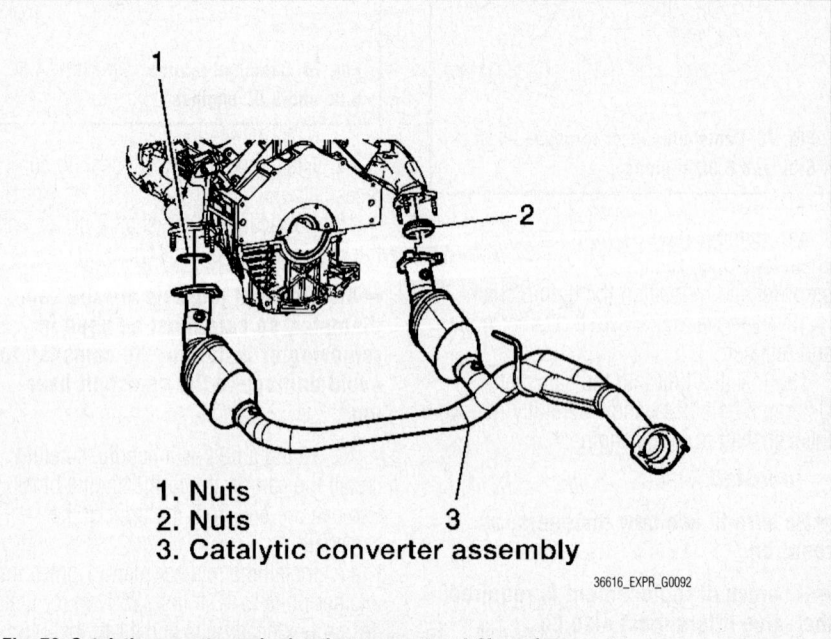

1. Nuts
2. Nuts
3. Catalytic converter assembly

Fig. 78 Catalytic converter and related components—4.3L engines

9. Position the converter assembly to its mounting.

10. Tighten the converter to exhaust manifold retaining nuts to 37 ft. lbs. (50 Nm).

11. Tighten the converter to muffler retaining nuts to 37 ft. lbs. (50 Nm).

12. Continue the installation in the reverse order of the removal procedure.

13. Start the engine and check for leaks.

14. Correct as required.

4.8L and 5.3L Engines

See Figure 79.

1. Before servicing the vehicle, refer to the Precautions Section.

2. Disconnect the negative battery cable.

3. Raise and support the vehicle safely.

4. Remove the oxygen sensors.

5. Remove the exhaust hanger bolts and hanger from the transmission.

6. Remove the converter to exhaust manifold nuts.

7. Remove the muffler to converter nuts.

8. Remove the catalytic converter assembly from the vehicle.

To install:

➡Be sure to use new fasteners, as required. Be sure to use new exhaust manifold seals.

9. Position the converter assembly to its mounting.

10. Tighten the converter to exhaust manifold retaining nuts to 37 ft. lbs. (50 Nm).

11. Tighten the converter to muffler retaining nuts to 37 ft. lbs. (50 Nm).

12. Continue the installation in the reverse order of the removal procedure.

13. Start the engine and check for leaks.

14. Correct as required.

6.0L Engines

See Figure 80.

1. Before servicing the vehicle, refer to the Precautions Section.

2. Disconnect the negative battery cable.

3. Raise and support the vehicle safely.

4. Disconnect the oxygen sensors.

5. Remove the exhaust hanger bolts and hanger.

6. Remove the converter to exhaust manifold nuts.

7. Remove the muffler to converter nuts.

8. Remove the catalytic converter from the vehicle.

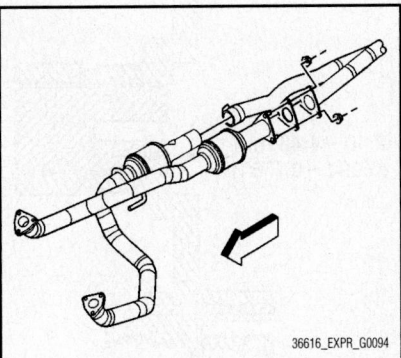

Fig. 80 Catalytic converter and related components—6.0L engines

To install:

➡Be sure to use new fasteners, as required. Be sure to use new exhaust manifold seals.

9. Position the converter assembly to its mounting.

10. Tighten the converter to exhaust manifold retaining nuts to 35 ft. lbs. (48 Nm).

11. Tighten the converter to muffler retaining nuts to 35 ft. lbs. (48 Nm).

12. Continue the installation in the reverse order of the removal procedure.

13. Start the engine and check for leaks.

14. Correct as required.

6.6L Engines

See Figure 81.

1. Before servicing the vehicle, refer to the Precautions Section.

2. Disconnect the negative battery cable.

3. Raise and support the vehicle safely.

4. Remove the converter to particulate filter nuts

5. Loosen the converter to exhaust pipe adaptor clamp.

6. Slide the exhaust pipe clamp up onto the exhaust pipe adapter.

7. Remove the converter hanger to transmission bolts.

8. With the converter hanger attached, remove the converter from the vehicle.

To install:

➡Be sure to use new fasteners, as required. Be sure to use new exhaust manifold seals. Be sure to use a new catalytic converter to particulate filter gasket.

9. Position the converter assembly to its mounting.

10. Tighten the converter to exhaust manifold retaining nuts to 30 ft. lbs. (40 Nm).

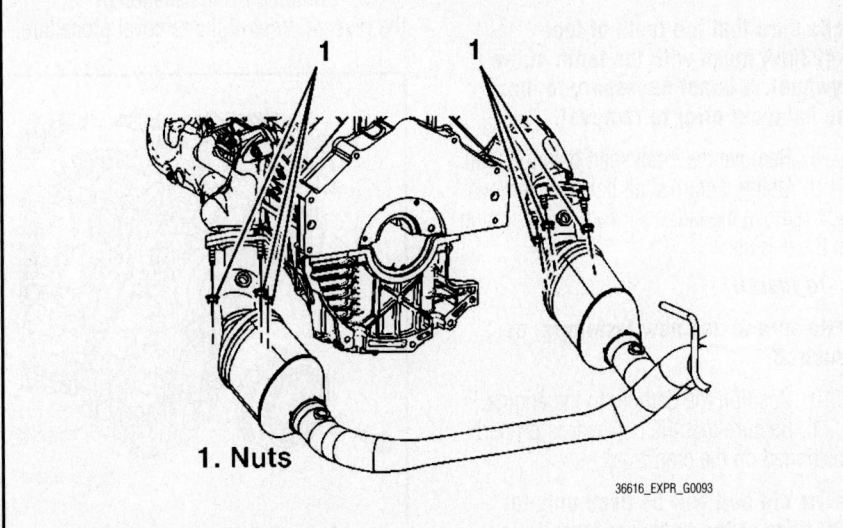

Fig. 79 Catalytic converter and related components—4.8L and 5.3L engines

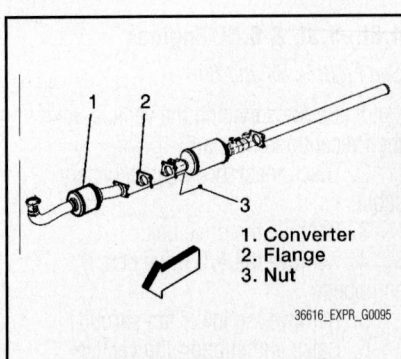

1. Converter
2. Flange
3. Nut

Fig. 81 Catalytic converter and related components—6.6L engines

11. Continue the installation in the reverse order of the removal procedure.
12. Start the engine and check for leaks.
13. Correct as required.

CRANKSHAFT DAMPER

REMOVAL & INSTALLATION

4.3L Engines

See Figure 82.

1. Before servicing the vehicle, refer to the Precautions Section.
2. Disconnect the negative battery cable.
3. Remove the drive belt.
4. Remove the cooling fan.
5. Remove the crankshaft balancer bolt and washer.
6. Remove the crankshaft pulley bolts and pulley.
7. Using a crankshaft balancer removal tool, remove the balancer from its mounting on the engine.

To install:

➡**Be sure to use new fasteners, as required.**

8. Position the damper to the engine.
9. Installation is the reverse of the removal procedure.

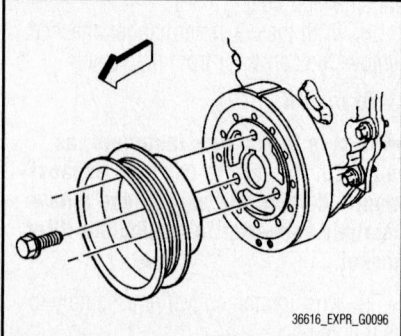

Fig. 82 Crankshaft damper and related components—4.3L engines

4.8L, 5.3L & 6.0L Engines

See Figures 83 and 84.

1. Before servicing the vehicle, refer to the Precautions Section.
2. Disconnect the negative battery cable.
3. Remove the drive belt.
4. Remove the A/C drive belt, if equipped.
5. Remove the lower fan shroud.
6. Raise and support the vehicle safely.
7. Remove the starter.

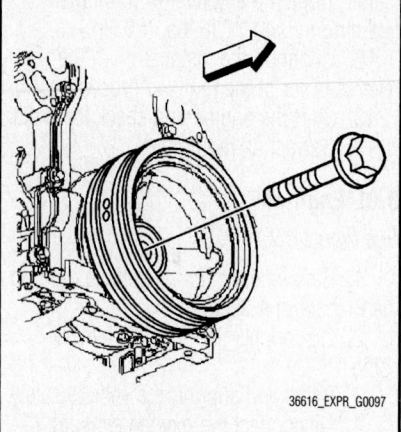

Fig. 83 Crankshaft damper and related components—4.8L, 5.3L and 6.0L engines

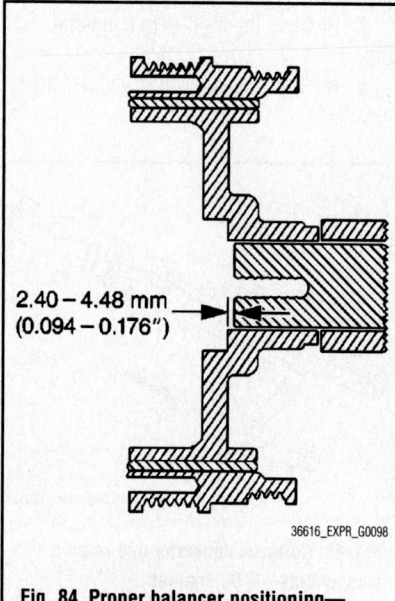

2.40 – 4.48 mm
(0.094 – 0.176")

Fig. 84 Proper balancer positioning— 4.8L, 5.3L and 6.0L engines

➡**Be sure that the teeth of tool J-42386A mesh with the teeth of the flywheel. It is not necessary to mark the balancer prior to removal.**

8. Remove the crankshaft balancer bolt.
9. Using a crankshaft balancer removal tool, remove the balancer from its mounting on the engine.

To install:

➡**Be sure to use new fasteners, as required.**

10. Position the damper to the engine.
11. Be sure that the balancer is properly positioned on the crankshaft.

➡**The old bolt will be used only for first pass of the balancer installation. Install a new bolt and tighten for the**

second, third and fourth pass of the procedure.

12. Tighten the old bolt to 240 ft. lbs. (330 NM). Remove and discard the old bolt.
13. Tighten the new bolt to 37 ft. lbs. (50 Nm). Retighten an additional 140 degrees.
14. Continue the installation in reverse order of the removal procedure.
15. Using the GM diagnostic scan tool, or equivalent, refer to the on-screen reprogramming directions and perform the crankshaft position system variation learn procedure.

6.6L Engines

See Figure 85.

1. Before servicing the vehicle, refer to the Precautions Section.
2. Disconnect the negative battery cable.
3. Remove the starter. Install tool J-44643 or equivalent to hold the flywheel in place.
4. Remove the radiator fan clutch assembly.
5. Remove the drive belt.
6. Remove the crankshaft damper bolt.
7. Remove the damper from its mounting on the engine.

To install:

➡**Be sure to use new fasteners, as required.**

8. Position the damper to the engine.
9. Tighten the bolt to 74 ft. lbs. (100 Nm). Retighten and additional 90 degrees.
10. Continue the installation in the reverse order of the removal procedure.

Fig. 85 Crankshaft damper and related components—6.6L engines

CRANKSHAFT FRONT SEAL

REMOVAL & INSTALLATION

4.3L Engines

1. Before servicing the vehicle, refer to the Precautions Section.
2. Disconnect the negative battery cable.
3. Remove the drive belt.
4. Remove the cooling fan.
5. Remove the crankshaft balancer bolt and washer.
6. Remove the crankshaft pulley bolts and pulley.
7. Using a crankshaft balancer removal tool, remove the balancer from its mounting on the engine.
8. Inspect the front cover seal bore area for damage.
9. Using a suitable puller, remove the seal.

To install:

➡**Be sure to use new fasteners, as required.**

10. Lubricate the exterior of the new seal with clean engine oil, prior to installation.
11. Using a seal installation tool and a hammer, install the new seal.
12. Be sure that the installed seal is flush and square to the front cover.
13. Continue the installation in the reverse order of the removal procedure.

4.8L, 5.3L & 6.0L Engines

1. Before servicing the vehicle, refer to the Precautions Section.
2. Disconnect the negative battery cable.
3. Remove the drive belt.
4. Remove the A/C drive belt, if equipped.
5. Remove the lower fan shroud.
6. Raise and support the vehicle safely.
7. Remove the starter.

➡**Be sure that the teeth of tool J-42386A mesh with the teeth of the flywheel. It is not necessary to mark the balancer prior to removal.**

8. Remove the crankshaft balancer bolt.
9. Using a crankshaft balancer removal tool, remove the balancer from its mounting on the engine.
10. Carefully remove the oil seal from the front cover.

To install:

➡**Be sure to use new fasteners, as required.**

➡**Do not lubricate the oil seal sealing surface. Do not reuse the old seal.**

11. Lubricate the outer edge of the new seal with clean engine oil, prior to installation.
12. Lubricate the front cover oil seal bore with clean engine oil.
13. Using a seal installation tool, install the new seal.
14. Be sure that the seal is installed evenly and completely into the front cover bore.
15. Continue the installation in the reverse order of the removal procedure.
16. Be sure that the balancer is properly positioned on the crankshaft.

➡**The old bolt will be used only for first pass of the balancer installation. Install a new bolt and tighten for the second, third and fourth pass of the procedure.**

17. Tighten the old bolt to 240 ft. lbs. (330 NM). Remove and discard the old bolt.
18. Tighten the new bolt to 37 ft. lbs. (50 Nm). Retighten an additional 140 degrees.
19. Using the GM diagnostic scan tool, or equivalent, refer to the on-screen reprogramming directions and perform the crankshaft position system variation learn procedure..

6.6L Engines

1. Before servicing the vehicle, refer to the Precautions Section.
2. Disconnect the negative battery cable.
3. Remove the starter. Install tool J-44643 or equivalent to hold the flywheel in place.
4. Remove the radiator fan clutch assembly.
5. Remove the drive belt.
6. Remove the crankshaft damper bolt.
7. Remove the damper from its mounting on the engine.
8. Install the seal removal tools on the front of the crankshaft. Carefully remove and discard the oil seal.

To install:

➡**Be sure to use new fasteners, as required.**

9. Lubricate the crankshaft seal bore and the crankshaft with clean engine oil, prior to installation.
10. Using a seal installation tool, install the new seal.
11. Continue the installation in the reverse order of the removal procedure.

CYLINDER HEAD

REMOVAL & INSTALLATION

4.3L Engines

Left Side

See Figures 86 and 87.

1. Before servicing the vehicle, refer to the Precautions Section.
2. Remove or disconnect the following:
   - Battery negative cable
   - Coolant
   - Accessory drive belt

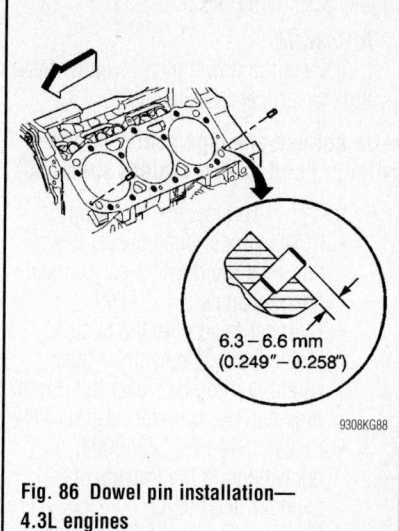

6.3 – 6.6 mm
(0.249"– 0.258")

9308KG88

Fig. 86 Dowel pin installation—4.3L engines

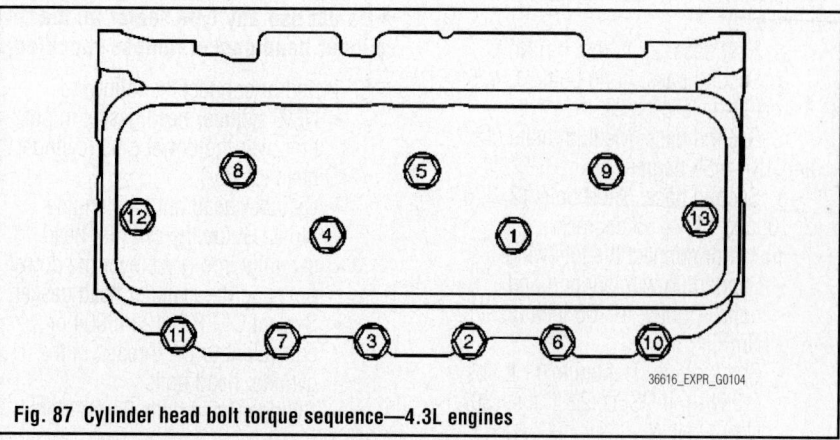

36616_EXPR_G0104

Fig. 87 Cylinder head bolt torque sequence—4.3L engines

- Cooling fan assembly
- Power steering pump mounting bracket
- Power steering pump mounting bracket stud from the cylinder head
- Lower intake manifold
- Exhaust manifold
- Spark plug wire harness and the spark plug wire support
- Valve pushrods
- Ground strap and ground wire bolt from the rear of the cylinder head
- Engine Coolant Temperature (ECT) sensor (if applicable)
- ECT gauge sensor (if applicable)
- Spark plugs
- Spark plug wire support
- Cylinder head bolts
- Cylinder head and the gasket

➡ **Clean all dirt, debris, and coolant from the engine block cylinder head bolt holes. Failure to remove all foreign material may result in damaged threads, improperly tightened fasteners or damage to components.**

3. Clean the cylinder head bolts and the engine block bolt holes.

To install:

4. Inspect the dowel pins (cylinder head locator) for proper installation.

➡ **Do not use any type sealer on the cylinder head gasket (unless specified).**

5. Install or connect the following:
- NEW cylinder head gasket in position over the dowel pins (cylinder head locator)
- Cylinder head onto the engine block. Guide the cylinder head carefully into place over the dowel pins and the cylinder head gasket.
- Sealant GM P/N 12346004, or equivalent, to the threads of the cylinder head bolts
- Cylinder head bolts finger–tight

6. Tighten the cylinder head bolts in sequence:
   a. First pass: 22 ft. lbs. (30 Nm).
   b. Second pass: Long bolts (1, 4, 5, 8, and 9)—+ 75 degrees.
   c. Second pass: Medium bolts (12 and 13)—+ 65 degrees.
   d. Second pass: Short bolts (2, 3, 6, 7, 10, and 11)—+ 55 degrees.
7. Install or connect the following:
- Spark plug wire support and bolts. Tighten to 106 inch lbs. (12 Nm).
- Spark plugs. Tighten to 11 ft. lbs. (15 Nm), if USED; 22 ft. lbs. (30 Nm), if NEW.

8. If reusing the ECT gauge sensor (if applicable), apply sealant GM P/N 12346004 or equivalent to the threads of the ECT gauge sensor. Install the ECT gauge sensor (if applicable). Tighten the sensor to 15 ft. lbs. (20 Nm).
9. Install or connect the following:
- Ground strap and the ground wire bolt. Tighten the bolt to 12 ft. lbs. (16 Nm).
- Valve pushrods
- Lower intake manifold
- Exhaust manifold
- Stud for the power steering pump mounting bracket to the cylinder head. Tighten the power steering pump mounting bracket stud to 15 ft. lbs. (20 Nm).
- Power steering pump mounting bracket
- Engine cooling fan assembly
- Coolant
- Battery negative cable

Right Side

See Figures 86 and 87.

1. Before servicing the vehicle, refer to the Precautions Section.
2. Remove or disconnect the following:
- Battery negative cable
- Coolant
- Engine cooling fan assembly
- Alternator mounting bracket
- Alternator mounting bracket stud from the cylinder head
- Lower intake manifold
- Exhaust manifold
- Spark plug wire harness and spark plug wire support
- Valve pushrods
- Cylinder head and the gasket
3. Clean the engine block and the cylinder head sealing surfaces.

To install:

4. Inspect the dowel pins (cylinder head locator) for proper installation.

➡ **Do not use any type sealer on the cylinder head gasket (unless specified).**

5. Install or connect the following:
- NEW cylinder head gasket in position over the dowel pins (cylinder head locator)
- Cylinder head onto the engine block. Guide the cylinder head carefully into place over the dowel pins and the cylinder head gasket.
- Sealant GM P/N 12346004 or equivalent to the threads of the cylinder head bolts
- Cylinder head bolts finger–tight

6. Tighten the cylinder head bolts in sequence:
   a. First pass: 22 ft. lbs. (30 Nm).
   b. Second pass: Long bolts (1, 4, 5, 8, and 9)—+ 75 degrees.
   c. Second pass: Medium bolts (12 and 13)—+ 65 degrees.
   d. Second pass: Short bolts (2, 3, 6, 7, 10, and 11)—+ 55 degrees.
7. Install or connect the following:
- Spark plug wire support and bolts. Tighten only the rear support bolt to 106 inch lbs. (12 Nm).

➡ **The front spark plug wire support bolt is used to fasten the oil level indicator tube, and will be installed within the oil level indicator tube installation procedure.**

- Front spark plug wire support bolt
- Spark plugs. Tighten to 11 ft. lbs. (15 Nm), if USED; 22 ft. lbs. (30 Nm), if NEW.
- Valve pushrods
- Lower intake manifold
- Spark plug wire harness and wire support. Tighten to 106 inch lbs. (12 Nm).
- Exhaust manifold
- Stud for the alternator mounting bracket. Tighten the alternator mounting bracket stud to 15 ft. lbs. (20 Nm).
- Alternator mounting bracket
- Engine cooling fan assembly
- Coolant
- Battery negative cable

4.8L, 5.3L & 6.0L Engines

Right Side

See Figures 88 through 91.

✳ CAUTION

Before servicing any electrical component, the ignition key must be in the OFF or LOCK position and all electrical loads must be OFF, unless instructed otherwise in these procedures.

1. Before servicing the vehicle, refer to the Precautions Section.
2. Remove or disconnect the following:
- Negative battery cable
- Coolant air bleed pipe
- Intake manifold
- Push rods
- Exhaust manifold(s)
- Alternator
- Alternator mounting bracket-to-cylinder head bolts
- Bolt behind the power steering pump

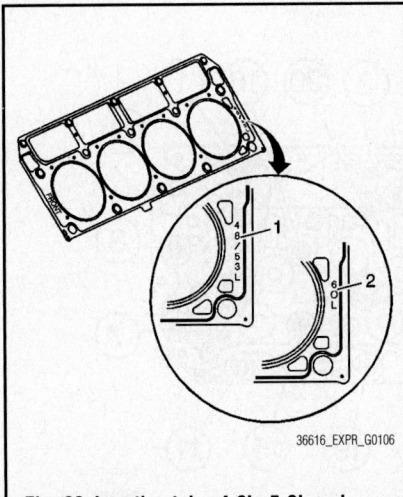

Fig. 88 Locating tab—4.8L, 5.3L and 6.0L engines

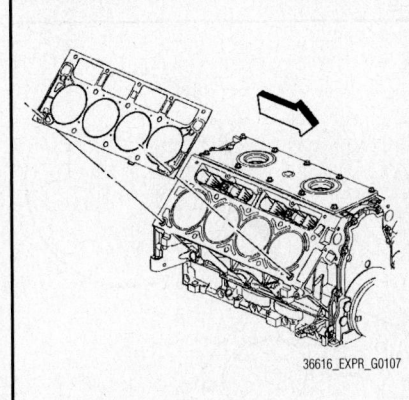

Fig. 89 Displacement markings—4.8L, 5.3L and 6.0L engines

- Alternator mounting bracket and set it aside
- Bolt holding the oil level indicator tube to the right side cylinder head
- Oil level indicator tube
- Cylinder head(s) from the engine
- Spark plugs

➡**The M11 cylinder head bolts are NOT reusable. Install NEW M11 cylinder head bolts during reassembly.**

- Cylinder head bolts

➡**After removal, place the cylinder head on two wood blocks to prevent damage.**

3. Remove the gasket. Discard the gasket. Discard the M11 cylinder head bolts.

To install:

➡**Do not use any type sealant on the cylinder head gasket (unless specified). The cylinder head gaskets must be installed in the proper direction and position.**

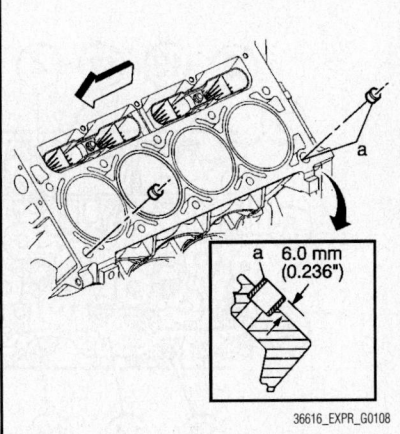

Fig. 90 Cylinder head gasket positioning—4.8L, 5.3L and 6.0L engines

a 6.0 mm (0.236")

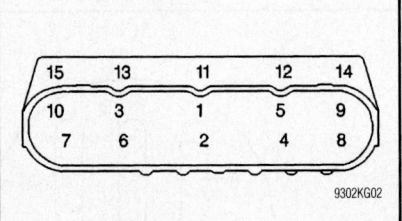

Fig. 91 Cylinder head bolt tightening sequence—4.8L, 5.3L and 6.0L engines

15	13	11	12	14
10	3	1	5	9
7	6	2	4	8

4. Clean the engine block cylinder head bolt holes (if required). Thread repair tool J 42385–107 may be used to clean the threads of old thread locking material.

5. Spray cleaner GM P/N 12346139, P/N 12377981, or equivalent into the hole.

6. Clean the cylinder head bolt holes with compressed air.

7. Check the cylinder head locating pins for proper installation.

➡**When properly installed, the tab on the right cylinder head gasket will be located right of center or closer to the front of the engine.**

8. Install or connect the following:
- NEW right cylinder head gasket onto the locating pins
- Cylinder head onto the locating pins and the gasket
- NEW M11 cylinder head bolts. Apply a 0.20 in. (5mm) band of threadlock GM P/N 12345382 or equivalent to the threads of the M8 cylinder head bolts.
- M8 cylinder head bolts.

9. Tighten the cylinder head bolts as follows:

a. M11 bolts (1–10) 1st pass: in sequence to 22 ft. lbs. (30 Nm).
b. M11 bolts (1–10) 2nd pass: in sequence + 90 degrees.
c. M11 bolts (1–10): + 70 degrees.
d. M8 cylinder head bolts (11,12,13,14,15) to 22 ft. lbs. (30 Nm). Begin with the center bolt (11) and alternating side-to-side, work outward tightening all of the bolts.

10. Install or connect the following:
- Alternator
- Exhaust manifold(s)
- Pushrods
- Intake manifold
- Negative battery cable

Left Side

See Figures 88 through 91.

❈❈ CAUTION

Before servicing any electrical component, the ignition key must be in the OFF or LOCK position and all electrical loads must be OFF, unless instructed otherwise in these procedures.

1. Before servicing the vehicle, refer to the Precautions Section.

2. Remove or disconnect the following:
- Negative battery cable
- Intake manifold
- Push rods
- Exhaust manifold(s)
- Alternator
- Alternator mounting bracket-to-cylinder head bolts
- Bolt behind the power steering pump
- Alternator mounting bracket and set it aside
- Oil level indicator tube-to-cylinder head bolt
- Oil level indicator tube
- Cylinder head from the engine
- Spark plugs

➡**The M11 cylinder head bolts are NOT reusable. Install NEW M11 cylinder head bolts during assembly.**

3. Remove the cylinder head bolts.

➡**After removal, place the cylinder head on two wood blocks to prevent damage.**

4. Remove the gasket. Discard the gasket. Discard the M11 cylinder head bolts.

To install:

➡**Do not use any type sealant on the cylinder head gasket (unless specified). The cylinder head gaskets must**

be installed in the proper direction and position.

5. Clean the engine block cylinder head bolt holes (if required). Thread repair tool J 42385–107 may be used to clean the threads of old thread locking material.

6. Spray cleaner GM P/N 12346139, P/N 12377981, or equivalent into the hole.

7. Clean the cylinder head bolt holes with compressed air.

8. Check the cylinder head locating pins for proper installation.

➡**When properly installed, the tab on the left cylinder head gasket will be located left of center or closer to the front of the engine.**

9. Install or connect the following:
- NEW left cylinder head gasket onto the locating pins
- Cylinder head onto the locating pins and the gasket
- NEW M11 cylinder head bolts.

10. Apply a 0.20 in. (5mm) band of threadlock GM P/N 12345382 or equivalent to the threads of the M8 cylinder head bolts.
- M8 cylinder head bolts
- M8 cylinder head bolts.

11. Tighten the cylinder head bolts as follows:

a. M11 bolts (1–10) 1st pass: in sequence to 22 ft. lbs. (30 Nm).

b. M11 bolts (1–10) 2nd pass: in sequence + 90 degrees.

c. M11 bolts (1–10): + 70 degrees.

d. M8 cylinder head bolts (11,12,13,14,15) to 22 ft. lbs. (30 Nm). Begin with the center bolt (11) and alternating side-to-side, work outward tightening all of the bolts.

12. Install or connect the following:
- Alternator mounting bracket. Tighten the four bolts to 37 ft. lbs. (50 Nm).
- Bolt at the rear of the power steering pump and tighten to 37 ft. lbs. (50 Nm).
- Exhaust manifold(s)
- Pushrods
- Intake manifold
- Negative battery cable

6.6L Engines

See Figures 92 through 95.

1. Before servicing the vehicle, refer to the Precautions Section.

2. Relieve the fuel system pressure.

3. Drain the coolant system.

4. Remove or disconnect the following:
- Negative battery cables
- Left or right front splash shield from the fender well, as applicable

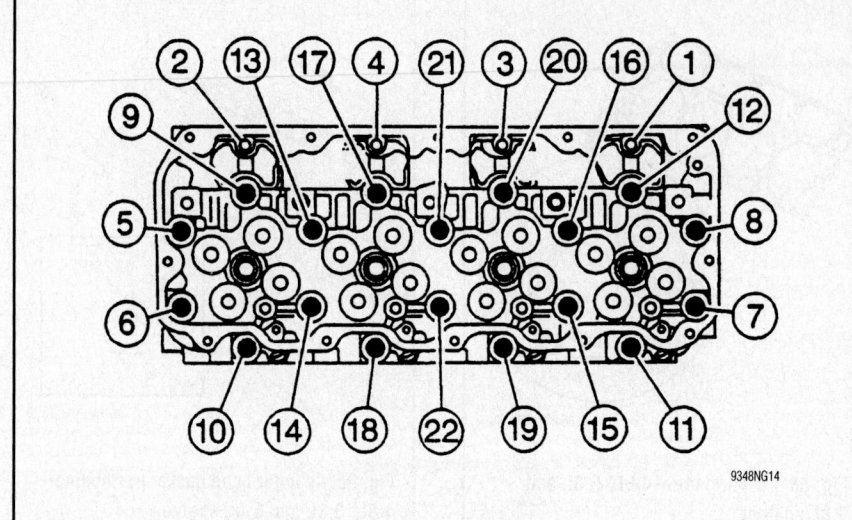

Fig. 92 Cylinder head bolt loosening sequence—6.6L engines

9348NG14

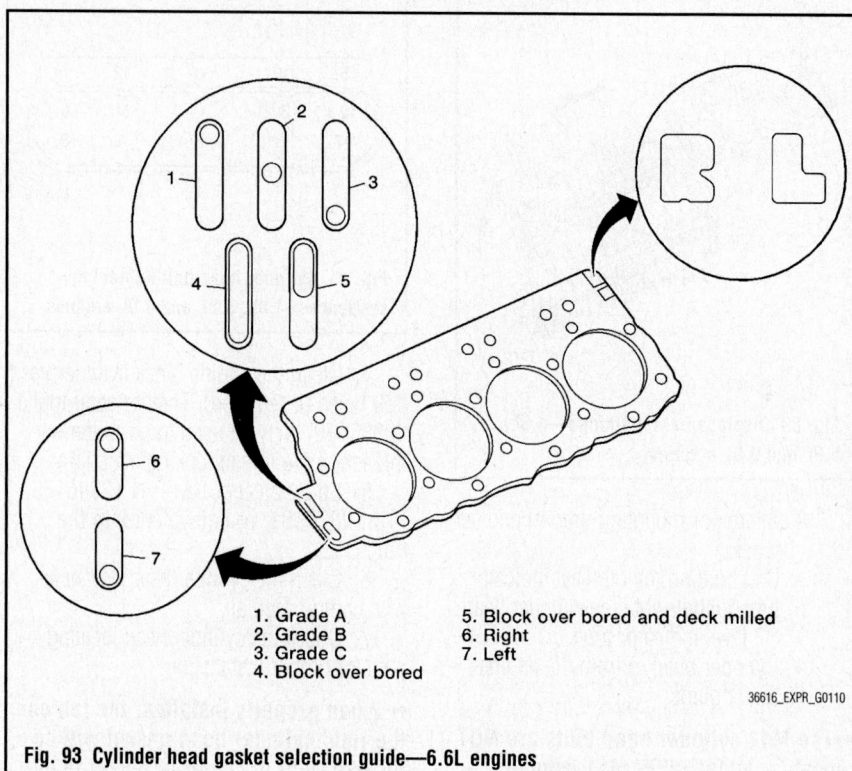

1. Grade A
2. Grade B
3. Grade C
4. Block over bored
5. Block over bored and deck milled
6. Right
7. Left

36616_EXPR_G0110

Fig. 93 Cylinder head gasket selection guide—6.6L engines

- Turbocharger
- Turbocharger charged air cooler inlet duct
- Thermostat housing crossover
- Left or right intake manifold, as necessary
- Upper left or right valve cover
- Fuel rail assembly
- Left or right exhaust manifold
- Bolt and ground straps from the rear of the cylinder head
- Lower left or right valve cover
- Rocker arm shaft assembly

- Glow plugs
- Fuel injector return pipe eye bolts and washers
- Fuel injector return pipe assembly
- Fuel injector bracket bolts
- Fuel injectors with the brackets, using a suitable removal tool
- Injector bracket pins
- Cylinder head bolts, in the proper sequence
- Cylinder head and gasket. Discard the gasket

Cylinder Head Gasket Grade	Ti Max (Piston Projection)		Compressed Gasket Thickness	
	Metric (mm)	English (in)	Metric (mm)	English (in)
Grade A	0.223-0.274	0.0088-0.0108	0.90-1.00	0.0354-0.0394
Grade B	0.274-0.325	0.0108-0.0128	0.95-1.05	0.0374-0.0413
Grade C	0.325-0.376	0.0128-0.0148	1.00-1.10	0.0394-0.0433
Block Over-Bored 0.010-0.030 in (0.254-0.762 mm)	0.223-0.376	0.0088-0.0148	1.00-1.10	0.0394-0.0433
Block Over-Bored 0.010-0.030 in (0.254-0.762 mm) and Deck Milled 0.008 in (0.203 mm)	0.4257-0.5777	0.0168-0.0228	1.25-1.35	0.0492-0.0532

36616_EXPR_G0111

Fig. 94 Cylinder head gasket selection specification data—6.6L engines

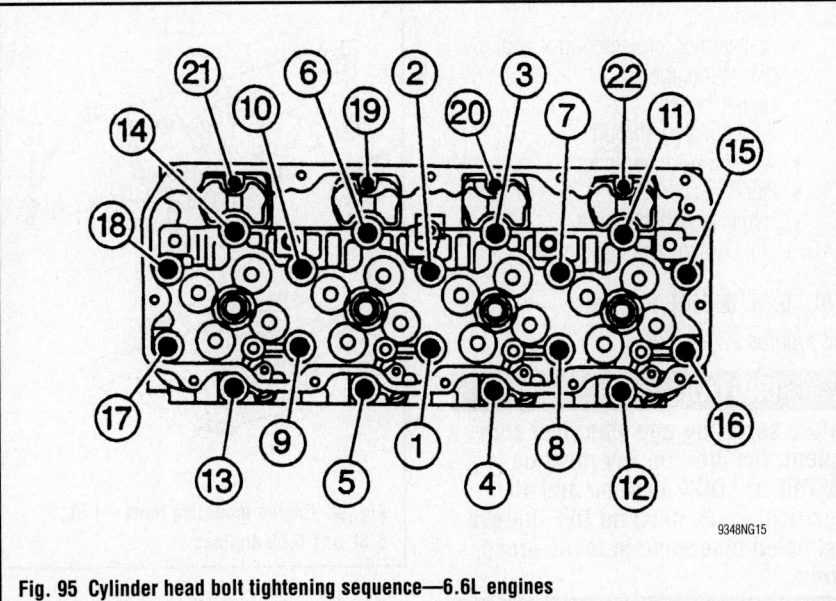

9348NG15

Fig. 95 Cylinder head bolt tightening sequence—6.6L engines

To install:

5. Clean the mating surfaces of the heads and block thoroughly.

6. Install the proper cylinder head gasket using the cylinder head gasket selection guide and specification data.

7. Position a new left or right side head gasket on the block. Note that the left and right side gaskets are NOT interchangeable.

➡**The cylinder head bolts on these vehicles are pre–coated with an application of a molybdenum disulfide for thread lubrication. Do not remove the coating or add any additional lubrication.**

8. Install the cylinder head and bolts.

9. Tighten the cylinder head bolts, in sequence, as follows:

a. Step 1: M12 bolts to 37 ft. lbs. (50 Nm).

b. Step 2: M12 bolts to 59 ft. lbs. (80 Nm).

c. Step 3: Using a torque angle meter, tighten the M12 bolts an additional 60 degrees.

d. Step 4: Using a torque angle meter, tighten the M12 bolts an additional 60 degrees.

e. Step 5: M8 bolts to 18 ft. lbs. (25 Nm).

10. Install or connect the following:

• New O–ring onto the fuel injectors after coating with clean engine oil
• New copper washer into the fuel injector bore in the cylinder head
• Fuel injector bracket pin

➡**If you are reusing the old injectors, clean the carbon from the tips, but do not use a wire brush.**

• Fuel injector bracket bolt and tighten to 37 ft. lbs. (50 Nm)
• Fuel injector return pipe assembly
• Fuel injector return pipe-to-injector eye bolts and washers. Tighten to 11 ft. lbs. (15 Nm).
• Fuel return pipe-to-cylinder head eye bolts and washers. Tighten to 11 ft. lbs. (15 Nm).
• Bolt and ground straps to the rear of the cylinder head. Tighten to 18 ft. lbs. (25 Nm).
• Valve rocker shaft assembly
• Lower and upper valve covers
• Glow plugs
• Exhaust manifold
• Fuel rail assembly
• Intake manifold
• Thermostat housing crossover
• Turbocharger charged air cooler duct
• Clamp and hose to the charged air cooler. Tighten to 53 inch lbs. (6 Nm).
• Turbocharger
• Fender splash shield
• Negative battery cables

11. Refill the cooling system with the proper type and quantity of antifreeze.

12. Evacuate and recharge the air conditioning system.

ENGINE ASSEMBLY

REMOVAL & INSTALLATION

4.3L Engines

See Figure 96.

1. Before servicing the vehicle, refer to the Precautions Section.

2. Properly relieve the fuel system pressure.

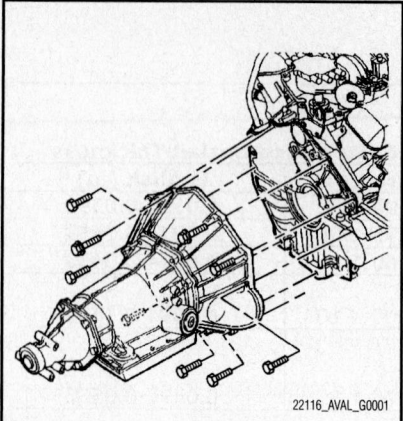

Fig. 96 Transmission mounting bolts— 4.3L engines

3. Drain the cooling system. Properly dispose of used coolant.

4. Drain the engine oil. Properly dispose of used engine oil.

5. Remove or disconnect the following:
- Negative battery cable
- Hood
- Air cleaner
- Accessory drive belt
- Fan
- Water pump pulley
- Radiator and shroud
- Heater hoses at the engine
- Accelerator, cruise control and detent linkage if used
- Air conditioning compressor, if used, and lay aside
- Power steering pump, if used, and lay aside
- Wiring from the engine
- Fuel line
- Vacuum lines from the intake manifold
- Exhaust pipes from the manifold
- Strut rods at the engine mountings, if used
- Flywheel or torque converter cover
- Wiring along the oil pan rail
- Starter
- Wire for the fuel gauge
- Converter-to-flex plate bolts, if equipped with automatic transmission

6. Support the transmission
- Bell housing to engine bolts
- Rear engine mounting to frame bolts and the front through bolts and the engine

To install:

7. Lower the engine.

8. Install or connect the following:
- Engine mounting bolts. Torque the rear engine mounting to frame

bolts or nuts to 45 ft. lbs. (54 Nm), the front through-bolts to 70 ft. lbs. (97 Nm) and the front nuts to 50 ft. lbs. (67 Nm).
- Bell housing to engine bolts and torque to 35 ft. lbs. (47 Nm)

9. Remove the transmission support.
- Converter-to-flex plate bolts and tighten to 35 ft. lbs. (47 Nm)
- Fuel gauge wiring
- Starter
- Flywheel or torque converter cover
- Strut rods at the engine mountings, if used
- Exhaust pipes at the manifold
- Vacuum lines to the intake manifold
- Fuel line
- Engine wiring harness
- Power steering pump, if used
- Air conditioning compressor, if used
- Accelerator, cruise control and detent linkage
- Heater hoses
- Radiator and shroud
- Accessory drive belts
- Hood
- Negative battery cable

10. Refill coolant and engine oil.

4.8L, 5.3L & 6.0L Engines

See Figures 97 and 98.

> ✳ **CAUTION**
>
> **Before servicing any electrical component, the ignition key must be in the OFF or LOCK position and all electrical loads must be OFF, unless instructed otherwise in these procedures.**

1. Before servicing the vehicle, refer to the Precautions Section.

2. Properly relieve the fuel system pressure.

3. Drain the cooling system. Properly dispose of used coolant.

4. Drain the engine oil. Properly dispose of used engine oil.

5. Remove the engine cover.

6. Disconnect the negative battery cable.

7. Recover the HVAC refrigerant.

8. Remove the sheet metal to radiator support bolts and supports from the vehicle.

9. Remove the air cleaner assembly.

10. Remove the coolant reservoir.

11. Remove the right and left headlamp capsules.

12. Remove the front bumper.

13. Remove the grille.

14. Remove the radiator inlet hose from the water pump.

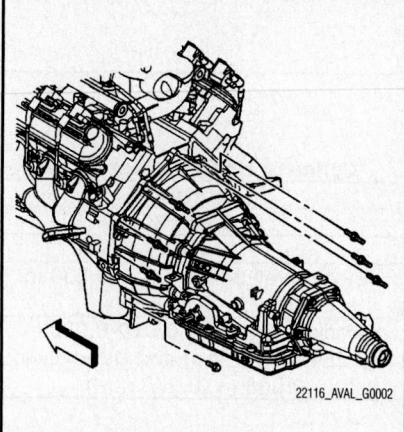

Fig. 97 Transmission mounting bolts— 4.8L, 5.3L and 6.0L engines

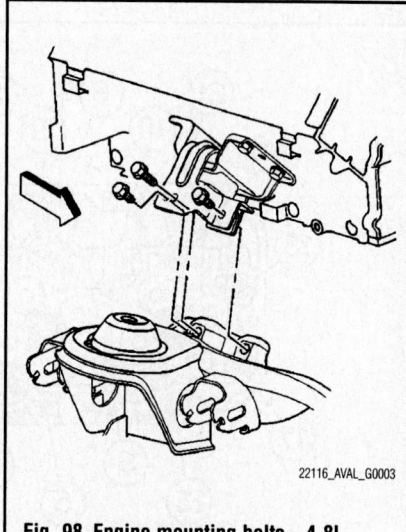

Fig. 98 Engine mounting bolts—4.8L, 5.3L and 6.0L engines

15. Remove the radiator outlet hose from the water pump.

16. Disconnect the transmission cooler lines from the radiator.

17. Disconnect the oil cooler line from the radiator, if equipped.

18. Disconnect and cap the HVAC lines from the condenser.

19. Disconnect the ground connection from the right hand inner fender and connector C4 at the underhood fuse block.

20. Disconnect the positive battery cable from the underhood fuse block and position aside.

21. Remove the core support retaining bolt.

22. With the aid of an assistant, remove the core support assembly with the radiator, condenser radiator hoses and fan shroud intact.

23. Remove the clutch fan.

24. Remove the accessory drive belt.

25. Remove the air bleed hose from the throttle body.

26. Remove the generator bracket from the engine. Leave the generator and power steering pump retained to the bracket. Use a suitable strap and position the bracket assembly aside.

27. Remove the radiator vent inlet hose from the throttle body.

28. Remove the ground straps from the frame and engine.

29. Remove the air conditioning compressor.

30. Disconnect the heater hoses from the water pump.

31. Remove the intake manifold.

32. Remove the ignition coils from the engine.

33. Remove the coolant air bleed pipe from the engine.

34. Raise and safely support the vehicle.

35. Remove the oil drain plug and drain the oil into a suitable container.

36. Remove the starter motor.

37. Disconnect the catalytic converter pipe from the exhaust manifolds.

38. Unplug the Crankshaft Position (CKP) sensor, engine oil level sensor, and the coolant heater, if equipped.

39. Remove the battery cable channel bolt.

40. Slide the channel pin out of the oil pan tab.

41. Gather all branches of the engine wiring harness and reposition off to the side.

42. Remove the lower 6 bell housing to engine studs and bolts. Leave the top 2 studs in place.

43. Remove the torque converter bolts.

44. Lower the vehicle.

45. Remove the left and right exhaust manifolds.

46. Install tool J42451−1 or similar lifting eye to the cylinder heads. Tighten the M10 engine lift bracket bolts to 37 ft. lbs. (50 Nm).

47. Remove the left and right engine mount-to-engine mount bracket bolts.

48. Remove the transmission oil level indicator tube nut.

49. Remove the transmission oil level indicator tube.

50. Remove the top 2 automatic transmission studs.

51. Position a floor jack under the transmission for support.

52. Install an engine hoist to the J 42451−1 lifting eyes.

53. Separate the engine from the automatic transmission, if equipped.

54. Install tool J 21366 to the transmission in order to hold the torque converter.

55. Remove the engine.

To install:

56. Installation is the reverse of removal. Note the following and observe the following torque specifications:

- Engine mount-to-engine mount bracket bolts to 48 ft. lbs. (65 Nm)
- If equipped with the 4L60-E, tighten the torque converter bolts to 37 ft. lbs. (63 Nm). If equipped with the 4L80-E, tighten the torque converter bolts to 44 ft. lbs. (60 Nm)
- If equipped with the 4L80-E automatic transmission, tighten the transmission converter cover bolts to 24 ft. lbs. (33 Nm)
- Tighten the automatic transmission bolts/studs to 37 ft. lbs. (50 Nm)
- Tighten the core support bolts to 18 ft. lbs. (25 Nm). Tighten the support nuts to 42 ft. lbs. (57 Nm)

57. Fill the engine to the proper level with oil and coolant.

58. Perform the CKP system variation learn procedure using a scan tool.

59. Check for and correct any leaks. Recharge the A/C system if equipped.

6.6L Engines

See Figures 99 and 100.

❋❋ CAUTION

Before servicing any electrical component, the ignition key must be in the OFF or LOCK position and all electrical loads must be OFF, unless instructed otherwise in these procedures.

1. Before servicing the vehicle, refer to the Precautions Section.

2. Remove the engine cover.

3. Properly relieve the fuel system pressure.

4. Disconnect the negative battery cable.

5. Recover the HVAC refrigerant.

6. Drain the cooling system.

7. Remove the cooling fan and accessory drive belt.

8. Unplug the generator electrical connector. Unbolt and reposition the generator to access the output wire nut. Remove the generator.

9. Disconnect the RH engine wiring harness connector. Remove the 2 RH engine wiring harness bracket bolts and position aside. Remove the 2 wiring harness routing bolts.

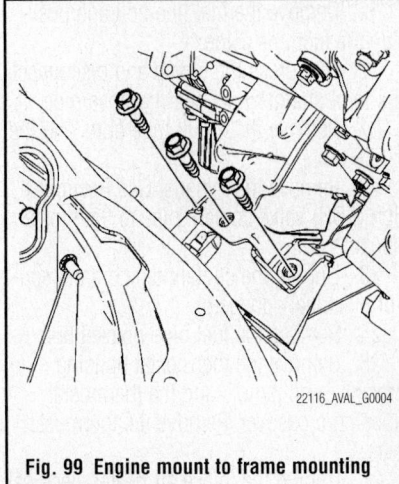

Fig. 99 Engine mount to frame mounting bolts—6.6L engines

Fig. 100 Engine mount to engine mounting bolts—6.6L engines

10. Remove the transmission tube bolt and reposition the transmission tube. Remove the oil indicator tube bracket bolt.

11. Remove the drive belt tensioner bolt and tensioner.

12. Remove the bolts and the generator mounting bracket.

13. If equipped, remove the auxiliary generator. Remove the auxiliary generator bracket bolt and bracket.

14. If equipped with a dual generator system, remove the bolt from the left side idler pulley and remove the idler pulley.

15. Unplug the A/C compressor clutch electrical connector and the A/C cut out switch electrical connector.

16. Disconnect the A/C suction and discharge lines at the compressor. Remove the A/C compressor.

17. Remove the power steering pump and bracket bolts. Position the power steering pump aside and secure.

18. Remove the A/C and power steering bracket mounting nuts/bolts and bracket.

19. Remove the fuel line bolt and position the fuel line aside.

20. Compress the clamp and disconnect the turbocharger inlet cooling hose/pipe.

21. Remove the oil fill tube bolts and the oil fill tube.

22. Remove the Exhaust Gas Recirculation (EGR) valve coolant pipe to thermostat housing bolt.

23. Unplug the coolant temperature sensor electrical connector.

24. Remove the fuel pipe bracket bolt.

25. Remove the thermostat housing crossover bolts/nuts and the thermostat housing crossover. Remove the thermostat pipe.

26. Unplug the intake air heater electrical connector.

27. Disconnect the engine harness electrical connector from the Manifold Absolute Pressure (MAP) sensor.

28. Disconnect the positive cable from the IAH.

29. Remove the intake manifold tube with the stud.

30. Remove and discard the 2 metal EGR gaskets from the EGR valve.

31. Remove and discard the O-ring seal from the center intake manifold.

32. Remove the air intake pipe.

33. Remove the right and left exhaust pipes.

34. Remove the EGR coolant hose.

35. Compress the clamp and disconnect the EGR heater inlet hose/pipe from the EGR cooler tube. Remove the EGR cooler tube bracket bolts.

36. Remove the crankcase ventilation hose/pipe.

37. Unplug the EGR solenoid electrical connector. Remove the EGR valve and EGR cooler tube as an assembly. Remove the 2 bolts and the EGR cooler tube bracket.

38. Unplug the engine wiring harness electrical connector from the turbocharger vane position sensor and solenoid valve.

39. Remove the turbocharger upper heat shield.

40. Reposition the turbocharger coolant outlet pipe clamp and remove the hose from the turbocharger pipe. Disconnect the fuel feed and return pipes.

41. Disconnect the positive battery cable from the glow plug control module. Remove the glow plug control module.

42. Remove the glow plug control module bracket bolts. Remove the fuel line bracket bolt.

43. Remove the turbocharger coolant inlet pipe bolt and remove the hose from the turbocharger.

44. Remove the turbocharger oil feed

pipe banjo bolt and washer. Discard the banjo bolt and washer. Reposition and secure the turbocharger oil fed pipe out of the way.

45. Remove the turbocharger oil return pipe nuts at the top of the flywheel housing.

46. Remove the turbocharger (with the oil return pipe).

47. Remove and discard the turbocharger oil return pipe gasket at the flywheel housing. Remove the turbocharger lower heat shield, oil feed pipe, washer, and pipe.

48. Unplug the LH main engine wiring harness connector and remove the bracket bolts.

49. Remove the LH glow plug nuts and the routing bolts.

50. Unplug the fuel injector electrical connectors, the Intake Air Temperature (IAT) sensor and fuel rail temperature sensor electrical connectors.

51. Unplug the Engine Coolant Temperature (ECT) wiring harness electrical connector and the oil pressure sensor electrical wiring harness electrical connector. Position the engine wiring harness over the RH side of engine.

52. Remove the fuel feed/return pipe bracket bolt. Disconnect the fuel hoses from the fuel pipe.

53. Remove the fuel line bracket bolt. Disconnect the fuel pump hose from the fuel pipe.

54. Disconnect the fuel injector return hoses from the return pipe assembly. Remove the fuel pipe. Remove the fuel pipe clamp bolt and turbocharger coolant inlet pipe bracket bolt.

55. Remove the center intake manifold.

56. Remove the fuel pump to LH fuel rail pipe. Compress the clamp and remove the fuel pressure relief hose. Remove the fuel pipe bracket bolt, disconnect the hose at the fuel pump and remove the fuel pipe/hose assembly.

57. Remove the LH to RH fuel rail pipe. Remove the LH fuel injector feed pipes. Remove the 2 bolts and the LH fuel rail.

58. Unplug the Fuel Rail Pressure (FRP) sensor electrical connector. Remove the RH fuel injector feed pipes. Remove the 2 bolts and the RH fuel rail.

59. Remove the 2 bolts and the turbocharger cooling outlet pipe.

60. Remove the intake manifolds.

61. Unplug the fuel pump electrical connector. Remove the 4 bolts and fuel injection pump.

62. Remove the transmission fill tube. Remove the engine oil indicator tube.

63. Remove the transmission.

64. Remove the engine flywheel.

65. Remove the upper oil pan.

66. Remove the engine flywheel housing.

67. Remove the oil pump pickup tube. Remove the oil filter adapter and the oil cooler assembly.

68. Remove the exhaust manifolds.

69. Disconnect any remaining ground straps from the engine.

70. Using tool J 36857 or similar engine lift hooks, install a suitable lifting device.

➡ **The engine will have to be angled in order to remove. Use a load positioning sling to assist in angling the engine.**

71. Raise the engine off the engine mounts.

72. Remove the left engine mount to engine mount frame bracket bolts. Remove the left engine mount to engine bolts. Remove the left engine mount bracket to frame bolts.

73. Remove the right engine mount to engine mount frame bracket bolts. Remove the right engine mount to engine bolts. Remove the right engine mount bracket to frame bolts.

74. Remove the engine from the vehicle.

To install:

75. Installation is the reverse of removal. Note the following and observe the following torque specifications:

- Engine mount bracket to frame bolts to 48 ft. lbs. (65 Nm)
- Engine mount to engine bolts to 43 ft. lbs. (58 Nm)
- Engine mount to engine mount bracket bolts to 48 ft. lbs. (65 Nm)

76. Fill the engine to the proper level with oil and coolant. Prime the fuel system.

77. Check for and correct any leaks. Recharge the A/C system if equipped.

EXHAUST MANIFOLD

REMOVAL & INSTALLATION

4.3L Engines

See Figure 101.

1. Before servicing the vehicle, refer to the Precautions Section.

2. Disconnect the negative battery cable.

3. Raise and support the vehicle safely.

4. Remove the tire and wheel assembly.

5. Remove the wheel house splash shield.

6. Remove the catalytic converter assembly.

7. Remove the spark plugs.

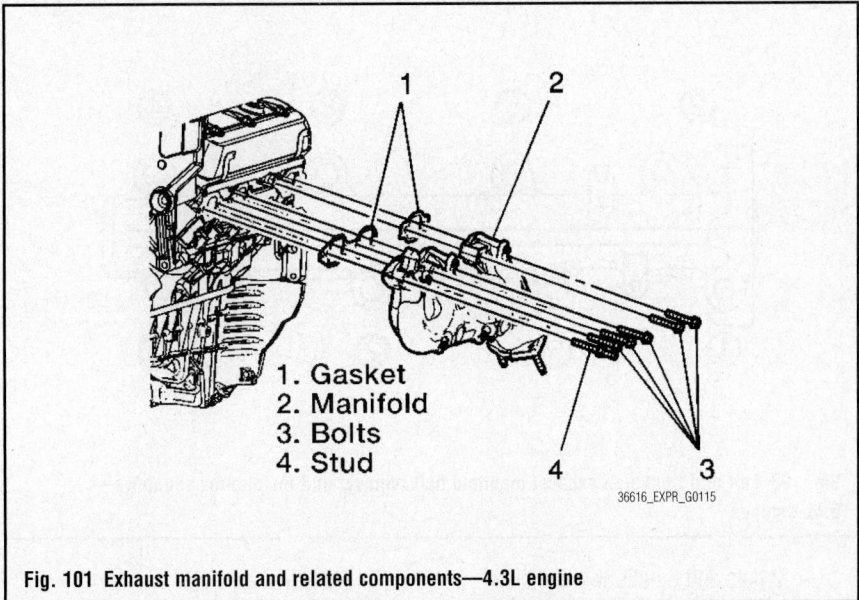

1. Gasket
2. Manifold
3. Bolts
4. Stud

36616_EXPR_G0115

Fig. 101 Exhaust manifold and related components—4.3L engine

8. Remove the exhaust manifold retaining bolts and stud.

9. Remove the component from the vehicle.

To install:

➡ Be sure to use new fasteners, as required. Be sure to use new exhaust manifold gaskets.

10. Position the exhaust manifold to the engine.

11. Tighten the retaining bolts to 11 ft. lbs. (15 Nm) first pass and 22 ft. lbs. (30 Nm) final pass.

12. Continue the installation in the reverse order of the removal procedure.

13. Start the engine and check for exhaust leaks, correct as required.

4.8L, 5.3L & 6.0L Engines

Left Side

See Figure 102.

1. Before servicing the vehicle, refer to the Precautions Section.

2. Disconnect the negative battery cable.

3. Raise and support the vehicle safely

4. Separate the catalytic converter from the exhaust manifold.

5. Lower the vehicle.

6. Remove the passenger's seat. Remove the engine cover.

7. Disconnect the EGR pipe from the exhaust manifold, if equipped.

8. Remove the spark plug wires.

9. Remove the exhaust manifold retaining bolts.

10. Remove the component from the vehicle.

To install:

➡ Be sure to use new fasteners, as required. Be sure to use new exhaust manifold gaskets.

➡ An improperly installed gasket or leaking exhaust system may effect On–Board Diagnostics (OBD) II system performance.

➡ Do not apply sealant to the first three threads of the bolt.

11. Install the heat shield and bolts. Tighten to 80 inch lbs. (9 Nm).

12. Install the exhaust pipe studs. Tighten to 15 ft. lbs (20 Nm).

13. Apply a 0.2 in. (5mm) wide band of threadlock GM P/N 12345493 or equivalent to the threads of the exhaust manifold bolts.

14. Install the exhaust manifold gasket and exhaust manifold

15. Install the exhaust manifold bolts and tighten, beginning with the center two bolts. Alternate from side-to-side, and work toward the outside bolts.

    a. Tighten the exhaust manifold bolts first pass to 11 ft. lbs. (15 Nm). Begin with the center 2 bolts, then alternate from side to side working outwards.

    b. Tighten the exhaust manifold bolts final pass to 15 ft. lbs. (20 Nm). Begin with the center 2 bolts, then alternate from side to side working outwards. Using a flat punch, bend over the exposed edge of the exhaust manifold gasket at the front of the right cylinder head.

16. Continue the installation in reverse order of the removal procedure.

17. Start the engine and check for exhaust leaks, correct as required.

Right Side

1. Before servicing the vehicle, refer to the Precautions Section.

2. Disconnect the negative battery cable.

3. Raise and support the vehicle safely

4. Separate the catalytic converter from the exhaust manifold.

5. Lower the vehicle.

6. Remove the passenger's seat. Remove the engine cover.

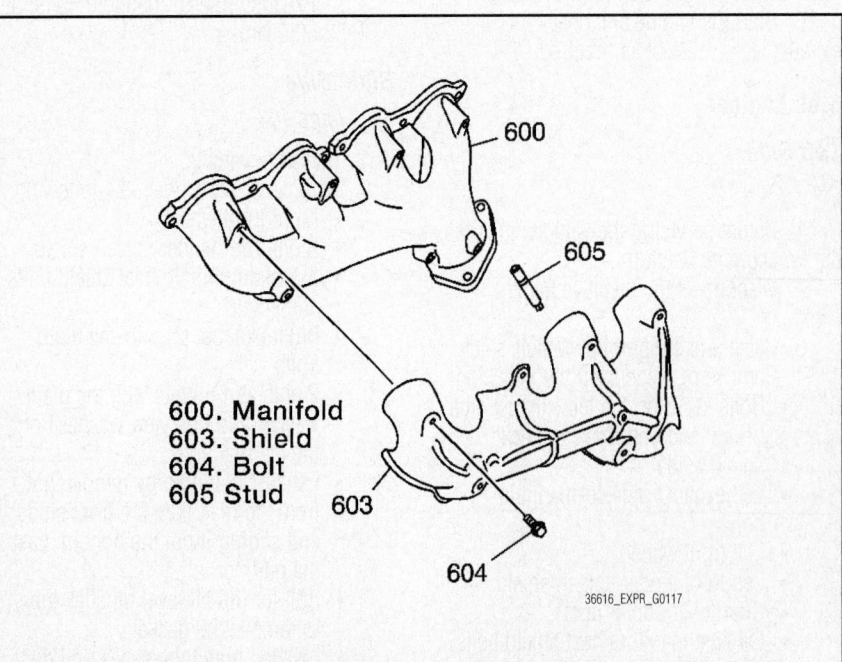

600. Manifold
603. Shield
604. Bolt
605 Stud

36616_EXPR_G0117

Fig. 102 Left side exhaust manifold and related components—4.8L, 5.3L and 6.0L engines

7. Remove the oil level indicator tube.

8. Remove the spark plug wires. Remove the spark plugs.

9. Remove the exhaust manifold retaining bolts.

10. Remove the component from the vehicle.

11. Remove the exhaust manifold studs.

To install:

➡**Be sure to use new fasteners, as required. Be sure to use new exhaust manifold gaskets.**

12. Install the exhaust manifold studs, into the new manifold.

13. Install the exhaust manifold gasket and exhaust manifold

14. Install the exhaust manifold bolts and tighten, beginning with the center two bolts. Alternate from side-to-side, and work toward the outside bolts.

   a. Tighten the exhaust manifold bolts first pass to 11 ft. lbs. (15 Nm). Begin with the center 2 bolts, then alternate from side to side working outwards.

   b. Tighten the exhaust manifold bolts final pass to 18 ft. lbs. (25 Nm). Begin with the center 2 bolts, then alternate from side to side working outwards. Using a flat punch, bend over the exposed edge of the exhaust manifold gasket at the front of the right cylinder head.

15. Continue the installation in the reverse order of the removal procedure.

16. Start the engine and check for exhaust leaks, correct as required.

6.6L Engines

Left Side

See Figure 103.

1. Before servicing the vehicle, refer to the Precautions Section.

2. Disconnect the negative battery cable.

3. Raise and support the vehicle safely

4. Remove or disconnect the following:
   - Bolts securing the left exhaust pipe heat shield and move the heat shield aside
   - Left exhaust pipe-to-manifold bolts
   - Left front wheel
   - Left front fender splash shield
   - Charge air cooler duct
   - Exhaust manifold heat shield bolts and shield

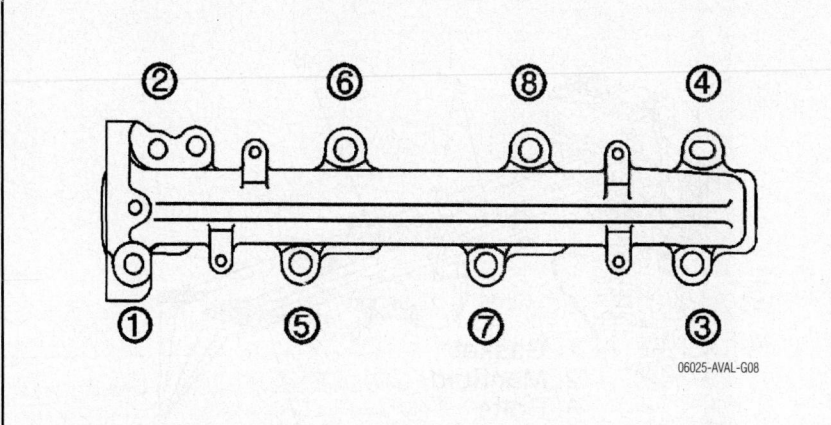

Fig. 103 Left and right side exhaust manifold bolt removal and installation sequence— 6.6L engines

06025-AVAL-G08

   - 2 nuts and 6 bolts with the plain washer and bell view washer from the left manifold
   - Exhaust manifold by removing it from the rear, then the front studs and sliding it out the bottom, past the oil filter
   - Exhaust manifold gasket and discard

To install:

5. Installation is the reverse of the removal procedure. Tighten the retainers as follows:

   a. Exhaust manifold nuts and bolts, in sequence, in 2 passes to 25 ft. lbs. (34 Nm).

   b. Heat shield bolts: 71 inch lbs. (8 Nm).

   c. Exhaust pipe-to-manifold bolts: 39 ft. lbs. (59 Nm).

Right Side

See Figure 103.

1. Raise the vehicle.

2. Remove or disconnect the following:
   - Right front wheel
   - Right front fender splash shield
   - Exhaust manifold heat shield bolts and shield
   - Right exhaust pipe-to-manifold bolts
   - 2 nuts and 6 bolts with the plain washer and bell view washer from the left manifold
   - Exhaust manifold by removing it from the rear, then the front studs and sliding it out the bottom, past the oil filter
   - Bolt for the oil level dipstick tube, to remove the gasket
   - Exhaust manifold gasket and discard

To install:

3. Installation is the reverse of the removal procedure. Tighten the retainers as follows:

   a. Oil level dipstick tube: 15 ft. lbs. (20 Nm).

   b. Exhaust manifold nuts and bolts, in sequence, in 2 passes: 25 ft. lbs. (34 Nm).

   c. Heat shield bolts: 71 inch lbs. (8 Nm).

   d. Exhaust pipe-to-manifold bolts: 39 ft. lbs. (59 Nm).

FLYWHEEL

REMOVAL & INSTALLATION

The ring gear is an integral part of the flywheel and is not replaceable.

1. Before servicing the vehicle, refer to the Precautions Section.

2. Disconnect the negative battery cable.

3. Raise and support the vehicle safely.

4. Remove the transmission.

5. Remove the bolts attaching the flexplate to the crankshaft flange, then remove it from the crankshaft.

To install:

6. Inspect the flexplate for cracks, and inspect the ring gear for burrs or worn teeth. Replace the flywheel if any damage is apparent. Remove burrs with a mill file.

7. If equipped with a spacer between the crankshaft and flexplate, reinstall the spacer.

8. Install the flexplate. The flexplate will only attach to the crankshaft in one position, as the bolt holes are unevenly spaced. Install the bolts and tighten in a criss-cross pattern. Refer to the Torque Specifications chart for the proper tightening torque values.

INTAKE MANIFOLD

REMOVAL & INSTALLATION

4.3L Engines

See Figures 104 through 109.

1. Before servicing the vehicle, refer to the Precautions Section.
2. Relieve the fuel system pressure.
3. Disconnect the negative battery cable.
4. Remove the passenger's seat. Remove the engine cover.
5. Remove or disconnect the following:
   - Air intake duct
   - Wiring harness connectors and brackets from the manifold
   - Throttle linkage and bracket from the upper manifold
   - Cruise control cable, if equipped
   - Fuel lines at the rear of the lower intake manifold
   - Brake booster vacuum hose from the upper intake manifold
   - Ignition coil and bracket
   - Purge solenoid and bracket
   - Studs and intake manifold attaching bolts, mark for reassembly
   - Upper intake manifold
   - Upper radiator hose from the thermostat housing
   - Heater hoses and the bypass hose from the lower intake manifold
   - Exhaust Gas Recirculation (EGR) valve
   - Transmission dipstick tube, if equipped
   - Positive Crankcase Ventilation (PCV) valve and hoses
   - Air conditioning compressor and bracket. Without disconnecting, position aside
   - Alternator bracket and bolt next to the thermostat housing, if needed
   - Lower intake manifold mounting bolts and the lower manifold

To install:

➡**Be sure to use new fasteners, as required.**

6. Clean all gasket mating surfaces thoroughly.

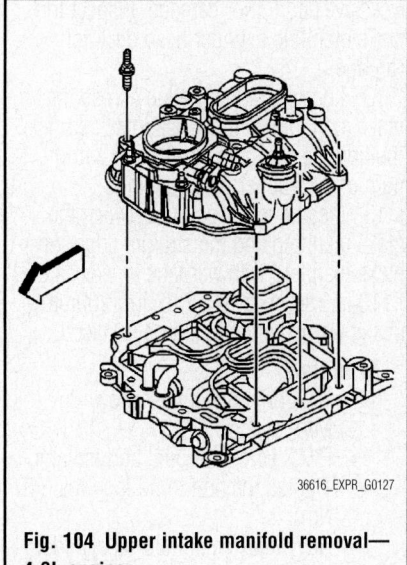

Fig. 104 Upper intake manifold removal—4.3L engines

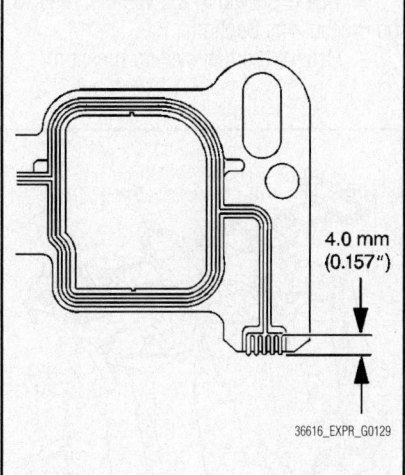

Fig. 106 Proper sealant application to cylinder head side of intake manifold—4.3L engines

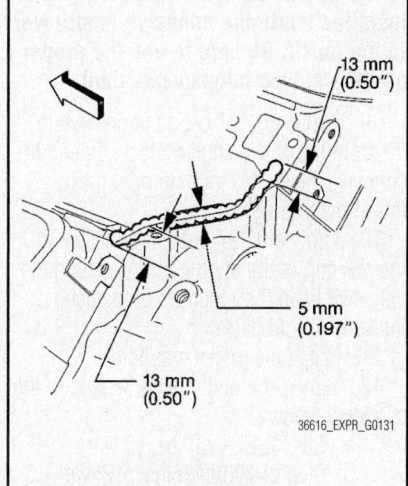

Fig. 108 Intake manifold sealant application top rear of engine block—4.3L engines

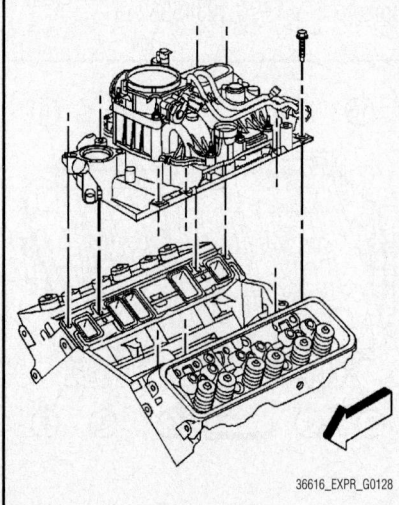

Fig. 105 Lower intake manifold removal—4.3L engines

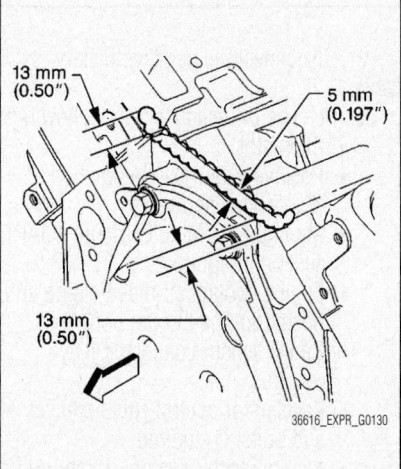

Fig. 107 Intake manifold sealant application top front of engine block—4.3L engines

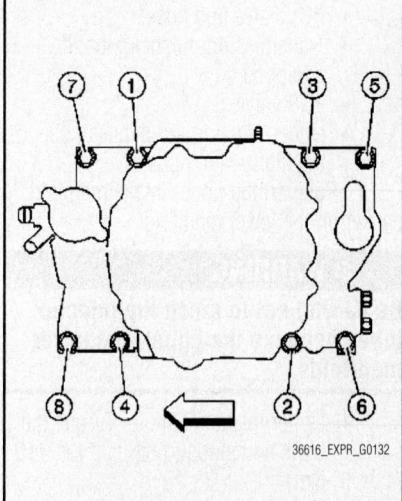

Fig. 109 Lower intake manifold bolt tightening sequence—4.3L engines

➡Apply the proper amount of sealant when assembling this component. Excessive use of sealant can prohibit the component from sealing properly. A component that is not sealed properly can leak and cause extensive engine damage.

7. Apply 0.157 inch patch of adhesive to the cylinder head side on the intake manifold gasket at each end.

➡The intake manifold gasket must be installed while the adhesive is still wet to the touch. Be sure to use the proper grade and type adhesive/sealant.

8. Install the intake manifold gasket onto the cylinder head. Use the gasket locating pins to properly seat the gasket.

➡The intake manifold gasket must be installed while the adhesive is still wet to the touch. Be sure to use the proper grade and type adhesive/sealant.

9. Apply a 0.197 bead of adhesive to the front top of the engine block. Extend the adhesive bead 0.50 inch up onto each intake manifold gasket.

10. Apply a 0.197 bead of adhesive to the rear top of the engine block. Extend the adhesive bead 0.50 inch up onto each intake manifold gasket.

11. Install the intake manifold.

12. Torque the bolts using 3 steps in the sequence shown:
 a. Step 1: 27 inch lbs. (3 Nm).
 b. Step 2: 106 inch lbs. (12 Nm).
 c. Step 3: 11 ft. lbs. (15 Nm).

13. Install or connect the following:
- Alternator bracket and bolts near the thermostat housing, if removed
- Air conditioning compressor
- PCV valve and hose
- Transmission dipstick tube, if equipped
- EGR valve
- Upper radiator and bypass hose to the thermostat housing

14. Position the upper intake manifold gasket on the lower manifold.

✳✳ WARNING

Be careful not to pinch the injector tubes between the upper and lower manifolds.

- Upper intake manifold. Torque the bolts and studs to 88 inch lbs. (10 Nm).
- Purge control bracket and valve
- Ignition coil
- Brake booster vacuum
- Fuel lines

- Accelerator cable
- Cruise control cable, if equipped
- Wiring harness brackets and connections
- Air intake duct
- Negative battery cable

15. Refill and bleed the cooling system.

16. Pressurize the fuel system and check for leaks.

4.8L, 5.3L & 6.0L Engines

See Figures 110 and 111.

➡The intake manifold, throttle body, fuel injection rail, and fuel injectors may be removed as an assembly. If not servicing the individual components, remove the manifold as a complete assembly.

1. Before servicing the vehicle, refer to the Precautions Section.

2. Relieve the fuel system pressure.

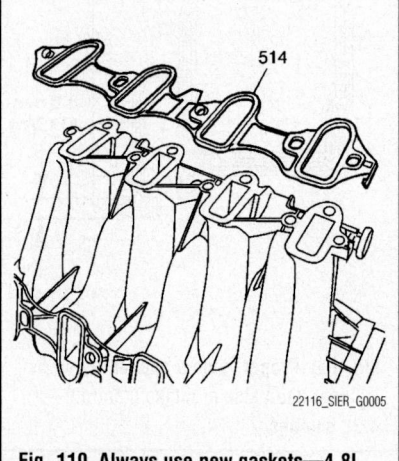

Fig. 110 Always use new gaskets—4.8L, 5.3L and 6.0L engines

3. Disconnect the negative battery cable.

4. Remove or disconnect the following:
- Alternator
- Positive Crankcase Ventilation (PCV) hose and valve
- Manifold Absolute Pressure (MAP) sensor, if required
- Engine coolant air bleed clamp and hose from the throttle body
- Knock sensor connector, if required.
- Accelerator control cable bracket and bolts, if required
- Fuel rail with injectors, if required
- EVAP solenoid, bolt, and isolator
- Any additional engine harness attachment points and set aside
- Intake manifold bolts

- Intake manifold with gaskets
- Intake manifold-to-cylinder head gaskets from the manifold. Discard the intake manifold gaskets.

5. Clean the intake manifold in solvent.

6. Dry the intake manifold with compressed air.

7. Inspect the intake manifold vacuum passages for debris or restrictions.

8. Inspect for damaged or broken vacuum fittings, damaged MAP sensor mounting bore, or broken MAP sensor retaining tabs.

9. Inspect the composite intake manifold assembly for cracks or other damage.

10. Inspect the areas between the intake runners. Inspect all the gasket sealing surfaces for damage.

11. Inspect the fuel injector bores for excessive scoring or damage. Inspect the intake manifold cylinder head deck for warpage.

12. Locate a straight edge across the intake manifold cylinder head deck surface. Position the straight edge across a minimum of two runner port openings.

13. Insert a feeler gauge between the intake manifold and the straight edge. An intake manifold with warpage in excess of 0.118 in. (3mm) over a 7.87 in. (200mm) area is warped and should be replaced.

To install:

14. Install or connect the following:
- MAP sensor
- EVAP solenoid, bolt, and isolator. Tighten the bolt to 89 inch lbs. (10 Nm).
- NEW intake manifold-to-cylinder head gaskets
- Intake manifold

15. Apply a 0.20 in. (5mm) band of threadlock GM P/N 12345382 or

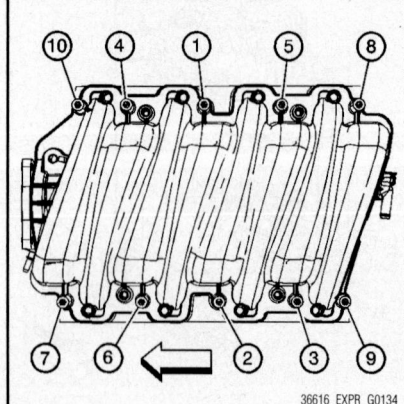

Fig. 111 Lower intake manifold bolt tightening sequence—4.8L, 5.3L and 6.0L engines

equivalent to the threads of the intake manifold bolts.

- Intake manifold bolts. Tighten intake manifold bolts first pass in sequence to 44 inch lbs. (5 Nm). Tighten intake manifold bolts final pass in sequence to 89 inch lbs. (10 Nm).
- PCV valve and hose
- Coolant air bleed hose and clamp onto the throttle body
- Accelerator control cable bracket and bolts. Tighten the bolts to 89 inch lbs. (10 Nm).
- Alternator

6.6L Engines

Center Manifold

See Figure 112.

1. Before servicing the vehicle, refer to the Precautions Section.
2. Disconnect the negative battery cable.
3. Remove the Exhaust Gas Recirculation (EGR) valve cooler tube.
4. Remove the intake manifold tube.
5. Remove and discard the 2 intake manifold tube gaskets.
6. Remove the turbocharger.
7. Remove the center intake manifold bolts/nuts.
8. Pull–up the center intake manifold in order to remove.
9. Remove and discard the gaskets.
10. Clean the center intake manifold in cleaning solvent and air dry.

To install:

11. Install new center intake manifold gaskets.
12. Install the center intake manifold.
13. Install the center intake manifold bolts/nuts and tighten to 89 inch lbs. (10 Nm).
14. Install the turbocharger.

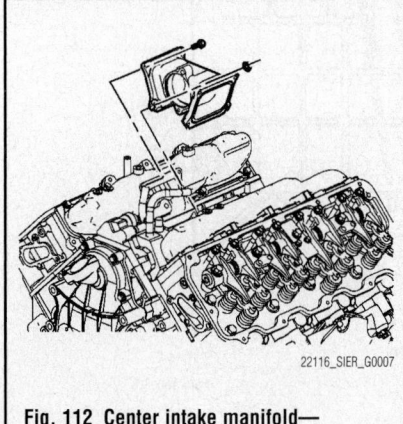

Fig. 112 Center intake manifold—6.6L engines

15. Install 2 new O–rings onto the intake manifold tube.
16. Lubricate the O–rings with clean engine oil to aid in the installation.
17. Install the intake manifold tube.
18. Install the EGR valve cooler tube.

Left & Right Manifolds

See Figures 113 through 115.

1. Before servicing the vehicle, refer to the Precautions Section.

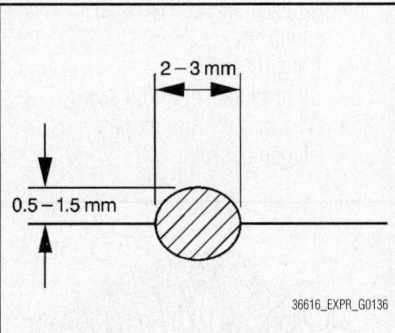

Fig. 113 Sealant application points—6.6L engines

2. Disconnect the negative battery cable.
3. Drain the cooling system. Properly dispose of used coolant.
4. Remove or disconnect the following:
- Batteries cables
- Center intake manifold
- Auxiliary alternator, if equipped
- Fuel junction block
- Left or right fuel rail
- Intake manifold tube
- 9 bolts and 2 nuts from the intake manifold. A bolt is located in the manifold opening.

➡The intake manifold uses sealer. If necessary, pry at the area by the common rail bolt holes and be careful to avoid damaging the sealing surfaces.

- Intake manifold from the head. Cover the head openings to prevent debris from entering.
5. Clean all gaskets surface.

To install:

6. Install or connect the following:
- A ⅛ in. (2–3mm) wide to ¹⁄₁₆ in (0.5–1.5mm) high bead of sealant

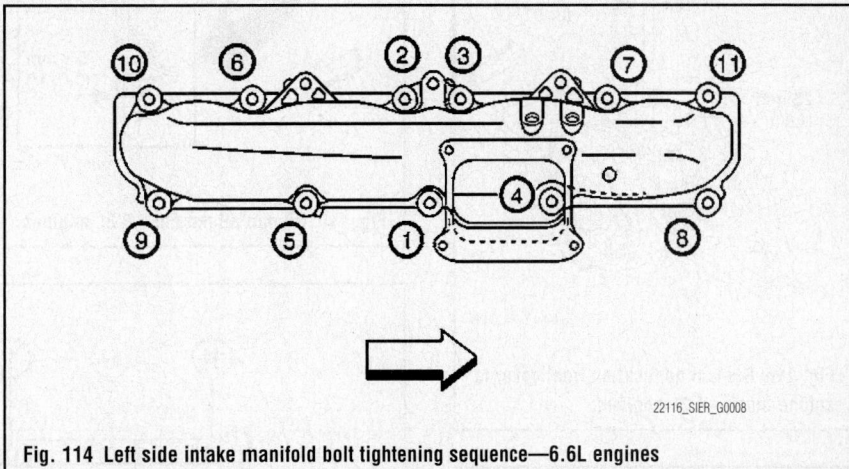

Fig. 114 Left side intake manifold bolt tightening sequence—6.6L engines

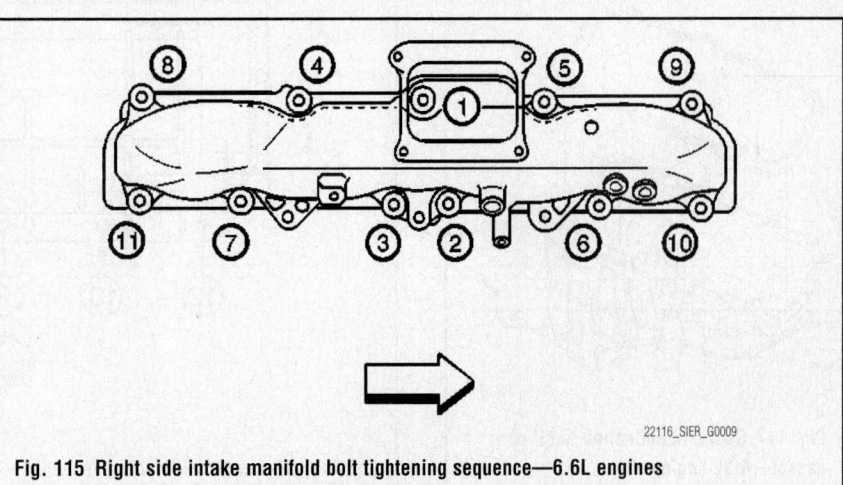

Fig. 115 Right side intake manifold bolt tightening sequence—6.6L engines

to the sealing surface of the intake manifold

➡ **The left and right side manifolds are NOT interchangeable.**

- Intake manifold
- Bolts and nuts. Tighten to 18 ft. lbs. (25 Nm), in sequence.
- Intake manifold tube
- Fuel rail
- Fuel junction block
- Turbocharger
- Negative battery cables
7. Fill cooling system.

OIL PAN

REMOVAL & INSTALLATION

4.3L Engines

See Figures 116 through 119.

1. Before servicing the vehicle, refer to the Precautions Section.
2. Disconnect the negative battery cable.
3. Raise and support the vehicle safely.

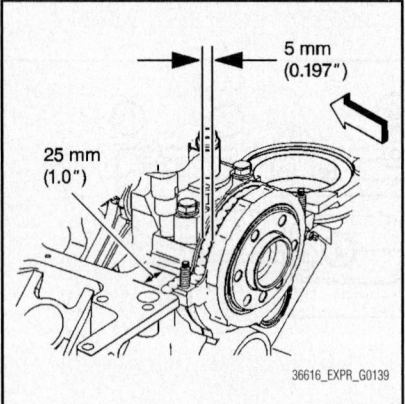

Fig. 116 Sealant application front cover to engine block—4.3L engines

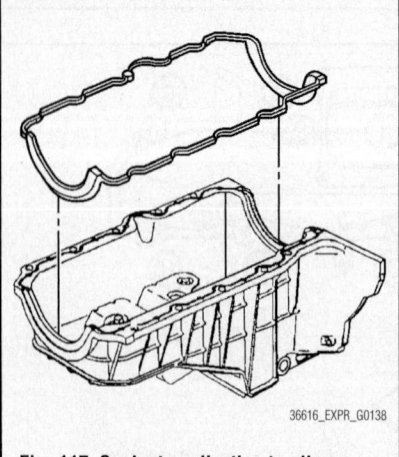

Fig. 117 Sealant application to oil pan gasket—4.3L engines

4. Drain the engine oil.
5. Remove or disconnect the following:
- Oil pan skid plate bolts and plate, if equipped
- Engine oil and filter
- Crossmember bolts and bar
- On 4WD, the front differential carrier
- Battery cable bracket bolts.
- Starter
- Transmission cover
- Positive battery cable clip bolt
- Oil level sensor electrical connector
- Transmission
- Oil level sensor and discard
- Oil pan bolts and oil pan
- Oil pan gasket

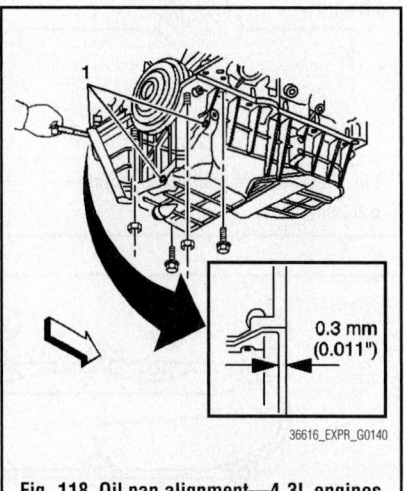

Fig. 118 Oil pan alignment—4.3L engines

To install:

➡ Be sure to use new fasteners, as required.

➡ Any time the transmission and oil pan are off the engine at the same time, install the transmission before the oil pan. This is to allow for proper oil pan alignment. Failure to achieve the correct oil pan alignment can result in transmission failure.

6. Thoroughly clean all gasket surfaces,
7. Apply a 5 mm wide and 25 mm long bead of sealant to both the right and left sides of the engine front cover to engine block junction at the oil pan sealing surfaces.
8. Apply a 5 mm wide and 25 mm long bead of sealant to both the right and left sides of the crankshaft rear oil seal housing to engine block junction at the oil pan sealing surfaces.
9. Install or connect the following:
- Transmission
- New gasket
- Oil pan and new gasket
- Install the oil pan bolts and nuts, but do not tighten
10. Measure the pan-to-transmission housing clearance using a feeler gage and a straight edge. Use a feeler gage to check the clearance between the oil pan-to-transmission housing measurement points. If the clearance exceeds 0.011 in. (0.3 mm) at any of the 3 oil pan-to-transmission housing measurement points (1), then repeat the step until the oil pan-to-transmission hous-

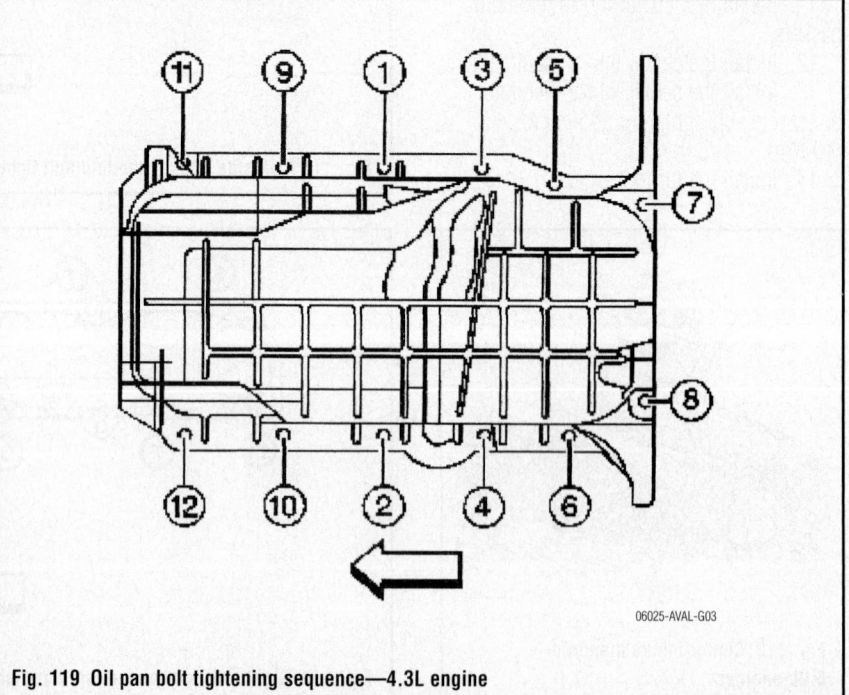

Fig. 119 Oil pan bolt tightening sequence—4.3L engine

ing clearance is within the specification. The oil pan must always be forward of the rear face of the engine block.

11. Install the oil pan bolts, nuts and reinforcements. Torque bolts in sequence to 18 ft. lbs. (25 Nm).

- Oil level sensor electrical connector
- Positive battery cable clip bolt
- Transmission cover
- Starter
- Battery cable bracket bolts.
- On 4WD, the front differential carrier
- Crossmember bolts and bar
- Engine oil and filter
- Oil pan skid plate bolts and plate, if equipped
- Negative battery cable

12. Refill the engine with oil.

4.8L, 5.3L & 6.0L Engines

See Figures 120 and 121.

➡The original oil pan gasket is retained and aligned to the oil pan by rivets. When installing a new gasket, it is not necessary to install new rivets. DO NOT reuse the oil pan gasket. When installing the oil pan, install a NEW oil pan gasket.

1. Before servicing the vehicle, refer to the Precautions Section.
2. Disconnect the negative battery cable.
3. Raise and support the vehicle safely.
4. Remove or disconnect the following:
- Front differential if equipped with AWD
- Under body shield from the vehicle
- Oil pan shield, if equipped
- Cross brace if equipped
- Engine oil and filter
- Transmission-to-oil pan bolts

- Oil level sensor electrical connector
- Two front wiring harness retainer bolts
- Engine wiring harness retainer bolts from the engine oil pan
- Engine oil cooler pipe-to-oil pan bolt
- Transmission oil cooler pipe retainer and the bolt from the oil pan
- Closeout covers and bolts (one each side of engine)
- Engine mount bolts each side
- Oil pan

To install:

➡The alignment of the structural oil pan is critical. The rear bolt hole locations of the oil pan provide mounting points for the transmission bell housing. To ensure the rigidity of the powertrain and correct transmission alignment, it is important that the rear of the block and the rear of the oil pan must NEVER protrude beyond the engine block and transmission bell housing plane.

5. Apply a 0.20 in. (5mm) bead of sealant GM P/N 12378190 or equivalent 0.8 in. (20mm) long to the engine block. Apply the sealant directly onto the tabs of the front cover gasket that protrudes into the oil pan surface.

➡Be sure to align the oil gallery passages in the oil pan and engine block properly with the oil pan gasket.

6. Pre-assemble the oil pan gasket to the pan. Install the oil pan bolts to the pan through the gasket.
7. Install or connect the following:
- Oil pan gasket
- Oil pan
- Oil pan bolts, finger-tight. Do not over tighten.

- Two lower bell housing bolts to position the oil pan correctly

8. Snug the lower bell housing bolt finger-tight. Do not over tighten. Tighten the oil pan-to-block and oil pan-to-oil pan front cover bolts to 18 ft. lbs. (25 Nm). Tighten the oil pan-to-rear cover bolts to 106 inch lbs. (12 Nm). Tighten the bell housing bolts to 37 ft. lbs. (50 Nm).

- Transmission oil cooler pipe retainer and the bolt to the oil pan
- Engine oil cooler pipe-to-oil pan bolt and tighten to 89 inch lbs. (10 Nm)
- Engine wiring harness retainer bolts to the engine oil pan
- Oil level sensor electrical connector
- Transmission-to-oil pan bolts and tighten to 41 ft. lbs. (55 Nm)
- Front differential, if equipped with AWD
- Underbody shield

9. Lower the vehicle. Fill the engine with oil and install the engine oil filter.
10. Connect the negative battery cable.

6.6L Engines

Lower Oil Pan

See Figures 122 and 123.

1. Before servicing the vehicle, refer to the Precautions Section.
2. Disconnect the negative battery cable.
3. Raise and support the vehicle safely.
4. Drain the engine oil.
5. Remove or disconnect the following:
- Oil pan skid plate, if equipped
- Crossbar
- Oil level sensor connector
- Lower oil pan bolts and nuts
- Lower oil pan from the lower crankcase
- Lower oil pan

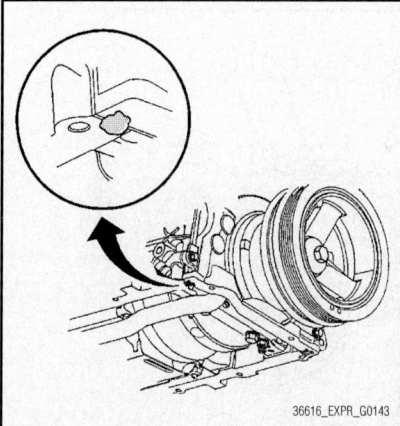

36616_EXPR_G0143

Fig. 120 Apply sealant at these points at the front of the block—4.8L, 5.3L and 6.0L engines

36616_EXPR_G0144

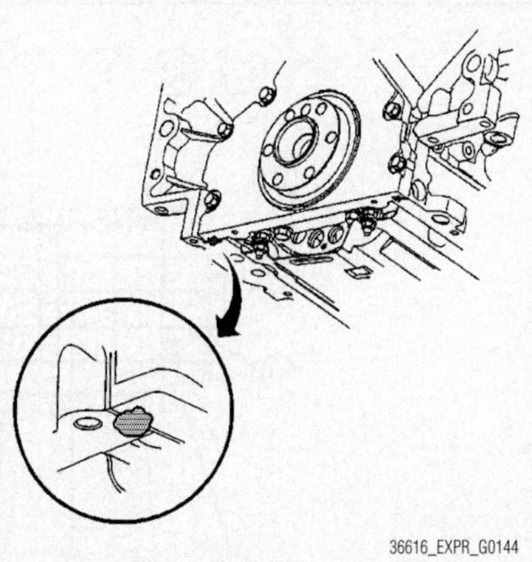

Fig. 121 Apply sealant at these points at the rear of the block—4.8L, 5.3L and 6.0L engines

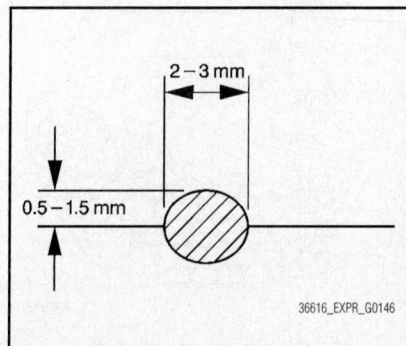

36616_EXPR_G0146

Fig. 122 Sealant application point—6.6L engines

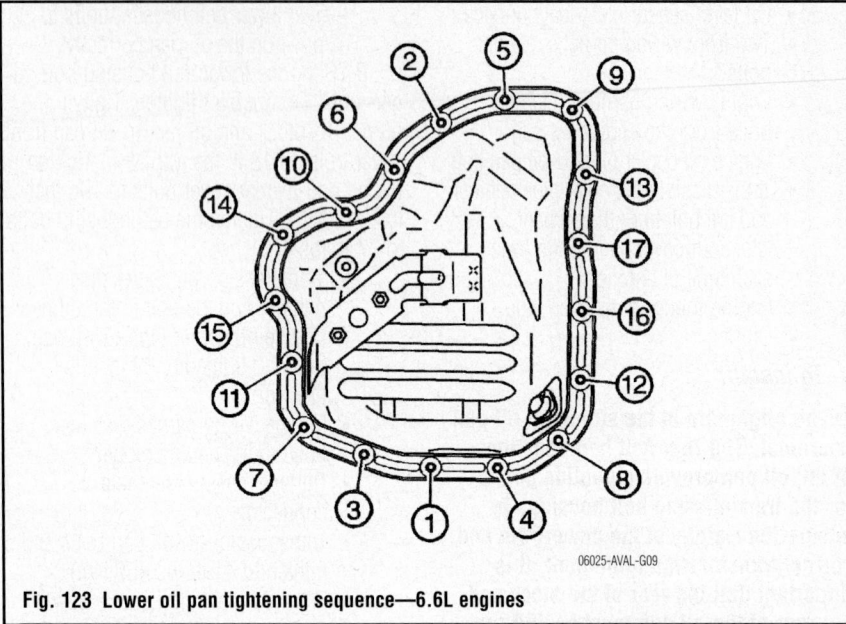

Fig. 123 Lower oil pan tightening sequence—6.6L engines

To install:

➡️**Be sure to use new fasteners, as required.**

6. Clean all sealing surfaces.

7. Apply a ⅛ in. (2mm) bead of sealant to the oil pan sealing surface.

8. Install the oil pan. Tighten the bolts and nuts in sequence to 89 inch lbs. (10 Nm)

9. The remainder of installation is the reverse of the removal procedure.

10. Refill engine with oil.

Upper Oil Pan

See Figures 124 through 126.

1. Before servicing the vehicle, refer to the Precautions Section.

2. Disconnect the negative battery cable.

3. Raise and support the vehicle safely.

4. Drain the engine oil.

5. Remove or disconnect the following:
   - Front differential carrier, if equipped

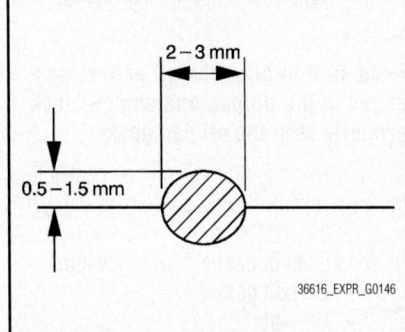

Fig. 125 Sealant application point—6.6L engines

- Relay rod from the pitman arm and idler arm (RWD)
- Transmission
- Lower oil pan
- Flexplate
- Positive and negative battery cable bracket bolts and bracket from the front of the upper oil pan
- Positive and negative battery cable bracket nut and bracket from the right side of the upper oil pan
- 2 engine flywheel housing to upper oil pan bolts (refer to denoted black triangles on accompanying figure)
- Upper oil pan bolts and any brackets
- Upper oil pan from the engine block
- Upper oil pan. The oil dipstick tube needs to be removed while lowering the upper oil pan.

To install:

➡️**Be sure to use new fasteners, as required.**

6. Clean all sealing surfaces.

7. Apply a ⅛ in. (2mm) bead of sealant to the oil pan and flywheel sealing surfaces.

8. Install or connect the following:
   - Upper oil pan; make sure the dipstick is installed into the upper pan
   - Upper pan bolts and brackets. Tighten, in sequence, to 15 ft. lbs. (20 Nm).
   - 2 engine flywheel housing to upper oil pan bolts (refer to denoted black triangles on accompanying figure). Torque to 37 ft. lbs. (50 Nm).

9. The remainder of installation is the reverse of the removal procedure.

10. Refill engine with oil.

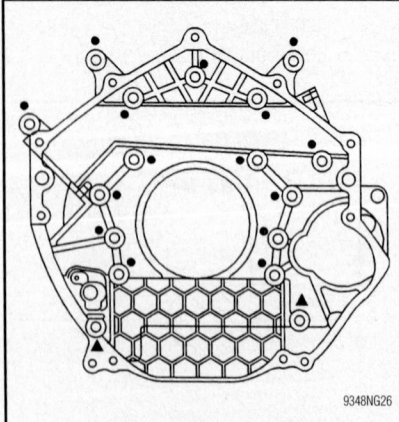

Fig. 124 Remove only the flywheel housing-to-upper oil pan bolts designated with a black triangle—6.6L engines

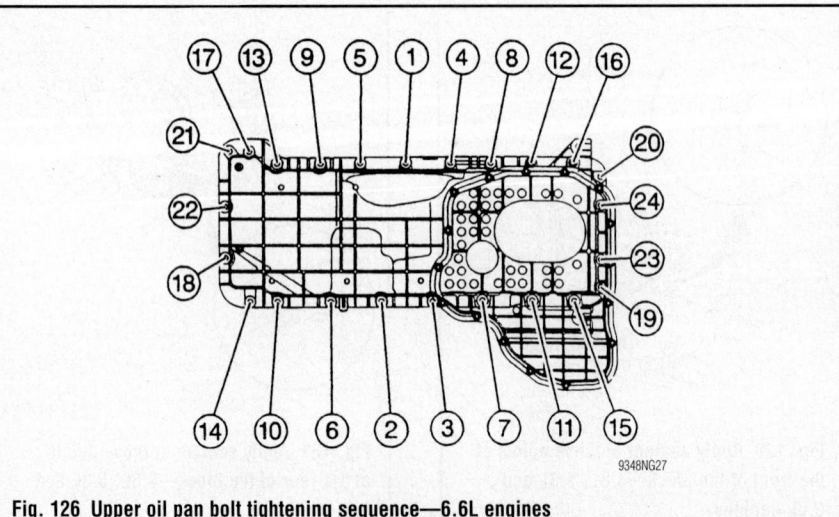

Fig. 126 Upper oil pan bolt tightening sequence—6.6L engines

OIL PUMP

REMOVAL & INSTALLATION

4.3L Engines

See Figures 127 and 128.

1. Before servicing the vehicle, refer to the Precautions Section.
2. Disconnect the negative battery cable.
3. Raise and support the vehicle safely.
4. Remove or disconnect the following:
   - Oil pan
   - Oil pump mounting bolt
   - Oil pump

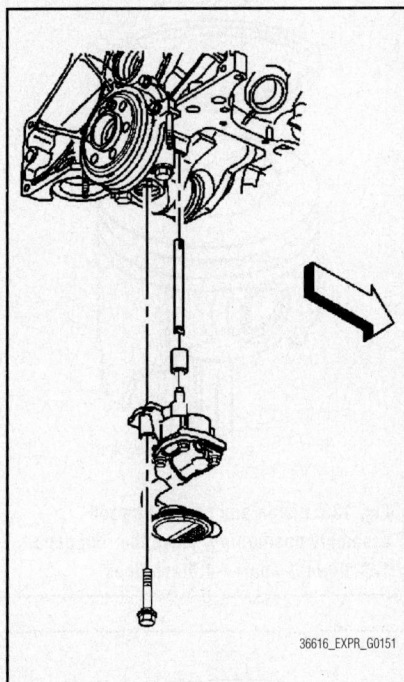

Fig. 127 Oil pump and related components—4.3L engines

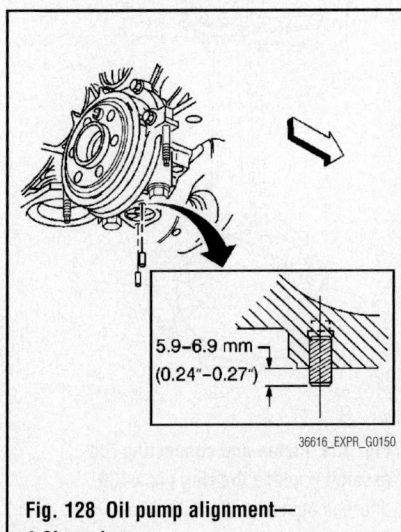

Fig. 128 Oil pump alignment—4.3L engines

To install:

5. Inspect the oil pump locator pins for damage, and replace if required.

➡**Do not reuse the oil pump driveshaft retainer. Install a new one.**

6. Clean and inspect the oil pump.
7. Position the oil pump onto the locator pins.
8. Install the oil pump bolt and tighten the bolt to 66 ft. lbs. (90 Nm).
9. Install the oil pan.

4.8L, 5.3L & 6.0L Engines

See Figures 129 and 130.

1. Before servicing the vehicle, refer to the Precautions Section.
2. Disconnect the negative battery cable.
3. Raise and support the vehicle safely.
4. Remove or disconnect the following:
   - Engine front cover
   - Oil pan
   - Oil pump screen bolt and nuts
   - Oil pump screen with O–ring seal.
   - O–ring seal from the pump screen. Discard the O–ring seal.

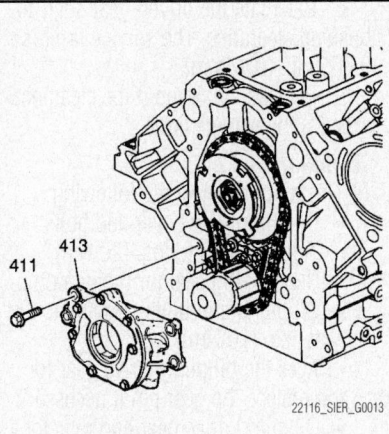

Fig. 129 Oil pump and related components—4.8L, 5.3L and 6.0L engines

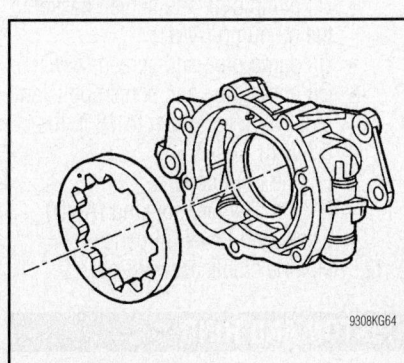

Fig. 130 Oil pump disassembly—4.8L, 5.3L and 6.0L engines

- Remaining crankshaft oil deflector nuts.
- Crankshaft oil deflector
- Oil pump bolts

➡**Do not allow dirt or debris to enter the oil pump assembly, cap ends as necessary.**

- Oil pump

➡**The internal parts of the oil pump assembly are not serviced separately (excluding the spring). If the oil pump components are worn or damaged, replace the oil pump as an assembly. Do not attempt to repair the wire mesh portion of the pump and screen assembly.**

To install:

➡**Inspect the oil pump and engine block oil gallery passages. These surfaces must be clear and free of debris or restrictions.**

5. Align the splined surfaces of the crankshaft sprocket and the oil pump drive gear and install the oil pump. Install the oil pump onto the crankshaft sprocket until the pump housing contacts the face of the engine block.
6. Install or connect the following:
   - Oil pump bolts. Tighten the oil pump bolts to 18 ft. lbs. (25 Nm).
   - Crankshaft oil deflector

➡**Lubricate a NEW oil pump screen O–ring seal with clean engine oil.**

- NEW O–ring seal onto the oil pump screen

➡**Push the oil pump screen tube completely into the oil pump prior to tightening the bolt. Do not allow the bolt to pull the tube into the pump.**

7. Align the oil pump screen mounting brackets with the correct crankshaft bearing cap studs.
8. Install or connect the following:
   - Oil pump screen
   - Oil pump screen bolt and the deflector nuts. Tighten the bolt to 106 inch lbs. (12 Nm) and the nuts to 18 ft. lbs. (25 Nm).
   - Oil pan
   - Engine front cover

6.6L Engines

See Figures 131 and 132.

1. Before servicing the vehicle, refer to the Precautions Section.
2. Disconnect the negative battery cable.

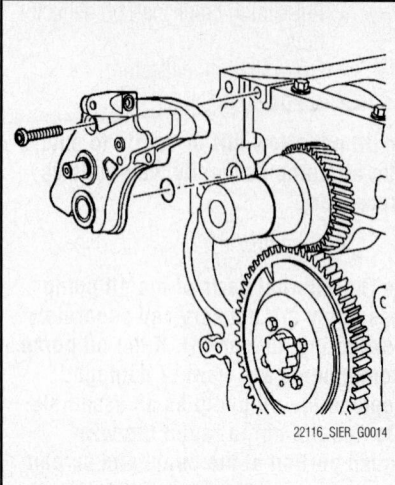

Fig. 131 Oil pump and related components—6.6L engines

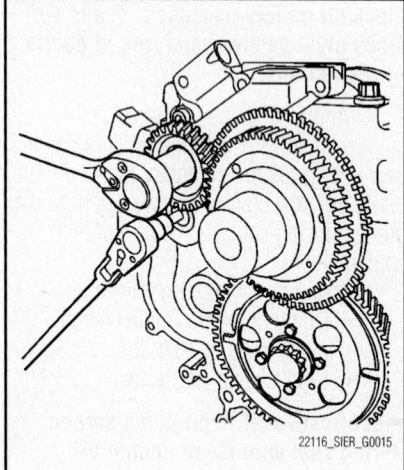

Fig. 132 Installing the oil pump drive gear—6.6L engines

3. Raise and support the vehicle safely.
4. Drain the engine oil.
5. Remove or disconnect the following:
   • Engine flywheel housing (RWD)
   • Engine front cover
   • Lower and upper oil pans
   • Oil pump pipe and screen and gasket
6. Block the crankshaft from turning with a wooden dowel.
   • Oil pump driven gear nut
   • Oil pump driven gear

➡**The crankshaft reluctor and oil pump drive gear are timed together at the factory. Do NOT remove the reluctor from the oil pump drive gear or damage the reluctor teeth.**

   • Oil pump drive gear and crankshaft reluctor assembly using a brass drift and tapping as close to the center of the reluctor assembly

   • 3 hex head and 1 Allen head bolt
   • Oil pump
   • Oil pump O–ring seal
   • Oil pump gear cover bolts and cover
7. Measure the clearance between the gear teeth and oil pump housing using a feeler gauge. The production clearance is 0.0049–0.0087 in. (0.125–0.221mm) and the service limit is 0.0087 in. (0.221mm). Replace the pump if the clearance exceeds the service limit.
8. Use a feeler gauge and a straightedge to measure the clearance between the side of the gear and the cover. The production clearance is 0.0025–0.0043 in. (0.064–0.109mm) and the service limit is 0.0043 in. (0.109mm). Replace the pump if the clearance exceeds the service limit.
9. Calculate the driven gear shaft-to-bushing clearance:
   a. Measure the driven gear shaft outside diameter. The production specification is 0.7853–0.7858 in. (19.947–19.960mm) and the service limit is 0.7819 in. (19.86mm).
   b. Measure the driven gear bushing inside diameter. The production value is 0.7874 in. (20mm).
   c. Calculate the driven gear shaft-to-bushing clearance. The service limit is 0.0055 in. (0.14mm).
   d. Replace the pump if the clearance exceeds the service limit.

To install:
10. Install or connect the following:
    • Oil pump gear cover and bolts. Tighten to 15 ft. lbs. (20 Nm).
    • New O–ring seal for the oil pump
    • Oil pump and bolts. Tighten to 15 ft. lbs. (20 Nm).
11. Check the oil pump drive gear for wear and replace the gear pin if necessary.
    • Oil pump drive gear and reluctor
    • Oil pump driven gear and nut. Block the crankshaft from moving, then tighten to 74 ft. lbs. (100 Nm).
    • Oil pump pipe and screen gasket to the oil pump (AWD)
    • Oil pump pipe and screen (AWD)
    • Oil pump pipe and screen bolts and nuts (AWD). Tighten to 18 ft. lbs. (25 Nm).
    • Engine front cover
    • Engine flywheel housing (AWD)
    • Upper and lower oil pans
12. Refill the crankcase with oil.

PISTON AND RING

POSITIONING

See Figures 133 through 135.

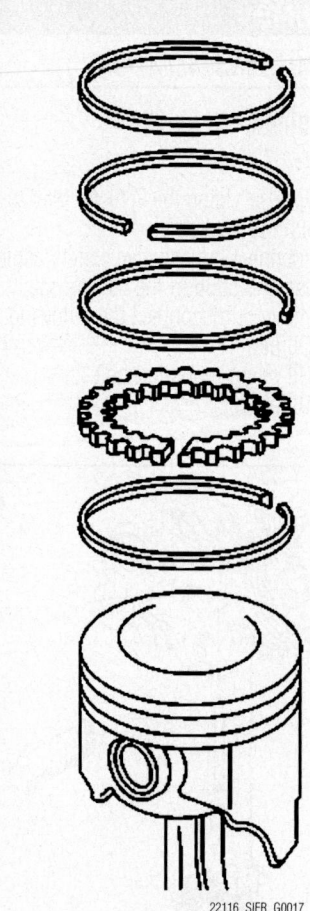

Fig. 133 Piston and connecting rod assembly positioning; place the ring gaps 120 degrees apart—4.3L engines

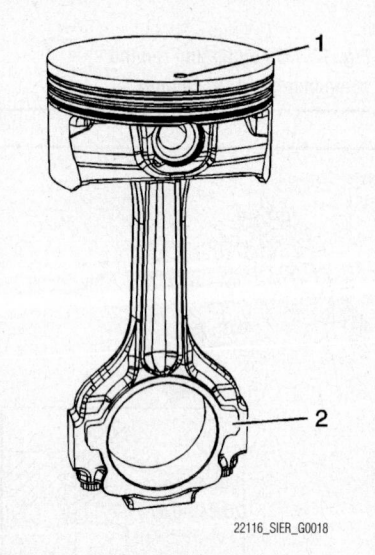

Fig. 134 Piston and connecting rod assembly; place the ring gaps 180 degrees apart—4.8L, 5.3L and 6.0L engines

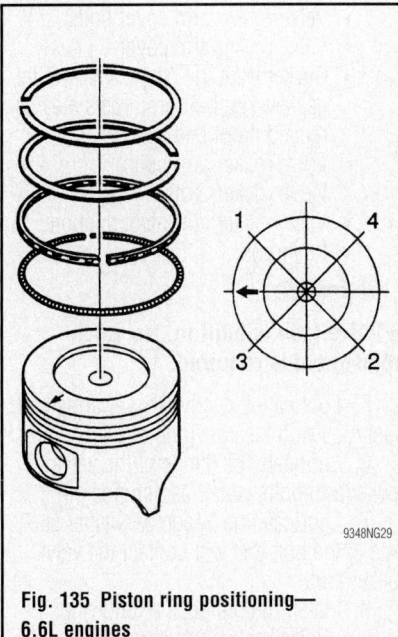

Fig. 135 Piston ring positioning—6.6L engines

REAR MAIN SEAL

REMOVAL & INSTALLATION

4.3L, 4.8L, 5.3L & 6.0L Engines

Please note that the entire transmission assembly and flexplate must be removed to perform this procedure.

1. Remove or disconnect the following:
   - Negative battery cable
   - Transfer case, if equipped
   - Transmission assembly
   - Clutch assembly and flywheel, if equipped with manual transmission
   - Flexplate, if equipped with automatic transmission
   - Crankshaft rear main oil seal by inserting a suitable prying tool and prying the seal out. Take care not to damage the crankshaft sealing surface.

To install:

2. Clean the oil seal bore in the block thoroughly before installation of the new seal.
3. Inspect the crankshaft for grit, rust or burrs and correct as necessary. Also inspect the portion of the crankshaft where the oil seal makes contact, for wear due to the rubbing action of the oil seal.
4. Clean the seal running surface of the crankshaft with a non–abrasive cleaner.
5. Lubricate the inner diameter of the new seal and the outer diameter of the crankshaft with engine oil.
6. Install or connect the following:
   - Rear main oil seal, using installation tool J 38841, J-35621–B or

J-41479, until the tool bottoms against the block and crankshaft rear main bearing cap.
   - Flywheel and clutch
   - Flexplate, as required
   - Transmission assembly
   - Transfer case, if equipped
   - Negative battery cable
7. Start the engine and verify no oil leaks.

6.6L Engines

Please note that the entire transmission assembly must be removed before performing this procedure. Before a new seal is installed, the Crankcase Depression Regulator (CDR) and crankcase ventilation system should be cleaned and inspected. In addition, use care removing the flywheel. Some models use a heavy, dual mass flywheel that must be handled with care.

1. Before servicing the vehicle, refer to the Precautions Section.
2. Remove or disconnect the following:
   - Negative battery cables
   - Transfer case, if equipped
   - Transmission assembly
   - Clutch assembly and flywheel, if equipped with manual transmission
   - Flexplate, if equipped with automatic transmission
   - Crankshaft rear main oil seal by inserting a suitable crankshaft seal removal tool and prying the seal out

To install:

3. Clean the oil seal bore in the block thoroughly before installation of the new seal.
4. Inspect the crankshaft for grit, rust or burrs and correct as necessary. Also inspect the portion of the crankshaft where the oil seal makes contact, for wear due to the rubbing action of the oil seal.

➡Because of rear crankshaft wear or grooving, the new oil seal should be seated in a new location. The J 39084 installation tool will control the seal positioning. This will provide a new surface on the crankshaft for the seal to ride on.

5. Clean the running surface of the crankshaft with a non–abrasive cleaner.
6. Lubricate the inner diameter of the new seal and the outer diameter of the crankshaft with engine oil.
7. Install or connect the following:
   - Rear main oil seal using a crankshaft rear oil seal installation tool
   - Flywheel.

   - Transmission assembly
   - Transfer case, if equipped
   - Negative battery cables
8. Start the engine and verify no oil leaks.

ROCKER ARMS/SHAFTS

REMOVAL & INSTALLATION

4.3L Engines

See Figures 136 and 137.

1. Before servicing the vehicle, refer to the Precautions Section.
2. Disconnect the negative battery cable.
3. Remove or disconnect the following:
   - Engine cover
   - Cylinder head cover
   - Rocker arm nut. If you are only replacing the pushrod, back the nut off until you can swing the rocker out of the way.
   - Rocker arms and balls as a unit

➡Always remove each set of rocker arms (1 set per cylinder) as a unit.

   - Pushrods and pushrod guides

To install:

4. Install or connect the following:
   - Pushrods and their guides. Be sure that they seat properly in each lifter.
5. Position a set of rocker arms (for 1 cylinder) in the proper location.

➡Install the rocker arms for each cylinder only when the lifters are off the cam lobe and both valves are closed.

6. Coat the replacement rocker arm with Molykote® or its equivalent, and the rocker

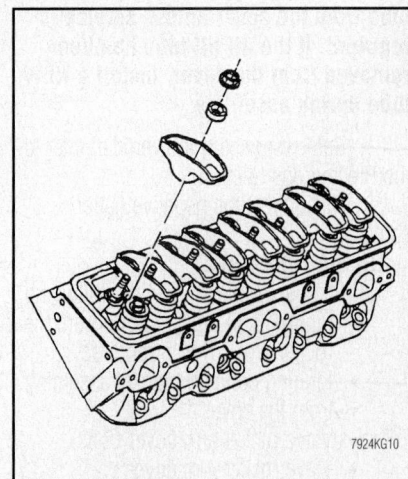

Fig. 136 Exploded view to the rocker arm and related components—4.3L engines

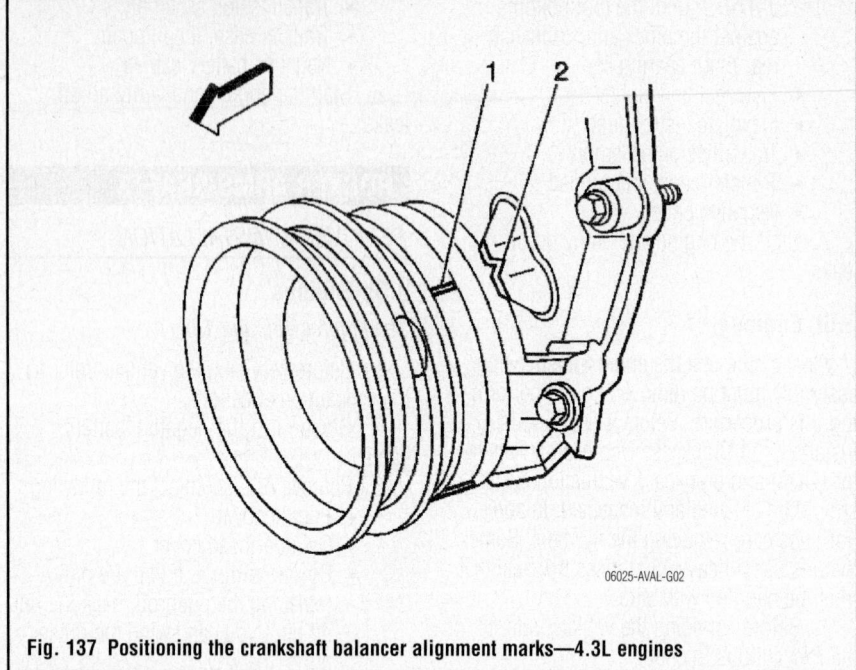

Fig. 137 Positioning the crankshaft balancer alignment marks—4.3L engines

arm and pivot with SAE 90 gear oil, and install the pivots.

- Nuts and finger tighten

7. Rotate the crankshaft balancer to position the crankshaft balancer alignment mark (1) 57–63 degrees clockwise or counterclockwise from the engine front cover alignment tab (2).

8. Tighten the rocker arm nuts to 22 ft. lbs. (30 Nm).

9. Install the rocker arm cover.

10. Install the engine cover.

4.8L, 5.3L & 6.0L Engines

See Figure 138.

➡️**Do not remove the ignition coils from the valve rocker arm cover unless required. Do not remove the oil fill tube from the cover unless service is required. If the oil fill tube has been removed from the cover, install a NEW tube during assembly.**

1. Before servicing the vehicle, refer to the Precautions Section.

2. Disconnect the negative battery cable.

On the right side:

3. Remove or disconnect the following:
- Ignition coil bracket bolts from the rocker arm cover, if required
- Ignition coil and bracket assembly from the cover
- Valve rocker arm cover bolts
- Valve rocker arm cover
- Gasket from the cover. Discard the gasket. The bolt grommets may be reused if not damaged.

- Oil fill cap from the oil fill tube
- Oil fill tube, if required. Discard the oil fill tube.

On the left side:

➡️**Do not remove the Positive Crankcase Ventilation (PCV) valve grommet from the cover unless service is required.**

4. Remove or disconnect the following:
- Ignition coil bracket bolts from the rocker arm cover (if required)
- Ignition coil and bracket assembly from the cover

- Valve rocker arm cover bolts
- Valve rocker arm cover
- Gasket from the cover. Discard the gasket. The bolt grommets may be reused if not damaged.
- Valve rocker arm bolts
- Valve rocker arms
- Valve rocker arm pivot support
- Pushrods

To install:

➡️**Valve lash is built in. No valve adjustment is required.**

5. Lubricate the valve rocker arms and pushrods with clean engine oil.

6. Lubricate the flange of the valve rocker arm bolts with clean engine oil.

7. Lubricate the flange or washer surface of the bolt that will contact the valve rocker arm.

8. Install or connect the following:
- Valve rocker arm pivot support

➡️**Make sure that the pushrods seat properly to the valve lifter sockets.**

- Pushrods

➡️**Make sure that the pushrods seat properly to the ends of the rocker arms.**

- Rocker arms and bolts. DO NOT tighten the rocker arm bolts at this time

9. Rotate the crankshaft until number one piston is at top dead center of compression stroke. In this position, cylinder number one rocker arms will be off lobe lift. The engine firing order is 1, 8, 7, 2, 6, 5, 4, 3.

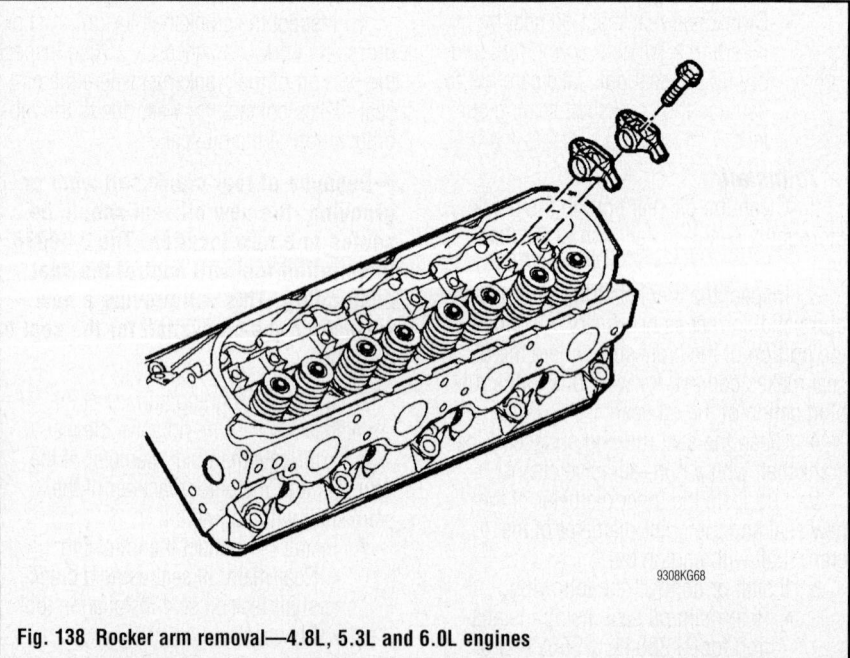

Fig. 138 Rocker arm removal—4.8L, 5.3L and 6.0L engines

Cylinders 1, 3, 5 and 7 are left bank. Cylinders 2, 4, 6, and 8 are right bank.

10. With the engine in the number one firing position, tighten the following valve rocker arm bolts:

  a. Tighten exhaust valve rocker arm bolts 1, 2, 7, and 8 to 22 ft. lbs. (30 Nm).

  b. Tighten intake valve rocker arm bolts 1, 3, 4, and 5 to 22 ft. lbs. (30 Nm).

11. Rotate the crankshaft 360 degrees. Tighten the following valve rocker arm bolts:

  a. Tighten exhaust valve rocker arm bolts 3, 4, 5, and 6 to 22 ft. lbs. (30 Nm).

  b. Tighten intake valve rocker arm bolts 2, 6, 7, and 8 to 22 ft. lbs. (30 Nm).

On the right side:

➡**The valve rocker arm cover bolt grommets may be reused. If the oil fill tube has been removed from the valve rocker arm cover, install a NEW oil fill tube during assembly.**

12. Lubricate the O–ring seal of the NEW oil fill tube with clean engine oil.

13. Install or connect the following:

  • NEW oil fill tube into the rocker arm cover and rotate the tube clockwise until locked in the proper position

  • Oil fill cap into the tube and rotate clockwise until locked in the proper position

  • NEW cover gasket into the valve rocker arm cover

  • Valve rocker arm cover onto the cylinder head

14. Install the cover bolts with grommets. Tighten the valve rocker arm cover bolts to 106 inch lbs. (12 Nm).

15. Apply threadlock GM P/N 12345382 or equivalent to the threads of the bracket bolts. Install the ignition coil and bracket assembly and bolts. Tighten the ignition coil and bracket assembly studs to 106 inch lbs. (12 Nm).

On the left side:

➡**DO NOT reuse the valve rocker arm cover gasket. The valve rocker arm cover bolt grommets may be reused. If the vapor vent grommet has been removed from the valve rocker arm cover, install a NEW vapor vent gourmet during assembly.**

16. Install or connect the following:

  • NEW cover gasket (1) into the valve rocker arm cover

  • Valve rocker arm cover onto the cylinder head

17. Install the cover bolts with grommets.

Tighten the valve rocker arm cover bolts to 106 inch lbs. (12 Nm).

18. Apply threadlock GM P/N 12345382 or equivalent to the threads of the bracket bolts. Install the ignition coils and bracket assembly and bolts. Tighten the ignition coil and bracket assembly bolts to 106 inch lbs. (12 Nm).

6.6L Engines

See Figures 139 through 142.

1. Before servicing the vehicle, refer to the Precautions Section.

2. Remove the lower valve (rocker arm) covers

3. Loosen the valve clearance lock nuts on each rocker arm

4. Loosen the valve clearance adjusting screw on each rocker arm to relieve tension on the valve train

➡**The rocker arm bolts retain the rocker arms on the shaft. Do not remove the bolts from the rocker arm shaft brackets.**

5. Loosen the rocker arm shaft bolts in the proper sequence, leaving the bolts in the rocker arm shaft brackets.

6. Remove or disconnect the following:

  • Rocker arm shaft assemblies from the cylinder head

  • Valve bridge pins

  • Valve bridges

  • Valve push rods

7. Clean all parts in a suitable solvent.

Disassemble the rocker arm shaft as necessary.

To install:

8. Lubricate the rocker arm shaft and the inside of the rocker arms with engine oil.

9. If disassembled, install or connect the following:

  • Rocker arm bracket on one end of the rocker arm shaft with the bolt

  • Rocker arm intake, spring, exhaust and the bracket with bolt. Continue in the same sequence to the last bracket.

  • Push the bracket to compress the springs and then install the bolt

10. Lubricate the top of the valves, the valve bridge stem, the valve bridge and the valve bridge pins.

11. Install or connect the following:

  • Valve bridge pins

  • Valve bridges

  • Pushrods. Make sure it is fully installed by gently pulling up on it. You should feel resistance from the pushrod trying to lift the valve lifter

12. Use clean engine oil to lubricate the rocker arm shaft bolt threads, tops of the push rods, rocker arms and rocker arm shaft.

  • Rocker arm shaft assembly to the cylinder head

  • Rocker arm shaft assembly bolts and tighten, in the proper sequence to 30 ft. lbs. (40 Nm)

13. Adjust the valve clearance, as follows:

  a. Remove the fan clutch.

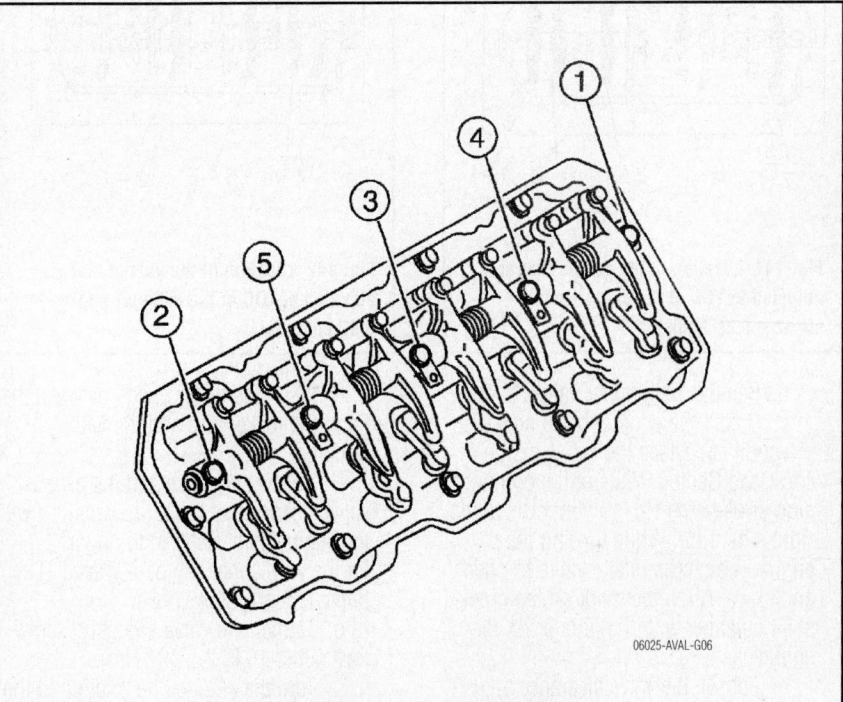

06025-AVAL-G06

Fig. 139 Rocker arm shaft bolt loosening sequence—6.6L engines

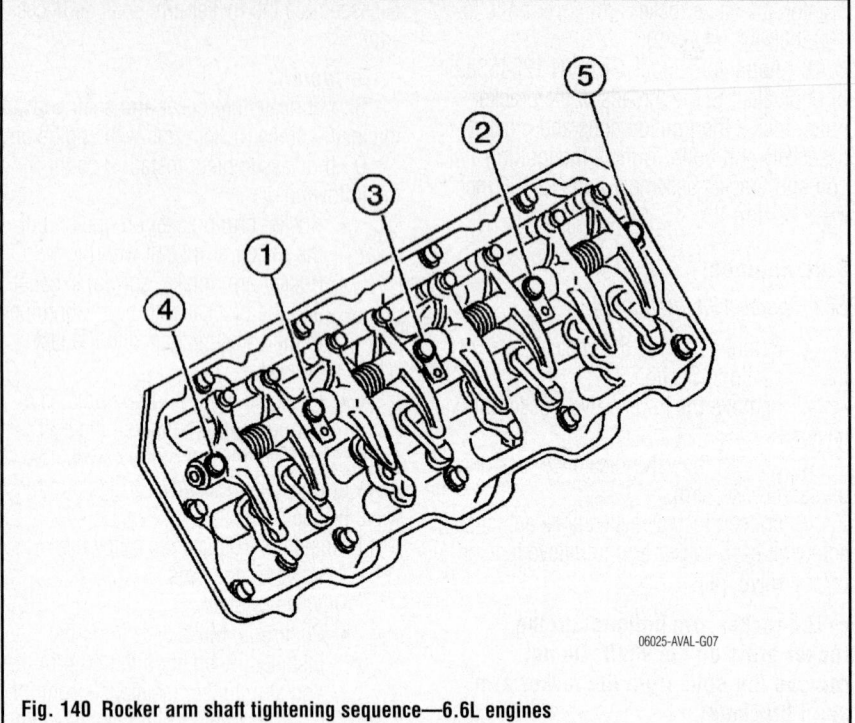

06025-AVAL-G07

Fig. 140 Rocker arm shaft tightening sequence—6.6L engines

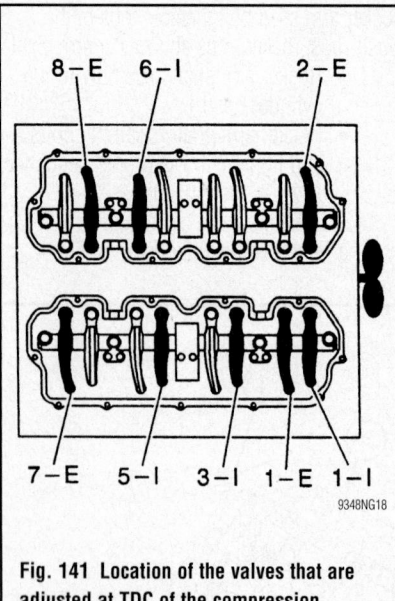

9348NG18

Fig. 141 Location of the valves that are adjusted at TDC of the compression stroke—6.6L engines

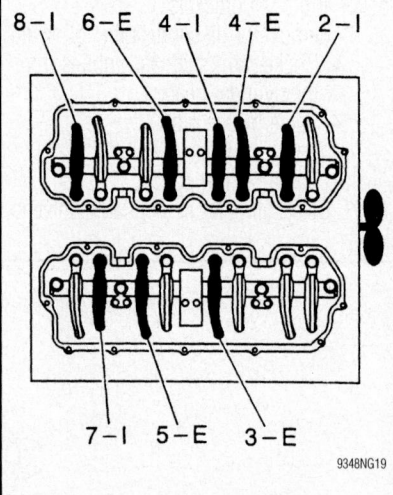

9348NG19

Fig. 142 Location of the valves that are adjusted at TDC of the exhaust stroke—6.6L engines

b. Remove both upper valve covers.

c. Rotate the engine in the normal direction and place the No. 1 piston at Top Dead Center (TDC) of the compression stroke. The No. 1 cylinder is at the right side front. While turning the engine, watch the intake valve to open and close. Align the mark on the crankshaft balancer with the pointer on the engine.

d. Loosen the valve clearance adjusting screws for the valve being adjusted.

e. Insert the feeler gauge between the tip of the rocker arm and the valve bridge.

f. Adjust the intake and the exhaust valve clearance to 0.012 in. (0.3mm) with the engine cold. Refer to the figure for the valves that can be adjusted TDC of the compression stroke.

g. Tighten the valve adjusting screw lock nut to 16 ft. lbs. (22 Nm).

h. Turn the engine one rotation in the normal direction and put the No. 1 piston

at TDC of the exhaust stroke to adjust the remaining valve clearance. While turning the engine, watch the exhaust valve to open and close. Align the mark on the crankshaft balancer with the pointer on the engine.

i. Loosen the valve clearance adjusting screws for the valves being adjusted.

j. Insert the feeler gauge between the tip of the rocker arm and the valve bridge.

k. Adjust the intake and the exhaust valve clearance to 0.012 in. (0.3mm) with the engine cold. Refer to the figure for the valves that can be adjusted TDC of the exhaust stroke.

l. Tighten the valve adjusting screw lock nut to 16 ft. lbs. (22 Nm).

14. Install the upper and lower valve cover and fan clutch, as necessary.

TURBOCHARGER

REMOVAL & INSTALLATION

6.6L Engines

See Figure 143.

1. Before servicing the vehicle, refer to the Precautions Section.

2. Disconnect the negative battery cables.

3. Open the hood and move the hinge bolts to the service position.

4. Raise the vehicle.

5. Drain the coolant.

6. Remove or disconnect the following:

• Left and right wheelhouse liners
• Exhaust pipe-to-exhaust outlet clamp. Move the clamp onto the exhaust pipe
• Transmission fluid fill tube-to-bell housing nuts if equipped with an A/T. Position the tube to the right side of the vehicle; it does not need to be removed from the transmission.

➡**If necessary, the entire transmission can be removed to gain additional clearance**

• 3 nuts and left exhaust heat shield from the front of the lower dash panel
• Left exhaust pipe heat shield bolts

7. Position the left exhaust pipe heat shield to access the left exhaust pipe-to-manifold bolts. Do not remove the heat shield from the vehicle at this time.

➡**Do not bend the exhaust pipe at the expansion area.**

- Left, then the right exhaust pipe-to-exhaust manifold bolts
- Gaskets and discard
- Lower bolt for the exhaust outlet shield

8. Lower the vehicle.
- Upper intake manifold sight shield front retaining bolt
- Sight shield
- Air cleaner outlet duct from the air cleaner and turbocharger. Cover the openings to prevent debris from entering
- Charged air cooler outlet duct-to-intake hose clamps (loosen only)
- Hose from the charged air cooler duct-to-intake manifold tube
- A/C compressor clutch electrical connector
- A/C cut-out switch connector
- Drive belt
- A/C compressor mounting bolts; position the compressor aside with the lines attached
- Turbocharger inlet coolant hose from the bypass valve
- Turbocharger outlet coolant hose from the turbocharger
- Crankcase hose from the left valve cover and position aside
- Wire connector from the intake heater
- Intake air heater relay, if equipped
- Heat shield-to-turbocharger bolts and heat shield
- Remaining 2 bolts from the exhaust outlet heat shield
- Exhaust outlet heat shield
- 4 bolts and 2 nuts from the exhaust outlet. You do not have to remove the outlet for turbocharger removal

9. Move the exhaust outlet to one side in order to access the right exhaust pipe-to-turbocharger bolts.
- Exhaust outlet gasket and discard
- Right exhaust pipe-to-turbocharger bolts
- Right exhaust pipe and gasket

10. Move the exhaust outlet to one side for access to the left pipe.
- Left exhaust pipe heat shield
- Left exhaust pipe-to-turbocharger bolts
- Left exhaust pipe and gasket
- Turbocharger oil supply hose eye bolt and washers. Move the hose aside
- Turbocharger oil drain pipe nuts from the flywheel housing
- Turbocharger mounting bolts
- Turbocharger with the oil drain pipe

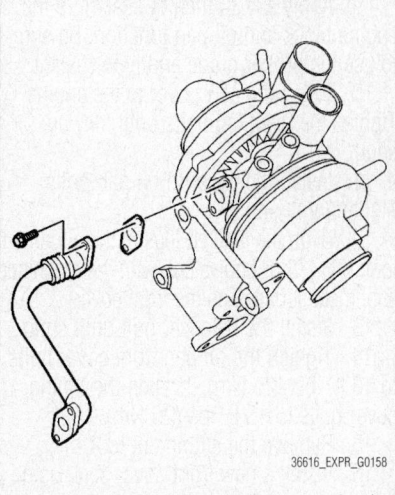

Fig. 143 Turbocharger assembly—6.6L engines

36616_EXPR_G0158

11. If replacing the turbocharger, remove the oil drain pipe and coolant hose.

To install:

12. Thoroughly clean the gasket surfaces.

13. Install or connect the following:
- Turbocharger oil drain pipe and new gasket. Tighten the bolts to 15 ft. lbs. (21 Nm).
- Turbocharger inlet coolant hose
- Turbocharger oil supply hose to the engine block
- Turbocharger oil supply hose eye bolt and washers
- Turbocharger lower heat shield
- Turbocharger. Tighten the 3 mounting bolts to 80 ft. lbs. (108 Nm).
- New gasket for oil drain pipe
- Oil drain pipe nuts

14. If installing a new turbocharger, pour 4–5 oz. of clean engine oil into the turbocharger supply hose opening, while rotating the impeller.
- Oil supply hose, using new washers. Tighten the eye bolt to 31 ft. lbs. (42 Nm) except on 2007 models. On 2007 models, tighten to 25 ft. lbs. (34 Nm)

15. Install the remaining components in the reverse order of removal, noting the following important points:
- When installing the exhaust pipe, use new gaskets and align the tabs and make sure the proper pipe flange is toward the turbocharger, as they are different. Tighten the exhaust pipe-to-turbocharger bolts to 39 ft. lbs. (53 Nm).
- Tighten the turbocharger heat shield bolts to 80 inch lbs. (9 Nm)

- Tighten the A/C compressor bolts to 37 ft. lbs. (50 Nm)
- Tighten the exhaust pipe clamp to 30 ft. lbs. (40 Nm)

16. Fill the cooling system and connect the negative battery cables.

➡Operate the engine at idle for at least 3 minutes after installing the turbocharger

TIMING CHAIN COVER AND SEAL

REMOVAL & INSTALLATION

4.3L Engines

See Figure 144.

1. Before servicing the vehicle, refer to the Precautions Section.
2. Disconnect the negative battery cable.
3. Drain the cooling system. Properly dispose of used coolant.
4. Remove the water pump.
5. Remove the crankshaft balancer.
6. Remove the oil pan.
7. Remove the engine shield.
8. Remove the engine wiring harness from the front cover.
9. Disconnect the Crankshaft Position (CKP) sensor electrical connector, if equipped.
10. Remove the CKP sensor and discard the O-ring.
11. Disconnect the engine wiring harness connector from the Camshaft Position (CMP) sensor.
12. Remove the CMP sensor.
13. Remove the front cover retaining bolts.
14. Remove the front cover from the engine.

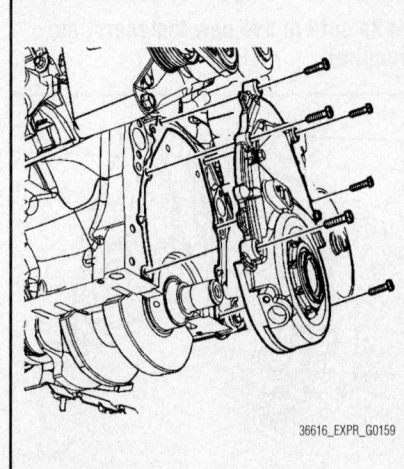

36616_EXPR_G0159

Fig. 144 Timing cover and related components—4.3L engines

→Do not reuse the front cover. It is a composite cover and must be replaced with a new cover.

To install:

→Be sure to use new fasteners, as required.

15. Install the new cover to the engine. Tighten the retaining bolts to 106 inch lbs. (12 Nm).

16. Using a new O–ring, lubricated with clean engine oil, install the CMP sensor. Tighten the retaining bolt to 89 inch lbs. (10 Nm).

17. Using a new O–ring, lubricated with clean engine oil, install the CKP sensor. Tighten the retaining bolt to 71 inch lbs. (8 Nm).

→Be sure that the sensor is correctly seated before tightening the retaining bolt.

18. Continue the installation in the reverse order of the removal procedure.

19. Start the engine and check for proper operation. Correct as required.

20. Check for leaks, correct as required.

4.8L, 5.3L & 6.0L Engines

See Figures 145 and 146.

1. Before servicing the vehicle, refer to the Precautions Section.

2. Disconnect the negative battery cable.

3. Drain the cooling system. Properly dispose of used coolant.

4. Remove the water pump.

5. Remove the crankshaft balancer.

6. Remove the oil pan to front cover bolts.

7. Remove the front cover retaining bolts.

8. Remove the front cover. Discard the gasket. Remove the oil seal.

To install:

→Be sure to use new fasteners, as required.

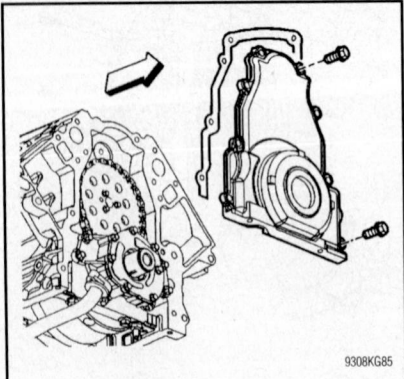

Fig. 145 Front cover and gasket—4.8L, 5.3L and 6.0L engines

9. Apply a 0.20 inch of sealant to the engine block and oil pan junction. Be sure to use the proper grade and type sealant.

10. Install the new cover to the engine. Tighten the retaining bolts until they are snug.

11. Install the cover to oil pan bolts. Tighten until snug.

12. Align the tapered legs of the alignment tool J-41476 or equivalent, with the machined alignment surfaces on the front cover.

13. Install the balancer bolt until snug.

14. Tighten the oil pan front cover bolts to 18 ft. lbs. (25 Nm). Tighten the timing cover bolts to 18 ft. lbs (25 Nm).

15. Remove the alignment tool.

16. Install a new front cover seal, using the proper seal installation tool.

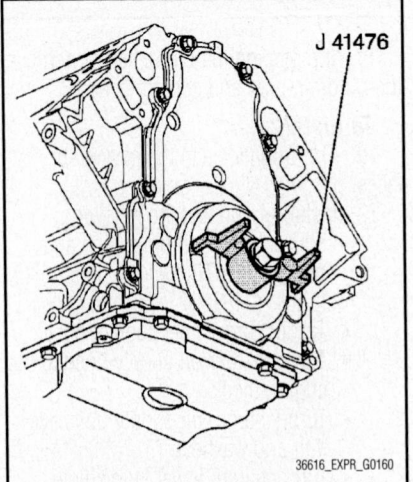

Fig. 146 Timing cover alignment tool installation—4.8L, 5.3L and 6.0L engines

17. Continue the installation in the reverse order of the removal procedure.

18. Start the engine and check for proper operation. Correct as required.

19. Check for leaks, correct as required.

6.6L Engines

See Figures 147 through 149.

1. Before servicing the vehicle, refer to the Precautions Section.

2. Disconnect the negative battery cables.

3. Remove the thermostat bypass pipe.

4. Remove the turbocharger coolant hoses and pipes.

5. Remove the upper oil pan.

6. Remove the cooling fan pulley.

7. Remove the water pump.

8. Remove the crankshaft balancer.

9. Remove the engine oil fill tube bolts. Remove the engine oil fill tube.

10. Remove the crankshaft position sensor bolt. Remove the sensor.

11. Remove the timing cover retaining bolts. Remove the timing cover from its mounting.

To install:

→Be sure to use new fasteners, as required.

12. Clean and inspect all sealing surfaces.

13. Install or connect the following:

- Oil pressure relief valve with a new O–ring. Tighten to 30 ft. lbs. (41 Nm).
- Apply a ⅛ in. (2–3mm) wide to ¹⁄₁₆ in. (0.5–1.5mm) high bead of sealant to the front cover sealing surfaces to the engine block and oil pan.

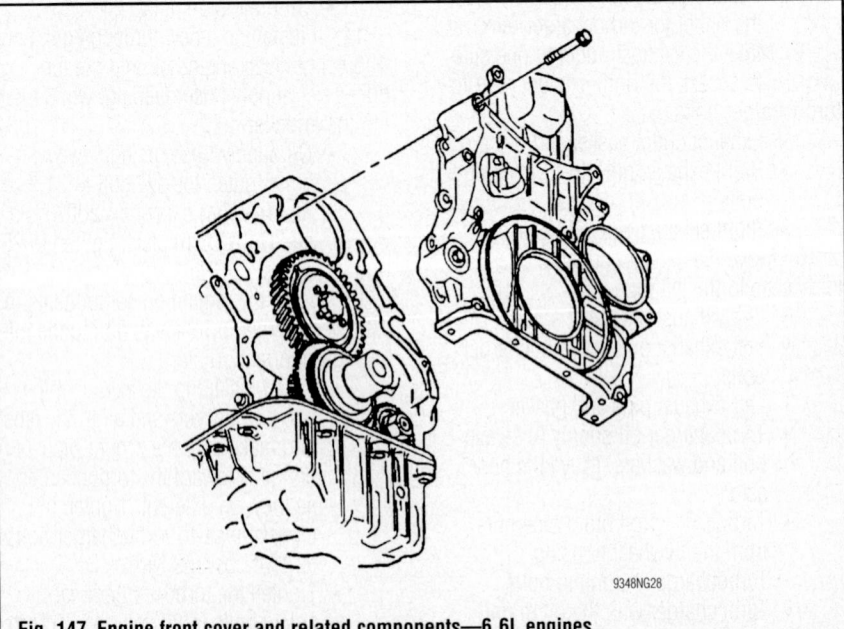

Fig. 147 Engine front cover and related components—6.6L engines

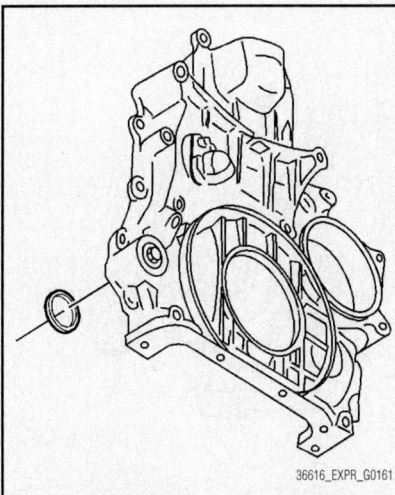

Fig. 148 Oil pressure relief valve seal location—6.6L engines

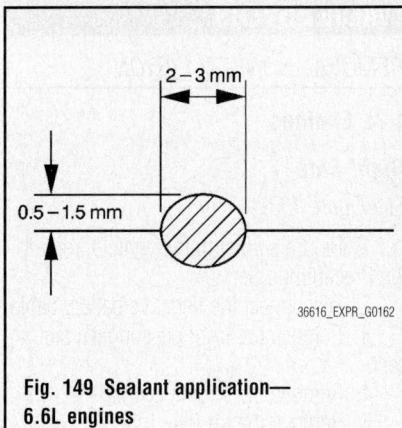

Fig. 149 Sealant application— 6.6L engines

- Front cover and bolts. Tighten to 18 ft. lbs. (25 Nm).

➡**The CKP sensor spacers are machined with different timing positions. If you have to replace a spacer, make sure it has the same part number.**

- CKP sensor spacer and spacer bolts. Tighten to 89 inch lbs. (10 Nm).
- CKP sensor and bolt. Tighten to 89 inch lbs. (10 Nm).

14. Continue the installation in the reverse order of the removal procedure.

15. Start the engine and check for proper operation. Correct as required.

16. Check for leaks, correct as required.

TIMING CHAIN AND SPROCKETS

REMOVAL & INSTALLATION

4.3L Engines
See Figure 150.

1. Before servicing the vehicle, refer to the Precautions Section.
2. Disconnect the negative battery cable.
3. Drain the cooling system. Properly dispose of used coolant.
4. Remove the water pump.
5. Remove the crankshaft balancer.
6. Remove the oil pan.
7. Remove the engine shield.
8. Remove the engine wiring harness from the front cover.
9. Disconnect the Crankshaft Position (CKP) sensor electrical connector, if equipped.
10. Remove the CKP sensor and discard the O–ring.
11. Disconnect the engine wiring harness connector from the Camshaft Position (CMP) sensor.
12. Remove the CMP sensor.
13. Remove the front cover retaining bolts.
14. Remove the front cover from the engine.

➡**Do not reuse the front cover. It is a composite cover and must be replaced with a new cover.**

15. Rotate the crankshaft until the timing marks on the camshaft and crankshaft sprockets are in proper alignment. This will put no. 4 cylinder at TDC.

16. Unsnap the timing chain tensioner shoe from the pin.

17. Remove or disconnect the following:
- Camshaft sprocket-to-camshaft nut and/or bolts
- Camshaft sprocket (along with the timing chain), if the sprocket is difficult to remove, use a plastic mallet to bump the sprocket from the camshaft.

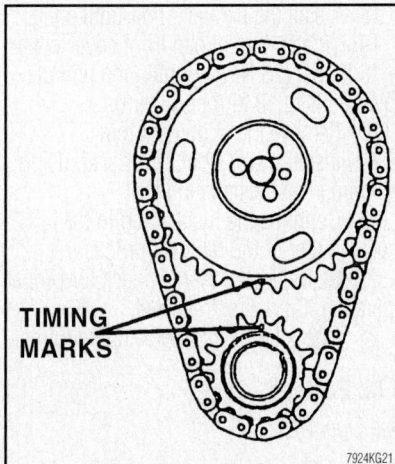

Fig. 150 Timing mark alignment for timing chain removal and installation— 4.3L engines

➡**The camshaft sprocket (located by a dowel) is lightly pressed onto the camshaft and should come off easily. The chain comes off with the camshaft sprocket.**

18. If necessary use J-5825–A, or equivalent, crankshaft sprocket removal tool to free the timing sprocket from the crankshaft.

19. Remove the crankshaft balancer key.

20. If necessary, remove the timing chain tensioner bracket bolt and bracket.

To install:

➡**Be sure to use new fasteners, as required.**

21. Inspect the timing chain and the timing sprockets for wear or damage, replace the damaged parts as necessary.

22. Clean the gasket mounting surfaces of all remaining traces of old gasket.

➡**During installation, coat the thrust surfaces lightly with Molykote® or equivalent pre–lube.**

23. If necessary, install the timing chain tensioner bracket and bolt and tighten to 106 inch lbs. (12 Nm).

24. Install the key into the crankshaft keyway. The crankshaft balancer key should be parallel to the crankshaft or with a slight incline.

25. Install or connect the following:
- Crankshaft sprocket onto the crankshaft, use tool J-5590, crankshaft sprocket installation tool, and a hammer, without disturbing the position of the engine.
- Timing chain, arrange the camshaft sprocket in such a way that the timing marks will align between the shaft centers and the camshaft locating dowel will enter the dowel hole in the cam sprocket.
- Cam sprocket, with the chain mounted under it in position on the front of the camshaft. Torque the camshaft sprocket-to-camshaft retainer bolts to 18 ft. lbs. (25 Nm).

26. Install the timing chain tensioner shoe onto the bracket and position the top of the shoe under the tab at the top of the bracket.

27. With the timing chain installed, turn the crankshaft 2 complete revolutions, then check to make certain that the timing marks are in correct alignment between the shaft centers.

28. Install the new cover to the engine. Tighten the retaining bolts to 106 inch lbs. (12 Nm).

29. Using a new O–ring, lubricated with clean engine oil, install the CMP

sensor. Tighten the retaining bolt to 89 inch lbs. (10 Nm).

30. Using a new O–ring, lubricated with clean engine oil, install the CKP sensor. Tighten the retaining bolt to 71 inch lbs. (8 Nm).

➡**Be sure that the sensor is correctly seated before tightening the retaining bolt.**

31. Continue the installation in the reverse order of the removal procedure.

32. Start the engine and check for proper operation. Correct as required.

33. Check for leaks, correct as required.

4.8L, 5.3L & 6.0L Engines

See Figure 151.

1. Before servicing the vehicle, refer to the Precautions Section.

2. Disconnect the negative battery cable.

3. Drain the cooling system. Properly dispose of used coolant.

4. Remove the water pump.

5. Remove the crankshaft balancer.

6. Remove the oil pan to front cover bolts.

7. Remove the front cover retaining bolts.

8. Remove the front cover. Discard the gasket. Remove the oil seal.

9. Remove the oil pump.

10. Rotate the crankshaft until the timing marks on the crankshaft and the camshaft sprockets are aligned.

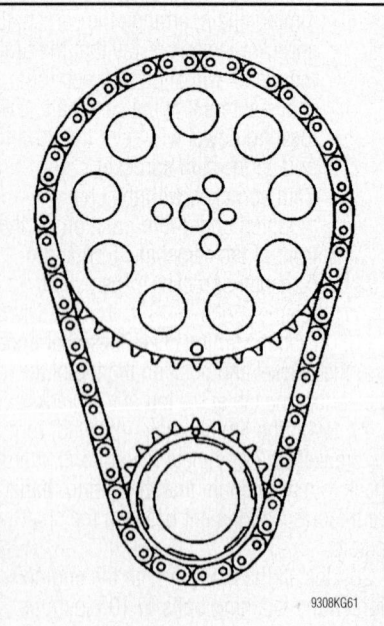

Fig. 151 Timing mark alignment—4.8L, 5.3L and 6.0L engines

➡**Do not turn the crankshaft assembly after the timing chain has been removed in order to prevent damage to the piston assemblies or the valves.**

11. Remove or disconnect the following:
• Camshaft sprocket bolts
• Camshaft sprocket and timing chain
• Crankshaft sprocket
• Crankshaft sprocket key

To install:

➡**Be sure to use new fasteners, as required.**

12. Install or connect the following:
• Key into the crankshaft keyway
• Crankshaft sprocket onto the front of the crankshaft. Align the crankshaft key with the crankshaft sprocket keyway. Rotate the crankshaft sprocket until the alignment mark is in the 12 o'clock position.
• Camshaft sprocket and timing chain. Locate the camshaft sprocket alignment mark in the 6 o'clock position.
• Camshaft sprocket bolts and tighten to 26 ft. lbs. (35 Nm).

13. Install the oil pump.

14. Apply a 0.20 inch of sealant to the engine block and oil pan junction. Be sure to use the proper grade and type sealant.

15. Install the new cover to the engine. Tighten the retaining bolts until they are snug.

16. Install the cover to oil pan bolts. Tighten until snug.

17. Align the tapered legs of the alignment tool J-41476 or equivalent, with the machined alignment surfaces on the front cover.

18. Install the balancer bolt until snug.

19. Tighten the oil pan front cover bolts to 18 ft. lbs. (25 Nm). Tighten the timing cover bolts to 18 ft. lbs (25 Nm).

20. Remove the alignment tool.

21. Install a new front cover seal, using the proper seal installation tool.

22. Continue the installation in the reverse order of the removal procedure.

23. Start the engine and check for proper operation. Correct as required.

24. Check for leaks, correct as required.

6.6L Engines

See Figure 152.

➡**The 6.6L engine uses gears in place of a timing chain. For removal and installation of the gears, please see the Camshaft and Lifters procedure.**

Fig. 152 Timing gears and related components—6.6L engines

VALVE COVERS

REMOVAL & INSTALLATION

4.3L Engines

Right Side

See Figure 153.

1. Before servicing the vehicle, refer to the Precautions Section.

2. Disconnect the negative battery cable.

3. Remove the front passenger's side seat.

4. Remove the engine cover.

5. Remove the oil filler tube.

6. Remove the PCV hose.

7. Remove the valve cover retaining bolts. Remove the valve cover from the engine. Discard the gasket.

To install:

➡**Be sure to use new fasteners, as required.**

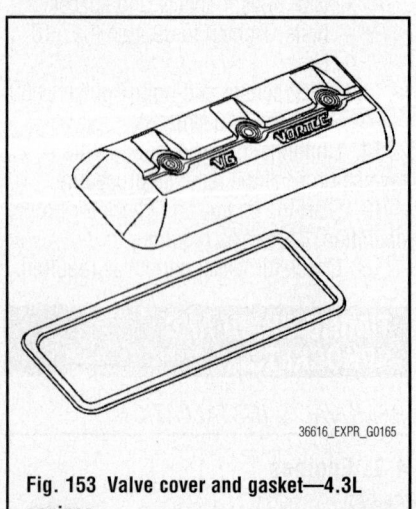

Fig. 153 Valve cover and gasket—4.3L engines

8. Using a new gasket, position the valve cover on the engine.

9. Install the retaining bolts. Tighten to 106 inch lbs. (12 Nm).

10. Continue the installation in the reverse order of the removal procedure.

11. Start the engine and check for leaks. Correct as required.

Left Side

1. Before servicing the vehicle, refer to the Precautions Section.

2. Disconnect the negative battery cable.

3. Remove the front passenger's side seat.

4. Remove the engine cover.

5. Remove the coil wiring harness bracket nut and bracket. Position unit to the side.

6. Disconnect the coolant temperature sensor electrical connector.

7. Disconnect the power brake booster vacuum hose.

8. Remove the PCV hose from the valve cover.

9. Remove the valve cover retaining bolts. Remove the valve cover from the engine. Discard the gasket.

To install:

➡**Be sure to use new fasteners, as required.**

10. Using a new gasket, position the valve cover on the engine.

11. Install the retaining bolts. Tighten to 106 inch lbs. (12 Nm).

12. Continue the installation in the reverse order of the removal procedure.

13. Start the engine and check for leaks. Correct as required.

4.8L, 5.3L & 6.0L Engines

Right Side

See Figure 154.

1. Before servicing the vehicle, refer to the Precautions Section.

2. Disconnect the negative battery cable.

3. Remove the front passenger's side seat.

4. Remove the engine cover.

5. Remove the upper transmission fill tube.

6. Remove the oil fill tube.

7. Disconnect the main electrical connector to the ignition coil wire harness.

8. Remove the harness clips. Reposition the harness, as required.

9. Remove the spark plug wires from the ignition coils. Remove the coil bracket

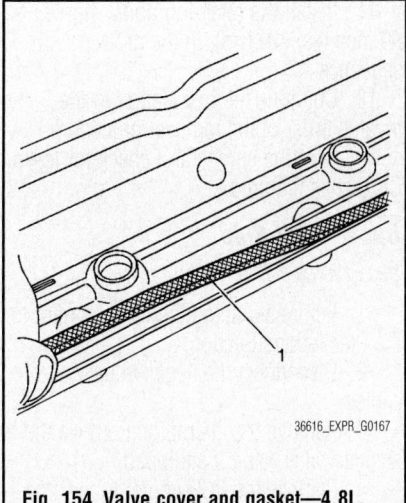

Fig. 154 Valve cover and gasket—4.8L, 5.3L and 6.0L engines

studs. Remove the coils and bracket from the valve cover.

10. Remove the vent hose from the valve cover.

11. Remove the valve cover retaining bolts. Remove the valve cover from the engine. Discard the gasket.

To install:

➡**Be sure to use new fasteners, as required.**

12. Using a new gasket, position the valve cover on the engine.

13. Install the retaining bolts. Tighten to 106 inch lbs. (12 Nm).

14. Continue the installation in the reverse order of the removal procedure.

15. Start the engine and check for leaks. Correct as required.

Left Side

See Figure 154.

1. Before servicing the vehicle, refer to the Precautions Section.

2. Disconnect the negative battery cable.

3. Remove the front passenger's side seat.

4. Remove the engine cover.

5. Remove the connector position assurance lock.

6. Disconnect the main electrical connector to the ignition coil wire harness.

7. Remove the harness clips. Reposition the harness, as required.

8. Remove the spark plug wires from the ignition coils. Remove the coil bracket studs. Remove the coils and bracket from the valve cover.

9. Remove the PCV vent hose from the valve cover.

10. Remove the valve cover retaining bolts. Remove the valve cover from the engine. Discard the gasket.

To install:

➡**Be sure to use new fasteners, as required.**

11. Using a new gasket, position the valve cover on the engine.

12. Install the retaining bolts. Tighten to 106 inch lbs. (12 Nm).

13. Continue the installation in the reverse order of the removal procedure.

14. Start the engine and check for leaks. Correct as required.

6.6L Engines

Lower Right Side

See Figures 155 and 156.

1. Before servicing the vehicle, refer to the Precautions Section.

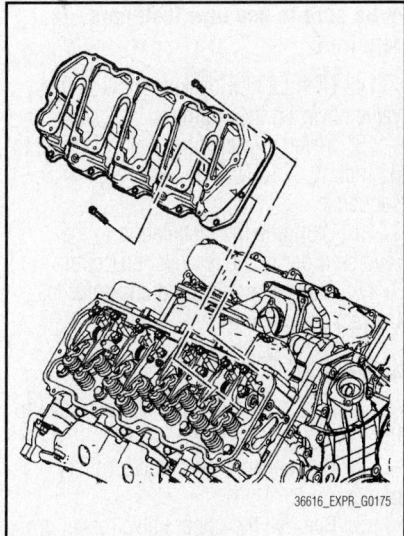

Fig. 155 Lower valve cover and related components—6.6L engines

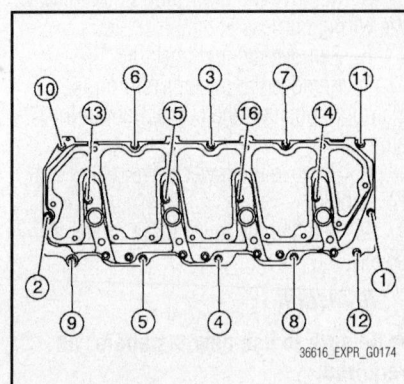

Fig. 156 Lower valve cover tightening sequence>6.6L engines

2. Disconnect the negative battery cables.

3. Remove the upper valve rocker arm cover.

4. Remove the fuel injectors.

5. Remove the injector return pipe clamp. Reposition the component to the side.

6. Remove the EGR cooler tube bracket bolt and nut.

7. Remove the front passenger's side seat.

8. Remove the engine cover.

9. Remove the right side fuel rail.

10. Remove the alternator mounting bracket.

11. Remove the EGR cooler tube bracket bolts and bracket.

12. Remove the lower valve rocker arm cover bolts.

13. Remove the lower valve rocker arm cover.

To install:

➡ Be sure to use new fasteners, as required.

14. Using a new gasket, position the valve cover on the engine.

15. Install the retaining bolts. Tighten to 89 inch lbs. (10 Nm), in the proper sequence.

16. Continue the installation in the reverse order of the removal procedure.

17. Start the engine and check for leaks. Correct as required.

Lower Left Side

1. Before servicing the vehicle, refer to the Precautions Section.

2. Disconnect the negative battery cables.

3. Remove the upper valve rocker arm cover.

4. Remove the air conditioning compressor and power steering pump bracket.

5. Remove the glow plug nuts. Remove the wiring harness at the glow plugs.

6. Remove the fuel injectors.

7. Remove the injector return pipe clamp. Reposition the component to the side.

8. Remove the lower valve rocker arm cover bolts.

9. Remove the lower valve rocker arm cover.

To install:

➡ Be sure to use new fasteners, as required.

10. Using a new gasket, position the valve cover on the engine.

11. Install the retaining bolts. Tighten to 89 inch lbs. (10 Nm), in the proper sequence.

12. Continue the installation in the reverse order of the removal procedure.

13. Start the engine and check for leaks. Correct as required.

Upper Right Side

See Figures 157 and 158.

1. Before servicing the vehicle, refer to the Precautions Section.

2. Disconnect the negative battery cables.

3. Remove the alternator. Remove the auxiliary alternator, if equipped.

4. Remove the EGR cooler tube.

5. Remove the glow plug nuts.

6. Remove the engine wiring harness from the glow plugs

7. Remove the glow plug harness bracket bolts and nut.

8. Remove the fuel pressure rail sensor electrical connector bracket bolt and nut.

9. Remove the bracket from the stud.

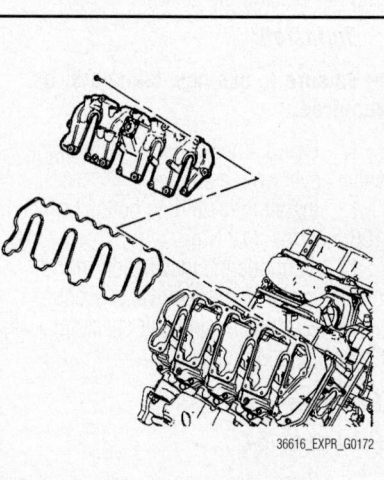

Fig. 157 Upper valve cover and gasket—6.6L engines

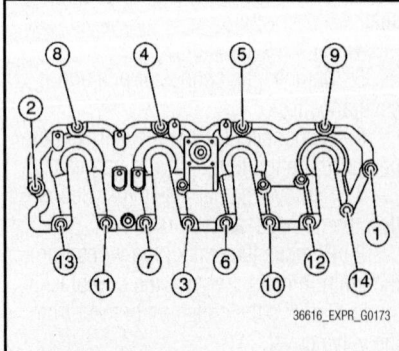

Fig. 158 Upper valve cover tightening sequence>6.6L engines

10. Remove the transmission support tube nut at the bell housing. Remove the transmission fill tube upper nut. Reposition the tube.

11. Remove the EGR heater inlet hose/pipe retainer stud at the rear of the engine. Remove the EGR heater inlet hose/pipe retainer nut at the center of the lower right cylinder head.

12. Remove the injector wire harness stud at the center lower right cylinder head.

➡ Label all the injector electrical connectors, for reassembly. Connecting the wrong wire to the injector will cause severe engine damage.

13. Disconnect the electrical wires from the injectors.

14. Remove the injector return line clip from the injector. Remove the injector return line fitting from the injector.

15. Complete the above for the remaining injectors.

16. Disconnect the right side main engine harness connector.

17. Remove the connector bracket bolts. Position the harness out of the way.

➡ Prior to removing the injector pipes, blow the area with compressed air to remove any debris. Do not use compressed air to clean debris after the injector pipes have been disconnected.

18. Remove the fuel injector pipes.

19. Remove the upper valve cover retaining bolts. Remove the valve cover from the engine. Discard the gasket.

To install:

➡ Be sure to use new fasteners, as required.

20. Using a new gasket, position the valve cover on the engine.

21. Install the retaining bolts. Tighten to 71 inch lbs. (8 Nm), in the proper sequence.

22. Continue the installation in the reverse order of the removal procedure.

23. Tighten the fuel injector pipes to 30 ft. lbs. (41 Nm).

24. Start the engine and check for leaks. Correct as required.

Upper Left Side

1. Before servicing the vehicle, refer to the Precautions Section.

2. Disconnect the negative battery cables.

3. Remove the alternator. Remove the auxiliary alternator, if equipped.

4. Remove the PCV valve hose/pipe.

5. Remove the glow plug control module. Remove the glow plug module bracket bolts and bracket.

→**Label all the injector electrical connectors, for reassembly. Connecting the wrong wire to the injector will cause severe engine damage.**

6. Disconnect the electrical wires from the injectors.

7. Remove the engine wiring bracket bolt.

8. Disconnect the left side main engine harness connector. Remove the wiring harness clip from the main connector bracket. Remove the connector bracket bolts.

9. Remove the glow plug wire harness retaining bolts at the lower part of the left valve cover. Reposition the harness out of the way.

→**Label all the injector electrical connectors, for reassembly. Connecting the wrong wire to the injector will cause severe engine damage.**

10. Disconnect the electrical wires from the injectors.

11. Remove the injector return line clip from the injector. Remove the injector return line fitting from the injector.

12. Complete the above for the remaining injectors.

13. Position the return line out of way.

→**Prior to removing the injector pipes, blow the area with compressed air to remove any debris. Do not use compressed air to clean debris after the injector pipes have been disconnected.**

14. Remove the fuel injector pipes.

15. Remove the number eight injector bracket bolt.

16. Install tool J-46594, or equivalent, into the number eight bracket bolt hole. Using the tool puller, pull the injector until it releases. Remove the tool. Remove the number eight injector and bracket.

17. Remove the upper valve cover retaining bolts. Remove the valve cover from the engine. Discard the gasket.

To install:

→**Be sure to use new fasteners, as required.**

18. Using a new gasket, position the valve cover on the engine.

19. Install the retaining bolts. Tighten to 71 inch lbs. (8 Nm), in the proper sequence.

20. Continue the installation in the reverse order of the removal procedure.

21. Tighten the fuel injector pipes to 30 ft. lbs. (41 Nm).

22. Start the engine and check for leaks. Correct as required.

VALVE LASH

ADJUSTMENT

→**All 4.3L, 4.8L, 5.3L and 6.0L engines use hydraulic lifters, which require no periodic adjustment.**

6.6L Engines

See Figures 159 and 160.

1. Before servicing the vehicle, refer to the Precautions Section.

2. Disconnect the negative battery cables.

3. Remove the front passenger's side seat.

4. Remove the engine cover.

5. Remove the upper fan shroud.

a. Rotate the engine in the normal direction and place the No. 1 piston at Top Dead Center (TDC) of the compression stroke. The No. 1 cylinder is at the right side front. While turning the engine, watch the intake valve to open and close. Align the mark on the crankshaft balancer with the pointer on the engine.

b. Loosen the valve clearance adjusting screws for the valve being adjusted.

c. Insert the feeler gauge between the tip of the rocker arm and the valve bridge.

d. Adjust the intake and the exhaust valve clearance to 0.012 in. (0.3mm) with the engine cold. Refer to the figure for the valves that can be adjusted TDC of the compression stroke.

e. Tighten the valve adjusting screw lock nut to 16 ft. lbs. (22 Nm).

f. Turn the engine one rotation in the normal direction and put the No. 1 piston at TDC of the exhaust stroke to adjust the remaining valve clearance. While turning the engine, watch the exhaust valve to open and close. Align the mark on the crankshaft balancer with the pointer on the engine.

g. Loosen the valve clearance adjusting screws for the valves being adjusted.

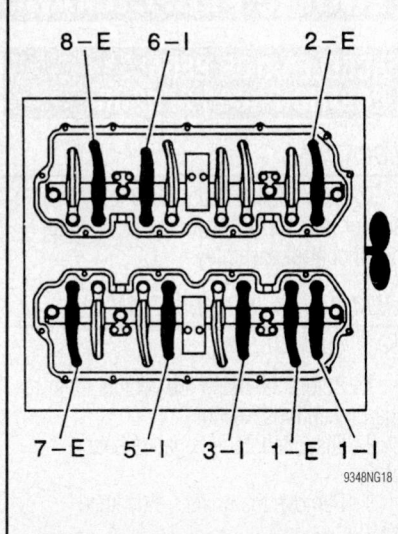

Fig. 159 Location of the valves that are adjusted at TDC of the compression stroke—6.6L engines

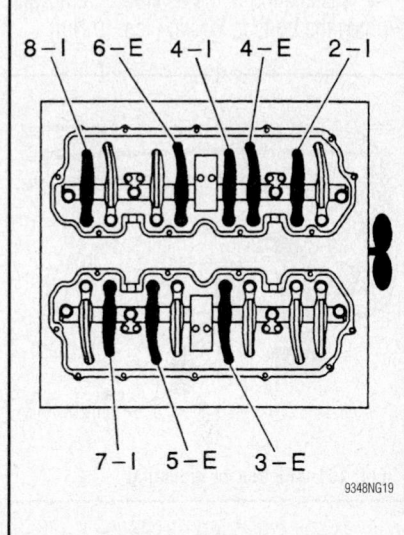

Fig. 160 Location of the valves that are adjusted at TDC of the exhaust stroke—6.6L engines

h. Insert the feeler gauge between the tip of the rocker arm and the valve bridge.

i. Adjust the intake and the exhaust valve clearance to 0.012 in. (0.3mm) with the engine cold. Refer to the figure for the valves that can be adjusted TDC of the exhaust stroke.

j. Tighten the valve adjusting screw lock nut to 16 ft. lbs. (22 Nm).

6. Install removed components.

7. Start the engine and check for leaks, correct as required.

ENGINE PERFORMANCE & EMISSION CONTROLS

ACCELERATOR PEDAL POSITION (APP) SENSOR

LOCATION

The Accelerator Pedal Position (APP) sensor is mounted inside the accelerator pedal control assembly.

REMOVAL & INSTALLATION

See Figure 161.

1. Before servicing the vehicle, refer to the Precautions Section.
2. Disconnect the negative battery cable.
3. Remove the driver's side knee bolster.
4. Push down on the small tab and disengage the electrical connector.
5. Remove the pedal bolts and remove the pedal and sensor assembly.
6. Installation is the reverse of removal. Tighten the bolts to 80 inch lbs. (9 Nm).

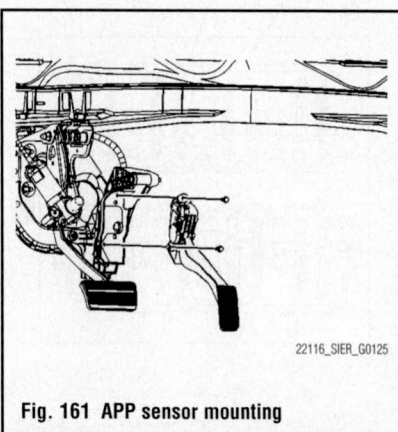

Fig. 161 APP sensor mounting

CAMSHAFT POSITION (CMP) SENSOR

LOCATION

The Camshaft Position (CMP) sensor is located above the crankshaft pulley.

REMOVAL & INSTALLATION

4.3L Engines

See Figure 162.

1. Before servicing the vehicle, refer to the Precautions Section.
2. Disconnect the negative battery cable.
3. Unplug the harness connector from the CMP sensor.
4. Remove the water pump.

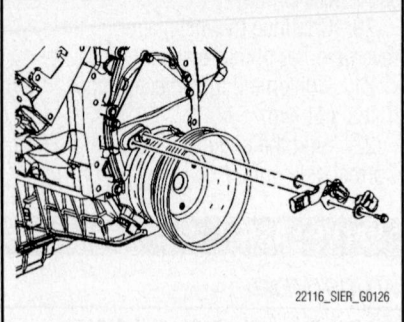

Fig. 162 CMP sensor mounting— 4.3L engines

5. Remove the CMP sensor bolt, then remove the sensor from the engine.
6. Installation is the reverse of removal. Lubricate a new O-ring with clean engine oil. Tighten the bolt to 89 inch lbs. (10 Nm).

4.8L, 5.3L & 6.0L Engines

See Figure 163.

1. Before servicing the vehicle, refer to the Precautions Section.
2. Disconnect the negative battery cable.
3. Unplug the harness connector from the CMP sensor.
4. Remove the CMP sensor harness bolts, then remove the sensor from the engine.
5. Installation is the reverse of removal. Lubricate a new O-ring with clean engine oil. Tighten the bolt to 106 inch lbs. (12 Nm).

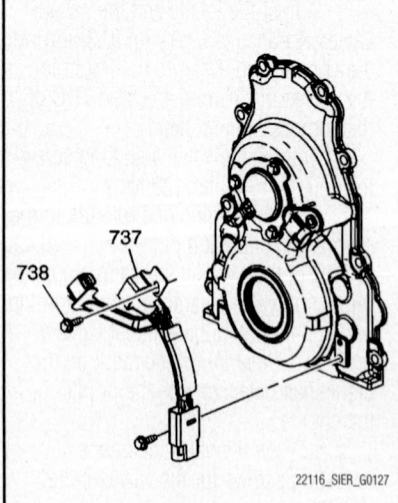

Fig. 163 CMP sensor harness mounting— 4.8L, 5.3L and 6.0L engines

6.6L Engines

See Figure 164.

1. Before servicing the vehicle, refer to the Precautions Section.
2. Disconnect the negative battery cable.
3. Remove the cooling fan pulley.
4. Unplug the harness connector from the CMP sensor.
5. Remove the CMP sensor bolt, then remove the sensor from the engine.
6. Installation is the reverse of removal. Tighten the bolt to 89 inch lbs. (10 Nm).

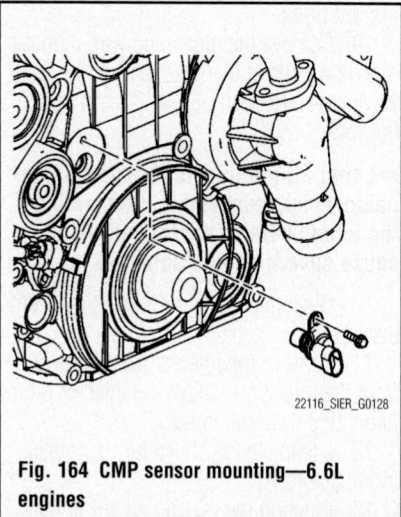

Fig. 164 CMP sensor mounting—6.6L engines

CRANKSHAFT POSITION (CKP) SENSOR

LOCATION

The Crankshaft Position (CKP) sensor is located next to the crankshaft pulley on the 4.3L and 6.6L engines. On the 4.8L, 5.3L and 6.0L engines the sensor is located on the side of the engine block.

REMOVAL & INSTALLATION

➡**Use of a scan tool is required to complete this procedure. Anytime the CKP sensor is replaced, the variation learn procedure must be performed.**

4.3L Engines

See Figure 165.

1. Before servicing the vehicle, refer to the Precautions Section.
2. Disconnect the negative battery cable.
3. Raise and safely support the vehicle.
4. Remove the skid plate, as required.
5. Unplug the harness connector from the sensor.

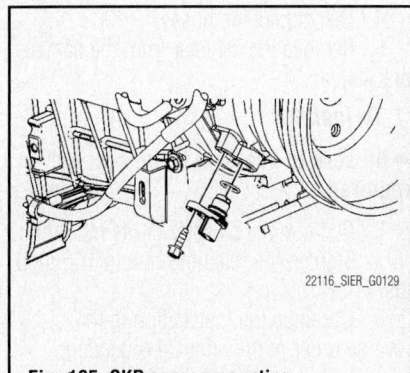

Fig. 165 CKP sensor mounting—4.3L engines

6. Remove the bolt securing the sensor, then remove it from the engine.

7. Installation is the reverse of removal. Lubricate a new O-ring with clean engine oil. Tighten the bolt to 89 inch lbs. (10 Nm). Connect the scan tool to the vehicle and perform the CKP sensor variation learn procedure.

4.8L, 5.3L & 6.0L Engines

See Figure 166.

1. Before servicing the vehicle, refer to the Precautions Section.

2. Disconnect the negative battery cable.

3. Raise and safely support the vehicle.

4. Remove the starter.

5. Working through the wheel well opening, unplug the harness connector from the sensor.

6. Clean the area around the sensor to prevent debris from entering the engine.

7. Remove the bolt securing the sensor, then remove it from the engine.

8. Installation is the reverse of removal. Lubricate a new O-ring with clean engine oil. Tighten the bolt to 18 ft. lbs. (25 Nm). Connect the scan tool to the vehicle and

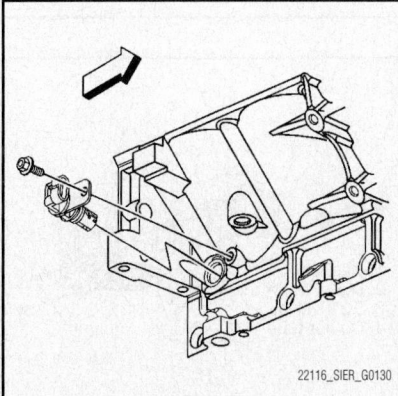

Fig. 166 CKP sensor mounting—4.8L, 5.3L and 6.0L engines

perform the CKP sensor variation learn procedure.

6.6L Engines

See Figure 167.

1. Before servicing the vehicle, refer to the Precautions Section.

2. Disconnect the negative battery cables.

3. Remove the right wheelhouse liner to gain access to the CKP sensor.

4. Unplug the harness connector from the CKP sensor.

5. Remove the CKP sensor bolt, then remove the sensor from the engine.

6. Installation is the reverse of removal. Tighten the bolt to 89 inch lbs. (10 Nm).

Fig. 167 CKP sensor mounting—6.6L engines

ENGINE COOLANT TEMPERATURE (ECT) SENSOR

LOCATION

The Engine Coolant Temperature (ECT) sensor is threaded into the cylinder head. The 6.6L engines use 2 ECT sensors which are located side by side.

REMOVAL & INSTALLATION

See Figures 168 through 170.

1. Before servicing the vehicle, refer to the Precautions Section.

2. Disconnect the negative battery cable (s).

3. Drain the cooling system to a level below the ECT sensor. Properly dispose of used coolant.

4. On 6.6L engines, remove the intake manifold tube.

5. Unplug the harness connector from the ECT sensor.

6. Remove the ECT sensor from the engine.

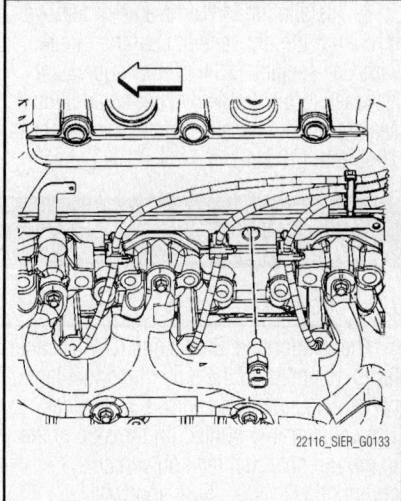

Fig. 168 ECT sensor mounting—4.3L engines

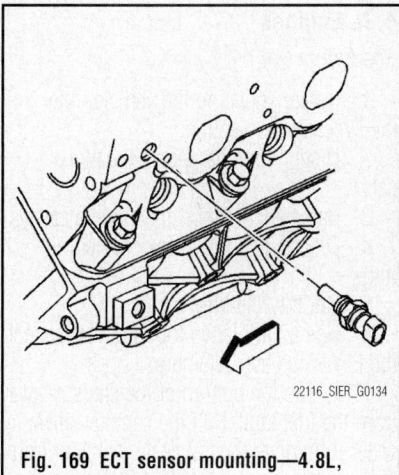

Fig. 169 ECT sensor mounting—4.8L, 5.3L and 6.0L engines

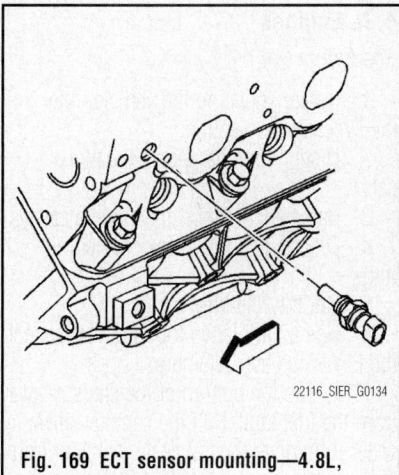

Fig. 170 ECT sensor mounting (1)—6.6L engines

7. Installation is the reverse of removal. If reusing the old sensor, coat the threads with GM sealant 12346004 or equivalent. New sensors are already coated; additional sealant is not needed. Tighten the sensor to 15 ft. lbs. (20 Nm).

EVAPORATIVE EMISSIONS (EVAP) CANISTER

LOCATION

The Evaporative Emissions (EVAP) canister is mounted on the side of the fuel tank on vehicles equipped with 4.3L engines. The canister is mounted on the side of the frame rail near fuel tank on vehicles equipped with 4.8L, 5.3L and 6.0L engines.

REMOVAL & INSTALLATION

4.3L Engines

See Figure 171.

1. Before servicing the vehicle, refer to the Precautions Section.
2. Disconnect the negative battery cable.
3. Raise and support the vehicle safely.
4. Disconnect the quick connect fittings.
5. Cut the retaining straps.
6. Use a flat bladed tool and disconnect the EVAP canister retainers.
7. Rotate the bottom of the canister away from the fuel tank. Pull the canister down in order to remove the top of the canister from the upper retainer.

To install:

➡Be sure to use new fasteners, as required.

8. Position the canister on its mounting.
9. Use new tie straps to hold the canister in place.
10. Continue the installation in the reverse order of the removal procedure.

4.8L, 5.3L & 6.0L Engines

See Figure 172.

1. Before servicing the vehicle, refer to the Precautions Section.
2. Disconnect the negative battery cable.
3. Raise and support the vehicle safely.

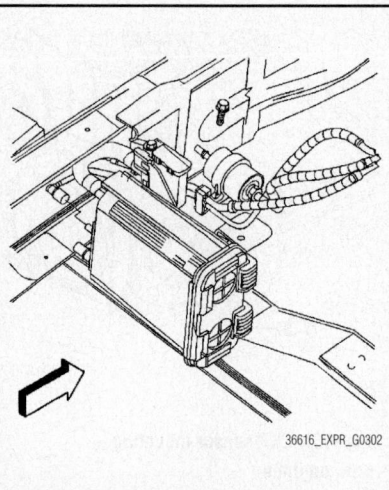

Fig. 172 EVAP canister and related components—4.8L, 5.3L and 6.0L engines

4. Disconnect the hoses.
5. Remove the canister from the canister bracket.

To install:

➡Be sure to use new fasteners, as required.

6. Position the canister on its mounting.
7. Tighten the retaining bolt to 106 inch lbs. (12 Nm).
8. Continue the installation in the reverse order of the removal procedure.

EXHAUST GAS RECIRCULATION (EGR) VALVE

LOCATION

The Exhaust Gas Recirculation (EGR) valve is used on the 6.6L engines. It is mounted to the exhaust gas recirculation valve cooler. The cooler is located on top of the engine, near the rear.

REMOVAL & INSTALLATION

See Figures 173 and 174.

1. Before servicing the vehicle, refer to the Precautions Section.

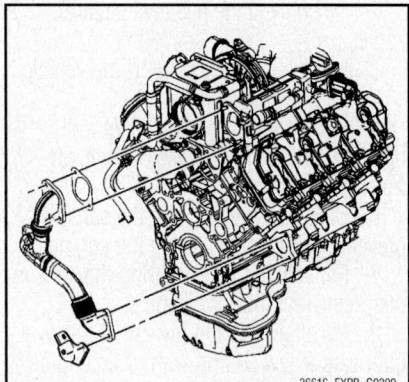

Fig. 173 Right exhaust pipe and related components—6.6L engines

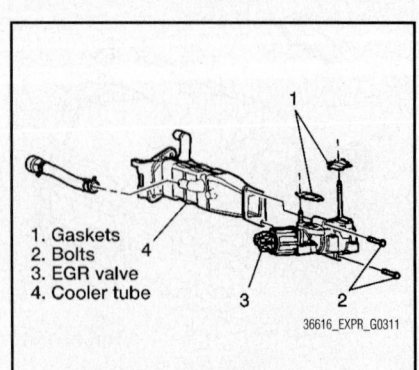

1. Gaskets
2. Bolts
3. EGR valve
4. Cooler tube

Fig. 174 EGR valve and related components—6.6L engines

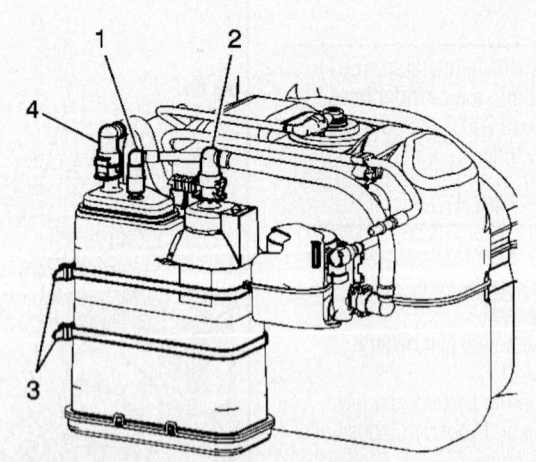

1. Quick connect fitting
2. Quick connect fitting
3. Straps
4. Quick connect fitting

Fig. 171 EVAP canister and related components—4.3L engines

2. Disconnect the negative battery cable(s).

➡In order to remove the engine cover the passenger side front seat must be removed.

3. Remove the engine cover.
4. Drain the cooling system. Properly dispose of used coolant.
5. Remove the alternator.
6. Remove the right exhaust pipe.
7. Remove the intake manifold tube.
8. Remove the EGR valve cooler.
9. Remove the EGR valve cooler tube bolts.
10. Separate the EGR valve from the cooler tube.
11. Remove and discard the intake manifold tube gaskets, as required.

To install:

➡Be sure to use new fasteners, as required.

12. Position the valve on its mounting.
13. Continue the installation in the reverse order of the removal procedure.

HEATED OXYGEN SENSOR (HO2S)

LOCATION

The Heated Oxygen Sensors (HO2S) are threaded into the exhaust pipes.

REMOVAL & INSTALLATION
See Figures 175 and 176.

➡Replace the sensor if the pigtail wiring, connector, or terminal is damaged. The external clean air reference is obtained by way of the sensor signal and heater wires. Any attempt to repair the wires or connectors could result in obstruction of the air reference. Make sure the lead wires are not sharply bent or kinked as the air reference could become blocked.

1. Before servicing the vehicle, refer to the Precautions Section.
2. Disconnect the negative battery cable.
3. Raise and support the vehicle safely.
4. Unplug the sensor connector. Remove the clip from the engine harness.
5. Remove the sensor from the exhaust pipe.

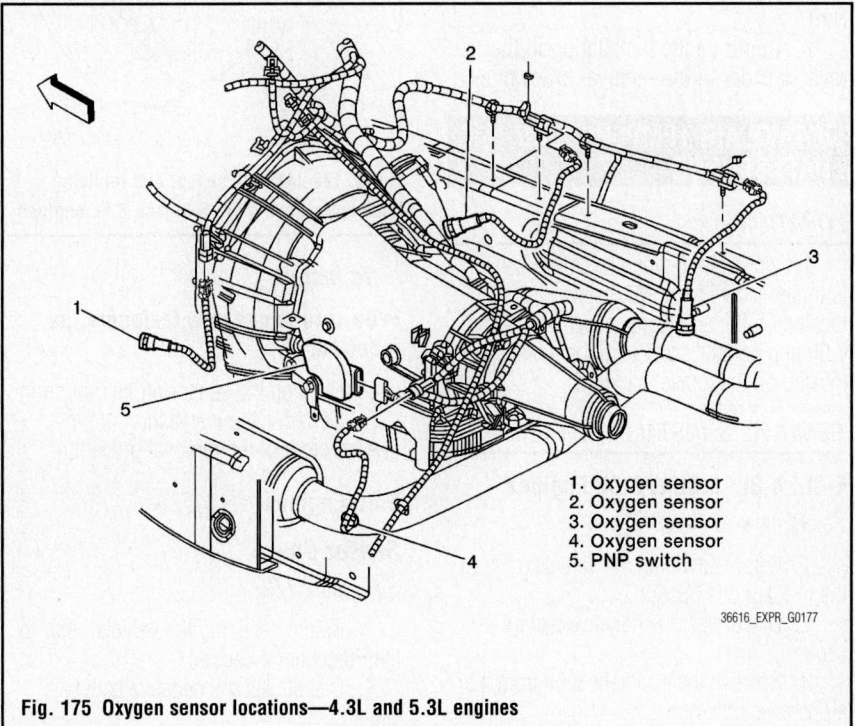

1. Oxygen sensor
2. Oxygen sensor
3. Oxygen sensor
4. Oxygen sensor
5. PNP switch

36616_EXPR_G0177

Fig. 175 Oxygen sensor locations—4.3L and 5.3L engines

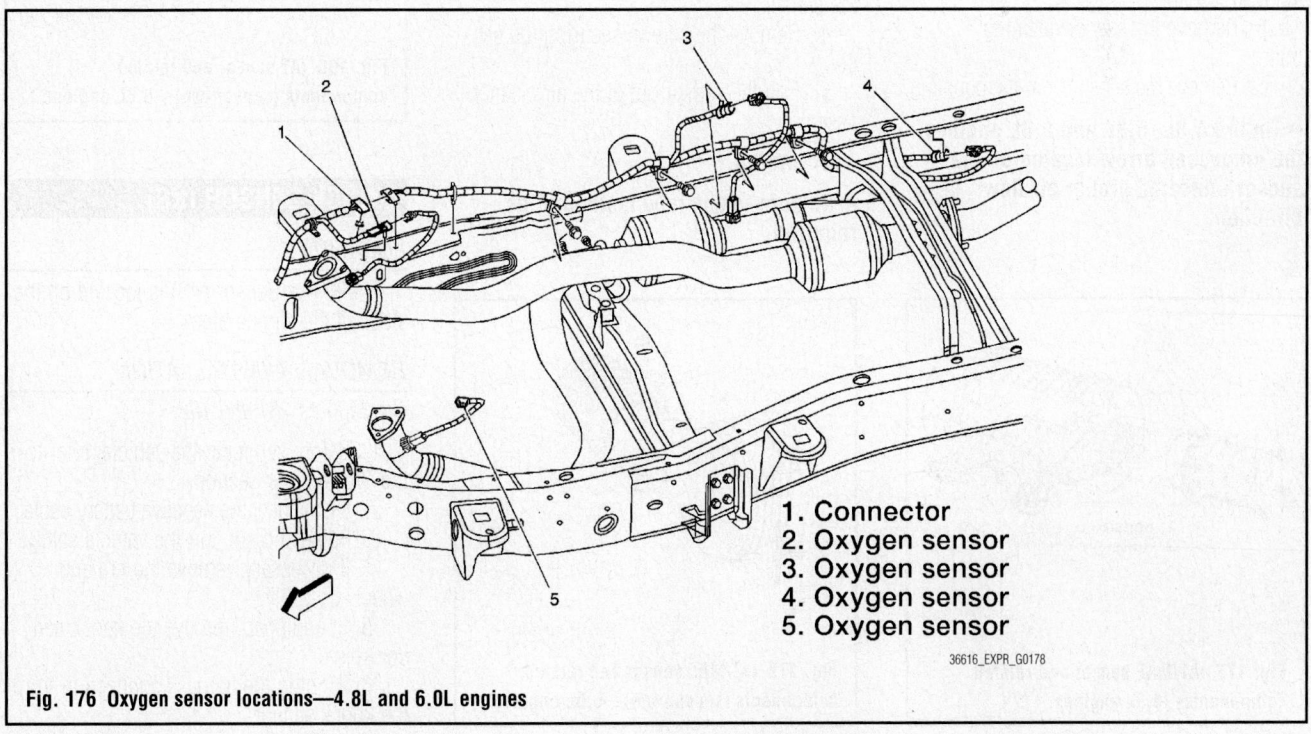

1. Connector
2. Oxygen sensor
3. Oxygen sensor
4. Oxygen sensor
5. Oxygen sensor

36616_EXPR_G0178

Fig. 176 Oxygen sensor locations—4.8L and 6.0L engines

To install:

➡ **Be sure to use new fasteners, as required.**

6. Position the sensor on its mounting.

7. If reusing the old sensor, coat the threads with GM antiseize compound 12377953 or equivalent.

8. New sensors are already coated; additional compound is not needed.

9. Tighten the sensor to 31 ft. lbs. (42 Nm).

10. Continue the installation in the reverse order of the removal procedure.

INTAKE AIR TEMPERATURE (IAT) SENSOR

LOCATION

The Intake Air Temperature (IAT) sensor is integrated with the MAF sensor, it is located on the air cleaner assembly. The 6.6L engine utilizes an additional IAT sensor located on the intake manifold.

REMOVAL & INSTALLATION

4.3L, 4.8L, 5.3L & 6.0L Engines

See Figures 177 and 178.

1. Before servicing the vehicle, refer to the Precautions Section.

2. Disconnect the negative battery cable.

3. Remove the air intake tube from the air cleaner assembly.

4. Detach the electrical connector from the MAF sensor.

5. Remove the sensor retaining bolts.

6. Remove the sensor from its mounting.

➡ **On the 4.8L, 5.3L and 6.0L engines, the embossed arrow located on the sensor indicated proper air flow direction.**

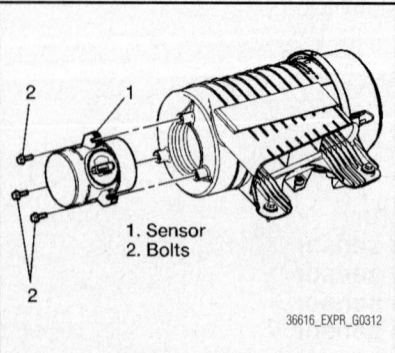

Fig. 177 IAT/MAF sensor and related components—4.3L engines

1. Sensor
2. Bolts

36616_EXPR_G0312

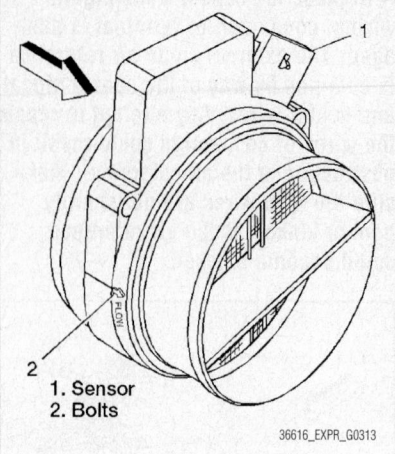

Fig. 178 IAT/MAF sensor and related components—4.8L, 5.3L and 6.0L engines

1. Sensor
2. Bolts

36616_EXPR_G0313

To install:

➡ **Be sure to use new fasteners, as required.**

7. Position the sensor on its mounting.

8. Continue the installation in the reverse order of the removal procedure.

6.6L Engines

Sensor One

See Figure 179.

1. Before servicing the vehicle, refer to the Precautions Section.

2. Disconnect the negative battery cable(s).

3. Detach the electrical connector from the sensor.

4. Remove the screws securing the sensor.

5. Pull the sensor out of the air cleaner assembly.

To install:

➡ **Be sure to use new fasteners, as required.**

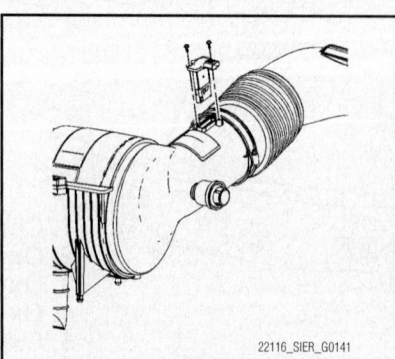

Fig. 179 IAT/MAF sensor and related components (sensor one)—6.6L engines

22116_SIER_G0141

6. Position the sensor on its mounting.

7. Continue the installation in the reverse order of the removal procedure.

Sensor Two

See Figure 180.

1. Before servicing the vehicle, refer to the Precautions Section.

2. Disconnect the negative battery cable(s).

3. Remove the air intake pipe.

4. Unplug the harness connector from the sensor.

5. Remove the sensor from the intake manifold.

To install:

➡ **Be sure to use new fasteners, as required.**

6. Position the sensor on its mounting.

7. Continue the installation in the reverse order of the removal procedure.

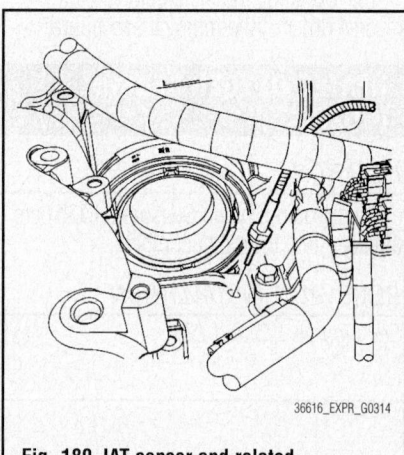

Fig. 180 IAT sensor and related components (sensor two)—6.6L engines

36616_EXPR_G0314

KNOCK SENSOR (KS)

LOCATION

The Knock Sensor (KS) is located on the sides of the engine block.

REMOVAL & INSTALLATION

See Figures 181 and 182.

1. Before servicing the vehicle, refer to the Precautions Section.

2. Disconnect the negative battery cable.

3. Raise and support the vehicle safely.

4. If necessary, remove the tire and wheel assembly.

5. If equipped, remove the knock sensor shield.

6. Unplug the harness connection from the knock sensor.

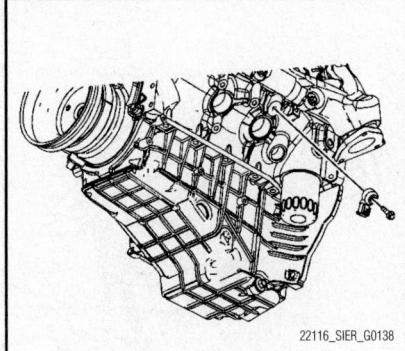

Fig. 181 Knock sensor mounting— 4.3L engines

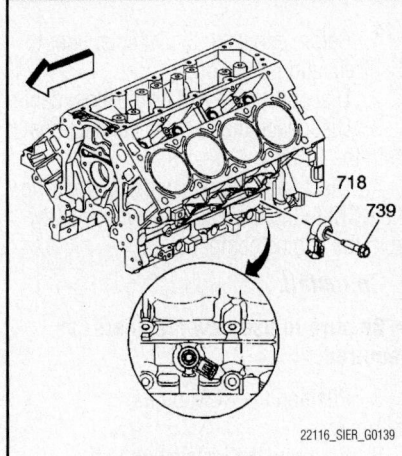

Fig. 182 Knock sensor mounting—4.8L, 5.3L and 6.0L engines

7. Remove the bolt securing the sensor, then remove it from the engine.

To install:

→**Be sure to use new fasteners, as required.**

8. Position the sensor on its mounting.
9. Tighten the bolt to 18 ft. lbs. (25 Nm).
10. Continue the installation in the reverse order of the removal procedure.

MALFUNCTION INDICATOR LIGHT (MIL)

RESET PROCEDURE

The MIL turns OFF after three consecutive ignition cycles in which a Test Passed has been reported for the diagnostic test that originally caused the MIL to illuminate. The DTC can be cleared as follows.

1. Connect the scan tool to the Diagnostic Link Connector (DLC).
2. Clear the DTC codes and command the MIL light off with the scan tool.

MASS AIR FLOW (MAF) SENSOR

LOCATION

The Mass Air Flow (MAF) sensor is integrated with the IAT sensor, it is located on the air cleaner assembly. The 6.6L engine utilizes an additional IAT sensor located on the intake manifold.

REMOVAL & INSTALLATION

4.3L, 4.8L, 5.3L & 6.0L Engines

1. Before servicing the vehicle, refer to the Precautions Section.
2. Disconnect the negative battery cable.
3. Remove the air intake tube from the air cleaner assembly.
4. Detach the electrical connector from the MAF sensor.
5. Remove the sensor retaining bolts.
6. Remove the sensor from its mounting.

→**On the 4.8L, 5.3L and 6.0L engines, the embossed arrow located on the sensor indicated proper air flow direction.**

To install:

→**Be sure to use new fasteners, as required.**

7. Position the sensor on its mounting.
8. Continue the installation in the reverse order of the removal procedure.

6.6L Engines

Sensor One

1. Before servicing the vehicle, refer to the Precautions Section.
2. Disconnect the negative battery cable(s).
3. Detach the electrical connector from the sensor.
4. Remove the screws securing the sensor.
5. Pull the sensor out of the air cleaner assembly.

To install:

→**Be sure to use new fasteners, as required.**

6. Position the sensor on its mounting.
7. Continue the installation in the reverse order of the removal procedure.

Sensor Two

See Figure 180.

1. Before servicing the vehicle, refer to the Precautions Section.
2. Disconnect the negative battery cable(s).

3. Remove the air intake pipe.
4. Unplug the harness connector from the sensor.
5. Remove the sensor from the intake manifold.

To install:

→**Be sure to use new fasteners, as required.**

6. Position the sensor on its mounting.
7. Continue the installation in the reverse order of the removal procedure.

MANIFOLD ABSOLUTE PRESSURE (MAP) SENSOR

LOCATION

The Manifold Absolute Pressure (MAP) sensor It is located on the intake manifold.

REMOVAL & INSTALLATION

See Figures 183 and 184.

1. Before servicing the vehicle, refer to the Precautions Section.

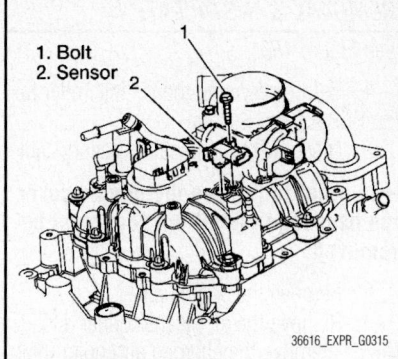

Fig. 183 MAP sensor and related components—4.3L engines

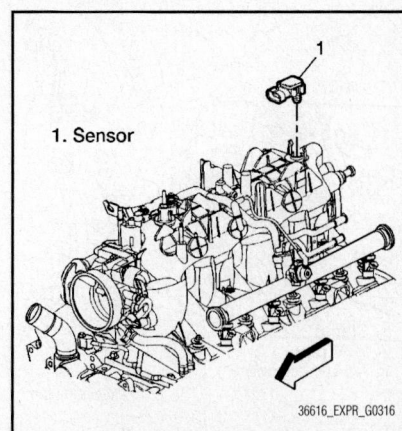

Fig. 184 MAP sensor and related components—4.8L, 5.3L and 6.0L engines

2. Disconnect the negative battery cable.

➡️ **In order to remove the engine cover the passenger side front seat must be removed.**

3. Remove the engine cover.

4. Disconnect the engine wiring harness electrical connector.

5. Remove the sensor retaining bolt, 4.3L engines.

To install:

➡️ **Be sure to use new fasteners, as required.**

6. Position the sensor on its mounting.

7. Tighten the retaining bolt to 89 inch lbs. (10 Nm), 4.3L engines.

8. Continue the installation in the reverse order of the removal procedure.

POSITIVE CRANKCASE VENTILATION (PCV) VALVE

LOCATION

On the 6.6L engine the PCV valve is located on the left valve cover. All other engines use a PCV orifice.

REMOVAL & INSTALLATION

See Figure 185.

1. Before servicing the vehicle, refer to the Precautions Section.

2. Disconnect the negative battery cable.

➡️ **In order to remove the engine cover the passenger side front seat must be removed.**

3. Remove the engine cover.

4. Remove the air cleaner outlet duct.

5. Remove the charged air cooler inlet pipe from the turbocharger.

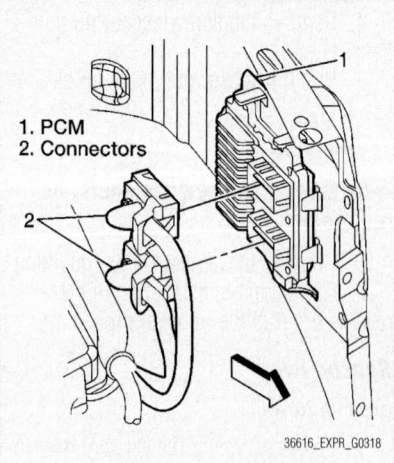

1. Clamp
2. PCV pipe
3. Air intake pipe

36616_EXPR_G0317

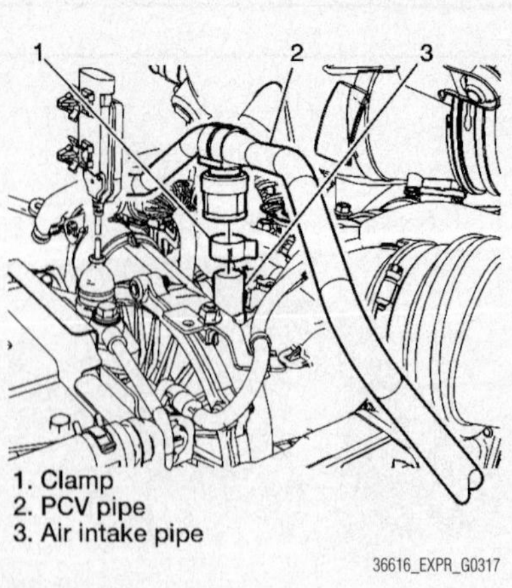

Fig. 185 PCV and related components—6.6L engines

6. Disconnect the wiring harness connector from the glow plug module.

7. Remove the glow plug wiring harness bracket bolts, position the harness to the side.

8. Remove the PCV pipe bolt and disconnect the PCV pipe from the left valve cover.

9. Remove the PCV pipe bolt and disconnect the PCV pipe from the right valve cover.

10. Compress the clamp and disconnect the pipe from the air intake pipe.

11. Remove the PCV hose/pipe.

To install:

➡️ **Be sure to use new fasteners, as required.**

12. Position the valve on its mounting.

13. Continue the installation in the reverse order of the removal procedure.

POWERTRAIN CONTROL MODULE (PCM)

LOCATION

The Powertrain Control Module (PCM) is located on a bracket on the side of the engine compartment.

REMOVAL & INSTALLATION

See Figures 186 and 187.

➡️ **It is necessary to record the remaining engine oil life. If the replacement module is not programmed with the remaining engine oil life, the engine oil life will default to 100 percent. If the replacement module is not programmed with the remaining engine oil life, the engine oil must be changed at 3,000 miles (5,000km) from the last oil change. A scan tool must be used to retrieve the PCM data. This information must be transferred to the new PCM.**

1. PCM
2. Connectors

36616_EXPR_G0318

Fig. 186 PCM and related components—4.3L, 4.8L, 5.3L and 6.0L engines

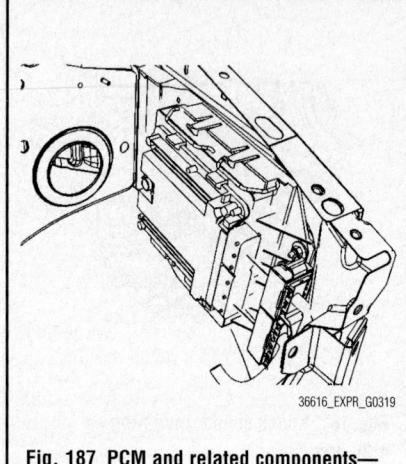

36616_EXPR_G0319

Fig. 187 PCM and related components—6.6L engines

1. Before servicing the vehicle, refer to the Precautions Section.

2. Disconnect the negative battery cable.

3. Disengage the harness connections from the PCM.

4. Disengage the retainer tabs securing the PCM to the bracket. Remove the PCM from the engine compartment.

To install:

➡️ **Be sure to use new fasteners, as required.**

5. Position the PCM on its mounting.

6. Continue the installation in the reverse order of the removal procedure.

➡️ **If a new PCM was installed using the GM diagnostic scan tool, or equivalent, refer to the on-screen reprogramming directions and reprogram the PCM.**

VEHICLE SPEED SENSOR (VSS)

LOCATION

The Vehicle Speed Sensor (VSS) is located on the tail section of the transmission on RWD models. On AWD models, it is located on the transfer case.

REMOVAL & INSTALLATION

See Figures 188 and 189.

1. Before servicing the vehicle, refer to the Precautions Section.

2. Disconnect the negative battery cable.

3. Raise and support the vehicle safely.

4. Detach the electrical connector from the VSS sensor.

5. Remove the sensor from the transmission or transfer case.

6. Remove the O-ring seal.

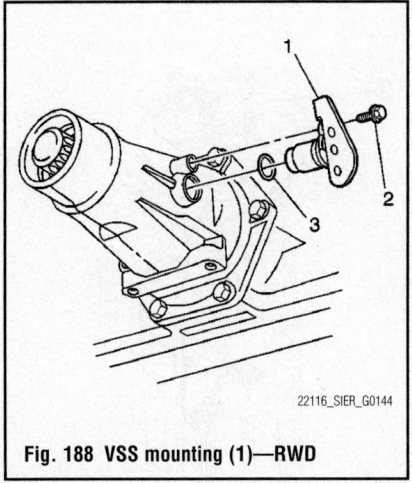

22116_SIER_G0144

Fig. 188 VSS mounting (1)—RWD

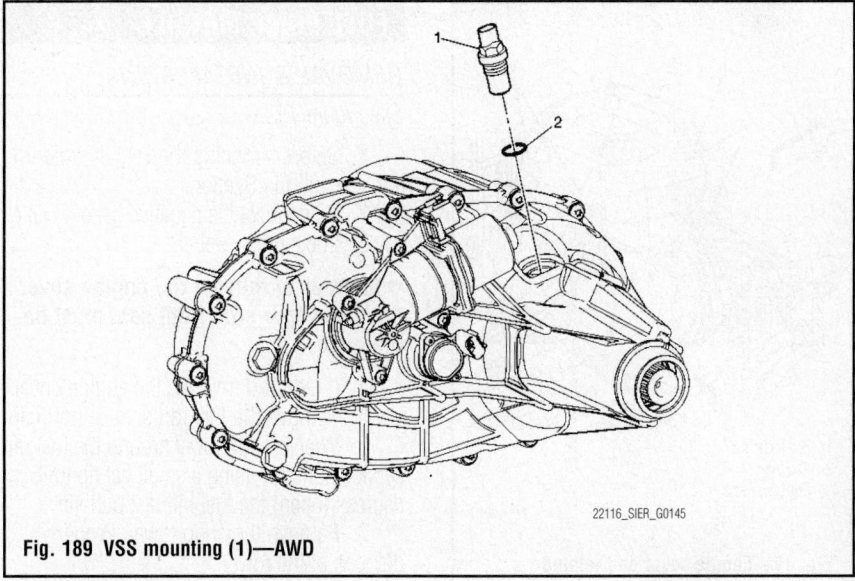

22116_SIER_G0145

Fig. 189 VSS mounting (1)—AWD

To install:

➡**Be sure to use new fasteners, as required.**

7. Coat a new O–ring with transmission fluid.

8. Position the sensor on its mounting.
9. Tighten the bolt to 97 inch lbs. (11 Nm) on RWD, or 13 ft. lbs. (17 Nm) on AWD.

10. Continue the installation in the reverse order of the removal procedure.

FUEL

GASOLINE FUEL INJECTION SYSTEM

FUEL SYSTEM SERVICE PRECAUTIONS

Safety is the most important factor when performing not only fuel system maintenance but any type of maintenance. Failure to conduct maintenance and repairs in a safe manner may result in serious personal injury or death. Maintenance and testing of the vehicle's fuel system components can be accomplished safely and effectively by adhering to the following rules and guidelines.

• To avoid the possibility of fire and personal injury, always disconnect the negative battery cable unless the repair or test procedure requires that battery voltage be applied.

• Always relieve the fuel system pressure prior to disconnecting any fuel system component (injector, fuel rail, pressure regulator, etc.), fitting or fuel line connection. Exercise extreme caution whenever relieving fuel system pressure to avoid exposing skin, face and eyes to fuel spray. Please be advised that fuel under pressure may penetrate the skin or any part of the body that it contacts.

• Always place a shop towel or cloth around the fitting or connection prior to loosening to absorb any excess fuel due to spillage. Ensure that all fuel spillage (should it occur) is quickly removed from engine surfaces. Ensure that all fuel soaked cloths or towels are deposited into a suitable waste container.

• Always keep a dry chemical (Class B) fire extinguisher near the work area.

• Do not allow fuel spray or fuel vapors to come into contact with a spark or open flame.

• Always use a back–up wrench when loosening and tightening fuel line connection fittings. This will prevent unnecessary stress and torsion to fuel line piping.

• Always replace worn fuel fitting O–rings with new. Do not substitute fuel hose or equivalent where fuel pipe is installed.

Before servicing the vehicle, make sure to also refer to the precautions in the beginning of this section as well.

RELIEVING FUEL SYSTEM PRESSURE

See Figures 190 and 191.

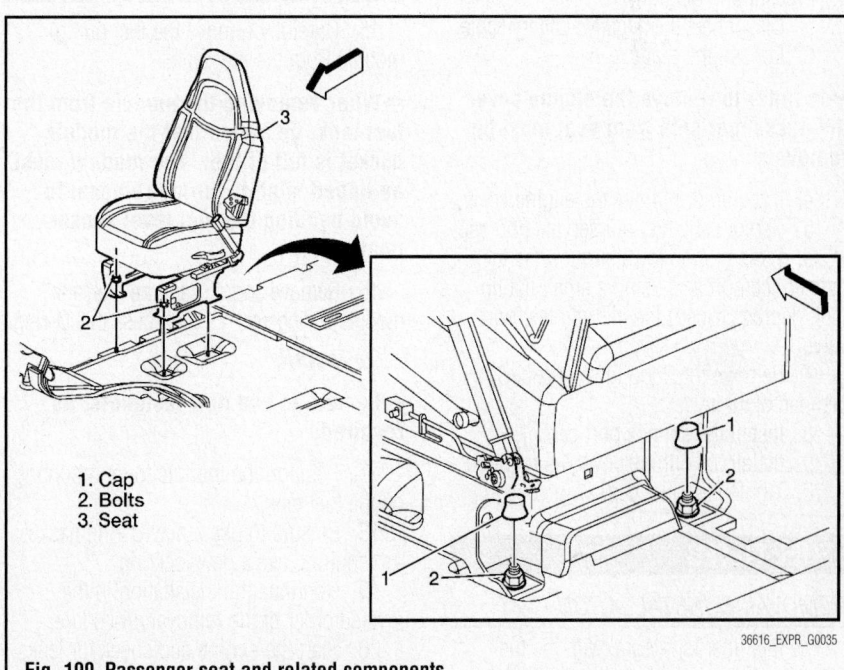

1. Cap
2. Bolts
3. Seat

36616_EXPR_G0035

Fig. 190 Passenger seat and related components

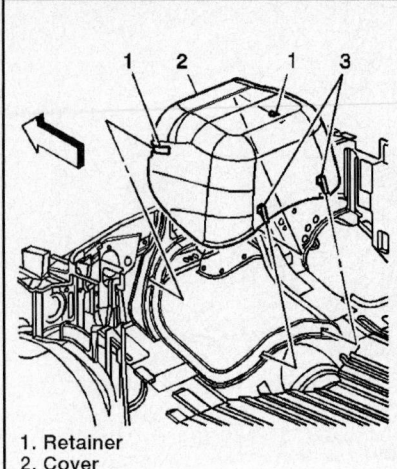

1. Retainer
2. Cover
3. Retainers

36616_EXPR_G0116

Fig. 191 Engine cover and related components

➡Remove the fuel tank cap and relieve the fuel system pressure before servicing the fuel system in order to reduce the risk of personal injury. After you relieve the fuel system pressure, a small amount of fuel may be released when servicing the fuel lines, the fuel injection pump, or the connections. In order to reduce the risk of personal injury, cover the fuel system components with a shop towel before disconnection. Place the shop towel in an approved container when the disconnection is complete.

1. Before servicing the vehicle, refer to the Precautions Section.
2. Disconnect the negative battery cable.
3. Loosen the fuel cap.

➡In order to remove the engine cover the passenger side front seat must be removed.

4. If required, remove the engine cover.
5. Remove the fuel rail service port cap.
6. Wrap a shop towel around the fuel rail service port and using a small flat tip tool, depress (open) the fuel rail test port valve.
7. Remove the shop towel. Properly dispose of the towel.
8. Install the service port cap.
9. Install the engine cover, as required.
10. Tighten the fuel cap.

FUEL FILTER

REMOVAL & INSTALLATION

The fuel filter is integral with the fuel pump/sender assembly in the fuel tank.

FUEL PUMP MODULE

REMOVAL & INSTALLATION

See Figure 192.

1. Before servicing the vehicle, refer to the Precautions Section.
2. Disconnect the negative battery cable.
3. Loosen the fuel cap.

➡In order to remove the engine cover the passenger side front seat must be removed.

4. If required, remove the engine cover.
5. Remove the fuel rail service port cap.
6. Wrap a shop towel around the fuel rail service port and using a small flat tip tool, depress (open) the fuel rail test port valve.
7. Remove the shop towel. Properly dispose of the towel.
8. Install the service port cap.
9. Tighten the fuel cap.
10. Remove the fuel tank.
11. Disconnect the fuel feed pipe quick connecting from the module.
12. Disconnect the EVAP pipe from the module.
13. Disconnect the front EVAP pipe from the module.
14. Using tool J-45722 or equivalent, remove the fuel tank module lockring. Use the proper tool to avoid damaging the lockring.

❋❋ WARNING

Do not handle the fuel sender assembly by the fuel pipes. The amount of leverage generated by handling the fuel pipes could damage the joints.

15. Carefully remove the fuel pump module from the fuel tank.

➡When removing the module from the fuel tank, be aware that the module bucket is full of fuel. The module must be tipped slightly during removal to avoid bending the fuel level sensor float arm

16. Remove and discard the fuel tank module O-ring seal. Do not reuse this O-ring.

To install:

➡Be sure to use new fasteners, as required.

17. Position the module to its mounting on the fuel tank.
18. Be sure to use a new O-ring gasket. As required, use a new lockring.
19. Continue the installation in the reverse order of the removal procedure.
20. Start the engine and check for leaks. Correct as required.

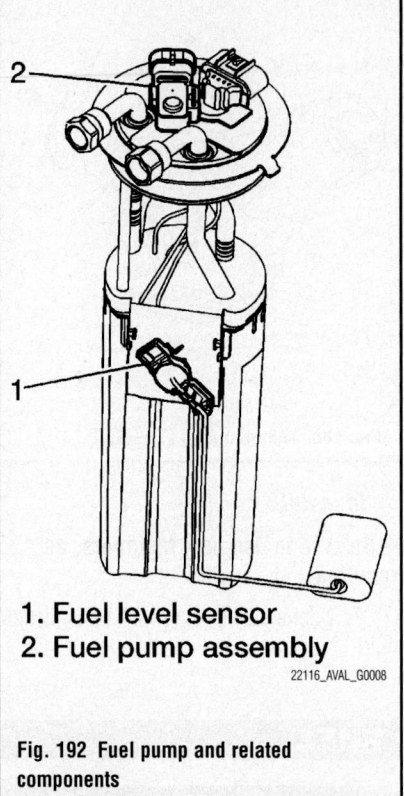

1. Fuel level sensor
2. Fuel pump assembly

22116_AVAL_G0008

Fig. 192 Fuel pump and related components

FUEL RAIL & INJECTORS

REMOVAL & INSTALLATION

4.3L Engines

See Figure 193.

1. Before servicing the vehicle, refer to the Precautions Section.
2. Disconnect the negative battery cable.
3. Loosen the fuel cap.

➡In order to remove the engine cover the passenger side front seat must be removed.

4. If required, remove the engine cover.
5. Remove the fuel rail service port cap.
6. Wrap a shop towel around the fuel rail service port and using a small flat tip tool, depress (open) the fuel rail test port valve.
7. Remove the shop towel. Properly dispose of the towel.
8. Install the service port cap.
9. Tighten the fuel cap.
10. Remove or disconnect the following:
    • Electrical connection
    • Fuel feed and return hoses from the engine fuel pipes
    • Upper manifold assembly
    • Poppet nozzle out of the casting socket

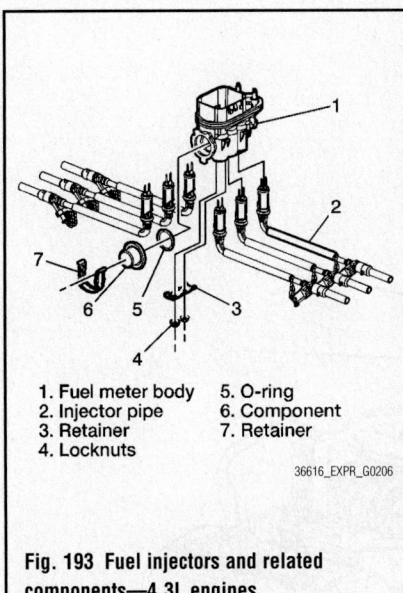

1. Fuel meter body
2. Injector pipe
3. Retainer
4. Locknuts
5. O-ring
6. Component
7. Retainer

36616_EXPR_G0206

Fig. 193 Fuel injectors and related components—4.3L engines

- Fuel meter body by releasing the locktabs

➡**Each injector is calibrated. When replacing the fuel injectors, be sure to replace it with the correct injector.**

- Lower hold–down plate and nuts

11. While pulling the poppet nozzle tube downward, push with a small prytool down between the injector terminals and remove the injectors.

To install:

➡**Be sure to use new fasteners, as required.**

12. Lubricate the new injector O–ring seats with engine oil.
13. Install or connect the following:
- O–rings on the injector
- Fuel injector into the fuel meter body injector socket
- Lower hold–down plate and nuts. Torque the nuts to 27 inch lbs. (3 Nm).
- Fuel meter body assembly into the intake manifold. Torque the fuel meter bracket retainer bolts to 88 inch. lbs. (10 Nm).

✳✳ CAUTION

To reduce the risk of fire or injury ensure that the poppet nozzles are properly seated and locked in their casting sockets

- Fuel meter body into the bracket and lock all the tabs in place
- Poppet nozzles into the casting sockets
- Electrical connections

- New O–ring seals on the fuel return and feed hoses
- Fuel feed and return hoses. Torque the fuel pipe nuts to 22 ft. lbs. (30 Nm).
- Negative battery cable

14. Turn the ignition **ON** for 2 seconds and then turn it **OFF** for 10 seconds. Again turn the ignition **ON** and check for leaks.
- Upper intake manifold

15. Start the engine and check for leaks. Correct as required.

4.8L, 5.3L & 6.0L Engines

See Figure 194.

1. Before servicing the vehicle, refer to the Precautions Section.
2. Disconnect the negative battery cable.
3. Loosen the fuel cap.

➡**In order to remove the engine cover the passenger side front seat must be removed.**

4. If required, remove the engine cover.
5. Remove the fuel rail service port cap.
6. Wrap a shop towel around the fuel rail service port and using a small flat tip tool, depress (open) the fuel rail test port valve.
7. Remove the shop towel. Properly dispose of the towel.
8. Install the service port cap.
9. Tighten the fuel cap.
10. Remove the air cleaner assembly.
11. Remove the engine wiring harness bracket.
12. Disconnect the electrical connectors from the EVAP, alternator and MAP sensor.
13. Remove the CPA retainer.
14. Disconnect the electrical connectors from the ignition coil main electrical connector.

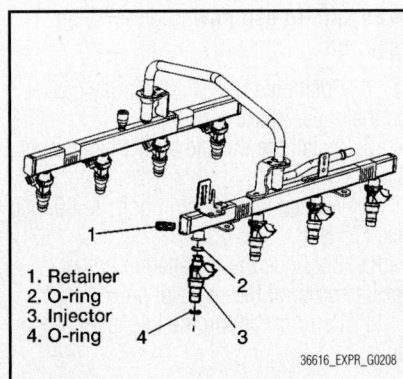

1. Retainer
2. O-ring
3. Injector
4. O-ring

36616_EXPR_G0208

Fig. 194 Fuel injectors and related components—4.8L, 5.3L and 6.0L engines

15. Disconnect the electrical connector from the electronic throttle control.
16. Disconnect the electrical connectors from the fuel injectors. Be sure to mark them for reassembly.

➡**Pull the CPA retainer on the connector up one click. Push the tab on the connector in. Disconnect the electrical connector.**

17. Remove the engine wiring harness clip from the alternator battery jumper cable and ignition coil bracket stud.
18. Remove the negative battery cable stud from the right cylinder head.
19. Remove the negative battery cable terminal and the engine wiring harness ground terminal from the cylinder head.
20. Remove the clip bolt from the alternator bracket.
21. Remove the PCV hose.
22. Disconnect the chassis fuel feed pipe quick connect fitting from the fuel rail.
23. Disconnect the EVAP fitting at the intake manifold.
24. Remove the EVAP tube and purge solenoid
25. Remove the fuel rail bolts. Remove the fuel rail assembly.
26. Remove the fuel injectors from the fuel rail assembly.

To install:

➡**Be sure to use new fasteners, as required.**

27. Lubricate the new injector O–ring seats with engine oil.
28. Install the injectors on the fuel rail assembly.
29. Position the fuel rail assembly to its mounting on the engine.
30. Tighten the retaining bolts to 89 inch lbs. (10 Nm).
31. Continue the installation in the reverse order of the removal procedure.
32. Start the engine and check for leaks. Correct as required.

FUEL TANK

REMOVAL & INSTALLATION

1. Before servicing the vehicle, refer to the Precautions Section.
2. Disconnect the negative battery cable.
3. Loosen the fuel cap.

➡**In order to remove the engine cover the passenger side front seat must be removed.**

4. If required, remove the engine cover.
5. Remove the fuel rail service port cap.

6. Wrap a shop towel around the fuel rail service port and using a small flat tip tool, depress (open) the fuel rail test port valve.

7. Remove the shop towel. Properly dispose of the towel.

8. Install the service port cap.

9. Tighten the fuel cap.

10. Drain the fuel tank.

11. Raise and support the vehicle safely.

➡Clean the fuel and EVAP connections before disconnecting them to prevent fuel system contamination. Cap the lines to prevent leakage and contamination.

12. Remove the fuel filler pipe and remove the tank shield, if equipped.

13. Label and disconnect the EVAP lines and electrical connection from the fuel tank assembly.

14. Disconnect the fuel line from the tank.

15. Support the fuel tank using a suitable jack. Remove the strap bolts and the straps.

16. Lower the tank halfway. Be sure the fill neck does not get hung up on the chassis harness. Detach the harness clip from the crossmember.

17. Lower the tank enough so that the electrical connections are accessible. Detach the connections then fully lower the tank and remove it from under the vehicle.

To install:

➡Be sure to use new fasteners, as required.

18. Installation is the reverse of removal. When installing the tank, be sure to inspect all lines, hoses and electrical connections first. Repair or replace as necessary. Tighten the strap bolts to 15 ft. lbs. (20 Nm).

19. To check for leaks, refill the tank then turn the ignition ON (engine OFF) for 2 seconds. Turn the ignition OFF for 10 seconds. Turn the ignition ON again (engine OFF) and inspect the tank and lines for leaks.

IDLE SPEED

ADJUSTMENT

Idle speed is maintained by the Powertrain Control Module (PCM). No adjustment is necessary or possible.

THROTTLE BODY

REMOVAL & INSTALLATION

4.3L Engines

See Figure 195.

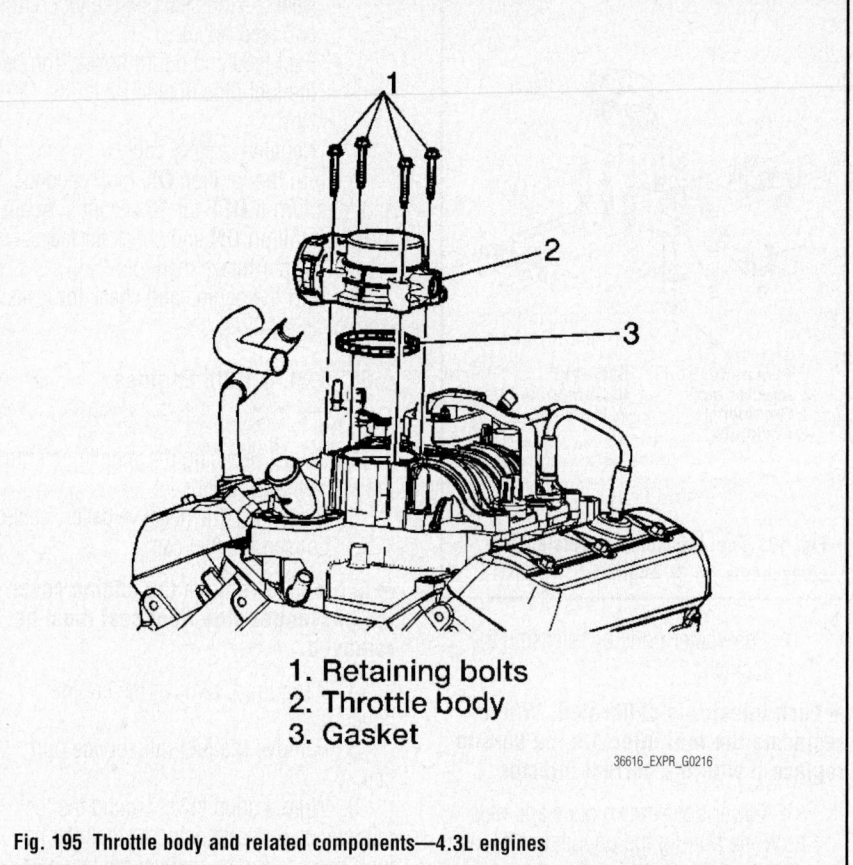

1. Retaining bolts
2. Throttle body
3. Gasket

36616_EXPR_G0216

Fig. 195 Throttle body and related components—4.3L engines

1. Before servicing the vehicle, refer to the Precautions Section.

2. Disconnect the negative battery cable.

3. Remove the air cleaner assembly.

4. Disconnect the engine wiring harness electrical connector from the throttle actuator.

5. Remove the throttle body retaining bolts.

6. Remove the component from its mounting.

To install:

➡Be sure to use new fasteners, as required.

7. Position a new throttle body gasket on the upper intake manifold.

8. Install the throttle body to its mounting.

9. Tighten the retaining bolts to 89 inch lbs. (10 Nm).

10. Continue the installation in the reverse order of the removal procedure.

11. Perform the throttle idle learn procedure.

➡Using the GM diagnostic scan tool, or equivalent, refer to the on-screen reprogramming directions and perform the throttle/idle learn procedure.

12. With the ignition ON and the engine OFF, perform the idle learn reset in mode setup, using the scan tool.

13. Start the engine and monitor the TB Idle Airflow Compensation parameter.

14. The value should equal zero percent and the engine should be idling at a normal idle speed.

15. Clear any DTC's.

4.8L, 5.3L & 6.0L Engines

See Figure 196.

1. Before servicing the vehicle, refer to the Precautions Section.

2. Disconnect the negative battery cable.

3. Remove the air cleaner assembly.

4. Disconnect the electrical connector.

5. Disconnect the vacuum hoses.

6. Remove the throttle body retaining nuts.

7. Remove the component from its mounting.

To install:

➡Be sure to use new fasteners, as required.

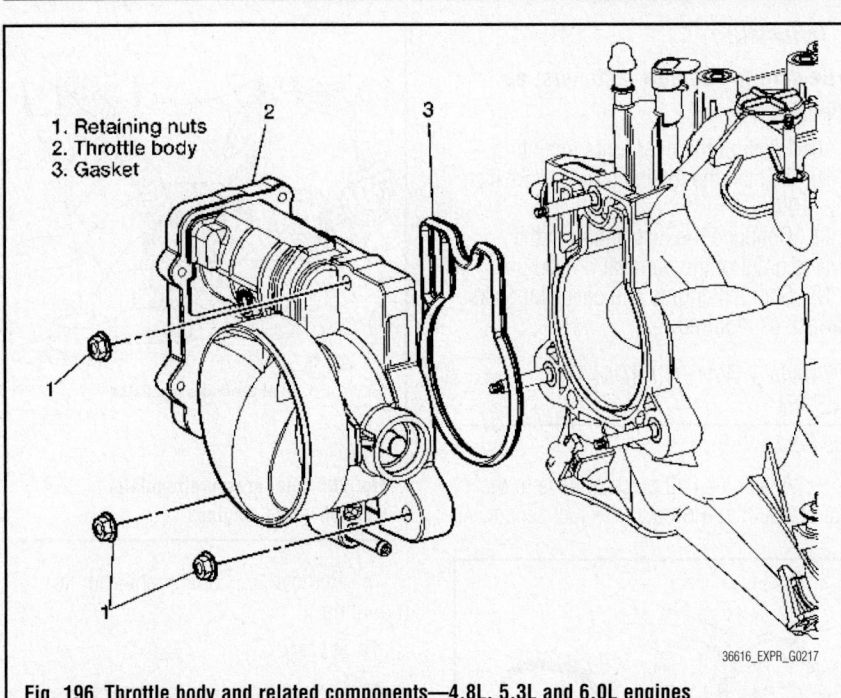

1. Retaining nuts
2. Throttle body
3. Gasket

36616_EXPR_G0217

Fig. 196 Throttle body and related components—4.8L, 5.3L and 6.0L engines

8. Position a new throttle body gasket on the upper intake manifold.

9. Install the throttle body to its mounting.

10. Tighten the retaining nuts to 89 inch lbs. (10 Nm).

11. Continue the installation in the reverse order of the removal procedure.

12. Perform the throttle idle learn procedure.

➡**Using the GM diagnostic scan tool, or equivalent, refer to the on-screen reprogramming directions and perform the throttle/idle learn procedure.**

13. With the ignition ON and the engine OFF, perform the idle learn reset in mode setup, using the scan tool.

14. Start the engine and monitor the TB Idle Airflow Compensation parameter.

15. The value should equal zero percent and the engine should be idling at a normal idle speed.

16. Clear any DTC's.

FUEL

DIESEL FUEL SYSTEM

FUEL SYSTEM SERVICE PRECAUTIONS

Safety is the most important factor when performing not only fuel system maintenance but any type of maintenance. Failure to conduct maintenance and repairs in a safe manner may result in serious personal injury or death. Maintenance and testing of the vehicle's fuel system components can be accomplished safely and effectively by adhering to the following rules and guidelines.

• To avoid the possibility of fire and personal injury, always disconnect the negative battery cable unless the repair or test procedure requires that battery voltage be applied.

• Always relieve the fuel system pressure prior to disconnecting any fuel system component (injector, fuel rail, pressure regulator, etc.), fitting or fuel line connection. Exercise extreme caution whenever relieving fuel system pressure to avoid exposing skin, face and eyes to fuel spray. Please be advised that fuel under pressure may penetrate the skin or any part of the body that it contacts.

• Always place a shop towel or cloth around the fitting or connection prior to loosening to absorb any excess fuel due to spillage. Ensure that all fuel spillage (should it occur) is quickly removed from engine surfaces. Ensure that all fuel soaked

cloths or towels are deposited into a suitable waste container.

• Always keep a dry chemical (Class B) fire extinguisher near the work area.

• Do not allow fuel spray or fuel vapors to come into contact with a spark or open flame.

• Always use a back-up wrench when loosening and tightening fuel line connection fittings. This will prevent unnecessary stress and torsion to fuel line piping.

• Always replace worn fuel fitting O-rings with new. Do not substitute fuel hose or equivalent where fuel pipe is installed.

Before servicing the vehicle, make sure to also refer to the precautions in the beginning of this section as well.

RELIEVING FUEL SYSTEM PRESSURE

Fuel system pressure can be released by wrapping a fuel fitting in a heavy shop towel and slightly loosening the fitting. NEVER perform this with any source of ignition nearby!

FUEL FILTER

REMOVAL & INSTALLATION

Except Primary Fuel Filter

See Figure 197.

1. Before servicing the vehicle, refer to the Precautions Section.

2. Disconnect the negative battery cables.

3. If necessary, remove the wheelhouse liner for additional access.

4. Drain the fuel from the fuel filter as follows:

a. Install a hose on the water drain on the water-in-fuel sensor.

b. Place the other end of the hose into an approved container.

c. Drain as much fuel as possible from the fuel filter housing.

d. Tighten the water drain on the water-in-fuel sensor.

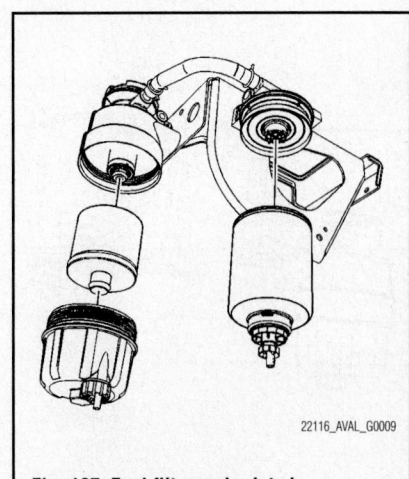

22116_AVAL_G0009

Fig. 197 Fuel filter and related components—6.6L engines

5. Remove or disconnect the following:
- Water–in–fuel sensor harness connector
- Fuel filter from the fuel filter/heater element housing
- Water–in–fuel sensor from the fuel filter

To install:

6. Install or connect the following:
- Water–in–fuel sensor in the fuel filter

➡ **Check the fuel filter/heater element housing and the filter for a dislocated filter seal or foreign debris. Contamination on the filter/heater housing may cause leakage at the fuel filter. Coat the seal with clean engine oil.**

- Fuel filter on the fuel filter/heater element housing
- Water–in–fuel harness connector
- Negative battery cables

7. Purge the fuel system.
8. Start the engine and check for leaks.

Primary Fuel Filter

See Figure 198.

1. Before servicing the vehicle, refer to the Precautions Section.
2. Disconnect the negative battery cables.
3. Raise and support the vehicle safely.
4. Drain the fuel from the fuel filter.
5. Disconnect the fuel lines.
6. Disconnect the electrical connectors.
7. Remove the filter bolts from the bracket.
8. Remove the filter.

36616_EXPR_G0220

Fig. 198 Primary fuel filter and related components—6.6L engines

To install:

➡ **Be sure to use new fasteners, as required.**

9. Position the filter to its mounting.
10. Tighten the retaining nuts to 89 inch lbs. (10 Nm).
11. Continue the installation in the reverse order of the removal procedure.
12. Start the engine and check for leaks. Correct, as required.

DRAINING WATER FROM THE SYSTEM

See Figure 199.

1. Attach a small piece of hose to the drain cock onto the water–in–fuel sensor.

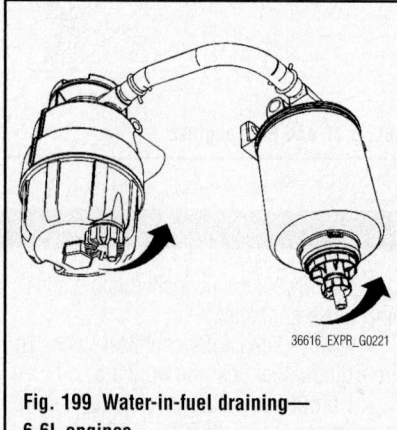

36616_EXPR_G0221

Fig. 199 Water-in-fuel draining— 6.6L engines

2. Place an approved fuel–resistant container under the fuel filter.
3. Open the drain cock 3 or 4 turns or until the water contaminated fuel seeps from the drain cock.
4. Perform the purging procedure until only diesel fuel drains from the assembly.
5. Tighten the drain cock.
6. Remove the container and hose.

FUEL PRESSURE REGULATOR

REMOVAL & INSTALLATION

See Figure 200.

1. Before servicing the vehicle, refer to the Precautions Section.
2. Disconnect the negative battery cables.
3. Remove the center intake manifold.
4. Disconnect the fuel pressure regulator electrical connector.
5. Reposition the distribution block hose clamps.
6. Remove the distribution block hoses from the distribution block.
7. Remove the fuel pressure regulator screws.

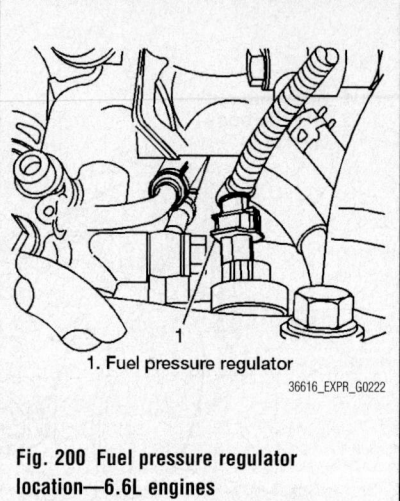

1. Fuel pressure regulator

36616_EXPR_G0222

Fig. 200 Fuel pressure regulator location—6.6L engines

8. Remove the component from its mounting.

To install:

➡ **Be sure to use new fasteners, as required.**

9. Lubricate new O-rings with clean engine oil.
10. Position the O-rings on the regulator.
11. Position the component on its mounting.
12. Tighten the retaining screws 35 inch lbs. (4 Nm), first pass and 62 inch lbs. (7 Nm), second pass.
13. Continue the installation in the reverse order of the removal procedure.
14. Prime (bleed) the fuel system.
15. Start the engine and check for leaks. Correct, as required.

FUEL SUPPLY PUMP

REMOVAL & INSTALLATION

See Figure 201.

1. Before servicing the vehicle, refer to the Precautions Section.
2. Disconnect the negative battery cables.

➡ **Clean the fuel connections before disconnecting them to prevent fuel system contamination. Cap the lines to prevent leakage and contamination.**

3. Relieve the fuel system pressure and open the fuel filler cap.
4. Raise and safely support the vehicle.
5. Detach the electrical connector from the pump.
6. Disconnect the fuel lines from the pump, then slide the pump out of its bracket.

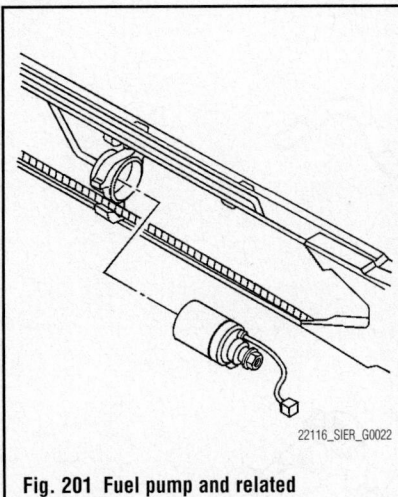

Fig. 201 Fuel pump and related components—6.6L engines

To install:

7. Install the pump using new O–rings. Tighten the fittings to 16 ft. lbs. (22 Nm).

8. Engage the electrical connection and install the fuel filler cap.

9. Purge the fuel system of air. Start the vehicle and check for leaks.

FUEL SYSTEM PURGING

BLEEDING

➡**Prior to priming the engine, ensure that there is fuel in the tank, the fuel filter is properly installed, fuel lines are properly connected, fuel filter is cool to the touch and any dirt has been removed from the fuel filter head and valve vent.**

1. Turn the ignition key ON for two minutes. The fuel pump will be operating and starting the priming process. Do not start the engine during the first two minutes.

2. After completing the initial priming (above step), turn the ignition OFF, then back to START and crank the engine for 15 seconds.

3. If the engine does not start, repeat the above two steps until the engine starts.

4. If the engine does not run after completing the above steps three times, turn the ignition key OFF for 60 seconds. This will allow the ECM to reset.

5. Repeat the procedure until the engine starts.

6. If the engine runs, but does not run smoothly, increase engine speed slightly by pressing the accelerator pedal. This will help fore air out of the system

7. If the engine starts and runs but

stalls again, turn the ignition key OFF for 60 seconds to reset the ECM. Repeat the above steps again.

8. Start the engine and allow it to idle for a few minutes.

9. Check for leaks.

GLOW PLUGS

REMOVAL & INSTALLATION

See Figures 202 and 203.

1. Before servicing the vehicle, refer to the Precautions Section.

2. Disconnect the negative battery cables.

➡**In order to remove the engine cover the passenger side front seat must be removed.**

3. Remove the engine cover.

4. It may be necessary to remove the left front tire and wheel assembly.

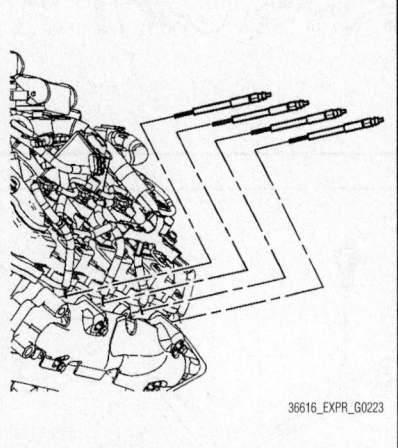

Fig. 202 Glow plug locations (bank one)—6.6L engines

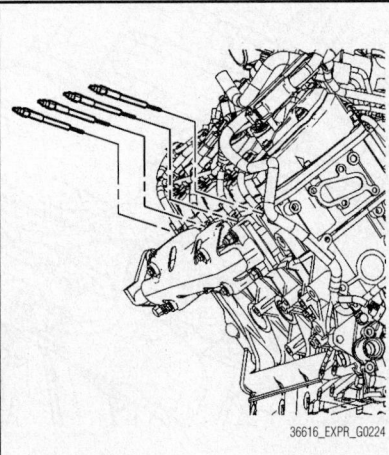

Fig. 203 Glow plug locations (bank two)—6.6L engines

5. Remove the front wheel house inner splash shield.

6. Remove the glow plug harness nuts. Remove the harness from the glow plugs.

To install:

7. Install the glow plugs.

8. Tighten to 13 ft. lbs. (18 Nm)

9. Continue the installation in the reverse order of the removal procedure.

10. Start the engine and check for proper operation.

INJECTION LINES

REMOVAL & INSTALLATION

See Figures 204 through 210.

1. Before servicing the vehicle, refer to the Precautions Section.

2. Disconnect the negative battery cables.

➡**In order to remove the engine cover the passenger side front seat must be removed.**

3. Remove the engine cover.

4. Remove the fuel feed pipe attaching nuts and bolts.

5. Remove the fuel feed pipe.

6. Disconnect the fuel rail balance pipe from fuel rails.

7. Remove the fuel rail balance pipe bolts.

8. Remove the fuel rail balance pipe.

9. Remove the left fuel return hose.

10. Remove the right fuel return hose.

11. Disconnect the fuel hoses from the fuel injector pump.

12. Remove the distribution block and fuel line assembly bolts.

13. Remove the distribution block and fuel line assembly.

14. Remove the fuel pipe assembly bracket bolts.

15. Remove the fuel pipe assembly bracket.

16. Remove the coolant pipe bolt and nut.

17. Remove the coolant pipe.

18. Remove the left fuel rail to pump pipe.

19. Remove the EGR mounting bracket bolts.

20. Remove the EGR mounting brackets.

21. Using compressed air to blow away any debris between the fuel injector line and the fittings. Wipe clean the fittings of debris.

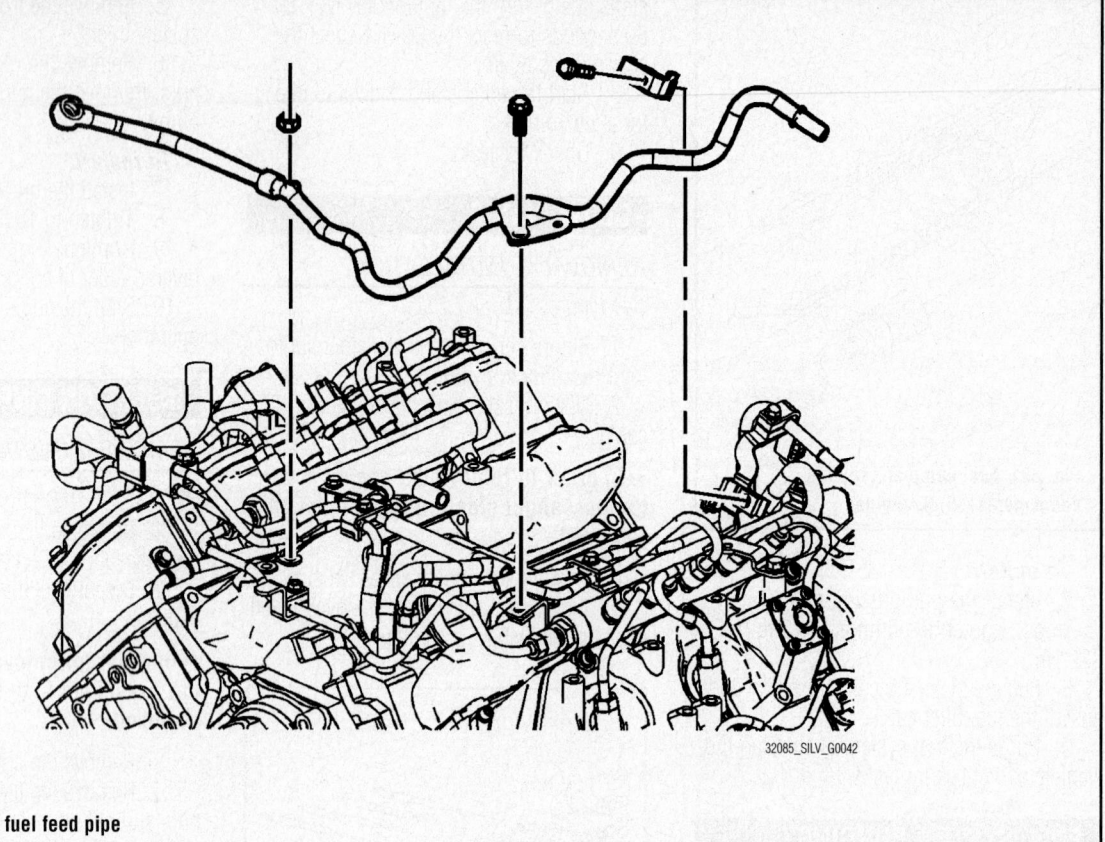

32085_SILV_G0042

Fig. 204 Remove the fuel feed pipe

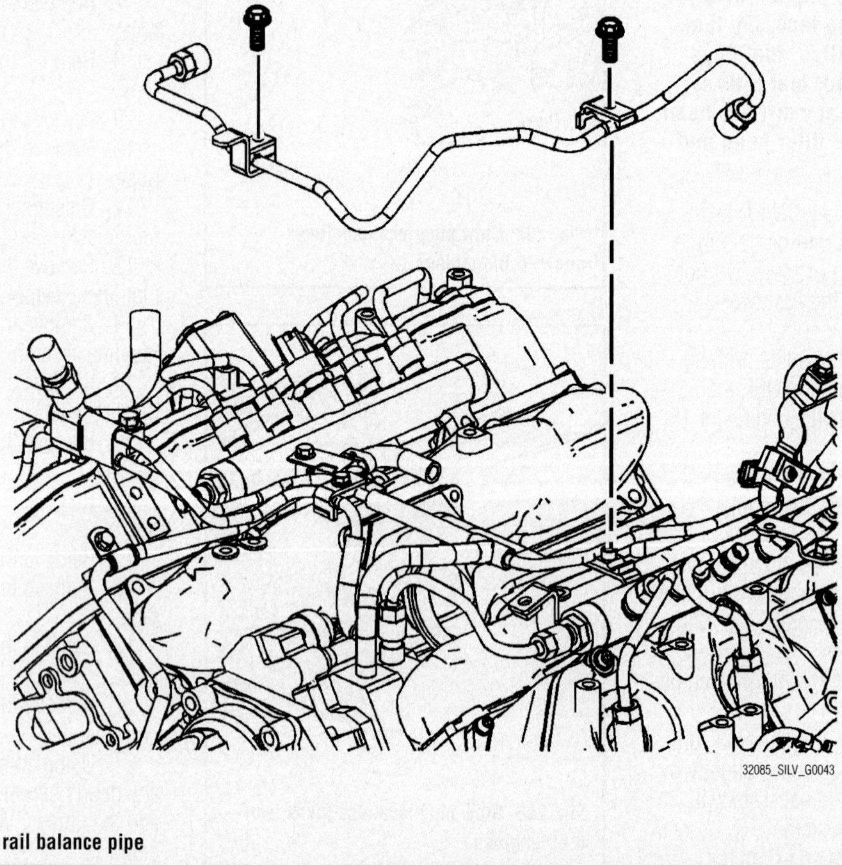

32085_SILV_G0043

Fig. 205 Remove the fuel rail balance pipe

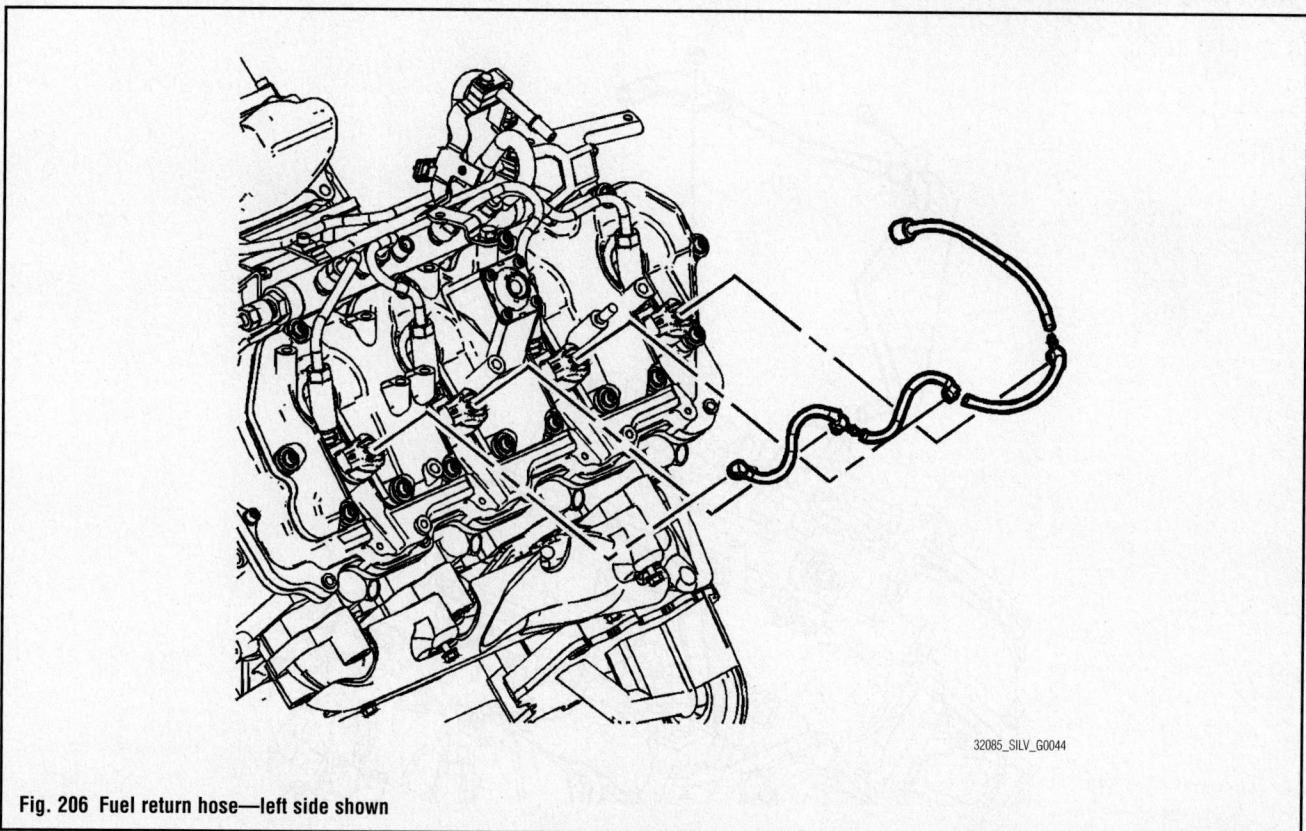

32085_SILV_G0044

Fig. 206 Fuel return hose—left side shown

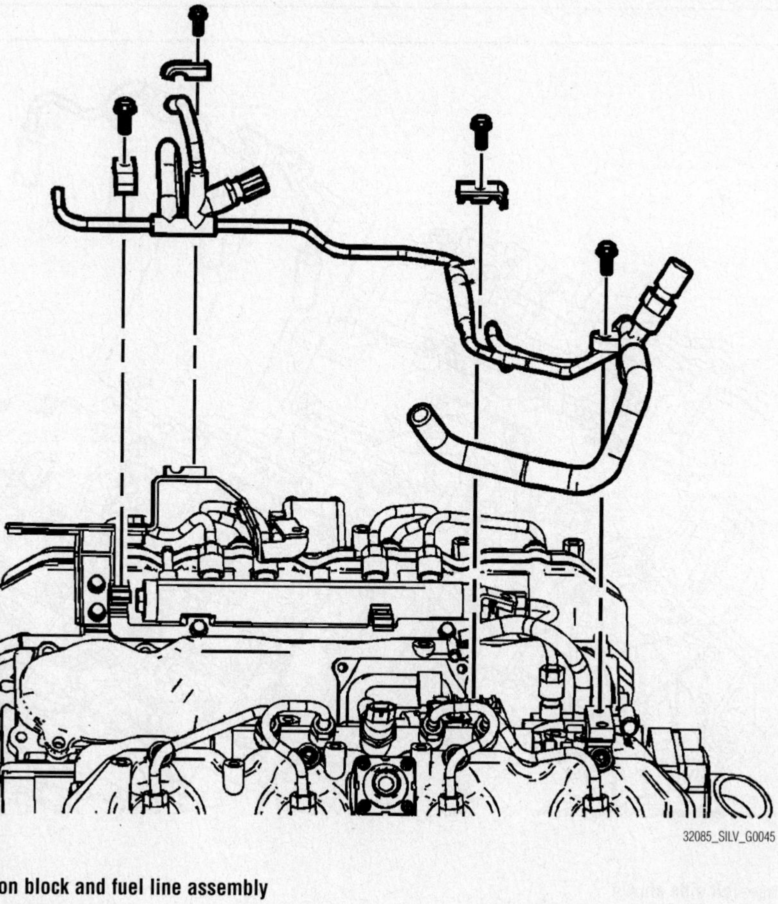

32085_SILV_G0045

Fig. 207 Remove the distribution block and fuel line assembly

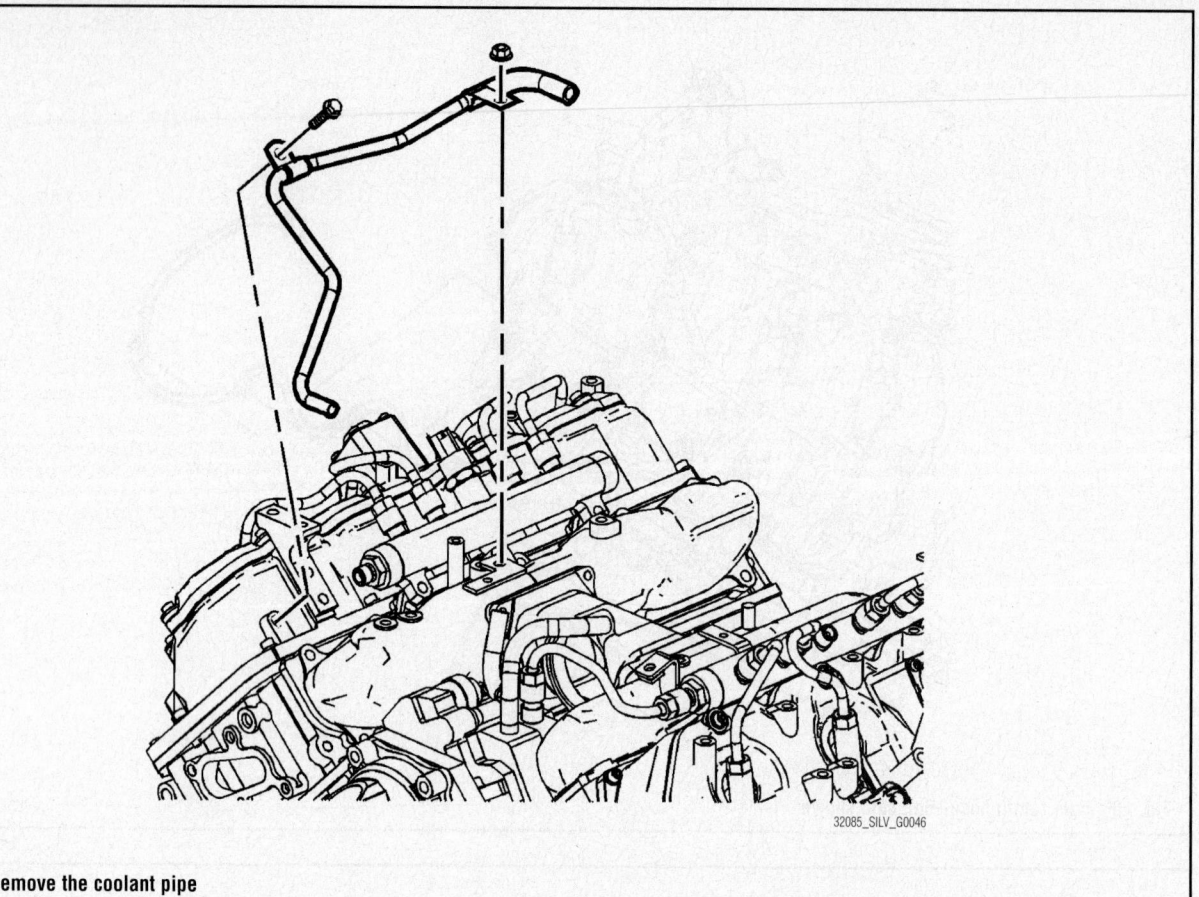

32085_SILV_G0046

Fig. 208 Remove the coolant pipe

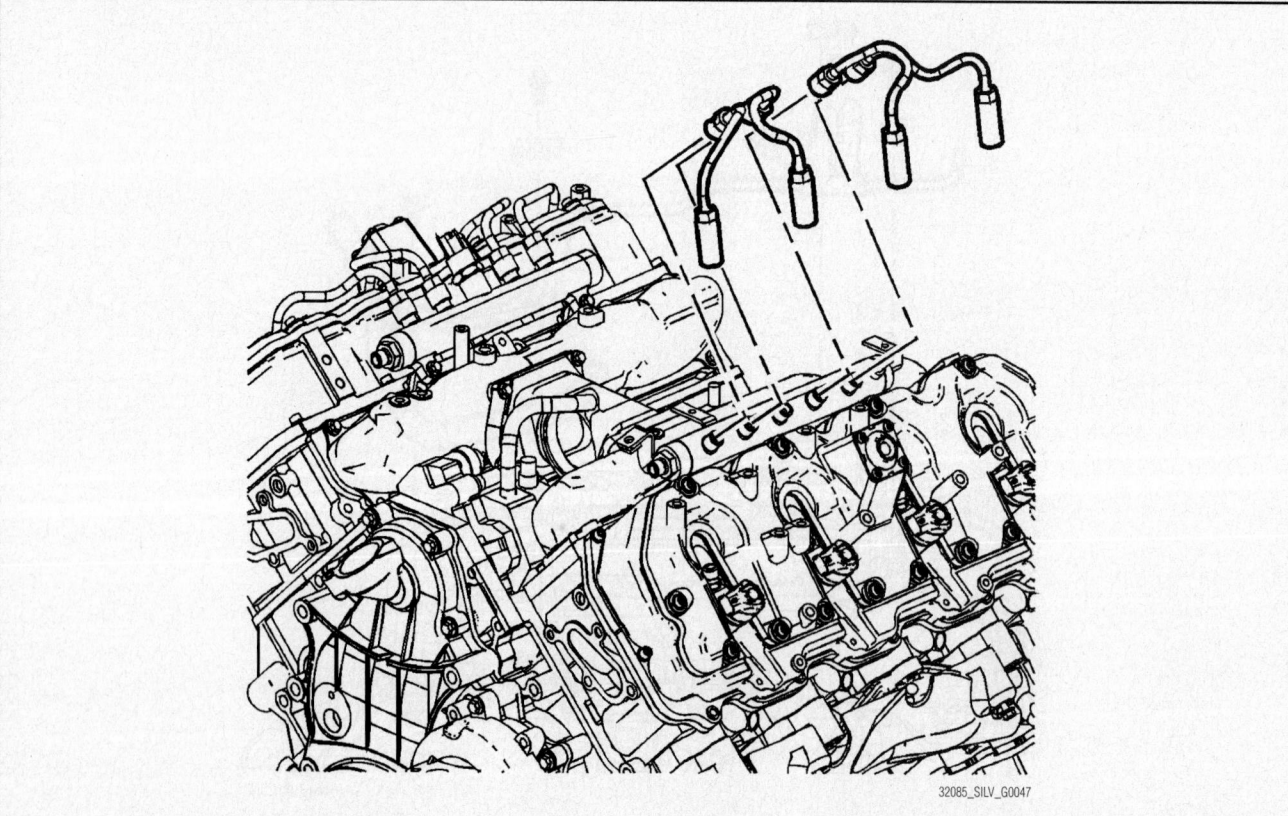

32085_SILV_G0047

Fig. 209 Fuel injector pipes—left side shown

Fig. 210 Fuel rail and bracket—left side shown

⁂ **WARNING**

DO NOT use compressed air to clean debris from the fuel injector inlet after the fuel line is removed. Using compressed air can allow debris to enter the fuel injector inlet and damage the fuel injector.

22. Spray lithium grease, GM P/N 12346293 or equivalent, between the fuel injector line and fitting to contain any debris during removal.

23. Remove the left fuel injector pipes.

24. Remove the right fuel injector pipes.

25. Remove the left fuel rail and bracket bolts.

26. Remove the left fuel rail and bracket.

27. Remove the right fuel rail bolts.

28. Remove the right fuel rail.

To install:

29. Install the right fuel rail.

30. Install the right fuel rail mounting bolts.

31. Tighten the right fuel rail mounting bolts to 18 ft. lbs. (25 Nm).

32. Install the left fuel rail.

33. Install the left fuel rail mounting bolts.

34. Tighten the left fuel rail mounting bolts to 18 ft. lbs. (25 Nm).

⁂ **CAUTION**

Improper torque methods of the fuel lines will result in fuel leaks and possible damage to the engine. Failure to follow proper fuel line fitting torque methods could result in serious personal injury.

35. Install the injection pipes to the right bank.

36. Tighten the injection pipes to 30 ft. lbs. (41 Nm)

37. Install the injection pipes to the left bank.

38. Tighten the injection pipes to 30 ft. lbs. (41 Nm)

39. Install the EGR mounting brackets.

40. Install the EGR mounting bracket bolts.

41. Tighten the EGR mounting bracket bolts to 15 ft. lbs. (20 Nm).

42. Install the left fuel rail to pump pipe.

43. Tighten the fuel rail to pump pipe nut to 30 ft. lbs. (41 Nm).

44. Install the coolant pipe.

45. Install the coolant pipe bolt and nut.

46. Tighten the coolant pipe bolt and nut to 18 ft. lbs. (25 Nm).

47. Install the fuel pipe assembly bracket.

48. Install the fuel pipe assembly bracket bolts.

49. Tighten the fuel pipe assembly bracket bolts to 18 ft. lbs. (25 Nm).

50. Install the distribution block and fuel line assembly.

51. Install the distribution block and fuel line assembly bolts.

52. Tighten the fuel line assembly bolts to 18 ft. lbs. (25 Nm).

53. Connect the fuel hoses to the fuel injector pump.

54. Install the right fuel return hose.

55. Install the left fuel return hose.

56. Install the fuel rail balance pipe.

57. Install the fuel rail balance pipe bolts.

58. Tighten the fuel rail balance pipe bolts to 15 ft. lbs. (21 Nm).

59. Connect the fuel rail balance pipe to the fuel rails.

60. Tighten the fuel rail balance pipe nuts to 30 ft. lbs. (41 Nm).

61. Install the fuel feed pipe.
62. Install the fuel feed pipe attaching nuts and bolts.
63. Tighten the fuel feed pipe bolts and nut to 18 ft. lbs. (25 Nm).

INJECTION PUMP

REMOVAL & INSTALLATION

See Figure 211.

➡**In order to remove the engine cover the passenger side front seat must be removed.**

1. Before servicing the vehicle, refer to the Precautions Section.
2. Disconnect the negative battery cables.
3. Remove the engine cover.
4. Properly relieve the fuel system pressure.
5. Drain the cooling system. Properly dispose of used engine coolant.
6. Remove the thermostat housing crossover.
7. Remove the left and right fuel rail feed pipes.
8. Remove the center intake manifold.
9. Disconnect the injection pump electrical connector.
10. Compress the injection pump hose clamps at the fuel line.
11. Disconnect the hoses from the fuel lines.
12. Remove the injection pump retaining bolts.
13. Remove the injection pump from its mounting.

To install:

➡**Be sure to use new fasteners, as required.**

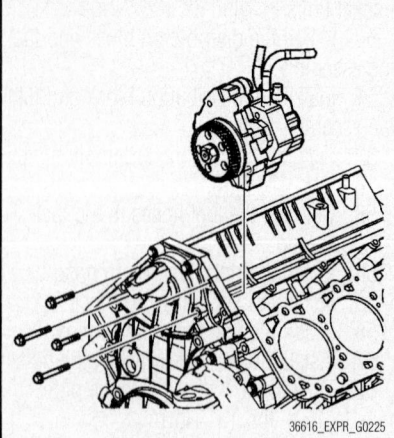

Fig. 211 Fuel injection pump and related components—6.6L engines

14. Prepare the fuel pump as follows:
   a. Hold the fuel pump by the drive gear in a vise with copper jaw liners.
   b. Loosen the gear nut until the nut is even with the end of the gear shaft.
   c. Separate the pump and adapter by removing the 3 bolts and spacers.
   d. Inspect the O–ring for damage on the pump adapter and replace if necessary. Lubricate the O–ring with clean engine oil.
   e. Clean all mating surfaces.
   f. Install the adapter on the pump.
   g. Using the bolts and spacers, reassemble the pump. Tighten the bolts to 15 ft. lbs. (20 Nm).
   h. Install the gear and nut and tighten to 52 ft. lbs. (70 Nm).
15. Position the pump assembly to its mounting on the engine.
16. Install the retaining bolts.
17. Tighten to 15 ft. lbs. (21 Nm).
18. Continue the installation in the reverse order of the removal procedure.
19. Prime (bleed) the fuel system.
20. Start the engine and check for leaks. Correct, as required.

INJECTION TIMING

ADJUSTMENT

The idle speed and injection timing is controlled by the Powertrain Control Module (PCM). There is no provision for adjustment.

INJECTOR RAILS

REMOVAL & INSTALLATION

See Figures 212 and 213.

1. Before servicing the vehicle, refer to the Precautions Section.
2. Disconnect the negative battery cables.

➡**In order to remove the engine cover the passenger side front seat must be removed.**

3. Remove the engine cover.
4. Remove the EGR valve cooler assembly.
5. Properly discharge the air conditioning system. Remove the air condition compressor.
6. Remove the right and left fuel injection feed lines.
7. Disconnect the FRP sensor electrical connector.
8. Disconnect the fuel feed pipe fittings from the fuel rails.
9. Remove the two fuel rail bolts and the fuel rail assembly.

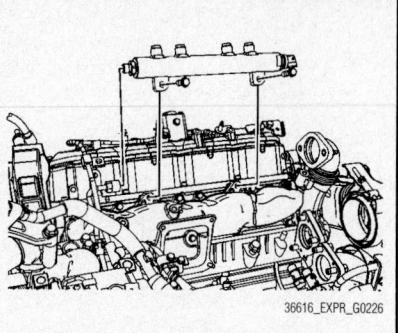

Fig. 212 Fuel injection rail assembly (bank one)—6.6L engines

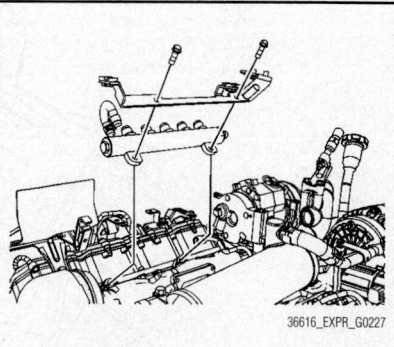

Fig. 213 Fuel injection rail assembly (bank two)—6.6L engines

10. Remove the fuel pressure sensor, as required.

To install:

➡**Be sure to use new fasteners, as required.**

11. Position the fuel rail on its mounting.
12. Install the retaining bolts.
13. Tighten them to 18 ft. lbs. (25 Nm).
14. Continue the installation in the reverse order of the removal procedure.
15. Prime (bleed) the fuel system.
16. Start the engine and check for leaks. Correct, as required.

INJECTORS

REMOVAL & INSTALLATION

Right Side

See Figure 214.

1. Before servicing the vehicle, refer to the Precautions Section.
2. Disconnect the negative battery cables.
3. Remove the right upper valve cover.
4. Remove the fuel injector bracket bolts.

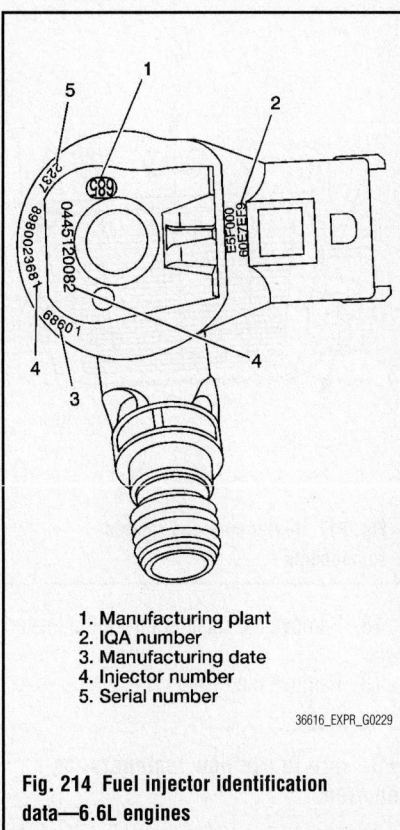

1. Manufacturing plant
2. IQA number
3. Manufacturing date
4. Injector number
5. Serial number

36616_EXPR_G0229

Fig. 214 Fuel injector identification data—6.6L engines

5. Install tool J-46594 or equivalent into the bolt hole. Install a flare nut wrench onto the tool and pull back, away from the injector, until the injector releases from the seat. Remove the tool

6. Remove the injectors with the brackets.

7. Remove and discard the copper washer from the injector bore. Remove and discard the O-ring.

To install:

➡ **Be sure to use new fasteners, as required.**

8. Position the injector rail on its mounting.

9. Continue the installation in the reverse order of the removal procedure.

10. When installing the upper valve cover, be sure to tighten the retaining bolts to specification.

11. If installing new injectors perform the fuel injector flow rate procedure.

➡ **Using the GM diagnostic scan tool or aftermarket equivalent reprogram the fuel injector flow rate. Be sure to follow the scan tool manufacturer's directions.**

12. Prime (bleed) the fuel system.

13. Start the engine and check for leaks. Correct, as required.

Left Side

1. Before servicing the vehicle, refer to the Precautions Section.

2. Disconnect the negative battery cables.

3. Remove the upper fan shroud.

4. Remove the auxiliary alternator, if equipped.

5. Remove the glow plug module and bracket. Remove the injector/glow plug wire harness retaining bolt, at the lower upper valve cover.

6. Disconnect the engine wiring harness connector.

7. Remove the engine wiring harness to bracket bolt, the two engine wiring harness

bracket to upper valve cover bolts and remove the bracket.

8. Remove the fuel injector pipes.

9. Remove the fuel return hose clips. Disconnect the fuel return hose from the injectors.

10. Label and disconnect the injector electrical connectors.

11. Remove the injector bracket bolts.

12. Install tool J-46594 or equivalent into the bolt hole. Install a flare nut wrench onto the tool and pull back, away from the injector, until the injector releases from the seat. Remove the tool

13. Remove the injectors with the brackets.

14. Remove and discard the copper washer from the injector bore. Remove and discard the O-ring.

To install:

➡ **Be sure to use new fasteners, as required.**

15. Position the injector on its mounting.

16. Tighten the retaining bolt to 22 ft. lbs. (30 Nm).

17. Continue the installation in the reverse order of the removal procedure.

18. If installing new injectors perform the fuel injector flow rate procedure.

➡ **Using the GM diagnostic scan tool or aftermarket equivalent reprogram the fuel injector flow rate. Be sure to follow the scan tool manufacturer's directions.**

19. Prime (bleed) the fuel system.

20. Start the engine and check for leaks. Correct, as required.

HEATING & AIR CONDITIONING SYSTEM

BLOWER MOTOR

REMOVAL & INSTALLATION

See Figure 215.

1. Before servicing the vehicle, refer to the Precautions Section.

2. Disconnect the negative battery cable.

3. Remove the coolant reservoir.

4. Remove the electrical connectors at the blower motor.

5. Remove the blower motor cooling tube.

6. Remove the retaining screws from the blower motor.

7. Remove the blower motor from the case.

8. Remove the retaining clip from the fan cage.

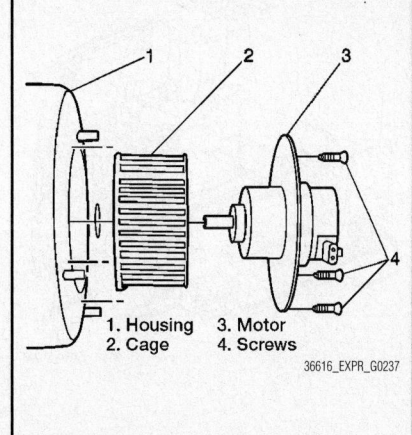

1. Housing
2. Cage
3. Motor
4. Screws

36616_EXPR_G0237

Fig. 215 Blower motor and related components

9. Remove the fan cage from the blower motor.

To install:

10. Install the fan cage to the blower motor.

11. Install the retaining clip to the fan cage.

12. Install the blower motor to the case.

13. Install the retaining screws to the blower motor.

14. Install the blower motor cooling tube (if equipped).

15. Install the electrical connectors at the blower motor.

16. If removed, install the coolant reservoir.

17. Verify the circuit operation.

HEATER CORE

REMOVAL & INSTALLATION

See Figures 216 and 217.

1. Before servicing the vehicle, refer to the Precautions Section.
2. Disconnect the negative battery cable.
3. Properly discharge the air conditioning system.
4. Drain the engine coolant. Properly dispose of used coolant.
5. Remove the air conditioning accumulator.

➡ **In order to remove the engine cover the passenger side front seat must be removed.**

6. Remove the engine cover.
7. Remove the right knee bolster bracket.
8. Remove the cowl drain tube bolts. Remove the cowl drain tube.
9. Disconnect and plug the heater hoses.
10. Remove the right hinge pillar trim.
11. Remove the harness connector and bracket at the right hinge pillar.
12. Disconnect the radio antenna cable.
13. Remove the heater outlet duct at the left side of the heater case.
14. Reposition the wire harness.
15. Remove the heater assembly retaining screws.

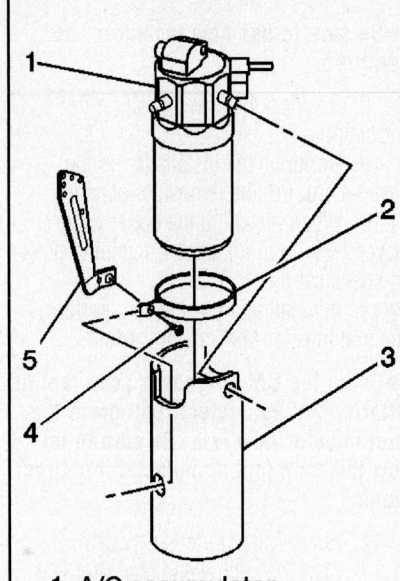

1. A/C accumulator
2. Clamp
3. Retainer
4. Nut

36616_EXPR_G0245

Fig. 216 Air conditioning accumulator and related components

16. Carefully open the heater core access door, in order to cut the heater core access door.
17. Cut the marked section of the heater core access door and remove the access door.

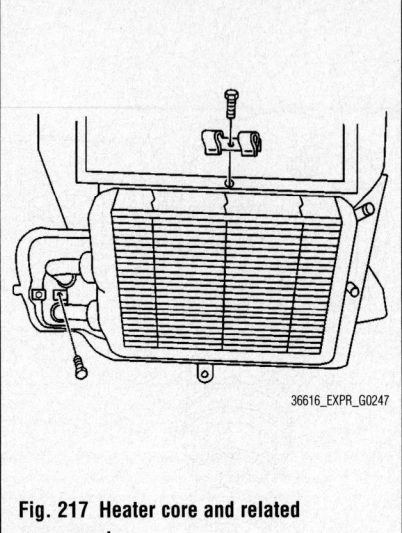

36616_EXPR_G0247

Fig. 217 Heater core and related components

18. Remove the retainers from the heater core.
19. Remove the heater core.

To install:

➡ **Be sure to use new fasteners, as required.**

20. Installation is the reverse of the removal procedure.
21. Be sure to properly charge the air conditioning system.
22. Be sure to refill all systems using the proper grade and type fluids.
23. Start the engine and check for leaks. Correct as required.

AUXILIARY HEATING & AIR CONDITIONING SYSTEM

BLOWER MOTOR

REMOVAL & INSTALLATION

See Figures 218 and 219.

1. Before servicing the vehicle, refer to the Precautions Section.
2. Disconnect the negative battery cable.
3. Remove the left body side panel.
4. Properly discharge the air conditioning system.
5. Remove the auxiliary HVAC module assembly.
6. Disconnect the electrical connectors from the auxiliary blower motor.
7. Remove the screws (1) from the auxiliary blower motor.
8. Remove the auxiliary blower motor (2).
9. Remove the retaining clip from the fan cage.
10. Remove the fan cage from the auxiliary blower motor.

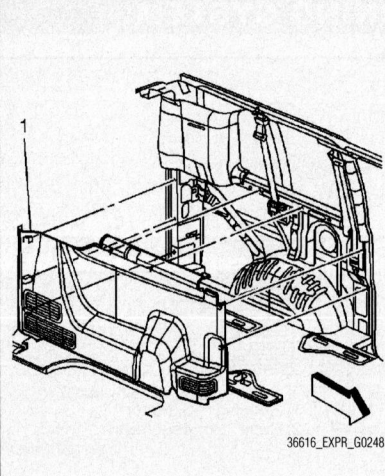

36616_EXPR_G0248

Fig. 218 Body side panel and related components—left side

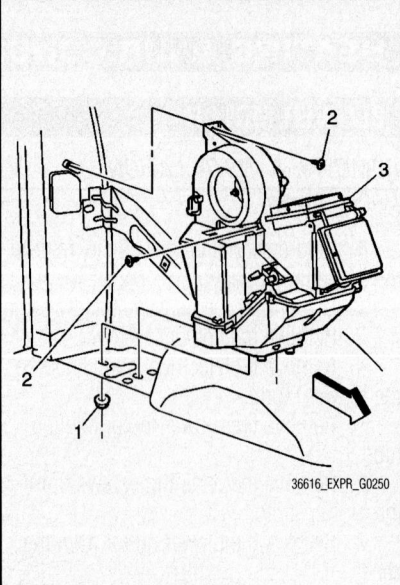

36616_EXPR_G0250

Fig. 219 Auxiliary HVAC module and related components

To install:

11. Install the fan cage to the auxiliary blower motor.

12. Install the retaining clip to the fan cage.

13. Install the auxiliary blower motor.

14. Install the screws (1) to the auxiliary blower motor (2).

    a. Tighten the screws to 44 inch lbs. (5 Nm).

15. Connect the electrical connectors to the auxiliary blower motor.

16. Install the auxiliary HVAC assembly.

17. Be sure to properly charge the air conditioning system.

18. Start the engine and check for leaks. Correct as required.

HEATER CORE

REMOVAL & INSTALLATION

See Figure 220.

1. Before servicing the vehicle, refer to the Precautions Section.

2. Drain the engine cooling system into a clean container for reuse.

3. Remove or disconnect the following:

- Negative battery cable
- Heater hoses from the rear auxiliary heater core
- Rear interior quarter trim panel from the left rear side
- Auxiliary HVAC module assembly
- Blower motor from the rear auxiliary heater case
- Rear auxiliary heater case retainers and the case
- Lower auxiliary heater case retainers and the lower case
- Rear heater core from the case

To install:

4. Install or connect the following:
- Rear auxiliary heater core to the case
- Lower case and the lower auxiliary heater case retainers
- Rear auxiliary heater case retainers and the case
- Blower motor to the rear auxiliary heater case
- Rear interior quarter trim panel
- Heater hoses to the rear auxiliary heater core

5. Refill the engine cooling system.

6. Connect the negative battery cable.

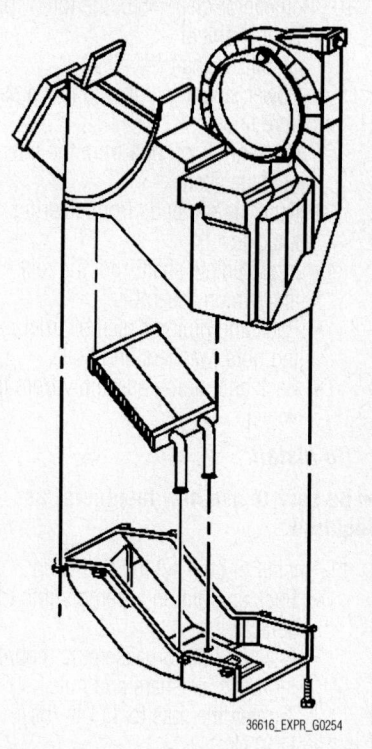

36616_EXPR_G0254

Fig. 220 Auxiliary heater core and related components

STEERING

POWER RACK & PINION STEERING GEAR

REMOVAL & INSTALLATION

See Figure 221.

1. Before servicing the vehicle, refer to the Precautions Section.

➡ **When performing service on or near the SRS components, or SRS wiring the SRS must be disabled. Failure to observe the correct procedure could cause deployment of the SRS components. Serious injury can occur.**

2. Position the steering wheel so the front wheels are in the straight ahead position.

3. Be sure the ignition switch is in the **OFF** position.

4. Disconnect the negative battery cable.

➡ **The SDM may have more than one fused power input. To ensure that there is no unwanted SRS deployment, personal injury, or unnecessary SRS system repairs, remove all fuses supplying power to the SDM. With all SDM fuses removed and the ignition**

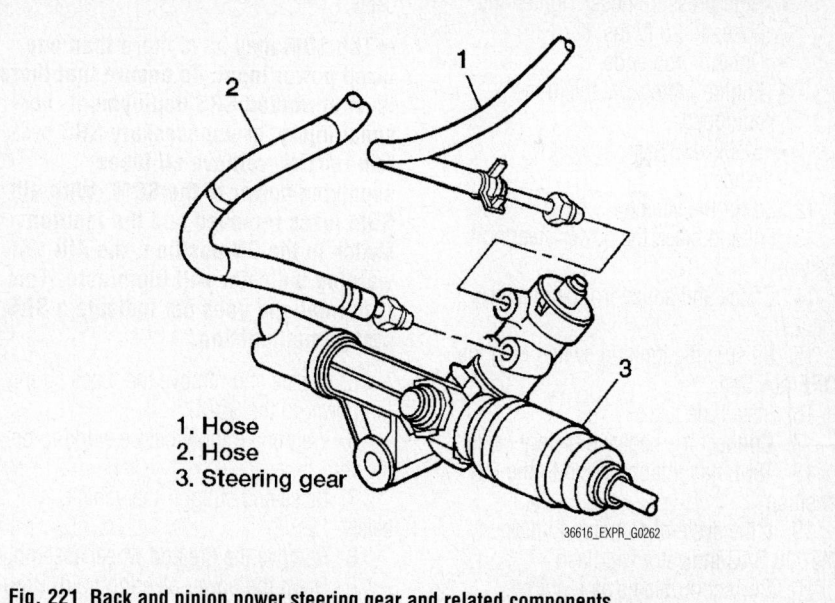

1. Hose
2. Hose
3. Steering gear

36616_EXPR_G0262

Fig. 221 Rack and pinion power steering gear and related components

switch in the ON position, the AIR BAG warning indicator will illuminate. This is normal and does not indicate a SRS system malfunction.

5. Locate and remove the fuses supplying power to the SDM.

6. Wait one minute before working on the vehicle.

7. Raise and support the vehicle safely.

8. Remove the tire and wheel assembly.

9. Drain the power steering fluid. Properly dispose of used fluid.

10. Remove or disconnect the following:
- Engine shield
- Stabilizer shaft
- Power steering high and low pressure lines
- Coupler clamp bolt from the intermediate shaft
- Outer tie rod ends from steering knuckle
- Intermediate shaft from the rack and pinion assembly
- Rack and pinion assembly mounting nuts, washers and bolts
- Rack and pinion assembly from the vehicle

To install:

➡**Be sure to use new fasteners, as required.**

11. Install or connect the following:
- Rack and pinion assembly into the vehicle
- Rack and pinion assembly mounting bolts, washers and nuts. Tighten the nuts to 111 ft. lbs. (150 Nm).
- Intermediate shaft to the rack and pinion assembly
- Coupler clamp bolt to the intermediate shaft. Tighten the bolt to 33 ft. lbs. (45 Nm).
- Low pressure hose
- High pressure hose. Tighten the hoses to 20 ft. lbs. (27 Nm).
- Outer tie rod ends
- Engine protection shield, if equipped
- Stabilizer shaft
- Wheels

12. Lower the vehicle.
13. Fill and bleed the power steering system
14. Check and adjust front end alignment.
15. Be sure the ignition switch is in the **OFF** position.
16. Install the fuses.
17. Connect the negative battery cable.
18. Turn the ignition switch to the **ON** position.
19. If the system is operating properly the AIR BAG indicator will flash
20. Correct problems as required.

POWER RECIRCULATING BALL STEERING GEAR

REMOVAL & INSTALLATION

See Figure 222.

1. Before servicing the vehicle, refer to the Precautions Section.

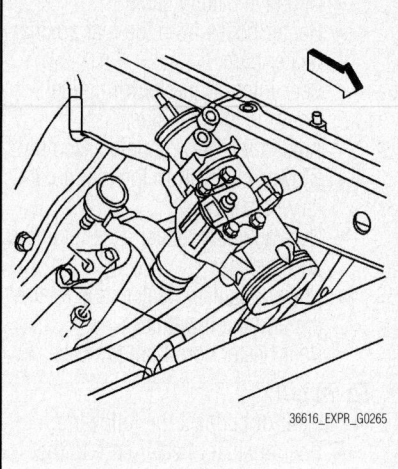

Fig. 222 Power steering gear and related components

➡**When performing service on or near the SRS components, or SRS wiring the SRS must be disabled. Failure to observe the correct procedure could cause deployment of the SRS components. Serious injury can occur.**

2. Position the steering wheel so the front wheels are in the straight ahead position.
3. Be sure the ignition switch is in the **OFF** position.
4. Disconnect the negative battery cable.

➡**The SDM may have more than one fused power input. To ensure that there is no unwanted SRS deployment, personal injury, or unnecessary SRS system repairs, remove all fuses supplying power to the SDM. With all SDM fuses removed and the ignition switch in the ON position, the AIR BAG warning indicator will illuminate. This is normal and does not indicate a SRS system malfunction.**

5. Locate and remove the fuses supplying power to the SDM.
6. Wait one minute before working on the vehicle.
7. Raise and support the vehicle safely.
8. Remove the tire and wheel assembly.
9. Drain the power steering fluid. Properly dispose of used fluid.
10. Remove the engine shield.
11. Disconnect the hoses from the steering gear. Plug the lines to prevent leakage and contamination.
12. Disconnect the steering shaft coupling from the gear.
13. Remove the pitman arm nut, then

separate the arm from the relay rod using puller J24319–B or equivalent.
14. Remove the steering gear bolts and remove the gear from the vehicle.

To install:

➡**Be sure to use new fasteners, as required.**

15. Install the gear in the vehicle. Tighten the bolts to 110 ft. lbs. (150 Nm).
16. Connect the pitman arm to the relay rod.
17. Connect the power steering hoses. Tighten the fittings to 24 ft. lbs. (32 Nm).
18. The remaining installation is the reverse of removal. Bleed the power steering system.
19. Check and adjust front end alignment.
20. Be sure the ignition switch is in the **OFF** position.
21. Install the fuses.
22. Connect the negative battery cable.
23. Turn the ignition switch to the **ON** position.
24. If the system is operating properly the AIR BAG indicator will flash
25. Correct problems as required.

POWER STEERING PUMP

REMOVAL & INSTALLATION

4.3L Engines

See Figures 223 and 224.

1. Before servicing the vehicle, refer to the Precautions Section.
2. Disconnect the negative battery cable.
3. Raise and support the vehicle safely.
4. Drain the power steering fluid. Properly dispose of used fluid.
5. Disconnect the hoses at the pump. When the hoses are disconnected, secure the ends in a raised position to prevent leakage. Cap the ends of the hoses to prevent the entrance of dirt.
6. Cap the pump fittings.
7. Loosen the belt tensioner.
8. Remove the pump drive belt.
9. Remove the pulley with a pulley puller such as J-29785–A.
10. Remove the following fasteners front mounting bolts
11. Lift out the pump.

To install:

12. Observe the following torque:
- Front mounting bolts: 37 ft. lbs. (50 Nm)

13. Install the pulley with J-25033–B.
14. Install the drive belt.
15. Install the hoses.
16. Fill and bleed the system.

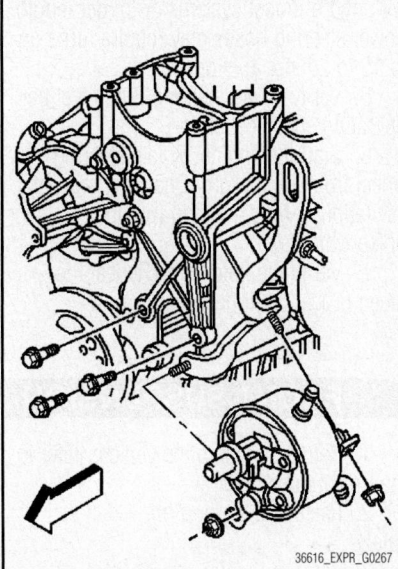

Fig. 223 Power steering pump and related components—4.3L engines

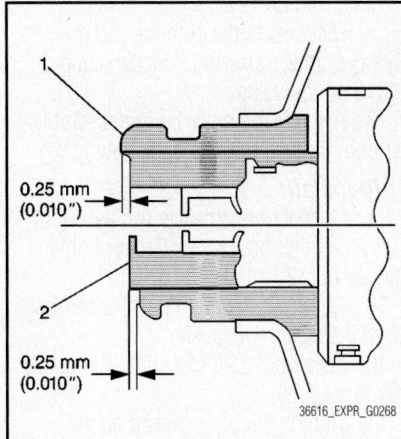

Fig. 224 Power steering pump pulley alignment—4.3L engines

4.8L, 5.3L & 6.0L Engines

See Figure 225.

1. Before servicing the vehicle, refer to the Precautions Section.
2. Disconnect the negative battery cable.
3. Drain the power steering fluid. Properly dispose of used fluid.
4. Remove the drive belt.
5. Remove the power steering pump pulley.
6. Disconnect the intermediate shaft to the gear retaining bolt. Disconnect the shaft from the gear.
7. Raise and support the vehicle safely.
8. Remove the tire and wheel assembly.

Fig. 225 Power steering pump and related components—4.8L, 5.3L and 6.0L engines

9. Disconnect the reservoir hose, from the pump thru the wheel well.
10. Disconnect and plug the power steering pump hoses.
11. Lower the vehicle.
12. Remove the pump retaining bolts. Remove the component from the vehicle.

To install:

→Be sure to use new fasteners, as required.

13. Install or connect the following:
- Power steering pump
- Bolts to the front and the rear of the pump. Tighten the front bolts to 37 ft. lbs. (50 Nm). Tighten the rear bolts to 30 ft. lbs. (41 Nm).
- Hoses to the pump. Tighten the nut to 20 ft. lbs. (28 Nm)
- Nut and clamp retaining the filler neck to the power steering pump, if equipped
- Pulley. Install the pulley with 0.020 in (0.5 mm) play
- Drive belt
14. Fill and bleed the power steering system.

6.6L Engines

See Figure 226.

1. Before servicing the vehicle, refer to the Precautions Section.
2. Disconnect the negative battery cable.
3. Drain the power steering fluid. Properly dispose of used fluid.
4. Remove the drive belt.
5. Remove the power steering pump pulley.
6. Disconnect the intermediate shaft to the gear retaining bolt. Disconnect the shaft from the gear.

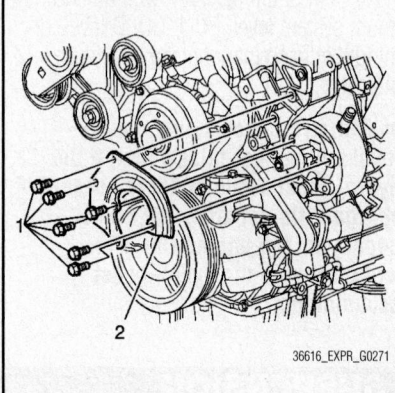

Fig. 226 Power steering pump and related components—6.6L engines

7. Raise and support the vehicle safely.
8. Remove the tire and wheel assembly.
9. Disconnect the reservoir hose, from the pump thru the wheel well.
10. Disconnect and plug the power steering pump hoses.
11. Lower the vehicle.
12. Remove the pump retaining bolts. Remove the component from the vehicle.

To install:

→Be sure to use new fasteners, as required.

13. Install or connect the following:
- Power steering pump
- Bolts to the front and the rear of the pump. Tighten the front bolts to 37 ft. lbs. (50 Nm). Tighten the rear bolts to 30 ft. lbs. (41 Nm).
- Hoses to the pump. Tighten the nut to 20 ft. lbs. (28 Nm)
- Nut and clamp retaining the filler neck to the power steering pump, if equipped
- Pulley. Install the pulley with 0.020 in (0.5 mm) play
- Drive belt
14. Fill and bleed the power steering system.

BLEEDING

Observe the following:
- Use clean, new power steering fluid type only
- Hoses touching the frame, body or engine may cause system noise. Verify that the hoses do not touch any other part of the vehicle.
- Loose connections may not leak, but could allow air into the steering system. Verify that all hose connections are tight.

→Power steering fluid level must be maintained throughout bleed procedure.

1. Fill pump reservoir with fluid to minimum system level, FULL COLD level, or middle of hash mark on cap stick fluid level indicator.

➡ **With hydro–boost only, the oil level will appear falsely high if the hydro–boost accumulator is not fully charged. Do not apply the brake pedal with the engine OFF. This will discharge the hydro–boost accumulator.**

2. If equipped with hydro–boost, fully charge the hydro–boost accumulator using the following procedure:
   a. Start the engine.
   b. Firmly apply the brake pedal 10–15 times.
   c. Turn the engine **OFF**
3. Raise the vehicle until the front wheels are off the ground.
4. With key in the **ON** position and the engine **OFF**, turn the steering wheel from stop to stop 12 times. Vehicles equipped

with hydro–boost systems or longer length power steering hoses may require turns up to 15 to 20 stop to stops.
5. Verify power steering fluid level per operating specification.
6. Start the engine. Rotate steering wheel from left to right. Check for sign of cavitation or fluid aeration (pump noise/whining).
7. Verify the fluid level. Repeat the bleed procedure if necessary.

SUSPENSION

COIL SPRING

REMOVAL & INSTALLATION

See Figure 227.

1. Before servicing the vehicle, refer to the Precautions Section.
2. Raise and support the vehicle safely.
3. Remove the tire and wheel assembly.
4. Remove the shock absorber.
5. Remove the stabilizer shaft link.
6. Properly support the lower control arm with a suitable jack.
7. Using the proper tool remove all tension from the lower control arm.
8. Remove the lower control arm pivot bolt retaining nuts and washers.
9. Remove the rear pivot bolt.
10. Remove the front pivot bolt.
11. Lower the lower control arm and remove the coil spring and insulator.
12. Remove the spring compressor tool from the spring. Remove the insulator.

To install:

➡ **Be sure to use new fasteners, as required.**

13. Installation is the reverse of the removal procedure.

➡ **The flat end of the coil spring and the upper insulator goes up into the shock tower and the pointed end of the coil spring goes on the lower control arm. Align the coil spring so that the end of the spring is seated in the pocket in the lower control arm.**

14. Tighten the lower control arm pivot nuts to 114 ft. lbs. (155 Nm) for W/O 14050/12300 GVW, 89 ft. lbs. (120 Nm) plus an additional 175 degrees for WITH 14050/12300 GVW and 6.6L engines.
15. Continue the installation in the reverse order of the removal procedure.

CONTROL LINKS

REMOVAL & INSTALLATION

See Figures 228 and 229.

FRONT SUSPENSION

1. Before servicing the vehicle, refer to the Precautions Section.
2. Raise and support the vehicle safely.
3. Remove the tire and wheel assembly.
4. Remove cotter pin (if equipped) and the nut from outer tie rod stud.
5. Loosen the jam nut (2) on the inner tie rod assembly (1).
6. Disconnect the outer tie rod assembly (2) from the steering knuckle using J 24319 or equivalent.
7. Remove the outer tie rod assembly (3) from the inner tie rod assembly (1).

To install:

8. Connect the outer tie rod assembly (3) to the inner tie rod (1). Do not tighten the jam nut (2).
9. Connect the outer tie rod assembly (3) to the steering knuckle.
10. Install outer tie rod nut to the outer tie rod stud (1).
11. Tighten the outer tie rod nut to 33–37 ft. lbs. (45–50 Nm).
12. If equipped with cotter pin install new cotter pin. If necessary further tighten nut until holes align and install cotter pin.

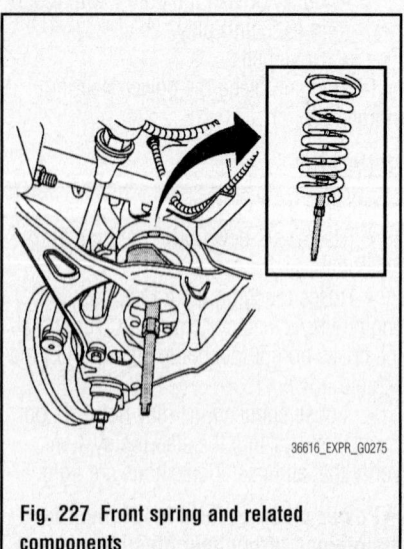

36616_EXPR_G0275

Fig. 227 Front spring and related components

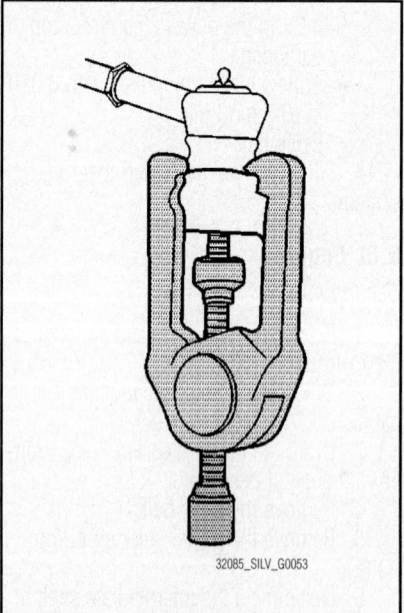

32085_SILV_G0053

Fig. 228 Disconnecting the outer tie rod from the steering knuckle

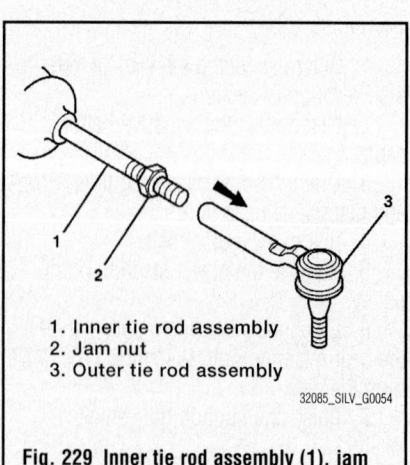

1. Inner tie rod assembly
2. Jam nut
3. Outer tie rod assembly

32085_SILV_G0054

Fig. 229 Inner tie rod assembly (1), jam nut (2) and outer tie rod assembly (3)

➡️If equipped with rack and pinion steering, make sure the rack and pinion boot is not twisted after the toe adjustment.

13. Check and adjust the wheel alignment as necessary.
14. Tighten jam nut (2).

LOWER BALL JOINT

REMOVAL & INSTALLATION

1. Before servicing the vehicle, refer to the Precautions Section.
2. Raise and support the vehicle safely.
3. Remove the tire and wheel assembly.
4. Remove the front coil spring.
5. Remove the lower control arm.
6. Position the control arm in a bench.
7. Remove the four securing crimps from the ball joint body.
8. Using a press, remove the ball joint from its mounting.

To install:

➡️Be sure to use new fasteners, as required.

9. Install the new ball joint, using a press.

➡️Use the outer flange of the ball joint in order to press the new ball joint into place.

10. Using a punch, install four crimps to the ball joint. Use the old ball joint as a reference.
11. Continue the installation in the reverse order of the removal procedure.
12. Check and adjust the front end alignment, as required.

LOWER CONTROL ARM

REMOVAL & INSTALLATION

RWD Models

See Figure 230.

1. Before servicing the vehicle, refer to the Precautions Section.
2. Raise and support the vehicle safely.
3. Remove the tire and wheel assembly.
4. Remove the front coil spring.
5. Remove and discard the lower ball joint retaining nut.
6. Using the proper ball joint removal tool, disconnect the lower ball joint from the steering knuckle.

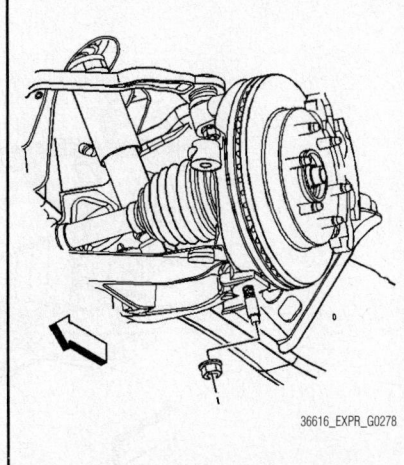

Fig. 230 Lower control arm and related components—RWD

7. Remove the lower control arm from its mounting on the vehicle.

To install:

➡️Be sure to use new fasteners, as required.

8. Install or connect the following:
- Lower control arm
- Tighten the lower control arm pivot nuts to 114 ft. lbs. (155 Nm) for W/O 14050/12300 GVW, 89 ft. lbs. (120 Nm) plus an additional 175 degrees for WITH 14050/12300 GVW and 6.6L engines.
- Ball joint stud to the steering knuckle
- Lower ball joint stud nut. Tighten the lower ball joint stud nut to 74 ft. lbs. (100 Nm)
- Front coil spring

9. Continue the installation in the reverse order of the removal procedure.
10. Check and adjust the front end alignment, as required.

AWD Models

See Figure 231.

1. Before servicing the vehicle, refer to the Precautions Section.
2. Raise and support the vehicle safely.
3. Remove the tire and wheel assembly.
4. Remove the torsion bar.
5. Remove the stabilizer link.
6. Remove the halfshaft.
7. Remove the lower shock absorber retaining nut and bolt.
8. Remove and discard the lower ball joint retaining nut.
9. Using the proper ball joint removal tool, remove the lower ball joint from steering knuckle.

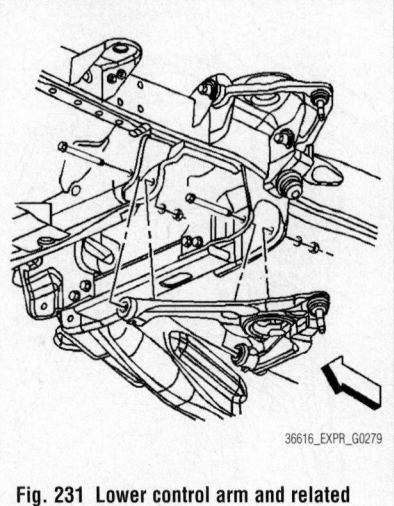

Fig. 231 Lower control arm and related components—AWD

10. Remove the lower control arm nuts and washers. Remove the bolts.
11. Remove the lower control arm from the vehicle.

To install:

➡️Be sure to use new fasteners, as required.

12. Position the lower control arm to its mounting.
13. Install the retaining bolts.
14. Tighten the lower control arm pivot nuts to 114 ft. lbs. (155 Nm) for W/O 14050/12300 GVW, 89 ft. lbs. (120 Nm) plus an additional 175 degrees for WITH 14050/12300 GVW and 6.6L engines.
15. Continue the installation in the reverse order of the removal procedure.
16. Check and adjust the front end alignment, as required.

SHOCK ABSORBERS

REMOVAL & INSTALLATION

See Figures 232 and 233.

1. Before servicing the vehicle, refer to the Precautions Section.
2. Raise and support the vehicle safely.
3. Remove the tire and wheel assembly.
4. Support the lower control arm with a jack or jack stand.
5. Remove the upper shock retaining nut, washer and rubber bushing.
6. Remove the lower shock retaining bolt and nut (AWD).
7. Remove the lower shock retaining bolts (RWD).
8. Remove the shock from the vehicle.

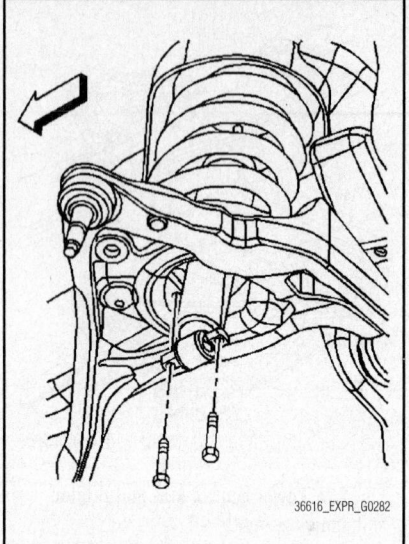

Fig. 232 Lower shock and retaining bolts—RWD

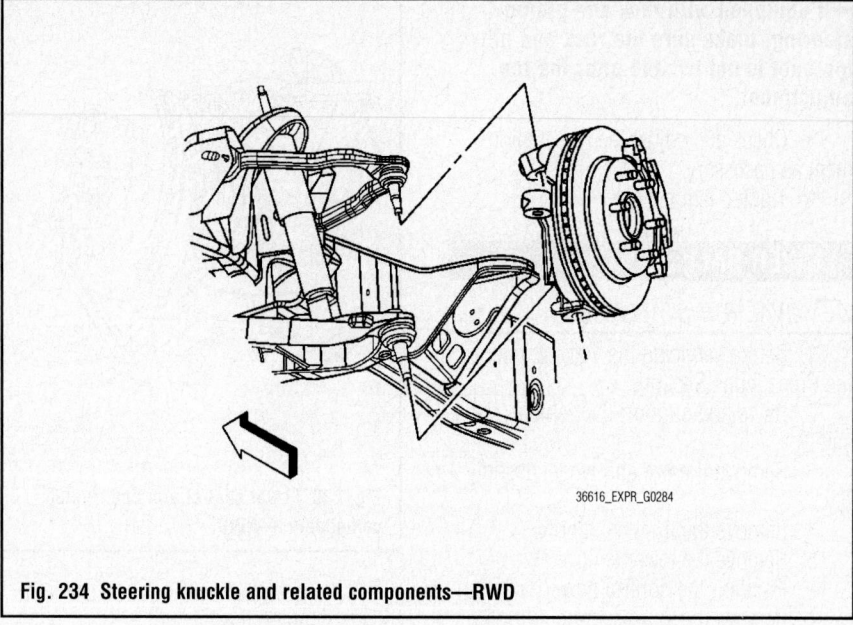

Fig. 234 Steering knuckle and related components—RWD

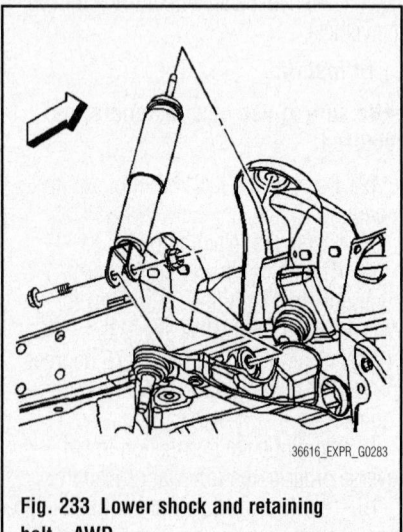

Fig. 233 Lower shock and retaining bolt—AWD

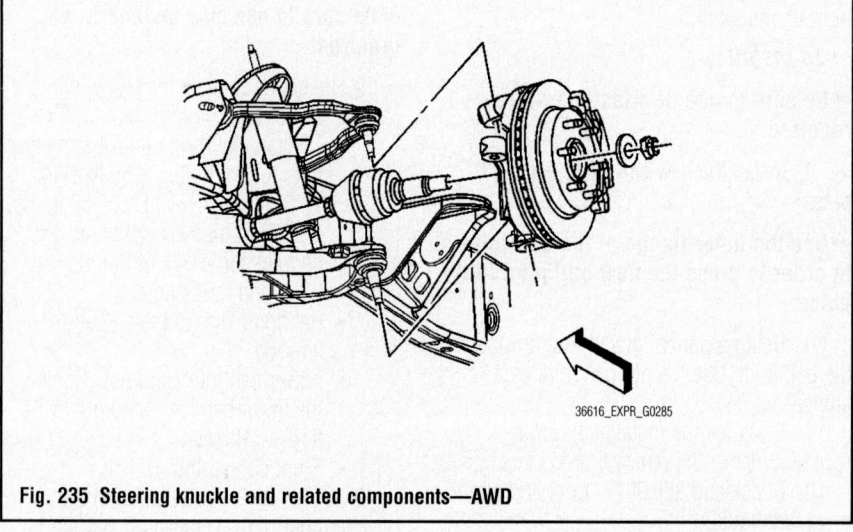

Fig. 235 Steering knuckle and related components—AWD

To install:

➡**Be sure to use new fasteners, as required.**

9. Install the shock absorber.

10. Install the lower retaining bolts. Tighten to 18 ft. lbs. (25 Nm).

11. Install the upper retaining bolt, bushing and washer. Tighten to 15 ft. lbs. (20 Nm).

12. Continue the installation in the reverse order of the removal procedure.

STEERING KNUCKLE

REMOVAL & INSTALLATION

See Figures 234 and 235.

1. Before servicing the vehicle, refer to the Precautions Section.

2. Raise and support the vehicle safely.

3. Remove the tire and wheel assembly.

4. Remove the wheel hub and bearing.

5. Support the lower control arm with a suitable jack.

6. Disconnect the outer tie rod from the knuckle.

7. Remove the brake hose bracket retaining bolt from the knuckle.

8. Remove the retaining nut and separate the upper and lower ball joints from the steering knuckle using a ball joint remover and adapters.

9. Remove the steering knuckle.

To install:

10. Clean all grease and contaminants from the tapered section and the threads of the upper ball joint, the lower ball joint, and the tie rod end.

11. Clean and inspect the taper holes and the mounting surfaces of the steering knuckle. If any of the tapered holes are elongated, out of round, or damaged, the replace the steering knuckle.

12. Install the steering knuckle.

13. Connect the lower ball joint to the steering knuckle and install the retaining nut and tighten to 74 ft. lbs. (100 Nm).

14. Connect the upper ball joint to the steering knuckle and install the retaining nut and tighten to 37 ft. lbs. (50 Nm).

15. Install the brake hose bracket retaining bolt to the knuckle.

16. Connect the outer tie rod to the steering knuckle.

17. Install the wheel hub and bearing.

18. Install the tire and wheel.

19. Remove the safety stands.

20. Lower the vehicle.
21. Check the front end alignment, adjust as required.

STABILIZER BAR

REMOVAL & INSTALLATION

1. Before servicing the vehicle, refer to the Precautions Section.
2. Raise and support the vehicle safely.
3. Remove the tire and wheel assembly.
4. Remove the stabilizer shaft nut from the link bolt.
5. Remove the stabilizer shaft link bolt.
6. Remove the stabilizer shaft link insulators and spacers.
7. Remove the oil pan skid plate, if equipped.
8. Remove the stabilizer shaft insulator bracket bolts.
9. Remove the stabilizer shaft bracket.
10. Remove the stabilizer shaft.
11. Remove the stabilizer shaft insulators.
12. Inspect all of the parts for wear and damage.

To install:

13. Installation is the reverse of the removal procedure.
14. For G2 and G3, tighten the insulator clamp bolts to 18 ft. lbs. (25 Nm). Place the stabilizer shaft insulators on the shaft with the slits facing toward the front of the vehicle. Tighten the insulator clamps mounting bolts to 34 ft. lbs. (46 Nm).
15. For AWD and G1, tighten the insulator clamps mounting bolts to 18 ft. lbs. (25 Nm). Place the stabilizer shaft insulators on the shaft with the slits facing toward the front of the vehicle.
16. Continue the installation in the reverse order of the removal procedure.
17. Check and adjust the front end alignment, as required.

TORSION BAR

REMOVAL & INSTALLATION

See Figures 236 through 239.

➡ This procedure requires the removal of both torsion bars.

1. Before servicing the vehicle, refer to the Precautions Section.
2. Raise and support the vehicle safely.
3. Mark the adjustment bolt setting. Install tool J36202 to the adjustment arm and the crossmember.
4. Increase the tension on the adjustment arm until the load is removed from the adjustment bolt and the adjuster nut.

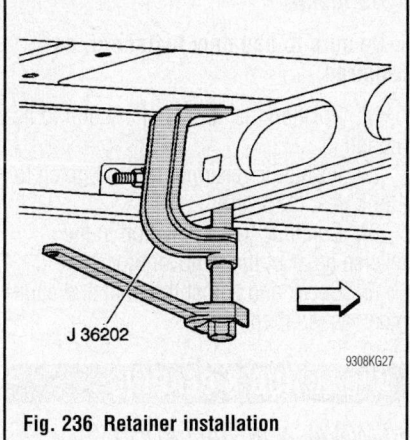

Fig. 236 Retainer installation

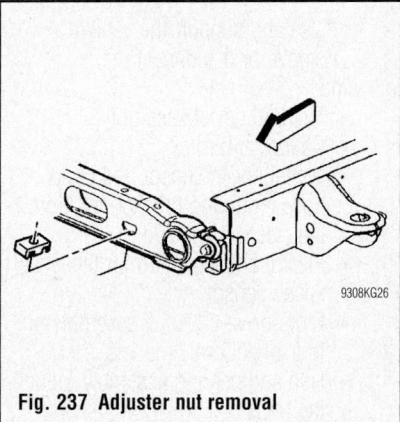

Fig. 237 Adjuster nut removal

5. Remove or disconnect the following:
• Adjustment bolt and the adjuster nut
• Tool, allowing the torsion bar to unload.
• Adjustment arm by sliding the torsion bar forward until the torsion bar clears the adjustment arm. Use your hand to support the adjustment arm as the adjustment arm releases from the torsion bar.
• Torsion bar crossmember bolts
• Torsion bar crossmember
• Torsion bars

➡ Note the position of the torsion bars as the left and right bars are different.

To install:

6. Install or connect the following:
• Torsion bars
• Torsion bar crossmember
• Torsion bar crossmember bolts. Tighten the bolt to 70 ft. lbs. (95 Nm)
7. While supporting the adjustment arm, slide the torsion bar rearward until the torsion bar fully engages the adjustment arm. Install tool J36202 to the adjustment

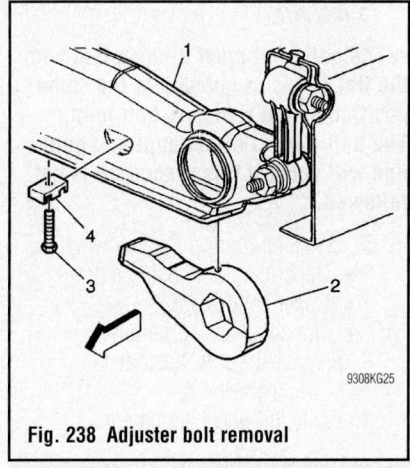

Fig. 238 Adjuster bolt removal

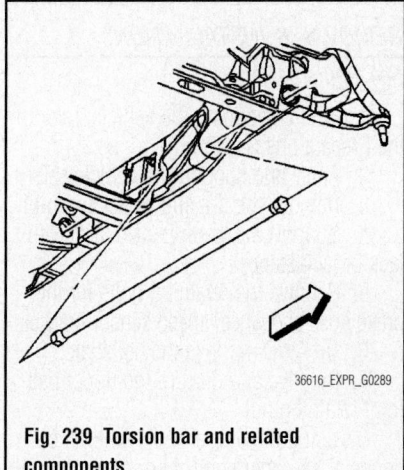

Fig. 239 Torsion bar and related components

arm and the crossmember. Increase the tension on the adjustment arm in order to load the torsion bar.
• Adjustment bolt and the adjuster nut
8. Remove the tool, releasing the tension on the torsion bar until the load is taken up by the adjustment bolt.
9. Remove the safety stands.
10. Lower the vehicle.
11. Measure the ride height.
12. Turn the adjustment bolt clockwise to increase the ride height and counterclockwise to decrease it.
13. Check and adjust the front end alignment, as required.

UPPER BALL JOINT

REMOVAL & INSTALLATION

1. Before servicing the vehicle, refer to the Precautions Section.
2. Raise and support the vehicle safely.
3. Remove the tire and wheel assembly.
4. Remove or disconnect the following:
• Upper control arm
• Upper ball joint, using a press

To install:

➡ **The ball joint must be installed with the flat edges or notches in the same position as the replaced ball joint. The ball joint is directional and damage will occur if this procedure is not followed.**

5. Install or connect the following:
   - Upper ball joint, using a press
   - Upper control arm
   - Tire and wheel assembly
6. Remove the safety stands.
7. Lower the vehicle.
8. Verify the wheel alignment.

UPPER CONTROL ARM

REMOVAL & INSTALLATION

See Figure 240.

1. Before servicing the vehicle, refer to the Precautions Section.
2. Raise and support the vehicle safely.
3. Remove the tire and wheel assembly.
4. Support the lower control arm with a jack or jack stand.
5. Remove the retaining bolts for the brake hose and wheel speed sensor brackets.
6. On AWD, remove the halfshaft.
7. Remove and discard the upper ball joint retaining nut.
8. Using the proper removal tool, disconnect the upper control arm from the steering knuckle.
9. Remove the upper control arm retaining nuts and adjustment cams.
10. Remove the retaining bolts.
11. Remove the control arm from the vehicle.

To install:

➡ **Be sure to use new fasteners, as required.**

12. Position the upper control arm to its mounting.
13. Install the retaining bolts. Tighten to 129 ft. lbs. (175 Nm).
14. Continue the installation in the reverse order of the removal procedure.
15. Check and adjust the front end alignment, as required.

WHEEL HUB & BEARING

REMOVAL & INSTALLATION

See Figures 241 and 242.

1. Raise and support the vehicle.
2. Remove or disconnect the following:
   - Tire and wheel assembly
   - Caliper and rotor
   - Wheel speed sensor and brake hose mounting bracket bolt from the steering knuckle
   - Electrical connection for the wheel speed sensor
   - Front drive halfshaft assembly on four wheel drive models
   - Hub and bearing assembly mounting bolts
   - Hub and bearing assembly

To install:

3. Clean all corrosion or contaminates from the steering knuckle bore and the hub and bearing assembly.
4. Install the O–ring to the steering knuckle (2500).

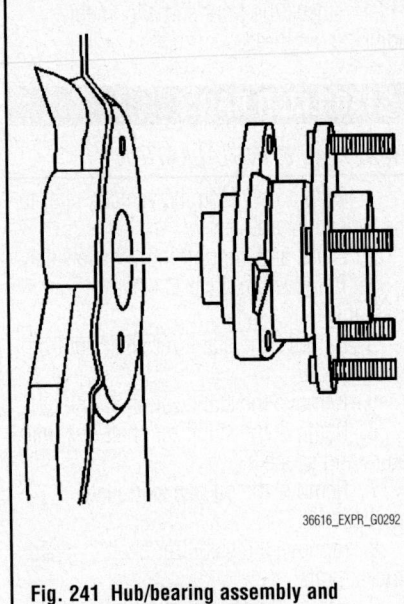

Fig. 241 Hub/bearing assembly and related components—RWD

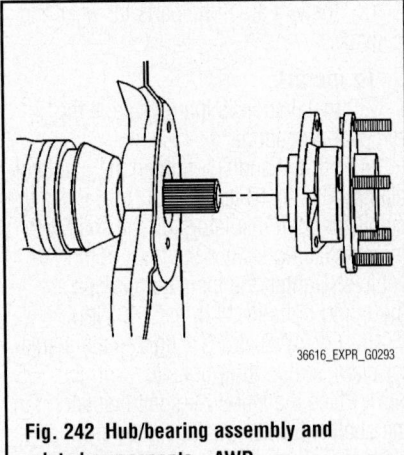

Fig. 242 Hub/bearing assembly and related components—AWD

5. Lubricate the steering knuckle bore with wheel bearing grease or the equivalent.
6. Install or connect the following:
   - Hub and bearing assembly
   - Hub and bearing assembly mounting bolts. Tighten the bolts to 133 ft. lbs. (180 Nm).
   - Front drive halfshaft assembly on four wheel drive models
   - Electrical connection for the wheel speed sensor
   - Wheel speed sensor and brake hose mounting bracket bolt to the steering knuckle. Tighten to 106 inch lbs. (12 Nm).
   - Rotor
   - Tire and wheel assembly.

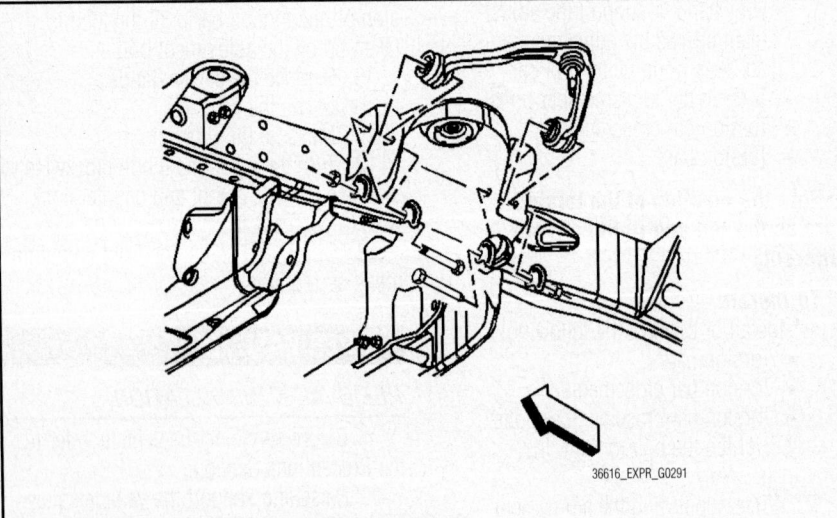

Fig. 240 Upper control arm and related components

LEAF SPRING

REMOVAL & INSTALLATION

1. Before servicing the vehicle, refer to the Precautions Section.
2. Raise and support the vehicle safely.
3. Remove the tire and wheel assembly.
4. Support the rear axle independently in order to relieve the tension on the leaf springs.
5. Remove or disconnect the following:
   - U–bolt nuts and U–bolts
   - Spring spacer and anchor plate
   - Shackle to the frame bracket nut and the bolt
   - Front spring bracket bolt
   - Leaf spring assembly from the vehicle
   - Shackle from the spring

To install:

6. Loosely assemble the spring shackle bracket to the frame. Install the shackle bolt. Install the shackle nut.
7. Install the leaf spring assembly to the vehicle.
8. Loosely assemble the spring to the front hanger bracket.
9. Install or connect the following:
   - Front spring hanger bracket bolt
   - Front spring hanger bracket nut
   - Shackle to the spring bolt
   - Shackle to the spring nut

➡ Do not reuse the U–bolts.

   - Spring spacer
   - U–bolts
   - Anchor plate
   - U–bolt nuts
10. Tighten in a crisscross pattern to:
    - 1500: 63 ft. lbs. (85 Nm)
    - 2500 and 3500: 103 ft. lbs. (140 Nm) plus 180 degrees

11. Tighten the front hanger bracket nut to 74 ft. lbs. (110 Nm) except 14200 GVW. Tighten the front hanger bracket nut to 211 ft. lbs. (300 Nm) plus 140 degrees, 14200 GVW.
12. Tighten the spring shackle to frame mounting nut to 85 ft. lbs. (115 Nm).
13. Tighten the spring shackle to leaf spring mounting nut to 63 ft. lbs. (85 Nm).
14. Remove the rear axle support.
15. Remove the safety stands. Lower the vehicle.

SHOCK ABSORBER

REMOVAL & INSTALLATION

See Figure 243.

1. Before servicing the vehicle, refer to the Precautions Section.
2. Raise and support the vehicle safely.
3. Remove the tire and wheel assembly.

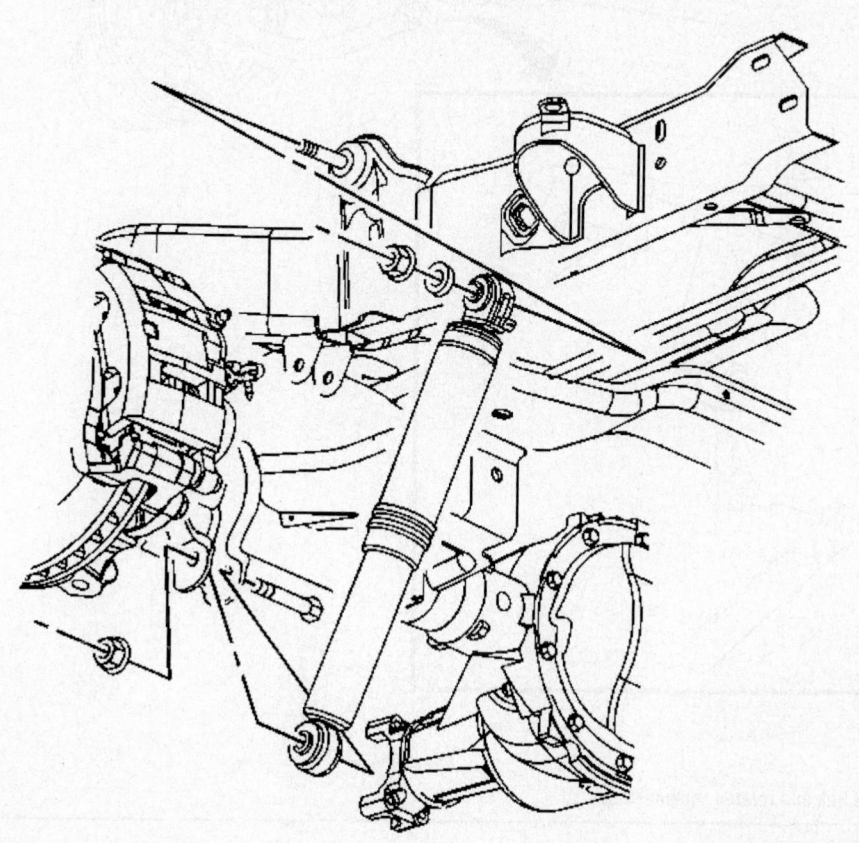

22116_SIER_G0039

Fig. 243 Rear shock absorber and related components

4. Remove or disconnect the following:
- Upper shock absorber nut and bolt
- Lower shock absorber nut and bolt
- Shock absorber

To install:

5. Installation is the reverse of removal. Tighten the nuts to 70 ft. lbs. (95 Nm).

6. Remove the safety stands.
7. Lower the vehicle.

STABILIZER SHAFT

REMOVAL & INSTALLATION

See Figure 244.

Please note at this time the manufacturer does not provide service information for this component.

1. Before servicing the vehicle, refer to the Precautions Section.
2. Raise and support the vehicle safely.

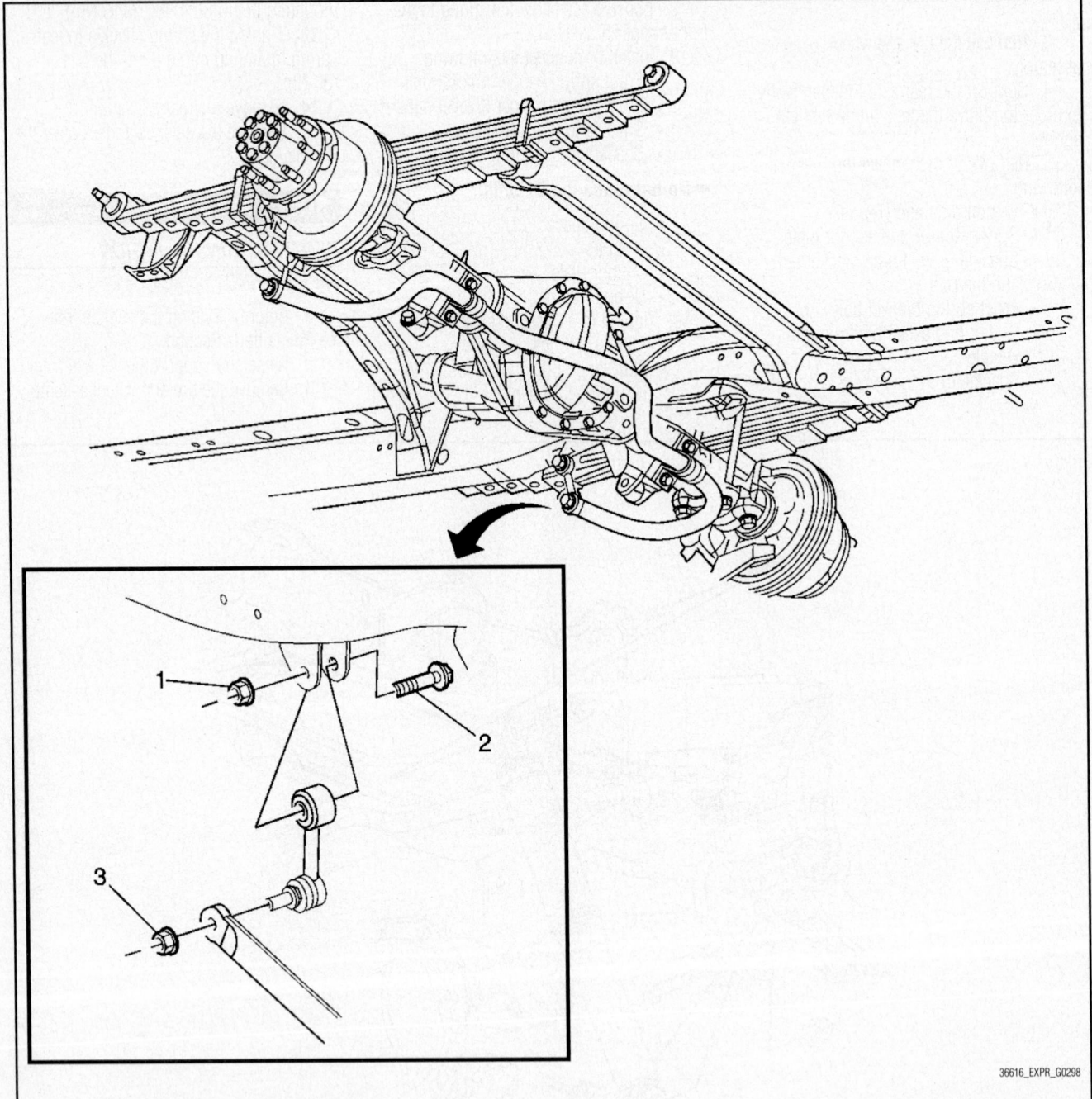

36616_EXPR_G0298

Fig. 244 Stabilizer shaft link and related components

PONTIAC

16

G6

SPECIFICATIONS AND MAINTENANCE CHARTS

VEHICLE AND ENGINE IDENTIFICATION CHART

Engine								Model Year	
Code ①	Liters	Cu. In.	Cyl.	Fuel Sys.	Engine Type	Eng. Mfg.		Code ②	Year
B	2.4	146	4	MFI	DOHC	General Motors		8	2008
7	3.6	217	6	SFI	DOHC	General Motors		9	2009
1	3.9	238	6	SFI	OHV	General Motors			
N	3.5	214	6	SFI	OHV	General Motors			

MFI: Multi-port Fuel Injection

SEFI: Sequential Multi-port Fuel Injection

① 8th position of VIN

② 10th position of VIN

36616_GMG6_C0001

GENERAL ENGINE SPECIFICATIONS
All measurements are given in inches.

Year	Model	Engine Displacement Liters	Engine Series (ID/VIN)	Net Horsepower @ rpm	Net Torque @ rpm (ft. lbs.)	Bore x Stroke (in.)	Compression Ratio	Oil Pressure @ rpm
2008	G6	2.4	B	164@6400	156@5000	3.46x3.85	10.4:1	50-80@1000
		3.5	N	219@5900	219@3200	3.90x3.00	9.8:1	30-45@1850
		3.6	7	252@6300	251@3200	3.70x3.37	10.2:1	20@2000
		3.9	1	222@5600	238@4000	3.90x3.31	9.8:1	30-45@1850
2009	G6	2.4	B	164@6400	156@5000	3.46x3.85	10.4:1	50-80@1000
		3.5	N	219@5900	219@3200	3.90x3.00	9.8:1	30-45@1850
		3.6	7	252@6300	251@3200	3.70x3.37	10.2:1	20@2000
		3.9	1	222@5600	238@4000	3.90x3.31	9.8:1	30-45@1850

36616_GMG6_C0002

GASOLINE ENGINE TUNE-UP SPECIFICATIONS

Year	Engine Displacement Liters	Engine VIN	Spark Plugs Gap (in.)	Ignition Timing (deg.) MT	Ignition Timing (deg.) AT	Fuel Pump (psi)	Idle Speed (rpm) MT	Idle Speed (rpm) AT	Valve Clearance In.	Valve Clearance Ex.
2008	2.4	B	0.043-0.37	①	①	50-60	①	①	HYD	HYD
	3.5	N	0.040	①	①	50-60	①	①	HYD	HYD
	3.6	7	0.043	①	①	50-60	①	①	HYD	HYD
	3.9	1	0.040	①	①	50-60	①	①	HYD	HYD
2009	2.4	B	0.040	①	①	50-60	①	①	HYD	HYD
	3.5	N	0.040	①	①	50-60	①	①	HYD	HYD
	3.6	7	0.043	①	①	50-60	①	①	HYD	HYD
	3.9	1	0.040	①	①	50-60	①	①	HYD	HYD

NOTE: The Vehicle Emission Control Information label often reflects specification changes changes made during production.

The label figures must be used if they differ from those in this chart.

HYD: Hydraulic

① Controlled by the Powertrain Control Module (PCM) and cannot be manually adjusted.

36616_GMG6_C0003

CAPACITIES

Year	Model	Engine Displacement Liters	Engine ID/VIN	Engine Oil with Filter (qts.)	Transmission (pts.)			Drive Axle		Fuel Tank (gal.)	Cooling System (qts.)
					4-Spd	6-Spd	Auto.	Front (pts.)	Rear (pts.)		
2008	G6	2.4	B	5.0	—	—	①	—	—	16.3	7.5
		3.5	N	4.0	—	—	①	—	—	16.3	9.7
		3.6	7	5.5	—	—	①	—	—	16.3	9.7
		3.9	1	4.0	—	—	①	—	—	16.3	9.8
2009	G6	2.4	B	5.0	—	—	①	—	—	16.3	7.5
		3.5	N	4.0	—	—	①	—	—	16.3	9.7
		3.6	7	5.5	—	—	①	—	—	16.3	9.7
		3.9	1	4.0	—	—	①	—	—	16.3	9.7

NOTE: All capacities are approximate. Add fluid gradually and check to be sure a proper fluid level is obtained.

① **4T45-E:** 14 pts. (bottom pan removal)

19 pts. (complete overhaul)

25.8 pts. (dry)

4T65-E: 14.8 pts. (bottom pan removal)

20 pts. (complete overhaul)

26.8 pts. (dry)

6T40/6T45: 10.6-14.8 pts. (valve body cover removal)

8.4-12.6 pts. (fluid change, drain plug)

17-18 pts. (overhaul)

6T70/6T75: 10.6-14.8 pts. (valve body cover removal)

8.4-12.6 (fluid change)

14.8-19.0 pts. (ovehaul)

36616_GMG6_C0004

FLUID SPECIFICATIONS

Year	Model	Engine Displacement Liters	Engine ID/VIN	Engine Oil	Auto. Trans. ①	Drive Axle	Power Steering Fluid	Brake Master Cylinder
2008	G6	2.4	B	5W-30	Dexron VI	75W-80	GM PS Fluid	DOT 3
		3.5	N	5W-30	Dexron VI	75W-80	GM PS Fluid	DOT 3
		3.6	7	5W-30	Dexron VI	75W-80	GM PS Fluid	DOT 3
		3.9	1	5W-30	Dexron VI	75W-80	GM PS Fluid	DOT 3
2009	G6	2.4	B	5W-30	Dexron VI	75W-80	GM PS Fluid	DOT 3
		3.5	N	5W-30	Dexron VI	75W-80	GM PS Fluid	DOT 3
		3.6	7	5W-30	Dexron VI	75W-80	GM PS Fluid	DOT 3
		3.9	1	5W-30	Dexron VI	75W-80	GM PS Fluid	DOT 3

DOT: Department Of Transpotation

① Manual Transmission GL-4 75W-80

36616_GMG6_C0011

VALVE SPECIFICATIONS

Year	Engine VIN	Engine Displacement Liters	Seat Angle (deg.)	Face Angle (deg.)	Spring Test Pressure (lbs. @ in.)	Spring Installed Height (in.)	Stem-to-Guide Clearance (in.)		Stem Diameter (in.)	
							Intake	Exhaust	Intake	Exhaust
2008	B	2.4	NA	NA	220@1.32	NA	0.0012-0.0022	0.0020-0.0026	0.2344-0.3140	0.2337-0.2343
	N	3.5	46	45	230@1.26	1.840	0.0009-0.0025	0.0009-0.0025	NA	NA
	7	3.6	45	44.25	NA	1.378	0.0010-0.0026	0.0014-0.0030	0.2344-0.2352	0.2341-0.2348
	1	3.9	46	45	230@1.26	1.84	0.0010-0.0027	0.0010-0.0027	NA	NA
2009	B	2.4	NA	NA	220@1.32	NA	0.0012-0.0022	0.0020-0.0026	0.2344-0.3140	0.2337-0.2343
	N	3.5	46	45	230@1.26	1.840	0.0009-0.0025	0.0009-0.0025	N/A	NA
	7	3.6	45	45.25	NA	1.378	0.0010-0.0026	0.0014-0.0030	0.2344-0.2352	0.2341-0.2348
	1	3.9	46	45	230@1.26	1.84	0.0009-0.0025	0.0009-0.0025	NA	NA

NA: Not Available

36616_GMG6_C0008

CAMSHAFT AND BEARING SPECIFICATIONS CHART
All measurements are given in inches.

Year	Engine Displ. Liters	Engine VIN	Journal Dia.	Brg. Oil Clearance	Shaft End-play	Runout	Journal Bore	Lobe Height	
								Intake	Exhaust
2008	2.4	B	1.0604-1.0614	—	0.0016-0.0057	NA	NA	NA	NA
	3.5	N	1.8680-1.8690	1.8710-1.8720	NA	0.001	NA	0.2727	0.2727
	3.6	7	①	②	0.0018-0.0085	0.002	0.0016-0.0033	1.6687-1.6805	1.6703-1.6821
	3.9	1	2.024-2.0250	2.0280-2.0290	0.0016-0.0035	0.001	NA	0.2727	0.2727
2009	2.4	B	1.0604-1.0614	—	0.0016-0.0057	NA	NA	NA	NA
	3.5	N	2.0240-2.0250	2.0280-2.0290	NA	0.001	NA	0.2727	0.2727
	3.6	7	①	②	0.0018-0.0085	0.002	0.0016-0.0033	1.6687-1.6805	1.6703-1.6821
	3.9	1	2.024-2.0250	2.0280-2.0290	NA	0.001	NA	0.2727	0.2727

NA: Not Available

① Front Number 1: 1.3754-1.3764 Middle and Rear 2-4: 1.0605-1.0614

② Front Number 1: 1.3779-1.3787 Middle and Rear Number 2-4: 1.0630-1.0638

36616_GMG6_C0006

CRANKSHAFT AND CONNECTING ROD SPECIFICATIONS

All measurements are given in inches.

Year	Engine Displ. Liters	Engine VIN	Crankshaft				Connecting Rod		
			Main Brg. Journal Dia.	Main Brg. Oil Clearance	Shaft End-play	Thrust on No.	Journal Diameter	Oil Clearance	Side Clearance
2008	2.4	B	2.2045-2.2050	0.012-0.0026	0.0012-0.0150	NA	1.9291-1.9297	0.0011-0.0027	0.0028-0.0146
	3.5	N	2.6473-2.6483	0.0008-0.0025	0.0024-0.0083	3	2.2489-2.2495	0.0007-0.0024	0.0078-0.0094
	3.6	7	2.6768-2.6775	0.0004-0.0024	0.0039-0.0130	NA	2.2044-2.205	0.0004-0.0028	0.0374-0.014
	3.9	1	2.6473-2.6483	①	0.0024-0.0083	3	2.2488-2.2495	0.0007-0.0024	0.008-0.009
2009	2.4	B	2.2045-2.2050	0.012-0.0026	0.0012-0.0150	NA	1.9291-2.2044	0.0011-0.0027	0.0028-0.0146
	3.5	N	2.6473-2.6483	0.0008-0.0025	0.0024-0.0083	3	2.2489-2.2495	0.0007-0.0024	0.0078-0.0094
	3.6	7	2.6768-2.6775	0.0004-0.0024	0.0039-0.0130	NA	2.2044-2.205	0.0004-0.0028	0.0374-0.014
	3.9	1	2.840-2.8410	①	0.0024-0.0083	3	2.2488-2.2495	0.0007-0.0024	0.008-0.009

① 0.0008-0.0025 except no. 3
0.0012-0.0030 on no. 3

36616_GMG6_C0007

PISTON AND RING SPECIFICATIONS

All measurements are given in inches.

Year	Engine Displ. Liters	Engine VIN	Piston Clearance	Ring Gap			Ring Side Clearance		
				Top Comp.	Bottom Comp.	Oil Control	Top Comp.	Bottom Comp.	Oil Control
2008	2.4	B	0.0004-0.0016	0.0060-0.0120	0.0080-0.0180	0.0060-0.0200	0.0015-0.0031	0.0012-0.0030	0.0011-0.0069
	3.5	N	①	0.0070-0.0150	0.0190-0.0290	0.0100-0.0290	0.0010-0.0030	0.0020-0.0030	0.004
	3.6	7	0.0010-0.0021	0.0059-0.0118	0.0110-0.0189	0.0059-0.0236	0.0012-0.0026	0.0006-0.0024	0.0012-0.0067
	3.9	1	②	0.006-0.0110	0.0098-0.0177	0.0060-0.0255	0.0011-0.0025	0.0007-0.0021	0.004
2009	2.4	B	0.0004-0.0016	0.0060-0.0120	0.0080-0.0180	0.0060-0.0200	0.0015-0.0031	0.0012-0.0027	0.0011-0.0069
	3.5	N	①	0.0007-0.0153	0.0190-0.0291	0.0100-0.0290	0.0010-0.0030	0.0020-0.0030	0.004
	3.6	7	0.0010-0.0021	0.0059-0.0118	0.0110-0.0189	0.0059-0.0236	0.0012-0.0026	0.0006-0.0024	0.0012-0.0067
	3.9	1	②	0.006-0.0110	0.0098-0.0177	0.0060-0.0255	0.0011-0.0025	0.0007-0.0021	0.004

① -0.0011-+0.011
② -0.0003-+0.0018

36616_GMG6_C0005

TORQUE SPECIFICATIONS
All readings in ft. lbs.

Year	Engine VIN	Engine Displacement Liters	Cylinder Head Bolts	Main Bearing Bolts	Rod Bearing Bolts	Crankshaft Damper Bolts	Flywheel Bolts	Manifold Intake	Exhaust	Spark Plugs	Oil Pan Drain Plug
2008	2.4	B	①	②	③	④	⑤	⑥	⑦	15	18
	3.5	N	⑧	⑨	③	⑩	52	⑪	15	11	18
	3.6	7	⑫	⑬	⑭	⑮	⑯	⑰	15	13	18
	3.9	1	①	②	③	⑬	52	⑱	15	11	18
2009	2.4	B	①	②	③	④	⑤	⑥	⑦	15	18
	3.5	N	⑧	⑨	③	⑩	52	⑪	15	11	18
	3.6	7	⑫	⑬	⑭	⑮	⑯	⑰	15	13	18
	3.9	1	⑧	⑨	③	⑩	52	⑱	15	11	18

① Step 1: 22 ft. lbs.
Step 2: plus 155 degrees

② Step 1: 15 ft. lbs.
Step 2: plus 70 degrees

③ Step 1: 18 ft. lbs.
Step 2: plus 110 degrees

④ Step 1: 74 ft. lbs.
Step 2: plus 125 degrees

⑤ Step 1: 39 ft. lbs.
Step 2: plus 25 degrees

⑥ Stud 53 INCH lbs.
Nut/bolts: 89 INCH lbs.

⑦ Step 1: 52 ft. lbs.
Step 2: plus 72 degrees

⑧ Step 1: 44 ft. lbs.
Step 2: plus 140 degrees

⑨ Step 1: 37 ft. lbs.
Step 2: plus 77 degrees

⑩ Step 1: 92 ft. lbs.
Step 2: plus 130 degrees

⑪ Lower manifold center bolt (first pass): 62 inch lbs.
Lower manifold center bolt (final pass): 115 inch lbs.
Lower manifold corner bolt (first pass): 62 inch lbs.
Lower manifold corner bolt (final pass): 18 ft. lbs.
Upper manifold: 18 ft. lbs.

⑫ M8: 11 ft. lbs. plus 75 degrees
M11: 22 ft. lbs. plus 150 degrees

⑬ Inner (Step 1): 15 ft. lbs.
Inner (Step 2): plus 80 degrees
Outer (Step 1): 10 ft. lbs.
Outer (Step 2): plus 110 degrees
Side (Step 1): 22 ft. lbs.
Side (Step 2): plus 60 degrees

⑭ Step 1: 22 ft. lbs.
Step 2: Loosen Bolts
Step 3: 18 ft. lbs.
Step 4: plus 110 degrees

⑮ Step 1: 74 ft. lbs.
Step 2: plus 150 degrees

⑯ Step 1: 22 ft. lbs.
Step 2: plus 45 degrees

⑰ Lower and Upper manifold bolts: 17 ft. lbs.

⑱ Lower manifold center bolt (first pass): 10 ft. lbs.
Lower manifold center bolt (final pass): 15 ft. lbs.
Lower manifold corner bolt (first pass): 10 ft. lbs.
Lower manifold corner bolt (final pass): 18 ft. lbs.
Upper manifold: 18 ft. lbs.

36616_GMG6_C0009

WHEEL ALIGNMENT

Year	Model			Caster Range (+/-Deg.)	Caster Preferred Setting (Deg.)	Camber Range (+/-Deg.)	Camber Preferred Setting (Deg.)	Toe-in (Deg.)
2008	G6	Front	Left	0.75	+2.90	0.75	-1.00	0.20+/-0.20
			Right	0.75	+2.90	0.75	-0.70	0.20+/-0.20
		Rear		—	—	0.60	-0.80	0.20+/-0.20
2009	G6	Front	Left	0.75	+2.90	0.75	-1.00	0.20+/-0.20
			Right	0.75	+2.90	0.75	-0.70	0.20+/-0.20
		Rear		—	—	0.60	-0.80	0.20+/-0.20

36616_GMG6_C0010

TIRE AND WHEEL SPECIFICATIONS

Year	Model	OEM Tires Standard	OEM Tires Optional	Tire Pressures (psi) Front	Tire Pressures (psi) Rear	Wheel Size	Wheel Lug Nut Torque (Ft. Lbs.)
2008	G6	P215/60R16	None	30	30	7J	100
	G6 GT	P225/50R17	None	30	30	7J	100
	G6 GTP	P225/50R18	None	35	35	7J	100
2009	G6	P195/60R15	P205/55R16	30	30	6.5J/7J	100
		P215/60R16	P225/50R17	30	30	7J	100
	G6 GT Conv.	P225/50R18	None	32	30	7J	100
	G6 GT	P225/50R17	P225/50R17	30	30	7J	100
	G6 GTP	P225/50R18	None	30	30	7J	100

OEM: Original Equipment Manufacturer

PSI: Pounds Per Square Inch

STD: Standard

OPT: Optional

36616_GMG6_C0013

BRAKE SPECIFICATIONS

All measurements in inches unless noted

Year	Model		Brake Disc Original Thickness	Brake Disc Minimum Thickness	Brake Disc Maximum Runout	Minimum Lining Thickness Front	Minimum Lining Thickness Rear	Brake Caliper Bracket Bolts (ft. lbs.)	Brake Caliper Mounting Bolts (ft. lbs.)
2008	G6	F	1.023	0.898	0.002	①	—	96	26
		R	0.551	0.465	0.002	—	①	96	26
2009	G6	F	1.023	0.898	0.002	①	—	96	26
		R	0.551	0.465	0.002	—	①	96	26

① Not available

36616_GMG6_C0012

MAINTENANCE I AND II SERVICE SCHEDULES
Pontiac G6

When the CHANGE ENGINE OIL light appears, certain services and inspections are required. Required services are described as Maintenance I and Maintenance II.

The first service on a vehicle should be Maintenance I, and the second service should be Maintenance II. Alternate between the 2 thereafter. However, in some cases, Maintenance II may be required more often.

Maintenance I: Use Maintenance I if the CHANGE ENGINE OIL light comes on within 10 months since vehicle was purchased or, if Maintenance II was performed.

Maintenance II: Use Maintenance II if the previous service performed was Maintenance I.

Always use Maintenance II whenever the CHANGE ENGINE OIL light comes on 10 months or more since the last service, or, if the CHANGE ENGINE OIL light has not come on at all for one year.

Service	Maintenance I	Maintenance II
Change the engine oil and filter. Reset the oil life system.	✓	✓
Visually inspect the vehicle for leaks or damage. A fluid loss in the vehicle system could indicate a problem. Inspected, repair and add fluid to the system if necessary.	✓	✓
Inspect the engine air cleaner filter. If necessary, replace the filter.	—	✓
Rotate the tires. Inspect the tire inflation pressures and the tire wear.	✓	✓
Visually inspect the brake lines and hoses for proper hook-up, binding, leaks, cracks, chafing, etc. Inspect the disc brake pads for wear and the rotors for surface condition. Inspect the drum brake linings for wear or cracks. Inspect other brake parts, including drums, wheel cylinders, calipers, parking brake, etc. Inspect the parking brake adjustment.	✓	✓
Inspect the engine coolant and the windshield washer fluid levels. Add fluid as needed.	✓	✓
Inspect the suspension and steering components. Inspect the front and rear suspension and the steering system for damaged, loose or missing parts, or signs of wear. Inspect the power steering lines and the hoses for proper hook-up, binding, leaks, cracks, chafing, etc.	—	✓
Visually inspect the coolant hoses and replace the hoses if they are cracked, swollen or deteriorated. Inspect all pipes, fittings and clamps; replace with GM parts as needed. To help ensure proper operation, a pressure test of the cooling system and pressure cap and cleaning the outside of the radiator and air conditioning condenser is recommended at least once a year.	—	✓
Inspect the wiper blades for wear or cracking.	—	✓
Inspect the restraint system components. Ensure the safety belt reminder light and all the belts, buckles, latch plates, retractors and anchorages are working properly. Look for any other loose or damaged safety belt system parts. If you see anything that might keep a safety belt system from working correctly, repair or replaced the damaged part. Replace torn or frayed safety belts, refer to Operational and Functional Checks in Seat Belts. Inspect for any opened or broken air bag coverings, and repair or replace as needed. The air bag system does require regular maintenance.	—	✓

36616_GMG6_C0014

MAINTENANCE I AND II SERVICE SCHEDULES
Pontiac G6

When the CHANGE ENGINE OIL light appears, certain services and inspections are required. Required services are described as Maintenance I and Maintenance II.

The first service on a vehicle should be Maintenance I, and the second service should be Maintenance II. Alternate between the 2 thereafter. However, in some cases, Maintenance II may be required more often.

Maintenance I: Use Maintenance I if the CHANGE ENGINE OIL light comes on within 10 months since vehicle was purchased or, if Maintenance II was performed.

Maintenance II: Use Maintenance II if the previous service performed was Maintenance I.

Always use Maintenance II whenever the CHANGE ENGINE OIL light comes on 10 months or more since the last service, or, if the CHANGE ENGINE OIL light has not come on at all for one year.

Service	Maintenance I	Maintenance II
Lubricate the body components.Lubricate all key lock cylinders, hood latch assemblies, secondary latches, pivots, spring anchor and release pawl, hood and door hinges, rear folding seats and liftgate hinges. Frequent lubrication may be required when exposed to a corrosive environment, refer to Fluid and Lubricant Recommendations . Applying dielectric silicone grease GM P/N 12345579 (Canadian P/N 1974984) or equivalent on the weatherstrips with a clean cloth.	—	✓
Inspect the transaxle fluid level and add fluid as needed.	—	✓
Inspect the suspension and steering components.Inspect the front and rear suspension and the steering system for damaged, loose or missing parts, or signs of wear. Inspect power steering lines and hoses for proper hook-up, binding, leaks, cracks, chafing, etc.	—	✓
Inspect the throttle system for interference or binding and for damaged or missing parts. Replace the parts as needed. Replace any components that have high effort or excessive wear. Do not lubricate the accelerator or the cruise control cables.	—	✓
Replace the passenger compartment air filter.	—	✓

36616_GMG6_C0015

PRECAUTIONS

Before servicing any vehicle, please be sure to read all of the following precautions, which deal with personal safety, prevention of component damage, and important points to take into consideration when servicing a motor vehicle:

• Never open, service or drain the radiator or cooling system when the engine is hot; serious burns can occur from the steam and hot coolant.

• Observe all applicable safety precautions when working around fuel. Whenever servicing the fuel system, always work in a well-ventilated area. Do not allow fuel spray or vapors to come in contact with a spark, open flame, or excessive heat (a hot drop light, for example). Keep a dry chemical fire extinguisher near the work area. Always keep fuel in a container specifically designed for fuel storage; also, always properly seal fuel containers to avoid the possibility of fire or explosion. Refer to the additional fuel system precautions later in this section.

• Fuel injection systems often remain pressurized, even after the engine has been turned **OFF**. The fuel system pressure must be relieved before disconnecting any fuel lines. Failure to do so may result in fire and/or personal injury.

• Brake fluid often contains polyglycol ethers and polyglycols. Avoid contact with the eyes and wash your hands thoroughly after handling brake fluid. If you do get brake fluid in your eyes, flush your eyes with clean, running water for 15 minutes. If eye irritation persists, or if you have taken brake fluid internally, IMMEDIATELY seek medical assistance.

• The EPA warns that prolonged contact with used engine oil may cause a number of skin disorders, including cancer. You should make every effort to minimize your exposure to used engine oil. Protective gloves should be worn when changing oil. Wash your hands and any other exposed skin areas as soon as possible after exposure to used engine oil. Soap and water, or waterless hand cleaner should be used.

• All new vehicles are now equipped with an air bag system, often referred to as a Supplemental Restraint System (SRS) or Supplemental Inflatable Restraint (SIR) system. The system must be disabled before performing service on or around system components, steering column, instrument panel components, wiring and sensors. Failure to follow safety and disabling procedures could result in accidental air bag deployment, possible personal injury and unnecessary system repairs.

• Always wear safety goggles when working with, or around, the air bag system. When carrying a non-deployed air bag, be sure the bag and trim cover are pointed away from your body. When placing a non-deployed air bag on a work surface, always face the bag and trim cover upward, away from the surface. This will reduce the motion of the module if it is accidentally deployed. Refer to the additional air bag system precautions later in this section.

• Clean, high quality brake fluid from a sealed container is essential to the safe and proper operation of the brake system. You should always buy the correct type of brake fluid for your vehicle. If the brake fluid becomes contaminated, completely flush the system with new fluid. Never reuse any brake fluid. Any brake fluid that is removed from the system should be discarded. Also, do not allow any brake fluid to come in contact with a painted surface; it will damage the paint.

• Never operate the engine without the proper amount and type of engine oil; doing so WILL result in severe engine damage.

• Timing belt maintenance is extremely important. Many models utilize an interference-type, non-freewheeling engine. If the timing belt breaks, the valves in the cylinder head may strike the pistons, causing potentially serious (also time-consuming and expensive) engine damage. Refer to the maintenance interval charts for the recommended replacement interval for the timing belt, and to the timing belt section for belt replacement and inspection.

• Disconnecting the negative battery cable on some vehicles may interfere with the functions of the on-board computer system(s) and may require the computer to undergo a relearning process once the negative battery cable is reconnected.

• When servicing drum brakes, only disassemble and assemble one side at a time, leaving the remaining side intact for reference.

• Only an MVAC-trained, EPA-certified automotive technician should service the air conditioning system or its components.

BRAKES

ANTI-LOCK BRAKE SYSTEM (ABS)

GENERAL INFORMATION

PRECAUTIONS

• Certain components within the ABS system are not intended to be serviced or repaired individually.

• Do not use rubber hoses or other parts not specifically specified for and ABS system. When using repair kits, replace all parts included in the kit. Partial or incorrect repair may lead to functional problems and require the replacement of components.

• Lubricate rubber parts with clean,

fresh brake fluid to ease assembly. Do not use shop air to clean parts; damage to rubber components may result.

• Use only DOT 3 brake fluid from an unopened container.

• If any hydraulic component or line is removed or replaced, it may be necessary to bleed the entire system.

• A clean repair area is essential. Always clean the reservoir and cap thoroughly before removing the cap. The slightest amount of dirt in the fluid may plug an orifice and impair the system function. Perform repairs after components have been thoroughly cleaned; use only denatured alcohol

to clean components. Do not allow ABS components to come into contact with any substance containing mineral oil; this includes used shop rags.

• The Anti-Lock control unit is a microprocessor similar to other computer units in the vehicle. Ensure that the ignition switch is **OFF** before removing or installing controller harnesses. Avoid static electricity discharge at or near the controller.

• If any arc welding is to be done on the vehicle, the control unit should be unplugged before welding operations begin.

BLEEDING PROCEDURE

Manual

> ❊❊ **CAUTION**
>
> **When adding fluid to the brake master cylinder reservoir, use only Delco Supreme 11®, GM P/N 12377967 (Canadian P/N 992667), or equivalent DOT-3 brake fluid from a clean, sealed brake fluid container. The use of any type of fluid other than the recommended type of brake fluid, may cause contamination which could result in damage to the internal rubber seals and/or rubber linings of hydraulic brake system components.**

1. Place a clean shop cloth beneath the brake master cylinder to catch brake fluid spills.
2. With the ignition OFF and the brakes cool, apply the brakes 3-5 times, or until the brake pedal effort increases significantly, in order to deplete the brake booster power reserve.
3. If you have performed a brake master cylinder bench bleeding on this vehicle, or if you disconnected the brake pipes from the master cylinder, or if you have disconnected the brake pipes from the proportioning valve assembly or the brake modulator assembly, you must perform the following steps to bleed air at the ports of the hydraulic component:

   a. Ensure that the brake master cylinder reservoir is full to the maximum-fill level. If necessary, add Delco Supreme 11®GM P/N 12377967 (Canadian P/N 992667), or equivalent DOT 3 brake fluid from a clean, sealed brake fluid container.

   If removal of the reservoir cap and diaphragm is necessary, clean the outside of the reservoir on and around the cap prior to removal.

   a. With the brake pipes installed securely to the master cylinder, proportioning valve assembly, or brake modulator assembly, loosen and separate one of the brake pipes from the port of the component.

   For the proportioning valve assembly or the brake modulator assembly, perform these steps in the sequence of system flow; begin with the fluid feed pipes from the master cylinder.

   a. Allow a small amount of brake fluid to gravity bleed from the open port of the component.

   b. Connect the brake pipe to the component and tighten securely.

   c. Have an assistant slowly press the brake pedal fully and maintain steady pressure on the pedal.

   d. Loosen the same brake pipe to purge air from the open port of the component.

   e. Tighten the brake pipe, then have the assistant slowly release the brake pedal.

   f. Wait 15 seconds, then repeat steps 3.3-3.7 until all air is purged from the same port of the component.

   g. With the brake pipe installed securely to the master cylinder, proportioning valve assembly, or brake modulator assembly, after all air has been purged from the first port of the component that was bled, loosen and separate the next brake pipe from the component, then repeat steps 3.3-3.8, until each of the ports on the component has been bled.

   h. After completing the final component port bleeding procedure, ensure that each of the brake pipe-to-component fittings are properly tightened.

4. Fill the brake master cylinder reservoir with Delco Supreme 11®GM P/N 12377967 (Canadian P/N 992667), or equivalent DOT 3 brake fluid from a clean, sealed brake fluid container. Ensure that the brake master cylinder reservoir remains at least half-full during this bleeding procedure. Add fluid as needed to maintain the proper level.

   Clean the outside of the reservoir on and around the reservoir cap prior to removing the cap and diaphragm.

5. Install a proper box-end wrench onto the RIGHT REAR wheel hydraulic circuit bleeder valve.
6. Install a transparent hose over the end of the bleeder valve.
7. Submerge the open end of the transparent hose into a transparent container partially filled with Delco Supreme 11® GM P/N 12377967 (Canadian P/N 992667), or equivalent DOT 3 brake fluid from a clean, sealed brake fluid container.
8. Have an assistant slowly press the brake pedal fully and maintain steady pressure on the pedal.
9. Loosen the bleeder valve to purge air from the wheel hydraulic circuit.
10. Tighten the bleeder valve, then have the assistant slowly release the brake pedal.
11. Wait 15 seconds, then repeat steps 8-10 until all air is purged from the same wheel hydraulic circuit.

12. With the right rear wheel hydraulic circuit bleeder valve tightened securely, after all air has been purged from the right rear hydraulic circuit, install a proper box-end wrench onto the LEFT FRONT wheel hydraulic circuit bleeder valve.
13. Install a transparent hose over the end of the bleeder valve, then repeat steps 7-11.
14. With the left front wheel hydraulic circuit bleeder valve tightened securely, after all air has been purged from the left front hydraulic circuit, install a proper box-end wrench onto the LEFT REAR wheel hydraulic circuit bleeder valve.
15. Install a transparent hose over the end of the bleeder valve, then repeat steps 7-11.
16. With the left rear wheel hydraulic circuit bleeder valve tightened securely, after all air has been purged from the left rear hydraulic circuit, install a proper box-end wrench onto the RIGHT FRONT wheel hydraulic circuit bleeder valve.
17. Install a transparent hose over the end of the bleeder valve, then repeat steps 7-11.
18. After completing the final wheel hydraulic circuit bleeding procedure, ensure that each of the 4 wheel hydraulic circuit bleeder valves are properly tightened.
19. Fill the brake master cylinder reservoir to the maximum-fill level with Delco Supreme 11® GM P/N 12377967 (Canadian P/N 992667), or equivalent DOT 3 brake fluid from a clean, sealed brake fluid container.
20. Slowly press and release the brake pedal. Observe the feel of the brake pedal.
21. If the brake pedal feels spongy, repeat the bleeding procedure again. If the brake pedal still feels spongy after repeating the bleeding procedure, perform the following steps:

    a. Inspect the brake system for external leaks.

    b. Pressure bleed the hydraulic brake system in order to purge any air that may still be trapped in the system.

22. Turn the ignition key ON, with the engine OFF. Check to see if the brake system warning lamp remains illuminated.

➡ **DO NOT allow the vehicle to be driven until it is diagnosed and repaired.**

Pressure

> ❊❊ **CAUTION**
>
> **When adding fluid to the brake master cylinder reservoir, use only Delco Supreme 11®, GM P/N 12377967 (Canadian P/N 992667), or equivalent DOT-3 brake fluid from a clean,**

sealed brake fluid container. The use of any type of fluid other than the recommended type of brake fluid, may cause contamination which could result in damage to the internal rubber seals and/or rubber linings of hydraulic brake system components.

1. Place a clean shop cloth beneath the brake master cylinder to catch brake fluid spills.

2. With the ignition OFF and the brakes cool, apply the brakes 3-5 times, or until the brake pedal becomes firm, in order to deplete the brake booster power reserve.

3. If you have performed a brake master cylinder bench bleeding on this vehicle, or if you disconnected the brake pipes from the master cylinder, or if you have disconnected the brake pipes from the proportioning valve assembly or the brake modulator assembly, you must perform the following steps to bleed air at the ports of the hydraulic component:

a. Ensure that the brake master cylinder reservoir is full to the maximum-fill level. If necessary, add Delco Supreme 11

b. GM P/N 12377967 (Canadian P/N 992667), or equivalent DOT 3 brake fluid from a clean, sealed brake fluid container.

If removal of the reservoir cap and diaphragm is necessary, clean the outside of the reservoir on and around the cap prior to removal.

a. With the brake pipes installed securely to the master cylinder, proportioning valve assembly, or brake modulator assembly, loosen and separate one of the brake pipes from the port of the component.

b. After completing the final component port bleeding procedure, ensure that each of the brake pipe-to-component fittings are properly tightened.

4. Fill the brake master cylinder reservoir to the maximum-fill level with Delco Supreme 11® GM P/N 12377967 (Canadian P/N 992667), or equivalent DOT 3 brake fluid from a clean, sealed brake fluid container.

Clean the outside of the reservoir on and around the reservoir cap prior to removing the cap and diaphragm.

5. Install the Brake Pressure Bleeder Adapter to the brake master cylinder reservoir.

6. Check the brake fluid level in the Diaphragm Type Brake Pressure Bleeder, or equivalent. Add Delco supreme 11® GM P/N 12377967 (Canadian P/N 992667), or equivalent DOT 3 brake fluid from a clean, sealed brake fluid container as necessary to bring the level to approximately the half-full point.

7. Connect the Brake Pressure Bleeder Adapter, or equivalent, to the Diaphragm Type Brake Pressure Bleeder.

8. Charge the Diaphragm Type Brake Pressure Bleeder, or equivalent, air tank to 25-30 psi (175-205 kPa).

9. Open the Diaphragm Type Brake Pressure Bleeder, or equivalent, fluid tank valve to allow pressurized brake fluid to enter the brake system.

10. Wait approximately 30 seconds, then inspect the entire hydraulic brake system in order to ensure that there are no existing external brake fluid leaks.

Any brake fluid leaks identified require repair prior to completing this procedure.

11. Install a proper box-end wrench onto the RIGHT REAR wheel hydraulic circuit bleeder valve.

12. Install a transparent hose over the end of the bleeder valve.

13. Submerge the open end of the transparent hose into a transparent container partially filled with Delco Supreme 11® GM P/N 12377967 (Canadian P/N 992667), or equivalent DOT 3 brake fluid from a clean, sealed brake fluid container.

14. Loosen the bleeder valve to purge air from the wheel hydraulic circuit. Allow fluid to flow until air bubbles stop flowing from the bleeder, then tighten the bleeder valve.

15. With the right rear wheel hydraulic circuit bleeder valve tightened securely, after all air has been purged from the right rear hydraulic circuit, install a proper box-end wrench onto the LEFT FRONT wheel hydraulic circuit bleeder valve.

16. Install a transparent hose over the end of the bleeder valve, then repeat steps 13-14.

17. With the left front wheel hydraulic circuit bleeder valve tightened securely, after all air has been purged from the left front hydraulic circuit, install a proper box-end wrench onto the LEFT REAR wheel hydraulic circuit bleeder valve.

18. Install a transparent hose over the end of the bleeder valve, then repeat steps 13-14.

19. With the left rear wheel hydraulic circuit bleeder valve tightened securely, after all air has been purged from the left rear hydraulic circuit, install a proper box-end wrench onto the RIGHT FRONT wheel hydraulic circuit bleeder valve.

20. Install a transparent hose over the end of the bleeder valve, then repeat steps 13-14.

21. After completing the final wheel hydraulic circuit bleeding procedure, ensure that each of the 4 wheel hydraulic circuit bleeder valves are properly tightened.

22. Close the Diaphragm Type Brake Pressure Bleeder, or equivalent, fluid tank valve, then disconnect the Diaphragm Type

Brake Pressure Bleeder, or equivalent, from the Brake Pressure Bleeder Adapter.

23. Remove the Brake Pressure Bleeder Adapter from the brake master cylinder reservoir.

24. Fill the brake master cylinder reservoir to the maximum-fill level with Delco Supreme 11® GM P/N 12377967 (Canadian P/N 992667), or equivalent DOT 3 brake fluid from a clean, sealed brake fluid container.

25. Slowly press and release the brake pedal. Observe the feel of the brake pedal.

26. If the brake pedal feels spongy perform the following steps:

a. Inspect the brake system for external leaks.

b. If equipped with antilock brakes, using a scan tool, perform the antilock brake system automated bleeding procedure to remove any air that may have been trapped in the BPMV.

c. Turn the ignition key ON, with the engine OFF. Check to see if the brake system warning lamp remains illuminated.

➡**DO NOT allow the vehicle to be driven until it is diagnosed and repaired.**

BLEEDING THE ABS SYSTEM

➡**Before performing the ABS Automated Bleed Procedure, first perform a manual or pressure bleed of the base hydraulic brake system.**

➡**The automated bleed procedure must be performed when a new brake pressure modulator valve (BPMV) is installed, because the secondary circuits of the new BPMV are not prefilled with brake fluid.**

➡**The automated bleed procedure is recommended when one of the following conditions exist:**

• Base brake system bleeding does not achieve the desired pedal height or feel
• Extreme loss of brake fluid has occurred
• Air ingestion is suspected in the secondary circuits of the brake modulator assembly

The ABS Automated Bleed Procedure uses a scan tool to cycle the system solenoid valves and run the pump in order to purge any air from the secondary circuits. These circuits are normally closed off, and are only opened during system initialization at vehicle start up and during ABS operation. The automated bleed procedure opens these secondary circuits and allows any air trapped in these circuits to flow out away from the brake modulator assembly, which is then forced out at the brake corners by the pressure bleeder.

The Auto Bleed Procedure may be terminated at any time during the process by pressing the EXIT button. No further Scan Tool prompts pertaining to the Auto Bleed procedure will be given. After exiting the bleed procedure, relieve bleed pressure and disconnect bleed equipment per manufacturer's instructions. Failure to properly relieve pressure may result in spilled brake fluid causing damage to components and painted surfaces.

1. Raise and support the vehicle.
2. Remove the tire and wheel assemblies.
3. Inspect the brake system for leaks and visual damage.
4. Lower the vehicle.
5. Prepare the brake bleeding equipment and the vehicle for a pressure bleed of the base hydraulic brake system.
6. Inspect the battery state of charge.
7. Install a scan tool.
8. Turn the ignition ON, with the engine OFF.
9. With the scan tool, perform the following steps:
   - Select Diagnostics
   - Select the appropriate vehicle information
   - Select Chassis
   - Select Electronic Brake Control Module (EBCM)
   - Select Special Functions
   - Select Automated Bleed
10. With an assistant ready, raise and support the vehicle.

➡**Apply the brake pedal when instructed, using moderate effort.**

➡**Ensure the pedal remains applied until instructed to release by the scan tool.**

➡**Do NOT exceed the time period allowed by the scan tool for having the bleeder valves open.**

➡**The bleed sequence for each corner is, left front, right front, right rear, left rear.**

11. Perform the automated bleed procedure as instructed by the scan tool.
12. If the automated bleed procedure is aborted, a malfunction exists.
13. After completion of the automated bleed procedure, press and hold the brake pedal to inspect for pedal firmness.
14. If the brake pedal feels spongy, repeat the bleed procedure completely.
15. Remove the scan tool.
16. Install the tire and wheel assemblies.
17. Lower the vehicle.
18. Adjust the brake fluid level.
19. Road test the vehicle while confirming the brake pedal remains high and firm.

BRAKES   FRONT DISC BRAKES

BRAKE CALIPER

REMOVAL & INSTALLATION

See Figure 1.

1. Remove enough brake fluid from the reservoir to reach the half fill mark.
2. Raise and support the vehicle.
3. Remove the tire and wheel.
4. Install and firmly hand tighten 2 wheel nuts to opposite wheel studs in order to retain the rotor to the hub.

5. Install a large C-clamp over the body of the brake caliper with the C-clamp ends against the rear of the caliper body and against the outer brake pad.
6. Tighten the C-clamp until the caliper piston is compressed into the caliper bore enough to allow the caliper to slide past the brake rotor.
7. Remove the C-clamp from the caliper.
8. Remove the brake hose from the brake caliper.

9. Cap or plug the opening in the brake caliper and the brake hose to prevent fluid loss and contamination.
10. Remove the brake caliper guide pin bolts.
11. Remove the brake caliper from the caliper bracket.

To install:
12. Install the brake caliper to the brake caliper bracket.
13. Install the brake caliper guide pin bolts and tighten to 26 ft. lbs. (35 Nm).
14. Remove the caps or plugs from the brake caliper opening and the brake hose.
15. Install new copper brake hose gaskets to the brake hose-to-caliper bolt and to the brake hose.
16. Install the brake hose and the brake hose-to-brake caliper bolt to the brake caliper and tighten to 37 ft. lbs. (50 Nm).
17. Bleed the hydraulic brake system.
18. Remove the wheel nuts retaining the brake rotor to the wheel hub.
19. Install the tire and wheel assembly.
20. Lower the vehicle.
21. With the engine off, gradually apply the brake pedal to approximately 2/3 of its travel distance.
22. Slowly release the brake pedal.
23. Wait 15 seconds, then repeat the steps until a firm brake pedal apply is obtained; this will properly seat the brake caliper piston and brake pads.

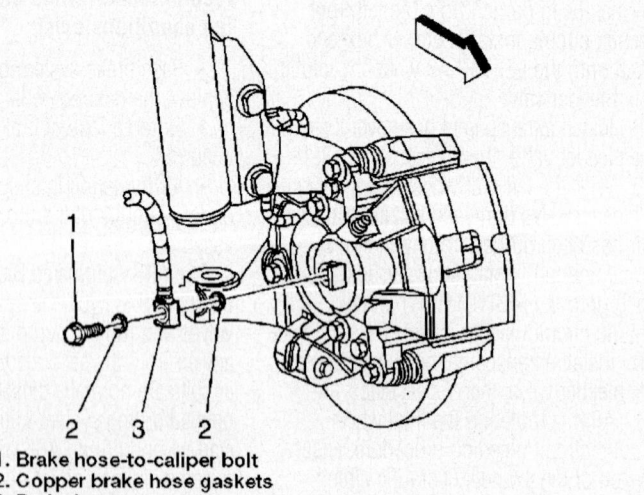

1. Brake hose-to-caliper bolt
2. Copper brake hose gaskets
3. Brake hose

36616_GMG6_G0049

Fig. 1 Removing and installing the front brake caliper

DISC BRAKE PADS

REMOVAL & INSTALLATION

See Figures 2 and 3.

1. Inspect the fluid level in the brake master cylinder reservoir.

2. If the brake fluid level is midway between the maximum-full point and the minimum allowable level, no brake fluid needs to be removed from the reservoir before proceeding.

3. If the brake fluid level is higher than midway between the maximum-full point and the minimum allowable level, remove brake fluid to the midway point before proceeding.

4. Raise and support the vehicle.

5. Remove the tire and wheel assembly.

6. Install and firmly hand tighten 2 wheel nuts to opposite wheel studs in order to retain the rotor to the hub.

7. Remove the brake caliper lower guide pin bolt.

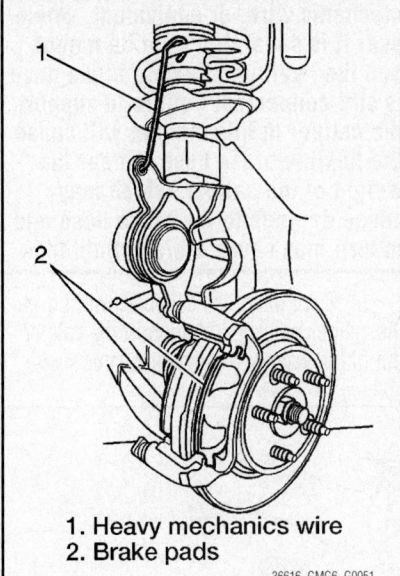

1. Heavy mechanics wire
2. Brake pads

36616_GMG6_G0051

Fig. 2 Removing the brake pads from the caliper mounting bracket (front)

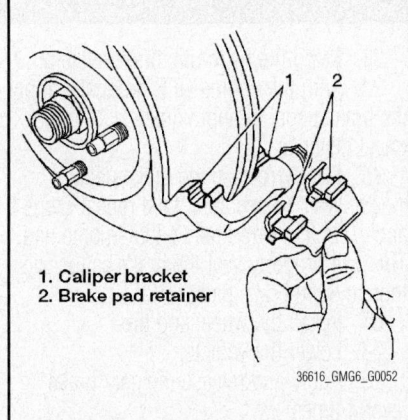

1. Caliper bracket
2. Brake pad retainer

36616_GMG6_G0052

Fig. 3 Removing the brake pad retainers

✴✴ CAUTION

Support the brake caliper with heavy mechanic wire, or equivalent, whenever it is separated from its mount and the hydraulic flexible brake hose is still connected. Failure to support the caliper in this manner will cause the flexible brake hose to bear the weight of the caliper, which may cause damage to the brake hose and in turn may cause a brake fluid leak.

8. Without disconnecting the hydraulic brake flexible hose, pivot the caliper upward and secure the caliper with heavy mechanics wire, or equivalent.

9. Remove the brake pads from the caliper mounting bracket.

10. Push the disc brake caliper piston into the caliper bore using an old inner disc brake pad and a disc brake piston installation tool.

11. Remove the brake pad retainers from the caliper bracket.

12. Thoroughly clean the brake pad hardware mating surfaces of the caliper bracket, of any debris and corrosion.

13. Inspect the brake caliper guide pins for freedom of movement, and inspect the condition of the guide pin boots. Move the guide pins inboard and outboard within the bracket bores, without disengaging the slides from the boots, and observe for the following:

- Restricted caliper guide pin movement
- Looseness in the brake caliper mounting bracket
- Seized or binding caliper guide pins
- Split or torn boots

14. If any of the conditions listed are found, the brake caliper guide pins and/or boots require replacement.

To install:

15. Ensure the brake pad hardware mating surfaces are clean.

16. Install the brake pad retainers to the brake caliper bracket.

➡The wear sensor equipped disc brake pad must be mounted inboard of the rotor with the leading edge of the sensor facing the brake rotor during forward wheel rotation, or at the top of the pad when installed in vehicle position.

17. Install the brake pads to the caliper bracket.

18. Remove the support, and rotate the brake caliper into position over the disc brake pads and to the caliper mounting bracket.

19. Install the lower brake caliper guide pin bolt and tighten to 26 ft. lbs. (35 Nm).

20. Remove the wheel nuts retaining the brake rotor to the hub.

21. Install the tire and wheel assembly.

22. Lower the vehicle.

23. With the engine OFF, gradually apply the brake pedal approximately ⅔ of its travel distance.

24. Slowly release the brake pedal.

25. Wait 15 seconds, then gradually apply the brake pedal approximately ⅔ of its travel distance again until a firm brake pedal apply is obtained. This will properly seat the brake caliper pistons and brake pads.

26. Fill the master cylinder auxiliary reservoir to the proper level.

27. Burnish the pads and rotors.

BRAKE CALIPER

REMOVAL & INSTALLATION

1. Remove enough brake fluid from the reservoir to reach the half fill mark.
2. Raise and support the vehicle.
3. Remove the tire and wheel.
4. Install and firmly hand tighten 2 wheel nuts to opposite wheel studs in order to retain the rotor to the hub.
5. Install a large C-clamp over the body of the brake caliper with the C-clamp ends against the rear of the caliper body and against the outer brake pad.
6. Tighten the C-clamp until the caliper piston is compressed into the caliper bore enough to allow the caliper to slide past the brake rotor.
7. Remove the C-clamp from the caliper.
8. Remove the brake hose from the brake caliper.
9. Remove and discard the 2 copper brake hose gasket. These gaskets may be stuck to the brake caliper and/or the brake hose end.
10. Cap or plug the opening in the brake caliper and the brake hose to prevent fluid loss and contamination.
11. On rear brakes, disconnect the parking brake cable from the caliper.
12. Remove the brake caliper guide pin bolts.
13. Remove the brake caliper from the caliper bracket.
14. Remove the park brake cable from the caliper.
15. Remove the brake caliper from the brake caliper bracket.

To install:

16. Inspect the caliper slide boots for cuts, tears, or deterioration. If damaged, replace the slides and boots.
17. Install the brake caliper to the brake caliper bracket.
18. Install the 2 brake caliper pin bolts and tighten to 26 ft. lbs. (35 Nm).
19. Install the park brake cable to the caliper.
20. Remove the caps or plugs from the brake caliper opening and the brake hose.

➡**DO NOT reuse the copper brake hose gaskets.**

21. Install NEW copper brake hose gaskets to the brake hose-to-caliper bolt and the brake hose.
22. Install the brake hose and brake hose-to-caliper bolt to the brake caliper and tighten the bolt to 37 ft. lbs. (50 Nm).

23. Bleed the hydraulic brake system.
24. With the engine OFF, gradually apply the brake pedal to approximately ⅔ of its travel distance.
25. Slowly release the brake pedal.
26. Wait 15 seconds, then repeat Steps 9 and 10 until a firm brake pedal is obtained. This will properly seat the brake caliper pistons and the brake pads.
27. Install the wheel and tire.
28. Lower the vehicle.
29. Apply and release the park brake lever 4 times.

DISC BRAKE PADS

REMOVAL & INSTALLATION

See Figure 4.

1. Inspect the fluid level in the brake master cylinder reservoir.
2. If the brake fluid level is midway between the maximum-full point and the minimum allowable level, no brake fluid needs to be removed from the reservoir before proceeding.
3. Raise and suitably support the vehicle.
4. Remove the tire and wheel assembly.

✳✳ CAUTION

When using a large C-clamp to compress a caliper piston into a caliper bore of a caliper equipped with an integral park brake mechanism, do not exceed more than 0.039 inch

(1 mm) of piston travel. Exceeding this amount of piston travel will cause damage to the internal adjusting mechanism and/or the integral park brake mechanism.

5. Install a large C-clamp over the body of the brake caliper with the C-clamp ends against the rear of the caliper body and against the outboard brake pad. Do not exceed 0.039 in (1 mm) of caliper piston travel.
6. Tighten the C-clamp until the caliper piston is compressed into the caliper bore enough to allow the caliper to slide past the brake rotor.
7. Remove the C-clamp from the caliper.
8. Remove the lower brake caliper guide pin bolt

✳✳ CAUTION

Support the brake caliper with heavy mechanic wire, or equivalent, whenever it is separated from its mount and the hydraulic flexible brake hose is still connected. Failure to support the caliper in this manner will cause the flexible brake hose to bear the weight of the caliper, which may cause damage to the brake hose and in turn may cause a brake fluid leak.

9. Pivot the brake caliper upward from the caliper bracket and support the caliper out of the way with heavy mechanic's wire

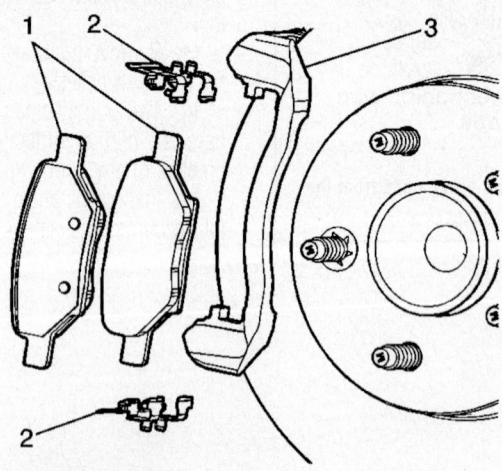

1. Brake pad
2. Brake pad retainers
3. Brake caliper mounting bracket

36616_GMG6_G0056

Fig. 4 Removing the rear disc brake pads

or equivalent; ensure that there is no tension on the hydraulic brake flexible hose. Do NOT disconnect the hydraulic brake flexible hose from the caliper.

10. Remove the brake pads from the brake caliper mounting bracket.

11. Remove and the brake pad retainers from the brake caliper mounting bracket.

To install:

12. Inspect the brake caliper guide pin bolts, pins, pin busing, bracket boots and bracket for damage and corrosion.

13. Do not attempt to clean away any corrosion. If damaged or corroded replace the necessary components.

14. Inspect the brake caliper piston boot for deterioration, replace if damaged.

15. Use a piston installation tool in order to twist the brake caliper piston into the brake caliper bore.

16. Install the brake pad retainers to the brake caliper mounting bracket.

17. Install the brake pads to the brake caliper mounting bracket.

18. Pivot the brake caliper downward, over the brake pads and into the caliper bracket.

19. Install the brake caliper guide pin bolt to the brake caliper guide pin and tighten the bolt to 26 ft. lbs. (35 Nm).

20. Install the tire and wheel assembly.

21. Lower the vehicle.

22. With the engine OFF, gradually apply the brake pedal to approximately ⅔ of its travel distance.

23. Slowly release the brake pedal.

24. Wait 15 seconds, then repeat steps 11 and 12 until a firm brake pedal apply is obtained; this will properly seat the brake caliper pistons and brake pads.

25. Fill the brake master cylinder reservoir to the proper level.

26. Apply and release the park brake lever 4 times.

27. Burnish the pads and rotors.

BRAKES   PARKING BRAKE

PARKING BRAKE CABLES

REMOVAL & INSTALLATION

See Figure 5.

1. Ensure that the park brake lever is in the fully released position.

2. Remove the floor console.

3. Remove the rear carpet.

4. Remove the right rear park brake cable or the left rear park brake cable from the console park brake bracket and the front park brake cable equalizer.

5. Raise and support the vehicle.

6. Remove the plastic retainer clip from the body.

7. Remove the tire and wheel assembly.

8. Remove the rear park brake cable retainer bolt.

9. Remove the rear park brake cable from the caliper park brake lever.

10. Lower the vehicle

11. Remove the plastic retainer clip from the stud.

12. Remove the park brake cable and pass-thru grommet from the body and remove the cable from the vehicle.

To install:

13. Install the park brake cable to the vehicle.

14. Install the park brake cable and pass-thru grommet to the body.

15. Install the plastic retainer clip to the stud.

16. Raise the vehicle.

17. Install the rear park brake cable to the caliper park brake lever.

18. Install the rear park brake cable retainer bolt.

19. Tighten the bolt to 89 inch lbs. (10 Nm).

20. Install the plastic retainer clip to the body.

21. Install the tire and wheel assembly

22. Lower the vehicle.

23. Install the right rear park brake cable or the left rear park brake cable to the console park brake bracket and the front park brake cable equalizer.

24. Install the rear carpet.

25. Install the floor console.

26. Cycle the park brake lever 3—5 times.

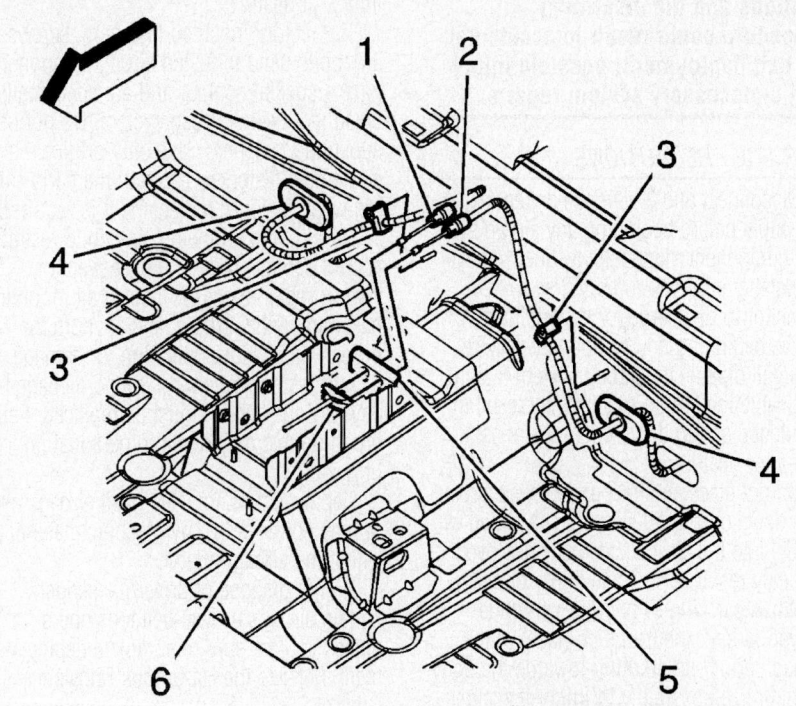

1. Right rear park brake cable
2. Console park brake bracket
3. Plastic retainer clip
4. Grommet
5. Console park brake bracket
6. Front park brake cable equalizer

22116_GMG6_G0085

Fig. 5 Inside vehicle parking brake cable components view

ADJUSTMENT

1. Apply and fully release the park brake lever several times. Verify that the park brake lever releases completely.

2. Turn ON the ignition. Verify the red BRAKE warning lamp is not illuminated.

3. If the red BRAKE warning lamp is illuminated, verify the park brake lever is in the fully released position and against the stop and there is no slack in the park brake cables.

4. Turn OFF the ignition.

5. Raise and support the vehicle.

6. With the park brake lever fully released, check the park brake apply levers on the rear calipers. The apply levers should be against the stops on the caliper housings. If the apply levers are not against the stops, binding may exist.

7. Fully apply and release the park brake lever 3—5 times in order for the cable tensioner to take up any slack in the park brake cables.

8. Fully apply the park brake lever, tension should be felt on the lever by pulling the lever less than one full pull.

9. Attempt to rotate the rear brake rotors. There should be no rotation forward or rearward.

10. Fully release the park brake lever.

11. Verify the park brake is released by rotating the rear brake rotors. The rotors should rotate freely and exhibit no brake drag.

12. Lower the vehicle.

CHASSIS ELECTRICAL

AIR BAG (SUPPLEMENTAL RESTRAINT SYSTEM)

GENERAL INFORMATION

✳✳ CAUTION

These vehicles are equipped with an air bag system. The system must be disarmed before performing service on, or around, system components, the steering column, instrument panel components, wiring and sensors. Failure to follow the safety precautions and the disarming procedure could result in accidental air bag deployment, possible injury and unnecessary system repairs.

SERVICE PRECAUTIONS

Disconnect and isolate the battery negative cable before beginning any airbag system component diagnosis, testing, removal, or installation procedures. Allow system capacitor to discharge for two minutes before beginning any component service. This will disable the airbag system. Failure to disable the airbag system may result in accidental airbag deployment, personal injury, or death.

Do not place an intact undeployed airbag face down on a solid surface. The airbag will propel into the air if accidentally deployed and may result in personal injury or death.

When carrying or handling an undeployed airbag, the trim side (face) of the airbag should be pointing towards the body to minimize possibility of injury if accidental deployment occurs. Failure to do this may result in personal injury or death.

Replace airbag system components with OEM replacement parts. Substitute parts may appear interchangeable, but internal differences may result in inferior occupant protection. Failure to do so may result in occupant personal injury or death.

Wear safety glasses, rubber gloves, and long sleeved clothing when cleaning powder residue from vehicle after an airbag deployment. Powder residue emitted from a deployed airbag can cause skin irritation. Flush affected area with cool water if irritation is experienced. If nasal or throat irritation is experienced, exit the vehicle for fresh air until the irritation ceases. If irritation continues, see a physician.

Do not use a replacement airbag that is not in the original packaging. This may result in improper deployment, personal injury, or death.

The factory installed fasteners, screws and bolts used to fasten airbag components have a special coating and are specifically designed for the airbag system. Do not use substitute fasteners. Use only original equipment fasteners listed in the parts catalog when fastener replacement is required.

During, and following, any child restraint anchor service, due to impact event or vehicle repair, carefully inspect all mounting hardware, tether straps, and anchors for proper installation, operation, or damage. If a child restraint anchor is found damaged in any way, the anchor must be replaced. Failure to do this may result in personal injury or death.

Deployed and non-deployed airbags may or may not have live pyrotechnic material within the airbag inflator.

Do not dispose of driver/passenger/curtain airbags or seat belt tensioners unless you are sure of complete deployment. Refer to the Hazardous Substance Control System for proper disposal.

Dispose of deployed airbags and tensioners consistent with state, provincial, local, and federal regulations.

After any airbag component testing or service, do not connect the battery negative cable. Personal injury or death may result if the system test is not performed first.

If the vehicle is equipped with the Occupant Classification System (OCS), do not connect the battery negative cable before performing the OCS Verification Test using the scan tool and the appropriate diagnostic information. Personal injury or death may result if the system test is not performed properly.

Never replace both the Occupant Restraint Controller (ORC) and the Occupant Classification Module (OCM) at the same time. If both require replacement, replace one, then perform the Airbag System test before replacing the other.

Both the ORC and the OCM store Occupant Classification System (OCS) calibration data, which they transfer to one another when one of them is replaced. If both are replaced at the same time, an irreversible fault will be set in both modules and the OCS may malfunction and cause personal injury or death.

If equipped with OCS, the Seat Weight Sensor is a sensitive, calibrated unit and must be handled carefully. Do not drop or handle roughly. If dropped or damaged, replace with another sensor. Failure to do so may result in occupant injury or death.

If equipped with OCS, the front passenger seat must be handled carefully as well. When removing the seat, be careful when setting on floor not to drop. If dropped, the sensor may be inoperative, could result in occupant injury, or possibly death.

If equipped with OCS, when the passenger front seat is on the floor, no one should sit in the front passenger seat. This uneven force may damage the sensing ability of the seat weight sensors. If sat on and damaged, the sensor may be inoperative, could result in occupant injury, or possibly death.

The following are general service instructions which must be followed in order to properly repair the vehicle and return it to its original integrity:

• Do not expose inflator modules to temperatures above 150°F (60°C).

• Verify the correct replacement part number. Do not substitute a component from a different vehicle.

• Use only original GM replacement parts available from your authorized GM dealer. Do not used salvaged parts for repairs to the SIR system.

Discard any of the following components if it has been dropped from a height of 3 feet or greater (91 cm).

• Inflatable restraint Sensing and Diagnostic Module (SDM)
• Inflatable restraint I/P module
• Inflatable restraint steering wheel module
• Inflatable restraint steering wheel module coil
• Inflatable restraint roof side rail modules
• Inflatable restraint Side Impact Sensor (SIS)
• Inflatable restraint seat belt retractor pretensioners
• Inflatable restraint front end sensors

DISARMING THE SYSTEM

Air Bag Fuse

1. Turn the steering wheel so that the vehicles wheels are pointing straight ahead.
2. Place the ignition in the OFF position.

➡**The SDM may have more than one fused power input. To ensure there is no unwanted SIR deployment, personal injury, or unnecessary SIR system repairs, remove all fuses supplying power to the SDM. With all SDM fuses removed and the ignition switch in the ON position, the AIR BAG warning indicator illuminates. This is normal operation, and does not indicate a SIR system malfunction.**

3. Locate and remove the fuse(s) supplying power to the SDM.
4. Wait for 1 minute before working on the system.

Negative Battery Cable

1. Turn the steering wheel so that the vehicles wheels are pointing straight ahead.
2. Place the ignition in the OFF position.
3. Disconnect the negative battery cable from the battery.
4. Wait 1 minute before working on the system.

ARMING THE SYSTEM

Air Bag Fuse

1. Place the ignition in the OFF position.
2. Install the fuse(s) supplying power to the SDM.
3. Turn the ignition switch to the ON position. The AIR BAG indicator will flash then turn OFF.
4. Perform the Diagnostic System Check - Vehicle if the AIR BAG warning indicator does not operate as described.

Negative Battery Cable

1. Place the ignition in the OFF position.
2. Connect the negative battery cable to the battery.
3. Turn the ignition switch to the ON position. The AIR BAG indicator will flash then turn OFF.
4. Perform the Diagnostic System Check - Vehicle if the AIR BAG warning indicator does not operate as described.

CLOCKSPRING CENTERING

See Figure 6.

1. Verify the following conditions before centering the supplemental inflatable restraint (SIR) steering wheel module coil:

a. The wheels on the vehicle are straight ahead.

b. The block tooth and the centering mark (1) of the steering shaft is in the 12 o'clock position. If available, remove the yellow retaining tab (1) from the SIR steering wheel module coil and save the tab for reassembly.

2. Hold the SIR steering wheel module coil face up by the casing (2).

a. Slowly turn the SIR steering wheel module coil hub (3) clockwise until the coil ribbon stops.

b. Slowly rotate the SIR steering wheel module coil hub (3) counterclockwise 2.5 revolutions until the centering window (4) turns yellow. This indicates the CENTER position.

➡**If the retaining tab is not available, the use of tape to secure the SIR steering wheel module coil is recommended for installation to the steering column.**

3. Install the yellow retaining tab (1) to the SIR steering wheel module coil.
4. Slide the centered SIR steering wheel module coil onto the steering shaft.

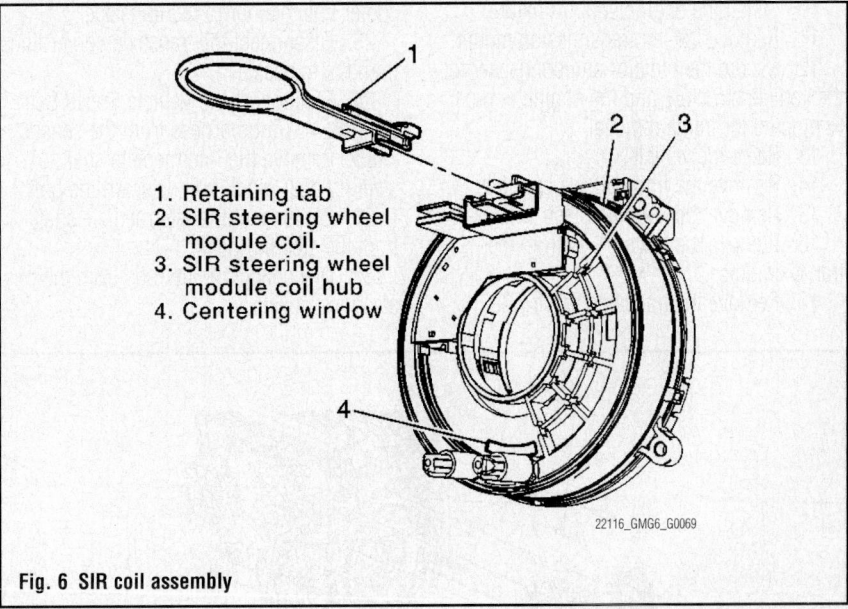

1. Retaining tab
2. SIR steering wheel module coil.
3. SIR steering wheel module coil hub
4. Centering window

22116_GMG6_G0069

Fig. 6 SIR coil assembly

DRIVE TRAIN

AUTOMATIC TRANSAXLE ASSEMBLY

REMOVAL & INSTALLATION

4T45-E

2.4L Engine

See Figures 7 through 9.

1. Remove the battery tray.
2. Disconnect the air cleaner outlet duct.
3. Disconnect the transaxle wiring harness from the transaxle and the Park Neutral Position (PNP) switch.
4. Disconnect the transaxle shift control cable terminal from the transaxle manual shift lever pin.
5. Remove the retainer from the transaxle shift control cable.
6. Press the locking tabs inward in order to release the transaxle shift control cable from the cable bracket.
7. Remove the shift cable bracket.
8. Remove the transaxle wiring harness from the retainer on the transaxle.
9. Remove the upper transaxle to engine studs (1, 2) and bolts (5, 6).
10. Install the engine support fixture.
11. Remove the left transmission mount.
12. Secure the radiator and condenser to the vehicle structure and the engine in order to prepare for frame removal.
13. Raise the vehicle.
14. Remove the front wheels and tires.
15. Remove the engine splash shields.
16. Remove the bolts (1, 2) from the transaxle brace.
17. Remove the transaxle brace (3).

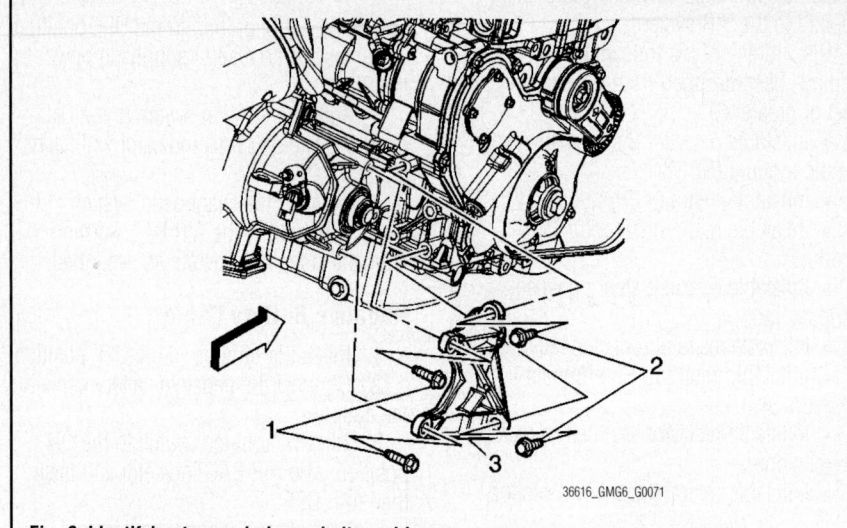
Fig. 8 Identifying transaxle brace bolts and brace

18. Remove the starter.
19. Mark the relationship of the flywheel to the torque converter for reassembly.
20. Use the flywheel holding tool to prevent the crankshaft from rotating.
21. Remove the torque converter to flywheel bolts.
22. Remove the nut holding the transaxle cooler line retainer to the transaxle.
23. Disconnect the transaxle cooler lines from the transaxle.
24. Disconnect the Vehicle Speed Sensor (VSS) wiring harness from the sensor.
25. Remove the intermediate shaft to steering gear pinch bolt. Discard the bolt.
26. Disconnect the intermediate shaft from the steering gear.
27. Disconnect the tie rods from the steering knuckle.

28. Disconnect the stabilizer shaft links from the stabilizer shaft.
29. Disconnect the ball joints from the steering knuckles.
30. Remove the frame.
31. Disconnect the wheel driveshafts from the transaxle. Secure the wheel driveshafts out of the way.
32. Support the transaxle with a suitable jack.
33. Remove the lower transaxle to engine bolts (5, 6, 7, 8, 9).
34. Separate the engine and the transaxle.
35. Remove the transaxle from the vehicle.
36. If the transaxle is being replaced, remove the PNP switch from the transaxle.
37. Flush the transaxle cooler and the lines with a transmission oil cooler flusher.

To install:

38. If previously removed, Install the PNP switch.
39. Position the transaxle in the vehicle.
40. Install the lower transaxle to engine bolts (5, 6, 7, 8, 9) and tighten to 55 ft. lbs. (75 Nm).
41. Install the wheel driveshafts to the transaxle.
42. Lubricate the transaxle cooler pipes before inserting into seals.
43. Connect the transaxle cooler pipes to the transaxle.
44. Install the transaxle cooler pipes retainer nut and tighten to 62 inch lbs. (7 Nm).
45. Use the fly wheel holding tool to prevent the crankshaft from rotating.
46. Install the torque converter to flywheel bolts and tighten to 44 ft. lbs. (60 Nm).

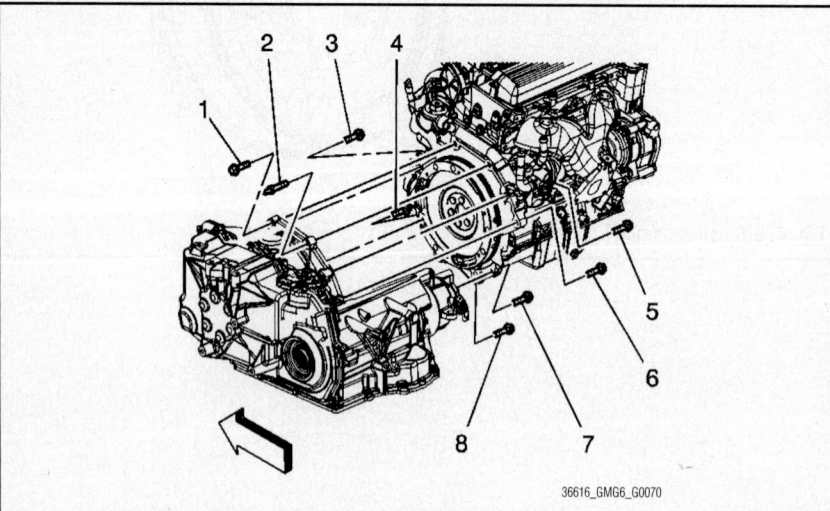
Fig. 7 Identifying transaxle to engine studs and bolts

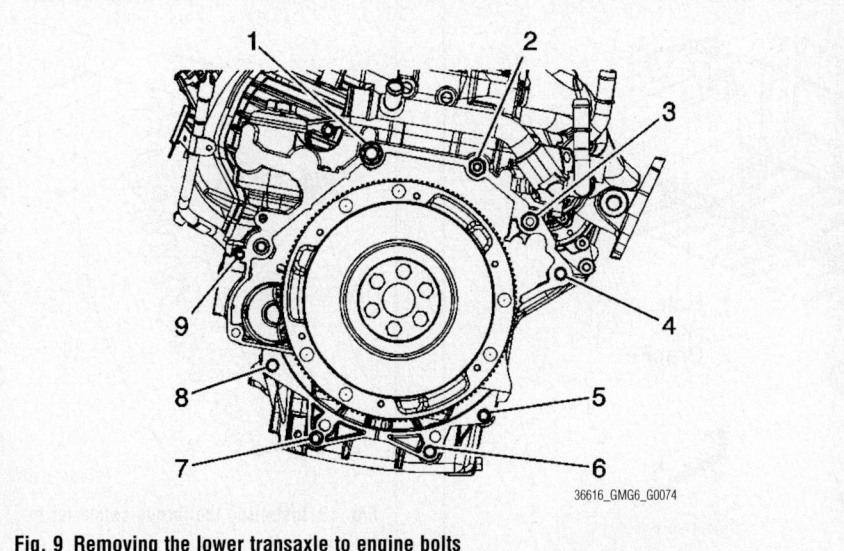

Fig. 9 Removing the lower transaxle to engine bolts

47. Install the starter.
48. Install the frame.
49. Connect the intermediate shaft to the steering gear shaft.
50. Install the new steering gear pinch bolt to the intermediate shaft and tighten to 36 ft. lbs. (49 Nm).
51. Connect the ball joints to the steering knuckles.
52. Connect the stabilizer shaft links to the stabilizer shaft.
53. Connect the wiring harness to the VSS.
54. Install the transaxle brace.
55. Install the transaxle brace bolts (1, 2) and tighten to 39 ft. lbs. (53 Nm).
56. Install the engine splash shields.
57. Install the front wheel and tire assemblies.
58. Lower the vehicle.
59. Install the left transaxle mount.
60. Install the upper transaxle to engine bolts (5, 6) and studs (1, 2) and tighten to 55 ft. lbs. (75 Nm).
61. Untie the radiator, air conditioning condenser, and fan module assembly.
62. Remove the engine support fixture.
63. Connect the transaxle wiring harness to the main transaxle electrical connector, and the PNP switch.
64. Install the shift cable bracket.
65. Install the transaxle shift control cable to the cable bracket
66. Install the retainer to the transaxle shift control cable.
67. Connect the transaxle shift control cable terminal to the transaxle manual shift lever pin.
68. Install the battery tray.
69. Connect the air cleaner outlet duct.
70. Add Automatic Transmission Fluid

(ATF) and verify the proper fluid level of the transaxle.

➡ **It is recommended that the Transmission Adaptive Pressure (TAP) information be reset. Resetting the TAP values using a scan tool will erase all learned values in all cells. As a result, the ECM, PCM, or TCM will need to relearn TAP values. Transmission performance may be affected as new TAP values are learned.**

71. Reset the TAP values.
72. Road test the vehicle.

3.5L Engine

See Figures 10 through 13.

1. Remove the air cleaner outlet duct.
2. Disconnect the negative battery cable.
3. Disconnect the transaxle wiring harness from the transaxle and the Park Neutral Position (PNP) switch.

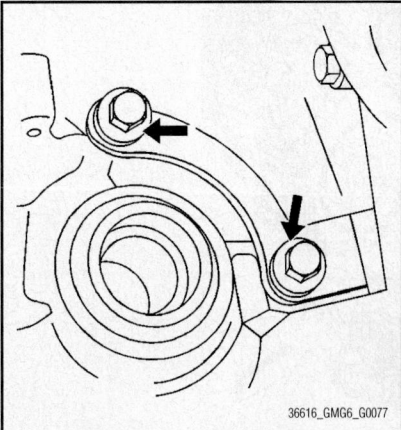

Fig. 10 Locating the transmission brace bolts

4. Remove the shift cable bracket front bolt and shift cable from the lever.
5. Remove the transmission wiring harness from the retainer on the transmission.
6. Disconnect bank 2, O2 sensor 1 electrical connector.
7. Remove the left exhaust manifold heat shield.
8. Remove the exhaust manifold heat shield.
9. Remove the front exhaust pipe nuts.
10. Remove the upper transmission to engine bolts and stud.
11. Install the engine support fixture.
12. Support the radiator and condenser from above using the condenser tabs on each side.
13. Raise the vehicle.
14. Remove the front wheels and tires.
15. Disconnect the bank 2, O2 sensor 2 electrical connector.
16. Remove the left catalytic converter to right catalytic converter nuts.
17. Remove the left catalytic converter.
18. Remove the steering gear intermediate shaft.

➡ **It is only necessary to remove the control arms from the frame if the frame is being replaced.**

19. Remove the frame.
20. Disconnect the wheel driveshafts from the transaxle.
21. Remove the 3 bolts from the transmission brace near the right axle shaft.
22. Remove the oil pan to bellhousing bolts and bracket.
23. Remove the flywheel inspection cover.
24. Remove the starter.
25. Mark the relationship of the flywheel to the torque converter for reassembly.
26. Remove the torque converter to flywheel bolts.
27. Remove the transmission oil cooler lines by removing the nut holding the bracket to the transaxle case.
28. Disconnect the Vehicle Speed Sensor (VSS) wiring harness from the sensor.
29. Disconnect the rear Heated Oxygen Sensor (HO2S) harness from the rear transmission mount.
30. Remove the remaining (rear) bolt from the shift cable bracket.
31. Remove the front transmission mount bracket from the transmission.
32. Use a transmission jack in order to support the transmission.
33. Remove the remaining bellhousing bolts (1, 3) and separate the transmission from the engine.
34. Lower the transmission with the

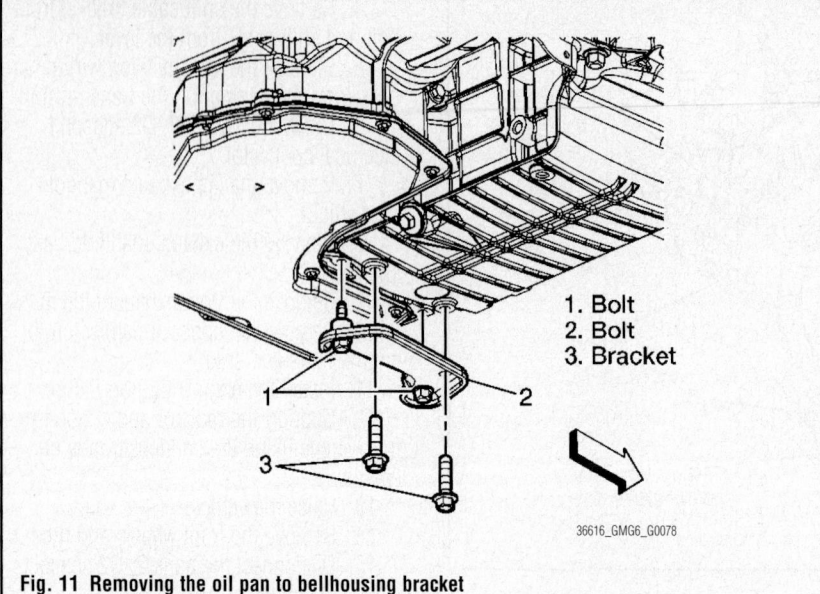

1. Bolt
2. Bolt
3. Bracket

Fig. 11 Removing the oil pan to bellhousing bracket

transmission jack far enough to remove the transmission.

35. If the transmission is being replace or installed in a holding fixture, remove the rear transmission mount bracket from the transmission.

36. If the transmission is being replaced, remove the PNP switch from the transmission.

37. If the transmission is being replaced, remove the transmission mount.

To install:

38. If the transmission is being replaced, install the following to the transmission:

- PNP switch
- Torque Converter Clutch (TCC) lock up clutch o-ring
- Transfer the transaxle from the bench fixture to the transmission jack

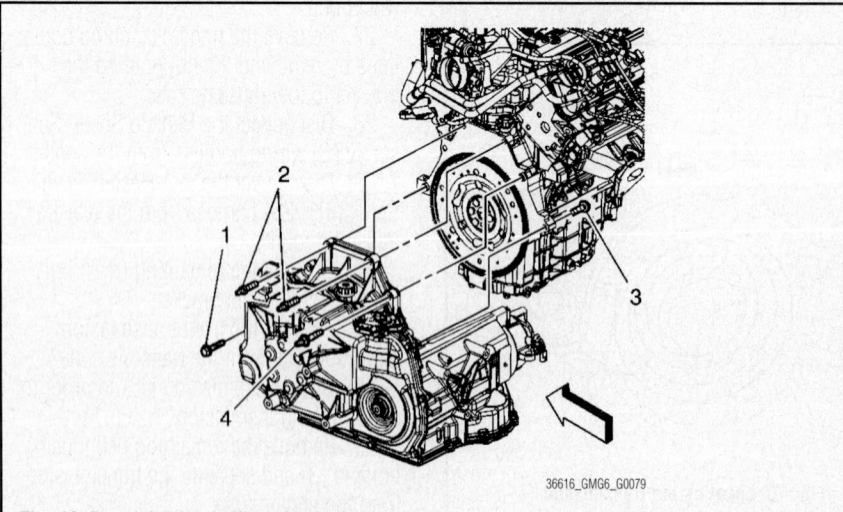

Fig. 12 Removing the bellhousing bolts

39. Install the side cover transmission mount bracket to the transmission.

40. Install the rear transmission mount bracket to the transmission.

41. Position the transaxle in the vehicle.

42. Install the lower transmission to engine bolts and tighten to 66 ft. lbs. (90 Nm).

43. Install the front transmission mount bracket to the transmission.

44. Install the wheel driveshafts to the transaxle.

45. Connect the wiring harness to the VSS.

46. Install the torque converter to flywheel bolts and tighten to 42 ft. lbs. (62 Nm).

47. Install the starter.

48. Install the flywheel inspection cover bolts and tighten to 89 inch lbs. (10 Nm).

49. Connect the transaxle oil cooler

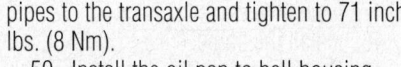

Fig. 13 Installing the torque converter to flywheel bolt

pipes to the transaxle and tighten to 71 inch lbs. (8 Nm).

50. Install the oil pan to bell housing bracket and bolts. Tighten the bolts to 53 ft. lbs. (72 Nm).

51. Install the 3 bolts to the transmission brace at the final drive area and tighten.

52. Remove the transmission jack.

53. Install the frame.

54. Install the engine splash shields.

55. Install the front wheels and tires.

56. Lower the vehicle.

57. Remove the radiator and condenser support and the engine support fixture.

58. Install the upper transmission to engine bolts and stud. Tighten the bolts/stud to 66 ft. lbs. (90 Nm).

59. Install the shift cable bracket and cable to the lever.

60. Install the catalytic converter.

61. Connect bank 2, O2 sensor 2 electrical connector.

62. Install the left exhaust manifold heat shield.

63. Install the heat shield bolts and tighten to 89 inch lbs. (10 Nm).

64. Connect the bank 2, O2 sensor 1 electrical connector.

65. Connect the electrical connectors to the PNP switch and transaxle.

66. Connect the negative battery cable.

67. Install the air cleaner outlet duct.

68. Add Automatic Transmission Fluid (ATF) and verify the proper fluid level of the transaxle.

➡️It is recommended that Transmission Adaptive Pressure (TAP) information be reset. Resetting the TAP values using a scan tool will erase all learned values in all cells. As a result, the ECM, PCM or TCM will need to relearn TAP values.

Transmission performance may be affected as new TAP values are learned.

69. Reset the TAP values.
70. Road test the vehicle.

4T65-E

See Figures 14 and 15.

1. Raise and support the vehicle.
2. Spray penetrating oil on the exposed threads of both lower ball joint bolt to facilitate their removal later in this procedure.
3. Lower the vehicle.
4. Remove the air cleaner outlet duct.
5. Disconnect the negative battery cable.
6. Disconnect the transaxle wiring harness from the transaxle and the Park Neutral Position (PNP) switch.
7. Remove the shift cable bracket and shift cable from the lever.
8. Remove the transmission wiring harness from the retainer on the transmission.
9. Remove the upper transmission to engine bolt (3) and studs (1, 4).
10. Install the engine support fixture.
11. Convertible ONLY, remove the transmission mount.
12. Support the radiator and condenser from above using the condenser tabs on each side.
13. Raise the vehicle.
14. Remove the front wheels and tires.
15. Remove the steering gear intermediate shaft.
16. Separate the control arm from the frame and the outer tie-rod end from the steering knuckles. Support the lower control arm with mechanic wire.
17. Remove the frame.
18. Remove the bolts from the transmission brace near the right axle shaft.
19. Remove the oil pan to bellhousing bracket bolts.

20. Remove the flywheel inspection cover.
21. Remove the starter.
22. Mark the relationship of the flywheel to the torque converter for reassembly.
23. Remove the torque converter to flywheel bolts.
24. Remove the transmission oil cooler lines by removing the nut holding the bracket to the transaxle case.
25. Disconnect the Vehicle Speed Sensor (VSS) wiring harness from the sensor.
26. Disconnect the rear Heated Oxygen Sensor (HO2S) harness from the bracket on the steering gear.
27. Disconnect the wheel driveshafts from the transaxle.
28. Remove the front transmission mount from the transmission.
29. Use a transmission jack in order to support the transmission.
30. Remove the remaining bellhousing bolts and studs and separate the transmission from the engine.
31. Lower the transmission with the transmission jack far enough to remove the transmission.
32. If the transmission is being replace or installed in a holding fixture, remove the rear transmission mount from the transmission.
33. Remove the PNP switch from the transmission.
34. Remove the transaxle to engine bolts (2, 5).
35. Separate the engine and the transaxle.
36. Remove the transaxle from the vehicle.
37. Remove the PNP switch.
38. Remove the shifter cable bracket.
39. Remove the lower transmission to engine stud.
40. Remove the left transmission mount bracket.

To install:
41. Install the PNP switch.
42. Install the Torque Converter Clutch (TCC) lock up clutch O-ring.

43. Install the torque converter.
44. Transfer the transaxle from the bench fixture to the transmission jack.
45. Install the left transmission mount bracket to the transmission.
46. Install the rear transmission mount to the transmission.
47. Position the transaxle in the vehicle.
48. Install the lower transmission to engine bolts (2, 5) and tighten to 66 ft. lbs. (90 Nm).
49. Install the front transmission mount to the transmission.
50. Install the wheel driveshafts to the transaxle.
51. Connect the wiring harness to the VSS.
52. Install the torque converter to flywheel bolts and tighten to 46 ft. lbs. (62 Nm).
53. Install the starter.
54. Install the flywheel inspection cover and tighten to 89 inch lbs. (10 Nm).
55. Connect the transaxle oil cooler pipes to the transaxle and tighten to 71 inch lbs. (8 Nm).
56. Install the oil pan to bellhousing bracket bolts and tighten to 53 ft. lbs. (72 Nm).
57. Install the bolts to the transmission brace at the final drive area and tighten.
58. Remove the transmission jack.
59. Install the frame.
60. Install the engine splash shields.
61. Install the front wheels and tires.
62. Lower the vehicle.
63. Convertible ONLE, install the transmission mount.
64. Remove the radiator and condenser support.
65. Remove the engine support fixture.
66. Install the upper transmission to engine bolt and studs and tighten to 66 ft. lbs. (90 Nm).
67. Install the shift cable bracket and shift cable to the lever.
68. Install the exhaust pipe upper bolts and heat shield.
69. Connect the electrical connectors to the PNP switch and transaxle.
70. Connect the negative battery cable.
71. Install the air cleaner outlet duct.

➡It is recommended that the Transmission Adaptive Pressure (TAP) information be reset. Resetting the TAP values using a scan tool will erase all learned values in all cells. As a result, the ECM, PCM or TCM will need to relearn the TAP values. Transmission performance may be affected as new TAP values are learned. Reset the TAP values.

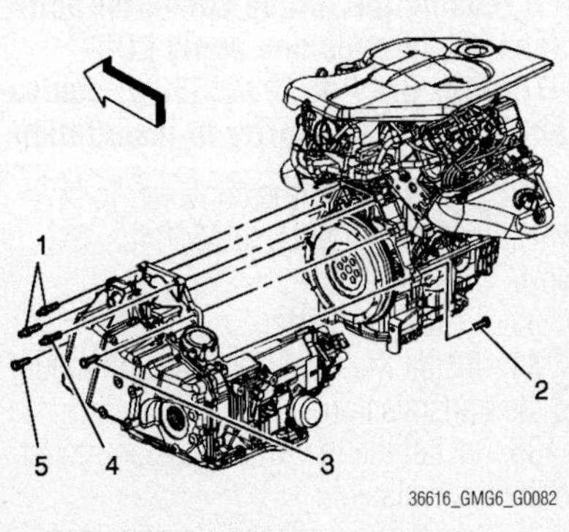

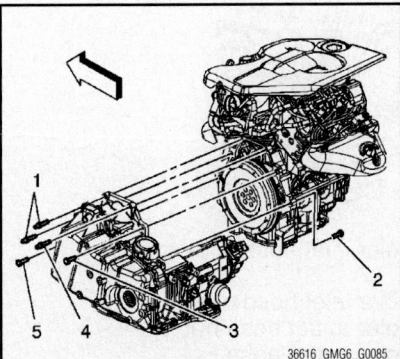

Fig. 14 Locating the transmission to engine bolts

Fig. 15 Identifying the transaxle to engine bolts

72. Add Automatic Transmission Fluid (ATF) and verify the proper fluid level of the transaxle.

73. Road test the vehicle.

6T40/6T45

See Figures 16 through 18.

1. Remove the battery tray.

2. Remove the transmission range select lever cable and bracket.

3. Drain the transmission fluid.

4. Disconnect the control valve body Transmission Control Module (TCM) electrical connector then unclip the connector from the transmission.

5. Remove the oil cooler inlet (1) and outlet (5) hoses from the retainer (2) on the control valve body cover.

6. Remove the transmission fluid cooler inlet hose nut (3) from the transmission.

7. Remove the transmission fluid cooler inlet hose (1) from the transmission.

8. Remove the transmission fluid cooler outlet hose nut (4) from the transmission.

9. Remove the transmission fluid cooler outlet hose (5) from the transmission.

10. Plug and/or cap the hose and transmission to prevent contamination.

11. Remove the upper transmission to engine bolts.

12. Remove the frame.

13. Disconnect the wheel driveshafts from the transmission.

14. Remove the intermediate driveshaft.

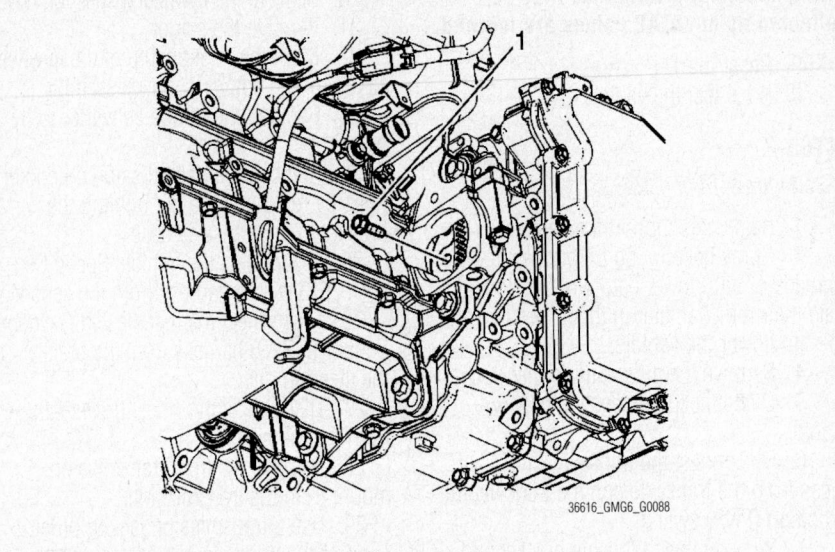

36616_GMG6_G0088

Fig. 17 Removing the torque converter to flywheel bolt

15. Remove the rear transmission mount from the transmission.

16. Remove the front transmission mount from the transmission.

17. Remove the starter.

18. Mark the relationship of the flywheel to the torque converter for reassembly.

19. Remove the torque converter to flywheel bolts.

20. Lower the vehicle.

21. Remove the 3 left transmission mount bolts from the transmission.

22. Lower the transmission side with the support fixture to allow clearance for removal.

23. Unclip the engine wiring harness from the transmission.

24. Raise the vehicle.

25. Use a transmission jack in order to support the transmission.

26. Remove the remaining transmission fasteners (1, 3, 4).

➡ **Insure the torque converter remains securely in place on the transmission input shaft while separating and removing the transmission.**

27. Separate the transmission from the engine.

28. Lower the transmission with the transmission jack far enough to remove the transmission.

To install:

29. Raise the transmission with the transmission jack and position the transmission to the engine.

30. Install the transmission bolts (1, 3, 4) and tighten to 55 ft. lbs. (75 Nm).

31. Remove the transmission jack.

➡ **If reusing the torque converter bolts, clean the threads and apply LOCTITE®242, GM P/N 12345382 or equivalent to the threads prior to installation.**

32. Install the torque converter to flywheel bolts and tighten to 46 ft. lbs. (62 Nm).

33. Install the starter.

34. Install the front transmission mount to the transmission.

35. Install the rear transmission mount to the transmission.

36. Install the intermediate driveshaft.

37. Install the wheel driveshafts to the transmission.

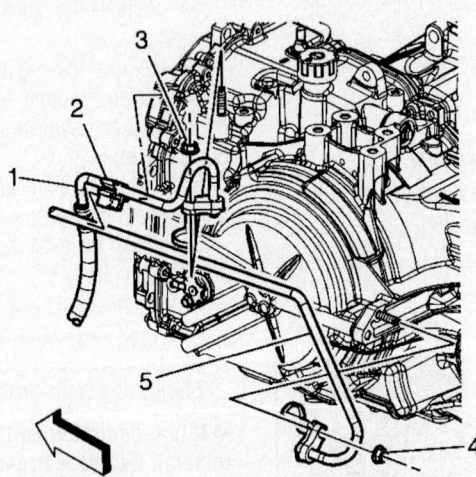

1. Transmission fluid cooler inlet hose
2. Retainer
3. Transmission fluid cooler inlet hose nut
4. Transmission fluid cooler outlet hose nut
5. Transmission fluid cooler outlet hose

36616_GMG6_G0087

Fig. 16 Removing the transmission fluid cooler hoses

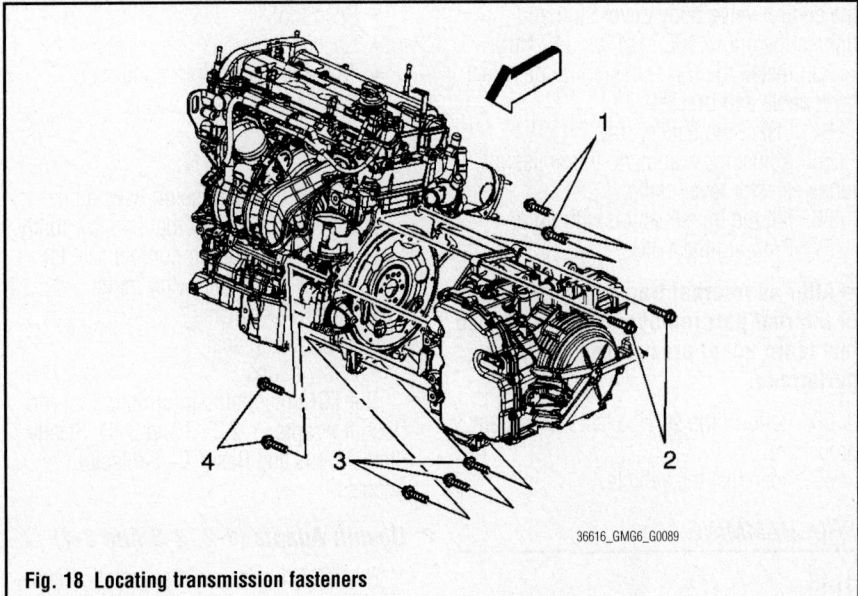

Fig. 18 Locating transmission fasteners

38. Install the frame.
39. Install the upper transmission to engine bolts and tighten to 55 ft. lbs. (75 Nm).
40. Install the transmission fluid cooler outlet hose to the transmission.
41. Install the transmission fluid cooler outlet hose retainer nut and tighten to 16 ft. lbs. (22 Nm).
42. Install the transmission fluid cooler inlet hose to the transmission.
43. Install the transmission fluid cooler inlet hose retainer nut.
44. Install the oil cooler inlet and outlet hoses to the retainer on the control valve body cover.
45. Connect the control valve body TCM electrical connector.
46. Install the transmission range select lever cable and bracket.
47. Install the battery tray.
48. Adjust the automatic transmission range selector lever cable.
49. Fill the transmission with fluid.
50. Program the TCM.

➡**After an internal transmission repair or internal part replacement the service fast learn adapt procedure should be performed.**

51. Perform the service fast learn adapt procedure.
52. Road test the vehicle.

6T70/6T75

See Figures 19 and 20.

1. Remove the battery tray.
2. Remove the transmission range select lever cable and bracket.
3. Drain the transmission fluid.

4. Remove the wire harness retainer from the control valve body cover stud.
5. Disconnect the control valve body Transmission Control Module (TCM) electrical connector
6. Remove the transmission fluid cooler pipe retainer nut.
7. Remove the transmission fluid cooler inlet hose and seal from the transmission.
8. Plug and/or cap the hose and transmission to prevent contamination.
9. Remove the transmission fluid cooler pipe retainer nut.
10. Remove the transmission fluid cooler outlet hose and seal from the transmission.
11. Plug and/or cap the hose and transmission to prevent contamination.
12. Disconnect both pipes from the retainer.

13. Install the engine support fixture.
14. Remove the rear transmission mount from the transmission.
15. Remove the front transmission mount from the transmission.
16. Remove the left transmission mount from the transmission.
17. Remove the upper transmission to engine bolts.
18. Remove the frame.
19. Disconnect the wheel driveshafts from the transmission.
20. Remove the intermediate driveshaft.
21. Remove the starter.
22. Mark the relationship of the flywheel to the torque converter for reassembly.
23. Remove the torque converter to flywheel bolts.
24. Use a transmission jack in order to support the transmission.
25. Remove the flywheel inspection cover bolts.
26. Remove the flywheel inspection cover.
27. Remove the remaining transmission bolts.

➡**Insure the torque converter remains securely in place on the transmission input shaft while separating and removing the transmission.**

28. Separate the transmission from the engine.
29. Lower the transmission with the transmission jack far enough to remove the transmission.

To install:

30. Raise the transmission with the transmission jack and position the transmission to the engine.
31. Install the transmission bolts and tighten to 55 ft. lbs. (75 Nm).

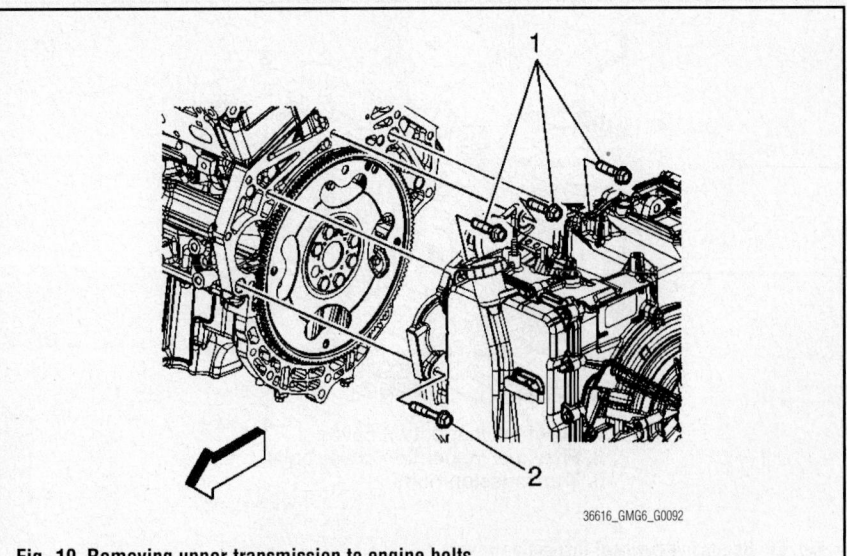

Fig. 19 Removing upper transmission to engine bolts

32. Install the flywheel inspection cover.
33. Install the flywheel inspection cover bolts and tighten to 55 ft. lbs. (75 Nm).
34. Remove the transmission jack.

➡**If reusing the torque converter bolts, clean the threads and apply LOC-TITE®242, GM P/N 12345382 or equivalent to the threads prior to installation.**

35. Install the torque converter to flywheel bolts and tighten to 46 ft. lbs. (62 Nm).
36. Install the starter.
37. Install the front transmission mount to the transmission.
38. Install the rear transmission mount to the transmission.
39. Install the left transmission mount to the transmission.
40. Install the transmission brace.
41. Install the transmission brace bolts and tighten to 37 ft. lbs. (50 Nm).
42. Install the intermediated driveshaft.
43. Install the wheel driveshafts to the transmission.
44. Install the frame.
45. Install the upper transmission to engine bolt and tighten to 55 ft. lbs. (75 Nm).
46. Remove the engine support fixture.
47. Install the transmission fluid cooler outlet hose and seal to the transmission.
48. Install the transmission fluid cooler pipe retainer nut and tighten to 16 ft. lbs. (22 Nm).
49. Install the transmission fluid cooler inlet hose and seal to the transmission.
50. Install the transmission fluid cooler pipe retainer nut and tighten to 16 ft. lbs. (22 Nm).
51. Connect the control valve body TCM electrical connector.
52. Install the wire harness retainer to

the control valve body cover stud and tighten the nut to 106 inch lbs. (12 Nm).
53. Install the transmission range select lever cable and bracket.
54. Install the battery tray.
55. Adjust the automatic transmission range selector lever cable.
56. Fill the transmission with fluid.
57. Program the TCM.

➡**After an internal transmission repair or internal part replacement the service fast learn adapt procedure should be performed.**

58. Perform the service fast learn adapt procedure.
59. Road test the vehicle.

PROGRAMMING

4T45

The 4T45 automatic transmission uses a line pressure control system, which has the ability to continuously adapt the system line pressure. This compensates for normal wear of the clutch fiber plates, seals and the springs.

The Transmission Control Module (TCM) maintains the Upshift Adapt parameters for the transmission. The TCM monitors the Input Speed Sensor (ISS) and the Output Speed Sensor (OSS) during commanded shifts in order to determine if a shift is occurring too fast or too slow. The TCM adjusts the signal from the Transmission Pressure Control (PC) solenoid in order to maintain a set shift feel.

Transmission adapts must be set again when the transmission is overhauled or replaced. In order to set the transmission adapts again, select the following:

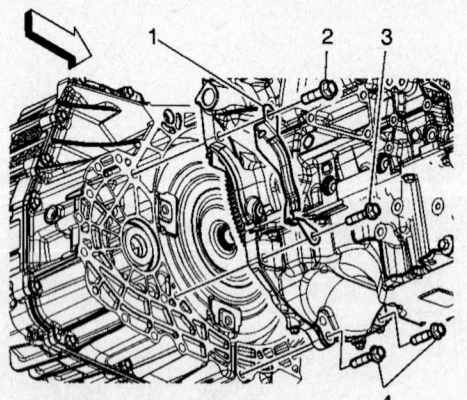

1. Flywheel inspection cover
2. Flywheel inspection cover bolts
3. Transmission bolts

36616_GMG6_G0093

Fig. 20 Removing flywheel inspection cover

- Scan tool
- Special functions
- Transmission output controls
- Reset transmission adapts

4T65-E

The 4T65-E transmission uses a line pressure control system that has the ability to adapt line pressure to compensate for normal wear of the following parts:
- Clutch fiber plates
- Springs and seal
- Apply bands

The TCM maintains information for the Upshift Adapts (1-2, 2-3 and 3-4), Steady State Adapts and Reset Transmission Adapts.

Upshift Adapts (1-2, 2-3 And 3-4)

The TCM monitors the automatic transmission Input Speed Sensor (ISS) and the Vehicle Speed Sensor (VSS) in order to determine when an upshift has started and completed. The TCM measures the time for the upshift. If the upshift time is longer than a calibrated value, then the TCM will adjust the current to the Pressure Control (PC) solenoid valve to increase the line pressure for the next shift in the same torque range. If the upshift time is shorter than the calibrated value, then the TCM will decrease the line pressure for the next shift in the same torque range.

Steady State Adapts

The TCM monitors the ISS and the VSS after an upshift in order to determine the amount of clutch slippage. If excessive slippage is detected, then the TCM will adjust the current to the PC solenoid valve in order to increase the line pressure to maintain the proper gear ratio for the commanded gear.

The TAP information is divided into 13 units, called cells. The cells are numbered 4 through 16. Each cell represents a given torque range. TAP cell 4 is the lowest adaptable torque range and TAP cell 16 is the highest adaptable torque range. It is normal for TAP cell values to display zero or negative numbers. This indicates that the TCM has adjusted line pressure at or below the calibrated base pressure.

Reset Transmission Adapts

Updating TAP information is a learning function of the TCM designed to maintain acceptable shift times. It is not recommended that TAP information be reset unless one of the following repairs has been made:
- Transmission overhaul or replacement
- Repair or replacement of an apply or

release component—clutch, band, piston, servo

• Repair or replacement of a component or assembly which directly affects line pressure

Resetting the TAP values using a scan tool will erase all learned values in all cells. As a result, the TCM will need to relearn TAP values. Transmission performance may be affected as new TAPs are learned. The TCM must also relearn TAP values when the TCM or the transmission is replaced.

6T40/6T45

TCM

1. The Transmission Control Module (TCM) must be programmed with the proper software/calibrations. Ensure that the following conditions exist in order to prepare for TCM programming:

• Battery is fully charged
• Ignition switch is in the RUN position
• Techline equipment cable connection at the Data Link Connector (DLC) is secure

2. Program the TCM using the latest software matching the vehicle. Refer to the up to date Techline equipment user instructions.

3. If the TCM fails to program:
   a. Ensure that the TCM connection is OK.
   b. Inspect the Techline equipment for the latest software version.
   c. Attempt to program the TCM. If the TCM still cannot be programmed properly, replace the TCM.

Service Fast Learn Adapts

Service Fast Learn Adapts is a procedure for 6 speed automatic transmissions in which a series of tests are run to allow the Transmission Control Module (TCM) to learn individual clutch characteristics. Once the clutch data is learned, Service Fast Learn Adapts translates it into the adaptive data cells, which the TCM uses for clutch control during shifts. The scan tool provides initiation of the Service Fast Learn Adapts procedure. This procedure is to be used following transmission repair.

The Service Fast Learn Adapts procedure must be performed when one of the following repairs have been made to the vehicle. Failure to perform the procedure after one of the following repairs may result in poor transmission performance, as well as transmission DTCs being set:

• Transmission internal service/overhaul
• Valve body repair or replacement

• Control solenoid (w/body and TCM) valve assembly replacement
• TCM software/calibration update
• Any service in response to a shift quality concern

➡Ensure the following conditions are met before performing the Service Fast Learn Adapts procedure:

• Drive wheels are blocked
• Parking brake is applied
• Service brake is applied
• Zero percent throttle and no external engine RPM control
• Transmission Fluid Temperature (TFT) is between 158-212°F (70-100°C)
• Transmission gear selector has been cycled from Park to Reverse 3 times in order to purge air from the Reverse clutches

1. Use the scan tool to navigate to Service Fast Lear Adapts selecting the following commands:
   a. F1: Transmission Control Module
   b. F5: Module Setup
   c. F0: Fast Learn Adapts Process

➡If at any time during the procedure, required conditions are not met, Service Fast Learn Adapts may abort and the process may need to be started again from the beginning.

2. Use the scan tool to perform the Service Fast Learn Adapts procedure. As the procedure is being performed, the scan tool data display will provide operator instructions. Follow the scan tool instructions as required.

3. Once the procedure is complete, shut OFF the engine and power down the TCM. You will lose communication to the scan tool.

4. Restart the engine. This will complete the Service Fast Learn Adapts procedure.

➡When the Service Fast Learn Adapts procedure is completed, the transmission will remain in a neutral state.

FRONT HALFSHAFTS (DRIVESHAFT)

REMOVAL & INSTALLATION
See Figures 21 through 23.

✳✳ WARNING

To prevent personal injury and/or component damage, do not allow the weight of the vehicle to load the front wheels, or attempt to operate the

vehicle, when the wheel driveshaft(s) or wheel driveshaft nut(s) are removed. To do so may cause the inner bearing race to separate, resulting in damage to brake and suspension components and loss of vehicle control.

✳✳ CAUTION

Wheel driveshaft boots, seals and clamps should be protected from sharp objects any time service is performed on or near the wheel driveshaft(s). Damage to the boot(s), the seal(s) or the clamp(s) may cause lubricant to leak from the joint and lead to increased noise and possible failure of the wheel driveshaft.

1. Raise and suitably support the vehicle.

2. Remove the wheel and the tire.

3. Insert a brass drift or punch between the brake rotor cooling fins and the brake caliper mounting bracket.

4. Using the appropriate size socket and breaker bar, loosen the wheel driveshaft nut.

➡DO NOT reuse the wheel driveshaft nut. Discard the nut and replace with a NEW one.

5. Remove the wheel driveshaft nut from the wheel driveshaft

6. Using the hub spindle remover, separate the brake rotor and wheel bearing/hub assembly.

7. Remove the outer tie rod assembly from the steering knuckle.

8. Remove the ball joint from the steering knuckle.

9. Using the Slide Hammer , the Axle Shaft Remove Extension, and the Axle Shaft Remover, remove the wheel driveshaft from the vehicle.

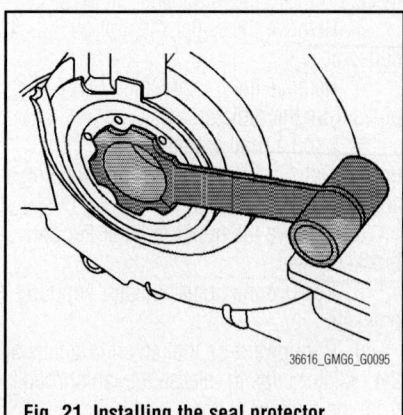

36616_GMG6_G0095

Fig. 21 Installing the seal protector

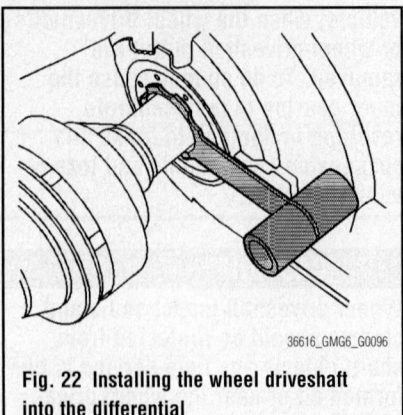

Fig. 22 Installing the wheel driveshaft into the differential

To install:

✳✳ CAUTION

The Seal Protector must be installed into the differential output shaft seal prior to removing and installing the wheel driveshaft. Failure to install the seal protector as indicated may cause the splines of the wheel driveshaft to cut the differential output seal.

10. Install the Seal Protector into the differential output shaft seal.

➡ **In order to prevent lubricant leaks, use care when installing the wheel driveshaft to the differential. Do not damage the oil seal. Replace the oil seal if it becomes nicked, distorted, or otherwise damaged.**

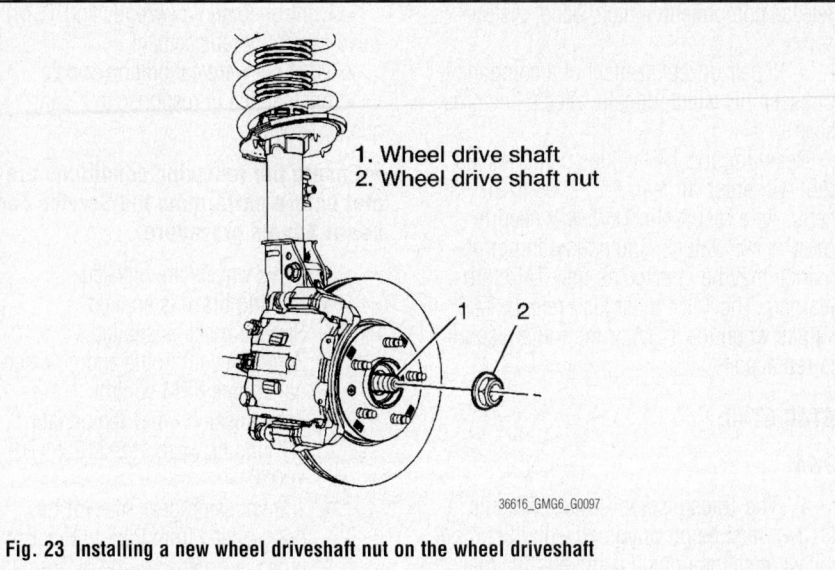

1. Wheel drive shaft
2. Wheel drive shaft nut

Fig. 23 Installing a new wheel driveshaft nut on the wheel driveshaft

11. Carefully install the wheel driveshaft into the differential until the splines are past the seal protector.

12. Remove the seal protector from the differential output shaft seal.

13. Install the wheel driveshaft into the differential until the retaining ring is fully seated.

14. Confirm that the front wheel driveshaft retaining ring is properly seated by holding the inner housing and pull the inner housing outward.

15. Install the front wheel driveshaft into the front wheel bearing/hub.

16. Install the ball joint to the steering knuckle.

17. Install the outer tie rod assembly to the steering knuckle.

18. Install the NEW wheel driveshaft nut on the wheel driveshaft.

19. Insert a drift or punch into the cooling fin of the brake rotor caliper and against the brake caliper mounting bracket.

20. Using a torque wrench and the appropriate size socket, tighten the wheel driveshaft nut to 159 ft. lbs. (215 Nm).

21. Install the wheel and tire.

22. Lower the vehicle.

23. Inspect the transaxle fluid level.

ENGINE COOLING

ENGINE FAN

REMOVAL & INSTALLATION

See Figures 24 through 26.

1. Partially drain the cooling system.
2. Remove the air cleaner air duct.
3. Remove the upper radiator air deflector.
4. Remove the transmission oil cooler pipes from the radiator.
5. Loop a rope around each of the upper 2 tabs of the condenser and tie a rope around the upper tie bar.
6. Remove the upper radiator support bracket bolts.
7. Remove the upper radiator support brackets.
8. Pry upward on the fan shroud tabs at the radiator clips to release the fan shroud from the radiator.

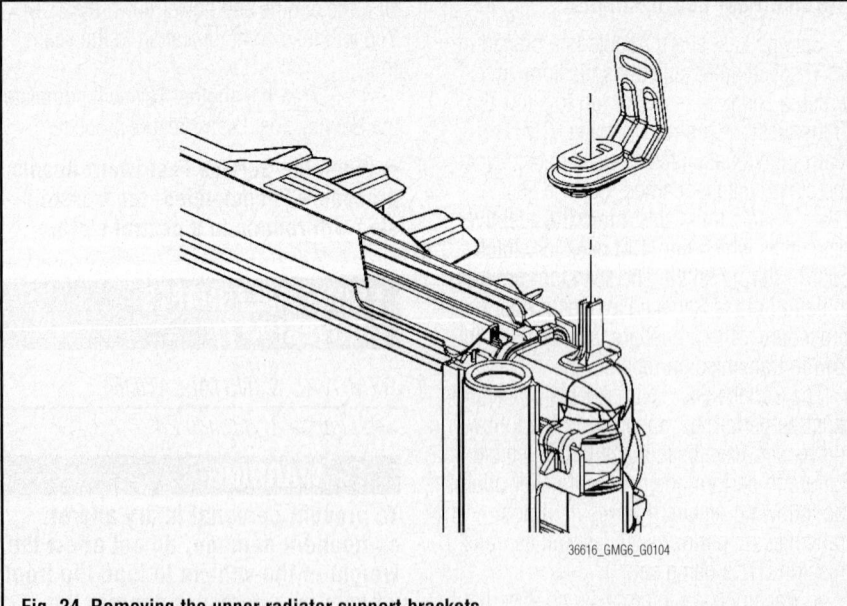

Fig. 24 Removing the upper radiator support brackets

9. Remove the lower radiator air deflector.

10. Lower the vehicle.

11. Remove the radiator inlet hose from the radiator.

12. Remove the radiator outlet hose from the radiator.

13. Disconnect the cooling fan wire harness connectors.

14. Remove the A/C compressor hose assembly.

15. Remove the lower radiator support bracket bolts.

16. Remove the lower radiator support brackets.

17. Remove the transmission oil cooler pipe clip from the fan shroud.

18. Remove the fan shroud assembly.

To install:

19. Install the fan shroud assembly.

20. Install the transmission oil cooler pipes to the radiator.

21. Install the transmission oil cooler pipe clip to the fan shroud.

22. Install the lower radiator support brackets.

23. Install the lower radiator support

bracket bolts and tighten to 44 ft. lbs. (60 Nm).

24. Install the cooling fan wire harness connectors.

25. Install the radiator outlet hose to the radiator.

26. Install the lower radiator air deflector.

27. Lower the vehicle.

28. Snap fan shroud tabs into the radiator clips.

29. Remove the rope attached to the condenser and upper tie bar.

30. Install the upper radiator support brackets.

31. Install the upper radiator support bracket bolts and tighten to 89 inch lbs. (10 Nm).

32. Install the radiator inlet hose to the radiator.

33. Install the A/C compressor hose assembly.

34. Install the upper radiator air deflector.

35. Install the air cleaner air duct.

36. Fill the cooling system.

37. Inspect the transmission fluid level.

RADIATOR

REMOVAL & INSTALLATION

2.4L Engine

See Figures 27 and 28.

1. Remove the cooling fan and shroud assembly.

2. Remove and discard the condenser mounting bolts.

3. Push upward on the condenser and downward on the radiator to unsnap the condenser mounting tabs from the radiator clips.

4. Remove and discard the condenser mounting nuts from the radiator.

5. Remove the radiator from the vehicle.

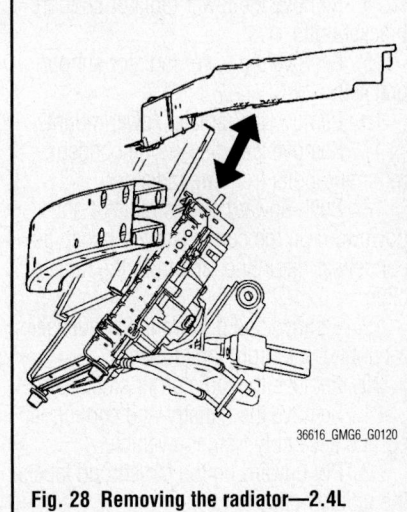

36616_GMG6_G0120

Fig. 28 Removing the radiator—2.4L engine

To install:

6. Install the radiator to the vehicle.

7. Push upward on the radiator and downward on the condenser to snap the condenser mounting tabs into the radiator clips.

8. Install new condenser mounting nut to the radiator and tighten the nut to 53 inch lbs. (6 Nm).

9. Install the cooling fan and shroud assembly.

3.5L & 3.9L Engines

See Figures 29 and 30.

1. Drain the coolant.

2. Loop a rope around each of the upper 2 tabs of the condenser and tie the rope around the upper tie bar.

3. Remove the upper radiator support brackets.

4. Reposition the radiator inlet hose clamp at the radiator using hose clamp pliers.

5. Remove the radiator inlet hose from the radiator.

6. Remove the front air dam.

7. Remove the right engine splash shield retainers.

8. Remove the right engine splash shield.

9. Remove the left engine splash shield retainers.

10. Remove the left engine splash shield.

11. Reposition the radiator outlet hose clamp at the radiator using the hose clamp pliers.

12. Remove the radiator outlet hose from the radiator.

13. Remove the transmission oil cooler pipes from the transmission.

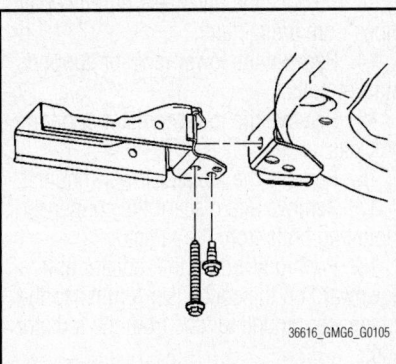

36616_GMG6_G0105

Fig. 25 Removing the lower radiator support brackets

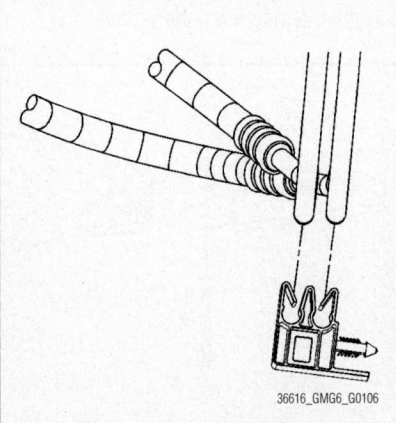

36616_GMG6_G0106

Fig. 26 Removing the transmission oil cooler pipe clip from the fan shroud

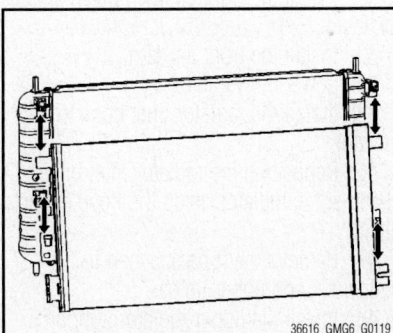

36616_GMG6_G0119

Fig. 27 Removing the condenser mounting bolts—2.4L engine

14. Remove the lower radiator support bracket bolts.

15. Remove the lower radiator support brackets.

16. Remove the radiator lower mounts.

17. Remove and discard the condenser mounting bolts from the radiator.

18. Push upward on the radiator and downward on the condenser to unsnap the condenser mounting tabs from the radiator clips.

19. Remove and discard the condenser mounting nuts from the radiator.

20. Remove the radiator air side seals.

21. Remove the radiator and cooling fan shroud assembly from the vehicle.

22. Pry upward on the fan shroud tabs at the radiator clips.

23. Remove the cooling fan and shroud assembly from the radiator.

To install:

24. Install the cooling fan and shroud assembly to the radiator.

25. Snap the fan shroud tabs into the radiator clips.

26. Install the radiator and cooling fan shroud assembly to the vehicle.

27. Install the radiator air side seals onto the condenser mounting tabs on the radiator.

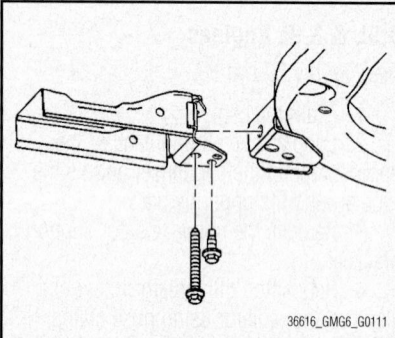

Fig. 29 Removing the lower radiator support brackets—3.5L and 3.9L engines

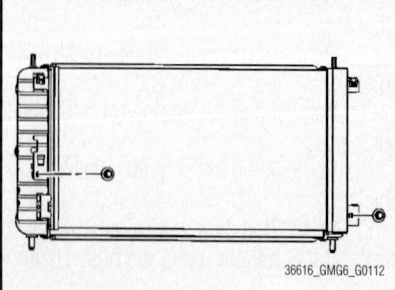

Fig. 30 Removing the condenser mounting bolts from the radiator—3.5L and 3.9L engines

❄❄ CAUTION

The bolt retaining the condenser to the radiator end tank is a special length and should be the ONLY bolt used upon reinstallation. The use of a longer bolt will damage the radiator end tank.

28. Install the condenser mounting nuts to the radiator.

29. Insert the condenser mounting tabs into the radiator clips.

30. Install the condenser to radiator bolts and tighten to 53 inch lbs. (6 Nm).

31. Bend the radiator air side seals and insert the seals into the channel of the intake air splash shields.

32. The radiator air side seals must be in the proper position for proper air flow.

➡Replace the radiator lower mounts as a pair or vibration may result.

33. Install the radiator lower mounts.

34. Install the lower radiator support brackets.

35. Install the lower radiator support bracket bolts and tighten to 44 ft. lbs. (60 Nm).

36. Install the transmission oil cooler pipes to the transmission.

37. Install the radiator outlet hose to the radiator.

38. Reposition the radiator outlet hose clamp at the radiator using the hose clamp pliers.

➡Engine splash shields must be properly installed or reduced A/C and engine cooling system performance could occur.

39. Install the left engine splash shield.

40. Install the left engine splash shield retainers.

41. Install the right engine splash shield.

42. Install the right engine splash shield retainers.

43. Install the front air dam.

44. Lower the vehicle.

45. Install the radiator inlet hose to the radiator.

46. Reposition the radiator inlet hose clamp at the radiator using the hose clamp pliers.

47. Remove the rope attached to the condenser and upper tie bar.

48. Install the upper radiator support brackets.

49. Fill the coolant.

50. Inspect the transmission fluid level.

3.6L Engine

See Figures 31 and 32.

1. Drain the coolant.

2. Loop a rope around each of the upper 2 tabs of the condenser and tie the rope around the upper tie bar.

3. Remove the upper radiator support brackets.

4. Reposition the radiator inlet hose clamp at the radiator using hose clamp pliers.

5. Remove the radiator inlet hose from the radiator.

6. Remove the front air dam.

7. Remove the right engine splash shield retainers.

8. Remove the right engine splash shield.

9. Remove the left engine splash shield retainers.

10. Remove the left engine splash shield.

11. Reposition the radiator outlet hose clamp at the radiator using the hose clamp pliers.

12. Remove the radiator outlet hose from the radiator.

13. Remove the transmission oil cooler pipes from the radiator.

14. Remove the lower radiator support bracket bolts.

15. Remove the lower radiator support brackets.

16. Remove the radiator lower mounts.

17. Remove and discard the condenser mounting bolts from the radiator.

18. Push upward on the radiator and downward on the condenser to unsnap the condenser mounting tabs from the radiator clips.

19. Remove and discard the condenser mounting nuts from the radiator.

20. Remove the radiator air side seals.

21. Remove the radiator and cooling fan shroud assembly from the vehicle.

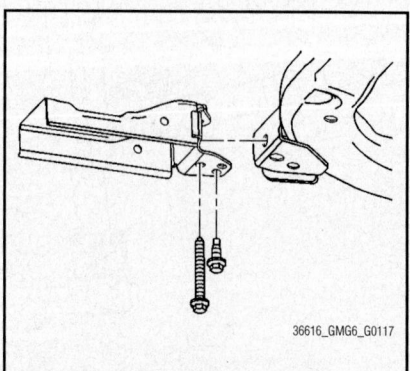

Fig. 31 Removing the lower radiator support brackets— 3.6L engine

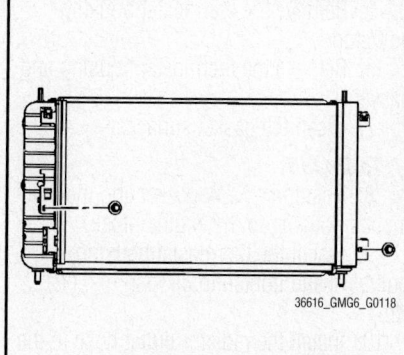

Fig. 32 Removing the condenser mounting bolts from the radiator— 3.6L engine

22. Pry upward on the fan shroud tabs at the radiator clips.

23. Remove the cooling fan and shroud assembly from the radiator.

To install:

24. Install the cooling fan and shroud assembly to the radiator.

25. Snap the fan shroud tabs into the radiator clips.

26. Install the radiator and cooling fan shroud assembly to the vehicle.

27. Install the radiator air side seals onto the condenser mounting tabs on the radiator.

✷✷ CAUTION

The bolt retaining the condenser to the radiator end tank is a special length and should be the ONLY bolt used upon reinstallation. The use of a longer bolt will damage the radiator end tank.

28. Install the condenser mounting nuts to the radiator.

29. Insert the condenser mounting tabs into the radiator clips.

30. Install the condenser to radiator bolts and tighten to 53 inch lbs. (6 Nm).

31. Bend the radiator air side seals and insert the seals into the channel of the intake air splash shields.

32. The radiator air side seals must be in the proper position for proper air flow.

➡**Replace the radiator lower mounts as a pair or vibration may result.**

33. Install the radiator lower mounts.

34. Install the lower radiator support brackets.

35. Install the lower radiator support bracket bolts and tighten to 44 ft. lbs. (60 Nm).

36. Install the transmission oil cooler pipes to the radiator.

37. Install the radiator outlet hose to the radiator.

38. Reposition the radiator outlet hose clamp at the radiator using the hose clamp pliers.

➡**Engine splash shields must be properly installed or reduced A/C and engine cooling system performance could occur.**

39. Install the left engine splash shield.

40. Install the left engine splash shield retainers.

41. Install the right engine splash shield.

42. Install the right engine splash shield retainers.

43. Install the front air dam.

44. Lower the vehicle.

45. Install the radiator inlet hose to the radiator.

46. Reposition the radiator inlet hose clamp at the radiator using the hose clamp pliers.

47. Remove the rope attached to the condenser and upper tie bar.

48. Install the upper radiator support brackets.

49. Fill the coolant.

50. Inspect the transmission fluid level.

THERMOSTAT

REMOVAL & INSTALLATION

2.4L Engine

See Figures 33 and 34.

1. Drain the cooling system.

➡**A drain has been provided at the bottom of the water pump for engine block coolant drainage.**

2. Remove the water pump drain plug and drain the coolant from the engine block at the water pump drain.

3. Lower the vehicle.

4. Disconnect the Engine Coolant Temperature (ECT) sensor electrical connector.

5. Disconnect the Heated Oxygen Sensor (HO2S) electrical connector clip from the bracket.

6. Remove the ECT sensor.

7. Remove the surge tank outlet hose from the thermostat housing.

8. Reposition the radiator outlet hose clamp at the thermostat housing.

9. Remove the radiator outlet hose from the thermostat housing.

10. Remove the exhaust heat shield bolts.

11. Remove the exhaust heat shield.

12. Reposition the heater inlet and outlet hose clamps at the thermostat housing pipes.

13. Disconnect the heater inlet and outlet hoses from the thermostat housing pipes.

14. Remove the thermostat housing bolts.

➡**Twist the water transfer pipe while pulling in order to remove it from the water pump.**

15. Remove the thermostat housing from the vehicle.

16. Remove the water transfer pipe from the thermostat housing, if necessary.

17. Remove and discard the water transfer pipe o-ring seals, if necessary.

18. Remove the thermostat housing cover bolts and cover, if necessary.

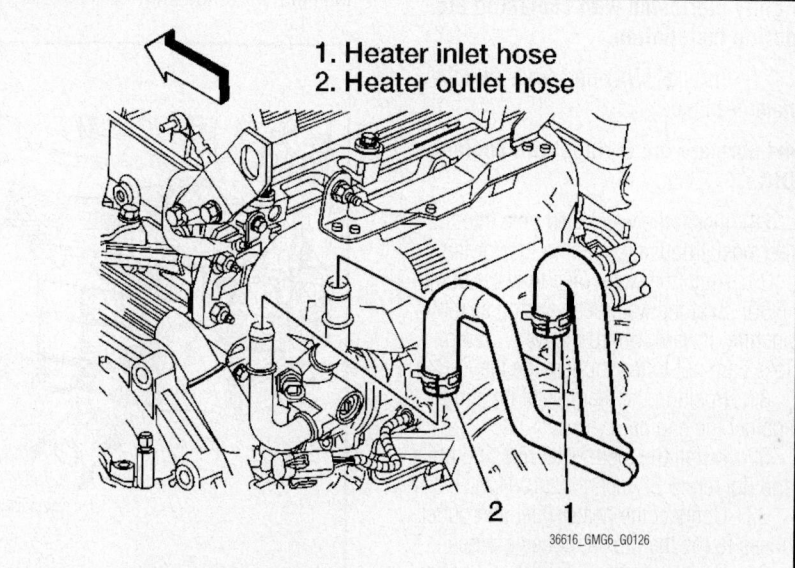

1. Heater inlet hose
2. Heater outlet hose

Fig. 33 Disconnecting the heater inlet and outlet hoses from the thermostat housing— 2.4L engine

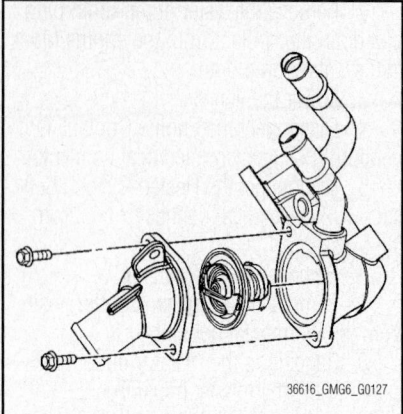

Fig. 34 Removing the thermostat—2.4L engine

19. Remove the thermostat, if necessary.

20. Remove and discard the thermostat housing O-ring seal, if necessary.

21. Remove all debris and thread sealant from the engine coolant temperature sensor and bolt holes if the housing is being re-used.

To install:

22. Install a NEW thermostat housing cover O-ring seal into the recess groove.

23. Install the thermostat, if necessary.

24. Install the thermostat housing cover bolts, if necessary. Tighten to 89 inch lbs. (10 Nm).

25. Install a NEW thermostat housing to engine O-ring seal onto the thermostat housing.

26. Load the thermostat housing assembly into position while the vehicle is lowered.

➡ **The water feed pipe seals can be lightly lubricated with coolant to aid during installation.**

27. Install NEW O-ring seals onto the water feed pipe.

➡ **Lubricate the O-rings with coolant ONLY.**

28. Install the water feed pipe into the thermostat housing aligning locator tab.

29. Align the water pipe to water pump.

30. Seat the water feed O-ring seal by pushing inward toward the water pump. Take care not to tear or damage the O-ring.

31. Position the thermostat housing against the engine.

32. Install the thermostat housing bolts and tighten to 89 inch lbs. (10 Nm).

33. Connect the heater inlet and outlet hoses to the thermostat housing pipes.

34. Position the heater inlet and outlet hose clamps at the thermostat housing pipes.

35. Install the exhaust heat shield.

36. Install the exhaust heat shield bolts and tighten to 17 ft. lbs. (23 Nm).

37. Install the radiator outlet hose to the thermostat housing.

38. Position the radiator outlet hose clamp at the thermostat housing.

39. Install the radiator outlet hose to the surge tank.

40. Position the radiator outlet hose clamp at the surge tank.

41. Apply sealant to the threads of the ECT sensor.

42. Install the ECT sensor and tighten to 15 ft. lbs. (20 Nm).

43. Connect the ECT sensor electrical connector.

44. Connect the HO2S electrical connector clip to the bracket.

45. Apply sealant GM P/N 12378521 or equivalent to the water pump drain plug.

46. Install the water pump drain plug and tighten to 15 ft. lbs. (20 Nm).

➡ **The vehicle must be level when filling the cooling system.**

47. Verify the drain valves at the radiator and water pump are closed.

48. Fill the cooling system.

49. Verify the repair and inspect for any leaks.

3.5L & 3.9L Engines

See Figure 35.

1. Drain the cooling system.

2. Remove the air cleaner outlet duct.

3. Reposition the radiator outlet hose clamp at the thermostat housing.

4. Remove the radiator outlet hose from the thermostat housing.

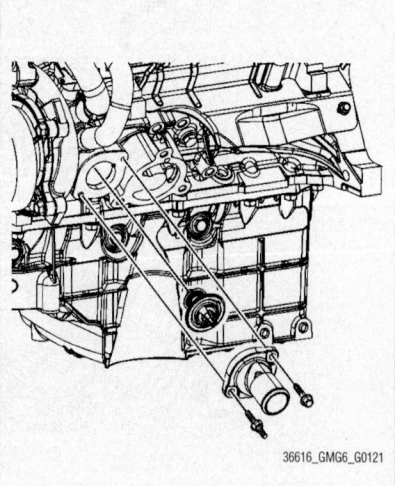

Fig. 35 Removing the thermostat—3.5L and 3.9L engines

5. Remove the thermostat housing bolt/stud.

6. Remove the thermostat housing and gasket.

7. Clean the gasket surfaces.

To install:

8. Position a NEW gasket and the thermostat housing to the engine block.

9. Install the thermostat housing bolt/stud and tighten to 89 inch lbs. (10 Nm).

10. Install the radiator outlet hose to the thermostat housing.

11. Position the radiator outlet hose clamp at the thermostat housing.

12. Install the air cleaner outlet duct.

13. Fill the cooling system.

14. Inspect the system for leaks.

WATER PUMP

REMOVAL & INSTALLATION

2.4L Engine

See Figures 36 through 38.

1. Remove the thermostat housing.

2. Remove the coolant heater.

3. Remove the water pump access plate from the front cover.

➡ **The water pump holding tool supports the sprocket and chain during water pump service. The tool must be used or the balance shaft must be re-timed.**

4. Install the water pump holding tool into position.

5. Tighten the bolts on the water pump holding tool into the threads on the water pump sprocket.

6. Install the access cover bolts that were removed earlier to secure the water pump holding tool to the front cover assembly.

7. Remove the 3 inner water pump sprocket to water pump bolts through the holes in the water pump holding tool.

➡ **Be sure to remove both water pump bolts from the front of the engine block.**

8. Remove the 2 water pump bolts.

9. Remove the 2 rear water pump bolts.

10. Remove the engine wiring harness clip nut from the water pump stud.

11. Remove the engine wiring harness clip from the stud.

12. Remove the water pump.

To install:

13. Apply sealant GM P/N 12378521 or equivalent to the water pump drain plug.

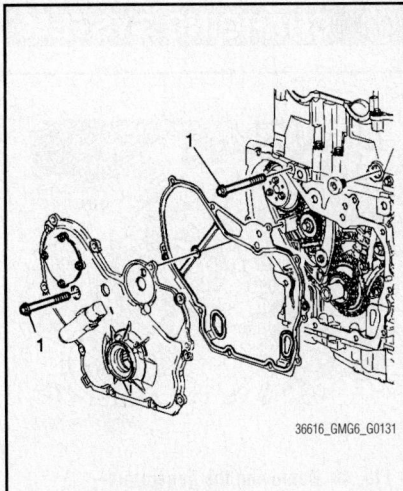

**Fig. 36 Identifying water pump bolts (1)—
2.4L engine**

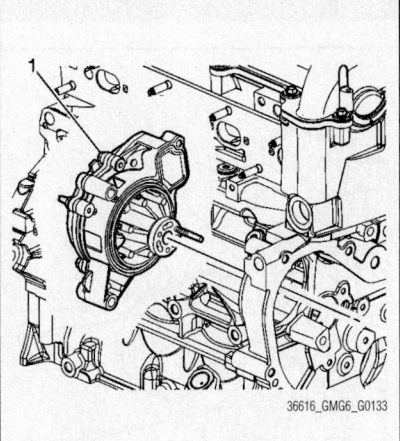

**Fig. 38 Removing the water pump (1)—
2.4L engine**

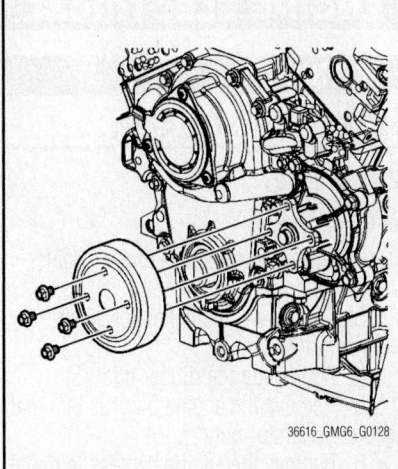

**Fig. 39 Removing the water pump
pulley—3.5L and 3.9L engines**

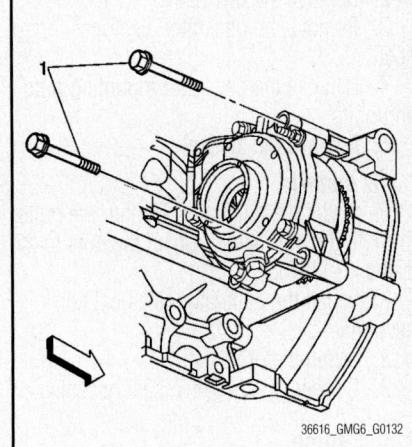

**Fig. 37 Removing the 2 rear water pump
bolts (1)—2.4L engine**

14. Install the water pump drain plug
and tighten to 15 ft. lbs. (20 Nm).

➡**A guide pin can be created to aid in
the water pump alignment. Use a
M6x6mm stud. Thread the pin into the
water pump sprocket.**

15. Using the dial indicator mounting
post, or a guide pin align the pin with the
water pump holding tool.
16. Position the water pump against the

engine block and hand tighten the water
pump bolts.
17. Install the inner water pump
sprocket bolts. After 2 are snug, remove
the guide pin and install the 3rd bolt.
Tighten the water pump bolts to 18 ft. lbs.
(25 Nm).
18. Tighten the water pump sprocket
bolts last. Tighten the water pump sprocket
bolts to 89 inch lbs. (10 Nm).
19. Remove the water pump holding
tool.
20. Install the coolant heater.
21. Install the water pump access plate
and bolts. Tighten the bolts to 89 inch lbs.
(10 Nm).
22. Install the thermostat housing.

3.5L & 3.9L Engines

See Figures 39 and 40.

1. Drain the cooling system.
2. Loosen the water pump pulley
bolts.
3. Remove the drive belt.
4. Remove the water pump pulley bolts
and pulley.
5. Remove the water pump bolts.
6. Remove the water pump and
gasket.
7. Clean the water pump mating
surfaces.

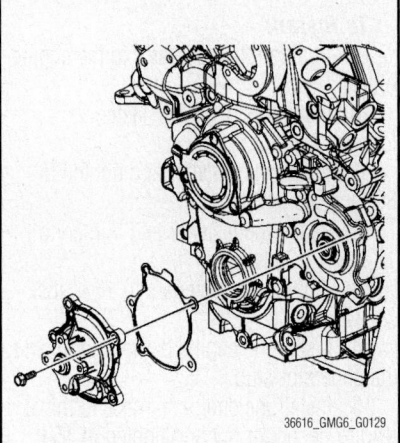

**Fig. 40 Removing the water pump—
3.5L and 3.9L engines**

To install:

8. Position a NEW water pump gasket
and the water pump to the engine front cover.
9. Install the water pump bolts and
tighten to 18 ft. lbs. (25 Nm).
10. Install the water pump pulley and bolts.
11. Install the drive belt.
12. Tighten the water pump pulley bolts
and tighten to 18 ft. lbs. (25 Nm).
13. Fill the cooling system.
14. Inspect for leaks.

ALTERNATOR

REMOVAL & INSTALLATION

2.4L Engine

See Figures 41 and 42.

1. Disconnect negative battery cable.
2. Remove the drive belt.
3. Disconnect the generator electrical connector (1).
4. Reposition the rubber boot (3).
5. Remove the engine harness terminal lead to generator nut (2).
6. Remove the engine harness terminal (4) from the generator stud.
7. Remove the generator fasteners (1,3,4).
8. Remove the generator.

To install:

9. Position the generator to the engine block.
10. Install the generator fasteners loosely.
11. Install the fastener and tighten to 89 inch lbs. (10 Nm).
12. Install the fastener and tighten to 16 ft. lbs. (22 Nm).
13. Tighten the fasteners to 16 ft. lbs. (22 Nm).
14. Install the engine harness terminal to the generator stud.
15. Install the engine harness terminal lead to generator nut and tighten to 15 ft. lbs. (20 Nm).
16. Position the rubber boot over the stud.
17. Connect the generator electrical connector.

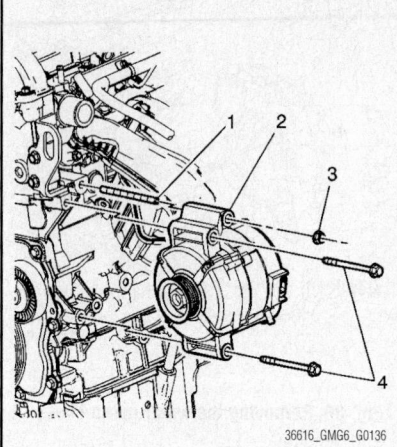

Fig. 42 Removing the generator—2.4L engine

18. Install the drive belt.
19. Connect negative battery cable.

3.5L Engine

See Figure 43.

➤The generator does not require periodic lubrication. The rotor shaft is mounted on bearings. Each bearing contains a permanent grease supply. Periodically check the mounting bolts for tightness, and the drive belt tension. The drive belt is self-adjusting, within the operating limits of the tensioner.

➤Service the generator as a complete unit.

36616_GMG6_G0138

Fig. 43 Removing the generator—3.5L engine

1. Disconnect the negative battery cable.
2. Remove the drive belt.
3. Remove the generator electrical connections.
4. Remove the generator mounting nuts and bolts.
5. Remove the generator.

To install:

6. Install the generator. Tighten the bolts to 37 ft. lbs. (50 Nm). Tighten the nuts to 22 ft. lbs. (30 Nm).
7. Install the generator electrical connections.
8. Install the drive belt.
9. Connect the negative battery cable.

3.6L Engine

See Figure 44.

1. Disconnect the negative battery cable.
2. Remove air cleaner outlet duct.
3. Reposition the positive battery cable boot at the generator terminal.
4. Remove the positive battery cable nut at the generator.
5. Remove the positive battery cable terminal from the generator.
6. Disconnect the engine harness electrical connector from the generator.
7. Remove the drive belt.
8. Remove the idler pulley.
9. Remove the generator bolts.

➤When removing the generator from the vehicle, it may be necessary to maneuver the generator to remove it from the vehicle.

10. Remove the generator.

To install:

11. Position the generator to the engine.
12. Loosely install the generator bolts.
13. Install the idler pulley.

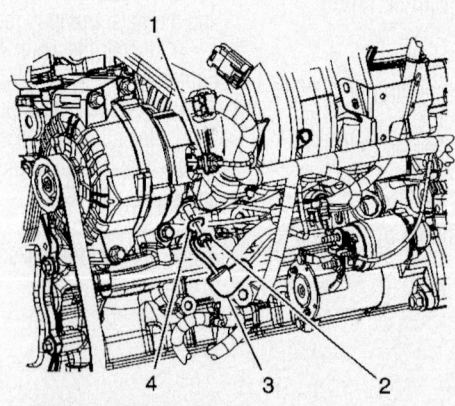

1. Generator electrical connector
2. Engine harness terminal lead to generator nut
3. Rubber boot
4. Engine harness terminal

36616_GMG6_G0135

Fig. 41 Disconnecting the generator—2.4L engine

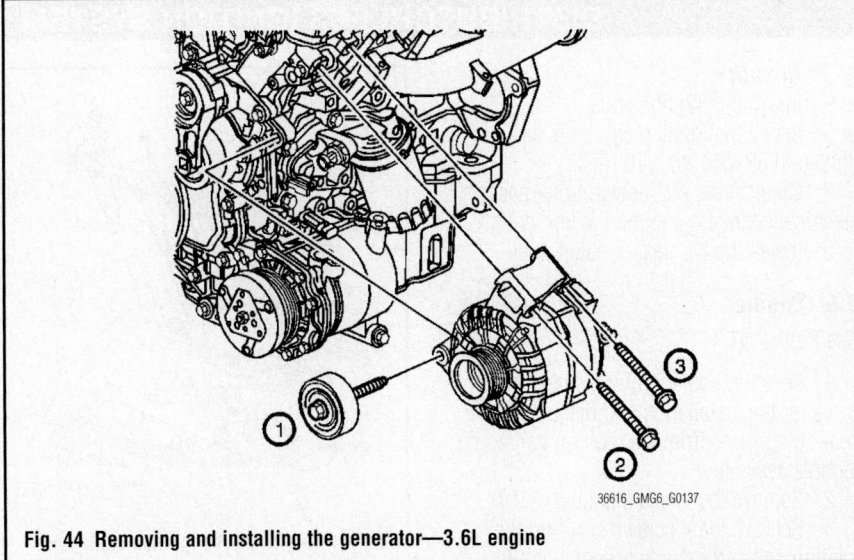

Fig. 44 Removing and installing the generator—3.6L engine

14. Tighten the generator bolts in the sequence shown to 37 ft. lbs. (50 Nm).

15. Install the drive belt.

16. Connect the engine harness electrical connector to the generator.

17. Install the positive battery cable terminal to the generator.

18. Install the positive battery cable nut at the generator and tighten to 15 ft. lbs. (20 Nm).

19. Position the positive battery cable boot at the generator terminal.

20. Connect the negative battery cable.

3.9L Engine

See Figures 45 through 47.

1. Disconnect the negative battery cable.

2. Remove the drive belt.

3. Disconnect the engine harness electrical connector.

4. Reposition the generator rubber boot.

5. Remove the engine harness terminal nut.

6. Remove the engine harness terminal.

7. Remove the generator lower bolt and stud.

8. Remove the generator upper bolt.

9. Remove the generator.

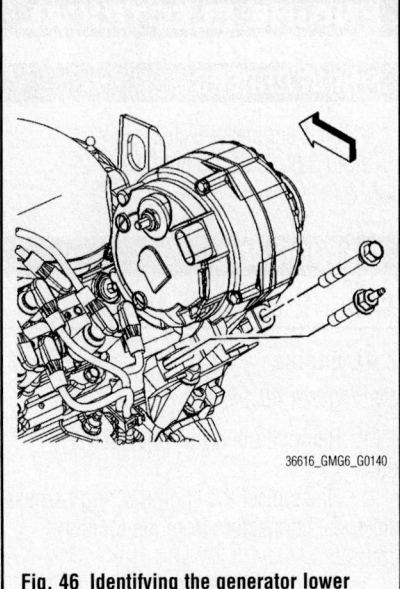

Fig. 46 Identifying the generator lower bolt and stud—3.9L engine

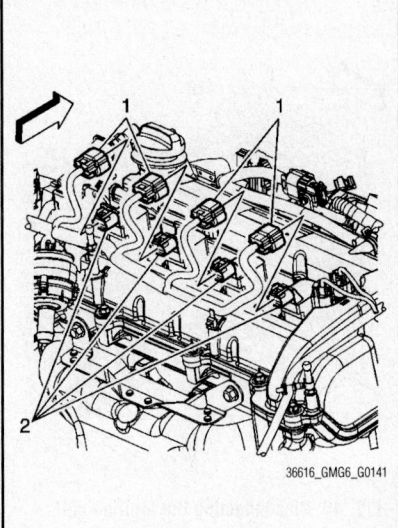

Fig. 47 Removing the generator— 3.9L engine

To install:

10. Install the generator.

11. Install the generator lower bolt and stud until snug.

12. Install the generator upper bolt and tighten to 37 ft. lbs. (50 Nm).

13. Install the engine harness terminal.

14. Install the engine harness terminal nut. Tighten to 22 ft. lbs. (30 Nm).

15. Position the generator rubber boot.

16. Connect the engine harness electrical connector.

17. Install the drive belt.

18. Connect the negative battery cable.

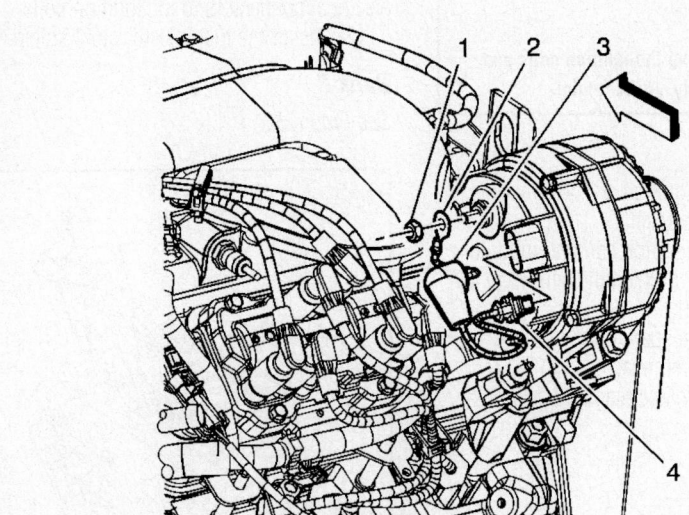

1. Engine harness terminal nut
2. Engine harness terminal
3. Generator rubber boot

Fig. 45 Disconnecting the generator—3.9L engine

ENGINE ELECTRICAL

DISTRIBUTORLESS IGNITION SYSTEM

FIRING ORDERS

2.4L L4 engine: 1-3-4-2
3.5L, 3.6L, 3.9L V6 engines: 1-2-3-4-5-6

IGNITION COIL

REMOVAL & INSTALLATION

2.4L Engine

See Figures 48 and 49.

1. Remove the air cleaner outlet duct.
2. Disconnect the engine wiring harness electrical connectors from the ignition coil(s).
3. Remove the ignition coil bolt(s).
4. Remove the ignition coil(s).

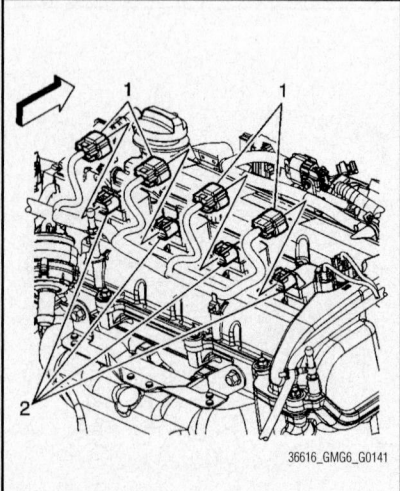

Fig. 48 Disconnecting the ignition coils

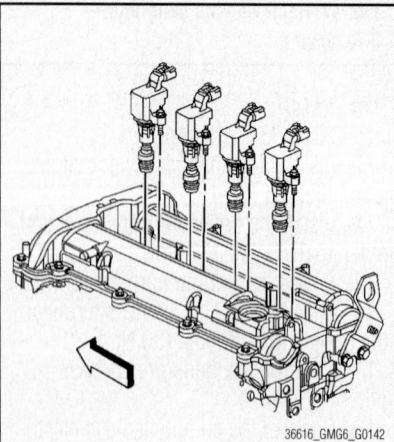

Fig. 49 Removing the ignition coils—2.4L engine

To install:

5. Install the ignition coils.
6. Install the ignition coil bolts and tighten to 89 inch lbs. (10 Nm).
7. Connect the engine wiring harness electrical connectors to the ignition coils.
8. Install the air cleaner outlet duct.

3.5L Engine

See Figure 50.

1. Note the position of the spark plug wires for the installation and disconnect the spark plug wires from the ignition coil and module assembly.
2. Remove the intake manifold cover.
3. Remove the 4 screws securing the ignition coil and module assembly to the bracket.
4. Remove the ignition coil and module assembly.

Fig. 50 Removing the ignition coils and module assembly—3.5L engine

To install:

5. Install the ignition coil and module assembly to the bracket.
6. Install the ignition coil and module assembly screws. Tighten the screws to 40 inch lbs. (4.5 Nm).
7. Connect the spark plug wires as noted during the removal.
8. Install the intake manifold cover.

3.6L Engine

Bank 1

See Figure 51.

1. Remove the fuel injector sight shield.
2. Disconnect the engine wiring harness electrical connectors from the ignition coils.
3. If removing the number 5 cylinder

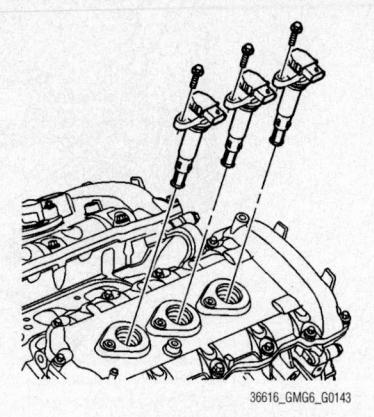

Fig. 51 Removing the ignition coils (bank 1)—3.6L engine

ignition coil, remove the Evaporative Emission (EVAP) canister purge tube.
4. If removing the number one ignition coil, remove the canister purge solenoid.
5. Remove the ignition coil bolts.
6. Remove the ignition coils.

To install:

7. Install the ignition coils.
8. Install the ignition coil bolts and tighten to 89 inch lbs. (10 Nm).
9. If the number 5 cylinder ignition coil was removed, install the EVAP canister purge tube.
10. If the number one ignition coil was removed, install the canister purge solenoid.
11. Connect the engine wiring harness electrical connectors to the ignition coils.
12. Install the fuel injector sight shield.

Bank 2

See Figure 52.

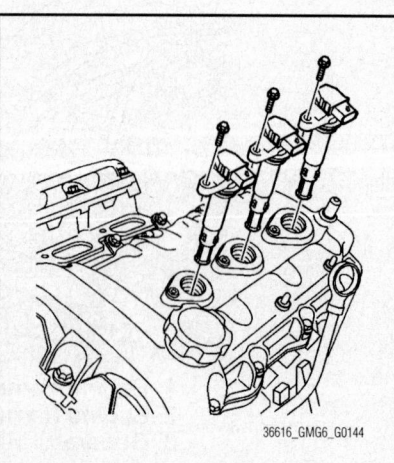

Fig. 52 Removing the ignition coils (bank 2)—3.6L engine

1. Remove the fuel injector sight shield.

2. Disconnect the engine wiring harness electrical connector(s) from the ignition coils.

3. Remove the ignition coil bolts.

4. Remove the ignition coils.

To install:

5. Install the ignition coils.

6. Install the ignition coil bolts and tighten 89 inch lbs. (10 Nm).

7. Connect the engine wiring harness electrical connectors to the ignition coils.

8. Install the fuel injector sight shield.

3.9L Engine

See Figures 53 and 54.

1. Remove the intake manifold cover.

2. Disconnect the Manifold Absolute Pressure (MAP) sensor electrical connector.

3. Disconnect the ignition coil electrical connector.

4. Disconnect the left side spark plug wires from the ignition coil.

5. Disconnect the right side spark plug wires from the ignition coil.

6. Remove the ignition coil bolts.

7. Remove the ignition coil nuts.

8. Remove the ignition coil.

9. Remove the ignition coil studs, if necessary.

To install:

10. Install the ignition coil studs, if necessary. Tighten the studs to 15 ft. lbs. (25 Nm).

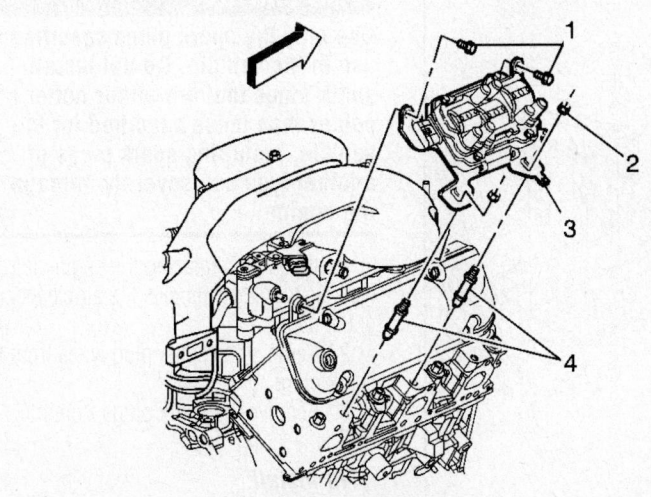

1. Ignition coil bolts
2. Ignition coil nuts
3. Ignition coil
4. Ignition coil studs

36616_GMG6_G0149

Fig. 54 Removing the ignition coils—3.9L engine

11. Install the ignition coil.

12. Install the ignition coil nuts and tighten to 15 ft. lbs. (25 Nm).

13. Install the ignition coil bolts and tighten to 15 ft. lbs. (25 Nm).

14. Connect the right side spark plug wires to the ignition coil.

15. Connect the left side spark plug wires to the ignition coil.

16. Connect the ignition coil electrical connector.

17. Connect the MAP sensor electrical connector.

18. Install the intake manifold cover.

IGNITION TIMING

ADJUSTMENT

The ignition timing is controlled by the Powertrain Control Module (PCM). No adjustment is necessary or possible.

SPARK PLUGS

REMOVAL & INSTALLATION

2.4L Engine

See Figure 55.

❋❋ WARNING

This engine has aluminum cylinder heads. Do not remove the spark plugs from a hot engine, allow it to cool first. Removing the spark plugs from a hot engine may cause spark plug thread damage or cylinder head damage.

1. Remove the ignition coils.

❋❋ WARNING

Make sure that any water and/or debris is blown out of the spark plug holes prior to removing the spark plugs.

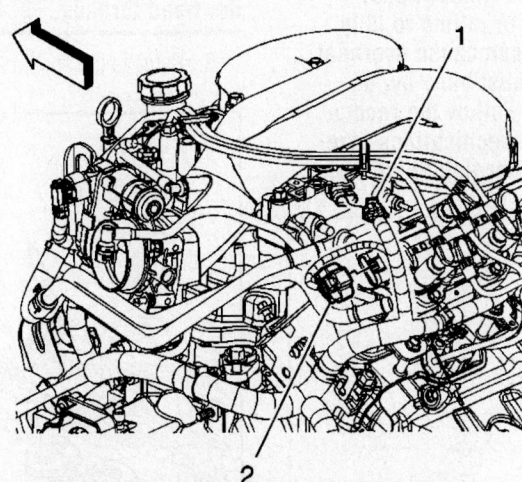

1. Manifold Absolute Pressure (MAP) sensor electrical connector
2. Ignition coil electrical connector

36616_GMG6_G0146

Fig. 53 Disconnecting the ignition coil connectors—3.9L engine

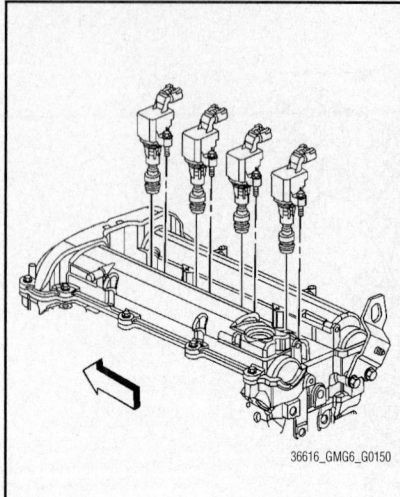

Fig. 55 Removing the spark plugs—2.4L engine

2. Remove the spark plugs using a⅝inch spark plug socket.

To install:

➡Do not coat spark plug threads with anti-seize compound. If anti-seize compound is used and spark plugs are over-torqued, damage to the cylinder head threads may result.

3. Check spark plug gap for specification, 0.042 inch. (1.06 mm).
4. Install the spark plugs.
5. Tighten spark plugs to 15 ft. lbs. (20 Nm).
6. Install the ignition coils and tighten mounting bolts to 89 inch lbs. (10 Nm).

3.5L Engine
See Figure 56.

> ✳✳ **CAUTION**
>
> Allow the engine to cool before removing the spark plugs. Attempting to remove spark plugs from a hot engine can cause the spark plugs to seize. This can damage the cylinder head threads.

> ✳✳ **CAUTION**
>
> Clean the spark plug recess area before removing the spark plug. Failure to do so can result in engine damage due to dirt or foreign material entering the cylinder head, or in contamination of the cylinder head threads. Contaminated threads may prevent proper seating of the new spark plug.

> ✳✳ **CAUTION**
>
> Use only the spark plugs specified for use in the vehicle. Do not install spark plugs that are either hotter or colder than those specified for the vehicle. Installing spark plugs of another type can severely damage the engine.

1. If you are replacing the engine left bank spark plugs, remove the air cleaner outlet duct.
2. Remove the spark plug wires from the spark plugs.
3. Remove the spark plugs from the engine.

To install:

> ✳✳ **CAUTION**
>
> It is important to check the gap of all new and reconditioned spark plugs before installation. Pre-set gaps may have changed during handling. Use a round wire feeler gauge to be sure of an accurate check, particularly on used plugs. Installing plugs with the wrong gap can cause poor engine performance and may even damage the engine.

4. Gap the spark plugs to the specifications

> ✳✳ **CAUTION**
>
> Be sure plug threads smoothly into cylinder head and is fully seated. Use a thread chaser if necessary to clean threads in cylinder head. Cross-threading or failing to fully seat spark plug can cause overheating of plug, exhaust blow-by, or thread damage. Follow the recommended torque specifications carefully. Over or under-tightening can

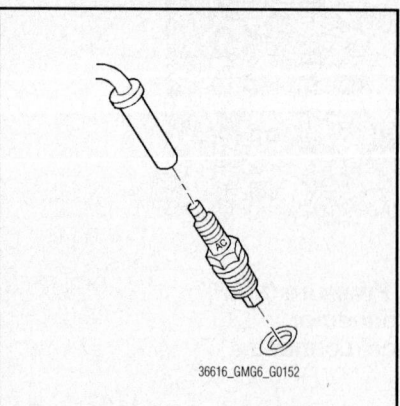

Fig. 56 Removing the spark plugs—3.5L engine

also cause severe damage to engine or spark plug.

5. Install the spark plugs to the engine. If installing the spark plugs to a new cylinder head tighten to plugs to 15 ft. lbs. (20 Nm). If installing the spark plugs to an existing cylinder head tighten to plugs to 11 ft. lbs. (15 Nm).
6. Install the spark plug wires to the spark plugs.

3.6L Engine
See Figure 57.

1. Remove the ignition coils.

> ✳✳ **CAUTION**
>
> Clean the spark plug recess area before removing the spark plug. Failure to do so could result in engine damage because of dirt or foreign material entering the cylinder head, or by the contamination of the cylinder head threads. The contaminated threads may prevent the proper seating of the new plug. Use a thread chaser to clean the threads of any contamination.

2. Use compressed air in order to remove debris from the spark plug cavity.

> ✳✳ **CAUTION**
>
> Allow the engine to cool before removing the spark plugs. Attempting to remove the spark plugs from a hot engine may cause the plug threads to seize, causing damage to the cylinder head threads.

3. Remove the spark plug.

Fig. 57 Removing the spark plugs—3.6L engine

To install:

❋❋ **CAUTION**

Use only the spark plugs specified for use in the vehicle. Do not install spark plugs that are either hotter or colder than those specified for the vehicle. Installing spark plugs of another type can severely damage the engine.

❋❋ **CAUTION**

Check the gap of all new and reconditioned spark plugs before installation. The pre-set gaps may have changed during handling. Use a round feeler gage to ensure an accurate check. Installing the spark plugs with the wrong gap can cause poor engine performance and may even damage the engine.

4. Ensure that the spark plug gap is equivalent to the spark plug gap specification.

❋❋ **CAUTION**

Be sure that the spark plug threads smoothly into the cylinder head and the spark plug is fully seated. Use a thread chaser, if necessary, to clean threads in the cylinder head. Cross-threading or failing to fully seat the spark plug can cause overheating of the plug, exhaust blow-by, or thread damage.

5. Install the spark plug. Tighten the spark plug to 15 ft. lbs. (20 Nm).
6. Install the ignition coils.

3.9L Engine

See Figures 58 through 60.

❋❋ **CAUTION**

Allow the engine to cool before removing the spark plugs. Attempting to remove spark plugs from a hot engine can cause the spark plugs to seize. This can damage the cylinder head threads.

❋❋ **CAUTION**

Clean the spark plug recess area before removing the spark plug. Fail-

ure to do so can result in engine damage due to dirt or foreign material entering the cylinder head, or in contamination of the cylinder head threads. Contaminated threads may prevent proper seating of the new spark plug.

❋❋ **CAUTION**

Use only the spark plugs specified for use in the vehicle. Do not install spark plugs that are either hotter or colder than those specified for the vehicle. Installing spark plugs of another type can severely damage the engine.

1. Remove the air cleaner outlet duct, if required.
2. Remove the intake manifold cover, if required.
3. Remove the left side spark plug wires from the spark plugs, if required.
4. Remove the right side spark plug wires from the spark plugs, if required.
5. Remove the spark plugs.

To install:

❋❋ **CAUTION**

It is important to check the gap of all new and reconditioned spark plugs before installation. Pre-set gaps may have changed during handling. Use a

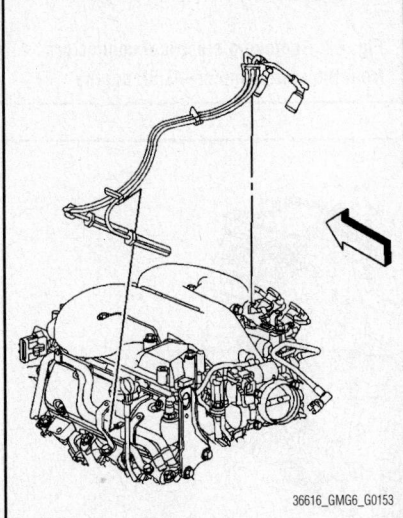

Fig. 58 Removing the left side plug wires—3.9L engine

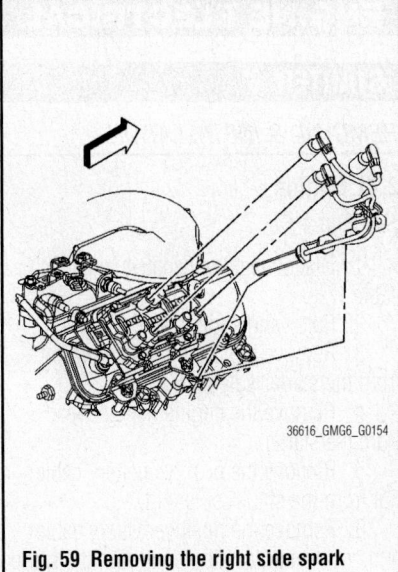

Fig. 59 Removing the right side spark plug wires—3.9L engine

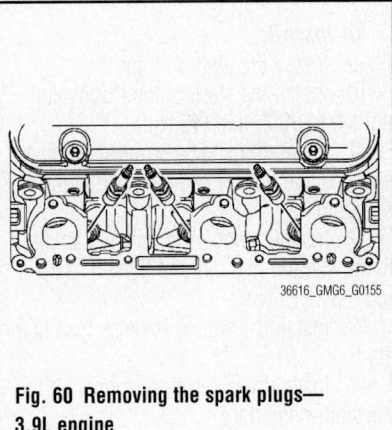

Fig. 60 Removing the spark plugs—3.9L engine

round wire feeler gauge to be sure of an accurate check, particularly on used plugs. Installing plugs with the wrong gap can cause poor engine performance and may even damage the engine.

6. Gap the NEW spark plugs.
7. Install the spark plugs and tighten to 15 ft. lbs. (20 Nm).
8. Install the right side spark plug wires to the spark plugs, if required.
9. Install the left side spark plug wires to the spark plugs, if required.
10. Install the intake manifold cover, if required.
11. Install the air cleaner outlet duct, if required.

STARTER

REMOVAL & INSTALLATION

2.4L Engine

See Figure 61.

1. Disconnect the negative battery cable.
2. Raise and support the vehicle.
3. Remove the S terminal connector from the starter solenoid.
4. Remove the engine harness lead from the starter.
5. Remove the positive battery cable nut from the starter solenoid.
6. Remove the positive battery cable and engine harness terminal from the starter solenoid.
7. Remove the starter motor bolts.
8. Remove the starter motor.

To install:

9. Install the starter motor.
10. Install the starter motor bolts and tighten to 30 ft. lbs. (40 Nm).
11. Install the engine harness terminal and positive battery cable to the starter solenoid.
12. Install the positive battery cable nut to the starter solenoid and tighten to 89 inch lbs. (10 Nm).
13. Install the engine harness lead to the starter.
14. Install the S terminal connector to the starter solenoid.
15. Lower the vehicle.
16. Connect the negative battery cable.

3.5L Engine

See Figures 62 and 63.

1. Disconnect the negative battery cable.
2. Raise the vehicle.
3. Remove the flywheel inspection cover bolts.
4. Remove the flywheel inspection cover.
5. Remove the electrical connections from the starter motor.
6. Remove the starter motor mounting bolts.
7. Remove the starter motor.

To install:

❋❋ CAUTION

Before installing the starter motor to the engine, tighten the nut next to the

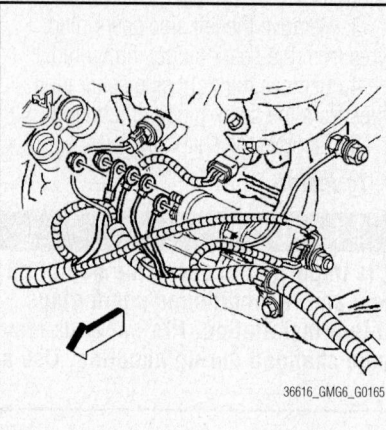

Fig. 62 Removing electrical connectors from the starter motor—3.5L engine

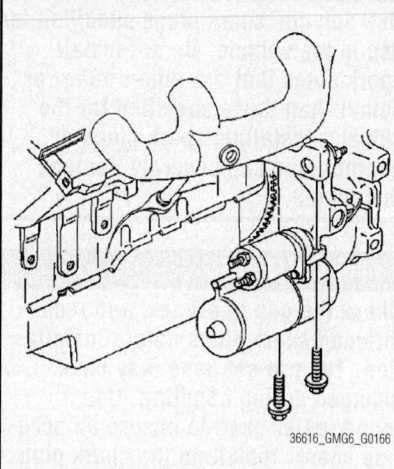

Fig. 63 Removing the starter motor—3.5L engine

cap on the solenoid BAT terminal. If this terminal is not tight in the solenoid cap, the cap may be damaged during installation of electrical connections and cause the starter motor to fail later.

8. Install the starter motor to the engine.
9. Install the starter motor mounting bolts and tighten to 30 ft. lbs. (40 Nm).
10. Install the electrical connection to the battery terminal on the solenoid and tighten to 13 ft. lbs. (17 Nm).
11. Install the electrical connections to the S terminal on the solenoid and tighten to 27 inch lbs. (3 Nm).
12. Install the flywheel inspection cover.
13. Install the flywheel inspection cover bolts and tighten to 89 inch lbs. (10 Nm).
14. Lower the vehicle.
15. Connect the negative battery cable.

3.6L Engine

See Figures 64 and 65.

1. Disconnect the negative battery cable.
2. Raise and support the vehicle.
3. Remove the starter solenoid BAT terminal nut.
4. Disconnect the engine harness electrical connector.
5. Unclip battery positive cable from starter bracket.
6. Disconnect the starter motor bolts and the starter.

To install:

7. Position the starter motor to the engine block.

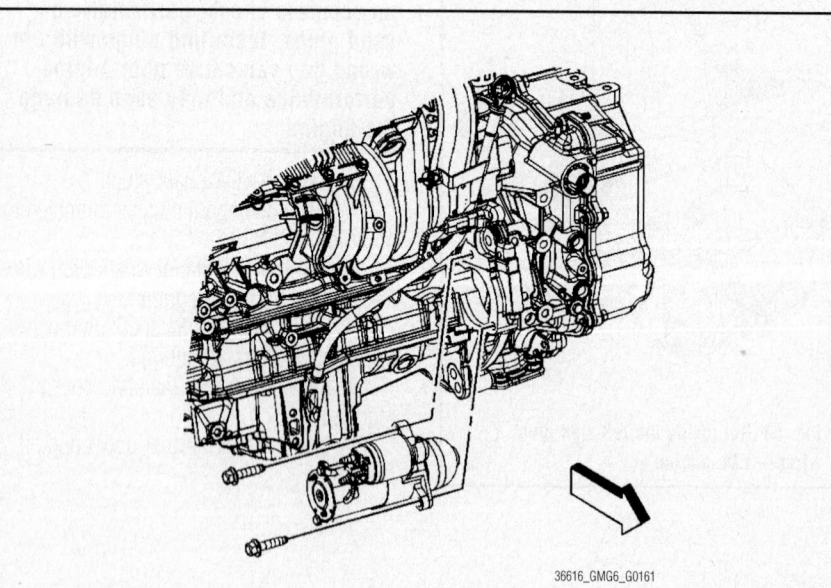

Fig. 61 Removing the starter—2.4L engine

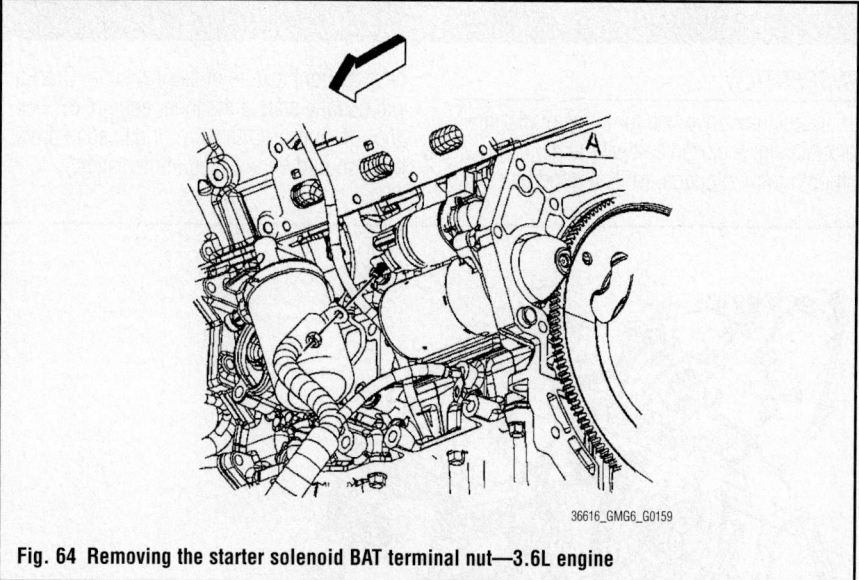

Fig. 64 Removing the starter solenoid BAT terminal nut—3.6L engine

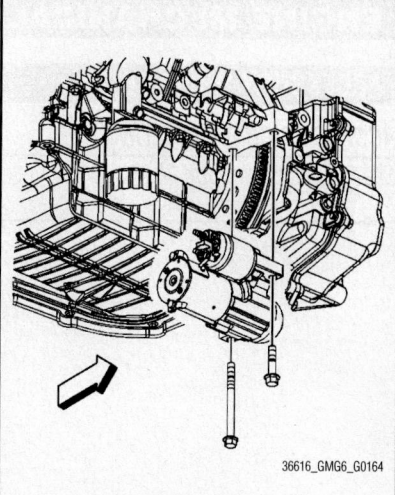

Fig. 66 Removing the starter—3.9L engine

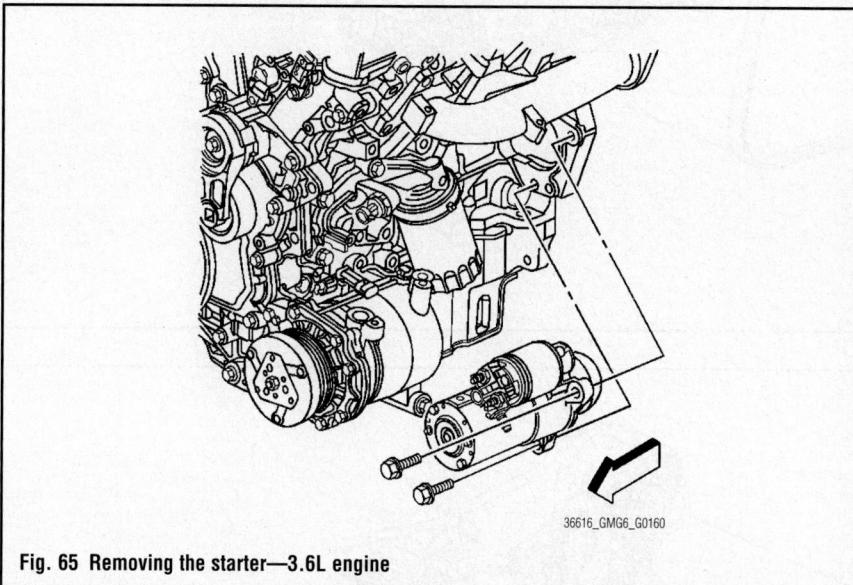

Fig. 65 Removing the starter—3.6L engine

8. Install the starter bolts and tighten to 37 ft. lbs. (50 Nm).

9. Connect the electrical connector to the starter.

10. Install the starter solenoid BAT terminal nut and tighten to 155 inch lbs. (13 Nm).

11. Install the knock sensor bank 2.

12. Install the left catalytic converter.

13. Lower the vehicle.

14. Connect the negative battery cable.

3.9L Engine

See Figure 66.

1. Disconnect the negative battery cable.

2. Raise and support the vehicle.

3. Remove the flywheel inspection cover bolts and cover.

4. Disconnect the engine harness electrical connector from the starter.

5. Remove the engine harness terminal nut.

6. Remove the positive battery cable terminal from the starter.

7. Remove the engine harness terminal from the starter.

8. Remove the starter motor bolts.

9. Remove the starter motor.

To install:

※※ CAUTION

Before installing the starter motor to the engine, tighten the nut next to the cap on the solenoid BAT terminal. If this terminal is not tight in the solenoid cap, the cap may be damaged during installation of electrical connections and cause the starter motor to fail later.

10. Install the starter motor.

11. Install the starter motor bolts and tighten to 30 ft. lbs. (40 Nm).

12. Install the engine harness terminal to the starter.

13. Install the positive battery cable terminal to the starter.

14. Install the engine harness terminal nut and tighten to 13 ft. lbs. (17 Nm).

15. Connect the engine harness electrical connector to the starter.

16. Install the flywheel inspection cover and bolts and tighten to 89 inch lbs. (10 Nm).

17. Lower vehicle.

18. Connect the negative battery cable.

ENGINE MECHANICAL

ACCESSORY DRIVE BELTS

ACCESSORY BELT ROUTING

See Figures 67 through 70.

INSPECTION

Inspect the drive belt for signs of glazing or cracking. A glazed belt will be perfectly smooth from slippage, while a good belt will have a slight texture of fabric visible. Cracks will usually start at the inner edge of the belt and run outward. All worn or damaged drive belts should be replaced immediately.

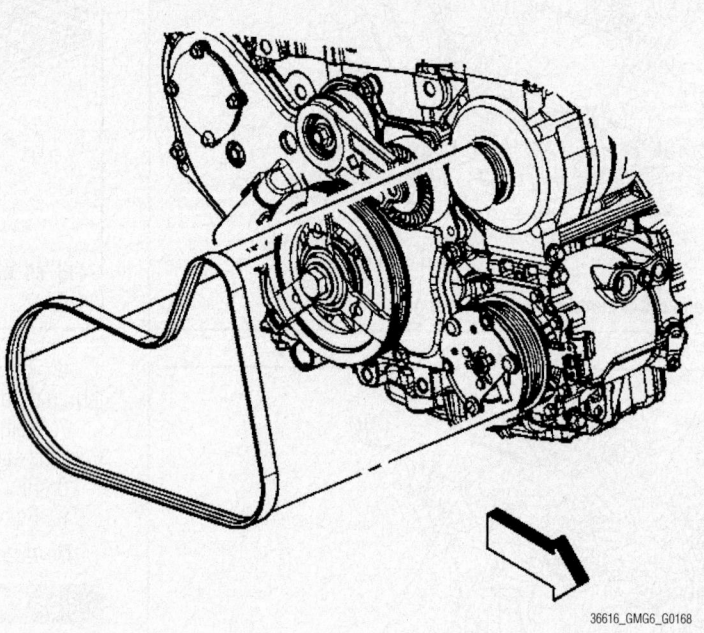

36616_GMG6_G0168

Fig. 67 Drive belt routing—2.4L & 3.6L engines

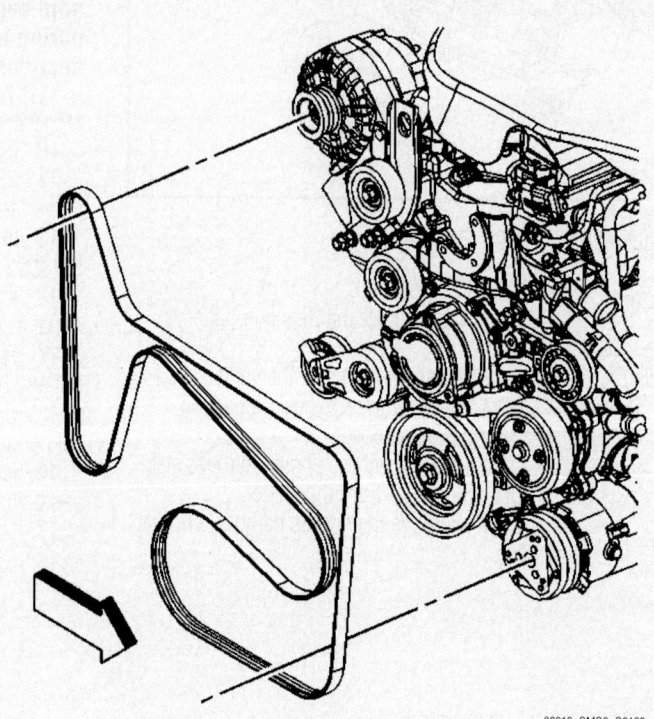

36616_GMG6_G0169

Fig. 68 Drive belt routing—3.5L engine

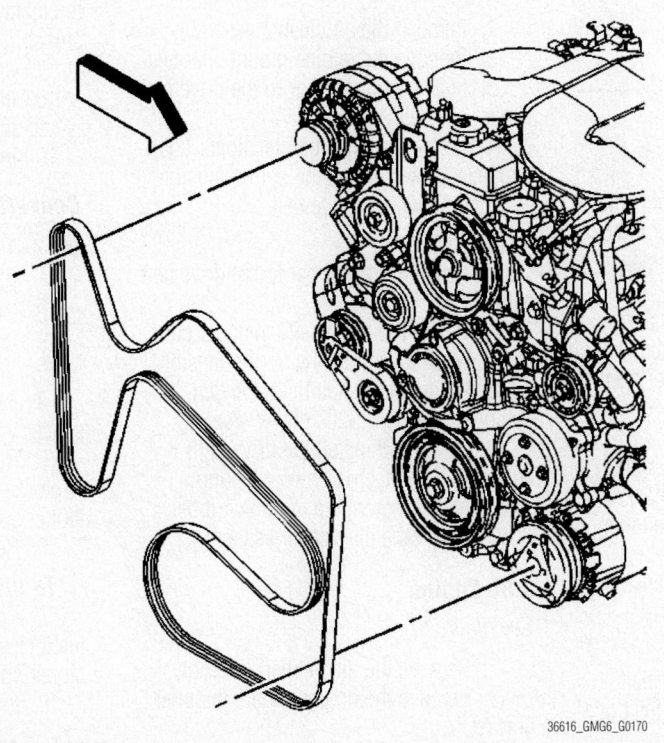

36616_GMG6_G0170

Fig. 69 Drive belt routing (coupe)—3.9L engine

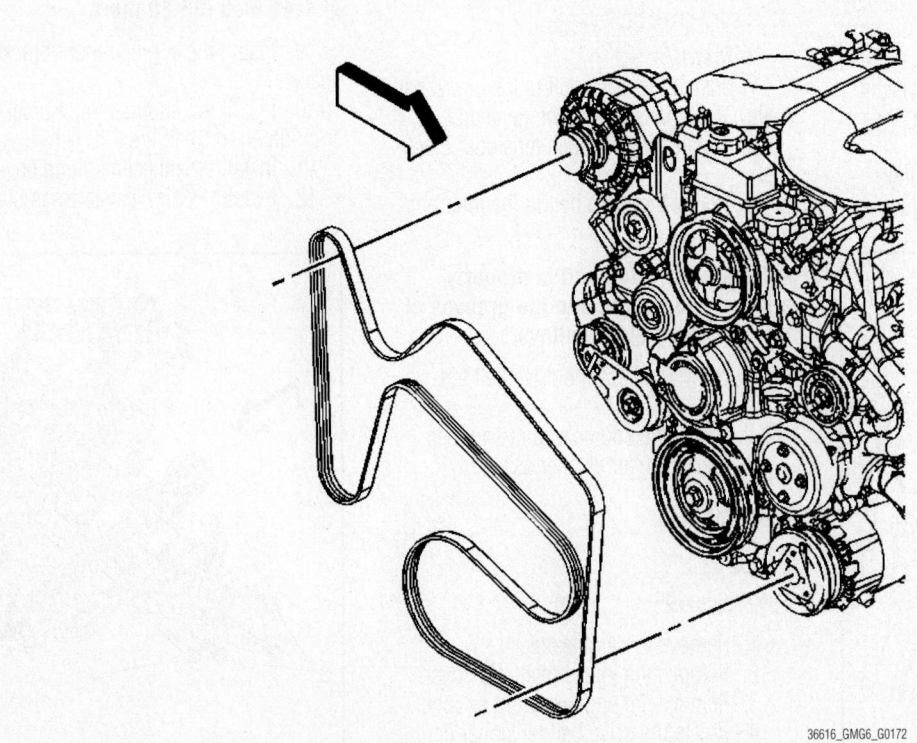

36616_GMG6_G0172

Fig. 70 Drive belt routing (convertible)—3.9L engine

ADJUSTMENT

Drive belts on this model have automatic adjusters.

REMOVAL & INSTALLATION

2.4L Engine

See Figures 67 and 71.

1. Remove the air cleaner outlet duct.
2. Remove the right front fender liner.
3. Install the accessory belt tensioner unloader to the drive belt tensioner.
4. Using the accessory belt tensioner unloader, rotate the tensioner counterclockwise in order to release the tensioner from the drive belt.
5. Remove the drive belt.
6. Slowly rotate the accessory belt tensioner unloader and the tensioner clockwise in order to allow the tensioner to rest.
7. Remove the accessory belt tensioner unloader from the drive belt tensioner.

To install:

8. Install and position the drive belt around all of the pulleys except for the drive belt tensioner.
9. Install the accessory belt tensioner unloader to the drive belt tensioner.
10. Using the accessory belt tensioner unloader, rotate the tensioner counterclockwise.
11. Position the drive belt under the tensioner pulley.
12. Using the accessory belt tensioner unloader, rotate the tensioner clockwise in order to seat the tensioner pulley onto the drive belt.
13. Install the right front fender liner.
14. Install the air cleaner outlet duct

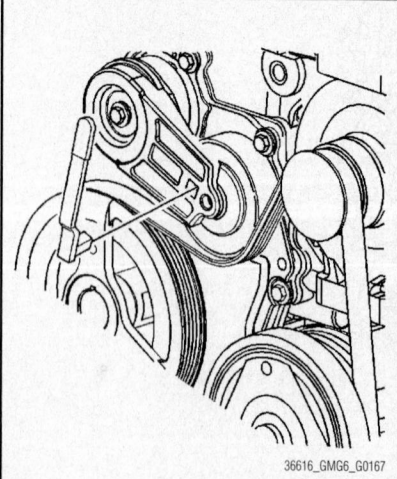

36616_GMG6_G0167

Fig. 71 Releasing tensioner from the drive belt—2.4L engine

3.5L Engine

See Figure 68.

1. Remove the air cleaner assembly.
2. Remove the engine mount snubber.
3. Install a breaker bar to the drive belt tensioner.
4. Rotate the drive belt tensioner counterclockwise to release the spring tension.
5. Remove the drive belt.

To install:

6. Install a breaker bar to the drive belt tensioner.
7. Rotate the drive belt tensioner counterclockwise to release the spring tension.
8. Route and install the drive belt, if equipped with hydraulic power steering.
9. Route and install the drive belt, if equipped with electric power steering.
10. Install the engine mount snubber.
11. Install the air cleaner assembly.

3.6L Engine

See Figure 67.

1. Remove the air cleaner assembly.
2. Remove the engine mount snubber bracket.
3. Rotate the drive belt tensioner clockwise to release the drive belt tension.
4. Slide the drive belt off of the belt idler pulley.
5. Slowly release the drive belt tensioner.
6. Remove the drive belt from the accessory drive pulleys.

To install:

7. Install the drive belt to the crankshaft pulley, the tensioner and the generator.
8. Rotate the drive belt tensioner clockwise.
9. Install the drive belt to the idler pulley (1).

➡**Ensure the drive belt is properly aligned and seated into the grooves of the accessory drive pulleys.**

10. Slowly release the drive belt tensioner.
11. Install the engine mount snubber.
12. Install the air cleaner assembly.

3.9L Engine

Coupe

See Figure 69.

1. Remove the air cleaner.
2. Remove the intake manifold cover.
3. Remove the engine mount snubber.
4. Rotate the drive belt tensioner counterclockwise in order to release the tensioner spring tension.
5. Remove the drive belt.

To install:

6. Rotate the drive belt tensioner counterclockwise in order to release the tensioner spring tension.
7. Install the drive belt.
8. Install the engine mount snubber.
9. Install the intake manifold cover.
10. Install the air cleaner.

Convertible

See Figures 70 and 72.

1. Remove the air cleaner assembly.
2. Remove the intake manifold cover.
3. Remove the engine mount bracket bolt.
4. Remove the engine mount bracket spacer.
5. Rotate the drive belt tensioner counterclockwise in order to release the tensioner spring tension.
6. Remove the drive belt.

To install:

7. Rotate the drive belt tensioner counterclockwise in order to release the tensioner spring tension.
8. Install the drive belt.

➡**The spacer has a nominal length of 1.42 inch (36.0 mm). If the spacer cannot be reinstalled, the spacer will require the ends to be buffed slightly using a crocus cloth or emery paper in order to bring the length to a minimum of 1.41 inch (35.80 mm).**

9. Install the engine mount bracket spacer.
10. Install the engine mount bracket bolt and tighten to 37 ft. lbs. (50 Nm).
11. Install the intake manifold cover.
12. Install the air cleaner assembly.

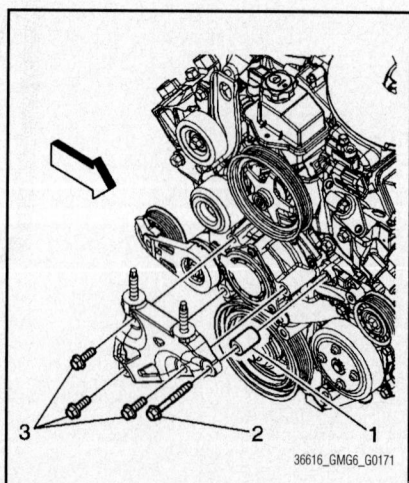

36616_GMG6_G0171

Fig. 72 Removing the engine mount bracket and spacer (convertible)—3.9L engine

BALANCE SHAFT

REMOVAL & INSTALLATION

2.4L Engine

See Figures 73 through 75.

1. Remove engine assembly.
2. Remove engine front cover and timing components.
3. Remove the balance shaft bearing carrier bolts.
4. Remove the balance shaft assemblies.

❈❈ WARNING

It is possible to install the intake side balance shaft into the exhaust side and vice versa. Please use care not to install the balance shafts into the wrong bores. Engine vibration will result. Do not remove the bolt holding the sprocket.

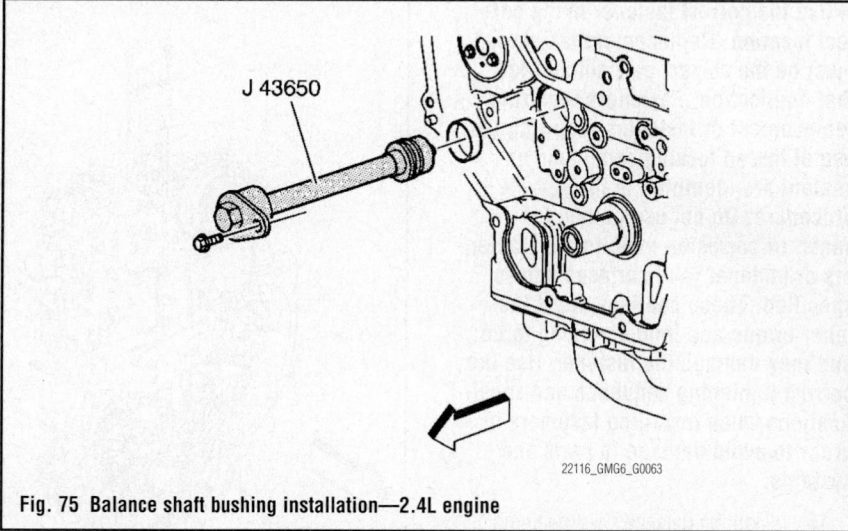
Fig. 75 Balance shaft bushing installation—2.4L engine

5. Install the J 43650 into the balance shaft hole. Insert the tool with the foot parallel to the shaft.
6. When the J 43650 is inserted in the block turn the J 43650 so that the foot becomes perpendicular to the shaft.
7. Center the foot of the J 43650 on the balance shaft bushing.
8. Once the J 43650 is centered on the balance shaft bushing, then insert the centering guide into the front balance shaft bore and tighten the nut with an appropriate wrench
9. When the J 43650 is properly installed, before removing the bushing, the end of the tool should be 4.6 inch. (116 mm) from the block face.
10. If the J 43650 is less than approximately 4.5 inch (114 mm) recheck the tool alignment.
11. Tighten the nut on the J 43650 until the tension releases. When the tension releases, remove the J 43650 and the balance shaft bushing.

To install:

12. Install the balance shaft bushing using the J 43650.
13. Seat the balance shaft bushing into the bore using the J 43650 and a wrench.
14. When the J 43650 is fully seated in the engine block, remove it with a wrench.

❈❈ WARNING

If the balance shafts are not properly timed to the engine, the engine may vibrate or make noise.

15. Install the balance shaft assemblies to the engine using the following steps:
   a. Place the number one piston at top dead center (TDC).
   b. Lubricate the balance shaft lobes with engine oil.
   c. Install the balance shafts into their bores.

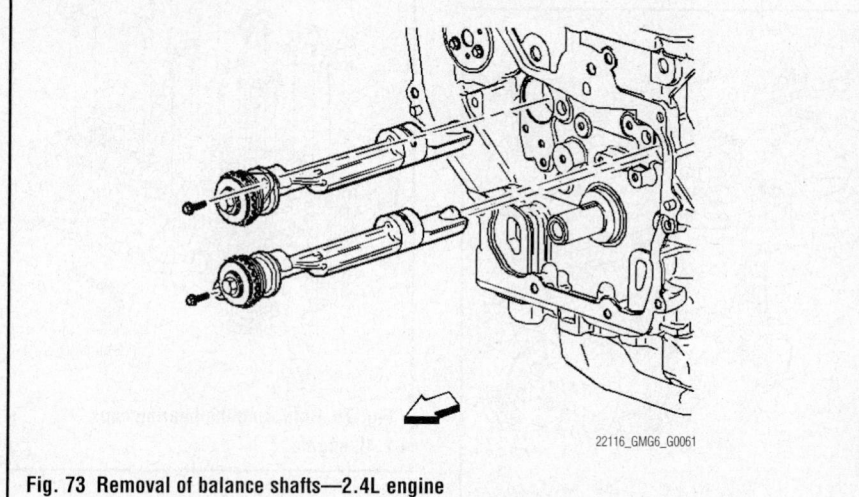
Fig. 73 Removal of balance shafts—2.4L engine

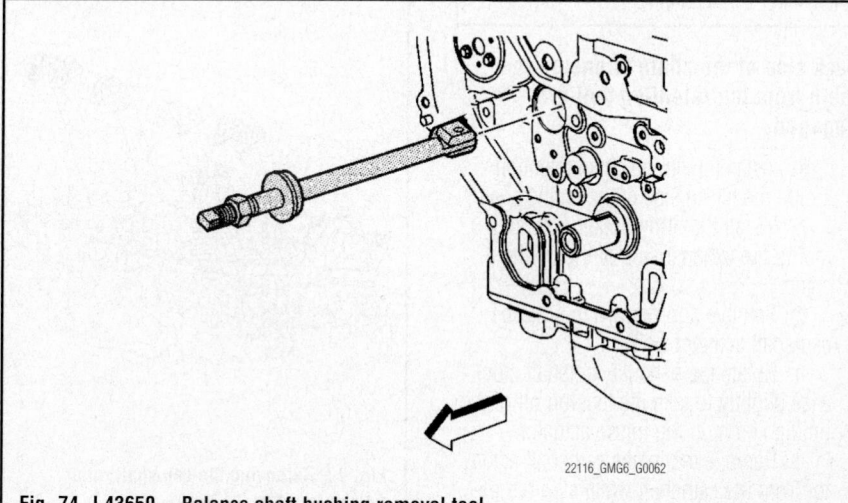
Fig. 74 J 43650— Balance shaft bushing removal tool

➡Use the correct fastener in the correct location. Replacement fasteners must be the correct part number for that application. Fasteners requiring replacement or fasteners requiring the use of thread locking compound or sealant are identified in the service procedure. Do not use paints, lubricants, or corrosion inhibitors on fasteners or fastener joint surfaces unless specified. These coatings affect fastener torque and joint clamping force and may damage the fastener. Use the correct tightening sequence and specifications when installing fasteners in order to avoid damage to parts and systems.

16. Install the balance shaft retaining bolts.

17. Tighten the balance shaft retaining bolts to 89 inch lbs. (10 Nm).

CAMSHAFT AND VALVE LIFTERS

REMOVAL & INSTALLATION

2.4L Engine (Intake)

See Figures 76 through 81.

1. Remove the intake camshaft position actuator.

a. Remove the camshaft cover.

b. Remove the spark plugs.

c. Rotate the crankshaft clockwise and install the camshaft actuator retainer.

d. Install the camshaft actuator retainer bolts and tighten to 89 inch lbs. (10 Nm).

e. Loosen, but DO NOT remove the intake camshaft actuator bolt.

f. Remove the camshaft actuator locking tool.

g. Clean the timing chain and gears with solvent.

➡Ensure the timing chain and the camshaft position actuators are marked for proper assembly.

h. Mark the intake and exhaust camshaft actuators and the respective locations on the timing chain.

i. Remove the upper timing chain guide bolts and guide.

j. Remove the timing chain tensioner.

➡The intake camshaft actuator should not rotate during the removal or installation.

➡Ensure the tips of the are fully engaged into the timing chain. The retention tool rod can be used on the

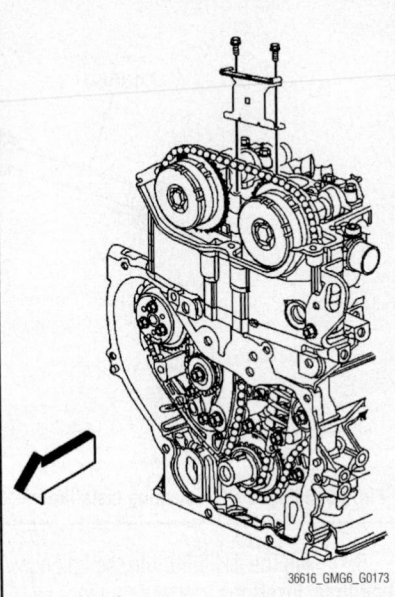

Fig. 76 Removing the upper timing chain guide—2.4L engine

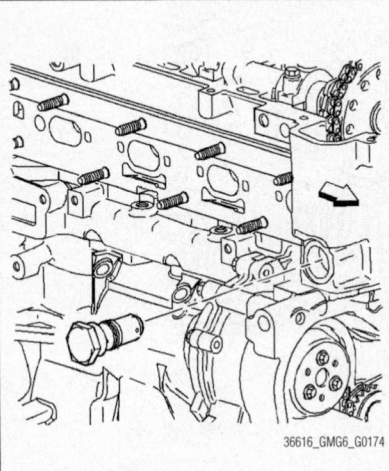

Fig. 77 Removing the timing chain tensioner—2.4L engine

back side of the chain to ensure the teeth from the retention tool are engaged.

k. Install the timing chain retention tool to the intake side of the timing chain.

l. Install the timing chain retention tool to the exhaust side of the timing chain.

m. Remove and discard the intake camshaft actuator bolt.

n. Rotate the exhaust camshaft clockwise slightly to take the tension off of the timing chain on the intake actuator.

o. Remove the intake camshaft actuator from the camshaft while also removing the actuator from the timing chain.

➡Remove each bolt on each cap one turn at a time until there is no spring tension pushing on the camshaft.

2. Mark the bearing caps to ensure they are installed in the original position.

3. Remove the bearing cap bolts.

4. Remove the bearing caps.

5. Remove the intake camshaft.

➡Keep all of the roller followers and hydraulic adjusters in order so that they can be reinstalled in their respective locations.

6. Remove the camshaft roller followers.

7. Remove the hydraulic lash adjusters.

To install:

8. Install the hydraulic element lash adjusters into their bores in the cylinder head.

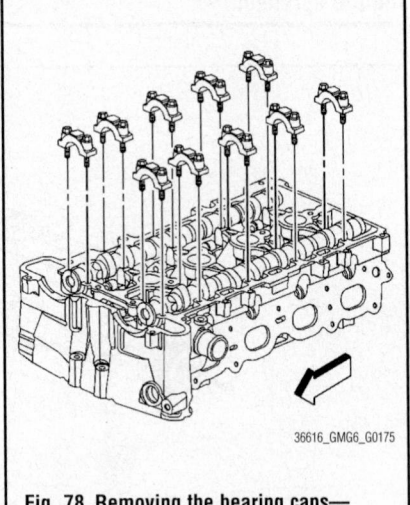

Fig. 78 Removing the bearing caps—2.4L engine

Fig. 79 Removing the camshaft roller followers—2.4L engine

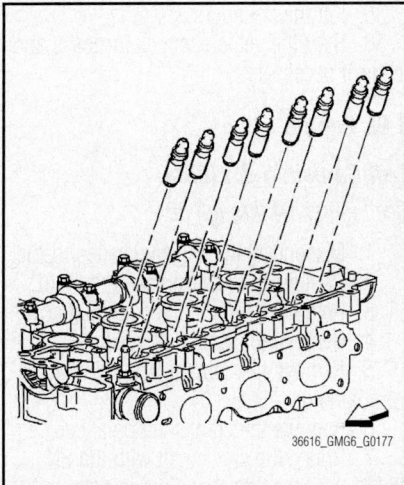

Fig. 80 Removing the hydraulic lash adjusters—2.4L engine

9. Lubricate the hydraulic lash adjusters with GM PN 12345501 or equivalent.

10. Lubricate the valve tips with GM PN 12345501 (Canadian PN 992704) or equivalent.

→**Used roller followers MUST be returned to their original position on the camshaft. If the camshaft is being replaced, the roller followers actuated by the camshaft must also be replaced.**

11. Position the camshaft roller followers on the tip of the valve stem and on the lash adjuster.

12. Lubricate the roller followers with GM PN 12345501 or equivalent.

13. Install the intake camshaft. Lubricate with GM PN 12345501 or equivalent.

14. Install the camshaft bearing caps. Hand tighten the cap bolts.

15. Tighten the bearing cap bolts in increments of 3 turns until they are seated. Tighten the bolts to 89 inch lbs. (10 Nm).

16. Install the intake camshaft position actuator.

→**Ensure that the alignment mark made previously on the intake camshaft actuator is still aligned properly with the mark on the timing chain.**

a. Install the timing chain onto the intake camshaft actuator.

b. Align the intake camshaft actuator alignment mark made previously with the timing chain mark and install the actuator onto the camshaft rotating the exhaust camshaft clockwise, if required.

c. Install a NEW intake camshaft actuator bolt (2) until snug.

d. Remove the timing chain retention tool (1) from the intake side of the timing chain.

→**Ensure that the alignment mark previously on the intake camshaft actuator is still aligned properly with the timing chain. If the mark made previously on the intake camshaft actuator is not aligned properly.**

e. Remove the timing chain retention tool (1) from the exhaust side of the timing chain.

→**Failure to reset the tensioner will allow the tensioner to over extends. limiting the timing chain life.**

f. Reset and install the timing chain tensioner.

g. Install the camshaft actuator retainer Camshaft Actuator Locking Tool.

h. Install the camshaft actuator retainer bolts and tighten to 89 inch lbs. (10 Nm).

i. Tighten the NEW camshaft actuator bolt to 22 ft. lbs (30 Nm) plus an additional 100 degrees.

→**You must have the Camshaft Actuator Locking Tool installed to perform this procedure.**

j. To release the tensioner apply a counterclockwise rotational torque to the crankshaft balancer bolt of 33 ft. lbs. (45 Nm).

k. Remove the camshaft actuator retainer.

l. Install the upper timing chain guide and bolts and tighten to 89 inch lbs. (10 Nm).

m. Install the spark plugs.

n. Install the camshaft cover.

3.5L & 3.9L Engines

See Figures 82 and 83.

1. Drain the engine oil and cooling system.

2. Relieve the fuel system pressure.

3. To remove the valve lifters, remove the valve covers.

4. Remove the intake manifolds.

5. Remove the rocker arm bolts.

6. Remove the rocker arms.

7. Remove the pushrods.

8. Remove the intake manifold oil splash shield.

9. Remove the lifter guide bolts.

10. Remove the valve lifter guides.

11. Remove the valve lifters.

12. Clean all gasket surfaces with degreaser.

13. Clean the valve train parts.

14. Inspect the valve lifters and the cam lobes for wear.

15. To remove the camshaft, remove the engine front cover, timing chain and sprockets.

16. Remove the camshaft position sensor.

17. Remove the camshaft thrust plate.

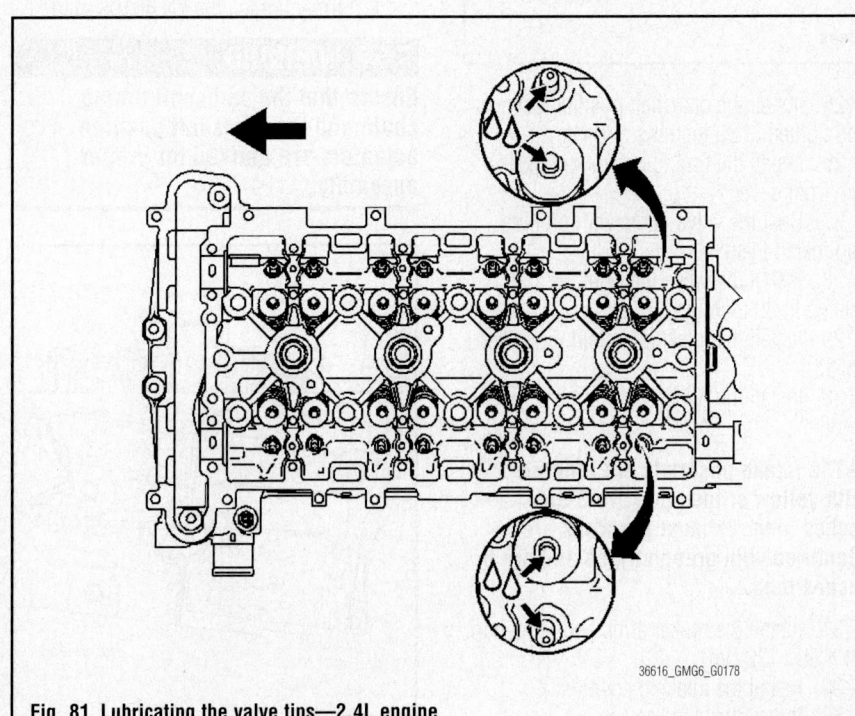

Fig. 81 Lubricating the valve tips—2.4L engine

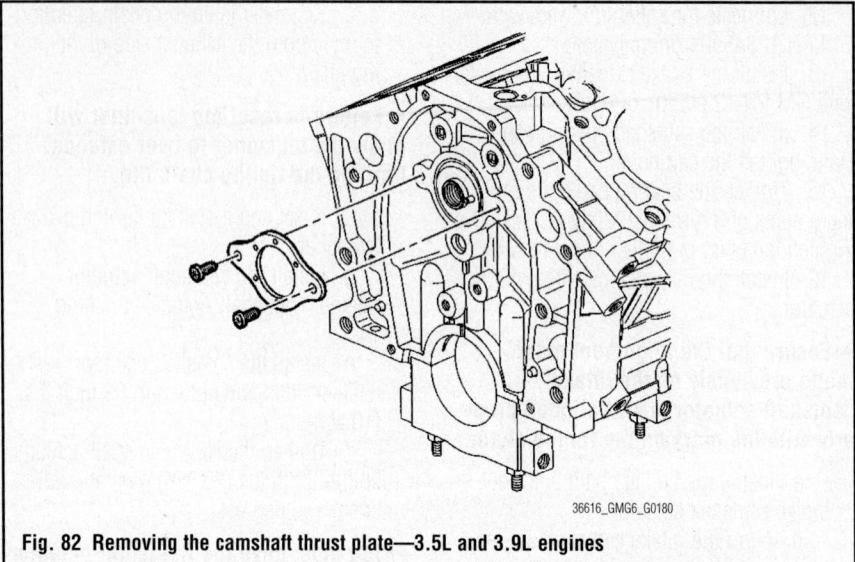

Fig. 82 Removing the camshaft thrust plate—3.5L and 3.9L engines

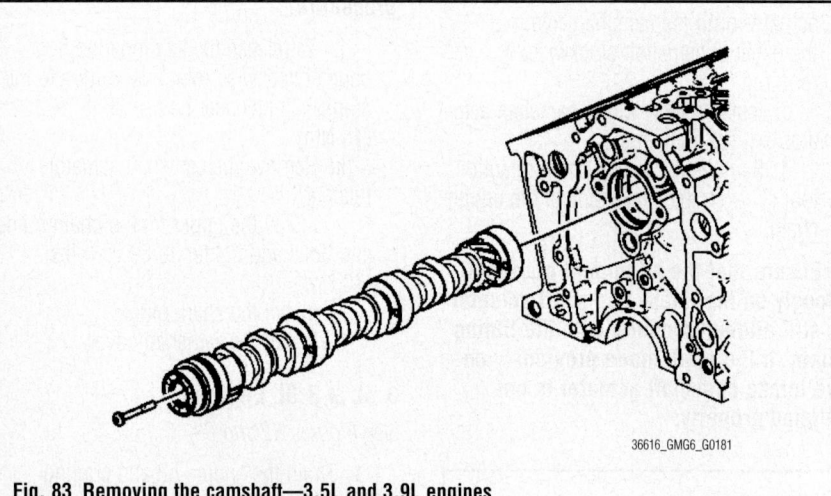

Fig. 83 Removing the camshaft—3.5L and 3.9L engines

❋❋ CAUTION

All camshaft journals are the same diameter, so care must be used in removing or installing the camshaft to avoid damage to the camshaft bearings.

18. Install the camshaft sprocket bolt into the camshaft. Tighten finger tight only.
19. Carefully rotate and remove the camshaft from the engine block.

To install:

20. Coat the camshaft journals with clean engine oil.
21. Coat the camshaft lobes with pre-lube.
22. Install the camshaft sprocket bolt into the camshaft. Tighten finger tight only.
23. Carefully rotate and install the camshaft to the engine block.
24. Install the camshaft thrust plate and tighten to 89 inch lbs. (10 Nm).

25. Install the camshaft position sensor and tighten to 89 inch lbs. (10 Nm).
26. Install the timing chain, sprockets and front cover.
27. Coat the valve lifters with prelube and install them.
28. Install the valve lifter guides and tighten to 89 inch lbs. (10 Nm).
29. Install the intake manifold oil splash shield.
30. Install the pushrods in their original locations.

➡**The intake pushrods are identified with yellow stripes and are 5-3/4 inches long. Exhaust pushrods are identified with green stripes and are 6 inches long.**

31. Install the rocker arms and tighten to 24 ft. lbs. (32 Nm).
32. Install the intake manifolds.
33. Install the valve covers.
34. Connect the negative battery cable.
35. Fill the cooling system.
36. Start the vehicle, check for leaks and repair if necessary.

3.6L Engine

Left Camshaft & Lifters

See Figures 84 through 89.

1. Disconnect the negative battery cable.
2. Remove the lower intake manifold.
3. Remove the left bank camshaft cover.
4. Remove the camshaft sensors.
5. Remove the camshaft position actuator solenoid.
6. Remove the crankshaft balancer
7. Rotate the crankshaft with the EN 46111 until the camshafts are in a neutral (low tension) position.
8. The camshaft flats will be parallel with the camshaft cover rail (1).

❋❋ WARNING

Use an open-end wrench at the camshaft hex to prevent camshaft/engine rotation. DO NOT remove the camshaft position actuator bolt at this time.

9. Loosen the camshaft position actuator bolt.

➡**Ensure that the tips of the EN 46108 are fully engaged into the timing chain (3 and 4).**

10. Install the EN 46108 (1 and 2) in order to retain the timing chain.
11. Firmly tighten the EN 46108 nuts.

❋❋ WARNING

Ensure that the camshaft timing chain and the camshaft position actuators are marked for proper assembly.

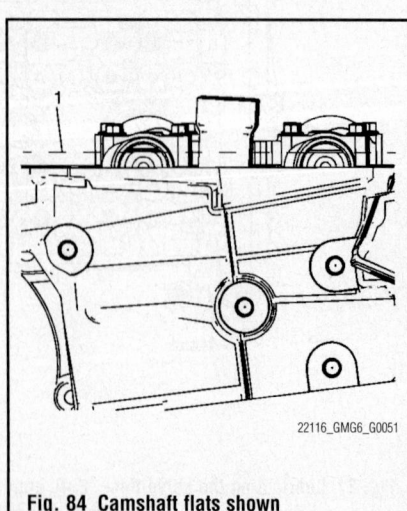

Fig. 84 Camshaft flats shown

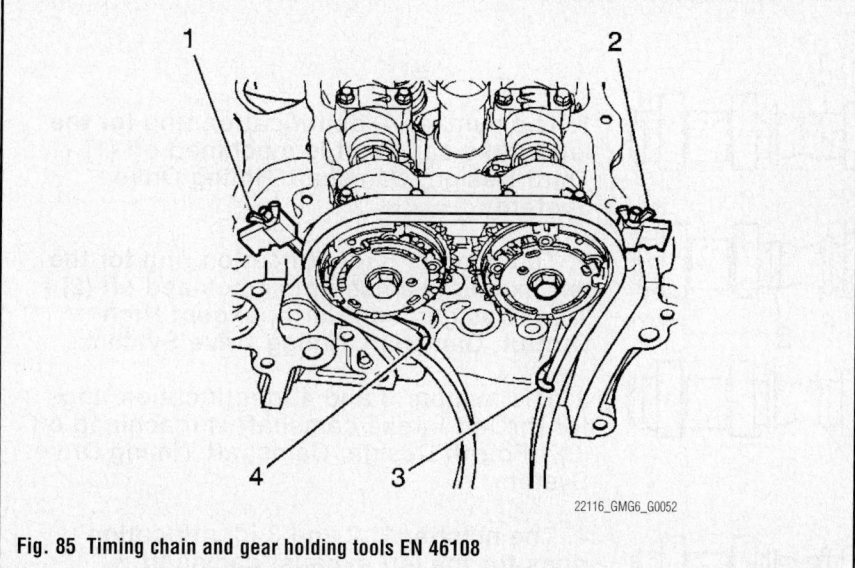

Fig. 85 Timing chain and gear holding tools EN 46108

12. Mark the timing chain and the respective locations on the camshaft position actuators (1-4).

13. Remove the camshaft position actuator bolt.

14. Observe the markings on the bearing caps. Each bearing cap is marked in order to identify its location.

15. The markings have the following meanings:

- The raised feature must always be oriented toward the center of the cylinder head.
- The I indicates the intake camshaft.
- The E indicates the exhaust camshaft
- The number indicates the journal position from the front of the engine

16. Remove the camshaft bearing cap bolts.

17. Remove the camshaft bearing caps.

18. Remove the camshafts.

19. Remove the rocker arms.

20. Remove lifters.

21. Replace the camshaft bearing caps and bolts.

To install:

⁑ **WARNING**

Ensure that the marks on the camshaft position actuator and the timing chain (1—4) are aligned. DO NOT tighten the camshaft position actuator bolt at this time.

22. Locate the camshafts to the cylinder head and assemble the camshaft actuators to the camshafts.

23. Ensure that the crankshaft is in the stage one timing drive assembly position using the EN 46111.

24. Ensure that the camshaft sealing rings (1) are in place in the camshaft grooves. Camshaft sealing rings must be in place below the surface of the camshaft journal in order to avoid being pinched between the cylinder head and the camshaft caps.

➡Ensure each valve lifter is filled with clean engine oil and the valve lifter does not tip over (plunger down) before the installation of the valve lifters. The loss of oil in the valve lifter lower pressure chamber or the dry stroking/cycling of the valve lifter plunger will allow air to travel into the high pressure chamber of the valve lifter. Air in the high pressure chamber of the valve lifter may not be purged causing extensive engine component damage.

25. Install valve lifters.

26. Install rocker arms.

27. Apply a liberal amount of lubricant to the camshaft journals and the left cylinder head camshaft carriers.

28. Place the left intake and left exhaust camshafts in position in the left cylinder head.

29. Position the camshaft lobes in a neutral position with the flats on the back of the camshafts up and parallel (1) with the left cylinder head camshaft cover rail.

30. Observe the markings on the left cylinder head camshaft bearing caps. Each

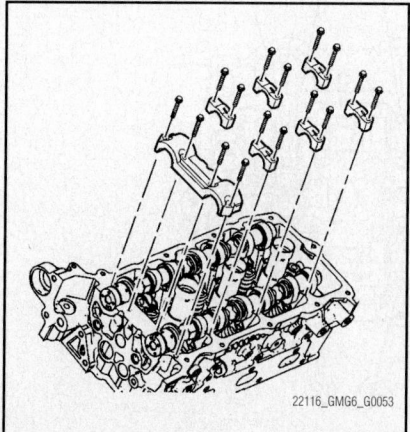

Fig. 86 Camshaft bearing cap removal— 3.6L engine

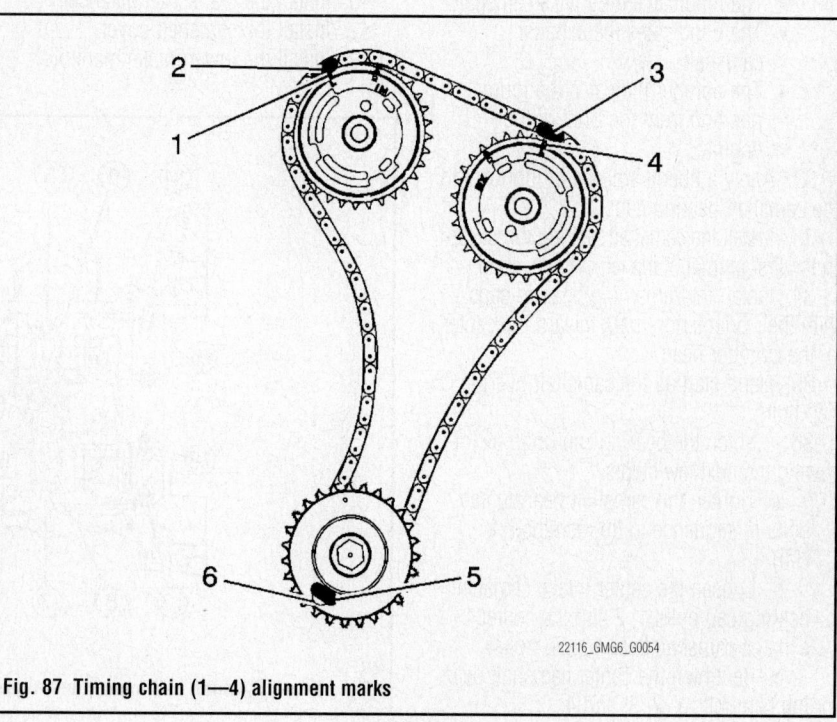

Fig. 87 Timing chain (1—4) alignment marks

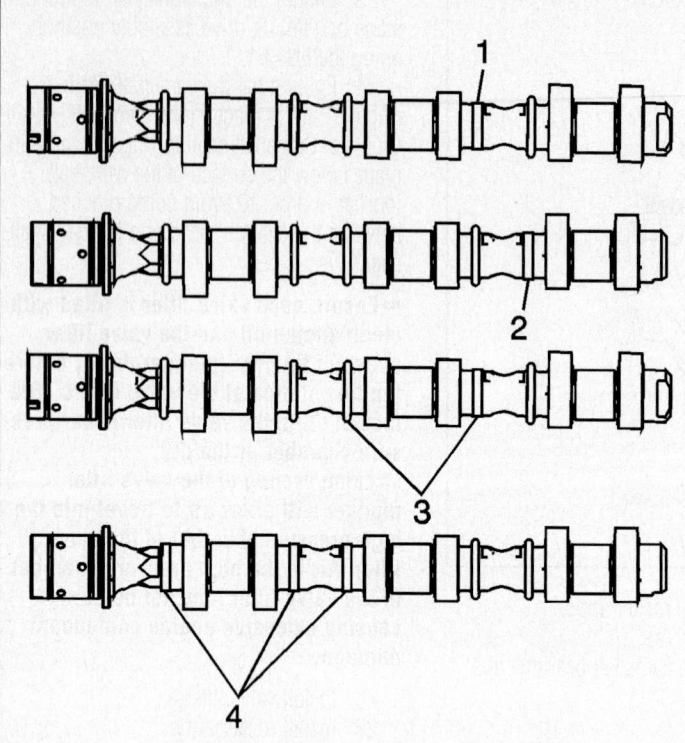

1. The number 4 identification ring for the left intake camshaft is machined off (1) - Third Design, Camshaft Timing Drive System.

2. The number 5 identification ring for the left exhaust camshaft is machined off (2) - Third Design and Fourth, except High Output, Camshaft Timing Drive System.

3. The number 3 and 4 identification rings for the left intake camshaft is machined off (3) - Fourth Design, Camshaft Timing Drive System.

4. The number 1, 2 and 3 identification rings for the left exhaust camshaft is machined off (4) - Fourth Design High Output, Camshaft Timing Drive System.

22116_GMG6_G0055

Fig. 88 Camshaft design identification—3.6L engine

bearing cap is marked in order to identify its location.

31. The markings have the following meanings:

- The raised feature must always be oriented toward the center of the cylinder head.
- The I indicates the intake camshaft.
- The E indicates the exhaust camshaft
- The number indicates the journal position from the front of the engine

32. Apply a liberal amount of lubricant to the camshaft bearing caps.

33. Install the camshaft bearing thrust cap in the first journal of the left cylinder head.

34. Install the remaining bearing caps with their orientation mark toward the center of the cylinder head.

35. Hand start all the camshaft bearing cap bolts.

36. Tighten the bearing cap bolts by following the next few steps:

a. Tighten the camshaft bearing cap bolts in sequence to 89 inch lbs.(10 Nm).

b. Loosen the center intake camshaft bearing cap bolts 1, 2 and the center exhaust camshaft bearing cap bolts.

c. Retighten the center camshaft bearing cap bolts 1, 2, 3, and 4.

d. Retighten the camshaft bearing cap bolts to 89 inch lbs.(10 Nm).

37. Install and tighten the camshaft position actuators.

38. Install the intake camshaft position actuator solenoid.

39. Install the camshaft sensors.

40. Install the crankshaft balancer.

41. Install the camshaft cover.

42. Install the lower intake manifold.

43. Connect the negative battery cable.

44. Drain crankcase and install recommended motor oil.

45. Start the vehicle, check for leaks and repair if necessary.

Right Camshaft & Lifters

See Figures 90 through 94.

1. Disconnect the negative battery cable.

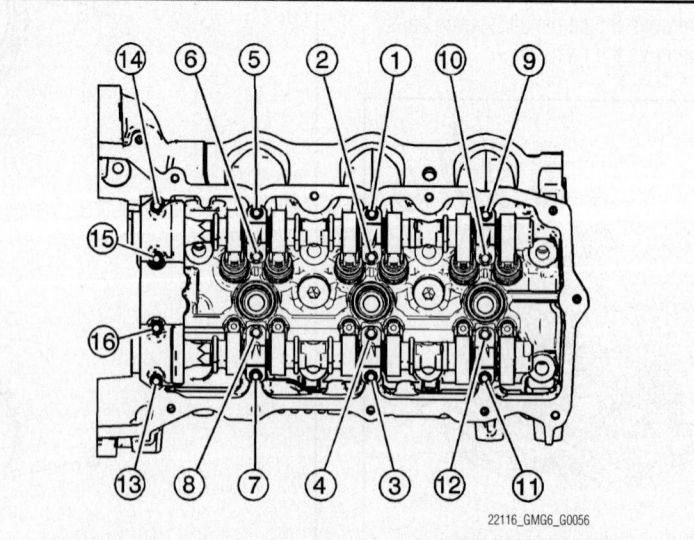

22116_GMG6_G0056

Fig. 89 Left camshaft bearing cap bolt tightening sequence—3.6L engine

2. Remove the lower intake manifold.
3. Remove the camshaft cover.
4. Remove the camshaft sensors.
5. Remove the intake camshaft position actuator solenoid.
6. Rotate the crankshaft with the EN 46111 until the camshafts are in a neutral (low tension) position. The camshaft flats will be parallel with the camshaft cover rail.

❋❋ WARNING

Use an open-end wrench at the camshaft hex to prevent camshaft/engine rotation. DO NOT remove the camshaft position actuator bolt at this time.

7. Loosen the camshaft position actuator bolt.

➡ **Ensure that the tips of the EN 46108 are fully engaged into the timing chain (3 and 4).**

8. Install the EN 46108 (1 and 2) in order to retain the timing chain.
9. Firmly tighten the EN 46108 nuts.

❋❋ WARNING

Ensure that the camshaft timing chain and the camshaft position actuators are marked for proper assembly.

10. Mark the timing chain and the respective locations on camshaft position actuators (15-18).
11. Remove the camshaft position actuator bolt.
12. Observe the markings on the right cylinder head camshaft bearing caps. Each

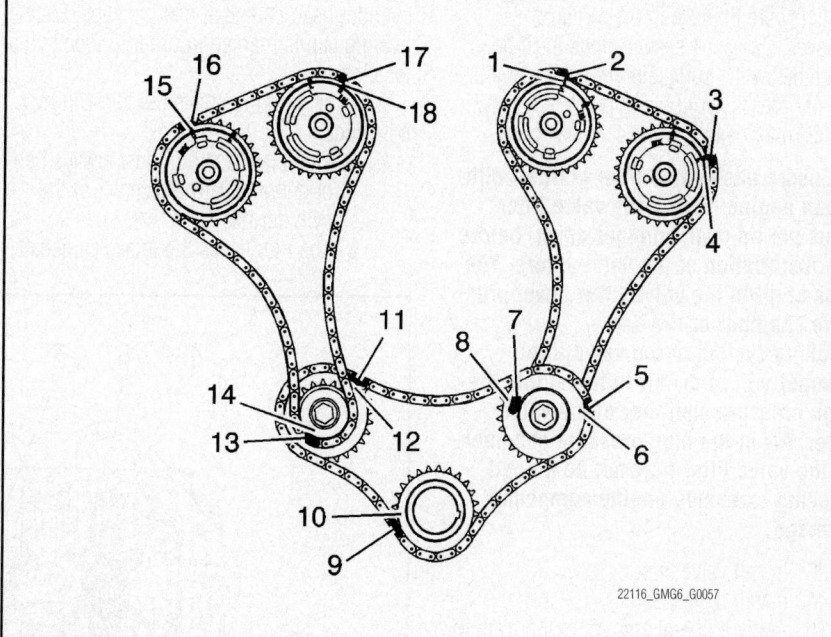

Fig. 91 Timing chain alignment marks —3.6L engine

bearing cap is marked in order to identify its location.
13. The markings have the following meanings:
- The raised feature must always be oriented toward the center of the cylinder head.
- The I indicates the intake camshaft.
- The E indicates the exhaust camshaft
- The number indicates the journal position from the front of the engine
14. Remove the camshaft bearing cap bolts.
15. Remove the camshaft bearing caps.
16. Remove the camshafts.

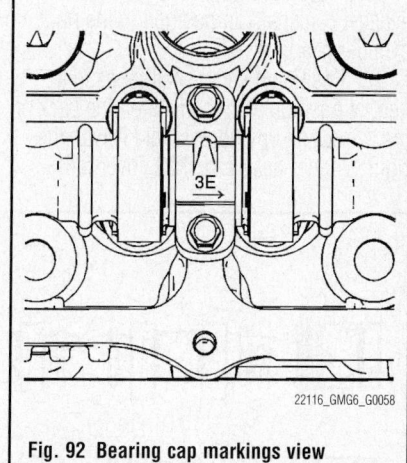

Fig. 92 Bearing cap markings view

17. Remove the rocker arms.
18. Remove lifters.
19. Replace the camshaft bearing caps and bolts.

To install:

❋❋ WARNING

Ensure that the marks on the camshaft position actuator and the timing chain (1—4) are aligned. DO NOT tighten the camshaft position actuator bolt at this time.

20. Locate the camshafts to the cylinder head and assemble the camshaft actuators to the camshafts.
21. Ensure that the crankshaft is in the stage one timing drive assembly position using the EN 46111.

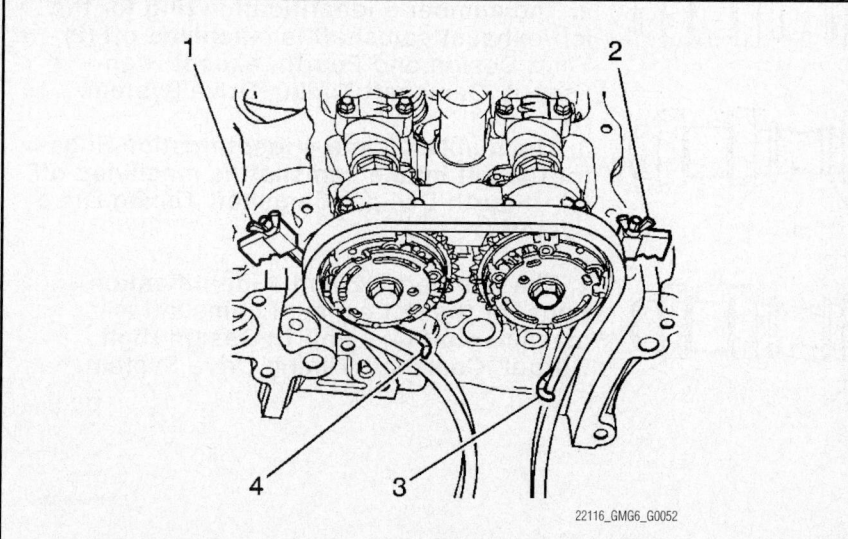

Fig. 90 Timing chain and gear holding tools EN 46108

22. Ensure that the camshaft sealing rings (1) are in place in the camshaft grooves. Camshaft sealing rings must be in place below the surface of the camshaft journal in order to avoid being pinched between the cylinder head and the camshaft caps.

➡**Ensure each valve lifter is filled with clean engine oil and the valve lifter does not tip over (plunger down) before the installation of the valve lifters. The loss of oil in the valve lifter lower pressure chamber or the dry stroking/cycling of the valve lifter plunger will allow air to travel into the high pressure chamber of the valve lifter. Air in the high pressure chamber of the valve lifter may not be purged causing extensive engine component damage.**

23. Install valve lifters.
24. Install rocker arms.
25. Apply a liberal amount of lubricant to the camshaft journals and the right cylinder head camshaft carriers.
26. Place the right intake and right exhaust camshafts in position in the right cylinder head.
27. Position the camshaft lobes in a neutral position with the flats on the back of the camshafts up and parallel (1) with the right cylinder head camshaft cover rail.

28. Observe the markings on the right cylinder head camshaft bearing caps. Each bearing cap is marked in order to identify its location.
29. The markings have the following meanings:
- The raised feature must always be oriented toward the center of the cylinder head.
- The I indicates the intake camshaft.

- The E indicates the exhaust camshaft
- The number indicates the journal position from the front of the engine

30. Apply a liberal amount of lubricant to the camshaft bearing caps.
31. Install the camshaft bearing thrust cap in the first journal of the right cylinder head.

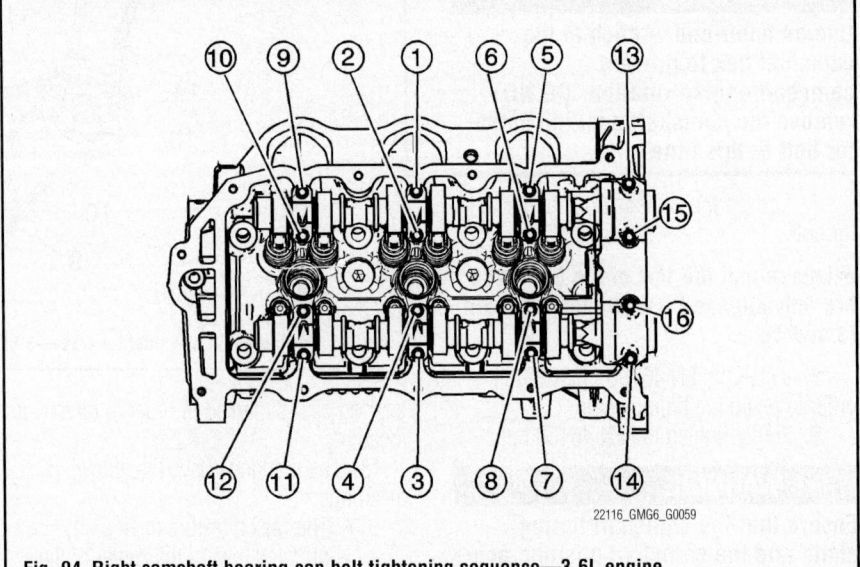

Fig. 94 Right camshaft bearing cap bolt tightening sequence—3.6L engine

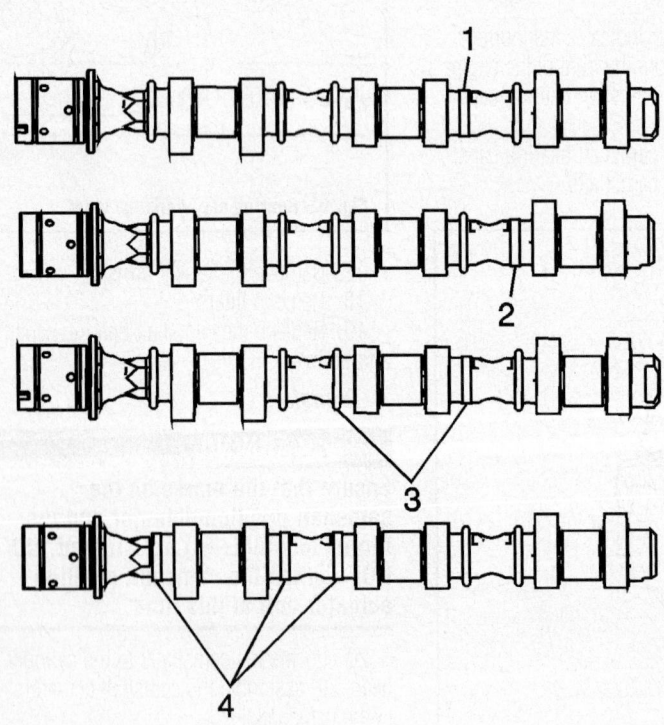

1. The number 4 identification ring for the left intake camshaft is machined off (1) - Third Design, Camshaft Timing Drive System.

2. The number 5 identification ring for the left exhaust camshaft is machined off (2) - Third Design and Fourth, except High Output, Camshaft Timing Drive System.

3. The number 3 and 4 identification rings for the left intake camshaft is machined off (3) - Fourth Design, Camshaft Timing Drive System.

4. The number 1, 2 and 3 identification rings for the left exhaust camshaft is machined off (4) - Fourth Design High Output, Camshaft Timing Drive System.

22116_GMG6_G0055

Fig. 93 Camshaft design identification—3.6L engine

32. Install the remaining bearing caps with their orientation mark toward the center of the cylinder head.

33. Hand start all the camshaft bearing cap bolts.

34. Tighten the bearing cap bolts by following the next few steps:

a. Tighten the camshaft bearing cap bolts in sequence to 89 inch lbs.(10 Nm).

b. Loosen the center intake camshaft bearing cap bolts (1, 2) and the center exhaust camshaft bearing cap bolts (3, 4).

c. Retighten the center camshaft bearing cap bolts 1, 2, 3, and 4.

d. Retighten the camshaft bearing cap bolts to 89 inch lbs.(10 Nm).

35. Install and tighten the camshaft position actuators.

36. Install the intake camshaft position actuator solenoid.

37. Install the camshaft sensors.

38. Install the crankshaft balancer.

39. Install the camshaft cover.

40. Install the lower intake manifold.

41. Connect the negative battery cable.

42. Drain crankcase and install recommended motor oil.

43. Start the vehicle, check for leaks and repair if necessary.

CATALYTIC CONVERTER

REMOVAL & INSTALLATION

2.4L Engine

See Figure 95.

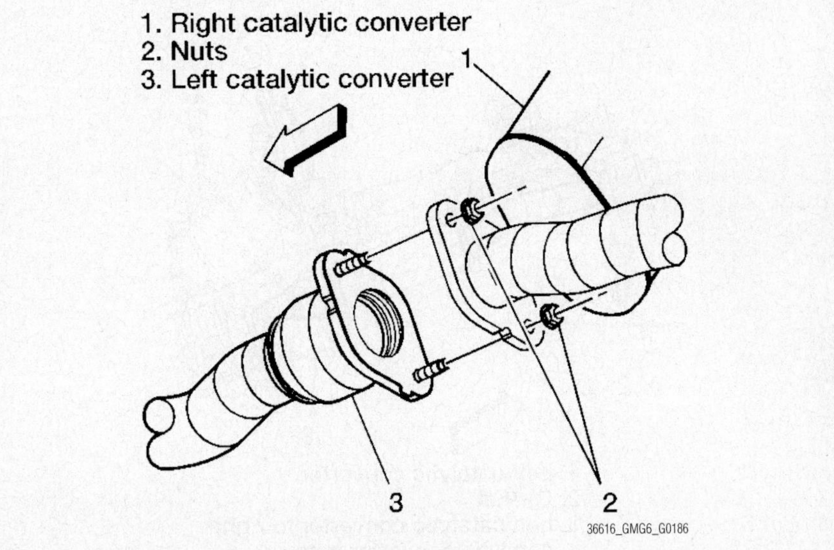

1. Remove the exhaust manifold shield.

2. Remove the catalytic converter to exhaust manifold nuts.

3. Raise and support the vehicle.

4. Remove the heated oxygen sensor.

5. Remove the catalytic converter to muffler nuts.

6. Separate the exhaust pipe from the catalytic converter studs.

7. Position and support the exhaust pipe out of the way.

8. Remove the converter to bracket bolt.

9. Remove the catalytic converter and gasket. Discard the Catalytic converter gaskets.

To install:

10. Install a NEW gasket to the catalytic converter.

11. Position the catalytic converter to the exhaust manifold and converter bracket.

12. Loosely install the converter to manifold nuts and converter bracket bolt.

1. Right catalytic converter
2. Nuts
3. Left catalytic converter

36616_GMG6_G0186

Fig. 95 Removing the catalytic converter—2.4L engine

13. Tighten the Converter to bracket bolt to 22 ft. lbs. (30 Nm).

14. Install a NEW gasket between the converter and exhaust pipe.

15. Connect the exhaust pipe to the converter and tighten the nuts to 18 ft. lbs. (25 Nm).

16. Install the heated oxygen sensor.

17. Lower the vehicle

18. Tighten the converter to manifold nuts to 18 ft. lbs. (25 Nm).

19. Install the exhaust manifold heat shield. Tighten the bolts to 89 inch lbs. (10 Nm).

3.5L Engine

See Figures 96 and 97.

1. Remove the left catalytic converter nuts at the exhaust manifold.

2. Remove the muffler assembly.

3. Remove the rear Heated Oxygen Sensor (HO2S) Connector Position Assurance (CPA) retainer.

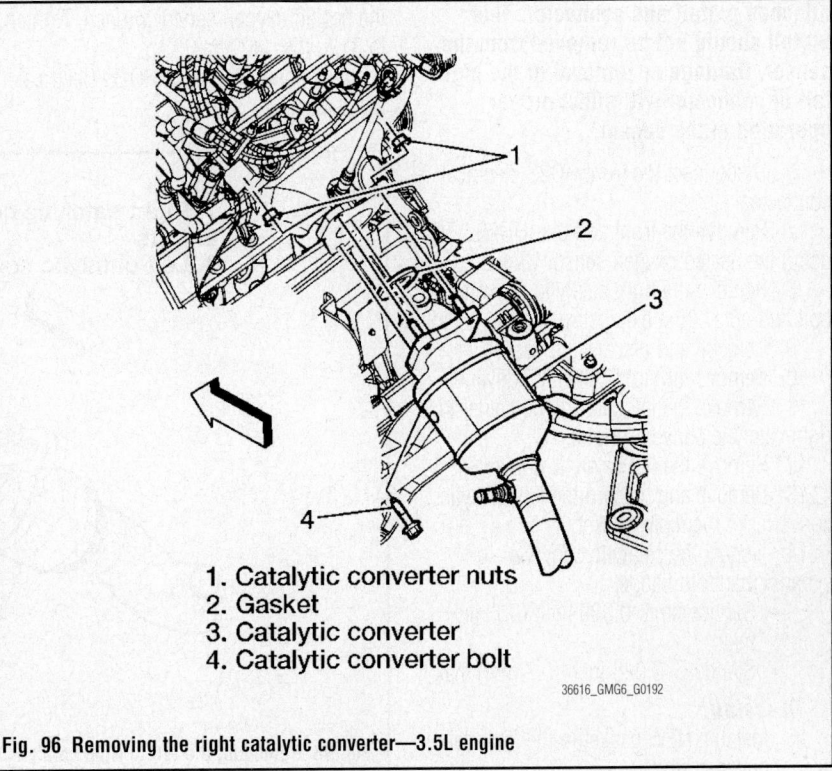

1. Catalytic converter nuts
2. Gasket
3. Catalytic converter
4. Catalytic converter bolt

36616_GMG6_G0192

Fig. 96 Removing the right catalytic converter—3.5L engine

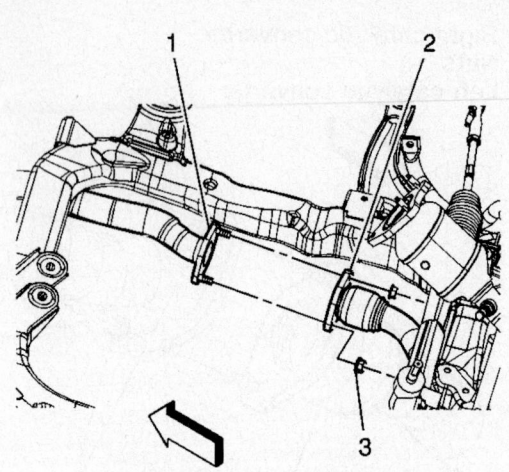

1. Left catalytic converter
2. Gasket
3. Left catalytic converter to right catalytic converter nuts

36616_GMG6_G0193

Fig. 97 Removing the left catalytic converter (powertrain shown for clarity)—3.5L engine

➡**The HO2S uses a permanently attached pigtail and connector. This pigtail should not be removed from the sensor. Damage or removal of the pigtail or connector will affect proper operation of the sensor.**

4. Disconnect the rear HO2S electrical connector.

5. Remove the front HO2S CPA retainer.

➡**The HO2S uses a permanently attached pigtail and connector. This pigtail should not be removed from the sensor. Damage or removal of the pigtail or connector will affect proper operation of the sensor.**

6. Disconnect the front HO2S electrical connector.

7. Remove the front and rear HO2S using the heated oxygen sensor wrench.

8. Remove the right catalytic converter bolt and nuts at the exhaust manifold.

9. Remove and discard the gasket.

10. Remove the right catalytic converter.

11. Remove the left catalytic converter to right catalytic converter nuts.

12. Remove the left catalytic converter.

13. Remove and discard the left catalytic converter to manifold gasket.

14. Inspect the catalytic converter-to-exhaust manifold flange.
   • Service limit: 0.028 inch (0.7 mm) max
   • Standard: 0.028 inch (0.7 mm) max

To install:

15. Install a NEW gasket to the front catalytic converter studs.

16. Install the left catalytic converter.

17. Install a NEW gasket to the right catalytic converter studs.

18. Install the right catalytic converter.

19. Install the right catalytic converter bolt and nuts at the exhaust manifold. Tighten the bolt and nuts to 23 ft. lbs. (31 Nm).

20. Install the left catalytic converter to right catalytic converter nuts. Tighten the nuts to 23 ft. lbs. (31 Nm).

21. Install the front and rear HO2S using the heated oxygen sensor wrench. Tighten to 31 ft. lbs. (42 Nm).

22. Connect the front HO2S electrical connector.

23. Install the front HO2S CPA retainer.

24. Disconnect the rear HO2S electrical connector.

25. Install the rear HO2S CPA retainer.

26. Install the muffler assembly.

27. Install the left catalytic converter nuts at the exhaust manifold. Tighten the nuts to 23 ft. lbs. (31 Nm).

28. Start the engine, and check for exhaust leaks.

3.6L Engine

Left Side

See Figures 98 and 99.

1. Remove the exhaust manifold heat shield.

2. Remove the fuel injector sight shield.

3. Remove the air cleaner outlet duct.

4. Remove the Connector Position Assurance (CPA) retainer from the HO2S electrical connection.

5. Disconnect the engine wiring harness electrical connector from the Heated Oxygen Sensor (HO2S) electrical connector.

6. Remove the HO2S electrical connector clip from the engine wiring harness tab.
   a. Remove the bank 2 sensor 1 heated oxygen sensor (HO2S) from the exhaust manifold.

7. Remove the left catalytic converter to exhaust manifold nuts.

8. Raise and support the vehicle.

9. Disconnect the bank 2 sensor 2 heated oxygen sensor (HO2S) electrical connector from the engine wiring harness electrical connector.

10. Remove the left catalytic converter to right catalytic converter nuts.

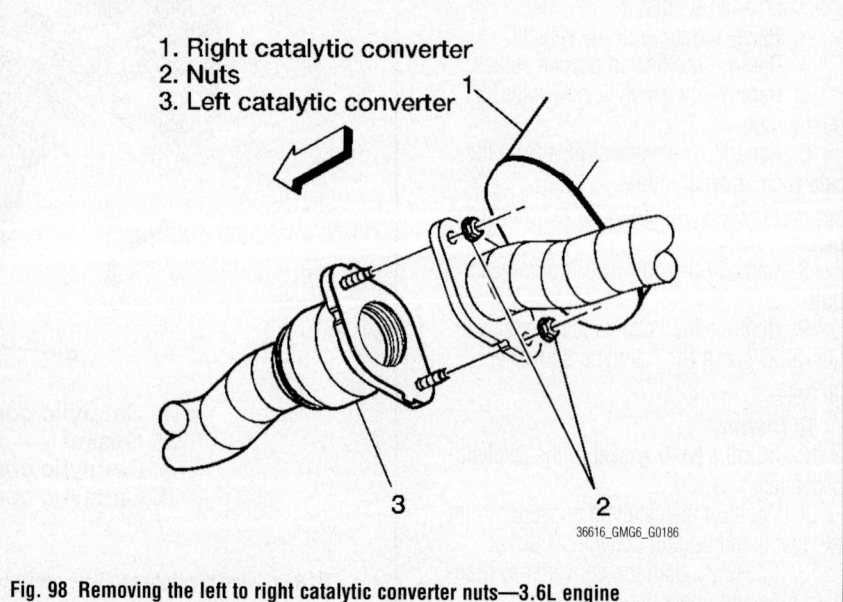

1. Right catalytic converter
2. Nuts
3. Left catalytic converter

36616_GMG6_G0186

Fig. 98 Removing the left to right catalytic converter nuts—3.6L engine

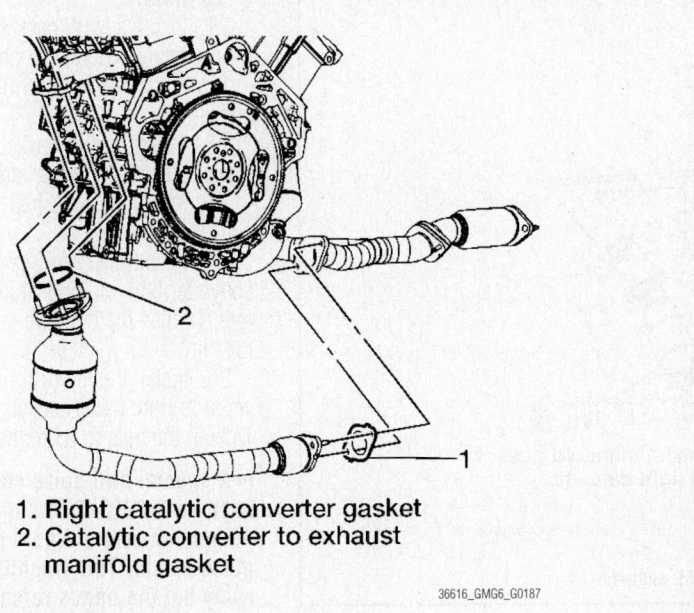

1. Right catalytic converter gasket
2. Catalytic converter to exhaust
   manifold gasket

36616_GMG6_G0187

Fig. 99 Removing the left catalytic converter—3.6L engine

11. Remove the left catalytic converter from the vehicle.

12. Discard the catalytic converter to exhaust manifold gasket.

13. Discard the left catalytic converter to right catalytic converter gasket.

To install:

14. Install a NEW catalytic converter seal onto the catalytic converter.

15. Install the catalytic converter to the vehicle.

16. Install a NEW left catalytic converter to right catalytic converter gasket.

17. Install the left catalytic converter to right catalytic converter nuts and tighten to 18 ft. lbs. (25 Nm).

18. Connect the bank 2 sensor 2 HO2S electrical connector to the engine wiring harness electrical connector.

19. Install the left catalytic converter to exhaust manifold nuts and tighten to 33 lb ft (45 Nm).

20. Install the exhaust manifold heat shield. Tighten the bolts to 89 inch lbs. (10 Nm).

➡A special anti-seize compound is used in the HO2S threads. The compound consists of liquid graphite and glass beads. The graphite tends to burn away, but the glass beads remain, making the sensor easier to remove. New, or service replacement sensors already have the compound applied to the threads. If the sensor is removed from an exhaust component and if for any reason the sensor is to reinstalled, the threads must have anti-seize

compound applied before the reinstallation.

  a. If reinstalling the old sensor, coat the threads with anti-seize compound GM P/N 12377953, or equivalent.

  b. Install the HO2S to the exhaust manifold and tighten the sensor to 31 ft. lbs. (42 Nm).

  c. Connect the engine wiring harness electrical connector to the HO2S electrical connector.

  d. Install the HO2S electrical connector clip to the engine wiring harness tab.

  e. Install the CPA retainer to the HO2S electrical connection.

  f. Install the air cleaner outlet duct.

  g. Install the fuel injector sight shield.

21. Lower the vehicle and inspect for exhaust leaks.

Right Side

See Figures 100 and 101.

1. Remove the exhaust manifold heat shield.

2. Remove the catalytic converter to exhaust manifold nuts.

3. Remove the bank 1 sensor 2 Heated Oxygen Sensor (HO2S).

4. Remove the left catalytic converter to right catalytic converter nuts.

5. Remove the exhaust pipe to right catalytic converter nuts.

6. Remove the catalytic converter from the vehicle.

7. Remove and discard the catalytic converter to exhaust manifold gasket.

8. Remove and discard the left catalytic converter to right catalytic converter gasket.

To install:

9. Install a NEW catalytic converter to exhaust manifold gasket onto the catalytic converter.

10. Install the catalytic converter to the vehicle.

11. Install a NEW left catalytic converter to right catalytic converter gasket between the converters.

12. Install the left catalytic converter to right catalytic converter nuts and tighten to 18 ft. lbs. (25 Nm).

13. Install the exhaust pipe to right catalytic converter nuts and tighten to 18 ft. lbs. (25 Nm).

14. Install the exhaust manifold heat shield.

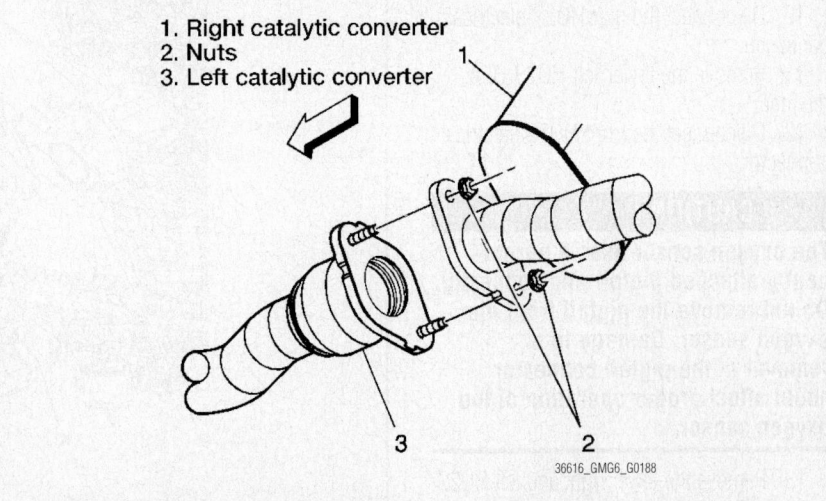

1. Right catalytic converter
2. Nuts
3. Left catalytic converter

36616_GMG6_G0188

Fig. 100 Removing the left catalytic converter to right catalytic converter nuts—3.6L engine

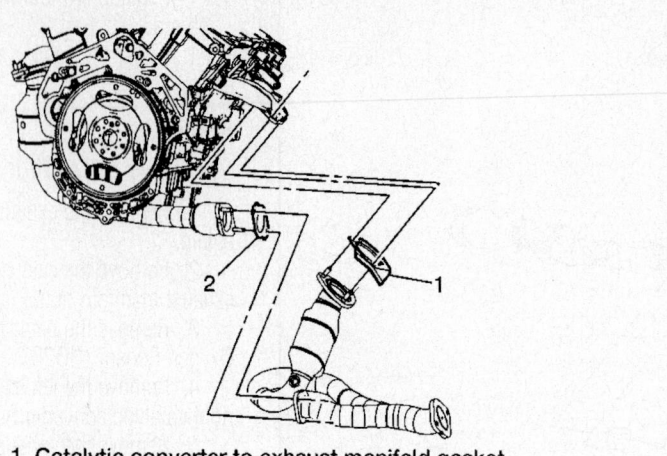

1. Catalytic converter to exhaust manifold gasket
2. Left catalytic converter to right catalytic converter gasket

36616_GMG6_G0189

Fig. 101 Removing the right catalytic converter—3.6L engine

3.9L Engine

Left Side

See Figure 102.

1. Remove the air cleaner assembly.
2. Remove the Connector Position Assurance (CPA) retainer.
3. Disconnect the Heated Oxygen Sensor (HO2S) electrical connector (4).
4. Remove the HO2S clip from the oil level indicator tube bracket.
5. Remove the exhaust manifold heat shield bolts.
6. Remove the exhaust manifold heat shield.
7. Remove the left (front) catalytic converter nuts at the exhaust manifold.
8. Remove the muffler assembly.
9. Remove the lower right heated oxygen sensor HO2S connector position assurance (CPA) retainer.
10. Disconnect the rear HO2S electrical connector.
11. Remove the lower left HO2S CPA retainer.
12. Disconnect the front HO2S electrical connector.

❋❋ CAUTION

The oxygen sensor uses a permanently attached pigtail and connector. Do not remove the pigtail from the oxygen sensor. Damage to or removal of the pigtail connector could affect proper operation of the oxygen sensor.

13. Remove the lower right and left HO2S using the heated oxygen sensor wrench.

14. Remove the left (front) catalytic converter to right (rear) catalytic converter nuts.
15. Remove the right (rear) catalytic converter bolt and nuts at the exhaust manifold.
16. Remove and discard the gasket.
17. Remove the right (rear) catalytic converter.
18. Remove the left (front) catalytic converter.
19. Remove and discard the left (front) catalytic converter to manifold gasket.
20. Inspect the catalytic converter-to-exhaust manifold flange. The catalytic converter to manifold flange warpage standard service limit is 0.028 inch (0.7 mm) max.

To install:

21. Install a NEW gasket to the left (front) catalytic converter studs.
22. Install the left (front) catalytic converter.
23. Install a NEW gasket to the right (rear) catalytic converter studs.
24. Install the right (rear) catalytic converter.
25. Install the right (rear) catalytic converter bolt and nuts at the exhaust manifold. Tighten the bolt and nuts to 23 ft. lbs. (31 Nm).
26. Install the left (front) catalytic converter to right (rear) catalytic converter nuts. Tighten the nuts to 23 ft. lbs. (31 Nm).

➡️**A special anti-seize compound is used on the HO2S threads. The compound consists of liquid graphite and glass beads. The graphite tends to burn away but the beads remain, making the sensor easier the remove. New, or service replacement sensors already have the compound applied to the threads. If the sensor is removed from an exhaust component and if for any reason the sensor is to be reinstalled, the threads must be have anti-seize compound applied before the reinstallation.**

27. If reinstalling the old HO2S, coat the threads with anti-seize compound GM P/N 12377953 or equivalent.
28. Install the lower right and left HO2S using the heated oxygen sensor wrench. Tighten the sensor to 31 ft. lbs. (42 Nm).
29. Connect the lower left HO2S electrical connector.
30. Install the lower left HO2S CPA retainer.

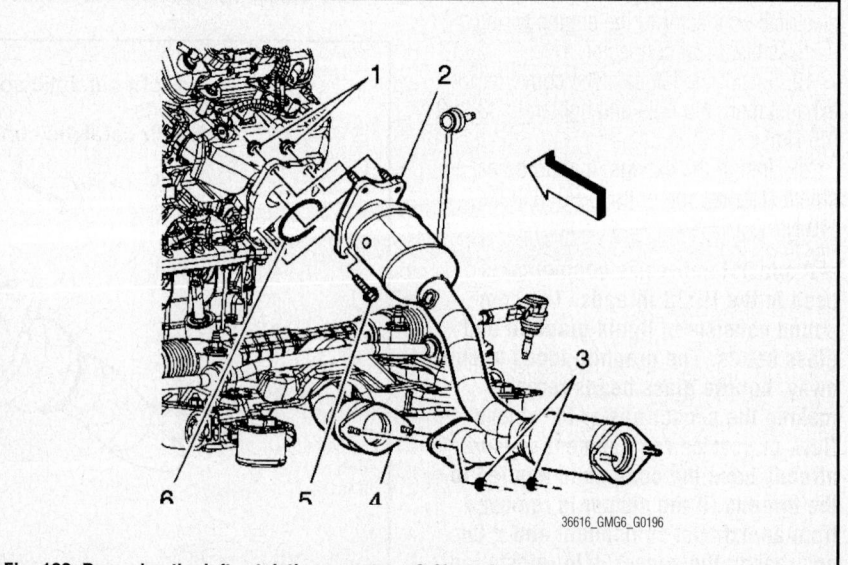

36616_GMG6_G0196

Fig. 102 Removing the left catalytic converter—3.9L engine

31. Connect the lower right HO2S electrical connector.

32. Install the lower right HO2S CPA retainer.

33. Install the muffler assembly.

34. Install the left (front) catalytic converter nuts at the exhaust manifold. Tighten the nuts to 23 ft. lbs. (31 Nm).

35. Install the exhaust manifold heat shield.

36. Install the exhaust manifold heat shield bolts. Tighten the bolts to 89 inch lbs. (10 Nm).

37. Connect the HO2S electrical connector.

38. Install the CPA retainer.

39. Install the HO2S clip to the oil level indicator tube bracket.

40. Install the air cleaner assembly.

41. Perform the engine mount position adjustment procedure.

42. Start the engine, and check for exhaust leaks.

Right Side (With 4T65-E)

See Figure 103.

1. Remove the muffler assembly.
2. Remove the rear stabilizer shaft.
3. Remove the Connector Position Assurance (CPA) retainer.
4. Disconnect the lower right Heated Oxygen Sensor (HO2S) electrical connector.

✳✳ CAUTION

The oxygen sensor uses a permanently attached pigtail and connector. Do not remove the pigtail from the oxygen sensor. Damage to or removal of the pigtail connector could affect proper operation of the oxygen sensor.

5. Remove the lower right HO2S using the heated oxygen sensor wrench.
6. Remove the left (front) catalytic converter to right (rear) catalytic converter nuts.
7. Remove the right (rear) catalytic converter bolt and nuts at the exhaust manifold.
8. Remove the right catalytic converter.
9. Remove and discard the gasket.
10. Inspect the catalytic converter-to-exhaust manifold flange. The catalytic converter to manifold flange warpage standard maximum service limit is 0.028 inch (0.7 mm).

To install:

11. Install a NEW gasket to the catalytic converter.
12. Install the right (rear) catalytic converter.
13. Install the right (rear) catalytic

converter bolt and nuts at the exhaust manifold. Tighten the nuts to 23 ft. lbs. (31 Nm).

14. Install the left (front) catalytic converter to right (rear) catalytic converter nuts. Tighten the nuts to 23 ft. lbs. (31 Nm).

➡ **A special anti-seize compound is used on the HO2S threads. The compound consists of liquid graphite and glass beads. The graphite tends to burn away but the beads remain, making the sensor easier the remove. New, or service replacement sensors already have the compound applied to the threads. If the sensor is removed from an exhaust component and if for any reason the sensor is to be reinstalled, the threads must be have anti-seize compound applied before the reinstallation.**

15. If reinstalling the old HO2S, coat the threads with anti-seize compound GM P/N 12377953 or equivalent.
16. Install the HO2S using the Heated Oxygen Sensor Wrench. Tighten the sensor to 31 ft. lbs. (42 Nm).
17. Connect the lower right HO2S electrical connector.
18. Install the CPA retainer.
19. Ensure that the HO2S connector clip is attached to the stud on the engine.
20. Install the rear stabilizer shaft.
21. Install the muffler assembly.
22. Perform the engine mount position adjustment procedure.
23. Start the engine, and check for exhaust leaks.

Right Side (With MT2)

See Figure 104.

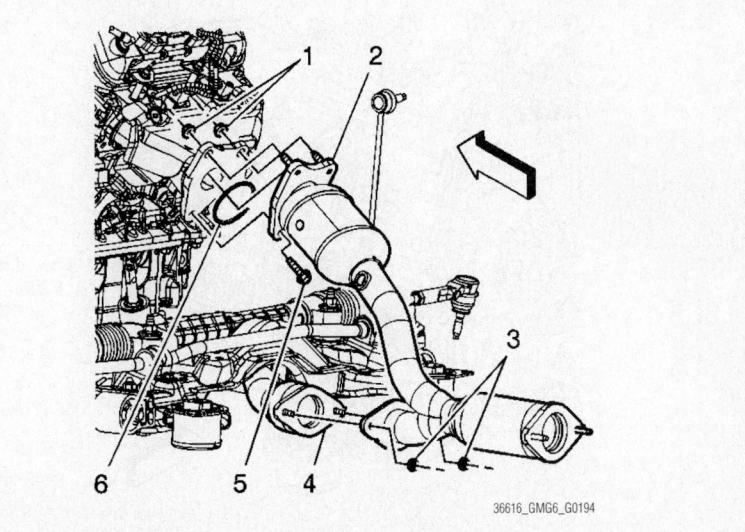

Fig. 103 Removing the right catalytic converter—3.9L engine

1. Remove the Connector Position Assurance (CPA) retainer.
2. Disconnect the engine harness electrical connector from the Heated Oxygen Sensor (HO2S).
3. Remove the HO2S clip from the oil level indicator tube bracket.
4. Remove the exhaust manifold heat shield bolts.
5. Remove the exhaust manifold heat shield.
6. Remove the right (rear) catalytic converter nuts.
7. Remove the muffler assembly.
8. Remove the rear stabilizer shaft.
9. Remove the CPA retainer.
10. Disconnect the HO2S electrical connector.

✳✳ CAUTION

The oxygen sensor uses a permanently attached pigtail and connector. Do not remove the pigtail from the oxygen sensor. Damage to or removal of the pigtail connector could affect proper operation of the oxygen sensor.

11. Remove the HO2S using the heated oxygen sensor wrench.
12. Remove the left (front) catalytic converter to right (rear) catalytic converter nuts.
13. Remove the right (rear) catalytic converter.
14. Remove and discard the gasket.
15. Inspect the catalytic converter-to-exhaust manifold flange. The catalytic converter to manifold flange warpage standard service limit is 0.028 inch (0.7 mm) max.

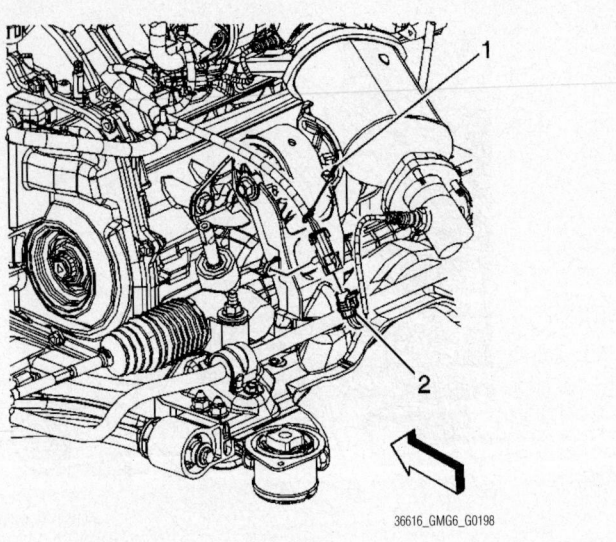

Fig. 104 Disconnecting the HO2S electrical connector—3.9L engine

To install:

16. Install a NEW gasket to the catalytic converter studs.

17. Install the right (rear) catalytic converter.

18. Install the left (front) catalytic converter to right (rear) catalytic converter nuts. Tighten the nuts to 23 ft. lbs. (31 Nm).

➡**A special anti-seize compound is used on the HO2S threads. The compound consists of liquid graphite and glass beads. The graphite tends to burn away but the beads remain, making the sensor easier the remove. New, or service replacement sensors already have the compound applied to the threads. If the sensor is removed from an exhaust component and if for any reason the sensor is to be reinstalled, the threads must be have anti-seize compound applied before the reinstallation.**

19. If reinstalling the old HO2S, coat the threads with anti-seize compound GM P/N 12377953 or equivalent.

20. Install the HO2S using the heated oxygen sensor wrench.

21. Tighten the sensor to 31 ft. lbs. (42 Nm).

22. Lower the vehicle to the ground, start the engine, and check for exhaust leaks.

23. Connect the HO2S electrical connector.

24. Install the CPA retainer.

25. Install the muffler assembly.

26. Install the rear stabilizer shaft.

27. Install the right (rear) catalytic converter nuts. Tighten the nuts to 23 ft. lbs. (31 Nm).

28. Install the exhaust manifold heat shield.

29. Install the exhaust manifold heat shield bolts. Tighten the bolts to 89 inch lbs. (10 Nm).Connect the engine harness electrical connector to the HO2S.

30. Install the CPA retainer.

31. Install the HO2S clip to the oil level indicator tube bracket.

32. Perform the engine mount position adjustment procedure.

33. Start the engine, and check for exhaust leaks.

CRANKSHAFT DAMPER

REMOVAL & INSTALLATION

2.4L Engine

See Figure 105.

1. Remove the engine drive belt.

2. Use the Balancer Holder J-38122-A in order to prevent the crankshaft from rotating while loosening the crankshaft balancer bolt.

3. Remove and discard the crankshaft balancer bolt.

4. Remove the crankshaft balancer.

To install:

➡**Ensure both components are aligned correctly or serious engine damage will occur.**

5. Install the crankshaft balancer holder into the end of the crankshaft.

6. Install the balancer onto the crankshaft balancer guide (EN-48585). Use care to properly align the keyway and flats on the balancer with the oil pump drive.

➡**The flywheel locking tool (J 43653) may be used instead of the crankshaft balancer holder (J 38112-A) to prevent crankshaft rotation.**

7. Install the crankshaft balancer holder.

➡**Always install a new crankshaft balancer retaining bolt and washer.**

8. Install a new retaining bolt and washer. Use the crankshaft balancer holder and a breaker bar to prevent the crankshaft from rotating when tightening the bolt. Tighten the bolt to 74 ft. lbs. (100 Nm) plus 125° using the angle meter (J 45059).

9. Install the camshaft actuator locking tool (EN-48953) and tighten the bolts into the cylinder head. Tighten the locking tool retaining bolts to 89 inch lbs. (10 Nm).

10. Release the timing chain tensioner by applying 33 ft. lbs. (45 Nm) counter-

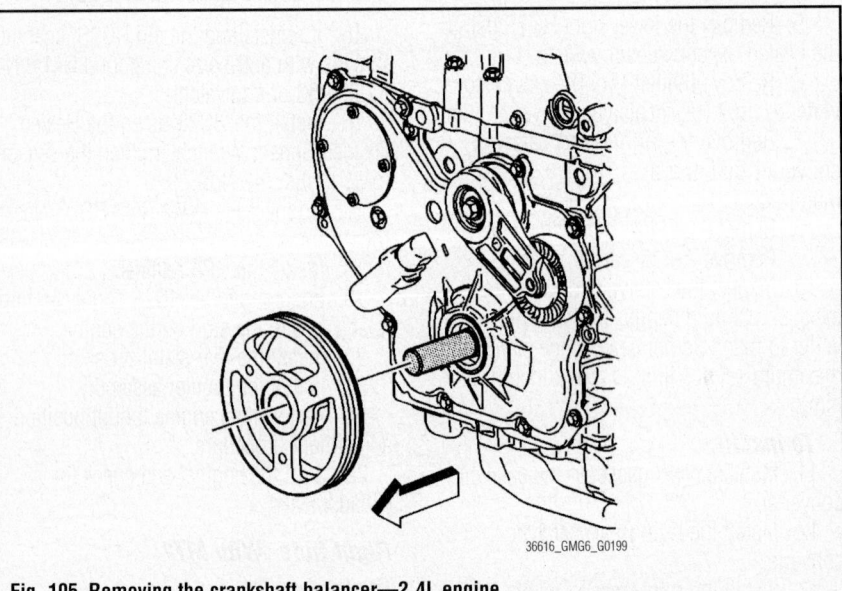

Fig. 105 Removing the crankshaft balancer—2.4L engine

clockwise torque to the crankshaft balancer bolt.

11. Remove the locking tool.

3.6L Engine

See Figures 106 and 107.

1. Install the flywheel holding tool (EN 46106) through the starter mounting hole.

2. Remove the crankshaft balancer bolt.

3. Install the crankshaft button (J 38416-2) in the nose of the crankshaft.

4. Install the crankshaft balancer remover (J 41816) in order to remove the crankshaft balancer.

5. Tighten the center bolt of the crankshaft balancer remover (J 41816) in order to pull the crankshaft balancer off of the crankshaft.

6. Remove the crankshaft balancer remover (J 41816) from the crankshaft balancer.

7. Remove the flywheel holding tool (EN 46106).

To install:

8. Install the flywheel holding tool (EN 46106).

9. Use the crankshaft balancer installer (J 41998-B), nut, bearing and washer to install the crankshaft balancer.

➥Do not lubricate the crankshaft front oil seal or crankshaft balancer sealing surfaces. The crankshaft balancer is installed into a dry seal.

10. Apply lubricant to the inside of the crankshaft balancer hub bore.

11. Place the crankshaft balancer in position on the crankshaft.

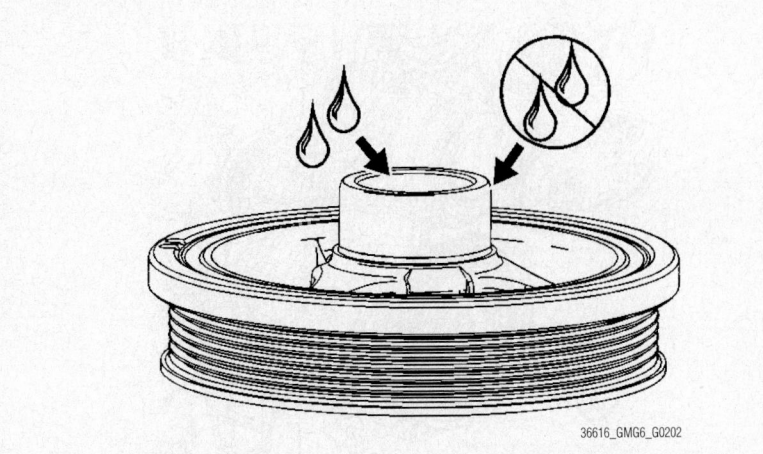

Fig. 107 Applying lubricant to the inside of the crankshaft balancer hub bore—3.6L engine

12. Thread the crankshaft balancer installer (J 41998-B) in the crankshaft. Ensure you engage at least 10 threads of the crankshaft balancer installer (J 41998-B) before pressing the crankshaft balancer in place.

13. Push the crankshaft balancer into position by tightening the nut on the crankshaft balancer installer (J 41998-B) until the large washer bottoms out on the crankshaft end.

14. Remove the crankshaft balancer installer (J 41998-B).

15. Install the crankshaft balancer bolt.

16. Tighten the crankshaft balancer bolt to 74 ft. lbs. (100 Nm). Tighten the bolt an additional 150° using the angle meter (J 45059).

17. Remove the flywheel holding tool (EN 46106).

3.5L & 3.9L Engines

See Figure 108.

1. Remove the crankshaft balancer bolt and washer.

✳✳ CAUTION

Do NOT use a power-assisted tool with the special tool in order to remove or install this component. You cannot properly control the alignment of this component using a power-assisted tool, and this can damage the component.

2. Remove the crankshaft balancer using the Crankshaft Balancer Remover (J-41816) along with (EN-46539) Puller End Protector.

To install:

3. Place the crankshaft balancer into position over the key in the crankshaft.

✳✳ CAUTION

Do NOT use a power-assisted tool with the special tool in order to remove or install this component. You cannot properly control the alignment of this component using a power-assisted tool, and this can damage the component.

4. Install the balancer and crank sprocket puller (J 29113) onto the crankshaft.

5. Rotate the hex nut on the balancer and crank sprocket puller (J 29113) to install the crankshaft balancer onto the crankshaft.

6. Remove the balancer and crank sprocket puller (J 29113) from the crankshaft.

Fig. 106 Removing the crankshaft balancer bolt—3.6L engine

Fig. 108 Removing the crankshaft balancer bolt and washer—3.5L and 3.9L engines

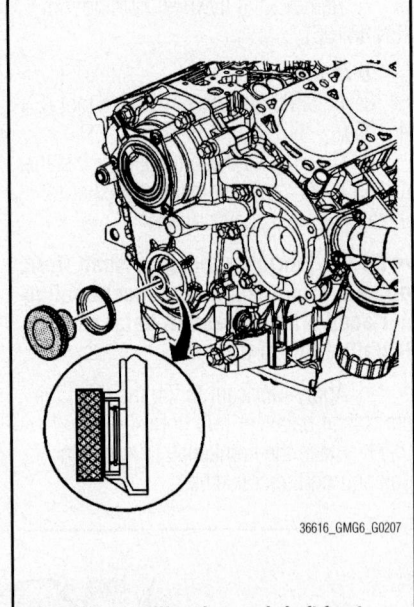

Fig. 111 Removing the crankshaft front seal—3.5L engine

7. Install the used crankshaft balancer bolt and tighten to 92 ft. lbs. (125 Nm).

8. Remove the used crankshaft balancer bolt.

9. Install the NEW crankshaft balancer bolt. Tighten the crankshaft balancer bolt a first pass to 92 ft. lbs. (125 Nm). Tighten the crankshaft balancer bolt a final pass to 130° using the angle meter (J 45059).

CRANKSHAFT FRONT SEAL

REMOVAL & INSTALLATION

2.4L Engine

See Figures 109 and 110.

1. Remove the crankshaft balancer.
2. Using a flat-bladed tool, remove the oil seal from the front cover.

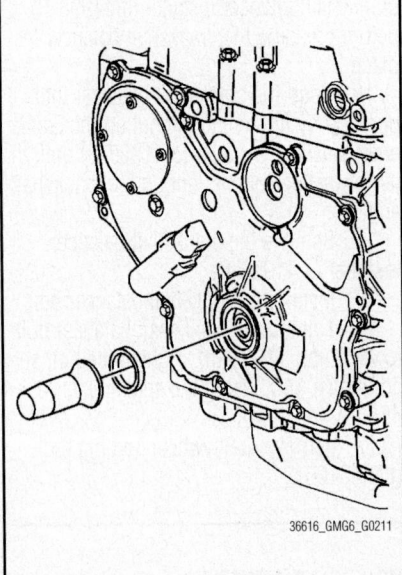

Fig. 110 Installing the crankshaft front oil seal—2.4L engine

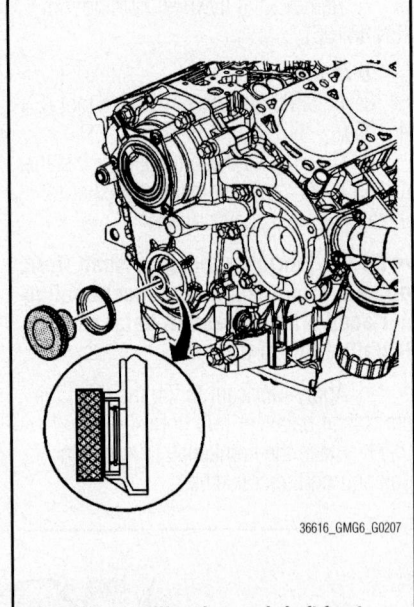

Fig. 112 Installing the crankshaft front seal—3.5L engine

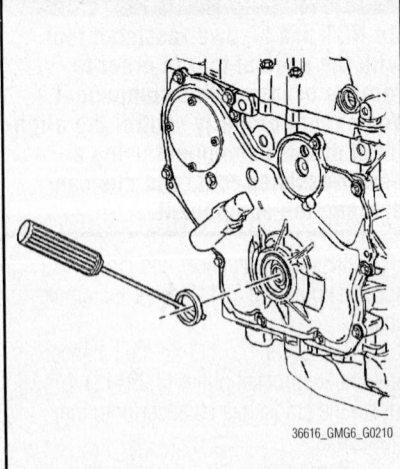

Fig. 109 Removing the crankshaft front oil seal—2.4L engine

To install:

3. Use the camshaft front/main seal installer (J 35268-A) in order to install the oil seal to the front cover.
4. Install the crankshaft balancer.

3.5L Engine

See Figures 111 and 112.

1. Remove the crankshaft balancer.
2. Remove the crankshaft key from the keyway.
3. Pry out the crankshaft front oil seal using a suitable tool. Use care not to damage the engine front cover or the crankshaft.

To install:

4. Lubricate the NEW oil seal with clean engine oil.
5. Align the front crankshaft seal installer (EN-48869) and the crankshaft front oil seal with the engine front cover and crankshaft.
6. Install the crankshaft front oil seal using crankshaft seal installer (EN-48869) and a suitable tool.
7. Install the crankshaft key into the keyway.
8. Install the crankshaft balancer.

3.6L Engine

See Figures 113 and 114.

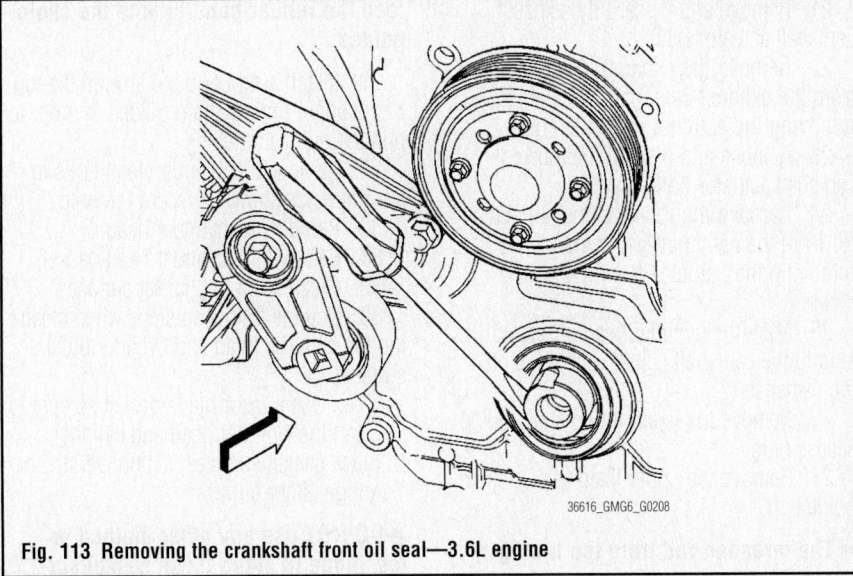

Fig. 113 Removing the crankshaft front oil seal—3.6L engine

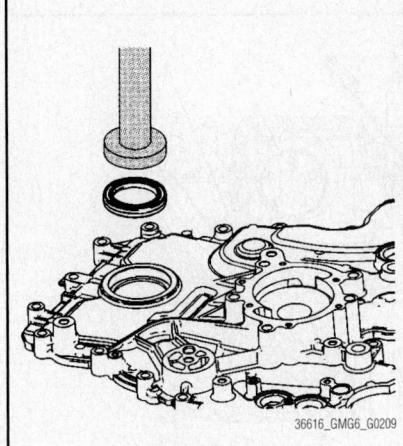

Fig. 114 Installing the crankshaft front oil seal—3.6L engine

1. Remove the crankshaft balancer.
2. Use a flat-bladed tool in order to remove the crankshaft oil seal. Use care not to damage the engine front cover or the crankshaft.

To install:

➡Do not lubricate the crankshaft front oil seal or the crankshaft balancer sealing surfaces.

3. Use the oil seal installer (J 29184) or equivalent to install the crankshaft front oil seal.
4. Install the crankshaft balancer.

3.9L Engine

See Figures 115 and 116.

1. Remove the crankshaft balancer.
2. Pry out the crankshaft front oil seal using a suitable tool. Use care not to

damage the engine front cover or the crankshaft.

To install:

3. Lubricate the NEW oil seal with clean engine oil.
4. Align the front crankshaft seal installer (EN-48869) and the crankshaft front oil seal with the engine front cover and crankshaft.
5. Install the crankshaft front oil seal using front crankshaft seal installer (EN-48869) and a suitable tool.
6. Install the crankshaft balancer.

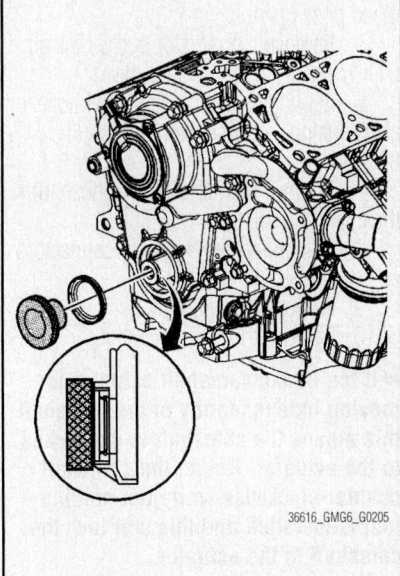

Fig. 116 Installing the crankshaft front oil seal—3.9L engine

CYLINDER HEAD

REMOVAL & INSTALLATION

2.4L Engine

See Figures 117 through 121.

1. Drain the cooling system.
2. Remove the exhaust manifold.
3. Remove the intake manifold.

Fig. 115 Removing the crankshaft front oil seal—3.9L engine

4. Reposition the radiator surge tank air bleed hose clamp.

5. Remove the radiator surge tank air bleed hose from the cylinder head.

6. Reposition the radiator inlet hose clamp using the hose clamp pliers (J 38185).

7. Remove the radiator inlet hose from the cylinder head.

8. Disconnect all electrical connectors as necessary.

9. Remove the spark plugs.

10. Remove the camshaft cover.

➡ **If the intake camshaft actuator is moving independently of the camshaft, this means the camshaft is not locked to the actuator. Rotate the camshaft counter-clockwise while the holding tool is installed and this will lock the camshaft to the actuator.**

11. Rotate the crankshaft clockwise to install the camshaft actuator locking tool (EN-48953) EGR Cooler Pressure Tester Adapter Set.

12. Install the camshaft actuator tool and bolts tighten to 89 inch lbs. (10 Nm).

13. Remove the upper timing chain guide bolts and guide.

14. Clean the timing chain and gears with solvent.

➡ **Ensure the timing chain and the camshaft position actuators are marked for proper assembly.**

15. Mark the timing gear sprockets and the timing chain. It is recommended that the paint marks are located in the 12 o'clock position.

16. Loosen, but do not remove the intake and exhaust camshaft actuator bolts.

17. Remove the camshaft actuator locking tool (EN-48953).

➡ **Ensure the tips of the timing chain retention tool (EN-48749) are fully engaged into the timing chain. The retention tool rod can be used on the back side of the chain to ensure the teeth from the retention tool are engaged.**

18. Install the timing chain retention tool (EN-48749) to the intake side of the timing chain.

19. Remove the timing chain tensioner.

➡ **The Intake camshaft and actuator should not rotate during the removal or installation.**

20. Install the timing chain retention tool (EN-48749) to the exhaust side of the timing chain.

21. Remove and discard the exhaust camshaft actuator bolt.

22. Remove the exhaust cam actuator from the exhaust camshaft while also removing the actuator from the chain.

23. Remove and discard the intake camshaft actuator bolt.

24. Remove the intake camshaft actuator from the camshaft while also removing the actuator from the timing chain.

25. Mark the cylinder head in relationship to the camshaft actuator notch is on the camshaft (2).

26. Remove the fixed timing chain guide access plug.

27. Remove the upper fixed timing chain guide bolt.

➡ **The threaded rod from the timing chain retention tool can be used to help feed the rubber band around the chain guides.**

28. Install a rubber band around the top of the upper timing chain guides in order to pull the guides together.

29. Remove the cylinder head bolts in the sequence shown. Discard the bolts.

30. Remove the cylinder head.

31. Remove the cylinder head gasket.

32. Clean all of the gasket surfaces.

33. Use the following steps when cleaning the cylinder head and cylinder block surfaces:

   a. Use a razor blade gasket scraper to clean the cylinder head and cylinder block gasket surfaces. Do not scratch or gouge either surface.

➡ **DO NOT use any other method or technique to clean these gasket surfaces.**

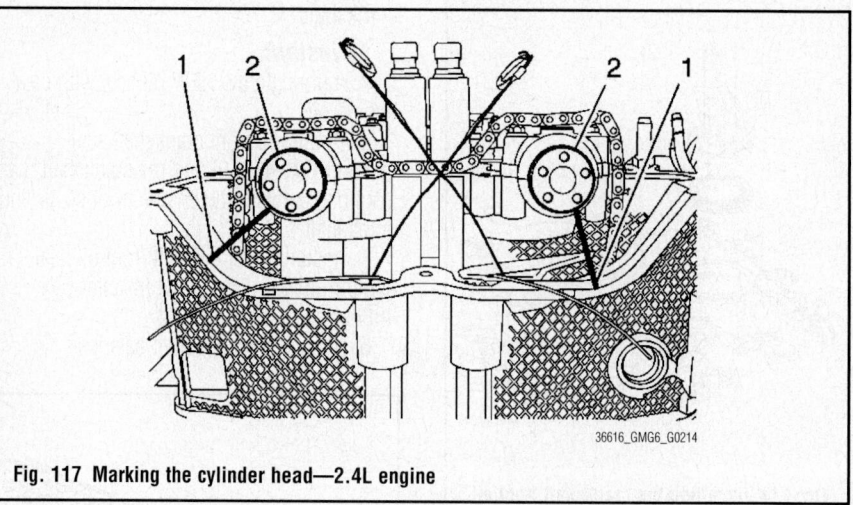

Fig. 117 Marking the cylinder head—2.4L engine

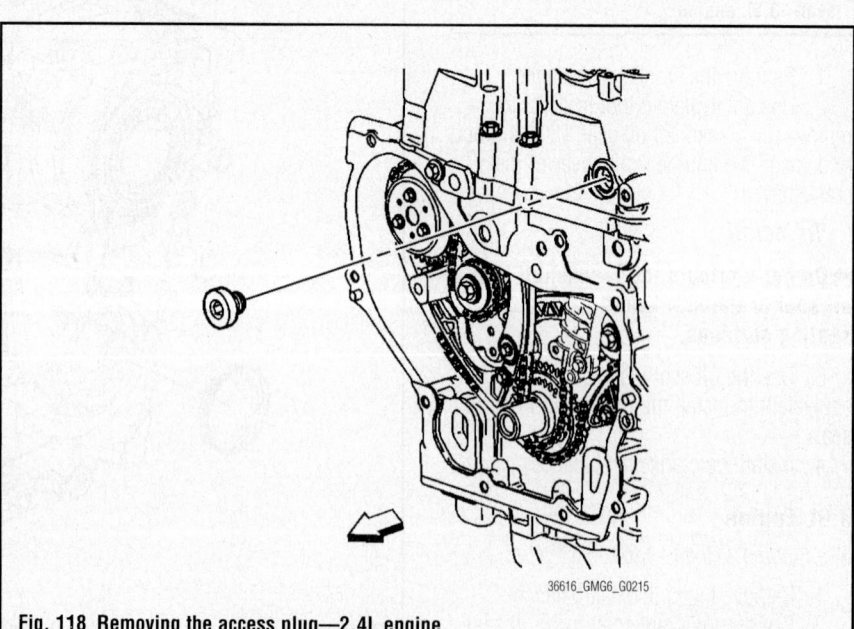

Fig. 118 Removing the access plug—2.4L engine

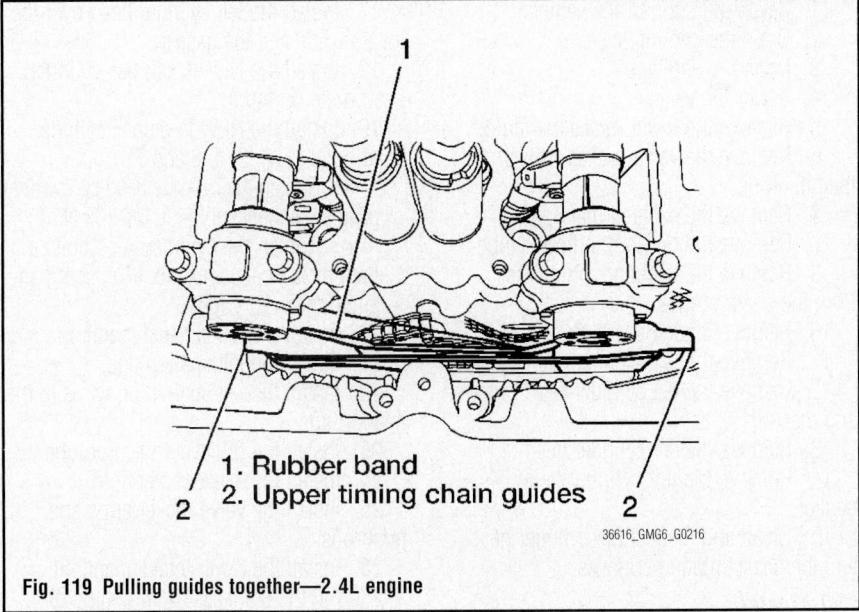

1. Rubber band
2. Upper timing chain guides

36616_GMG6_G0216

Fig. 119 Pulling guides together—2.4L engine

b. Use a NEW razor blade on the cylinder head and a NEW blade on the cylinder block.

➡ **Be careful not to gouge or scratch the gasket surfaces. DO NOT gouge or scrape the combustion chamber surfaces. The feel of the gasket surface is important, not the appearance. There will be indentations from the gasket left in the cylinder head after all of the gasket material is removed. These small indentations will be filled in by the NEW gasket.**

c. Hold the razor blade as parallel to the gasket surface as possible.

34. Clean the oil sealer/lube and any dirt from around the bolt holes.

➡ **DO NOT use a tap to clean the cylinder head bolt holes.**

35. Clean the bolt holes with a nylon bristle brush.

36. When cleaning the cylinder head bolt holes use suitable commercial spray liquid solvent and compressed air from an extended tip blow gun in order to reach the bottom of the holes.

37. If replacing the cylinder head, transfer all parts as necessary.

To install:

➡ **DO NOT use any sealing material.**

38. Install the cylinder head gasket.
39. Install the cylinder head.
40. Install NEW cylinder head bolts.

41. Install and tighten the cylinder head bolts in the sequence shown to 22 ft. lbs. (30 Nm) plus an additional 155 degrees using the angle meter (J 45059).

42. Install the NEW front cylinder head bolts and tighten the bolts to 26 ft. lbs. (35 Nm).

43. Ensure the cylinder head and the camshaft are correctly aligned.

44. Remove the rubber band from around the top of the upper timing chain guides.

45. Install the fixed guide bolt into the cylinder head and tighten to 106 inch lbs. (12 Nm).

46. Apply sealant compound to thread and install the timing chain guide bolt access hole plug.

47. Install the fixed timing chain guide access plug and tighten the plug to 59 ft. lbs. (90 Nm).

➡ **Ensure that the alignment mark made previously on the intake camshaft actuator is still aligned properly with the mark on the timing chain. If the mark made previously on the intake camshaft actuator is not aligned properly, refer to Camshaft Timing Chain, Sprocket, and Tensioner.**

48. Install the timing chain onto the intake camshaft actuator.

49. Align the intake camshaft actuator alignment mark made previously with the timing chain mark and install the actuator onto the camshaft.

50. Install a NEW intake camshaft actuator bolt until snug.

51. Remove the timing chain retention tool (EN-48749) from the intake side of the timing chain.

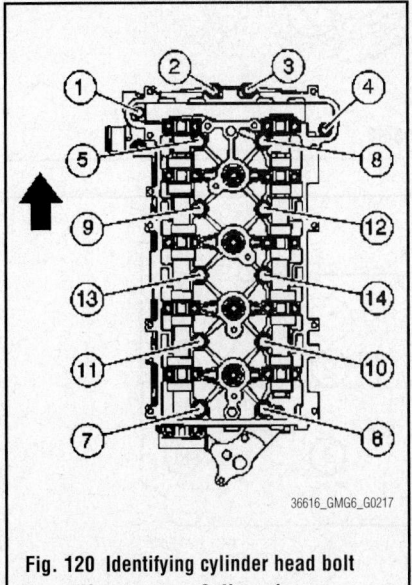

36616_GMG6_G0217

Fig. 120 Identifying cylinder head bolt removal sequence—2.4L engine

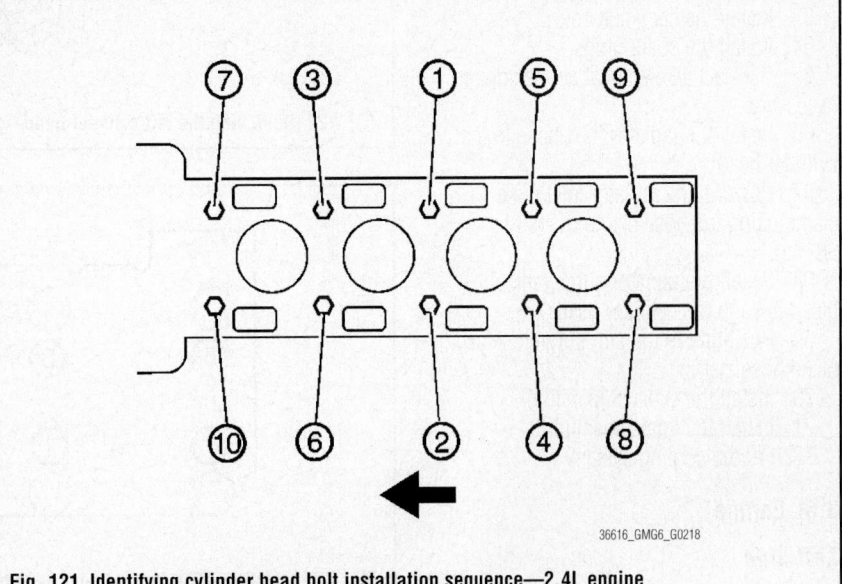

36616_GMG6_G0218

Fig. 121 Identifying cylinder head bolt installation sequence—2.4L engine

➡**Ensure that the alignment mark made previously on the exhaust camshaft actuator is still aligned properly with the mark on the timing chain. The exhaust cam may have to be rotated clockwise to install the exhaust actuator.**

52. Install the timing chain onto the exhaust camshaft actuator.

53. Align the exhaust camshaft actuator alignment mark made previously with the timing chain mark and install the actuator onto the camshaft.

54. Install a NEW exhaust camshaft actuator bolt until snug.

55. Remove the timing chain retention tool (EN-48749) from the exhaust side of the timing chain.

➡**Failure to reset the chain tensioner will put excess tension on the chain, limiting the chains life.**

56. Reset and install the timing chain tensioner.

57. Install the camshaft actuator locking tool (EN-48953) to the actuators.

58. Install the camshaft actuator locking tool bolts and tighten to 89 inch lbs. (10 Nm).

59. Tighten the NEW camshaft actuator bolt to 22 ft. lbs. (30 Nm), plus an additional 100° using the angle meter (J 45059).

60. Release the tensioner by applying a counterclockwise rotational torque of 33 ft. lbs. (45 Nm) to the harmonic balancer bolt.

61. Remove the camshaft actuator locking tool.

62. Install the upper timing chain guide bolts and guide. Tighten the bolts to 89 inch lbs. (10 Nm).

63. Install the camshaft cover.

64. Install the spark plugs.

65. Connect all electrical connectors as necessary.

66. Install the radiator inlet hose to the cylinder head.

67. Position the radiator inlet hose clamp using the hose clamp pliers (J 38185).

68. Install the radiator surge tank air bleed hose to the cylinder head.

69. Position the radiator surge tank air bleed hose clamp.

70. Install the exhaust manifold.

71. Install the intake manifold.

72. Fill the cooling system.

3.5L Engine

Left Side

See Figures 122 and 123.

---

1. Raise and support the vehicle.
2. Drain the cooling system.
3. Drain the engine oil.
4. Lower the vehicle.
5. Remove the lower intake manifold.
6. Remove the valve rocker arms and the pushrods.
7. Remove the exhaust manifold.
8. Remove the oil level indicator tube.
9. Remove the left spark plug wires from the spark plugs.
10. Remove the left spark plugs.
11. Remove the left exhaust manifold.
12. Remove the left cylinder head bolts and discard.
13. Remove the left cylinder head.
14. Remove the left cylinder head gasket.
15. Clean and inspect the cylinder head and the gasket mating surfaces.

To install:

16. Install a new left cylinder head gasket.

---

17. Install the left cylinder head over the locator pins and the gasket.

18. Install the NEW small hex cylinder head bolts (5 and 8).

19. Install the NEW large hex cylinder head bolts (1, 2, 3, 4, 6 and 7).

   a. Tighten the cylinder head bolts a first pass in sequence to 44 ft. lbs. (60 Nm).

   b. Tighten the cylinder head bolts a final pass in sequence to 140° using an angle meter (J 45059).

20. Install the left exhaust manifold.

21. Install the left spark plugs.

22. Install the left spark plug wires to the spark plugs.

23. Install the oil level indicator tube.

24. Install the exhaust manifold.

25. Install the valve rocker arms and pushrods.

26. Install the lower intake manifold.

27. Fill the crankcase with engine oil.

28. Fill the cooling system.

29. Inspect for leaks.

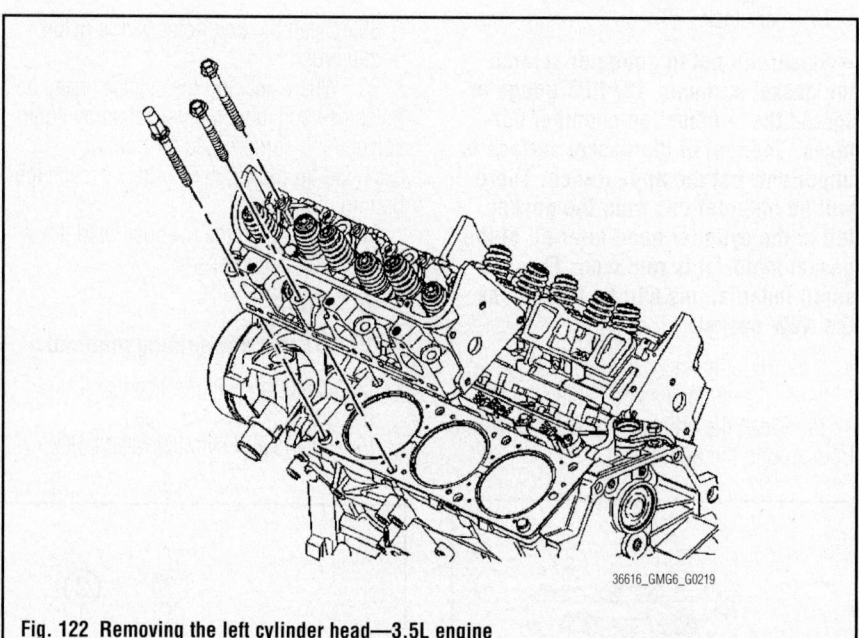

Fig. 122 Removing the left cylinder head—3.5L engine

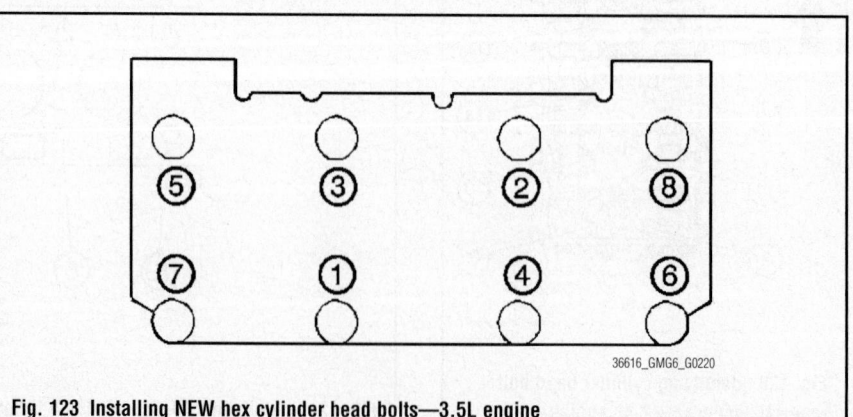

Fig. 123 Installing NEW hex cylinder head bolts—3.5L engine

Right Side

See Figures 124 and 125.

1. Raise and support the vehicle.
2. Drain the cooling system.
3. Drain the engine oil.
4. Lower the vehicle.
5. Remove the lower intake manifold.
6. Remove the valve rocker arms and push rods.
7. Remove the exhaust manifold.
8. Remove the right spark plug wires from the spark plugs.
9. Remove the right spark plugs.
10. Remove the fuel line bracket bolt and the stud.
11. Remove the fuel line bracket.
12. Remove the generator.
13. Remove the right exhaust manifold.
14. Remove the right cylinder head bolts and discard.
15. Remove the right cylinder head.
16. Remove the right cylinder head gasket.

17. Clean and inspect the cylinder head and the gasket mating surfaces.

To install:

18. Install a new right cylinder head gasket.
19. Install the right cylinder head over the locator pins and the gasket.
20. Install the NEW small hex cylinder head bolts (5 and 8).
21. Install the NEW large hex cylinder head bolts (1, 2, 3, 4, 6 and 7).
    a. Tighten the cylinder head bolts a first pass in sequence to 44 ft. lbs. (60 Nm).
    b. Tighten the cylinder head bolts a final pass in sequence to 140 ° using an angle meter (J 45059).
22. Install the right exhaust manifold.
23. Install the generator.
24. Install the fuel line bracket.
25. Install the fuel line bracket bolt and the stud. Tighten the bolt and the stud to 37 ft. lbs. (50 Nm).

26. Install the right spark plugs.
27. Install the right spark plug wires to the spark plugs.
28. Install the exhaust manifold.
29. Install the push rods and valve rocker arms.
30. Install the lower intake manifold.
31. Fill the crankcase with engine oil.
32. Fill the cooling system.
33. Inspect for leaks.

3.6L Engine

Left Side

See Figure 126.

1. Remove the left bank secondary timing chain.
2. Remove the oil level indicator.
3. Disconnect the coolant temperature sensor electrical connector.
4. Remove the wiring harness ground from the cylinder head.
5. Remove the catalytic converter.
6. Remove the cylinder head with the exhaust manifold.
7. Remove and discard the cylinder head gasket.
8. Clean and inspect the cylinder head and the engine block sealing surfaces.

To install:

9. Install a NEW cylinder head gasket.
10. Carefully install the cylinder head with the exhaust manifold to the engine. Install the catalytic converter to the exhaust manifold.
11. Install the catalytic converter to the exhaust manifold.
12. Connect the wiring harness electrical connector located at the side of the cylinder head.
13. Install the wiring harness ground to the cylinder head. Tighten the wiring

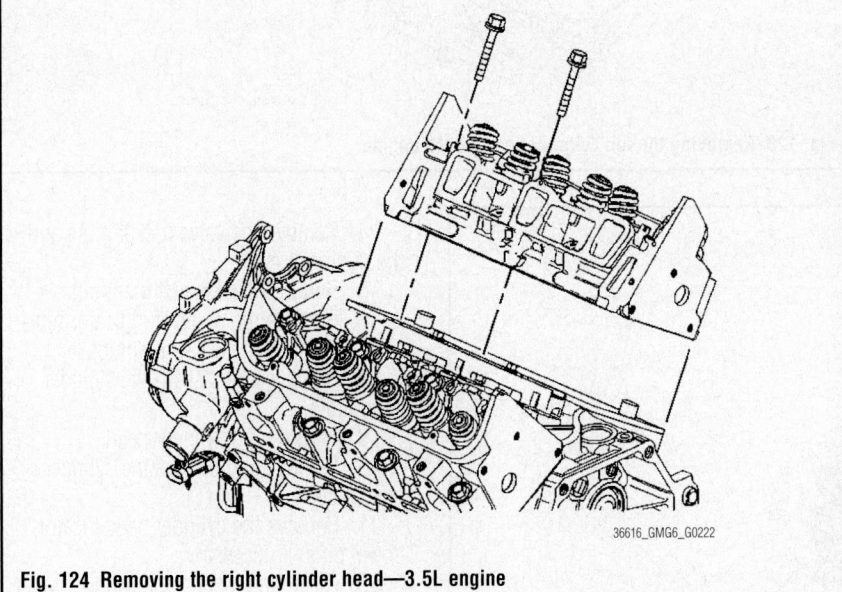

Fig. 124 Removing the right cylinder head—3.5L engine

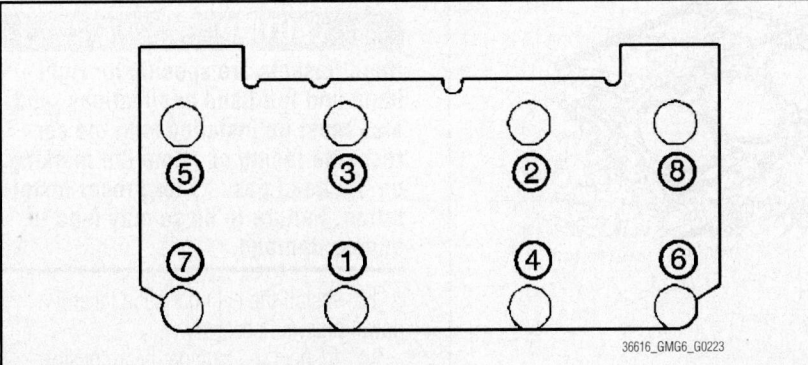

Fig. 125 Installing the NEW hex cylinder head bolts—3.5L engine

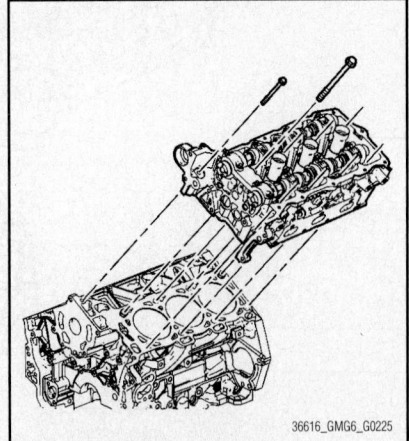

Fig. 126 Removing the left cylinder head with the exhaust manifold—3.6L engine

harness ground bolt to 89 inch lbs. (10 Nm).

14. Install the coolant temperature sensor electrical connector.

15. Install the oil level indicator.

16. Install the left bank secondary timing chain.

Right Side

See Figure 127.

1. Remove the hood.
2. Remove the right bank secondary timing chain.
3. Remove the right cylinder head bolts.
4. With the aid of an assistant, remove the cylinder head with the exhaust manifold.
5. Remove and discard the cylinder head gasket.
6. Clean and inspect the cylinder head and the engine block sealing surfaces.

To install:

7. Install a NEW cylinder head gasket.
8. With the aid of an assistant, carefully install the cylinder head with the exhaust manifold to the engine.
9. Install the right bank secondary timing chain.
10. Install the hood.

3.9L Engine

Left Side

See Figures 128 and 129.

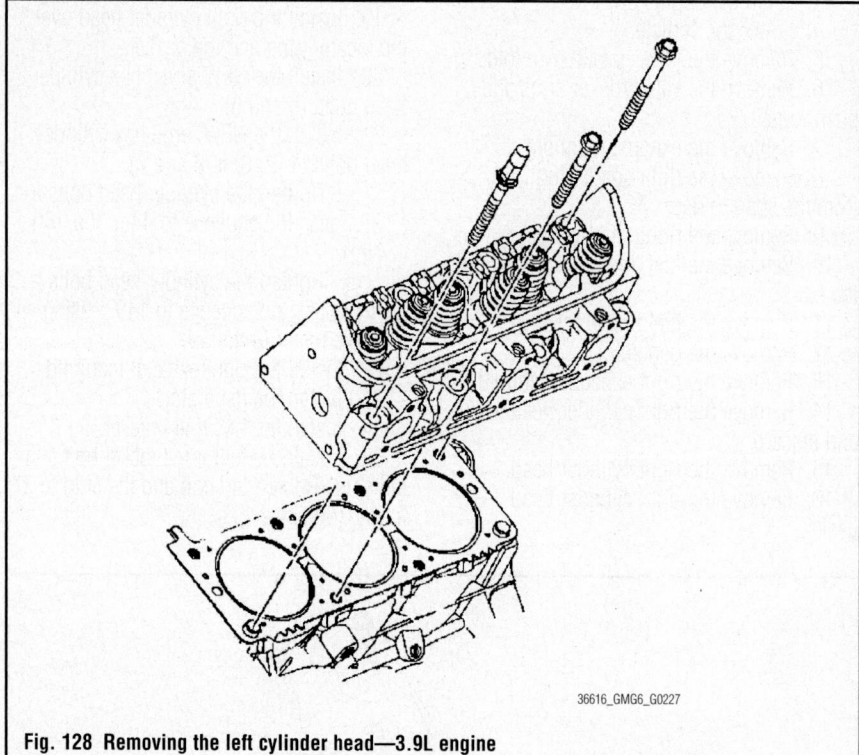

36616_GMG6_G0227

Fig. 128 Removing the left cylinder head—3.9L engine

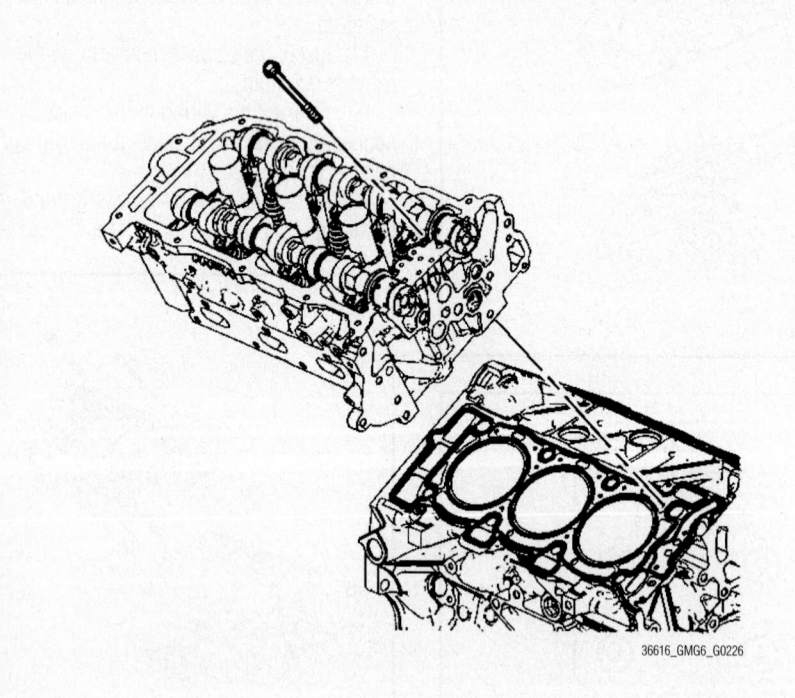

36616_GMG6_G0226

Fig. 127 Removing the right cylinder head—3.6L engine

1. Drain the engine oil.
2. Lower the vehicle.
3. Remove the lower intake manifold.

4. Remove the valve rocker arms and the pushrods.
5. Remove the exhaust manifold.
6. Remove the oil level indicator tube.
7. Remove the left spark plugs.
8. Remove and discard the cylinder head bolts.
9. Remove the cylinder head.
10. Remove and discard the cylinder head gasket.
11. Remove the cylinder head locator dowel pins, if necessary.
12. Clean and inspect the cylinder head.

To install:

> ✳✳ **CAUTION**
>
> **Head gaskets are specific for right hand and left hand applications, and also must be installed with the correct side facing up. Note the marking on the head gaskets for proper installation. Failure to do so may lead to engine damage.**

13. Install the cylinder head locator dowel pins, if necessary.
14. Inspect the cylinder head locator dowel pins for proper installation.

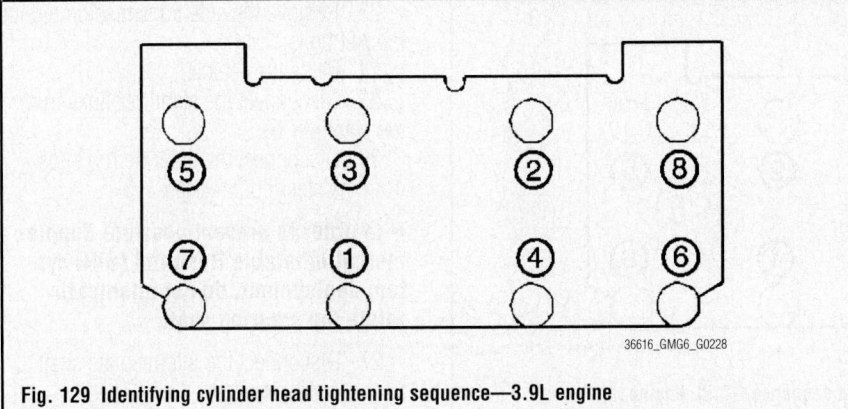

Fig. 129 Identifying cylinder head tightening sequence—3.9L engine

15. Install a NEW cylinder head gasket.
16. Install the cylinder head onto the locator pins and the engine.

⁕⁕ **CAUTION**

This component uses torque-to-yield bolts. When servicing this component do not reuse the bolts, New torque-to-yield bolts must be installed. Reusing used torque-to-yield bolts will not provide proper bolt torque and clamp load. Failure to install NEW torque-to-yield bolts may lead to engine damage.

17. Install NEW cylinder head bolts finger tight.
18. Install the NEW small hex cylinder head bolts (5 and 8).
19. Install the NEW large hex cylinder head bolts (1, 2, 3, 4, 6 and 7).
   a. Tighten the cylinder head bolts a first pass in sequence to 44 ft. lbs. (60 Nm).
   b. Tighten the cylinder head bolts a final pass in sequence to 140° using the angle meter (J 45059).
20. Install the left spark plugs.
21. Install the oil level indicator tube.
22. Install the exhaust manifold.
23. Install the valve rocker arms and the pushrods.
24. Install the lower intake manifold.
25. Fill the engine with oil.
26. Inspect for leaks.

Right Side

See Figures 130 and 131.

1. Drain the engine oil.
2. Lower the vehicle.
3. Remove the lower intake manifold.
4. Remove the valve rocker arms and pushrods.
5. Remove the exhaust manifold.
6. Remove the right spark plugs.
7. Remove the fuel line bracket bolt and stud.

8. Remove the fuel line bracket.
9. Remove the generator.
10. Remove and discard the cylinder head bolts.
11. Remove the cylinder head.
12. Remove and discard the cylinder head gasket.
13. Remove the cylinder head locator dowel pins, if necessary.
14. Clean and inspect the cylinder head.

To install:

⁕⁕ **CAUTION**

Head gaskets are specific for right hand and left hand applications, and also must be installed with the correct side facing up. Note the markings on the head gaskets for proper

installation. Failure to do so may lead to engine damage.

15. Install the cylinder head locator dowel pins, if necessary.
16. Inspect the cylinder head locator dowel pins for proper installation.
17. Install a NEW cylinder head gasket.
18. Install the cylinder head onto the locator pins and the engine.

⁕⁕ **CAUTION**

This component uses torque-to-yield bolts. When servicing this component do not reuse the bolts, New torque-to-yield bolts must be installed. Reusing used torque-to-yield bolts will not provide proper bolt torque and clamp load. Failure to install NEW torque-to-yield bolts may lead to engine damage.

19. Install NEW cylinder head bolts finger tight.
20. Install the NEW small hex cylinder head bolts (5 and 8).
21. Install the NEW large hex cylinder head bolts (1, 2, 3, 4, 6 and 7).
   a. Tighten the cylinder head bolts a first pass in sequence to 44 ft. lbs. (60 Nm).
   b. Tighten the cylinder head bolts a final pass in sequence to 140 degrees using the J 45059 .

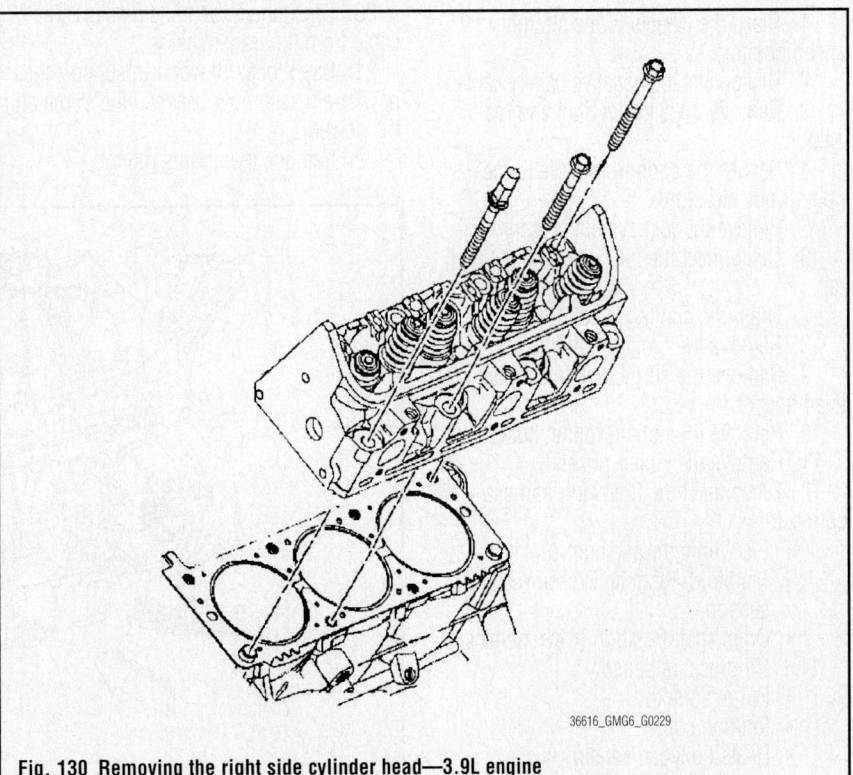

Fig. 130 Removing the right side cylinder head—3.9L engine

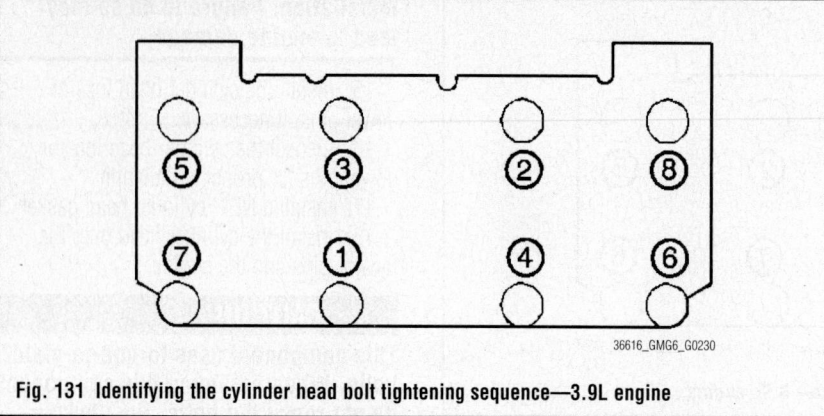

36616_GMG6_G0230

Fig. 131 Identifying the cylinder head bolt tightening sequence—3.9L engine

22. Install the generator.

23. Position the fuel line bracket to the cylinder head.

24. Install the fuel line bracket bolt and stud and tighten to 37 ft. lbs. (50 Nm).

25. Install the right spark plugs.

26. Install the exhaust manifold.

27. Install the valve rocker arms and pushrods.

28. Install the lower intake manifold.

29. Fill the engine with oil.

30. Inspect for leaks.

ENGINE ASSEMBLY

REMOVAL & INSTALLATION

2.4L Engine

See Figure 132.

1. Place the wheels in the straight ahead position.

2. Disconnect the negative battery cable.

3. Remove the air inlet duct and resonator.

4. Secure the cooling module to the upper body structure.

5. Relieve the fuel system pressure.

6. Disconnect the fuel line from the fuel rail.

7. Drain the cooling system.

8. Remove the radiator inlet hose.

9. Remove the surge tank to cylinder head hose.

10. Remove the radiator outlet hose.

11. Remove the heater hoses.

12. Disconnect the following harness connectors:

- Electronic throttle control
- Manifold Absolute Pressure (MAP) sensor
- Crankshaft Position (CKP) sensor
- Oil pressure sensor
- Purge solenoid
- Ignition coils
- Heated oxygen sensor
- Vehicle Speed Sensor (VSS)
- Engine Coolant Temperature (ECT) sensor
- Back-up light switch
- Camshaft position actuator solenoid control valves
- Fuel rail
- Remove the ground wires from the left side of the cylinder head

13. Raise and support the vehicle.

14. Remove the drive belt.

15. Remove the AC compressor bolts and set the compressor aside.

16. Disconnect the starter and alternator connectors.

17. Disconnect the front exhaust pipe from the exhaust manifold.

18. Lower the vehicle.

19. Disconnect the transmission harness connectors.

20. Disconnect the transmission shift cable from the transmission.

21. Use blocks of wood to support the powertrain assembly between the frame and the powertrain.

22. Remove the engine mount.

23. Remove the side transmission mount bracket bolts.

24. Raise the vehicle.

25. Disconnect the stabilizer links from the stabilizer bar.

26. Disconnect the outer tie rod ends from the steering knuckles.

➡**In order to prevent possible Supplemental Inflatable Restraint (SIR) system deployment, do not attempt to rotate the steering shaft.**

27. Disconnect the intermediate shaft from the steering gear.

28. Disconnect the lower control arms from the steering knuckles.

29. Disconnect the drive axles from the transaxle and support with wire or bungee cords.

30. Use a paint pen or magic marker in order to mark the frame to body position.

31. Lower the vehicle to about 3 feet off the ground in order to position the lift table under the frame.

32. Use wood blocks as necessary between the lift table and the frame to support the assembly.

33. Remove the front frame bolts, the frame support bracket and bolt and then the rear frame bolts.

34. Slowly raise the vehicle off of the frame and powertrain.

35. Attach an engine lift hoist to the engine lift hooks.

36. Remove the starter.

37. Remove the torque converter-to-flywheel bolts.

38. Remove the transaxle to engine bolts.

39. Separate the engine from the transaxle.

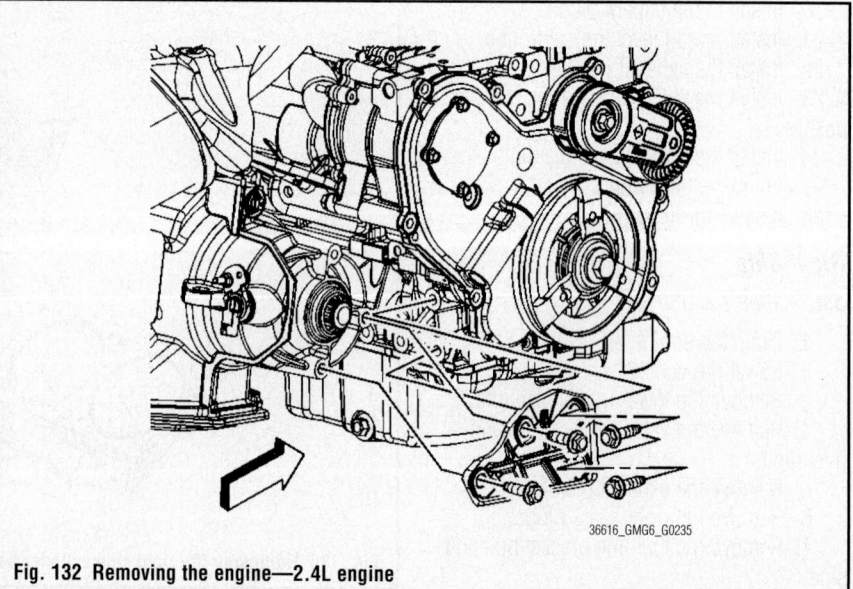

36616_GMG6_G0235

Fig. 132 Removing the engine—2.4L engine

40. Remove the following components:
- Exhaust manifold
- Engine mount bracket.
- Engine block heater
- Thermostat housing and feed pipe
- Alternator
- Fuel rail
- Drive belt tensioner
- Engine flywheel

41. Install the engine to a suitable engine stand.

To install:

42. Attach a lifting device to the lifting hooks.

43. Install the following components:
- Exhaust manifold
- Engine mount bracket.
- Engine block heater
- Thermostat housing and feed pipe
- Alternator
- Fuel rail
- Drive belt tensioner.

44. Lower the engine into the vehicle and install the engine to the transaxle bolts and tighten to 55 ft. lbs. (75 Nm).

45. Install the torque converter bolts and tighten to 46 ft. lbs. (62 Nm).

46. Position the transaxle brace to the engine and transaxle and install the brace to the transaxle bolts.

47. Install the transaxle brace to the engine block bolts and tighten to 37 ft. lbs. (50 Nm).

48. Install the starter.

49. Remove the engine lift from the engine.

50. Lower vehicle slowly over frame and powertrain.

51. Hand start all the frame bolts while aligning the frame to the paint marks.

52. Tighten the frame bolts to 74 ft. lbs. (100 Nm) plus an additional 180 degrees.

53. Remove the lift table.

54. Connect the drive axles to the transaxle.

55. Connect the lower control arm to the steering knuckle.

56. Connect the intermediate steering shaft to the steering gear.

57. Connect the outer tie rod ends to the steering knuckles.

58. Connect the stabilizer links to the stabilizer bar.

59. Install the side transmission mount bracket bolts and tighten to 37 ft. lbs. (50 Nm).

60. Install the engine mounts and tighten to 37 ft. lbs. (50 Nm).

61. Remove the wood blocks between the powertrain and frame.

62. Connect the transmission shift cable to the transmission.

63. Connect the transmission harness connector.

64. Install the catalytic converter to the exhaust manifold and tighten to 22 ft. lbs. (30 Nm).

65. Lower the vehicle.

66. Install the alternator and starter connections.

67. Install the AC compressor to the engine.

68. Install the engine drive belt.

69. Connect all electrical connectors disconnect previously.

70. Install the heater hoses.

71. Install the radiator outlet hose.

72. Connect the fuel line to the fuel rail.

73. Release the cooling module from the upper body structure.

74. Install the air inlet duct and resonator.

75. Connect the negative battery cable.

76. Fill and bleed the cooling system.

77. Fill the engine with clean oil.

78. Fill the transaxle to the proper level.

79. Start the vehicle, check for leaks and repair if necessary.

80. Road test the vehicle.

3.5L Engine

See Figures 133 through 135.

1. Disconnect the negative battery cable.

2. Remove the intake manifold cover.

3. Drain the cooling system.

4. Drain the engine oil.

5. Remove the air cleaner assembly.

6. Remove the hood.

7. Remove the engine mount snubber and drive belt.

8. Disconnect the following electrical connectors:
- The Knock Sensor (KS)
- The Camshaft Position (CMP) sensor
- The Crankshaft Position (CKP) sensor
- The Heated Oxygen Sensor (HO2S)
- The Manifold Absolute Pressure (MAP) sensor
- The Exhaust Gas Recirculation (EGR) valve
- The Evaporative Emission (EVAP) canister purge solenoid
- The electronic throttle control
- The ignition coil
- The body wiring harness to engine harness

9. Raise and support the vehicle.

10. Remove the catalytic converters.

11. Remove the engine wiring harness grounds from the transaxle.

12. Remove the engine mount lower nuts.

13. Remove the torque converter covers.

14. Remove the starter motor.

15. Remove the Air Conditioning (A/C) compressor. DO NOT discharge the A/C system. Support the compressor.

16. Remove the torque converter bolts.

17. Remove the engine mount bracket bolts and bracket.

18. Remove the engine wiring harness clip from the rear of the transaxle brace.

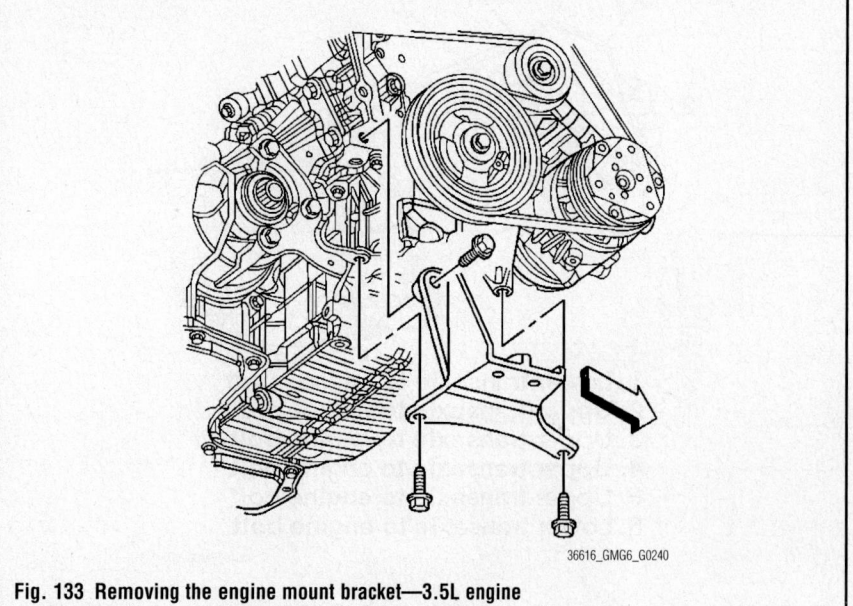

36616_GMG6_G0240

Fig. 133 Removing the engine mount bracket—3.5L engine

19. Remove the transaxle brace bolts and remove the brace.

20. Remove the transaxle to oil pan brace bolts and brace.

21. Remove the lower transaxle-to-engine bolt (6) and the stud (1).

22. Remove the radiator outlet hose from the engine.

23. Lower the vehicle and support the transaxle.

24. Remove the heater outlet and inlet hoses from the engine.

25. Remove the vacuum hoses from the upper intake manifold.

26. Remove the brake booster vacuum hose from the upper intake manifold.

27. Remove the fuel lines from the fuel rail.

28. Remove the radiator inlet hose from the engine.

29. Install the engine lifting device to the engine.

30. Remove the upper transaxle-to-engine bolts (3, 4, 5) and the stud (2).

31. Remove the engine from the vehicle.

32. Remove the flywheel.

33. Install the engine to the engine stand.

To install:

34. Remove the engine from the engine stand.

35. Install the flywheel.

36. Install the engine to the vehicle.

37. Install the upper transaxle-to-engine bolts (3, 4, 5) and the stud (2) and tighten to 55 ft. lbs. (75 Nm).

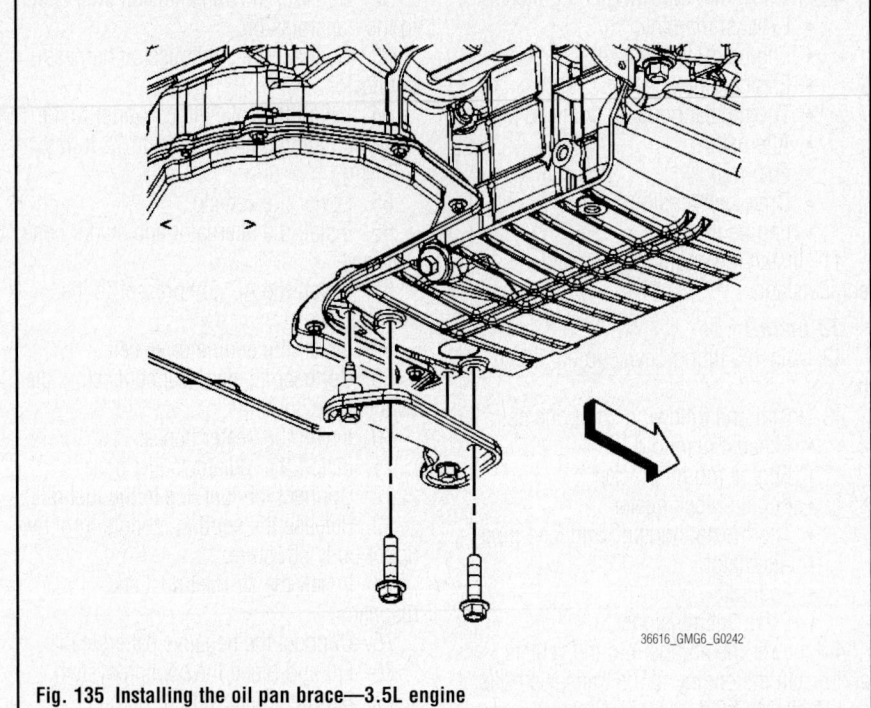

Fig. 135 Installing the oil pan brace—3.5L engine

38. Remove the engine lifting device.

39. Install the radiator inlet hose to the engine.

40. Install the fuel lines to the fuel rail.

41. Install the brake booster vacuum hose to the upper intake manifold.

42. Install the vacuum hoses to the upper intake manifold.

43. Install the heater inlet and outlet hoses to the engine.

44. Raise the vehicle and remove the transaxle support.

45. Install the radiator outlet hose to the engine.

46. Install the lower transaxle-to-engine bolt (6) and the stud (1) and tighten to 55 ft. lbs. (75 Nm).

47. Position the transaxle to oil pan brace and install the bolts. Tighten the bolts to 37 ft. lbs. (50 Nm).

48. Position the transaxle brace to the transaxle and install the bolts until snug.

49. Install the engine wiring harness clip to the rear of the transaxle brace.

50. Position the engine mount bracket to the engine and install the bolts until snug.

51. Tighten the engine mount bracket bolts and transaxle brace bolts.

   a. Tighten the engine mount bracket upper bolt to 66 ft. lbs. (90 Nm).

   b. Tighten the engine mount bracket lower bolts to 37 ft. lbs. (50 Nm).

   c. Tighten the transaxle brace bolts to 53 ft. lbs. (72 Nm)

52. Install the torque converter bolts.

53. Install the A/C compressor.

54. Install the starter motor.

55. Install the torque converter covers.

56. Install the engine mount lower nuts and tighten to 32 ft. lbs. (43 Nm).

57. Install the engine wiring harness grounds to the transaxle.

58. Install the engine wiring harness ground nut to the transaxle stud and tighten the nut to 26 ft. lbs. (35 Nm).

59. Install the catalytic converters.

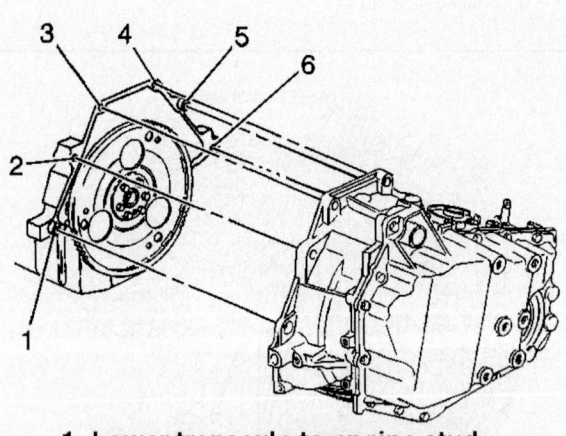

1. Lower transaxle to engine stud
2. Upper transaxle to engine stud
3. Upper transaxle to engine bolt
4. Upper transaxle to engine bolt
5. Upper transaxle to engine bolt
6. Lower transaxle to engine bolt

Fig. 134 Removing the transaxle to engine bolts and studs—3.5L engine

60. Lower the vehicle.

61. Connect the following electrical connectors:

- The body wiring harness to engine harness
- The ignition coil
- The electronic throttle control
- The EVAP canister purge solenoid
- The EGR valve
- The MAP sensor
- The HO2S
- The CKP sensor
- The CMP sensor
- The KS

62. Install the drive belt and engine mount snubber.

63. Install the hood.

64. Install the air cleaner assembly.

65. Connect the negative battery cable.

66. Fill the crankcase with engine oil.

67. Fill cooling system.

68. Perform a CKP system variation learn procedure.

69. Install the intake manifold cover.

70. Inspect for leaks.

3.6L Engine

See Figures 136 through 138.

1. Disconnect the negative battery cable.

2. Remove the intake manifold cover.

3. Drain the cooling system.

4. Drain the engine oil.

5. Remove the air cleaner assembly.

6. Remove the hood.

7. Remove the engine mount strut.

8. Remove the drive belt.

9. Disconnect the front knock sensor (KS).

10. Disconnect the rear KS and the crank sensor.

11. Re-position the plastic wire loom/shield on each valve cover, then disconnect the camshaft position (CMP) sensors.

12. Disconnect the manifold absolute pressure (MAP) sensor.

13. Disconnect the evaporative emission (EVAP) canister purge solenoid.

14. Disconnect the front and rear ignition coils.

15. Disconnect the A/C compressor.

16. Disconnect the coolant temperature sensor.

17. Disconnect the following electrical connectors:

- The heated oxygen sensor (HO2S)
- The exhaust gas recirculation (EGR) valve
- The electronic throttle control
- The body wiring harness-to-engine harness

18. Raise and support the vehicle.

19. Remove the catalytic converters.

20. Remove the engine wiring harness grounds from the transaxle.

21. Remove the engine mount lower bolts .

22. Remove the torque converter covers.

23. Remove the starter motor.

24. Remove the air conditioning (A/C) compressor. DO NOT discharge the A/C system. Support the compressor and set aside.

25. Remove the power steering pump and position aside.

26. Remove the torque converter bolts.

27. Remove the engine mount bracket.

28. Remove the transaxle to oil pan brace bolts and brace.

29. Remove the lower transaxle-to-engine bolt and the stud.

30. Remove the radiator outlet hose from the engine.

31. Lower the vehicle and support the transaxle.

32. Remove the engine coolant thermostat housing from the engine.

33. Remove the vacuum hoses from the upper intake manifold.

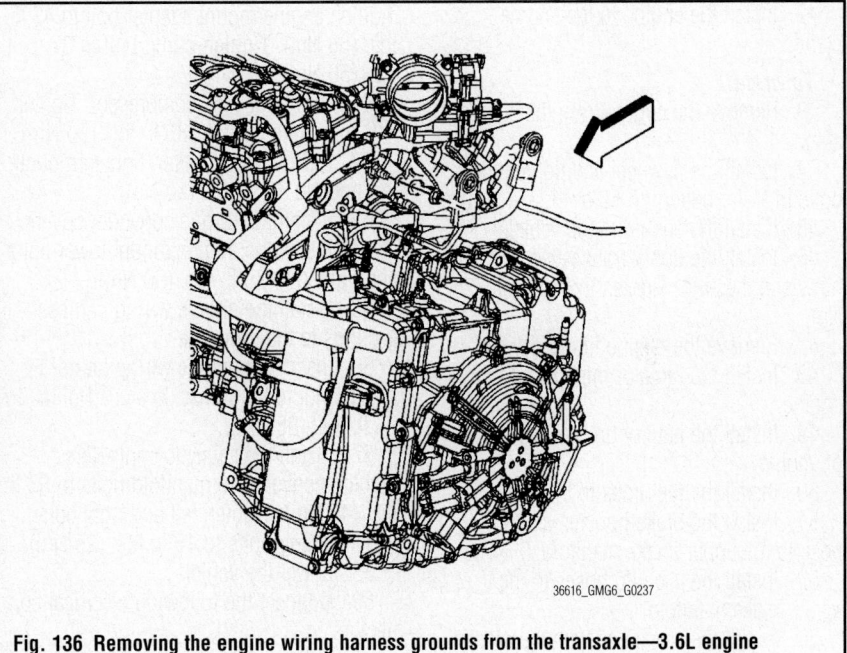

36616_GMG6_G0237

Fig. 136 Removing the engine wiring harness grounds from the transaxle—3.6L engine

36616_GMG6_G0238

Fig. 137 Removing the transaxle to oil pan brace—3.6L engine

34. Remove the brake booster vacuum hose from the upper intake manifold.

35. Remove the fuel lines from the fuel rail.

36. Remove the battery ground from the rear of engine.

37. Remove the radiator inlet hose from the engine

38. Install the engine lifting device to the engine.

39. Remove the upper transaxle-to-engine bolts and the stud.

40. Remove the engine from the vehicle.

41. Remove the flywheel.

42. Install the engine to the engine stand.

To install:

43. Remove the engine from the engine stand.

44. Install the flywheel and tighten the bolts in a star pattern to 52 ft. lbs (71 Nm).

45. Install the engine to the vehicle

46. Install the upper transaxle-to-engine bolts and the stud. Tighten to 55 ft. lbs. (75 Nm).

47. Remove the engine lifting device.

48. Install the radiator inlet hose to the engine.

49. Install the battery ground to the rear of engine.

50. Install the fuel lines to the fuel rail.

51. Install the brake booster vacuum hose to the upper intake manifold.

52. Install the vacuum hoses to the upper intake manifold.

53. Install the engine coolant thermostat housing to the engine. Tighten mounting bolts to 18 ft. lbs. (25 Nm).

54. Raise the vehicle and remove the transaxle support.

55. Install the radiator outlet hose to the engine.

56. Install the lower transaxle-to-engine bolt and the stud. Tighten to 55 ft. lbs. (75 Nm).

57. Position the transaxle to oil pan brace, install and tighten the bolts to 37 ft. lbs. (50 Nm).

58. Install the engine mount bracket. Tighten the Upper and lower bracket bolts to 37 ft. lbs. (50 Nm).

59. Install the torque converter bolts.

60. Install the power steering pump. Tighten engine mount adapter bolt to 43 ft. lbs. (58 Nm). Tighten pump bolt to 37 ft. lbs. (50 Nm).

61. Install the A/C compressor. Tighten A/C mounting bolts to 37 ft. lbs. (50 Nm).

62. Install starter motor, tighten mounting bolts to 37 ft. lbs. (50 Nm).

63. Install the torque converter covers.

64. Install the engine mount lower bolts and tighten to 38 ft. lbs. (50 Nm).

65. Install the engine wiring harness grounds to the transaxle.

66. Install the engine wiring harness ground nut to the transaxle stud. Tighten to 26 ft. lbs. (35 Nm).

67. Install the catalytic converters. Tighten converter to manifold bolts to 33 ft. lbs. (45 Nm). Tighten left and right converter joining bolts to 18 ft. lbs. (25 Nm).

68. Lower the vehicle.

69. Connect the following electrical connectors:

- The body wiring harness-to-engine harness

- The electronic throttle control
- The EGR valve
- The HO2S
- Coolant temperature sensor
- A/C compressor
- Front and rear ignition coils
- EVAP canister purge solenoid
- MAP sensor

70. Connect the CMP sensors, then reposition the plastic wire loom/shield on each valve cover.

71. Connect the rear KS

72. Connect the front KS and the crank sensor.

73. Install the drive belt.

74. Install the engine mount strut. Tighten the bolt to 81 ft. lbs. (110 Nm).

75. Install the hood and mounting bolts, tighten to 89 inch lbs. (10 Nm).

76. Install the air cleaner assembly.

77. Connect the negative battery cable.

78. Fill the crankcase with engine oil.

79. Fill and bleed cooling system.

80. Perform a CKP system variation learn procedure.

81. Install the intake manifold cover

82. Start the vehicle, check for leaks and repair if necessary

3.9L Engine

See Figures 139 through 142.

1. Disconnect the negative battery cable.

2. Remove the air cleaner assembly.

3. Remove the hood.

4. Remove the intake manifold cover.

5. Remove the engine mount snubber and drive belt.

6. Remove the power steering pump and disconnect the power steering lines, if equipped.

7. Drain the cooling system.

8. Drain the engine oil.

9. Remove the oil pressure sensor heat shield nuts and shield.

10. Disconnect the oil pressure sensor electrical connector.

11. Disconnect the knock sensor electrical connector.

12. Disconnect the air conditioning (A/C) compressor electrical connector.

13. Lower the vehicle.

14. Disconnect the Evaporative Emission (EVAP) canister purge solenoid electrical connector.

15. Disconnect the Electronic Throttle Control (ETC) electrical connector.

16. Remove the Connector Position Assurance (CPA) retainer.

17. Disconnect the Heated Oxygen Sensor (HO2S) electrical connector.

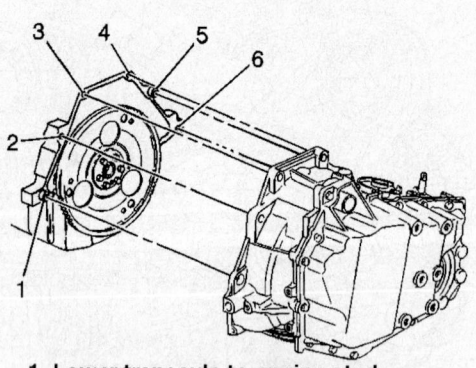

1. Lower transaxle to engine stud
2. Upper transaxle to engine stud
3. Upper transaxle to engine bolt
4. Upper transaxle to engine bolt
5. Upper transaxle to engine bolt
6. Lower transaxle to engine bolt

36616_GMG6_G0239

Fig. 138 Removing the transaxle to engine bolts and studs—3.6L engine

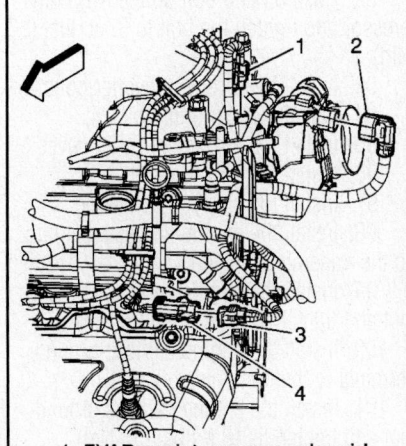

1. EVAP canister purge solenoid
2. ETC electrical connector
3. CPA retainer
4. HO2S electrical connector

36616_GMG6_G0246

Fig. 139 Disconnecting the EVAP canister purge solenoid, ETC connector, CPA retainer and HO2S connector— 3.9L engine

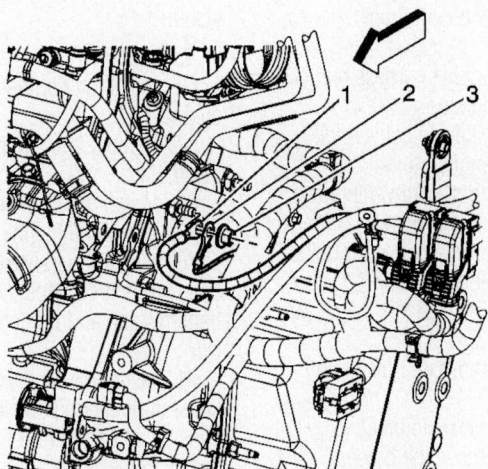

1. Engine harness ground terminal
2. Engine harness ground nut

36616_GMG6_G0251

Fig. 141 Removing the engine harness ground terminal from the transmission stud— 3.9L engine

18. Disconnect the Manifold Absolute Pressure (MAP) sensor electrical connector.

19. Disconnect the ignition control module electrical connector.

20. Disconnect the inlet manifold valve electrical connector.

21. Disconnect the fuel injector inline electrical connector.

22. Disconnect the camshaft phasor sensor electrical connector.

23. Remove the CPA retainer.

24. Disconnect the rear upper HO2S electrical connector.

25. Disconnect the Knock Sensor (KS) electrical connector.

26. Disconnect the Crankshaft Position (CKP) sensor electrical connector.

27. Disconnect the engine harness connector from the body harness connector.

28. Disconnect the body harness electrical connector from the Powertrain Control Module (PCM).

29. Disconnect the engine harness electrical connectors from the PCM.

30. Disconnect the engine harness electrical connector from the Transmission Control Module (TCM).

31. Remove the engine harness clip nut.

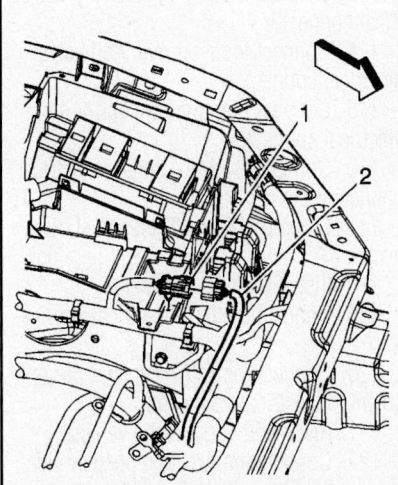

1. Engine harness connector
2. Body harness connector

36616_GMG6_G0250

Fig. 140 Disconnecting the engine harness connector from the body harness connector—3.9L engine

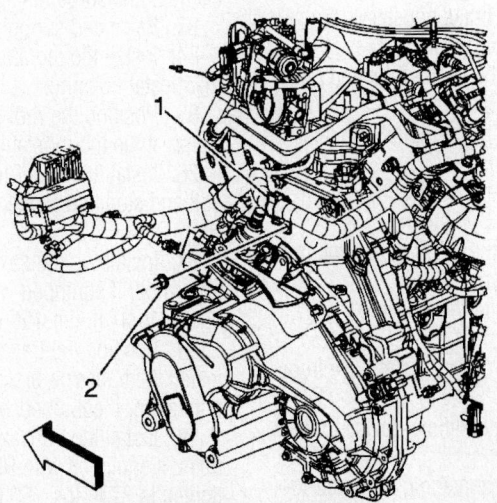

1. Engine harness rear clip
2. Engine harness rear clip nut

36616_GMG6_G0252

Fig. 142 Removing the engine harness rear clip from the transmission stud—3.9L engine

32. Remove the engine harness clip from the transmission stud.

33. Remove the engine harness rear clip nut.

34. Remove the engine harness rear clip from the transmission stud.

35. Remove the catalytic converters.

36. Remove the engine mount.

37. Remove the torque converter cover.

38. Remove the starter motor.

39. Remove the torque converter bolts.

40. Unbolt and reposition the A/C compressor to the side. DO NOT discharge the A/C system.

41. Remove the transaxle brace to oil pan bolts.

42. Remove the transaxle brace to transaxle bolt and remove the brace.

43. Remove the transaxle brace to oil pan bolts, if equipped with RPO MT2.

44. Remove the transaxle brace to transaxle bolt and remove the brace, if equipped with RPO MT2.

45. Remove the transaxle brace to oil pan lower bolt, if equipped with RPO M15.

46. Remove the lower transaxle-to-engine bolt and stud.

47. Reposition the radiator outlet hose clamp at the thermostat housing.

48. Remove the radiator outlet hose from the thermostat housing.

49. Lower the vehicle and support the transaxle.

50. Reposition the radiator surge tank hose clamp at the surge tank pipe.

51. Remove the radiator surge tank hose from the surge tank pipe.

52. Reposition the brake booster vacuum hose clamp at the intake manifold.

53. Remove the brake booster vacuum hose from the intake manifold.

54. Reposition the heater inlet and outlet hose clamps at the engine.

55. Remove the heater outlet and inlet hoses from the engine.

56. Disconnect the fuel feed line from the fuel rail.

57. Disconnect the EVAP purge line from the canister purge solenoid.

58. Reposition the radiator inlet hose clamp at the engine.

59. Remove the radiator inlet hose from the engine.

60. Install a engine lifting device to the engine.

61. Remove the remaining transaxle-to-engine bolts/studs if equipped with a manual transmission.

62. Remove the remaining transaxle-to-engine bolts/studs if equipped with a automatic transmission.

63. Remove the engine from the vehicle.

64. Remove the flywheel.

65. Install the engine to the engine stand.

To install:

66. Install an engine lifting device to the engine.

67. Remove the engine from the engine stand.

68. Install the flywheel.

69. Install the engine to the vehicle.

70. Install the transaxle-to-engine bolts/studs if equipped with a automatic transmission and tighten to 55 ft. lbs. (75 Nm).

71. Install the transaxle-to-engine bolts/studs if equipped with a manual transmission and tighten to 55 ft. lbs. (75 Nm).

72. Remove the engine lifting device from the engine.

73. Install the radiator inlet hose to the engine.

74. Position the radiator inlet hose clamp at the engine.

75. Connect the EVAP purge line to the canister purge solenoid.

76. Connect the fuel feed line to the fuel rail.

77. Install the heater outlet and inlet hoses to the engine.

78. Position the heater inlet and outlet hose clamps at the engine.

79. Install the brake booster vacuum hose to the intake manifold.

80. Position the brake booster vacuum hose clamp at the intake manifold.

81. Install the radiator surge tank hose to the surge tank pipe.

82. Position the radiator surge tank hose clamp at the surge tank pipe.

83. Raise and support the vehicle.

84. Install the radiator outlet hose to the thermostat housing.

85. Position the radiator outlet hose clamp at the thermostat housing.

86. Install the lower transaxle-to-engine bolt and stud and tighten to 55 ft. lbs. (75 Nm).

87. Install the transaxle brace to oil pan lower bolt, if equipped with RPO M15 and tighten to 37 ft. lbs. (50 Nm).

88. Position the transaxle brace and install the transaxle brace to transaxle bolt until snug, if equipped with RPO MT2.

89. Install the transaxle brace to oil pan bolts, if equipped with RPO MT2 and tighten to 37 ft. lbs. (50 Nm).

90. Position the transaxle brace and install the transaxle brace to transaxle bolt until snug.

91. Install the transaxle brace to oil pan bolts and tighten to 37 ft. lbs. (50 Nm).

92. Position and bolt up the A/C compressor and tighten the bolt to 37 ft. lbs. (50 Nm).

93. Install the torque converter bolts.

94. Install the starter motor.

95. Install the torque converter cover.

96. Install the engine mount.

97. Install the catalytic converters.

98. Install the engine harness rear clip to the transmission stud.

99. Install the engine harness rear clip nut and tighten to 18 ft. lbs. (25 Nm).

100. Install the engine harness ground terminal to the transmission stud.

101. Install the engine harness ground nut and tighten to 18 ft. lbs. (25 Nm).

102. Install the engine harness clip to the transmission stud.

103. Install the engine harness clip nut and tighten to 18 ft. lbs. (25 Nm).

104. Connect the engine harness electrical connector to the TCM.

105. Connect the engine harness electrical connectors to the PCM.

106. Connect the body harness electrical connector to the PCM.

107. Connect the engine harness connector to the body harness connector (2).

108. Connect the CKP sensor electrical connector.

109. Connect the knock sensor electrical connector.

110. Connect the rear upper HO2S electrical connector.

111. Install the CPA retainer.

112. Connect the camshaft phasor sensor electrical connector.

113. Connect the fuel injector inline electrical connector.

114. Connect the inlet manifold valve electrical connector.

115. Connect the ignition control module electrical connector.

116. Connect the MAP sensor electrical connector.

117. Connect the HO2S electrical connector.

118. Install the CPA retainer.

119. Connect the ETC electrical connector.

120. Connect the EVAP canister purge solenoid electrical connector.

121. Raise and support the vehicle.

122. Connect the A/C compressor electrical connector.

123. Connect the knock sensor electrical connector.

124. Connect the oil pressure sensor electrical connector.

125. Install the oil pressure sensor heat shield and nuts and tighten the nuts to 18 ft. lbs. (25 Nm).

126. Lower the vehicle.

127. Connect the power steering lines and install the power steering pump, if equipped.

128. Install the drive belt and engine mount snubber.

129. Install the intake manifold cover.

130. Install the hood.

131. Install the air cleaner assembly.

132. Fill the engine with oil.

133. Fill the cooling system.

134. Connect the negative battery cable.

135. Inspect for leaks.

EXHAUST MANIFOLD

REMOVAL & INSTALLATION

2.4L Engine

See Figures 143 through 145.

1. Remove the secondary air injection bolts and nuts.

2. Remove the secondary air injection studs.

3. Remove the secondary air injection valve assembly

4. Remove the secondary air injection gasket and discard.

5. Remove the exhaust manifold heat shield bolt.

6. Remove the exhaust manifold heat shield.

7. Remove the block heater if equipped.

8. Remove the oxygen sensor.

9. Remove the exhaust manifold brace bolts (2) and brace (1).

10. Remove and discard the exhaust manifold to cylinder head retaining nuts.

11. Remove the exhaust manifold.

12. Remove the exhaust manifold gasket.

13. Clean all of the sealing surfaces.

14. If the exhaust manifold is being replaced, transfer the exhaust manifold heat shield and the oxygen sensor.

15. Remove the secondary air injection pipe assembly bolts.

16. Remove the secondary air injection pipe assembly.

To install:

17. Install new exhaust manifold studs and tighten to 89 inch lbs. (10 Nm).

18. Install the secondary air injection pipe assembly.

19. Install the secondary air injection pipe assembly bolts and tighten to 89 inch lbs. (10 Nm).

20. Install the exhaust manifold gasket.

21. Install the exhaust manifold to the cylinder head.

22. Install NEW exhaust manifold to cylinder head retaining nuts finger tight.

23. Install the exhaust manifold brace and bolts. Tighten the bolts to 43 ft. lbs. (58 Nm).

24. Tighten the NEW exhaust manifold to cylinder head retaining nuts two passes in sequence. Tighten the nuts to 124 inch lbs. (14 Nm).

25. Coat the threads of the oxygen sensor with anti-seize GM P/N 12397953 or equivalent.

26. Install the oxygen sensor and tighten to 31 ft. lbs. (42 Nm).

27. Install the block heater, if equipped. Tighten the block heater to 89 inch lbs. (10 Nm).

28. Install the exhaust manifold heat shield.

29. Install the exhaust manifold heat shield bolt and tighten to 18 ft. lbs. (25 Nm).

30. Install the secondary air injection studs and tighten to 89 inch lbs. (10 Nm).

31. Install the secondary air injection valve assembly with a NEW gasket.

32. Install the secondary air injection bolts and nuts.

a. Tighten the secondary air injection assembly and exhaust manifold heat shield bolts to 16 ft. lbs. (22 Nm).

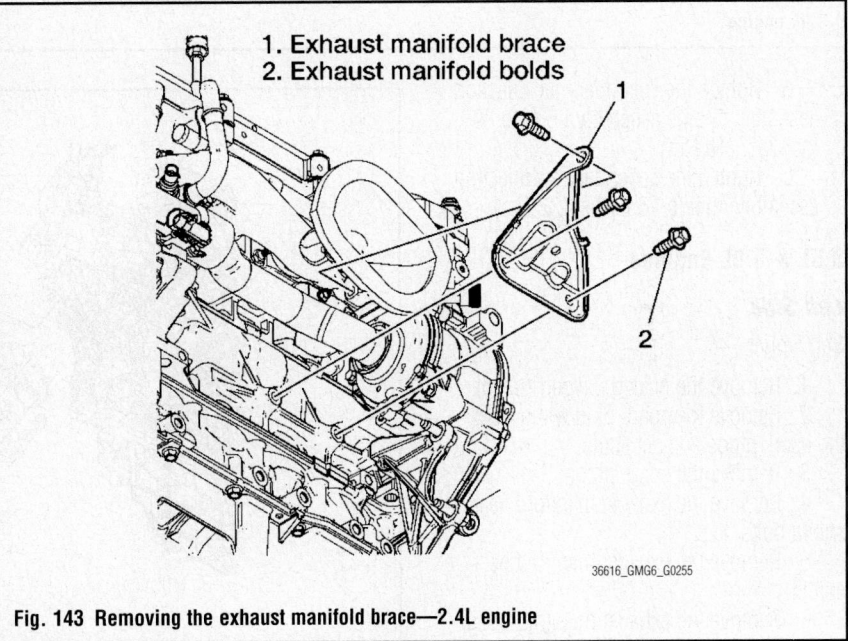

1. Exhaust manifold brace
2. Exhaust manifold bolds

36616_GMG6_G0255

Fig. 143 Removing the exhaust manifold brace—2.4L engine

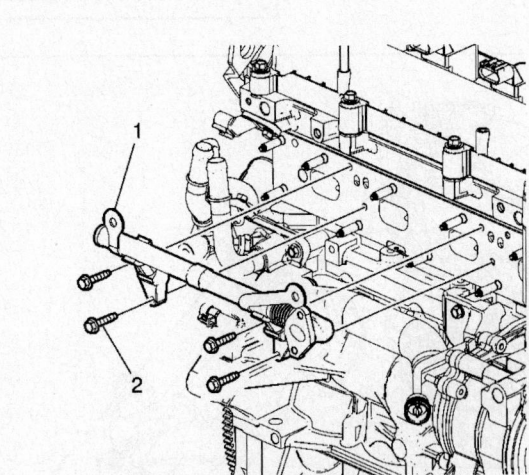

1. Secondary air injection pipe assembly
2. Secondary air injection pipe assembly bolts

36616_GMG6_G0256

Fig. 144 Removing the secondary air injection pipe assembly—2.4L engine

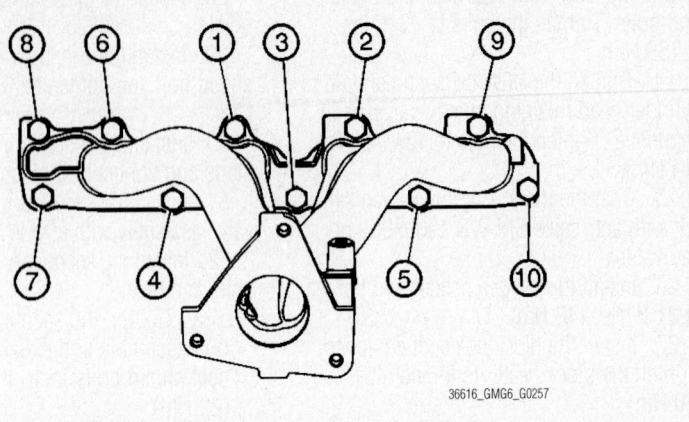

Fig. 145 Identifying the exhaust manifold to cylinder head retaining nut tightening sequence—2.4L engine

b. Tighten the secondary air injection assembly to pipe assembly bolts to 89 inch lbs. (10 Nm).

c. Tighten the secondary air injection assembly nuts to 16 ft. lbs. (22 Nm).

3.5L & 3.9L Engines

Left Side

See Figure 146.

1. Remove the heated oxygen sensor.
2. Remove the spark plug wires from the spark plugs and set aside.
3. Remove the spark plugs.
4. Remove the exhaust manifold heat shield bolts.
5. Remove the exhaust manifold heat shield.
6. Remove the exhaust manifold bolts.
7. Remove the exhaust manifold.
8. Remove the exhaust manifold gasket.

To install:

9. Install the exhaust manifold gasket.
10. Install the exhaust manifold.
11. Install the exhaust manifold bolts and tighten to 15 ft. lbs. (20 Nm).
12. Install the exhaust manifold heat shield.
13. Install the exhaust manifold heat shield bolts and tighten to 89 inch lbs. (10 Nm).
14. Install the spark plugs and tighten to 11 ft. lbs. (15 Nm).
15. Install the spark plug wires.
16. Install the heated oxygen sensor and tighten to 31 ft. lbs. (42 Nm).

Right Side

See Figure 147.

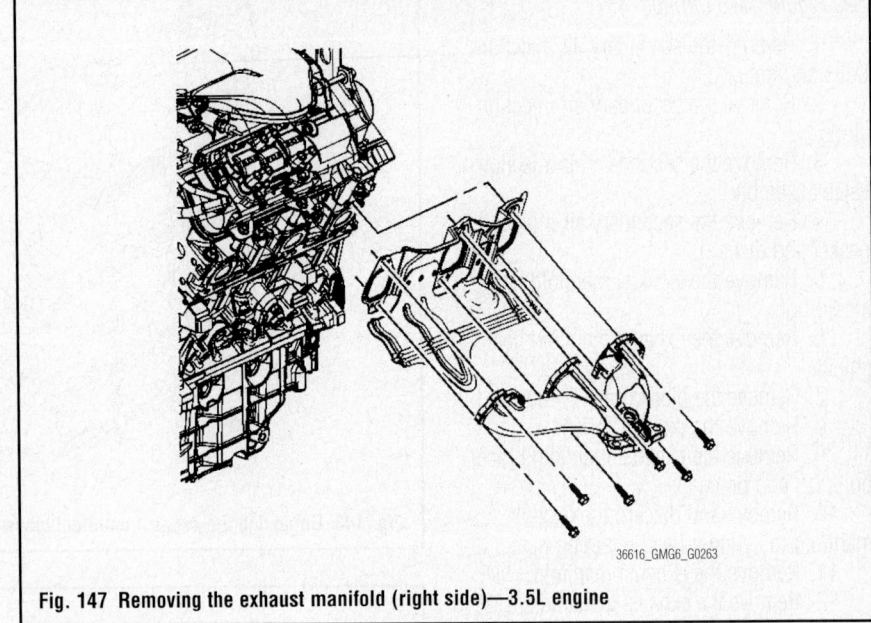

Fig. 147 Removing the exhaust manifold (right side)—3.5L engine

1. Remove the heated oxygen sensor.
2. Remove the spark plug wires.
3. Remove the spark plugs.
4. Remove the exhaust manifold heat shield bolts.
5. Remove the exhaust manifold heat shields.
6. Remove the exhaust manifold bolts.
7. Remove the exhaust manifold.
8. Remove the exhaust manifold gasket.

To install:

9. Install the exhaust manifold gasket.
10. Install the exhaust manifold and tighten the bolts to 15 ft. lbs. (20 Nm).
11. Install the exhaust manifold heat shield.
12. Install the exhaust manifold heat shield bolts and tighten to 89 inch lbs. (10 Nm).

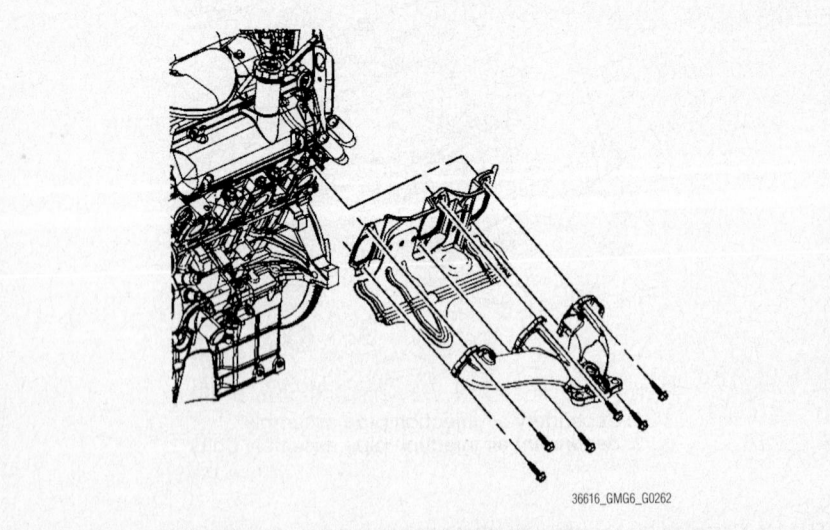

Fig. 146 Removing the exhaust manifold (left side)—3.5L engine

13. Install the spark plugs and tighten to 11 ft. lbs. (15 Nm).

14. Install the spark plug wires.

15. Install the heated oxygen sensor and tighten to 31 ft. lbs. (42 Nm).

3.6L Engine

Left Side

See Figures 148 through 150.

1. Remove the left exhaust manifold heat shield bolts.

2. Remove the left exhaust manifold heat shield.

3. Remove the left exhaust manifold lower bolts from the left cylinder head.

4. Remove the left exhaust manifold upper bolts from the left cylinder head.

5. Remove the left exhaust manifold.

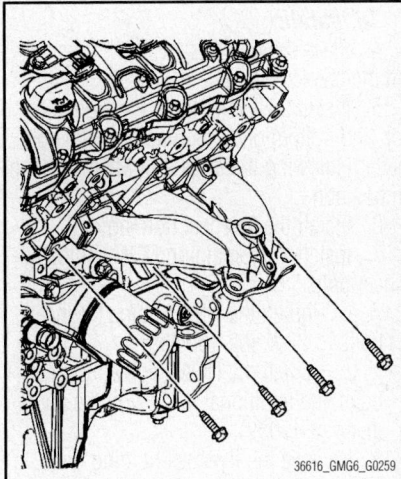

Fig. 148 Removing left exhaust manifold lower bolts—3.6L engine

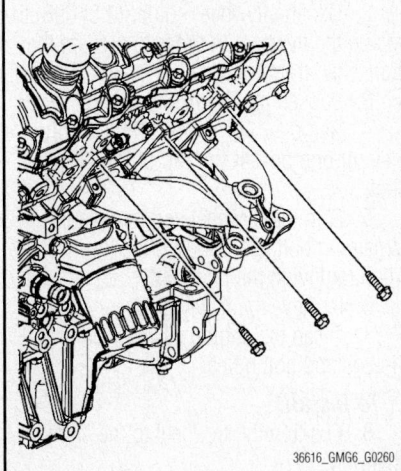

Fig. 149 Removing left exhaust manifold upper bolts—3.6L engine

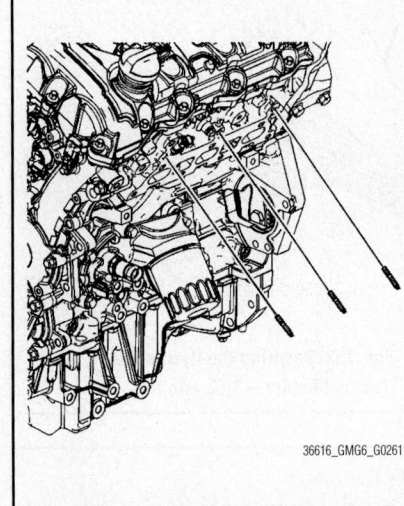

Fig. 150 Installing the studs into the left cylinder head—3.6L engine

6. Remove and discard the left exhaust manifold gasket.

To install:

7. Install the studs into the left cylinder head.

8. Install a NEW left exhaust manifold gasket.

9. Install the left exhaust manifold.

10. Loosely install the left exhaust manifold upper bolts into the left cylinder head.

11. Loosely install the left exhaust manifold lower bolts into the left cylinder head.

12. Tighten the left exhaust manifold bolts to 18 ft. lbs. (25 Nm).

13. Place the left exhaust manifold heat shield in position.

14. Install the exhaust manifold heat shield bolts and tighten to 89 inch lbs. (10 Nm).

Right Side

See Figure 151.

1. Remove the right exhaust manifold heat shield bolts.

2. Remove the right exhaust manifold heat shield.

3. Remove the right exhaust manifold lower bolts from the right cylinder head.

4. Remove the right exhaust manifold upper bolts from the right cylinder head.

5. Remove the right exhaust manifold.

6. Remove and discard the right exhaust manifold gasket.

To install:

7. Install a NEW right exhaust manifold gasket.

8. Install the right exhaust manifold.

9. Loosely install the right exhaust manifold upper bolts into the right cylinder head.

10. Tighten the right exhaust manifold bolts and tighten to 18 ft. lbs. (25 Nm).

11. Place the right exhaust manifold heat shield in position.

12. Install the exhaust manifold heat shield bolts and tighten to 89 inch lbs. (10 Nm).

FLYWHEEL

REMOVAL & INSTALLATION

2.4L Engine

See Figure 152.

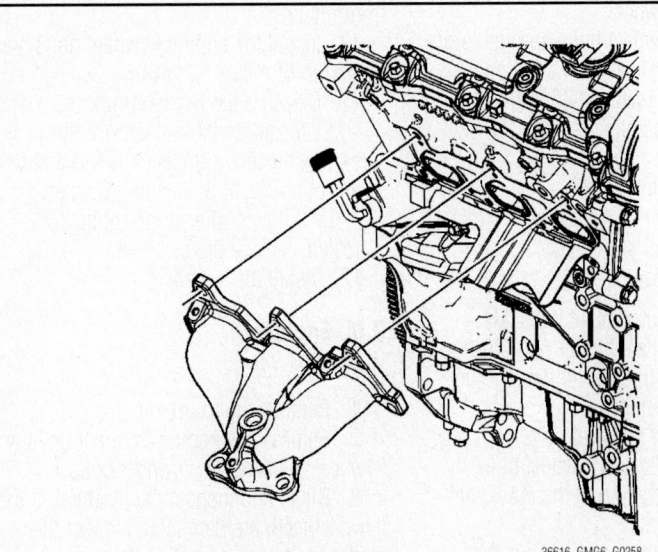

Fig. 151 Removing the right exhaust manifold—3.6L engine

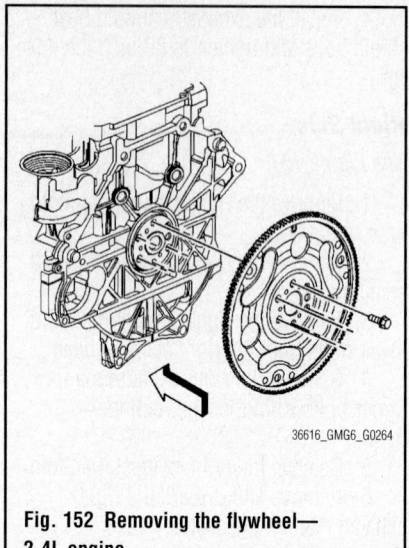

Fig. 152 Removing the flywheel—2.4L engine

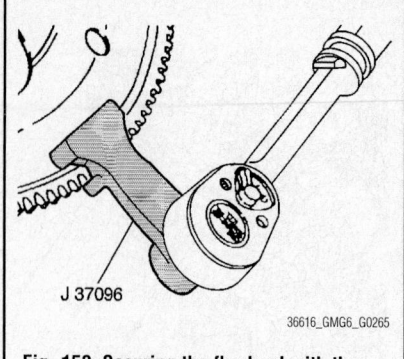

Fig. 153 Securing the flywheel with the flywheel holder—3.5L engine

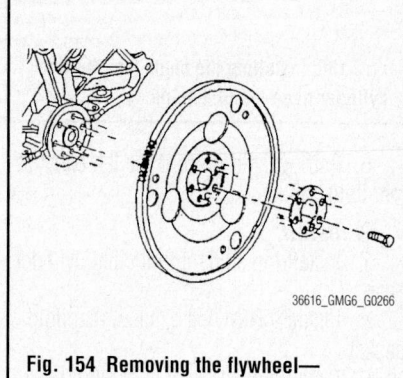

Fig. 154 Removing the flywheel—3.5L engine

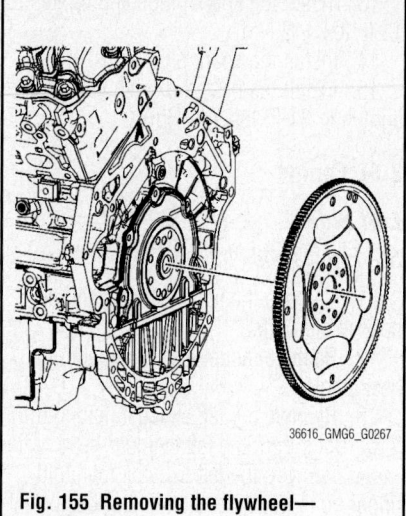

Fig. 155 Removing the flywheel—3.6L engine

1. Remove the transmission.
2. Using the crankshaft balancer holder (J 38122-A), hold the crankshaft balancer.

➡It may be necessary to remove the chamfer (bevel) from the edge of an 18 mm socket in order to get full engagement on the thin-headed flywheel bolts.

3. Remove the flywheel bolts.

➡Do not orientate the flywheel to the crankshaft. It is balanced separately from the engine.

4. Remove the flywheel.
5. Clean the thread adhesive from the flywheel bolt holes. Use a nylon bristle brush to clean the holes in the crankshaft.

To install:
6. Install the flywheel.
7. Install the flywheel bolts and tighten to 39 ft. lbs. (53 Nm), plus an additional 25° using an angle meter (J 45059).
8. Remove the crankshaft balancer holder (J 38122-A).
9. Install the transmission.

3.5L Engine
See Figures 153 and 154.

1. Remove the automatic transaxle.
2. Use the flywheel holder (J 37096) to secure the flywheel in order to prevent the crankshaft from rotating.
3. Loosen the 6 flywheel bolts.
4. Remove 5 of the 6 flywheel bolts leaving one bolt at the top of the crankshaft rotation.
5. Grip the flywheel and remove the remaining bolt. Do not drop the flywheel when removing the final bolt.

6. Remove the engine flywheel retainer and the flywheel.
7. Clean the engine flywheel bolt threads and bolt holes.

To install:
8. Install the flywheel and the flywheel retainer.
9. Use the flywheel holder to secure the flywheel in order to prevent the crankshaft from rotating.
10. Install the engine flywheel bolts and tighten to 52 ft. lbs. (71 Nm).
11. Measure the flywheel runout:
    a. Install a dial indicator on the engine block and inspect the engine flywheel runout at 3 attaching bosses.
    b. If the condition cannot be corrected, replace the flywheel.
12. Install the transaxle.

3.6L Engine
See Figure 155.

1. Remove the transaxle.
2. Remove the engine flywheel bolts and flywheel. Discard the flywheel bolts.
3. Clean and inspect the flywheel. If the flywheel teeth are damaged, inspect the starter for proper operation. Replace the starter if you find excessive wear or damage to the starter drive.

To install:
4. Place the engine flywheel in position on the crankshaft.
5. Install 2 NEW bolts in location at the top and bottom of the engine flywheel bolt pattern allowing the engine flywheel to hang in position.
6. Install the flywheel holding tool.
7. Install the remaining NEW engine flywheel bolts.
    a. Tighten the NEW engine flywheel bolts to 22 ft. lbs. (30 Nm).
    b. Tighten the NEW engine flywheel bolts and additional 45° using the angle meter (J 45059).
8. Remove the flywheel holding tool.
9. Install the transaxle.

3.9L Engine
See Figure 156.

1. Remove the transaxle.
2. Use the flywheel holder (J 37096) to secure the flywheel in order to prevent the crankshaft from rotating.
3. Loosen the flywheel bolts.
4. Remove 5 of the 6 flywheel bolts leaving one bolt at the top of the crankshaft.
5. Grip the flywheel and remove the remaining bolt. Do not drop the flywheel when removing the final bolt.
6. Remove the flywheel.
7. Clean the engine flywheel bolt threads and bolt holes.

To install:
8. Position the flywheel to the crankshaft.
9. Install the flywheel bolts finger tight.
10. Use the flywheel holder (J 37096) to secure the flywheel in order to prevent the crankshaft from rotating.

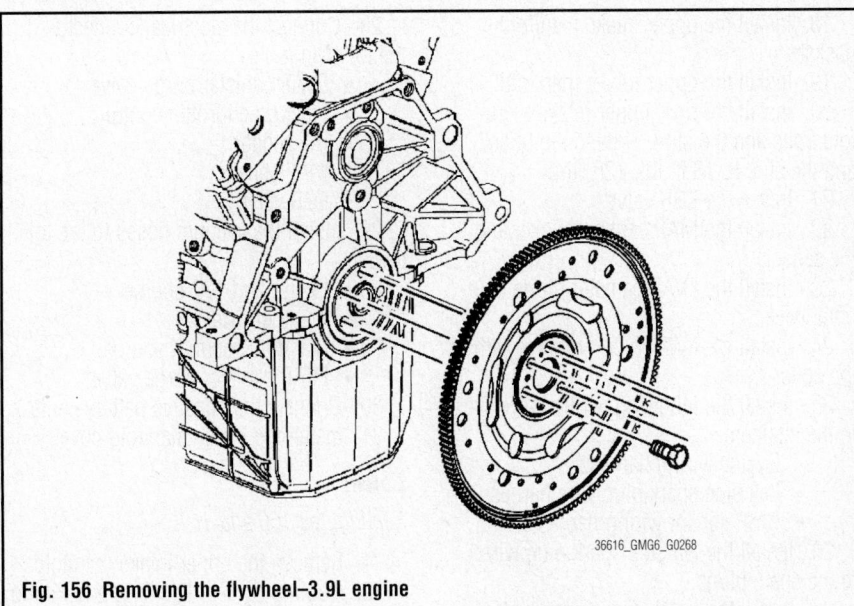

Fig. 156 Removing the flywheel–3.9L engine

11. Tighten the engine flywheel bolts. Tighten the bolts to 52 ft. lbs. (70 Nm).

12. Install the automatic transaxle.

INTAKE MANIFOLD

REMOVAL & INSTALLATION

2.4L Engine

See Figure 157.

1. Remove the throttle body.
2. Remove the fuel rail.
3. Remove the Evaporative Emission (EVAP) canister purge solenoid valve tube.
4. Reposition the brake booster vacuum hose clamp at the intake manifold.
5. Remove the brake booster hose from the intake manifold.
6. Remove the oil level indicator tube bolt.
7. Disconnect the engine harness electrical connector from the fuel injector inline electrical connector.
8. Remove the fuel injector inline connector clip from the intake manifold.
9. Disconnect the engine harness electrical connector from the knock sensor harness.
10. Remove the knock sensor connector clip from the oil level indicator tube.
11. Remove the intake manifold bolts and nuts.
12. Remove the intake manifold.

➡The intake manifold gasket is reusable. Only replace the gasket if damage has occurred. Remove the intake manifold gasket, if necessary.

To install:

13. Install the intake manifold gasket, if necessary.
14. Install the intake manifold.
15. Install the intake manifold bolts and nuts. Tighten the bolts and nuts to 89 inch lbs. (10 Nm).
16. Connect the engine harness electrical connector to the knock sensor harness.
17. Install the knock sensor connector clip to the oil level indicator tube.
18. Connect the engine harness electrical connector to the fuel injector inline electrical connector.
19. Install the fuel injector inline connector clip to the intake manifold.
20. Install the oil level indicator tube bolt. Tighten the bolt to 89 inch lbs. (10 Nm).

21. Install the brake booster hose to the intake manifold.
22. Position the brake booster vacuum hose clamp at the intake manifold.
23. Install the EVAP canister purge solenoid valve tube.
24. Install the fuel rail.
25. Install the throttle body.

3.5L Engine

Upper

See Figures 158 and 159.

1. Disconnect the negative battery cable.
2. Remove the intake manifold cover.
3. Remove the vacuum hoses from the following:
   - Evaporative Emissions (EVAP) canister purge valve
   - Manifold vacuum source
   - Brake booster
   - Heater and Air Conditioning (A/C) source
4. Disconnect the electrical connectors from the following:
   - Exhaust Gas Recirculation (EGR) valve
   - Mass Air Flow (MAF) sensor
   - Intake Air Temperature (IAT) sensor
   - Electronic throttle control
   - EVAP canister purge valve
5. Remove the air cleaner outlet duct.
6. Remove the left side spark plug wires from the spark plugs.
7. Remove the following wiring harnesses from the retainers:
   - Camshaft Position (CMP) sensor wiring harness

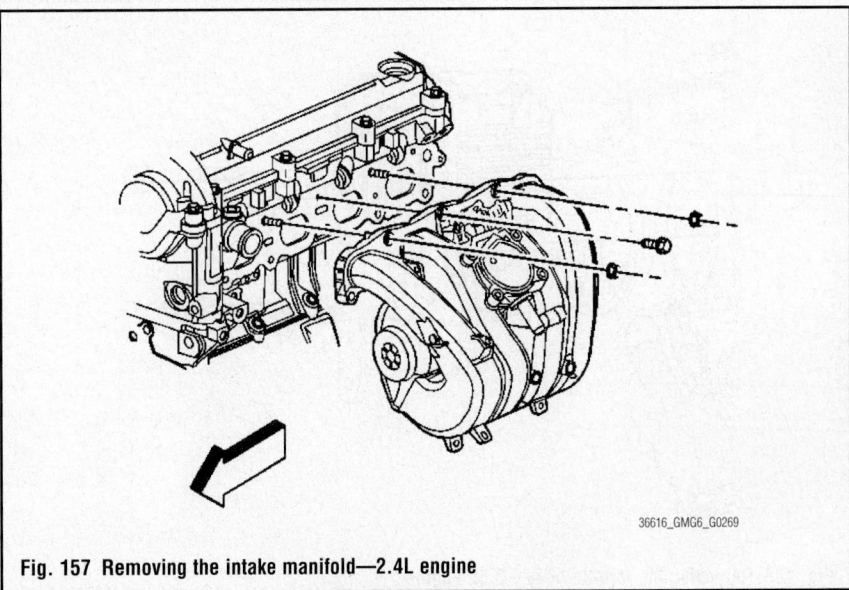

Fig. 157 Removing the intake manifold—2.4L engine

- Left side spark plug wire harness
- Engine wiring harness

8. Remove the ignition coil bracket with the coils.

9. Remove the EVAP canister purge solenoid valve.

10. Remove the Manifold Absolute Pressure (MAP) sensor and the bracket.

11. Remove the EGR valve.

12. Remove the upper intake manifold bolts and the stud.

13. Remove the upper intake manifold.

14. Remove the upper intake manifold gaskets.

15. If replacing the upper intake manifold, remove the throttle body.

16. Clean the upper intake gasket mating surfaces.

To install:

17. If removed, install the throttle body.

18. Install the upper intake manifold gaskets.

19. Install the upper intake manifold.

20. Install the right upper intake manifold bolts and the stud. Tighten the bolts and the stud to 18 ft. lbs. (25 Nm).

21. Install the EGR valve.

22. Install the MAP sensor bracket and the sensor.

23. Install the EVAP canister purge solenoid valve.

24. Install the ignition coil bracket with the coils.

25. Install the following wiring harnesses to the retainers:

- Engine wiring harness
- Left side spark plug wire harness
- CMP sensor wiring harness

26. Install the left side spark plug wires to the spark plugs.

27. Install the air cleaner outlet duct.

28. Connect the electrical connectors to the following:

- EVAP canister purge valve
- Electronic throttle control
- IAT sensor
- MAF sensor
- EGR valve

29. Install the vacuum hoses to the following:

- Heater and A/C source
- Brake booster
- Manifold vacuum source
- EVAP canister purge valve

30. Connect the negative battery cable.

31. Install the intake manifold cover.

Lower

See Figures 160 and 161.

1. Remove the upper intake manifold.
2. Cooling System Draining and Filling.
3. Remove the valve rocker arm covers.
4. Remove the coolant crossover pipe.
5. Disconnect the fuel injector wiring harness electrical connector from the Engine Coolant Temperature (ECT) sensor.
6. Disconnect the engine wiring harness electrical connector (2) from the fuel injector inline electrical connector.
7. Disconnect the fuel injector wiring harness electrical connector from the Camshaft Position (CMP) sensor.
8. Remove the fuel injector wiring harness connector bracket bolt from the intake manifold.
9. Remove the fuel rail bolts and rail.
10. Remove the lower intake manifold bolts.
11. Remove the lower intake manifold.
12. Remove the rocker arms.
13. Remove the push rods. The intake push rods measure 5.81 inch (147.51 mm). The exhaust push rods measure 6.1 inch (154.87 mm).
14. Remove the lower intake manifold gaskets and seals.
15. Clean the lower intake manifold gasket and seal surfaces on the cylinder heads and the engine block.
16. Clean the gasket and seal surfaces on the lower intake manifold with degreaser.
17. Remove all the loose Room Temperature Vulcanizing (RTV) sealer

To install:

➡All gasket-mating surfaces need to be free of oil and foreign material. Use cleaner to clean the surfaces.

➡RTV sealer is NOT to be placed under the lower intake manifold gaskets.

18. Install the lower intake manifold gaskets and seals.

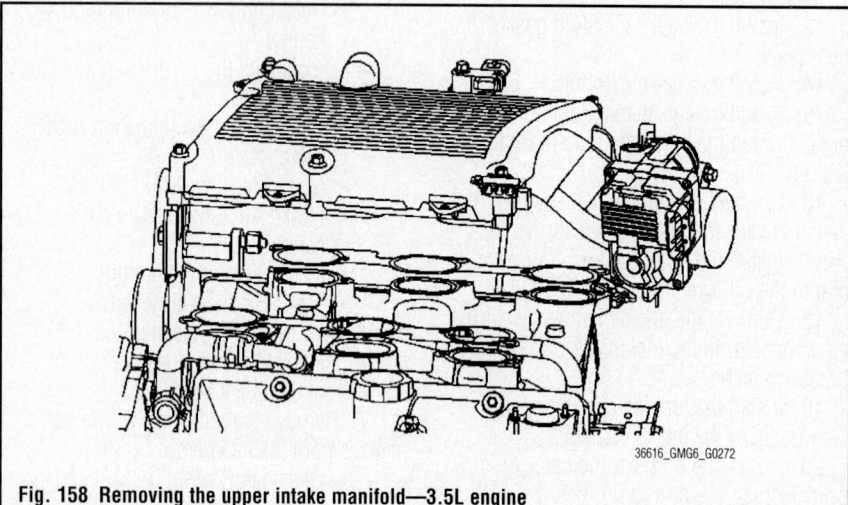

Fig. 158 Removing the upper intake manifold—3.5L engine

36616_GMG6_G0272

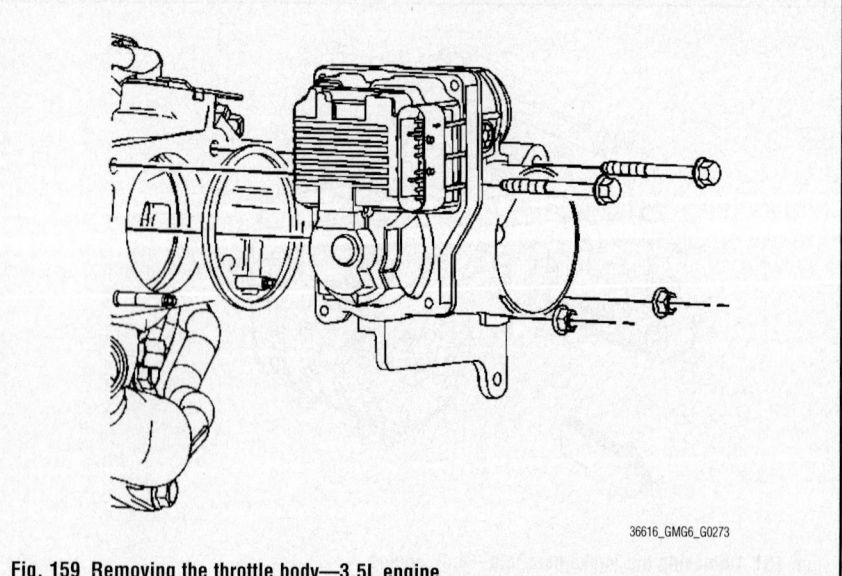

Fig. 159 Removing the throttle body—3.5L engine

36616_GMG6_G0273

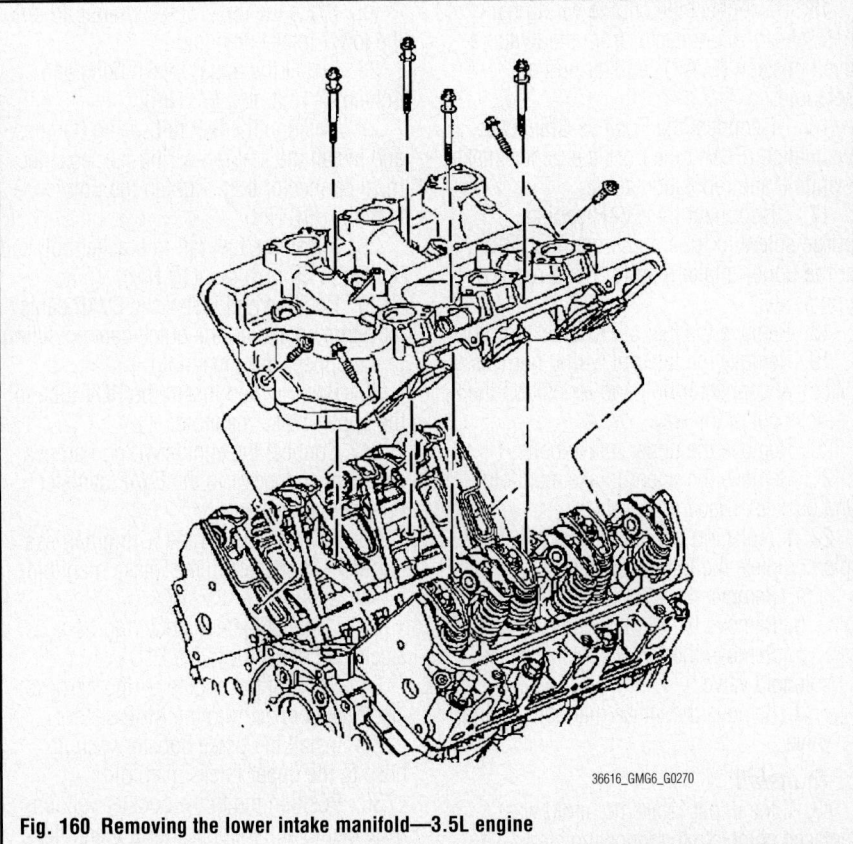

Fig. 160 Removing the lower intake manifold—3.5L engine

19. Coat the ends of the push rods using prelube GM P/N 12345501 (Canadian P/N 992704) or equivalent.

20. Install push rods in their original location. The intake pushrods are identified with yellow stripes. The exhaust pushrods are identified with green stripes.

21. Coat the rocker arm friction surfaces using prelube GM P/N 12345501 or equivalent.

➡ **Shims (P/N 88894006) may be required under the valve rocker arm pedestals if reconditioning has been performed on the cylinder head or its components.**

22. Install the rocker arms in their original locations.

23. Install the rocker arm bolts. Tighten the bolts to 25 ft. lbs. (34 Nm).

24. With the NEW gaskets and seals in place, apply a small drop, 0.31-0.39 inch (8-10 mm) of RTV sealer to the 4 corners of the intake manifold to block joints.

25. Install the lower intake manifold.

❋❋ CAUTION

Maximum gasket performance is achieved when using new fasteners, which contain a thread-locking patch. If the fasteners are not replaced, a thread locking chemical must be applied to the fastener threads. Failure to replace the fasteners or apply a thread-locking chemical MAY reduce gasket sealing capability.

❋❋ CAUTION

Failure to tighten vertical bolts before the diagonal bolts may cause an oil leak.

26. Apply sealer to the lower intake manifold bolt threads.

27. Install the lower intake manifold bolts.

28. Tighten the lower intake manifold bolts in the sequence shown.

a. Tighten the center lower intake manifold bolts (1, 2, 3, 4) in sequence to 15 ft. lbs. (20 Nm).

b. Tighten the visible corner lower intake manifold bolts (5, 8) to 18 ft. lbs. (25 Nm).

c. Tighten the hidden corner lower intake manifold bolts (6, 7) to 18 ft. lbs. (25 Nm).

29. Inspect the fuel rail, fuel injectors for damage and replace as necessary.

30. Lubricate and install NEW injector lower O-rings seals onto the injectors. Lubricate the NEW O-rings seals with GM P/N 12345616.

31. Install the injector nozzles into the lower intake manifold injector bores.

32. Press on the injector rail using the palms of both hands until the injectors are fully seated.

33. Install the fuel injector rail bolts. Tighten the bolts to 89 inch lbs. (10 Nm).

34. Position the fuel injector wiring harness electrical connector bracket to the intake manifold and install the bolt. Tighten the bolt to 10 ft. lbs. (14 Nm).

35. Connect the fuel injector wiring harness electrical connector to the CMP sensor.

36. Connect the engine wiring harness electrical connector to the fuel injector inline electrical connector.

37. Connect the fuel injector wiring harness electrical connector to the ECT sensor.

38. Install the coolant crossover pipe.

39. Install the valve rocker arm covers.

40. Install the upper intake manifold.

41. Fill the coolant system.

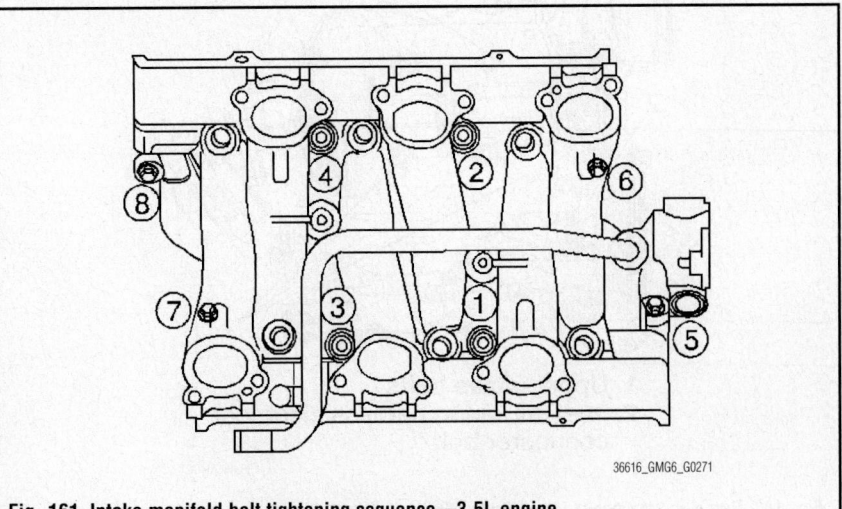

Fig. 161 Intake manifold bolt tightening sequence—3.5L engine

3.6L Engine

Upper

See Figure 162.

1. Remove the fuel injector sight shield.

2. Remove the air cleaner outlet duct.

3. Disconnect the fuel feed line quick connect fitting from the fuel rail.

4. Remove the fuel feed pipe line nut and remove the fuel feed line clip from the stud.

5. Reposition the fuel feed line out of the way.

6. Remove the coolant air bleed hose/pipe clip bolt from the upper intake manifold.

7. Reposition the coolant air bleed hose clamp at the water outlet.

8. Remove the coolant air bleed hose from the water outlet.

9. Remove the coolant air bleed hose/pipe clip from the upper intake manifold stud and reposition out of the way.

10. Reposition the brake booster vacuum hose clamp at the upper intake manifold.

11. Remove the brake booster vacuum hose from the upper intake manifold.

12. Disconnect the engine wiring harness electrical connector from the Manifold Absolute Pressure (MAP) sensor.

13. Disconnect the engine wiring harness electrical connector from the Electronic Throttle Control (ETC).

14. Disconnect the engine wiring harness electrical connector from the intake manifold tuning valve.

15. Disconnect the engine wiring harness electrical connector from the Evaporative Emission (EVAP) canister purge solenoid.

16. Disconnect the Positive Crankcase Ventilation (PCV) tube from the upper intake manifold and reposition aside.

17. Disconnect the EVAP canister purge solenoid tube quick connect fitting at the upper intake manifold and reposition aside.

18. Remove the fuel rail to bracket bolt.

19. Remove the fuel rail wiring harness electrical connector bolt and reposition the harness out of the way.

20. Remove the upper intake bolts.

21. Remove the upper intake manifold and gaskets. Discard gaskets.

22. If replacing the upper intake manifold complete the following steps:

 a. Remove the MAP sensor.

 b. Remove the throttle body.

 c. Remove the EVAP canister purge solenoid valve.

 d. Remove the intake manifold tuning valve.

To install:

23. If the upper intake manifold was replaced complete the following steps:

 a. Install the MAP sensor.

 b. Install the throttle body.

 c. Install the EVAP canister purge solenoid valve.

 d. Install the intake manifold tuning valve.

24. Place NEW upper intake manifold gaskets onto the lower intake manifold.

25. Place the upper intake manifold onto the lower intake manifold.

26. Install the upper intake bolts and tighten to 17 ft. lbs. (23 Nm).

27. Position the fuel rail wiring harness and install the fuel rail wiring harness electrical connector bolt. Tighten the bolt to 89 inch lbs. (10 Nm).

28. Install the fuel rail to bracket bolt and tighten to 89 inch lbs. (10 Nm).

29. Position and install the EVAP canister purge solenoid tube quick connect fitting to the upper intake manifold.

30. Position and install the PCV tube to the upper intake manifold.

31. Connect the engine wiring harness electrical connector to the EVAP canister purge solenoid.

32. Connect the engine wiring harness electrical connector to the intake manifold tuning valve.

33. Connect the engine wiring harness electrical connector to the ETC.

34. Connect the engine wiring harness electrical connector to the MAP sensor.

35. Install the brake booster vacuum hose to the upper intake manifold.

36. Position the brake booster vacuum hose clamp at the upper intake manifold.

37. Position and install the coolant air bleed hose/pipe clip to the upper intake manifold stud.

38. Install the coolant air bleed hose to the water outlet.

39. Position the coolant air bleed hose clamp at the water outlet.

40. Install the coolant air bleed hose/pipe clip bolt to the upper intake manifold and tighten to 89 inch lbs. (10 Nm).

41. Position the fuel feed line and install the fuel feed line clip to the stud.

42. Install the fuel feed line nut and tighten to 89 inch lbs. (10 Nm).

43. Connect the fuel feed line quick connect fitting to the fuel rail.

44. Install the air cleaner outlet duct.

45. Install the fuel injector sight shield.

Lower

See Figure 163.

1. Remove the fuel injectors and fuel rail.

2. Remove the lower intake manifold bolts.

3. Remove the lower intake manifold and gasket. Discard the gasket.

4. Clean and inspect the intake manifold and sealing surfaces.

To install:

5. Place a NEW lower intake manifold gasket onto the cylinder heads.

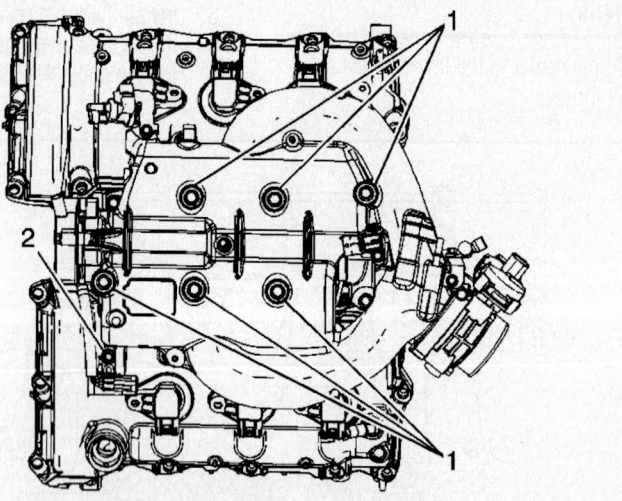

1. Upper intake bolts
2. Fuel rail wiring harness electrical connector bolt

36616_GMG6_G0274

Fig. 162 Removing the upper intake bolts—3.6L engine

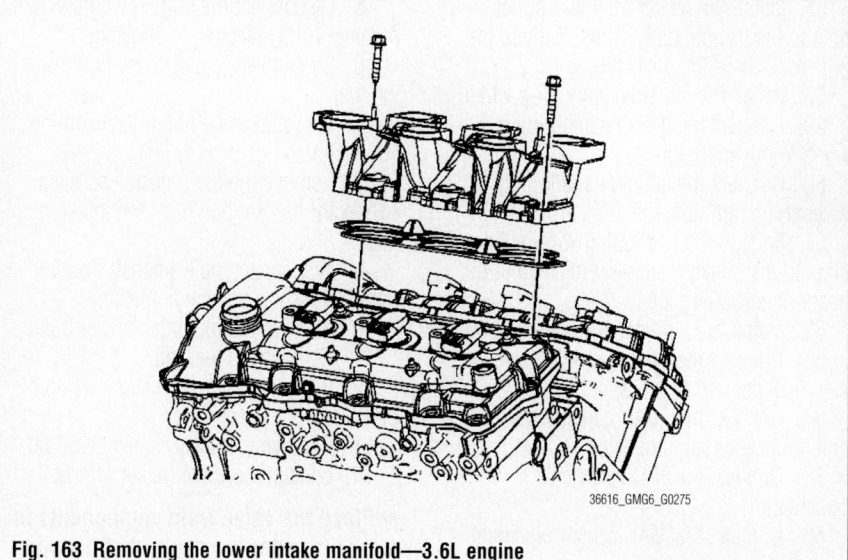

Fig. 163 Removing the lower intake manifold—3.6L engine

6. Place the lower intake manifold onto the cylinder heads.

7. Install the lower intake manifold bolts. Tighten the bolts to 17 ft. lbs. (23 Nm).

8. Install the fuel injectors and fuel rail.

3.9L Engine

Upper

See Figures 164 and 165.

1. Remove the intake manifold cover.

2. Relieve the fuel system pressure.

3. Disconnect the fuel feed pipe quick connect fitting from the fuel rail.

4. Disconnect the evaporative (EVAP) emission pipe from the purge solenoid.

5. Open the retaining clip, and remove the fuel and EVAP pipes from the clip.

6. Drain the cooling system.

7. Remove the Positive Crankcase Ventilation (PCV) fresh air tube.

8. Remove the PCV foul air tube.

9. Reposition the brake booster vacuum hose clamp at the intake manifold.

10. Remove the vacuum hose from the intake manifold.

11. Reposition the radiator surge tank inlet hose clamp.

12. Remove the radiator surge tank inlet hose from the inlet pipe.

13. Remove the radiator surge tank inlet pipe bolts.

14. Remove the radiator surge tank inlet pipe.

15. Disconnect the Manifold Absolute Pressure (MAP) sensor electrical connector.

16. Disconnect the Evaporative Emission (EVAP) canister purge solenoid electrical connector.

17. Disconnect the Electronic Throttle Control (ETC) electrical connector (2).

18. Disconnect the inlet manifold valve electrical connector.

19. Remove the air cleaner outlet duct.

20. Disconnect the left side spark plug wires from the spark plugs.

21. Disconnect the left side spark plug wires from the ignition coil.

22. Disengage the spark plug wire retainer clips from the intake manifold bracket and the heater inlet/outlet pipe.

23. Remove the left side spark plug wires.

24. Remove the heater inlet and outlet pipe nuts from the throttle body studs.

25. Remove the inlet and outlet pipe from the studs.

26. Remove the 2 ignition coil bolts.

27. Remove the generator upper bolt.

28. Remove the generator ball stud.

29. Remove the generator rear brace.

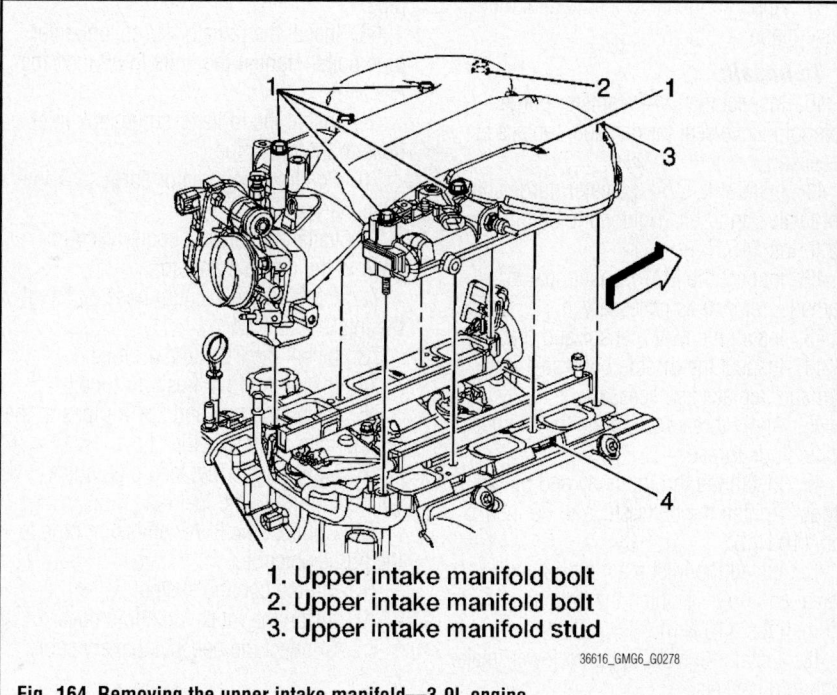

1. Upper intake manifold bolt
2. Upper intake manifold bolt
3. Upper intake manifold stud

Fig. 164 Removing the upper intake manifold—3.9L engine

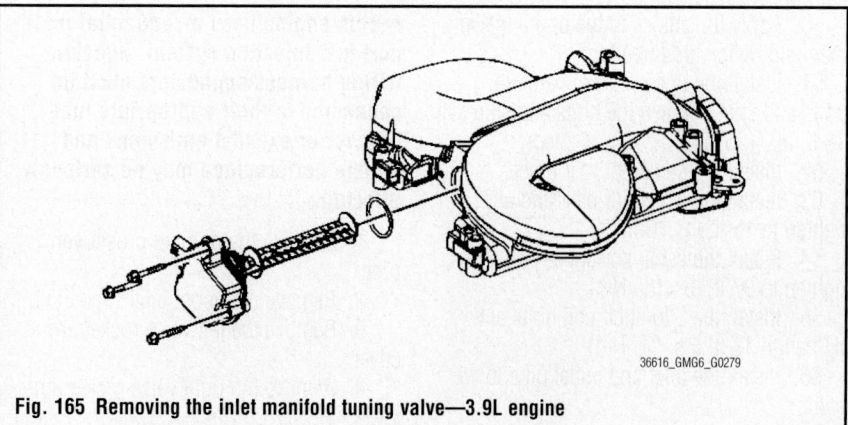

Fig. 165 Removing the inlet manifold tuning valve—3.9L engine

30. Remove the upper intake manifold bolts and stud.

31. Separate and remove the upper intake manifold from the lower intake manifold.

32. Remove the upper to lower intake manifold gaskets.

33. Remove the inlet manifold tuning valve bolts and valve.

34. Remove the throttle body bolts/studs and throttle body.

35. Remove the MAP sensor bracket and sensor.

36. Remove the EVAP canister purge solenoid valve bolt and valve.

37. Clean the upper intake to lower intake gasket mating surfaces.

38. Inspect the intake manifold tuning valve seal for damage. The tuning valve blade attachment to the motor should be tight, with no looseness or slack present, Replace as necessary.

39. Apply lubricant to the nose of the valve blade.

To install:

40. Inspect the EVAP canister purge solenoid valve seal for damage, replace as necessary.

41. Install the EVAP canister purge solenoid valve and bolt. Tighten the bolt to 12 ft. lbs. (16 Nm).

42. Inspect the MAP sensor seal for damage, replace as necessary.

43. Install the MAP sensor and bracket.

44. Inspect the throttle body seal for damage, replace as necessary.

45. Apply threadlock to the throttle body bolts/studs threads.

46. Install the throttle body and bolts/studs. Tighten the bolts/studs to 89 inch lbs. (10 Nm).

47. Install the inlet manifold tuning valve, and bolts. Tighten the bolts to 89 inch lbs. (10 Nm).

48. Install the NEW upper to lower intake manifold gaskets.

49. Set the upper intake manifold onto the lower intake manifold.

50. Apply threadlock to the upper intake manifold bolts/stud threads.

51. Install the upper intake manifold bolts and stud. Tighten the bolts and stud to 18 ft. lbs. (25 Nm).

52. Install the generator rear brace.

53. Install the generator ball stud and tighten to 15 ft. lbs. (20 Nm).

54. Install the generator upper bolt and tighten to 37 ft. lbs. (50 Nm).

55. Install the 2 ignition coil bolts and tighten to 18 ft. lbs. (25 Nm).

56. Install the inlet and outlet pipe to the studs.

57. Install the heater inlet and outlet pipe nuts to the throttle body studs. Tighten the nuts to 89 inch lbs. (10 Nm).

58. Install the left side spark plug wires.

59. Connect the left side spark plug wires to the spark plugs.

60. Connect the left side spark plug wires to the ignition coil.

61. Engage the spark plug wire retainer clips to the intake manifold bracket and the heater inlet/outlet pipe.

62. Install the air cleaner outlet duct.

63. Connect the inlet manifold valve electrical connector.

64. Connect the EVAP canister purge solenoid electrical connector.

65. Connect the ETC electrical connector.

66. Connect the MAP sensor electrical connector.

67. Install the radiator surge tank inlet pipe.

68. Install the radiator surge tank inlet pipe bolts. Tighten the bolts to 89 inch lbs. (10 Nm).

69. Install the radiator surge tank inlet hose to the inlet pipe.

70. Position the radiator surge tank inlet hose clamp.

71. Install the brake booster vacuum hose to the intake manifold.

72. Position the vacuum hose clamp at the intake manifold.

73. Install the PCV foul air tube.

74. Install the PCV fresh air tube.

75. Install the fuel and EVAP pipes to the retainer clip and close the clip.

76. Connect the fuel feed pipe quick connect fitting to the fuel rail.

77. Connect the EVAP emission pipe to the purge solenoid.

78. Fill the cooling system.

79. Install the intake manifold cover.

80. Connect the negative battery cable.

Lower

See Figures 166 and 167.

➥This engine uses a sequential multi-port fuel injection system. Injector wiring harness connectors must be connected to their appropriate fuel injector or exhaust emissions and engine performance may be seriously affected.

1. Remove the coolant crossover pipe.

2. Remove the upper intake manifold.

3. Remove the left valve rocker arm cover.

4. Remove the right valve rocker arm cover.

5. Disconnect the Engine Coolant Temperature (ECT) electrical connector.

6. Disconnect the fuel feed line from the fuel rail.

7. Disconnect the fuel injector inline connector.

8. Remove the fuel injector harness connector bracket bolt from the intake manifold.

9. Disconnect the Camshaft Position (CMP) sensor electrical connector.

10. Remove the fuel injector rail bolts.

11. Remove the fuel rail.

12. Remove the lower intake manifold bolts.

13. Remove the lower intake manifold.

14. Loosen the valve rocker arm bolts.

➥Place the valve train components in a rack in order to ensure that the components are installed in the same location from which they were removed.

15. Remove the valve rocker arms.

16. Remove the push rods. The intake push rods measure 5.81 inch (147.51 mm). The exhaust push rods measure 6.1 inch (154.87 mm).

17. Remove the lower intake manifold gaskets and seals.

18. Clean the lower intake manifold gasket and seal surfaces on the cylinder heads and the engine block.

19. Clean the gasket and seal surfaces on the lower intake manifold with degreaser.

20. Remove all the loose Room Temperature Vulcanizing sealer (RTV).

To install:

➥All gasket mating surfaces need to be free of oil and foreign material. Use lubricant to clean the surfaces.

➥RTV sealer is NOT to be placed under the lower intake manifold gaskets.

21. Install the lower intake manifold gaskets and seals.

22. Coat the ends of the push rods using prelube.

➥The intake valve push rods measure 5.75 inch (146.0 mm) and the exhaust valve push rods measure 6.0 inch (152.5 mm).

23. Install the push rods in their original location.

24. Coat the rocker arm friction surfaces using prelube.

➥Shims (P/N 88894006) may be required under the valve rocker arm pedestals if reconditioning has been performed on the cylinder head or its components.

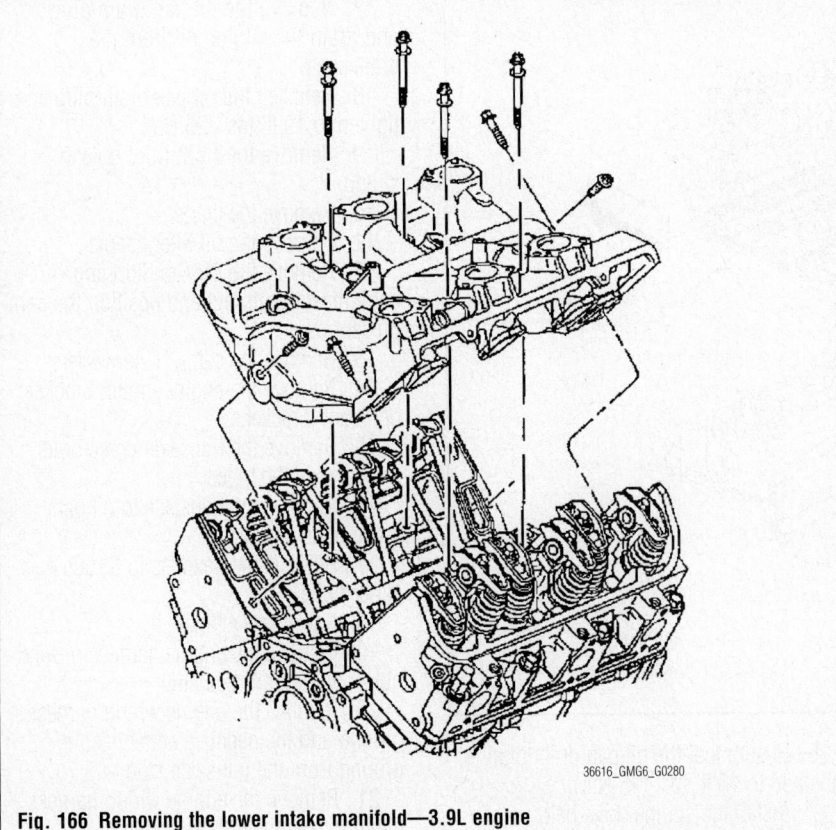

Fig. 166 Removing the lower intake manifold—3.9L engine

25. Install the valve rocker arms in their original positions.

26. Install the valve rocker arm bolts. Tighten the bolts to 25 ft. lbs. (34 Nm).

27. With the NEW gaskets and seals in place, apply a small drop, 0.031-0.39 inch (8-10 mm) of RTV sealer to the 4 corners of the intake manifold to engine block joints.

28. Install the lower intake manifold.

✳✳ CAUTION

Maximum gasket performance is achieved when using new fasteners, which contain a thread-locking patch. If the fasteners are not replaced, a thread locking chemical must be applied to the fastener threads. Failure to replace the fasteners or apply a thread-locking chemical MAY reduce gasket sealing capability.

✳✳ CAUTION

Failure to tighten vertical bolts before the diagonal bolts may cause an oil leak.

29. Apply sealer to the lower intake manifold bolt threads.

30. Install the lower intake manifold bolts.

31. Tighten the lower intake manifold bolts in the sequence shown.

a. Tighten the bolts (1, 2, 3, 4) in sequence to 12 ft. lbs. (16 Nm).

b. Tighten the bolts (5, 6, 7, 8) in sequence to 18 ft. lbs. (25 Nm).

32. Inspect the fuel rail, fuel injectors and fuel injector O-rings for damage and replace as necessary.

33. Lubricate the fuel injector O-rings using lubricant.

34. Install the injector nozzles into the lower intake manifold injector bores.

35. Press on the injector rail using the palms of both hands until the injector is fully seated.

36. Install the fuel injector rail bolts. Tighten the bolts to 89 inch lbs. (10 Nm).

37. Connect the CMP sensor electrical connector.

38. Position the fuel injector harness connector bracket to the intake manifold.

39. Install the fuel injector harness connector bracket bolt. Tighten the bolt to 71 inch lbs. (8 Nm).

40. Connect the fuel injector inline connector.

41. Connect the fuel feed line to the fuel rail.

42. Connect the ECT electrical connector.

43. Install the right valve rocker arm cover.

44. Install the left valve rocker arm cover.

45. Install the upper intake manifold.

46. Install the coolant crossover pipe.

OIL PAN

REMOVAL & INSTALLATION

2.4L Engine

See Figures 168 and 169.

1. Raise and support the vehicle.

2. Place a drain pan under the oil pan drain plug.

3. Remove the oil pan drain plug.

4. Drain the engine oil.

5. Remove the engine drive belt.

6. Remove the lower AC compressor bolt.

7. Remove the oil pan bolts.

8. Remove the oil pan

9. Remove any old oil pan sealant.

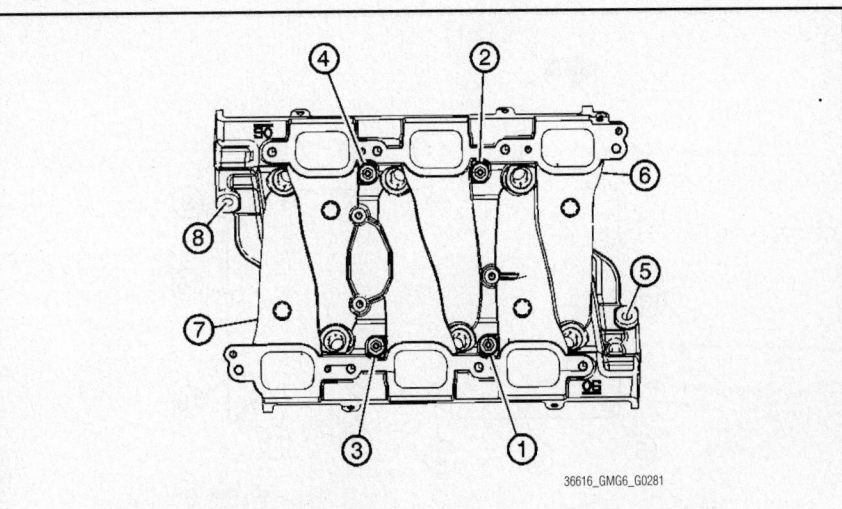

Fig. 167 Identifying the lower intake manifold bolt tightening sequence—3.9L engine

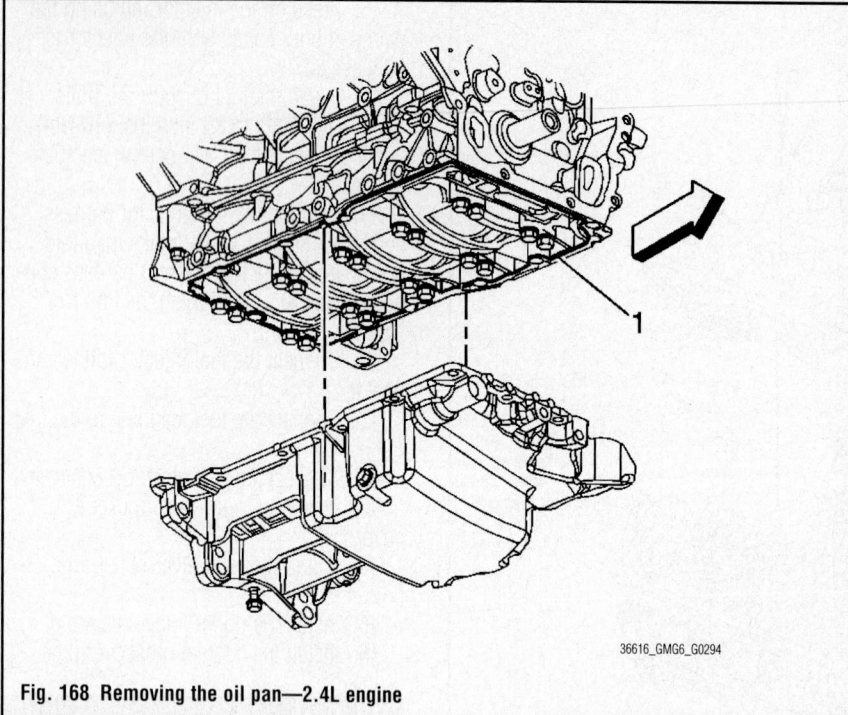

Fig. 168 Removing the oil pan—2.4L engine

To install:

10. Ensure that the oil pan and the sealing surface on the lower crankcase are free of all oil and debris.

11. Apply a 0.079 inch (2 mm) bead of sealant around the perimeter of the oil pan and the oil suction port opening. DO NOT over apply the sealant. More than a 0.079 inch (2 mm) bead is not required.

12. Install the oil pan.

13. Install the oil pan bolts.

14. Tighten the oil pan bolts in the sequence shown. Tighten the bolts to 18 ft. lbs. (25 Nm).

15. Install the A/C compressor bolt and tighten to 37 ft. lbs. (50 Nm).

16. Ensure that the oil pan drain plug is tightened to 18 ft. lbs. (25 Nm).

17. Install the engine drive belt.

18. Lower the vehicle.

19. Fill the crankcase with oil.

3.5L Engine

See Figures 170 through 172.

1. Disconnect the negative battery cable.

2. Remove the engine mount snubber and the drive belt.

3. Remove the air cleaner inlet duct.

4. Install the engine support fixture.

5. Raise and support the vehicle.

6. Place a suitable drain pan under the oil pan drain plug.

7. Remove the oil pan drain plug and drain the engine oil from the crankcase.

8. Reinstall the oil pan drain plug and tighten to 19 ft. lbs. (26 Nm).

9. Remove the right front splash shield.

10. Remove the starter.

11. Remove the oil filter adapter.

12. Remove the Air Conditioning (A/C) compressor bolts/nut and position the compressor aside.

13. Remove the catalytic converters.

14. Remove the engine mount bracket bolts and bracket.

15. Remove the transaxle brace bolts and remove the brace.

16. Remove the transaxle to oil pan brace bolts and brace.

17. Remove the flexplate to torque converter bolts.

18. Lower the vehicle.

19. Remove the engine harness ground nut from the transaxle stud.

20. Remove the engine wiring harness ground and the negative battery cable ground from the transaxle stud.

21. Remove the engine wiring harness clip nut from the transaxle stud.

22. Remove the engine wiring harness clip from the transaxle stud.

23. Remove the engine wiring harness clips from the oil pan.

24. Loosen, DO NOT REMOVE the transaxle studs and bolts.

25. Using the engine support fixture, raise the engine and transaxle slightly.

26. Raise and support the vehicle.

27. Remove the oil pan bolts.

28. Separate the engine and transaxle approximately 1/2 inch (13 mm).

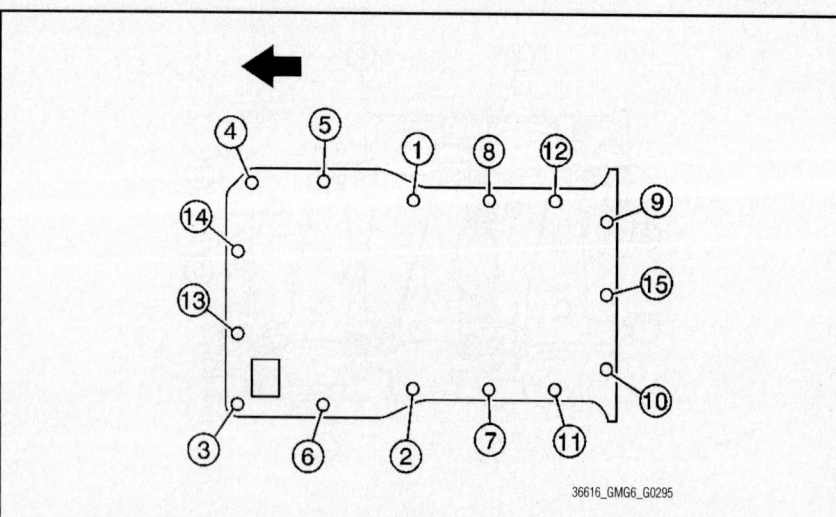

Fig. 169 Identifying oil pan bolt tightening sequence—2.4L engine

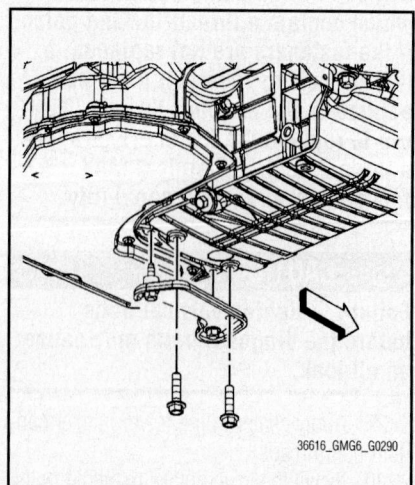

Fig. 170 Removing the oil pan brace—3.5L engine

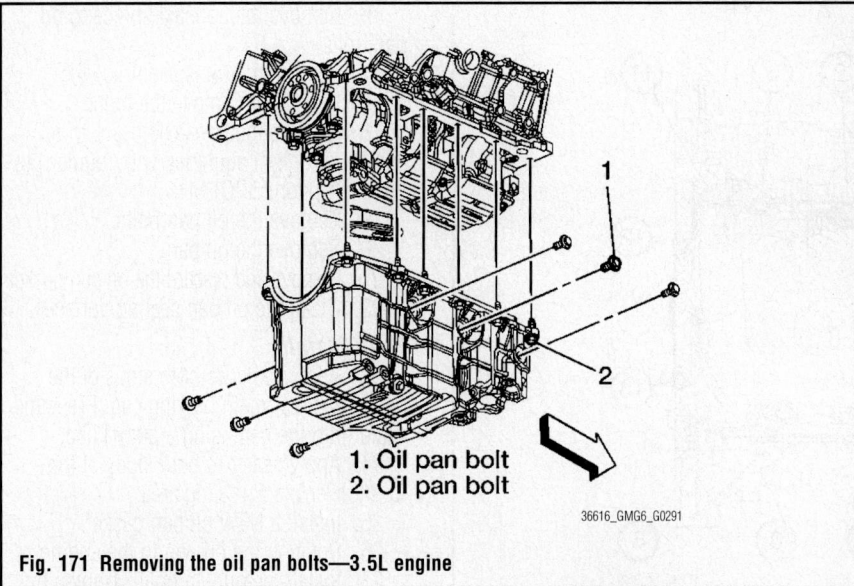

1. Oil pan bolt
2. Oil pan bolt

36616_GMG6_G0291

Fig. 171 Removing the oil pan bolts—3.5L engine

29. Ensure that when removing the oil pan, the pan clears the boss on the transaxle.

30. Remove the oil pan. If the oil pan cannot be removed, use the engine support fixture to raise the engine until the pan can be removed.

31. Remove and discard the oil pan gasket.

32. Clean the oil pan sealing surfaces.

To install:

33. Apply sealer to both sides of the front cover/block mating area.

34. Apply sealer to both sides of the crankcase rear main bearing cap. Press the sealer into the gap using a putty knife.

35. Install a NEW oil pan gasket.

36. Install the oil pan.

37. Install the oil pan bolts. Tighten bolt (1) to 37 ft. lbs. (50 Nm) + 50°. Tighten bolt (2) to 18 ft. lbs. (25 Nm).

38. Lower the vehicle.

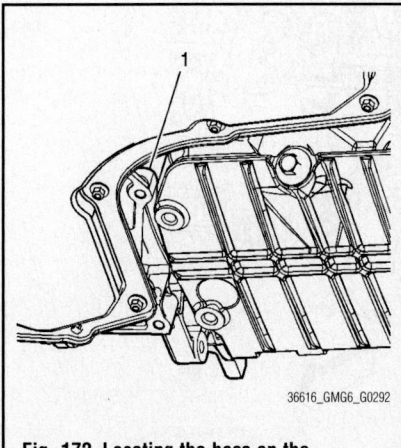

36616_GMG6_G0292

Fig. 172 Locating the boss on the transaxle—3.5L engine

39. Using the engine support fixture, lower the engine and transaxle.

40. Tighten the transaxle studs and bolts to 55 ft. lbs. (75 Nm).

41. Install the engine wiring harness clips to the oil pan.

42. Install the engine wiring harness clip to the transaxle stud.

43. Install the engine wiring harness clip nut to the transaxle stud and tighten to 18 ft. lbs. (25 Nm).

44. Install the negative battery cable ground and the engine wiring harness ground to the transaxle stud.

45. Install the engine harness ground nut to the transaxle stud and tighten the nut to 18 ft. lbs. (25 Nm).

46. Raise and support the vehicle.

47. Install the flexplate to torque converter bolts and tighten to 46 ft. lbs. (62 Nm).

48. Position the transaxle to the oil pan brace and install the bolts. Tighten the bolts to 37 ft. lbs. (50 Nm).

49. Position the transaxle brace to the transaxle and install the bolts until snug.

50. Install the engine wiring harness clip to the rear of the transaxle brace.

51. Position the engine mount bracket to the engine and install the bolts until snug.

52. Tighten the engine mount bracket bolts and transaxle brace bolts.

   a. Tighten the engine mount bracket upper bolt to 66 ft. lbs. (90 Nm).

   b. Tighten the engine mount bracket lower bolts to 37 ft. lbs. (50 Nm).

   c. Tighten the transaxle brace bolts to 53 ft. lbs. (72 Nm).

53. Install the catalytic converters.

54. Position the A/C compressor and install the bolts. Tighten the bolts to 37 ft. lbs. (50 Nm).

55. Install the oil filter adapter.

56. Install the starter.

57. Install the right front splash shield.

58. Ensure that the oil pan drain plug is tighten to 19 ft. lbs. (26 Nm).

59. Lower the vehicle.

60. Remove the engine support fixture.

61. Install the air cleaner inlet duct.

62. Install the drive belt and the engine mount snubber.

63. Fill the crankcase with oil.

64. Connect the negative battery cable.

65. Start the engine and inspect for leaks.

3.6L Engine

See Figures 173 through 175.

1. Raise and support the vehicle.

2. Drain the engine oil and remove the oil filter.

3. Remove the catalytic converter.

4. Remove the Air Conditioning (A/C) compressor bolts and reposition.

5. Remove the oil pan to transmission bolts.

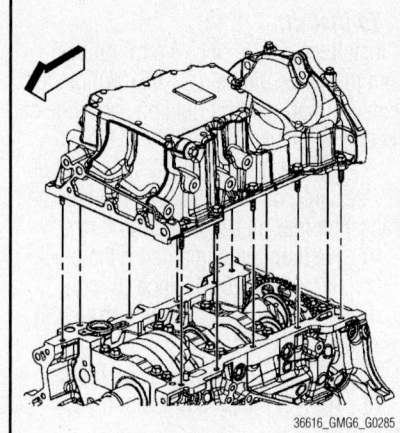

36616_GMG6_G0285

Fig. 173 Removing the oil pan—3.6L engine

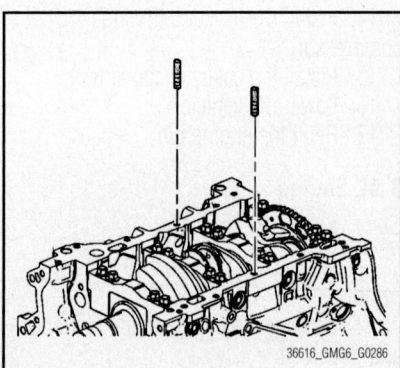

36616_GMG6_G0286

Fig. 174 Installing guide pins—3.6L engine

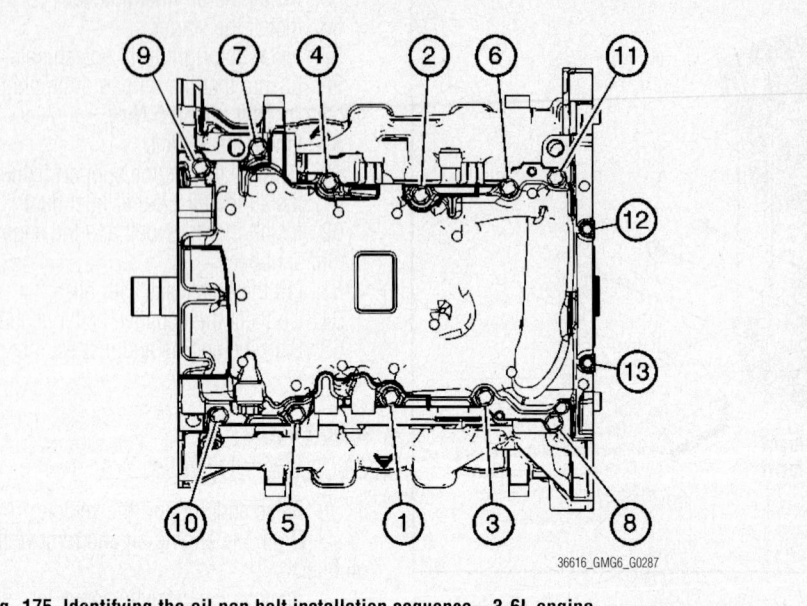

Fig. 175 Identifying the oil pan bolt installation sequence—3.6L engine

6. Remove the oil pan bolts.

7. Remove the oil pan.

8. Clean the oil pan and the engine block gasket surface.

To install:

Install the 0.315 inch (8 mm) guides from the guide pin set (EN-46109) into the center oil pan rail bolt hole on each side of the engine block.

9. Place a 0.118 inch (3 mm) bead of RTV sealant , on the block pan rail and the crankshaft rear oil seal housing.

10. Position the oil pan onto the block.

11. Remove the 0.315 inch (8 mm) guides from the guide pin set (EN-46109) from the engine block.

12. Loosely install the oil pan bolts.

13. Tighten the oil pan bolts in sequence.

   a. Tighten the 8 mm bolts (1-11) to 17 ft. lbs.

   b. Tighten the 6 mm bolts (12, 13) to 89 inch lbs. (10 Nm).

14. Install the air conditioning (A/C) compressor.

15. Install the catalytic converter.

16. Lower the vehicle.

17. Refill the engine oil.

3.9L Engine

See Figures 176 and 177.

1. Disconnect the negative battery cable.

2. Remove the engine mount snubber and drive belt.

3. Remove the air cleaner inlet duct.

4. Install the engine support fixture.

5. Raise and support the vehicle.

6. Place a suitable drain pan under the oil pan drain plug.

7. Remove the oil pan drain plug and drain the engine oil from the crankcase.

8. Reinstall the oil pan drain plug until snug.

9. Remove the right front splash shield.

10. Remove the starter.

11. Remove the engine oil cooler.

12. Remove the oil filter adapter.

13. Remove the Air Conditioning (A/C) compressor bolts and position the compressor aside.

14. Disconnect the oil level sensor electrical connector.

15. Remove the catalytic converter.

16. Remove the transaxle brace to oil pan bolts.

17. Remove the transaxle brace to transaxle bolt and remove the brace.

18. Remove the transaxle brace to oil pan lower bolt, if equipped with regular production option (RPO) M15.

19. Remove the oil pan bolts.

20. Remove the oil pan.

21. Remove and discard the oil pan gasket.

22. Clean the oil pan sealing surfaces.

To install:

23. Apply sealer to both sides of the crankshaft rear main bearing cap. Press the sealer into the gap using a putty knife.

24. Apply sealer to both sides of the front cover/block mating area.

25. Install a NEW oil pan gasket.

26. Position the oil pan to the engine.

27. Install the oil pan bolts. Tighten bolt (1) to 37 ft. lbs. (50 Nm) + 50°. Tighten bolt (2) to 18 ft. lbs. (25 Nm).

28. Install the transaxle brace to oil pan lower bolt, if equipped with (RPO) M15 and tighten to 37 ft. lbs. (50 Nm).

29. Position the transaxle brace and install the transaxle brace to transaxle bolt until snug.

30. Install the transaxle brace to oil pan bolts and tighten to 37 ft. lbs. (50 Nm).

31. Connect the oil level sensor electrical connector.

32. Install the catalytic converter.

33. Position the A/C compressor and install the bolts. Tighten the bolts to 37 ft. lbs. (50 Nm).

34. Install the right front splash shield.

35. Install the oil filter adapter.

36. Install the oil cooler.

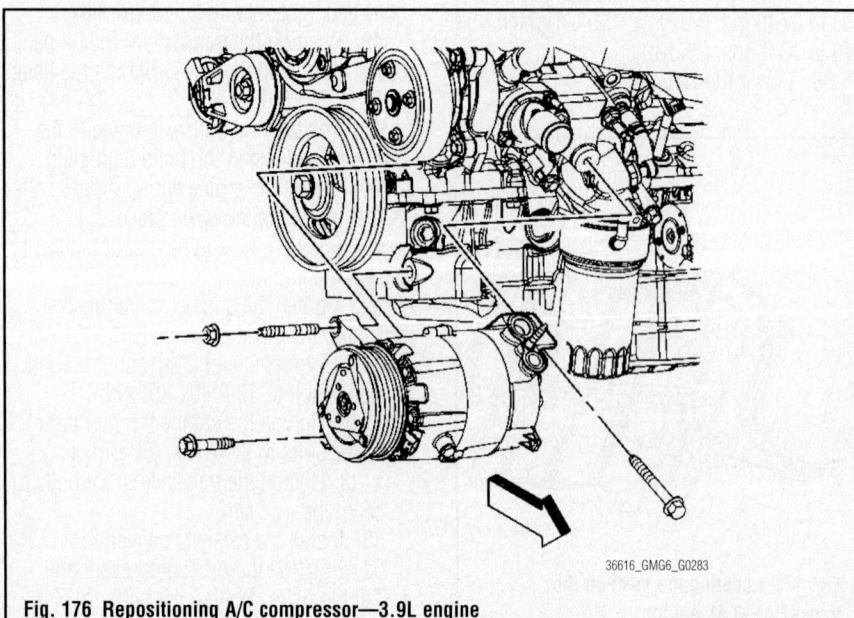

Fig. 176 Repositioning A/C compressor—3.9L engine

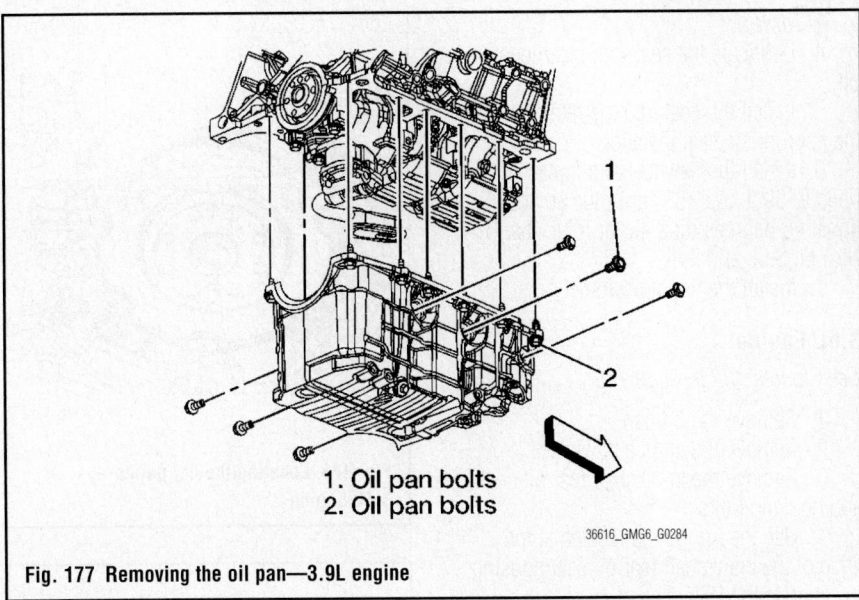

1. Oil pan bolts
2. Oil pan bolts

36616_GMG6_G0284

Fig. 177 Removing the oil pan—3.9L engine

37. Ensure that the oil pan drain plug is tightened. Tighten to 19 ft. lbs. (26 Nm).
38. Lower the vehicle.
39. Remove the engine support fixture.
40. Install the air cleaner inlet duct.
41. Install the engine mount snubber and drive belt.
42. Fill the crankcase.
43. Connect the negative battery cable.

OIL PUMP

REMOVAL & INSTALLATION

3.5L Engine

See Figure 178.

1. Remove the oil pan.
2. Remove the oil pump bolt.

3. Remove the oil pump and the oil pump driveshaft.
4. Inspect the oil pump driveshaft and the oil pump.

To install:

➡Rotate the oil pump driveshaft as necessary in order to obtain the engagement with the oil pump drive unit.

5. Install the oil pump driveshaft and the oil pump.
6. Install the oil pump bolt and tighten to 30 ft. lbs. (41 Nm).
7. Install the oil pan.

3.6L Engine

See Figure 179.

➡Do not remove the left bank idler sprocket.

1. Remove the primary timing chain.
2. Remove the oil pump bolts and the oil pump.

To install:

3. Align the oil pump drive gear with the crankshaft flats and install the oil pump to the engine block.
4. Align the pump body with the mounting holes in the cylinder block.
5. Install the oil pump bolts and tighten to 17 ft. lbs. (23 Nm).
6. Install the primary timing chain.

3.9L Engine

See Figure 181.

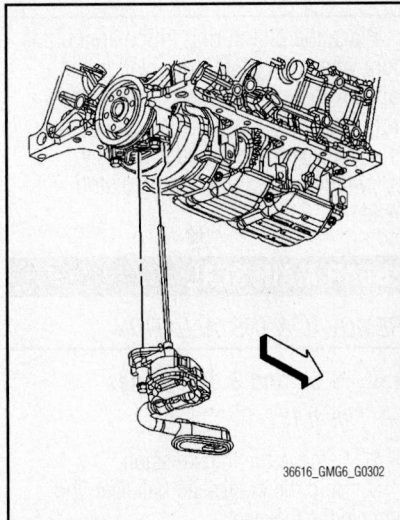

36616_GMG6_G0302

Fig. 180 Removing the oil pump—3.9L engine

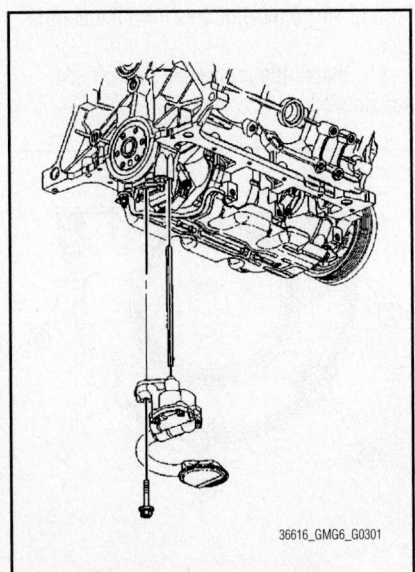

36616_GMG6_G0301

Fig. 178 Removing the oil pump—3.5L engine

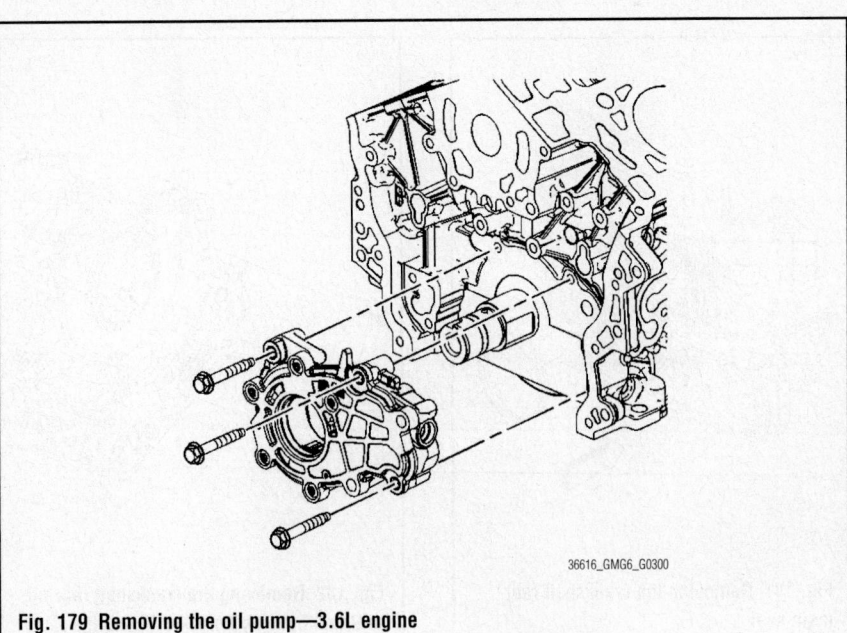

36616_GMG6_G0300

Fig. 179 Removing the oil pump—3.6L engine

1. Remove the oil pan.
2. Remove the oil pump bolt.
3. Remove the oil pump and the oil pump driveshaft.

To install:

→Rotate the oil pump driveshaft as necessary in order to obtain the engagement with the oil pump drive unit.

- Install the oil pump driveshaft and the oil pump.
4. Install the oil pump bolt and tighten to 30 ft. lbs. (41 Nm).
5. Install the oil pan.

PISTON AND RING

POSITIONING

Place the piston ring in the area of the bore where the piston ring will travel (approximately or 1 inch (25 mm) down from the deck surface). Be sure the ring is square with the cylinder bore by positioning the ring with the piston head.

REAR MAIN SEAL

REMOVAL & INSTALLATION

2.4L, 3.5L and 3.9L Engines

See Figure 181.

1. Remove the transmission.
2. Hold the crankshaft balancer and remove the flywheel.
3. Carefully pry the seal out of the retainer without damaging the crankshaft or the seal retainer.

To install:

4. Lubricate the seal with clean engine oil.

5. Install the seal into the retainer using the appropriate seal installer.

6. Install the flywheel and tighten the bolts to 39 ft. lbs. (53 Nm) plus an additional 25 degrees on 2.4L, or 52 ft. lbs. (71 Nm) on 3.5L and 3.9L.

7. Install the transmission.

3.6L Engine

See Figures 182 through 185.

1. Remove the oil pan.
2. Remove the engine flywheel.
3. Remove the crankshaft rear oil seal and housing bolts.
4. Use the pry points located at the edge of the crankshaft rear oil seal housing to separate the RTV sealant.
5. Remove and discard the crankshaft rear oil seal housing.

To install:

6. Install the 0.236 inch (6 mm) guides from the EN-46109 pin set into the 2 crankshaft rear oil seal housing corner bolt holes of the engine block.

7. Install the crankshaft rear oil seal installation tool (EN-47839) tool with the handle (J-42183) onto the rear of the crankshaft flange.

8. Place a 0.118 inch (3 mm) bead of RTV sealant, GM P/N 12378521 or equivalent, to the NEW crankshaft rear oil seal housing as shown.

→DO NOT allow any engine oil on the area where the crankshaft rear oil seal housing is to be installed.

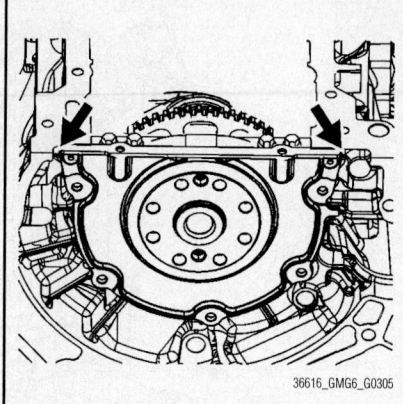

Fig. 183 Locating the pry points—3.6L engine

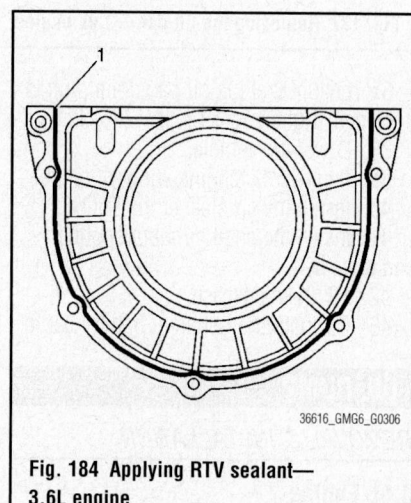

Fig. 184 Applying RTV sealant—3.6L engine

9. Install the crankshaft rear oil seal housing to the engine block.

10. Install the pin set (EN-46109) pin set 0.236 inch (6 mm) guides from the engine block.

11. Install the crankshaft rear oil seal housing bolts.

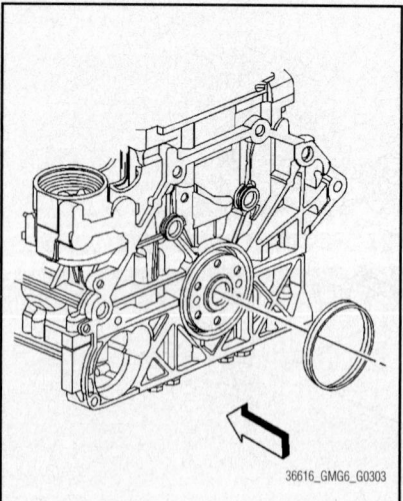

Fig. 181 Removing the crankshaft rear main seal

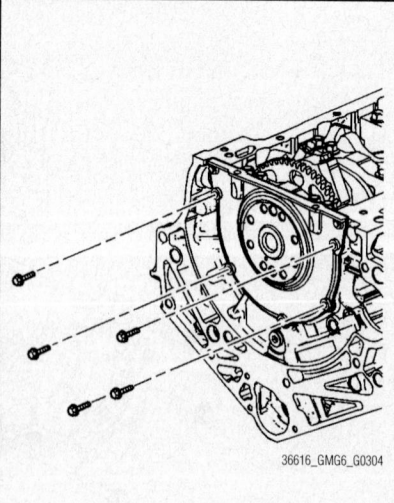

Fig. 182 Removing the crankshaft rear oil seal and housing bolts—3.6L engine

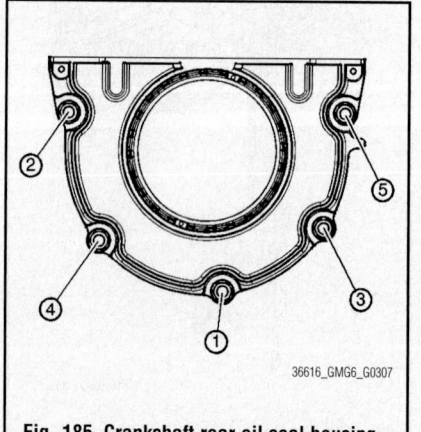

Fig. 185 Crankshaft rear oil seal housing bolt torque sequence—3.6L engine

12. Tighten the crankshaft rear oil seal housing bolts in sequence and tighten to 89 inch lbs. (10 Nm).

13. Remove the crankshaft rear oil seal installation tool (EN-47839) and the handle (J-42183) from the crankshaft flange.

ROCKER ARMS/SHAFTS

REMOVAL & INSTALLATION

3.5L & 3.9L Engines

1. Relieve the fuel system pressure.
2. Disconnect the negative battery cable.
3. Remove the valve rocker arm covers.
4. Remove the rocker arm bolts.
5. Remove the rocker arms.
6. Remove the pushrods.

To install:

7. Install the pushrods in the original location. Ensure that the pushrods seat in the lifter.

➡ **The intake pushrods are identified with yellow stripes and are 5-3/4 inches long. Exhaust pushrods are identified with green stripes on 3.5L and blue stripes on 3.9L and are 6 inches long.**

8. Install the rocker arms.
9. Install the rocker arm bolts and tighten to 25 ft. lbs. (34 Nm).
10. Install the valve rocker covers.
11. Connect the negative battery cable.
12. Start the vehicle, check for leaks and repair if necessary.

3.6L Engine

1. Remove valve cover.
2. Remove the applicable camshaft(s). Refer to Camshaft Replacement.
3. Remove the valve rocker arms, camshaft followers.
4. Clean and inspect the camshaft(s) and the rocker arm(s). Repair or replace as necessary.

To install:

5. Apply a liberal amount of lubricant GM P/N 12345501 or equivalent to the pivot pocket, roller and valve slot areas of the camshaft followers.

➡ **The follower must be positioned squarely on the valve tip so that the full width of the roller will completely contact the camshaft lobe. If the followers are being reused you must put them back in their original location.**

6. Place the camshaft followers in position on the valve tip and stationary hydraulic lash adjuster (SHLA).

7. The rounded head end of the follower goes on the SHLA while the flat end goes on the valve tip.

8. Clean the camshaft journals and carriers with a clean, lint-free cloth.

TIMING CHAIN AND SPROCKETS

REMOVAL & INSTALLATION

2.4L Engine

See Figures 186 through 193.

1. Remove the number 1 cylinder spark plug.
2. Rotate the crankshaft in the engine rotational direction clockwise, until the number 1 piston is at Top Dead Center (TDC) on the exhaust stroke.
3. Remove the camshaft cover.
4. Remove the engine front cover.
5. Remove the upper timing chain guide bolts and guide.

➡ **The timing chain tensioner must be removed to unload chain tension before the timing chain is removed. If it is not, the timing chain will become cocked and it will be difficult to remove.**

6. Remove the timing chain tensioner.
7. Install a 24 mm wrench on the hex on the exhaust camshaft in order to hold the camshaft.

8. Remove and discard the exhaust camshaft actuator bolt.
9. Remove the exhaust camshaft actuator from the camshaft and timing chain.
10. Remove the timing chain tensioner guide bolt and guide.
11. Remove the fixed timing chain guide access plug.
12. Remove the fixed timing chain guide bolts and guide.
13. Install a 24 mm wrench on the hex on the intake camshaft in order to hold the camshaft.
14. Remove and discard the intake camshaft actuator bolt.
15. Remove the intake camshaft actuator, and the timing chain through the top of the cylinder head.

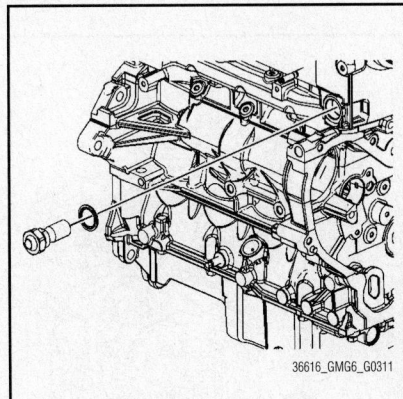

36616_GMG6_G0311

Fig. 187 Removing the timing chain tensioner—2.4L engine

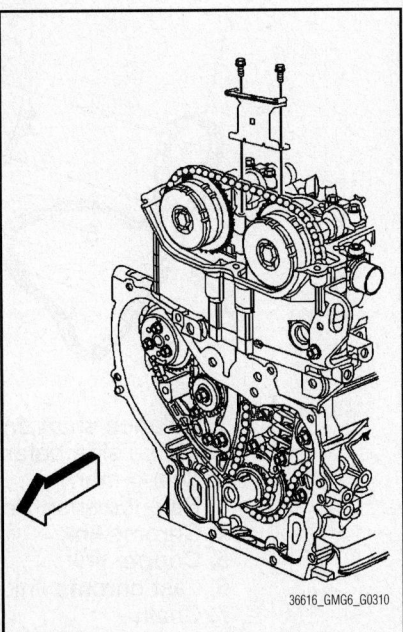

36616_GMG6_G0310

Fig. 186 Removing the upper timing chain guide—2.4L engine

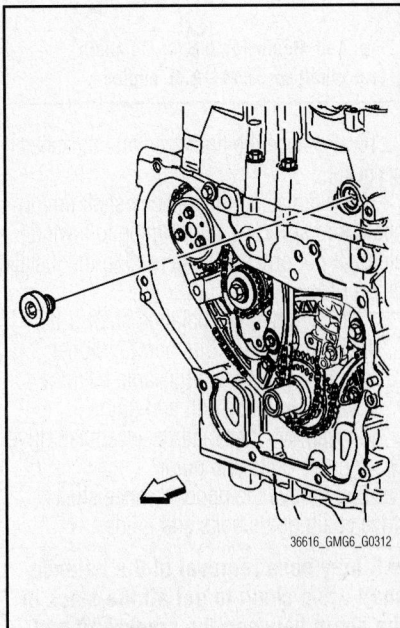

36616_GMG6_G0312

Fig. 188 Removing the fixed timing chain guide access plug—2.4L engine

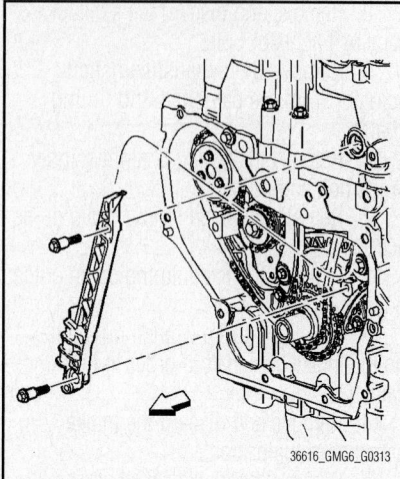

Fig. 189 Removing the fixed timing chain guide bolts and guide—2.4L engine

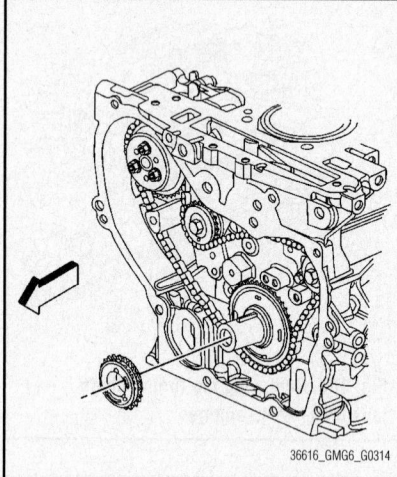

Fig. 190 Removing the timing chain crankshaft sprocket—2.4L engine

16. Remove the timing chain crankshaft sprocket.

17. If replacing the balance shaft timing chain and sprocket, perform the following steps; if not proceed to step 10 in the installation procedure.

    a. Remove the balance shaft drive chain tensioner bolts and tensioner.

    b. Remove the adjustable balance shaft chain guide bolt and guide.

18. Remove the small balance shaft drive chain guide bolts and guide.

19. Remove the upper balance shaft drive chain guide bolts and guide.

➡**It may ease removal of the balance shaft drive chain to get all the slack in the chain between the crankshaft and water pump sprockets.**

20. Remove the balance shaft drive chain.

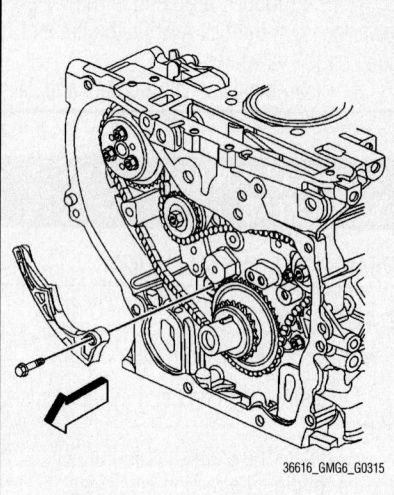

Fig. 191 Removing the adjustable balance shaft chain guide—2.4L engine

21. Remove the balance shaft drive sprocket.

To install:

22. If replacing the balance shaft timing chain, perform the following steps, if not proceed to step 10.

23. Install the balance shaft drive sprocket.

➡**If the balance shafts are not properly timed to the engine, the engine may vibrate or make noise.**

24. Install the balance shaft drive chain with the colored link lined up with the marks on the balance shaft sprockets and the balance shaft drive sprocket. There are three colored links on the chain. Two are chrome and one is copper. Use the following steps in order to line up the links with the sprockets.

    a. Place the copper link so that it lines up with the timing mark on the intake side balance shaft sprocket.

    b. Working clockwise around the chain, place the chrome link in line with the timing mark (3) on the balance shaft drive sprocket. (Approximately 6 o'clock position on the sprocket).

    c. Place the chain on the water pump drive sprocket. The alignment is not critical.

    d. Align the last chrome link with the timing mark on the exhaust side balance shaft drive sprocket.

25. Install the upper balance shaft drive chain guide and bolts. Tighten to 11 ft. lbs. (15 Nm).

26. Install the small balance shaft drive chain guide and bolts. Tighten to 11 ft. lbs. (15 Nm).

27. Install the adjustable balance shaft chain guide and bolt and tighten to 89 inch lbs. (10 Nm).

28. Reset the timing chain tensioner by performing the following steps:

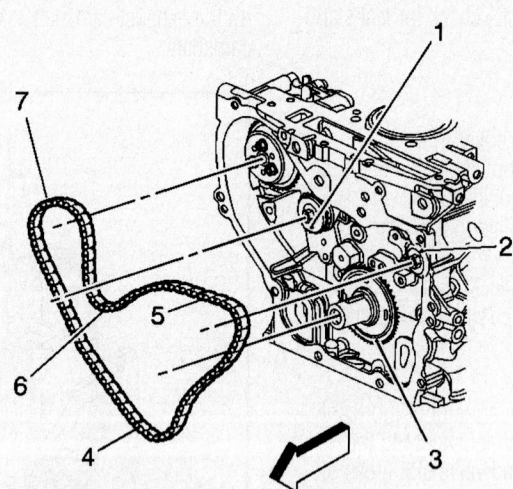

1. Balance shaft timing chain
2. Intake side balance shaft sprocket timing mark
3. Balance shaft drive sprocket timing mark
4. Chrome link
5. Copper link
6. Last chrome link
7. Chain

Fig. 192 Replacing the balance shaft timing chain—2.4L engine

a. Rotate the tensioner plunger 90° in its bore and compress the plunger.

b. Rotate the tensioner back to the original 12 o'clock position and insert a paper clip through the hole in the plunger body and into the hose in the tensioner plunger.

29. Install the balance shaft drive chain tensioner and bolts. Tighten the bolts to 89 inch lbs. (10 Nm).

30. Remove the paper clip from the balance shaft drive chain tensioner.

31. Ensure the intake camshaft notch is in the 5 o'clock position (2) and the exhaust camshaft notch is in the 7 o'clock position (1). The number 1 piston should be at TDC, crankshaft key at 12 o'clock.

32. Install the timing chain drive sprocket to the crankshaft with the timing mark in the 5 o'clock position and the front of the sprocket facing out.

➡There are 3 colored links on the timing chain. 2 links are of matching color, and 1 link is of a unique color. Use the following procedure to line up the links with the actuators. Orient the chain so that the colored links are visible.

➡Always use new actuator bolts.

33. Assemble the intake camshaft actuator into the timing chain with the timing mark lined up with the uniquely colored link.

34. Lower the timing chain through the opening in the cylinder head. Use care to ensure that the chain goes around both sides of the cylinder block bosses.

35. Install the intake camshaft actuator onto the intake camshaft while aligning the dowel pin into the camshaft slot.

36. Hand tighten the new intake camshaft actuator bolt.

37. Route the timing chain around the crankshaft sprocket and line up the first matching colored link with the timing mark on the crankshaft sprocket, in approximately the 5 o'clock position.

38. Rotate the crankshaft clockwise to remove all chain slack. Do not rotate the intake camshaft.

39. Install the adjustable timing chain guide down through the opening in the cylinder head and install the adjustable timing chain bolt. Tighten the adjustable timing chain guide bolt to 89 inch lbs. (10 Nm).

➡Always install NEW actuator bolts.

40. Install the exhaust camshaft actuator into the timing chain with the timing mark lines up with the second matching colored link.

41. Install the exhaust camshaft actuator onto the exhaust camshaft, aligning the dowel pin into the camshaft slot.

42. Using a 23 mm open end wrench, rotate the exhaust camshaft approximately 45 degrees until the dowel pin in the camshaft actuator goes into the camshaft slot.

43. When the actuator seats on the cam, tighten the new exhaust camshaft actuator bolt hand tight.

44. Verify that all of the colored links and the appropriate timing marks are still aligned. If they are

45. not aligned, repeat the portion of the procedure necessary to align the timing marks.

46. Install the fixed timing chain guide and bolts. Tighten the fixed timing chain guide bolts to 106 inch lbs. (12 Nm).

47. Install the upper timing chain guide and bolts. Tighten the upper timing chain guide bolts to 89 inch lbs. (10 Nm).

48. Reset the timing chain tensioner by performing the following steps:

a. Remove the snap ring.

b. Remove the piston assembly from the body of the timing chain tensioner.

c. Install the tensioner tool (J 45027-2) into a vise.

d. Install the notch end of the piston assembly into the tensioner tool.

e. Using the tensioner tool, turn the ratchet cylinder into the piston.

f. Reinstall the piston assembly into the body of the tensioner.

g. Install the snap ring.

49. Inspect the timing chain tensioner seal for damage. If damaged, replace the seal.

50. Inspect to ensure all dirt and debris is removed from the timing chain tensioner threaded hole in the cylinder head.

➡Ensure the timing chain tensioner seal is centered throughout the torque procedure to eliminate the possibility of an oil leak.

51. Install the timing chain tensioner assembly. Tighten the timing chain tensioner to 55 ft. lbs. (75 Nm).

52. The timing chain tensioner is released by compressing it 2 mm (0.079 in), which will release the locking mechanism in the ratchet. To release the timing chain tensioner, use a suitable tool with a rubber tip on the end. Feed the tool down through the cam drive chest to rest on the cam chain. Then give a sharp jolt diagonally downwards to release the tensioner.

53. Using a 23 mm wrench, engage the hex on the intake camshaft, and using a torque wrench, tighten the camshaft actuator bolt. Tighten the intake camshaft position actuator bolt to 22 ft. lbs. (30 Nm), plus 100°.

54. Using a 23 mm wrench, engage the hex on the exhaust camshaft, and using a torque wrench, tighten the camshaft actuator bolt. Tighten the exhaust camshaft position actuator bolt to 22 ft. lbs. (30 Nm), plus 100°.

55. Install the timing chain oiling nozzle. Tighten the timing chain oiling nozzle bolt to 89 inch lbs. (10 Nm).

56. Apply sealant compound GM P/N 12345382 to the thread of the timing chain guide bolt access hole plug.

57. Install the timing chain guide bolt access hole plug. Tighten the access hole plug to 66 ft. lbs. (90 Nm).

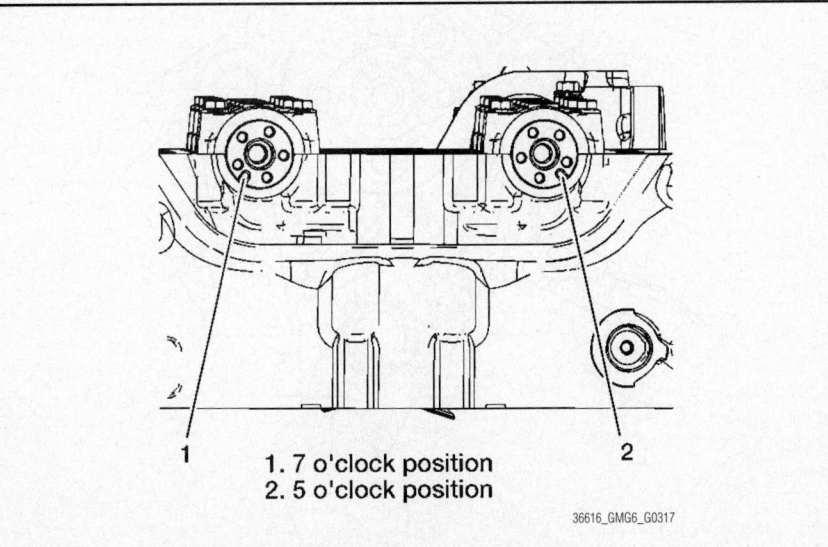

1. 7 o'clock position
2. 5 o'clock position

36616_GMG6_G0317

Fig. 193 Ensuring the intake camshaft and exhaust camshaft is in the correct position—2.4L engine

58. Install the engine front cover.
59. Install the camshaft cover.
60. Install the number 1 cylinder spark plug.

3.5L Engine

See Figures 194 through 196.

1. Remove the engine front cover.
2. Align the crankshaft timing mark to the timing mark on the bottom of the timing chain tensioner.
3. Align the timing mark on the camshaft position actuator gear with the timing mark on top of the timing chain tensioner.
4. Remove the camshaft position actuator bolts.
5. Remove the timing chain, camshaft position actuator, and crankshaft sprockets.
6. Remove the timing chain tensioner bolts.
7. Remove the timing chain tensioner.
8. Remove the crankshaft sprocket.
9. Remove the timing chain dampener bolts.
10. Remove the timing chain dampener.
11. Remove and discard the camshaft position actuator filter from the end of the camshaft.

To install:

→Always install a NEW camshaft position actuator filter anytime the camshaft actuator is removed.

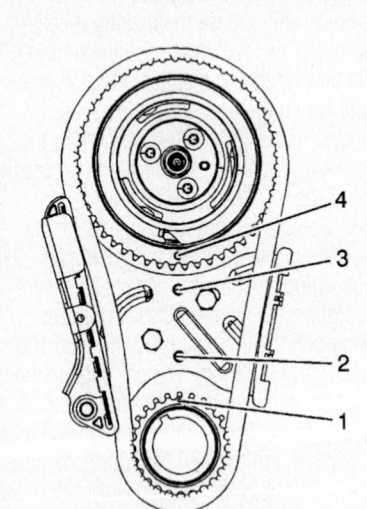

1. Crankshaft timing mark
2. Timing chain bottom timing mark
3. Timing chain top timing mark
4. Camshaft position actuator gear timing mark

36616_GMG6_G0318

Fig. 194 Aligning the timing marks— 3.5L engine

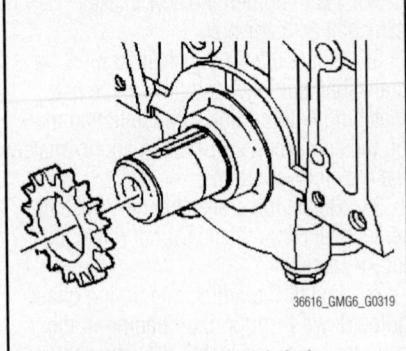

36616_GMG6_G0319

Fig. 195 Removing the crankshaft sprocket—3.5L engine

12. Install a NEW the camshaft position actuator filter to the end of the camshaft.
13. Install the crankshaft sprocket.
14. Apply prelube to the crankshaft sprocket thrust surface.
15. Install the timing chain tensioner.
16. Install the timing chain tensioner bolts. Tighten the bolts to 15 ft. lbs. (21 Nm).
17. Using the Tensioner compressor (EN-47719), fully collapse the tensioner, and place he tensioner retaining pin into the retaining hole.
18. Align the crankshaft timing mark to the timing mark on the bottom of the timing chain tensioner.
19. Hold the camshaft sprocket with the timing chain hanging down and install the timing chain to the crankshaft gear.
20. Align the timing mark on the camshaft position actuator gear with the timing mark on top of the timing chain tensioner.

21. Align the dowel in the camshaft position actuator with the dowel hole in the camshaft.
22. Install the camshaft position actuator bolts.

✳✳ CAUTION

Use only a Torx Plus®Bit when removing or installing the camshaft position actuator fasteners. The Torx Plus®design differs from typical Torx® fastener. Use of a standard Torx® bit on Torx Plus® fasteners may result in a rounded out fastener head or incorrect faster torque.

➥DO NOT use any type of threadlocking compound on the camshaft position actuator bolts. Usage of a threadlocking compound on the threads could lead to contamination of the camshaft position actuator, possibly resulting in potential damage to the actuator.

23. Draw the camshaft actuator onto the camshaft using the bolts. Tighten the bolts to 12 ft. lbs. (16 Nm).
24. Remove the retaining pin from the timing chain tensioner in order to make the tensioner active.
25. Coat the crankshaft and camshaft sprockets with clean engine oil.
26. Install the engine front cover.

3.6L Engine

Primary

See Figures 197 through 201.

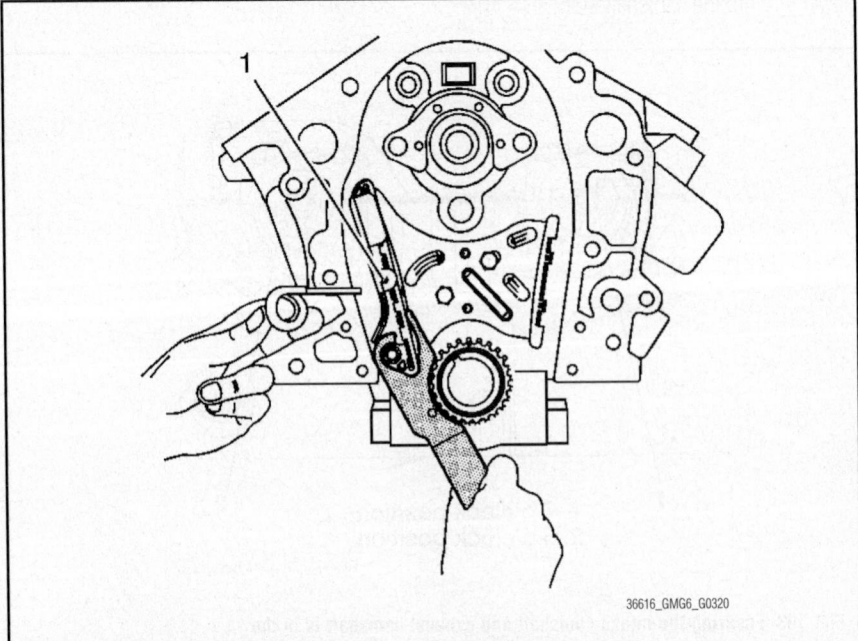

36616_GMG6_G0320

Fig. 196 Inserting the retaining pin into the retaining hole—3.5L engine

1. Remove the spark plugs in order to ease crankshaft/engine rotation.

2. Remove the engine front cover.

3. Remove the right bank secondary camshaft drive chain tensioner.

4. Remove the right bank secondary camshaft drive chain shoe.

5. Remove the right bank secondary camshaft drive chain guide.

6. Remove the right bank secondary camshaft drive chain.

7. Remove the primary camshaft drive chain tensioner.

8. Remove the primary camshaft drive chain upper guide.

9. Remove the primary camshaft timing chain.

10. Remove the crankshaft sprocket from the nose of the crankshaft.

To install:

11. Ensure the crankshaft sprocket is installed with the timing mark visible.

12. Install the crankshaft sprocket on to the nose of the crankshaft.

13. Align the notch in the crankshaft sprocket with the pin in the crankshaft.

14. Slide the crankshaft sprocket on the crankshaft nose until the crankshaft sprocket contacts the step in the crankshaft.

15. Ensure the crankshaft is in the stage one timing position with the crankshaft sprocket timing mark aligned to the stage one timing mark on the oil pump cover using

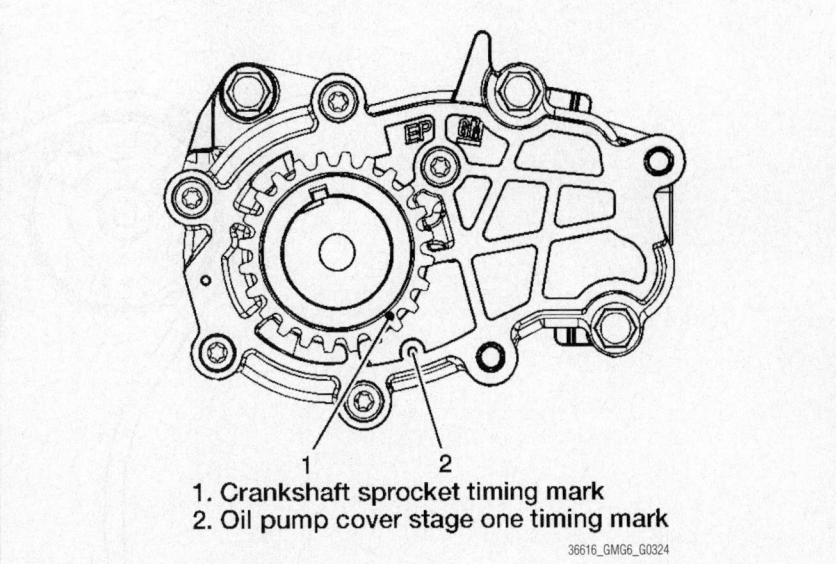

1. Crankshaft sprocket timing mark
2. Oil pump cover stage one timing mark

36616_GMG6_G0324

Fig. 198 Identifying timing marks—3.6L engine

the EN 46111 . Refer to camshaft timing drive chain alignment diagram - stage one.

16. Install the primary camshaft timing chain.

17. Install the primary upper camshaft drive chain guide. Tighten the bolts to 18 ft. lbs. (25 Nm).

18. Install the primary camshaft drive chain tensioner.

a. Ensure that the primary camshaft drive chain tensioner is being installed.

b. Using the tensioner tool (J-45027), reset the primary camshaft drive chain tensioner plunger.

c. Install the plunger into the primary camshaft drive chain tensioner body.

d. Compress the plunger into the body and lock the primary camshaft drive chain tensioner by inserting the tensioner retraction pins (EN-46112) into the access hole in the side of the primary camshaft drive chain tensioner body.

e. Slowly release pressure on the primary camshaft drive chain tensioner. The primary camshaft drive chain tensioner should remain compressed.

f. Install a NEW primary camshaft drive chain tensioner gasket to the primary camshaft drive chain tensioner.

g. Install the primary camshaft drive chain tensioner bolts through the primary camshaft drive chain tensioner and gasket.

h. Ensure the primary camshaft drive chain tensioner mounting surface on the engine block does not have any burrs or defects that would degrade the sealing of the NEW primary camshaft drive chain tensioner gasket.

i. Place the primary camshaft drive chain tensioner into position and loosely install the bolts to the block.

j. Verify the proper placement of the primary camshaft drive chain tensioner gasket tab. Tighten the tensioner bolts the first pass to 44 inch lbs. (5 Nm). For the final pass tighten the bolts to 17 ft. lbs. (23 Nm).

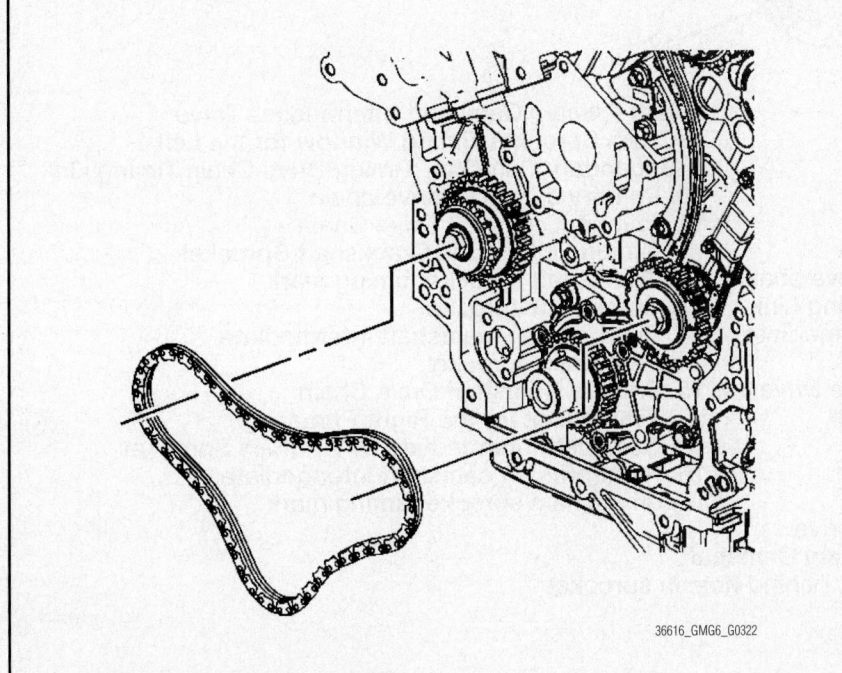

36616_GMG6_G0322

Fig. 197 Removing the primary camshaft timing chain—3.6L engine

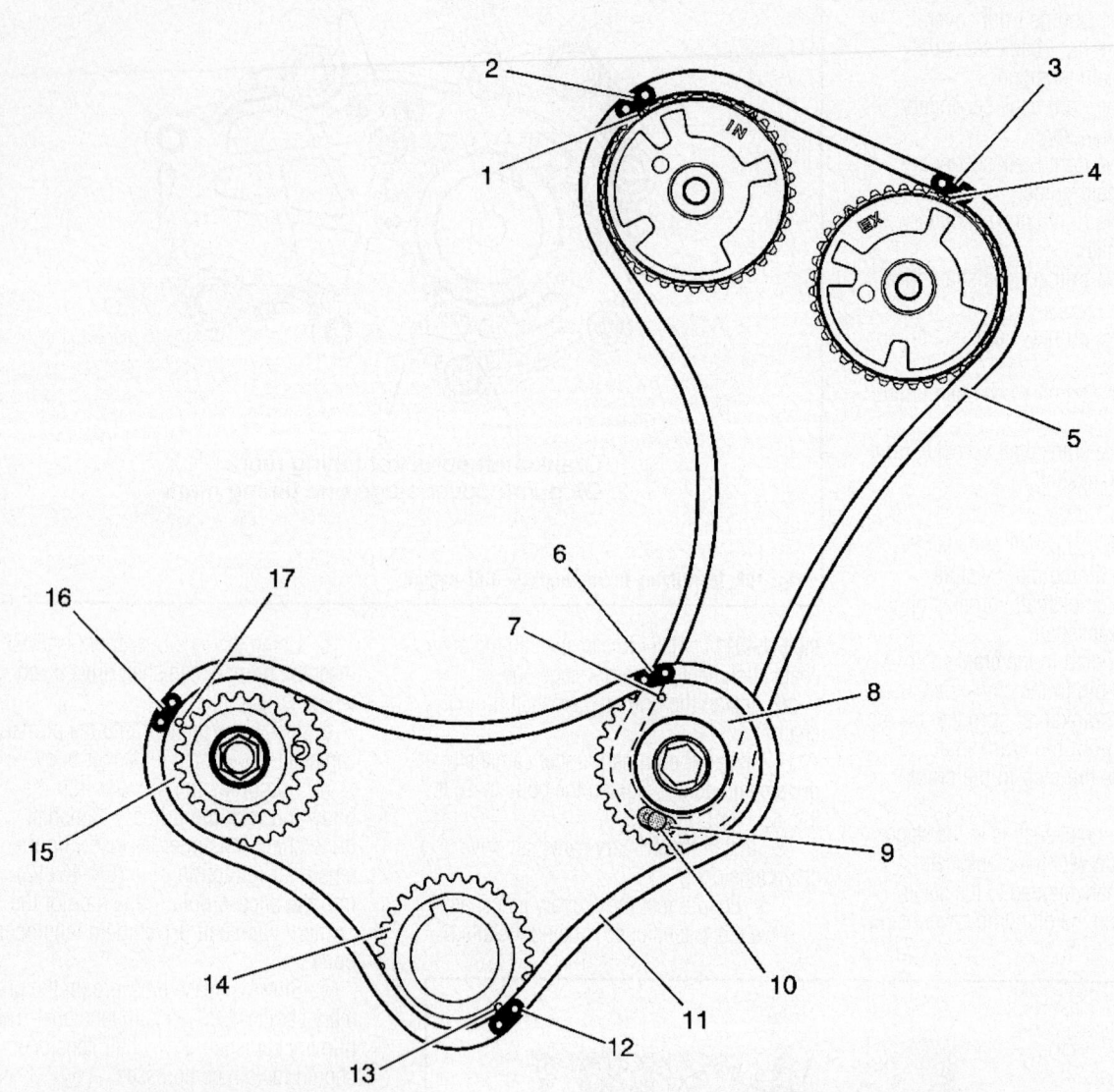

1. Left intake secondary camshaft timing drive chain timing link
2. Left exhaust secondary camshaft timing drive chain timing link
3. Left exhaust camshaft position (CMP) actuator timing mark - circle
4. Left secondary camshaft timing drive chain
5. Primary Camshaft Drive Chain Timing Link for the Left Primary Camshaft Intermediate Drive Chain Sprocket
6. Left Primary Camshaft Intermediate Drive Chain Sprocket Timing Mark for the Primary Camshaft Drive Chain
7. Left primary camshaft intermediate drive chain sprocket
8. Left Secondary Camshaft Timing Drive Chain Timing Link for the Left Primary Camshaft Intermediate Drive Chain Sprocket, behind hole in sprocket
9. Left Primary Camshaft Intermediate Drive Chain Sprocket Timing Window for the Left Secondary Camshaft Timing Drive Chain Timing Link
10. Primary camshaft drive chain
11. Primary Camshaft Drive Chain Timing Link for the Crankshaft Sprocket
12. Crankshaft sprocket timing mark
13. Crankshaft sprocket
14. Right primary camshaft intermediate drive chain sprocket
15. Primary Camshaft Drive Chain Timing Link for the Right Primary Camshaft Intermediate Drive Chain Sprocket
16. Right primary camshaft intermediate drive chain sprocket timing mark

36616_GMG6_G0323

Fig. 199 Camshaft timing drive chain alignment diagram (stage one)—3.6L engine

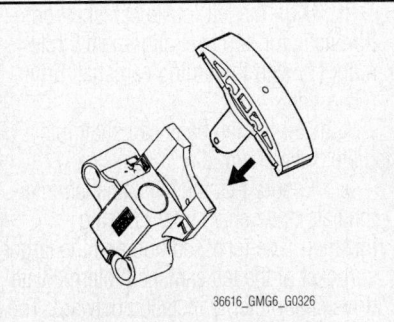

Fig. 200 Installing plunger into the primary camshaft drive chain tensioner body—3.6L engine

k. Release the primary camshaft drive chain tensioner by pulling out the tensioner retraction pins (EN-46112) pins and unlocking the tensioner plunger.

l. Verify the primary and left secondary camshaft drive chain timing mark alignments.

m. Remove the camshaft retaining tools (EN 48383-1) from the rear of the left camshafts.

Using the socket (EN-48589), rotate the crankshaft and crankshaft sprocket from the stage 1 alignment position to the stage 2 alignment position, 115 crankshaft degrees, in order to install the right secondary camshaft drive chain components.

n. Install the camshaft retaining tools (EN 48383-2) onto the rear of the left camshafts.

o. Install the (EN 48383-3) onto the rear of the right camshafts.

19. Install the right bank secondary camshaft drive chain.

20. Install the right bank secondary camshaft drive chain guide.

21. Install the right bank secondary camshaft drive chain shoe.

22. Install the right bank secondary camshaft drive chain tensioner.

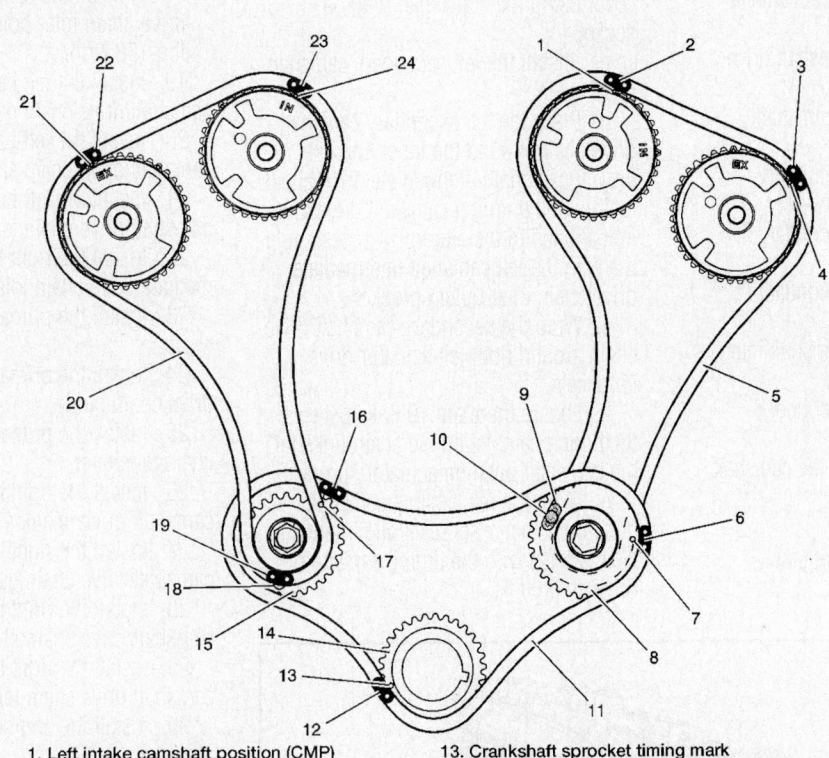

1. Left intake camshaft position (CMP) actuator timing mark - circle
2. Left intake secondary camshaft timing drive chain timing link
3. Left exhaust secondary camshaft timing drive chain timing link
4. Left exhaust camshaft position (CMP) actuator timing mark - circle
5. Left secondary camshaft timing drive chain
6. Primary Camshaft Drive Chain Timing Link for the Left Primary Camshaft Intermediate Drive Chain Sprocket
7. Left Primary Camshaft Intermediate Drive Chain Sprocket Timing Mark for the Primary Camshaft Drive Chain
8. Left primary camshaft intermediate drive chain sprocket
9. Left Secondary Camshaft Timing Drive Chain Timing Link for the Left Primary Camshaft Intermediate Drive Chain Sprocket, behind hole in sprocket
10. Left primary camshaft intermediate drive chain sprocket timing window
11. Primary camshaft drive chain
12. Primary Camshaft Drive Chain Timing Link for the Crankshaft Sprocket

13. Crankshaft sprocket timing mark
14. Crankshaft sprocket
15. Right primary camshaft intermediate drive chain sprocket
16. Primary Camshaft Drive Chain Timing Link for the Right Primary Camshaft Intermediate Drive Chain Sprocket
17. Right Primary Camshaft Intermediate Drive Chain Sprocket Timing Mark for the Primary Camshaft Drive Chain
18. Right Primary Camshaft Intermediate Drive Chain Sprocket Timing Mark/Window for the Right Secondary Camshaft Timing Drive Chain
19. Right Secondary Camshaft Timing Drive Chain Timing Link for the Right Primary Camshaft Intermediate Drive Chain Sprocket
20. Right secondary camshaft timing drive chain
21. Right exhaust camshaft position (CMP) actuator timing mark - triangle
22. Right exhaust secondary camshaft timing drive chain timing link
23. Right intake secondary camshaft timing drive chain timing link
24. Right intake camshaft position (CMP) actuator timing mark - triangle

Fig. 201 Camshaft timing drive chain alignment (stage one)—3.6L engine

23. Install the spark plugs.
24. Install the engine front cover.

Secondary—Left Side

See Figure 202.

1. Remove the engine front cover.
2. Remove the right bank secondary camshaft drive chain tensioner.
3. Remove the right bank secondary camshaft drive chain shoe.
4. Remove the right bank secondary camshaft drive chain guide.
5. Remove the right bank secondary camshaft drive chain.
6. Remove the primary camshaft drive chain tensioner.
7. Remove the primary upper camshaft drive chain guide.
8. Remove the primary camshaft drive chain.
9. Remove the right bank camshaft intermediate drive chain idler.
10. Remove the left bank secondary camshaft drive chain tensioner.
11. Remove the left bank secondary camshaft drive chain shoe.
12. Remove the left bank secondary camshaft drive chain guide.
13. Remove the left bank camshaft intermediate drive chain idler.
14. Remove the left bank secondary camshaft drive chain.
15. Clean and inspect all of the camshaft timing drive components.

To install:

16. Install the left bank secondary camshaft drive chain.

➡There should be no need to rotate the camshaft more than 10 degrees. Using the hex cast into the camshaft rotate the camshaft in order to install the camshaft retaining tools.

17. Install the camshaft retaining tools onto the rear of the left camshafts.

a. All camshafts must be locked in place before installation of any camshaft drive chains.

Ensure that the camshaft retaining tools is fully seated onto the camshafts.

b. Ensure the crankshaft is in the stage one timing position with the crankshaft sprocket timing mark aligned to the stage one timing mark on the oil pump cover using the crankshaft rotation socket.

c. Install the left secondary camshaft drive chain.

d. Place the left secondary camshaft drive chain around the inner sprocket of the left camshaft intermediate drive chain idler with the timing camshaft drive chain link aligned to the alignment access hole made in the left camshaft intermediate drive chain idler outer sprocket.

e. Wrap the secondary camshaft drive chain around both left actuator drive sprockets.

f. Ensure there are 10 links between the timing camshaft drive chain links for the camshaft position actuator sprockets.

g. Align the left exhaust camshaft position actuator sprocket alignment circle mark (2) with the timing camshaft drive chain link.

h. Align the left intake camshaft position actuator sprocket alignment circle mark (1) with the timing camshaft drive chain link.

18. Install the left bank camshaft intermediate drive chain idler.

a. Ensure that the left camshaft intermediate drive chain idler is being installed. The recessed hub and the larger sprocket of the left camshaft intermediate drive chain idler is installed outward. The raised hub and the smaller sprocket of the left camshaft intermediate drive chain idler is installed towards the block.

b. Place the left camshaft intermediate drive chain idler to the cylinder block.

c. Install the camshaft intermediate drive chain idler bolt and tighten 43 ft. lbs. (58 Nm).

19. Install the left bank secondary camshaft drive chain guide.
20. Install the left bank secondary camshaft drive chain shoe.
21. Install the left bank secondary camshaft drive chain tensioner.
22. Install the right bank camshaft intermediate drive chain idler.
23. Install the primary camshaft drive chain.
24. Install the primary upper camshaft drive chain guide.
25. Install the primary camshaft drive chain tensioner.
26. Install the right bank secondary camshaft drive chain.
27. Install the right bank secondary camshaft drive chain guide.
28. Install the right bank secondary camshaft drive chain shoe.
29. Install the right bank secondary camshaft drive chain tensioner.
30. Install the engine front cover.

3.9L Engine

See Figure 203.

1. Remove the engine front cover.
2. Align the crankshaft timing mark to the timing mark on the bottom of the timing chain tensioner.
3. Align the timing mark on the camshaft gear with the timing mark on top of the timing chain tensioner.
4. Remove the camshaft sprocket bolts.
5. Remove the timing chain, camshaft, and crankshaft sprockets.
6. Remove the timing chain tensioner bolts.
7. Remove the timing chain tensioner.
8. Remove and discard the camshaft position actuator filter (1) from the end of the camshaft.

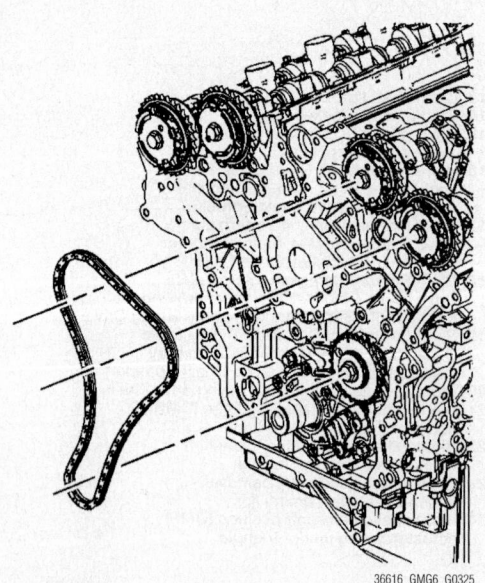

36616_GMG6_G0325

Fig. 202 Removing the left bank secondary camshaft drive chain—3.6L engine

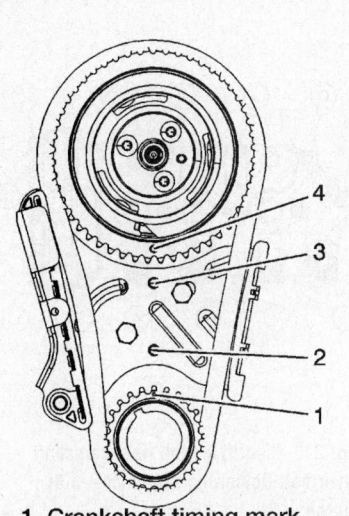

1. Crankshaft timing mark
2. Timing chain tensioner bottom timing mark
3. Timing chain tensioner top timing mark
4. Camshaft gear timing mark

36616_GMG6_G0321

Fig. 203 Aligning timing marks—3.9L engine

To install:

➡**Always install a NEW camshaft position actuator filter anytime the camshaft position actuator is removed.**

9. Install a NEW camshaft position actuator filter (1) to the end of the camshaft.

10. Install the crankshaft sprocket.

11. Apply prelube to the crankshaft sprocket thrust surface.

12. Install the timing chain tensioner.

13. Install the timing chain tensioner bolts and tighten to 15 ft. lbs. (21 Nm).

14. Using the Tensioner Compressor (EN-47719), fully collapse the tensioner, and place the tensioner retaining pin into the retaining hole.

15. Align the crankshaft timing mark to the timing mark on the bottom of the timing chain tensioner.

16. Hold the camshaft sprocket with the timing chain hanging down and install the timing chain to the crankshaft gear.

17. Align the timing mark on the camshaft gear with the timing mark on top of the timing chain tensioner.

18. Align the dowel in the camshaft sprocket with the dowel hole in the camshaft.

19. Draw the camshaft sprocket onto the camshaft using the mounting bolts. Tighten the bolts to 12 ft. lbs. (16 Nm).

20. Remove the retaining pin from the timing chain tensioner in order to make the tensioner active.

21. Coat the crankshaft and camshaft sprockets with clean engine oil.

22. Install the engine front cover.

VALVE COVERS

REMOVAL & INSTALLATION

2.4L Engine

See Figures 204 through 206.

1. Remove the camshaft cover ground strap.

2. Remove the front lift bracket.

3. Remove the rear lift bracket.

4. Remove the bolt and coil.

5. Remove the camshaft position actuator solenoid valve bolts.

6. Remove the camshaft position actuator solenoid valves.

7. Remove the camshaft cover assembly.

8. Remove and discard the camshaft cover gasket, camshaft cover grommets,

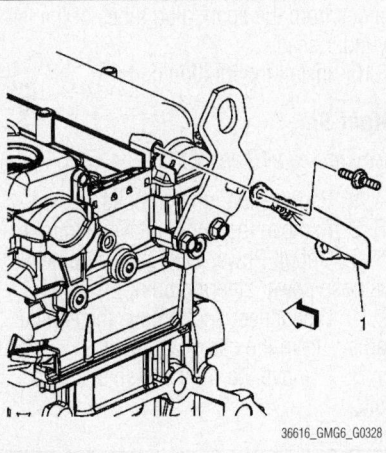

36616_GMG6_G0328

Fig. 204 Removing the camshaft cover ground strap—2.4L engine

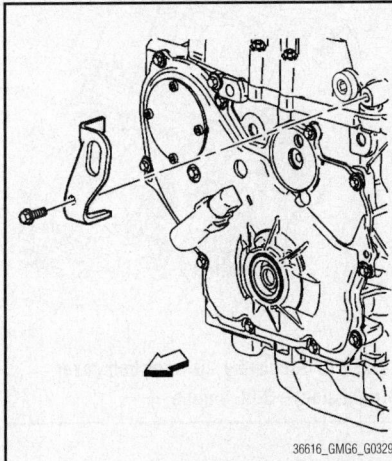

36616_GMG6_G0329

Fig. 205 Removing the front lift bracket—2.4L engine

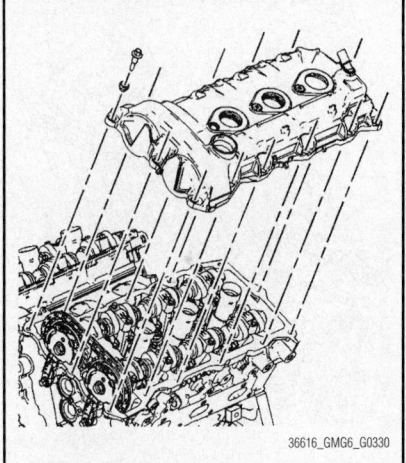

36616_GMG6_G0330

Fig. 206 Removing the rear lift bracket—2.4L engine

and camshaft cover bolts if they are serviced with the grommet.

To install:

9. Install NEW camshaft cover grommets and camshaft cover bolts if they are serviced with the grommet.

10. Assemble the camshaft cover and a NEW gasket. Ensure that the gasket is located in the retaining groove in the camshaft cover.

11. Install the cover on the cylinder head and hand start the bolts. Tighten the bolts to 89 inch lbs. (10 Nm).

12. Install the front lift bracket.

13. Install the front lift bracket bolt and tighten to 18 ft. lbs. (25 Nm).

14. Install the rear lift bracket.

15. Install the rear lift bracket bolts and tighten to 18 ft. lbs. (25 Nm).

16. Install the ground strap and tighten the bolts to 89 inch lbs. (10 Nm).

17. Install the spark plugs and tighten to 15 ft. lbs. (20 Nm).

18. Install the ignition coil and tighten the bolt to 89 inch lbs. (10 Nm).

19. Install the camshaft position actuator solenoid valves.

20. Install the camshaft position actuator solenoid valve bolts and tighten to 89 inch lbs. (10 Nm).

3.6L Engine

Left Side

See Figures 207 through 209.

1. Remove the ignition coils.

2. Disconnect and remove the engine harness from the camshaft cover.

3. Remove the upper intake manifold.

4. Remove the left camshaft cover bolts.

5. Remove the left camshaft cover from the left cylinder head.

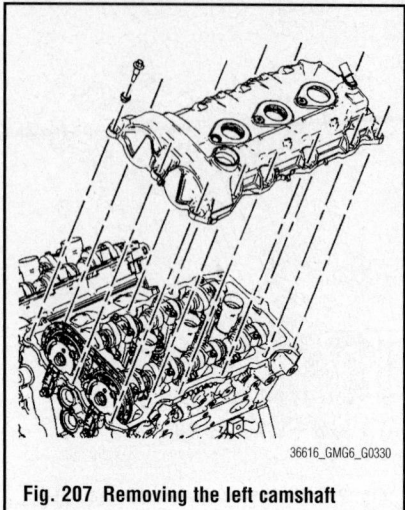

Fig. 207 Removing the left camshaft cover—3.6L engine

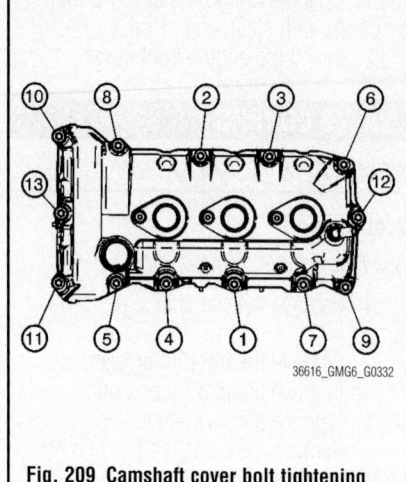

Fig. 209 Camshaft cover bolt tightening sequence—3.6L engine

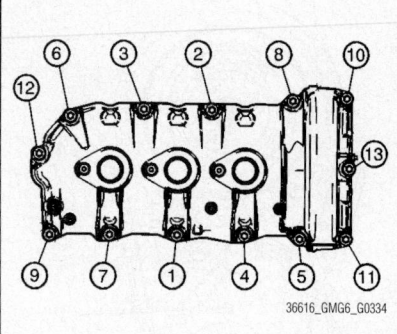

Fig. 211 Identifying the right camshaft cover bolt tightening sequence—3.6L engine

6. Clean the mating surfaces of the cylinder head and the camshaft cover.

7. Install the (EN 46101) onto the spark plug tubes of the left cylinder head.

To install:

8. Install the new camshaft cover bolt grommets prior to installing the camshaft cover bolts.

9. Place a bead 0.3150 inch (8 mm) in diameter by 0.1575 inch (4 mm) in height of RTV, GM P/N 12378521 or equivalent, on the engine front cover split lines.

10. Place the left camshaft cover into position onto the left cylinder head.

11. Loosely install the left camshaft cover bolts.

12. Tighten the left camshaft cover bolts in the sequence shown to 89 inch lbs. (10 Nm).

13. Connect and install the engine harness to the camshaft cover.

14. Install the upper intake manifold.

15. Remove the spark plug tube seal guides from the spark plug tubes of the left cylinder head.

16. Install the ignition coils.

Right Side

See Figures 210 and 211.

1. Remove the ignition coils.

2. Remove the upper intake manifold.

3. Unbolt Power Steering Pump, leave the hose power steering pump.

4. Disconnect and remove the engine harness from the camshaft cover.

5. Remove the right camshaft cover bolts.

6. Remove the right camshaft cover from the right cylinder head.

7. Clean the mating surfaces of the cylinder head and the camshaft cover.

8. Install the spark plug tube seal guides onto the spark plug tubes of the left cylinder head.

To install:

9. Install new camshaft cover bolt grommets prior to installing the camshaft cover bolts.

10. Place a bead 0.3150 inch (8 mm) in diameter by 0.1575 inch (4 mm) in height of RTV sealant, GM P/N 12378521 or equivalent, on the engine front cover split lines.

11. Place the right camshaft cover into position onto the right cylinder head.

12. Loosely install the right camshaft cover bolts.

13. Tighten the camshaft cover bolts in the sequence shown. Tighten the bolts to 89 inch lbs. (10 Nm).

14. Connect and install the engine harness to the camshaft cover.

15. Install the upper intake manifold.

16. Remove the spark plug tube seal guides from the spark plug tubes of the right cylinder head.

17. Install the ignition coils.

VALVE LASH

ADJUSTMENT

Hydraulic lash adjusters are used on all engines and no adjustment is necessary.

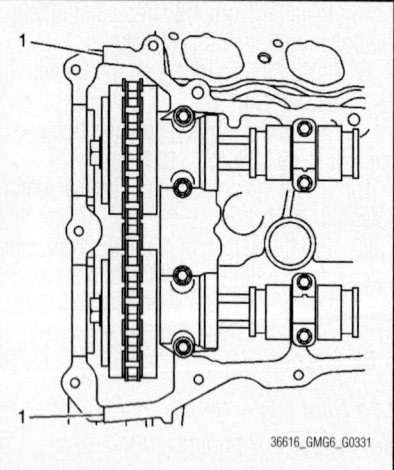

Fig. 208 Applying sealant to the engine front cover split lines—3.6L engine

Fig. 210 Removing the camshaft cover (right side)—3.6L engine

ENGINE PERFORMANCE & EMISSION CONTROLS

ACCELERATOR PEDAL POSITION (APP) SENSOR

LOCATION

The Accelerator Pedal Position (APP) sensor is located below the left side of the instrument panel, attached to the accelerator pedal assembly.

REMOVAL & INSTALLATION

See Figure 212.

1. Disconnect the Accelerator Pedal Position (APP) sensor electrical connector.
2. Remove the APP sensor bolts.
3. Remove the APP sensor.

To install:
4. Install the APP sensor.
5. Install the APP bolts and tighten to 89 inch lbs. (10 Nm).
6. Connect the APP sensor electrical connector.
7. Confirm that the APP sensor connector locking clip is fully secured.

CAMSHAFT POSITION (CMP) SENSOR

LOCATION

The 2.4L engines Camshaft Position (CMP) sensor (exhaust) is located on the upper left rear of the engine, near the camshaft cover. The CMP (intake) is located on the upper front of the engine, near the camshaft cover.

The 3.5L and 3.9L engines Camshaft Position (CMP) sensor is located in the right side of the engine compartment, above the timing chain cover, below the power steering pump.

The 3.6L engines Camshaft Position (CMP) (bank 1 exhaust) sensor is located on the right side of the engine, near the rear. The CMP (bank 1 intake) sensor is located on the rear of the engine, at the right side. The CMP (bank 2 exhaust) is located on the right side of the engine, near the front. The CMP (bank 2 intake) sensor is located on the right side of the engine, near the front.

REMOVAL & INSTALLATION

2.4L Engine

Intake

See Figure 213.

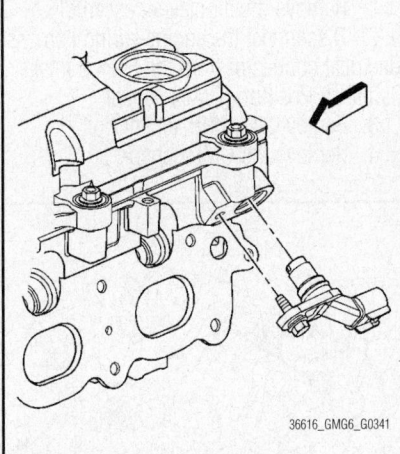

Fig. 213 Locating the CMP sensor (intake)—2.4L engine

1. Remove the air cleaner outlet duct.
2. Disconnect the engine wiring harness electrical connector from the intake camshaft position (CMP) sensor.
3. Remove the CMP sensor bolt.
4. Remove the CMP sensor.

To install:

➡Inspect the CMP sensor for damage, replace as necessary.

5. Lubricate the CMP sensor O-ring seal with clean engine oil.
6. Install the CMP sensor.
7. Install the CMP sensor bolt and tighten to 89 inch lb. (10 Nm).
8. Connect the engine wiring harness electrical connector to the intake CMP sensor.
9. Install the air cleaner outlet duct.

Exhaust

See Figure 214.

1. Disconnect the exhaust Camshaft Position (CMP) sensor electrical connector.
2. Remove the CMP sensor bolt. Intake CMP shown, exhaust CMP similar.
3. Remove the CMP sensor.

To install:

➡Inspect the CMP sensor for damage, replace as necessary.

4. Lubricate the CMP sensor O-ring seal with clean engine oil.
5. Install the CMP sensor. Intake CMP shown, exhaust CMP similar.
6. Install the CMP sensor bolt. Tighten the bolt to 89 inch lbs. (10 Nm).

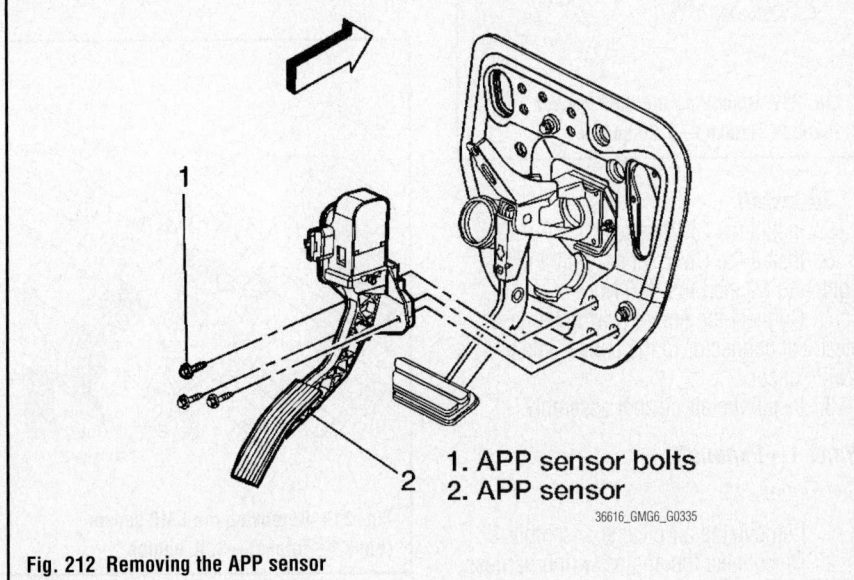

1. APP sensor bolts
2. APP sensor

Fig. 212 Removing the APP sensor

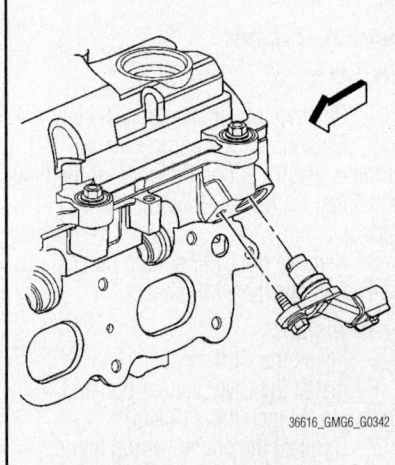

Fig. 214 Identifying the CMP sensor (intake shown exhaust similar)—2.4L engine

7. Connect the exhaust CMP sensor electrical connector.

3.5L Engine

See Figure 215.

1. Disconnect the Camshaft Position (CMP) sensor electrical connector.
2. Remove the CMP sensor bolt.
3. Remove the CMP sensor.
4. Inspect the sensor O-ring for wear, cracks, or leakage if the sensor is not being replaced.

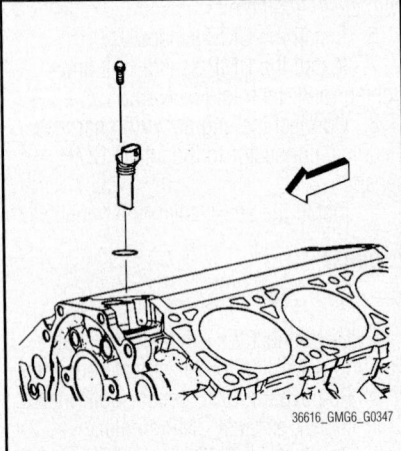

Fig. 215 Removing the CMP sensor—3.5L engine

To install:

5. Lubricate the o-ring with clean engine oil and replace the o-ring if damaged.
6. Install the CMP sensor.
7. Install the CMP sensor bolt and tighten to 89 inch lbs. (10 Nm).
8. Connect the CMP sensor electrical connector.

3.6L Engine

Bank 2—Exhaust

See Figure 216.

1. Remove the air cleaner assembly.
2. Disconnect the engine wiring harness electrical connector from the bank 2 exhaust Camshaft Position (CMP) sensor.
3. Remove the CMP sensor bolt.
4. Remove the CMP sensor.

To install:

5. Install the CMP sensor.
6. Install the CMP sensor bolt and tighten to 89 inch lbs. (10 Nm).
7. Connect the engine wiring harness electrical connector to the bank 2 exhaust CMP sensor.
8. Install the air cleaner assembly.

Fig. 216 Removing the CMP sensor (bank 2—exhaust)—3.6L engine

Bank 2—Intake

See Figure 217.

1. Remove the air cleaner assembly.
2. Disconnect the engine wiring harness electrical connector from the bank 2 intake Camshaft Position (CMP) sensor.
3. Remove the CMP sensor bolt.
4. Remove the CMP sensor.

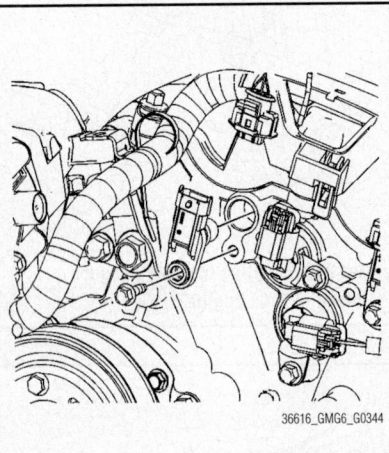

Fig. 217 Removing the CMP sensor (bank 2—intake)—3.6L engine

To install:

5. Install the CMP sensor.
6. Install the CMP sensor bolt and tighten to 89 inch lbs. (10 Nm).
7. Connect the engine wiring harness electrical connector to the bank 2 intake CMP sensor.
8. Install the air cleaner assembly.

Bank 1—Exhaust

See Figure 218.

1. Remove the air cleaner assembly.
2. Disconnect the engine wiring harness

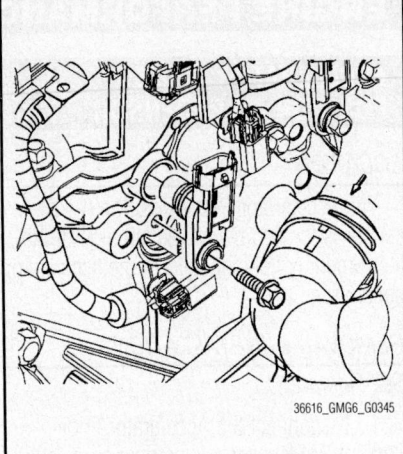

Fig. 218 Removing the CMP sensor (bank 1—exhaust)—3.6L engine

electrical connector from the bank 1 exhaust Camshaft Position (CMP) sensor.
3. Remove the CMP sensor bolt.
4. Remove the CMP sensor.

To install:

5. Install the CMP sensor.
6. Install the CMP sensor bolt and tighten to 89 inch lbs. (10 Nm).
7. Connect the engine wiring harness electrical connector to the bank 1 exhaust CMP sensor.
8. Install the air cleaner assembly.

Bank 1—Intake

See Figure 219.

1. Remove the air cleaner assembly.
2. Disconnect the engine wiring harness electrical connector from the bank 1 intake camshaft position (CMP) sensor.
3. Remove the CMP sensor bolt.
4. Remove the CMP sensor.

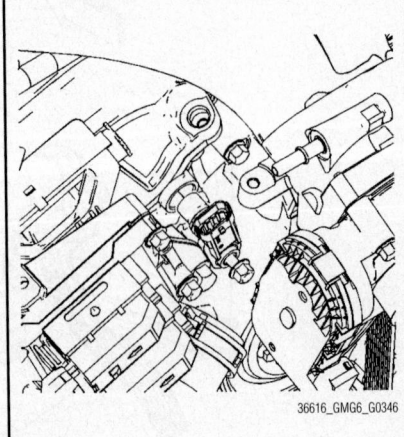

Fig. 219 Removing the CMP sensor (bank 1—intake)—3.6L engine

To install:

5. Install the CMP sensor.

6. Install the CMP sensor bolt and tighten to 89 inch lbs. (10 Nm).

7. Connect the engine wiring harness electrical connector to the bank 1 intake CMP sensor.

8. Install the air cleaner assembly.

3.9L Engine

See Figure 220.

1. Remove the power steering pump.

2. Disconnect the Camshaft Position (CMP) sensor electrical connector.

3. Remove the CMP sensor bolt.

4. Remove the CMP sensor.

5. Inspect the sensor O-ring for wear, cracks, or leakage if the sensor is not being replaced.

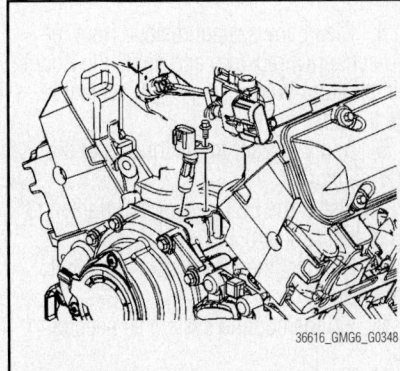

Fig. 220 Removing the CMP sensor— 3.9L engine

To install:

6. Replace the O-ring if damaged, lubricate the NEW O-ring with clean engine oil.

7. Install the CMP sensor.

8. Install the CMP sensor bolt and tighten to 89 inch lbs. (10 Nm).

9. Connect the CMP sensor electrical connector.

10. Install the power steering pump.

CRANKSHAFT POSITION (CKP) SENSOR

LOCATION

The 2.4L engine Crankshaft Position (CKP) sensor is located on the left front side of the engine, above the starter.

The 3.5L and 3.9L engine CKP sensor is located on the right side of the engine, at the end of the crankshaft, behind the harmonic balancer.

The 3.6L engine CKP sensor is located at the rear of the engine, at the left side of the engine block near the transmission/flywheel.

REMOVAL & INSTALLATION

2.4L Engine

See Figure 221.

1. Disconnect the Crankshaft Position (CKP) sensor electrical connector.

2. Remove the oil level indicator tube.

3. Remove the positive battery cable nut from the starter solenoid.

4. Remove the positive battery cable from the starter solenoid.

5. Remove the CKP sensor bolt.

6. Remove the CKP sensor.

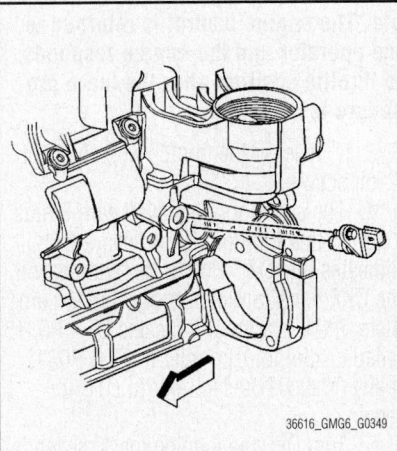

Fig. 221 Removing the CKP sensor— 2.4L engine

To install:

7. Lubricate the CKP sensor O-ring seal with clean engine oil.

8. Install the CKP sensor.

9. Install the CKP sensor bolt and tighten to 89 inch lbs. (10 Nm).

➡**Ensure that the engine harness terminal is still installed on the starter solenoid.**

10. Install the positive battery cable to the starter solenoid.

11. Install the positive battery cable nut to the starter solenoid and tighten to 89 inch lbs. (10 Nm).

12. Connect the CKP sensor electrical connector.

13. Install the oil level indicator tube.

3.5L Engine

See Figure 222.

1. Raise and support the vehicle.

2. Disconnect the Crankshaft Position (CKP) sensor electrical connector.

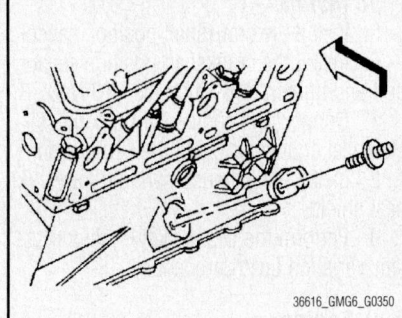

Fig. 222 Removing the CKP sensor— 3.5L engine

3. Remove the CKP sensor bolt.

4. Remove the CKP sensor.

5. Inspect for wear, cracks, or leakage if the sensor is not being replaced.

To install:

6. Lubricate the O-ring with clean engine oil before installation and replace the O-ring if necessary.

7. Install the CKP sensor.

8. Install the CKP sensor bolt and tighten to 97 inch lbs. (11 Nm).

9. Connect the CKP sensor electrical connector.

10. Lower the vehicle.

11. Perform the CKP system variation learn procedure.

3.6L Engine

See Figure 223.

1. Remove the exhaust manifold lower heat shield.

2. Disconnect the engine wiring harness electrical connector from the crankshaft position (CKP) sensor.

3. Remove the crankshaft sensor bolt.

4. Remove the crankshaft sensor.

Fig. 223 Removing the CKP sensor— 3.6L engine

To install:

5. Install the crankshaft position sensor.

6. Install the crankshaft position sensor bolt and tighten to 89 inch lbs. (10 Nm).

7. Connect the engine wiring harness electrical connector (2) to the CKP sensor.

8. Install the exhaust manifold lower heat shield.

9. Perform the Crankshaft Position System Variation Learn procedure.

3.9L Engine

See Figure 224.

1. Raise and support the vehicle.

2. Disconnect the Crankshaft Position (CKP) sensor electrical connector.

3. Remove the CKP sensor stud.

4. Remove the CKP sensor.

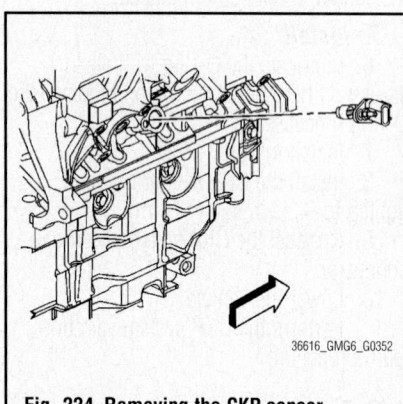

36616_GMG6_G0352

Fig. 224 Removing the CKP sensor— 3.9L engine

To install:

5. Lubricate the CKP sensor O-ring with clean engine oil.

6. Install the CKP sensor.

7. Install the CKP sensor stud and tighten to 89 inch lbs. (10 Nm).

8. Connect the CKP sensor electrical connector.

9. Lower the vehicle.

PROGRAMMING

Crankshaft Position System Variation Learn

1. Install a scan tool.

2. Monitor the ECM for DTCs with a scan tool. If other DTCs are set, except DTC P0315, refer to the applicable DTC for repair.

3. With a scan tool, select the CKP system variation learn procedure and perform the following:

a. Observe the fuel cut-off for the applicable engine.

b. Block the drive wheels.

c. Set the parking brake.

d. Place the vehicle's transmission in Park or Neutral.

e. Turn the Air Conditioning (A/C) OFF.

f. Cycle the ignition from OFF to ON.

g. Apply and hold the brake pedal for the duration of the procedure.

h. Start and idle the engine.

i. Accelerate to Wide Open Throttle (WOT). The engine should not accelerate beyond the calibrated fuel cut-off RPM value noted in the first step. Release the throttle immediately if the value is exceeded.

➡**While the learn procedure is in progress, release the throttle immediately when the engine starts to decelerate. The engine control is returned to the operator and the engine responds to throttle position after the learn procedure is complete.**

j. Release the throttle when fuel cut-off occurs.

4. The scan tool displays Learn Status: Learned this Ignition. If the scan tool indicates that DTC P0315 ran and passed, the CKP variation learn procedure is complete. If the scan tool indicates DTC P0315 failed or did not run, refer to DTC P0315. If any other DTCs set, refer to DTC for repair.

5. Turn OFF the ignition for 30 seconds after the learn procedure is completed successfully

ENGINE COOLANT TEMPERATURE (ECT) SENSOR

LOCATION

The 2.4L Engine Coolant Temperature (ECT) sensor is located on the rear of the engine, below the camshaft position exhaust sensor.

The 3.5L and 3.9L Engine Coolant Temperature (ECT) sensor is mounted in the rear cylinder head, below the coolant reservoir.

The 3.6L Engine Coolant Temperature (ECT) sensor is located on the front center of the engine, between cylinders 2 and 4 exhaust ports.

REMOVAL & INSTALLATION

2.4L Engine

See Figure 225.

1. Partially drain the cooling system.

2. Disconnect the Engine Coolant Temperature (ECT) sensor electrical connector.

3. Remove the ECT sensor.

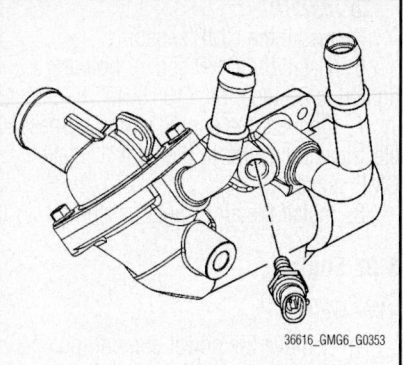

36616_GMG6_G0353

Fig. 225 Removing the ECT sensor— 2.4L engine

To install:

➡**Use a tap in order to remove any sealant residue in the sensor hole in the thermostat housing.**

4. Clean any sealant residue from the old sensor (if reusing) and apply the Room Temperature Vulcanizing (RTV) sealant to the threads.

5. Apply sealant to the threads of the ECT sensor.

6. Install the ECT sensor and tighten to 15 ft. lbs. (20 Nm).

7. Connect the ECT sensor electrical connector.

8. Fill the cooling system as needed.

3.5L Engine

See Figure 226.

❋❋ CAUTION

Use care when handling the coolant sensor. Damage to the coolant sensor will affect the operation of the fuel control system.

1. Partially drain the cooling system.

2. Disconnect the Engine Coolant

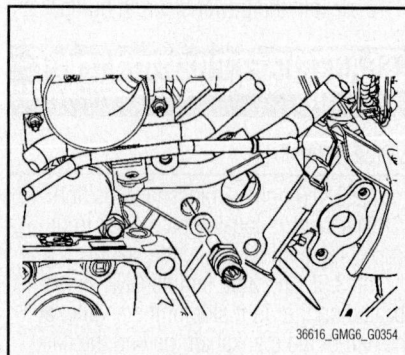

36616_GMG6_G0354

Fig. 226 Removing the ECT sensor— 3.5L engine

Temperature (ECT) sensor electrical connector.

3. Remove the ECT sensor.

To install:

✳✳ CAUTION

Replacement components must be the correct part number for the application. Components requiring the use of the thread locking compound, lubricants, corrosion inhibitors, or sealants are identified in the service procedure. Some replacement components may come with these coatings already applied. Do not use these coatings on components unless specified. These coatings can affect the final torque, which may affect the operation of the component. Use the correct torque specification when installing components in order to avoid damage.

4. Coat the threads with sealer GM P/N 13246004 or equivalent.

5. Install the ECT sensor and tighten to 15 ft. lbs. (20 Nm).

6. Connect the ECT electrical connector.

7. Fill the cooling system.

3.6L Engine

See Figure 227.

1. Disconnect the engine wiring harness electrical connector (1) from the Engine Coolant Temperature (ECT) sensor.

2. Remove the ECT sensor.

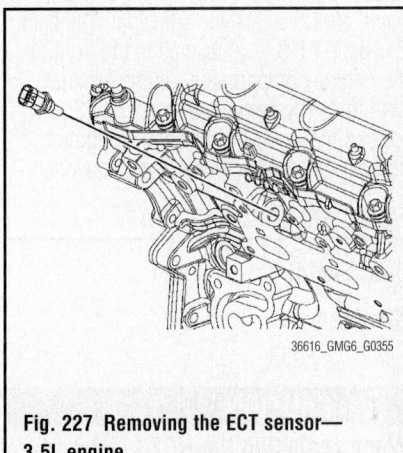

Fig. 227 Removing the ECT sensor— 3.5L engine

To install:

3. Install the ECT sensor and tighten to 16 ft. lbs. (22 Nm).

4. Connect the engine wiring harness electrical connector to the ECT sensor.

3.9L Engine

See Figure 228.

✳✳ CAUTION

Use care when handling the coolant sensor. Damage to the coolant sensor will affect the operation of the fuel control system.

1. Drain the cooling system.

2. Remove the intake manifold cover, if necessary.

3. Disconnect the Engine Coolant Temperature (ECT) sensor electrical connector.

4. Remove the ECT sensor.

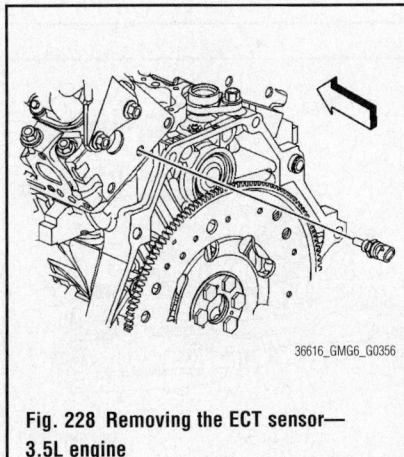

Fig. 228 Removing the ECT sensor— 3.5L engine

To install:

✳✳ CAUTION

Replacement components must be the correct part number for the application. Components requiring the use of the thread locking compound, lubricants, corrosion inhibitors, or sealants are identified in the service procedure. Some replacement components may come with these coatings already applied. Do not use these coatings on components unless specified. These coatings can affect the final torque, which may affect the operation of the component. Use the correct torque specification when installing components in order to avoid damage.

5. Coat the threads of the ECT sensor with sealer GM P/N 13246004 or equivalent.

6. Install the ECT sensor and tighten to 15 ft. lbs. (20 Nm).

7. Connect the ECT electrical connector.

8. Install the intake manifold cover, if necessary.

9. Fill the cooling system.

EVAPORATIVE EMISSIONS (EVAP) CANISTER

REMOVAL & INSTALLATION

2.4L Engine

See Figure 229.

1. Remove the fuel tank.

2. Disconnect the Evaporative Emission (EVAP) canister to EVAP canister vent solenoid valve line quick connect fitting.

3. Disconnect the fuel tank EVAP vapor line to EVAP canister quick connect fitting.

4. From under the fuel tank, remove the TORX® bolt attaching the EVAP canister to bracket.

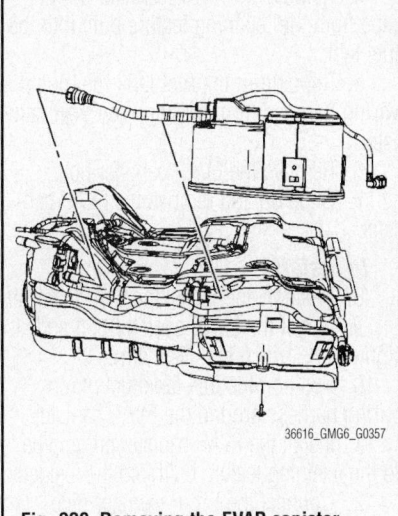

Fig. 229 Removing the EVAP canister— 2.4L engine

To install:

5. Slide the NEW EVAP canister down into the bracket.

6. From under the fuel tank, install the Torx® bolt attaching the EVAP canister to bracket and tighten to 89 inch lbs. (10 Nm).

7. Connect the fuel tank EVAP vapor line to EVAP canister quick connect fitting.

8. Connect the EVAP canister to EVAP canister vent solenoid valve line quick connect fitting.

9. Install the fuel tank.

3.6L Engine

See Figure 230.

1. Remove the fuel tank.

2. Disconnect the fuel tank vent pipe quick connect fitting from the EVAP canister.

3. Disconnect the Evaporative Emission (EVAP) canister pipe quick connect fitting from the EVAP canister vent solenoid valve.

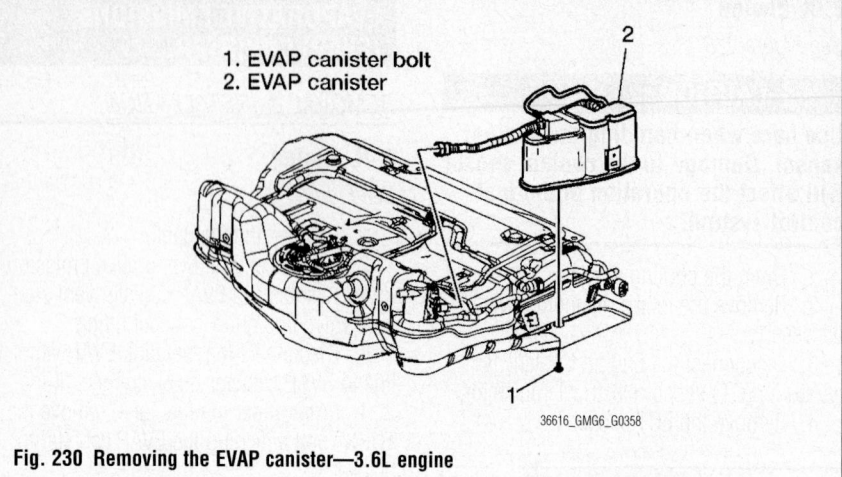

1. EVAP canister bolt
2. EVAP canister

36616_GMG6_G0358

Fig. 230 Removing the EVAP canister—3.6L engine

4. Remove the EVAP canister purge pipe from the retaining feature built into the fuel tank.

5. Reposition the fuel tank fuel pump wiring harness from around the EVAP canister.

6. Remove the EVAP canister bolt.

7. Slide up and remove the EVAP canister.

To install:

8. Position and install the EVAP canister.

9. Install the EVAP canister bolt and tighten to 31 inch lbs. (3.5 Nm).

10. Position the fuel tank fuel pump wiring harness around the EVAP canister.

11. Install the EVAP canister purge pipe to the retaining feature built into the fuel tank.

12. Connect the EVAP canister pipe quick connect fitting to the EVAP canister vent solenoid valve.

13. Connect the EVAP canister vent pipe quick connect fitting to the EVAP canister.

14. Install the fuel tank.

3.5L & 3.9L Engines

See Figure 231.

1. Remove the fuel tank.

2. Disconnect the Evaporative Emission (EVAP) canister to EVAP canister vent solenoid valve line quick connect fitting.

3. Disconnect the fuel tank EVAP vapor line to EVAP canister quick connect fitting.

4. From under the fuel tank, remove the TORX®bolt attaching the EVAP canister to bracket.

5. Slide the EVAP canister upward from the bracket.

To install:

6. Slide the NEW EVAP canister down into the bracket.

7. From under the fuel tank, install the TORX® bolt attaching the EVAP canister to bracket and tighten to 89 inch lbs. (10 Nm).

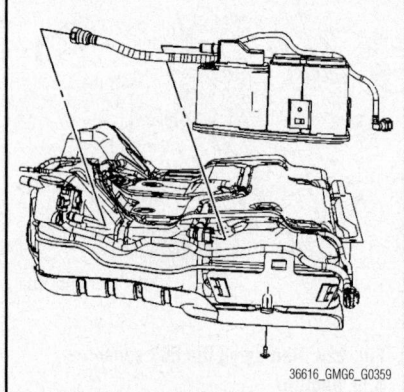

36616_GMG6_G0359

Fig. 231 Removing the EVAP canister—3.5L engine

8. Connect the fuel tank EVAP vapor line to EVAP canister quick connect fitting.

9. Connect the EVAP canister to EVAP canister vent solenoid valve line quick connect fitting.

10. Install the fuel tank.

EXHAUST GAS RECIRCULATION (EGR) VALVE

REMOVAL & INSTALLATION

3.5L Engine

See Figure 232.

1. Disconnect the Exhaust Gas Recirculation (EGR) valve electrical connector.

2. Remove the EGR pipe bolt and carefully pull the pipe assembly back.

3. Remove the EGR valve bolts.

4. Remove EGR valve.

5. Remove the EGR valve gasket.

6. Clean and inspect the EGR valve gasket mating surfaces.

To install:

7. Install a new EGR valve gasket.

8. Install the EGR valve.

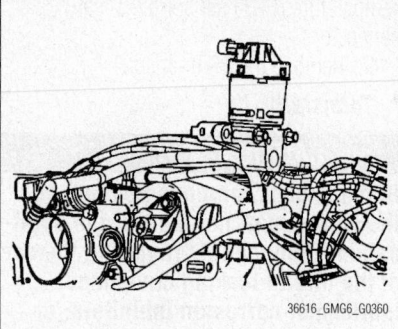

36616_GMG6_G0360

Fig. 232 Removing the EGR valve— 3.5L engine

9. Install the EGR valve bolts. Tighten the bolt to 22 ft. lbs. (30 Nm).

10. Install the EGR pipe to the EGR valve.

11. Install the EGR pipe. Tighten the bolt to 18 ft. lbs. (25 Nm).

12. Connect the EGR valve electrical connector.

HEATED OXYGEN (HO2S) SENSOR

LOCATION

The 2.4L engine Heated Oxygen Sensor (HO2S) 1 is located on the rear of the engine, between the exhaust manifold and the catalytic converter. The HO2S 2 is located on the rear of the engine, below the catalytic converter.

The 3.5L, 3.6L and 3.9L engines Heated Oxygen Sensor (HO2S) bank 1 sensor 1 is located in the center of the rear exhaust manifold. The bank 1 sensor 2 HO2S is located at the rear of the engine compartment, after the catalytic converter. The bank 2 sensor 1 HO2S is located in the front of the engine compartment, on the exhaust manifold. The bank 2 sensor 2 HO2S is located in the lower front of the engine compartment, after the catalytic converter.

REMOVAL & INSTALLATION

2.4L Engine

Sensor 1

See Figure 233.

❋❋ CAUTION

When replacing the HO2S clear codes with a scan tool, regardless of whether or not a DTC is set. Perform a HO2S heater resistance learn reset with a scan tool, where available. Perform this procedure in order to reset the HO2S resistance learned value and avoid possible HO2S failure.

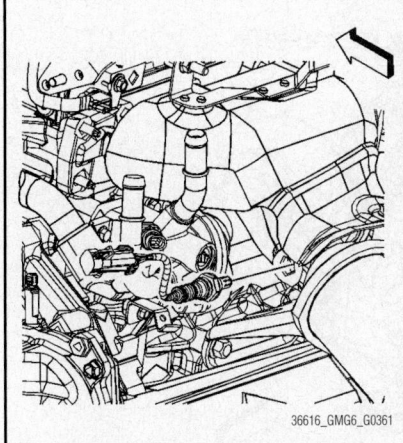

Fig. 233 Removing the HO2S (sensor 1)—
2.4L engine

✳✳ **CAUTION**

The oxygen sensor uses a permanently attached pigtail and connector.
Do not remove the pigtail from the
oxygen sensor. Damage to or removal
of the pigtail connector could affect
proper operation of the oxygen sensor.

✳✳ **CAUTION**

The use of excessive force may damage the threads in the exhaust mani-
fold/pipe.

➡The in-line connector and louvered
end must be kept clear of grease, dirt
or other contaminants. Avoid using
cleaning solvents of any type. DO NOT
drop or roughly handle the HO2S.

➡The HO2S may be difficult to remove
when the engine temperature is less
than 120°F (48°C).

1. Remove the connector position assurance (CPA) retainer.
2. Disconnect the HO2S electrical connector.
3. Remove the HO2S electrical connector clip from the thermostat housing.
4. Remove the HO2S.

To install:

➡A special anti-seize compound is
used on the HO2S threads. The compound consists of a liquid graphite and
glass beads. The graphite will burn
away, but the glass beads will remain,
making the sensor easier to remove.
New or service sensors will have the
compound applied to the threads. If a
sensor is removed and is to be reinstalled, the threads must have an anti-

seize compound applied before installation.

5. If reinstalling the old HO2S, coat the
threads with anti-seize compound GM P/N
12377953 or equivalent.
6. Install the HO2S. Tighten the sensor
to 30 ft. lbs. (41 Nm).
7. Install the HO2S electrical connector
clip to the thermostat housing.
8. Connect the HO2S electrical connector.
9. Install the CPA retainer.

Sensor 2

See Figures 234 and 235.

✳✳ **CAUTION**

When replacing the HO2S clear
codes with a scan tool, regardless of
whether or not a DTC is set. Perform
a HO2S heater resistance learn reset
with a scan tool, where available.
Perform this procedure in order to
reset the HO2S resistance learned
value and avoid possible HO2S failure.

✳✳ **CAUTION**

The oxygen sensor uses a permanently attached pigtail and connector.
Do not remove the pigtail from the
oxygen sensor. Damage to or removal
of the pigtail connector could affect
proper operation of the oxygen sensor.

✳✳ **CAUTION**

The use of excessive force may damage the threads in the exhaust mani-
fold/pipe.

➡The in-line connector and louvered
end must be kept clear of grease, dirt
or other contaminants. Avoid using
cleaning solvents of any type. DO NOT
drop or roughly handle the HO2S.

➡The HO2S may be difficult to remove
when the engine temperature is less
than 120°F (48°C).

1. Raise and support the vehicle.
2. Remove the Connector Position
Assurance (CPA) retainer.
3. Disconnect the HO2S electrical connector.
4. Using the oxygen sensor wrench,
remove the HO2S.

To install:

➡A special anti-seize compound is used
on the HO2S threads. The compound
consists of a liquid graphite and glass
beads. The graphite will burn away but

Fig. 234 Disconnecting the HO2S
(sensor 2)—2.4L engine

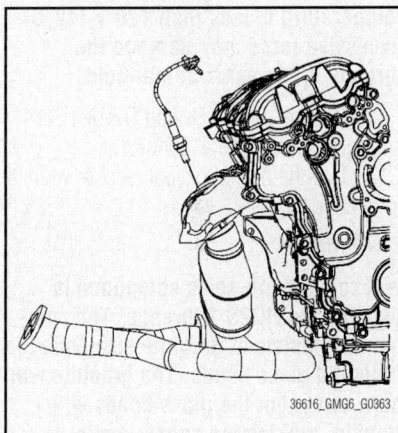

Fig. 235 Removing the HO2S (sensor 2)—
2.4L engine

the glass beads will remain, making the
sensor easier to remove. New or service
sensors already have the compound
applied to the threads. If the sensor is
removed and is to be reinstalled, the
threads must be coated with an anti-
seize compound before reinstallation.

5. If reinstalling the old HO2S, coat the
threads with anti-seize compound GM P/N
12377953 or equivalent.
6. Using the oxygen sensor wrench,
install the HO2S. Tighten the HO2S to 30 ft.
lbs. (41 Nm).
7. Connect the HO2S electrical connector.
8. Install the CPA retainer.
9. Lower the vehicle.

3.5L Engine

Bank 1 Sensor 1

See Figure 236.

➡The Heated Oxygen Sensor (HO2S) 1
may be difficult to remove when engine

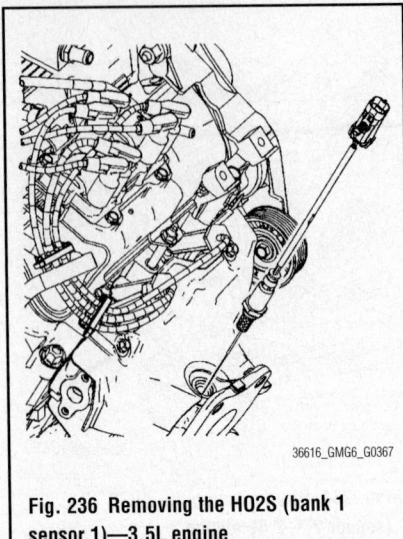

Fig. 236 Removing the HO2S (bank 1 sensor 1)—3.5L engine

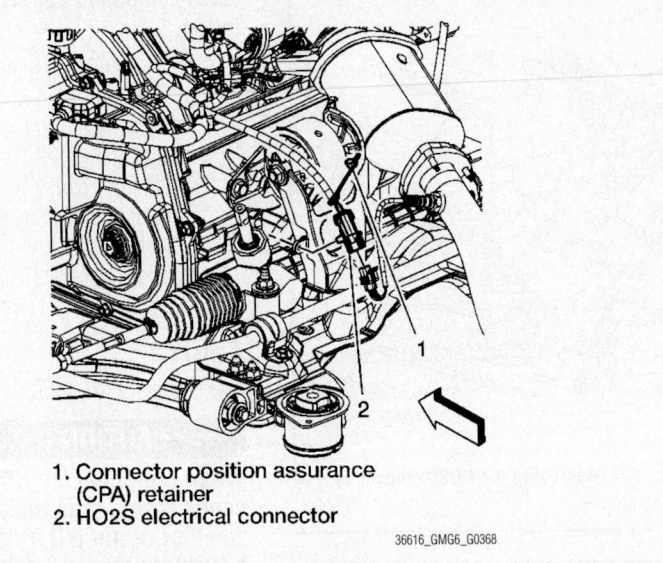

1. Connector position assurance (CPA) retainer
2. HO2S electrical connector

36616_GMG6_G0368

Fig. 237 Disconnecting the HO2S electrical connector (bank 1 sensor 2)—3.5L engine

temperature is less than 120°F (48°C). Excessive force may damage the threads in the exhaust manifold.

1. Disconnect the Heated Oxygen Sensor (HO2S) 1 electrical connector.
2. Use the heated oxygen sensor wrench to remove the HO2S 1.

To install:

➡A special anti-seize compound is used on the HO2S 1 threads. The compound consists of graphite suspended in fluid and glass beads. The graphite will burn away, but the glass beads will remain, making the sensor easier to remove. New or service sensors will already have the compound applied to the threads. If a sensor is removed from an engine and is to be reinstalled, the threads must have anti-seize compound applied before the reinstallation.

3. Coat the threads of the HO2S 1 with anti-seize compound GM P/N 12377953 or an equivalent, if necessary.
4. Install the HO2S 1. Tighten the sensor with the heated oxygen sensor wrench to 30 ft. lbs. (41 Nm).
5. Connect the HO2S 1 electrical connector.

Bank 1 Sensor 2

See Figure 237.

➡The Heated Oxygen Sensor (HO2S) may be difficult to remove when engine temperature is less than 48°C (120°F). Excessive force may damage the threads in the exhaust pipe.

1. Raise and support the vehicle.
2. Remove the Connector Position Assurance (CPA) retainer.

3. Disconnect the HO2S electrical connector.
4. Using the heated oxygen sensor wrench, remove the HO2S.

To install:

➡A special anti-seize compound is used on the HO2S 2 threads. The compound consists of graphite suspended in fluid and glass beads. The graphite will burn away, but the glass beads will remain, making the sensor easier to remove. New or service sensors will already have the compound applied to the threads. If a sensor is removed from an engine and is to be reinstalled, the threads must have anti-seize compound applied before reinstallation.

5. Coat the threads of the HO2S 2 with anti-seize compound GM P/N 12377953 or an equivalent, if necessary.
6. Install the HO2S and tighten the sensor 30 ft. lbs. (41 Nm).
7. Connect the HO2S electrical connector.
8. Install the CPA retainer.
9. Lower the vehicle.

Bank 2 Sensor 1

See Figure 238.

➡The Heated Oxygen sensor (HO2S) 1 may be difficult to remove when the engine temperature is less than 120°F (48°C). Excessive force may damage the threads in the exhaust manifold.

1. Disconnect the HO2S electrical connector.
2. Use the heated oxygen sensor wrench to remove the HO2S 1.

To install:

➡A special anti-seize compound is used on the HO2S 1 threads. The compound consists of graphite suspended in fluid and glass beads. The graphite will burn away, but the glass beads will remain, making the sensor easier to remove. New or service sensors will already have the compound applied to the threads. If a sensor is removed from an engine and is to be reinstalled, the threads must have anti-seize compound applied before the reinstallation.

3. Coat the threads of the HO2S 1 with anti-seize compound GM P/N 12377953 or an equivalent, if necessary.
4. Install the HO2S 1. Use the heated oxygen sensor wrench to tighten the sensor to 30 ft. lbs. (41 Nm).

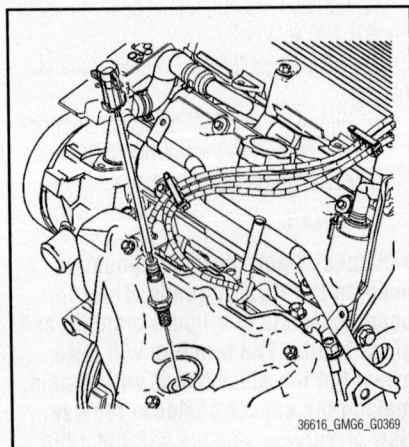

36616_GMG6_G0369

Fig. 238 Removing the HO2S 1—3.6L engine

5. Connect the HO2S 1 electrical connector.

Bank 2 Sensor 2

See Figure 239.

➡The Heated Oxygen sensor (HO2S) 1 may be difficult to remove when the engine temperature is less than 120°F (48°C). Excessive force may damage the threads in the exhaust manifold.

1. Raise and support the vehicle.
2. Remove the Connector Position Assurance (CPA) retainer.
3. Disconnect the HO2S electrical connector.
4. Using the heated oxygen sensor wrench, remove the HO2S.

To install:

➡A special anti-seize compound is used on the HO2S 1 threads. The compound consists of graphite suspended in fluid and glass beads. The graphite will burn away, but the glass beads will remain, making the sensor easier to remove. New or service sensors will already have the compound applied to the threads. If a sensor is removed from an engine and is to be reinstalled, the threads must have anti-seize compound applied before the reinstallation.

5. Coat the threads of the HO2S 2 with anti-seize compound GM P/N 12377953 or an equivalent, if necessary.
6. Install the HO2S and tighten to 30 ft. lbs. (41 Nm).
7. Connect the HO2S electrical connector.

8. Install the CPA retainer.
9. Lower the vehicle.

3.6L Engine

Bank 1 Sensor 1

See Figure 240.

1. Raise and support the vehicle.
2. Remove the engine wiring harness Heated Oxygen Sensor (HO2S) electrical connector clip from the engine harness.
3. Remove the Connector Position Assurance (CPA) retainer from the HO2S electrical connection.
4. Disconnect the engine wiring harness electrical connector from the HO2S electrical connector (1).
5. Raise and support the vehicle to an appropriate height to reach the HO2S.
6. Remove the HO2S from the exhaust manifold.

To install:

➡A special anti-seize compound is used in the HO2S threads. The compound consists of liquid graphite and glass beads. The graphite tends to burn away, but the glass beads remain, making the sensor easier to remove. New, or service replacement sensors already have the compound applied to the threads. If the sensor is removed from an exhaust component and if for any reason the sensor is to reinstalled, the threads must have anti-seize compound applied before the reinstallation.

7. If reinstalling the old sensor, coat the threads with anti-seize compound GM P/N 12377953, or equivalent.

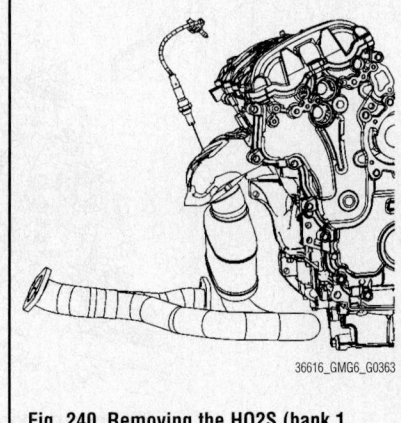

Fig. 240 Removing the HO2S (bank 1 sensor 1)—3.6L engine

8. Install the HO2S to the exhaust manifold and tighten the sensor to 31 ft. lbs. (42 Nm).
9. Lower the vehicle.
10. Connect the engine wiring harness electrical connector to the HO2S electrical connector.
11. Install the engine wiring harness HO2S electrical connector clip to the engine harness.
12. Install the CPA retainer to the HO2S electrical connection.

Bank 1 Sensor 2

See Figure 241.

1. Raise and support the vehicle.
2. Remove the Connector Position Assurance (CPA) retainer from the HO2S electrical connection.
3. Disconnect the Heated Oxygen Sensor (HO2S) electrical connector from the engine wiring harness electrical connector.
4. Remove the bank 1 sensor 2 HO2S from the catalytic converter.

To install:

➡A special anti-seize compound is used in the HO2S threads. The compound consists of liquid graphite and glass beads. The graphite tends to burn away, but the glass beads remain, making the sensor easier to remove. New, or service replacement sensors already have the compound applied to the threads. If the sensor is removed from an exhaust component and if for any reason the sensor is to reinstalled, the threads must have anti-seize compound applied before the reinstallation.

5. If reinstalling the old sensor, coat the threads with anti-seize compound GM P/N 12377953, or equivalent.

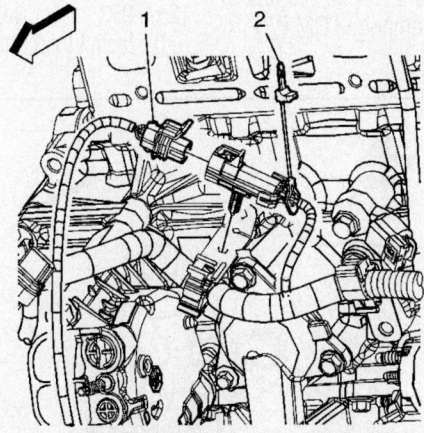

1. Connector position assurance (CPA) retainer
2. HO2S electrical connector

36616_GMG6_G0370

Fig. 239 Disconnecting the HO2S electrical connector (bank 2 sensor 2)—3.6L engine

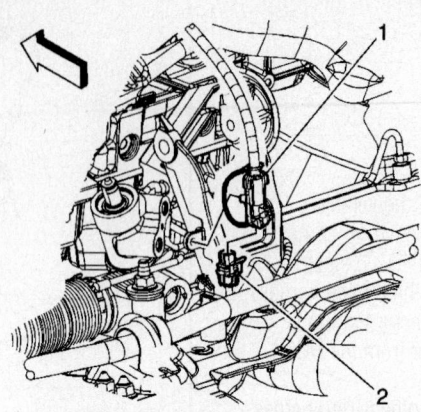

1. Connector position assurance (CPA) retainer
2. Heated Oxygen Sensor (bank 1 sensor 2)

36616_GMG6_G0364

Fig. 241 Disconnecting the HO2S electrical connector (bank 1 sensor 2)—3.6L engine

6. Install the bank 1 sensor 2 HO2S to the catalytic converter and tighten the sensor to 31 ft. lbs. (42 Nm).

7. Connect the HO2S electrical connector to the engine wiring harness electrical connector.

8. Install the CPA retainer to the HO2S electrical connection.

9. Lower the vehicle.

Bank 2 Sensor 1

See Figure 242.

1. Remove the fuel injector sight shield.

2. Remove the air cleaner outlet duct.

3. Remove the Connector Position Assurance (CPA) retainer from the HO2S electrical connection.

4. Disconnect the engine wiring harness electrical connector from the Heated Oxygen Sensor (HO2S) electrical connector.

5. Remove the HO2S electrical

connector clip from the engine wiring harness tab.

6. Remove the HO2S from the exhaust manifold.

To install:

➡A special anti-seize compound is used in the HO2S threads. The compound consists of liquid graphite and glass beads. The graphite tends to burn away, but the glass beads remain, making the sensor easier to remove. New, or service replacement sensors already have the compound applied to the threads. If the sensor is removed from an exhaust component and if for any reason the sensor is to reinstalled, the threads must have anti-seize compound applied before the reinstallation.

7. If reinstalling the old sensor, coat the threads with anti-seize compound GM P/N 12377953, or equivalent.

8. Install the HO2S to the exhaust manifold and tighten the sensor to 31 ft. lbs. (42 Nm).

9. Connect the engine wiring harness electrical connector to the HO2S electrical connector (3).

10. Install the HO2S electrical connector clip to the engine wiring harness tab.

11. Install the CPA retainer to the HO2S electrical connection.

12. Install the air cleaner outlet duct.

13. Install the fuel injector sight shield.

Bank 2 Sensor 2

See Figure 243.

1. Raise and support the vehicle.

2. Remove the Connector Position Assurance (CPA) retainer from the HO2S electrical connection.

3. Disconnect the Heated Oxygen Sensor (HO2S) electrical connector from the engine wiring harness electrical connector

4. Remove the bank 2 sensor 2 HO2S from the catalytic converter.

To install:

➡A special anti-seize compound is used in the HO2S threads. The compound consists of liquid graphite and glass beads. The graphite tends to burn away, but the glass beads remain, making the sensor easier to remove. New, or service replacement sensors already have the compound applied to the threads. If the sensor is removed from an exhaust component and if for any reason the sensor is to reinstalled, the threads must have anti-seize compound applied before the reinstallation.

5. If reinstalling the oil sensor, coat the threads with anti-seize compound GM P/N 12377953, or equivalent.

6. Install the bank 2 sensor 2 HO2S to

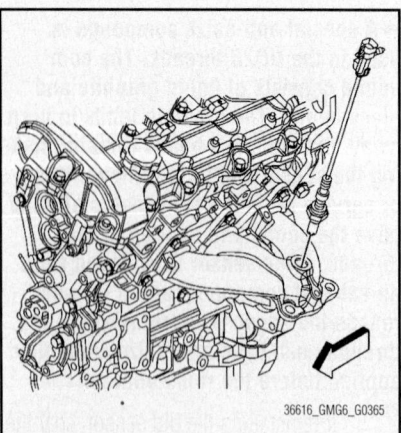

36616_GMG6_G0365

Fig. 242 Removing the HO2S (bank 1 sensor 1)—3.6L engine

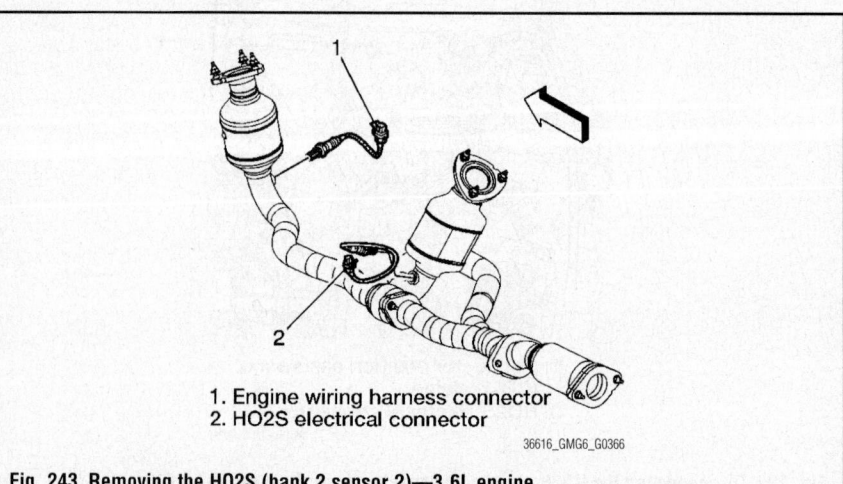

1. Engine wiring harness connector
2. HO2S electrical connector

36616_GMG6_G0366

Fig. 243 Removing the HO2S (bank 2 sensor 2)—3.6L engine

the catalytic converter and tighten the sensor to 31 ft. lbs. (42 Nm).

7. Connect the HO2S electrical connector to the engine wiring harness electrical connector.

8. Install the CPA retainer to the HO2S electrical connection.

9. Lower the vehicle.

3.9L Engine

Bank 1 Sensors 1 & 2

See Figure 244.

1. Remove the intake manifold cover.
2. Remove the Connector Position Assurance (CPA) retainer.
3. Disconnect the Heated Oxygen Sensor (HO2S) electrical connector.
4. Remove the HO2S clip from the ignition control module bracket.

➡**The HO2S may be difficult to remove when the engine temperature is less than 120°F (48°C). Excessive force may damage the threads in the exhaust manifold.**

5. Remove the HO2S using the heated oxygen sensor wrench.

To install:

➡**A special anti-seize compound is used in the HO2S threads. The compound consists of liquid graphite and glass beads. The graphite tends to burn away, but the glass beads remain, making the sensor easier to remove. New, or service replacement sensors already have the compound applied to the threads. If the sensor is removed from an exhaust component and if for any reason the sensor is to reinstalled, the**

threads must have anti-seize compound applied before the reinstallation.

6. Coat the threads of the HO2S with anti-seize compound GM P/N 12377953 or equivalent, if necessary.

7. Install the HO2S and tighten to 31 ft. lbs. (42 Nm) using the heated oxygen sensor wrench.

8. Connect the HO2S electrical connector.

9. Install the CPA retainer.

10. Install the HO2S clip to the ignition control module bracket.

11. Install the intake manifold cover.

Bank 2 Sensor 1

See Figure 245.

1. Remove the Connector Position Assurance (CPA) retainer.
2. Disconnect the Heated Oxygen Sensor (HO2S) electrical connector.
3. Remove the HO2S clip from the oil level indicator tube bracket.

➡**The HO2S may be difficult to remove when the engine temperature is less than 120°F (48°C). Excessive force may damage the threads in the exhaust manifold.**

4. Remove the HO2S using the heated oxygen sensor wrench.

To install:

➡**A special anti-seize compound is used in the HO2S threads. The compound consists of liquid graphite and glass beads. The graphite tends to burn away, but the glass beads remain, making the sensor easier to remove. New, or service replacement sensors already have the compound applied to the threads. If the sensor is removed**

from an exhaust component and if for any reason the sensor is to reinstalled, the threads must have anti-seize compound applied before the reinstallation.

5. Coat the threads of the HO2S with anti-seize compound GM P/N 12377953 or equivalent, if necessary.

6. Install the HO2S and tighten to 31 ft. lbs. (42 Nm) using the heated oxygen sensor wrench.

7. Connect the HO2S electrical connector.

8. Install the CPA retainer.

9. Install the HO2S clip to the oil level indicator tube bracket.

Bank 2 Sensor 2

1. Raise and support the vehicle.
2. Remove the Connector Position Assurance (CPA) retainer.
3. Disconnect the Heated Oxygen Sensor (HO2S) electrical connector.

➡**The HO2S may be difficult to remove when the engine temperature is less than 120°F (48°C). Excessive force may damage the threads in the exhaust manifold.**

4. Remove the HO2S using the heated oxygen sensor wrench.

To install:

➡**A special anti-seize compound is used in the HO2S threads. The compound consists of liquid graphite and glass beads. The graphite tends to burn away, but the glass beads remain, making the sensor easier to remove. New, or service replacement sensors already have the compound applied to the threads. If the sensor is removed from an exhaust component and if for any reason the sensor is to reinstalled, the threads must have anti-seize compound applied before the reinstallation.**

5. Coat the threads of the HO2S with anti-seize compound GM P/N 12377953 or equivalent, if necessary.

6. Install the HO2S and tighten to 31 ft. lbs. (42 Nm) using the heated oxygen sensor wrench.

7. Connect the HO2S electrical connector.

8. Install the CPA retainer.

9. Ensure that the HO2S connector clip is attached to the stud on the engine.

10. Lower the vehicle.

KNOCK SENSOR (KS)

LOCATION

The 2.4L engine Knock Sensor (KS) is located on the front of the engine, below the intake manifold.

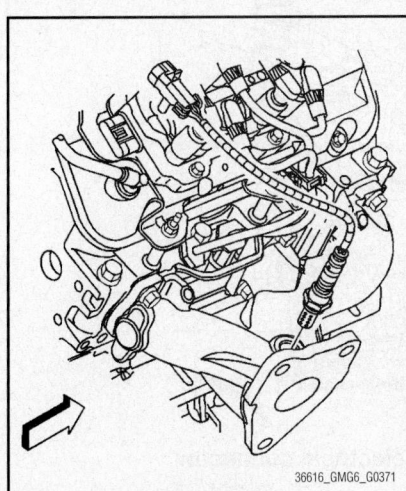

36616_GMG6_G0371

Fig. 244 Removing the HO2S (bank 1 sensor 1)—3.9L engine

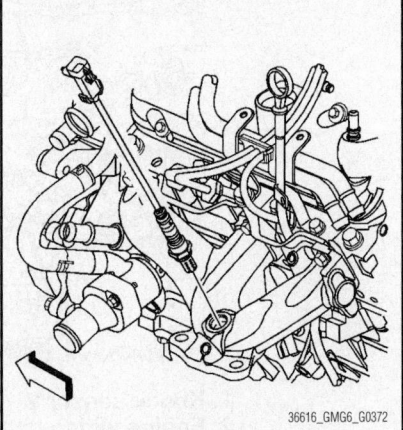

36616_GMG6_G0372

Fig. 245 Removing the HO2S (bank 2 sensor 1)—3.9L engine

The 3.5L and 3.9L engine Knock Sensor (KS) 1 is located at the rear of the engine, below the exhaust manifold, above the transaxle. The KS 2 is located at the front of the engine, above the starter.

The 3.6L engine Knock Sensor (KS) 1 is located on the center rear side of the engine block. The KS 2 is located on the center front side of the engine block.

REMOVAL & INSTALLATION

2.4L Engine

See Figure 246.

1. Disconnect the Knock Sensor (KS) electrical connector.
2. Remove the KS electrical connector clip from the oil level indicator tube bracket.
3. Remove the oil level indicator tube.
4. Remove the KS bolt.
5. Remove the KS.

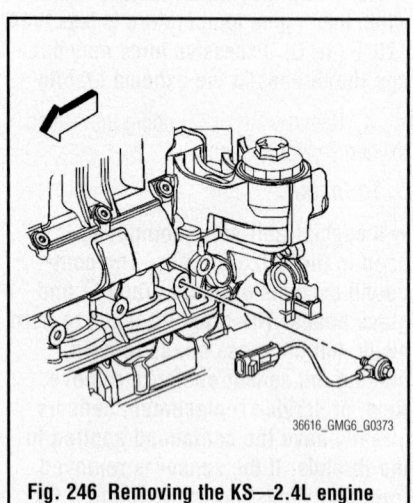

Fig. 246 Removing the KS—2.4L engine

To install:

➡ **Rotate the pigtail 90° from vertical before securing the fastener.**

6. Install the KS.
7. Install the KS bolt. Tighten the bolt to 18 ft. lbs. (25 Nm).
8. Connect the KS electrical connector.
9. Install the oil level indicator tube.
10. Install the KS electrical connector clip to the oil level indicator tube bracket.

3.5L & 3.9L Engines

Bank 1

See Figure 247.

1. Raise and support the vehicle.
2. Disconnect the engine wiring harness electrical connector from the knock sensor.

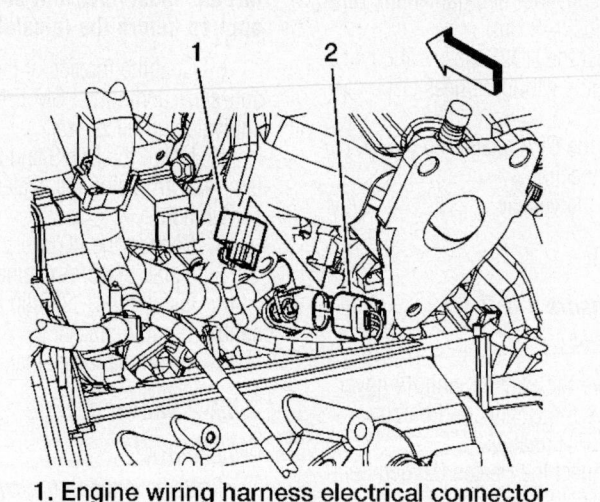

1. Engine wiring harness electrical connector
2. Knock sensor 1

36616_GMG6_G0374

Fig. 247 Disconnecting the KS 1—3.5L engine

3. Remove the knock sensor bolt and sensor.

To install:

4. Position the knock sensor to the engine block and install the knock sensor bolt and tighten to 18 ft. lbs. (25 Nm).
5. Connect the engine wiring harness electrical connector to the knock sensor.
6. Lower the vehicle.

Bank 2

See Figure 248.

1. Raise and support the vehicle.
2. Disconnect the engine wiring harness electrical connector from the knock sensor.

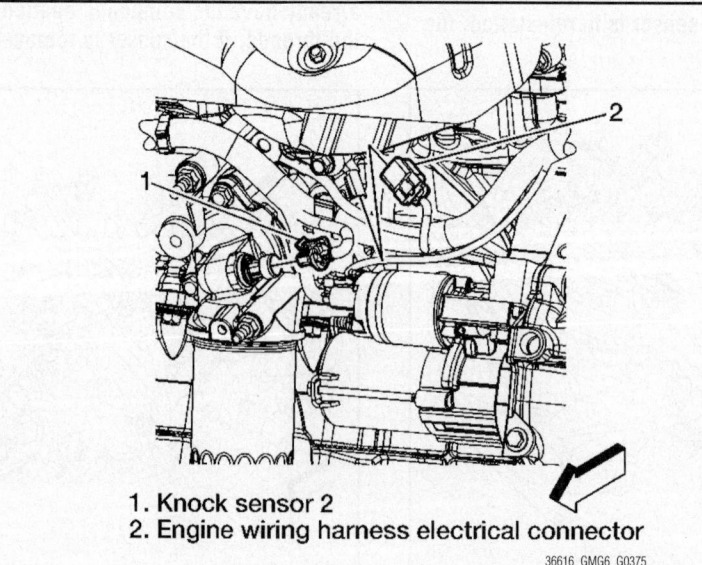

1. Knock sensor 2
2. Engine wiring harness electrical connector

36616_GMG6_G0375

Fig. 248 Disconnecting the KS 2—3.5L engine

3. Remove the knock sensor bolt and sensor.

To install:

4. Position the knock sensor to the engine block and install the knock sensor bolt.
5. Connect the engine wiring harness electrical connector to the knock sensor.
6. Lower the vehicle.

3.6L Engine

Bank 1

See Figures 249 and 250.

1. Remove the exhaust manifold lower heat shield.

1. Engine wiring harness electrical connector
2. Knock sensor 1

36616_GMG6_G0376

Fig. 249 Disconnecting the KS 1—3.6L engine

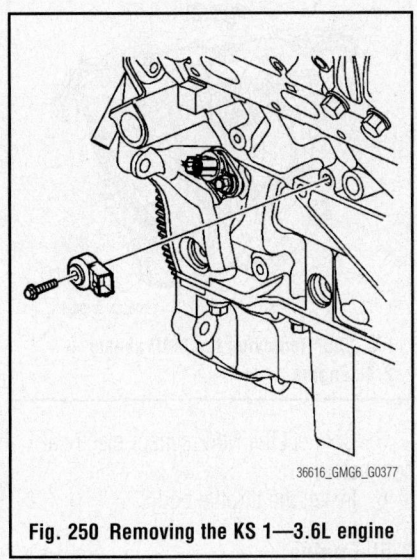

36616_GMG6_G0377

Fig. 250 Removing the KS 1—3.6L engine

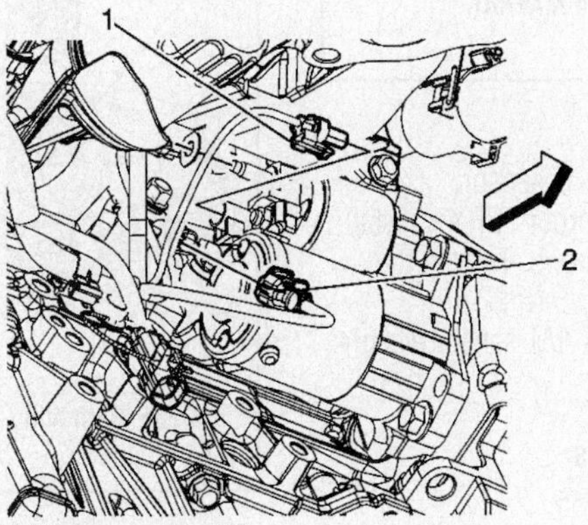

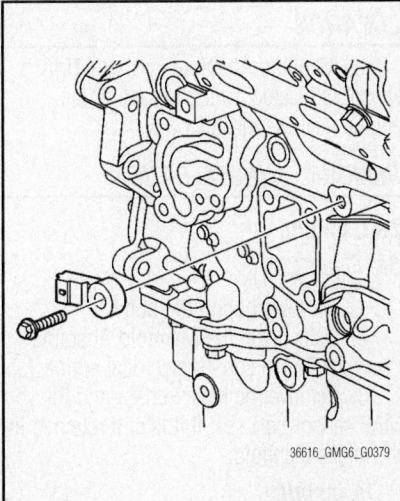

1. Knock sensor 2
2. Engine wiring harness electrical connector

36616_GMG6_G0378

Fig. 251 Disconnecting the KS 2—3.6L engine

2. Disconnect the engine wiring harness electrical connector from the bank 1 knock sensor.

3. Loosen the knock sensor bolt and remove the knock sensor.

To install:

Position the knock sensor and tighten the knock sensor bolt to 17 ft. lbs. (23 Nm).

Connect the engine wiring harness electrical connector to the bank 1 knock sensor.

Install the exhaust manifold lower heat shield.

Bank 2

See Figures 251 and 252.

1. Raise and support the vehicle.

2. Disconnect the engine wiring harness electrical connector from the bank 2 knock sensor.

36616_GMG6_G0379

Fig. 252 Removing the KS 2—3.6L engine

3. Loosen the knock sensor bolt and remove the knock sensor.

To install:

4. Position the knock sensor and tighten the knock sensor bolt to 17 ft. lbs. (23 Nm).

5. Connect the engine wiring harness electrical connector to the bank 2 knock sensor.

6. Lower the vehicle.

MALFUNCTION INDICATOR LIGHT (MIL)

RESET PROCEDURE

Here are 3 methods for clearing codes from the PCM memory:

• Use the Scan Tool (also clears Freeze Frame & Failure Records)

• If battery power to the PCM is removed (battery cable or PCM fuse), all current data (DTC, Freeze Frame, Fail Records, Statistical Filters and I/M Readiness Flags) will be cleared

• If the fault that caused a DTC to set has been corrected, the PCM will begin to count warm—up cycles. Once it has counted 40 warm—up cycles with no further faults detected, the DTC is cleared

MASS AIR FLOW (MAF)/INTAKE AIR TEMPERATURE (IAT) SENSOR

LOCATION

The Mass Air Flow (MAF)/Intake Air Temperature (IAT) sensor is located on the top right side of the engine, at the air cleaner.

REMOVAL & INSTALLATION

2.4L Engine

See Figure 253.

1. Disconnect the Mass Air Flow (MAF)/Intake Air Temperature (IAT) sensor electrical connector.

2. Using a tamper proof TORX®, remove the MAF/IAT sensor screws.

3. Remove the MAF/IAT sensor.

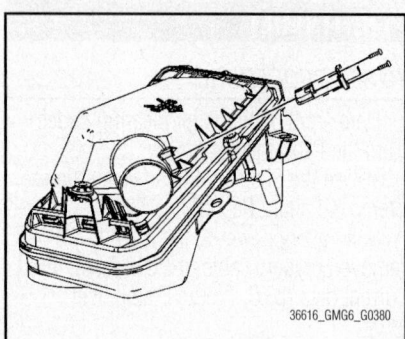

36616_GMG6_G0380

Fig. 253 Removing the MAF/IAT sensor—2.4L engine

To install:

4. Install the MAF/IAT sensor.

5. Using a tamper proof TORX®, install the MAF/IAT sensor screws. Tighten the screws to 5 inch lbs. (0.6 Nm).

6. Connect the MAF/IAT sensor electrical connector.

3.5L & 3.9L Engines

See Figures 254 and 255.

1. Remove the Positive Crankcase Ventilation (PCV) fresh air tube from the air cleaner intake duct.

2. Disconnect the Mass Air Flow (MAF) sensor electrical connector.

3. Loosen the clamps and remove the air cleaner intake duct with the MAF sensor from the throttle body and the air cleaner housing cover.

4. Loosen the clamp and remove the MAF sensor from the air cleaner intake duct.

To install:

5. Install the MAF sensor to the air cleaner intake duct. Tighten the clamp to 18 inch lbs. (2 Nm).

6. Install the air cleaner intake duct with the MAF sensor to the throttle body and the air cleaner housing cover. Tighten the clamps to 18 inch lbs. (2 Nm).

7. Connect the MAF sensor electrical connector.

8. Install the PCV fresh air tube to the air cleaner intake duct.

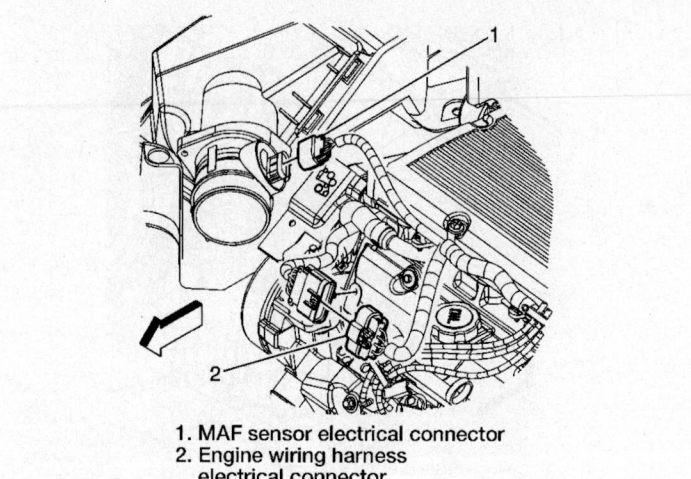

1. MAF sensor electrical connector
2. Engine wiring harness electrical connector

36616_GMG6_G0382

Fig. 254 Disconnecting the MAF sensor—3.5L engine

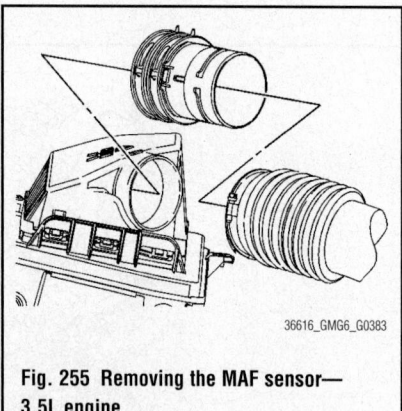

36616_GMG6_G0383

Fig. 255 Removing the MAF sensor—3.5L engine

9. Start and idle the engine.
10. Inspect the air intake duct for leaks.

MANIFOLD ABSOLUTE PRESSURE (MAP) SENSOR

LOCATION

The Manifold Absolute Pressure (MAP) sensor is located on the top left of the engine near the throttle body.

REMOVAL & INSTALLATION

2.4L Engine

See Figure 256.

1. Remove the throttle body.

2. Disconnect the Manifold Absolute Pressure (MAP) sensor electrical connector.

3. Remove the MAP sensor and the MAP sensor port seal if it is still retained in the intake manifold.

To install:

4. Install the MAP sensor with the port seal into the intake manifold.

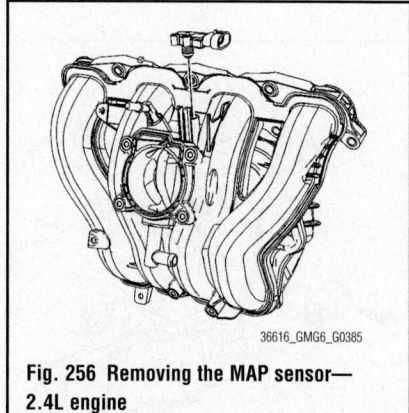

36616_GMG6_G0385

Fig. 256 Removing the MAP sensor—2.4L engine

5. Connect the MAP sensor electrical connector.

6. Install the throttle body.

3.5L Engine

See Figure 257.

1. Remove the intake manifold cover.

2. Disconnect the Manifold Absolute Pressure (MAP) sensor electrical connector.

3. Remove the MAP sensor attaching screw.

4. Remove the MAP sensor and MAP sensor seal from the upper intake manifold.

To install:

5. Install the MAP sensor and MAP sensor seal into the upper intake manifold.

6. Install the MAP sensor attaching screw and tighten to 57 inch lbs. (6.5 Nm).

7. Connect the MAP sensor electrical connector.

8. Install the intake manifold cover.

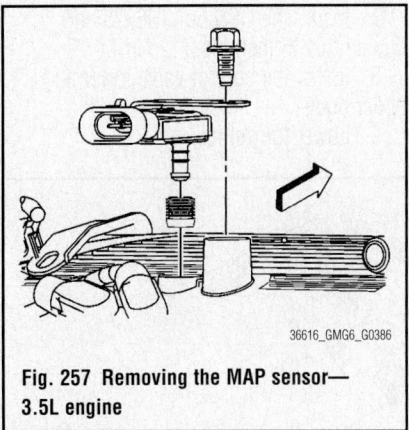

Fig. 257 Removing the MAP sensor—
3.5L engine

3.6L Engine

See Figure 258.

1. Remove the fuel injector sight shield.
2. Disconnect the engine wiring harness electrical connector from the Manifold Absolute Pressure (MAP) sensor.
3. Remove the MAP sensor bolt and sensor.

To install:

4. Lubricate the MAP sensor O-ring seal with clean engine oil.

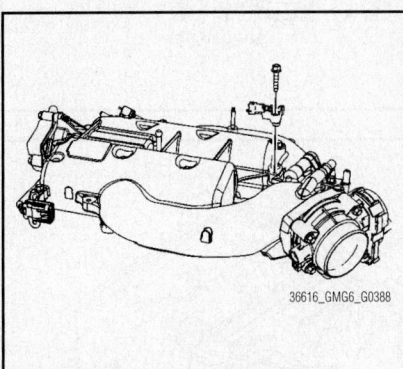

Fig. 258 Removing the MAP sensor—
3.6L engine

5. Install the MAP sensor and bolt and tighten the bolt to 89 inch lbs. (10 Nm).
6. Connect the engine wiring harness electrical connector to the MAP sensor.
7. Install the fuel injector sight shield.

3.9L Engine

See Figure 259.

1. Remove the intake manifold cover.
2. Disconnect the Manifold Absolute Pressure (MAP) sensor electrical connector.
3. Remove the spark plug wire clip from the intake manifold bracket, if necessary.
4. Remove the MAP sensor bolt.
5. Remove the MAP sensor and MAP sensor seal from the upper intake manifold.

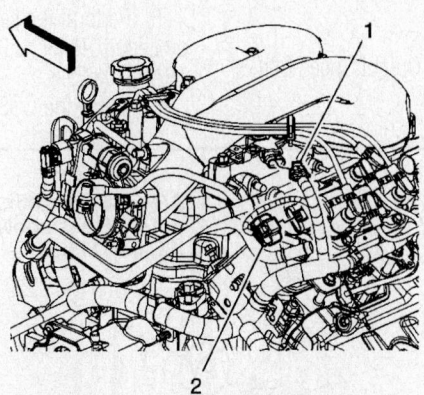

1. MAP sensor electrical connector
2. Engine wiring harness electrical connector

Fig. 259 Removing the MAP sensor—3.9L engine

To install:

6. Install the MAP sensor seal into the upper intake manifold.
7. Install the MAP sensor.
8. Install the MAP sensor bolt and tighten to 89 inch lbs. (10 Nm).
9. If required, install the spark plug wire clip to the intake manifold bracket.
10. Connect the MAP sensor electrical connector.
11. Install the intake manifold cover.

OUTPUT SHAFT SPEED (OSS) SENSOR

REMOVAL & INSTALLATION

4T45-E

See Figure 260.

1. Rotate the transmission so that the case side cover is facing upward in order to drain the transmission fluid through the stub shaft end of the transmission.
2. Remove the speed sensor stud.
3. Remove the speed sensor assembly. Pull the speed sensor assembly straight out from the transmission case in order to prevent damage to the case bore.
4. Remove the O-ring.
5. Rotate the transmission with the oil pan facing upward.

To install:

6. Inspect the vehicle speed sensor for damage to the sensor, the electrical connector, or the O-ring.
7. Clean and dry the vehicle speed sensor.
8. Install the O-ring onto the speed sensor.
9. Install the speed sensor into the transmission case.
10. Install the speed sensor stud. Tighten the speed sensor stud to 9 ft. lbs. (12 Nm).

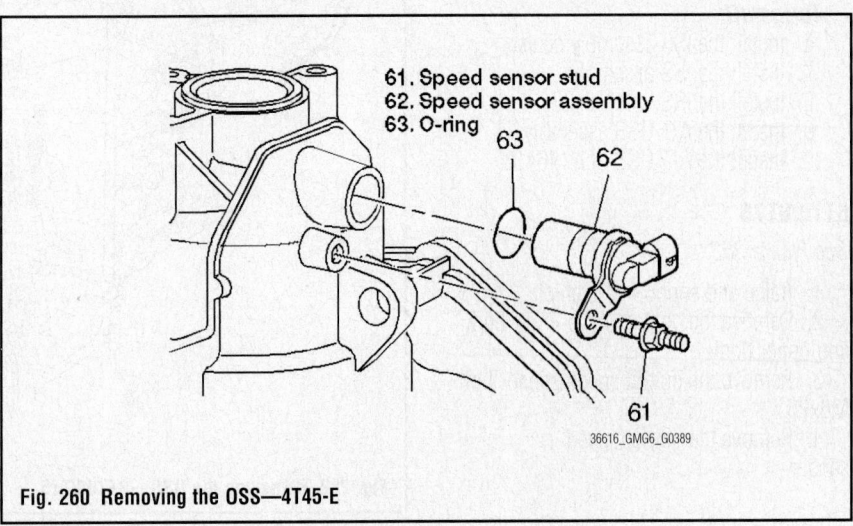

61. Speed sensor stud
62. Speed sensor assembly
63. O-ring

Fig. 260 Removing the OSS—4T45-E

6T40/6T45

See Figure 261.

1. Remove the A/T Output Speed Sensor (OSS) bolt M6x18.

To install:

5. Perform the service fast learn adapt procedure. Refer to PROGRAMMING in TRANSAXLE.

6. Install the OSS.

7. Install the OSS bolt M6x25 and tighten to 106 inch lbs. (12 Nm).

8. Install the control valve lower and upper body.

9. Lower the vehicle.

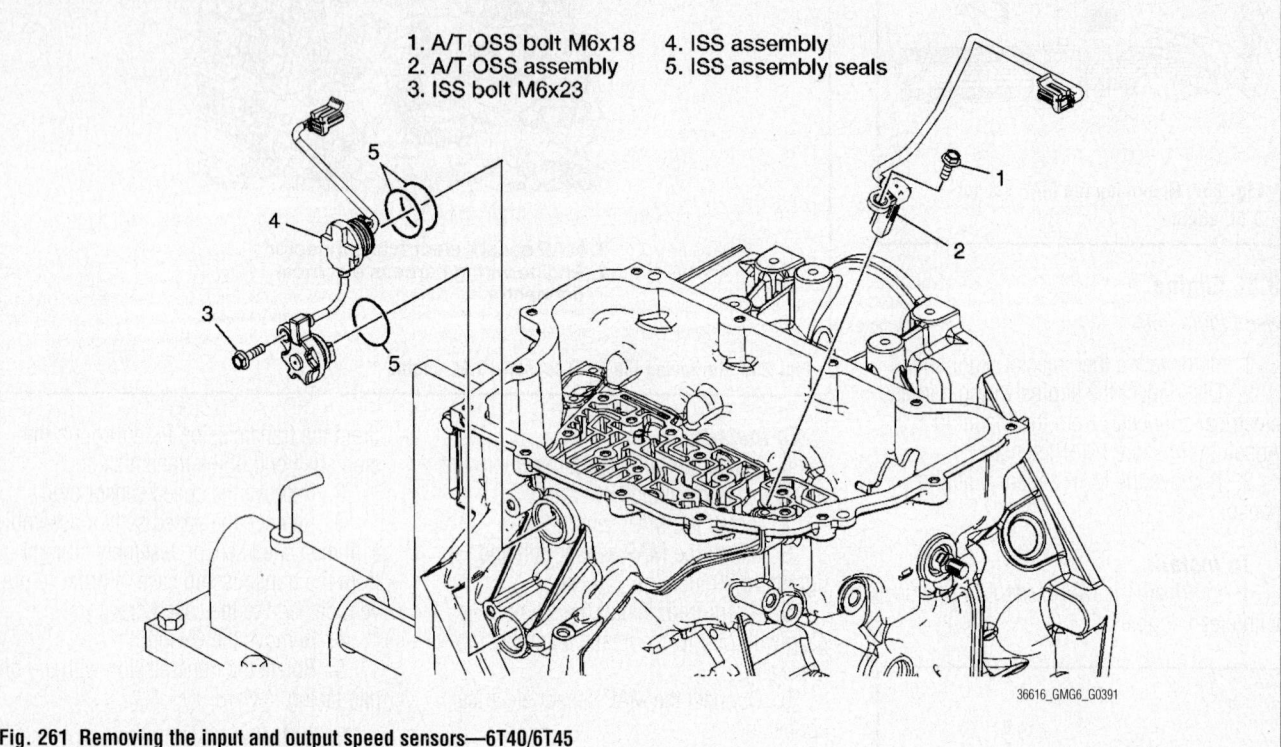

1. A/T OSS bolt M6x18
2. A/T OSS assembly
3. ISS bolt M6x23
4. ISS assembly
5. ISS assembly seals

36616_GMG6_G0391

Fig. 261 Removing the input and output speed sensors—6T40/6T45

2. Remove the A/T OSS assembly.
3. Remove the Input Speed Sensor (ISS) bolt M6x23.
4. Remove the ISS assembly. Compress the locking tabs on the plug to release it from the case and to avoid damaging the retainers.
5. Remove the ISS assembly seals. Discard the seals as they are not reusable.

To install:

6. Install the ISS assembly seals.
7. Install the ISS assembly.
8. Install the ISS bolt M6x23.
9. Install the A/T OSS assembly.
10. Install the A/T OSS bolt M6x18.

6T70/6T75

See Figure 262.

1. Raise and support the vehicle.
2. Remove the control valve lower body and upper body.
3. Remove the output speed sensor bolt M6x25.
4. Remove the output speed sensor.

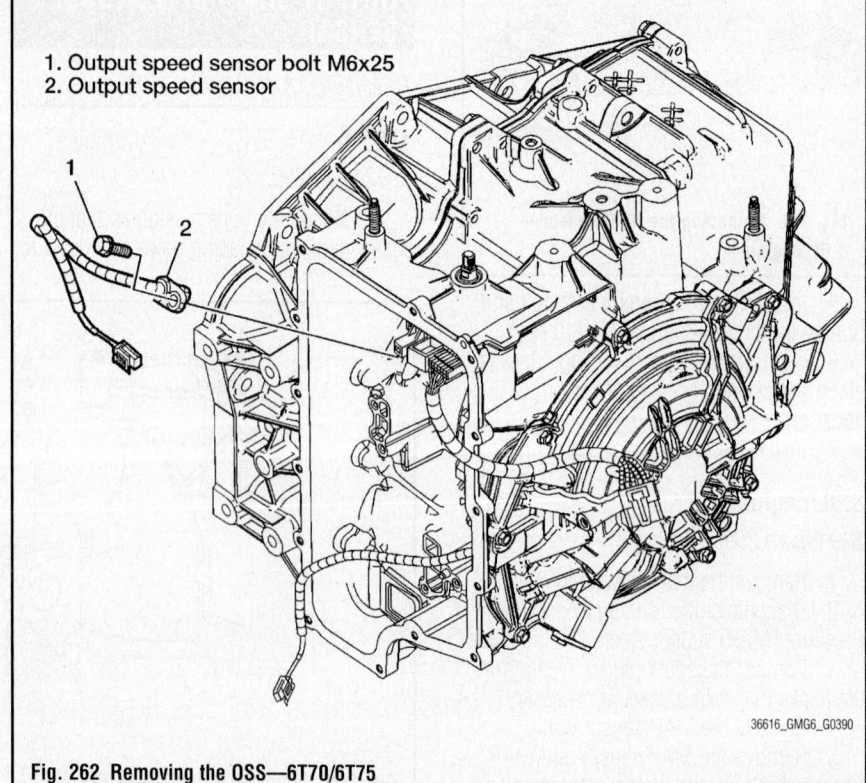

1. Output speed sensor bolt M6x25
2. Output speed sensor

36616_GMG6_G0390

Fig. 262 Removing the OSS—6T70/6T75

VEHICLE SPEED SENSOR (VSS)

REMOVAL & INSTALLATION

4T45-E

See Figure 263.

✳✳ WARNING

Ensure that the vehicle is properly supported and squarely positioned. To help avoid personal injury when a vehicle is on a hoist, provide additional support for the vehicle on the opposite end from which the components are being removed.

1. Position the vehicle on a hoist and raise the vehicle.
2. Disconnect the Vehicle Speed Sensor (VSS) electrical connector.

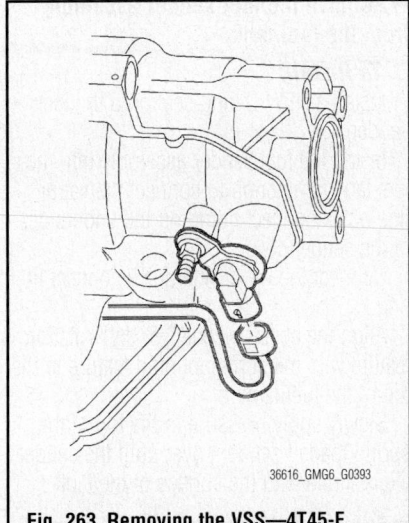

36616_GMG6_G0393

Fig. 263 Removing the VSS—4T45-E

3. Remove the VSS electrical harness retainer from the VSS stud.
4. Remove the VSS stud.
5. Remove the output VSS from the transmission case.

➡**Inspect the O-ring for damage and replace if necessary.**

6. Remove the O-ring from the VSS.

To install:

7. Install the O-ring onto the VSS.
8. Install the output VSS into the transmission case.
9. Install the VSS stud and tighten the stud to 106 inch lbs. (12 Nm).
10. Install the VSS electrical harness retainer to the VSS stud.
11. Connect the VSS electrical connector.
12. Lower the vehicle.

4T65-E

See Figures 264 and 265.

1. Raise and support the vehicle.
2. Remove the right front tire and wheel.
3. Disconnect the Vehicle Speed Sensor (VSS) electrical connector.
4. Remove the VSS bolt.
5. Remove the VSS from the extension case.
6. Remove the O-ring from the VSS.

To install:

7. Install the O-ring to the VSS.
8. Install the VSS.
9. Install the VSS bolt and tighten to 106 inch lbs. (12 Nm).
10. Connect the VSS electrical connector.
11. Install the right front tire and wheel
12. Lower the vehicle.

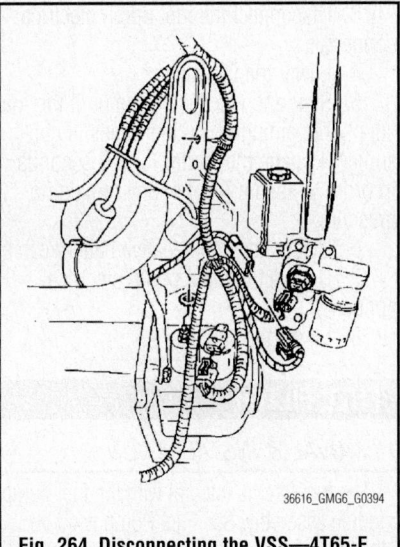

36616_GMG6_G0394

Fig. 264 Disconnecting the VSS—4T65-E

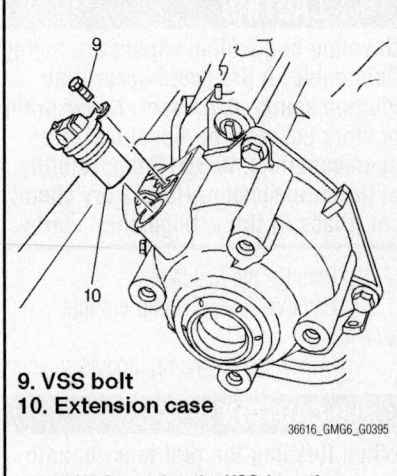

9. VSS bolt
10. Extension case

36616_GMG6_G0395

Fig. 265 Removing the VSS from the extension case—4T65-E

FUEL

GASOLINE FUEL INJECTION SYSTEM

FUEL SYSTEM SERVICE PRECAUTIONS

Safety is the most important factor when performing not only fuel system maintenance but any type of maintenance. Failure to conduct maintenance and repairs in a safe manner may result in serious personal injury or death. Maintenance and testing of the vehicle's fuel system components can be accomplished safely and effectively by adhering to the following rules and guidelines.

• To avoid the possibility of fire and personal injury, always disconnect the negative battery cable unless the repair or test procedure requires that battery voltage be applied.

• Always relieve the fuel system pressure prior to disconnecting any fuel system component (injector, fuel rail, pressure regulator, etc.), fitting or fuel line connection. Exercise extreme caution whenever relieving fuel system pressure to avoid exposing skin, face and eyes to fuel spray. Please be advised that fuel under pressure may penetrate the skin or any part of the body that it contacts.

• Always place a shop towel or cloth around the fitting or connection prior to loosening to absorb any excess fuel due to spillage. Ensure that all fuel spillage (should it occur) is quickly removed from engine surfaces. Ensure that all fuel soaked cloths or towels are deposited into a suitable waste container.

• Always keep a dry chemical (Class B) fire extinguisher near the work area.

• Do not allow fuel spray or fuel vapors to come into contact with a spark or open flame.

• Always use a back-up wrench when loosening and tightening fuel line connection fittings. This will prevent unnecessary stress and torsion to fuel line piping.

• Always replace worn fuel fitting O-rings with new. Do not substitute fuel hose or equivalent where fuel pipe is installed.

Before servicing the vehicle, make sure to also refer to the precautions in the beginning of this section as well.

RELIEVING FUEL SYSTEM PRESSURE

1. Loosen the fuel fill cap in order to relieve the tank pressure. Do not tighten at this time.
2. Raise and support the vehicle.

3. Disconnect the fuel pump electrical connector.

4. Lower the vehicle.

5. Start and run the engine until the fuel supply remaining in the fuel pipes is consumed. Engage the starter for 3.0 seconds in order to assure relief of any remaining pressure.

6. Disconnect the negative battery cable.

7. Connect the fuel pump electrical connector.

8. Lower the vehicle.

FUEL FILTER

REMOVAL & INSTALLATION

The fuel filter is integral with the fuel pump module assembly. See Fuel Pump Module.

FUEL SYSTEM CLEANING

✳✳ CAUTION

Gasoline or gasoline vapors are highly flammable. A fire could occur if an ignition source is present. Never drain or store gasoline or diesel fuel in an open container, due to the possibility of fire or explosion. Have a dry chemical (Class B) fire extinguisher nearby.

1. Remove the fuel tank.

2. Remove the fuel pump module assembly.

3. Inspect the fuel pump module strainer.

✳✳ CAUTION

When flushing the fuel tank, handle the fuel and water mixture as a hazardous material. Handle the fuel and water in accordance with all applicable local, state, and federal laws and regulations

4. Flush the fuel tank with hot water.

5. Pour the water out of the fuel sender assembly opening in the fuel tank. Rock the fuel tank in order to be sure that the removal of the water from the fuel tank is complete.

6. Allow the tank to dry completely before reassembly.

7. Disconnect the fuel feed pipe at the engine fuel rail.

➡**Only use oil-free compressed air to blow out the fuel pipes.**

8. Clean the fuel pipes by applying air pressure in the opposite direction of the fuel flow.

9. Connect the fuel feed pipe to the engine fuel rail.

10. Install the fuel pump module assembly.

11. Install the fuel tank.

FUEL PUMP

REMOVAL & INSTALLATION

Fuel Tank Pump Module

2.4L & 3.5L Engines

See Figure 266.

✳✳ WARNING

In order to reduce the risk of fire and personal injury that may result from a fuel leak, always replace the fuel sender gasket when reinstalling the fuel sender assembly.

1. Remove the fuel tank.

2. Disconnect the fuel pressure sensor and sender electrical connections.

3. Disconnect the Evaporative Emission (EVAP) vapor line quick connect fittings.

4. Disengage the fuel feed line from the retaining features built into the fuel tank.

✳✳ CAUTION

Avoid damaging the lock ring. Use only the fuel sender lock ring wrench (J-45722) to prevent damage to the lock ring.

✳✳ CAUTION

Do Not handle the fuel sender assembly by the fuel pipes. The amount of leverage generated by handling the fuel pipes could damage the joints.

➡**Do NOT use impact tools. Significant force will be required to release the lock ring. The use of a hammer and screwdriver is not recommended. Secure the fuel tank in order to prevent fuel tank rotation. Use the fuel sender**

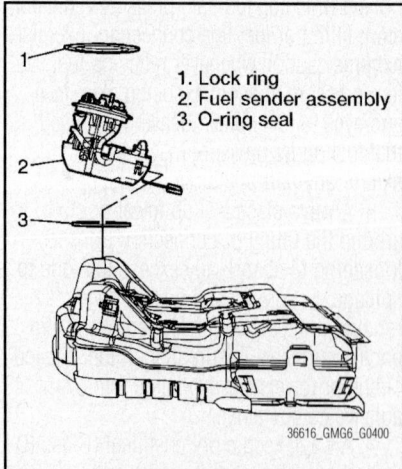

1. Lock ring
2. Fuel sender assembly
3. O-ring seal

36616_GMG6_G0400

Fig. 266 Removing the fuel sender assembly from the fuel tank—2.4L engine

lock ring wrench J-45722 and a long breaker-bar in order to unlock the fuel sender lock ring.

➡**The fuel sender assembly may spring up from its position. When removing the fuel sender assembly from the fuel tank, be aware that the reservoir bucket is full of fuel. It must be tipped slightly during the removal to avoid damage to the float. Discard the sender assembly o-ring and replace it with a new one. Carefully discard the fuel in the reservoir bucket into an approved container.**

➡**Raise the fuel sender assembly out of the tank far enough to access the vapor line quick connect fitting on the underside of the sender cover.**

➡**Disconnect the vapor line quick connect fitting.**

➡**Remove the fuel sender assembly from the fuel tank.**

To install:

Install a NEW O-ring seal onto the fuel sender.

Install the fuel sender assembly into the fuel tank far enough to connect the vapor line quick connect fitting on the underside of the sender cover.

Connect the vapor line quick connect fitting.

Align the cover "paddle" or anti-rotation feature with the corresponding feature in the top of the fuel tank.

Slowly apply pressure to the top of the spring loaded sender cover until the sender aligns flush with the surface of the tank.

➡**Some lock rings were manufactured with "DO NOT REUSE" stamped into them. These lock rings may be reused if they are not damaged or warped.**

➡**Inspect the lock ring for damage due to improper removal or installation procedures. If damage is found, install the NEW lock ring. Check the lock ring for flatness.**

➡**Always replace the fuel sender seal when installing the fuel sender assembly. Replace the lock ring if necessary. DO NOT apply any type of lubrication in the seal groove. Ensure the lock ring is installed with the correct side facing upward. A correctly installed lock ring will only turn in a clockwise direction.**

5. Use the J-45722 wrench in order to install the fuel sender lock ring. Turn the fuel sender lock ring in a clockwise direction.

6. Turn the lock ring until the ring seats on the second detent.

7. Engage the fuel feed line to the retaining features built into the fuel tank.

8. Connect the EVAP vapor line quick connect fittings.

9. Connect the fuel pressure sensor and sender electrical connections.

10. Install the fuel tank.

11. Lower the vehicle.

12. Refill the tank.

13. Connect the negative battery cable.

14. Inspect for fuel leaks through the following steps:

a. Turn the ignition to the ON position for 2 seconds.

b. Turn the ignition to the OFF position for 10 seconds.

c. Turn the ignition to the ON position.

d. Inspect for fuel leaks.

FUEL RAIL & INJECTORS

REMOVAL & INSTALLATION

2.4L Engine

See Figure 267.

✷✷ CAUTION

Observe all applicable safety precautions when working around fuel. Whenever servicing the fuel system, always work in a well ventilated area. Do not allow fuel spray or vapors to come in contact with a spark or open flame. Keep a dry chemical fire extinguisher near the work area. Always keep fuel in a container specifically designed for fuel storage; also, always properly seal fuel containers to avoid the possibility of fire or explosion.

1. Relieve the fuel system pressure.

2. Remove the air cleaner outlet duct.

3. Disconnect the fuel feed line quick connect fitting from the fuel rail.

4. Disconnect the engine wiring harness electrical connector from the fuel injector wiring harness electrical connector.

5. Disconnect the fuel injector wiring harness electrical from the Manifold Absolute Pressure (MAP) sensor.

6. Remove the engine wiring harness clips from the fuel rail tabs.

7. Remove the fuel rail bolts.

➡**Use care when removing the fuel rail assembly in order to prevent damage to the fuel injector spray tips.**

8. Pull the fuel rail back and upward in order to release the fuel injectors from the cylinder head ports.

9. Remove the fuel rail.

➡**The fuel injector tip insulators may be located on the injector or may still be located in the cylinder head. Either way, ensure that all 4 injector tip insulators are removed and discarded.**

10. Remove and discard the fuel injector tip insulators.

11. Disconnect the fuel injector wiring harness electrical connectors from the fuel injectors.

12. Remove the fuel injector wiring harness clips from the fuel rail.

13. Remove the fuel injector wiring harness from the fuel rail.

14. Remove the fuel injectors, if necessary.

To install:

15. Install the fuel injectors, if necessary.

16. Install the fuel injector wiring harness clips to the fuel rail.

17. Connect the fuel injector wiring harness electrical connectors to the fuel injectors.

18. Lubricate the NEW fuel injector tip insulators with clean engine oil.

19. Install the NEW fuel injector tip insulators to the cylinder head.

20. Lubricate the fuel injector O-rings with clean engine oil.

21. With the fuel injectors positioned downward, lower the fuel injectors into the cylinder head ports.

22. Carefully push down on the fuel rail in order to insert the injectors into the cylinder head ports.

23. Install the fuel rail bolts and tighten to 89 inch lbs. (10 Nm).

24. Install the engine wiring harness clips to the fuel rail tabs.

25. Connect the fuel injector wiring harness electrical to the MAP sensor.

26. Connect the engine wiring harness electrical connector to the fuel injector wiring harness electrical connector.

27. Connect the fuel feed line quick connect fitting to the fuel rail.

28. Install the air cleaner outlet duct.

29. Connect the negative battery cable.

30. Inspect for fuel leaks using the following procedure

• Turn ON the ignition, with the engine OFF for 2 seconds.

• Turn OFF the ignition for 10 seconds.

• Turn ON the ignition.

• Inspect for fuel leaks.

3.5L Engine

See Figure 268.

An 8-digit identification number is stamped on the fuel rail. Refer to this number if servicing or part replacement is required.

1. Remove the engine fuel feed pipe from the fuel rail.

✷✷ WARNING

In order to reduce the risk of fire and personal injury that may result from a fuel leak, always install the fuel injector O-rings in the proper position. If the upper and lower O-rings are different colors (black and brown), be sure to install the black O-ring in the upper position and the brown O-ring in the lower position on the fuel injector. The O-rings are the same size but are made of different materials.

✷✷ CAUTION

Cap the fittings and plug the holes when servicing the fuel system in order to prevent dirt and other contaminants from entering the open pipes and passages.

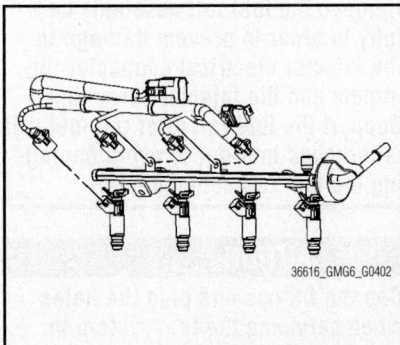

Fig. 267 Removing the fuel injector wiring harness from the fuel rail—2.4L engine

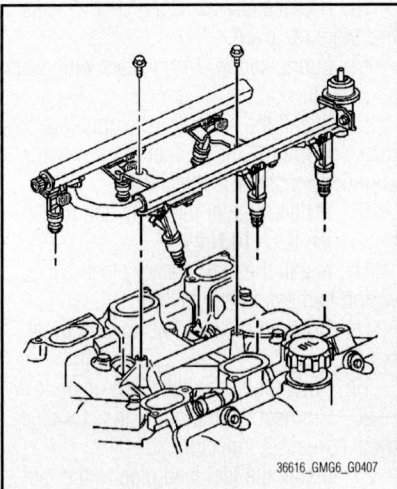

Fig. 268 Removing the fuel rail assembly—3.5L engine

2. Relieve fuel system pressure.

3. Remove the upper intake manifold.

4. Disconnect the main injector harness electrical connector.

5. Disconnect the main fuel injector electrical harness connector.

6. Pull up the lock release of the fuel injector electrical connectors.

7. Depress the lock tabs and disconnect the fuel injector electrical connectors.

8. Remove the fuel injector electrical wiring harness from the fuel rail.

9. Remove the fuel rail bolts.

10. Remove the fuel rail assembly.

11. Remove the fuel injector O-ring seal from the spray tip end of each injector.

12. Remove and discard O-rings if damaged.

To install:

> ### ✳✳ CAUTION
> Use care when servicing the fuel system components, especially the fuel injector electrical connectors, the fuel injector tips, and the injector O-rings. Plug the inlet and the outlet ports of the fuel rail in order to prevent contamination.

> ### ✳✳ CAUTION
> Do not use compressed air to clean the fuel rail assembly as this may damage the fuel rail components.

> ### ✳✳ CAUTION
> Do not immerse the fuel rail assembly in a solvent bath in order to prevent damage to the fuel rail assembly.

13. Replace any damaged O-ring seals that were removed.

14. Lubricate the O-ring seals with clean engine oil.

15. Install the fuel rail assembly into the intake manifold. Tilt the fuel rail assembly slightly to install the injectors.

16. Install the fuel rail bolts and tighten to 89 inch lbs. (10 Nm).

17. Install the fuel injector electrical wiring harness to the fuel rail.

18. Connect the fuel injector electrical connectors.

19. Push the slide locks into position.

20. Connect the main fuel injector electrical harness connector.

21. Install the fuel feed pipe to the fuel rail.

22. Install the upper pontake manifold.

23. Connect the negative battery cable.

24. Inspect for fuel leaks with the following procedure:
- Turn ON the ignition, with the engine OFF for 2 seconds.
- Turn OFF the ignition for 10 seconds.
- Turn ON the ignition.
- Inspect for fuel leaks.

3.6L Engine

See Figures 269 through 271.

> ### ✳✳ CAUTION
> Observe all applicable safety precautions when working around fuel. Whenever servicing the fuel system, always work in a well ventilated area. Do not allow fuel spray or vapors to come in contact with a spark or open flame. Keep a dry chemical fire extinguisher near the work area. Always keep fuel in a container specifically designed for fuel storage; also, always properly seal fuel containers to avoid the possibility of fire or explosion.

1. Remove the fuel injector sight shield.

2. Disconnect the engine wiring harness electrical connector from the fuel injector wiring harness electrical connector.

3. Disconnect the fuel feed pipe quick connect fitting from the fuel rail.

4. Remove the upper intake manifold.

> ### ✳✳ WARNING
> Wear safety glasses when using compressed air in order to prevent eye injury. Use compressed air in order to remove any debris from the around the area where the fuel injectors enter the lower intake manifold. Remove the fuel rail bolts.

> ### ✳✳ CAUTION
> Remove the fuel rail assembly carefully in order to prevent damage to the injector electrical connector terminals and the injector spray tips. Support the fuel rail after the fuel rail is removed in order to avoid damaging the fuel rail components.

> ### ✳✳ CAUTION
> Cap the fittings and plug the holes when servicing the fuel system in order to prevent dirt and other contaminants from entering open pipes and passages.

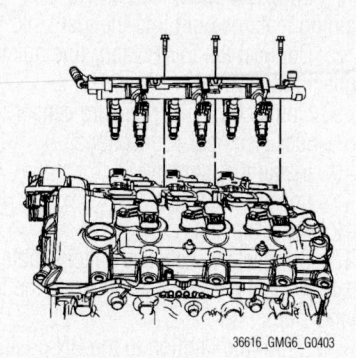

Fig. 269 Removing the fuel rail with fuel injectors from the lower intake manifold— 3.6L engine

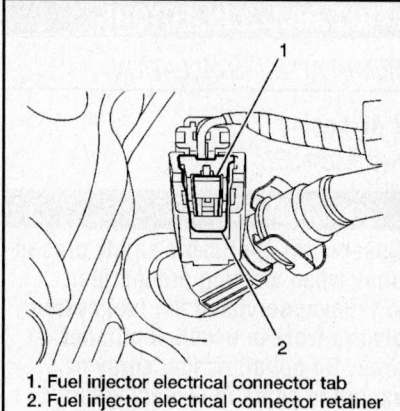

1. Fuel injector electrical connector tab
2. Fuel injector electrical connector retainer

36616_GMG6_G0404

Fig. 270 Disconnecting the fuel injector electrical connector—3.6L engine

5. Remove the fuel rail with fuel injectors from the lower intake manifold.

6. Lift up the fuel injector electrical connector retainer.

7. Push in the fuel injector electrical connector tab in order to disconnect the connector from the injector.

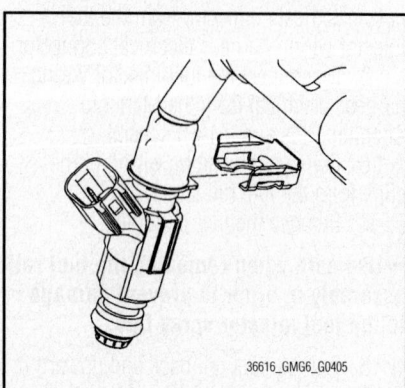

36616_GMG6_G0405

Fig. 271 Installing the fuel injector retaining clip—3.6L engine

8. Remove the fuel injector retainer clip.

9. Remove the fuel injector.

10. Remove and discard the fuel injector seals.

To install:

11. Install NEW fuel injector seals.

12. Install the fuel injector.

13. Install the fuel injector retainer clip

14. Install the fuel injector electrical connector.

15. Push down on the fuel injector electrical connector retainer, securing the electrical connector.

16. Install the fuel rail with fuel injectors to the lower intake manifold.

17. Install the fuel rail bolts and tighten to 89 inch lbs. (10 Nm).

18. Install the upper intake manifold.

19. Connect the fuel feed pipe quick connect fitting to the fuel rail.

20. Connect the engine wiring harness electrical connector (1) to the fuel injector wiring harness electrical connector.

21. Install the fuel injector sight shield.

3.9L Engine

See Figures 272 through 274.

An 8-digit identification number is stamped on the fuel rail. Refer to this number if servicing or part replacement is required.

❈❈ WARNING

In order to reduce the risk of fire and personal injury that may result from a fuel leak, always install the fuel injector O-rings in the proper position. If the upper and lower O-rings are different colors (black and brown), be sure to install the black O-ring in the upper position and the brown O-ring in the lower position on the fuel injector. The O-rings are the same size but are made of different materials.

❈❈ CAUTION

Cap the fittings and plug the holes when servicing the fuel system in order to prevent dirt and other contaminants from entering the open pipes and passages.

➡If the fuel injectors are found to be leaking, the engine oil may be contaminated with fuel.

1. Disconnect the fuel feed pipe from the fuel rail.

2. Disconnect any remaining electrical connectors.

3. Remove the upper intake manifold.

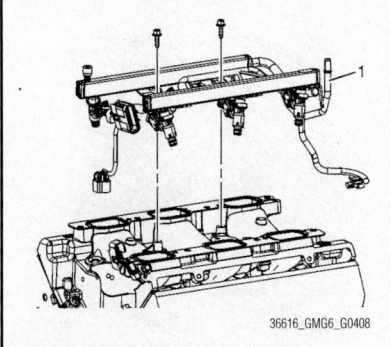

Fig. 272 Removing the fuel rail—3.9L engine

4. Remove the fuel injector harness connector bracket bolt from the intake manifold.

5. Disconnect the Camshaft Position (CMP) sensor electrical connector.

6. Remove the fuel rail bolts.

7. Remove the fuel rail.

8. Remove and discard the O-rings from the spray tip end of each injector.

❈❈ CAUTION

Use care in removing the fuel injectors in order to prevent damage to the fuel injector electrical connector pins or the fuel injector nozzles. Do not immerse the fuel injector in any type of cleaner. The fuel injector is an electrical component and may be damaged by this cleaning method.

9. Remove the fuel injector retaining clip, if required.

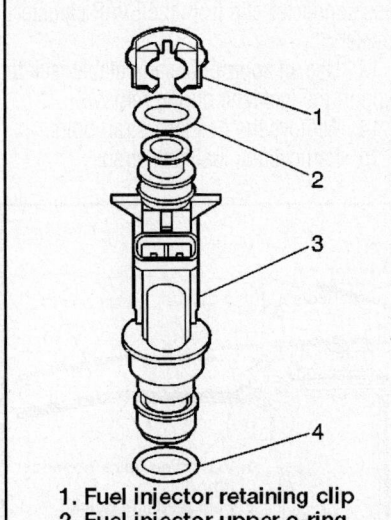

1. Fuel injector retaining clip
2. Fuel injector upper o-ring
3. Fuel injector
4. Fuel injector lower o-ring

Fig. 273 Removing the fuel injector—3.9L engine

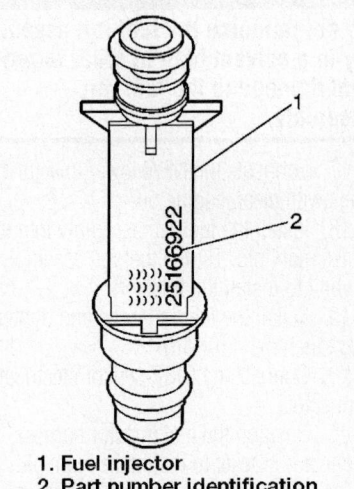

1. Fuel injector
2. Part number identification

Fig. 274 Locating the fuel injector part identification number—3.9L engine

10. Remove the fuel injector from the fuel rail, if required.

11. Remove and discard the fuel injector upper O-ring.

To install:

➡DO NOT reuse the fuel injector O-ring seals. Install NEW O-ring seals during assembly.

➡Ensure to use the correct part number when ordering the replacement fuel injectors.

12. The fuel injector is stamped with a part number identification.

13. Lubricate the NEW injector O-rings with clean engine oil.

14. Install the NEW fuel injector upper O-ring.

15. Install the fuel injector to the fuel rail, if required.

16. Install the fuel injector retaining clip, if required.

❈❈ CAUTION

Use care when servicing the fuel system components, especially the fuel injector electrical connectors, the fuel injector tips, and the injector O-rings. Plug the inlet and the outlet ports of the fuel rail in order to prevent contamination.

❈❈ CAUTION

Do not use compressed air to clean the fuel rail assembly as this may damage the fuel rail components.

Do not immerse the fuel rail assembly in a solvent bath in order to prevent damage to the fuel rail assembly.

17. Lubricate the NEW lower injector O-rings with clean engine oil.

18. Install the fuel rail assembly into the intake manifold. Tilt the fuel rail assembly slightly to install the injectors.

19. Install the fuel rail bolts and tighten to 89 inch lbs. (10 Nm).

20. Connect the CMP sensor electrical connector.

21. Position the fuel injector harness connector bracket to the intake manifold.

22. Install the fuel injector harness connector bracket bolt and tighten to 71 inch lbs. (8 Nm).

23. Install the upper intake manifold.

24. Connect any remaining electrical connectors.

25. Connect the fuel feed pipe to the fuel rail.

26. Inspect for fuel leaks with the following procedure:
- Turn ON the ignition, with the engine OFF for 2 seconds.
- Turn OFF the ignition for 10 seconds.
- Turn ON the ignition.
- Inspect for fuel leaks.

FUEL TANK

REMOVAL & INSTALLATION

✳✳ CAUTION

Observe all applicable safety precautions when working around fuel. Whenever servicing the fuel system, always work in a well ventilated area. Do not allow fuel spray or vapors to come in contact with a spark or open flame. Keep a dry chemical fire extinguisher near the work area. Always keep fuel in a container specifically designed for fuel storage; also, always properly seal fuel containers to avoid the possibility of fire or explosion.

2.4L Engine

See Figures 275 and 276.

1. Relieve the fuel system pressure.
2. Drain the fuel tank.
3. Raise and support the vehicle.
4. Loosen the fuel fill pipe hose clamp at the fuel tank.

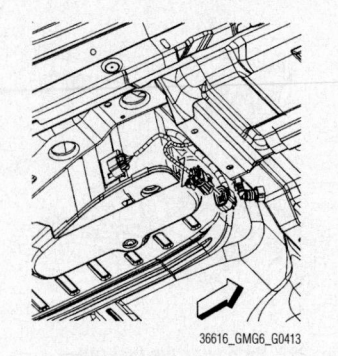

Fig. 275 Disconnecting the fuel tank jumper electrical connector—2.4L engine

5. Disconnect and reposition the rear stabilizer shaft.

6. Disconnect the vapor recirculation line quick connect fitting.

7. Disconnect the fuel fill pipe hose from the fuel tank.

8. Release the exhaust pipe insulators from the underbody hangers.

9. Release the muffler insulator from the underbody hanger and slowly lower the exhaust to rest on a tall jackstand. If this is not possible, remove the rear half of the exhaust system at the take down flange.

10. If applicable, disengage the rear Antilock Brake System (ABS) wiring harness connector clip from the side of the EVAP canister bracket.

11. Disconnect the fuel tank jumper electrical connector from the underbody wiring harness.

12. Disengage the underbody wiring harness connector clip from the EVAP canister bracket.

13. Use an appropriate adjustable jack to support the fuel tank during removal.

14. Remove the fuel tank strap bolts.

15. Remove the fuel tank straps.

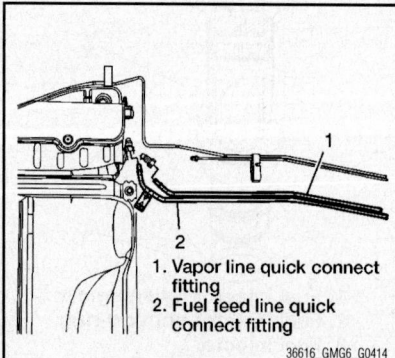

1. Vapor line quick connect fitting
2. Fuel feed line quick connect fitting

Fig. 276 Disconnecting the fuel feed and vapor line quick connect fittings—2.4L engine

16. Disconnect the fuel feed and vapor line quick connect fittings.

17. Cap or plug the fuel feed and vapor lines in order to prevent fuel loss and/or system contamination.

18. In order to clear the exhaust pipe, slowly lower the right side of the fuel tank.

19. Once the tank is clear of the right frame rail, remove the fuel tank down and forward toward the right side of the vehicle.

20. If the fuel tank is being replaced, disconnect and remove the fuel tank electrical harness.

21. If the fuel tank is being replaced, perform the following:
   a. Disconnect and remove the fuel tank vapor line.
   b. Remove the EVAP canister.
   c. Remove the EVAP canister vent solenoid valve.
   d. Remove the fuel pump module.

To install:

22. If the fuel tank is being replaced, perform the following:
   a. Install the fuel pump module.
   b. Install the EVAP canister vent solenoid valve.
   c. Install the he EVAP canister.
   d. Install and connect the fuel tank vapor line.

23. If the fuel tank is being replaced, install and connect the fuel tank electrical harness.

24. Begin to install the left side of the fuel tank over the exhaust pipe.

25. Raise the right side of the fuel tank into position inboard of the right frame rail. Use care in feeding the fuel feed, EVAP vapor line, and the fuel sender electrical harness over the exhaust system.

26. Completely raise and install the fuel tank into position.

➡**Ensure that the strap marked with the "L" is installed on the left side and the strap marked "R" is installed on the right side.**

27. Install the fuel tank straps.

28. Install the fuel tank strap bolts and tighten to 15 ft. lbs. (20 Nm).

29. Remove the adjustable jack from under the fuel tank.

30. Remove the caps or plugs from the fuel feed and vapor lines.

31. Connect the fuel feed and vapor line quick connect fittings.

32. Connect the fuel tank jumper electrical connector to the underbody wiring harness.

33. Engage the underbody wiring harness connector clip to the EVAP canister bracket.

34. If applicable, engage the rear ABS

wiring harness connector clip to the side of the EVAP canister bracket.

35. Raise the exhaust into position and install the muffler insulator to the underbody hanger.

36. Install the exhaust extension pipe insulators to the underbody hangers.

37. Connect the fuel fill pipe hose to the fuel tank.

38. Install the fuel fill pipe hose clamp and tighten to 35 inch lbs. (4 Nm).

39. Connect the vapor recirculation line quick connect fitting.

40. Position and connect the rear stabilizer shaft.

41. Lower the vehicle.

42. Refill the fuel tank.

43. Connect the negative battery cable.

44. Inspect for fuel leaks using the following procedure:

   a. Turn ON the ignition, with the engine OFF for 2 seconds.

   b. Turn OFF the ignition for 10 seconds.

   c. Turn ON the ignition, with the engine OFF.

   d. Inspect for fuel leaks.

IDLE SPEED

ADJUSTMENT

Idle speed is maintained by the Powertrain Control Module (PCM). No adjustment is necessary or possible.

THROTTLE BODY

REMOVAL & INSTALLATION

2.4L Engine
See Figure 277.

CAUTION

Do not use solvent of any type when cleaning the gasket surfaces on the intake manifold and the throttle body assembly, as damage to the gasket surfaces and throttle body assembly may result.

CAUTION

Use care in cleaning the gasket surfaces on the intake manifold and the throttle body assembly, as sharp tools may damage the gasket surfaces.

CAUTION

Do not use any solvent that contains Methyl Ethyl Ketone (MEK). This sol-

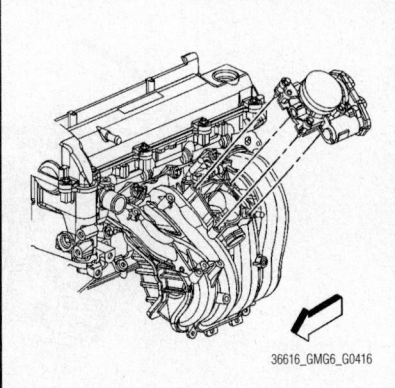

Fig. 277 Removing the throttle body— 2.4L engine

vent may damage fuel system components.

➡ DO NOT prop open the throttle blade with the ignition key in the ON position as it may set a Diagnostic Trouble Code (DTC).

1. Remove the air cleaner outlet duct.

2. Disconnect the engine wiring harness electrical connector from the Electronic Throttle Control (ETC).

3. Remove the throttle body bolts.

4. Remove the throttle body.

5. Inspect the throttle body gasket, and replace if necessary.

To install:

6. Install the throttle body.

7. Install the throttle body bolts and tighten to 89 inch lbs. (10 Nm).

8. Connect the engine wiring harness electrical connector to the ETC.

9. Install the air cleaner outlet duct.

10. Perform the Throttle Learn procedure.

3.5L Engine
See Figure 278.

1. Remove the air cleaner outlet duct.

2. Disconnect the Electronic Throttle Control (ETC) electrical connector.

3. Remove the heater pipe nut at the throttle body.

4. Remove the nuts and the bolts from the throttle body.

5. Remove the throttle body assembly.

6. Remove the throttle body gasket.

CAUTION

Do not use solvent of any type when cleaning the gasket surfaces on the intake manifold and the throttle body assembly, as damage to the gasket surfaces and throttle body assembly may result.

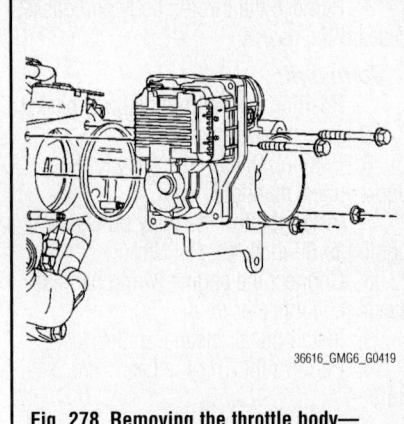

Fig. 278 Removing the throttle body— 3.5L engine

CAUTION

Use care in cleaning the gasket surfaces on the intake manifold and the throttle body assembly, as sharp tools may damage the gasket surfaces.

7. Clean and inspect the throttle body gasket mating surfaces.

To install:

8. Install a new gasket, if necessary.

9. Install the throttle body assembly.

10. Install the throttle body nuts and the bolts and tighten to 89 inch lbs. (10 Nm).

11. Install the heater pipe nut to the throttle body and tighten to 18 ft. lbs. (25 Nm).

12. Connect the ETC electrical connector.

13. Install the air cleaner outlet duct.

14. Perform the Throttle Learn Procedure.

3.6L Engine
See Figure 280.

1. Remove the air cleaner outlet duct.

2. Disconnect the engine wiring harness electrical connector from the Electronic Throttle Control (ETC).

3. Remove the throttle body bolts.

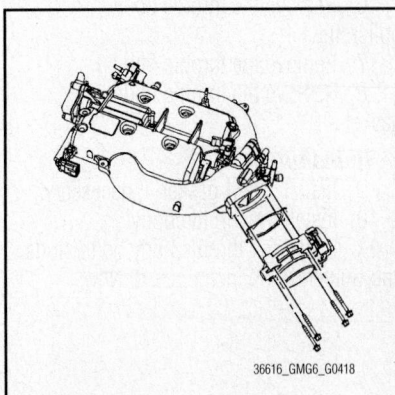

Fig. 279 Removing the throttle body— 3.6L engine

4. Remove the throttle body and gasket. Discard the gasket.

To install:

5. Position a NEW throttle body gasket to the upper intake manifold.

6. Position the throttle body to the upper intake manifold.

7. Install the throttle body bolts and tighten to 89 inch lbs. (10 Nm).

8. Connect the engine wiring harness electrical connector to the ETC.

9. Install the air cleaner outlet duct.

10. Perform the Throttle Learn Procedure.

3.9L Engine

See Figure 280.

> ❋❋ **CAUTION**
>
> **Do not use solvent of any type when cleaning the gasket surfaces on the intake manifold and the throttle body assembly, as damage to the gasket surfaces and throttle body assembly may result.**

> ❋❋ **CAUTION**
>
> **Use care in cleaning the gasket surfaces on the intake manifold and the throttle body assembly, as sharp tools may damage the gasket surfaces.**

1. Remove the intake manifold cover.

2. Remove the air cleaner outlet duct.

3. Disconnect the Electronic Throttle Control (ETC) electrical connector.

4. Remove the heater inlet and outlet pipe nuts.

5. Remove the heater inlet and outlet pipe bracket from the throttle body studs. Reposition the pipes.

6. Remove the throttle body bolts/studs.

7. Remove the throttle body.

8. Remove the throttle body gasket.

To install:

9. Install a new gasket, if necessary.

10. Install the throttle body.

11. Install the throttle body bolts/studs and tighten to 89 inch lbs. (10 Nm).

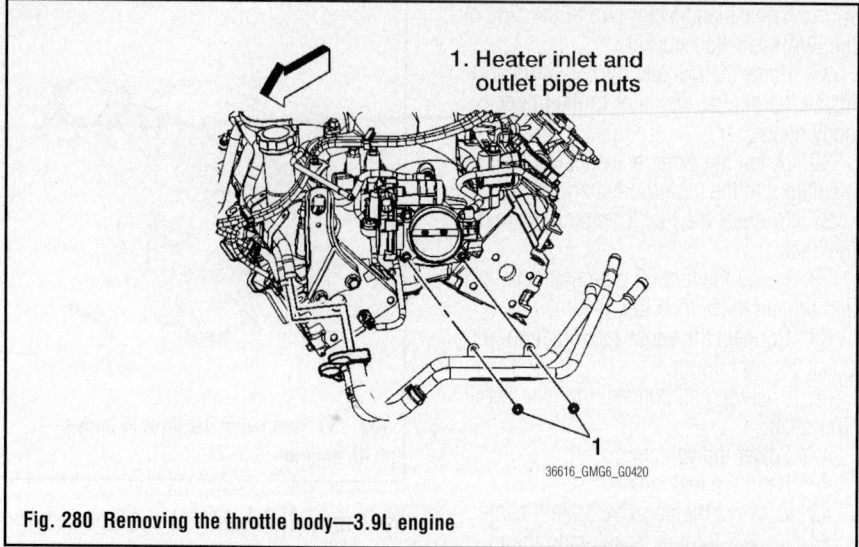

1. Heater inlet and outlet pipe nuts

36616_GMG6_G0420

Fig. 280 Removing the throttle body—3.9L engine

12. Position the heater inlet and outlet pipes and install the pipe bracket to the throttle body studs.

13. Install the heater inlet and outlet pipe nuts and tighten to 89 inch lbs. (10 Nm).

14. Connect the ETC electrical connector.

15. Install the air cleaner outlet duct.

16. Install the intake manifold cover.

PROGRAMMING

Throttle Learn

With Scan Tool-Reset

1. Ignition ON, engine OFF. With a scan tool, perform the Idle Learn Reset in Module Setup.

2. Start the engine, monitor the TB Idle Airflow Compensation parameter. The TB Idle Airflow Compensation parameter value should equal 0 percent and the engine should be idling at a normal idle speed. If the engine is not idling normally, proceed with the Learn portion of the diagnostic.

3. Clear the DTCs and return to the diagnostic that referred you here.

Without Scan Tool-Learn

> ❋❋ **CAUTION**
>
> **Do NOT perform the Without Scan Tool-Learn procedure if DTCs are set.**

1. The engine speed is between 450-4,000 RPM.

2. The Manifold Absolute Pressure (MAP) is greater than 5 kPa.

3. The Mass Air Flow (MAF) is greater than 2 g/s.

4. The ignition 1 voltage is greater than 10 volts.

5. Start and idle the engine in Park for 3 minutes.

6. With a scan tool, monitor desired and actual RPM.

7. The ECM will start to learn the new idle cells and Desired RPM should start to decrease.

8. Ignition OFF for 60 seconds.

9. Start and idle the engine in Park for 3 minutes.

> ❋❋ **CAUTION**
>
> **During the drive cycle the check engine light may come on with idle speed DTCs. If idle speed codes are set, clear codes so the ECM can continue to learn.**

10. After the 3 minute run time the engine should be idling normal. If the engine idle speed has not been learned the vehicle will need to be driven at speeds above 44 mph (70 km/h) with several decelerations and extended idles.

11. After the drive cycle, the engine should be idling normally. If the engine idle speed has not been learned, turn OFF the ignition for 60 seconds and repeat step 6.

12. Once the engine speed has returned to normal, clear DTCs.

HEATING & AIR CONDITIONING SYSTEM

BLOWER MOTOR

REMOVAL & INSTALLATION

See Figure 281.

1. Remove the right closeout panel.
2. Remove the blower motor wire harness connector.

➡**Cut through the case as straight as possible because the motor cup must be replaced. In order to prevent damage to the component, do not cut any deeper than necessary to remove the motor cup.**

3. Cut out the blower motor using a utility knife in the narrow groove of the lower case.
4. Remove the blower motor.
5. Remove the blower motor nuts.
6. Remove the blower motor from the blower motor cup.

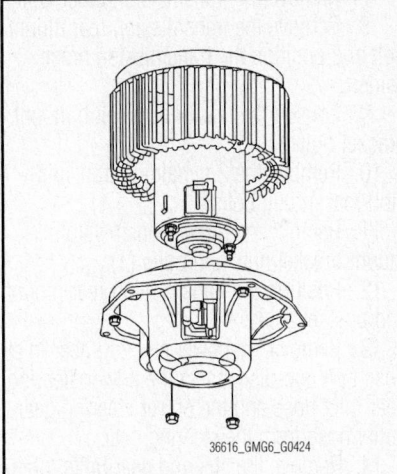

36616_GMG6_G0424

Fig. 281 Removing the blower motor from the blower motor cup

To install:

7. Install the new blower motor to the blower motor cup.
8. Install the blower motor nuts and tighten to 21 inch lbs. (2.4 Nm).
9. Install the motor blower seal to the blower motor service ring.
10. Install the blower motor.
11. Install the blower motor attachment ring.
12. Install the blower motor screws and tighten to 13 inch lbs. (1.5 Nm).
13. Install the blower motor wire harness connector.
14. Install the right closeout panel.

HEATER CORE

REMOVAL & INSTALLATION

See Figure 282.

1. Remove the HVAC module assembly.
2. Remove the center floor air outlet duct screws.
3. Remove the center floor air outlet duct.
4. Drill out the heater core cover heat stakes.
5. Remove the heater core cover screws.
6. Remove the heater core cover.
7. Remove the heater core.

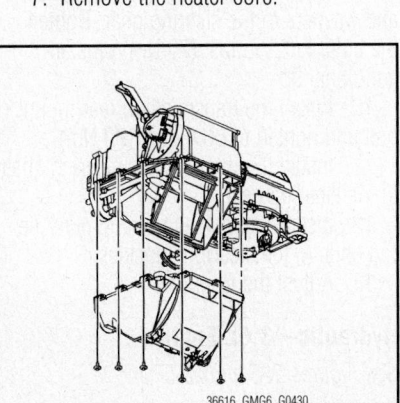

36616_GMG6_G0430

Fig. 282 Removing the heater core cover

To install:

8. Install the heater core.
9. Install the heater core cover.
10. Install the heater core cover screws and tighten to 13 inch lbs. (1.5 Nm).
11. Install the center floor air outlet duct.
12. Install the upper floor air outlet duct screws and tighten to 13 inch lbs. (1.5 Nm).
13. Install the HVAC module assembly.

HVAC MODULE

REMOVAL & INSTALLATION

See Figures 283 and 284.

1. Remove the Air Conditioner (A/C) lines from the thermal expansion valve.
2. Remove the heater hose from the heater core.
3. Remove the Instrument Panel (I/P) assembly.
4. Remove the recirculation actuator wire harness connector.
5. Remove the air temperature actuator wire harness connector.
6. Remove the mode actuator wire harness connector.
7. Remove the blower motor wire harness connector.

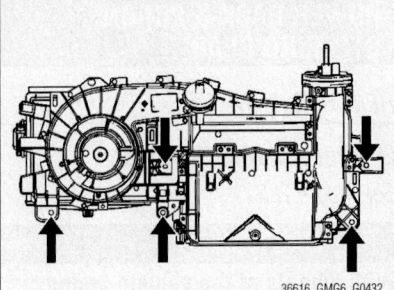

36616_GMG6_G0432

Fig. 283 Removing the HVAC module assembly mounting bolts

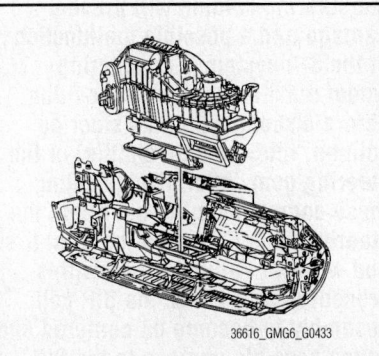

36616_GMG6_G0433

Fig. 284 Removing the HVAC module assembly

8. Remove the blower motor resistor wire harness connector.
9. Remove the left hand side window defogger outlet duct.
10. Remove the HVAC module assembly mounting bolts.
11. Remove the HVAC module assembly.

To install:

12. Install the HVAC module assembly.
13. Install the HVAC module assembly mounting bolts and tighten to 44 inch lbs. (5 Nm).
14. Install the left hand side window defogger outlet duct.
15. Install the blower motor resistor wire harness connector.
16. Install the blower motor wire harness connector.
17. Install the mode actuator wire harness connector.
18. Install the air temperature actuator wire harness connector.
19. Install the recirculation actuator wire harness connector.
20. Install the I/P assembly.
21. Install the heater hoses to the heater core.
22. Install the A/C lines to the thermal expansion valve.

STEERING

POWER RACK & PINION STEERING GEAR

REMOVAL & INSTALLATION

Electronic Power Steering

See Figure 285.

❋❋ CAUTION

With wheels of the vehicle facing straight ahead, secure the steering wheel utilizing steering column anti-rotation pin, steering column lock, or a strap to prevent rotation. Locking of the steering column will prevent damage and a possible malfunction of the SIR system. The steering wheel must be secured in position before disconnecting the steering column, intermediate shaft(s) or the steering gear. After disconnecting these components, do not rotate the steering wheel or move the front tires and wheels. Failure to follow this procedure may cause the SIR coil assembly to become un-centered and cause possible damage to the SIR coil. If you think the SIR coil has became un-centered, refer to your specific SIR coil's centering procedure to re-center SIR Coil.

1. Turn the front wheels to the straight forward position and secure the steering wheel from moving.
2. Disengage the rack and pinion outer tie rod ends from the steering knuckles.
3. Separate the intermediate steering shaft from the steering gear.
4. Remove the transmission rear mount bolt.
5. Remove the steering gear bolts, nuts, and washers from the steering gear.

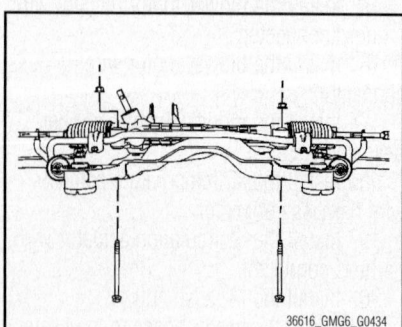

Fig. 285 Removing the steering gear (electronic power steering)

➡ **The position of the steering gear will need to be manipulated to remove it through the left front wheel opening.**

6. Remove the steering gear through the left front wheel opening.
7. Transfer any parts as needed.

To install:

8. Install the steering gear through the left front wheel opening.

➡ **Start all of the bolts and nuts by hand before finalizing any torques.**

9. Install the steering gear bolts, nuts, and washers to the steering gear. Tighten the bolts to 52 ft. lbs. (70 Nm) plus an additional 90°.
10. Install the transmission rear mount bolt and tighten to 66 ft. lbs. (90 Nm).
11. Install the intermediate steering shaft to the steering gear.
12. Install the rack and pinion outer tie rod ends to the steering knuckles.
13. Adjust the front toe.

Hydraulic—3.6L Engine

See Figures 286 and 287.

❋❋ CAUTION

With wheels of the vehicle facing straight ahead, secure the steering wheel utilizing steering column anti-rotation pin, steering column lock, or a strap to prevent rotation. Locking of the steering column will prevent damage and a possible malfunction of the SIR system. The steering wheel must be secured in position before disconnecting the steering column, intermediate shaft(s) or the steering gear. After disconnecting these components, do not rotate the steering wheel or move the front tires and wheels. Failure to follow this procedure may cause the SIR coil assembly to become un-centered and cause possible damage to the SIR coil. If you think the SIR coil has became un-centered, refer to your specific SIR coil's centering procedure to re-center SIR Coil.

1. Turn the front wheels to the straight forward position and secure the steering wheel from moving.
2. Remove as much power steering fluid from the remote power steering fluid reservoir as possible.
3. Place drain pans under the vehicle as needed.

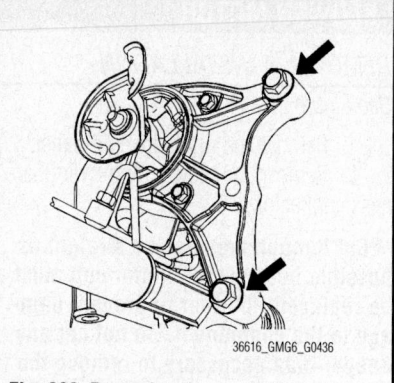

Fig. 286 Removing the remaining transmission rear mount bolts

4. Disengage the rack and pinion outer tie rod ends from the steering knuckles.
5. Separate the intermediate steering shaft from the steering gear.
6. Remove the steering gear heat shield from the steering gear.
7. Remove the transmission brace bolt.
8. Remove the transmission rear mount bolt and position the transmission brace aside.
9. Loosen the rear transmission mount bracket bolt.
10. Remove the 2 remaining transmission rear mount bolts.
11. Remove the 3 rear transmission mount bracket nuts and bolts (1).
12. Position the transmission rear mount and bracket aside.
13. Remove the power steering gear inlet hose bolt and disconnect the power steering gear inlet hose and the power steering gear outlet hose from the steering gear.
14. Remove the steering gear bolts, nuts, and washers from the steering gear.

➡ **The position of the steering gear will need to be manipulated to remove it through the left front wheel opening.**

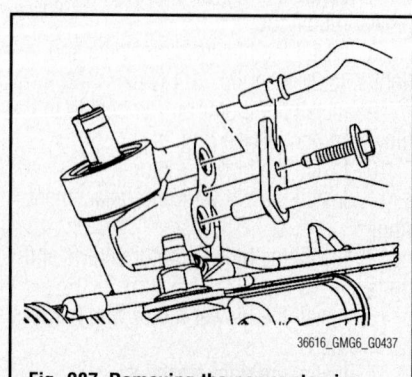

Fig. 287 Removing the power steering gear (hydraulic)—3.6L engine

15. Remove the steering gear through the left front wheel opening.

16. Transfer any parts as needed.

To install:

17. Install the steering gear through the left front wheel opening.

➡ **Start all of the bolts and nuts by hand before finalizing any torques.**

18. Install the steering gear bolts, nuts, and washers to the steering gear. Tighten the bolts and nuts to 81 ft. lbs. (110 Nm).

19. Connect the power steering gear inlet hose and the power steering gear outlet hose to the steering gear and install the power steering gear inlet hose bolt and tighten to 20 ft. lbs. (27 Nm).

20. Position the transmission rear mount and bracket in place.

21. Install the 3 rear transmission mount bracket bolts and nuts and tighten to 37 ft. lbs. (50 Nm).

22. Install the 2 remaining transmission rear mount bolts.

23. Place the transmission brace in the proper position. Install the bolt in order to secure the transmission brace to the transmission rear mount. Tighten the 3 transmission rear mount bolts to 37 ft. lbs. (50 Nm).

24. Install the transmission brace bolt and tighten to 37 ft. lbs. (50 Nm).

25. Tighten the rear transmission mount bracket bolt and tighten to 37 ft. lbs. (50 Nm).

26. Install the steering gear heat shield to the steering gear.

27. Clean any excess power steering fluid from the vehicle and remove the drain pans.

28. Install the intermediate steering shaft to the steering gear.

29. Install the rack and pinion outer tie rod ends to the steering knuckles.

30. Fill and bleed the power steering system.

31. Adjust the front toe.

Hydraulic—3.5L & 3.9L Engines

See Figures 288 and 289.

1. Turn the steering wheel to the straight forward position, support it from movement, and remove the key from the ignition.

2. Raise and support the vehicle.

3. Remove the front tires and wheels.

4. Remove the tie rod end castle nuts.

☀☀ CAUTION

Do not free the ball stud by using a pickle fork or a wedge-type tool. Damage to the seal or bushing may result.

5. Using the universal steering linkage

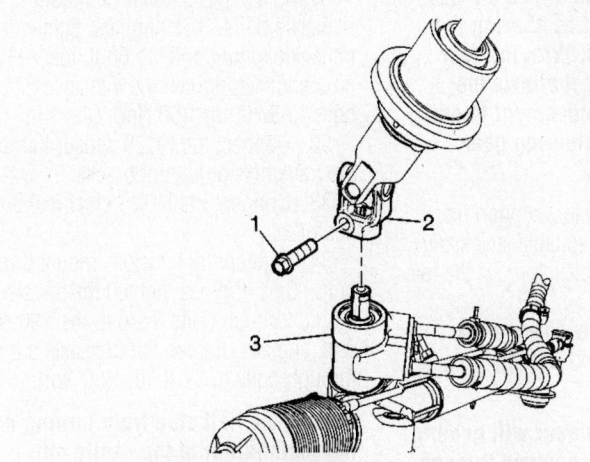

1. Intermediate shaft to steering gear pinch bolt
2. Intermediate shaft
3. Steering gear

36616_GMG6_G0438

Fig. 288 Separating the intermediate shaft from the steering gear—3.5L and 3.9L engines

and tie rod puller, separate the tie rod ends from the steering knuckles.

6. Remove the intermediate shaft to steering gear pinch bolt. Discard the bolt.

➡ **Secure the steering wheel in the straight forward position before separating the intermediate shaft from the steering gear, or damage to the SIR coil will occur.**

7. Separate the intermediate shaft from the steering gear.

8. Loosen the transaxle mount through bolt.

9. Disconnect the Heated Oxygen Sensor (HO2S) electrical connector.

10. Disconnect the HO2S sensor harness from the transmission mount bracket.

11. Remove the 3 transaxle mount to transaxle bolts.

12. Remove the 3 transaxle bracket to frame nuts.

13. Position the transaxle bracket and rear mount aside.

14. Remove the bolt and disconnect the power steering gear inlet and outlet pipe/hoses from the power steering gear. Cap off the pipe/hoses and position aside.

15. Remove the power steering gear outlet pipe routing pin-style retainer from the right rear side of the frame.

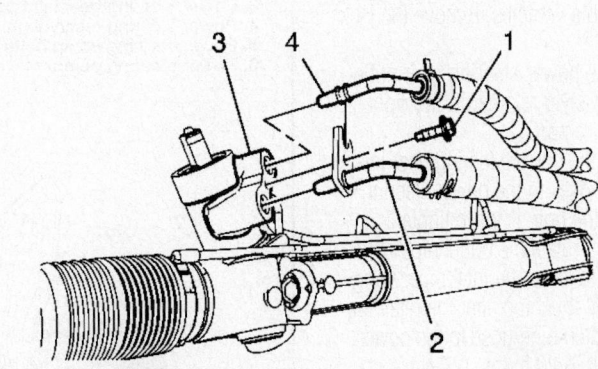

1. **Bolt**
2. **Power steering gear inlet hose/pipe**
3. **Power steering gear outlet hose/pipe**
4. **Power steering gear**

36616_GMG6_G0439

Fig. 289 Disconnecting the power steering gear inlet and outlet pipe/hoses from the power steering gear—3.5L and 3.9L engine

➡Convertible vehicles utilize a cross brace that is installed by sharing the frame mounting bolts. With the rear frame bolts removed, it allows the cross brace to have movement to gain access to the power steering gear mounting bolts.

16. Convertible vehicles, support the rear of the frame with a suitable jack stand.

17. Convertible vehicles, remove the rear frame mount bolts.

18. Remove the power steering gear mounting bolts, nuts, and washers from the gear.

➡The power steering gear will need to be rotated while it is removed through the left wheel opening.

19. Remove the power steering gear through the left wheel opening.

20. If the power steering gear is to be replaced, transfer the outer tie rod ends to the new steering gear.

To install:

➡The power steering gear will need to be rotated while it is installed through the left wheel opening.

21. Position the power steering gear into the vehicle.

22. Connect the intermediate steering shaft to the steering gear.

23. Install the power steering gear mounting bolts, nuts and washers to the power steering gear. Tighten the mounting bolts/nuts to 81 ft. lbs. (110 Nm).

24. Convertible vehicles, install the rear frame mounting bolts. Tighten the rear frame mounting bolts to 73 ft. lbs. (100 Nm) plus an additional 180° rotation.

25. Convertible vehicles, remove the jack stand.

26. Install the power steering gear outlet pipe routing pin-style retainer to the right rear side of the frame.

27. Connect the power steering gear inlet and outlet pipe/hoses to the power steering gear and install the bolt. Prior to tightening the retaining bolt, rotate the outlet pipe clockwise/down so it touches the inlet pipe. Verify the hoses are still touching after the retaining bolt is tight. Tighten pipe/hose to the power steering gear bolt to 20 ft. lbs. (27 Nm).

28. Install the new intermediate steering shaft to steering gear pinch bolt and tighten to 36 ft. lbs. (49 Nm).

29. Position the transaxle bracket and rear mount back to their original position.

30. Install the 3 transaxle bracket to frame nuts. Tighten the transaxle bracket to from nuts to 37 ft. lbs. (50 Nm).

31. Install the 3 transaxle mount to transaxle bolts. 3.5L engines, tighten the transaxle mount bolts to 66 ft. lbs. (90 Nm). 3.9L engines, tighten the transaxle mount bolts to 37 ft. lbs. (50 Nm).

32. Connect the HO2S sensor harness to the transmission mount bracket.

33. Connect the HO2S electrical connector.

34. Tighten the transaxle mount through bolt. . 3.5L engines, tighten the transaxle mount through bolts to 66 ft. lbs. (90 Nm). 3.9L engines, tighten the transaxle mount through bolts to 37 ft. lbs. (50 Nm).

➡Hold the ball stud from turning during installation of the castle nut.

35. Install new torque castle nuts to the tie rod end ball studs. Tighten the nuts to 18 ft. lbs. (25 Nm) plus an additional 90° rotation.

36. Install the front tires and wheels.

37. Lower the vehicle.

38. Fill and bleed the power steering system.

39. Measure the wheel alignment and adjust as necessary.

POWER STEERING PUMP

REMOVAL & INSTALLATION

3.5L & 3.9L Engines

See Figure 290.

1. Remove the intake manifold cover.

2. Remove the drive belt and engine mount snubber.

3. Remove the drive belt idler pulley.

4. Remove the air cleaner assembly.

5. Remove the power steering pump pulley.

6. Remove the engine lift bracket bolts.

7. Remove the engine lift bracket.

8. Remove the power steering gear inlet pipe/hose fitting.

a. Use an appropriate tool to remove the power steering fluid from the reservoir before removing the hoses from the pump.

b. Use a NEW o-ring for installation.

9. Remove the power steering reservoir inlet pipe/hose. Compress the clamp and to disconnect the return hose from the power steering reservoir.

10. Remove the power steering pump bolts.

11. Remove the power steering pump.

To install:

12. Install the power steering pump. After installation, fill and bleed the power steering system.

13. Install the power steering pump bolts and tighten to 18 ft. lbs. (25 Nm).

14. Install the power steering reservoir inlet pipe/hose.

15. Install the power steering gear inlet pipe/hose fitting. Install a NEW o-ring. Tighten the fitting to 20 ft. lbs. (27 Nm).

16. Install the engine lift bracket.

17. Install the engine lift bracket bolts and tighten to 37 ft. lbs. (50 Nm).

18. Install the power steering pump pulley.

19. Install the air cleaner assembly.

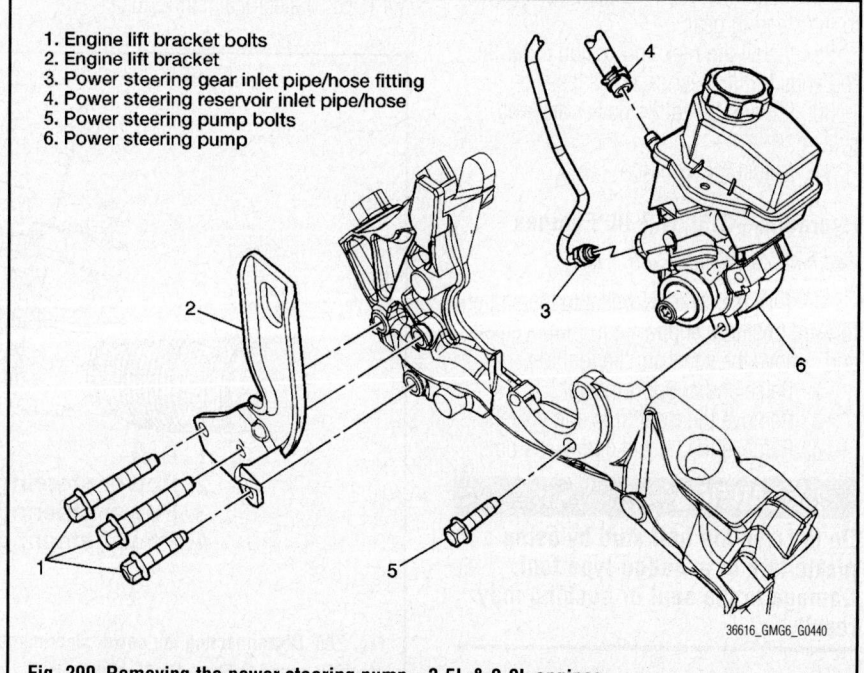

1. Engine lift bracket bolts
2. Engine lift bracket
3. Power steering gear inlet pipe/hose fitting
4. Power steering reservoir inlet pipe/hose
5. Power steering pump bolts
6. Power steering pump

36616_GMG6_G0440

Fig. 290 Removing the power steering pump—3.5L & 3.9L engines

20. Install the drive belt idler pulley.
21. Install the drive belt and engine mount snubber.
22. Install the intake manifold cover.

BLEEDING

➡ **Use clean, new power steering fluid type only. See the Maintenance and Lubrication subsection for fluid specifications.**

➡ **Hoses touching the frame, body or engine may cause system noise. Verify that the hoses do not touch any other part of the vehicle.**

➡ **Loose connections may not leak, but could allow air into the steering system. Verify that all hose connections are tight.**

➡ **Power steering fluid level must be maintained throughout bleed procedure.**

1. Fill pump reservoir with fluid to minimum system level, FULL COLD level, or middle of hash mark on cap stick fluid level indicator.

➡ **With hydro-boost only, the oil level will appear falsely high if the hydro-boost accumulator is not fully charged. Do not apply the brake pedal with the engine OFF. This will discharge the hydro-boost accumulator.**

2. If equipped with hydro-boost, fully charge the hydro-boost accumulator using the following procedure:
   a. Start the engine.
   b. Firmly apply the brake pedal 10-15 times.
   c. Turn the engine OFF.
3. Raise the vehicle until the front wheels are off the ground.
4. Key On engine OFF, turn the steering wheel from stop to stop 12 times. Vehicles equipped with hydro-boost systems or longer length power steering hoses may require turns up to 15-20 stop to stops.
5. Verify the power steering fluid level per operating specifications.
6. Start the engine. Rotate the steering wheel from left to right. Check for any sign of cavitations or fluid aeration (pump noise/whining).
7. Verify the fluid level. Repeat the bleed procedure, if necessary.

SUSPENSION

FRONT SUSPENSION

LOWER CONTROL ARM

REMOVAL & INSTALLATION

See Figure 291.

1. Raise and support the vehicle.
2. Remove the tire and wheel.

➡ **DO NOT re-use the lower ball joint bolt. Discard and use NEW only.**

3. Remove the lower ball joint to knuckle nut and bolt.
4. Separate the lower control arm from the knuckle.
5. If removing the left lower control arm, remove the left side transmission mount.

6. If removing the right lower control arm, remove the right engine mount.
7. Remove the front lower control arm bolt.
8. Remove the rear lower control arm bushing nuts and bolts.
9. Remove the lower control arm from the cradle.

To install:
10. Position the lower control arm in the cradle.
11. Install and hand tighten the rear lower control arm bushing nuts and bolts.
12. Install and hand tighten the front lower control arm bolt.
13. Install the ball joint to knuckle bolt and nut and tighten to 37 ft. lbs. (50 Nm). Reverse the nut ¾ of a turn. Tighten to 37 ft. lbs. (50 Nm) plus 30°.
14. Load the front suspension with the proper jack stand before tightening the bolts to specifications.
15. Tighten the front lower control arm bolt to 37 ft. lbs. (50 Nm) plus 90°.
16. Tighten the rear bushing to frame bolts 37 ft. lbs. (50 Nm) plus 90°.
Remove the jack stand.
If installing the left lower control arm, install the left side transmission mount.
If installing the right lower control arm, install the right engine mount.
17. Install the tire and wheel.
18. Verify the wheel alignment.
19. Remove the support and lower the vehicle.

STEERING KNUCKLE

REMOVAL & INSTALLATION

See Figure 292.

1. Raise and support the vehicle.
2. Remove the wheel bearing/hub.
3. Separate the outer tie rod end from the knuckle.
4. Remove the nuts and bolts from the strut to the knuckle.
5. Separate the lower ball joint from the knuckle.
6. Remove the steering knuckle.

To install:
7. Verify the front end alignment.
8. Connect the lower ball joint to the knuckle.
9. Install the nuts and bolts to the strut and knuckle.
10. Connect the outer tie rod end to the knuckle.
11. Install the wheel bearing/hub.
12. Lower the vehicle.

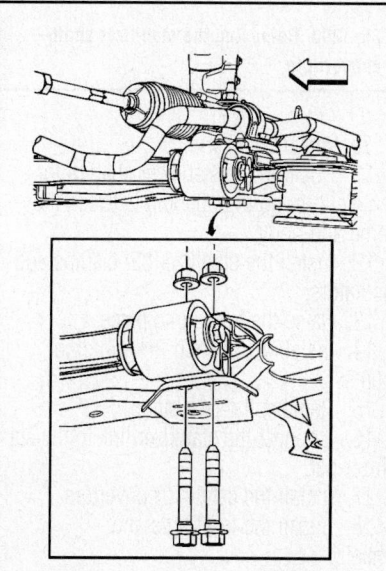

36616_GMG6_G0444

Fig. 291 Removing the lower control arm nuts and bolts

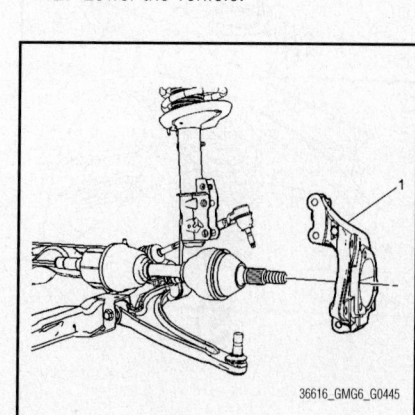

36616_GMG6_G0445

Fig. 292 Removing the steering knuckle (1)

STRUT

REMOVAL & INSTALLATION

See Figure 293.

1. Raise and support the vehicle.
2. Remove the front wheel.
3. Disconnect the stabilizer link from the strut.
4. Remove the strut to steering knuckle nuts.
5. If applicable, reposition the wheel speed sensor/ABS harness and bracket.
6. Remove the strut to steering knuckle bolts.
7. Remove the upper strut cap to body nuts.

➡**In order to prevent damage to the CV joint boot, place a shop towel over the CV joint.**

8. Remove the strut from the vehicle.

To install:

➡**It may be necessary to rotate the upper strut mount cover guide to match the hole in the strut tower.**

9. Position the strut to the vehicles strut tower, using the alignment pin as a guide.
10. Install the upper strut cap to body nuts and tighten to 18 ft. lbs. (25 Nm).
11. Install the strut to steering knuckle bolts leaving the nuts off.
12. If applicable, place the wheel speed sensor harness and bracket to the bolt end.
13. Install the strut to steering knuckle nuts. Tighten the nuts to 89 ft. lbs. (120 Nm).

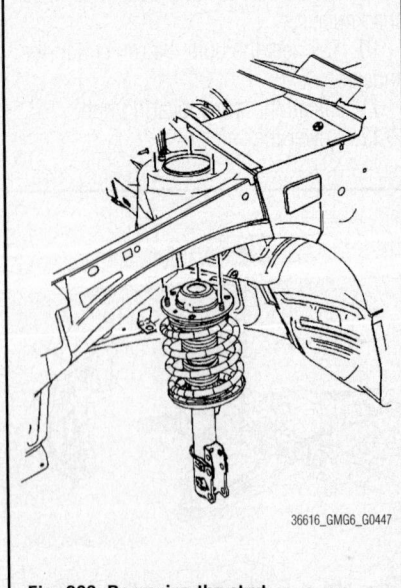

Fig. 293 Removing the strut

14. Connect the stabilizer link to the strut and tighten to 48 ft. lbs. (65 Nm).
15. Install the front wheel.
16. Lower the vehicle.
17. Road test the vehicle and test for leads and pulls.

STABILIZER SHAFT

REMOVAL & INSTALLATION

Sedan/Coupe

See Figure 294.

1. Install the engine support fixture.
2. Raise and support the vehicle.
3. Remove the tires and wheels.
4. Disconnect the stabilizer links from the stabilizer shaft.
5. Remove the stabilizer bar clamps and insulators.
6. Remove the catalytic convertors for the 3.5L, 3.6L and 3.9L engines.
7. Lower the frame in order to gain clearance to the stabilizer shaft.
8. Remove the stabilizer shaft through the opening between the frame and body.

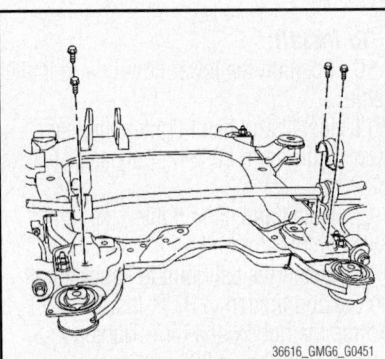

Fig. 294 Removing the stabilizer bar—coupe/sedan

To install:

9. Position the stabilizer shaft to the frame.
10. Install the stabilizer bar clamps and insulators.
11. Raise the frame into place.
12. Remove the jack stand.
13. Connect the stabilizer link to the stabilizer bar.
14. For the 3.5L, 3.6L and 3.9L engines install the catalytic convertors.
15. Install the front tire and wheel.
16. Lower the vehicle.
17. Remove the engine support fixture.

Convertible

See Figure 295.

1. Install the engine support fixture.
2. Raise and support the vehicle.
3. Remove the front tires and wheels.
4. Remove the LH and RH reinforcements.
5. Remove the catalytic convertors.
6. Disconnect the stabilizer links from the stabilizer shaft.
7. Lower the frame in order to gain access to the stabilizer shaft.
8. Support the rear of the frame assembly with a suitable jack stand.
9. Remove the stabilizer bar clamps and insulators.
10. Remove the stabilizer shaft thru the opening between the frame and body.

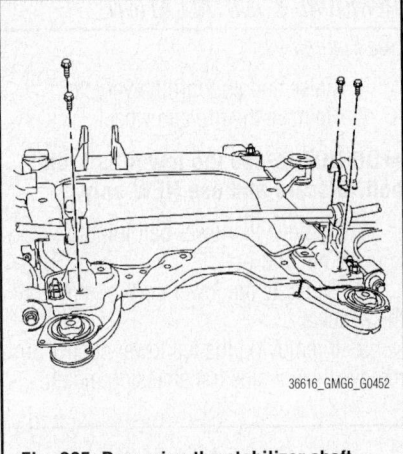

Fig. 295 Removing the stabilizer shaft—convertible

To install:

11. Position the stabilizer shaft to the vehicle through the opening between the frame and body.
12. Install the stabilizer bar clamps and insulators.
13. Raise the frame into place.
14. Install the LH and RH reinforcements.
15. Remove the jack stand.
16. Connect the stabilizer link to the stabilizer bar.
17. Install the catalytic convertors.
18. Install the front tires and wheels.
19. Lower the vehicle.
20. Remove the engine support fixture.

WHEEL HUB & BEARING

REMOVAL & INSTALLATION

See Figure 296.

1. Raise and support the vehicle.
2. Remove the brake rotor.
3. Disconnect the wheel speed sensor electrical connector, if equipped.
4. Remove the wheel speed sensor electrical connector from the mounting bracket, if needed.
5. Loosen the wheel driveshaft from the wheel bearing/hub.
6. Remove the wheel bearing/hub mounting bolts.
7. Remove the wheel bearing/hub and backing plate from the steering knuckle.

To install:

8. Position the backing plate and wheel bearing/hub assembly in the steering knuckle.
9. Install the wheel bearing/hub mounting bolts and tighten to 85 ft. lbs. (115 Nm).
10. Reconnect the wheel speed senor electrical connector, if needed.
11. Install the wheel speed sensor electrical connector on the retaining bracket, if needed.
12. Install the brake rotor.
13. Install the wheel driveshaft retaining nut and washer.
14. Remove the support and lower the vehicle.

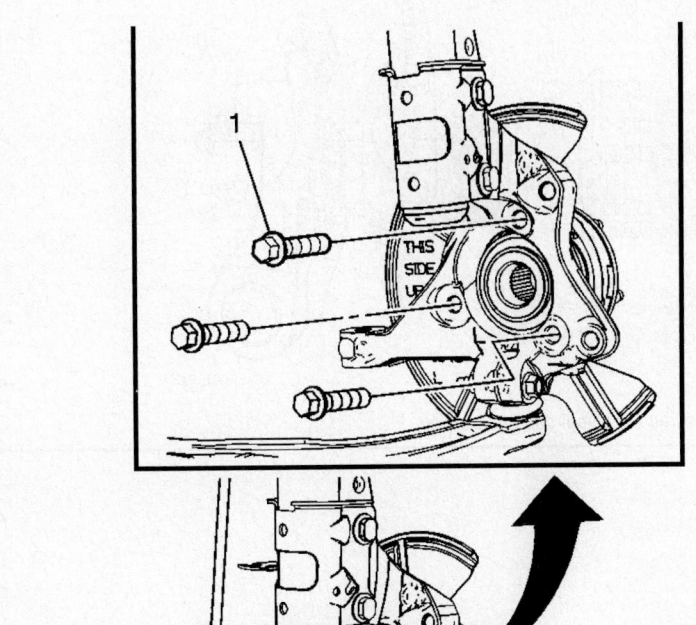

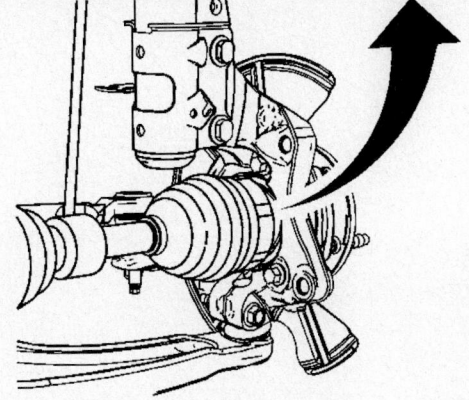

36616_GMG6_G0454

Fig. 296 Removing the wheel bearing/hub mounting bolts

SUSPENSION

SHOCK ABSORBER

REMOVAL & INSTALLATION

See Figure 297.

1. Raise and support the vehicle.
2. Remove the tire and wheel.
3. Using a suitable jack stand, raise the rear knuckle to remove spring tension.
4. Remove the lower shock bolt.
5. Remove the upper shock nuts.
6. Remove the shock from the vehicle.

To install:

7. Place the shock in the vehicle.
8. Install the shock absorber to body nuts and tighten to 18 ft. lbs. (25 Nm).
9. Install the shock absorber to

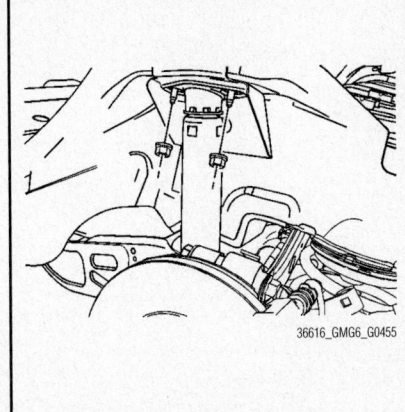

36616_GMG6_G0455

Fig. 297 Removing the rear shock

knuckle bolt and tighten to 133 ft. lbs. (180 Nm).
10. Remove the jack stand from the rear knuckle.

REAR SUSPENSION

11. Install the tire and wheel.
12. Lower the vehicle.

WHEEL HUB & BEARING

REMOVAL & INSTALLATION

See Figure 298.

1. Raise and support the vehicle.
2. Remove the tire and wheel assembly.
3. Remove the brake rotor.
4. Disconnect the electrical connector from the wheel speed sensor, if equipped with ABS.
5. Remove the stabilizer link bolt at the knuckle and position the stabilizer link out of the way in order to provide access to the wheel bearing/hub nuts.
6. Remove the 4 wheel bearing/hub assembly nuts.

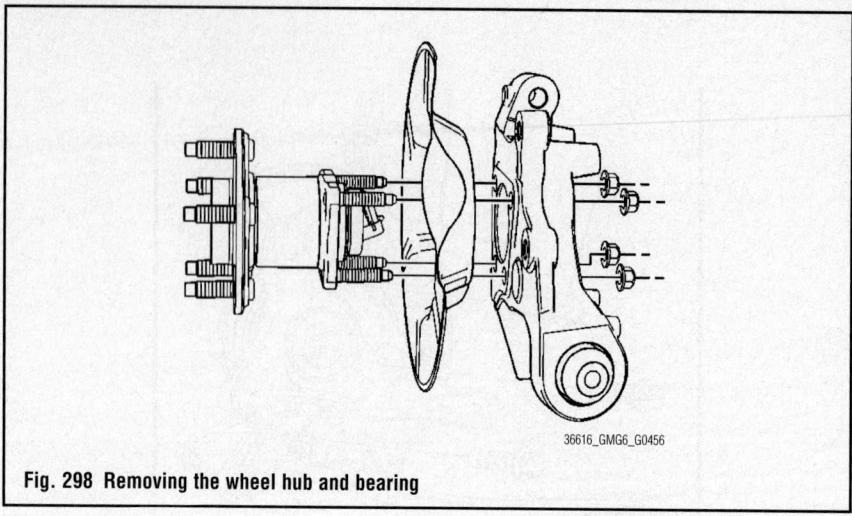

36616_GMG6_G0456

Fig. 298 Removing the wheel hub and bearing

7. Remove the wheel bearing/hub assembly from the knuckle.

To install:

8. Install the wheel bearing/hub assembly to the knuckle.

9. Install the 4 wheel bearing/hub assembly nuts and tighten to 47 ft. lbs. (63 Nm).

10. Connect the stabilizer link bolt at the knuckle.

11. Connect the electrical connector to the wheel speed sensor, if equipped with ABS.

12. Install the brake rotor.

13. Install the tire and wheel assembly.

14. Lower the vehicle.

PONTIAC

G8

SPECIFICATIONS AND MAINTENANCE CHARTS

ENGINE AND VEHICLE IDENTIFICATION

	Engine							Model Year	
Code ①	Liters (cc)	Cu. In.	Cyl.	Fuel Sys.	Engine Type	Eng. Mfg.		Code ②	Year
7	3.6 (3564)	218	6	SFI	DOHC	GM		8	2008
Y	6.0 (5703)	348	8	SFI*	OHV	GM		9	2009

SFI: Sequential Fuel Injection

DOHC: Double Overhead Camshafts

SFI*: Sequential Fuel Injection with Active Fuel management

36616_GMG8_C0001

GENERAL ENGINE SPECIFICATIONS

Year	Model	Engine Displacement Liters (cc)	Engine ID/VIN	Fuel System Type	Net Horsepower @ rpm	Net Torque @ rpm (ft. lbs.)	Bore x Stroke (in.)	Com-pression Ratio	Oil Pressure @ rpm
2008	G8	3.6 (3564)	7	SFI	256@6300	248@2100	3.70x3.37	10.2:1	20@2000
		6.0 (5703)	Y	SFI*	355@5300	385@4400	4.00x3.62	10.4:1	18@2000
2009	G8	3.6 (3564)	7	SFI	256@6300	248@2100	3.70x3.37	10.2:1	20@2000
		6.0 (5703)	Y	SFI*	355@5300	385@4400	4.00x3.62	10.4:1	18@2000

SFI: Sequential Fuel Injection

SFI*: Sequential Fuel Injection with Active Fuel management

36616_GMG8_C0002

ENGINE TUNE-UP SPECIFICATIONS

Year	Engine Displacement Liters	Engine ID/VIN	Spark Plug Gap (in.)	Ignition Timing (deg.) MT	AT	Fuel Pump (psi) ①	Idle Speed (rpm) MT ②	AT ②	Valve Clearance In.	Ex.
2008	3.6	7	0.043	NA	①	50-60	NA	②	HYD	HYD
	6.0	Y	0.040	NA	①	55-60	NA	②	HYD	HYD
2009	3.6	7	0.043	NA	①	50-60	NA	②	HYD	HYD
	6.0	Y	0.040	NA	①	55-60	NA	②	HYD	HYD

NOTE: The Vehicle Emission Control Information label often reflects specification changes made during production.

The label figures must be used if they differ from those in this chart.

NA: Not Applicable

HYD: Hydraulic

① Engines equipped with Distributorless Ignition System (DIS). Ignition timing is not adjustable

② Idle speed is computer controlled and is not adjustable

36616_GMG8_C0003

CAPACITIES

Year	Engine Displacemen Liters	Engine VIN	Engine Oil with Filter (qts.)	Transmission pts. ①	Transfer Case (pts.)	Front Axle (pts.)	Rear Axle (pts.)	Fuel Tank (gal.)	Cooling System (qts.)
2008	3.6	7	6.9	①	NA	NA	2.3	19.3	10.6
	6.0	Y	8.0	②	NA	NA	2.3	19.3	11.6
2009	3.6	7	6.9	①	NA	NA	2.3	19.3	10.6
	6.0	Y	8.0	②	NA	NA	2.3	19.3	11.6

NA: Not applicable

① 5 speed w/ pan removal: 7.4 qts.

② 6 speed w/ pan removal: 6.0 qts., w/ oil cooler: 6.45 qts.

36616_GMG8_C0004

FLUID SPECIFICATIONS

Year	Model	Engine Displacement Liters (VIN)	Engine Oil	Auto. Trans.	Drive Axle	Power Steering Fluid	Brake Master Cylinder
2008	G8	3.6 (7) 6.0 (Y)	5W-30	Dexron VI	①	Dexron VI	DOT 4
		3.6 (7) 6.0 (Y)	5W-30	Dexron VI	①	Dexron VI	DOT 4
2009	G8	3.6 (7) 6.0 (Y)	5W-30	Dexron VI	①	Dexron VI	DOT 4
		3.6 (7) 6.0 (Y)	5W-30	Dexron VI	①	Dexron VI	DOT 4

DOT: Department Of Transpotation

① Castrol SAF Carbon Mod. GM P/N 92184900

36616_GMG8_C0010

VALVE SPECIFICATIONS

Year	Engine Displ. Liters	Engine ID/VIN	Seat Angle (deg.)	Face Angle (deg.)	Spring Test Pressure (lbs. @ in.)	Spring Free-Length (in.)	Stem-to-Guide Clearance (in.) Intake	Exhaust	Stem Diameter (in.) Intake	Exhaust
2008	3.6	7	45	44.25	①	1.6555-	0.0010	0.0014	0.2344	0.2341
						1.766	0.0026	0.0030	0.2352	0.2348
	6.0	Y	46	45	② ③	2.08	0.0037	0.0037	0.3130	0.3130
2009	3.6	7	45	44.25	①	1.6555-	0.0010	0.0014	0.2344	0.2341
						1.766	0.0026	0.0030	0.2352	0.2348
	6.0	Y	46	45	② ③	2.08	0.0037	0.0037	0.3130	0.3130

① Valve spring load closed: 56-61 lbs @ installed height.

② Valve spring load closed: 76 lbs. @ 1.8 inhes

③ Valve spring load open: 220 lbs. @ 1.32 inches

36616_GMG8_C0006

CRANKSHAFT AND CONNECTING ROD SPECIFICATIONS

All measurements are given in inches.

Year	Engine Displacement Liters	Engine ID/VIN	Crankshaft				Connecting Rod		
			Main Brg. Journal Dia.	Main Brg. Oil Clearance	Shaft End-play	Thrust on No.	Journal Diameter	Oil Clearance	Side Clearance
2008	3.6	7	2.6768-2.6775	0.0004-0.0024	0.0039-0.0130	3	2.2044-2.2050	0.0004-0.0028	0.0374-0.0140
	6.0	Y	2.558-2.559	0.0008-0.0021	0.0015-0.0078	3	2.0991-2.0999	0.0009-0.0030	0.0043-0.0200
2009	3.6	7	2.6768-2.6775	0.0004-0.0024	0.0039-0.0130	3	2.2044-2.2050	0.0004-0.0028	0.0374-0.0140
	6.0	Y	2.558-2.559	0.0008-0.0021	0.0015-0.0078	3	2.0991-2.0999	0.0009-0.0030	0.0043-0.0200

36616_GMG8_C0005

PISTON AND RING SPECIFICATIONS

All measurements are given in inches.

Year	Engine Displ. Liters	Engine ID/VIN	Piston Clearance	Ring Gap			Ring Side Clearance		
				Top Compression	Bottom Compression	Oil Control	Top Compression	Bottom Compression	Oil Control
2008	3.6	7	0.0008-0.0013	0.0059-0.0118	0.0110-0.0189	0.0059-0.0236	0.0012-0.0026	0.0006-0.0024	0.0012-0.0067
	6.0	Y	0.0009-0.0031	0.008-0.016	0.0015-0.027	0.009-0.031	0.0012-0.0040	0.0014-0.0031	0.0005-0.0080
2009	3.6	7	0.0008-0.0013	0.0059-0.0118	0.0110-0.0189	0.0059-0.0236	0.0012-0.0026	0.0006-0.0024	0.0012-0.0067
	6.0	Y	0.0009-0.0031	0.008-0.016	0.0015-0.027	0.009-0.031	0.0012-0.0040	0.0014-0.0031	0.0005-0.0080

36616_GMG8_C0007

TORQUE SPECIFICATIONS
All readings in ft. lbs.

Year	Engine Displacement Liters	Engine ID/VIN	Cylinder Head Bolts	Main Bearing Bolts	Rod Bearing Bolts	Crankshaft Damper Bolts	Flexplate Bolts	Manifold		Spark Plugs	Oil Pan Drain Plug
								Intake	Exhaust		
2008	3.6	7	①	②	③	④	⑤	⑥	15	13	18
	6.0	Y	⑦	⑧	⑨	⑩	⑪	⑫	⑬	11	18
2009	3.6	7	①	②	③	④	⑤	⑥	15	13	18
	6.0	Y	⑦	⑧	⑨	⑩	⑪	⑫	⑬	11	18

① M8 bolt
   Step 1: 11 ft. lbs.
   Step 2: Plus 60 degrees
   M11 bolt
   Step 1: 33 ft. lbs.
   Step 2: Back off 120 degrees
   Step 3: 22 ft. lbs.
   Step 2: Plus 150 degrees

② Inner Bolts
   Step 1: 15 ft. lbs.
   Step 2: Plus 80 degrees
   Outer Bolts
   Step 1: 10 ft. lbs.
   Step 2: Plus 110 degrees
   Side Bolts
   Step 1: 22 ft. lbs.
   Step 2: Plus 60 degrees

③ Step 1: 22 ft. lbs.
   Step 2: back off to zero
   Step 3: 18 ft. lbs
   Step 4: Plus 110 degrees

④ 74 ft. lbs. Plus 150 degrees

⑤ 22 ft. lbs. Plus 75 degrees

⑥ Intake manifold bolts:
   Cover ball stud to upper intake: 62 inch lbs.
   Runner solenoid to upper intake: 89 inch lbs.
   Upper intake manifold to cyl head - long: 17 ft. lbs.
   Upper intake manifold to cyl head - short: 17 ft. lbs.
   Upper intake manifold to lower manifold: 17 ft. lbs.

⑦ M8 bolt
   Step 1: 22 ft. lbs.
   M11 bolt
   Step 1: 22 ft. lbs.
   Step 2: Plus 90 degrees
   Step 3: Plus 70 degrees

⑧ M8 bolts
   Step 1: 18 ft. lbs.
   M10 bolts
   Step 1: 15 ft. lbs.
   Step 2: Plus 80 degrees
   M10 studs
   Step 1: 15 ft. lbs.
   Step 2: Plus 51 degrees

⑨ M8 bolts
   Step 1: 15 ft. lbs.
   Step 2: Plus 85 degrees

⑩ Step 1: 110 ft. lbs.
   Step 2: Loosen 360 degrees
   Step 3: 37 ft. lbs
   Step 4: Plus 230 degrees

⑪ Step 1: 15 ft. lbs.
   Step 2: 37 ft. lbs.
   Step 3: 74 ft. lbs

⑫ Step 1: 44 inch lbs.
   Step 2: 89 inch lbs.

⑬ Step 1: 11 ft. lbs.
   Step 2: 15 fl

36616_GMG8_C0008

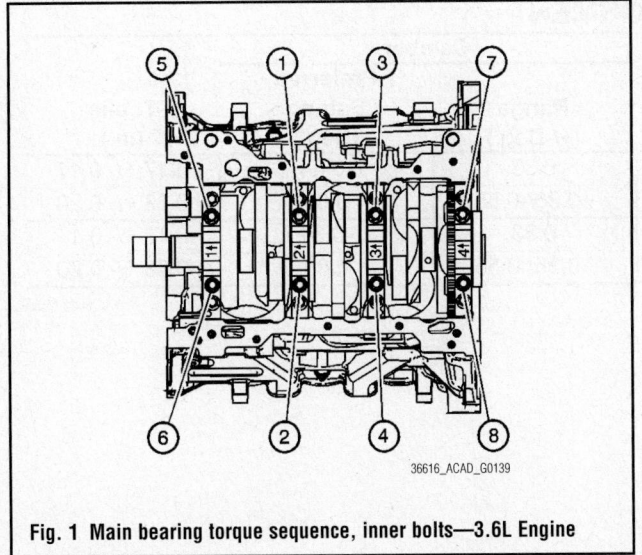

36616_ACAD_G0139

Fig. 1 Main bearing torque sequence, inner bolts—3.6L Engine

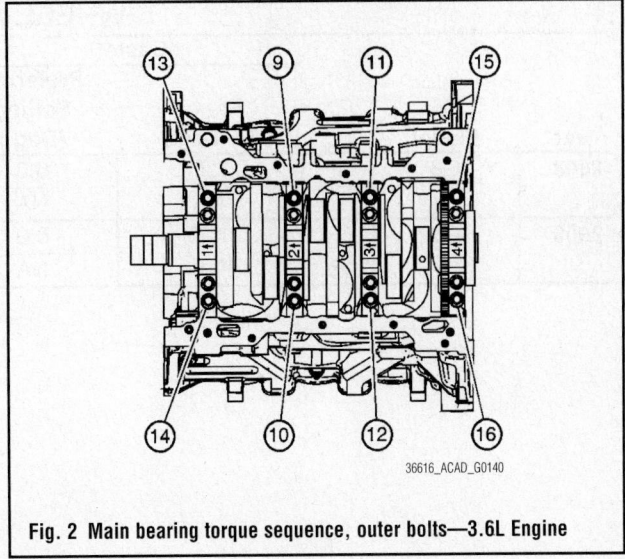

36616_ACAD_G0140

Fig. 2 Main bearing torque sequence, outer bolts—3.6L Engine

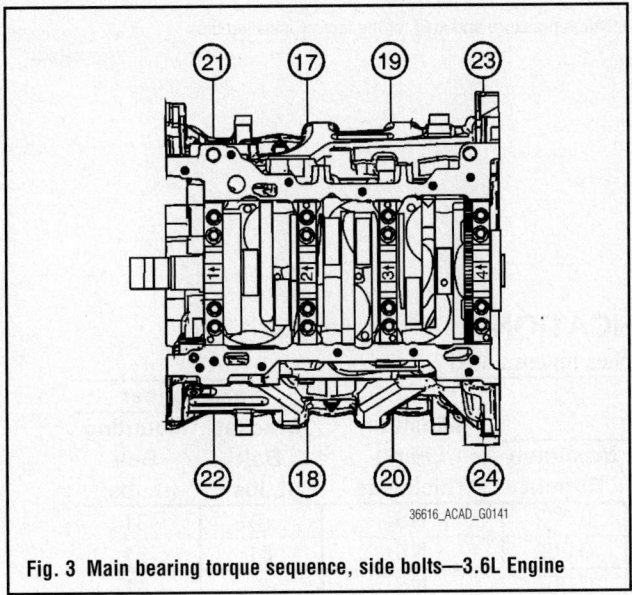

36616_ACAD_G0141

Fig. 3 Main bearing torque sequence, side bolts—3.6L Engine

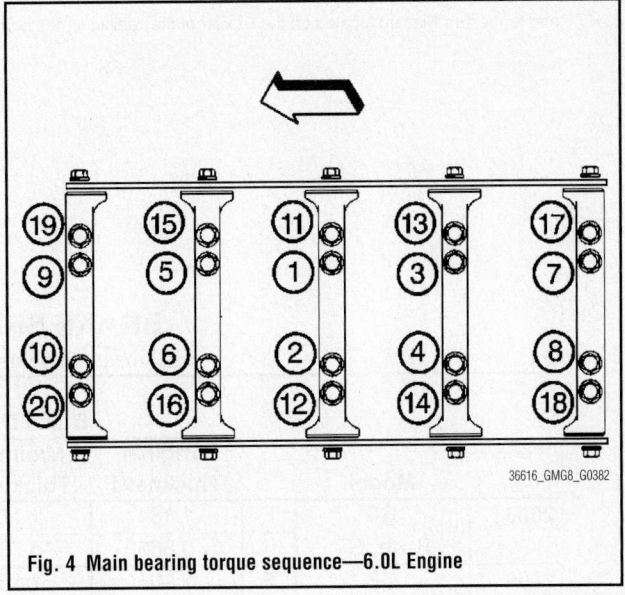

36616_GMG8_G0382

Fig. 4 Main bearing torque sequence—6.0L Engine

WHEEL ALIGNMENT

Year	Model		Caster Range (+/-Deg.)	Caster Preferred Setting (Deg.)	Camber Range (+/-Deg.)	Camber Preferred Setting (Deg.)	Toe-in (in.)
2008	G8	F	1.25	6.0	0.33	-0.34	0.17 +/- 0.17
		R	NA	NA	+0.35/-0.55	0.80	0.33 +/- 0.20
2009	G8	F	1.25	6.0	0.33	-0.34	0.17 +/- 0.17
		R	NA	NA	+0.35/-0.55	0.80	0.33 +/- 0.20

36616_GMG8_C0009

TIRE, WHEEL AND BALL JOINT SPECIFICATIONS

Year	Model	OEM Tires Standard	OEM Tires Optional	Tire Pressures (psi) Front	Tire Pressures (psi) Rear	Wheel Size	Ball Joint Inspection	Lug Nut (ft. lbs.)
2008	G8	245/45RX18	245/40RX19	①	①	8JX18, 8JX19	0.125 in	125
2009	G8	245/45RX18	245/40RX19	①	①	8JX18, 8JX19	0.125 in	125

OEM: Original Equipment Manufacturer

PSI: Pounds Per Square Inch

① Refer to the Tire Placard located on the B pillar of the vehicle for the correct tire inflation pressure and load for the factory installed tires.

36616_GMG8_C0011

BRAKE SPECIFICATIONS
All measurements in inches unless noted

Year	Model		Brake Disc Original Thickness	Brake Disc Minimum Thickness	Brake Disc Maximum Runout	Minimum Lining Thickness	Brake Caliper Bracket Bolt (ft. lbs.)	Brake Caliper Mounting Bolt (ft. lbs.)
2008	G8	F	1.181	1.102	0.002	NS	①	31
	Base, GT	R	0.866	0.787	0.002	NS	81	31
2009	G8	F	1.181	1.102	0.002	NS	①	31
	Base, GT	R	0.866	0.787	0.002	NS	81	31

NS: Not Specified

F: Front

R: Rear

① Step 1: 44 ft. lbs.
   Step 2: Plus 120 degrees

36616_GMG8_C0012

MAINTENANCE I AND II SERVICE SCHEDULES
Pontiac G8

When the CHANGE ENGINE OIL light appears, certain services and inspections are required. Services are described below. Generally, it is recommended that the first service be Maintenance I, second service be Maintenance II, and that services are then alternated from Maintenance I and Maintenance II thereafter. In some Required services are described as Maintenance I and Maintenance II.

The first service of a vehicle should be Maintance I, and the second service should be Maintenance II. Alternate between the 2 services thereafter. However, in some cases, Maintenance II may be required more

Maintenance I: Use Maintenance I if the Service Engine Oil light comes on within 10 months since the vehicle was purcahses or, if Maintenance II was performed.

Maintenance II: Use Maintenance II if the previous service performed was Maintenance I. Always used Maintenance II whenever the CHANGE ENGINE OIL light comes on 10 months or more since the last service, or, if the CHANGE ENGINE OIL light has not come on at all for one year.

Service	Maintenance I	Maintenance II
Change engine oil and filter. Reset oil life system.	✓	✓
Visually check for any leaks or damage. A fluid loss in the vehicle system could indicate a problem. Inspect, repair and add fluid to the system, if necessary.	✓	✓
Inspect engine air cleaner filter. If necessary, replace filter.	—	✓
Rotate tires and check inflation pressures and wear.	✓	✓
Visually inspect brake lines and hoses for proper hook-up, binding, leaks, cracks, chafing, etc. Inspect the disc brake pads for wear and the rotors for surface condition. Inspect the drum brake lings for wear or cracks. Inspect other brake parts, including drums, wheel cylinders, calipers, parking brake, etc. Inspect parking brake adjustment.	✓	✓
Check engine coolant and windshield washer fluid levels and add fluid as	✓	✓
Perform any needed additional services.	✓	✓
Inspect the suspension and steering components. Inspect the front and rear suspension systems and steering system for damaged, loose, or missing parts, or signs of wear. Inspect the power steering lines and the hoses for proper hook-up, binding, leaks, cracks, chafing, etc.	—	✓
Inspect the coolant hoses and replace the hoses if they are crackes, swollen or deteriorated. Inspect all pipes, fittings and clamps; replace with OEM parts as needed. To help ensure proper operation, a pressure test of the cooling system and pressure cap, and cleaning the outside of the radiator and A/C condesnser is recommended at least once a year.	—	✓
Inspect wiper blades for wear or cracking		✓
Inspect restraint system components.		✓
Lubricate all key lock cylinders, latch assemblies and hinges		✓
Replace passenger compartment air filter.		✓

To reset the CHANGE ENGINE OIL LIGHT:

1. Turn the ignition key to ON/RUN with the engine off.

2. Fully press and release the accelerator pedal three times within five seconds. If the percentage does not return to 100% or if the CHANGE ENGINE OIL SOON message comes back on when the vehicle is started, the engine oil life system was not properly reset. Repeat the procedure.

36616_GMG8_C0013

ADDITIONAL MAINTENANCE SERVICES
Pontiac G8

TO BE SERVICED	TYPE OF SERVICE	VEHICLE MILEAGE INTERVAL (x1000)					
		25	50	75	100	125	150
Air cleaner filter	R		✓		✓		✓
Accessory drive belt	I						✓
Auto. Trans. Fluid ①	R		✓		✓		✓
Cooling system hoses and	S/I						✓
Engine coolant	R						✓
Fuel system	I	✓	✓	✓	✓	✓	✓
Exhaust system & heat shields	S/I	✓	✓	✓	✓	✓	✓
Brake fluid ②	R						
Spark plugs	R				✓		

R: Replace

S/I: Inspect and service, if necessary

① Replace if any of the following condition are met:

Heavy city traffic where the outside temperature regularly reaches 90 degrees F (32 degrees C) or higher.

Hilly or mountainous terrain

Frequent trailer towing

Taxi, police or delivery service

Otherwise, change every 100,000 miles

② Drain, flush, and refill brake hydraulic system at a re

service interval (I or II) every two years.

36616_GMG8_C0014

PRECAUTIONS

Before servicing any vehicle, please be sure to read all of the following precautions, which deal with personal safety, prevention of component damage, and important points to take into consideration when servicing a motor vehicle:

• Never open, service or drain the radiator or cooling system when the engine is hot; serious burns can occur from the steam and hot coolant.

• Observe all applicable safety precautions when working around fuel. Whenever servicing the fuel system, always work in a well-ventilated area. Do not allow fuel spray or vapors to come in contact with a spark, open flame, or excessive heat (a hot drop light, for example). Keep a dry chemical fire extinguisher near the work area. Always keep fuel in a container specifically designed for fuel storage; also, always properly seal fuel containers to avoid the possibility of fire or explosion. Refer to the additional fuel system precautions later in this section.

• Fuel injection systems often remain pressurized, even after the engine has been turned **OFF**. The fuel system pressure must be relieved before disconnecting any fuel lines. Failure to do so may result in fire and/or personal injury.

• Brake fluid often contains polyglycol ethers and polyglycols. Avoid contact with the eyes and wash your hands thoroughly after handling brake fluid. If you do get brake fluid in your eyes, flush your eyes with clean, running water for 15 minutes. If eye irritation persists, or if you have taken brake fluid internally, IMMEDIATELY seek medical assistance.

• The EPA warns that prolonged contact with used engine oil may cause a number of skin disorders, including cancer. You should make every effort to minimize your exposure to used engine oil. Protective gloves should be worn when changing oil. Wash your hands and any other exposed skin areas as soon as possible after exposure to used engine oil. Soap and water, or waterless hand cleaner should be used.

• All new vehicles are now equipped with an air bag system, often referred to as a Supplemental Restraint System (SRS) or Supplemental Inflatable Restraint (SIR) system. The system must be disabled before performing service on or around system components, steering column, instrument panel components, wiring and sensors. Failure to follow safety and disabling procedures could result in accidental air bag deployment, possible personal injury and unnecessary system repairs.

• Always wear safety goggles when working with, or around, the air bag system. When carrying a non-deployed air bag, be sure the bag and trim cover are pointed away from your body. When placing a non-deployed air bag on a work surface, always face the bag and trim cover upward, away from the surface. This will reduce the motion of the module if it is accidentally deployed. Refer to the additional air bag system precautions later in this section.

• Clean, high quality brake fluid from a sealed container is essential to the safe and proper operation of the brake system. You should always buy the correct type of brake fluid for your vehicle. If the brake fluid becomes contaminated, completely flush the system with new fluid. Never reuse any brake fluid. Any brake fluid that is removed from the system should be discarded. Also, do not allow any brake fluid to come in contact with a painted surface; it will damage the paint.

• Never operate the engine without the proper amount and type of engine oil; doing so WILL result in severe engine damage.

• Timing belt maintenance is extremely important. Many models utilize an interference-type, non-freewheeling engine. If the timing belt breaks, the valves in the cylinder head may strike the pistons, causing potentially serious (also time-consuming and expensive) engine damage. Refer to the maintenance interval charts for the recommended replacement interval for the timing belt, and to the timing belt section for belt replacement and inspection.

• Disconnecting the negative battery cable on some vehicles may interfere with the functions of the on-board computer system(s) and may require the computer to undergo a relearning process once the negative battery cable is reconnected.

• When servicing drum brakes, only disassemble and assemble one side at a time, leaving the remaining side intact for reference.

• Only an MVAC-trained, EPA-certified automotive technician should service the air conditioning system or its components.

BRAKES

GENERAL INFORMATION

PRECAUTIONS

• Certain components within the ABS system are not intended to be serviced or repaired individually.

• Do not use rubber hoses or other parts not specifically specified for and ABS system. When using repair kits, replace all parts included in the kit. Partial or incorrect repair may lead to functional problems and require the replacement of components.

• Lubricate rubber parts with clean, fresh brake fluid to ease assembly. Do not use shop air to clean parts; damage to rubber components may result.

• Use only DOT 3 brake fluid from an unopened container.

• If any hydraulic component or line is removed or replaced, it may be necessary to bleed the entire system.

• A clean repair area is essential. Always clean the reservoir and cap thoroughly before removing the cap. The slightest amount of dirt in the fluid may plug an orifice and impair the system function. Perform repairs after components have been thoroughly cleaned; use only denatured alcohol to clean components. Do not allow ABS components to come into contact with any substance containing mineral oil; this includes used shop rags.

• The Anti-Lock control unit is a microprocessor similar to other computer units in the vehicle. Ensure that the ignition switch is **OFF** before removing or installing con-

ANTI-LOCK BRAKE SYSTEM (ABS)

troller harnesses. Avoid static electricity discharge at or near the controller.

• If any arc welding is to be done on the vehicle, the control unit should be unplugged before welding operations begin.

WHEEL SPEED SENSORS

REMOVAL & INSTALLATION

Front

➡**The front wheel speed sensors are integral with the hub and bearing assemblies. If a front wheel speed sensor needs replacement, you must replace the entire hub and bearing assembly. Refer to Wheel Bearing in Suspension.**

Rear

See Figure 5.

1. Before servicing the vehicle, refer to the Precautions Section.

❊❊ CAUTION

To avoid any vehicle damage, serious personal injury or death when major components are removed from the vehicle and the vehicle is supported by a hoist, support the vehicle with jack stands at the opposite end from which the components are being removed and strap the vehicle to the hoist.

2. Raise and support the vehicle.
3. Remove the rear wheels.

4. Disconnect the wheel speed sensor electrical connector (1).

5. Remove the wheel speed sensor to knuckle retaining bolt (3).

6. Remove the wheel speed sensor (2) from the knuckle (1).

Fig. ***To install:***

7. Install the wheel speed sensor to the knuckle.

8. Install the wheel speed sensor to knuckle retaining bolt and tighten to 62 inch lbs. (7 Nm).

9. Connect the wheel speed sensor jumper harness electrical connector.

10. Install the rear wheels.

11. Lower the vehicle.

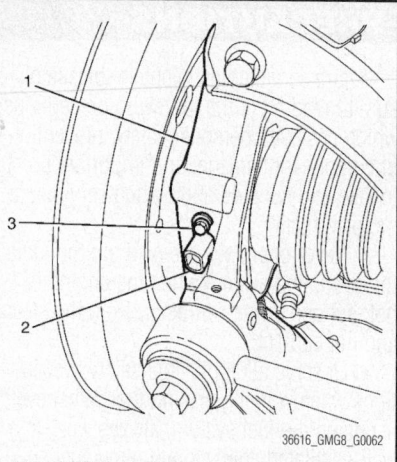

36616_GMG8_G0062

Fig. 5 Wheel speed sensor electrical connector and retaining bolt location

---

BRAKES

BLEEDING THE BRAKE SYSTEM

BLEEDING PROCEDURE

Manual Bleeding

1. Before servicing the vehicle, refer to the Precautions Section.

❊❊ CAUTION

To avoid any vehicle damage, serious personal injury or death when major components are removed from the vehicle and the vehicle is supported by a hoist, support the vehicle with jack stands at the opposite end from which the components are being removed and strap the vehicle to the hoist.

2. Place a clean suitable container beneath the brake master cylinder to catch brake fluid spills.

➡**When adding fluid to the brake master cylinder reservoir, use only Super DOT 4 or DOT 4 Plus brake fluid from a clean, sealed brake fluid container. The use of any type of fluid other than the recommended type of brake fluid may cause contamination which could result in damage to the internal rubber seals and/or rubber linings of hydraulic brake system components.**

➡**With the ignition OFF and the brakes cool, apply the brakes 3–5 times, or until the brake pedal effort increases significantly, in order to deplete the brake booster power reserve.**

3. Deplete the brake booster power reserve.

4. If you have performed a brake master cylinder bench bleed, disconnected the

brake pipes from the master cylinder or the hydraulic modulator assembly, you MUST perform the following steps to bleed air at the ports of the hydraulic component:

• Clean the outside of the reservoir on and around the reservoir cap prior to removal.

• With the brake pipes installed securely to the master cylinder or hydraulic modulator assembly, loosen and separate one of the brake pipes from the port of the component:

➡**For the hydraulic modulator assembly, perform these steps in the sequence of system flow; begin with the fluid feed pipes from the master cylinder.**

• Allow a small amount of brake fluid to gravity bleed from the open port of the component.

• Reconnect the brake pipe to the component and tighten securely.

• With the aid of an assistant slowly depress the brake pedal fully and maintain steady pressure on the pedal.

• Loosen the same brake pipe to purge air from the open port of the component.

• Tighten the brake pipe, then have the assistant slowly release the brake pedal.

• Wait 15 seconds, then repeat the above steps until all air is purged from the same port of each component.

• With the brake pipe installed securely to the master cylinder or

hydraulic modulator assembly, and after all air has been purged from the first port of the component that was bled, loosen and separate the next brake pipe from the component, then repeat the previous steps until each of the ports on the component has been bled.

• After completing the final component port bleeding procedure, make sure that each of the brake pipe to component fittings is correctly tightened.

5. Clean the outside of the brake master cylinder reservoir on and around the reservoir cap.

➡**Make sure the brake master cylinder reservoir remains at least half-full during this bleeding procedure. Add fluid as needed to maintain the correct level.**

6. Remove the master cylinder reservoir cap.

7. Raise and support the vehicle.

8. Remove the wheels.

9. Fit a correct sized ring spanner onto the LEFT REAR wheel hydraulic circuit bleeder valve.

10. Install a transparent hose over the end of the wheel hydraulic circuit bleeder valve.

11. Submerge the open end of the transparent hose into a container partially filled with brake fluid from a clean, sealed brake fluid container.

12. Have an assistant slowly depress the brake pedal fully and maintain steady pressure on the pedal.

13. Loosen the bleeder valve to purge air from the wheel hydraulic circuit.

14. Tighten the bleeder valve, then have the assistant slowly release the brake pedal.

15. Wait 15 seconds, then repeat steps 12–14 until all air is purged from the wheel hydraulic circuit.

16. Tighten the wheel circuit bleeder valve securely.

17. Fit a correct sized ring spanner onto the RIGHT REAR wheel hydraulic circuit bleeder valve.

18. Repeat steps 10–16.

19. Fit a correct sized ring spanner onto the LEFT FRONT wheel hydraulic circuit (inboard other) bleeder valve.

20. Repeat steps 10–16.

21. For other models, fit a correct sized ring spanner onto the LEFT FRONT wheel hydraulic circuit outer bleeder valve.

22. Repeat steps 10–16.

23. Fit a correct sized ring spanner onto the RIGHT FRONT wheel hydraulic circuit (inboard other) bleeder valve.

24. Repeat steps 10–16.

25. For other models, fit a correct sized ring spanner onto the RIGHT FRONT wheel hydraulic circuit outer bleeder valve.

26. Repeat steps 10–16.

27. After completing the final wheel hydraulic circuit bleeding procedure, make sure that each of the 4 wheel hydraulic circuit bleeder valves is correctly tightened.

28. Install the wheels.

29. Lower the vehicle.

30. Fill the brake master cylinder reservoir to the maximum fill level with brake fluid from a clean, sealed brake fluid container.

31. Slowly depress and release the brake pedal. Observe the feel of the brake pedal.

➡**If it is determined that air was inducted into the system upstream of the hydraulic modulator assembly prior to servicing, the Antilock Brake System Automated Bleed Procedure must be performed. Refer to Automated Bleed Procedure in Antilock Brake System.**

32. If the brake pedal feels spongy, repeat the bleeding procedure again. If the brake pedal still feels spongy after repeating the bleeding procedure, perform the following steps:
- Inspect the brake system for external leaks. Refer to Brake System External Leak Inspection.
- Pressure bleed the hydraulic brake system in order to purge any air that may still be trapped in the system.

33. Turn the ignition ON, engine OFF. Check to see if the brake system warning lamp is illuminated.

➡**DO NOT allow the vehicle to be driven until it is diagnosed and repaired.**

34. If the brake system warning lamp is illuminated, perform Diagnostic System Check in General information.

Pressure Bleeding

1. Before servicing the vehicle, refer to the Precautions Section.

✳✳ CAUTION

To avoid any vehicle damage, serious personal injury or death when major components are removed from the vehicle and the vehicle is supported by a hoist, support the vehicle with jack stands at the opposite end from which the components are being removed and strap the vehicle to the hoist.

2. Place a clean suitable container beneath the brake master cylinder to catch brake fluid spills.

➡**When adding fluid to the brake master cylinder reservoir, use only Super DOT 4 or DOT 4 Plus brake fluid from a clean, sealed brake fluid container. The use of any type of fluid other than the recommended type of brake fluid may cause contamination which could result in damage to the internal rubber seals and/or rubber linings of hydraulic brake system components.**

➡**With the ignition OFF and the brakes cool, apply the brakes 3–5 times, or until the brake pedal effort increases significantly, in order to deplete the brake booster power reserve.**

3. Deplete the brake booster power reserve.

4. If you have performed a brake master cylinder bench bleed, disconnected the brake pipes from the master cylinder or the hydraulic modulator assembly, you MUST perform the following steps to bleed air at the ports of the hydraulic component:
- Clean the outside of the reservoir on and around the reservoir cap prior to removal.
- With the brake pipes installed securely to the master cylinder or hydraulic modulator assembly, loosen and separate one of the brake pipes from the port of the component:

➡**For the hydraulic modulator assembly, perform these steps in the sequence of system flow; begin with the fluid feed pipes from the master cylinder.**

- Allow a small amount of brake fluid to gravity bleed from the open port of the component.
- Reconnect the brake pipe to the component and tighten securely.
- With the aid of an assistant slowly depress the brake pedal fully and maintain steady pressure on the pedal.
- Loosen the same brake pipe to purge air from the open port of the component.
- Tighten the brake pipe, then have the assistant slowly release the brake pedal.
- Wait 15 seconds, then repeat the above steps until all air is purged from the same port of each component.
- With the brake pipe installed securely to the master cylinder or hydraulic modulator assembly, and after all air has been purged from the first port of the component that was bled, loosen and separate the next brake pipe from the component, then repeat the previous steps until each of the ports on the component has been bled.
- After completing the final component port bleeding procedure, make sure that each of the brake pipe to component fittings is correctly tightened.

5. Clean the outside of the brake master cylinder reservoir on and around the reservoir cap.

6. Remove the master cylinder reservoir cap and diaphragm.

7. Fill the brake master cylinder reservoir to the maximum-fill level with brake fluid from a clean, sealed brake fluid container.

8. Set up the brake pressure bleeder following the manufacturer instructions.

9. Open the brake pressure bleeder fluid valve to allow pressurized brake fluid to enter the brake system.

➡**Any brake fluid leaks identified require repair prior to completing this procedure.**

10. Wait approximately 30 seconds, then inspect the entire hydraulic brake system in order to make sure that there are no existing external brake fluid leaks.

11. Raise and support the vehicle.

12. Remove the wheels.

➡Make sure the brake master cylinder reservoir remains at least half-full during this bleeding procedure. Add fluid as needed to maintain the correct level.

13. Fit a suitable tool onto the LEFT REAR wheel hydraulic circuit bleeder valve (1).

14. Install a transparent hose over the end of the wheel hydraulic circuit bleeder valve (1).

15. Submerge the open end of the transparent hose into a container partially filled with brake fluid from a clean, sealed brake fluid container.

16. Loosen the bleeder valve to purge air from the wheel hydraulic circuit. Allow fluid to flow until air bubbles stop flowing from the bleeder, then tighten the bleeder valve.

17. Tighten the wheel circuit bleeder valve securely.

18. Fit a suitable tool onto the RIGHT REAR wheel hydraulic circuit bleeder valve.

19. Repeat steps 14–16.

20. Tighten the wheel circuit bleeder valve securely.

21. Fit a suitable tool onto the LEFT FRONT wheel hydraulic circuit bleeder valve.

22. Repeat steps 14–16.

23. Tighten the wheel circuit bleeder valve securely.

24. For other models, fit a correct sized ring spanner onto the LEFT FRONT wheel hydraulic circuit outer bleeder valve.

25. Repeat steps 14–16.

26. Tighten the wheel circuit bleeder valve securely.

27. Fit a suitable tool onto the RIGHT FRONT wheel hydraulic circuit bleeder valve.

28. Repeat steps 14–16.

29. Tighten the wheel circuit bleeder valve securely.

30. For other models, fit a correct sized ring spanner onto the RIGHT FRONT wheel hydraulic circuit outer bleeder valve.

31. Repeat steps 14–16.

32. Tighten the wheel circuit bleeder valve securely.

33. After completing the final wheel hydraulic circuit bleeding procedure, make sure that each wheel hydraulic circuit bleeder valve is correctly tightened.

34. Close the brake pressure bleeder fluid valve.

35. Install the wheels.

36. Lower the vehicle.

37. Remove the brake pressure bleeder from the brake master cylinder reservoir.

38. Fill the brake master cylinder reservoir to the maximum-fill level with brake fluid from a clean, sealed brake fluid container.

39. Slowly depress and release the brake pedal. Observe the feel of the brake pedal.

➡If it is determined that air was inducted into the system upstream of the BPMV prior to servicing, the Antilock Brake System Automated Bleed Procedure must be performed. Refer to Automated Bleed Procedure in Antilock Brake System

40. If the brake pedal feels spongy, repeat the bleeding procedure again. If the brake pedal still feels spongy after repeating the bleeding procedure, inspect the brake system for external leaks.

41. Turn the ignition ON, engine OFF. Check to see if the brake system warning lamp is illuminated.

➡DO NOT allow the vehicle to be driven until it is diagnosed and repaired.

42. If the brake system warning lamp is illuminated, refer to Diagnostic System Check in General information.

ABS AUTOMATED BLEED PROCEDURE

1. Before servicing the vehicle, refer to the Precautions Section.

※ CAUTION

To avoid any vehicle damage, serious personal injury or death when major components are removed from the vehicle and the vehicle is supported by a hoist, support the vehicle with jack stands at the opposite end from which the components are being removed and strap the vehicle to the hoist.

➡Before performing the Antilock Brake System Automated Bleed Procedure, first perform a pressure bleed of the base brake system. Refer to Bleeding the Brake System. The automated bleed procedure is recommended when one of the following conditions exist:

- Base brake system bleeding does not achieve the desired pedal height or feel.
- Extreme loss of brake fluid has occurred.
- Air ingestion is suspected in the secondary circuits of the hydraulic modulator assembly.

➡The Antilock Brake System Automated Bleed Procedure uses a scan tool to cycle the system solenoid valves and run the pump in order to purge any air from the secondary circuits. These circuits are normally closed off and are only opened during system initialization at vehicle start up and during ABS operation. The automated bleed procedure opens these secondary circuits and allows any air trapped in these circuits to flow out toward the brake calipers.

※※ WARNING

The Auto Bleed Procedure may be terminated at any time during the process by pressing the EXIT button. No further Scan Tool prompts pertaining to the Auto Bleed procedure will be given. After exiting the bleed procedure, relieve bleed pressure and disconnect bleed equipment per manufacturer's instructions. Failure to properly relieve pressure may result in spilled brake fluid causing damage to components and painted surfaces.

2. Raise and support the vehicle.

3. Remove all 4 wheels.

4. Inspect the brake system for leaks and visual damage.

5. Lower the vehicle.

6. Inspect the battery state of charge.

7. Install a scan tool.

8. Turn the key to the ignition ON, engine OFF position.

9. With the scan tool, establish communications with the ABS system.

10. Following the directions given on the scan tool, pressure bleed the base brake system. Refer to Bleeding the Brake System.

11. Follow the scan tool directions until the desired brake pedal height is achieved.

If the bleed procedure is aborted, a malfunction exists. Perform the following steps before resuming the bleed procedure:

- If a DTC is detected, refer to Diagnostic Trouble Codes
- If the brake pedal feels spongy, perform the conventional brake bleed procedure again.

12. When the desired pedal height is achieved, press the brake pedal to inspect for firmness.

13. Lower the vehicle.

14. Remove the scan tool.

15. Install the tire and wheel assemblies.

16. Inspect the brake fluid level.

17. Road test the vehicle while inspecting that the pedal remains high and firm.

BRAKES   **FRONT DISC BRAKES**

BRAKE CALIPER

REMOVAL & INSTALLATION

See Figure 6.

1. Before servicing the vehicle, refer to the Precautions Section.

✲✲ CAUTION

To avoid any vehicle damage, serious personal injury or death when major components are removed from the vehicle and the vehicle is supported by a hoist, support the vehicle with jack stands at the opposite end from which the components are being removed and strap the vehicle to the hoist.

2. Inspect the fluid level in the master cylinder reservoir.

➡**If the brake fluid level is midway between the maximum fill level and the minimum allowable level, no brake fluid needs to be removed from the master cylinder reservoir before proceeding.**

➡**DO NOT completely empty the master cylinder reservoir or remove any brake lines otherwise complete bleeding of the braking system will be necessary.**

➡**DO NOT re use the removed fluid.**

3. If the brake fluid level is higher than midway between the maximum fill level and the minimum allowable level, using a hand vacuum pump, siphon the brake fluid to the midway point before proceeding.

4. Raise and support the vehicle.

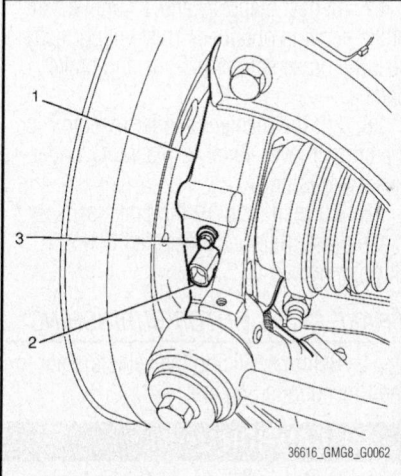

36616_GMG8_G0062

Fig. 6 Brake caliper assembly removal

5. Remove the front wheels.

6. Install 2 wheel nuts in reverse to opposite wheel studs to retain the brake disc to the hub.

➡**Position the ends of the G-clamps against the rear of the brake caliper and against the outboard brake pad.**

7. Install large G-clamps over the body of the brake caliper.

8. Tighten the G-clamps evenly until the brake caliper pistons bottom in each brake caliper bore.

9. Remove the G-clamps from the brake caliper.

10. Place a clean suitable container under the brake caliper assembly.

11. Remove the brake hose to brake caliper banjo retaining bolt (4).

➡**Install a rubber cap or plug on the exposed brake hose end in order to prevent fluid loss and contamination.**

12. Separate the brake hose to brake caliper banjo retaining bolt (4) from the brake hose (2).

➡**Copper brake hose sealing washers become work hardened due to the heat generated with brake applications and will not reseal. Install NEW copper brake hose sealing washers (3) whenever the brake hose to brake caliper banjo retaining bolt (4) is removed.**

13. Remove and discard the 2 copper brake hose sealing washers (3). The copper brake hose sealing washers (4) may be stuck to the brake caliper (1) and/or the brake hose (2).

➡**Bolts with micro-encapsulated thread sealant must be discarded after removal.**

14. Remove the brake caliper anchor plate to knuckle retaining bolts (5) and discard.

15. Remove the brake caliper assembly (1) from the front hub assembly.

To install:

✲✲ WARNING

Make sure the brake hose is not twisted or kinked after installation. Damage to the hose could result.

16. Clean the front brake caliper anchor plate mounting surfaces to the front steering knuckle.

17. Check the serviceability of the brake pads.

➡**The brake pads are marked as inner and outer only. Failure to install the brake pads in their correct position will cause the brake pads not to seat correctly in the brake caliper.**

18. Install the existing or NEW brake pads as required.

19. Press the inner brake pad by using a suitable tool to make sure the brake caliper pistons bottom in each brake caliper bore.

20. Position the front brake caliper assembly over the front brake disc.

21. Install the NEW front brake caliper anchor plate to front steering knuckle retaining bolts and tighten to 44 ft. lbs. plus 120° (60 Nm plus 120°)

✲✲ WARNING

Make sure the brake hose is not twisted or kinked after installation. Damage to the hose could result.

➡**Install NEW copper brake hose sealing washers.**

22. Install the front brake hose to brake caliper banjo retaining bolt and NEW copper brake hose sealing washers to the front brake caliper. Tighten the banjo bolt to 25 ft. lbs. (35 Nm).

23. Bleed the braking system. Refer to Bleeding the Brake System.

24. Remove the 2 wheel nuts retaining the brake disc to the hub.

25. Install the front wheels.

26. Lower the vehicle to the ground.

27. With the engine OFF, gradually apply the brake pedal to approximately ⅔ of its travel distance.

28. Slowly release the brake pedal.

29. Repeat steps 12 and 13 until a firm brake pedal is obtained. This will correctly seat the brake caliper pistons and brake pads.

30. Fill the master cylinder reservoir to the correct level.

31. Burnish (bed in) the brake pads and brake discs if required. Refer to Brake Pad & Rotor Burnishing in Rotor.

DISC BRAKE PADS

REMOVAL & INSTALLATION

See Figure 7.

1. Before servicing the vehicle, refer to the Precautions Section.

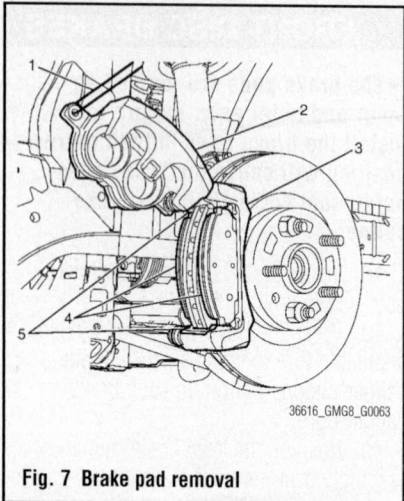

36616_GMG8_G0063

Fig. 7 Brake pad removal

✳✳ CAUTION

To avoid any vehicle damage, serious personal injury or death when major components are removed from the vehicle and the vehicle is supported by a hoist, support the vehicle with jack stands at the opposite end from which the components are being removed and strap the vehicle to the hoist.

2. Inspect the fluid level in the master cylinder reservoir.

➡**If the brake fluid level is midway between the maximum fill level and the minimum allowable level, no brake fluid needs to be removed from the master cylinder reservoir before proceeding.**

➡**DO NOT completely empty the master cylinder reservoir or remove any brake lines otherwise complete bleeding of the braking system will be necessary.**

➡**DO NOT re use the removed fluid.**

3. If the brake fluid level is higher than midway between the maximum fill level and the minimum allowable level, using a hand vacuum pump, siphon the brake fluid to the midway point before proceeding.

4. Raise and support the vehicle.

5. Remove the front wheels.

6. Install 2 wheel nuts in reverse to opposite wheel studs to retain the brake disc to the hub.

➡**Position the ends of the G-clamps against the rear of the brake caliper and against the outboard brake pad.**

7. Install large G-clamps over the body of the brake caliper.

8. Tighten the G-clamps evenly until the brake caliper pistons bottom in each brake caliper bore.

9. Remove the G-clamps from the brake caliper

➡**Bolts with micro-encapsulated thread sealant must be discarded after removal.**

10. Remove the brake caliper lower guide pin bolt (1). Discard the bolt (1).

✳✳ WARNING

Support the brake caliper with heavy mechanic wire, or equivalent, whenever it is separated from its mount and the hydraulic flexible brake hose is still connected. Failure to support the caliper in this manner will cause the flexible brake hose to bear the weight of the caliper, which may cause damage to the brake hose and in turn may cause a brake fluid leak.

➡**DO NOT disconnect the brake hose from the brake caliper (2).**

11. Pivot the brake caliper (2) upward and secure with heavy mechanics wire (1), or equivalent.

12. Remove the brake pads (4) from the brake caliper anchor plate (3).

13. Remove the brake pad retainers (5) from the brake caliper anchor plate (3).

14. Clean the brake pad brake pad retainer surfaces of the brake caliper anchor plate (3).

➡**Inspect the brake caliper guide pins for freedom of movement and the condition of the guide pin boots. This is achieved by moving the guide pins inboard and outboard within the brake caliper anchor plate (3) bores, without disengaging the slides from the boots.**

15. Inspect the brake caliper guide pins and boots for the following conditions:
- Restricted brake caliper guide pin movement
- Too much brake caliper guide pin play in the brake caliper anchor plate (3)
- Seized or binding brake caliper guide pins
- Split or torn boots

a. If any of the conditions listed are found, overhaul or replace the brake caliper (2).

To install:

✳✳ CAUTION

To avoid any vehicle damage, serious personal injury or death when major components are removed from the vehicle and the vehicle is supported by a hoist, support the vehicle with jack stands at the opposite end from which the components are being removed and strap the vehicle to the hoist.

16. Clean the piston to brake pad contact faces as required.

17. Install the brake pad retainers (5) to the brake caliper anchor plate (3).

➡**The brake pads (4) are marked as inner and outer only. Failure to install the brake pads (4) in their correct position will cause the brake pads (4) not to seat correctly in the brake caliper (2).**

18. Install the brake pads (4) to the brake caliper anchor plate (3).

✳✳ WARNING

Make sure the brake hose is not twisted or kinked after installation. Damage to the hose could result.

19. Remove the mechanics wire (1) or equivalent, and rotate the brake caliper (2) into position over the brake pads (4) and to the brake caliper anchor plate (3).

20. Make sure the brake hose is correctly located in its mounting bracket.

21. Install the NEW lower brake caliper guide pin bolt and tighten to 31 ft. lbs. (42 Nm).

22. Remove the 2 wheel nuts retaining the brake disc to the hub.

23. Install the front wheels.

24. Lower the vehicle to the ground.

25. With the engine off, gradually apply the brake pedal approximately ⅔ of its travel distance.

26. Slowly release the brake pedal.

27. Repeat steps 10 and 11 until a firm brake pedal is obtained. This will correctly seat the brake caliper pistons and brake pads.

28. Fill the master cylinder reservoir to the correct level. Refer to Master Cylinder Reservoir Filling.

29. Burnish (bed in) the brake pads and brake discs. Refer to Brake Pad & Rotor Burnishing.

BRAKE PAD & ROTOR BURNISHING

1. Before servicing the vehicle, refer to the Precautions Section.

✳✳ CAUTION

Road test a vehicle under safe conditions and while obeying all traffic

laws. Do not attempt any maneuvers that could jeopardize vehicle control. Failure to adhere to these precautions could lead to serious personal injury and vehicle damage.

➡Burnishing the brake pads and brake discs is necessary whenever the brake discs have been refinished or replaced, and/or whenever the brake pads have

been replaced to make sure that the braking surfaces are correctly prepared.

2. Select a smooth road with little or no traffic.
3. Accelerate the vehicle to 43 mph (70 km/h).

➡Use care to avoid overheating the brakes while performing this step as it may adversely affect the heating characteristics of the NEW brake pad material.

➡DO NOT allow the brakes to lock.

4. Using moderate pressure, apply the brakes to bring the vehicle to a stop.
5. Repeat steps 3 and 4 until approximately 20 stops have been completed. Allow sufficient cooling periods of no less than 500 meters between stops in order to correctly burnish the brake pads and brake discs.

BRAKES

BRAKE CALIPER

REMOVAL & INSTALLATION
See Figure 8.

1. Before servicing the vehicle, refer to the Precautions Section.

✻✻ CAUTION

To avoid any vehicle damage, serious personal injury or death when major components are removed from the vehicle and the vehicle is supported by a hoist, support the vehicle with jack stands at the opposite end from which the components are being removed and strap the vehicle to the hoist.

2. Inspect the fluid level in the master cylinder reservoir.

➡If the brake fluid level is midway between the maximum fill level and the minimum allowable level, no brake fluid needs to be removed from the master cylinder reservoir before proceeding.

➡DO NOT completely empty the master cylinder reservoir or remove any brake lines otherwise complete bleeding of the braking system will be necessary.

➡DO NOT re use the removed fluid.

3. If the brake fluid level is higher than midway between the maximum fill level and the minimum allowable level, using a hand vacuum pump, siphon the brake fluid to the midway point before proceeding.
4. Raise and support the vehicle.
5. Remove the rear wheels.
6. Install 2 wheel nuts in reverse to opposite wheel studs to retain the brake disc to the hub.

➡Position the ends of the G-clamps against the rear of the brake caliper and against the outboard brake pad.

7. Install a large G-clamp over the body of the brake caliper (1).
8. Tighten the G-clamp until the brake caliper piston bottoms out in the brake caliper bore.
9. Remove the G-clamps from the brake caliper (1).
10. Place a drain tray beneath the brake caliper assembly.
11. Remove the brake hose to brake caliper banjo retaining bolt (5).

➡Install a rubber cap or plug on the exposed brake hose end in order to prevent fluid loss and contamination.

12. Separate the brake hose to brake caliper banjo retaining bolt (5) from the brake hose (1).

➡Copper brake hose sealing washers become work hardened due to the heat generated with brake applications and will not reseal. Install NEW copper brake hose sealing washers (4) whenever the brake hose to brake caliper banjo retaining bolt (5) is removed.

13. Remove and discard the 2 copper brake hose sealing washers (4). The copper

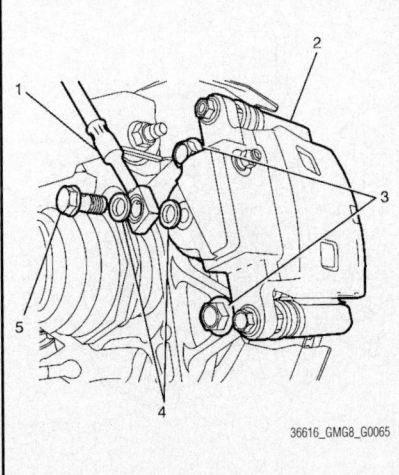

Fig. 8 Brake caliper removal—rear

REAR DISC BRAKES

brake hose sealing washers (4) may be stuck to the brake caliper (2) and/or the brake hose (1).

➡Bolts with micro-encapsulated thread sealant must be discarded after removal.

14. Remove and discard the front brake caliper anchor plate to front steering knuckle retaining bolts (3).
15. Remove the front brake caliper assembly (2) from the vehicle.

To install:

✻✻ CAUTION

To avoid any vehicle damage, serious personal injury or death when major components are removed from the vehicle and the vehicle is supported by a hoist, support the vehicle with jack stands at the opposite end from which the components are being removed and strap the vehicle to the hoist.

16. Clean the front brake caliper anchor plate mounting surfaces.
17. Check the serviceability of the brake pads.

➡The inner brake pads are marked as left and right side only.

18. Install the existing or NEW brake pads as required.
19. Press the inner brake pad by using a suitable tool to make sure the brake caliper piston bottoms out in the brake caliper bore.
20. Position the front brake caliper assembly over the brake disc.
21. Install the NEW front brake caliper anchor plate to front steering knuckle retaining bolts and tighten to 81 ft. lbs. (110 Nm).

✻✻ WARNING

Make sure the brake hose is not twisted or kinked after installation. Damage to the hose could result.

22. Install the front brake hose to brake caliper banjo retaining bolt and NEW copper sealing washers to the brake caliper. Tighten the banjo bolt to 26 ft. lbs. (35 Nm).

23. Bleed the braking system. Refer to Bleeding the Brake System.

24. Remove the 2 wheel nuts retaining the brake disc to the hub.

25. Install the rear wheels.

26. Lower the vehicle to the ground.

27. With the engine OFF, gradually apply the brake pedal to approximately ⅔ of its travel distance.

28. Slowly release the brake pedal.

29. Repeat steps 12 and 13 until a firm brake pedal is obtained. This will correctly seat the brake caliper pistons and brake pads.

30. Fill the master cylinder reservoir to the correct level. Refer to Master Cylinder Reservoir Filling.

31. Burnish (bed in) the brake pads and brake discs if required. Refer to Brake Pad & Rotor.

DISC BRAKE PADS

REMOVAL & INSTALLATION

See Figure 9.

1. Before servicing the vehicle, refer to the Precautions Section.

⁑ CAUTION

To avoid any vehicle damage, serious personal injury or death when major components are removed from the vehicle and the vehicle is supported by a hoist, support the vehicle with jack stands at the opposite end from which the components are being removed and strap the vehicle to the hoist.

2. Inspect the fluid level in the master cylinder reservoir.

➡ **If the brake fluid level is midway between the maximum fill level and the minimum allowable level, no brake fluid needs to be removed from the master cylinder reservoir before proceeding.**

➡ **DO NOT completely empty the master cylinder reservoir or remove any brake lines otherwise complete bleeding of the braking system will be necessary.**

➡ **DO NOT re use the removed fluid.**

3. If the brake fluid level is higher than midway between the maximum fill level and the minimum allowable level, using a hand vacuum pump, siphon the brake fluid to the midway point before proceeding.

4. Raise and support the vehicle.

5. Remove the rear wheels.

6. Install 2 wheel nuts in reverse to opposite wheel studs to retain the brake disc to the hub.

➡ **Position the ends of the G-clamps against the rear of the brake caliper and against the outboard brake pad.**

7. Install a large G-clamp over the body of the brake caliper (1).

8. Tighten the G-clamp until the brake caliper piston bottoms out in the brake caliper bore.

9. Remove the G-clamps from the brake caliper (1).

➡ **Bolts with micro-encapsulated thread sealant must be discarded after removal.**

10. Remove the brake caliper lower guide pin bolt (1) and discard.

⁑ WARNING

Support the brake caliper with heavy mechanic wire, or equivalent, whenever it is separated from its mount and the hydraulic flexible brake hose is still connected. Failure to support the caliper in this manner will cause the flexible brake hose to bear the weight of the caliper, which may cause damage to the brake hose and in turn may cause a brake fluid leak.

➡ **DO NOT disconnect the brake hose (1) from the brake caliper (3).**

11. Pivot the brake caliper (3) upward and secure with heavy mechanics wire (2), or equivalent.

12. Remove the brake pads (5) from the brake caliper anchor plate (4).

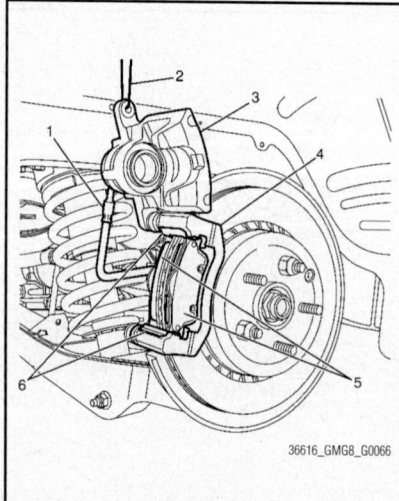

Fig. 9 Brake pad removal—rear

36616_GMG8_G0066

13. Remove the brake pad retainers (6) from the brake caliper anchor plate (4).

14. Clean the brake pad retainer mating surfaces of the brake caliper anchor plate (4).

➡ **Inspect the brake caliper guide pins for freedom of movement and the condition of the guide pin boots. This is achieved by moving the guide pins inboard and outboard within the brake caliper anchor plate (4) bores, without disengaging the slides from the boots.**

15. Inspect the brake caliper guide pins and boots for the following conditions:
- Restricted brake caliper guide pin movement
- Too much brake caliper guide pin play in the brake caliper anchor plate (4)
- Seized or binding brake caliper guide pins
- Split or torn boots

a. If any of the conditions listed are found, overhaul or replace the brake caliper (3).

To install:

16. Thoroughly clean both piston to brake pad contact faces as required.

17. Install the brake pad retainers (6) to the brake caliper anchor plate (4).

➡ **The brake pads (5) are marked as left hand inner and right hand inner and must only be fitted to their respective positions to optimize brake pad life and performance.**

18. Install the brake pads (5) to the brake caliper anchor plate (4).

⁑ WARNING

Make sure the brake hose is not twisted or kinked after installation. Damage to the hose could result.

19. Remove the mechanics wire (2) or equivalent, and rotate the brake caliper (3) into position over the brake pads (5) and to the brake caliper anchor plate (4).

20. Make sure the brake hose (1) is correctly located in its mounting bracket.

21. Install the NEW lower brake caliper guide pin bolt and tighten to 31 ft. lbs. (42 Nm).

22. Remove the 2 wheel nuts retaining the brake disc to the hub.

23. Install the rear wheels.

24. Lower the vehicle to the ground.

25. With the engine off, gradually apply the brake pedal approximately ⅔ of its travel distance.

26. Slowly release the brake pedal.

27. Repeat steps 10 and 11 until a firm

brake pedal is obtained. This will correctly seat the brake caliper pistons and brake pads.

28. Fill the master cylinder reservoir to the correct level.

29. Burnish (bed in) the brake pads and brake discs. Refer to Brake Pad & Rotor Burnishing.

BRAKE PAD & ROTOR BURNISHING

1. Before servicing the vehicle, refer to the Precautions Section.

> ✳✳ **CAUTION**
>
> **Road test a vehicle under safe conditions and while obeying all traffic**

laws. Do not attempt any maneuvers that could jeopardize vehicle control. Failure to adhere to these precautions could lead to serious personal injury and vehicle damage.

➡Burnishing the brake pads and brake discs is necessary whenever the brake discs have been refinished or replaced, and/or whenever the brake pads have been replaced to make sure that the braking surfaces are correctly prepared.

2. Select a smooth road with little or no traffic.

3. Accelerate the vehicle to 43 mph (70 km/h).

➡Use care to avoid overheating the brakes while performing this step as it may adversely affect the heating characteristics of the NEW brake pad material.

➡DO NOT allow the brakes to lock.

4. Using moderate pressure, apply the brakes to bring the vehicle to a stop.

5. Repeat steps 3 and 4 until approximately 20 stops have been completed. Allow sufficient cooling periods of no less than 500 meters between stops in order to correctly burnish the brake pads and brake discs.

BRAKES

PARKING BRAKE CABLES

ADJUSTMENT

See Figures 10 and 11.

1. Before servicing the vehicle, refer to the Precautions Section.

> ✳✳ **CAUTION**
>
> **To avoid any vehicle damage, serious personal injury or death when major components are removed from the vehicle and the vehicle is supported by a hoist, support the vehicle with jack stands at the opposite end from which the components are being removed and strap the vehicle to the hoist.**

➡The park brake cable adjustment bolt cover trim is retained by 2 clips. Gently pry upwards with fingers at the front floor console armrest latch to remove.

2. Remove the park brake cable adjustment bolt cover trim.

3. Loosen the park brake cable adjustment bolt (1) several turns to allow slack in the park brake rear cables.

4. Make sure that the park brake actuator arms have fully retracted.

5. Raise and support the vehicle.

6. Remove the rear wheels.

7. Install 2 wheel nuts in reverse to opposite wheel studs to retain the brake disc to the hub.

8. Make sure that the brake disc is free and does not bind. If the brake disc is binding refer to the following procedures:
   - Brake Rotor Thickness Variation Measurement
   - Brake Rotor Assembled Lateral Runout Measurement
   - Brake Caliper Inspection

9. Remove the access hole plug (1) from the brake disc (3).

PARKING BRAKE

10. Using a suitable lever such as a screwdriver, tighten the adjuster nut, until the brake disc is locked.

11. Loosen the adjuster nut 3–5 clicks. Make sure that the brake disc is free and does not bind.

12. Install the access hole plug.

13. Remove the 2 wheel nuts retaining the brake disc to the hub.

14. Install the rear wheels.

15. Lower the vehicle.

16. Apply the park brake until the lever is extended 4–6 clicks.

17. Tighten the park brake cable adjustment bolt to remove any excess slack from the park brake cable.

18. Make sure that this adjustment applies the park brake shoes by attempting to turn each rear wheel.

19. Release the park brake and inspect that each rear wheel is free and does not bind.

20. Lower the vehicle to the ground.

21. Install the park brake cable adjustment bolt cover trim.

PARKING BRAKE SHOES

REMOVAL & INSTALLATION

See Figure 12.

1. Before servicing the vehicle, refer to the Precautions Section.

> ✳✳ **CAUTION**
>
> **To avoid any vehicle damage, serious personal injury or death when major components are removed from the vehicle and the vehicle is supported by a hoist, support the vehicle with jack stands at the opposite end from which the components are being removed and strap the vehicle to the hoist.**

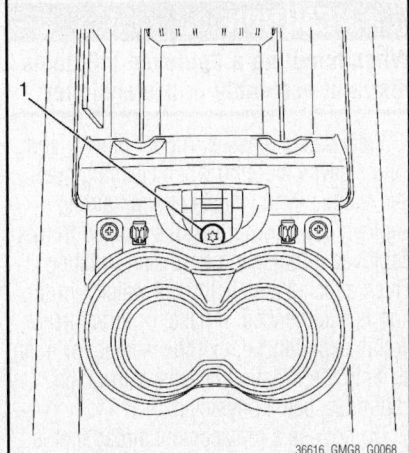

36616_GMG8_G0068

Fig. 10 Park brake cable adjustment bolt location (1)

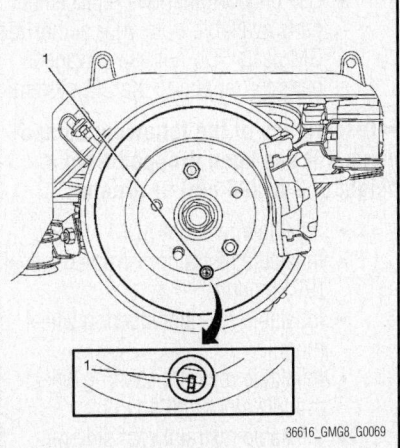

36616_GMG8_G0069

Fig. 11 Adjustment access hole plug location (1)

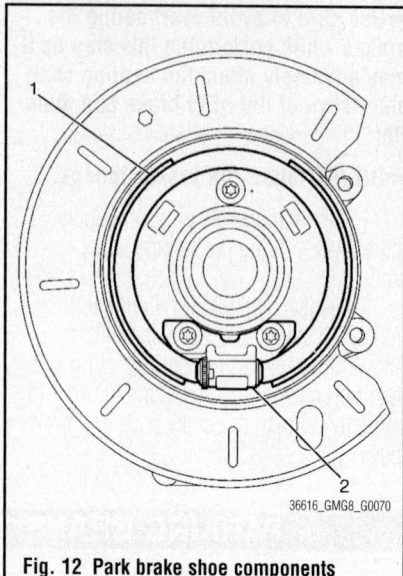

Fig. 12 Park brake shoe components

2. Raise and support the vehicle.
3. Remove the rear tire and wheel assembly.

4. Remove the park brake adjustment access hole plug from the brake disc.
5. Rotate the park brake adjuster nut until all park brake shoe adjustment has been removed.
6. Remove the rear brake caliper and brake disc. Refer to Rear Brake Caliper.
7. Remove the wheel bearing and hub assembly. Refer to Rear Wheel Bearing in Suspension.
8. Remove the park brake shoe retaining spring.

➡ Detach the park brake shoe (1) from the actuator assembly (2) by grasping the park brake shoe assembly (1) and pushing upwards.

9. Detach the park brake shoe (1) from the actuator assembly (2).
10. Remove the park brake shoe (1).

To install:

➡ Attach the park brake shoe assembly (1) to the actuator assembly (2) by

grasping the park brake shoe assembly (1) and spreading slightly while pulling the shoe over the actuator assembly (2).

11. Attach the park brake shoe assembly (1) to the actuator assembly (2).
12. Install the parking brake shoe retaining spring.
13. Install the wheel bearing and hub assembly. Refer to Rear Wheel Bearing in Suspension.
14. Install the rear brake disc and rear brake caliper. Refer to Rear Brake Caliper.
15. Adjust the park brake. Refer to Park Brake Adjustment.
16. Install the rear tire and wheel assembly.
17. Lower the vehicle.

ADJUSTMENT

Refer to Parking Brake Cables, Adjustment.

CHASSIS ELECTRICAL

AIR BAG (SUPPLEMENTAL RESTRAINT SYSTEM)

GENERAL INFORMATION

✳✳ CAUTION

These vehicles are equipped with an air bag system. The system must be disarmed before performing service on, or around, system components, the steering column, instrument panel components, wiring and sensors. Failure to follow the safety precautions and the disarming procedure could result in accidental air bag deployment, possible injury and unnecessary system repairs.

SERVICE PRECAUTIONS

✳✳ CAUTION

When performing service on or near the SIR components or the SIR wiring, the SIR system must be disabled. Refer to AIR BAG (SUPPLEMENTAL RESTRAINT SYSTEM). Failure to observe the correct procedure could cause deployment of the SIR components, personal injury, or unnecessary SIR system repairs.

➡ The sensing and diagnostic module (SDM) maintains a reserved energy supply. The reserved energy supply provides deployment power for the SIR modules. Deployment power may be

available for up to 2 minutes after disconnecting the vehicle power. Disabling the SIR system prevents deployment of the SIR modules from the reserved energy supply.

➡ The following are general service instructions which must be followed in order to properly repair the vehicle and return it to its original integrity:

- Do not expose inflator modules to temperatures above 147°F (65°C).
- Verify the correct replacement part number. Do not substitute a component from a different vehicle
- Use only original GM replacement parts available from your authorized GM dealer. Do not use salvaged parts for repairs to the SIR system

➡ Discard any of the following components if it has been dropped from a height of 3 ft. (96 cm) or greater:

- Inflatable restraint SDM
- Inflatable restraint instrument panel (I/P) module
- Inflatable restraint steering wheel module
- Inflatable restraint steering wheel module clock-spring coil
- Inflatable restraint roof side rail modules
- Inflatable restraint side impact sensors (SIS)

- Inflatable restraint seat belt pre-tensioners
- Electronic front sensors
- Front seat (with side impact module)
- Do not apply power to an inflatable restraint except as specified.
- Do not attempt to make any repairs to the inflatable restraint assembly or front/side-impact sensors. A damaged or defective component must be replaced.
- Do not weld, solder, braze, hammer, machine drill, or heat any supplemental restraint system (SIR) component.

✳✳ CAUTION

When handling a deployed inflatable restraint assembly or pretensioner:

Wear safety glasses, rubber gloves, and long sleeved clothing when cleaning powder residue from vehicle after an airbag deployment. Powder residue emitted from a deployed airbag can cause skin irritation. Flush affected area with cool water if irritation is experienced. If nasal or throat irritation is experienced, exit the vehicle for fresh air until the irritation ceases. If irritation continues, see a physician.

Do not use a replacement airbag that is not in the original packaging. This may result in improper deployment, personal injury, or death.

The factory installed fasteners, screws and bolts used to fasten airbag components have a special coating and are specifically designed for the airbag system. Do not use substitute fasteners. Use only original equipment fasteners listed in the parts catalog when fastener replacement is required.

• During any service operation that requires removal and reinstallation of a steering column fitted with an inflatable restraint assembly, always carry the steering column with two hands and with the steering wheel away from your body.

• Do not set a steering column on the floor with the steering wheel facing towards the floor.

• When carrying out steering gear removal and installation procedures, remove the ignition key from the lock and ensure the steering column is locked. If this operation is not carried out and the steering wheel is spun while the steering gear is removed, the clock spring coil will be destroyed. This will result in the sensing diagnostic module (SDM) setting a DTC, and non-deployment of the steering wheel inflatable restraint assembly.

❋❋ CAUTION

Failure to observe the special tool recommendations and instructions could cause SIR deployment, personal injury, or unnecessary SIR system repairs.

❋❋ CAUTION

When carrying an undeployed inflator module: Do not carry the inflator module by the wires or connector. Make sure the air bag opening points away from you. Failure to observe these guidelines may result in personal injury.

❋❋ CAUTION

When storing an undeployed inflator module: Make sure the air bag opening points away from the surface on which

the inflator module rests. Provide free space for the air bag to expand in case of an accidental deployment. When storing a steering column, do not rest the column with the air bag opening facing down and the column vertical. Lay the column on its side. Failure to observe these guidelines may result in personal injury.

❋❋ CAUTION

In order to prevent accidental deployment and the risk of personal injury, do not dispose of an undeployed inflator module as normal shop waste. Undeployed inflator modules contain substances that could cause severe illness or personal injury if their sealed containers are damaged during disposal. Use the following deployment procedures to safely dispose of an undeployed inflator module. Failure to observe the following disposal methods may be a violation of federal, state, or local laws.

DISABLING PROCEDURE—AIR BAG FUSE

1. Before servicing the vehicle, refer to the Precautions Section.
2. Turn the steering wheel so that the vehicles wheels are pointing straight ahead.
3. Place the ignition in the OFF position.

➥ The SDM may have more than one fused power input. To ensure there is no unwanted SIR deployment, personal injury, or unnecessary SIR system repairs, remove all fuses supplying power to the SDM. With all SDM fuses removed and the ignition switch in the ON position, the AIR BAG warning indicator illuminates. This is normal operation, and does not indicate a SIR system malfunction.

4. Locate and remove the fuse(s) supplying power to the SDM. Refer to Underhood Electrical Center in Chassis Electrical.

5. Wait 1 minute before working on the system.

ENABLING PROCEDURE—AIR BAG FUSE

1. Before servicing the vehicle, refer to the Precautions Section.
2. Place the ignition in the OFF position.
3. Install the fuse(s) supplying power to the SDM. Refer to Underhood Electrical Center in Chassis Electrical.
4. Turn the ignition switch to the ON position. The AIR BAG indicator will flash then turn OFF.
5. Perform the Diagnostic System Check if the AIR BAG warning indicator does not operate as described.

DISABLING PROCEDURE—NEGATIVE BATTERY CABLE

1. Before servicing the vehicle, refer to the Precautions Section.
2. Turn the steering wheel so that the vehicles wheels are pointing straight ahead.
3. Place the ignition in the OFF position.
4. Disconnect the negative battery cable from the battery. Refer to Battery Negative Cable Disconnection & Connection in Engine Electrical.
5. Wait 1 minute before working on system.

ENABLING PROCEDURE—NEGATIVE BATTERY CABLE

1. Before servicing the vehicle, refer to the Precautions Section.
2. Place the ignition in the OFF position.
3. Connect the negative battery cable to the battery. Refer to Battery Negative Cable Disconnection & Connection in Engine Electrical.
4. Turn the ignition switch to the ON position. The AIR BAG indicator will flash then turn OFF.
5. Perform the Diagnostic System Check if the AIR BAG warning indicator does not operate as described.

DRIVE TRAIN

AUTOMATIC TRANSMISSION ASSEMBLY

REMOVAL & INSTALLATION

V6 Engine

See Figures 13 through 17.

1. Before servicing the vehicle, refer to the Precautions Section.

2. Remove the radiator support brackets from top of radiator by raising the securing lock 10mm and then sliding the bracket off the radiator slide pin. Carry out same procedure for other bracket.

3. Disconnect the battery negative cable. Refer to Battery Negative Cable Disconnection & Connection in Engine Electrical.

4. Remove the air cleaner outlet duct. Refer to Air Cleaner in Engine Mechanical.

5. Disconnect the evaporative (EVAP) emission canister purge pipe.

✷✷ CAUTION

To avoid any vehicle damage, serious personal injury or death when major components are removed from the vehicle and the vehicle is supported by a hoist, support the vehicle with jack stands at the opposite end from which the components are being removed and strap the vehicle to the hoist.

6. Remove the engine dress cover. Refer to Engine Cover in Engine Mechanical.

7. Remove the exhaust system. Refer to Exhaust System in Engine Mechanical.

8. Remove the propeller shaft. Refer to Propeller Shaft in Rear Drive Axle.

9. Remove the front air deflector.

10. Remove the engine splash shield.

11. Remove the transmission manual shift shaft retaining nut.

12. Disconnect the shift linkage from the transmission.

13. Disconnect the transmission wiring harness connector from the transmission by rotating the locking latch counterclockwise.

14. Disconnect the wiring harness clips from the transmission, and position the wiring harness aside.

15. Remove the starter motor to gain access to the torque converter bolts. Refer to Starter in Engine Electrical.

16. Mark the torque converter to flex-plate/flywheel orientation to make sure proper realignment.

17. Repeat the following steps for all 3 torque converter bolts:

   a. Rotate the harmonic balancer centre bolt clockwise ONLY, in order to align the torque converter bolt with the starter motor opening in the engine block.

   b. Remove and discard the torque converter bolt. The bolt is self locking and is NOT reusable.

18. Using inspection hole push torque converter back towards transmission pump.

19. Place an oil drain pan under the transmission fluid cooler pipes.

20. Remove the bolt securing the transmission fluid cooler pipes brace to the engine.

21. Disconnect the fluid cooler pipes from the transmission.

22. Plug the open outlet ports to prevent fluid loss and contamination.

23. Disconnect the engine wiring harness retaining clips to the transmission mounting bolts.

24. Disconnect the steering shaft from the steering rack.

25. Remove the engine close out cover.

➡ **The engine mounts must NOT bend or deflect from the vertical position. Damage to the mount will occur.**

26. Support the power train with a suitable jack or table.

27. Remove the front sub-frame rear retaining bolts and fit bolts from special tool kit EN-48536.

28. Install bolt till stepped shank (1) is 2 mm below sub-frame (2).

29. Remove the front sub-frame front retaining bolts and fit bolts from special tool kit EN-48536.

30. Install bolt till stepped shank (1) is 2 mm below chassis rail flange (2).

31. Remove all 4 transmission mount to body retaining bolts and install 2 bolts from

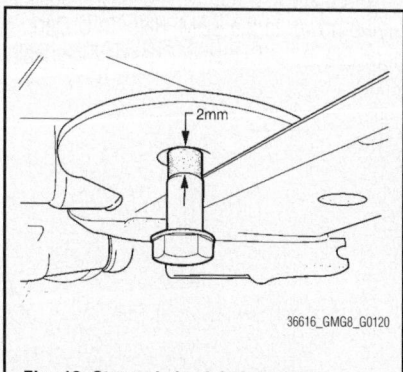

Fig. 13 Stepped shank bolt location— Sub-frame

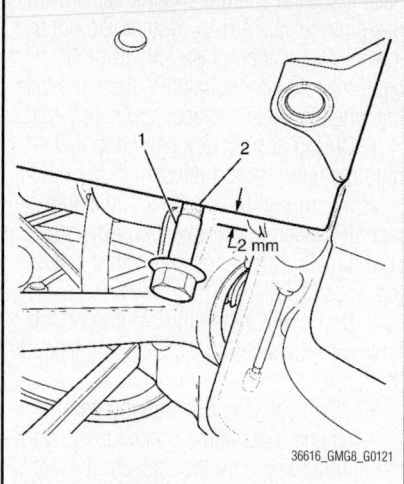

Fig. 14 Stepped shank bolt location— Chassis rail flange

special tool kit in diagonal holes e.g. left hand front and right hand rear.

32. Install the bolts until 65 mm is measured between the bolt heads (1) and transmission mount (2).

33. Remove the front sub-frame middle bolts.

34. Lower the power train slowly until the sub-frame and transmission mount are resting on bolts.

35. Insert the 65 mm spacer blocks (1) between the sub-frame (2) and chassis rails (3).

36. Tension the front sub-frame front and rear bolts. Tighten the bolts to 70 ft. lbs. (95 Nm).

37. Install and tension the middle sub-frame bolts and tighten to 70 ft. lbs. (95 Nm).

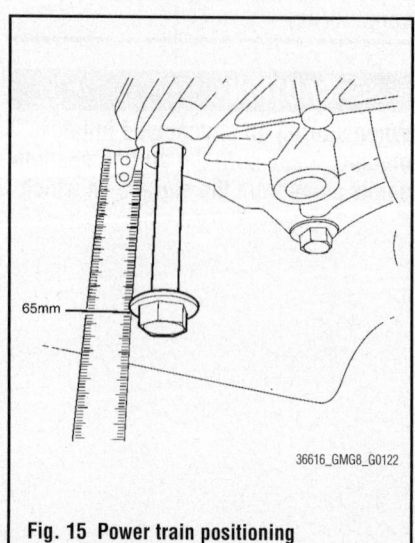

Fig. 15 Power train positioning

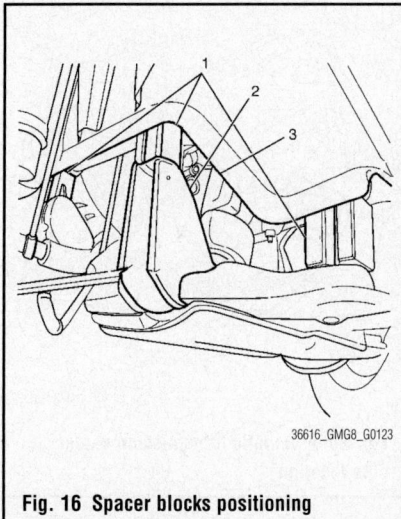

Fig. 16 Spacer blocks positioning

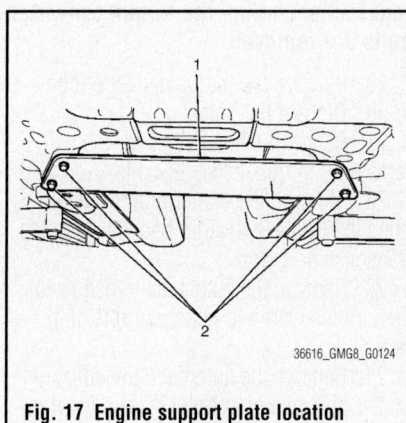

Fig. 17 Engine support plate location

38. Remove the supporting jack or table

39. Install engine support plate (1) to the front sub-frame.

40. Install the engine support plate retaining bolts (2) and tighten to 89 inch Lbs. (10 Nm).

41. Remove the transmission retaining bolts.

42. Pull the transmission free from the engine dowels.

➡**Ensure clearance is maintained between the transmission and the following:**

- The catalytic converters
- The wiring harnesses
- The cooler pipes
- The propeller shaft

43. Carefully lower the transmission from the vehicle.

44. Flush the transmission oil cooler.

To install:

➡**The engine mounts must NOT bend or deflect from the vertical position. Damage to the mount will occur.**

➡**Ensure clearance is maintained between the transmission and the following:**

- The catalytic converters
- The wiring harnesses
- The cooler pipes
- The propeller shaft

45. Using the transmission jack, carefully raise the transmission to the vehicle. Align the transmission with the engine dowels.

46. Install the right hand side transmission retaining bolts and tighten to 37 ft. lbs. (50 Nm).

47. Install the remaining transmission retaining bolts.

48. Install the engine close out cover and tighten the studs to 89 inch lbs. (10 Nm).

49. Remove the engine and transmission lowering blocks and engine balance plate.

50. Install the front sub frame to front chassis rail retaining bolts and tighten to 118 ft. lbs. (120 Nm).

51. Install the centre sub frame to front chassis rail retaining bolts and tighten to 118 ft. lbs. (120 Nm).

52. Install the rear sub frame to front chassis rail retaining bolts and tighten to 178 ft. lbs (240 Nm).

53. Connect the engine wiring harness retaining clips to the transmission mounting bolts.

54. Install the steering shaft to the steering rack.

55. Replace the O-rings seals if cracked, cut, or distorted.

56. Lubricate the O-rings seals with automatic transmission fluid.

57. Install the O-rings seals onto the cooler pipes prior to inserting the cooler pipes into the transmission.

58. Insert the transmission fluid cooler pipes into the transmission.

59. Install the bolt securing the transmission fluid cooler pipe retainer to the transmission and tighten to 18 ft. lbs (25 Nm).

60. Install the bolt securing the transmission fluid cooler pipes brace to the engine and tighten to 37 ft. lbs. (50 Nm).

61. Align the torque converter to flexplate/flywheel orientation marks made during the removal procedure.

➡**Torque converter bolts are self locking and must be replaced with NEW torque converter bolts every time the bolts are removed.**

62. Repeat the following steps for all 3 torque converter bolts:

- Rotate the harmonic balancer center bolt clockwise ONLY, in order to align the torque converter bolt holes in the flexplate/flywheel with the starter motor opening in the engine block.

- To aid in alignment of the torque converter to the flexplate/flywheel, install all 3 NEW torque converter retaining bolts before fully tightening. Tighten the bolts to 48 ft. lbs (65 Nm).

63. Install the starter motor. Refer to Starter in Engine Electrical.

64. Install the air deflector front.

65. Connect the wiring harness clips to the transmission.

66. Connect the transmission wiring harness connector to the transmission by rotating the locking latch clockwise.

67. Install the propeller shaft coupler to the transmission flange. Refer to Propeller Shaft in Rear Drive Axle.

68. Place the transmission in the park position by rotating the shift shaft fully counterclockwise.

69. Connect the shift linkage to the transmission.

70. Install the transmission manual shift shaft retaining nut and tighten to 11 ft. lbs (15 Nm).

71. Check the transmission fluid level (fill if necessary).

72. Adjust the shift control linkage. Refer to Shift Control Linkage Adjustment.

73. Install the engine splash shield.

74. Install the front air deflector.

75. Install the propeller shaft. Refer to Propeller Shaft in Rear Drive Axle.

76. Install the exhaust system. Refer to Exhaust System in Engine Mechanical.

77. Lower the vehicle.

78. Install the radiator retaining brackets onto the radiator slide pin.

79. Secure the retaining brackets by pushing the securing lock downwards until the lock reaches the bottom of the radiator bracket. Carry out the same procedure for the other bracket.

80. Install the air cleaner outlet duct.

81. Connect the negative battery cable. Refer to Battery Negative Cable Disconnection & Connection in Engine Electrical.

82. The transmission control module must be programmed with the proper software/calibrations.

83. Perform final inspection:

a. With the ignition OFF or disconnected, turn the engine by hand several times. Listen for any unusual noises or evidence that any parts are binding.

b. Start the engine and listen for abnormal sounds.

c. While the engine continues to idle, raise and support the vehicle.

d. Inspect for fluid leaks while the engine is idling.

e. Lower the vehicle.

f. Perform a final inspection for the proper fluid level.

g. Road test the vehicle.

Shift Control Linkage Adjustment

See Figure 18.

1. Before servicing the vehicle, refer to the Precautions Section.

2. Position the shift lever in PARK.

3. Raise and support the vehicle.

4. Loosen the shift control linkage adjustment bolt to allow the adjuster (1) to slide freely.

5. Hold the selector lever on the transmission against the rear stop to eliminate any play. Tighten the shift control linkage adjustment nut 80 inch lbs. (9 Nm)

6. Lower the vehicle.

7. Check the operation of the starting system with the shift lever in each position. The engine should only crank when the lever is in the PARK or NEUTRAL position.

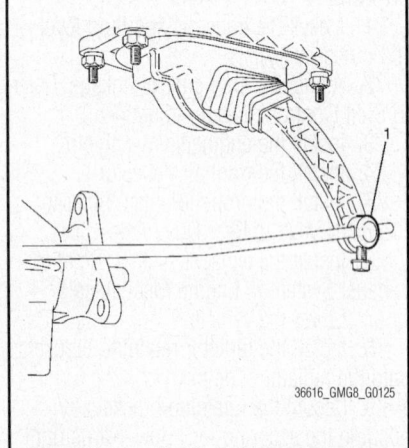

Fig. 18 Transmission linkage adjustment location

V8 Engine

See Figures 19 through 31.

1. Before servicing the vehicle, refer to the Precautions Section.

2. Place the transmission in the Park position.

3. Disconnect the battery negative cable. Refer to Battery Negative Cable Disconnection & Connection in Engine Electrical.

4. Remove the air cleaner outlet duct from the engine. Refer to Air Cleaner in Engine Mechanical.

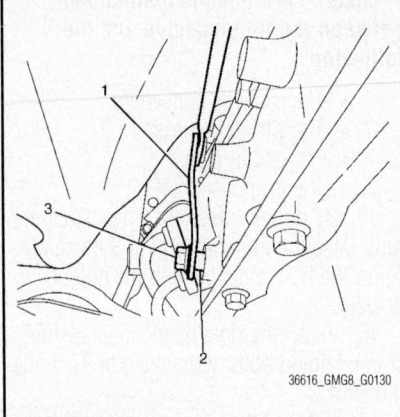

Fig. 19 Transmission manual shift shaft nut and linkage location

5. Remove the radiator support brackets from top of radiator by raising the securing lock 10mm and then sliding the bracket off the radiator slide pin. Carry out same procedure for other bracket.

6. Disconnect the evaporative (EVAP) emission canister purge pipe.

> ※※ **CAUTION**
>
> **To avoid any vehicle damage, serious personal injury or death when major components are removed from the vehicle and the vehicle is supported by a hoist, support the vehicle with jack stands at the opposite end from which the components are being removed and strap the vehicle to the hoist.**

7. Raise and support the vehicle.

8. Remove the exhaust system. Refer to Exhaust System in Engine Mechanical.

9. Remove the propeller shaft. Refer to Propeller Shaft in Rear Drive Axle.

10. Remove the front air deflector.

11. Remove the engine splash shield.

12. Remove the transmission manual shift shaft nut (3).

13. Disconnect the shift linkage (1) from the transmission shift shaft (2).

14. Remove the starter motor. Refer to Starter in Engine Electrical.

15. Remove the right flexplate inspection cover.

16. Remove the left flexplate inspection cover.

17. Rotate the harmonic balancer centre bolt clockwise ONLY, in order to align the torque converter bolt with the starter motor opening in the engine block.

18. Mark the torque converter to flexplate orientation to make sure of correct realignment.

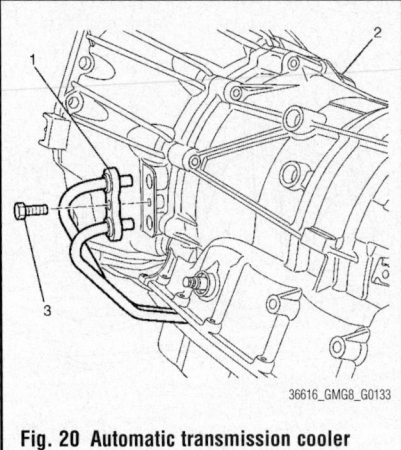

Fig. 20 Automatic transmission cooler pipe location

➡ **NEW torque converter bolts will be required each time the torque converter bolts are removed.**

19. Remove the torque converter bolt.

20. Discard the bolt.

21. Repeat previous steps for the remaining torque converter bolts.

22. Through the starter motor opening, push the torque converter back towards the transmission pump.

23. Remove the automatic transmission cooler pipe clamp to generator retaining nut.

24. Remove the automatic transmission cooler pipe retaining bolt (3) from the transmission assembly (2).

➡ **Make sure that the O-rings remain with the cooler pipes.**

25. Position the automatic transmission cooler pipes aside.

> ※※ **CAUTION**
>
> **The front wheels of the vehicle must be maintained in the straight ahead position and the steering column must be in the LOCK position before disconnecting the steering column or intermediate shaft. If these procedures are not followed, incorrect alignment of some components during installation will result and damage to the SIR coil assembly will occur.**

➡ **Observing the orientation of the intermediate steering shaft (1) with reference to the pinion shaft (3) will minimize the potential of incorrect steering column assembly alignment.**

26. Mark the intermediate steering shaft (1) in relation to the pinion shaft (3).

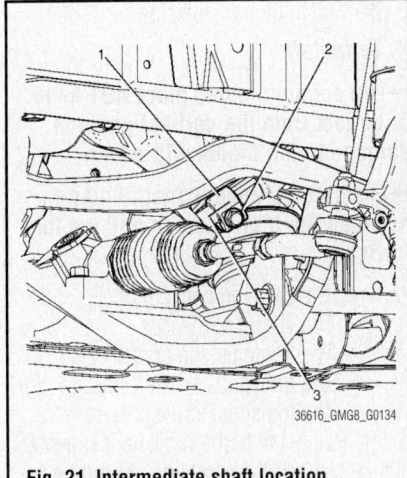

Fig. 21 Intermediate shaft location

➤ **Bolts with micro-encapsulated thread sealant must be discarded after removal.**

27. Remove the intermediate shaft to pinion shaft retaining bolt (2).

28. Discard the bolt.

29. Disconnect the intermediate shaft (2) from the pinion shaft (3).

30. Support the power train with a suitable jack or table.

31. Remove the transmission support to body retaining bolts (1).

➤ **The engine mounts must NOT bend or deflect from the vertical position. Damage to the mount will occur.**

32. Remove the front and rear sub frame to front chassis rail retaining bolts (1).

➤ **Do not tighten the bolts at this stage.**

33. Replace the front and rear sub frame to body retaining bolts with four (M16 x 2.0) 160 mm bolts from special tool kit EN-48536.

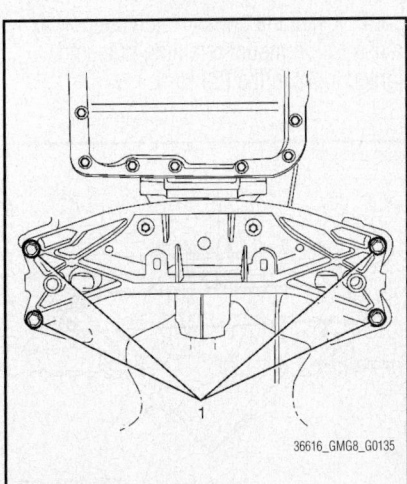

Fig. 22 Transmission support to body retaining bolt location

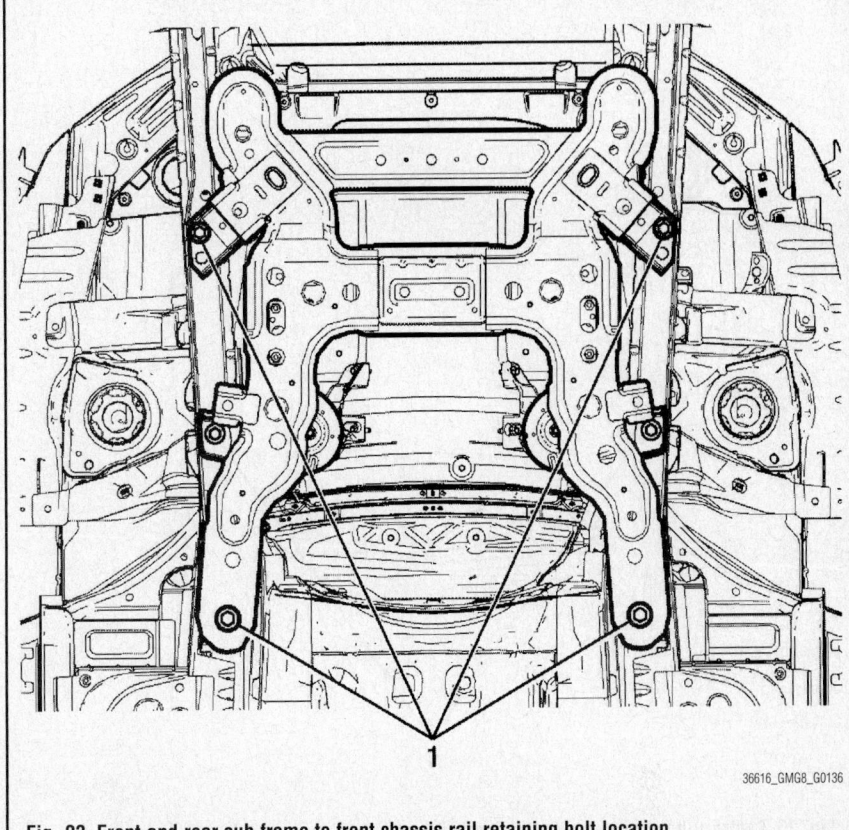

Fig. 23 Front and rear sub frame to front chassis rail retaining bolt location

34. Install the bolts until 2 mm of the thread remains visible below the sub frame.

➤ **Do not tighten the bolts at this stage.**

35. Replace the transmission support to body retaining bolts with the two (M10 x 1.5) 115 mm bolts (2) from special tool kit EN-48536 adjacent to each other. e.g. Left hand front and Right hand rear.

36. Install the bolts until 65 mm of bolt remains visible (A) between the bolt heads (2) and the transmission mount (1).

37. Remove the centre sub frame to body retaining bolts (1).

38. Lower the power train slowly until the sub frame and transmission assembly is resting on the bolt heads.

39. Insert the 65 mm spacer blocks (1) between the sub frame (2) and chassis rails (3).

40. Tighten the front and rear sub frame retaining bolts to 70 ft. lbs (95 Nm).

41. Install the remaining two (M16 x 2.0) 115 mm centre sub frame to body retaining bolts from special tool kit

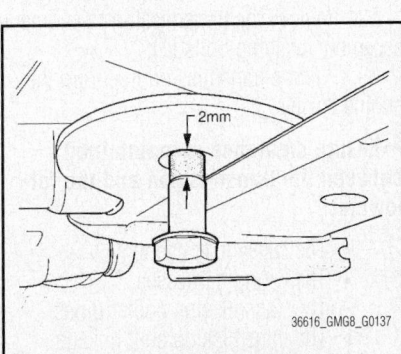

Fig. 24 Install the bolts until 2 mm of the thread remains visible below the sub frame

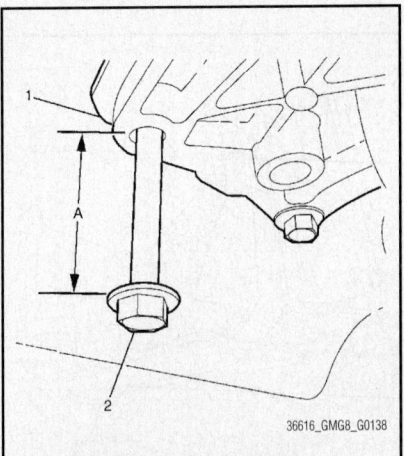

Fig. 25 Install the bolts until 65 mm of bolt remains visible between the bolt heads and the transmission mount.

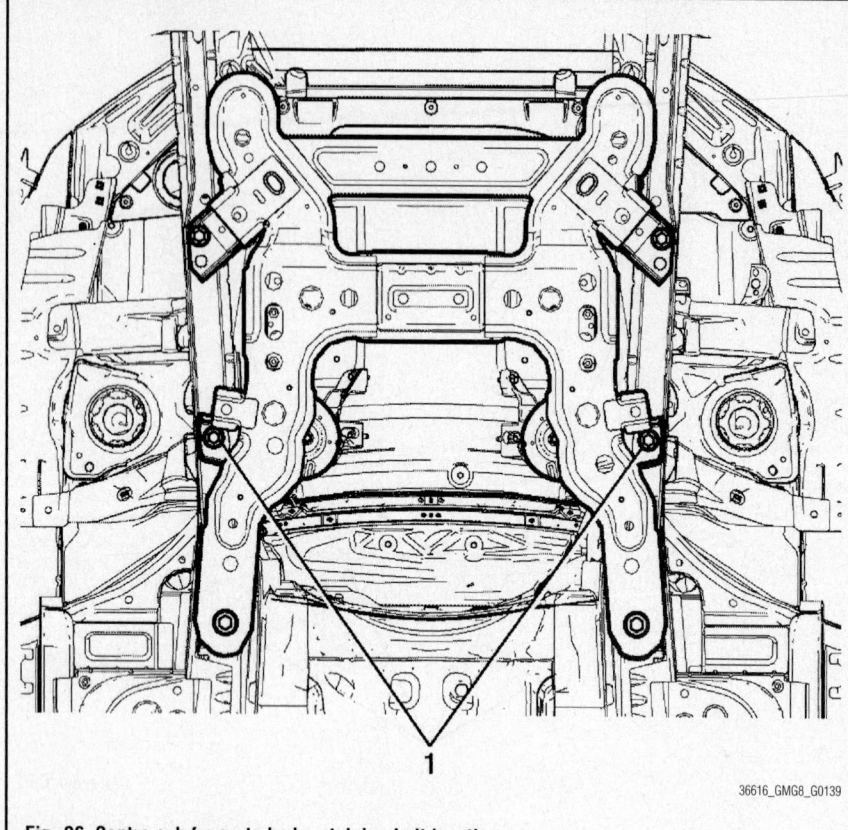

Fig. 26 Centre sub frame to body retaining bolt location

36616_GMG8_G0139

EN-48536 to the front sub frame and tighten to 70 ft. lbs (95 Nm).

42. Position the engine support plate (1) to the front sub frame.

43. Install the four (M8 x 1.25) 28 mm engine support plate to front sub frame retaining bolts (2) from special tool kit EN-48536 and tighten to 89 inch lbs. (10 Nm).

44. Support the transmission with a suitable jack or table.

45. Disconnect the transmission vent hose from the transmission.

46. Disconnect the transmission wiring harness connector from the transmission by rotating the locking latch counter-clockwise.

47. Remove the wiring harness retaining bolts (2) from the transmission.

48. Disconnect the wiring harness clips (1) from the transmission, and position the wiring harness aside.

49. Remove the transmission support to transmission mount retaining nuts.

50. Remove the two (M10 x 1.5) 115 mm special tool kit EN-48536 transmission support to body retaining bolts (1).

51. Remove the transmission mount.

52. Remove the transmission to engine assembly retaining bolts (1).

53. Pull the transmission free from the engine dowels.

➡**Ensure clearance is maintained between the transmission and the following:**

- The catalytic converters
- The wiring harnesses
- The transmission cooler pipes
- The transmission shift linkage
- The transmission vent hose.

54. Carefully lower the transmission from the vehicle.

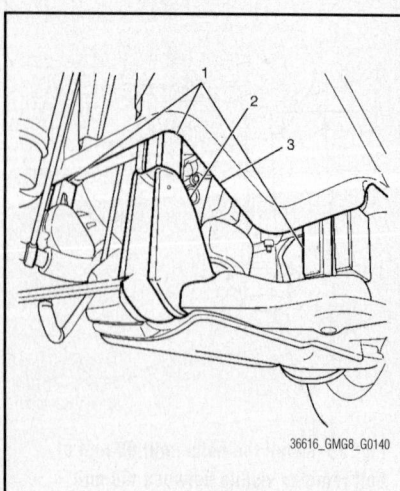

Fig. 27 65 mm spacer block location

36616_GMG8_G0140

55. Flush the transmission oil cooler.

To install:

➡**The engine mounts must NOT bend or deflect from the vertical position, damage to the mount will occur.**

➡**Ensure clearance is maintained between the transmission and the following:**

- The catalytic converters
- The wiring harnesses
- The transmission cooler pipes
- The transmission shift linkage
- The transmission vent hose

56. Rotate the harmonic balancer centre bolt clockwise ONLY to align the torque converter bolt hole that has the flexplate to torque converter alignment mark with the starter motor opening.

57. Prepare the transmission for installation by rotating the torque converter clockwise ONLY to align the torque converter bolt hole that has the alignment mark with the starter motor opening.

58. Using a suitable transmission jack, carefully raise the transmission to the vehicle.

59. Align the transmission with the engine dowels.

60. Install the transmission to engine retaining bolts (1) and tighten to 43 ft. lbs (59 Nm).

61. Install the transmission mount and tighten to 43 ft. lbs (59 Nm).

62. Install the two (M10 x 1.5) 115 mm bolts from special tool kit EN-48536 adjacent to each other. e.g. Left hand front and Right hand rear.

63. Install the bolts until 65 mm of bolt remains visible between the upper surface of the transmission mount and the vehicle body.

64. Install the transmission support to transmission mount retaining nuts and tighten to 43 ft. lbs (59 Nm).

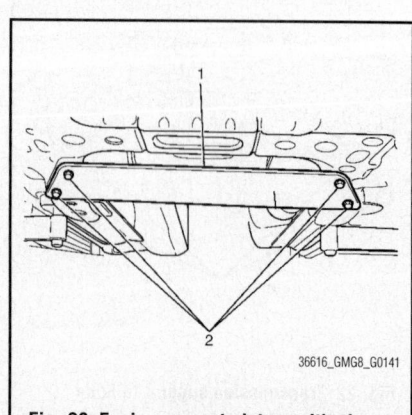

Fig. 28 Engine support plate positioning

36616_GMG8_G0141

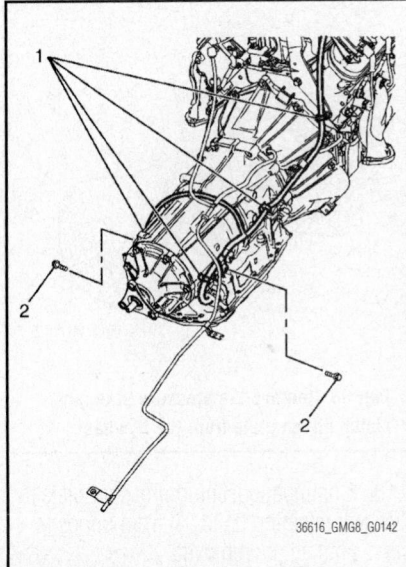

Fig. 29 Wiring harness clips and bolt locations

65. Position the transmission wiring harness to the transmission and connect the wiring harness clips to the transmission.

66. Install the wiring harness retaining bolts to the transmission and tighten to 106 inch lbs. (12 Nm).

67. Connect the transmission wiring harness connector to the transmission by rotating the locking latch clockwise.

68. Connect the transmission vent hose to the transmission.

69. Remove the four (M8 x 1.25) 28 mm engine support plate to front sub frame retaining bolts.

70. Remove the engine support plate from the front sub frame.

71. Loosen the six sub frame to front chassis rail retaining bolts by one turn each.

72. Remove the 65 mm spacer blocks from between the sub frame and chassis rails.

73. Raise the power train slowly until the sub frame and transmission mount are lifted off the bolt heads and the power train is positioned back up into the engine bay.

74. Remove the six sub frame to front chassis rail retaining bolts.

75. Install the original front and centre sub frame to front chassis rail retaining bolts and tighten to 118 ft. lbs. (160 Nm).

76. Install the original rear sub frame to front chassis rail retaining bolts and tighten to 177 ft. lbs. (240 Nm).

77. Remove the two (M10 x 1.5) 115 mm special tool kit EN-48536 transmission support to body retaining bolts.

78. Install the four original transmission support to lower sub frame retaining bolts and tighten to 43 ft. lbs. (58 Nm).

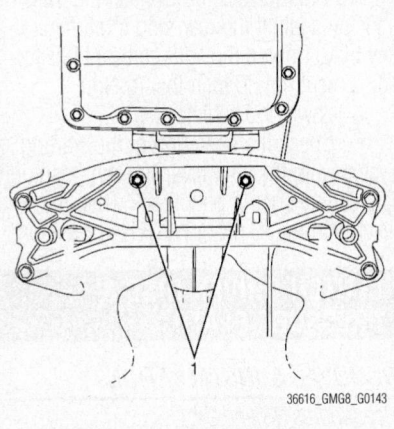

Fig. 30 Transmission support to transmission mount retaining nut locations

79. Remove the support from under the power train.

➡ **The intermediate steering shaft and pinion shaft splines must be installed in the position recorded during removal and aligned with the marks previously made.**

80. Connect the intermediate steering shaft to the pinion shaft.

81. Install a NEW intermediate steering shaft to pinion shaft retaining bolt and tighten to 18 ft. lbs. (25 Nm).

➡ **Replace the O-rings if cracked, cut, or distorted.**

82. Lubricate the O-rings with automatic transmission fluid.

83. Install the O-rings onto the cooler pipes prior to inserting the cooler pipes into the transmission.

84. Insert the transmission fluid cooler pipes into the transmission.

85. Install the automatic transmission cooler pipe retaining bolt and tighten to 15 ft. lbs. (20 Nm)

86. Install the automatic transmission cooler pipe to generator retaining nut and tighten to 17 ft. lbs (22 Nm).

87. Align the torque converter to flexplate orientation marks made during the removal procedure.

➡ **Torque converter bolts are self locking and must be replaced with NEW torque converter bolts every time the bolts are removed.**

88. Repeat the following steps for all 3 torque converter bolts:
   • Rotate the harmonic balancer centre bolt clockwise ONLY, in order to align the torque converter bolt holes in the flexplate with the

starter motor opening in the engine block.
   • To aid in alignment of the torque converter to the flexplate. Install all 3 NEW torque converter bolts before fully tightening to 46 ft. lbs (63 Nm).

89. Install the left flexplate inspection cover and tighten the retaining bolt to 89 inch lbs. (10 Nm).

90. Install the right flexplate inspection cover and tighten the retaining bolt to 89 inch lbs. (10 Nm).

91. Install the starter motor. Refer to Starter in Engine Electrical.

92. Place the transmission in the park position by rotating the shift shaft fully counter clockwise.

93. Connect the shift linkage to the transmission manual shift shaft.

94. Install the transmission manual shift shaft nut and tighten to 11 ft. lbs. (15 Nm).

95. Adjust the shift control linkage. Refer to Range Selector Lever Link Adjustment

96. Install the engine splash shield.

97. Install the front air deflector.

98. Install the propeller shaft. Refer to Propeller Shaft in Rear Drive Axle.

99. Install the exhaust system. Refer to Exhaust System in Engine Mechanical.

100. Lower the vehicle.

101. Connect the evaporative (EVAP) emission canister purge pipe.

102. Install the radiator retaining brackets onto the radiator slide pin.

103. Secure the retaining brackets by pushing the securing lock downwards until the lock reaches the bottom of the radiator bracket. Carry out the same procedure for the other bracket.

104. Install the air cleaner outlet duct to the engine. Refer to Air Cleaner Outlet Duct Replacement.

105. Connect the battery negative cable. Refer to Battery Negative Cable Disconnection & Connection in Engine Electrical.

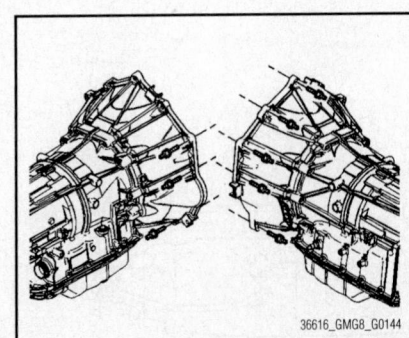

Fig. 31 Transmission to engine assembly retaining bolts locations

106. The transmission control module must be programmed with the proper software/calibrations. Programming the transmission requires a proprietary Service Programming System.

107. Perform final test:

a. Disable the ignition and fuel system:

- Remove the fuel pump fuse from the under hood body electrical centre.
- Remove the ignition relay from the under hood body electrical centre.

b. Crank the engine several times. Listen for any unusual noises or evidence that any parts are binding.

c. Enable the ignition and fuel system:

- Install the fuel pump fuse to the under hood body electrical centre.
- Install the ignition relay to the under hood body electrical centre.

d. Start the engine and listen for abnormal conditions.

e. While the engine continues to idle raise and support the vehicle.

f. Inspect for fluid leaks while the engine is idling.

g. Check the transmission fluid level (fill if necessary).

h. Lower the vehicle.

i. Road test the vehicle.

Range Selector Lever Link Adjustment

See Figure 32.

1. Before servicing the vehicle, refer to the Precautions Section.
2. Position the shift lever in PARK.
3. Raise and support the vehicle.
4. Loosen the shift control linkage adjustment bolt to allow the adjuster to slide freely.

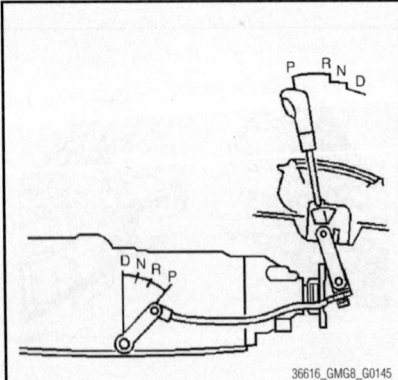

36616_GMG8_G0145

Fig. 32 Transmission linkage adjustment

5. Hold the selector lever on the transmission against the rear stop to eliminate any play. Tighten the shift control linkage adjustment nut 80 inch lbs. (9 Nm)
6. Lower the vehicle.
7. Check the operation of the starting system with the shift lever in each position. The engine should only crank when the lever is in the PARK or NEUTRAL position.

CLUTCH DRIVEN DISC & PRESSURE PLATE

REMOVAL & INSTALLATION

See Figures 33 and 34.

1. Before servicing the vehicle, refer to the Precautions Section.

> ※※ **CAUTION**
>
> **When servicing clutch parts, do not create dust by grinding or sanding the clutch disc or by cleaning parts with a dry brush or with compressed air. A water-dampened cloth NOT SOAKED should be used. The clutch disc contains asbestos fibers which can become airborne if dust is created during servicing. Breathing dust containing asbestos fibers may cause serious bodily harm.**

2. Disable the SIR system. Refer to Refer to Air Bag Disabling Procedure & Enabling Procedure in Chassis Electrical
3. Disconnect the battery negative cable. Refer to Battery Negative Cable Disconnection & Connection in Engine Electrical.

> ※※ **CAUTION**
>
> **To avoid any vehicle damage, serious personal injury or death when major components are removed from the vehicle and the vehicle is supported by a hoist, support the vehicle with jack stands at the opposite end from which the components are being removed and strap the vehicle to the hoist.**

4. Raise and support the vehicle.
5. Remove or disconnect the following:
6. Remove the transmission assembly. Refer to Manual Transmission Removal & Installation.

➡ **Marking of the flywheel is not required as it has dowel pins to ensure correct alignment.**

7. Loosen all of the pressure plate to flywheel retaining bolts (4) working from opposite sides to avoid distortion.

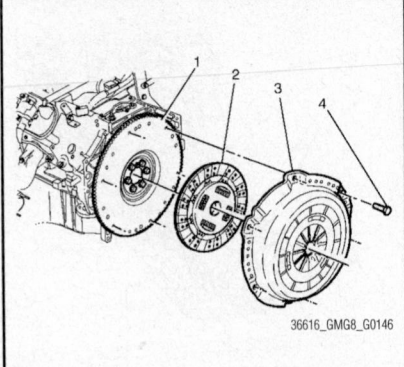

36616_GMG8_G0146

Fig. 33 Remove the pressure plate and clutch driven plate from the flywheel

8. Continue loosening pressure plate to flywheel retaining bolts (4) from opposite sides until all are removed.
9. Remove the pressure plate (3) and clutch driven plate (2) from the flywheel (1).

To install:

➡ **Before installation of the pressure and clutch driven plate, ensure that the locating dowel pins are secure in the flywheel, also ensure the self-adjusting system is reset.**

➡ **Apply any a small amount of grease to clutch driven plate splines or transmission input shaft splines.**

➡ **Install the clutch driven plate (2) with the short boss facing the flywheel (1). Flywheel side is stamped on the clutch driven plate hub (FW Side).**

10. While holding the pressure plate (3) and clutch driven plate (2) together, align them to the flywheel (1).

➡ **The pressure plate to flywheel retaining bolts (4) must not to be tightened at this stage.**

11. Install the pressure plate to flywheel retaining bolts (4).
12. Do not tighten at this stage.
13. Using a clutch driven plate centering tool (5) align the clutch driven plate (2) to the flywheel (1).
14. Install the pressure plate bolts (4), and insert the clutch centering tool (5).
15. Tighten the pressure plate to flywheel retaining bolts, using the sequence shown.

- Tighten the bolts a first pass to 11 ft. lbs. (15 Nm).
- Tighten the bolts a second pass to 26 ft. lbs. (35 Nm).
- Tighten the bolts a third pass to 41 ft. lbs (55 Nm).

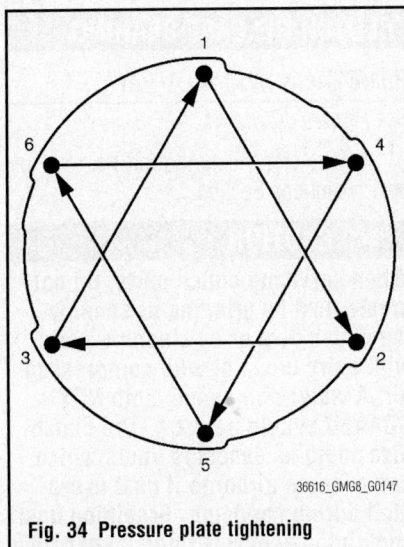

Fig. 34 Pressure plate tightening sequence

- Tighten the bolts a fourth pass to 52 Ft. lbs. (70 Nm).

16. Install the transmission assembly. Refer to Manual Transmission Removal & Installation.

17. Bleed the clutch hydraulic system. Refer to Clutch Bleeding.

18. Connect the battery negative cable. Refer to Battery Negative Cable Disconnection & Connection in Engine Electrical.

19. Enable the SIR. Refer to Refer to Air Bag Disabling Procedure & Enabling Procedure in Chassis Electrical

20. Press the clutch pedal several times to allow the self-adjusting pressure plate function to take effect.

21. Road test vehicle for correct clutch operation.

ADJUSTMENTS

See Figures 35 and 36.

1. Before servicing the vehicle, refer to the Precautions Section.

❋❋ CAUTION

When servicing clutch parts, do not create dust by grinding or sanding the clutch disc or by cleaning parts with a dry brush or with compressed air. A water-dampened cloth NOT SOAKED should be used. The clutch disc contains asbestos fibers which can become airborne if dust is created during servicing. Breathing dust containing asbestos fibers may cause serious bodily harm.

➡**Before installing the pressure plate, the self adjusting feature must be preset.**

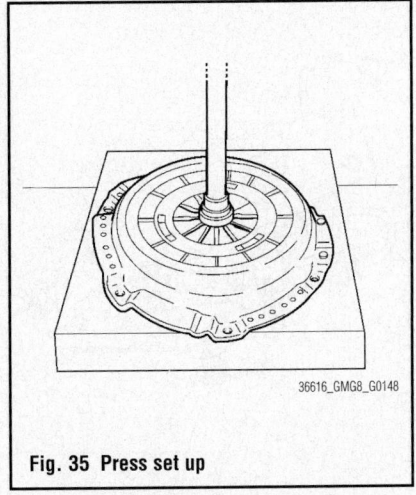

Fig. 35 Press set up

2. Place the flat side of the clutch driven plate downwards on the flat press plates, then place the pressure plate assembly over it.

➡**Do not compress the pressure plate too far, as damage may occur to the plate.**

3. Using a hydraulic press, compress the pressure plate diaphragm spring until tension is release from the clutch driven plate.

4. Hold using a suitable tool against the step adjusting ring tension spring stop in front of the adjusting ring tension spring.

➡**Do not force the adjustment ring as damage to the pressure plate may occur.**

➡**Minimal effort is required to rotate the adjustment ring.**

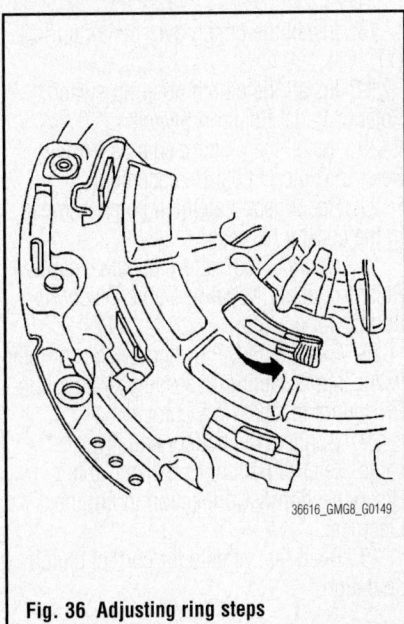

Fig. 36 Adjusting ring steps

5. Using a suitable tool, rotate the stepped adjusting ring counter-clockwise, compressing the tension springs, until the adjusting ring steps are fully adjusted out, then continue to hold in position.

6. Release the press pressure from the pressure plate diaphragm spring fingers.

7. Release the adjusting ring tension spring stops.

8. Remove the pressure plate from the press.

CLUTCH MASTER CYLINDER

REMOVAL & INSTALLATION

See Figures 37 through 39.

1. Before servicing the vehicle, refer to the Precautions Section.

❋❋ CAUTION

When servicing clutch parts, do not create dust by grinding or sanding the clutch disc or by cleaning parts with a dry brush or with compressed air. A water-dampened cloth NOT SOAKED should be used. The clutch disc contains asbestos fibers which can become airborne if dust is created during servicing. Breathing dust containing asbestos fibers may cause serious bodily harm.

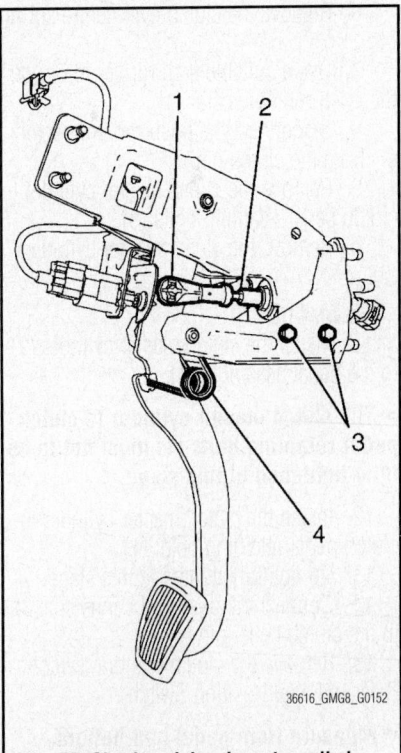

Fig. 37 Clutch pedal and master cylinder attachment locations

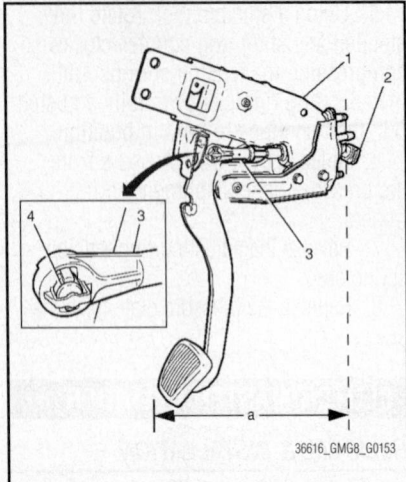

Fig. 38 Clutch pedal and master cylinder installation

2. Disable the SIR system. Refer to Refer to Air Bag Disabling Procedure & Enabling Procedure in Chassis Electrical

3. Disconnect the battery negative cable. Refer to Battery Negative Cable Disconnection & Connection in Engine Electrical.

4. Remove the clutch pedal assembly. Refer to Pedal.

5. Place the clutch pedal on a suitable work surface.

➡**Note the position of the clutch over centre spring (4).**

6. Remove the clutch over centre spring (4).

7. Use a suitable screwdriver to pry off the push rod connector (1).

8. Disconnect the push rod connector (1) from the clutch pedal.

9. Remove the clutch master cylinder to clutch pedal retaining bolts (3).

10. Remove the clutch master cylinder (2).

To install:

11. Install the clutch master cylinder (2) to the pedal assembly (1).

➡**The clutch master cylinder to clutch pedal retaining bolts (1) must not to be fully tightened at this stage.**

12. Install the clutch master cylinder to clutch pedal retaining bolts (1).

13. Do not fully tighten at this stage.

14. Connect the push rod connector (3) to the clutch pedal pin (4).

15. Remove the clutch position switch. Refer to Pedal Position Switch.

➡**Measure from pedal pad bottom edge when at the top of travel to mod plate surface plane.**

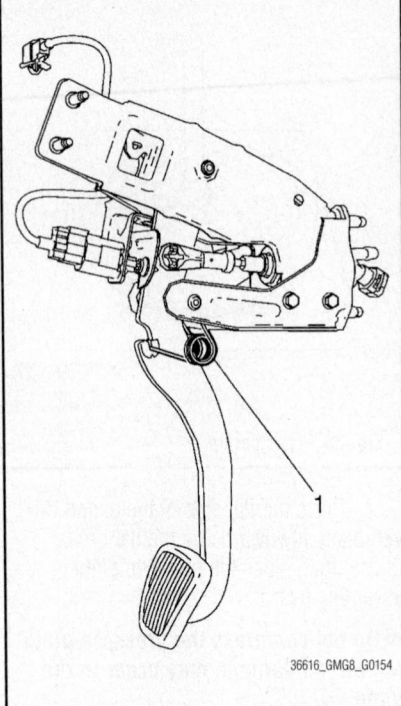

Fig. 39 Clutch over centre spring location

16. With an assistant raise clutch pedal to a height of 224 mm (a) to achieve the correct pedal height.

17. Tighten the clutch master cylinder to clutch pedal retaining bolts (1) and tighten to 106 inch lbs. (12 Nm)

➡**Pushing the pedal to the bottom of travel will assist with the clutch over centre spring (1) installation.**

➡**Make sure that the clutch over centre spring (1) is installed in its original position.**

18. Install the clutch over centre spring (1).

19. Install the clutch position switch. Refer to Pedal Position Switch.

20. Install the clutch pedal assembly. Refer to Clutch Pedal Replacement.

21. Reconnect the clutch patch harness to the cockpit harness.

22. Connect the battery negative cable. Refer to Battery Negative Cable Disconnection & Connection.

23. Enable the SIR system. Refer to Refer to Air Bag Disabling Procedure & Enabling Procedure in Chassis Electrical

24. Connect the battery negative cable. Refer to Battery Negative Cable Disconnection & Connection in Engine Electrical.

25. Road test vehicle for correct clutch operation.

CLUTCH RELEASE BEARING

REMOVAL & INSTALLATION

See Figures 40 and 41.

1. Before servicing the vehicle, refer to the Precautions Section.

❋❋ **CAUTION**

When servicing clutch parts, do not create dust by grinding or sanding the clutch disc or by cleaning parts with a dry brush or with compressed air. A water-dampened cloth NOT SOAKED should be used. The clutch disc contains asbestos fibers which can become airborne if dust is created during servicing. Breathing dust containing asbestos fibers may cause serious bodily harm.

2. Disable the SIR system. Refer to Refer to Air Bag Disabling Procedure & Enabling Procedure in Chassis Electrical

3. Disconnect the battery negative cable. Refer to Battery Negative Cable Disconnection & Connection in Engine Electrical.

❋❋ **CAUTION**

To avoid any vehicle damage, serious personal injury or death when major components are removed from the vehicle and the vehicle is supported by a hoist, support the vehicle with jack stands at the opposite end from which the components are being removed and strap the vehicle to the hoist.

4. Raise and support the vehicle.

5. Remove the transmission assembly. Refer to Manual Transmission.

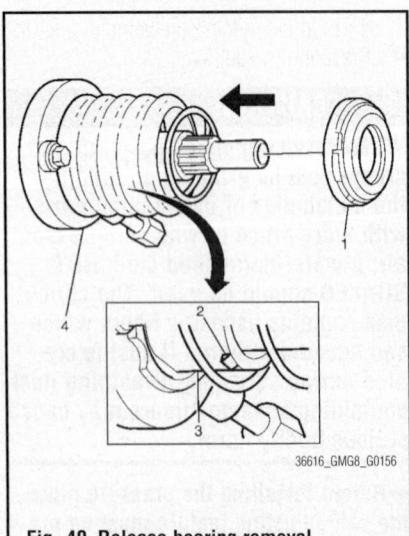

Fig. 40 Release bearing removal

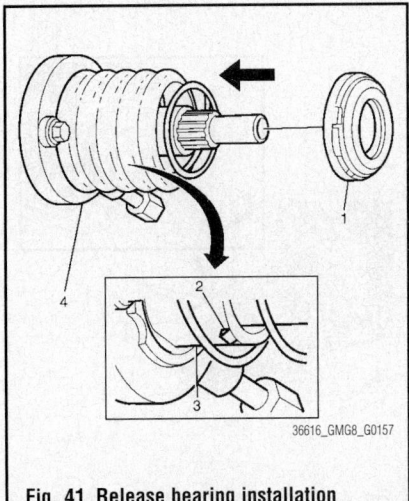

Fig. 41 Release bearing installation

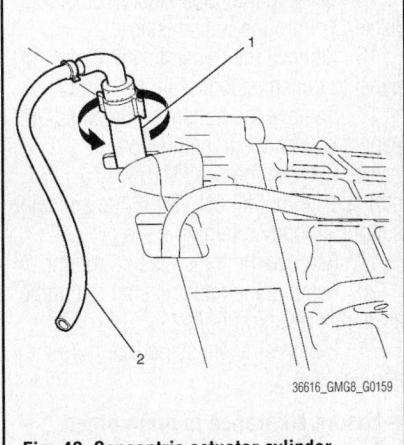

Fig. 42 Concentric actuator cylinder bleeder screw location

➡**Twist and pull the release bearing (1) to release it from the concentric actuator cylinder (3) to throw-out bearing locking tab (2).**

6. Remove the release bearing (1) from the concentric actuator cylinder (3).

To install:

7. Clean the exposed section of the concentric actuator cylinder (4) guide sleeve (3).

8. Lubricate the concentric actuator cylinder guide sleeve (3).

9. The release bearing (2) must lock into the concentric actuator cylinder to throw-out bearing locking tab (2).

10. Install the release bearing (1) to the concentric actuator cylinder guide sleeve (3).

11. Install the transmission assembly. Refer to Manual Transmission Removal & Installation.

12. Bleed the clutch hydraulic system. Refer to Clutch Bleeding.

13. Enable the SIR system. Refer to Air Bag Disabling Procedure & Enabling Procedure in Chassis Electrical

14. Connect the battery negative cable. Refer to Battery Negative Cable Disconnection & Connection in Engine Electrical.

15. Road test vehicle for correct operation.

CLUTCH HYDRAULIC BLEEDING PROCEDURE

See Figure 42.

1. Before servicing the vehicle, refer to the Precautions Section.

✳ CAUTION

When servicing clutch parts, do not create dust by grinding or sanding the clutch disc or by cleaning parts with a dry brush or with compressed air. A water-dampened cloth NOT SOAKED should be used. The clutch disc contains asbestos fibers which can become airborne if dust is created during servicing. Breathing dust containing asbestos fibers may cause serious bodily harm.

2. Clean any dirt from around the clutch fluid reservoir cap (1).

✳ WARNING

DO NOT use fluid which has been bled from a hydraulic clutch system, in order to fill the clutch master cylinder reservoir, due to the possibility that the fluid may be aerated, have too much moisture content, or be contaminated and may cause system or vehicle damage.

3. Remove the clutch fluid reservoir cap (1) and ensure the clutch fluid reservoir (2) is filled to the fill line with new hydraulic fluid. Add fluid if required from a clean sealed container.

4. Stroke the clutch pedal from the up stop to the down stop position at least 15 times slowly to avoid aeration of fluid.

✳ CAUTION

Wear Safety Glasses for the procedure.

✳ CAUTION

To avoid any vehicle damage, serious personal injury or death when major components are removed from the vehicle and the vehicle is supported by a hoist, support the vehicle with jack stands at the opposite end from which the components are being removed and strap the vehicle to the hoist.

5. Raise and support the vehicle.

6. Loosen the concentric actuator cylinder bleeder screw (1).

7. Connect one end of a rubber tube (2) to the concentric actuator cylinder bleed screw (1).

➡**Make sure that the end of the rubber tube (2) always stays submerged in a suitable container.**

8. Insert the other end of the rubber tube (2) into a clean container filled with clean brake fluid.

➡**Do not pump the clutch pedal repeatedly as entrapped air will cause fluid to foam.**

9. Using an assistant, slowly depress the clutch pedal to the down stop position.

10. Open the concentric actuator cylinder bleed screw (1) ¼ turn to release trapped air.

11. Close the concentric actuator cylinder bleed screw (1) and slowly return the clutch pedal to the up stop position.

12. Open the concentric actuator cylinder bleed screw (1) and slowly depress the clutch pedal from the up stop to the down stop position until fluid escapes through the bleeder assembly (1).

13. Close the concentric actuator cylinder bleed screw (1).

14. Return the clutch pedal to the up stop position.

15. Depress the clutch pedal from the up stop to the down stop position.

16. Open the concentric actuator cylinder bleed screw (1) and allow fluid with air bubbles to escape.

17. Close the concentric actuator cylinder bleed screw (1).

➡**Always make sure that the clutch fluid reservoir remains filled with new clean hydraulic fluid.**

18. Repeat steps 14–17 until fluid without air bubbles escapes into the container.

19. Tighten the concentric actuator cylinder bleed screw (1), with the clutch pedal still depressed, to 70 inch lbs. (8 Nm).

20. Lower the vehicle to the ground.

21. Make sure fluid level is correct.

22. Road test vehicle for correct clutch operation.

MANUAL TRANSMISSION ASSEMBLY

REMOVAL & INSTALLATION

See Figures 43 and 44.

1. Before servicing the vehicle, refer to the Precautions Section.

2. Disable the SIR system. Refer to Air Bag Disabling Procedure & Enabling Procedure in Chassis Electrical

3. Disconnect the battery negative cable. Refer to Battery Negative Cable Disconnection & Connection in Engine Electrical.

4. Remove the shift control shift close out boot.

5. Remove the shift control assembly.

➡**The engine mounts must NOT bend or deflect from the vertical position, damage to the mount will occur.**

6. Support the transmission with a suitable jack or table.

7. Disconnect the electrical connectors from the transmission.

8. Disengage the wiring harness retainers from the transmission.

9. Disconnect the electrical connectors from the transmission.

10. Disengage the wiring harness retainers from the transmission and position the wiring harness aside.

11. Using a suitable tool, disconnect the clutch hydraulic hose at the concentric slave cylinder.

12. Remove the transmission auxiliary oil cooler pipes (if necessary).

13. Remove the starter motor. Refer to Starter in Engine Electrical.

14. Remove the transmission close out panel to transmission retaining bolt (2).

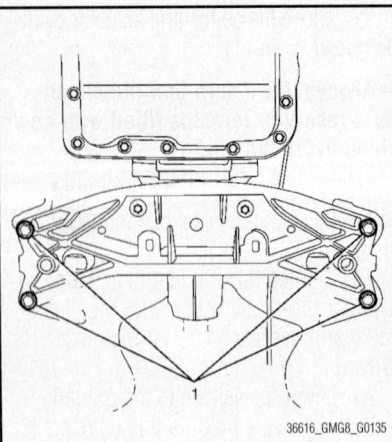

Fig. 43 Transmission support to body retaining bolt locations

36616_GMG8_G0135

15. Remove the transmission close out panel (1) from the transmission.

16. Remove the transmission close out panel to transmission retaining bolt (2).

17. Remove the transmission close out panel (1) from the transmission.

18. Remove the two (M10 x 1.5) 115 mm special tool kit EN-48536 transmission support to body retaining bolts (1).

19. Remove the transmission mount.

20. Remove the transmission to engine assembly retaining bolts (1,2,3,4).

21. Pull the transmission free from the engine dowels.

➡**Ensure clearance is maintained between the transmission and the following:**

- The catalytic converters
- The wiring harnesses
- The transmission cooler pipes

22. Carefully lower the transmission from the vehicle.

23. Flush the transmission oil cooler.

To install:

➡**The engine mounts must NOT bend or deflect from the vertical position, damage to the mount will occur.**

➡**Engage third gear on the transmission to allow for alignment of the input spline of the transmission to the clutch assembly.**

➡**Ensure clearance is maintained between the transmission and the following:**

- The catalytic converters
- The wiring harnesses
- The transmission cooler pipes

24. Using a suitable transmission jack, carefully raise the transmission to the vehicle.

25. Align the transmission with the engine dowels.

26. Install the transmission to engine block retaining bolts and tighten to 35 ft. lbs. (48 Nm)

27. Install the transmission mount. Refer to Transmission Mount Replacement.

28. Install the two (M10 x 1.5) 115 mm bolts from special tool kit EN-48536 adjacent to each other. e.g. Left hand front and Right hand rear.

29. Install the bolts until 65 mm of bolt remains visible between the upper surface of the transmission mount and the vehicle body.

30. Install the transmission close out panel to the transmission.

31. Install the transmission close out panel to transmission retaining bolt and tighten to 15 ft. lbs. (20 Nm).

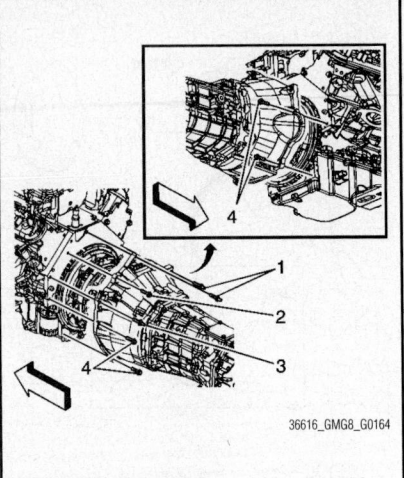

Fig. 44 Transmission to engine assembly retaining bolt locations

36616_GMG8_G0164

32. Install the transmission close out panel to the transmission.

33. Install the transmission close out panel to transmission retaining bolt and tighten to 15 ft. lbs. (20 Nm).

34. Install the starter motor. Refer to Starter in Engine Electrical.

35. Install the transmission auxiliary oil cooler pipes (if necessary).

36. Using a suitable tool, connect the clutch hydraulic hose at the concentric slave cylinder.

37. Position the transmission wiring harness to the transmission and connect the wiring harness retaining clips to the transmission.

38. Connect the electrical connectors to the transmission.

39. Connect the wiring harness retaining clips to transmission.

40. Connect the electrical connectors to the transmission.

41. Install the shift control assembly.

42. Check the transmission fluid and fill as necessary.

43. Install the shift control shift close out boot.

44. Install the console trim plate.

45. Enable the SIR system. Refer to Air Bag Disabling Procedure & Enabling Procedure in Chassis Electrical

46. Connect the battery negative cable. Refer to Battery Negative Cable Disconnection & Connection in Engine Electrical.

REAR HALFSHAFTS

REMOVAL & INSTALLATION

See Figures 45 through 49.

1. Before servicing the vehicle, refer to the Precautions Section.

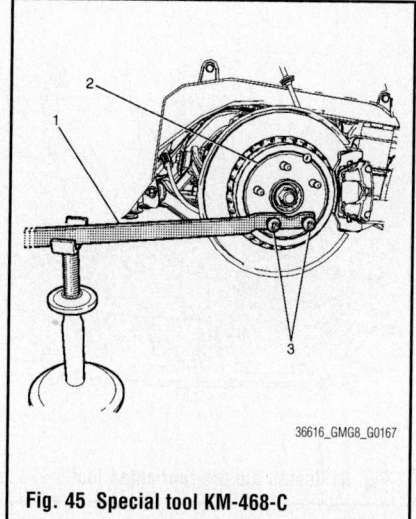

Fig. 45 Special tool KM-468-C

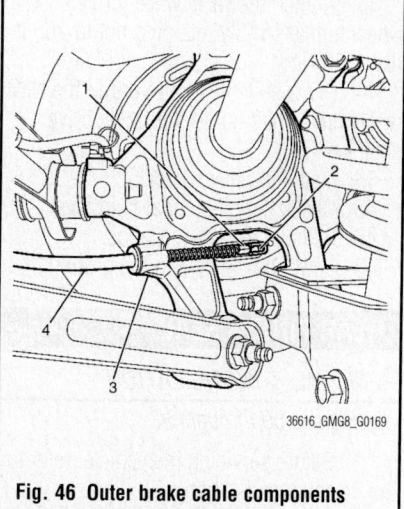

Fig. 46 Outer brake cable components

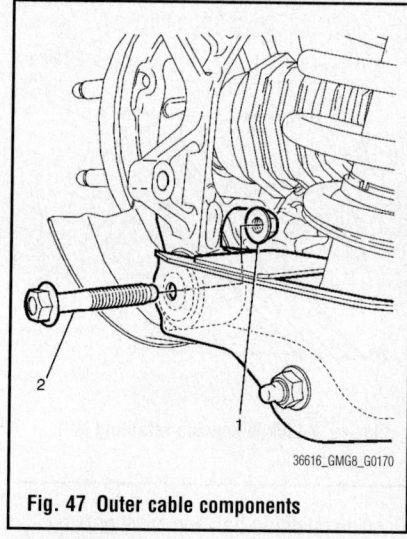

Fig. 47 Outer cable components

2. Raise and support the vehicle.

3. Remove the rear tire and wheel assemblies.

4. Install the KM-468-C (1) to the wheel hub (2) with 2 inverted wheel nuts (3).

5. Support the KM-468-C (1) outer end on a safety stand.

➡Use a suitable tool to release the crimping on the wheel drive shaft retaining nut.

➡The wheel drive shaft retaining nut must be discarded after removal.

6. Remove the wheel drive shaft retaining nut.

7. Discard the nut.

8. Remove the wheel drive shaft washer.

9. Discard the washer.

10. Remove the KM-468-C from the wheel hub.

11. Disconnect the wheel speed sensor electrical connector.

12. Detach the wheel speed sensor wiring harness mounting clip from the knuckle.

➡Using a suitable tool, detach the rear park brake cable and clevis (1) from the park brake actuator (2) by pivoting the rear park brake cable and clevis (1) rearward.

13. Detach the rear park brake cable and clevis (1) from the park brake actuator (2).

➡Remove the outer cable (4) from the rear knuckle (3) by pulling the outer cable (4) forward.

14. Remove the outer cable (4) from the rear knuckle (3).

➡Nuts with micro-encapsulated thread sealant must be discarded after removal.

15. Remove the lower control arm to knuckle retaining bolt (2) and nut (1).

16. Discard the nut.

17. Remove the I-Link to knuckle retaining bolt (1) and washer (2).

18. Remove the Y-Link to the knuckle retaining bolt (2) and nut (1).

19. Discard the nut.

➡Do not hammer the end of the wheel drive shaft to remove use 7208 .

20. Use 7208 to remove the wheel drive shaft from the wheel hub assembly.

21. Place a suitable container under the differential in order to collect draining fluid.

➡Do not pull on the interconnecting shaft as it will pull apart the inboard joint.

➡Do not damage the axle seal when disconnecting the wheel drive shaft from the differential. Cuts or abrasions will damage the axle seal and result in lubricant leakage from this area.

➡Use a suitable tool to pry the inner constant velocity joint out of the differential to release the snap ring.

➡Support the wheel drive shaft when removing as the rear sub-frame may cut the inner constant velocity boot.

22. Disconnect the wheel drive shaft from the differential.

23. Remove the wheel drive shaft from the vehicle.

24. The snap ring is a single use part and must be discarded after removal.

25. Remove the snap ring from the inner constant velocity joint.

26. Discard the snap ring.

To install:

➡The gap in the snap ring must be at the bottom.

27. Install the NEW snap ring to the wheel drive inner constant velocity joint.

➡Do not damage the axle seal when installing the wheel drive shaft to the differential. Cuts or abrasions will damage the axle seal and result in subsequent lubricant leakage from this area.

28. Install the wheel drive shaft to the differential.

➡Pull the wheel hub assembly outwards to position the wheel drive shaft through the wheel hub assembly.

29. Position the wheel drive shaft through the wheel hub assembly.

30. Install the lower control arm to

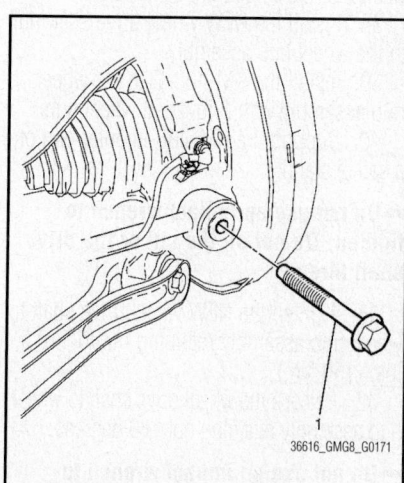

Fig. 48 I-Link to knuckle retaining bolt locations

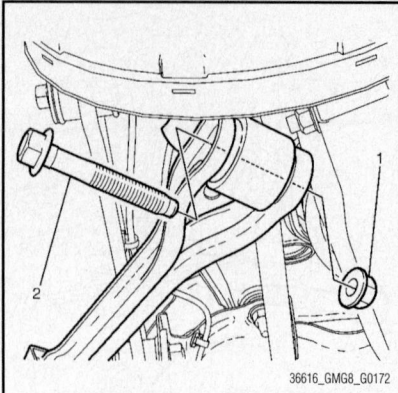

Fig. 49 Y-Link to knuckle retaining bolt locations

knuckle retaining bolt and NEW nut and tighten to 77 ft. lbs. (105 Nm).

31. Install the rear park brake cable into the rear knuckle.

32. Make sure that the rear park brake cables are properly seated.

➡**Attach the rear park brake cable and clevis to the park brake actuator by pivoting the rear park brake cable and clevis rearward using pliers.**

33. Attach the rear park brake cable and clevis to the park brake actuator.

34. Install the I-Link to knuckle retaining bolt and washer and tighten to 77 ft. lbs. (105 Nm).

35. Install the Y-Link to the knuckle retaining bolt and NEW nut and tighten to 126 ft. lbs. (170 Nm).

➡**The wheel speed sensor cable must be secured to protect it from damage.**

36. Connect the wheel speed sensor electrical connector.

37. Install the NEW wheel drive shaft washer to the wheel hub assembly.

38. Install the NEW wheel drive shaft nut to the wheel hub assembly.

39. Install the KM-468-C to the wheel hub assembly with 2 inverted wheel nuts.

40. Support the KM-468-C outer end on a safety stand.

➡**Do not use an impact wrench to tighten. Do not oil the nut or the drive shaft thread.**

41. Tighten the NEW wheel drive shaft to wheel hub assembly retaining nut to 110 ft. lbs. (150 Nm).

42. Release the wheel drive shaft to wheel hub assembly retaining nut 180 degrees.

➡**Do not use an impact wrench to tighten. Do not oil the nut or the drive shaft thread.**

43. Tighten the NEW wheel drive shaft to wheel hub assembly retaining nut to 266 ft. lbs. (360 Nm).

44. Use a suitable tool to crimp the NEW wheel drive shaft nut to the wheel drive shaft keyway.

45. Install the rear wheel.

46. Check the differential fluid level.

47. Remove the safety stands.

48. Lower the vehicle to the ground.

REAR PINION SEAL

REMOVAL & INSTALLATION

See Figures 50 through 54.

1. Before servicing the vehicle, refer to the Precautions Section.

2. A pre-fabricated tool will need to made prior to starting this procedure. Follow the steps below:

- Make from a 13mm piece of wood.
- Drill a hole at (1) and attach a one meter length of string at this point, knotted at one end.
- Drill three 8.5mm holes at a PCD of 96mm and 120 degrees apart.
- Drill three 8.5mm holes at a PCD of 110mm and 120 degrees apart.
- Drill a 50mm hole in the centre of the tool.

✸✸ CAUTION

To avoid any vehicle damage, serious personal injury or death when major components are removed from the vehicle and the vehicle is supported by a hoist, support the vehicle with jack stands at the opposite end from

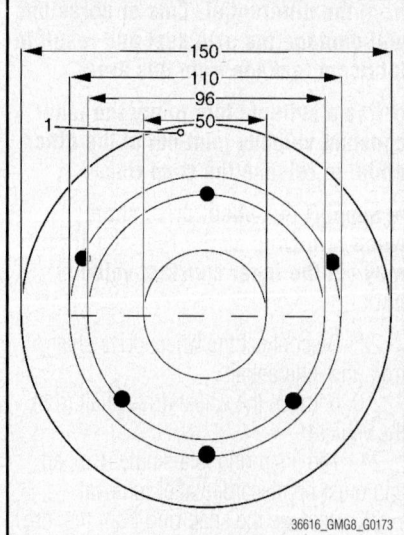

Fig. 50 Pre-fabricated tool dimensions

which the components are being removed and strap the vehicle to the hoist.

3. Raise and support vehicle.

4. Remove the intermediate exhaust assembly. Refer to Exhaust System in Engine Mechanical

5. Remove the rear tire and wheel assemblies.

6. Disconnect the propeller shaft and rubber coupling from the differential pinion flange. Refer to Propeller Shaft.

7. Secure the propeller shaft with a wire to protect it from damage.

➡**Make sure that the hand brake is off and the brake rotors freely rotate.**

8. Install the pre-fabricated tool (1) to the pinion flange.

9. Attach the spring balance (2) to the string of the pre-fabricated tool (1).

➡**The torque reading will different for in and out of the vehicle measurement.**

➡**The torque reading is required to correctly reset pinion pre-load on assembly.**

10. Pull the spring balance (2) and record the reading.

11. Example:

- With a pulley diameter of 150 mm, the radius is 75 mm, which equals .075 m. With a spring balance reading of 25 N, the pre-load equals. 075 m x 25 N = 1.875 Nm.

12. Install the 6613 (2) to the pinion flange (1).

13. While holding the 6613 (2) remove the prevailing torque pinion flange retaining nut from the differential.

14. Discard the prevailing torque pinion flange retaining nut.

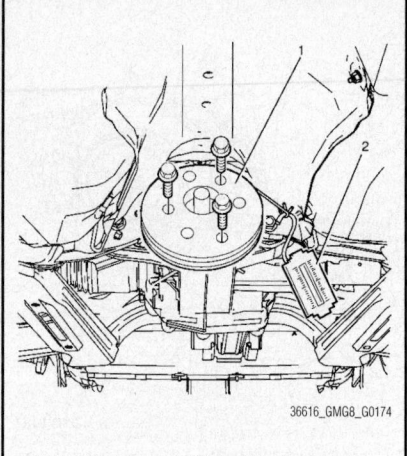

Fig. 51 Install the pre-fabricated tool

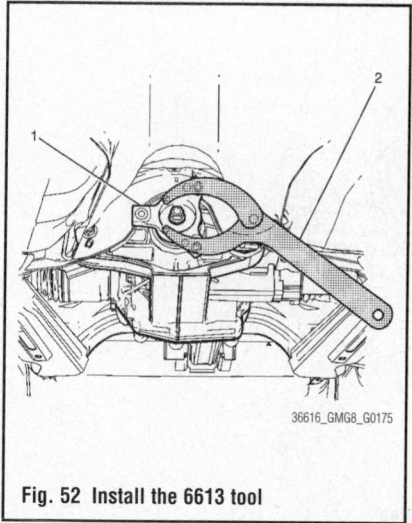

Fig. 52 Install the 6613 tool

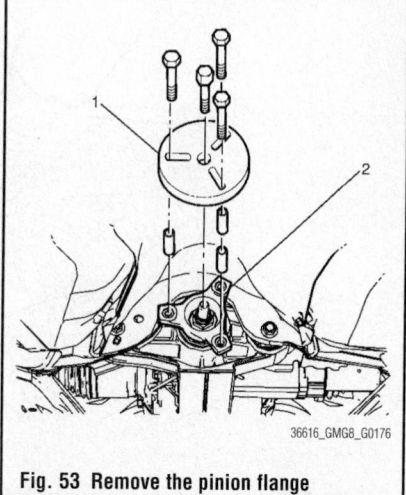

Fig. 53 Remove the pinion flange

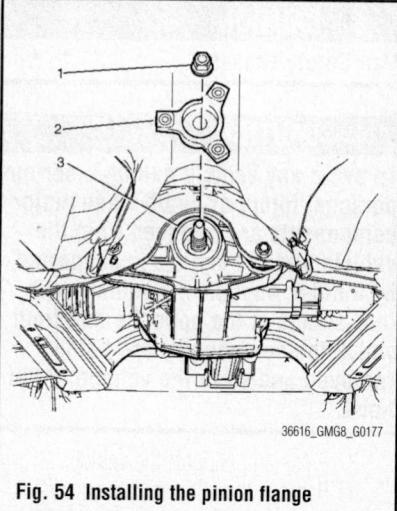

Fig. 54 Installing the pinion flange

15. Remove the 6613 (2) from the pinion flange (1).

➡**Use a suitable puller (1) to remove the pinion flange (2).**

16. Install the puller (1) to the pinion flange (2).

17. Place a large suitable container under the differential in order to collect draining fluid.

18. Use the puller (1) to remove the pinion flange (2).

19. Remove the pinion flange from the differential.

➡**The pinion flange oil seal should be replaced when replacing the pinion flange.**

20. Check the pinion flange oil seal for wear and/or damage. Replace if necessary.

21. Use E-308 to remove the pinion flange oil seal from the differential.

22. Discard the pinion flange oil seal.

To install:

23. Lubricate the NEW pinion flange oil seal with the correct grease.

➡**Do not damage any sealing surfaces when fitting the pinion flange oil seal. Cuts or abrasions will damage the assembly and result in lubricant leakage from this area.**

➡**Use DT-48727 to obtain correct seal depth.**

24. Install the NEW pinion flange oil seal to the differential with DT-48727.

25. Position the pinion flange (2) to the differential (3).

26. Lubricate the contact surface of the NEW prevailing torque pinion flange retaining nut (1) with correct grease.

27. Apply Loctite®2701 (alternative

Loctite®648) to the thread of the NEW prevailing torque pinion flange retaining nut (1).

➡**Do not fully tighten the NEW prevailing torque pinion flange retaining nut at this stage.**

28. Install the NEW prevailing torque pinion flange retaining nut (1) to the differential (3).

29. Install the 6613 to the pinion flange.

➡**Do NOT over tighten the NEW prevailing torque pinion flange retaining nut. If the prevailing torque pinion flange retaining nut is over tightened the differential will have to be disassembled.**

30. Tighten the NEW prevailing torque pinion flange retaining nut carefully until the pinion flange has no play.

31. Remove the 6613 from the pinion flange.

➡**The torque reading will different for in and out of the vehicle measurement.**

32. Install the pre-fabricated tool to the pinion flange.

33. Attach the spring balance to the string of the pre-fabricated tool.

34. Turning torque must be equal to the value recorded in the removal procedure.

➡**Do NOT over tighten the prevailing torque pinion flange retaining nut. If the prevailing torque pinion flange retaining nut is over tightened the differential will have to be disassembled.**

35. If the turning torque is below the value recorded in the removal procedure, tighten the NEW prevailing torque pinion flange retaining nut in small steps and check turning torque until specified turning torque is reached.

36. If the turning torque is above the value recorded in the removal procedure a NEW collapsible spacer must be fitted.

37. Make sure the pinion gear is free from excessive Loctite.

38. Install the propeller shaft and rubber coupling to differential flange retaining bolts. Refer to Propeller Shaft.

39. Install the intermediate exhaust assembly. Refer to Exhaust System in Engine Mechanical.

40. Check differential fluid level.

41. Remove safety stands.

42. Lower the vehicle to the ground.

PROPELLER SHAFT

REMOVAL & INSTALLATION

See Figures 55 and 56.

1. Before servicing the vehicle, refer to the Precautions Section.

2. Select park/1st gear position in the transmission and apply the park brake.

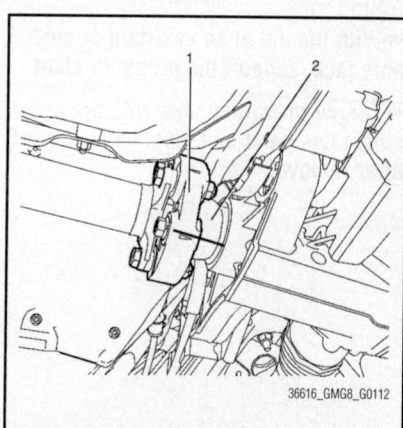

Fig. 55 Matchmarking rubber couplings with reference to the differential flange

✳✳ CAUTION

To avoid any vehicle damage, serious personal injury or death when major components are removed from the vehicle and the vehicle is supported by a hoist, support the vehicle with jack stands at the opposite end from which the components are being removed and strap the vehicle to the hoist.

3. Raise and support the vehicle.
4. Remove the intermediate exhaust assembly. Refer to Exhaust System in Engine Mechanical.
5. Remove the propeller shaft heat shield.

➡Observe the orientation of the rubber couplings with reference to the differential flange and the transmission flange. This will minimize the potential of incorrect propeller shaft installation.

6. Mark the rubber coupling (1) in relation to the differential flange (2).

➡With the aid of an assistant or suitable jack support the propeller shaft (2).

7. Remove the rubber coupling to differential flange retaining bolts (1).

➡Observe the orientation of the rubber couplings with reference to the differential flange and the transmission flange. This recommendation will minimize the potential of incorrect propeller shaft installation.

8. Mark the rubber coupling in relation to the transmission flange.

➡With the aid of an assistant or suitable jack, support the propeller shaft.

➡Torque prevailing nuts with are single use parts and must be discarded after removal.

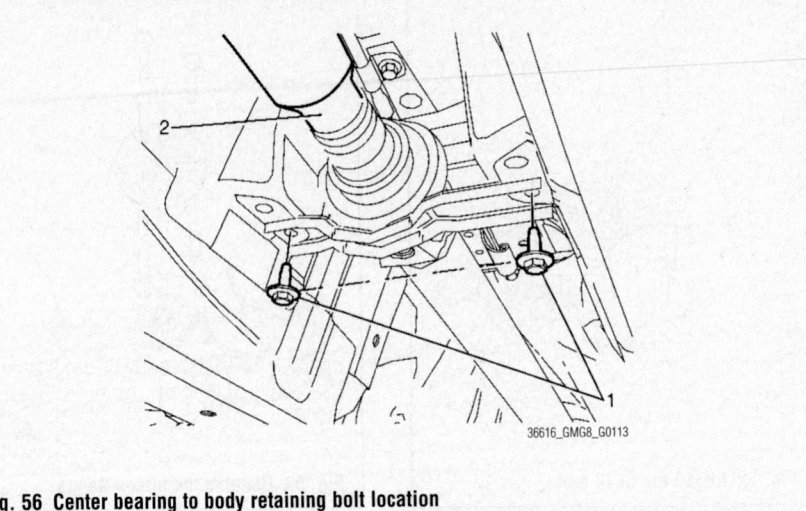

Fig. 56 Center bearing to body retaining bolt location

9. Remove the rubber coupling to transmission flange retaining bolts and torque prevailing nuts.
10. Discard the nuts.

➡With the aid of an assistant or suitable jack support the propeller shaft (2).

11. Remove the centre bearing to body retaining bolts (1).
12. Disconnect the propeller shaft (2) from the differential flange.
13. Remove the propeller shaft (2) from the vehicle.
14. Inspect the propeller shaft (2) assembly for excessive wear and/or damage.

To install:

➡Align the marks on the rubber coupling to differential flange made prior to removal.

15. Connect the rubber coupling to the differential flange.

➡With the aid of an assistant or suitable jack support the propeller shaft to the differential flange.

16. Install the rubber coupling to differential flange retaining bolts and tighten to 85 ft. lbs. (115 Nm).

➡Align the marks on the rubber coupling to transmission flange made prior to removal.

17. Connect the rubber coupling to transmission flange.

➡With the aid of an assistant or suitable jack support the propeller shaft.

➡The centre bearing to body retaining bolts must not be fully tightened at this stage.

18. Install the centre bearing to body retaining bolts.

➡With the aid of an assistant or suitable jack support the propeller shaft.

19. Install the rubber coupling to transmission flange bolts and NEW torque prevailing nuts and tighten to 72 ft. lbs. (100 Nm).
20. Tighten the centre bearing to body retaining bolts and tighten to 16 ft. lbs. (22 Nm).
21. Install the propeller shaft heat shield.
22. Install the intermediate exhaust assembly.
23. Lower the vehicle to the ground.

ENGINE COOLING

ENGINE FAN

REMOVAL & INSTALLATION

See Figures 57 and 58.

1. Before servicing the vehicle, refer to the Precautions Section.

2. Disconnect the battery ground cable from the battery. Refer to Battery Negative Cable Disconnection & Connection in Engine Electrical.

3. Remove the radiator air baffle and deflector.

4. Remove the mass air flow sensor. Refer to Mass Airflow Sensor/Intake Air Temperature Sensor in Engine Performance & Emission Controls.

5. Remove the air intake duct. Refer to Air Cleaner in Engine Mechanical.

6. Remove the radiator inlet hose. Refer to Radiator in Engine Cooling.

7. Detach and remove the coolant recovery hose from the coolant recovery hose retaining locks.

8. Detach the coolant recovery reservoir hose from the coolant recovery reservoir.

9. Detach the cooling fan motor electrical connector from the main wiring harness.

❄ CAUTION

To avoid any vehicle damage, serious personal injury or death when major components are removed from the vehicle and the vehicle is supported by a hoist, support the vehicle with jack stands at the opposite end from which the components are being removed and strap the vehicle to the hoist.

10. Raise and support the vehicle.

11. Detach the transmission cooling hoses from the fan shroud.

12. Lower the vehicle.

13. Remove the fan shroud (3) by pressing down on retaining lugs (1) to release it from the radiator assembly (2).

➡ **When removing or installing the fan assembly always hold it by the fan motor mounting struts.**

➡ **Do not grasp the assembly by the fan rings as this may cause vibrations when the fans are in motion.**

14. While holding the fan motor mounting struts remove the cooling fan and shroud assembly (1).

To install:

15. Install the cooling fan and shroud assembly.

16. Install the cooling fan and shroud assembly onto the radiator by pushing assembly forward until tabs lock into radiator retaining lugs. Listen for an audible click to confirm fitting.

❄ CAUTION

To avoid any vehicle damage, serious personal injury or death when major components are removed from the vehicle and the vehicle is supported by a hoist, support the vehicle with jack stands at the opposite end from which the components are being removed and strap the vehicle to the hoist.

17. Raise and support the vehicle.

18. Install the transmission cooling hoses onto the fan assembly.

19. Attach the cooling fan electrical connector to the main wiring harness.

20. Attach the coolant recovery hose into the coolant recovery hose retaining locks.

21. Install the radiator inlet hose. Refer to Radiator in Engine Cooling.

22. Install the air intake duct.

23. Install the MAF sensor. Refer to Mass Airflow Sensor/Intake Air Temperature Sensor in Engine Performance & Emission Controls.

24. Install the radiator air baffle and deflector.

25. Connect the battery ground lead to the vehicle. Refer to Battery Negative Cable Disconnection & Connection in Engine Electrical.

26. Start and run engine until the cooling fans are activated.

Fan Motor

See Figure 59.

1. Before servicing the vehicle, refer to the Precautions Section.

2. Remove the cooling fan and shroud assembly.

➡ **Armature shaft and nut is left hand thread.**

3. Remove the cooling fans (2) retaining nuts (3).

4. Remove the cooling fans (2) from the cooling fan motor (1).

To install:

➡ **When installing the cooling fans, ensure they are install as per removal.**

5. Install the cooling fans to the cooling fan motor.

6. Install the cooling fan to fan motor retaining nut and tighten to 53 inch lbs. (6 Nm).

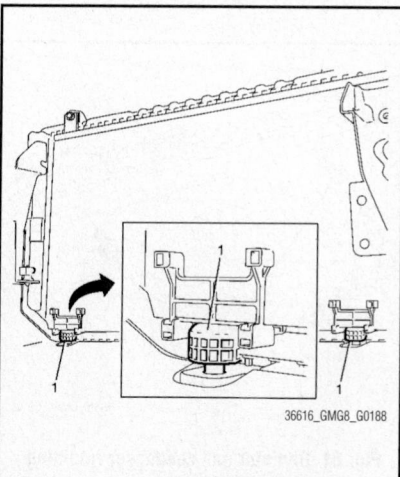

36616_GMG8_G0188

Fig. 57 Fan shroud mounting location

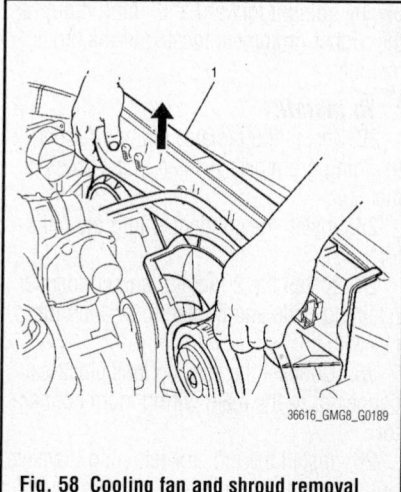

36616_GMG8_G0189

Fig. 58 Cooling fan and shroud removal

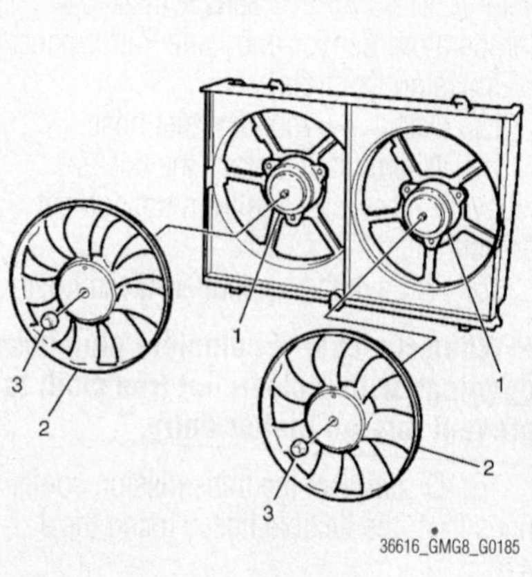

36616_GMG8_G0185

Fig. 59 Cooling fans removed

7. Install the cooling fan and shroud assembly.

8. Start and run engine until cooling fans are activated.

RADIATOR

REMOVAL & INSTALLATION

See Figures 60 and 61.

1. Before servicing the vehicle, refer to the Precautions Section.

2. Disconnect the battery ground cable from the battery. Refer to Battery Negative Cable Disconnection & Connection in Engine Electrical

✳✳ CAUTION

Ensure engine is below 50°C before removing the coolant pressure cap.

✳✳ CAUTION

To avoid any vehicle damage, serious personal injury or death when major components are removed from the vehicle and the vehicle is supported by a hoist, support the vehicle with jack stands at the opposite end from which the components are being removed and strap the vehicle to the hoist.

3. Raise and support vehicle.

4. If needed, place a suitable container beneath the radiator and engine.

5. Drain the cooling system.

6. Remove the air deflector.

7. Detach the radiator outlet hose. Refer to Radiator Outlet Hose.

8. Lower the vehicle.

9. Remove the engine cover.

10. Remove the radiator air baffle and deflector.

11. Remove the air intake duct.

12. Remove the mass air flow meter. Refer to Mass Airflow Sensor/Intake Air Temperature Sensor in Engine Performance & Emission Controls

13. Detach the radiator inlet hose.

14. Where fitted, detach the coolant recovery reservoir hose from the coolant pressure cap.

15. Remove the coolant air bleed hose.

➡**When removal is complete plug hose openings with a clean lint free cloth to prevent foreign matter entry.**

16. Disconnect the transmission cooler lines from the flexible hoses using the J 41623-B .

• Detach plastic cover from hose fitting and slide along pipe.

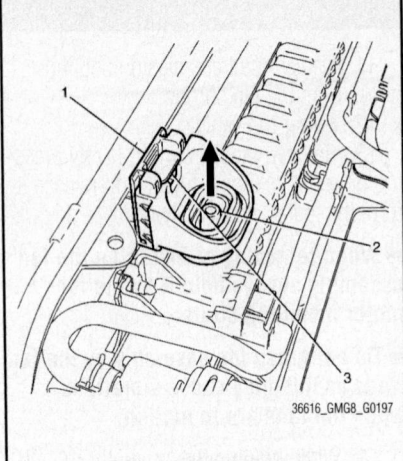

36616_GMG8_G0197

Fig. 60 Radiator support brackets

• Open the J 41623-B then close and clip around the hose to be disconnected.

• While holding the flexible hose push the hose inwards with one hand, then pull back to separate from the steel hose piping.

• Repeat procedure for the second fitting.

17. Remove the radiator support brackets (2) from top of radiator by raising the securing lock (3) 10 mm and then sliding the bracket off the radiator slide pin (1). Carry out same procedure for other bracket.

18. Disconnect the cooling fans electrical connector from the main wiring loom connector.

19. Remove the two radiator and condenser retaining bolts (1).

➡**When maneuvering the condenser take care not to fracture the A/C lines.**

20. Detach the condenser by lifting it out of the retaining brackets located on the radiator assembly.

21. Remove the radiator and fan assembly, by tilting it forward and lifting it out of the rubber grommets located in the cross member.

To install:

22. Install the radiator into the rubber retaining grommets located in the cross member.

23. Install the condenser into the radiator

24. Install the 2 radiator and condenser retaining bolts and tighten to 97 inch lbs. (11 Nm).

25. Connect the cooling fans electrical connector to the main wiring loom connector.

26. Install the radiator retaining brackets, onto the radiator slide pin.

27. Secure the retaining brackets by pushing the securing lock downwards until lock reaches bottom of radiator bracket.

➡**Make sure the cloth protecting the hose openings from contamination is removed from the hose openings before carrying out the installation procedure.**

28. Connect the flexible hoses to the transmission cooler lines. Listen for an audible click to confirm fitting.

29. Push plastic cover forward along pipe and clip onto hose fitting.

30. Install the coolant air bleed hose.

31. Where fitted, install the coolant recovery reservoir hose to the coolant pressure cap.

32. Install the radiator inlet hose.

33. Install the mass air flow meter. Refer to Mass Airflow Sensor/Intake Air Temperature Sensor in Engine Performance & Emission Controls.

34. Install the air intake duct. Refer to Air Cleaner in Engine Mechanical.

35. Install the radiator air baffle and deflector.

✳✳ CAUTION

To avoid any vehicle damage, serious personal injury or death when major components are removed from the vehicle and the vehicle is supported by a hoist, support the vehicle with jack stands at the opposite end from which the components are being removed and strap the vehicle to the hoist.

36. Raise and support vehicle.

37. Install the radiator outlet hose. Refer to Radiator Outlet Hose.

38. Install the air deflector.

39. Fill the cooling system.

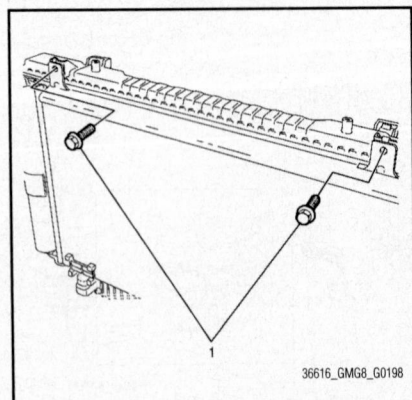

36616_GMG8_G0198

Fig. 61 Radiator and condenser retaining bolt locations

40. Lower the vehicle.
41. Install the battery ground lead to the vehicle. Refer to Battery Negative Cable Disconnection & Connection in Engine Electrical.
42. Inspect cooling system for leaks.

THERMOSTAT

REMOVAL & INSTALLATION

3.6L Engine

See Figures 62 and 63.

1. Before servicing the vehicle, refer to the Precautions Section.
2. Disconnect the battery ground cable from the battery.

> ❋❋ **CAUTION**
>
> **Ensure engine is below 50°C before removing the coolant pressure cap.**

3. Remove the radiator air baffle and deflector.
4. Remove the air intake duct.

> ❋❋ **CAUTION**
>
> **To avoid any vehicle damage, serious personal injury or death when major components are removed from the vehicle and the vehicle is supported by a hoist, support the vehicle with jack stands at the opposite end from which the components are being removed and strap the vehicle to the hoist.**

5. Raise and support the vehicle.
6. Drain the coolant into a suitable container.
7. Lower the vehicle.
8. Release the retaining hose clamp and detach the hose from the thermostat housing end.
9. Remove the thermostat housing (2)

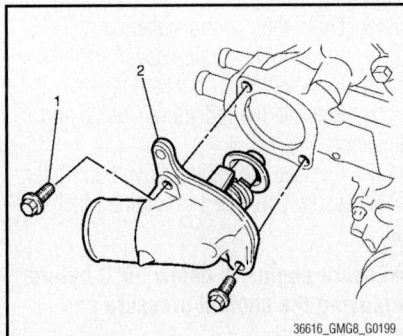

Fig. 62 Thermostat housing location— 3.6L Engine

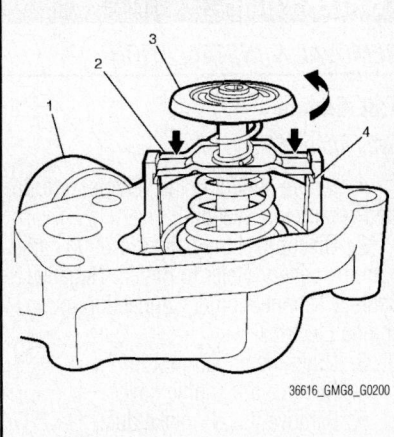

36616_GMG8_G0200

Fig. 63 Thermostat removal—3.6L Engine

to water pump retaining bolts (1), and remove thermostat housing.
10. If the housing is to be replaced, discard the O-ring.
11. Place thermostat housing in a soft jaw vice.
12. While depressing the thermostat (3), rotate the retaining bar (2) counterclockwise in the housing (1) until it clears the retaining lugs (4).
13. Carefully release the thermostat spring force.
14. Remove the thermostat from its housing.

To install:
15. Install thermostat.
   a. While pressing the thermostat, rotate the retaining bar clockwise in the housing until it locks into the retaining lugs.
16. Ensure all mating surfaces are thoroughly cleaned, using only a fine abrasive material.

➡**Ensure a new O-ring seal is used.**

17. Install the thermostat housing.
18. Install the thermostat housing to water pump retaining bolts and tighten to 124 inch lbs. (14 Nm).
19. Install the hose to the thermostat housing by opening the retaining hose clamp and securing it over the hose.

➡ **Ensure that the hoses are not twisted.**

20. Install the radiator air baffle and deflector.
21. Install the air intake duct.
22. Fill the cooling system.
23. Connect the battery ground cable to the battery. Refer to Battery Negative Cable Disconnection & Connection in Engine Electrical.
24. Inspect cooling system for leaks.

6.0L Engine

See Figures 64 and 65.

1. Before servicing the vehicle, refer to the Precautions Section.
2. Disconnect the battery ground cable from the battery.

> ❋❋ **CAUTION**
>
> **Ensure engine is below 50°C before removing the coolant pressure cap.**

3. Remove the radiator air baffle and deflector.
4. Remove the air intake duct.

> ❋❋ **CAUTION**
>
> **To avoid any vehicle damage, serious personal injury or death when major components are removed from the vehicle and the vehicle is supported by a hoist, support the vehicle with jack stands at the opposite end from which the components are being removed and strap the vehicle to the hoist.**

5. Raise and support the vehicle.
6. Drain the coolant into a suitable container.
7. Release the retaining hose clamp and detach the hose from the thermostat housing end.
8. Remove the thermostat housing to water pump retaining bolts, and remove thermostat housing.
9. If the housing is to be replaced, discard the O-ring.
10. Place thermostat housing in a soft jaw vice.
11. Press and rotate the springs of the thermostat to release it from the thermostat housing.

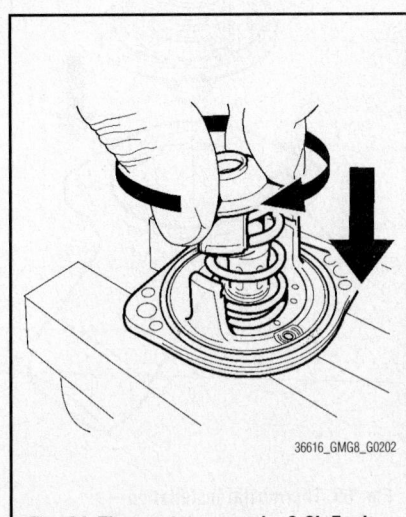

36616_GMG8_G0202

Fig. 64 Thermostat removal—6.0L Engine

12. Remove the thermostat from the thermostat housing.

To install:

13. Install thermostat.

a. Assure that the air bleed ball is not jammed by slightly shaking the assembly.

b. Place the thermostat (1) assembly into the thermostat housing (2).

c. Install the thermostat by rotating and locking it into the thermostat housing.

14. Ensure all mating surfaces are thoroughly cleaned, using only a fine abrasive material.

➡**Ensure a new O-ring seal is used.**

15. Install the thermostat housing.

16. Install the thermostat housing to water pump retaining bolts and tighten to 124 inch lbs. (14 Nm).

17. Install the hose to the thermostat housing by opening the retaining hose clamp and securing it over the hose.

➡**Ensure the hoses are not twisted.**

18. Install the radiator air baffle and deflector.

19. Install the air intake duct.

20. Fill the cooling system.

21. Connect the battery ground cable to the battery. Refer to Battery Negative Cable Disconnection & Connection in Engine Electrical.

22. Inspect cooling system for leaks.

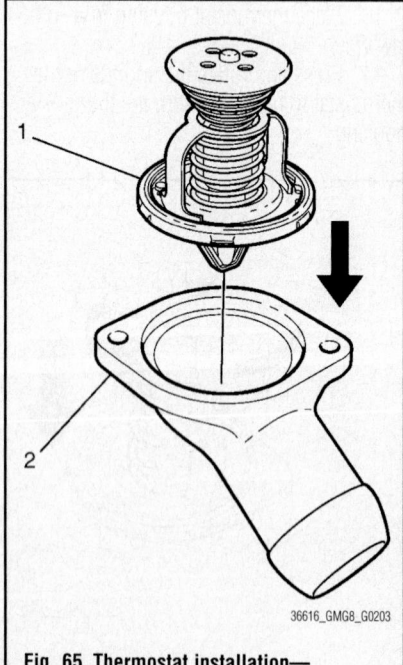

**Fig. 65 Thermostat installation—
6.0L Engine**

WATER PUMP

REMOVAL & INSTALLATION

3.6L Engine

See Figures 66 and 67.

1. Before servicing the vehicle, refer to the Precautions Section.

2. Disconnect the battery ground cable from the battery. Refer to Battery Negative Cable Disconnection & Connection in Engine Electrical.

3. Drain the cooling system.

4. Remove the engine cover.

5. Remove the air intake duct.

6. Remove the radiator air baffle and deflector.

7. Remove the engine drive belt. Refer to Accessory Drive Belt in Engine Mechanical.

➡**Ensure engine is below 50°C before removing the coolant pressure cap.**

8. Remove the water pump pulley to water pump retaining bolts (1).

9. Remove the water pump pulley (2) from the water pump (3).

➡**Use a soft hammer to separate the water pump from the engine cover.**

10. Remove the water pump to engine front cover retaining bolts (3).

11. Remove the water pump (1).

12. Remove the water pump gasket (2).

13. Discard the gasket.

To install:

14. Using a water sealant install the water pump and gasket to front engine cover.

15. Make sure all retaining bolts are clean and free of debris.

16. Install the water pump and NEW gasket.

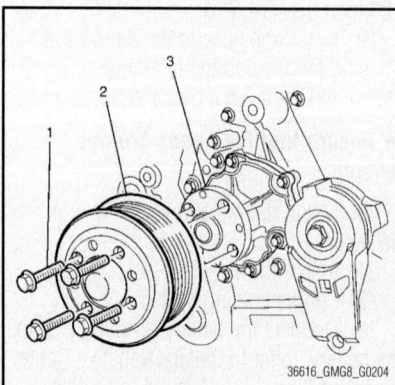

Fig. 66 Water pump pulley retaining bolt locations—3.6L Engine

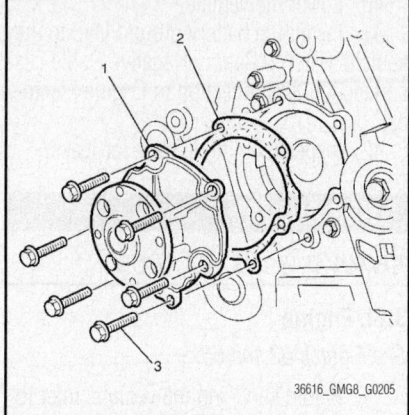

Fig. 67 Water pump retaining bolt locations—3.6L Engine

17. Install the water pump to engine front cover retaining bolts and tighten to 89 inch lbs. (10 Nm).

18. Install the water pump pulley to the water pump.

19. Install the water pump pulley to water pump retaining bolts and tighten to 89 inch lbs. (10 Nm).

20. Install the drive belt. Refer to Accessory Drive Belt in Engine Mechanical.

21. Install the air intake duct.

22. Install the radiator air baffle and deflector.

23. Install the engine cover.

24. Connect the battery ground cable to the battery. Refer to Battery Negative Cable Disconnection & Connection in Engine Electrical.

25. Fill cooling system.

26. Start engine and check for leaks.

6.0L Engine

See Figure 68.

1. Before servicing the vehicle, refer to the Precautions Section.

2. Disconnect the battery ground cable from the battery. Refer to Battery Negative Cable Disconnection & Connection in Engine Electrical.

3. Drain the cooling system.

4. Remove the engine cover.

5. Remove the air intake duct.

6. Remove the radiator air baffle and deflector.

7. Remove the engine drive belt. Refer to Accessory Drive Belt in Engine Mechanical.

➡**Ensure engine is below 50°C before removing the coolant pressure cap.**

8. Remove the coolant pressure cap.

9. Detach the inlet hose.

10. Detach the outlet hose.

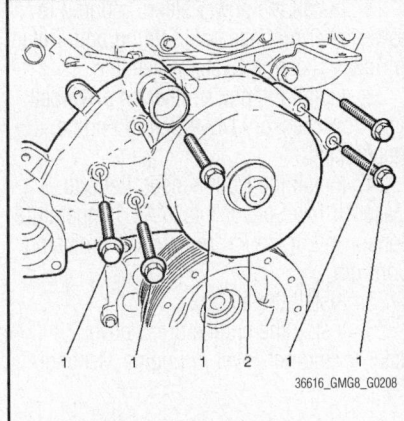

Fig. 68 Water pump retaining bolt locations—6.0L Engine

11. Detach the heater hoses from the water pump.

12. Remove drive belt tensioner. Refer to Accessory Drive Belt Tensioner in Engine Mechanical.

13. Remove the water pump (2) retaining bolts (1).

➡ **Use of a soft hammer will aid in the removal of the water pump.**

14. Remove the water pump.

To install:

➡ **Ensure all mating surfaces are clean and free of grease.**

15. Insert 2 retaining bolts at each end of the pump, place the new gasket of the bolts and use this as a guide to install the pump.

16. Install and tighten the remaining bolts a first pass to 11 ft. lbs. (15 Nm). Tighten the bolts at final pass to 18 ft. lbs. (25 Nm).

17. Install drive belt tensioner. Refer to Accessory Drive Belt Tensioner in Engine Mechanical.

18. Install the outlet hose to the water pump. Refer to Radiator Outlet Hose.

19. Install the inlet hose to the water pump.

20. Install the heater hoses to the water pump.

21. Install the engine drive belt. Refer to Accessory Drive Belt in Engine Mechanical.

22. Install the air intake duct.

23. Install the radiator air baffle and deflector.

24. Install the ground battery lead to the vehicle. Refer to Battery Negative Cable Disconnection & Connection in Engine Electrical.

25. Fill the cooling system.

26. Inspect cooling system for leaks.

ENGINE ELECTRICAL

ALTERNATOR

REMOVAL & INSTALLATION

3.6L Engine

See Figures 69 and 70.

1. Before servicing the vehicle, refer to the Precautions Section.

2. Raise and support the vehicle.

3. Disconnect the battery negative cable. Refer to Battery Negative Cable Disconnection & Connection.

4. Remove the drive belt from the alternator. Refer to Accessory Drive Belt in Engine Mechanical.

5. Disconnect the electrical connector (3) from the alternator.

6. Reposition the protective boot from the alternator output terminal for access.

7. Remove the alternator output terminal nut and disconnect the battery positive lead from the alternator.

8. Remove the alternator to alternator retaining nuts (1).

9. Remove the alternator to alternator bracket retaining studs (2).

10. Remove the alternator from the vehicle (3).

To install:

11. Install the alternator to the alternator mounting bracket.

12. Install the alternator to alternator bracket retaining studs and tighten to 13 ft. lbs. (18 Nm).

13. Install the alternator to alternator bracket retaining nuts and tighten to 13 ft. lbs. (18 Nm).

14. Install the battery positive lead and

CHARGING SYSTEM

the alternator terminal nut to the alternator and tighten to 115 inch lbs. (13 Nm).

15. Install the terminal boot.

16. Connect the electrical connector to the alternator.

17. Lower the vehicle.

18. Install the drive belt to the alternator. Refer to Accessory Drive Belt in Engine Mechanical.

19. Connect the battery negative cable.

6.0L Engine

See Figures 71 through 73.

1. Before servicing the vehicle, refer to the Precautions Section.

2. Disconnect the battery negative cable. Refer to Battery Negative Cable Disconnection & Connection.

3. Remove the engine cover.

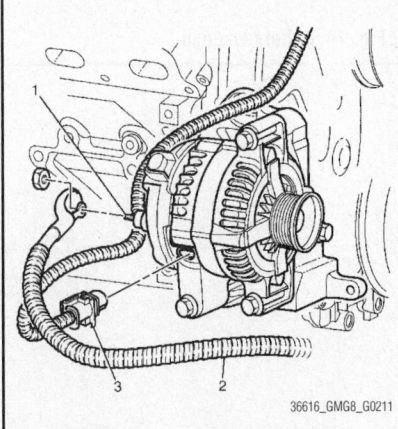

Fig. 69 Alternator electrical connectors—3.6L Engine

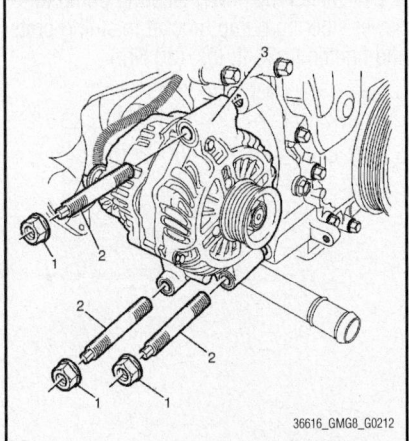

Fig. 70 Alternator bolt and nut locations

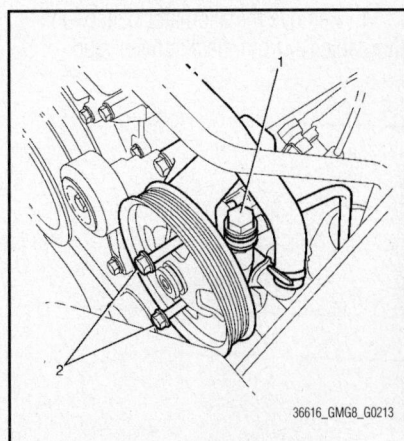

Fig. 71 Power steering pump to power steering hose banjo bolt location

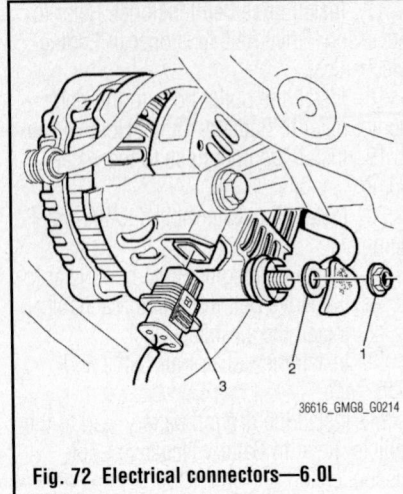

Fig. 72 Electrical connectors—6.0L Engine

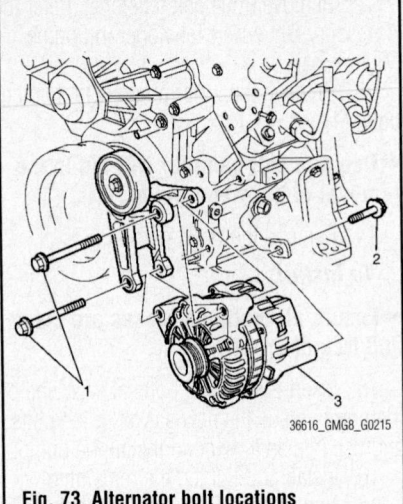

Fig. 73 Alternator bolt locations

4. Remove air filter assembly.

5. Remove the induction tube from throttle body. Refer to Air Cleaner in Engine Mechanical.

6. Remove the mass air flow (MAF) sensor. Refer to Mass Airflow Sensor/Intake Air Temperature Sensor in Engine Performance & Emission Controls.

7. Remove the drive belt. Refer to Accessory Drive Belt in Engine Mechanical.

8. Remove the power steering pump to power steering hose banjo bolt (1).

➡ **Bolts with micro-encapsulated thread sealant must be discarded after removal.**

9. Remove the power steering pump to power steering pump bracket retaining bolts (2).
- Discard the bolts.
- Place the power steering pump to allow access to the alternator.

10. Remove the alternator battery positive cable nut (1) from the alternator.

11. Remove the alternator battery positive cable (2) from the alternator stud.

➡ **Press the retainer tabs to remove electrical connector.**

12. Remove the electrical connector (3) from the alternator.

13. Remove the alternator retaining bolts (1, 2).

14. Remove the alternator (3) from the vehicle.

To install:

15. Install the alternator to the alternator mounting bracket.

16. Install alternator retaining bolts and tighten to 43 ft. lbs. (58 Nm).

17. Install the alternator battery positive cable to the alternator stud.

18. Install the alternator battery cable nut to the alternator and tighten to 89 inch lbs. (10 Nm).

➡ **Ensure locking tabs are located into the correct position.**

19. Install the electrical connector.

20. Install the power steering pump to the power steering pump bracket.

21. Install the power steering pump to power steering pump bracket retaining bolts and tighten to 23 ft. lbs. (30 Nm).

22. Install the power steering pump to power steering hose banjo fitting bolt. Refer to Power Steering System Bleeding.

23. Install the power steering drive belt. Refer to Accessory Drive Belt in Engine Mechanical.

24. Install the MAF sensor. Refer to Mass Airflow Sensor/Intake Air Temperature Sensor in Engine Performance & Emission Controls

25. Install the air box.

26. Install the engine dress cover. Refer to Engine Cover in Engine Mechanical.

BATTERY NEGATIVE CABLE

DISCONNECTION & CONNECTION PROCEDURE

See Figure 74.

1. Open the rear compartment lid.

2. Remove the left-hand cargo area carpet side access panel (1) from the left-hand cargo area carpet side (2).

➡ **Clean any existing corrosion from the battery terminal and the battery negative cable end.**

3. Remove the battery negative cable to battery terminal retaining nut (1).

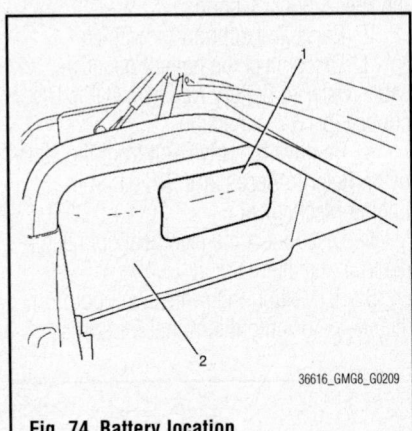

Fig. 74 Battery location

FIRING ORDERS

3.6L V6 Engine: 1-2-3-4-5-6
6.0L V8 Engine: 1-8-4-3-6-5-7-2

IGNITION COIL

REMOVAL & INSTALLATION

3.6L Engine

Bank 1

See Figure 75.

1. Before servicing the vehicle, refer to the Precautions Section.
2. Turn the ignition OFF.
3. Remove the engine cover.
4. Remove the upper intake manifold. Refer to Upper Intake Manifold in Engine Mechanical.
5. Remove the ignition coil harness connector from the ignition coil.
6. Remove the ignition coil to camshaft cover retaining bolts (1).
7. Remove the ignition coils (2) from the vehicle.

To install:

8. Install the ignition coil to the engine.
9. Install the ignition coil to camshaft cover retaining bolts and tighten to 89 inch lbs. (10 Nm).
10. Install the ignition coil harness connector to the ignition coil.
11. Install the upper intake manifold. Refer to Upper Intake Manifold in Engine Mechanical.
12. Install the engine cover. Refer to Engine Cover in Engine Mechanical.

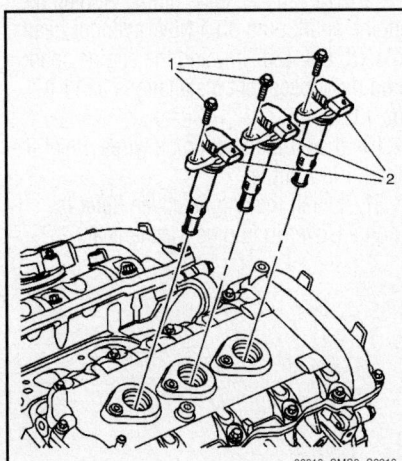

Fig. 75 Ignition coil bank 1 locations— 3.6L Engine

Bank 2

See Figure 76.

1. Before servicing the vehicle, refer to the Precautions Section.
2. Turn the ignition OFF.
3. Remove the engine cover.
4. Remove the upper intake manifold. Refer to Upper Intake Manifold in Engine Mechanical.
5. Remove the ignition coil harness connector from the ignition coil.
6. Remove the ignition coil to camshaft cover retaining bolts (1).
7. Remove the ignition coils (2) from the vehicle.

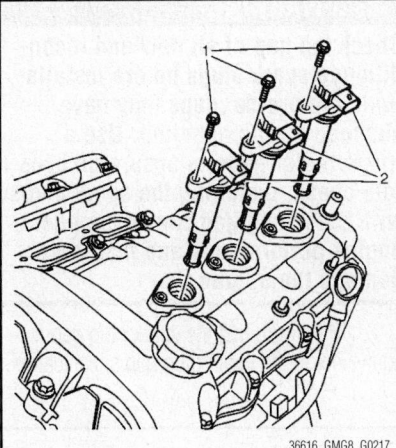

Fig. 76 Ignition coil bank 2 locations— 3.6L Engine

To install:

8. Install the ignition coil to the engine.
9. Install the ignition coil to camshaft cover retaining bolts and tighten to 89 inch lbs. (10 Nm).
10. Install the ignition coil harness connector to the ignition coil.
11. Install the upper intake manifold. Refer to Upper Intake Manifold in Engine Mechanical.
12. Install the engine cover. Refer to Engine Cover in Engine Mechanical.

6.0L Engine

See Figures 77 and 78.

1. Before servicing the vehicle, refer to the Precautions Section.
2. Disconnect the battery ground cable from the battery. Refer to Battery Negative Cable Disconnection & Connection in Engine Electrical.
3. Remove the engine cover.

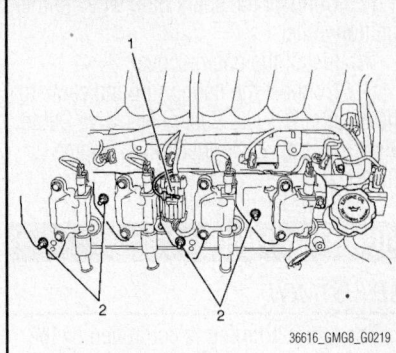

Fig. 77 Ignition coil assembly to rocker cover retaining bolt locations— 6.0L Engine

4. Disconnect the spark plug wires from the ignition coils.
5. Disconnect the main ignition coil harness connector from the ignition coil assembly.
6. Remove the ignition coil assembly to rocker cover retaining bolts.
7. Remove the ignition coil assembly from the engine.
8. Disconnect the ignition coil to ignition coil wiring harness connectors.
9. Remove the ignition coil to ignition coil assembly retaining bolts (1).
10. Remove the ignition coils from the ignition coil assembly.

To install:

11. Install the ignition coil assembly.
12. Install the ignition coil to ignition coil assembly retaining bolts and tighten to 106 inch lbs. (12 Nm).
13. Connect the ignition coil to ignition coil wiring harness connectors.
14. Install the ignition coil assembly to the engine.
15. Install the ignition coil assembly to rocker cover retaining bolts and tighten to 106 inch lbs. (12 Nm).

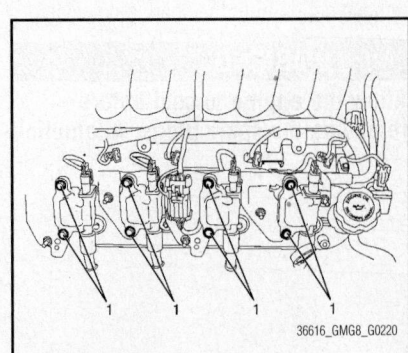

Fig. 78 Ignition coil retaining bolt locations—6.0L Engine

16. Connect the main ignition coil harness connector to the ignition coil assembly.

17. Connect the spark plug wires to the ignition coils.

18. Install the engine cover.

19. Connect the battery ground cable to the battery. Refer to Battery Negative Cable Disconnection & Connection in Engine Electrical.

IGNITION TIMING

ADJUSTMENT

The ignition timing is controlled by the Powertrain Control Module (PCM). No adjustment is necessary or possible.

SPARK PLUGS

REMOVAL & INSTALLATION

3.6L Engine

See Figure 79.

1. Before servicing the vehicle, refer to the Precautions Section.

2. Turn the ignition OFF.

3. Remove the ignition coil. Refer to Ignition Coil.

✳✳ WARNING

Clean the spark plug recess area before removing the spark plug. Failure to do so could result in engine damage because of dirt or foreign material entering the cylinder head, or by the contamination of the cylinder head threads. The contaminated threads may prevent the proper seating of the new plug. Use a thread chaser to clean the threads of any contamination.

✳✳ CAUTION

Use safety glasses.

4. Use compressed air in order to remove debris from the spark plug cavity.

✳✳ WARNING

Allow the engine to cool before removing the spark plugs. Attempting to remove the spark plugs from a hot engine may cause the plug threads to seize, causing damage to cylinder head threads.

5. Remove the spark plugs (1) from the cylinder head.

To install:

✳✳ WARNING

Use only the spark plugs specified for use in the vehicle. Do not install spark plugs that are either hotter or colder than those specified for the vehicle. Installing spark plugs of another type can severely damage the engine.

✳✳ WARNING

Check the gap of all new and reconditioned spark plugs before installation. The pre-set gaps may have changed during handling. Use a round feeler gage to ensure an accurate check. Installing the spark plugs with the wrong gap can cause poor engine performance and may even damage the engine.

6. Make sure that the spark plug gap is equivalent to the spark plug gap specification.

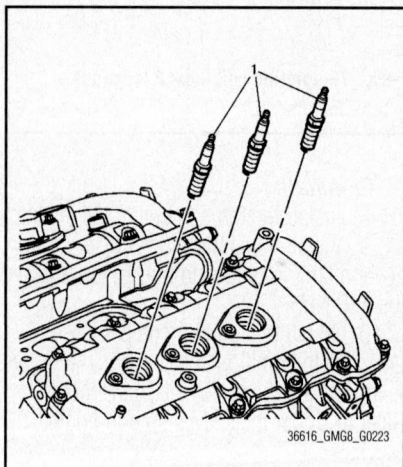

36616_GMG8_G0223

Fig. 79 Spark plug removal

✳✳ WARNING

Be sure that the spark plug threads smoothly into the cylinder head and the spark plug is fully seated.

7. Use a thread chaser, if necessary, to clean threads in the cylinder head. Cross-threading or failing to fully seat the spark plug can cause overheating of the plug, exhaust blow-by, or thread damage.

8. Install the spark plug and tighten to 15 ft. lbs. (20 Nm).

9. Install the ignition coil. Refer to Ignition Coil.

6.0L Engine

1. Before servicing the vehicle, refer to the Precautions Section.

2. Remove the engine cover.

3. Remove the spark plug wires. Refer to Spark Plug Wires.

4. Loosen each spark plug 1 or 2 turns.

✳✳ CAUTION

Use safety glasses.

5. Use a brush, or use compressed air in order to remove any dirt from the spark plugs.

6. Remove the spark plugs one at a time and place each plug in a tray marked with the corresponding cylinder numbers.

To install:

7. Inspect each spark plug gap. Adjust each plug as needed.

a. Spark plug gap: 0.040 inches (1.02 mm).

8. Hand start the spark plugs in the corresponding cylinders.

9. Tighten the spark plugs. Tighten the engine spark plug on a NEW cylinder head to 15 ft. lbs. (20 Nm) and the engine spark plug on subsequent installations to 11 ft. lbs. (15 Nm).

10. Install the spark plug wires. Refer to Spark Plug Wires.

11. Install the engine cover. Refer to Engine Cover in Engine Mechanical.

STARTER

REMOVAL & INSTALLATION

3.6L Engine

See Figures 80 and 81.

1. Before servicing the vehicle, refer to the Precautions Section.

2. Disconnect the battery negative cable. Refer to Battery Negative Cable Disconnection & Connection in Engine Electrical.

⁂ CAUTION

To avoid any vehicle damage, serious personal injury or death when major components are removed from the vehicle and the vehicle is supported by a hoist, support the vehicle with jack stands at the opposite end from which the components are being removed and strap the vehicle to the hoist.

3. Raise and support the vehicle.

4. Remove the right catalytic converter from the vehicle. Refer to Catalytic Converter in Engine Mechanical.

5. Remove the starter motor heat shield to starter motor retaining screw (1).

6. Detach the starter motor heat shield to starter motor retaining clip (2) from the starter motor (3).

7. Remove the starter motor heat shield (4).

8. Remove the starter motor to bell housing retaining bolts (2).

9. Remove the starter motor (1) from the bell housing.

10. Remove the engine wiring harness lead nut (1).

11. Remove the engine wiring harness lead terminal (4) from the starter motor.

12. Remove battery positive cable retaining nut (3) from the starter motor solenoid.

13. Remove the battery positive cable (2) from the starter motor.

To install:

14. Install the engine wiring harness lead terminal from the starter motor.

15. Install the engine wiring harness lead nut and tighten to 53 inch lbs. (6 Nm).

16. Install the battery positive cable from the starter motor.

17. Install battery positive cable retaining nut to the starter motor solenoid and tighten to 89 inch lbs. (10 Nm).

18. Maneuver the starter motor into place, locating into the correct position on the bell housing.

19. Install the starter motor to bell housing retaining bolts and tighten to 43 ft. lbs. (58 Nm).

➡**Make sure the heat shield to starter motor retaining clip is correctly attached to the starter motor.**

20. Attach the heat shield to the starter motor.

21. Install the heat shield to starter motor retaining bolt and tighten to 44 inch lbs. (5 Nm).

22. Install the right catalytic converter to the vehicle. Refer to Catalytic Converter in Engine Mechanical.

23. Lower the vehicle.

24. Connect the battery negative cable. Refer to Battery Negative Cable Disconnection & Connection in Engine Electrical.

6.0L Engine

See Figures 82 and 83.

1. Before servicing the vehicle, refer to the Precautions Section.

2. Disconnect the battery negative cable. Refer to Battery Negative Cable Disconnection & Connection in Engine Electrical.

⁂ WARNING

To avoid any vehicle damage, serious personal injury or death when major components are removed from the vehicle and the vehicle is supported by a hoist, support the vehicle with jack stands at the opposite end from which the components are being removed and strap the vehicle to the hoist.

3. Raise and support the vehicle.

4. Remove the right catalytic converter from the vehicle. Refer to Catalytic Converter in Engine Mechanical.

5. Remove the starter motor heat shield to starter motor retaining bolts.

6. Remove the heat shield from the vehicle.

7. Remove the engine wiring harness lead nut (1).

8. Remove the engine wiring harness lead terminal (4) from the starter motor.

9. Remove battery positive cable retaining nut (2) from the starter motor solenoid.

10. Remove the battery positive cable (3) from the starter motor.

11. Remove starter motor to engine block retaining bolts (1).

12. Maneuver the starter motor (2) out

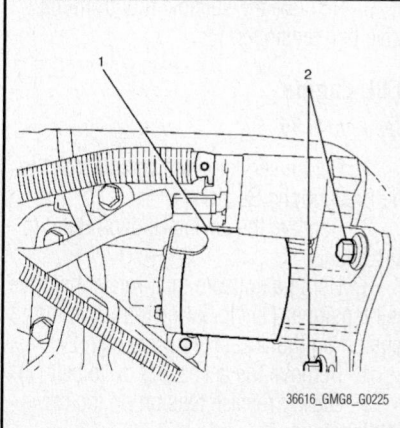

Fig. 80 Starter motor bolt locations— 3.6L Engine

36616_GMG8_G0225

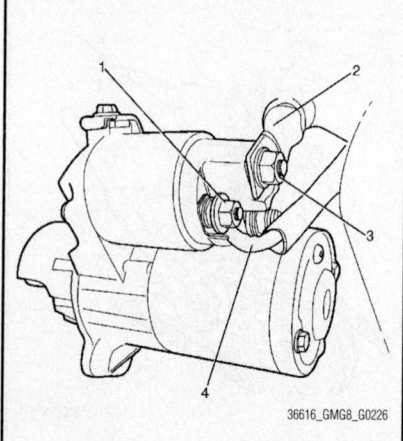

Fig. 81 Starter attachments—3.6L Engine

36616_GMG8_G0226

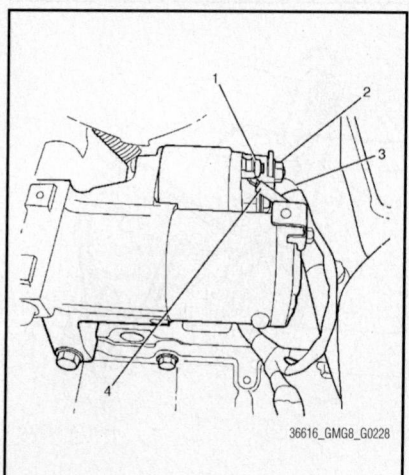

Fig. 82 Starter attachments—6.0L Engine

36616_GMG8_G0228

and down between the transmission bell housing and body sub frame.

To install:

13. Maneuver the starter motor into position between the transmission bell housing and body sub frame.

14. Install starter motor to bell housing retaining bolts and tighten to 37 ft. lbs. (50 Nm).

15. Install the engine wiring harness lead terminal from the starter motor.

16. Install the engine wiring harness lead nut and tighten to 53 inch lbs. (6 Nm).

17. Install the battery positive cable from the starter motor.

18. Install battery positive cable retaining nut from the starter motor solenoid.

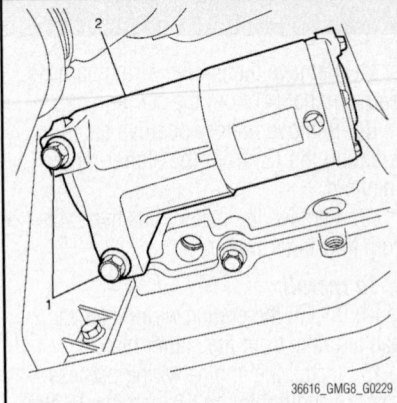

Fig. 83 Starter motor bolt locations—6.0L Engine

19. Install battery positive cable retaining nut to the starter motor battery positive terminal and tighten to 89 inch lbs. (10 Nm).

20. Install the heat shield to the vehicle.

21. Install the heat shield to starter motor retaining bolts and tighten to 44 inch lbs. (5 Nm).

22. Install the right catalytic converter to the vehicle. Refer to Catalytic Converter in Engine Mechanical.

23. Lower the vehicle.

24. Connect the battery negative cable. Refer to Battery Negative Cable Disconnection & Connection in Engine Electrical.

ENGINE MECHANICAL

ACCESSORY DRIVE BELTS

ACCESSORY BELT ROUTING

See Figures 84 and 85.

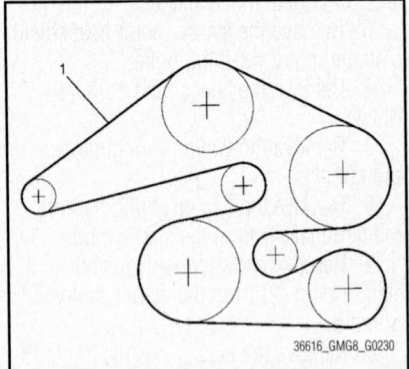

Fig. 84 Accessory drive belt routing—3.6L Engine

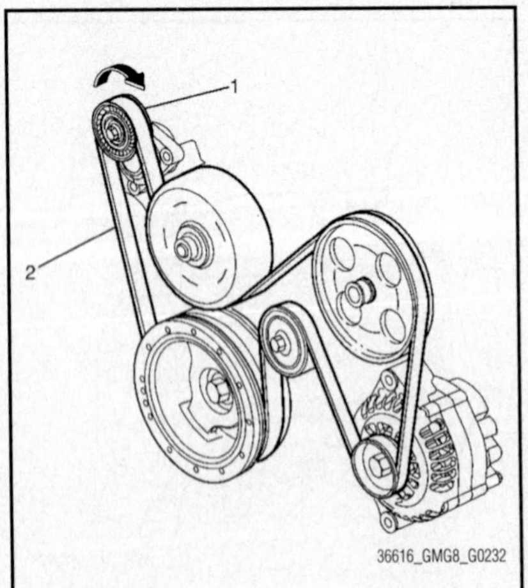

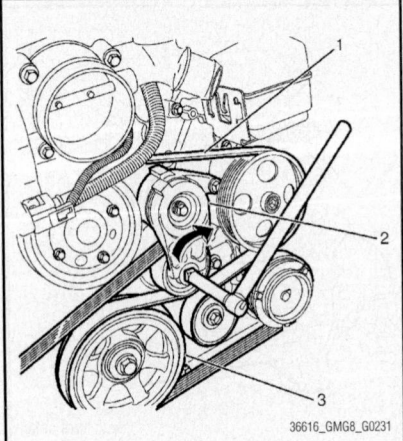

Fig. 85 Accessory drive belt routing—6.0L Engine

INSPECTION

1. Inspect the drive belts for cuts, tears, sections of ribs missing, or damaged belt plies.

2. Inspection of the accessory drive pulleys should include inspecting for bends, dents or other damage that May prevent the drive belt from seating correctly in the pulley grooves or on the smooth surface of a pulley when the back side of the drive belts are used to drive the pulley.

ADJUSTMENT

No Adjustment is necessary, as the belt tensioner applies constant tension to keep belt at the proper adjustment.

REMOVAL & INSTALLATION

3.6L Engine

See Figure 86.

Fig. 86 Accessory drive belt removal—3.6L Engine

1. Before servicing the vehicle, refer to the Precautions Section.

2. Rotate the drive belt tensioner (2) clockwise in order to release tension on the drive belt (1).

3. Remove the drive belt (1) from the crankshaft pulley (3).

4. Slowly release the drive belt tensioner (2).

5. Remove the drive belt (1).

To install:

6. Using a suitable tool rotate the drive belt tensioner clockwise.

➡Refer to Accessory Drive Belt Routing.

7. Install the drive belt to the crankshaft pulley.

➡Make sure the drive belt is correctly aligned and seated into the grooves of the accessory drive pulleys.

8. Slowly release the drive belt tensioner.

9. Remove the suitable tool from the drive belt tensioner.

6.0L Engine

See Figure 85.

1. Before servicing the vehicle, refer to the Precautions Section.

2. Remove the air intake duct. Refer to Air Cleaner.

3. Using a suitable tool, rotate the drive belt tensioner (1) clockwise to relieve the tension on the accessory drive belt (2).

4. Remove the accessory drive belt (2).

5. Slowly release tension on the drive belt tensioner (1).

6. Clean and inspect the drive belt surfaces of all the pulleys.

To install:

7. Route the accessory drive belt around all the pulleys except the water pump pulley.

8. Using a suitable tool, rotate the drive belt tensioner clockwise.

9. Install the accessory drive belt under the water pump pulley.

10. Slowly release the drive belt tensioner.

11. Install the air intake duct. Refer to Air Cleaner.

12. Inspect the accessory drive belt for correct alignment.

CAMSHAFT AND VALVE LIFTERS

REMOVAL & INSTALLATION

3.6L Engine

Right Side

See Figures 87 through 95.

1. Before servicing the vehicle, refer to the Precautions Section.

2. Remove the intake manifold. Refer to Intake Manifold.

3. Remove the camshaft cover.

4. Remove the camshaft sensors.

5. Remove the intake camshaft position actuator solenoid.

6. Remove the crankshaft balancer. Refer to Crankshaft Damper.

7. Rotate the crankshaft with the EN 46111 until the camshafts are in a neutral (low tension) position.

➡ **The camshaft flats will be parallel with the camshaft cover rail (1).**

✳ WARNING

A wrench must be used on the hex of the camshaft when loosening or tightening in order to prevent component damage. Failure to prevent the

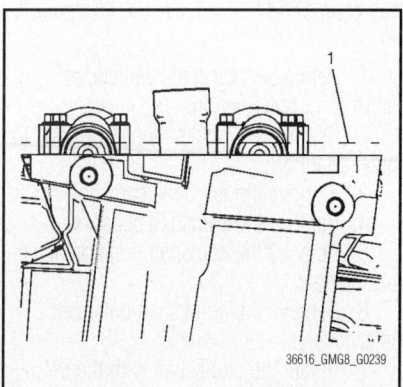

Fig. 87 Right side camshaft positioning

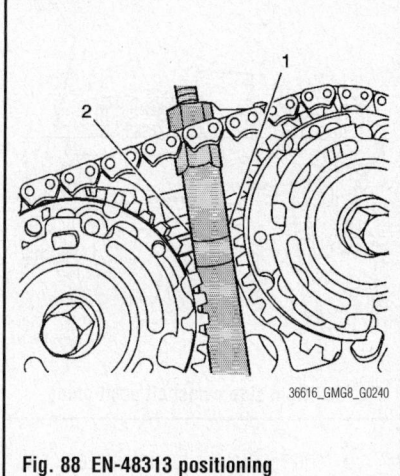

Fig. 88 EN-48313 positioning

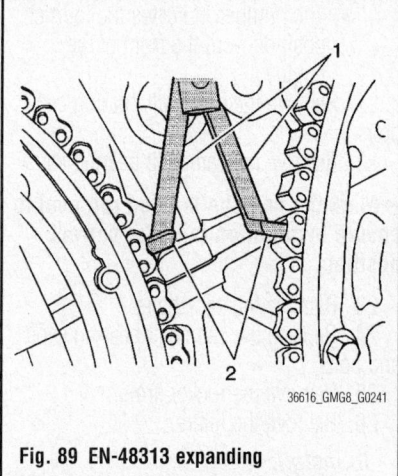

Fig. 89 EN-48313 expanding

torque reaction against the timing drive chain can lead to timing drive chain failure.

➡ **Use an open-end wrench at the camshaft hex to prevent camshaft/engine rotation. DO NOT remove the camshaft position actuator bolt at this time.**

8. Loosen the camshaft position actuator bolt.

9. Unscrew the EN-48313 so the legs of the tool are retracted.

10. Insert the EN-48313 between the camshaft actuators, rearward of the timing chain until the top line that is scribed in the body of the tool (1) is adjacent to the top surface of the cylinder head (2). This is the approximate installed position.

➡ **The engine front cover is removed for clarity in the following graphics, but NOT required to perform the procedure.**

11. Ensure that the feet (2) on the legs of the tool are facing the front of the engine.

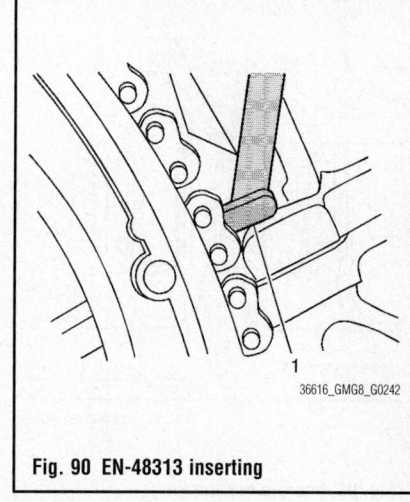

Fig. 90 EN-48313 inserting

12. Partially expand the legs (1) of the EN-48313 by turning the T-shaped handle clockwise.

13. Continue expanding the EN-48313 until the feet (2) contact the timing chain. Do not tighten at this time.

➡ **Ensure that the foot (1) of the EN-48313 is engaged into one of the link pockets to prevent chain slippage during tightening of the EN-48313. Do not allow the body of the EN-48313 to rotate when tightening the T-handle.**

14. Hand tighten the EN-48313.

✳ WARNING

A wrench must be used on the hex of the camshaft when loosening or tightening in order to prevent component damage. Failure to prevent the torque reaction against the timing drive chain can lead to timing drive chain failure.

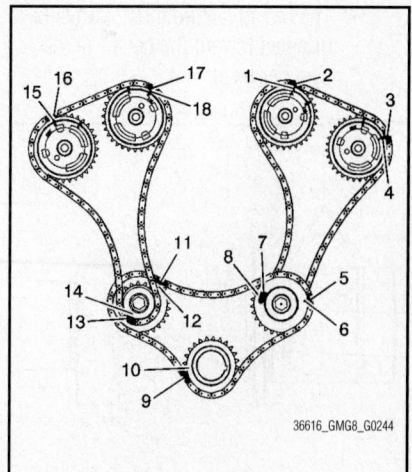

Fig. 91 Timing chain to actuator marking

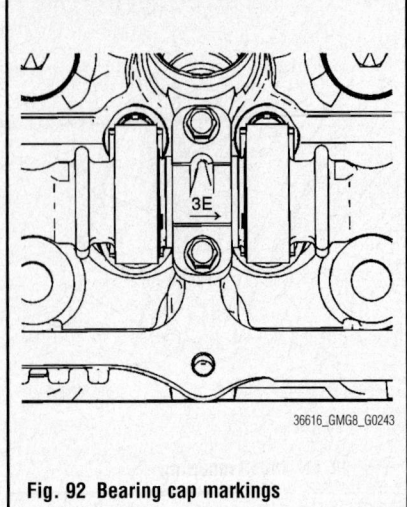

Fig. 92 Bearing cap markings

15. Use an open end wrench on the hex cast into the body of the EN-48313 and hand tighten the T-handle.

16. Use an open end wrench on the hex cast into the right intake and exhaust camshafts and rotate the camshafts towards each other in order to create slack in the chain between the actuators.

➡**The EN-48313 is now properly installed to hold the timing chain in position.**

➡**Ensure that the camshaft timing chain and the camshaft position actuators are marked for proper assembly.**

17. Mark the timing chain and the respective locations on camshaft position actuators (15-18).

18. Remove the camshaft position actuator bolt.

19. Observe the markings on the bearing caps. Each bearing cap is marked in order to identify its location.

20. The markings have the following meanings:

- The raised feature must always be oriented toward the center of the cylinder head.

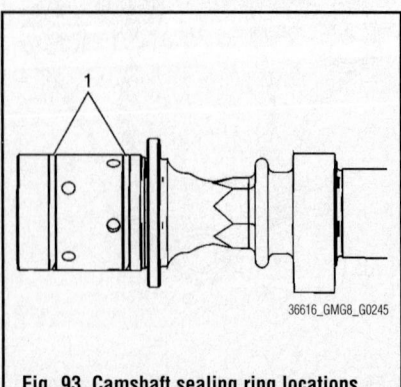

Fig. 93 Camshaft sealing ring locations

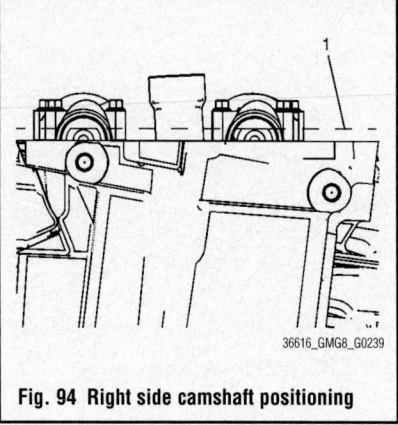

Fig. 94 Right side camshaft positioning

- The I indicates the intake camshaft.
- The E indicates the exhaust camshaft.
- The number indicates the journal position from the front of the engine.

21. Remove the camshaft bearing cap bolts.

22. Remove the camshaft bearing caps.

➡**Mark the camshafts upon removal to ensure installation is in the correct position.**

23. Remove the camshafts.

24. Replace the camshaft bearing caps and bolts.

25. Remove the rocker arms.

26. Remove the lifters.

To install:

27. Install the lifters.

28. Install the rocker arms.

29. Ensure that the camshaft sealing rings (1) are in place in the camshaft grooves. Camshaft sealing rings must be in place below the surface of the camshaft journal in order to avoid being pinched between the cylinder head and the camshaft caps.

30. Apply a liberal amount of lubricant GM P/N 12345501 (Canadian P/N 992704) or equivalent to the camshaft journals and the right cylinder head camshaft carriers.

31. Place the right intake and right exhaust camshafts in position in the right cylinder head.

32. Position the camshaft lobes in a neutral position with the flats on the back of the camshafts up and parallel (1) with the right cylinder head camshaft cover rail.

33. Observe the markings on the right cylinder head camshaft bearing caps. Each bearing cap is marked in order to identify its location. The markings have the following meanings:

- The raised feature must always be oriented toward the center of the cylinder head.

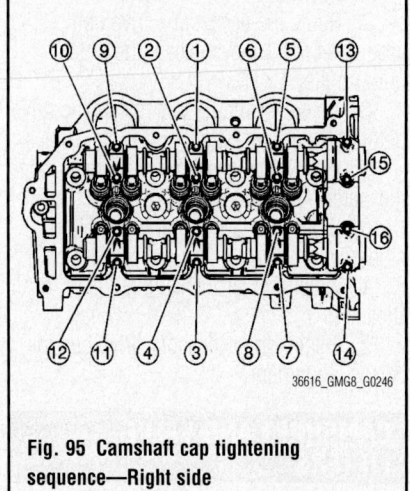

Fig. 95 Camshaft cap tightening sequence—Right side

- The I indicates the intake camshaft.
- The E indicates the exhaust camshaft.
- The number 1, 3, 5 indicates the cylinder position from the front of the engine.

34. Apply a liberal amount of lubricant GM P/N 12345501 (Canadian P/N 992704) or equivalent to the camshaft bearing caps.

35. Install the camshaft bearing thrust caps in the first journal of the right cylinder head.

36. Install the remaining bearing caps with their orientation mark toward the center of the cylinder head.

37. Hand start all the camshaft bearing cap bolts.

38. Tighten the camshaft bearing cap bolts in the sequence shown and tighten to 89 inch lbs. (10 Nm).

39. Loosen the center intake camshaft bearing cap bolts (1, 2) and the center exhaust camshaft bearing cap bolts (3, 4).

40. Retighten the center camshaft bearing cap bolts (1, 2, 3, 4) to 89 inch lbs. (10 Nm).

Left Side

See Figures 88 through 91, 93, 96 through 98.

1. Before servicing the vehicle, refer to the Precautions Section.

2. Remove the intake manifold. Refer to Intake Manifold.

3. Remove the left bank camshaft cover.

4. Remove the camshaft sensors.

5. Remove the camshaft position actuator solenoid.

6. Remove the crankshaft balancer. Refer to Crankshaft Damper.

7. Rotate the crankshaft with the EN 46111 until the camshafts are in a neutral (low tension) position.

Fig. 96 Left side camshaft positioning

➥The camshaft flats will be parallel with the camshaft cover rail (1).

⁂ WARNING

A wrench must be used on the hex of the camshaft when loosening or tightening in order to prevent component damage. Failure to prevent the torque reaction against the timing drive chain can lead to timing drive chain failure.

➥Use an open-end wrench at the camshaft hex to prevent camshaft/engine rotation. DO NOT remove the camshaft position actuator bolt at this time.

8. Loosen the camshaft position actuator bolt.

9. Unscrew the EN-48313 so that the legs of the tool are retracted.

10. Insert the EN-48313 between the camshaft actuators, rearward of the timing chain until the bottom line that is scribed in the body of the tool is adjacent to the top surface of the cylinder head. This is the approximate installed position.

11. Ensure that the feet on the legs of the tool are facing the front of the engine.

12. Partially expand the legs of the EN-48313 by turning the T-shaped handle clockwise.

13. Insert the leg of the tool behind the timing chain guide.

14. Continue expanding the EN-48313 until the legs contact the timing chain. Do not tighten at this time.

➥Ensure that the foot of the EN-48313 is engaged into one of the link pockets to prevent tool slippage during tightening of the EN-48313 .

15. Hand tighten the EN-48313 .

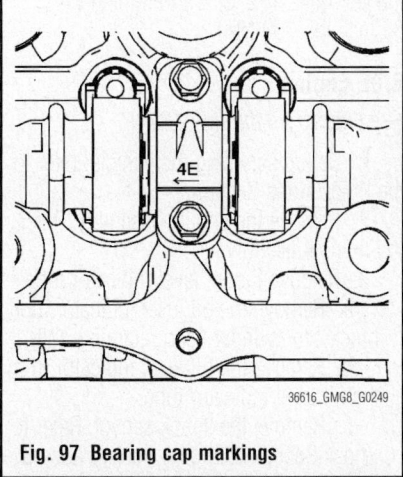

Fig. 97 Bearing cap markings

⁂ WARNING

A wrench must be used on the hex of the camshaft when loosening or tightening in order to prevent component damage. Failure to prevent the torque reaction against the timing drive chain can lead to timing drive chain failure.

16. Use an open end wrench on the hex cast into the left intake and exhaust camshafts and rotate the camshafts toward

each other in order to create slack in the chain between the actuators.

17. The EN-48313 is now properly installed to hold the timing chain in position.

➥Ensure that the camshaft timing chain and the camshaft position actuators are marked for proper assembly.

18. Mark the timing chain and the respective locations on the camshaft position actuators (1–4).

19. Remove the camshaft position actuator bolt.

20. Observe the markings on the bearing caps. Each bearing cap is marked in order to identify its location.

21. The markings have the following meanings:

- The raised feature must always be oriented toward the center of the cylinder head.
- The I indicates the intake camshaft.
- The E indicates the exhaust camshaft.
- The number indicates the journal position from the front of the engine.

22. Remove the camshaft bearing cap bolts.

23. Remove the camshaft bearing caps.

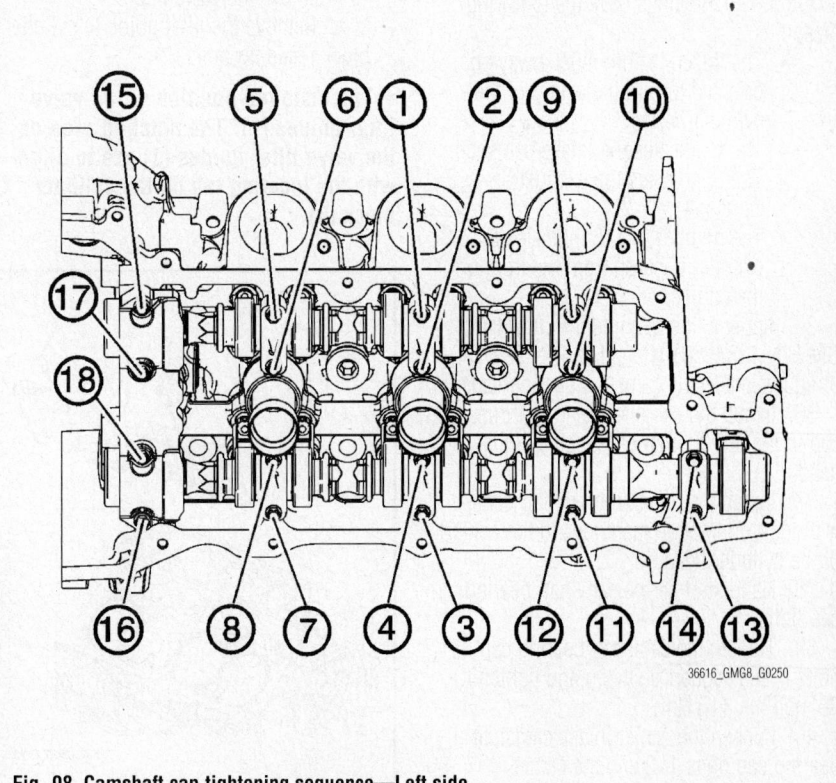

Fig. 98 Camshaft cap tightening sequence—Left side

➡**Mark the camshafts upon removal to ensure installation is in the correct position.**

24. Remove the camshafts.
25. Replace the camshaft bearing caps and bolts.
26. Remove the rocker arms.
27. Remove the lifters.

To install:

28. Install the lifters.
29. Install the rocker arms.
30. Ensure that the camshaft sealing rings (1) are in place in the camshaft grooves. Camshaft sealing rings must be in place below the surface of the camshaft journal in order to avoid being pinched between the cylinder head and the camshaft caps.
31. Apply a liberal amount of lubricant GM P/N 12345501 (Canadian P/N 992704) or equivalent to the camshaft journals and the left cylinder head camshaft carriers.
32. Place the left intake and left exhaust camshafts in position in the left cylinder head.
33. Position the camshaft lobes in a neutral position with the flats on the back of the camshafts up and parallel with the left cylinder head camshaft cover rail.
34. Observe the markings on the left cylinder head camshaft bearing caps. Each bearing cap is marked in order to identify its location. The markings have the following meanings:

- The raised feature must always be oriented toward the center of the cylinder head.
- The I indicates the intake camshaft.
- The E indicates the exhaust camshaft.
- The number 2, 4, 6 indicates the cylinder position from the front of the engine.

35. Apply a liberal amount of lubricant GM P/N 12345501 (Canadian P/N 992704) or equivalent to the camshaft bearing caps.
36. Install the camshaft bearing thrust cap in the first journal of the left cylinder head.
37. Install the remaining bearing caps with their orientation mark toward the center of the cylinder head.
38. Hand start all the camshaft bearing cap bolts.
39. Tighten the camshaft bearing cap bolts in the sequence shown and tighten to 89 inch lbs. (10 Nm).
40. Loosen the center intake camshaft bearing cap bolts 1, 2 and the center exhaust camshaft bearing cap bolts 3, 4.
41. Retighten the center camshaft bear-

ing cap bolts 1, 2, 3, 4 and tighten to 89 inch lbs. (10 Nm).

6.0L Engine

See Figures 99 through 104.

1. Before servicing the vehicle, refer to the Precautions Section.
2. Remove the engine assembly. Refer to Engine Assembly.
3. Remove the oil level indicator tube:
   a. Remove the oil level indicator tube bracket to cylinder head retaining bolt.
   b. Remove the oil level indicator from the oil level indicator tube.
   c. Remove the knock sensor. Refer to Knock Sensor in Engine Performance & Emission Controls.
   d. Remove the oil level indicator tube up through the exhaust manifold.
   e. Remove and discard the O-ring from the oil level indicator tube if damaged.
4. Remove the left and right exhaust manifolds. Refer to Exhaust Manifold.
5. Remove the intake manifold. Refer to Intake Manifold.
6. Remove the coolant air bleed pipe. Refer to Coolant Air Bleed Pipe in Engine Cooling.
7. Remove the left and right valve rocker arm covers. Refer to Valve Covers.
8. Remove the left and right cylinder heads. Refer to Cylinder Head.
9. Remove the valve lifters.
   a. Remove the lifter guide to cylinder block retaining bolts (2).

➡**The installed position of the valve lifter guides (1). The notched area of the valve lifter guides (1) are to align with the locating tab on the cylinder block (3).**

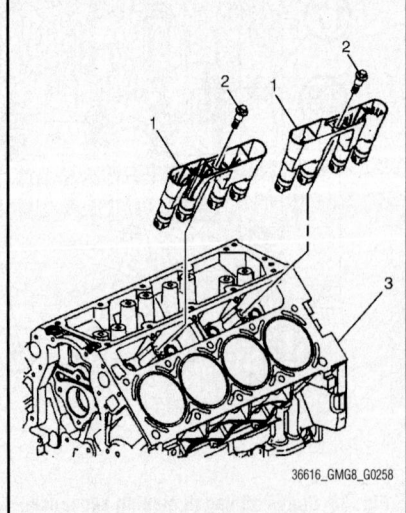

Fig. 99 Valve lifter guides location

10. Remove the valve lifter guides (1) and valve lifters as an assembly from the cylinder block (3).
11. Remove the valve lifters from the valve lifter guide.

➡**Some valve lifters may be stuck in their bores because of gum or varnish deposits.**

12. Use valve Lifter Remover or equivalent in order to remove the valve lifters, if required.

➡**The cylinder deactivation lifters (4) are installed into the guide (5) by aligning the notched area of the guide (1) with the raised surface on the side of the lifter (2).**

13. When using the valve train components again, always install the components to the original location and position.
14. Clean and inspect the valve lifters, if required.
15. Remove the water pump. Refer to Water Pump in Engine Cooling.
16. Remove the crankshaft balancer. Refer to Crankshaft Damper.
17. Remove the engine front cover. Refer to Engine Timing Chain Cover & Seal.
18. Inspect the sprockets for correct alignment. The mark on the camshaft sprocket should be located in the 6 o'clock position and the mark on the crankshaft sprocket should be located in the 12 o'clock position.

✹✹ WARNING

Do not turn the crankshaft assembly after the timing chain has been removed in order to prevent damage to the piston assemblies or the valves.

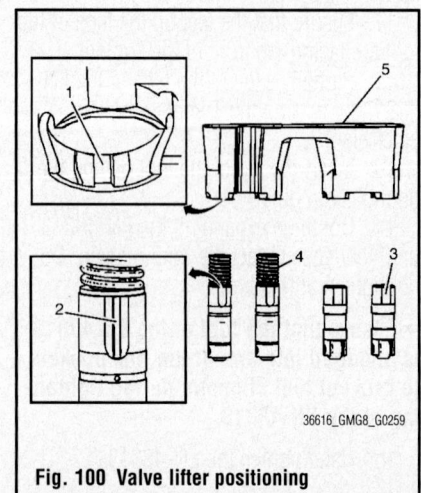

Fig. 100 Valve lifter positioning

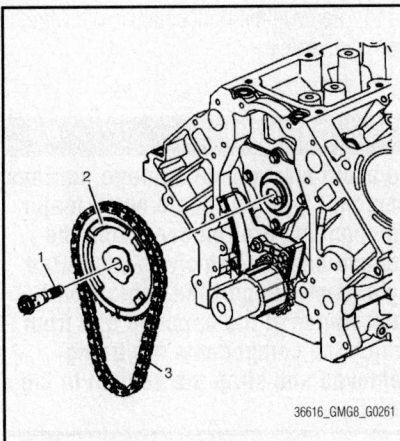

Fig. 101 Camshaft sprocket bolt location—6.0L Engine

19. Remove the camshaft sprocket bolt (1).
20. Remove the camshaft sprocket (2) and timing chain (3).
21. Remove the camshaft retainer to cylinder block retaining bolts (1) and remove the camshaft retainer (2).

✳✳ WARNING

All camshaft journals are the same diameter, so care must be used in removing or installing the camshaft to avoid damage to the camshaft bearings.

22. Remove the camshaft (2).
   - Install M8 -1.25 x 100 mm (M8 - 1.25 x 4.0 in) bolts (1) in the front of the camshaft (2).
   - Using the bolts (1) as a handle, carefully rotate and pull the camshaft (2) out of the cylinder block (3).
   - Remove the bolts (1) from the camshaft.

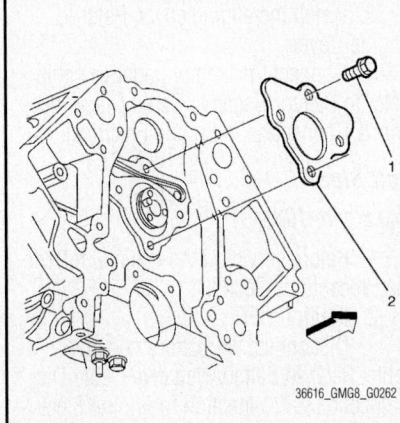

Fig. 102 Camshaft retainer location— 6.0L Engine

To install:

➡️ **If camshaft replacement is required, the valve lifters must also be replaced.**

23. Lubricate the camshaft journals and the bearings with clean engine oil.
24. Install the camshaft sprocket bolt into the camshaft front bolt hole.

✳✳ WARNING

All camshaft journals are the same diameter, so care must be used in removing or installing the camshaft to avoid damage to the camshaft bearings.

25. Using the bolt as a handle, carefully install the camshaft into the engine block.
26. Remove the bolt from the front of the camshaft.

➡️ **The gasket surface on the engine block should be clean and free of dirt or debris.**

27. Install the camshaft retainer (203) and the bolts (204). Install the retainer with the sealing gasket facing the front of the engine block.
28. Tighten the camshaft retainer bolts.
   - Tighten the first design hex head bolts to 18 ft. lbs. (25 Nm).
   - Tighten the second design Torx® head bolts to 11 ft. lbs. (15 Nm).
29. Align the camshaft sprocket alignment mark (1, 2), in the 6 o'clock position.
30. Install the camshaft sprocket and timing chain.
31. Install the camshaft sprocket to camshaft retaining bolt (1) and tighten to 18 ft. lbs. (25 Nm).
32. Install the engine front cover. Refer to Engine Timing Chain Cover & Seal.
33. Install a NEW crankshaft front oil seal. Refer to Engine Timing Chain Cover & Seal.
34. Install the crankshaft balancer. Refer to Crankshaft Damper.

➡️ **When using the non-Active Fuel Management (AFM) valve lifters again, install the lifters to their original locations. If camshaft replacement is required, the valve lifters must also be replaced.**

35. Lubricate the valve lifters and engine block valve lifter bores with clean engine oil.
36. Insert the valve lifters into the lifter guides.
37. Align the flat area on the top of the lifter with the flat area in the lifter guide

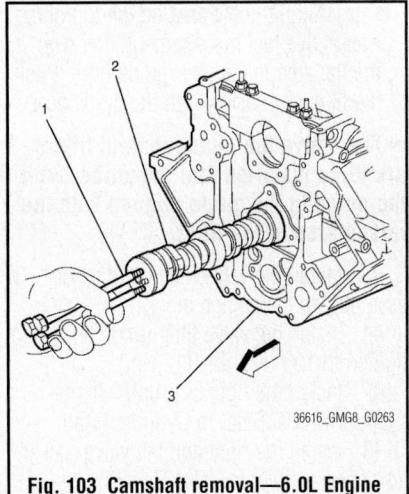

Fig. 103 Camshaft removal—6.0L Engine

bore. Push the lifter completely into the guide bore.

➡️ **When using the AFM valve lifters again, install the lifters to their original locations.**

   - If camshaft replacement is required, the valve lifters must also be replaced.
   - Each of the 4 valve guide assemblies will contain 2 active fuel management valve lifters and 2 non-active fuel management valve lifters.
   - With the lifters and guides properly installed, cylinders 1, 4, 6, and 7 lifter bores will each contain 2 active fuel management valve lifters.

38. Lubricate the valve lifters and engine block valve lifter bores with clean engine oil.
39. Insert the valve lifters into the lifter guides.

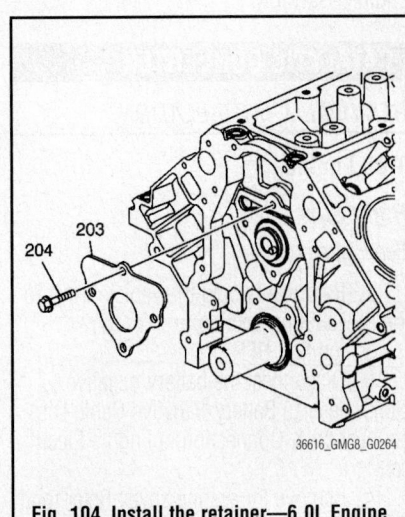

Fig. 104 Install the retainer—6.0L Engine

a. Align the flat area on the top of the non-active fuel management lifter with the flat area in the lifter guide bore. Push the lifter completely into the guide bore.

➡The active fuel management lifters are to be installed into the guide, with the notch in the guide aligned with the raised area of the lifter.

40. Install the valve lifters and guide assembly to the engine block.

41. Install the valve lifter guide bolts and tighten to 106 inch lbs. (12 Nm).

42. Install the right side and left side cylinder heads. Refer to Cylinder Head.

43. Install the right and left valve rocker arm covers. Refer to Valve Covers.

44. Install the coolant air bleed pipe. Refer to Coolant Air Bleed Pipe in Engine Cooling.

45. Install the intake manifold. Refer to Intake Manifold.

46. Install the water pump. Refer to Water Pump in Engine Cooling.

47. Install the left and right exhaust manifolds. Refer to Exhaust Manifold.

48. Install the oil level indicator tube.

a. Inspect the O-ring seal for cuts or damage. If the oil level indicator tube O-ring seal is not cut or damaged, it may be used again.

b. Lubricate the O-ring seal with clean engine oil.

c. Install the O-ring seal onto the oil level indicator tube.

d. Install the oil level indicator tube into the engine block and rotate into proper position.

e. Install the tube bolt and tighten to 18 ft. lbs. (25 Nm).

f. Install the oil level indicator into the tube.

49. Install the engine assembly. Refer to Engine Assembly.

CATALYTIC CONVERTER

REMOVAL & INSTALLATION

3.6L Engine

Right Side

See Figure 105.

1. Before servicing the vehicle, refer to the Precautions Section.

2. Ignition OFF.

3. Disconnect the battery negative cable. Refer to Battery Negative Cable Disconnection & Connection in Engine Electrical.

4. Remove the engine cover. Refer to Engine Cover.

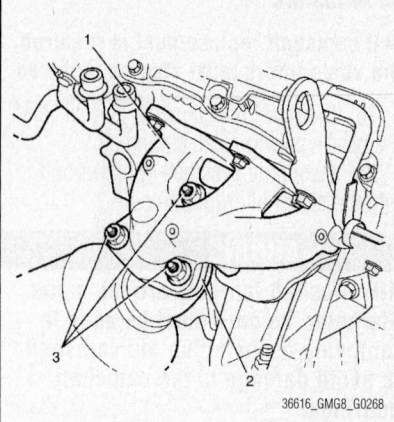

Fig. 105 Catalytic converter to exhaust manifold retaining nut locations—3.6L Engine right side

5. Remove the right pre-catalytic converter heated oxygen sensor (HO2S) sensor. Refer to Heated Oxygen Sensor in Engine Performance & Emission Controls.

6. Remove the right exhaust manifold heat shield.

➡The right catalytic converter to exhaust manifold retaining nuts (1) are single use parts. They must be discarded after removal.

7. Remove the right catalytic converter to exhaust manifold retaining nuts (3).

8. Discard the nuts.

✳✳ CAUTION

To avoid any vehicle damage, serious personal injury or death when major components are removed from the vehicle and the vehicle is supported by a hoist, support the vehicle with jack stands at the opposite end from which the components are being removed and strap the vehicle to the hoist.

9. Raise and support the vehicle.

➡The exhaust crossover pipe assembly to right catalytic converter retaining nuts are single use parts. They must be discarded after removal.

10. Remove the exhaust crossover pipe assembly to right catalytic converter retaining nuts.

11. Discard the nuts.

12. Pull down and back on the right catalytic converter to disconnect from the exhaust manifold.

13. Disconnect the exhaust crossover pipe assembly from the right catalytic converter.

14. Remove the right catalytic converter from the vehicle.

To install:

✳✳ CAUTION

To avoid any vehicle damage, serious personal injury or death when major components are removed from the vehicle and the vehicle is supported by a hoist, support the vehicle with jack stands at the opposite end from which the components are being removed and strap the vehicle to the hoist.

15. Raise and support the vehicle.

➡Make sure that a NEW sealing ring is fitted prior to installation. Failure to comply may cause the exhaust system to perform poorly.

16. Install the right catalytic converter to the vehicle.

17. Align the exhaust crossover pipe assembly to the right catalytic converter.

18. Install NEW exhaust crossover pipe assembly to right catalytic converter retaining nuts and tighten to 30 ft. lbs. (40 Nm).

19. Lower the vehicle.

20. Install NEW right catalytic converter to exhaust manifold retaining nuts and tighten to 33 ft. lbs. (45 Nm).

21. Make sure that the exhaust system is clear of all other components and chassis. If the exhaust system is not clear of all the other components loosen all retaining nuts and re-align.

22. Install the right exhaust manifold heat shield.

23. Install the right pre-catalytic converter HO2S sensor. Refer to Heated Oxygen Sensor in Engine Performance & Emission Controls.

24. Install the engine cover. Refer to Engine Cover.

25. Connect the battery negative cable. Refer to Battery Negative Cable Disconnection & Connection in Engine Electrical.

Left Side

See Figure 106.

1. Before servicing the vehicle, refer to the Precautions Section.

2. Ignition OFF.

3. Disconnect the battery negative cable. Refer to Battery Negative Cable Disconnection & Connection in Engine Electrical.

4. Remove the engine cover. Refer to Engine Cover.

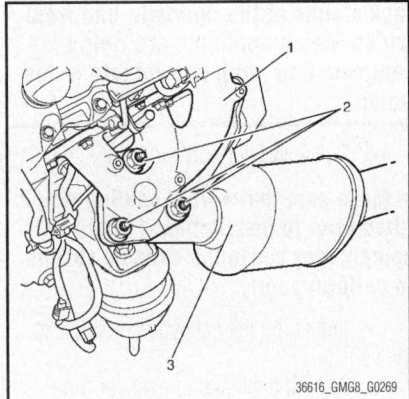

Fig. 106 Catalytic converter to exhaust manifold retaining nut locations—3.6L Engine left side

5. Remove the left pre-catalytic converter heated oxygen sensor (HO2S) sensor. Refer to Heated Oxygen Sensor in Engine Performance & Emission Controls.

6. Remove the left exhaust manifold heat shield.

➡ **The right catalytic converter to exhaust manifold retaining nuts (1) are single use parts. They must be discarded after removal.**

7. Remove the oil level indicator tube.

8. Remove the left catalytic converter to exhaust manifold retaining nuts (3).

9. Discard the nuts.

❊❊ CAUTION

To avoid any vehicle damage, serious personal injury or death when major components are removed from the vehicle and the vehicle is supported by a hoist, support the vehicle with jack stands at the opposite end from which the components are being removed and strap the vehicle to the hoist.

10. Raise and support the vehicle.

➡ **The exhaust crossover pipe assembly to left catalytic converter retaining nuts are single use parts. They must be discarded after removal.**

11. Remove the exhaust crossover pipe assembly to left catalytic converter retaining nuts.

12. Discard the nuts.

13. Pull down and back on the left catalytic converter to disconnect from the exhaust manifold.

14. Disconnect the exhaust crossover pipe assembly from the left catalytic converter.

15. Remove the left catalytic converter from the vehicle.

To install:

❊❊ CAUTION

To avoid any vehicle damage, serious personal injury or death when major components are removed from the vehicle and the vehicle is supported by a hoist, support the vehicle with jack stands at the opposite end from which the components are being removed and strap the vehicle to the hoist.

16. Raise and support the vehicle.

➡ **Make sure that a NEW sealing ring is fitted prior to installation. Failure to comply may cause the exhaust system to perform poorly.**

17. Install the left catalytic converter to the vehicle.

18. Align the exhaust crossover pipe assembly to the left catalytic converter.

19. Install NEW exhaust crossover pipe assembly to left catalytic converter retaining nuts and tighten to 30 ft. lbs. (40 Nm).

20. Lower the vehicle.

21. Install NEW left catalytic converter to exhaust manifold retaining nuts and tighten to 33 ft. lbs. (45 Nm).

22. Make sure that the exhaust system is clear of all other components and chassis. If the exhaust system is not clear of all the other components loosen all retaining nuts and re-align.

23. Install the oil level indicator tube.

24. Install the left exhaust manifold heat shield.

25. Install the left pre-catalytic converter HO2S sensor. Refer to Heated Oxygen Sensor in Engine Performance & Emission Controls.

26. Install the engine cover. Refer to Engine Cover.

27. Connect the battery negative cable. Refer to Battery Negative Cable Disconnection & Connection in Engine Electrical.

6.0L Engine

Right Side

See Figure 107.

1. Before servicing the vehicle, refer to the Precautions Section.

2. Ignition OFF.

3. Disconnect the battery negative cable. Refer to Battery Negative Cable Disconnection & Connection in Engine Electrical.

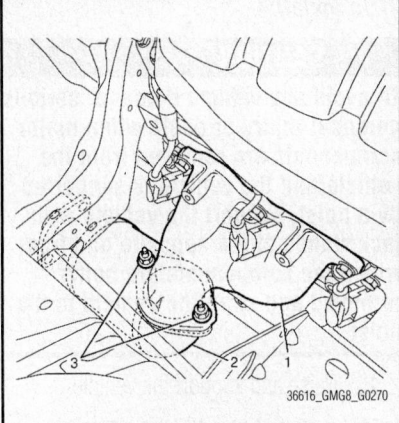

Fig. 107 Catalytic converter to exhaust manifold retaining nut locations—6.0L Engine right side

4. Remove the right pre-catalytic converter heated oxygen sensor (HO2S) sensor. Refer to Heated Oxygen Sensor in Engine Performance & Emission Controls.

➡ **The right catalytic converter to exhaust manifold retaining nuts (1) are single use parts. They must be discarded after removal.**

5. Remove the right catalytic converter to exhaust manifold retaining nuts (3).

6. Discard the nuts.

❊❊ CAUTION

To avoid any vehicle damage, serious personal injury or death when major components are removed from the vehicle and the vehicle is supported by a hoist, support the vehicle with jack stands at the opposite end from which the components are being removed and strap the vehicle to the hoist.

7. Raise and support the vehicle.

➡ **The exhaust crossover pipe assembly to right catalytic converter retaining nuts are single use parts. They must be discarded after removal.**

8. Remove the exhaust crossover pipe assembly to right catalytic converter retaining nuts.

9. Discard the nuts.

10. Pull down and back on the right catalytic converter to disconnect from the exhaust manifold.

11. Disconnect the exhaust crossover pipe assembly from the right catalytic converter.

12. Remove the right catalytic converter from the vehicle.

To install:

❊❊ CAUTION

To avoid any vehicle damage, serious personal injury or death when major components are removed from the vehicle and the vehicle is supported by a hoist, support the vehicle with jack stands at the opposite end from which the components are being removed and strap the vehicle to the hoist.

13. Raise and support the vehicle.

➡**Make sure that a NEW sealing ring is fitted prior to installation. Failure to comply may cause the exhaust system to perform poorly.**

14. Install the right catalytic converter to the vehicle.

15. Align the exhaust crossover pipe assembly to the right catalytic converter.

16. Install NEW exhaust crossover pipe assembly to right catalytic converter retaining nuts and tighten to 30 ft. lbs. (40 Nm).

17. Lower the vehicle.

18. Install NEW right catalytic converter to exhaust manifold retaining nuts and tighten to 33 ft. lbs. (45 Nm).

19. Make sure that the exhaust system is clear of all other components and chassis. If the exhaust system is not clear of all the other components loosen all retaining nuts and re-align.

20. Install the right pre-catalytic converter HO2S sensor. Refer to Heated Oxygen Sensor in Engine Performance & Emission Controls.

21. Connect the battery negative cable. Refer to Battery Negative Cable Disconnection & Connection in Engine Electrical.

Left Side

See Figure 108.

1. Before servicing the vehicle, refer to the Precautions Section.

2. Ignition OFF.

3. Disconnect the battery negative cable. Refer to Battery Negative Cable Disconnection & Connection in Engine Electrical.

4. Remove the left pre-catalytic converter heated oxygen sensor (HO2S) sensor. Refer to Heated Oxygen Sensor in Engine Performance & Emission Controls.

➡**The right catalytic converter to exhaust manifold retaining nuts (1) are single use parts. They must be discarded after removal.**

5. Remove the oil level indicator tube.

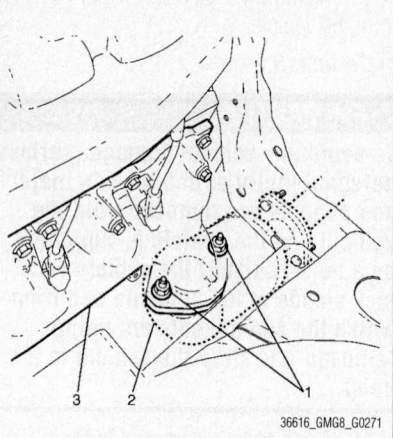

Fig. 108 Catalytic converter to exhaust manifold retaining nut locations—6.0L Engine left side

36616_GMG8_G0271

6. Remove the left catalytic converter to exhaust manifold retaining nuts.

7. Discard the nuts.

❊❊ CAUTION

To avoid any vehicle damage, serious personal injury or death when major components are removed from the vehicle and the vehicle is supported by a hoist, support the vehicle with jack stands at the opposite end from which the components are being removed and strap the vehicle to the hoist.

8. Raise and support the vehicle.

➡**The exhaust crossover pipe assembly to left catalytic converter retaining nuts are single use parts. They must be discarded after removal.**

9. Remove the exhaust crossover pipe assembly to left catalytic converter retaining nuts.

10. Discard the nuts.

11. Pull down and back on the left catalytic converter to disconnect from the exhaust manifold.

12. Disconnect the exhaust crossover pipe assembly from the left catalytic converter.

13. Remove the left catalytic converter from the vehicle.

To install:

❊❊ CAUTION

To avoid any vehicle damage, serious personal injury or death when major components are removed from the vehicle and the vehicle is supported by a hoist, support the vehicle with

jack stands at the opposite end from which the components are being removed and strap the vehicle to the hoist.

14. Raise and support the vehicle.

➡**Make sure that a NEW sealing ring is fitted prior to installation. Failure to comply may cause the exhaust system to perform poorly.**

15. Install the left catalytic converter to the vehicle.

16. Align the exhaust crossover pipe assembly to the left catalytic converter.

17. Install NEW exhaust crossover pipe assembly to left catalytic converter retaining nuts and tighten to 30 ft. lbs. (40 Nm).

18. Lower the vehicle.

19. Install NEW left catalytic converter to exhaust manifold retaining nuts and tighten to 33 ft. lbs. (45 Nm).

20. Make sure that the exhaust system is clear of all other components and chassis. If the exhaust system is not clear of all the other components loosen all retaining nuts and re-align.

21. Install the oil level indicator tube.

22. Install the left pre-catalytic converter HO2S sensor. Refer to Heated Oxygen Sensor in Engine Performance & Emission Controls.

23. Connect the battery negative cable. Refer to Battery Negative Cable Disconnection & Connection in Engine Electrical.

CRANKSHAFT DAMPER

REMOVAL & INSTALLATION

3.6L Engine

See Figures 109 through 112.

1. Before servicing the vehicle, refer to the Precautions Section.

2. Remove the drive belt. Refer to Accessory Drive Belt.

❊❊ CAUTION

To avoid any vehicle damage, serious personal injury or death when major components are removed from the vehicle and the vehicle is supported by a hoist, support the vehicle with jack stands at the opposite end from which the components are being removed and strap the vehicle to the hoist.

3. Raise and support the vehicle.

4. Remove the starter motor. Refer to Starter in Engine Electrical.

5. Install the EN 46106 (1) through the starter mounting hole.

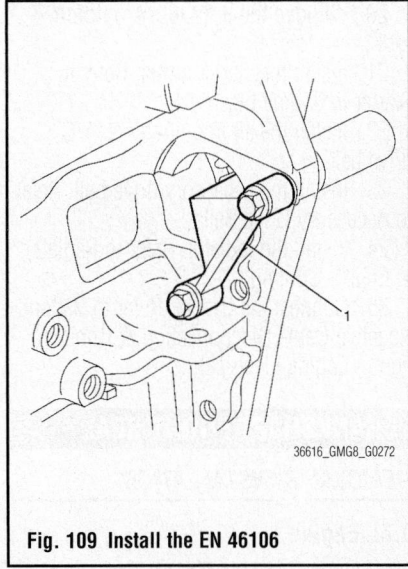

Fig. 109 Install the EN 46106

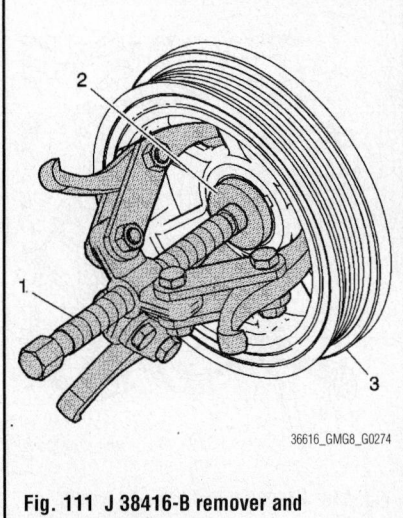

Fig. 111 J 38416-B remover and J 38416-2 button

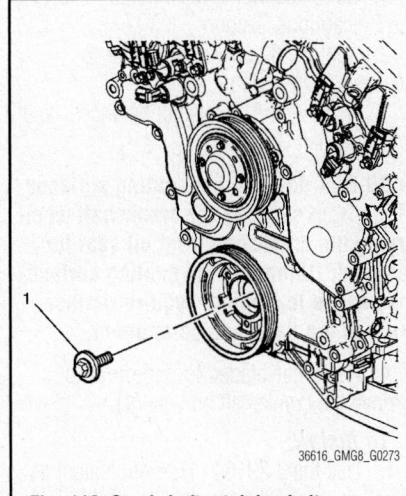

Fig. 110 Crankshaft retaining bolt location (1)

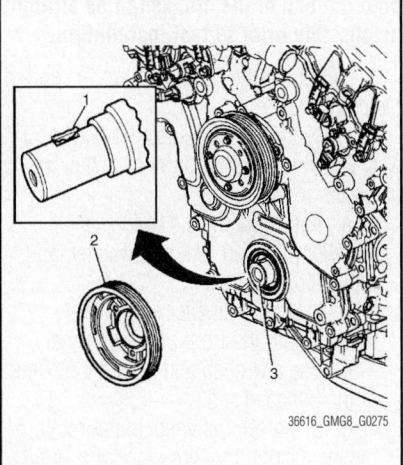

Fig. 112 Crankshaft key location— 3.6L Engine

6. Lower the vehicle.

7. Remove the front air deflector.

8. Remove the crankshaft balancer to crankshaft retaining bolt (1).

9. Install the J 38416-B remover (1) and J 38416-2 button (2).

➡**Remove the crankshaft balancer by tightening the center bolt on the J 38416-B remover (1) until the crankshaft balancer (3) is removed from the crankshaft.**

10. Remove the crankshaft balancer (3).

11. Remove the J 38416-B remover (1) and J 38416-2 button (2) from the crankshaft balancer.

To install:

➡**DO NOT lubricate the crankshaft front oil seal or crankshaft balancer sealing surfaces. The crankshaft balancer is installed into a dry seal.**

12. Apply lubricant to the inside of the crankshaft balancer hub bore.

➡**Make sure the key (1) located on the top of the crankshaft is correctly installed in the crankshaft.**

❊❊ WARNING

Failure to adhere to this may cause engine damage.

13. Install the crankshaft balancer (2) on to the crankshaft (3).

14. Install the crankshaft balancer to crankshaft retaining bolt.
- Tighten the bolt to 74 ft. lbs. (100 Nm).
- Tighten the crankshaft balancer to

crankshaft retaining bolt an additional 150 degrees using the J 45059 meter .

15. Raise the vehicle

16. Install the front air deflector.

17. Remove EN 46106 from the starter mounting hole.

18. Install the starter motor. Refer to Starter in Engine Electrical.

19. Install the drive belt. Refer to Accessory Drive Belt.

6.0L Engine

See Figures 113 through 116.

1. Before servicing the vehicle, refer to the Precautions Section.

2. Disconnect the battery. Refer to Battery Negative Cable Disconnection & Connection in Engine Electrical.

3. Remove the radiator. Refer to Radiator in Engine Cooling.

4. Remove the accessory drive belt. Refer to Accessory Drive Belt.

5. Remove the air conditioning (A/C) drive belt.

6. Remove the starter motor. Refer to Starter in Engine Electrical.

➡**Do not use the crankshaft balancer bolt again. Install a NEW crankshaft balancer bolt during final assembly.**

7. Install the J 42386-A holding tool and bolts.

8. Use one M10 - 1.5 x 120 mm and one M10 - 1.5 x 45 mm bolt for proper tool operation. Tighten the J 42386-A holding tool bolts to 37 ft. lbs. (50 Nm).

9. Remove the crankshaft balancer bolt.

10. Do not discard the crankshaft balancer bolt. The balancer bolt will be used during the balancer installation procedure.

Fig. 113 Holding tool location

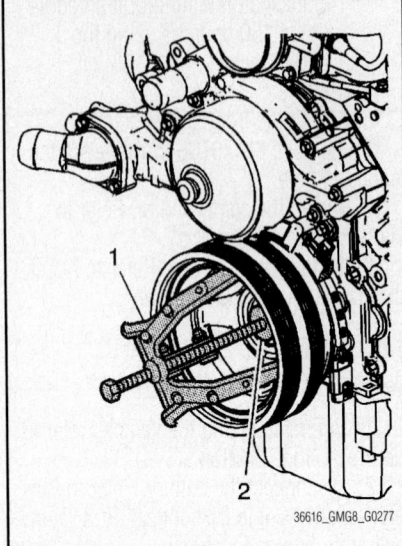

Fig. 114 J 41816 remover and the J 41816-2 protector

11. Use the J 41816 remover (1) and the J 41816-2 protector (2) in order to remove the crankshaft balancer.

12. Remove the crankshaft balancer.

13. Remove the J 42386-A holding tool and bolts.

To install:

➡ The used crankshaft balancer bolt is used only during the installation procedure. Install a NEW crankshaft balancer bolt during final assembly.

14. Install the J 42386-A holding tool and bolts.

15. Use 1 M10 - 1.5 x 120 mm and 1 M10 - 1.5 x 45 mm bolt for proper tool operation. Tighten the J 42386-A holding tool bolts to 37 ft. lbs. (50 Nm).

16. Install the crankshaft balancer washer (1) onto the crankshaft balancer.

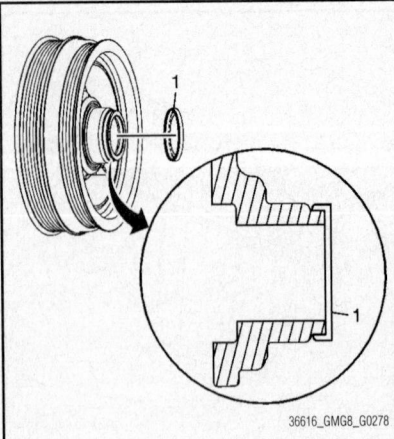

Fig. 115 Crankshaft balancer washer location

Fig. 116 J 41665 installer and J 41478 tools

➡ The balancer should be positioned onto the end of the crankshaft as straight as possible prior to tool installation.

17. Position the balancer onto the end of the crankshaft.

18. Use the J 41665 installer and the J 41478 seal installer in order to install the balancer.

   a. Assemble the J 41478 seal installer threaded rod, nut, washer, and the J 41665 installer .

   b. Insert the smaller end of the installer into the front of the balancer.

   c. Use a wrench and hold the hex end of the threaded rod.

   d. Use a second wrench and rotate the installation tool nut clockwise until the balancer is started onto the crankshaft.

   e. Remove the tool and reverse the installation tool.

   f. Position the larger end of the installer against the front of the balancer.

   g. Use a wrench and hold the hex end of the threaded rod.

   h. Use a second wrench and rotate the installation tool nut clockwise until the balancer is installed onto the crankshaft.

   i. Remove the balancer installation tools.

19. Install the NEW crankshaft balancer bolt.

   a. Tighten the crankshaft balancer bolt a first pass to 110 ft. lbs. (150 Nm).

   b. Loosen the crankshaft balancer bolt a second pass 360 degrees.

   c. Tighten the crankshaft balancer bolt a third pass to 37 ft. lbs. (50 Nm).

   d. Tighten the crankshaft balancer bolt a final pass to 230 degrees using the J 45059 meter .

20. Remove the J 42386-A holding tool .

21. Install the starter motor. Refer to Starter in Engine Electrical.

22. Install the air conditioning (A/C) drive belt.

23. Install the accessory drive belt. Refer to Accessory Drive Belt.

24. Install the radiator. Refer to Radiator in Engine Cooling.

25. Connect the battery. Refer to Battery Negative Cable Disconnection & Connection in Engine Electrical.

CRANKSHAFT FRONT SEAL

REMOVAL & INSTALLATION

3.6L Engine

See Figures 117 and 118.

1. Before servicing the vehicle, refer to the Precautions Section.

2. Remove the drive belt. Refer to Accessory Drive Belt.

3. Remove the crankshaft balancer. Refer to Crankshaft Damper.

➡ DO NOT damage the sealing surfaces of the front cover or the crankshaft when prying the crankshaft front oil seal for removal. Damaging the sealing surface may cause leakage or require replacement of the damaged component.

4. Use a flat-bladed tool in order to remove the crankshaft oil seal (1).

To install:

5. Use the J 29184 (1) or equivalent to install the crankshaft front oil seal (2).

6. Install the crankshaft balancer. Refer to Crankshaft Damper.

7. Install the drive belt. Refer to Accessory Drive Belt.

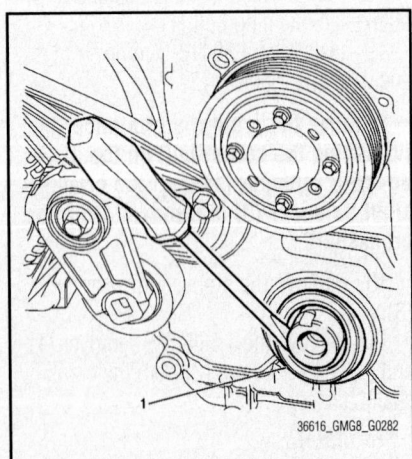

Fig. 117 Prying the crankshaft oil seal from the front engine cover—3.6L Engine

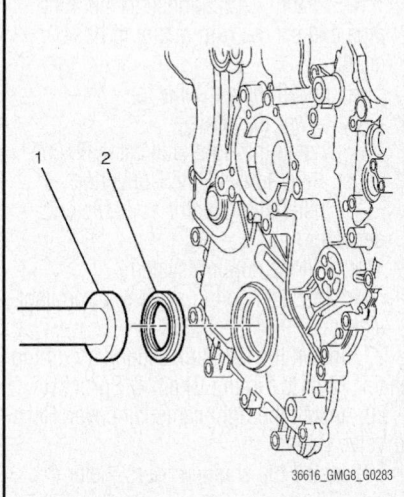

Fig. 118 Installing crankshaft oil seal into the front engine cover—6.0L Engine

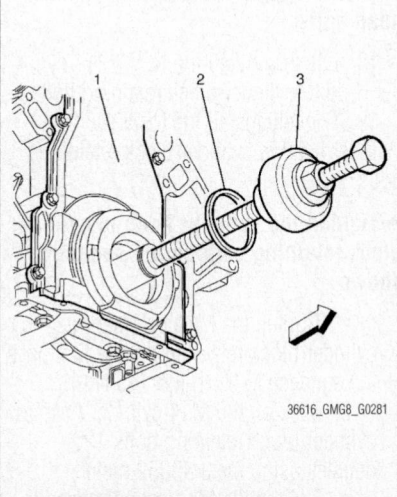

Fig. 120 Installing crankshaft oil seal into the front engine cover—6.0L Engine

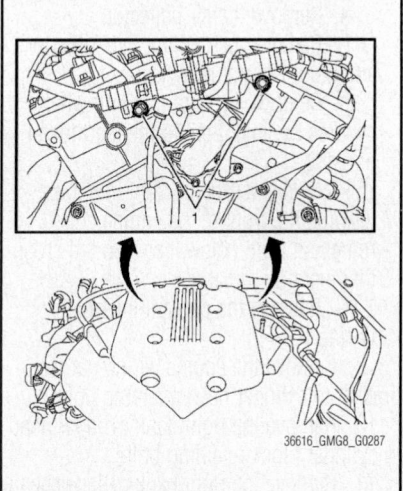

Fig. 121 Additional wiring harness ground locations—3.6L Engine

6.0L Engine

See Figures 119 and 120.

1. Before servicing the vehicle, refer to the Precautions Section.

2. Disconnect the battery. Refer to Battery Negative Cable Disconnection & Connection in Engine Electrical.

3. Remove the radiator. Refer to Radiator in Engine Cooling.

4. Remove the accessory drive belt. Refer to Accessory Drive Belt.

5. Remove the air conditioning (A/C) drive belt.

6. Remove the starter motor. Refer to Starter in Engine Electrical.

7. Remove the crankshaft balancer. Refer to Crankshaft Damper.

8. Using tool E-308 (2) gently pry the crankshaft oil seal (1) from the front engine cover (3).

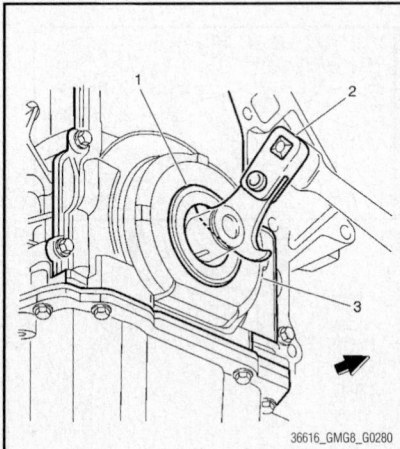

Fig. 119 Prying the crankshaft oil seal from the front engine cover—6.0L Engine

To install:

9. Install the crankshaft front oil seal onto the J 41478 (3) guide.

10. Install the J 41478 (3) threaded rod (with nut, washer, guide, and oil seal) into the end of the crankshaft.

11. Use the J 41478 (3) in order to install the oil seal (2) into the front engine cover (1) bore.

  a. Use a wrench and hold the hex on the installer tool.

  b. Use a second wrench and rotate the installer nut clockwise until the seal bottoms in the front engine cover (1) bore.

  c. Remove the tool.

  d. Inspect the oil seal for correct installation. The oil seal should be installed evenly and completely into the front cover bore.

12. Install the starter motor. Refer to Starter in Engine Electrical.

13. Install the air conditioning (A/C) drive belt.

14. Install the accessory drive belt. Refer to Accessory Drive Belt.

15. Install the radiator. Refer to Radiator in Engine Cooling.

16. Connect the battery. Refer to Battery Negative Cable Disconnection & Connection in Engine Electrical.

CYLINDER HEAD

REMOVAL & INSTALLATION

3.6L Engine

Right Side

See Figures 121 and 122.

1. Before servicing the vehicle, refer to the Precautions Section.

2. Disconnect the battery ground cable. Refer to Battery Negative Cable Disconnection & Connection in Engine Electrical.

3. Remove the engine covers. Refer to Engine Cover.

4. Remove the right camshaft cover. Refer to Valve Cover.

5. Remove the left bank secondary timing chain. Refer to Timing Chain and Sprockets.

6. Remove the wiring harness ground to cylinder head retaining bolts.

7. Remove the wiring harness ground from the side of the cylinder head.

8. Remove the coolant inlet pipe.

  a. Ensure engine is below 50°C before removing the coolant pressure cap.

  b. Remove the radiator air baffle and deflector.

  c. Remove the air intake duct. Refer to Air Cleaner.

  d. Drain the cooling system.

  e. Remove the right side catalytic converter.

  f. Detach the lower radiator hose by removing the retaining hose clamp and removing it from the coolant inlet pipe.

✳✳ CAUTION

To avoid any vehicle damage, serious personal injury or death when major components are removed from the vehicle and the vehicle is supported by a hoist, support the vehicle with jack stands at the opposite end from which the components are being removed and strap the vehicle to the hoist.

g. Raise and support the vehicle.

h. Remove the air deflector.

i. Remove the coolant inlet pipe to alternator bracket retaining.

j. Remove the retaining bolt which secures the inlet pipe to the thermostat housing.

k. Maneuver the coolant inlet pipe towards the front of the engine and remove it from below, between the cross member and radiator.

l. Remove the coolant inlet pipe O-ring.

9. Remove the engine wiring harness bracket to cylinder head retaining bolts.

10. Remove the right bank cylinder head to cylinder block retaining bolts.

11. Remove the right bank cylinder head.

12. Remove and discard the right cylinder head gasket.

➡**Cylinder head gaskets must be discarded whenever the cylinder head has been removed from the cylinder block**

13. Clean and inspect the cylinder head and the cylinder block sealing surfaces.

To install:

➡**Make sure that the crankshaft is in the timing drive assembly position using the EN 46111 socket .**

14. Make sure the cylinder head locating pins are securely mounted in the cylinder block deck face.

15. Install a NEW right cylinder head gasket using the deck face locating pins for retention.

16. Align the right cylinder head with the deck face locating pins.

17. Place the right cylinder head in position on the deck face.

➡ **DO NOT allow oil on the cylinder head bolt bosses.**

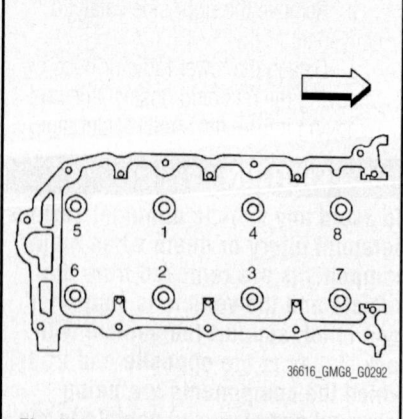

Fig. 122 Cylinder head bolt tightening sequence right side—3.6L Engine

➡**DO NOT reuse the old M11 cylinder head bolts.**

18. Loosely install the NEW M11 cylinder head to cylinder block retaining bolts.

19. Loosely install the NEW M8 front cylinder head to cylinder block retaining bolts.

➡**Tighten the cylinder head to cylinder block retaining bolts in the sequence shown.**

a. Tighten the M11 cylinder head to cylinder block retaining bolts a first pass in sequence to 33 ft. lbs. (45 Nm).

b. Back off the M11 cylinder head to cylinder block retaining bolts 120 degrees using the J 45059 meter

c. Tighten the M11 cylinder head to cylinder block retaining bolts a second pass in sequence to 22 ft. lbs. (30 Nm).

d. Tighten the M11 cylinder head to cylinder block retaining bolts a third pass in sequence an additional 150 degrees using the J 45059 meter J 45059.

e. Install the 2 front M8 right cylinder head to cylinder block retaining bolts (9, 10).

f. Tighten the M8 cylinder head to cylinder block retaining bolts (9, 10) a first pass to 11 ft. lbs. (15 Nm).

20. Tighten the M8 cylinder head to cylinder block retaining bolts (9, 10) a second pass in sequence an additional 60 degrees using the J 45059 meter.

21. Install the catalytic converter to the exhaust manifold. Refer to Catalytic Converter.

22. Install the engine wiring harness bracket to cylinder head retaining bolts.

23. Install the wiring harness bracket using the cylinder head retaining bolts and tighten to 89 inch lbs. (10 Nm).

24. Install the wiring harness ground to the side of the cylinder head.

25. Install the wiring harness ground to the right cylinder head retaining bolt (3) and tighten to 89 inch lbs. (10 Nm).

26. Install the coolant inlet pipe. Refer to Engine Coolant Inlet Pipe Replacement.

a. Ensure all mating surfaces are thoroughly cleaned, using only a fine abrasive material.

b. Install the coolant inlet pipe at the thermostat end.

c. Install the coolant inlet pipe retaining bolt and tighten to 16 ft. lbs (22 Nm).

d. Raise and support the front of the vehicle.

e. Install the coolant inlet pipe to alternator bracket retaining nut and tighten to 16 ft. lbs. (22 Nm).

f. Attach the inlet hose to the inlet pipe and secure with retaining hose clamp.

g. Install the air deflector.

h. Lower the vehicle.

i. Install the right side catalytic converter. Refer to Catalytic Converter.

j. Install the radiator air baffle and deflector.

k. Fill the cooling system.

l. Inspect cooling system for coolant leaks.

27. Install the left bank secondary timing chain. Refer to Timing Chain & Sprockets.

28. Install the right camshaft cover. Refer to Valve Cover.

29. Install the engine covers. Refer to Engine Cover.

30. Connect the battery ground cable. Refer to Battery Negative Cable Disconnection & Connection in Engine Electrical.

Left Side

See Figures 123 through 125.

1. Before servicing the vehicle, refer to the Precautions Section.

2. Disconnect the battery ground cable. Refer to Battery Negative Cable Disconnection & Connection in Engine Electrical.

3. Remove the engine covers. Refer to Engine Cover.

4. Remove the right camshaft cover. Refer to Valve Cover.

5. Remove the left bank secondary timing chain. Refer to Timing Chain & Sprockets.

6. Remove the oil level indicator tube.

a. Remove the oil level indicator tube bracket to cylinder head retaining bolt.

b. Remove the oil level indicator from the oil level indicator tube.

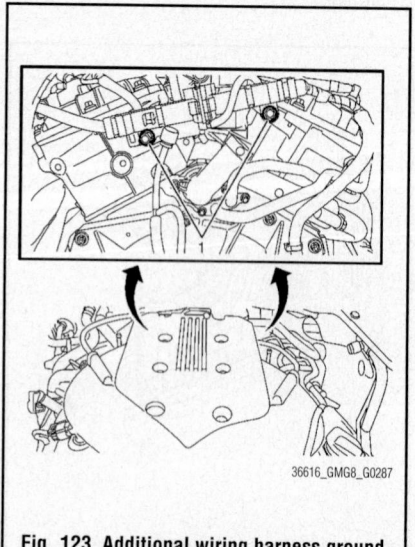

Fig. 123 Additional wiring harness ground locations—3.6L Engine

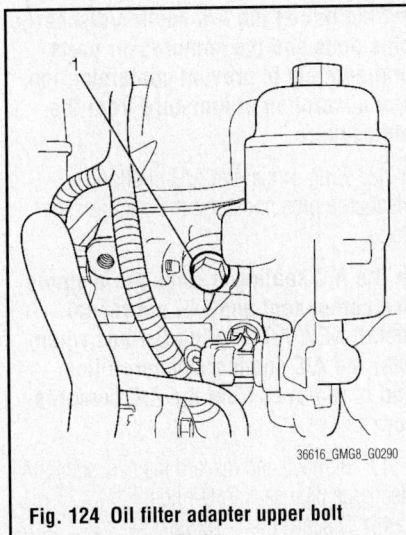

Fig. 124 Oil filter adapter upper bolt locations—3.6L Engine

c. Remove the knock sensor. Refer to Knock Sensor in Engine Performance & Emission Controls.

d. Remove the oil level indicator tube up through the exhaust manifold.

e. Remove and discard the O-ring from the oil level indicator tube if damaged.

7. Disconnect the coolant temperature sensor electrical connector. Refer to Engine Coolant Temperature Sensor.

8. Remove the wiring harness ground to cylinder head retaining bolt.

9. Remove the wiring harness ground from the cylinder head.

10. Remove the upper intake manifold with the lower intake manifold. Refer to Intake Manifold.

11. Remove the left engine cover mounting bracket to cylinder head retaining bolt.

12. Remove the left engine cover mounting bracket from the cylinder head.

13. Remove the engine wiring harness bracket to cylinder head retaining bolts.

14. Remove the catalytic converter. Refer to Catalytic Converter.

➡ **DO NOT remove the oil filter adapter.**

15. Remove the oil filter adapter upper bolt (1).

16. Remove the left bank cylinder head to cylinder block retaining bolts.

17. Remove the left bank cylinder head.

18. Remove and discard the left cylinder head gasket.

19. Clean and inspect the cylinder head and the cylinder block sealing surfaces.

To install:

➡ **Make sure that the crankshaft is in the timing drive assembly position using the EN 46111 socket .**

20. Make sure the cylinder head locating pins are securely mounted in the cylinder block deck face.

21. Install a NEW left cylinder head gasket using the deck face locating pins for retention.

22. Align the left cylinder head with the deck face locating pins.

23. Place the left cylinder head in position on the deck face.

➡ **DO NOT allow oil on the cylinder head bolt bosses.**

➡**DO NOT reuse the old M11 cylinder head bolts.**

24. Loosely install the NEW M11 cylinder head to cylinder block retaining bolts.

25. Loosely install the NEW M8 front cylinder head to cylinder block retaining bolts.

➡**Tighten the cylinder head to cylinder block retaining bolts in the sequence shown.**

a. Tighten the M11 cylinder head to cylinder block retaining bolts a first pass in sequence to 33 ft. lbs. (45 Nm).

b. Back off the M11 cylinder head to cylinder block retaining bolts 120 degrees using the J 45059 meter

c. Tighten the M11 cylinder head to cylinder block retaining bolts a second pass in sequence to 22 ft. lbs. (30 Nm).

d. Tighten the M11 cylinder head to cylinder block retaining bolts a third pass in sequence an additional 150 degrees using the J 45059 meter J 45059.

e. Install the 2 front M8 left cylinder head to cylinder block retaining bolts (9, 10).

f. Tighten the M8 cylinder head to cylinder block retaining bolts (9, 10) a first pass to 11 ft. lbs. (15 Nm).

26. Tighten the M8 cylinder head to cylinder block retaining bolts (9, 10) a second pass in sequence an additional 60 degrees using the J 45059 meter.

27. Install the oil filter adapter upper retaining bolt and tighten to 48 ft. lbs. (65 Nm).

28. Install the catalytic converter to the exhaust manifold. Refer to Catalytic Converter.

29. Install the wiring harness bracket to the rear of the cylinder head.

Install the wiring harness bracket using the cylinder head retaining bolts (1) and tighten to 89 inch lbs. (10 Nm).

30. Install the left engine cover mounting bracket to the cylinder head.

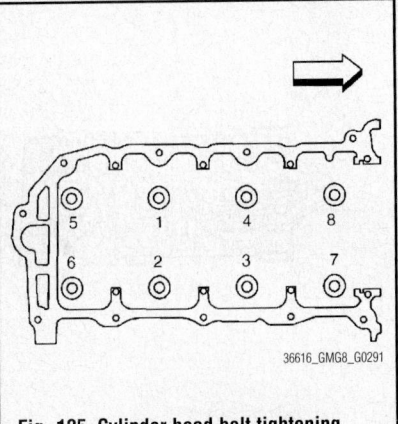

Fig. 125 Cylinder head bolt tightening sequence left side—3.6L Engine

31. Install the left engine cover mounting bracket using the cylinder head retaining bolt and tighten to 43 ft. lbs. (58 Nm).

32. Install the left engine cover mounting bracket to cylinder head retaining bolt.

33. Install the upper intake manifold with the lower intake manifold. Refer to Intake Manifold.

34. Install the wiring harness ground to the cylinder head.

35. Install the wiring harness ground to the cylinder head retaining bolt and tighten to 89 inch lbs. (10 Nm).

36. Connect the coolant temperature sensor electrical connector.

37. Install the oil level indicator.

38. Install the left bank secondary timing chain. Refer to Timing Chain & Sprockets.

39. Install the left camshaft cover. Refer to Valve Cover.

40. Install the engine covers. Refer to Engine Cover.

41. Connect the battery ground cable. Refer to Battery Negative Cable Disconnection & Connection in Engine Electrical.

ENGINE ASSEMBLY

REMOVAL & INSTALLATION

3.6L Engine

See Figures 126 through 136.

1. Before servicing the vehicle, refer to the Precautions Section.

2. Turn the ignition key to the LOCK position.

3. Disconnect the battery ground cable. Refer to Battery Negative Cable Disconnection & Connection in Engine Electrical.

4. Remove the engine covers. Refer to Engine Cover Replacement.

5. Remove the radiator air intake baffle.

6. Recover the air conditioning (A/C) refrigerant.

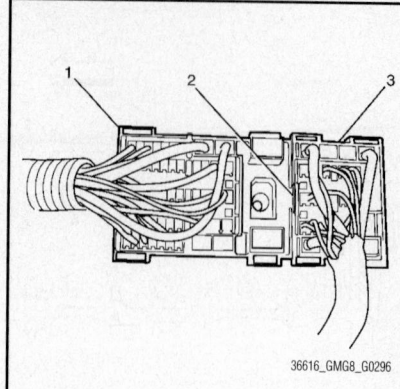

Fig. 126 Separate the body harness connector from the engine connector—3.6L Engine

7. Remove the air intake duct. Refer to Air Cleaner.

8. Depressurize the fuel system. Refer to Fuel Pressure Relief.

9. Drain the cooling system.

10. Remove the radiator outlet hose. Refer to Radiator Outlet Hose.

11. Compress the coolant bleed hose retaining clamp at the outlet housing end and slide 50 mm (2 in) along the coolant bleed hose.

12. Remove the coolant bleed hose from the outlet housing.

➡ **Twist and pull the coolant recovery hose to remove from the outlet housing.**

13. Disconnect the coolant recovery hose from the outlet housing.

➡ **Plug or cap the hoses and inlets when separating the cooling system components, this prevents dirt and other contaminants from entering the cooling system.**

14. Plug or cap the cooling system hoses and inlets

➡ **The inlet and outlet heater hoses are retained to the heater pipes by quick connect fittings.**

15. Disconnect the heater hose quick connect fittings by releasing the retaining clips with a suitable tool.

16. Disconnect the heater hose from the heater pipe in two places.

17. Compress the vacuum hose retaining clamp at the intake manifold vacuum port and slide 50 mm (2 in) back along the vacuum hose.

18. Disconnect the vacuum hose from the intake manifold vacuum port and secure away from the engine.

19. Remove the engine coolant heater cord if fitted.

20. Rotate the engine control module (ECM) electrical connector levers up to the unlocked position.

21. Disconnect ECM electrical connectors from the ECM.

22. Disconnect the 56 pin engine wiring harness to main wiring harness electrical connector.

23. Disconnect the two pin engine wiring harness to main wiring harness electrical connector.

24. Remove the under hood body electrical centre (BEC) cover.

25. Remove the positive cable protective cover.

26. Remove the positive cable to under hood BEC plate retaining bolt.

27. Disconnect the positive cable from the upper under hood BEC plate.

28. Remove the under hood BEC upper plate to lower plate retaining bolts.

29. Raise the upper under hood BEC plate from the lower under hood BEC plate.

30. Detach the protector from the base of the under hood BEC connector.

➡ **Use a suitable tool to depress the connector locking tang (2), then pull the body harness connector (1) upward and the engine connector (3) downward to separate the body harness connector (1) from the engine connector (3).**

31. Separate the body harness connector (1) from the engine connector (3).

32. Reposition and secure the engine wiring harness and connector (3) on the engine.

33. Remove the vehicle body ground cable to cylinder head ground stud retaining nut.

34. Detach the vehicle body ground cable from the cylinder head ground stud.

35. Remove the remote positive battery post cover from the remote positive battery post.

36. Remove the remote positive battery post to wiring harness retaining nut.

37. Remove the wiring harness from the remote positive battery post.

38. Disconnect the A/C pressure transducer electrical connector.

39. Disconnect the A/C compressor electrical connector.

40. Remove the suction/discharge line pad to A/C compressor retaining nut.

41. Disconnect the A/C suction/discharge line pad from the A/C compressor.

➡ **Plug or cap the A/C suction/discharge pipe ends and the compressor ports immediately to prevent contamination and absorption of moisture from the atmosphere.**

42. Plug or cap the A/C suction/discharge pipe ends and the compressor ports.

➡ **The A/C sealing O-rings are a single use component and will not reseal. Install NEW A/C sealing O-rings whenever the A/C suction/discharge line pad is removed from the A/C compressor.**

43. Remove and discard the A/C suction/discharge pipe sealing O-rings.

44. Discard the O-rings.

45. Remove the A/C suction pipe pad to A/C suction pipe retaining nut.

46. Disconnect the upper A/C suction pipe from the lower A/C suction tube.

47. Plug or cap the A/C suction pipe ends immediately to prevent contamination and absorption of moisture from the atmosphere.

48. Plug or cap the A/C suction pipe ends.

➡ **The A/C suction pipe sealing O-ring is a single use component and will not reseal. Install a NEW A/C suction pipe sealing O-ring whenever the upper A/C suction pipe is removed from the lower A/C suction pipe.**

49. Remove and discard the A/C suction pipe sealing O-ring.

50. Discard the O-ring.

51. Reposition and retain the A/C suction/discharge pipes away from the engine.

52. Disconnect the fuel feed hose from the fuel feed pipe.

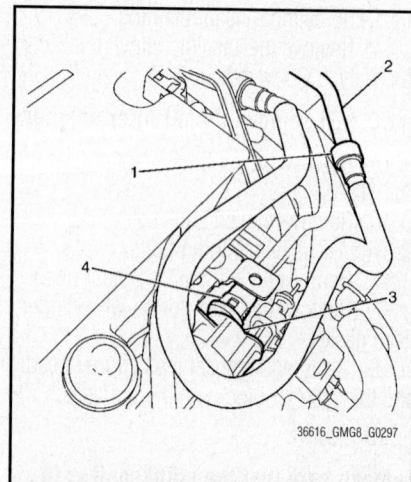

Fig. 127 Fuel and EVAP line locations—3.6L Engine

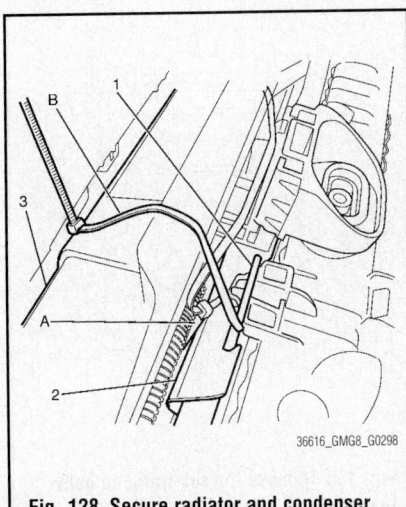

Fig. 128 Secure radiator and condenser assembly—3.6L Engine

➡Plug or cap the fuel feed pipe and fuel feed hose ends to prevent fuel leaks and/or contamination.

53. Disconnect the evaporative emission (EVAP) purge line (4) from the purge solenoid (3).

54. Plug or cap the (EVAP) purge line (4) and the purge solenoid (3) ends.

➡The flexible hoses are not serviced separately. Therefore if the hose's require replacement, then the hose and radiator to hose cooler hose assembly must be fitted.

➡When removal is complete plug hose openings with a clean lint free cloth to prevent foreign matter entry.

55. Place a suitable container beneath the radiator and engine.

56. Using the cooler quick connect tool J 41623-B disconnect the transmission cooler line from the flexible hose.
- Open the cooler quick connect tool J 41623-B then close and clip around the hose to be disconnected.
- While holding the flexible hose push the hose inwards with one hand, then pull back to separate from the steel hose piping.
- Repeat for the second fitting.

57. Reposition and secure the flexible hoses away from the engine and sub-frame.

➡It is necessary to secure the radiator and condenser assembly to the front end assembly as the radiator and condenser assembly is supported to the sub-frame.

➡Thread zip tie A around the front end assembly and zip tie B through the radiator and condenser mount (1). Insert zip tie A into the retainer of zip tie B and insert zip tie B into the retainer of zip tie A.

58. Secure radiator and condenser assembly (2) to the front end assembly (3) with large zip ties or equivalent.

✳✳ CAUTION

To avoid any vehicle damage, serious personal injury or death when major components are removed from the vehicle and the vehicle is supported by a hoist, support the vehicle with jack stands at the opposite end from which the components are being removed and strap the vehicle to the hoist.

59. Raise and support the vehicle.
60. Remove the front air deflector.
61. Remove the Engine Splash Shield.
62. Disconnect the radiator inlet hose.
63. Place a suitable container under the power steering cooler.

➡The power steering cooler (3) must be plugged to prevent the entry of foreign particles into the power steering system.

64. Release the power steering gear outlet hose spring clamp (2) and disconnect the power steering gear outlet hose (1) from the power steering cooler (3).

65. Plug the power steering cooler (3) and power steering gear outlet hose (1).

➡The power steering cooler (3) must be plugged to prevent the entry of foreign particles into the power steering system.

66. Release the power steering reservoir inlet hose spring clamp (1) and disconnect the power steering reservoir inlet hose (2) from the power steering cooler (3).

67. Plug the power steering cooler (3) and power steering reservoir inlet hose (2).

68. Disconnect the oil level/temperature sensor electrical connector.

69. Remove the exhaust system. Refer to Exhaust System.

70. Remove the centre exhaust heat shield. Refer to Exhaust System.

71. Remove the propeller shaft. Refer to Propeller Shaft in Rear Drive Axle.

72. Remove the shift selector linkage rod to shift selector shaft retaining nut. Refer to Transmission.

73. Remove the shift selector linkage rod from the shift selector shaft.

74. Remove the starter motor. Refer to Starter in Engine Electrical.

75. Partially lower the vehicle.
76. Remove the front wheels.
77. Detach the front brake hose from the strut mounted brake hose retaining bracket. Repeat for opposite side.

➡Bolts with micro-encapsulated thread sealant must be discarded after removal.

➡Make sure all the bolt holes are thoroughly cleaned and all micro-encapsulated thread sealant is removed.

78. Remove the front brake caliper anchor plate to knuckle retaining bolts. Repeat for opposite side.
   a. Discard the bolts.
   b. Clean the bolt holes.

➡DO NOT disconnect the hydraulic brake flexible hose from the brake caliper otherwise complete bleeding of the braking system will be necessary.

79. Remove the front brake caliper from the front steering knuckle. Repeat for opposite side.

✳✳ WARNING

Support the brake caliper with heavy mechanic wire, or equivalent, whenever it is separated from its mount and the hydraulic flexible brake hose is still connected. Failure to support the caliper in this manner will cause the flexible brake hose to bear the weight of the caliper, which may cause damage to the brake hose and in turn may cause a brake fluid leak.

80. Support the front brake caliper with heavy mechanic's wire, or equivalent. Repeat for opposite side.

81. Install two wheel nuts to retain the front brake disc to the hub. Repeat for opposite side.

82. Disconnect the front wheel speed sensor jumper harness electrical connector

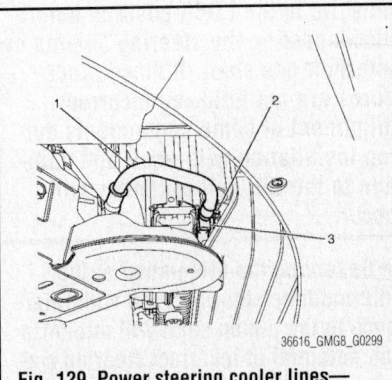

Fig. 129 Power steering cooler lines—3.6L Engine

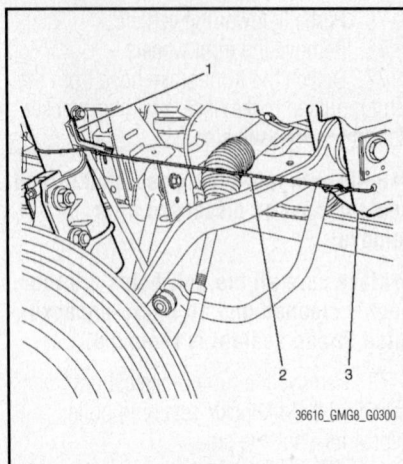

Fig. 130 Strut assembly must be secured to the sub-frame—3.6L Engine

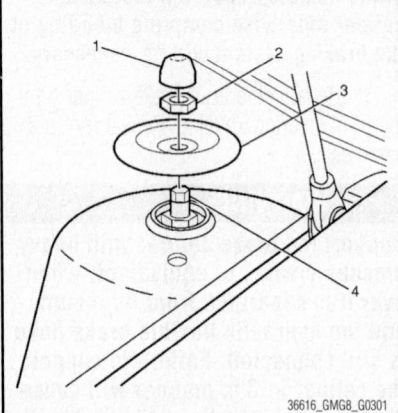

Fig. 131 Remove the strut assembly to front wheelhouse retaining plate— 3.6L Engine

and secure away from the sub-frame and suspension components. Repeat for opposite side.

❊❊ WARNING

The front wheels of the vehicle must be maintained in the straight ahead position and the steering column must be in the LOCK position before disconnecting the steering column or intermediate shaft. If these procedures are not followed incorrect alignment of some components during installation will result and damage to the SIR coil assembly will occur.

➡ Observing the orientation of the intermediate steering shaft with reference to the pinion shaft will minimize the potential of incorrect steering column assembly alignment. Refer to Intermediate Shaft in Steering.

83. Mark the intermediate steering shaft in relation to the pinion shaft.

84. Remove the intermediate steering shaft to pinion shaft retaining bolt.

➡ Bolts with micro-encapsulated thread sealant must be discarded after removal.

➡ Make sure the bolt hole is thoroughly cleaned and all micro-encapsulated thread sealant is removed.

85. Disconnect the intermediate shaft from the pinion shaft.
   a. Discard the bolt.
   b. Clean the bolt hole.
86. Lower the vehicle.

➡ The strut assembly (1) must be secured to the sub-frame (3) to prevent damage to the front wheelhouse liner, fenders and suspension components.

87. Retain the front strut assembly (1) to the front sub-frame (3) using heavy mechanics wire or equivalent (2). Repeat for opposite side.

88. Remove the stud dust cover (1) from the strut assembly to front wheelhouse retaining nut (2).

➡ The strut assembly (4) must be supported from underneath before the strut assembly to front wheelhouse retaining nut (2) is removed.

89. Remove the strut assembly to front wheelhouse retaining nut (2) while holding the strut piston shaft (4) with a suitable tool.

90. Discard the nut.

91. Remove the strut assembly to front wheelhouse retaining plate (3).

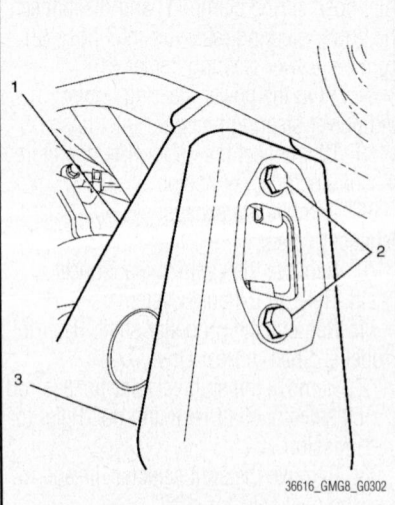

Fig. 132 Sub-frame reinforcement plate bolt location—3.6L Engine

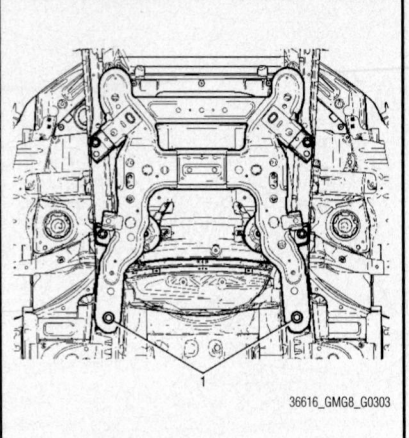

Fig. 133 Remove the sub-frame to body rear retaining bolt location—3.6L Engine

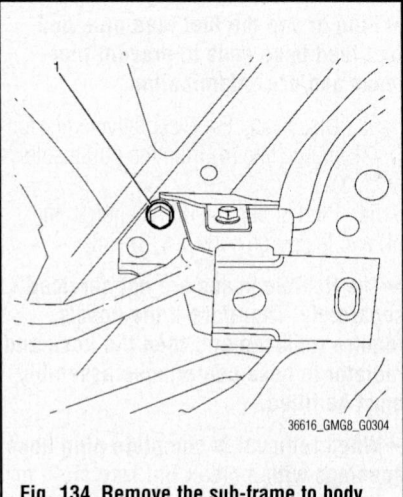

Fig. 134 Remove the sub-frame to body front retaining bolt location—3.6L Engine

92. Position a suitable powertrain and/or engine lift table below the frame, engine and transmission.

93. Raise the lift table and/or lower the vehicle to support the frame, engine and transmission.

94. Remove the transmission support to body retaining bolts (1).

95. Remove the sub-frame reinforcement plate to sub-frame retaining bolts (2).

96. Remove the sub-frame reinforcement plate (3) from the sub-frame (1).

97. Remove the sub-frame to body rear retaining bolts (1).

➡ Only right side depicted in graphic, left side similar.

98. Remove the sub-frame to body front retaining bolt (1). Repeat for opposite side.

➡ Only right side depicted in graphic, left side similar.

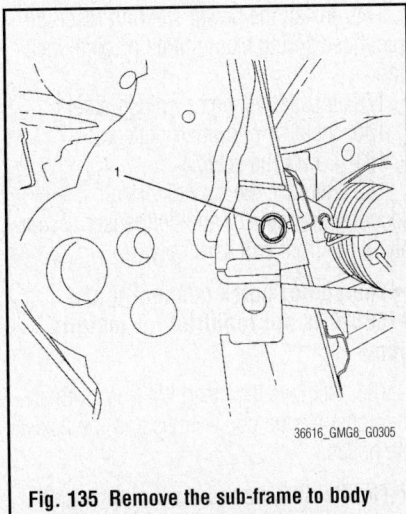

Fig. 135 Remove the sub-frame to body retaining bolt (1)—3.6L Engine

99. Remove the sub-frame to body retaining bolt. Repeat for opposite side.

➡**Make sure that all the hoses, wires, pipes and front struts clear the vehicle during the removal process.**

100. With the aid of an assistant, lower the table and/or raise the vehicle to remove the engine, transmission, front suspension and sub-frame assembly from the vehicle.

101. Remove the engine and transmission wiring harness and related components.

102. Remove the transmission cooler line clamp to alternator mounting bracket retaining nut.

103. Remove the transmission cooler line clamp and transmission cooler lines from the alternator mounting bracket.

104. Position the EN 46114 on the engine.

105. Install the J 41798 to the cylinder head retaining bolts and tighten to 36 ft. lbs. (50 Nm).

106. Connect a suitable lifting crane to the engine lift brackets and raise the suitable lifting crane to support the engine.

107. Position a second powertrain lift table below the transmission.

108. Remove the transmission. Refer to Transmission.

109. Remove the engine flywheel. Refer to Flywheel.

110. Remove the catalytic converters. Refer to Catalytic Converter.

111. Remove the drive belt. Refer to Accessory Drive Belt.

➡**The locking tang on the power steering reservoir bracket must be released before removing the power steering reservoir. Release the locking tang on the power steering reservoir bracket with a suitable tool.**

112. Separate power steering fluid reservoir from the power steering fluid reservoir bracket.

➡**DO NOT disconnect the power steering pipes/hoses.**

➡**Bolts with micro-encapsulated thread sealant must be discarded after removal.**

➡**Make sure all the bolt holes are thoroughly cleaned and all micro-encapsulated thread sealant is removed.**

113. Remove the power steering pump to power steering pump bracket retaining bolts.
   a. Discard the bolts.
   b. Clean the bolt hole.

114. Remove the power steering pump from the power steering pump bracket position the power steering pump aside.

115. Remove the A/C compressor.

116. Remove the A/C compressor mounting bracket.

117. Remove the alternator. Refer to Alternator.

118. Attach a suitable lifting chain and hooks to the EN 46114 .

119. Using a suitable lifting crane, raise the engine to clear the engine mount stud.

120. Remove the engine mount brackets with the engine mounts.

121. Remove the engine from the sub-frame

122. If required mount the engine on a suitable engine stand.

To install:

123. Use a floor crane in order to install the engine to the frame.

124. Install the engine mount brackets with the engine mounts.
   a. Install the engine mount bracket using the cylinder block retaining bolts and tighten to 43 ft. lbs. (58 Nm).
   b. Position the engine mount on the engine mount bracket.
   c. Install the engine mount using the engine mount bracket retaining nut and tighten to 59 ft. lbs. (80 Nm).

125. Raise the floor crane to partially support the engine

126. Install the alternator bracket and alternator. Refer to Alternator in Engine Electrical.

127. Install the A/C compressor.

128. Install the power steering pump to the power steering pump bracket.

129. Install the NEW power steering pump to the power steering pump bracket

retaining bolts and tighten to 22 ft. Lbs. (27 Nm).

➡**Make sure the power steering reservoir and the power steering reservoir bracket locking tang are engaged to avoid an induced rattle condition.**

130. Install the power steering fluid reservoir to the power steering fluid reservoir bracket.

131. Install the drive belt. Refer to Accessory Drive Belt.

132. Install the catalytic converters. Refer to Catalytic Converter.

133. Install the flywheel. Refer to Flywheel.

134. Install the transmission. Refer to Transmission in Drive Train.

135. Install the transmission cooler line clamp and transmission cooler lines to the alternator mounting bracket

136. Install the transmission cooler line clamp to the alternator mounting bracket retaining nut and tighten to 16 ft. lbs. (22 Nm).

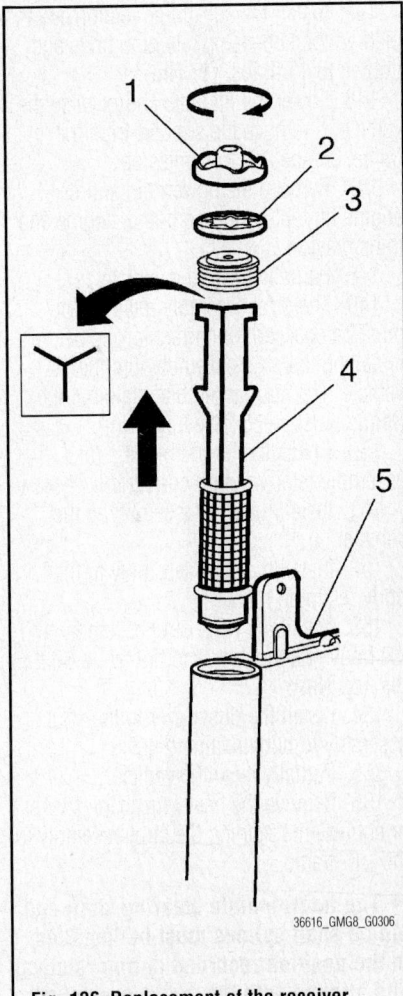

Fig. 136 Replacement of the receiver dehydrator cartridge from the condenser

137. Install the engine and transmission wiring harness and related components.

138. Remove the EN 46114 lift brackets from the engine.

➡ **Make sure that all the hoses, wires, pipes and shock modules clear the vehicle during the installation process.**

139. With the aid of an assistant, raise the table and/or lower the vehicle to install the engine, transmission, front suspension and sub-frame assembly to the vehicle.

140. Install the transmission support to the body retaining bolts and tighten to 43 ft. lbs. (58 Nm).

141. Install the sub-frame to the body retaining bolts and tighten to 118 ft. lbs. (160 Nm).

142. Install the sub-frame to the body front retaining bolts and tighten to 118 ft. lbs. (160 Nm).

143. Install the sub-frame to the body rear retaining bolts and tighten to 177 ft. lbs. (240 Nm).

144. Install the sub-frame reinforcement plate to the sub-frame.

145. Install the sub-frame reinforcement plate to the sub-frame retaining bolts and tighten to 13 ft. lbs. (17 Nm).

146. Lower the lift table and/or raise the vehicle to remove the support from the frame, engine and transmission.

147. Remove the powertrain and/or engine lift table from the frame, engine and transmission.

148. Partially lower the vehicle.

149. The strut assembly retaining nut must be checked for correct torque before installing the strut assembly into the vehicle. The strut assembly retaining nut torque must be 55 ft. lbs. (75 Nm).

150. Check the torque of the strut assembly retaining nut, correct if necessary.

151. Install the strut assembly to the vehicle.

152. Install the strut assembly to the body retaining plate.

153. Install the NEW strut assembly to the body retaining nut and tighten to 40 ft. lbs. (55 Nm).

154. Install the dust cover to the strut assembly to body retaining nut.

155. Partially raise the vehicle.

156. Remove the heavy mechanics wire or equivalent retaining the strut assembly to the sub-frame.

➡ **The intermediate steering shaft and pinion shaft splines must be installed in the position recorded during removal and aligned with the marks previously made.**

157. Connect the intermediate steering shaft to the pinion shaft.

158. Install the NEW intermediate steering shaft to the pinion shaft retaining bolt and tighten to 18 ft. lbs.(25 Nm).

159. Connect the wheel speed sensor jumper harness electrical connector.

160. Remove the heavy mechanic's wire, or equivalent support from the brake caliper.

161. Remove the wheel nuts retaining the brake disc to the hub.

✷✷ WARNING

Make sure the brake hose is not twisted or kinked after installation. Damage to the hose could result.

162. Install the brake caliper assembly to the steering knuckle.

163. Install the NEW brake caliper anchor plate to the knuckle retaining bolts and tighten to 44 ft. lbs. (60 Nm) plus 120°.

✷✷ WARNING

Make sure the brake hose is not twisted or kinked after installation. Damage to the hose could result.

164. Attach the brake hose to the strut mounted brake hose retaining bracket.

165. Install the front wheels.

166. Install the shift selector linkage rod to the shift selector shaft.

167. Install the shift selector linkage rod using the shift selector shaft retaining nut and tighten to 11 ft. lbs. (15 Nm).

168. Install the starter motor. Refer to Starter in Engine Electrical.

169. Install the propeller shaft. Refer to Propeller Shaft in Replacement.

170. Install the centre exhaust heat shield.

171. Install the Exhaust system. Refer to Exhaust System.

172. Connect the low oil level sensor electrical connector.

173. Remove the plug from the power steering cooler and power steering reservoir inlet hose.

174. Connect the power steering reservoir inlet hose to the power steering cooler.

175. Install the power steering reservoir inlet hose spring clamp to its original location.

176. Remove the plug from the power steering cooler and power steering reservoir inlet hose.

177. Connect the power steering reservoir inlet hose to the power steering cooler.

178. Install the power steering reservoir inlet hose spring clamp to its original location

179. Install the engine splash shield.

180. Install the front air deflector.

181. Lower the vehicle.

182. Remove the zip ties or equivalent securing the radiator and condenser assembly to the front end assembly.

➡ **The cooler quick connect tool J 41623-B is not required for installation.**

183. Remove the clean lint free cloth at the transmission cooler lines and the flexible hoses.

➡ **The flexible hoses are not serviced separately. Therefore if the hose's require replacement, then the hose and radiator to hose cooler hose assembly must be fitted.**

184. Align both flexible hose's with both steel cooler lines.

➡ **Listen for an audible click to confirm fitting.**

185. Hold the cooler line and connect the flexible hose by pushing together. Repeat procedure for other hose.

➡ **When adding or changing transmission fluid use only recommended automatic transmission fluid.**

186. Check and top up transmission fluid level if required.

187. Remove the plug or cap at the fuel feed hose and fuel feed pipe ends.

188. Connect the fuel feed hose to the fuel feed pipe.

189. Remove the plug or cap at the EVAP purge line and the purge solenoid ends.

190. Connect the EVAP purge line to the purge solenoid.

➡ **DO NOT coat the new sealing washer with oil. They must be fitted dry. The use of mineral oil will render the washer useless, as the washer WILL swell causing refrigerant to leak out.**

191. Note the following:

a. Install a NEW sealing washer to suction pipe joint.

b. Position the upper suction pipe to the lower suction pipe.

c. Install the A/C suction pipe pad to the A/C suction pipe retaining nut and tighten to 16 ft lbs. (22 Nm).

d. Remove the plug or cap at the A/C suction/discharge pipe ends and the compressor ports.

➡ **The A/C sealing O-rings must be fitted dry. DO NOT lubricate the A/C sealing O-rings.**

    e. Fit the NEW A/C suction/discharge pipe sealing O-ring to the suction pipe.

    f. Connect the A/C suction/discharge line pad to the A/C compressor.

    g. Install the suction/discharge line pad to A/C compressor retaining nut.

    h. Connect the A/C compressor electrical connector.

    i. Connect the A/C pressure transducer electrical connector.

192. Install the wiring harness.

193. Install the remote battery positive post to the wiring harness retaining nut and tighten to 11 ft. lbs. (15 Nm).

➡ **Make sure the clips on the remote battery positive post cover are engaged to avoid an induced rattle condition.**

194. Install the remote battery positive post cover.

195. Attach the vehicle body ground cable to the cylinder head ground stud.

196. Install the vehicle body ground cable to the cylinder head ground stud retaining nut and tighten to 18 ft. lbs. (25 Nm).

➡ **Listen for a audible click from the locking tang to confirm fitting.**

197. Slide the engine connector into the body harness connector to join.

198. Attach the protector to the base of the under hood BEC connector.

199. Install the upper under hood BEC plate to the lower under hood BEC plate.

➡ **The under hood BEC upper plate to lower plate retaining bolts DO NOT have a torque specification.**

200. Listen for an audible clicking sound whilst tightening the under hood BEC upper plate to lower plate retaining bolts to confirm correct fitting.

201. Install the under hood BEC upper plate to lower plate retaining bolts.

202. Connect the positive cable to the upper under hood BEC plate.

203. Install the positive cable to the under hood BEC plate retaining bolt and tighten to 89 inch lbs. (10 Nm).

204. Install the positive cable protective cover.

205. Install the under hood body electrical centre (BEC) lid.

206. Connect the 56 pin engine wiring harness to main wiring harness electrical connector.

207. Connect the 2 pin engine wiring harness to main wiring harness electrical connector.

208. Connect ECM electrical connectors.

209. Rotate the engine control module (ECM) electrical connector levers to the locked position.

210. Install the engine coolant heater cord if fitted.

211. Connect the vacuum hose to the intake manifold vacuum port.

212. Compress the vacuum hose retaining clamp and slide along the vacuum hose to the correct location to secure the vacuum hose to the intake manifold vacuum port.

✳✳ WARNING

Do not twist hoses upon installation.

➡ **Listen for a audible click to confirm fitting in two places**

213. Attach the heater hose quick connect fitting by pushing the hose onto the heater pipe.

214. Remove the plug or cap at the cooling system hoses and inlets

215. Install the coolant bleed hose to the outlet housing.

216. Compress the coolant bleed hose retaining clamp and position back to its original location on the coolant bleed hose.

217. Connect the coolant recovery hose from the outlet housing.

218. Install the radiator outlet hose. Refer to Radiator Outlet Hose in Engine Cooling.

219. Connect the battery ground cable. Refer to Battery Negative Cable Disconnection & Connection in Engine Electrical.

220. Refill the cooling system.

221. Install the air intake duct. Refer to Air Cleaner.

➡ **The receiver and dehydrator is a single use only component. A NEW receiver and dehydrator must be installed whenever a closed A/C system is opened or exposed to atmosphere. If the receiver and dehydrator has been replaced following a service/repair and it is deemed necessary to immediately re-open the A/C system it is not necessary to replace the receiver and dehydrator again, providing the A/C system is plugged/capped correctly.**

222. Replace the receiver and dehydrator:

    a. Remove the receiver dehydrator plastic screw cap (1) from the condenser (5).

➡ **The circlip (2) cannot be removed if any gas pressure is present in A/C system.**

➡ **To gain adequate clearance for removal of the circlip (2), use a suit-**

able tool to gently tap the receiver dehydrator bottle plug (3) downwards.

    b. Remove the circlip (2).

➡ **Screw a suitable bolt into the threaded hole in the receiver dehydrator bottle plug (3). Pull upwards on the bolt to remove the receiver dehydrator bottle plug (3) from the condenser (5).**

    c. Remove the receiver dehydrator bottle plug (3) from the condenser (5).

➡ **Using a suitable tool, grip the lower lip on the receiver dehydrator cartridge (4) and pull upwards to remove the receiver dehydrator cartridge (4) from the condenser (5).**

    d. Remove the receiver dehydrator cartridge (4) from the condenser (5).

    e. To install, reverse removal procedure.

223. Recharge the air conditioning (A/C) system.

224. Install the radiator air intake baffle.

225. Install the engine covers. Refer to Engine Cover.

226. Disable the ignition system.

227. Crank the engine several times. Listen for any unusual noises or evidence that parts are binding.

228. Enable the ignition system.

229. Start the engine and listen for unusual noises.

230. Check the vehicle oil pressure gauge and confirm that the engine has acceptable oil pressure.

231. If necessary, install an oil pressure gauge and measure the engine oil pressure.

232. Run the engine speed at about 1,000 RPM until the engine has reached normal operating temperature.

233. Listen for sticking stationary hydraulic lash adjuster, and other unusual noises.

234. Inspect for fuel, oil, and/or other coolant leaks while the engine is running.

6.0L Engine

See Figures 126, 128 through 136, 137 through 145.

1. Before servicing the vehicle, refer to the Precautions Section.

2. Turn the ignition key to the LOCK position.

3. Disconnect the battery negative cable. Refer to Battery Negative Cable Disconnection & Connection in Engine Electrical.

4. Remove the engine cover. Refer to Engine Cover.

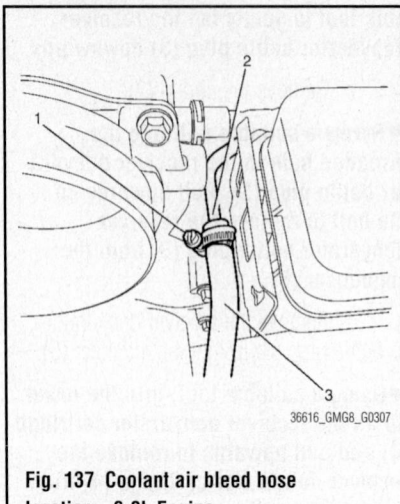

Fig. 137 Coolant air bleed hose location—6.0L Engine

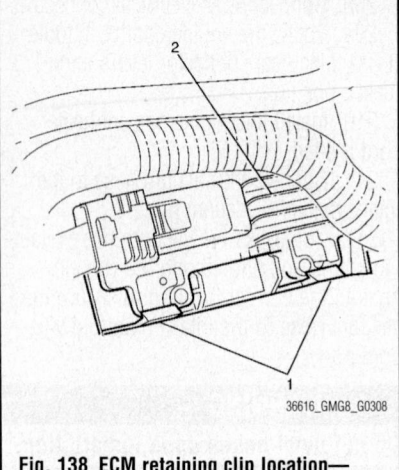

Fig. 138 ECM retaining clip location—6.0L Engine

5. Remove the radiator air baffle and deflector.

6. Recover the air conditioning (A/C) refrigerant.

7. Remove the air intake duct. Refer to Air Cleaner.

8. Depressurize the fuel system. Refer to Fuel Pressure Relief.

9. Drain the cooling system.

10. Remove the radiator outlet hose. Refer to Radiator Outlet Hose in Engine Cooling.

11. Loosen the coolant bleed hose retaining clamp (1) at the cylinder head end and slide 50 mm (2 in) along the coolant bleed hose (3).

12. Disconnect the coolant air bleed hose (3) from the coolant bleed pipe (2).

➡ **Disconnect the heater hose assembly quick connect fittings by releasing the retaining clips using a suitable tool.**

13. Disconnect the inlet and outlet heater hoses from the heater hose assembly quick connect fittings.

⚹⚹ **WARNING**

Do not touch the connector pins or soldered components on the circuit board in order to prevent possible electrostatic discharge (ESD) damage to the PCM.

14. Release the ECM retaining clips and detach the ECM.

15. Move the connector lock levers to the unlock position and disconnect the ECM electrical connectors.

16. Remove the under hood Body Electrical Centre (BEC) cover.

17. Remove the positive cable protective cover.

18. Remove the positive cable to under hood BEC plate retaining bolt.

19. Disconnect the positive cable from the upper under hood BEC plate.

20. Raise the upper under hood BEC plate from the lower under hood BEC plate.

21. Detach the protector from the base of the under hood BEC connector.

➡ **Use a suitable tool to depress the connector locking tang (2), then pull the body harness connector (1) upward and the engine connector (3) downward to separate the body harness connector (1) from the engine connector (3).**

22. Separate the body harness connector (1) from the engine connector (3).

23. Reposition and secure the engine wiring harness and connector (3) on the engine.

24. Remove the under hood BEC upper plate to lower plate retaining bolts.

25. Raise the upper under hood BEC plate from the lower under hood BEC plate.

26. Detach the protector from the base of the under hood BEC connector.

27. Remove the vehicle body ground cable to cylinder head ground stud retaining nut (3).

28. Detach the vehicle body ground cable (1) from the cylinder head ground stud (2).

29. Disconnect the A/C electrical connector from the A/C compressor.

30. Disconnect the electrical connector from the A/C Refrigerant Pressure Sensor.

31. Remove the suction/discharge pipes pad to compressor retaining bolt.

32. Disconnect the suction/discharge pipes from the compressor.

➡ **Sealing washers are single use and must be discarded after use.**

➡ **Seal pipes immediately to prevent absorption of moisture from the atmosphere.**

➡ **The plugs for A/C compressor ports must be sufficient to stop oil escaping when tilting A/C compressor for removal.**

33. Remove and discard the port sealing washers.

34. Discard the port sealing washers.

➡ **Cap or plug the ports immediately to prevent absorption of moisture from the atmosphere.**

35. Cap or plug the A/C compressor ports.

36. Cap or plug the A/C hoses.

37. Remove the engine coolant heater cord if fitted. Refer to Coolant Heater Cord Replacement.

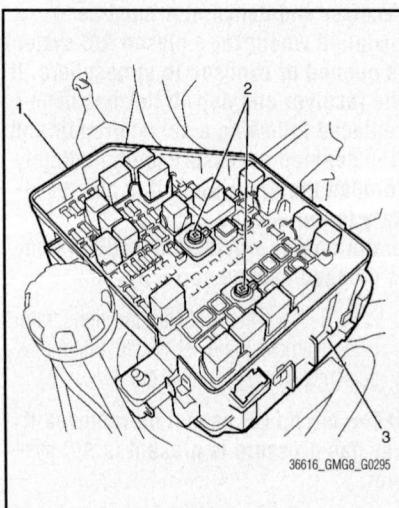

Fig. 139 Under hood BEC upper plate to lower plate retaining bolt locations

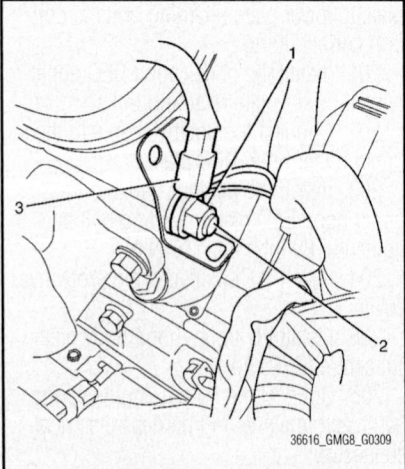

Fig. 140 Detach the vehicle body ground cable from the cylinder head ground stud—6.0L Engine

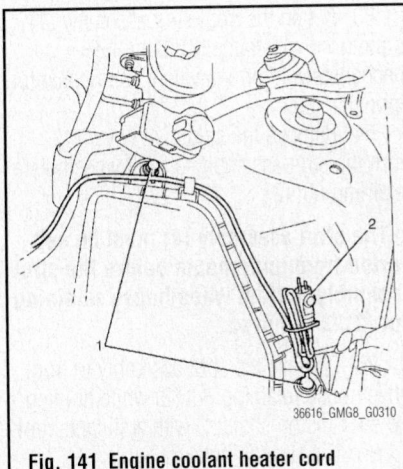

Fig. 141 Engine coolant heater cord location—6.0L Engine

38. Compress the vacuum hose retaining clamp (2) at the intake manifold vacuum port (1) and slide 2 inches (50 mm) back along the vacuum hose (3).

39. Disconnect the vacuum hose (3) from the intake manifold vacuum port (1).

➡ Plug or cap the fuel feed pipe and fuel rail tube ends to prevent fuel leaks and/or contamination.

40. Disconnect the fuel rail feed pipe quick connect fitting.

41. Remove the remote positive battery post cover from the remote positive battery post.

42. Remove the remote positive battery post to wiring harness retaining nut.

43. Remove the wiring harness from the remote positive battery post.

➡ Plug or cap the throttle body to EVAP purge valve hose (3) and EVAP purge valve (1) ends to prevent fuel leaks and/or contamination.

44. Disconnect the throttle body to EVAP

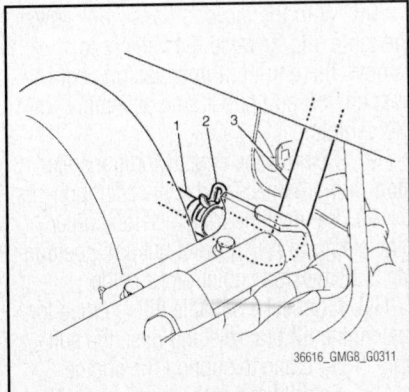

Fig. 142 Vacuum hose location— 6.0L Engine

purge valve hose (3) from the EVAP purge valve (1).

➡ Plug or cap the EVAP purge valve to fuel tank hose (2) and EVAP purge valve (1) ends to prevent fuel leaks and/or contamination.

45. Disconnect the EVAP purge valve to fuel tank hose (2) from the EVAP purge valve (1).

46. Remove the A/C suction pipe pad to lower A/C suction pipe retaining nut.

47. Disconnect the upper A/C suction pipe from the lower A/C suction pipe.

➡ Plug or cap the A/C suction pipe ends immediately to prevent contamination and absorption of moisture from the atmosphere.

48. Plug or cap the A/C suction pipe ends.

➡ The A/C suction pipe sealing O-ring is a single use component and will not reseal. Install a NEW A/C suction pipe sealing O-ring whenever the upper A/C suction pipe is removed from the lower A/C suction pipe.

49. Remove and discard the A/C suction pipe sealing O-ring.

50. Discard the A/C suction pipe sealing O-ring.

51. Reposition and retain the A/C suction/discharge pipes away from the engine.

➡ It is necessary to secure the radiator and condenser assembly to the front end assembly as the radiator and condenser assembly is supported to the sub-frame.

➡ Thread zip tie A around the front end assembly and zip tie B through the radiator and condenser mount (1). Insert zip tie A into the retainer of zip tie B and insert zip tie B into the retainer of zip tie A.

52. Secure radiator and condenser assembly (2) to the front end assembly (3) with large zip ties or equivalent.

➡ The next few steps do not apply to manual transmission vehicles.

➡ The flexible hoses are not serviced separately. Therefore if the hose's require replacement, then the hose and radiator to hose assembly must be fitted.

➡ When removal is complete plug hose openings with a clean lint free cloth to prevent foreign matter entry.

53. Place a suitable container beneath the radiator and engine.

54. Using the cooler quick connect tool J 41623-B disconnect the transmission cooler line from the flexible hose.
   - Open the cooler quick connect tool J 41623-B then close and clip around the hose to be disconnected.
   - While holding the flexible hose push the hose inwards with one hand, then pull back to separate from the steel hose piping.
   - Repeat for the second fitting if required.

55. Reposition and secure the flexible hoses away from the engine and sub-frame.

✳✳ CAUTION

To avoid any vehicle damage, serious personal injury or death when major components are removed from the vehicle and the vehicle is supported by a hoist, support the vehicle with jack stands at the opposite end from which the components are being removed and strap the vehicle to the hoist.

56. Raise and support the vehicle.

57. Remove the front air deflector.

58. Remove the Engine Splash Shield.

59. Disconnect the radiator inlet hose.

60. Place a suitable container under the power steering cooler.

➡ The power steering cooler (3) must be plugged to prevent the entry of foreign particles into the power steering system.

61. Release the power steering gear outlet hose spring clamp (2) and disconnect

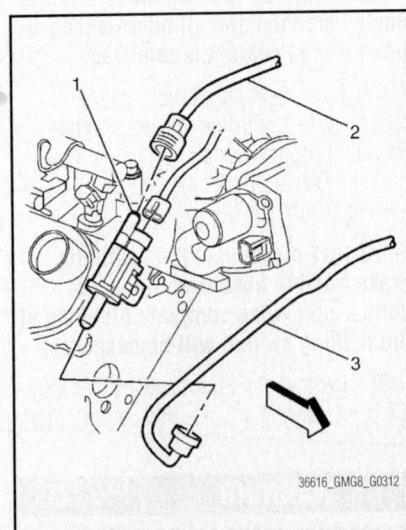

Fig. 143 EVAP purge valve to fuel tank hose location—6.0L Engine

the power steering gear outlet hose (1) from the power steering cooler (3).

62. Plug the power steering cooler (3) and power steering gear outlet hose (1).

➡ The power steering cooler (3) must be plugged to prevent the entry of foreign particles into the power steering system.

63. Release the power steering reservoir inlet hose spring clamp (1) and disconnect the power steering reservoir inlet hose (2) from the power steering cooler (3).

64. Plug the power steering cooler (3) and power steering reservoir inlet hose (2).

65. Remove the exhaust system. Refer to Exhaust System.

66. Remove the centre exhaust heat shield. Refer to Exhaust System.

67. Remove the propeller shaft. Refer to Propeller Shaft in Rear Drive Axle.

68. For automatic transmission:

   a. Remove the shift selector linkage rod to shift selector shaft retaining nut. Refer to Automatic Transmission.

   b. Remove the shift selector linkage rod from the shift selector shaft.

69. For manual transmission, remove the shift control assembly. Refer to Manual Transmission.

70. Remove the starter motor. Refer to Starter in Engine Electrical.

71. Partially lower the vehicle.

72. Remove the front wheels.

73. Detach the front brake hose from the strut mounted brake hose retaining bracket. Repeat for opposite side.

➡ Bolts with micro-encapsulated thread sealant must be discarded after removal.

➡ Make sure all the bolt holes are thoroughly cleaned and all micro-encapsulated thread sealant is removed.

74. Remove the front brake caliper anchor plate to knuckle retaining bolts. Repeat for opposite side.

   a. Discard the bolts.

   b. Clean the bolt holes.

➡ DO NOT disconnect the hydraulic brake flexible hose from the brake caliper otherwise complete bleeding of the braking system will be necessary.

75. Remove the front brake caliper from the front steering knuckle. Repeat for opposite side.

✳✳ WARNING

Support the brake caliper with heavy mechanic wire, or equivalent, whenever it is separated from its mount and the hydraulic flexible brake hose is still connected. Failure to support the caliper in this manner will cause the flexible brake hose to bear the weight of the caliper, which may cause damage to the brake hose and in turn may cause a brake fluid leak.

76. Support the front brake caliper with heavy mechanic's wire, or equivalent. Repeat for opposite side.

77. Install two wheel nuts to retain the front brake disc to the hub. Repeat for opposite side.

78. Disconnect the front wheel speed sensor jumper harness electrical connector and secure away from the sub-frame and suspension components. Repeat for opposite side.

✳✳ WARNING

The front wheels of the vehicle must be maintained in the straight ahead position and the steering column must be in the LOCK position before disconnecting the steering column or intermediate shaft. If these procedures are not followed incorrect alignment of some components during installation will result and damage to the SIR coil assembly will occur.

➡ Observing the orientation of the intermediate steering shaft with reference to the pinion shaft will minimize the potential of incorrect steering column assembly alignment. Refer to Intermediate Shaft in Steering.

79. Mark the intermediate steering shaft in relation to the pinion shaft.

80. Remove the intermediate steering shaft to pinion shaft retaining bolt.

➡ Bolts with micro-encapsulated thread sealant must be discarded after removal.

➡ Make sure the bolt hole is thoroughly cleaned and all micro-encapsulated thread sealant is removed.

81. Disconnect the intermediate shaft from the pinion shaft.

   a. Discard the bolt.

   b. Clean the bolt hole.

82. Lower the vehicle.

➡ The strut assembly (1) must be secured to the sub-frame (3) to prevent damage to the front wheelhouse liner, fenders and suspension components.

83. Retain the front strut assembly (1) to the front sub-frame (3) using heavy mechanics wire or equivalent (2). Repeat for opposite side.

84. Remove the stud dust cover (1) from the strut assembly to front wheelhouse retaining nut (2).

➡ The strut assembly (4) must be supported from underneath before the strut assembly to front wheelhouse retaining nut (2) is removed.

85. Remove the strut assembly to front wheelhouse retaining nut (2) while holding the strut piston shaft (4) with a suitable tool.

86. Discard the nut.

87. Remove the strut assembly to front wheelhouse retaining plate (3).

88. Position a suitable powertrain and/or engine lift table below the frame, engine and transmission.

89. Raise the lift table and/or lower the vehicle to support the frame, engine and transmission.

90. Remove the transmission support to body retaining bolts (1).

91. Remove the sub-frame reinforcement plate to sub-frame retaining bolts (2).

92. Remove the sub-frame reinforcement plate (3) from the sub-frame (1).

93. Remove the sub-frame to body rear retaining bolts (1).

➡ Only right side depicted in graphic, left side similar.

94. Remove the sub-frame to body front retaining bolt (1). Repeat for opposite side.

➡ Only right side depicted in graphic, left side similar.

95. Remove the sub-frame to body retaining bolt. Repeat for opposite side.

➡ Make sure that all the hoses, wires, pipes and front struts clear the vehicle during the removal process.

96. With the aid of an assistant, lower the table and/or raise the vehicle to remove the engine, transmission, front suspension and sub-frame assembly from the vehicle.

97. Remove the engine and transmission wiring harness and related components.

98. Remove the transmission cooler pipe clamp to A/C bracket nut and position the transmission cooler pipes aside.

99. Connect a suitable lifting crane to the engine lift brackets and raise the suitable lifting crane to support the engine.

100. Position a second powertrain lift table below the transmission.

101. Remove the transmission. Refer to

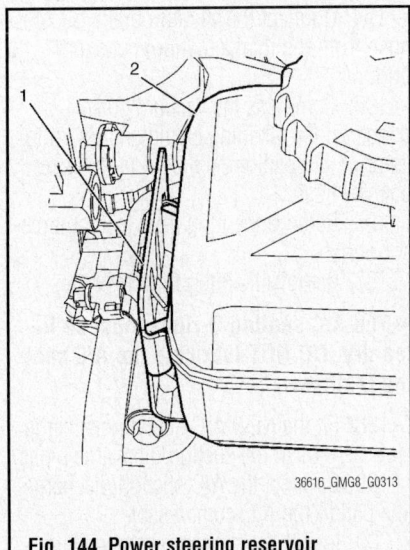

Fig. 144 Power steering reservoir tang location

Automatic Transmission. Or Manual Transmission in Drive Train.

102. Remove the engine flywheel. Refer to Flywheel.

103. Remove the accessory drive belt. Refer to Accessory Drive Belt.

104. Remove the A/C drive belt.

105. The locking tang on the power steering reservoir bracket (1) must be released before removing the power steering reservoir (2).

106. Remove the power steering reservoir (2) from the power steering pump power steering reservoir bracket (1) and position the power steering reservoir (2) aside.

107. Remove the power steering pump to power steering pump bracket retaining bolts and position the power steering pump away

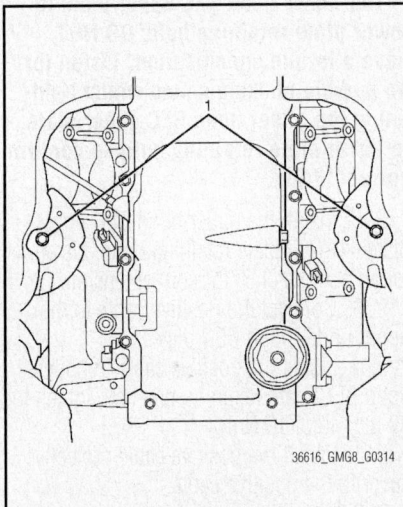

Fig. 145 Lower engine mount to front sub-frame retaining nut location

from the power steering pump bracket. Refer to Power Steering Pump in Steering.

108. Position the J 41798 lift bracket on the cylinder head.

109. Install the J 41798 to cylinder head retaining bolts and tighten to 63 ft. lbs. (50 Nm).

110. Attach a suitable lifting chain and hooks to the engine lifting brackets.

111. Remove the lower engine mount to front sub-frame retaining nut (1) from both engine mounts.

112. Using a suitable lifting crane, raise the engine to clear the engine mount stud.

113. Remove the engine from the sub-frame

114. If required mount the engine on a suitable engine stand.

To install:

115. Remove the engine from the engine stand.

116. Lower the engine onto the front sub-frame .

117. Position the engine mounts to the front sub-frame .

118. Install the lower engine mount to front sub-frame retaining nuts on both engine mounts and tighten to 59 ft. lbs. (80 Nm).

119. Position the power steering pump to the power steering pump bracket.

120. Install NEW power steering pump to power steering pump bracket retaining bolts and tighten to 23 ft. lbs. (30 Nm).

➡**Make sure the power steering reservoir and the power steering reservoir bracket locking tang are engaged to avoid an induced rattle condition.**

121. Install the power steering reservoir to the power steering pump power steering reservoir bracket.

122. Install the A/C drive belt.

123. Install the accessory drive belt.

124. Install the engine flywheel.

125. Connect a suitable lifting crane to the engine lift brackets and raise the suitable lifting crane to support the engine.

126. Install the transmission.

127. Position the transmission cooler pipes to the engine.

128. Install the transmission cooler pipe clamp to A/C bracket retaining nut and tighten to 16 ft. lbs. (22 Nm).

129. Install the engine and transmission wiring harness and related components.

➡**Make sure that all the hoses, wires, pipes and shock modules clear the vehicle during the installation process.**

130. With the aid of an assistant, raise the table and/or lower the vehicle to install

the engine, transmission, front suspension and sub-frame assembly to the vehicle.

131. Install the transmission support to the body retaining bolts and tighten to 43 ft. lbs. (58 Nm).

132. Install the sub-frame to the body retaining bolts and tighten to 118 ft. lbs. (160 Nm).

133. Install the sub-frame to the body front retaining bolts and tighten to 118 ft. lbs. (160 Nm).

134. Install the sub-frame to the body rear retaining bolts and tighten to 177 ft. lbs. (240 Nm).

135. Install the sub-frame reinforcement plate to the sub-frame.

136. Install the sub-frame reinforcement plate to the sub-frame retaining bolts and tighten to 13 ft. lbs. (17 Nm).

137. Lower the lift table and/or raise the vehicle to remove the support from the frame, engine and transmission.

138. Remove the powertrain and/or engine lift table from the frame, engine and transmission.

139. Partially lower the vehicle.

140. The strut assembly retaining nut must be checked for correct torque before installing the strut assembly into the vehicle. The strut assembly retaining nut torque must be 55 ft. lbs. (75 Nm).

141. Check the torque of the strut assembly retaining nut, correct if necessary.

142. Install the strut assembly to the vehicle.

143. Install the strut assembly to the body retaining plate.

144. Install the NEW strut assembly to the body retaining nut and tighten to 40 ft. lbs. (55 Nm).

145. Install the dust cover to the strut assembly to body retaining nut.

146. Partially raise the vehicle.

147. Remove the heavy mechanics wire or equivalent retaining the strut assembly to the sub-frame.

➡ **The intermediate steering shaft and pinion shaft splines must be installed in the position recorded during removal and aligned with the marks previously made.**

148. Connect the intermediate steering shaft to the pinion shaft.

149. Install the NEW intermediate steering shaft to the pinion shaft retaining bolt and tighten to 18 ft. lbs.(25 Nm).

150. Connect the wheel speed sensor jumper harness electrical connector.

151. Remove the heavy mechanic's wire, or equivalent support from the brake caliper.

152. Remove the wheel nuts retaining the brake disc to the hub.

✳✳ WARNING

Make sure the brake hose is not twisted or kinked after installation. Damage to the hose could result.

153. Install the brake caliper assembly to the steering knuckle.

154. Install the NEW brake caliper anchor plate to the knuckle retaining bolts and tighten to 44 ft. lbs. (60 Nm) plus 120°.

✳✳ WARNING

Make sure the brake hose is not twisted or kinked after installation. Damage to the hose could result.

155. Attach the brake hose to the strut mounted brake hose retaining bracket.

156. Install the front wheels.

157. For automatic transmission, install the shift selector linkage rod to the shift selector shaft.

158. For automatic transmission, install the shift selector linkage rod using the shift selector shaft retaining nut and tighten to 11 ft. lbs. (15 Nm).

159. For manual transmission, install the shift control assembly. Refer to Manual Transmission in Drive Train.

160. Install the starter motor. Refer to Starter in Engine Electrical.

161. Install the propeller shaft. Refer to Propeller Shaft in Replacement.

162. Install the centre exhaust heat shield.

163. Install the Exhaust system. Refer to Exhaust System.

164. Remove the plug from the power steering cooler and power steering reservoir inlet hose.

165. Connect the power steering reservoir inlet hose to the power steering cooler.

166. Install the power steering reservoir inlet hose spring clamp to its original location.

167. Remove the plug from the power steering cooler and power steering reservoir inlet hose.

168. Connect the power steering reservoir inlet hose to the power steering cooler.

169. Install the power steering reservoir inlet hose spring clamp to its original location

170. Install the engine splash shield.

171. Install the front air deflector.

172. Lower the vehicle.

173. Remove the zip ties or equivalent securing the radiator and condenser assembly to the front end assembly.

174. Remove the clean lint free cloth at the transmission cooler lines and the flexible hoses.

➡ **The flexible hoses are not serviced separately. Therefore if the hose's require replacement, then the hose and radiator to hose cooler hose assembly must be fitted.**

175. Align both flexible hose's with both steel cooler lines.

➡ **Listen for an audible click to confirm fitting.**

176. Hold the cooler line and connect the flexible hose by pushing together. Repeat procedure for other hose.

➡ **When adding or changing transmission fluid use only recommended automatic transmission fluid.**

177. Check and top up transmission fluid level if required.

178. Remove the large zip ties or equivalent securing the radiator and condenser assembly to the front end assembly.

179. Remove the plug or cap at the A/C suction pipe ends.

180. The A/C sealing O-rings must be fitted dry. DO NOT lubricate the A/C sealing O-rings.

181. Fit the NEW A/C suction pipe sealing O-ring to the suction pipe.

182. Install the upper A/C suction pipe to the lower A/C suction pipe.

183. Install the A/C suction pipe pad to A/C suction pipe retaining nut and tighten to 16 ft. lbs. (22 Nm).

184. Remove the plug from the throttle body to EVAP purge valve tube and EVAP purge valve ends.

185. Connect the throttle body to EVAP purge valve tube to the EVAP purge valve.

186. Remove the plug from the EVAP purge valve to fuel tank tube and EVAP purge valve ends.

187. Connect the EVAP purge valve to fuel tank tube to the EVAP purge valve.

188. Install the wiring harness to the remote positive battery post.

189. Install the remote positive battery post to wiring harness retaining bolt and tighten to 11 ft. lbs. (15 Nm).

➡ **Make sure the clips on the remote positive battery post cover are engaged to avoid an induced rattle condition.**

190. Install the remote positive battery post cover.

191. Remove the plug from the fuel feed pipe and fuel rail pipe ends.

192. Connect the fuel rail feed pipe quick connect fitting.

193. Install the engine coolant heater cord if fitted.

194. Connect the vacuum brake booster hose from the intake manifold vacuum port.

195. Compress the vacuum brake booster hose retaining clamp and return to its original position on the vacuum brake booster hose.

196. Remove the plug from the compressor ports.

197. Remove the plug from the pipes.

➡ **The A/C sealing O-rings must be fitted dry. DO NOT lubricate the A/C sealing O-rings.**

198. Fit the NEW A/C suction/discharge pipe O-rings to the suction/discharge pipes.

199. Connect the A/C suction/discharge line pad to the A/C compressor.

200. Install the suction/discharge line pad to compressor and tighten the retaining bolt to the correct torque specification and tighten to 16 ft. lbs. (22 Nm).

201. Connect the electrical connector to the A/C Refrigerant Pressure Sensor to the A/C refrigerant sensor.

202. Connect the A/C electrical connector to the A/C compressor.

203. Attach the vehicle body ground cable to the cylinder head ground stud.

204. Install the vehicle body ground cable to the cylinder head ground stud retaining nut and tighten to 18 ft. lbs. (25 Nm).

➡ **Listen for a audible click from the locking tang to confirm fitting.**

205. Slide the engine connector into the body harness connector to join.

206. Install the protector to the base of the under hood BEC connector.

207. Install the upper under hood BEC plate to the lower under hood BEC plate.

➡ **The under hood BEC upper plate to lower plate retaining bolts DO NOT have a torque specification. Listen for an audible clicking sound whilst tightening the under hood BEC upper plate to lower plate retaining bolts to confirm correct fitting.**

208. Install the under hood BEC upper plate to lower plate retaining bolts. Listen for an audible click for correct tension.

209. Connect the positive cable to the upper under hood BEC plate.

210. Install the positive cable to under hood BEC plate retaining bolt and tighten to 89 inch lbs. (10 Nm).

211. Install the positive cable protective cover to the positive cable.

212. Install the under hood body electrical centre (BEC) cover.

✳✳ WARNING

In order to prevent any possible electrostatic discharge damage to the ECM, do not touch the connector pins or the soldered components on the circuit board.

213. Connect the ECM electrical connectors to the ECM.
214. Engage the ECM retaining clips to secure the ECM.

➡️ **Listen for a audible click to confirm fitting.**

215. Connect the inlet and outlet heater hoses at the heater hose assembly quick connect fittings.
216. Connect the coolant air bleed hose to the coolant bleed pipe.
217. Reposition the coolant bleed hose retaining clamp to its original position on the coolant bleed hose.
218. Tighten the coolant bleed hose retaining clamp.
219. Install the radiator outlet hose.
220. Fill the cooling system.
221. Install the air intake duct.

➡️ **The receiver and dehydrator is a single use only component. A NEW receiver and dehydrator must be installed whenever a closed A/C system is opened or exposed to atmosphere. If the receiver and dehydrator has been replaced following a service/repair and it is deemed necessary to immediately re-open the A/C system it is not necessary to replace the receiver and dehydrator again, providing the A/C system is plugged/capped correctly.**

222. Replace the receiver and dehydrator.
    a. Remove the receiver dehydrator plastic screw cap (1) from the condenser (5).

➡️ **The circlip (2) cannot be removed if any gas pressure is present in A/C system.**

➡️ **To gain adequate clearance for removal of the circlip (2), use a suitable tool to gently tap the receiver dehydrator bottle plug (3) downwards.**

    b. Remove the circlip (2).

➡️ **Screw a suitable bolt into the threaded hole in the receiver dehydrator bottle plug (3). Pull upwards on the bolt to remove the receiver dehydrator bottle plug (3) from the condenser (5).**

    c. Remove the receiver dehydrator bottle plug (3) from the condenser (5).

➡️ **Using a suitable tool, grip the lower lip on the receiver dehydrator cartridge (4) and pull upwards to remove the receiver dehydrator cartridge (4) from the condenser (5).**

    d. Remove the receiver dehydrator cartridge (4) from the condenser (5).
    e. To install, reverse removal procedure
223. Recharge the air conditioning (A/C) system.
224. Install the radiator air baffle and deflector.
225. Install the engine cover.
226. Connect the battery negative cable. Refer to Battery Negative Cable Disconnection & Connection in Engine Electrical.
227. Crank the engine several times. Listen for any unusual noises or evidence that parts are binding.
228. Enable the ignition system.
229. Start the engine and listen for unusual noises.
230. Check the vehicle oil pressure gauge and confirm that the engine has acceptable oil pressure.
231. If necessary, install an oil pressure gauge and measure the engine oil pressure.
232. Run the engine speed at about 1,000 RPM until the engine has reached normal operating temperature.
233. Listen for sticking lifters and other unusual noises.
234. Inspect for fuel, oil, and/or other coolant leaks while the engine is running.

ENGINE COVER

REMOVAL & INSTALLATION

V6 Engine

See Figure 146.

1. Before servicing the vehicle, refer to the Precautions Section.

➡️ **Apply suitable pressure on the front edge of the engine cover (2) to disengage the locator legs (1).**

➡️ **Disengage the engine cover insulator legs (1) by raising the engine cover (2) upwards and moving it suitably forward to release the retention hooks (3).**

2. Remove the engine cover (2).
3. Disengage the sound insulator from the two hooks on the intake manifold sight shield bracket.
4. Remove the sound insulator ensuring it safely releases from behind the water outlet housing.

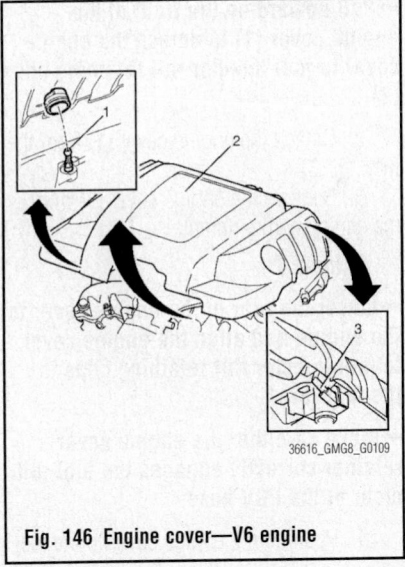

36616_GMG8_G0109

Fig. 146 Engine cover—V6 engine

To install:

➡️ **Make sure the sound insulator correctly locates behind the water outlet housing.**

5. Install the sound insulator.
6. Engage the sound insulator onto the two retention hooks on the intake manifold sight shield bracket.

➡️ **When installing the engine cover onto the engine assembly, make sure to correctly engage the retention hooks.**

7. Install the engine cover onto the engine assembly, engaging the engine cover insulator legs.

V8 Engine

See Figure 147.

1. Before servicing the vehicle, refer to the Precautions Section.

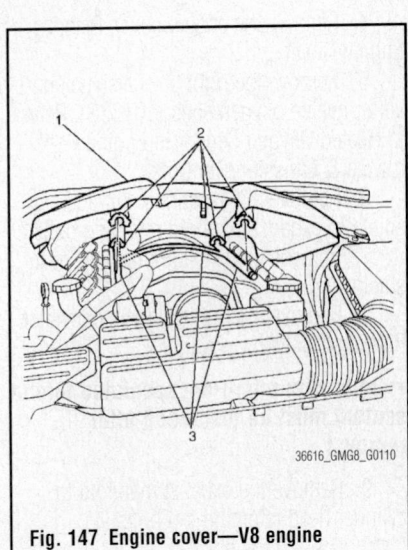

36616_GMG8_G0110

Fig. 147 Engine cover—V8 engine

➡Pull upward on the front of the engine cover (1) to detach the engine cover to fuel injector rail retaining clips (2).

2. Detach the engine cover (1) from the fuel rail (3).

3. Remove the engine cover (1) from the engine compartment.

To install:

➡Lower the rear of the engine cover to the engine and align the engine cover to fuel injector rail retaining clips to the fuel rail.

➡Make sure that the engine cover retainer correctly engages the fuel rail, clear of the PCV hose.

4. Position the engine cover to the fuel rail.

➡Press down on the engine cover to ensure the engine cover to fuel injector rail retaining clips are fully engaged to prevent an induced rattle condition.

5. Install the engine cover to the fuel rail.

EXHAUST MANIFOLD

REMOVAL & INSTALLATION

V6 Engine

Right Side

See Figure 148.

1. Before servicing the vehicle, refer to the Precautions Section.

2. Ignition OFF.

3. Disconnect the battery negative cable. Refer to Battery Negative Cable Disconnection & Connection in Engine Electrical.

4. Remove the engine cover. Refer to Engine Cover.

5. Remove the right pre-catalytic converter heated oxygen sensor (HO2S). Refer to Heated Oxygen Sensor in Engine Performance & Emission Controls.

6. Remove the exhaust manifold heat shield to exhaust manifold retaining bolts.

7. Remove the exhaust manifold heat shield.

8. Remove the right catalytic converter. Refer to Catalytic Converter.

➡Bolts with micro-encapsulated thread sealant must be discarded after removal.

9. Remove the exhaust manifold to cylinder head retaining top bolts (1).

10. Discard the bolts.

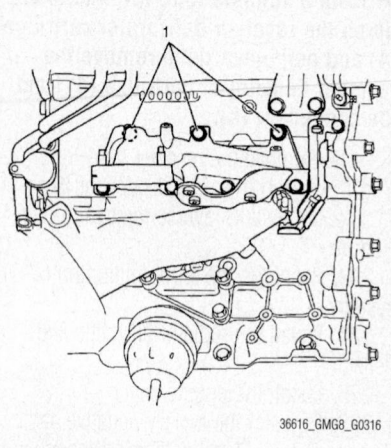

Fig. 148 Exhaust manifold bolt location right side top shown—V6 engine

✳✳ CAUTION

To avoid any vehicle damage, serious personal injury or death, always use the jackstands to support the vehicle when lifting the vehicle with a jack.

11. Raise and support the vehicle.

➡Bolts with micro-encapsulated thread sealant must be discarded after removal.

12. Remove the exhaust manifold to cylinder head retaining bottom bolts.

13. Discard the bolts.

➡Make sure that the surrounding wiring harness and electrical connectors are not damaged when removing the exhaust manifold.

➡The exhaust manifold gasket and sealing ring are single use parts. They must be discarded after removal.

14. Remove the exhaust manifold from the engine assembly.

15. Separate the exhaust manifold from the exhaust manifold gasket and sealing ring.

16. Discard the exhaust manifold gasket and sealing ring.

To install:

17. Inspect the exhaust manifold before installation.

➡Make sure the sealing ring is seated correctly.

18. Install a NEW exhaust manifold gasket and NEW sealing ring to the exhaust manifold.

19. A suitable support must be used to support the exhaust manifold while the vehicle is being lowered.

20. Install the exhaust manifold assembly to the engine.

➡Do not fully tighten the exhaust manifold to cylinder head retaining bolts at this stage.

21. Install NEW exhaust manifold to cylinder head retaining bolts.

22. Tighten the exhaust manifold to cylinder head retaining bolts working from the centre to the outside to 15 ft. lbs. (20 Nm).

23. Lower the vehicle.

24. Do not fully tighten the exhaust manifold to cylinder head retaining bolts at this stage.

25. Install NEW exhaust manifold to cylinder head retaining bolts.

26. Tighten the exhaust manifold to cylinder head retaining bolts working from the centre to the outside to 15 ft. lbs. (20 Nm).

27. Install the right catalytic converter.

28. Install the exhaust manifold heat shield to exhaust manifold retaining bolts and tighten to 89 inch lbs. (10 Nm).

29. Install the right pre-catalytic converter HO2S.

30. Install the engine cover.

31. Connect the battery negative cable. Refer to Battery Negative Cable Disconnection & Connection in Engine Electrical.

Left Side

See Figure 149.

1. Before servicing the vehicle, refer to the Precautions Section.

2. Ignition OFF.

3. Disconnect the battery negative cable. Refer to Battery Negative Cable Disconnection & Connection in Engine Electrical.

4. Remove the engine cover. Refer to Engine Cover.

5. Remove the left pre-catalytic converter heated oxygen sensor (HO2S). Refer to Heated Oxygen Sensor in Engine Performance & Emission Controls.

6. Remove the exhaust manifold heat shield to exhaust manifold retaining bolts.

7. Remove the exhaust manifold heat shield.

8. Remove the oil level indicator tube.

9. Remove the left catalytic converter. Refer to Catalytic Converter.

10. Remove the battery positive cable retaining nut from the starter motor solenoid.

11. Remove the battery positive cable from the starter motor. Refer to Starter in Engine Electrical.

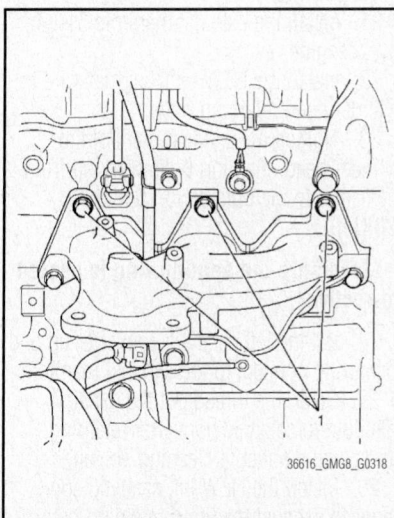

Fig. 149 Exhaust manifold bolt location left side top shown—V6 engine

➡Bolts with micro-encapsulated thread sealant must be discarded after removal.

12. Remove the exhaust manifold to cylinder head retaining bolts (1).
13. Discard the bolts.

✳✳ CAUTION

To avoid any vehicle damage, serious personal injury or death, always use the jackstands to support the vehicle when lifting the vehicle with a jack.

14. Raise and support the vehicle.

➡Bolts with micro-encapsulated thread sealant must be discarded after removal.

15. Remove the exhaust manifold to cylinder head retaining bolts.
16. Discard the bolts.

➡Make sure that the surrounding wiring harness and electrical connectors are not damaged when removing the exhaust manifold.

➡The exhaust manifold gasket and sealing ring are single use parts. They must be discarded after removal.

17. Remove the exhaust manifold from the engine assembly.
18. Separate the exhaust manifold from the exhaust manifold gasket and sealing ring.
19. Discard the exhaust manifold gasket and sealing ring.

To install:
20. Inspect the exhaust manifold before installation.

➡Make sure the sealing ring is seated correctly.

21. Install a NEW exhaust manifold gasket and NEW sealing ring to the exhaust manifold.
22. A suitable support must be used to support the exhaust manifold while the vehicle is being lowered.
23. Install the exhaust manifold assembly to the engine.

➡Do not fully tighten the exhaust manifold to cylinder head retaining bolts at this stage.

24. Install NEW exhaust manifold to cylinder head retaining bolts.
25. Tighten the exhaust manifold to cylinder head retaining bolts working from the centre to the outside to 15 ft. lbs. (20 Nm).
26. Lower the vehicle.
27. Do not fully tighten the exhaust manifold to cylinder head retaining bolts at this stage.
28. Install NEW exhaust manifold to cylinder head retaining bolts.
29. Tighten the exhaust manifold to cylinder head retaining bolts working from the centre to the outside to 15 ft. lbs. (20 Nm).
30. Install the left catalytic converter.
31. Install the exhaust manifold heat shield to exhaust manifold retaining bolts and tighten to 89 inch lbs. (10 Nm).
32. Install the right pre-catalytic converter HO2S.
33. Install the engine cover.
34. Connect the battery negative cable. Refer to Battery Negative Cable Disconnection & Connection in Engine Electrical.

V8 Engine

Right Side
See Figure 150.

1. Before servicing the vehicle, refer to the Precautions Section.
2. Ignition OFF.
3. Disconnect the battery negative cable. Refer to Battery Negative Cable Disconnection & Connection in Engine Electrical.
4. Remove the engine cover. Refer to Engine Cover.
5. Remove the oil level indicator tube.
6. Remove the right side spark plug leads. Refer to Spark Plug Wires in Engine Electrical.
7. Remove the right side spark plugs from the cylinder head. Refer to Spark Plugs in Engine Electrical.

8. Remove the right side exhaust manifold heat shield.
9. Remove the exhaust manifold heat shield to exhaust manifold retaining bolts.
10. Remove the exhaust manifold heat shield (1) from the exhaust manifold.

➡The right catalytic converter to exhaust manifold retaining nuts are single use parts. They must be discarded after removal.

11. Remove the right catalytic converter to exhaust manifold retaining nuts.
12. Discard the nuts.
13. Disconnect the right catalytic converter (4) from the exhaust manifold (3).
14. Loosen the exhaust manifold to cylinder head retaining bolts (2) working from the outside to the centre.

➡Bolts with micro-encapsulated thread sealant must be discarded after removal.

15. Remove the exhaust manifold to cylinder head retaining bolts (2).
16. Discard the bolts.

➡Make sure that the surrounding wiring harness and electrical connectors are not damaged when removing the exhaust manifold.

➡The exhaust manifold gasket and sealing ring are single use parts. They must be discarded after removal.

17. Remove the exhaust manifold.
18. Discard the exhaust manifold gasket and sealing ring.

To install:
19. Clean and inspect the exhaust manifold.
20. Install NEW exhaust manifold gasket

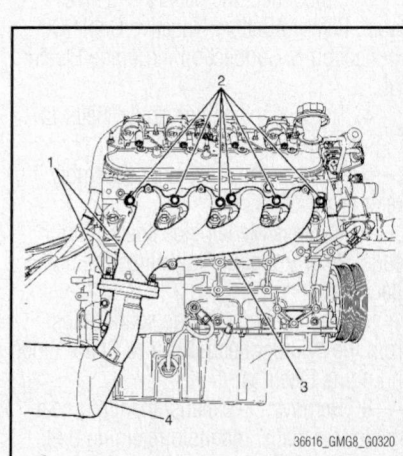

Fig. 150 Exhaust manifold bolt location right side—V8 engine

and NEW sealing ring to the exhaust manifold.

21. Install the exhaust manifold assembly to engine.

22. Install the NEW exhaust manifold to cylinder head retaining bolts.

23. Tighten the exhaust manifold to cylinder head retaining bolts working from the centre to the outside to 15 ft. lbs. (20 Nm).

→ **Make sure the sealing ring is seated correctly.**

24. Lift the right catalytic converter up and forward to connect to the exhaust manifold.

25. Clean the threads of the exhaust manifold to catalytic converter retaining studs with a suitable cleaning solvent.

26. Install the NEW right catalytic converter to exhaust manifold retaining nuts and tighten to 33 ft. lbs. (45 Nm).

27. Position the exhaust manifold heat shield to the exhaust manifold.

28. Install the exhaust manifold heat shield to exhaust manifold retaining bolts and tighten to 89 inch lbs. (10 Nm).

29. Install the right side spark plugs to the cylinder head.

30. Install the right side spark plug leads.

31. Install the oil level indicator tube.

32. Install the engine cover.

33. Connect the battery negative cable. Refer to Battery Negative Cable Disconnection & Connection in Engine Electrical.

Left Side
See Figure 151.

1. Before servicing the vehicle, refer to the Precautions Section.

2. Ignition OFF.

3. Disconnect the battery negative cable. Refer to Battery Negative Cable Disconnection & Connection in Engine Electrical.

4. Remove the engine cover. Refer to Engine Cover.

5. Remove the air cleaner assembly. Refer to Air Cleaner.

6. Remove the left side spark plug leads. Refer to Spark Plug Wires in Engine Electrical.

7. Remove the left side spark plugs from the cylinder head. Refer to Spark Plugs in Engine Electrical.

8. Remove the exhaust manifold heat shield to exhaust manifold retaining bolts.

9. Remove the exhaust manifold heat shield from the exhaust manifold.

10. Remove the engine coolant tempera-

ture sensor. Refer to Engine Coolant Temperature Sensor in Engine Performance & Emission Controls.

→ **The left catalytic converter to exhaust manifold retaining nuts are single use parts. They must be discarded after removal.**

11. Remove the left catalytic converter to exhaust manifold retaining nuts.

12. Discard the nuts.

13. Disconnect the left catalytic converter from the exhaust manifold.

14. Loosen the exhaust manifold to cylinder head retaining bolts working from the outside to the centre.

→ **Bolts with micro-encapsulated thread sealant must be discarded after removal.**

15. Remove the exhaust manifold to cylinder head retaining bolts.

16. Discard the bolts.

→ **Make sure that the surrounding wiring harness and electrical connectors are not damaged when removing the exhaust manifold.**

→ **The exhaust manifold gasket and sealing ring are single use parts. They must be discarded after removal.**

17. Remove the exhaust manifold.

18. Discard the exhaust manifold gasket and sealing ring.

To install:
19. Clean and inspect the exhaust manifold.

20. Install NEW exhaust manifold gasket and NEW sealing ring to the exhaust manifold.

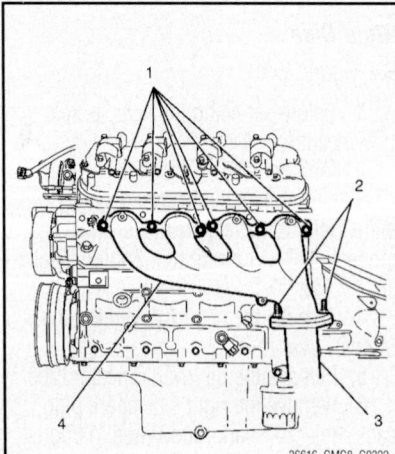

Fig. 151 Exhaust manifold bolt location left side—V8 engine

36616_GMG8_G0322

21. Install the exhaust manifold assembly to engine.

22. Install the NEW exhaust manifold to cylinder head retaining bolts.

23. Tighten the exhaust manifold to cylinder head retaining bolts working from the centre to the outside to 15 ft. lbs. (20 Nm).

→ **Make sure the sealing ring is seated correctly.**

24. Lift the left catalytic converter up and forward to connect to the exhaust manifold.

25. Clean the threads of the exhaust manifold to catalytic converter retaining studs with a suitable cleaning solvent.

26. Install the NEW left catalytic converter to exhaust manifold retaining nuts and tighten to 33 ft. lbs. (45 Nm).

27. Install the engine coolant temperature sensor.

28. Position the exhaust manifold heat shield to the exhaust manifold.

29. Install the exhaust manifold heat shield to exhaust manifold retaining bolts and tighten to 89 inch lbs. (10 Nm).

30. Install the left side spark plugs to the cylinder head.

31. Install the left side spark plug leads.

32. Install the air cleaner assembly.

33. Install the engine cover.

34. Connect the battery negative cable. Refer to Battery Negative Cable Disconnection & Connection in Engine Electrical.

FLYWHEEL/FLEXPLATE

REMOVAL & INSTALLATION

Manual Transmission
See Figures 152 and 153.

1. Before servicing the vehicle, refer to the Precautions Section.

2. Disable the SIR system. Refer to Air Bag Disabling Procedure & Enabling Procedure in Chassis Electrical

3. Disconnect the battery negative cable. Refer to Battery Negative Cable Disconnection & Connection in Engine Electrical.

❋❋ CAUTION

To avoid any vehicle damage, serious personal injury or death when major components are removed from the vehicle and the vehicle is supported by a hoist, support the vehicle with jack stands at the opposite end from which the components are being removed and strap the vehicle to the hoist.

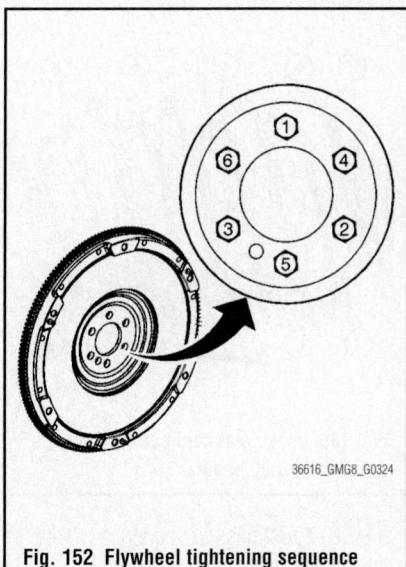

Fig. 152 Flywheel tightening sequence

4. Raise and support the vehicle.
5. Remove or disconnect the following:
6. Remove the transmission assembly. Refer to Manual Transmission Removal & Installation.

➡**Marking of the flywheel is not required as it has dowel pins to ensure correct alignment.**

7. Loosen all of the pressure plate to flywheel retaining bolts working from opposite sides to avoid distortion.
8. Continue loosening pressure plate to flywheel retaining bolts from opposite sides until all are removed.
9. Remove the pressure plate and clutch driven plate from the flywheel.
10. Remove flywheel bolts and flywheel.

To install:
11. Install flywheel. Tighten flywheel bolts in sequence to:
   a. Tighten the bolts (1–6) a first pass in sequence to 15 ft. lbs. (20 Nm).
   b. Tighten the bolts (1–6) a second pass in sequence to 37 ft. lbs. (50 Nm).
   c. Tighten the bolts (1–6) a final pass in sequence to 74 ft. lbs. (100 Nm).

➡**Before installation of the pressure and clutch driven plate, ensure that the locating dowel pins are secure in the flywheel, also ensure the self-adjusting system is reset.**

➡**Apply any a small amount of grease to clutch driven plate splines or transmission input shaft splines.**

➡**Install the clutch driven plate (2) with the short boss facing the flywheel (1). Flywheel side is stamped on the clutch driven plate hub (FW Side).**

12. While holding the pressure plate (3) and clutch driven plate (2) together, align them to the flywheel (1).

➡**The pressure plate to flywheel retaining bolts (4) must not to be tightened at this stage.**

13. Install the pressure plate to flywheel retaining bolts (4).
14. Do not tighten at this stage.
15. Using a clutch driven plate centering tool (5) align the clutch driven plate (2) to the flywheel (1).
16. Install the pressure plate bolts (4), and insert the clutch centering tool (5).
17. Tighten the pressure plate to flywheel retaining bolts, using the sequence shown, to:
- Tighten the bolts a first pass to 11 ft. lbs. (15 Nm).
- Tighten the bolts a second pass to 26 ft. lbs. (35 Nm).
- Tighten the bolts a third pass to 41 ft. lbs (55 Nm).
- Tighten the bolts a fourth pass to 52 Ft. lbs. (70 Nm).
18. Install the transmission assembly. Refer to Manual Transmission Removal & Installation.
19. Bleed the clutch hydraulic system. Refer to Clutch Bleeding.
20. Connect the battery negative cable. Refer to Battery Negative Cable Disconnection & Connection in Engine Electrical.
21. Enable the SIR. Refer to Air Bag Disabling Procedure & Enabling Procedure in Chassis Electrical
22. Press the clutch pedal several times to allow the self-adjusting pressure plate function to take effect.

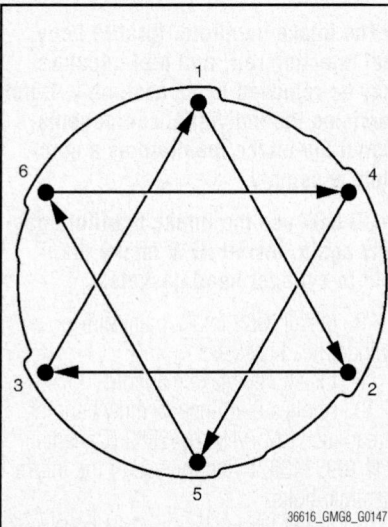

Fig. 153 Pressure plate tightening sequence

23. Road test vehicle for correct clutch operation.

Automatic Transmission
See Figure 154.

1. Before servicing the vehicle, refer to the Precautions Section.
2. Remove transmission.
3. Remove the flexplate to crankshaft retaining bolts (2).
4. Remove the flexplate (1).

To install:
5. Apply thread lock GM P/N 12345382 (Canadian P/N 10953489), or equivalent, to the threads of the flexplate bolts.
6. Install flexplate and bolts.
7. Tighten flexplate bolts in sequence to:
   a. Tighten the bolts (1–6) a first pass in sequence to 15 ft. lbs. (20 Nm).
   b. Tighten the bolts (1–6) a second pass in sequence to 37 ft. lbs. (50 Nm).
   c. Tighten the bolts (1–6) a final pass in sequence to 74 ft. lbs. (100 Nm).
8. Install transmission.

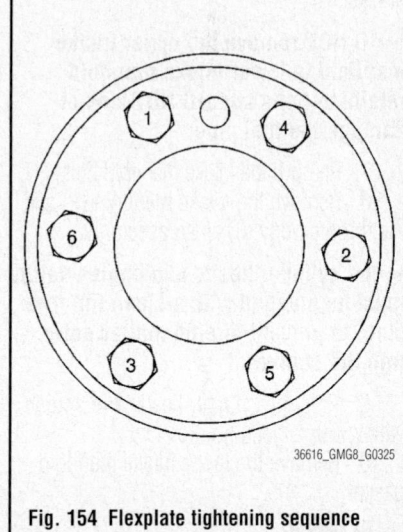

Fig. 154 Flexplate tightening sequence

INTAKE MANIFOLD

REMOVAL & INSTALLATION

3.6L Engine
See Figure 155.

1. Before servicing the vehicle, refer to the Precautions Section.
2. Remove the PCV tube and PCV fresh air tubes.
3. Disconnect the EVAP hose from the intake manifold.
4. Remove the fuel injector harness electrical connector/EVAP valve mounting bracket to intake manifold retaining bolt.

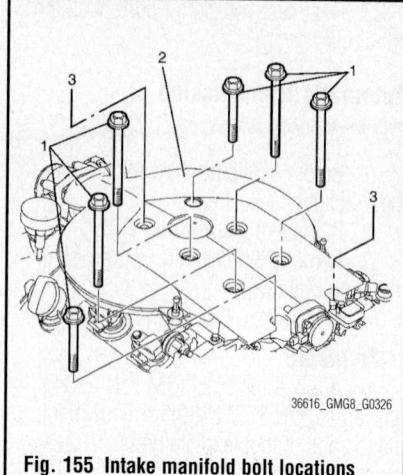

Fig. 155 Intake manifold bolt locations

Refer to EVAP system in Engine Performance & Emission Controls.

5. Detach the fuel injector harness electrical connector from the fuel injector harness electrical connector/EVAP valve mounting bracket.

6. Remove the fuel injector harness electrical connector/EVAP valve mounting bracket.

➡**DO NOT remove the upper intake manifold to lower intake manifold retaining bolts and DO NOT kink or damage the fuel pipe.**

7. Remove the intake manifold bolts (1).

8. Remove the intake manifold (2) and the throttle body (3) as an assembly.

➡**The cylinder heads and engine valley must be plugged with a clean lint free cloth to prevent foreign matter entry into the engine.**

9. Plug the cylinder heads and engine valley with a clean lint free cloth.

10. Remove the lower intake manifold gasket.

To install:

11. Install the NEW intake manifold gasket.

12. Install the intake manifold and the throttle body as an assembly as an assembly.

➡**Tighten the intake manifold bolts in a circular pattern starting at the center (long bolts) and moving outward.**

13. Install the intake manifold bolts and tighten to 17 ft. lbs. (23 Nm).

14. Install the fuel injector harness electrical connector/EVAP valve mounting bracket.

15. Install the fuel injector harness electrical connector/EVAP valve mounting bracket to intake manifold retaining bolt and tighten to 80 inch lbs. (9 Nm).

16. Attach the fuel injector harness electrical connector to the fuel injector harness electrical connector/EVAP valve mounting bracket.

17. Connect the EVAP hose to the upper intake manifold.

18. Install the PCV tube and PCV fresh air tubes.

6.0L Engine

See Figure 156.

1. Before servicing the vehicle, refer to the Precautions Section.

➡**The intake manifold, throttle body, fuel injection rail, and fuel injectors may be removed as an assembly. If not servicing the individual components, remove the manifold as a complete assembly.**

➡**Removal of the intake manifold to cylinder head retaining bolts (1–10) should be performed in sequence. Failing to do so may distort the intake manifold (B).**

2. Remove the intake manifold to cylinder head retaining bolts in reverse of tightening sequence.

3. Remove the intake manifold from the engine.

4. Plug the engine with a clean lint free cloth.

5. Remove the intake manifold to cylinder head gaskets.

6. Discard the intake manifold to cylinder head gaskets.

7. Clean and inspect the intake manifold.

To install:

➡**The intake manifold, throttle body, fuel injection rail, and fuel injectors may be removed as an assembly. If not servicing the individual components, install the intake manifold as a complete assembly.**

➡**DO NOT use the intake manifold gaskets again. Install NEW intake manifold-to-cylinder head gaskets.**

8. Install NEW intake manifold-to-cylinder head gaskets.

9. Install the intake manifold.

10. Apply a 0.20 inch (5 mm) band of thread lock GM P/N 12345382 (Canadian P/N 10953489) to the threads of the intake manifold bolts.

11. Install the intake manifold bolts and fuel rail stop brackets.

12. Tighten the intake manifold bolts.

a. Tighten the intake manifold bolts

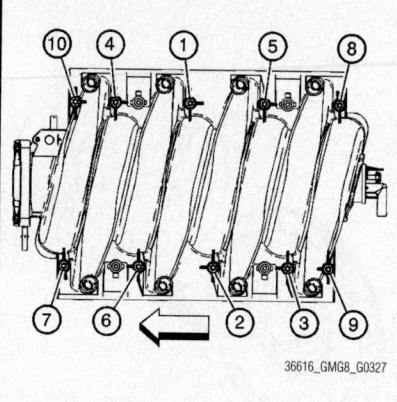

Fig. 156 Intake manifold bolt tightening sequence—6.0L engine

(1–10) a first pass in sequence to 44 inch lbs. (5 Nm).

b. Tighten the intake manifold bolts (1–10) a final pass in sequence to 89 inch lbs. (10 Nm).

13. Lubricate the Manifold Absolute Pressure (MAP) sensor grommet with clean engine oil.

14. Install the MAP sensor and grommet.

15. Install the MAP sensor bolt.

16. Install the positive crankcase ventilation (PCV) dirty air hose.

17. Install the PCV fresh air hose.

18. Install the Evaporative Emission (EVAP) canister purge solenoid valve, bracket, and bolt and tighten the bolt to 37 ft. lbs. (50 Nm).

19. Install the EVAP tubes.

20. Install the fuel rail.

OIL PAN

REMOVAL & INSTALLATION

3.6L Engine

See Figures 157 and 158.

1. Before servicing the vehicle, refer to the Precautions Section.

2. Disconnect the battery ground cable. Refer to Battery Negative Cable Disconnection & Connection in Engine Electrical.

✴✴ CAUTION

To avoid any vehicle damage, serious personal injury or death when major components are removed from the vehicle and the vehicle is supported by a hoist, support the vehicle with jack stands at the opposite end from which the components are being removed and strap the vehicle to the hoist.

3. Raise and support the vehicle.

4. Drain the engine oil.

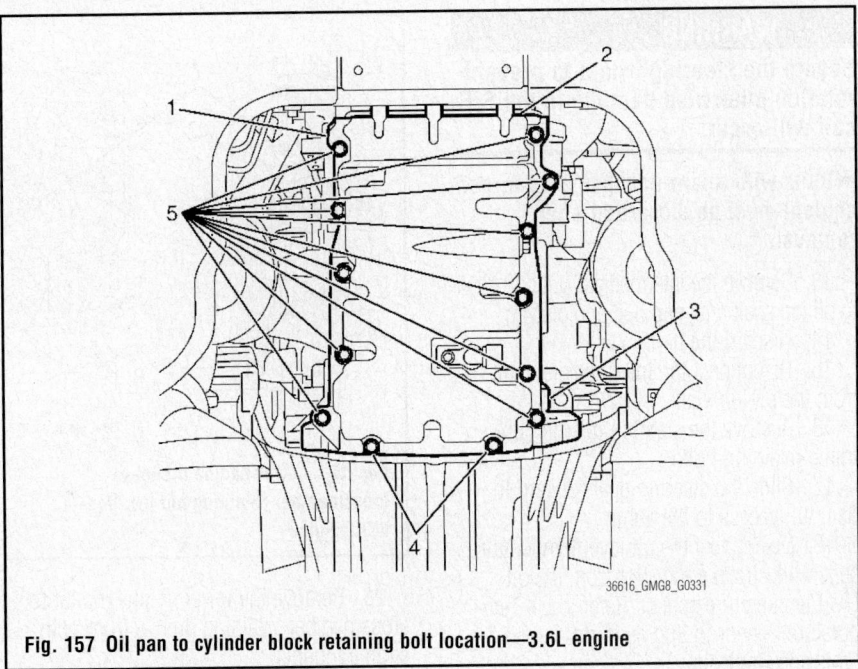

Fig. 157 Oil pan to cylinder block retaining bolt location—3.6L engine

5. Remove the engine splash shield.
6. Remove the front air deflector.

➡**Observing the orientation of the intermediate steering shaft with reference to the pinion shaft will minimize the potential of incorrect steering column assembly alignment.**

7. Mark the intermediate steering shaft in relation to the pinion shaft. Refer to intermediate shaft in Steering.

➡**Bolts with micro-encapsulated thread sealant must be discarded after removal.**

8. Remove the intermediate steering shaft to pinion shaft retaining bolt and discard.
9. Discard the bolt.

➡**Make sure all the bolt hole is thoroughly cleaned and all micro-encapsulated thread sealant is removed.**

10. Disconnect the intermediate shaft from the pinion shaft.
11. Clean the bolt hole.
12. Remove the steering gear to subframe retaining bolts.
13. Slide the steering gear forward to gain full access to the sump.
14. Disconnect the oil level/temperature sensor electrical connector from the oil level/temperature sensor.
15. Remove the front cover to oil pan retaining bolts (1).
16. Remove the transmission to oil pan retaining bolts (1).
17. Remove the rear oil pan to cylinder block retaining bolts (4).

18. Remove the oil pan to cylinder block retaining bolts (5).

➡**Using the pry points (1 and 3) to shear the RTV sealant.**

19. Remove the oil pan (2) from the engine block.

To install:

20. Place a 0.118 inch (3 mm) bead of RTV sealant (1) on the block pan rail and the crankshaft rear oil seal housing.
21. Position the oil pan onto the engine block.
22. Install the oil pan to cylinder block

retaining bolts in the sequence shown and tighten.
- The eight mm bolts (1–11) to 16 ft. lbs. (22 Nm).
- The six mm bolts (12, 13) to 80 inch lbs. (9 Nm).

23. Install the transmission to the oil pan retaining bolts and tighten to 35 ft. lbs. (48 Nm).
24. Install the front cover using the oil pan retaining bolts and tighten a first pass to 15 ft. lbs. (20 Nm) plus 60 degrees.
25. Connect the oil level/temperature sensor electrical connector to the oil level/temperature sensor.
26. Position the steering gear in the correct location.
27. Install the steering gear using the sub-frame retaining bolts and tighten to 48 ft. lbs. (65 Nm).

➡**The intermediate steering shaft and pinion shaft splines must be installed in the position recorded during removal and aligned with the marks previously made.**

28. Connect the intermediate steering shaft to the pinion shaft.
29. Install the NEW intermediate steering shaft to the pinion shaft retaining bolt and tighten to 18 ft. lbs. (25 Nm).
30. Install the engine splash shield.
31. Install the front air deflector.
32. Lower the vehicle to the ground
33. Fill the engine with new engine oil.
34. Connect the battery ground cable.
Refer to Battery Negative Cable Disconnection & Connection in Engine Electrical.

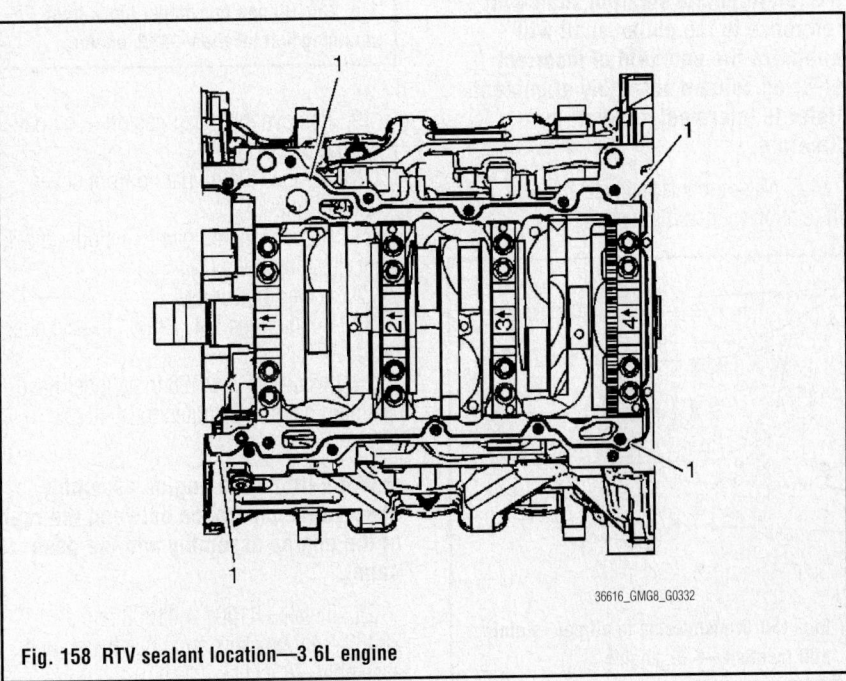

Fig. 158 RTV sealant location—3.6L engine

6.0L Engine

See Figures 159 through 166.

1. Before servicing the vehicle, refer to the Precautions Section.
2. Disconnect the battery ground cable. Refer to Battery Negative Cable Disconnection & Connection in Engine Electrical.

❋❋ CAUTION

To avoid any vehicle damage, serious personal injury or death when major components are removed from the vehicle and the vehicle is supported by a hoist, support the vehicle with jack stands at the opposite end from which the components are being removed and strap the vehicle to the hoist.

3. Raise and support the vehicle.
4. Remove the air deflector.
5. Drain the engine oil and remove the oil filter.
6. Remove the engine splash shield.
7. Remove the starter motor. Refer to Starter in Engine Electrical.
8. Remove the left side close out cover to cylinder block retaining bolt (2).
9. Remove the left side close out cover (1).
10. Remove the right side close out cover to cylinder block retaining bolt (2).
11. Remove the right side close out cover (1).

➡**Observing the orientation of the intermediate steering shaft with reference to the pinion shaft will minimize the potential of incorrect steering column assembly alignment. Refer to Intermediate Shaft in Steering.**

12. Mark the intermediate steering shaft in relation to the pinion shaft.

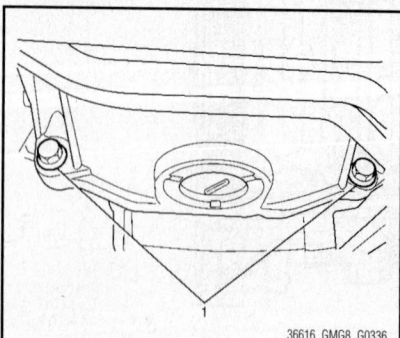

Fig. 159 Transmission to oil pan retaining bolt location—6.0L engine

❋❋ WARNING

Secure the steering wheel to prevent rotation otherwise damage to the SIR coil will occur.

➡**Bolts with micro-encapsulated thread sealant must be discarded after removal.**

13. Remove the intermediate steering shaft to pinion shaft retaining bolt and discard.
14. Discard the bolt.
15. Disconnect the intermediate shaft from the pinion shaft.
16. Remove the steering gear to subframe retaining bolts.
17. Slide the steering gear forward to gain full access to the sump.
18. Disconnect the oil level/temperature sensor electrical connector from the oil level/temperature sensor. Refer to Oil Temperature Sensor in Engine Performance & Emission Controls.

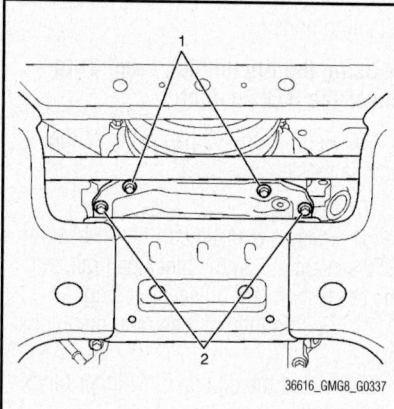

Fig. 160 Oil pan to cylinder block front retaining bolt location—6.0L engine

19. Remove the transmission to oil pan retaining bolts (1).
20. Remove the oil pan to front cover retaining bolts (1).
21. Remove the oil pan to cylinder block front retaining bolts (2).
22. Lower the vehicle.
23. Position the J 41798 on the cylinder head.
24. Install the J 41798 to cylinder head retaining bolts and tighten to 36 ft. lbs. (50 Nm).

➡**When lifting the engine assembly, observe the clearance between the rear of the engine assembly and the dash panel.**

25. Install J 41803 J-41803 and J 28467-B lift brackets and raise the engine assembly .78 inches (20 mm).

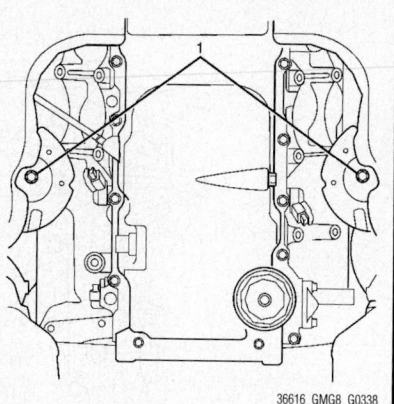

Fig. 161 Lower engine mount to crossmember retaining nut location— 6.0L engine

26. Remove the lower engine mount to crossmember retaining nut (1) from both engine mounts.
27. Remove the oil pan to engine rear cover retaining bolts (2).
28. Remove the oil pan to cylinder block retaining bolts (1).
29. Remove the oil pan (3).

➡**DO NOT allow foreign material to enter the oil passages of the oil pan, cap, or cover the openings, as required.**

➡**Take care not to gouge, score, or damage the oil pan sealing surface.**

30. Drill out the retaining rivets (3) from the oil pan, if required.

➡**The oil pan gasket and rivets are single use only components and must be replaced whenever the oil pan is removed from the cylinder block.**

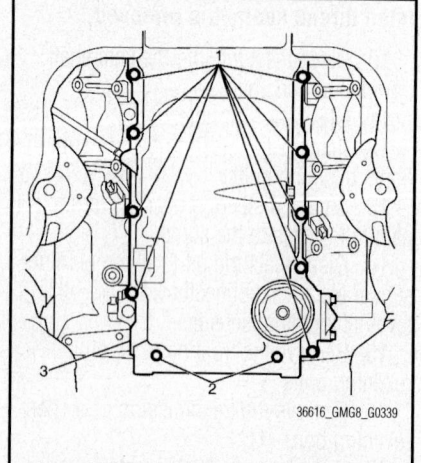

Fig. 162 Oil pan retaining bolts location— 6.0L engine

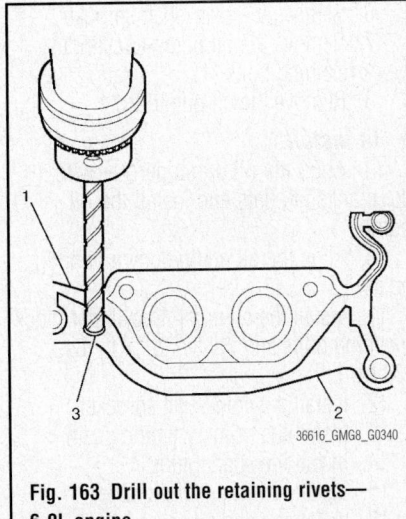

Fig. 163 Drill out the retaining rivets—6.0L engine

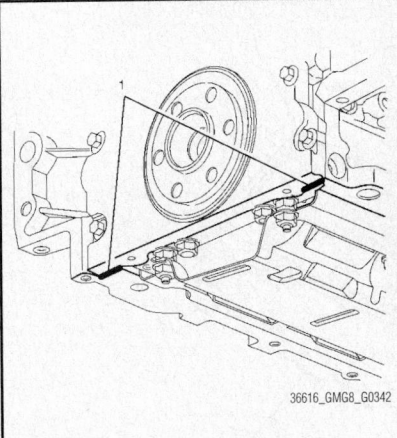

Fig. 165 Apply a 0.2 inches (5 mm) bead of sealant 0.8 in (20 mm) long to the rear engine block—6.0L engine

31. Remove the oil pan gasket from the oil pan.

32. Discard the gasket and rivets.

33. Clean and inspect the oil pan as necessary.

To install:

➡️**The alignment of the structural oil pan is critical. The rear bolt hole locations of the oil pan provide mounting points for the transmission housing. To ensure the rigidity of the powertrain and correct transmission alignment, it is important that the rear of the block and the rear of the oil pan are flush. The rear of the oil pan must NEVER protrude beyond the engine block and transmission housing plane.**

➡️**The original oil pan gasket is retained and aligned to the oil pan by rivets. When installing a new gasket, it is not necessary to install new oil pan gasket rivets.**

34. It is not necessary to rivet the NEW gasket to the oil pan.

35. Apply a 0.2 inches (5 mm) bead of sealant 0.8 in (20 mm) long to the engine block (1). Apply the sealant directly onto the tabs of the front cover gasket that protrude into the oil pan surface.

36. Apply a 0.2 inches (5 mm) bead of sealant 0.8 in (20 mm) long to the engine block (1). Apply the sealant directly onto the tabs of the rear cover gasket that protrude into the oil pan surface.

➡️**Make sure to align the oil gallery passages in the oil pan and engine block correctly, with the oil pan gasket.**

37. Preassemble the oil pan gasket (2) to the oil pan (3).

38. Install the oil pan gasket (2) to the oil pan (3).

39. Install the oil pan retaining bolts (1) to the oil pan (3) and through the oil pan gasket (2).

40. Install the oil pan assembly.

41. Install the oil pan to cylinder block retaining bolts finger tight. Do not over tighten.

42. Install the oil pan to engine rear cover retaining bolts finger tight. Do not over tighten.

43. Lower the vehicle.

44. Lower the engine to engage the engine mounts to the front sub-frame.

45. Raise the vehicle.

46. Install the lower engine mount to front sub-frame retaining nuts on both engine mounts and tighten to 59 ft. lbs. (80 Nm).

47. Lower the vehicle.

48. Remove J 41803 and J 28467-B lift brackets from the engine.

49. Remove the J 41798 to cylinder head retaining bolts.

50. Remove the J 41798 from the cylinder head.

51. Install the oil pan to front cover retaining bolts finger tight. Do not over tighten.

52. Install the oil pan to cylinder block retaining bolts finger tight. Do not over tighten.

53. Place a straight edge across the rear of the engine block and the rear of the oil pan at the transmission housing mounting surfaces.

54. Align the oil pan until the rear of engine block and the rear of oil pan are flush or even.

55. Measure the oil pan-to-engine block alignment.

    a. Place a straight edge across the rear of the engine block and rear of the oil pan at the transmission housing mounting surfaces.

➡️**The rear of the oil pan must NEVER protrude beyond the engine block and transmission housing mounting surfaces.**

    b. Insert a feeler gage between the straight edge and the oil pan transmission housing mounting surface and check to make sure that there is no more than a 0.01 inch (0.25 mm) gap between the pan and the straight edge.

    c. If the oil pan alignment is not within specifications, remove the oil pan and repeat the previous procedures.

56. Tighten the oil pan to cylinder block retaining bolts (1) to 25 Nm (18 lb ft).

57. Tighten the oil pan to engine rear oil seal housing retaining bolts (2) to 12 Nm (106 lb in).

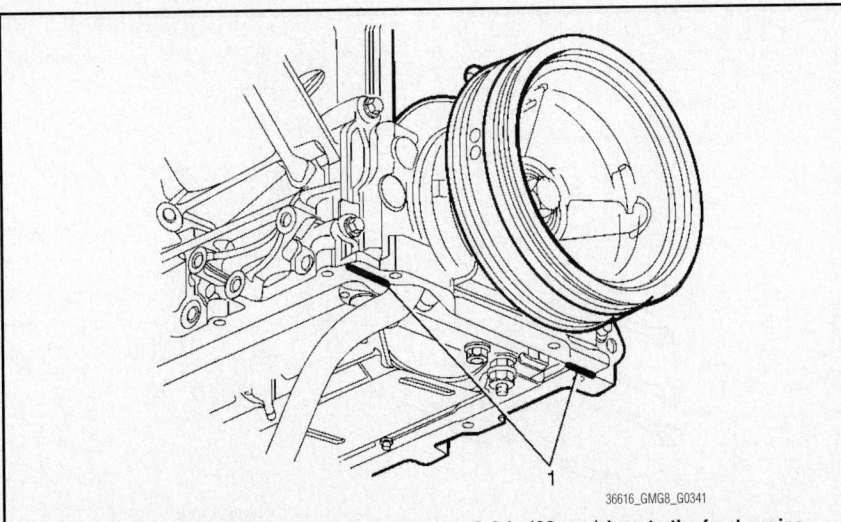

Fig. 164 Apply a 0.2 inches (5 mm) bead of sealant 0.8 in (20 mm) long to the front engine block (1)—6.0L engine

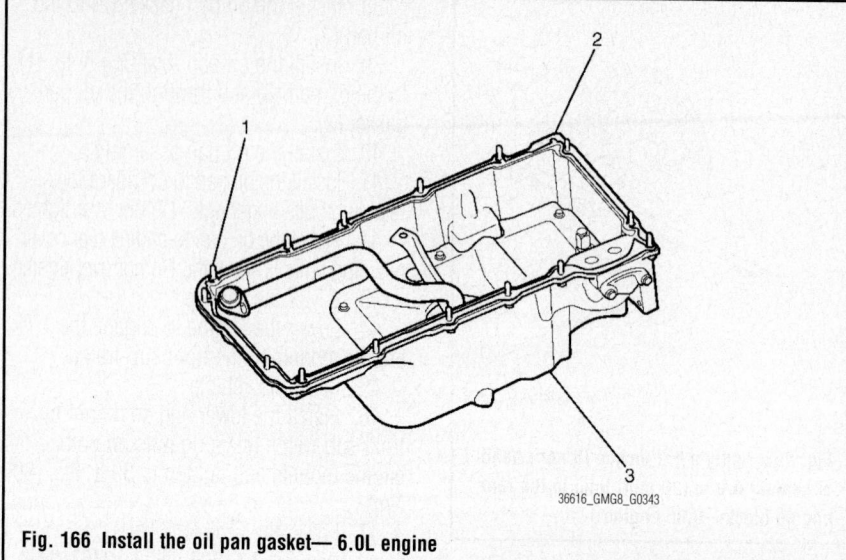

Fig. 166 Install the oil pan gasket— 6.0L engine

58. Tighten the oil pan to cylinder block retaining bolts to 18 ft. lbs. (25 Nm).

59. Tighten the oil pan to front cover retaining bolts to 18 ft. lbs. (25 Nm).

60. Position the steering gear in the correct location.

61. Install the steering gear to subframe retaining bolts and tighten to 48 ft. lbs. (65 Nm).

➡**The intermediate steering shaft and pinion shaft splines must be installed in the position recorded during removal and aligned with the marks previously made.**

62. Connect the intermediate steering shaft to the pinion shaft.

63. Install the intermediate steering shaft to pinion shaft NEW retaining bolt and tighten to 18 ft. lbs. (25 Nm).

64. Install the right side close out cover.

65. Install the right side close out cover to cylinder block retaining bolt and tighten to 106 inch lbs. (12 Nm).

66. Install the left side close out cover.

67. Install the left side close out cover to cylinder block retaining bolt and tighten to 106 inch lbs. (12 Nm).

68. Connect the oil level/temperature sensor electrical connector to the oil level/temperature sensor.

69. Install the starter motor.

70. Install the air deflector.

71. Install the engine splash shield.

72. Lower the vehicle to the ground

73. Connect the battery ground cable. Refer to Battery Negative Cable Disconnection & Connection in Engine Electrical.

74. Replace the engine oil and oil filter.

OIL PUMP

REMOVAL & INSTALLATION

3.6L Engine

See Figure 167.

1. Before servicing the vehicle, refer to the Precautions Section.

2. Remove the engine covers. Refer to Engine Cover.

3. Remove the spark plugs in order to ease crankshaft/engine rotation. Refer to Spark Plugs in Engine Electrical.

4. Remove the engine front cover. Refer to Timing Chain Cover and Seal.

➡**DO NOT remove the left bank idler sprocket.**

5. Remove the primary timing chain. Refer to Timing Chain and Sprockets.

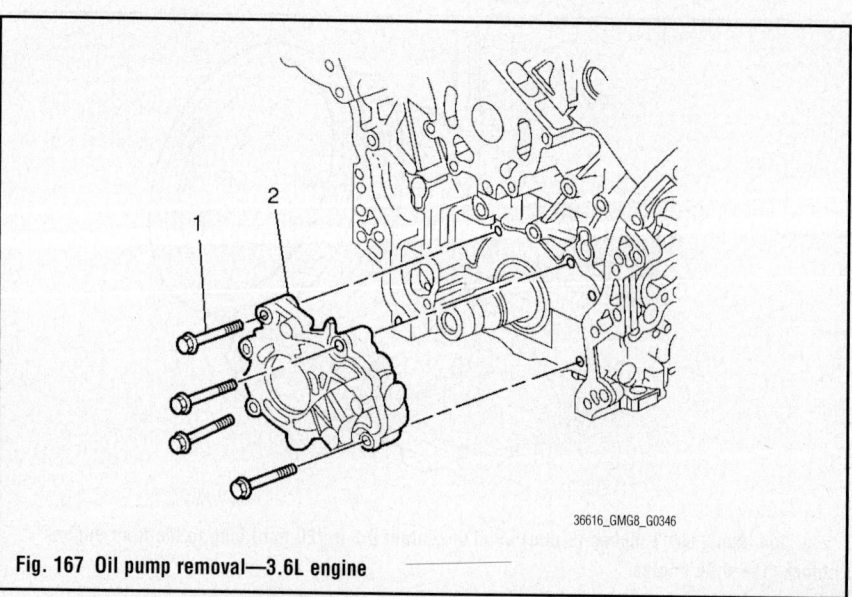

Fig. 167 Oil pump removal—3.6L engine

6. Remove the crankshaft sprocket.

7. Remove the oil pump to cylinder block retaining bolts (1).

8. Remove the oil pump (2).

To install:

9. Align the oil pump gerotor with the crankshaft flats and install the oil pump.

10. Align the oil pump body mounting holes.

11. Install the oil pump to cylinder block retaining bolts and tighten to 17 ft. lbs. (23 Nm).

12. Install the crankshaft sprocket.

13. Install the primary timing chain.

14. Install the spark plugs.

15. Install the engine front cover.

16. Install the engine covers.

6.0L Engine

See Figures 168 through 170.

1. Before servicing the vehicle, refer to the Precautions Section.

2. Remove the engine oil pan. Refer to Oil Pan.

3. Remove the engine front cover. Refer to Timing Chain Cover and Seal.

4. Remove the oil pump screen and tube assembly to oil pump retaining bolt (1).

5. Remove the oil pump screen and tube assembly to crankshaft oil deflector retaining nut (4).

6. Remove the oil pump screen and tube assembly (3) from the oil pump (2).

➡**The oil pump screen and tube assembly O-ring seal is a single use only component and must be replaced**

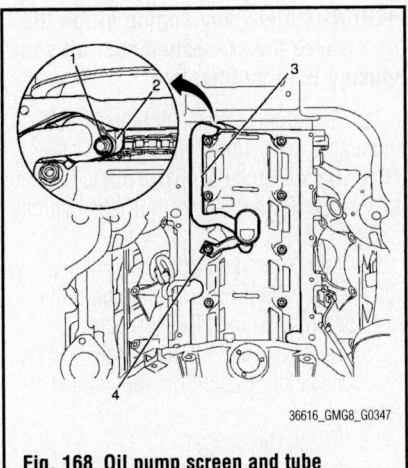

Fig. 168 Oil pump screen and tube assembly—6.0L engine

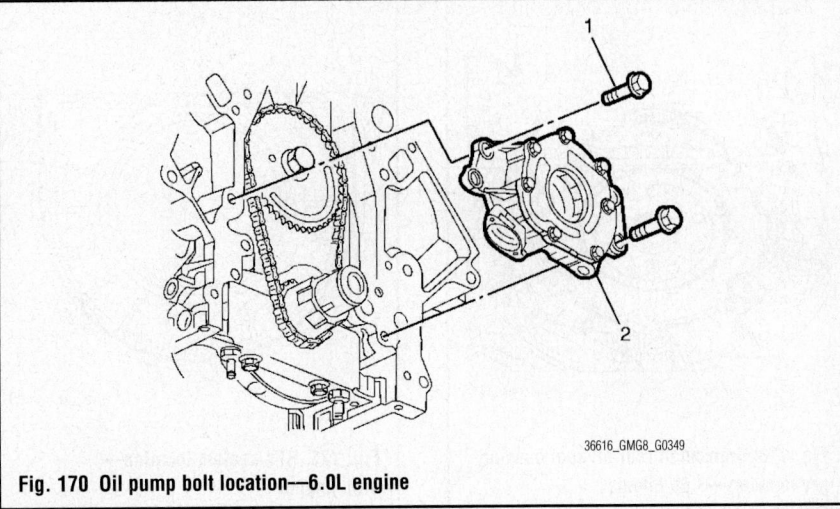

Fig. 170 Oil pump bolt location—6.0L engine

whenever the oil pump screen and tube assembly is removed.

7. Remove the oil pump screen and tube assembly O-ring seal from the oil pump screen and tube assembly.

8. Discard the oil pump screen and tube assembly O-ring seal.

9. Remove the remaining crankshaft oil deflector retaining nuts (2).

10. Remove the crankshaft oil deflector (1).

11. Remove the oil pump bolts (1).

➡Do not allow dirt or debris to enter the oil pump. Cap the ends as necessary.

12. Remove the oil pump (2).

To install:

➡Inspect the engine block oil gallery passages. These surfaces must be clear and free of debris or restrictions.

13. Align the splined surfaces of the crankshaft sprocket and the oil pump drive gear and install the oil pump.

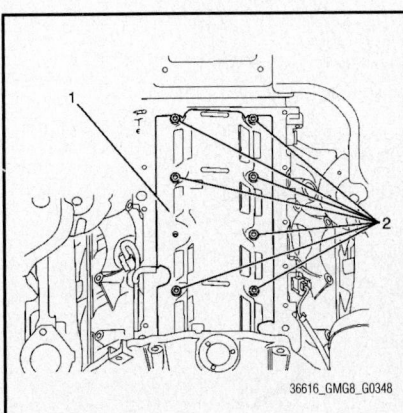

Fig. 169 Crankshaft oil deflector—6.0L engine

14. Install the oil pump to engine block retaining bolts and tighten to 18 ft. lbs. (25 Nm).

15. Install the crankshaft oil deflector.

16. Install the crankshaft oil deflector retaining nuts and tighten to 89 inch lbs. (10 Nm).

17. Lubricate a NEW oil pump screen and tube assembly O-ring seal with clean engine oil.

18. Install the NEW oil pump screen and tube assembly O-ring seal onto the oil pump screen and tube assembly.

➡Push the oil pump screen and tube assembly completely into the oil pump prior to tightening the oil pump screen and tube assembly to oil pump retaining bolt. Do not allow the oil pump screen and tube assembly to oil pump retaining bolt to pull the oil pump screen and tube assembly into the oil pump.

➡Align the oil pump screen brackets with the correct crankshaft bearing cap studs.

19. Install the oil pump screen and tube assembly.

20. Install the oil pump screen and tube assembly to oil pump retaining bolt and tighten to 80 inch lbs. (9 Nm).

21. Install the oil pump screen and tube assembly to crankshaft oil deflector retaining nut and tighten to 89 inch lbs. (10 Nm).

22. Install the engine front cover.

23. Install the engine oil pan.

PISTON AND RING

POSITIONING

See Figure 171.

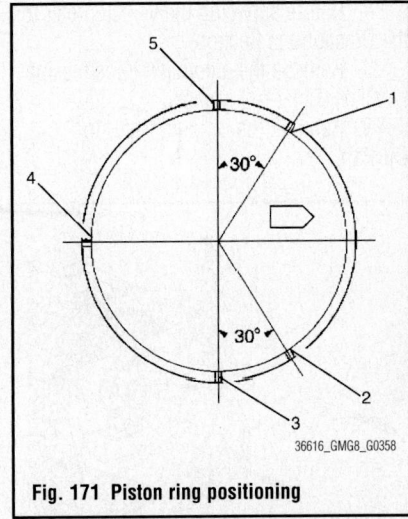

Fig. 171 Piston ring positioning

REAR MAIN SEAL

REMOVAL & INSTALLATION

3.6L Engine

See Figures 172 through 176.

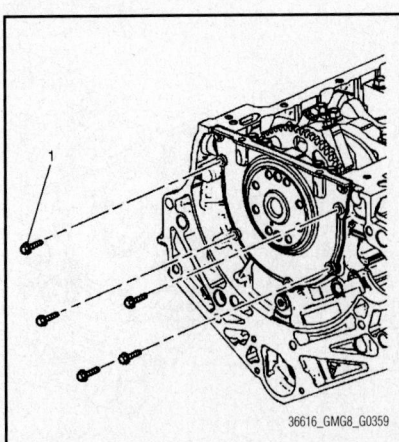

Fig. 172 Crankshaft rear oil seal housing bolt location—3.6L Engine

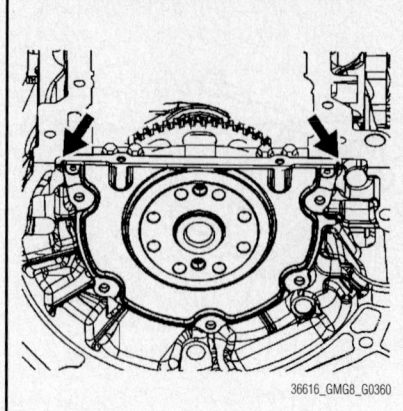

Fig. 173 Crankshaft rear oil seal housing pry location—3.6L Engine

1. Before servicing the vehicle, refer to the Precautions Section.

2. Remove the automatic transmission flexplate. Refer to Flywheel.

3. Remove the oil pan. Refer to Oil Pan.

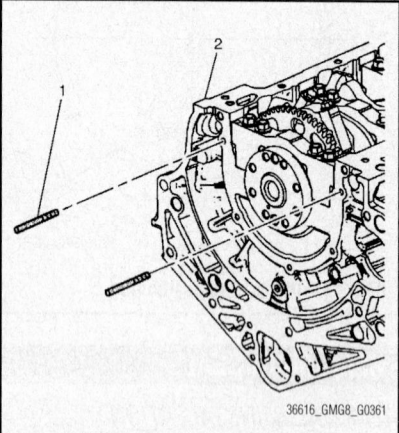

Fig. 174 Crankshaft rear oil seal guide location—3.6L Engine

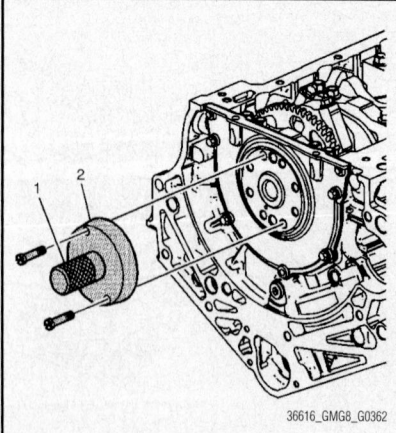

Fig. 175 Install the J 42183 handle with the EN 47839 installation tool—3.36L Engine

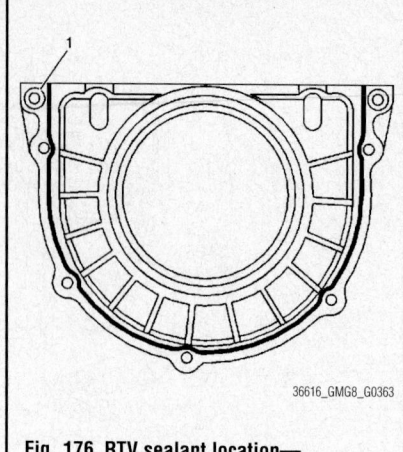

Fig. 176 RTV sealant location—3.6L Engine

4. Remove the crankshaft rear oil seal housing bolts (1).

5. Using the pry points located at the edge of the crankshaft rear oil seal housing shear the RTV sealant.

6. Remove and discard the crankshaft rear oil seal housing from the cylinder block.

To install:

7. Install the 0.236 inch (6 mm) guides from the EN 46109 guide pin set (1) into the 2 crankshaft rear oil seal housing corner bolt holes of the cylinder block (2).

8. Install the J 42183 handle (1) with the EN 47839 installation tool (2) onto the rear of the crankshaft flange.

9. Place a 0.118 inch (3 mm) bead of RTV sealant (1) to the NEW crankshaft rear oil seal housing as shown.

➡ DO NOT allow any engine oil on the area where the crankshaft rear oil seal housing is to be installed.

10. Install the crankshaft rear oil seal housing to the cylinder block.

11. Remove the EN 46109 guide pin set 0.236 inch (6 mm) guides from the cylinder block.

12. Install the crankshaft rear oil seal housing to cylinder block retaining bolts and tighten to 89 inch lbs. (10 Nm).

13. Remove the J 42183 handle and EN 47839 installation tool from the crankshaft flange.

14. Install the oil pan.

15. Install the automatic transmission flexplate.

6.0L Engine

See Figures 177 and 178.

1. Before servicing the vehicle, refer to the Precautions Section.

2. Remove the engine flywheel or flexplate. Refer to Flywheel.

3. Gently pry the crankshaft rear oil seal (1) from the rear cover (2).

To install:

4. Inspect the seal and identify the part number markings for proper orientation.

➡ Do not lubricate the oil seal inside diameter (ID) of the crankshaft surface. Do not reuse the crankshaft rear oil seal.

5. Lubricate the outside diameter (OD) of the oil seal with clean engine oil.

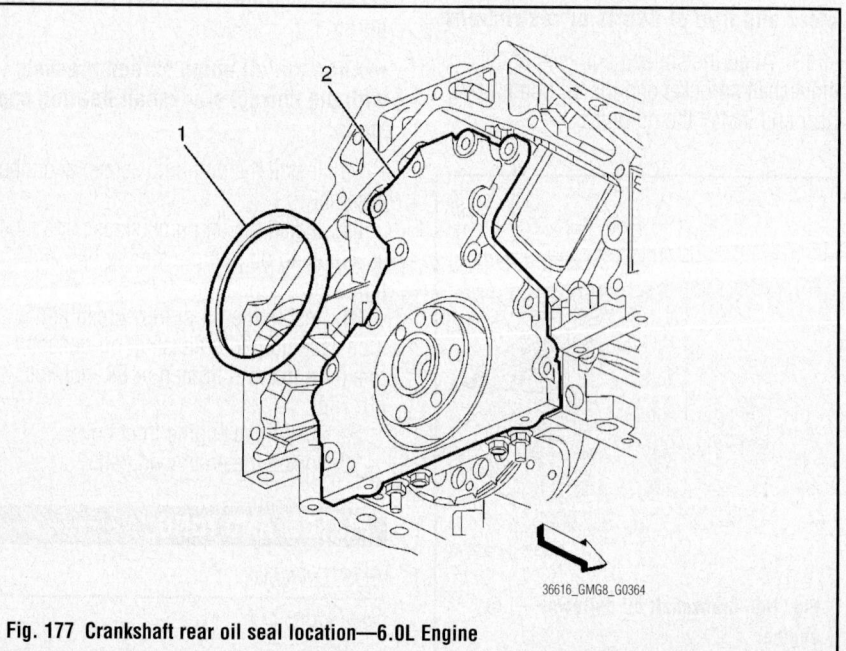

Fig. 177 Crankshaft rear oil seal location—6.0L Engine

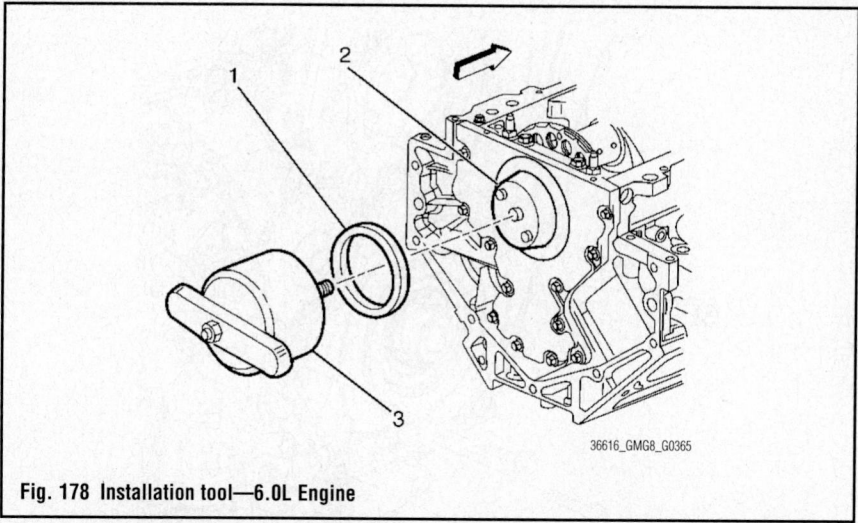

Fig. 178 Installation tool—6.0L Engine

➤**DO NOT allow oil or other lubricants to contact the seal surface.**

6. Lubricate the rear cover oil seal bore with clean engine oil.

➤**DO NOT allow oil or other lubricants to contact the crankshaft surface.**

7. Install the J 41479-2A (2) cone and bolts onto the rear of the crankshaft.

➤**Do not over tighten the bolts.**

8. Tighten the bolts.

9. Install the rear oil seal (1) onto the J 41479 (3) and push the seal to the rear cover bore (2).

10. Thread the J 41479 (3) threaded rod into the tapered cone until the J 41479 (3) contacts the rear oil seal (1).

11. Align the rear oil seal (1) onto the J 41479 (3).

12. Rotate the handle of the J 41479 (3) clockwise until the rear oil seal (1) enters and bottoms into the rear cover bore (2).

13. Remove the J 41479 (3) and J 41479-2A .

ROCKER ARMS/SHAFTS

REMOVAL & INSTALLATION

3.6L Engine

Refer to Camshaft & Valve Lifters

6.0L Engine

1. Before servicing the vehicle, refer to the Precautions Section.

2. Remove the valve rocker arm covers. Refer to Valve Covers.

✳✳ WARNING

Place the valve rocker arms, valve pushrods, and pivot support, in a

rack so they can be installed in the same location from which they were removed.

3. Remove the valve rocker arm bolts.
4. Remove the valve rocker arms.

To install:

➤**When using the valve train components again, always install the components to the original location and position.**

➤**Valve lash is net build, no valve adjustment is required.**

5. Lubricate the valve rocker arms and pushrods with clean engine oil.

6. Lubricate the flange of the valve rocker arm bolts with clean engine oil.

➤**Make sure the pushrods seat correctly to the ends of the rocker arms.**

➤**DO NOT tighten the rocker arm bolts at this time.**

7. Install the rocker arms and rocker arm retaining bolts.

➤**The Number 1 piston is at the compression stroke when the Number 6 cylinder inlet and exhaust valves are rocking, that is when the exhaust valve is at the end of its upward travel while the intake valve starts its downward movement.**

➤**The engine firing order is 1-8-7-2-6-5-4-3. Cylinder numbers are 1-3-5-7 are on the left bank and 2-4-6-8 are on the right bank.**

8. Rotate the crankshaft until number one piston is at top dead centre of compression stroke.

9. With the engine in the number one

firing position, tighten the following valve rocker arm retaining bolts:

a. Tighten exhaust valve rocker arm retaining bolts 1, 2, 7, and 8 to 22 ft. lbs. (30 Nm).

b. Tighten intake valve rocker arm retaining bolts 1, 3, 4, and 5 to 22 ft. lbs. (30 Nm).

10. Rotate the crankshaft 360 degrees.

11. Tighten the following valve rocker arm retaining bolts:

a. Tighten exhaust valve rocker arm retaining bolts 3, 4, 5, and 6 to 22 ft. lbs. (30 Nm).

b. Tighten intake valve rocker arm retaining bolts 2, 6, 7, and 8 to 22 ft. lbs. (30 Nm).

12. Install the valve rocker arm covers.

TIMING CHAIN COVER AND SEAL

REMOVAL & INSTALLATION

3.6L Engine

See Figures 179 through 183.

1. Before servicing the vehicle, refer to the Precautions Section.

2. Remove engine. See Engine Assembly in Engine Mechanical.

3. Remove the intake manifold. See Intake Manifold in Engine Mechanical.

4. Remove the valve covers. See Valve Covers in Engine Mechanical.

5. Remove the water outlet housing assembly.

6. Remove the drive belt tensioner. See Accessory Drive Belts in Engine Mechanical.

7. Remove the water pump pulley. See Water Pump in Engine Cooling.

8. Remove the power steering pump. See Power Steering Pump in Steering.

Fig. 179 Front cover guide pin locations

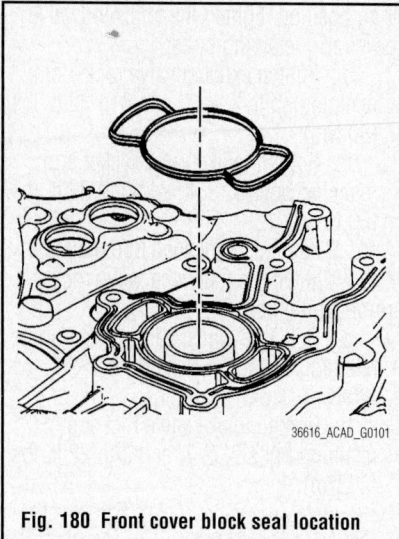

Fig. 180 Front cover block seal location

9. Remove the crankshaft balancer. See Crankshaft Damper in Engine Mechanical.

10. Remove the camshaft position sensors. See Camshaft Position Sensor in Engine Performance & Emission Controls.

11. Remove the camshaft position actuator solenoid valves from the front cover. See Camshaft Position Actuator Solenoid Valves in Engine Performance & Emission Controls.

12. Remove the alternator. See Alternator in Engine Electrical.

✱✱ WARNING

There are a total of 22 M8 bolts that must be removed and 3 optional M12 bolts that may need to be removed before the front cover will separate from the engine block.

13. Remove the engine front cover.

14. Use a flat-bladed tool in order to remove the crankshaft oil seal. Use care not

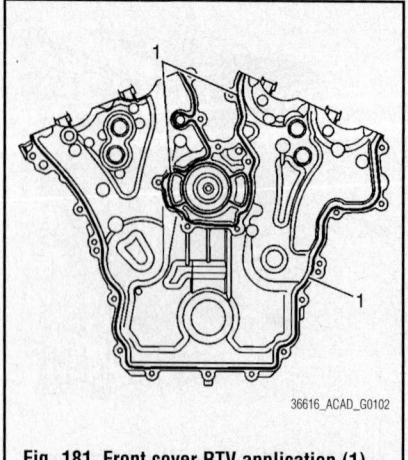

Fig. 181 Front cover RTV application (1)

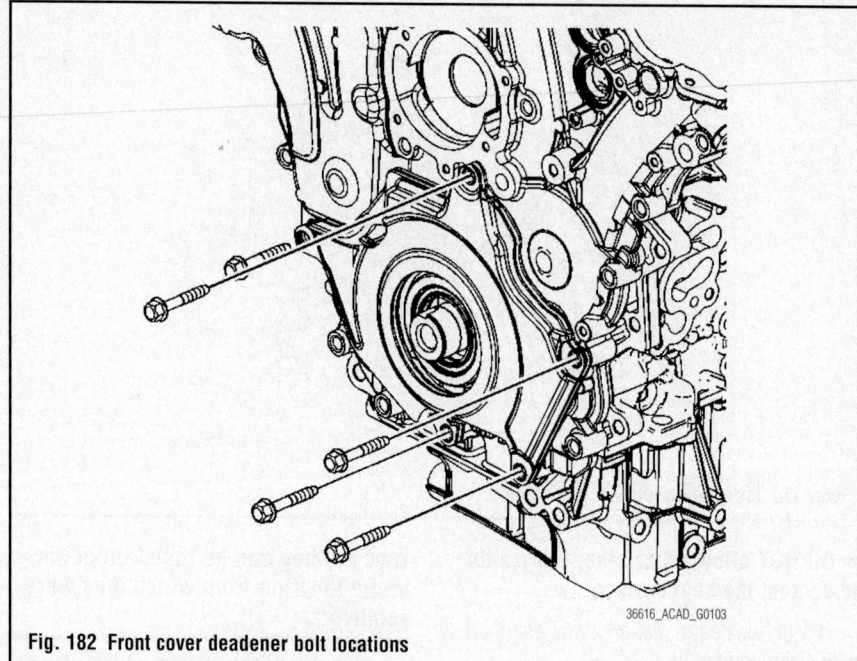

Fig. 182 Front cover deadener bolt locations

to damage the engine front cover or the crankshaft.

To install:

15. Use the J 29184 or equivalent to install the crankshaft front oil seal.

16. Install front cover:

   a. Install the 8 mm (0.315 in) guide from the EN-46109 pins into the cylinder block positions as shown.

   b. Install the NEW engine front cover to cylinder block seal.

   c. Place a 3 mm (0.118 in) bead of RTV sealant, GM P/N 12378521 (Canadian P/N 88901148) or equivalent, on the engine front cover.

   d. Place the engine front cover onto the EN-46109 pins and slide into position.

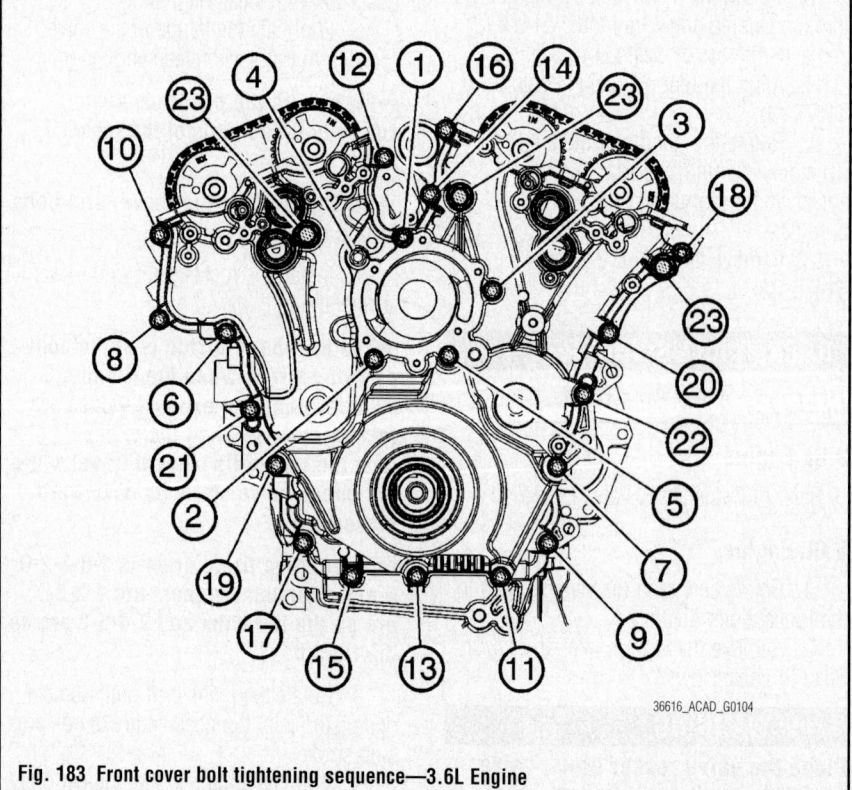

Fig. 183 Front cover bolt tightening sequence—3.6L Engine

e. Remove the EN-46109 pins from the cylinder block.

f. Install the engine front cover deadener.

➤The front cover and deadener may vary in appearance depending on application but are retained by the same number of bolts.

g. Loosely install the engine front cover bolts to hold the engine front cover deadener into position.

h. Loosely install the remaining engine front cover bolts.

➤Engine front cover bolts in the number (23) location are model dependent and may not apply.

i. Tighten the engine front cover bolts (1–22) in sequence shown to 14 ft lbs. (20 Nm).

j. Tighten the engine front cover bolts (1–22) a second pass in sequence an additional 60 degrees.

k. Tighten the engine front cover bolts (23) to 48 ft. lbs. (65 Nm).

17. Install the alternator.

18. Install the camshaft position actuator solenoid valves to the front cover.

19. Install the camshaft position sensors.

20. Install the crankshaft balancer.

21. Install the power steering pump.

22. Install the water pump pulley.

23. Install the water outlet housing assembly.

24. Install the drive belt tensioner.

25. Remove the EN-48383 from the right camshafts.

26. Remove the EN-48383 from the left camshafts.

27. Install the valve covers.

28. Install the intake manifold.

29. Install engine.

30. Start engine and check for leaks.

6.0L Engine

See Figures 184 through 190.

1. Before servicing the vehicle, refer to the Precautions Section.

2. Remove the oil pan. Refer to Oil Pan.

3. Remove the crankshaft balancer. Refer to Crankshaft Damper.

4. Remove the engine front cover to cylinder block retaining bolts (1).

➤The engine front cover gasket (3) is a single use only component and must be replaced whenever the engine front cover (2) is removed.

5. Remove the engine front cover (2) and gasket (3).

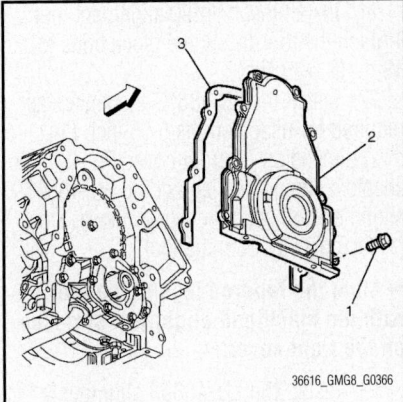

Fig. 184 Front cover bolt location— 6.0L Engine

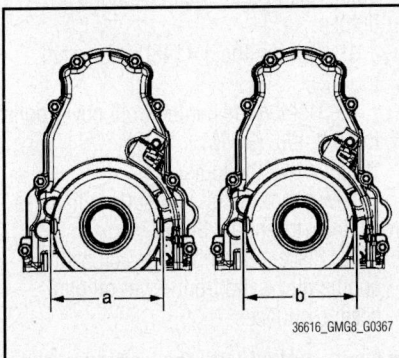

Fig. 185 Front cover measuring— 6.0L Engine

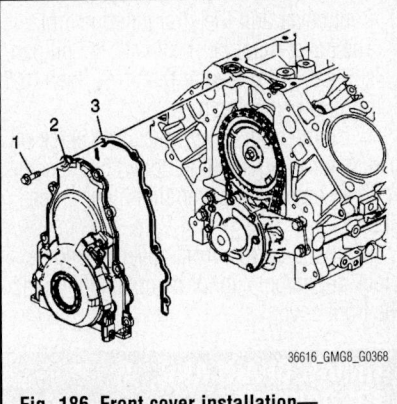

Fig. 186 Front cover installation— 6.0L Engine

6. Remove the engine front cover gasket (3).

7. Discard the engine front cover gasket (3).

To install:

8. Measure the alignment tab distance on the front cover.

➤For 2009 model year, the engine front cover may have either a 5.55 inch (141 mm) dimension (a) or 6.26 inch (159 mm) dimension (b) alignment tab

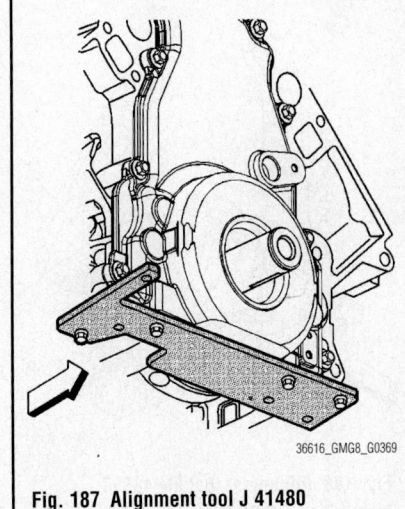

Fig. 187 Alignment tool J 41480 installation—6.0L Engine

distance. The EN-48853 front cover alignment tool is designed to properly align both design front covers. For the 5.55 inch (141 mm) cover, the EN 48853-2 adapters must be used.

➤Do not use the crankshaft oil seal or the engine front cover gasket again. Do not apply any type of sealant to the front cover gasket, unless specified. The special tools in this procedure are used to properly align the engine front cover at the oil pan surface and to center the crankshaft front oil seal.

- All gasket surfaces should be free of oil or other foreign material during assembly.
- The crankshaft front oil seal MUST be centered in relation to the crankshaft.
- The oil pan sealing surface at the front cover and engine block MUST be aligned within specifications.

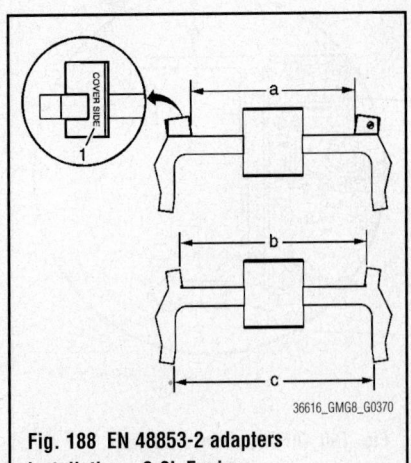

Fig. 188 EN 48853-2 adapters installation—6.0L Engine

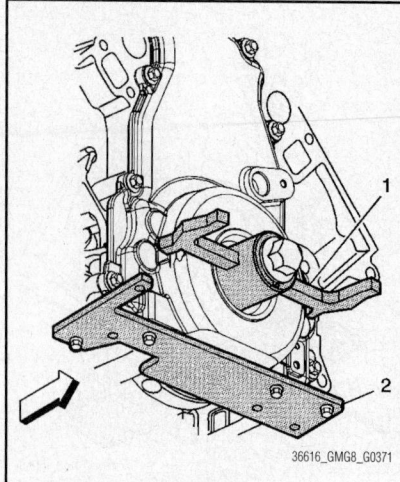

Fig. 189 Alignment tool EN-48853 installation—6.0L Engine

- An improperly aligned front cover may cause premature front oil seal wear and/or engine assembly oil leaks.

9. Install the front cover gasket (3), front cover (2), and bolts (1).

10. Tighten the cover bolts finger tight. Do not overtighten.

➡**Start the tool-to-front cover bolts. Do not tighten the bolts at this time.**

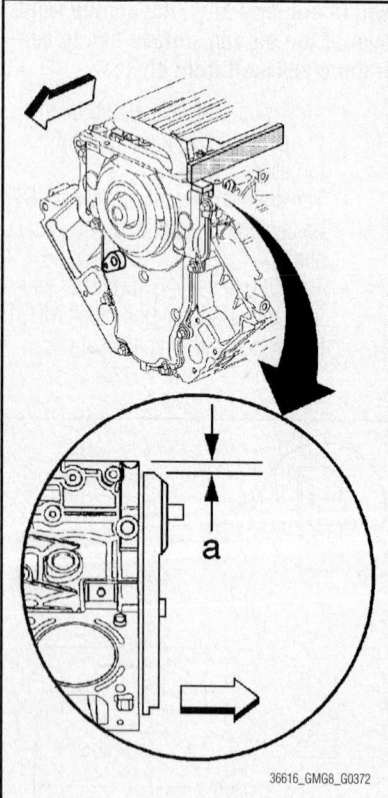

Fig. 190 Oil pan surface flatness measurement—6.0L Engine

11. Install the J 41480 alignment tool . Tighten the tool-to-engine block bolts to 18 ft. lbs. (25 Nm).

12. Install the EN 48853-2 adapters as required for usage on the 5.55 inch (141 mm) dimension (a) front cover. Position the adapters against the legs of the EN-48853 alignment tool with the words "cover side" (1) facing away from the tool.

➡**Align the tapered legs of the tool with the machined alignment surfaces on the front cover.**

13. Install the EN-48853 alignment tool (1).

14. Install the crankshaft balancer bolt.

   a. Tighten the crankshaft balancer bolt by hand until snug. Do not over-tighten.

   b. Tighten the J 41480 alignment tool (2).

   c. Tighten the engine front cover bolts to 18 ft. lbs. (25 Nm).

15. Remove the tools.

16. Measure the oil pan surface flatness, front cover-to-engine block.

   a. Place a straight edge across the engine block and front cover oil pan sealing surfaces.

➡**Avoid contact with the portion of the gasket that protrudes into the oil pan surface.**

   b. Insert a feeler gage between the front cover and the straight edge tool. The cover must be flush with the oil pan surface, or no greater than 0.02 inch (0.5 mm)(a) below flush.

17. If the front cover-to-engine block oil pan surface alignment is not within specifications, repeat the cover alignment procedure.

18. If the correct front cover-to-engine block alignment cannot be obtained, replace the front cover.

TIMING CHAIN AND SPROCKETS

REMOVAL & INSTALLATION

3.6L Engine

See Figures 191 through 226.

1. Before servicing the vehicle, refer to the Precautions Section.

2. Remove the spark plugs in order to ease crankshaft/engine rotation.

3. Remove front cover. See Timing Chain Cover and Seal in Engine Mechanical.

4. Using the EN-48589, rotate the

Fig. 191 Right bank secondary camshaft drive chain tensioner

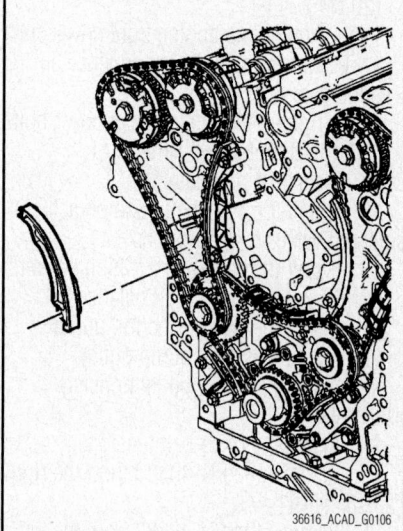

Fig. 192 Right bank secondary camshaft drive chain shoe

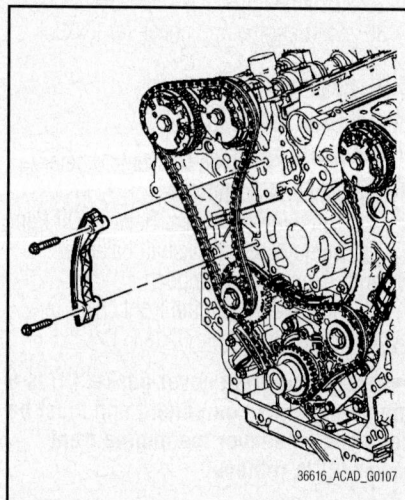

Fig. 193 Right bank secondary camshaft drive chain guide

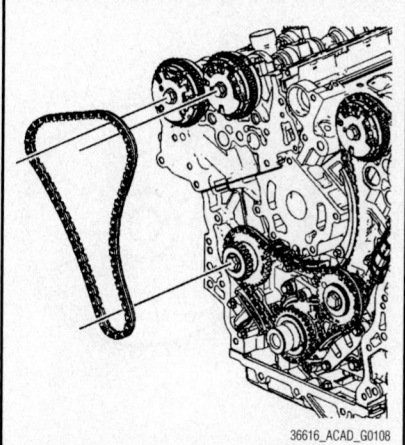

Fig. 194 Right bank secondary camshaft drive chain

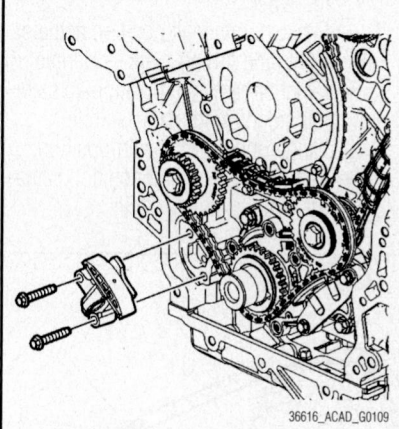

Fig. 195 Primary camshaft drive chain tensioner

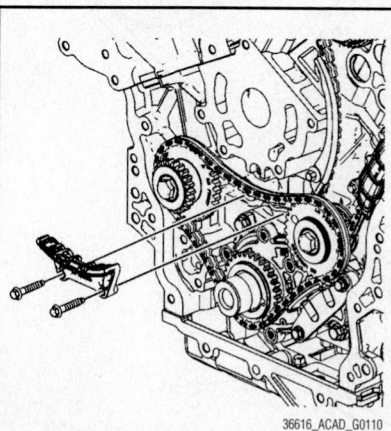

Fig. 196 Primary camshaft drive chain upper guide

crankshaft until the left cylinder head camshafts align with the EN-48383 and the right cylinder head camshafts align with the EN-48383.

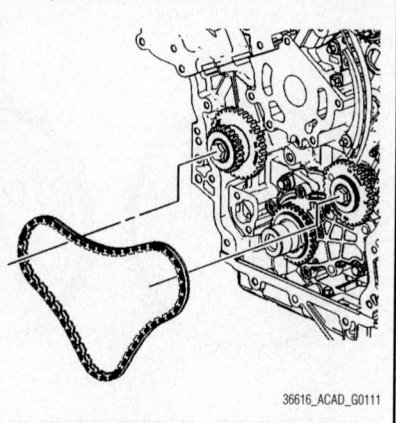

Fig. 197 Primary camshaft timing chain

5. Install the EN-48383-1 to the left camshafts.

6. Remove the right bank secondary camshaft drive chain tensioner.

7. Remove and discard the right secondary camshaft drive chain tensioner gasket.

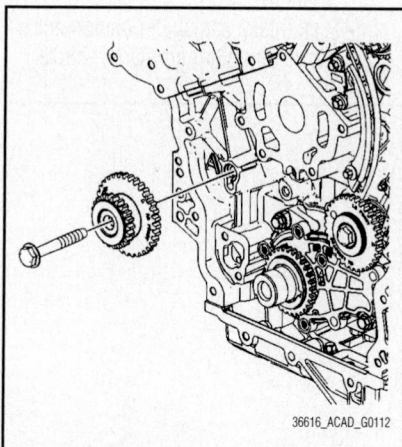

Fig. 198 Right bank camshaft intermediate drive chain idler

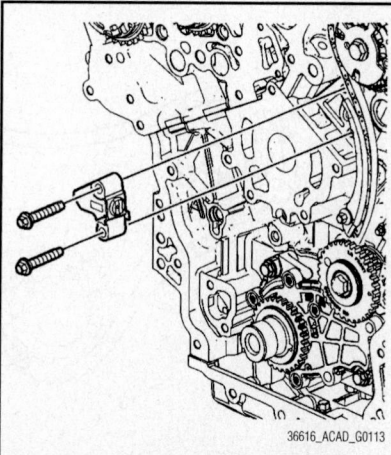

Fig. 199 Left bank secondary camshaft drive chain tensioner

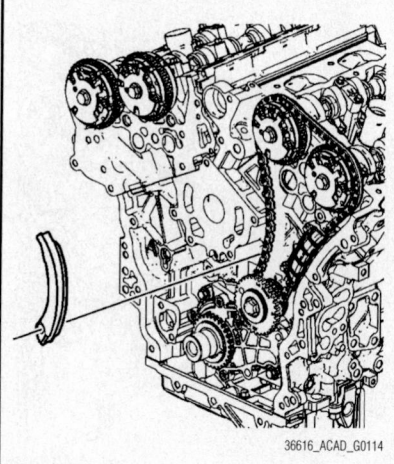

Fig. 200 Left bank secondary camshaft drive chain shoe

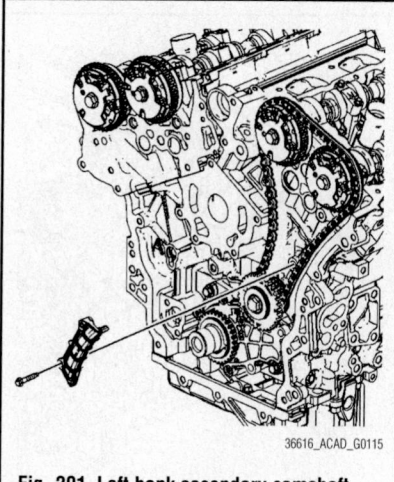

Fig. 201 Left bank secondary camshaft drive chain guide

8. Remove the right bank secondary camshaft drive chain shoe.

9. Remove the right bank secondary camshaft drive chain guide.

10. Remove the right secondary camshaft drive chain from the right camshaft position actuators and the right camshaft intermediate drive chain idler sprocket.

11. Remove the primary camshaft drive chain tensioner.

12. Remove and discard the primary camshaft drive chain tensioner gasket.

13. Remove the primary camshaft drive chain upper guide.

14. Remove the primary camshaft timing chain.

15. Remove the right bank camshaft intermediate drive chain idler.

16. Remove the left bank secondary camshaft drive chain tensioner.

17. Remove and discard the left

Fig. 202 Left bank camshaft intermediate drive chain idler

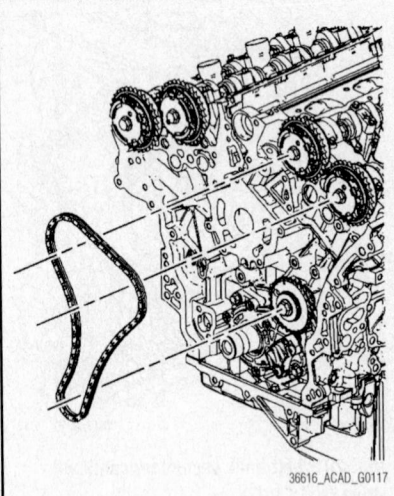

Fig. 203 Left bank secondary camshaft drive chain

secondary camshaft drive chain tensioner gasket.

18. Remove the left bank secondary camshaft drive chain shoe.

19. Remove the left bank secondary camshaft drive chain guide.

20. Remove the left bank camshaft intermediate drive chain idler.

21. Remove the left bank secondary camshaft drive chain.

22. Clean and inspect all of the camshaft timing drive components. Replace components as necessary.

To install:

✳✳ WARNING

All camshafts must be locked in place before installation of any camshaft drive chains.

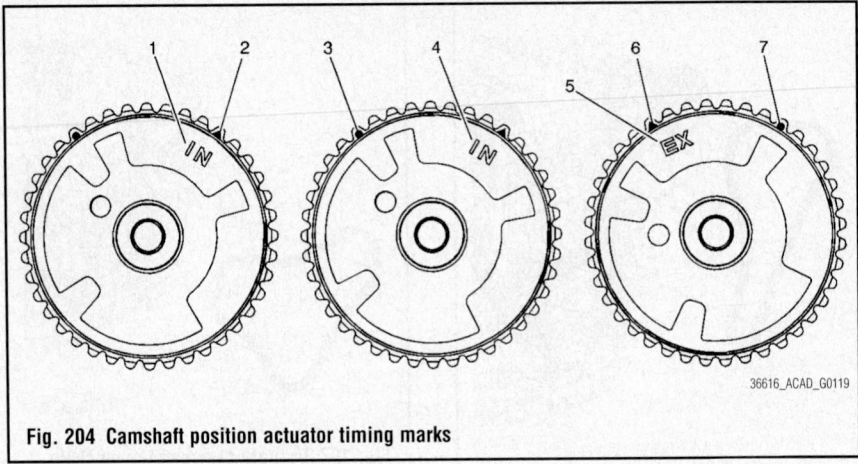

Fig. 204 Camshaft position actuator timing marks

23. Camshaft and timing chain positioning:

   a. Camshaft Position (CMP) actuator timing marks.
- Right intake camshaft position actuator identifier
- Right intake camshaft position actuator right side timing mark—triangle
- Left intake camshaft position actuator left side timing mark—circle
- Left intake camshaft position actuator identifier
- Exhaust camshaft position actuator identifier
- Exhaust camshaft position actuator right side timing mark—triangle
- Exhaust camshaft position actuator left side timing mark—circle

   b. Stage one timing chain position:
- Left intake camshaft position actuator timing mark—circle

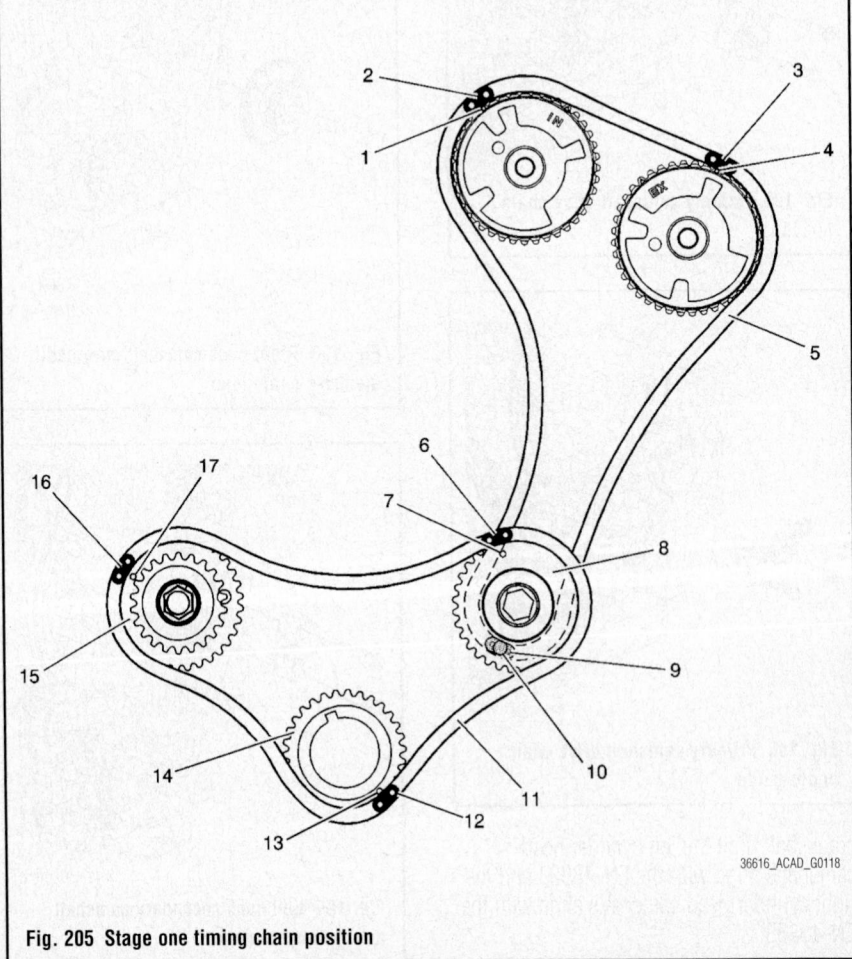

Fig. 205 Stage one timing chain position

- Left intake secondary camshaft timing drive chain timing link
- Left exhaust secondary camshaft timing drive chain timing link
- Left exhaust camshaft position actuator timing mark—circle
- Left secondary camshaft timing drive chain
- Primary camshaft drive chain timing link for the left primary camshaft intermediate drive chain sprocket
- Left primary camshaft intermediate drive chain sprocket timing mark for the primary camshaft drive chain
- Left primary camshaft intermediate drive chain sprocket
- Left secondary camshaft timing drive chain timing link for the left primary camshaft intermediate drive chain sprocket, behind hole in sprocket

- Left primary camshaft intermediate drive chain sprocket timing window for the left secondary camshaft timing drive chain timing link
- Primary camshaft drive chain
- Primary camshaft drive chain timing link for the crankshaft sprocket
- Crankshaft sprocket timing mark
- Crankshaft sprocket
- Right primary camshaft intermediate drive chain sprocket
- Primary camshaft drive chain timing link for the right primary camshaft intermediate drive chain sprocket
- Right primary camshaft intermediate drive chain sprocket timing mark
c. Stage two timing chain position:
- Left intake CMP actuator timing mark—circle
- Left intake secondary camshaft timing drive chain timing link

- Left exhaust secondary camshaft timing drive chain timing link
- Left exhaust CMP actuator timing mark—circle
- Left secondary camshaft timing drive chain
- Primary camshaft drive chain timing link for the left primary camshaft intermediate drive chain sprocket
- Left primary camshaft intermediate drive chain sprocket timing mark for the primary camshaft drive chain
- Left primary camshaft intermediate drive chain sprocket
- Left secondary camshaft timing drive chain timing link for the left primary camshaft intermediate drive chain sprocket, behind hole in sprocket
- Left primary camshaft intermediate drive chain sprocket timing window

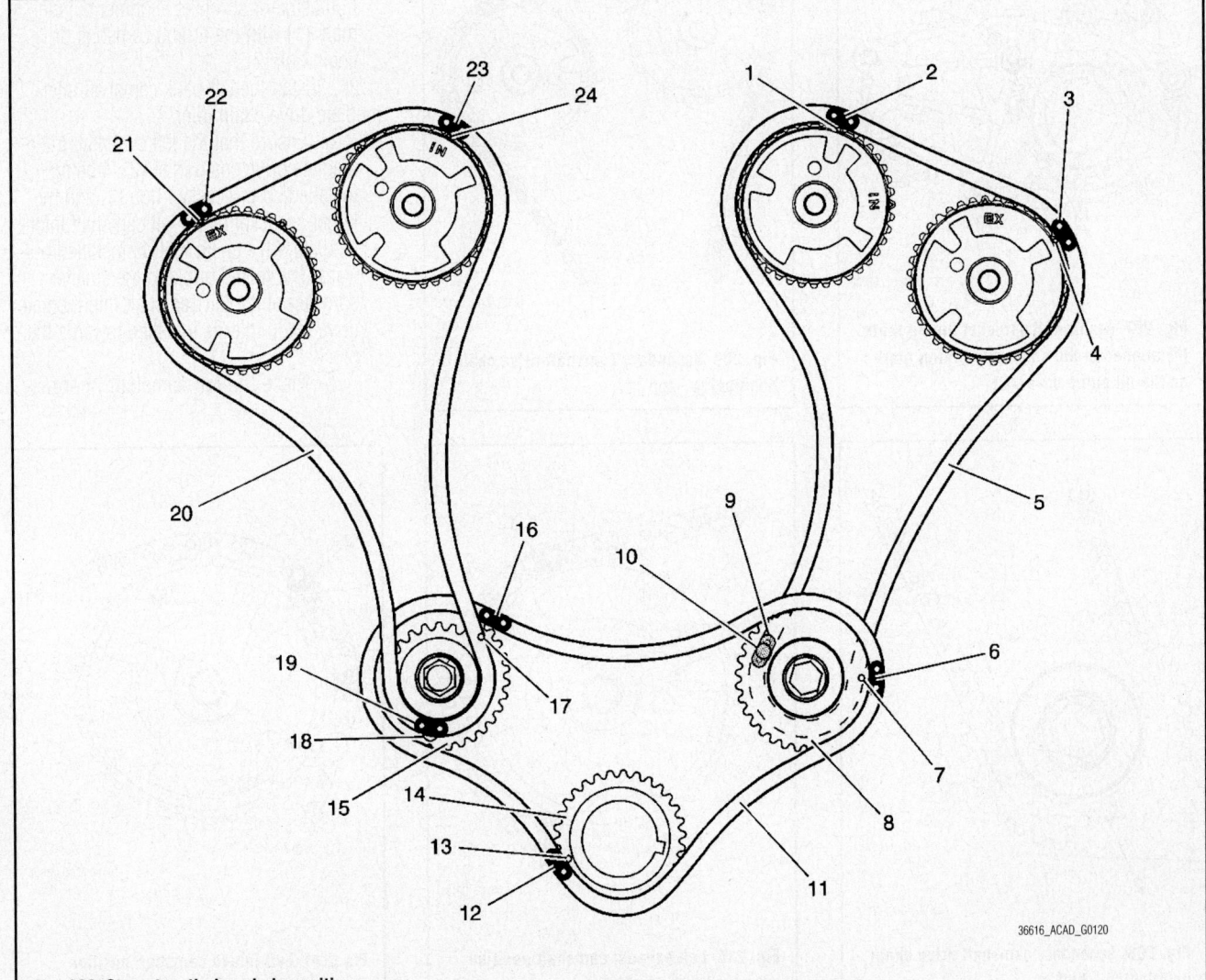

Fig. 206 Stage two timing chain position

36616_ACAD_G0120

- Primary camshaft drive chain
- Primary camshaft drive chain timing link for the crankshaft sprocket
- Crankshaft sprocket timing mark
- Crankshaft sprocket
- Right primary camshaft intermediate drive chain sprocket
- Primary camshaft drive chain timing link for the right primary camshaft intermediate drive chain sprocket
- Right primary camshaft intermediate drive chain sprocket timing mark for the primary camshaft drive chain
- Right primary camshaft intermediate drive chain sprocket timing mark/window for the right secondary camshaft timing drive chain

- Right secondary camshaft timing drive chain timing link for the right primary camshaft intermediate drive chain sprocket
- Right secondary camshaft timing drive chain
- Right exhaust CMP actuator timing mark—triangle
- Right exhaust secondary camshaft timing drive chain timing link
- Right intake secondary camshaft timing drive chain timing link
- Right intake CMP actuator timing mark—triangle

24. Ensure the crankshaft is in the stage one timing position with the crankshaft sprocket timing mark (1) aligned to the

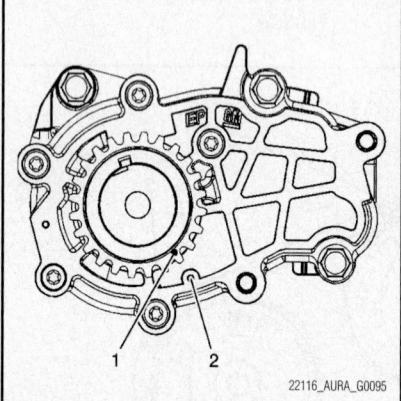

Fig. 207 Crankshaft sprocket timing mark (1) aligned to the stage one timing mark on the oil pump cover (2)

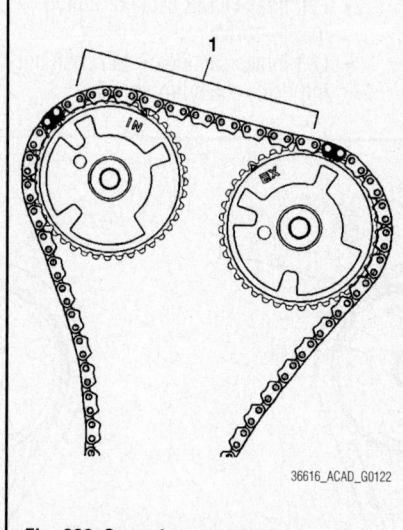

Fig. 209 Secondary camshaft drive chain positioning—top

stage one timing mark on the oil pump cover (2).

25. Install the left secondary camshaft drive chain.

a. Place the left secondary camshaft drive chain around the inner sprocket of the left camshaft intermediate drive chain idler with the timing camshaft drive chain link (1) aligned to the alignment access hole (2) made in the left camshaft intermediate drive chain idler outer sprocket.

b. Wrap the secondary camshaft drive chain around both left actuator drive sprockets.

c. Ensure there are 10 links (1) between the timing camshaft drive chain links for the camshaft position actuator sprockets.

d. Align the left exhaust camshaft position actuator sprocket alignment circle mark (2) with the timing camshaft drive chain link (1).

e. Align the left intake camshaft position actuator sprocket alignment circle mark (1) with the timing camshaft drive chain link (2).

26. Install the left bank camshaft intermediate drive chain idler.

a. Ensure that the left camshaft intermediate drive chain idler (2) is being installed. The recessed hub (3) and the larger sprocket of the left camshaft intermediate drive chain idler is installed outward. The raised hub and the smaller sprocket of the left camshaft intermediate drive chain idler is installed towards the block.

b. Place the left camshaft interme-

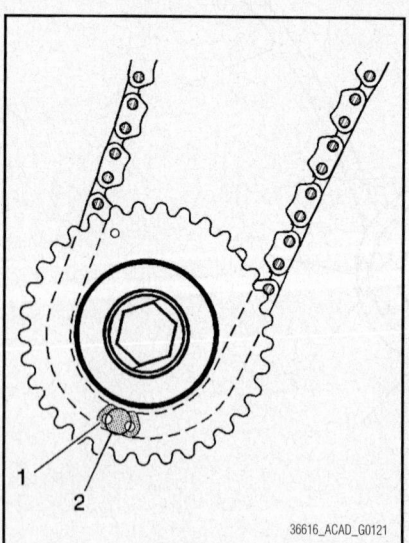

Fig. 208 Secondary camshaft drive chain positioning—bottom

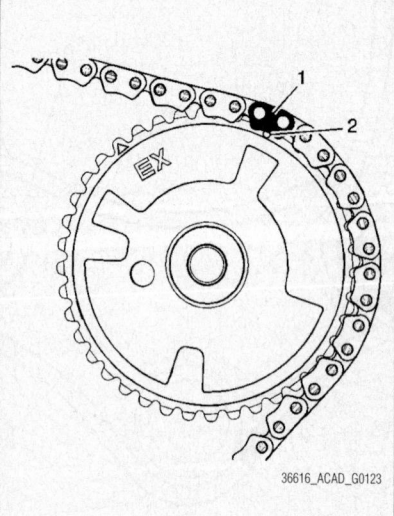

Fig. 210 Left exhaust camshaft position actuator sprocket alignment

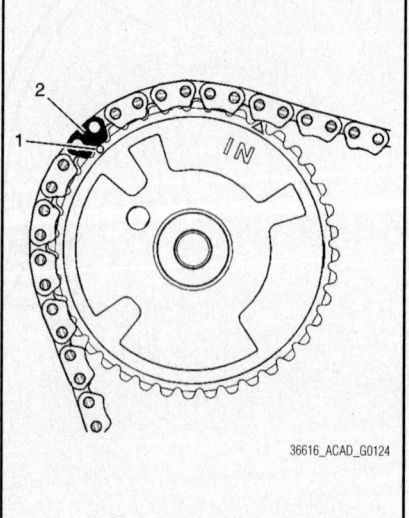

Fig. 211 Left intake camshaft position actuator sprocket alignment

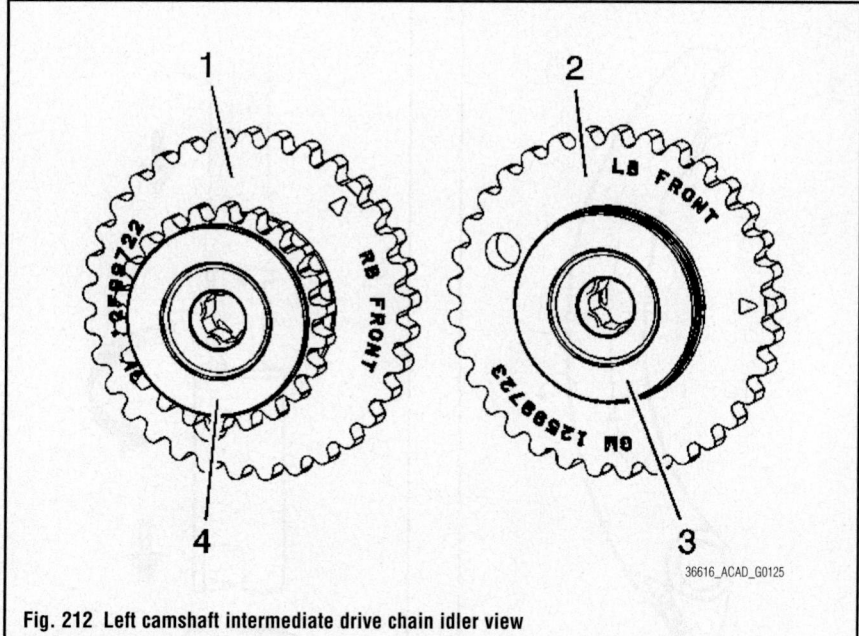

Fig. 212 Left camshaft intermediate drive chain idler view

diate drive chain idler to the cylinder block.

c. Install the camshaft intermediate drive chain idler bolt and tighten to 43 ft. lbs. (58 Nm).

27. Install the left bank secondary camshaft drive chain guide.

a. Ensure that the left secondary camshaft drive chain guide (2) is being installed.

b. Position the left secondary camshaft drive chain guide.

c. Install the secondary camshaft drive chain guide bolts and tighten to 17 ft. lbs. (23 Nm).

28. Install the left bank secondary camshaft drive chain shoe.

a. Ensure that the left secondary camshaft drive chain shoe (2) is being installed.

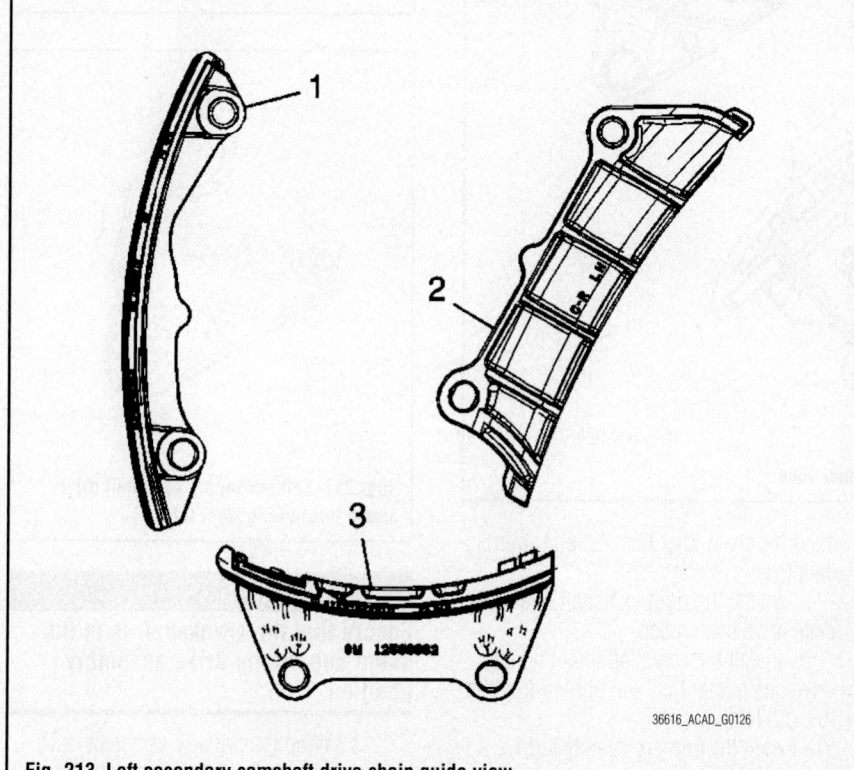

Fig. 213 Left secondary camshaft drive chain guide view

b. Position the left secondary camshaft drive chain shoe.

c. Install the secondary camshaft drive chain shoe bolt and tighten to 17 ft. lbs. (23 Nm).

29. Install the left bank secondary camshaft drive chain tensioner.

a. Ensure that the left secondary camshaft drive chain tensioner (2) is being installed.

b. Using the J-45027 tool , reset the left secondary camshaft drive chain tensioner plunger.

c. Compress the plunger into the body and lock the left secondary camshaft drive chain tensioner by inserting the EN-46112 pins into the access hole in the side of the left secondary camshaft drive chain tensioner body.

d. Slowly release pressure on the left secondary camshaft drive chain tensioner. The left secondary camshaft drive chain tensioner should remain compressed.

e. Install a NEW left secondary camshaft drive chain tensioner gasket to the left secondary camshaft drive chain tensioner.

f. Install the left secondary camshaft drive chain tensioner bolts through the left secondary camshaft drive chain tensioner and gasket.

g. Ensure the left secondary camshaft drive chain tensioner mounting surface on the left cylinder head does not have any burrs or defects that would degrade the sealing of the NEW left secondary camshaft drive chain tensioner gasket.

h. Place the left secondary camshaft drive chain tensioner into position and loosely install the bolts to the block.

i. Verify the proper placement of the left secondary camshaft drive chain tensioner gasket tab (1).

j. First pass, tighten the left secondary camshaft drive chain tensioner bolts to 44 inch lbs. (5 Nm).

k. Second pass, tighten the left secondary camshaft drive chain tensioner bolts to 17 ft. lbs. (23 Nm).

l. Release the left secondary camshaft drive chain tensioner by pulling out the EN-46112 pins and unlocking the tensioner plunger.

m. Verify the left secondary camshaft drive chain timing mark alignments by referring to camshaft timing drive chain alignment diagram—stage one timing chain position.

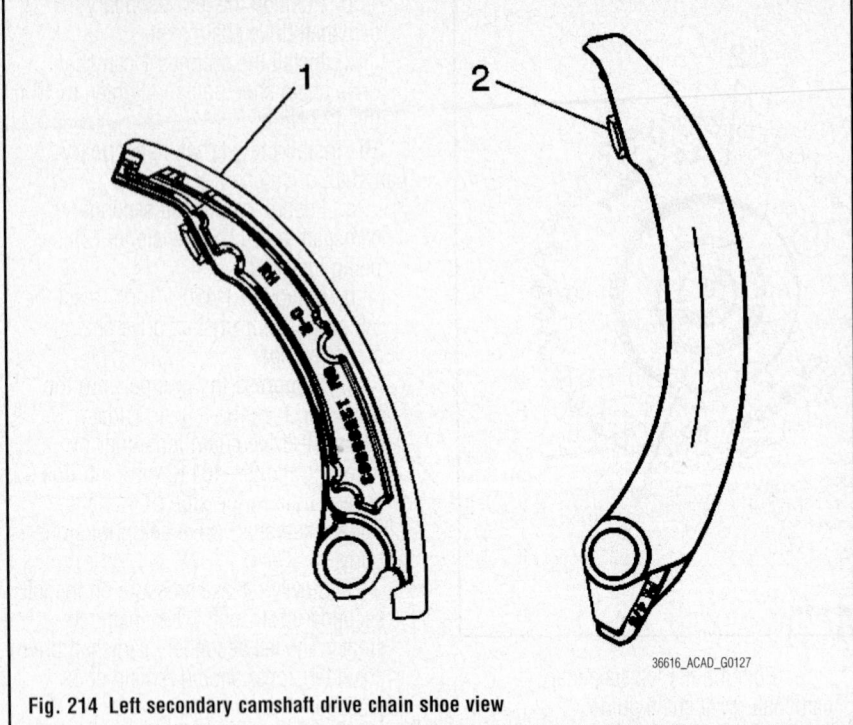

Fig. 214 Left secondary camshaft drive chain shoe view

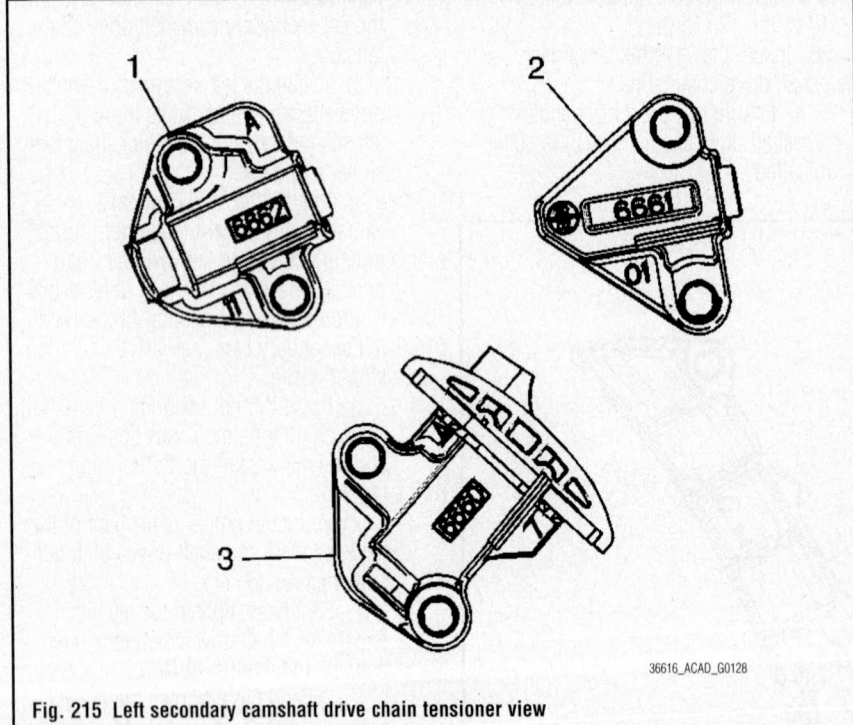

Fig. 215 Left secondary camshaft drive chain tensioner view

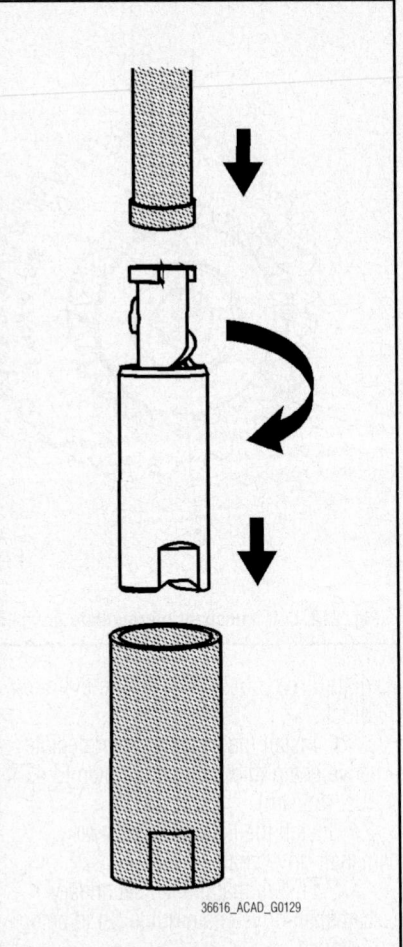

Fig. 216 Left secondary camshaft drive chain tensioner plunger reset

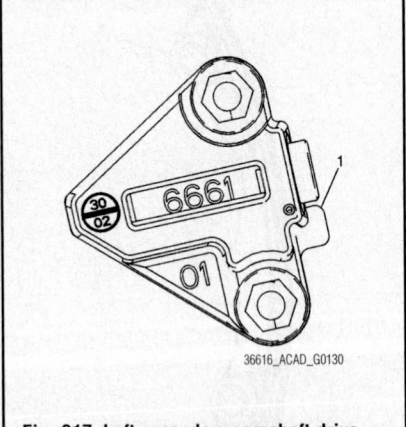

Fig. 217 Left secondary camshaft drive chain tensioner gasket tab

30. Install the right bank camshaft intermediate drive chain idler.

a. Ensure that the right camshaft intermediate drive chain idler (1) is being installed. The recessed hub (4) and the smaller sprocket of the right camshaft intermediate drive chain idler is installed outward. The raised hub and the larger sprocket of the right camshaft intermediate drive chain idler is installed towards the block.

b. Install the right camshaft intermediate drive chain idler.

c. Install the camshaft intermediate drive chain idler bolt and tighten to 43 ft. lbs. (58 Nm).

31. Install the primary camshaft drive chain.

✳✳ WARNING

Ensure that the crankshaft is in the stage one timing drive assembly position.

a. Wrap the primary camshaft drive chain around the large sprockets of each

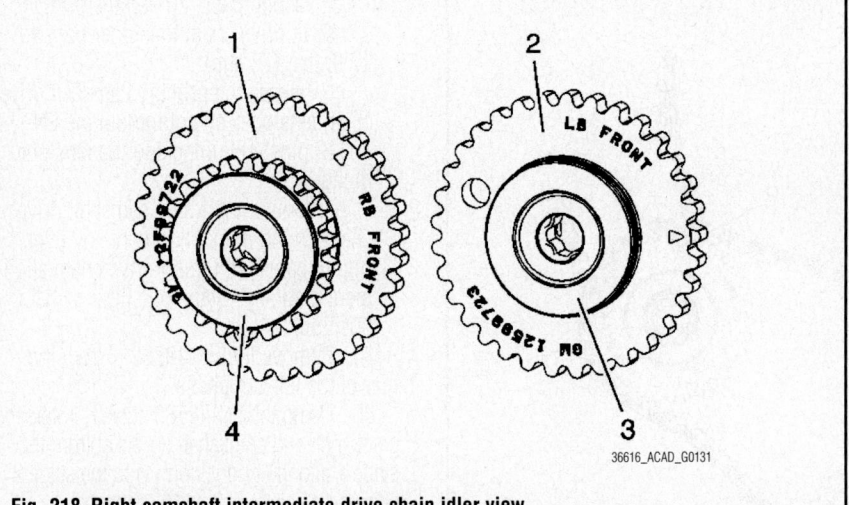

Fig. 218 Right camshaft intermediate drive chain idler view

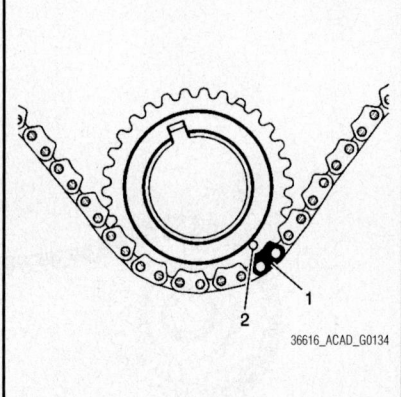

Fig. 221 Crankshaft sprocket timing mark will align with a timing camshaft drive chain link

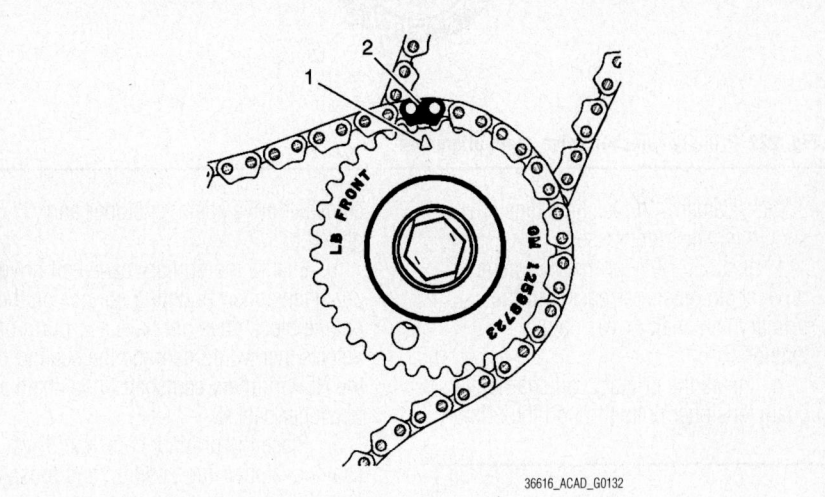

Fig. 219 Left camshaft intermediate drive chain idler timing mark will align with a timing camshaft drive chain link

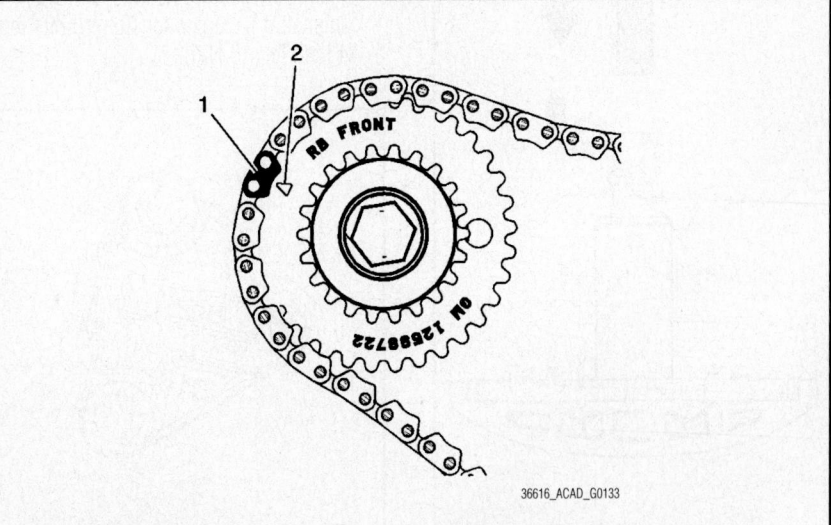

Fig. 220 Right camshaft intermediate drive chain idler timing mark will align with a timing camshaft drive chain link

camshaft intermediate drive chain idler and the crankshaft sprocket.

b. The left camshaft intermediate drive chain idler timing mark (1) will align with a timing camshaft drive chain link (2).

c. The right camshaft intermediate drive chain idler timing mark (2) will align with a timing camshaft drive chain link (1).

d. The crankshaft sprocket timing mark (2) will align with a timing camshaft drive chain link (1).

e. Ensure all the timing marks (2, 3, 6) are properly aligned with the timing camshaft drive chain links (1, 4, 5).

32. Install the primary upper camshaft drive chain guide.

a. Ensure the upper primary camshaft drive chain guide (3) is being installed.

b. Install the upper primary camshaft drive chain guides.

c. Install the upper primary camshaft drive chain guide bolts and tighten to 17 ft. lbs. (23 Nm).

33. Install the primary camshaft drive chain tensioner.

a. Ensure that the primary camshaft drive chain tensioner (3) is being installed.

b. Using the J-45027 tool, reset the primary camshaft drive chain tensioner plunger.

c. Install the plunger into the primary camshaft drive chain tensioner body.

d. Compress the plunger into the body and lock the primary camshaft drive chain tensioner by inserting the EN-46112 pins into the access hole in the side of the primary camshaft drive chain tensioner body.

e. Slowly release pressure on the primary camshaft drive chain tensioner. The

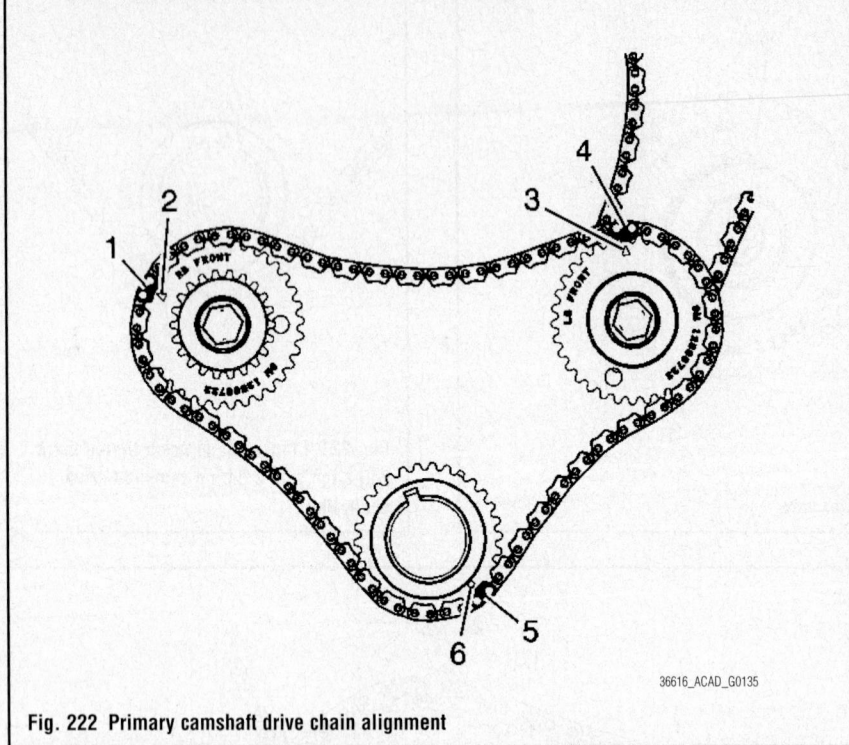

Fig. 222 Primary camshaft drive chain alignment

primary camshaft drive chain tensioner should remain compressed.

f. Install a NEW primary camshaft drive chain tensioner gasket to the primary camshaft drive chain tensioner.

g. Install the primary camshaft drive chain tensioner bolts through the primary

camshaft drive chain tensioner and gasket.

h. Ensure the primary camshaft drive chain tensioner mounting surface on the engine block does not have any burrs or defects that would degrade the sealing of the NEW primary camshaft drive chain tensioner gasket.

i. Place the primary camshaft drive chain tensioner into position and loosely install the bolts to the block.

j. Verify the proper placement of the primary camshaft drive chain tensioner gasket tab (1).

k. First pass, tighten the primary camshaft drive chain tensioner bolts to 44 inch lbs. (5 Nm).

l. Second pass, tighten the primary camshaft drive chain tensioner bolts to 17 ft. lbs. (23 Nm).

m. Release the primary camshaft drive chain tensioner by pulling out the EN-46112 pins and unlocking the tensioner plunger.

n. Verify the primary camshaft drive chain timing mark alignments by referring to camshaft timing drive chain alignment diagram - stage one timing chain position.

34. Remove the EN 48383-1 from the rear of the left camshafts.

35. Using the EN-48589 socket , rotate the crankshaft and crankshaft sprocket from the stage 1 alignment position (1) to the stage 2 alignment position (2), 115 crankshaft degrees, in order to install the right secondary camshaft drive chain components.

36. Install the EN-48383-2 onto the rear of the left camshafts.

37. Install the EN 48383-3 onto the rear of the right camshafts.

38. Install the right bank secondary camshaft drive chain guide.

39. Ensure that the right secondary camshaft drive chain guide (1) is being installed.

a. Position the right secondary camshaft drive chain guide.

b. Install the secondary camshaft drive chain guide bolts and tighten to 17 ft. lbs. (23 Nm).

40. Install the right bank secondary camshaft drive chain shoe.

a. Ensure that the right secondary camshaft drive chain shoe (1) is being installed.

b. Position the right secondary camshaft drive chain shoe.

c. Install the secondary camshaft drive chain shoe bolt and tighten to 17 ft. lbs. (23 Nm).

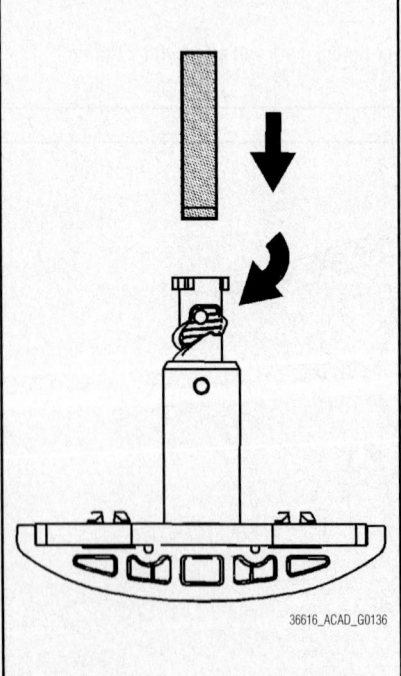

Fig. 223 Primary camshaft drive chain tensioner reset

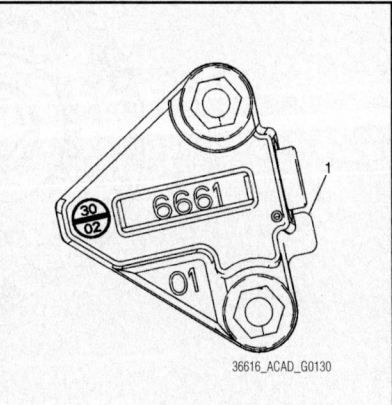

Fig. 224 Primary camshaft drive chain tensioner gasket tab

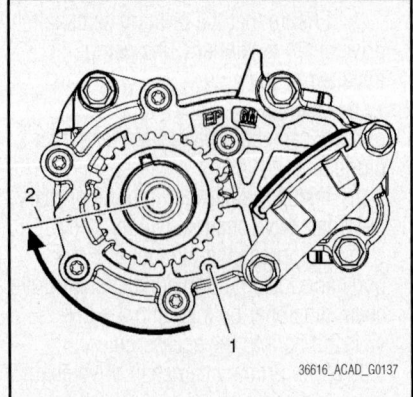

Fig. 225 Crankshaft sprocket stage 2 position

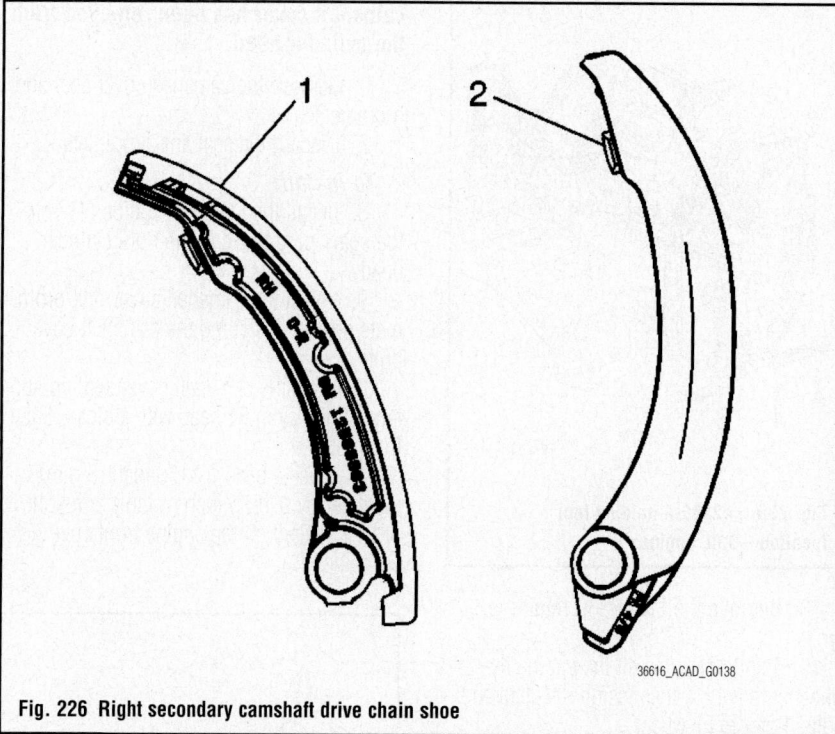

Fig. 226 Right secondary camshaft drive chain shoe

36616_ACAD_G0138

41. Install the right bank secondary camshaft drive chain tensioner.

a. Ensure that the right secondary camshaft drive chain tensioner (1) is being installed.

b. Using the J 45027 tool, reset the right secondary camshaft drive chain tensioner plunger.

c. Install the plunger into the right secondary camshaft drive chain tensioner body.

d. Compress the plunger into the body and lock the right secondary camshaft drive chain tensioner by inserting the EN 46112 pins into the access hole in the side of the right secondary camshaft drive chain tensioner body.

e. Slowly release pressure on the right secondary camshaft drive chain tensioner. The right secondary camshaft drive chain tensioner should remain compressed.

f. Install a NEW right secondary camshaft drive chain tensioner gasket to the right secondary camshaft drive chain tensioner.

g. Install the right secondary camshaft drive chain tensioner bolts through the right secondary camshaft drive chain tensioner and gasket.

h. Ensure the right secondary camshaft drive chain tensioner mounting surface on the right cylinder head does not have any burrs or defects that would degrade the sealing of the NEW right secondary camshaft drive chain tensioner gasket

i. Place the right secondary drive chain tensioner into position and loosely install the bolts to the block.

j. Verify the proper placement of the right secondary camshaft drive chain tensioner gasket tab (1).

k. First pass, tighten the right secondary camshaft drive chain tensioner bolts to 44 inch lbs. (5 Nm).

l. Second pass, tighten the right secondary camshaft drive chain tensioner bolts to 17 ft. lbs. (23 Nm).

m. Release the right secondary camshaft drive chain tensioner by pulling out the EN-46112 pins and unlocking the tensioner plunger.

n. Verify the right secondary camshaft drive chain timing mark alignments by referring to camshaft timing drive chain alignment diagram - stage two timing chain position.

42. Remove the EN-48383 from the right camshafts.

43. Remove the EN-48383 from the left camshafts.

44. Install the engine front cover. See Timing Chain Cover and Seal in Engine Mechanical.

6.0L Engine

See Figures 227 through 230.

1. Before servicing the vehicle, refer to the Precautions Section.

2. Remove the crankshaft balancer. Refer to Crankshaft Damper.

3. Remove the engine front cover. Refer to Timing Chain Cover & Seal.

4. Remove the oil pump. Refer to Oil Pump.

> ☀☀ **WARNING**
>
> **Do not turn the crankshaft assembly after the timing chain has been removed in order to prevent damage to the piston assemblies or the valves.**

5. Inspect the sprockets for correct alignment. The mark on the camshaft sprocket (1) should be located in the 6 o'clock position and the mark on the crankshaft sprocket (2) should be located in the 12 o'clock position.

6. Remove the camshaft sprocket bolt.

7. Remove the camshaft sprocket and timing chain.

8. Remove the timing chain tension bolts (1) and tensioner (2).

9. Using the J 41816-2 protector, the J 41558 remove, bolts and the J 8433-1 puller in order to remove the crankshaft sprocket.

10. Remove the crankshaft sprocket.

To install:

11. Use the J 41478 seal installer and the J 41665 balancer and sprocket installer in order to install the crankshaft sprocket.

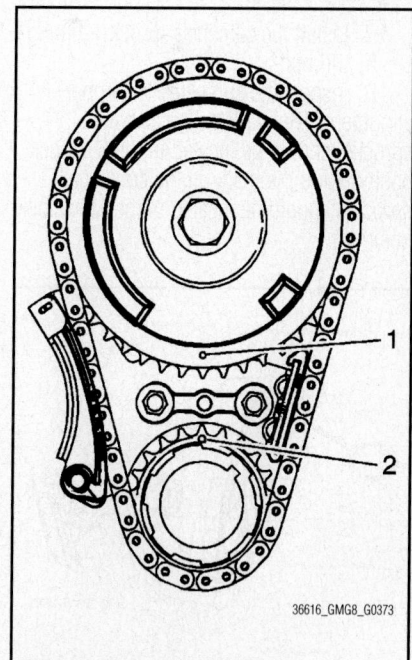

36616_GMG8_G0373

Fig. 227 Timing chain and sprocket alignment—6.0L Engine

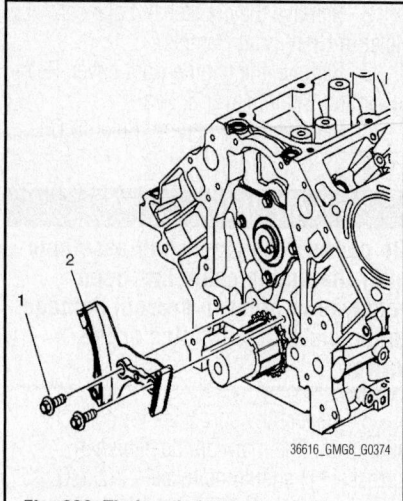

Fig. 228 Timing chain tensioner—6.0L Engine

12. Install the sprocket onto the crankshaft until fully seated against the crankshaft flange.

13. Rotate the crankshaft sprocket until the alignment mark is in the 12 o'clock position.

14. Compress the timing chain tensioner guide and install the EN 46330 retaining pin.

15. Install the timing chain tensioner and bolts. Tighten the timing chain tensioner bolts to 18 ft. lbs. (25 Nm).

➡**The sprocket teeth and timing chain must mesh.**

➡**The camshaft and the crankshaft sprocket alignment marks MUST be aligned properly.**

16. Install the camshaft sprocket, timing chain, and bolt.

17. Inspect the sprockets for proper alignment. The mark on the camshaft sprocket should be located in the 6 o'clock position and the mark on the crankshaft sprocket should be located in the 12 o'clock position.

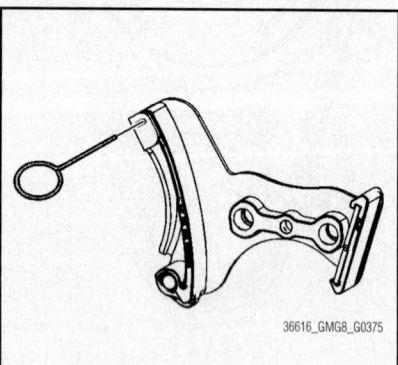

Fig. 229 EN 46330 retaining pin—6.0L Engine

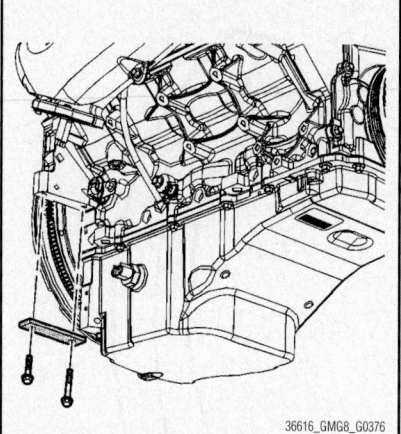

Fig. 230 J 42386-A holding tool location—6.0L Engine

18. Remove the EN 46330 retaining pin.

19. Temporarily install the engine flywheel automatic transmission flexplate and bolts. Refer to Flywheel

20. Install the J 42386-A holding tool and bolts. Use 1 M10-1.5 x 120 mm bolt and 1 M10-1.5 x 45 mm bolt for proper tool operation. Tighten the J 42386-A holding tool bolts to 37 ft. lbs. (50 Nm).

21. Tighten the camshaft sprocket bolt.

   a. Tighten the camshaft sprocket bolt a first pass to 55 ft. lbs. (75 Nm).

   b. Tighten the camshaft sprocket bolt a final pass an additional 50 degrees using the J 45059 meter.

22. Remove the J 42386-A holding tool and bolts.

23. Remove the engine flywheel.

24. Install the oil pump.

25. Install the engine front cover.

26. Install the crankshaft balancer.

VALVE COVERS (CAMSHAFT COVERS)

REMOVAL & INSTALLATION

3.6L Engine

See Figures 231 through 234.

1. Before servicing the vehicle, refer to the Precautions Section.

2. Remove the ignition coils. Refer to Ignition Coil in Engine Electrical.

3. Remove the spark plugs.

4. Remove the camshaft cover to cylinder head retaining bolts.

5. Remove the camshaft cover from the cylinder head.

➡**The camshaft cover seal and grommets must be discarded whenever the camshaft cover has been removed from the cylinder head.**

6. Remove the camshaft cover seal and grommets.

7. Discard the seal and grommets

To install:

8. Install the EN 46101 guide (1) onto the spark plug tubes of the right cylinder head.

9. Install the camshaft cover bolt grommets prior to installing the camshaft cover bolts.

10. Wipe the camshaft cover sealing surface on the cylinder head with a clean, lint-free cloth.

11. Place a bead 0.3150 inch (8 mm) in diameter by 0.1575 inch (4 mm) in height of RTV sealant on the engine front cover split lines (1).

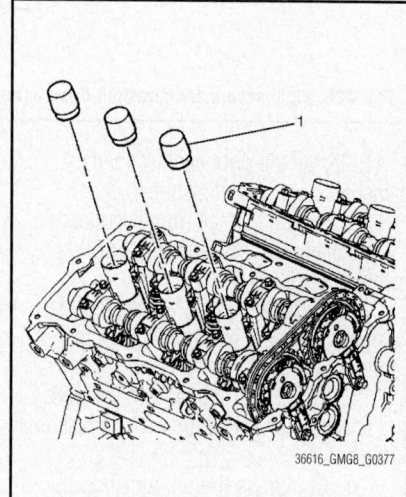

Fig. 231 EN 46101 guide tool location—3.6L Engine

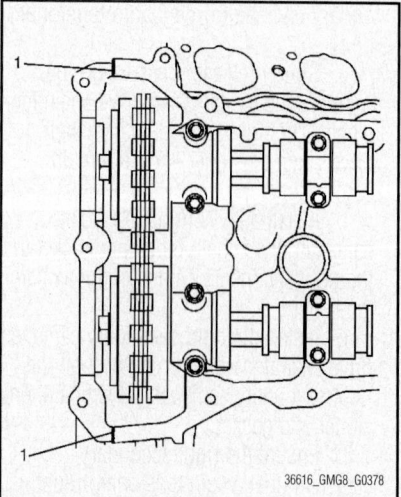

Fig. 232 RTV sealant location (1)—3.6L Engine

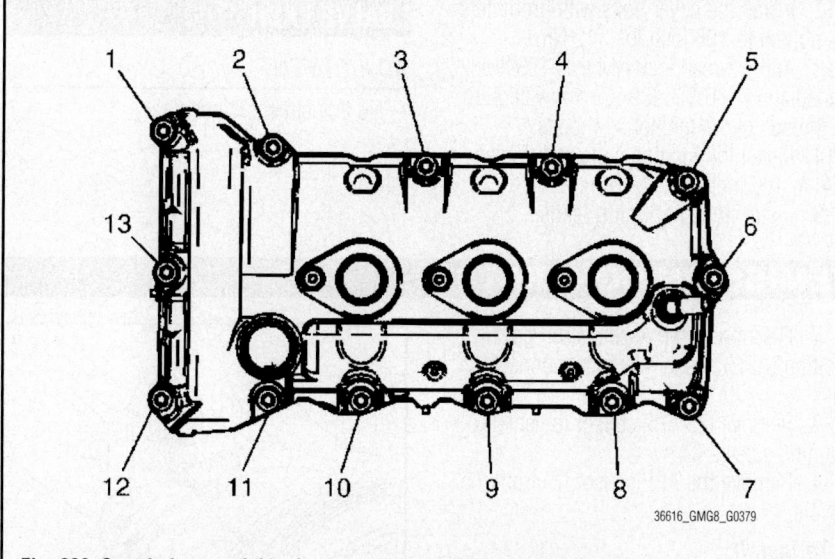

Fig. 233 Camshaft cover tightening sequence right side—3.6L Engine

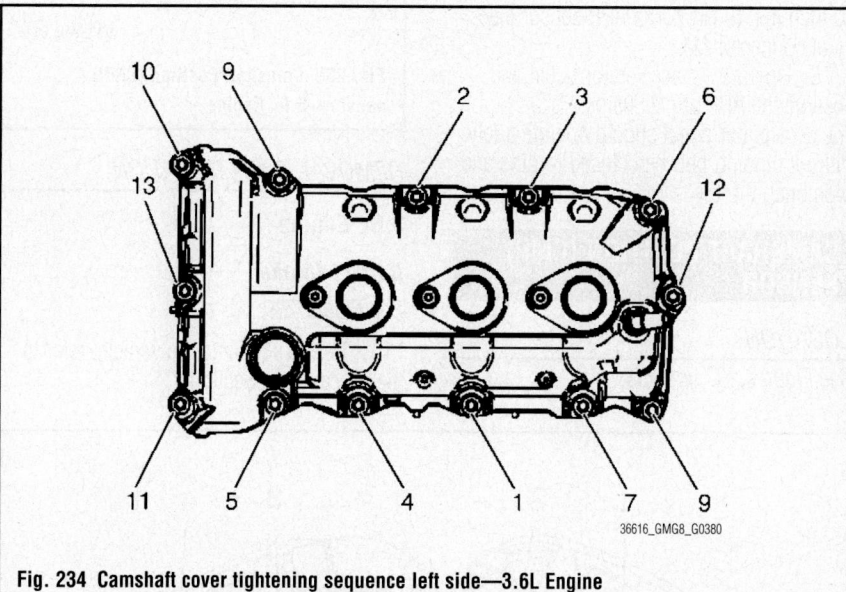

Fig. 234 Camshaft cover tightening sequence left side—3.6L Engine

6.0L Engine

See Figure 235.

1. Before servicing the vehicle, refer to the Precautions Section.

2. Remove the spark plug leads.

➡Do not remove the oil fill tube from the cover, unless service is required. If the oil fill tube has been removed from the cover, install a NEW tube during assembly (Right side only).

3. Remove the ignition coil and bracket assembly. Refer to Ignition Coil in Engine Electrical.

4. Remove the valve rocker arm cover retaining bolts (2) and valve rocker arm cover (1).

5. Remove and discard the valve rocker arm cover gasket, valve rocker arm cover grommets and valve rocker arm cover bolts if they are serviced with the grommet.

➡The valve rocker arm cover gasket is a single use only component and must be replaced whenever the valve rocker arm cover is removed from the cylinder head.

6. Remove the valve rocker arm cover gasket.

7. Discard the valve rocker arm cover gasket.

To install:

➡All gasket surfaces should be free of oil or other foreign material during assembly. DO NOT use the valve rocker arm cover gasket again.

8. Install NEW valve rocker arm cover grommets and use NEW valve rocker arm cover bolts if they are serviced with the grommet.

12. Place the camshaft cover into position onto the cylinder head.

13. Loosely install the camshaft cover bolts.

14. Tighten the camshaft cover to cylinder head retaining bolts in the sequence shown and tighten in sequence to 89 inch lbs. (10 Nm).

15. Remove the EN 46101 guide from the spark plug tubes of the cylinder head.

16. Install the NEW spark plugs and tighten to 15 ft. lbs. (20 Nm).

➡DO NOT damage the spark plug and/or the seal in the left camshaft cover or an engine misfire condition may result.

17. Install the ignition coils.

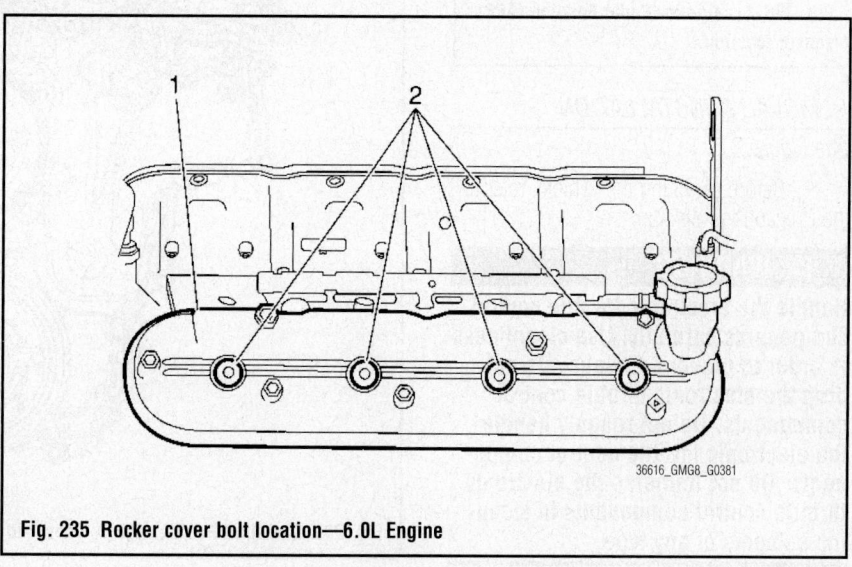

Fig. 235 Rocker cover bolt location—6.0L Engine

9. Install a NEW gasket into the valve rocker arm cover.

10. Install a NEW oil fill tube and seal to the valve rocker arm cover (Right side only).

11. Install the valve rocker arm cover onto the cylinder head.

12. Install the cover bolts with grommets and tighten to 106 inch lbs. (12 Nm).

13. Apply thread lock GM P/N 12345382 (Canadian P/N 10953489), or equivalent, to the threads of the ignition coil bolts.

14. Install the ignition coils and tighten bolts to 106 inch lbs. (12 Nm).

15. Install the spark plug leads.

VALVE LASH

ADJUSTMENT

No adjustment is necessary.

ENGINE PERFORMANCE & EMISSION CONTROLS

ACCELERATOR PEDAL POSITION (APP) SENSOR

LOCATION

See Figure 236.

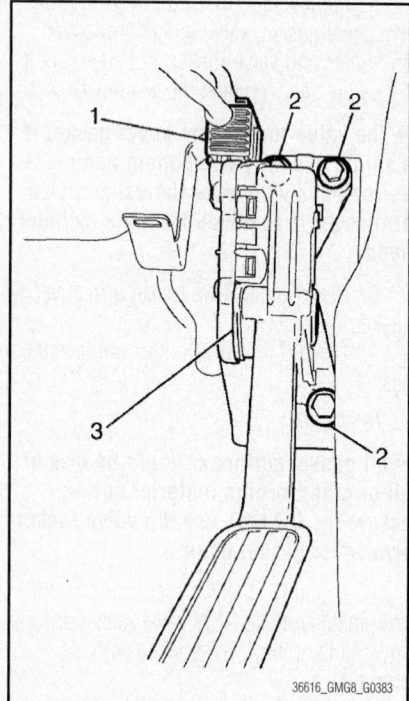

Fig. 236 Accelerator Pedal Position (APP) sensor location

REMOVAL & INSTALLATION

See Figure 236.

1. Before servicing the vehicle, refer to the Precautions Section.

✳✳ WARNING

Handle the electronic throttle control components carefully. Use cleanliness in order to prevent damage. Do not drop the electronic throttle control components. Do not roughly handle the electronic throttle control components. Do not immerse the electronic throttle control components in cleaning solvents of any type.

2. Disconnect the Accelerator Pedal Position (APP) sensor electrical connector (1).

3. Remove the APP sensor to vehicle retaining screws (2).

4. Remove the APP sensor (3) from the vehicle.

To install:

5. Install the APP sensor (3) to the vehicle and tighten the bracket screws (2) to 80 inch lbs. (9 Nm). The APP sensor electrical connector (1).

6. Operate the accelerator pedal and observe the APP angles using a scan tool. The accelerator pedal should operate freely, without binding between closed throttle and wide open throttle.

CAMSHAFT POSITION (CMP) SENSOR

LOCATION

See Figures 237 and 238.

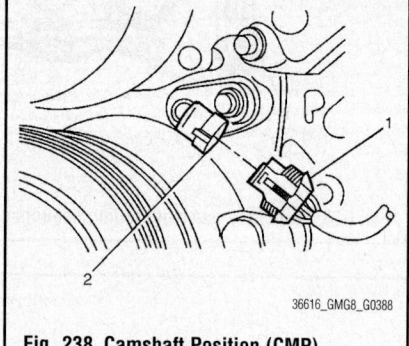

Fig. 238 Camshaft Position (CMP) sensor—6.0L Engine

REMOVAL & INSTALLATION

3.6L Engine

Bank 1 Intake

See Figure 239.

1. Before servicing the vehicle, refer to the Precautions Section.

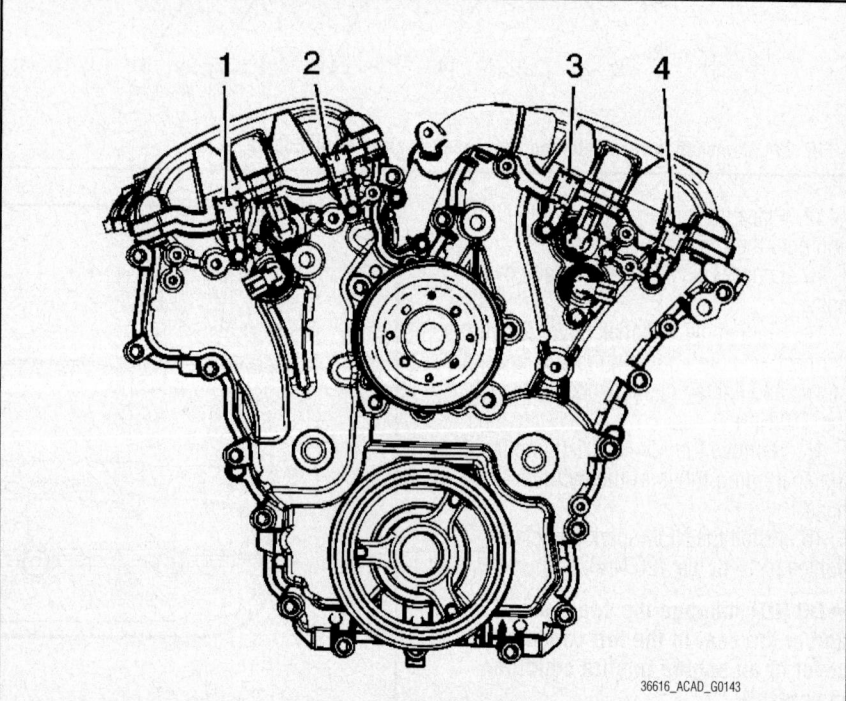

Fig. 237 Camshaft Position (CMP) sensor locations—3.6L Engine

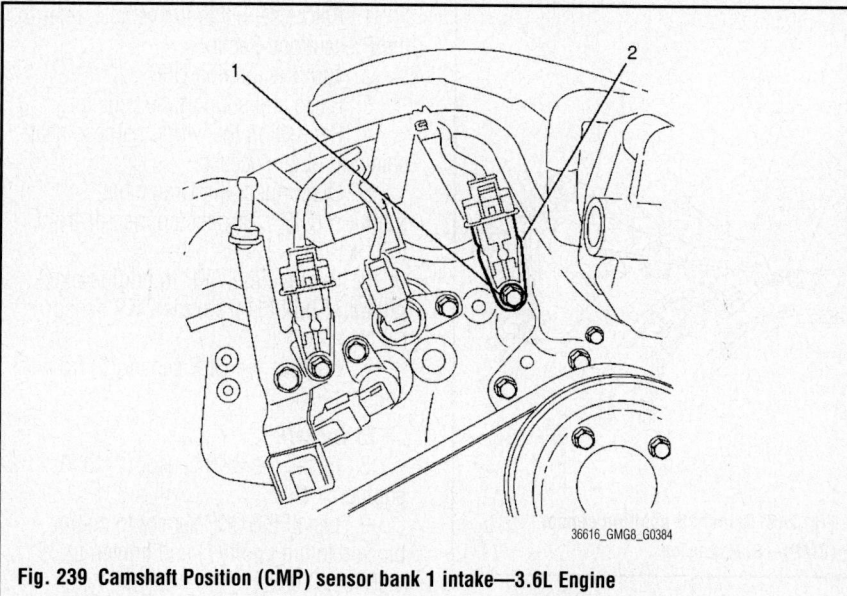

Fig. 239 Camshaft Position (CMP) sensor bank 1 intake—3.6L Engine

2. Turn the ignition OFF.

3. Remove the Camshaft Position (CMP) sensor electrical connector (1) from the CMP sensor (2).

4. Remove the CMP sensor to engine front cover retaining bolt (1).

5. Remove the CMP sensor from the engine front cover (2).

To install:

6. Install the CMP sensor (2) to the engine front cover.

7. Install the CMP sensor to engine front cover retaining bolt (1) and tighten to 89 inch lbs. (10 Nm).

8. Install the CMP sensor electrical connector (1) to the CMP sensor.

Bank 1 Exhaust

See Figure 240.

1. Before servicing the vehicle, refer to the Precautions Section.

2. Turn the ignition OFF.

3. Remove the remote earth post bracket to engine front cover retaining bolts and reposition the remote earth post bracket in order to provide access.

4. Remove the Camshaft Position (CMP) sensor electrical connector (1) from the CMP sensor (2).

5. Remove the CMP sensor to engine front cover retaining bolt (1).

6. Remove the CMP sensor from the engine front cover (2).

To install:

7. Install the CMP sensor (2) to the engine front cover.

8. Install the CMP sensor to engine

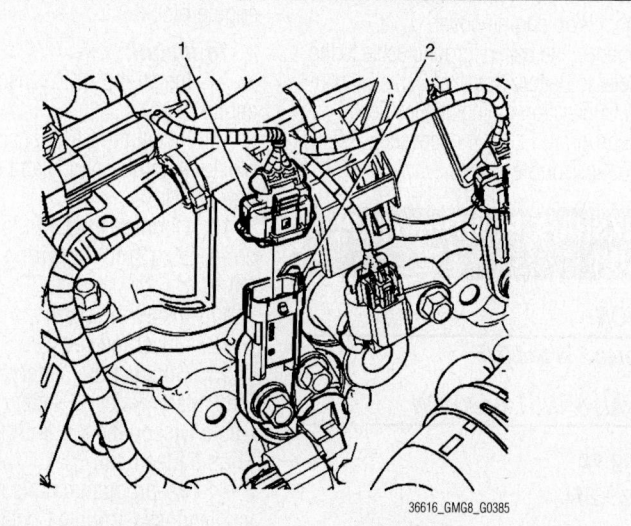

Fig. 240 Camshaft position (CMP) sensor bank 1 exhaust—3.6L Engine

front cover retaining bolt (1) and tighten to 89 inch lbs. (10 Nm).

9. Install the CMP sensor electrical connector (1) to the CMP sensor.

10. Install the remote earth post bracket to engine front cover retaining bolts and tighten to 89 inch lbs. (10 Nm).

Bank 2 Intake

See Figure 241.

1. Before servicing the vehicle, refer to the Precautions Section.

2. Turn the ignition OFF.

3. Remove the power steering fluid reservoir bolts and reposition the power steering fluid reservoir in order to provide access. Refer to Power Steering Reservoir in Steering.

4. Remove the Camshaft Position (CMP) sensor electrical connector (1) from the CMP sensor (2).

5. Remove the CMP sensor to engine front cover retaining bolt (1).

6. Remove the CMP sensor from the engine front cover (2).

To install:

7. Install the CMP sensor (2) to the engine front cover.

8. Install the CMP sensor to engine front cover retaining bolt (1) and tighten to 89 inch lbs. (10 Nm).

9. Install the CMP sensor electrical connector (1) to the CMP sensor.

10. Install the power steering fluid reservoir.

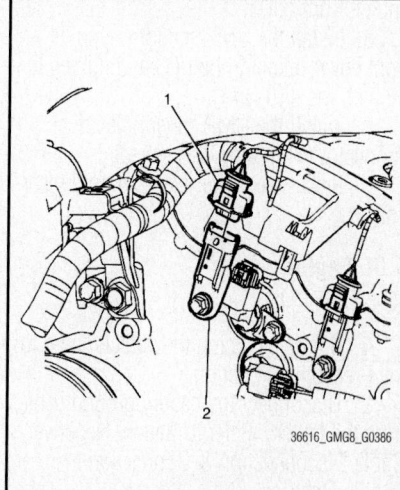

Fig. 241 Camshaft position (CMP) sensor bank 2 intake—3.6L Engine

Bank 2 Exhaust

See Figure 242.

1. Before servicing the vehicle, refer to the Precautions Section.

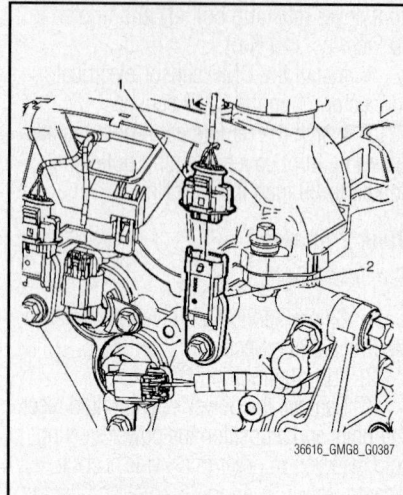

Fig. 242 Camshaft position sensor (CMP) bank 2 exhaust—3.6L Engine

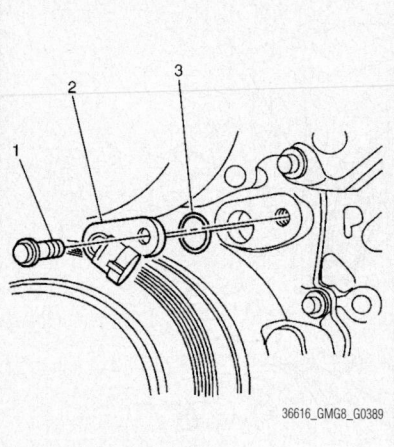

Fig. 243 Camshaft position sensor (CMP)—6.0L Engine

2. Turn the ignition OFF.

3. Remove the power steering fluid reservoir bolts and reposition the power steering fluid reservoir in order to provide access. Refer to Power Steering Reservoir in Steering.

4. Remove the Camshaft Position (CMP) sensor electrical connector (1) from the CMP sensor (2).

5. Remove the CMP sensor to engine front cover retaining bolt (1).

6. Remove the CMP sensor from the engine front cover (2).

To install:

7. Install the CMP sensor (2) to the engine front cover.

8. Install the CMP sensor to engine front cover retaining bolt (1) and tighten to 89 inch lbs. (10 Nm).

9. Install the CMP sensor electrical connector (1) to the CMP sensor.

10. Install the power steering fluid reservoir.

6.0L Engine

See Figure 243.

1. Before servicing the vehicle, refer to the Precautions Section.

2. Disconnect the battery ground cable from the battery. Refer to Battery Negative Cable Disconnection & Connection in Engine Electrical.

3. Remove the engine cover. Refer to Engine Cover.

4. Disconnect the Camshaft Position (CMP) sensor electrical connector (1).

5. Remove the CMP sensor to engine front cover retaining bolt (1).

6. Remove the CMP sensor (2) from the engine front cover.

7. Remove the CMP sensor O-ring (3) from the CMP sensor and discard.

8. Discard the O-ring.

To install:

➡ **Install a NEW O-ring to the camshaft sensor**

➡ **Before installing the camshaft sensor, apply a small amount of clean motor oil to the O-ring (3).**

9. Install a NEW O-ring (3) to the CMP sensor.

10. Install the CMP sensor (2) to the engine front cover.

11. Install the CMP sensor to engine front cover retaining bolt (1) and tighten to 80 inch lbs. (9 Nm).

12. Connect the CMP sensor electrical connector (1) to wiring harness.

13. Install the engine cover.

14. Connect the battery ground cable to the battery. Refer to Battery Negative Cable Disconnection & Connection in Engine Electrical.

15. Reprogram ECM, if necessary. Refer to Diagnostic Trouble Codes.

CRANKSHAFT POSITION (CKP) SENSOR

LOCATION

See Figures 244 and 245.

REMOVAL & INSTALLATION

3.6L Engine

See Figure 244.

1. Before servicing the vehicle, refer to the Precautions Section.

2. Turn the ignition OFF.

3. Raise and support the vehicle.

4. Reposition the wiring harness heat shield to obtain access.

5. Disconnect the Crankshaft Position (CKP) harness connector from the CKP.

6. Remove the CKP to engine block retaining bolt (1) from the CKP sensor (2).

7. Remove the CKP sensor (2) from the engine block.

To install:

8. Install the CKP sensor (2) to the engine block.

9. Install the CKP sensor to engine block retaining bolt (1) and tighten to 89 inch lbs. (10 Nm).

10. Connect the CKP electrical connector (3) to the CKP sensor.

11. Lower the vehicle.

6.0L Engine

See Figure 245.

1. Before servicing the vehicle, refer to the Precautions Section.

2. Disconnect the battery ground cable from the battery. Refer to Battery Negative Cable Disconnection & Connection in Engine Electrical.

3. Raise and support the vehicle.

4. Remove the starter. Refer to Starter in Engine Electrical.

5. Disconnect the Crankshaft Position (CKP) sensor electrical connector (2) from the wiring harness (1).

6. Remove the CKP sensor to engine block retaining bolt (1).

7. Remove the CKP sensor (2) from the engine block.

To install:

8. Install the CKP sensor (2) to the engine block.

9. Install the CKP sensor to engine block retaining bolt (1) and tighten to 18 ft. lbs. (25 Nm).

10. Connect the CKP sensor electrical connector (2) to the wiring harness (1).

11. Install the starter.

12. Lower the vehicle.

13. Connect the battery ground cable to the battery. Refer to Battery Negative Cable Disconnection & Connection in Engine Electrical.

14. Re-programming is required. Refer to Diagnostic Trouble Codes.

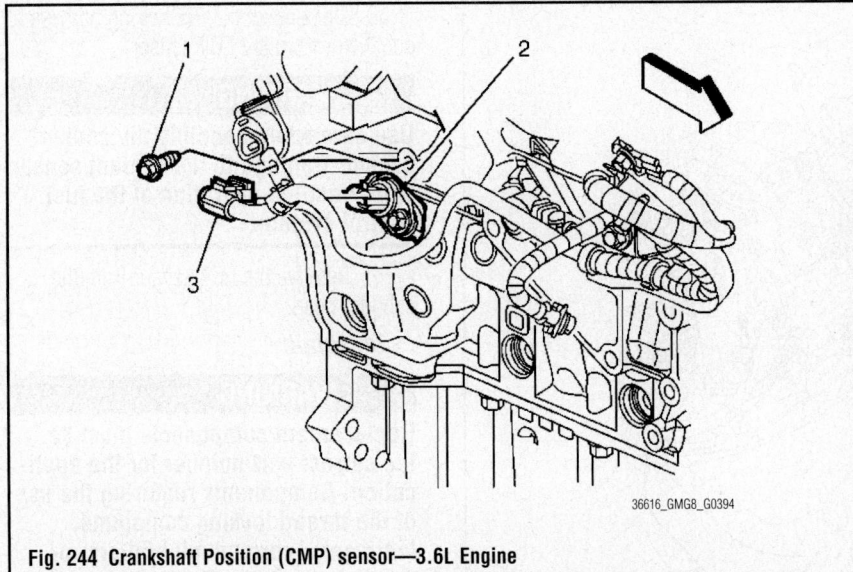

36616_GMG8_G0394

Fig. 244 Crankshaft Position (CMP) sensor—3.6L Engine

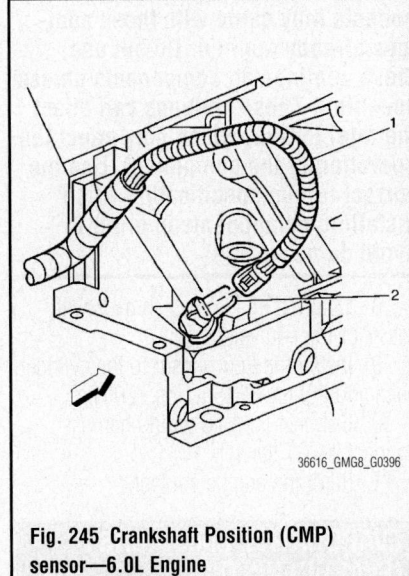

36616_GMG8_G0396

Fig. 245 Crankshaft Position (CMP) sensor—6.0L Engine

ELECTRONIC CONTROL MODULE (ECM)

REMOVAL & INSTALLATION

Pre-removal

1. Before servicing the vehicle, refer to the Precautions Section.

➡**Reprogramming the ECM requires a proprietary Service Programming System.**

➡**It is necessary to record the remaining engine oil life. If the replacement module is not programmed with the remaining engine oil life, the engine oil life will default to 100%. If the replacement module is not programmed with the remaining engine oil**

life, the engine oil will need to be changed at 5000 km (3,000 mi) from the last engine oil change.

2. Using a scan tool, retrieve the percentage of remaining engine oil and the remaining automatic transmission fluid life. Record the remaining engine oil and the remaining automatic transmission fluid life.

3. If the engine control module (ECM) is replaced, the following procedures must be performed:

➡**When replacing the ECM, the ECM must be reset prior to removal. Failure to perform this procedure will result in the inability to:**

- Test the ECM for warranty purposes.
- Install the ECM into other vehicles.
- ECM reset procedure.
- ECM reprogramming
- Theft Deterrent programming

Removal

1. Before servicing the vehicle, refer to the Precautions Section.

✳✳ CAUTION

Always turn the ignition off when installing or removing the ECM connectors in order to prevent damage to the components.

2. Turn the ignition OFF.
3. Disconnect the battery negative cable. Refer to Battery Negative Cable Disconnection & Connection in Engine Electrical.

➡**Disconnect the rear electrical connector from the ECM first.**

4. Unlock the ECM electrical connector lock levers and disconnect the ECM electrical connectors.

5. Remove the ECM from the ECM housing by pushing both ECM retaining clips outwards.

To install:

6. Install the ECM to the ECM housing. Ensure the ECM retaining clips are located correctly.

7. Connect the ECM electrical connectors and lock the connector lock levers into place.

8. Connect the battery negative cable to the battery. Refer to Battery Negative Cable Disconnection & Connection in Engine Electrical.

9. Program the ECM. Reprogramming the ECM requires a proprietary Service Programming System.

➡**If you encounter an ECM programming error, with a display message of "Starting Disabled, Remove Key" on the driver information center, with a diagnostic test code (DTC) of P1631, perform the "10-Minute Relearn Procedure". Theft Deterrent Control Module Programming and Setup requires a proprietary Service Programming System.**

10. Turn OFF the ignition for at least 5 seconds after the programming event is complete.

11. Perform the throttle learn procedure. Refer to Throttle/Idle Learn.

12. Use the scan tool to clear all DTCs.

RESET

Reprogramming the ECM requires a proprietary Service Programming System.

ENGINE COOLANT TEMPERATURE (ECT) SENSOR

LOCATION

See Figures 246 and 247.

REMOVAL & INSTALLATION

3.6L Engine

See Figure 246.

1. Before servicing the vehicle, refer to the Precautions Section.

2. Turn the ignition OFF.

3. Remove the engine coolant temperature sensor harness connector (1) from the coolant temperature sensor (2).

4. Remove the engine coolant temperature sensor (1) from the engine (2).

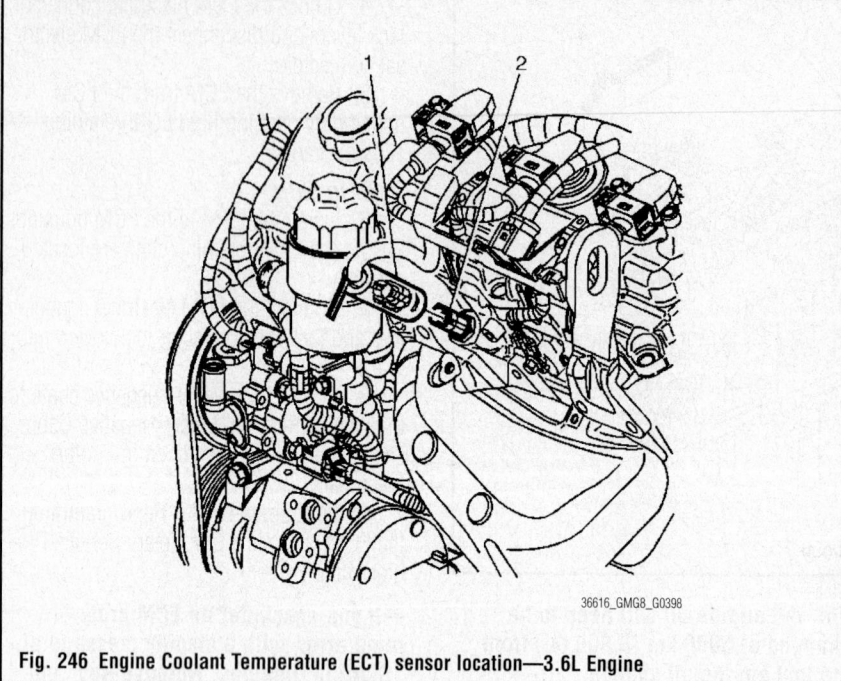

36616_GMG8_G0398

Fig. 246 Engine Coolant Temperature (ECT) sensor location—3.6L Engine

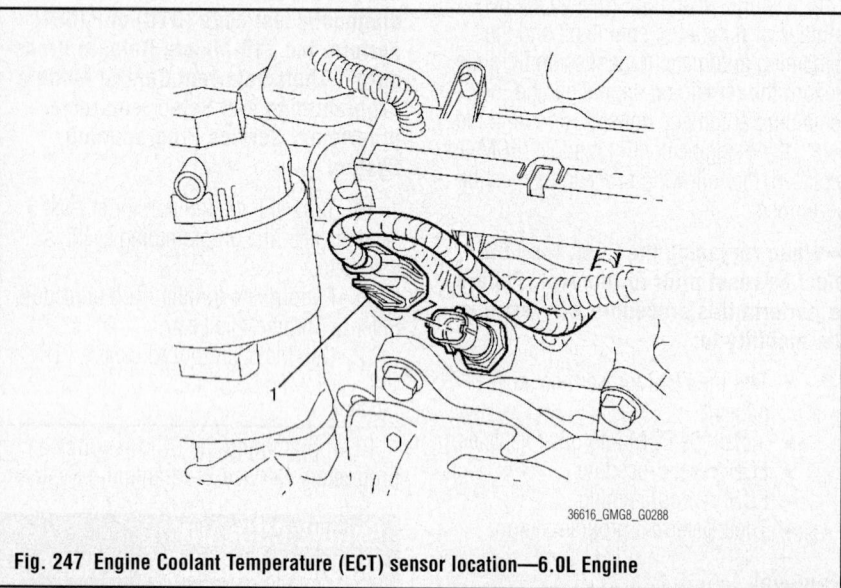

36616_GMG8_G0288

Fig. 247 Engine Coolant Temperature (ECT) sensor location—6.0L Engine

To install:

5. Install the coolant temperature sensor (1) to the engine and tighten to 15 ft. lbs. (20 Nm).

6. Install the coolant temperature sensor electrical connector (1) to the coolant temperature sensor.

7. Inspect and fill the cooling system as necessary.

6.0L Engine

See Figure 247.

1. Before servicing the vehicle, refer to the Precautions Section.

2. Turn OFF the ignition.

✻✻ CAUTION

To avoid any vehicle damage, serious personal injury or death when major components are removed from the vehicle and the vehicle is supported by a hoist, support the vehicle with jack stands at the opposite end from which the components are being removed and strap the vehicle to the hoist.

3. Raise the vehicle.

4. Drain the engine coolant below the level of the engine coolant temperature (ECT) sensor.

5. Lower the vehicle.

6. Disconnect the ETC wiring harness connector from the ECT sensor.

✻✻ WARNING

Use care when handling the coolant sensor. Damage to the coolant sensor will affect the operation of the fuel control system.

7. Remove the ECT sensor from the cylinder head.

To install:

✻✻ WARNING

Replacement components must be the correct part number for the application. Components requiring the use of the thread locking compound, lubricants, corrosion inhibitors, or sealants are identified in the service procedure. Some replacement components may come with these coatings already applied. Do not use these coatings on components unless specified. These coatings can affect the final torque, which may affect the operation of the component. Use the correct torque specification when installing components in order to avoid damage.

8. Coat the ECT sensor threads with sealer or the equivalent.

9. Install the ECT sensor to the cylinder head and tighten to 15 ft. lbs. (20 Nm).

10. Connect the ETC wiring harness connector ECT sensor.

11. Refill the engine coolant.

EVAPORATIVE EMISSIONS (EVAP) CANISTER

LOCATION

See Figure 248.

REMOVAL & INSTALLATION

See Figure 248.

1. Before servicing the vehicle, refer to the Precautions Section.

2. Remove the fuel tank assembly. Refer to Fuel Tank in Fuel System.

3. Support the evaporative (EVAP) emission canister assembly (1).

4. Remove the EVAP emission canister assembly to chassis retaining bolts (2).

5. Remove the EVAP emission canister assembly (1) from the vehicle.

To install:

6. Install the NEW EVAP emission canister assembly (1) to the vehicle.

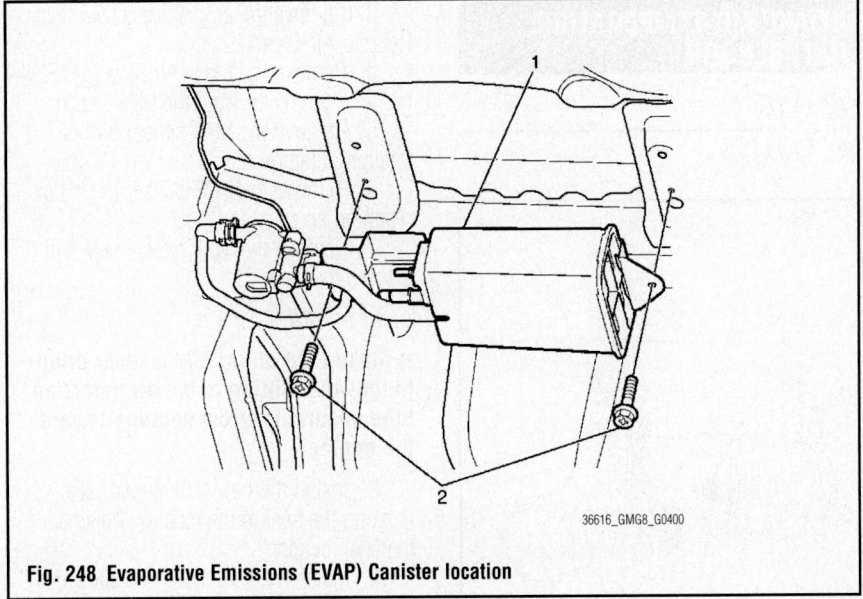

Fig. 248 Evaporative Emissions (EVAP) Canister location

7. Support the EVAP emission canister assembly (1).

8. Install the EVAP emission canister assembly to chassis retaining bolts (2) and tighten to 53 inch lbs. (6 Nm).

9. Install the fuel tank assembly.

HEATED OXYGEN (HO2S) SENSOR

LOCATION

See Figures 249 through 254.

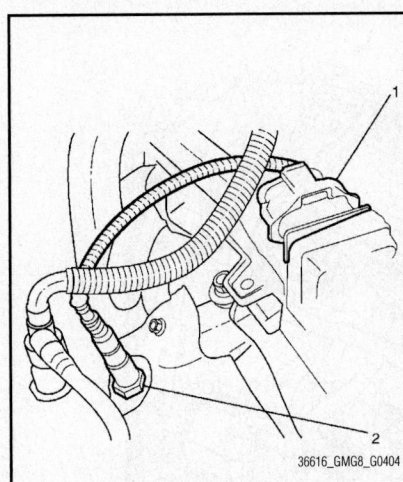

Fig. 249 Heated Oxygen (HO2S) Sensor Bank 1 Sensor 1—3.6L Engine

REMOVAL & INSTALLATION

Sensor 1

1. Before servicing the vehicle, refer to the Precautions Section.

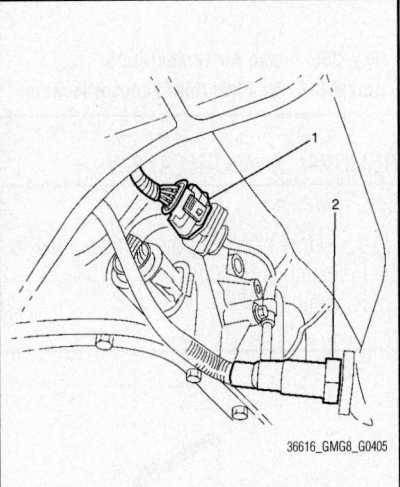

Fig. 250 Heated Oxygen (HO2S) Sensor Bank 1 Sensor 2—3.6L & 6.0L Engines

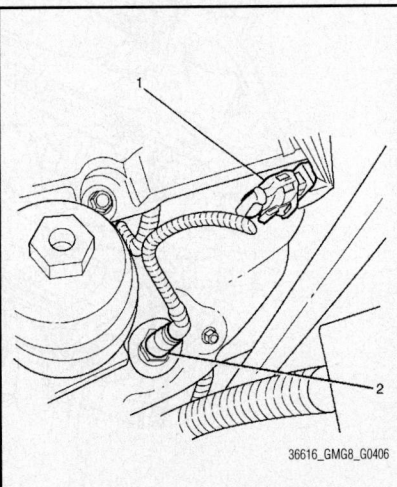

Fig. 251 Heated Oxygen (HO2S) Sensor Bank 2 Sensor 1—3.6L Engine

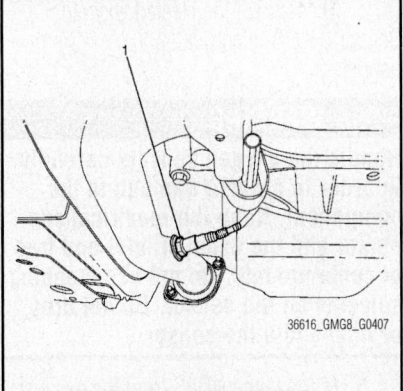

Fig. 252 Heated Oxygen (HO2S) Sensor Bank 2 Sensor 2—3.6L & 6.0L Engines

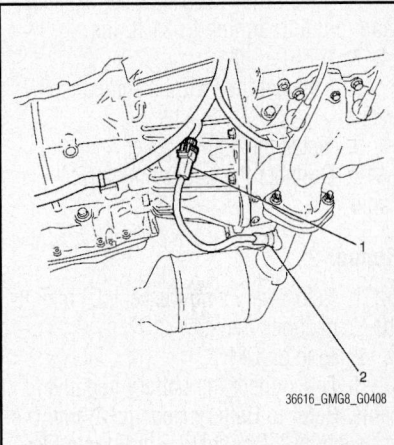

Fig. 253 Heated Oxygen (HO2S) Sensor Bank 1 Sensor 1—6.0L Engine

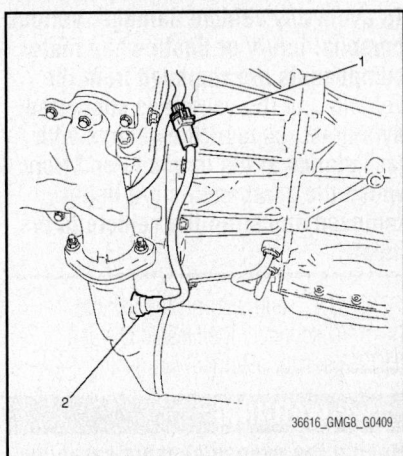

Fig. 254 Heated Oxygen (HO2S) Sensor Bank 2 Sensor 1—6.0L Engine

2. Ignition OFF.

3. Disconnect the battery negative cable. Refer to Battery Negative Cable Disconnection & Connection in Engine Electrical.

4. Remove the engine cover, if necessary. Refer to Engine Cover.

5. Disconnect the Heated Oxygen Sensor (HO2S) electrical connector.

✳✳ WARNING

Handle the oxygen sensors carefully in order to prevent damage to the component. Keep the electrical connector and the exhaust inlet end free of contaminants. Do not use cleaning solvents on the sensor. Do not drop or mishandle the sensor.

6. Remove the HO2S from the exhaust manifold.

To install:

7. Install the HO2S into the exhaust manifold and tighten to 31 ft. lbs. (42 Nm).
8. Connect the HO2S electrical connector.
9. Install the engine cover.
10. Connect the battery negative cable.

Sensor 2

1. Before servicing the vehicle, refer to the Precautions Section.
2. Ignition OFF.
3. Disconnect the battery negative cable. Refer to Battery Negative Cable Disconnection & Connection in Engine Electrical.

✳✳ CAUTION

To avoid any vehicle damage, serious personal injury or death when major components are removed from the vehicle and the vehicle is supported by a hoist, support the vehicle with jack stands at the opposite end from which the components are being removed and strap the vehicle to the hoist.

4. Raise and support the vehicle.
5. Disconnect the Heated Oxygen (HO2S) sensor electrical connector.

✳✳ WARNING

Handle the oxygen sensors carefully in order to prevent damage to the component. Keep the electrical connector and the exhaust inlet end free of contaminants. Do not use cleaning solvents on the sensor. Do not drop or mishandle the sensor.

6. Remove the HO2S from the exhaust crossover pipe assembly.

INTAKE AIR TEMPERATURE (IAT) SENSOR

LOCATION

See Figure 255.

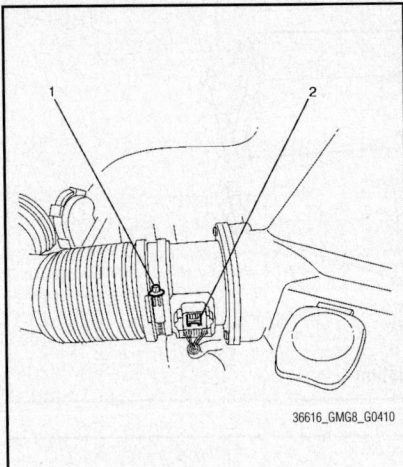

36616_GMG8_G0410

Fig. 255 Intake Air Temperature (IAT)/Mass Air Flow (MAF) sensor location

REMOVAL & INSTALLATION

See Figure 255.

1. Before servicing the vehicle, refer to the Precautions Section.
2. Ignition OFF.

3. Remove the air cleaner intake duct. Refer to Air Cleaner.
4. Remove the Mass Air Flow (MAF) harness connector from the MAF sensor.
5. Remove the MAF sensor air box retaining clamps.
6. Remove the MAF sensor to air box retaining screws.
7. Remove the MAF sensor seal and discard the seal.

To install:

➡**Make note of the MAF sensor orientation when fitting to the air induction tube ensuring, arrow pointing toward the engine.**

8. Install the new MAF sensor seal locating the seal in the location holes and the MAF sensor.
9. Install the MAF sensor to air box retaining screws and tighten to 35 inch lbs. (4 Nm).
10. Install the air cleaner intake duct.
11. Install the mass air flow (MAF) harness connector.
12. Install the MAF sensor clamps to the MAF sensor.

KNOCK SENSOR (KS)

LOCATION

See Figures 256 through 259.

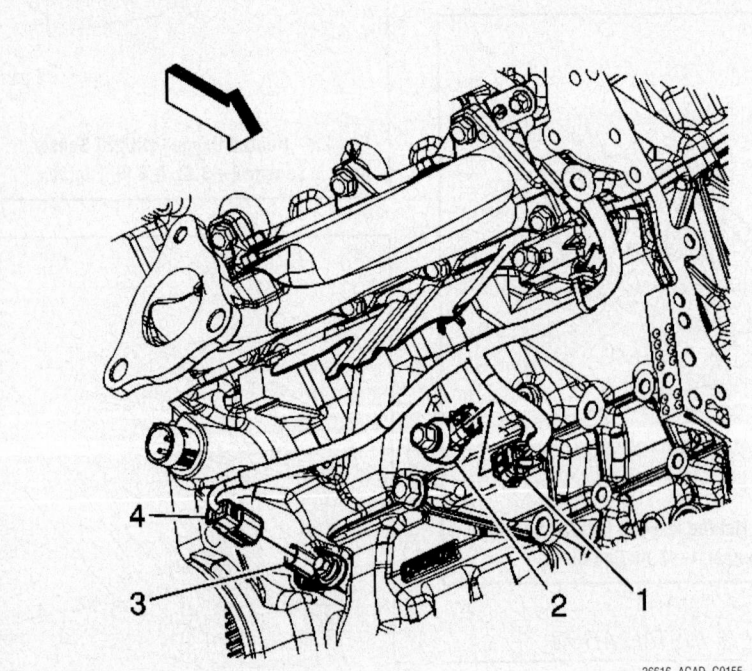

36616_ACAD_G0155

Fig. 256 Knock Sensor (KS) location bank 1—3.6L Engine

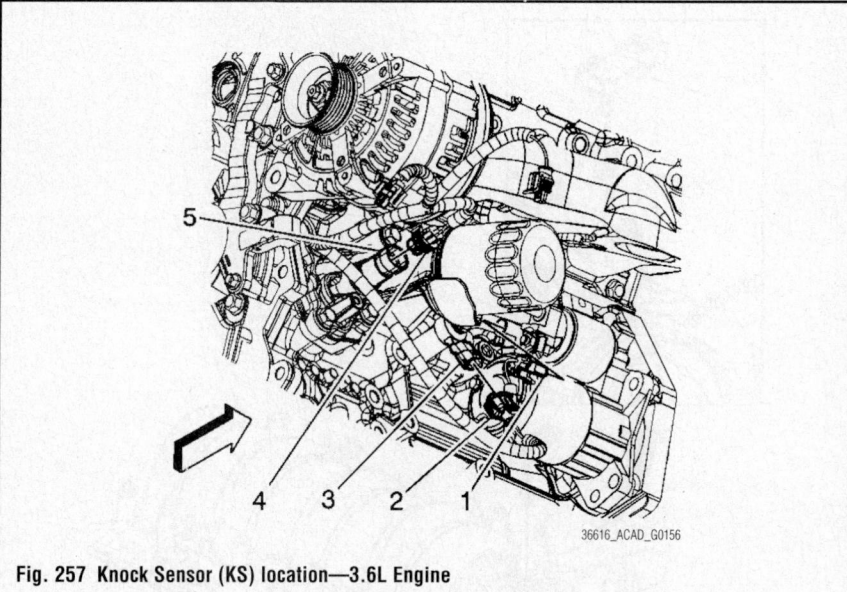

Fig. 257 Knock Sensor (KS) location—3.6L Engine

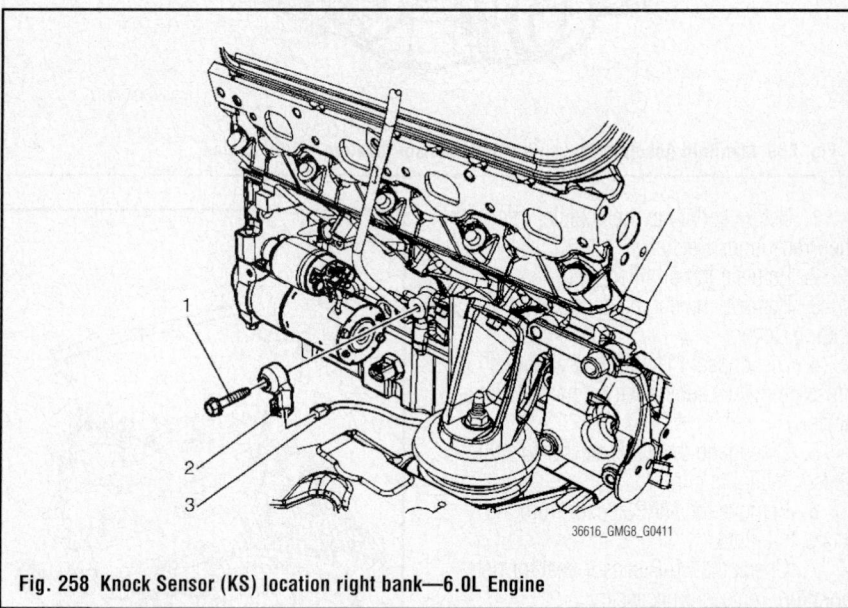

Fig. 258 Knock Sensor (KS) location right bank—6.0L Engine

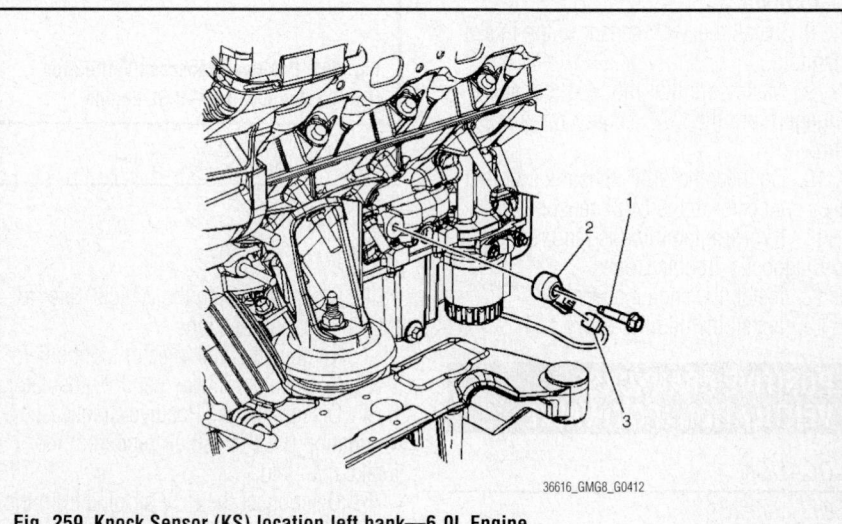

Fig. 259 Knock Sensor (KS) location left bank—6.0L Engine

REMOVAL & INSTALLATION

3.6L Engine

Bank 1

See Figure 256.

1. Before servicing the vehicle, refer to the Precautions Section.

2. Disconnect the negative battery cable.

3. Remove the exhaust manifold lower heat shield.

4. Disconnect the engine wiring harness electrical connector from the Knock Sensor (KS).

5. Remove the knock sensor bolt and sensor.

To install:

6. Installation is the reverse of removal. Tighten the KS bolt to 17 ft. lbs. (23 Nm).

Bank 2

See Figure 257.

1. Before servicing the vehicle, refer to the Precautions Section.

2. Disconnect the negative battery cable.

3. Raise and support the vehicle.

4. Remove the engine oil filter.

5. Lower the vehicle.

6. Disconnect the engine wiring harness electrical connector from the Knock Sensor (KS).

7. Remove the knock sensor bolt and sensor.

To install:

8. Installation is the reverse of removal. Tighten the KS bolt to 17 ft. lbs. (23 Nm).

9. Install a new oil filter.

6.0L Engine

Right Bank

See Figure 258.

1. Before servicing the vehicle, refer to the Precautions Section.

2. Disconnect the battery ground cable from the battery. Refer to Battery Negative Cable Disconnection & Connection in Engine Electrical.

3. Raise and support the vehicle.

4. Remove the starter motor. Refer to Starter in Engine Electrical.

5. Disconnect the engine wiring harness (3) from the knock sensor (2).

6. Remove the knock sensor to engine block retaining bolt (1).

7. Remove the knock sensor (2) from the engine block.

To install:

8. Connect the engine wiring harness (3) to the knock sensor (2).

9. Position the knock sensor (2) on the engine block.

10. Install the knock sensor to engine block retaining bolt (1) and tighten to 15 ft. lbs. (20 Nm).

11. Install the starter motor.

12. Connect the battery ground cable to the battery.

Left Bank

See Figure 259.

1. Before servicing the vehicle, refer to the Precautions Section.

2. Disconnect the battery ground cable from the battery. Refer to Battery Negative Cable Disconnection & Connection in Engine Electrical.

3. Raise and support the vehicle.

4. Disconnect the engine wiring harness (3) from the knock sensor (2).

5. Remove the knock sensor to engine block retaining bolt (1).

6. Remove the knock sensor (2) from the engine block.

To install:

7. Connect the engine wiring harness (3) to the knock sensor (2).

8. Position the knock sensor (2) on the engine block.

9. Install the knock sensor to engine block retaining bolt (1) and tighten to 15 ft. lbs. (20 Nm).

10. Connect the battery ground cable to the battery.

MALFUNCTION INDICATOR LIGHT (MIL)

RESET PROCEDURE

Clearing Diagnostic Trouble Codes, resets MIL.

MASS AIR FLOW (MAF) SENSOR

LOCATION

Refer to Intake Air Temperature Sensor.

REMOVAL & INSTALLATION

Refer to Intake Air Temperature Sensor

MANIFOLD ABSOLUTE PRESSURE (MAP) SENSOR

LOCATION

See Figure 260.

REMOVAL & INSTALLATION

See Figure 260.

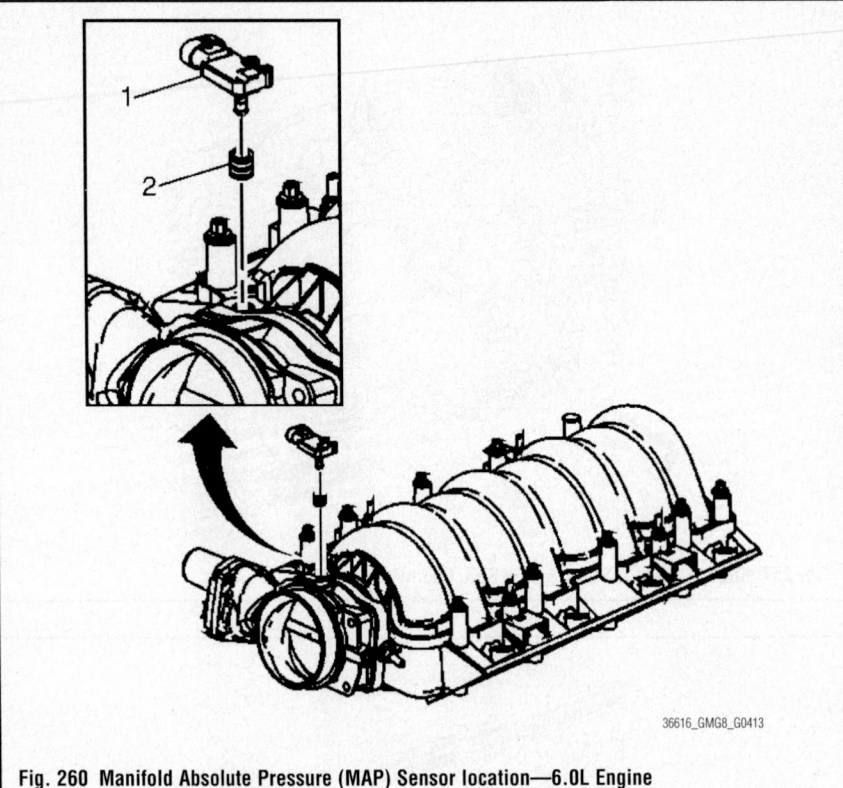

Fig. 260 Manifold Absolute Pressure (MAP) Sensor location—6.0L Engine

1. Before servicing the vehicle, refer to the Precautions Section.

2. Remove the oil filler cap.

3. Remove the engine cover. Refer to Engine Cover.

4. Disconnect the manifold absolute pressure (MAP) sensor wiring harness connector.

5. Disengage the MAP sensor to MAP sensor retaining clip.

6. Remove the MAP sensor from the intake manifold.

7. Check the MAP sensor seal for deterioration, replace if necessary.

To install:

8. Install the MAP sensor to the intake manifold.

9. Make sure that the MAP sensor is engaged into the MAP sensor retaining clip.

10. Connect the MAP sensor wiring harness connector to the MAP sensor.

11. If re-programming is required. Refer to Diagnostic Trouble Codes.

12. Install the engine cover.

13. Install the oil filler cap.

POSITIVE CRANKCASE VENTILATION (PCV) VALVE

LOCATION

See Figure 261.

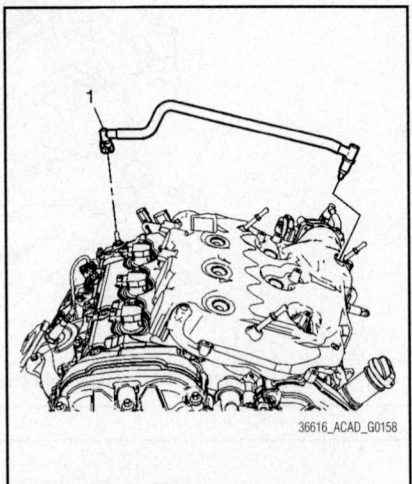

Fig. 261 Positive Crankcase Ventilation (PCV) Valve location—3.6L Engine

REMOVAL & INSTALLATION

3.6L Engine

See Figure 261.

1. Before servicing the vehicle, refer to the Precautions Section.

2. Remove the fuel injector sight shield.

3. Remove the intake manifold insulator.

4. Disconnect the Positive Crankcase Ventilation (PCV) fresh air pipe from the intake manifold.

5. Disconnect the PCV air pipe from the camshaft cover.

To install:

6. Connect the PCV air pipe to the camshaft cover valve.

7. Connect the PCV air pipe to the intake manifold.

8. Remove the intake manifold insulator.

9. Install the fuel injector sight shield.

THROTTLE ACTUATOR CONTROL (TAC)

LOCATION

See Figures 262 and 263.

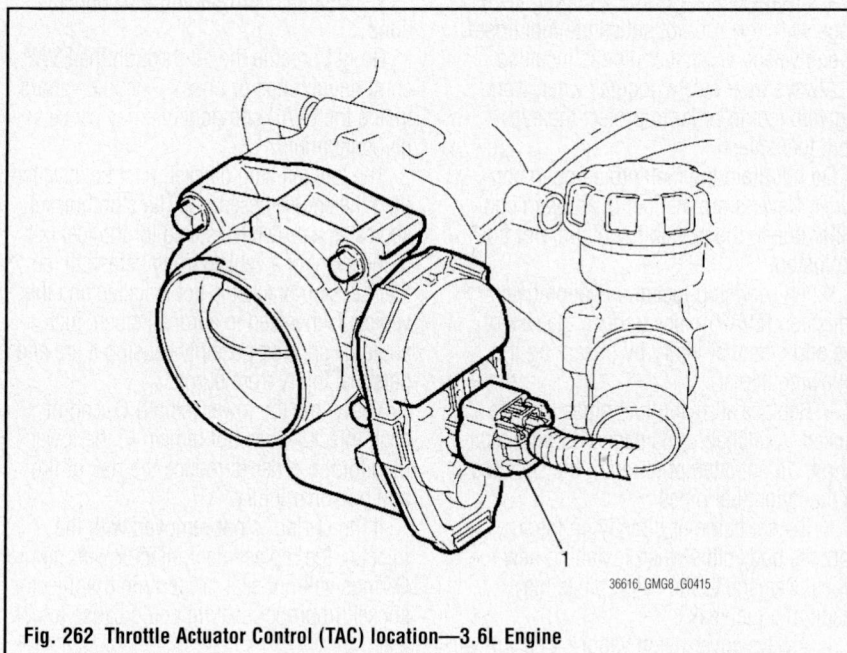

Fig. 262 Throttle Actuator Control (TAC) location—3.6L Engine

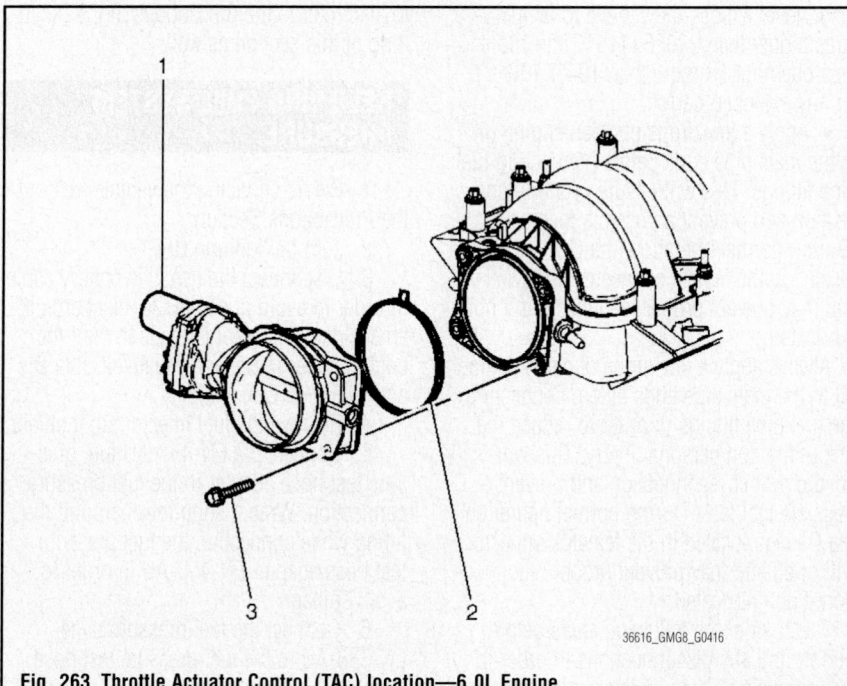

Fig. 263 Throttle Actuator Control (TAC) location—6.0L Engine

REMOVAL & INSTALLATION

See Figures 262 and 263.

1. Before servicing the vehicle, refer to the Precautions Section.

2. Remove the air intake duct. Refer to Air Cleaner.

> ※※ **WARNING**
>
> **Do not insert any tools into the throttle body bore in order to avoid damage to the throttle valve plate.**

> ※※ **WARNING**
>
> **Handle the electronic throttle control components carefully. Use cleanliness in order to prevent damage. Do not drop the electronic throttle control components. Do not roughly handle the electronic throttle control components. Do not immerse the electronic throttle control components in cleaning solvents of any type.**

➡ **The intake manifold, throttle body, fuel injection rail, and fuel injectors may be removed as an assembly. If not servicing the individual components, remove the manifold as a complete assembly.**

3. Remove the electrical wire harness connector from the throttle body.

4. Remove the throttle body to intake manifold retaining bolts.

5. Remove the throttle body.

➡ **The throttle body gasket is a single use part. The gasket must be discarded after removal.**

6. Remove the throttle body to intake manifold gasket, and discard.

7. Discard the throttle body gasket.

8. Clean the throttle body and intake manifold mating surfaces.

To install:

9. Install a new throttle body to intake manifold gasket. Align the locating tab of the gasket with the notch in the manifold.

10. Install the throttle body to the intake manifold.

11. Install the throttle body to intake manifold retaining bolts and tighten to 89 inch lbs. (10 Nm) for 3.6L engine, 106 inch lbs. (12 Nm) for 6.0L engine.

12. Install the electrical wire harness connector from the throttle body.

13. Install the air intake duct to the throttle body.

14. If re-programming is required.

THROTTLE LEARN

1. The following conditions must be met before performing relearn:

- DTCs P0121, P0122, P0123, P0221, P0222, P0223, P0638, P2100, P2101, P2105, and P2119 are not set.
- The engine speed is less than 40 RPM.
- The vehicle speed is 0 km/h (0 mph).

- The accelerator pedal position is less than 14.9 percent.
- The ignition 1 voltage is more than 10 volts.
- The engine coolant temperature is between 5–85°C (41–185°F).
- The intake air temperature is between 5–60°C (41–140°F).

➡Ensure the above conditions are met before performing with this procedure.

➡Do not perform this procedure if a throttle position (TP) sensor or other throttle actuator control (TAC) system DTCs are set other than P2176. The ECM will not perform the idle learn procedure with a DTC set.

2. Turn OFF the ignition for 30 seconds.
3. Turn ON the ignition, with the engine OFF for 60 seconds.
4. Turn OFF the ignition.
5. Turn ON the ignition, with the engine OFF.
6. Clear the DTCs with a scan tool.

FUEL

GASOLINE FUEL INJECTION SYSTEM

FUEL SYSTEM SERVICE PRECAUTIONS

Safety is the most important factor when performing not only fuel system maintenance but any type of maintenance. Failure to conduct maintenance and repairs in a safe manner may result in serious personal injury or death. Maintenance and testing of the vehicle's fuel system components can be accomplished safely and effectively by adhering to the following rules and guidelines:

- To avoid the possibility of fire and personal injury, always disconnect the negative battery cable unless the repair or test procedure requires that battery voltage be applied.
- Always relieve the fuel system pressure prior to disconnecting any fuel system component (injector, fuel rail, pressure regulator, etc.), fitting or fuel line connection. After you relieve the fuel system pressure, a small amount of fuel may be released when servicing the fuel lines, the fuel injection pump, or the connections. In order to reduce the risk of personal injury, cover the fuel system components with a shop towel before disconnection. This will catch any fuel that may leak out. Place the towel in an approved container when the disconnection is complete. Please be advised that fuel under pressure may penetrate the skin or any part of the body that it contacts.
- Always place a shop towel or cloth around the fitting or connection prior to loosening to absorb any excess fuel due to spillage. Ensure that all fuel spillage (should it occur) is quickly removed from engine surfaces. Ensure that all fuel soaked cloths or towels are deposited into a suitable waste container.
- Always keep a dry chemical (Class B) fire extinguisher near the work area.
- Do not allow fuel spray or fuel vapors to come into contact with a spark or open flame.
- Always use a back-up wrench when loosening and tightening fuel line connec-

tion fittings. This will prevent unnecessary stress and torsion to fuel line piping.

- Always replace worn fuel fitting O-rings with new. Do not substitute fuel hose or equivalent where fuel pipe is installed.

Always wear safety goggles when working with fuel in order to protect the eyes from fuel splash.

Do not drain the fuel into an open container. Never store the fuel in an open container due to the possibility of a fire or an explosion.

When servicing fuel and Evaporative Emission (EVAP) pipes, reduce the risk of fire and personal injury by observing the following items:

- Replace all nylon fuel pipes that are nicked, scratched or damaged during installation, do not attempt to repair the sections of the nylon fuel pipes
- Do not hammer directly on the fuel harness body clips when installing new fuel pipes. Damage to the nylon pipes may result in a fuel leak.
- Always cover nylon vapor pipes with a wet towel before using a torch near them. Also, never expose the vehicle to temperatures higher than 239°F (115°C) for more than one hour, or more than 194°F (90°C) for any extended period.
- Apply a few drops of clean engine oil to the male pipe ends before connecting fuel pipe fittings. This will ensure proper reconnection and prevent a possible fuel leak. (During normal operation, the O-rings located in the female connector will swell and may prevent proper reconnection if not lubricated.)

Always apply a few drops of clean engine oil to the male pipe ends before connecting the fuel pipe fittings in order to reduce the risk of fire and personal injury. This will ensure proper reconnection and prevent a possible fuel leak. During normal operation, the O-rings located in the female connector will swell and may prevent proper reconnection if not lubricated.

Clean all of the following areas before performing any disconnections in order to avoid possible contamination in the system:

- The fuel pipe connections
- The hose connections
- The areas surrounding the connections

Do not breathe the air through the EVAP component tubes or hoses. The fuel vapors inside the EVAP components may cause personal injury.

The fuel rail stop bracket must be installed onto the engine assembly. The stop bracket serves as a protective shield for the fuel rail in the event of a vehicle frontal crash. If the fuel rail stop bracket is not installed and the vehicle is involved in a frontal crash, fuel could be sprayed possibly causing a fire and personal injury from burns.

Verify that the lower (small) O-ring of each injector does not remain in the lower manifold in order to reduce the risk of fire and personal injury.

If the O-ring is not removed with the injector, the replacement injector with new O-rings will not seat properly in the injector socket. Improper seating could cause a fuel leak.

Before servicing the vehicle, make sure to also refer to the precautions in the beginning of this section as well.

RELIEVING FUEL SYSTEM PRESSURE

1. Before servicing the vehicle, refer to the Precautions Section.
2. Turn the ignition OFF.
3. Disconnect the negative battery cable in order to avoid possible fuel discharge if an accidental attempt is made to start the engine. Refer to Battery Negative Cable Disconnection & Connection.
4. Remove the fuel injector sight shield.
5. Connect the EN-453-AU fuel pressure test hose adapter to the fuel pressure connection. Wrap a shop towel around the fitting while connecting the fuel pressure test hose adapter EN-453-AU in order to avoid spillage.
6. Connect the fuel pressure gage EN-338-AU to the fuel pressure test hose adapter EN-453-AU.

7. Wrap a shop towel around the fitting while connecting the gage in order to avoid spillage.

8. Install the bleed hose into an approved container.

9. Open the valve in order to bleed the system pressure. Fuel connections are now safe for servicing.

10. Disconnect and remove the fuel pressure gage EN-338-AU from the vehicle.

11. Drain any fuel remaining in the gage into an approved container.

12. Disconnect and remove the fuel pressure test hose adapter EN-453-AU from the vehicle.

13. Install the fuel injector sight shield.

14. Connect the negative battery cable.

FUEL FILTER

REMOVAL & INSTALLATION

See Figures 264 and 265.

1. Before servicing the vehicle, refer to the Precautions Section.

2. Remove fuel pump module.

3. Carefully detach and remove the fuel pump housing (2) from the primary fuel module lower half (4).

4. Detach the fuel filter (1) from the fuel pump housing (2) using a suitable tool.

To install:

➡ **Listen for audible clicks to confirm correct installation of the fuel filter to the fuel pump housing.**

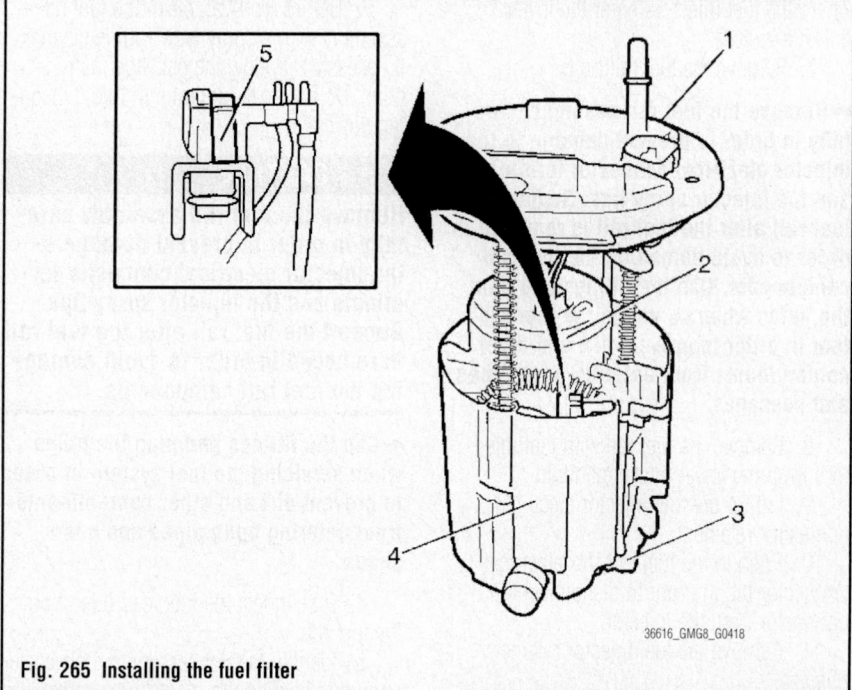

Fig. 265 Installing the fuel filter

➡ **Make sure that all the retainers of the fuel filter (1) engages the fuel pump housing (2).**

5. Install the fuel filter (1) to the fuel pump housing (2).

➡ **Observe the routing of the pipes.**

➡ **Do not damage the pipe connectors.**

➡ **Listen for audible clicks to confirm correct installation of the fuel pump housing to the primary fuel module lower half.**

FUEL RAIL & INJECTORS

REMOVAL & INSTALLATION

3.6L Engine

1. Before servicing the vehicle, refer to the Precautions Section.

✳✳ CAUTION

Gasoline or gasoline vapors are highly flammable. A fire could occur if an ignition source is present. Never drain or store gasoline or diesel fuel in an open container, due to the possibility of fire or explosion. Have a dry chemical (Class B) fire extinguisher nearby.

✳✳ CAUTION

Wear safety glasses in order to avoid eye damage.

2. Remove the fuel injector sight shield.

3. Disconnect the engine wiring harness electrical connector from the fuel injector wiring harness electrical connector.

4. Disconnect the fuel feed pipe quick connect fitting from the fuel rail.

5. Remove the upper intake manifold.

✳✳ CAUTION

Wear safety glasses while using the compressed air to avoid eye injury.

6. Use compressed air in order to remove any debris from the around the area

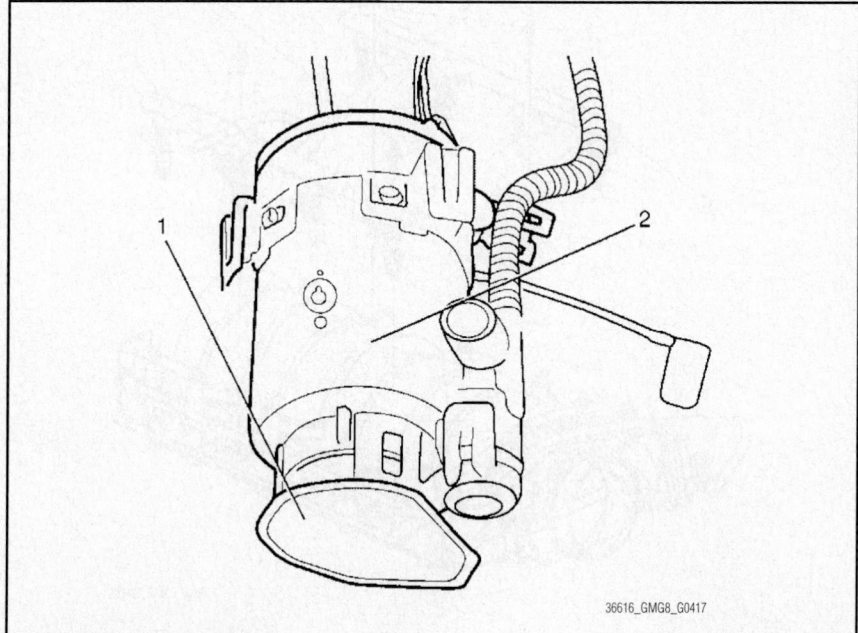

Fig. 264 Detach the fuel filter

where the fuel injectors enter the lower intake manifold.

7. Remove the fuel rail bolts.

➡ **Remove the fuel rail assembly carefully in order to prevent damage to the injector electrical connector terminals and the injector spray tips. Support the fuel rail after the fuel rail is removed in order to avoid damaging the fuel rail components. Cap the fittings and plug the holes when servicing the fuel system in order to prevent dirt and other contaminants from entering open pipes and passages.**

8. Remove the fuel rail with fuel injectors from the lower intake manifold.

9. Lift up the fuel injector electrical connector retainer.

10. Push in the fuel injector electrical connector tab in order to disconnect the connector from the injector.

11. Remove the fuel injector retainer clip.

12. Remove the fuel injector.

13. Remove and discard the fuel injector seals.

To install:

14. Install NEW fuel injector seals.

15. Install the fuel injector.

16. Install the fuel injector retainer clip.

17. Install the fuel injector electrical connector.

18. Push down on the fuel injector electrical connector retainer, securing the electrical connector.

19. Install the fuel rail with fuel injectors to the lower intake manifold. Tighten the bolts to 89 in. lbs. (10 Nm).

20. Install the upper intake manifold.

21. Connect the fuel feed pipe quick connect fitting to the fuel rail.

22. Connect the engine wiring harness electrical connector to the fuel injector wiring harness electrical connector.

23. Inspect for fuel leaks using the following procedure:

a. Turn ON the ignition, with the engine OFF for 2 seconds.

b. Turn OFF the ignition for 10 seconds.

c. Turn ON the ignition.

d. Inspect for fuel leaks.

24. Install the fuel injector sight shield.

6.0L Engine

See Figure 266.

1. Before servicing the vehicle, refer to the Precautions Section.

2. Relieve the fuel system pressure. Refer to Relieving Fuel System Pressure.

3. Before removal, clean the fuel rail assembly with a spray type engine cleaner, if necessary. Follow the package instructions. Do not soak fuel rails in liquid cleaning solvent.

✳✳ CAUTION

Remove the fuel rail assembly carefully in order to prevent damage to the injector electrical connector terminals and the injector spray tips. Support the fuel rail after the fuel rail is removed in order to avoid damaging the fuel rail components.

➡ **Cap the fittings and plug the holes when servicing the fuel system in order to prevent dirt and other contaminants from entering open pipes and passages.**

4. Disconnect the fuel feed hose from the fuel rail.

5. Identify the connectors to their corresponding injectors to make sure correct sequential injector firing order after reassembly.

6. Disconnect the injector electrical connectors to the injectors.

7. Disconnect the electrical harness from the fuel rail brackets.

8. Remove the fuel rail ground strap to intake manifold retaining bolt.

9. Remove the fuel rail to intake manifold retaining bolts.

10. Lift evenly on both sides of the fuel rail , and remove the fuel rail assembly.

11. Remove the injector lower O-ring seal from the spray tip end of each injector and discard.

12. Discard the O-ring seals.

To install:

13. Lubricate the NEW lower injector O-ring seals with clean engine oil.

14. Install the new O-ring seals on the spray tip end of each injector.

15. Install the fuel rail assembly to the intake manifold.

16. Apply a 0.02 inch (0.5 mm) band of approved thread lock to the threads of the fuel rail retaining bolts.

17. Install the fuel rail to intake manifold retaining bolts and tighten to 89 inch lbs. (10 Nm).

18. Install the fuel rail ground strap to intake manifold retaining bolts and tighten to 89 inch lbs. (10 Nm).

19. Connect the injector electrical connectors to the injectors:

- Install each connector on the proper injector in order to make sure correct sequential injector firing order.
- Rotate the injectors as required in order to avoid stretching the wire harness.

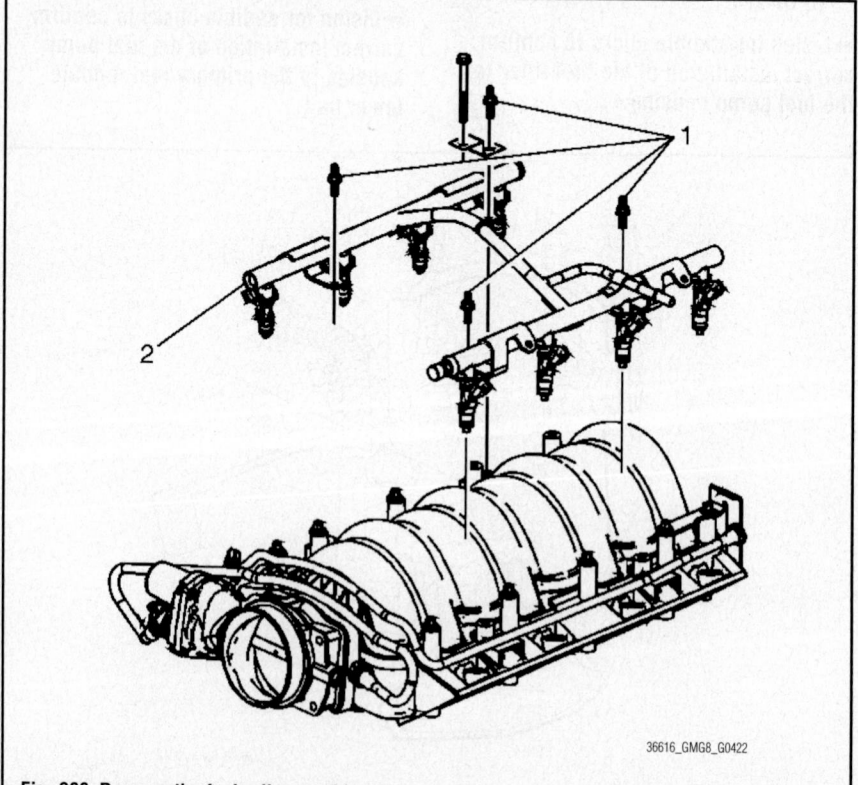

36616_GMG8_G0422

Fig. 266 Remove the fuel rail assembly

20. Connect the electrical harness to the fuel rail brackets.

21. Connect the fuel feed hose to the fuel rail fuel pipe.

22. Connect the negative battery cable.

23. Inspect for leaks.

    a. Turn ON the ignition for 2 seconds.

    b. Turn OFF the ignition for 10 seconds.

    c. Turn ON the ignition.

    d. Inspect for fuel leaks.

FUEL TANK

REMOVAL & INSTALLATION

See Figures 267 through 269.

1. Before servicing the vehicle, refer to the Precautions Section.

2. Ignition OFF.

3. Disconnect the battery negative cable. Refer to Battery Negative Cable Disconnection & Connection in Engine Electrical.

❋❋ CAUTION

Refer to Precautions.

4. Drain the fuel tank into a suitable container.

❋❋ CAUTION

To avoid any vehicle damage, serious personal injury or death when major components are removed from the vehicle and the vehicle is supported by a hoist, support the vehicle with jack stands at the opposite end from which the components are being removed and strap the vehicle to the hoist.

❋❋ WARNING

Do not bend the fuel tank straps. Bending the fuel tank straps may damage the straps.

5. Raise and support the vehicle.

6. Remove the right rear wheel.

7. Remove the exhaust system for access. Refer to Exhaust System in Engine Mechanical.

8. Remove the propeller shaft. Refer to Propeller Shaft in Drive Train.

9. Remove the park brake cables.

10. Disconnect the lower Evaporative Emission (EVAP) line from the upper EVAP line.

11. Remove the retaining hose clamp from the fuel filler hose.

12. Remove the fuel filler hose from the vehicle.

13. Disconnect the fuel feed line.

14. Disconnect the EVAP line.

15. Disconnect the fuel tank electrical connector from the chassis electrical harness.

16. Support the rear frame assembly using a suitable tool.

17. Remove the rear frame to chassis retaining bolts (1, 2) and discard.

➡ **Make sure that the bolts (2) extends 50mm (2 in) from the rear frame.**

18. Install the frame support tool EN-48536 (2) to the rear frame mounts (1).

➡ **When lowering the rear frame do not to damage the rear brake hoses.**

19. Lower the rear frame onto the frame support tool EN-48536 (2).

20. Disconnect the EVAP canister hose connector from the EVAP canister

21. Disconnect the EVAP canister hose connector from the EVAP canister.

22. Disconnect the electrical connector from the EVAP canister vent solenoid.

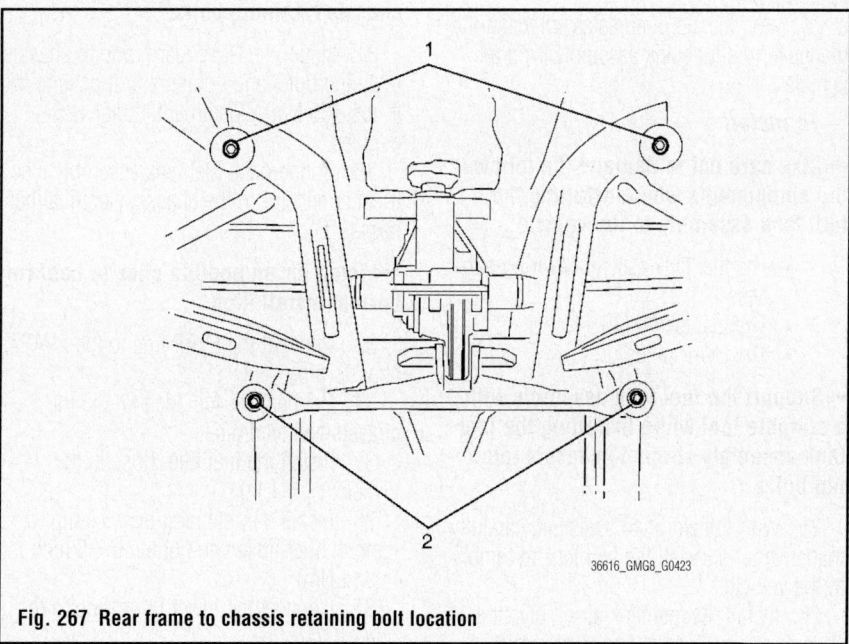

36616_GMG8_G0423

Fig. 267 Rear frame to chassis retaining bolt location

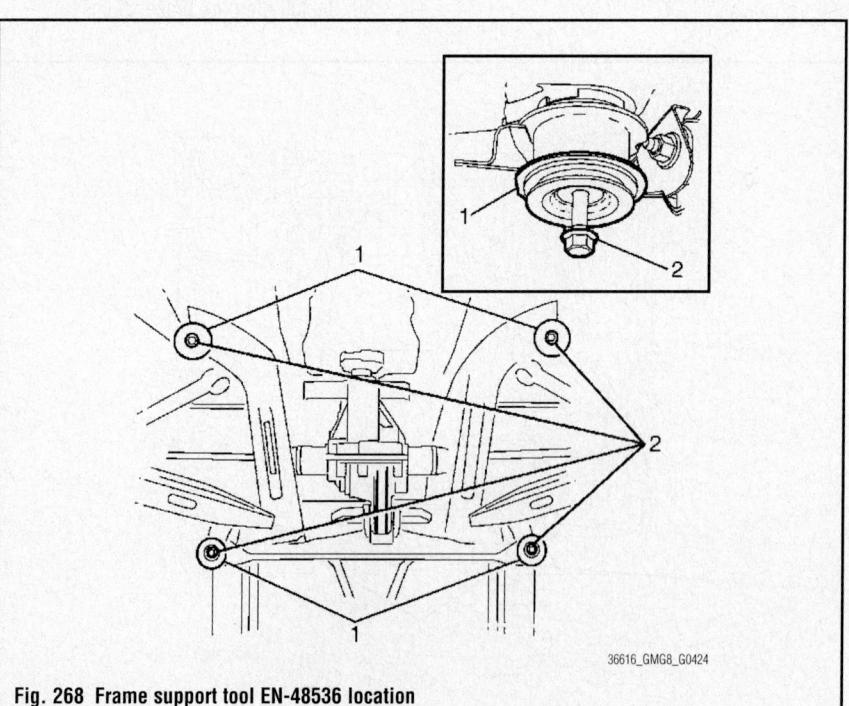

36616_GMG8_G0424

Fig. 268 Frame support tool EN-48536 location

➡Take care not to damage the following components when lowering the fuel tank assembly:

- The fuel tank assembly wiring harness
- The fuel feed pipe
- The EVAP pipes

➡Support the fuel tank assembly with a suitable tool before removing the fuel tank assembly straps to chassis retaining bolts (1).

23. Remove the fuel tank strap to chassis retaining bolts (1).

24. With the aid of an assistant, carefully maneuver the fuel tank assembly from the vehicle.

To install:

➡Take care not to damage the following components when installing the fuel tank assembly to the vehicle:

- The fuel tank assembly wiring harness
- The fuel feed pipe
- The EVAP pipes

➡Support the fuel tank assembly with a suitable tool while installing the fuel tank assembly straps to chassis retaining bolts.

25. With the aid of an assistant, carefully maneuver and install the fuel tank assembly to the vehicle.

26. Install the fuel tank assembly strap to chassis retaining bolts and tighten to 22 ft. lbs. (30 Nm).

➡Listen for an audible click to confirm correct installation.

27. Connect the electrical connector to the EVAP emission canister vent solenoid.

28. Connect the EVAP canister hose connector to the EVAP canister.

29. Raise and support the rear frame assembly into its position using a suitable tool.

30. Remove the rear frame support tool EN-48536 from the rear frame mounts.

➡Using a suitable tool clean the threaded holes of the rear frame to chassis retaining bolts.

31. Install the NEW rear frame to chassis retaining bolts and tighten a first pass to 48 ft. lbs. (65 Nm) plus an additional 125 degrees.

32. Connect the fuel tank assembly electrical connector to the chassis electrical harness.

➡Listen for an audible click to confirm correct installation.

33. Connect the EVAP line to the EVAP chassis pipe.

34. Connect the fuel feed line to the chassis fuel feed pipe.

35. Install the fuel filler hose to the vehicle.

36. Install the retaining hose clamp to the fuel filler hose and tighten to 35 inch lbs. (4 Nm).

37. Connect the lower EVAP line to the upper EVAP line.

38. Install the park brake cables.

39. Install the propeller shaft.
40. Install the exhaust system.
41. Install the right rear wheel.
42. Lower the vehicle to the ground.
43. Fill the fuel tank with the drained fuel.
44. Connect the battery negative cable.
45. Inspect for fuel leaks using the following procedure:

- Turn ON the ignition, with the engine OFF for 2 seconds
- Turn OFF the ignition, for 10 seconds
- Turn ON the ignition, with the engine OFF
- Inspect for leaks

FUEL TANK MODULE

REMOVAL & INSTALLATION

Primary

See Figures 270 and 271.

1. Before servicing the vehicle, refer to the Precautions Section.
2. Ignition OFF.
3. Disconnect the battery negative cable. Refer to Battery Negative Cable Disconnection & Connection in Engine Electrical.

❊❊ CAUTION

Refer to Precautions section.

❊❊ CAUTION

To avoid any vehicle damage, serious personal injury or death when major components are removed from the vehicle and the vehicle is supported by a hoist, support the vehicle with jack stands at the opposite end from which the components are being removed and strap the vehicle to the hoist.

4. Remove the fuel tank assembly. Refer to Fuel Tank.

5. Press the release tab of the secondary fuel tank module electrical connector to release the connector.

6. Disconnect the primary fuel tank module electrical connector from the primary fuel tank module assembly.

➡The primary fuel tank module is spring loaded. Take care when loosening the cam lock ring.

7. Rotate the cam lock ring (2) counterclockwise using CH-48482 fuel sender lock ring wrench (1).

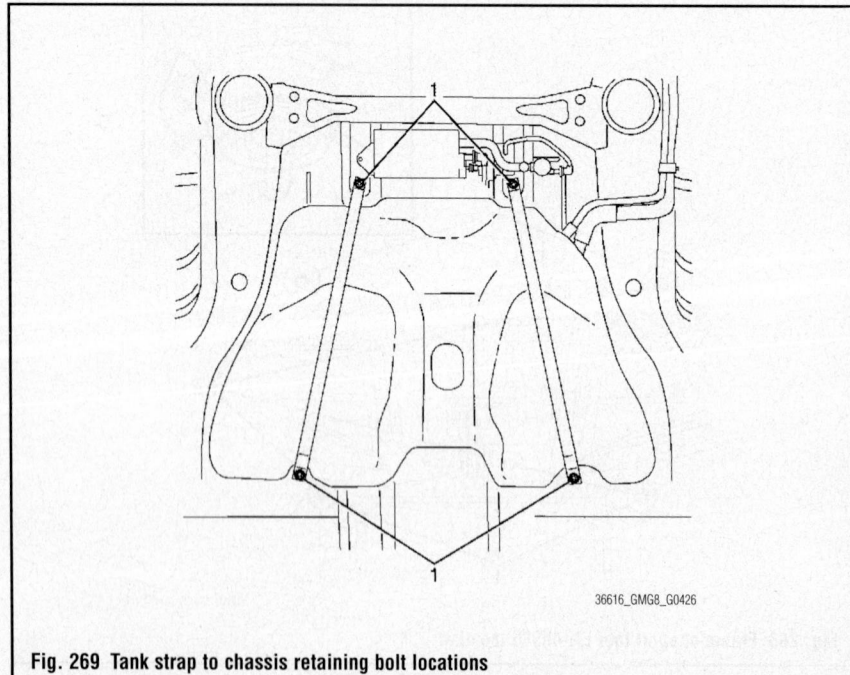

36616_GMG8_G0426

Fig. 269 Tank strap to chassis retaining bolt locations

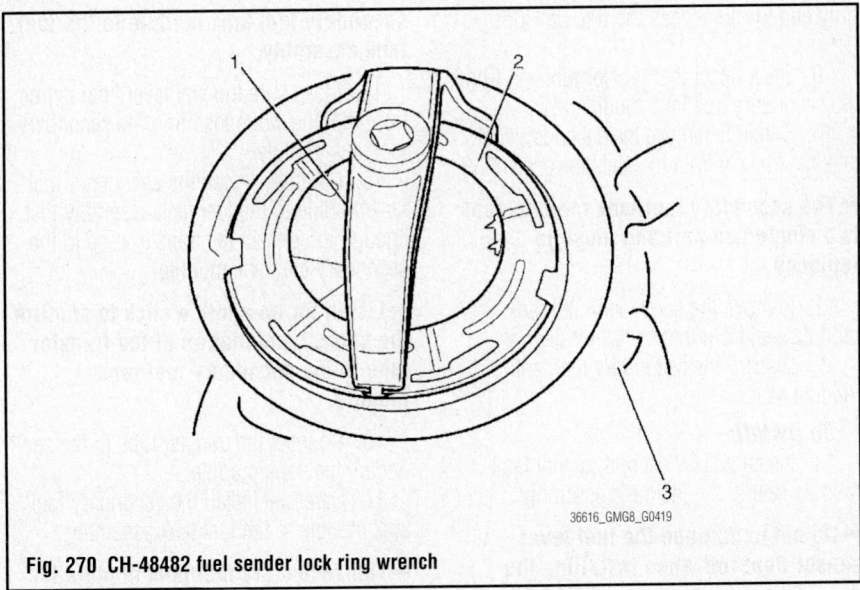

Fig. 270 CH-48482 fuel sender lock ring wrench

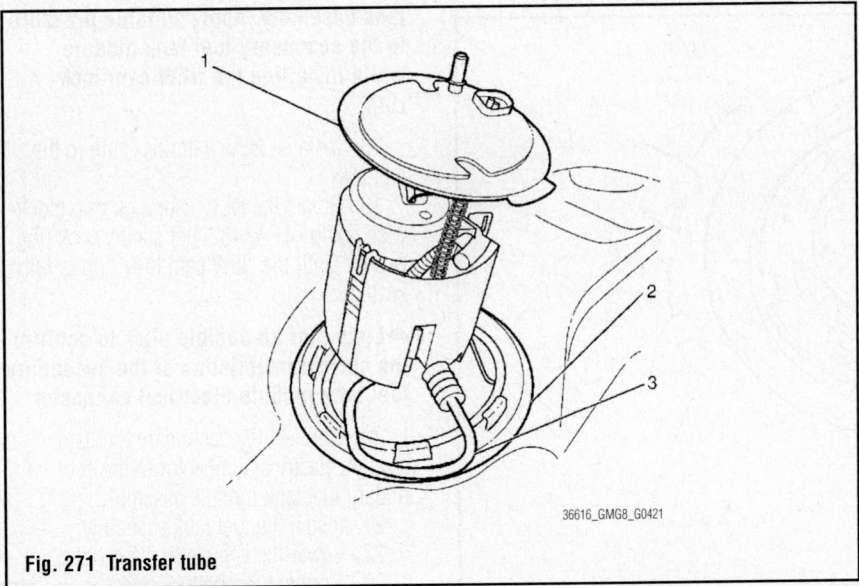

Fig. 271 Transfer tube

➡**Observe the orientation of the secondary fuel tank module (1) in relation to the fuel tank assembly.**

➡**Do not damage the fuel level sensor float rod when removing the secondary fuel tank module (1) from the fuel tank assembly.**

8. Carefully lift the primary fuel tank module (1) out of the fuel tank assembly only enough to access the transfer tube (3).

9. Disconnect the transfer tube (3) from the secondary fuel tank module (1).

10. Carefully remove the secondary fuel tank module (1) from the fuel tank assembly.

➡**The primary fuel tank module seal is a single use part and must be replaced.**

11. Remove the primary fuel tank module seal from the fuel tank assembly.

12. Discard the primary fuel tank module seal.

To install:
13. Install a NEW primary fuel tank module seal to the fuel tank assembly.

➡**Do not to damage the fuel level sensor float rod when installing the secondary fuel tank module to the fuel tank assembly.**

14. Make sure the fuel level float is free from binding while inserting the secondary fuel tank module.

15. Carefully install the primary fuel tank module to the fuel tank assembly just enough to connect the transfer tube to the primary fuel tank module.

➡**Listen for an audible click to confirm the correct installation of the transfer tube to the primary fuel tank module.**

16. Connect the transfer tube to the primary fuel tank module.

17. Carefully install the primary fuel tank module to the fuel tank assembly.

➡**The primary fuel tank module is spring loaded when installed in the fuel tank assembly. Apply suitable pressure to the primary fuel tank module while installing the NEW cam lock ring.**

18. Install a NEW cam lock ring to the fuel tank.

19. Rotate the NEW cam lock ring clockwise using CH-48482 fuel sender lock ring wrench until the NEW cam lock ring is fully seated.

➡**Listen for an audible click to confirm the correct installation of the primary fuel tank module electrical connector.**

20. Connect the primary fuel tank module electrical connector to the primary fuel tank module assembly.

21. Install the fuel tank assembly.

22. Lower the vehicle to the ground.

23. Connect the battery negative cable.

Secondary

See Figures 272 and 273.

1. Before servicing the vehicle, refer to the Precautions Section.

2. Ignition OFF.

3. Disconnect the battery negative cable. Refer to Battery Negative Cable Disconnection & Connection in Engine Electrical.

⚠ **CAUTION**

Refer to Precautions section.

⚠ **CAUTION**

To avoid any vehicle damage, serious personal injury or death when major components are removed from the vehicle and the vehicle is supported by a hoist, support the vehicle with jack stands at the opposite end from which the components are being removed and strap the vehicle to the hoist.

4. Remove the fuel tank assembly. Refer to Fuel Tank.

5. Press the release tab of the secondary fuel tank module electrical connector to release the connector.

6. Disconnect the secondary fuel tank module electrical connector from the secondary fuel tank module assembly.

➡**The secondary fuel tank module is spring loaded. Take care when loosening the cam lock ring.**

7. Rotate the cam lock ring (2) counterclockwise using CH-48482 fuel sender lock ring wrench (1).

➡**Observe the orientation of the secondary fuel tank module (1) in relation to the fuel tank assembly.**

➡**Do not damage the fuel level sensor float rod when removing the secondary fuel tank module (1) from the fuel tank assembly.**

8. Carefully lift the secondary fuel tank module (1) out of the fuel tank assembly

only enough to access the transfer tube (2).

9. Disconnect the transfer tube (2) from the secondary fuel tank module (1).

10. Carefully remove the secondary fuel tank module (1) from the fuel tank assembly.

➡**The secondary fuel tank module seal is a single use part and must be replaced.**

11. Remove the secondary fuel tank module seal from the fuel tank assembly.

12. Discard the secondary fuel tank module seal.

To install:

13. Install a NEW secondary fuel tank module seal to the fuel tank assembly.

➡**Do not to damage the fuel level sensor float rod when installing the**

secondary fuel tank module to the fuel tank assembly.

14. Make sure the fuel level float is free from binding while inserting the secondary fuel tank module.

15. Carefully install the secondary fuel tank module to the fuel tank assembly just enough to connect the transfer tube to the secondary fuel tank module.

➡**Listen for an audible click to confirm the correct installation of the transfer tube to the secondary fuel tank module.**

16. Connect the transfer tube to the secondary fuel tank module.

17. Carefully install the secondary fuel tank module to the fuel tank assembly.

➡**The secondary fuel tank module is spring loaded when installed in the fuel tank assembly. Apply suitable pressure to the secondary fuel tank module while installing the NEW cam lock ring.**

18. Install a NEW cam lock ring to the fuel tank.

19. Rotate the NEW cam lock ring clockwise using CH-48482 fuel sender lock ring wrench until the NEW cam lock ring is fully seated.

➡**Listen for an audible click to confirm the correct installation of the secondary fuel tank module electrical connector.**

20. Connect the secondary fuel tank module electrical connector to the secondary fuel tank module assembly.

21. Install the fuel tank assembly.

22. Lower the vehicle to the ground.

23. Connect the battery negative cable.

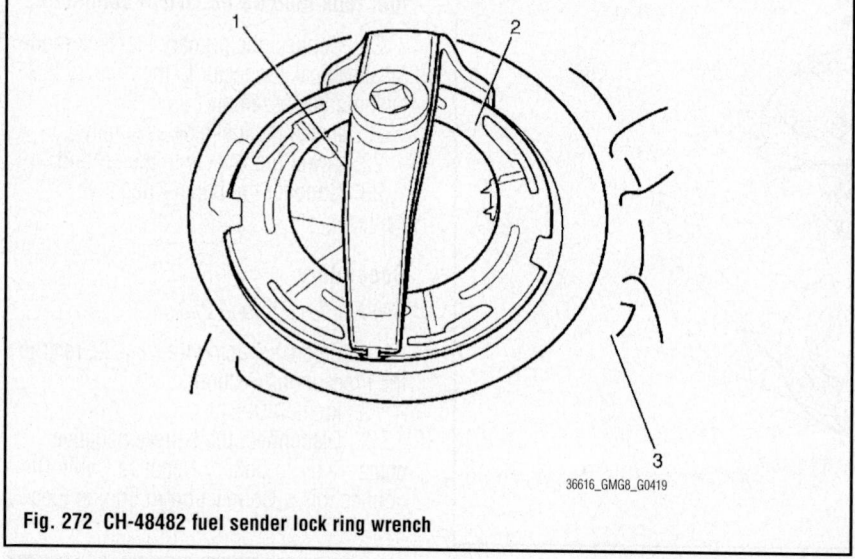

36616_GMG8_G0419

Fig. 272 CH-48482 fuel sender lock ring wrench

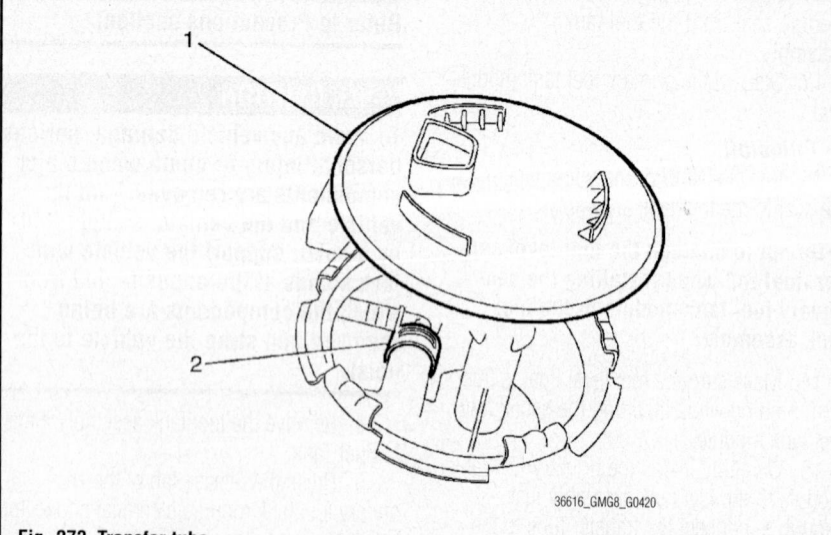

36616_GMG8_G0420

Fig. 273 Transfer tube

IDLE SPEED

ADJUSTMENT

Idle Speed is not adjustable.

THROTTLE BODY

REMOVAL & INSTALLATION

1. Before servicing the vehicle, refer to the Precautions Section.

2. Remove the air intake duct. Refer to Air Cleaner.

✳✳ WARNING

Do not insert any tools into the throttle body bore in order to avoid damage to the throttle valve plate.

WARNING

Handle the electronic throttle control components carefully. Use cleanliness in order to prevent damage. Do not drop the electronic throttle control components. Do not roughly handle the electronic throttle control components. Do not immerse the electronic throttle control components in cleaning solvents of any type.

➡The intake manifold, throttle body, fuel injection rail, and fuel injectors may be removed as an assembly. If not servicing the individual components,

remove the manifold as a complete assembly.

3. Remove the electrical wire harness connector from the throttle body.
4. Remove the throttle body to intake manifold retaining bolts.
5. Remove the throttle body.

➡The throttle body gasket is a single use part. The gasket must be discarded after removal.

6. Remove the throttle body to intake manifold gasket, and discard.
7. Discard the throttle body gasket.
8. Clean the throttle body and intake manifold mating surfaces.

To install:

9. Install a new throttle body to intake manifold gasket. Align the locating tab of the gasket with the notch in the manifold.
10. Install the throttle body to the intake manifold.
11. Install the throttle body to intake manifold retaining bolts and tighten to 89 inch lbs. (10 Nm) for 3.6L engine, 106 inch lbs. (12 Nm) for 6.0L engine.
12. Install the electrical wire harness connector from the throttle body.
13. Install the air intake duct to the throttle body.
14. If re-programming is required.

HEATING & AIR CONDITIONING SYSTEM

BLOWER MOTOR

REMOVAL & INSTALLATION

See Figure 274.

1. Before servicing the vehicle, refer to the Precautions Section.
2. Remove the right closeout insulator panel.
3. Remove the instrument panel (I/P) compartment.
4. Remove the right side floor air outlet duct.
5. Disconnect the blower motor electrical connector (1).
6. Remove the blower motor to HVAC module assembly retaining screws (1).

7. Remove the blower motor from the HVAC module assembly.

To install:

8. Install the blower motor to the HVAC module assembly.
9. Install the blower motor to HVAC module assembly retaining screws and tighten to 9 inch lbs. (1 Nm).
10. Connect the blower motor electrical connector.
11. Install the right side floor air outlet duct.
12. Install the instrument panel (I/P) compartment.
13. Install the right closeout insulator panel.

HEATER CORE

REMOVAL & INSTALLATION

See Figures 275 through 277.

1. Before servicing the vehicle, refer to the Precautions Section.
2. Remove the HVAC module assembly. Refer to HVAC Module Assembly.
3. Remove the foam seal from the heater core pipes.
4. Remove the heater core pipes locating plate to HVAC module assembly retaining screws (1).
5. Remove the heater core pipes locating plate (2) from the HVAC module assembly (3).

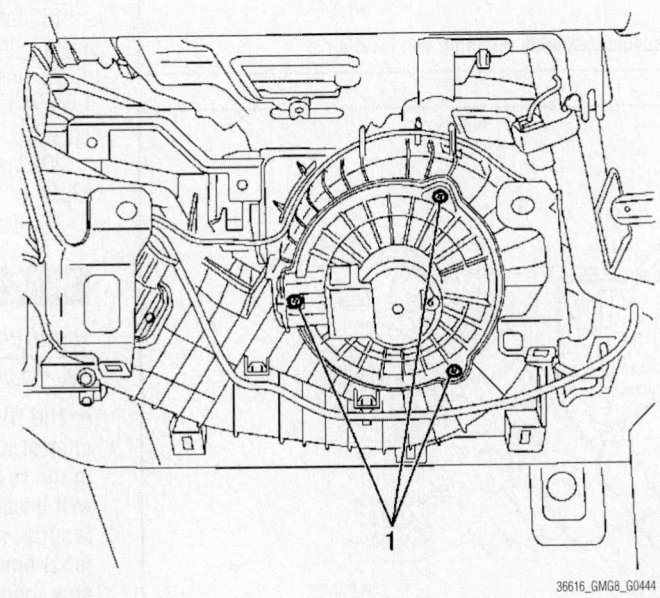

36616_GMG8_G0444

Fig. 274 Blower motor to HVAC module assembly retaining screw locations

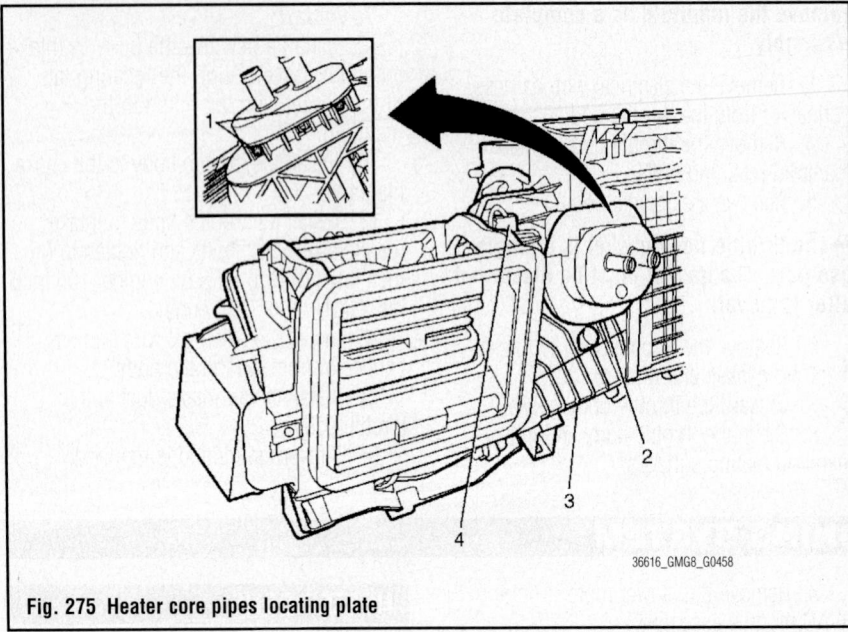

Fig. 275 Heater core pipes locating plate

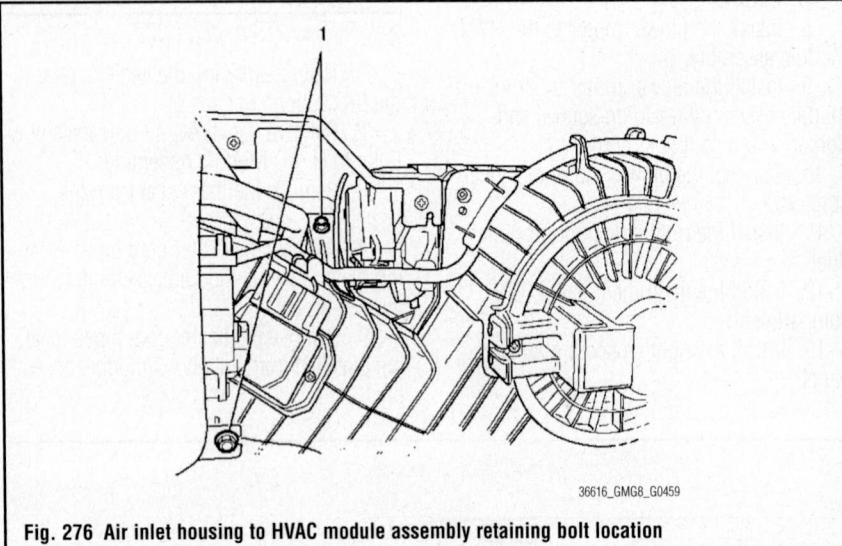

Fig. 276 Air inlet housing to HVAC module assembly retaining bolt location

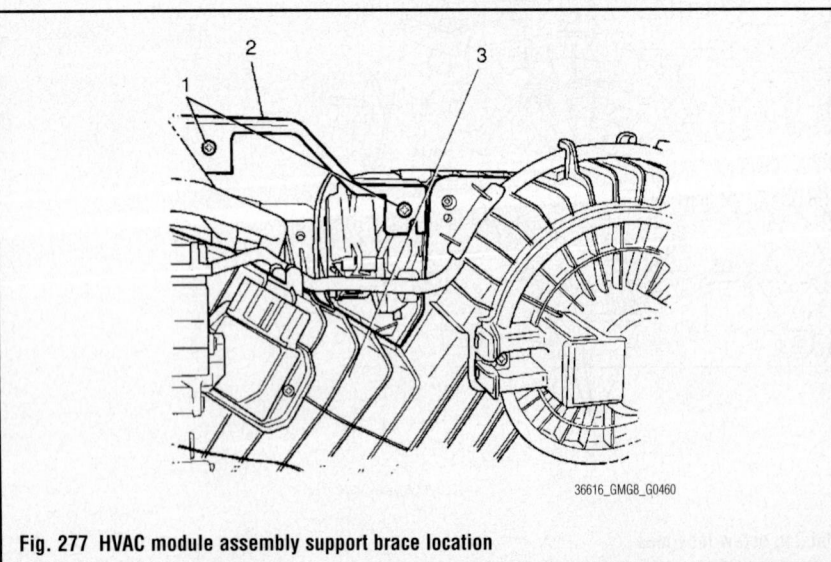

Fig. 277 HVAC module assembly support brace location

6. Disconnect the recirculation actuator electrical connector (4).

7. Remove the air inlet housing to HVAC module assembly retaining bolts (1).

8. Remove the HVAC module assembly support brace to HVAC module assembly retaining screws (1).

9. Remove the HVAC module assembly support brace (2) from the HVAC module assembly (3).

10. Separate the air inlet housing from the HVAC module assembly.

➡**Remove the heater core by sliding the heater core out of the HVAC module assembly.**

11. Remove the heater core from the HVAC module assembly.

To install:

➡**Install the heater core by sliding the heater core into the HVAC module assembly.**

12. Install the heater core to the HVAC module assembly.

13. Install the air inlet housing to the HVAC module assembly.

14. Install the air inlet assembly to HVAC module assembly retaining bolts and tighten to 80 inch lbs. (9 Nm).

15. Install the HVAC module assembly support brace to the HVAC module assembly.

16. Install the HVAC module assembly support brace to HVAC module assembly retaining screws and tighten to 9 inch lbs. (1 Nm).

17. Connect the recirculation actuator electrical connector.

18. Install the heater core pipes locating plate to the HVAC module assembly.

19. Install the heater core pipes locating plate to HVAC module assembly retaining screws.

20. Install the foam seal to the heater pipes.

21. Install the HVAC module assembly.

HVAC MODULE ASSEMBLY

REMOVAL & INSTALLATION

See Figures 278 through 283.

➡**The HVAC manual or HVAC automatic control modules are replaced, an automatic re-calibration of all the actuators will occur. For the best re-calibration results, start and run the engine for at least one minute after installing the new module . Do not adjust any controls on the HVAC control module during the re-calibration procedure. If** interrupted, improper HVAC performance may result. No additional procedures are necessary.

1. Before servicing the vehicle, refer to the Precautions Section.
2. Recover the refrigerant.
3. Disconnect the battery negative cable. Refer to Battery Negative Cable Disconnection & Connection in Engine Electrical.
4. Remove the engine cover.
5. Remove the windscreen wiper arms.
6. Remove the air inlet grill panel.
7. Remove the air filter assembly.
8. Drain the cooling system.

➡**Heater hoses for 3.6L engine are shown. 6.0L engine heater hoses are similar.**

➡**Mark position of heater hoses (3) and heater hose retaining clamps (1) before removal to make sure of correct alignment during assembly.**

9. Using J 38185 compress the heater hose retaining clamps (1) and slide along the heater hose (3).
10. Remove the heater hoses (3) from the heater core pipes (2).
11. Disconnect the vacuum hose and the vacuum brake booster check valve from the vacuum brake booster.
12. Detach the vacuum hose from the bulkhead mounted vacuum hose retaining bracket and position aside.
13. Remove the remote battery positive post cover.

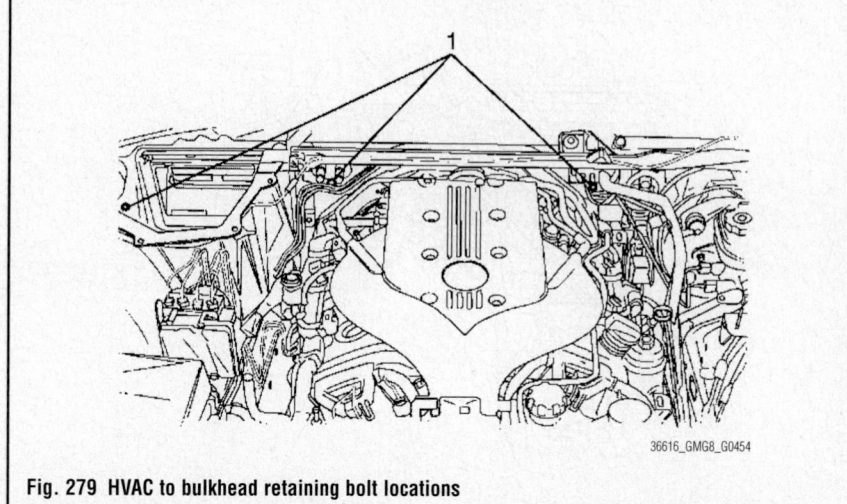

Fig. 279 HVAC to bulkhead retaining bolt locations

14. Remove the remote battery positive post to wiring harness retaining bolt.
15. Remove the starter motor power cable and position aside.
16. Remove the suction pipe upper to suction pipe lower retaining nut.
17. Remove the suction pipe/liquid pipe retaining clip to left front chassis rail retaining bolt.
18. Detach the liquid pipe from the suction pipe/liquid pipe retaining clip.
19. Disconnect the suction pipe upper from suction pipe lower.

➡**The sealing washer is a single use item and must be discarded after use.**

20. Remove the sealing washer.
21. Discard the sealing washer

➡**Cover any opening of the A/C system with a suitable cap or tape immediately, to prevent absorption of moisture from the atmosphere.**

22. Cap or plug the suction pipe upper and the suction pipe lower.
23. Remove the suction pipe/liquid pipe pad to TX valve retaining nut.
24. Disconnect the suction pipe/liquid pipe pad from the TX valve.

➡**The sealing washers are a single use item and must be discarded after use.**

25. Remove the sealing washers.
26. Discard the sealing washers

➡**Cover any opening of the A/C system with a suitable cap or tape immediately, to prevent absorption of moisture from the atmosphere.**

27. Cap or plug the suction pipe, liquid pipe and the TX valve.

➡**HVAC to bulkhead retaining bolt locations are shown in a 3.6L engine compartment. 6.0L engine compartment HVAC to bulkhead retaining bolt locations are the same.**

28. Remove the HVAC to bulkhead retaining bolts (1).
29. Disconnect the blower motor electrical connector.
30. Disconnect the HVAC module electrical connectors.
31. Disconnect the blower motor control processor electrical connector.
32. Detach the I/P wiring harness to HVAC module assembly retaining clips.
33. Remove the instrument panel (I/P) pad.

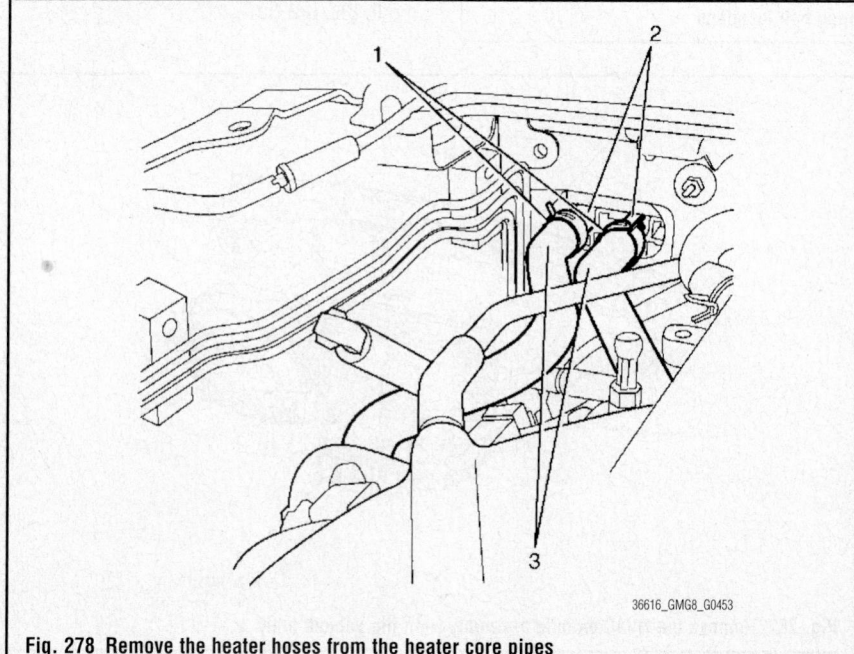

Fig. 278 Remove the heater hoses from the heater core pipes

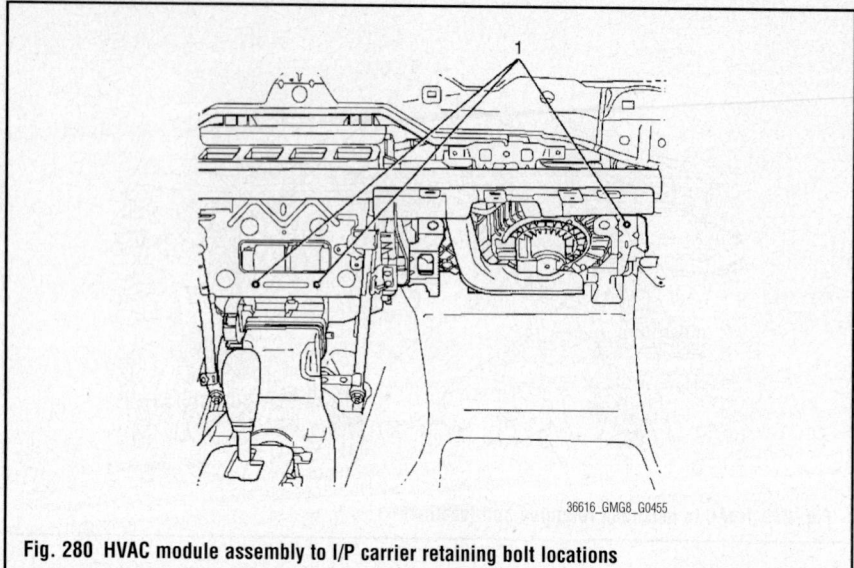

Fig. 280 HVAC module assembly to I/P carrier retaining bolt locations

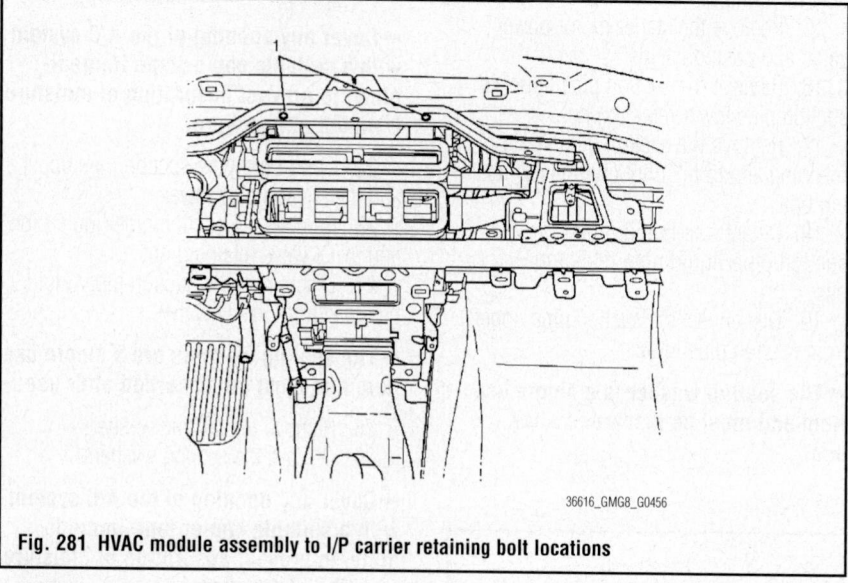

Fig. 281 HVAC module assembly to I/P carrier retaining bolt locations

34. Remove the instrument panel centre support bracket.

35. Remove the HVAC module assembly to I/P carrier retaining bolts (1).

36. Remove the I/P carrier.

➡To remove the HVAC module assembly (2) from the vehicle (1) rotate the HVAC module assembly (2) downwards and towards the back of the vehicle (1).

37. Remove the HVAC module assembly (2) from the vehicle body (1).

To install:

➡To install the HVAC module assembly to the vehicle rotate the HVAC module assembly upwards and towards the front of the vehicle.

➡Make sure the HVAC module assembly fits into the drain assembly.

38. Install the HVAC module assembly to the vehicle body.

39. Install the I/P carrier.

40. Install the HVAC module assembly to I/P carrier retaining bolts and tighten to 80 inch lbs. (9 Nm).

➡HVAC to bulkhead retaining bolt locations are shown in a 3.6L engine compartment. 6.0L engine compartment HVAC to bulkhead retaining bolt locations are the same.

41. Install the HVAC module assembly to bulkhead retaining bolts and tighten to 62 inch lbs. (7 Nm).

42. Connect the blower motor control processor electrical connector.

43. Connect the HVAC module electrical connectors.

44. Connect the blower motor electrical connector.

45. Attach the I/P wiring harness to HVAC module assembly retaining clips.

46. Install the I/P upper trim pad.

47. Install the I/P retainer bracket.

48. Remove the plugs or caps from the suction pipe, liquid pipe and the TX valve.

➡DO NOT coat the NEW sealing washers with oil, they must be fitted dry. The use of mineral oil will render the sealing washers useless, as the sealing washers WILL swell causing refrigerant to leak out.

49. Install NEW sealing washers.

50. Position the suction pipe/liquid pipe pad to the TX Valve.

51. Install the suction pipe/liquid pipe pad to TX valve retaining nut and tighten to 16 ft. lbs. (22 Nm).

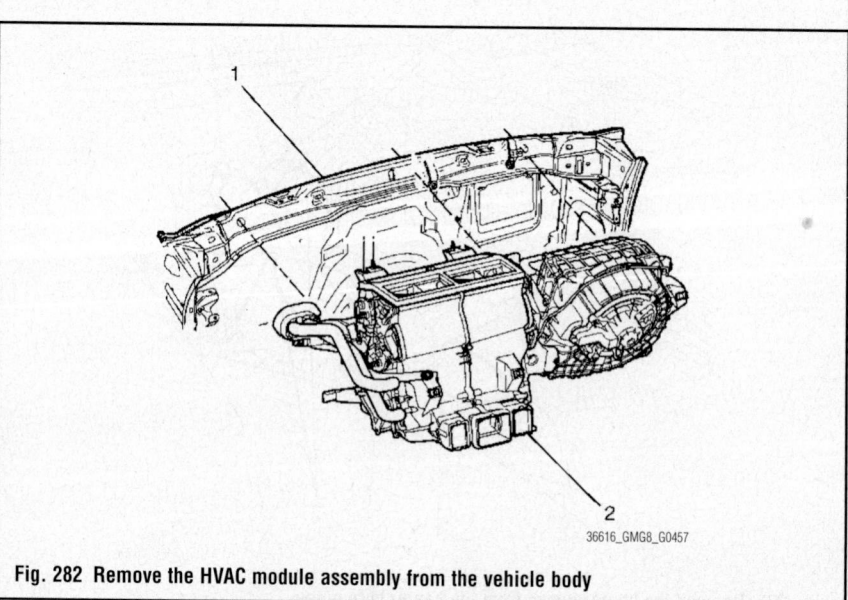

Fig. 282 Remove the HVAC module assembly from the vehicle body

52. Remove the plugs or caps from the suction pipe upper and the suction pipe lower.

➡**DO NOT coat the NEW sealing washer with oil, they must be fitted dry. The use of mineral oil will render the sealing washer useless, as the sealing washer WILL swell causing refrigerant to leak out.**

53. Install a NEW sealing washer.
54. Install the suction pipe upper to the suction pipe lower.
55. Attach the liquid pipe to the suction pipe/liquid pipe retaining clip.
56. Install the suction pipe/liquid pipe retaining clip to left front chassis rail retaining bolt.
57. Install the suction pipe upper to suction pipe lower retaining nut and tighten to 16 ft. lbs. (22 Nm).
58. Install the starter motor positive cable to the remote battery positive post.
59. Install the remote battery positive post to wiring harness retaining bolt and tighten to 11 ft. lbs. (15 Nm).

➡**Make sure the clips on the remote battery positive post cover are engaged to avoid an induced rattle condition.**

60. Install the remote battery positive post cover.
61. Connect the vacuum hose and the vacuum brake booster check valve to the vacuum brake booster.
62. Attach the vacuum hose to the bulkhead mounted vacuum hose retaining bracket.

➡**Heater hoses for 3.6L engine are shown. 6.0L engine heater hoses are similar.**

➡**If reusing the heater hoses, align the heater hoses with the marks made on the heater core inlet pipe during the removal procedure.**

63. Connect the heater hoses to the heater core pipes.

64. Using J 38185, slide the heater hose retaining clamps back into the original position on the heater hoses.
65. Install the engine cover.
66. Install windscreen wiper arms.
67. Install the air inlet grill panel.
68. Install the air filter assembly.
69. Connect the battery negative cable.
70. Fill the cooling system.

➡**The receiver and dehydrator is a single use only component. A NEW receiver and dehydrator must be installed whenever a closed A/C system is opened or exposed to atmosphere. If the receiver and dehydrator has been replaced following a service/repair and it is deemed necessary to immediately re-open the A/C system it is not necessary to replace the receiver and dehydrator again, providing the A/C system is plugged/capped correctly.**

71. Replace the receiver and dehydrator.
   a. Remove the receiver dehydrator plastic screw cap (1) from the condenser (5).

➡**The circlip (2) cannot be removed if any gas pressure is present in A/C system.**

➡**To gain adequate clearance for removal of the circlip (2), use a suitable tool to gently tap the receiver dehydrator bottle plug (3) downwards.**

   b. Remove the circlip (2).

➡**Screw a suitable bolt into the threaded hole in the receiver dehydrator bottle plug (3). Pull upwards on the bolt to remove the receiver dehydrator bottle plug (3) from the condenser (5).**

   c. Remove the receiver dehydrator bottle plug (3) from the condenser (5).

➡**Using a suitable tool, grip the lower lip on the receiver dehydrator cartridge**

(4) and pull upwards to remove the receiver dehydrator cartridge (4) from the condenser (5).

   d. Remove the receiver dehydrator cartridge (4) from the condenser (5).
   e. To install, reverse removal procedure.
72. Evacuate and recharge the A/C system.
73. Connect the battery negative cable.
74. Leak test the HVAC module assembly pipe connections.

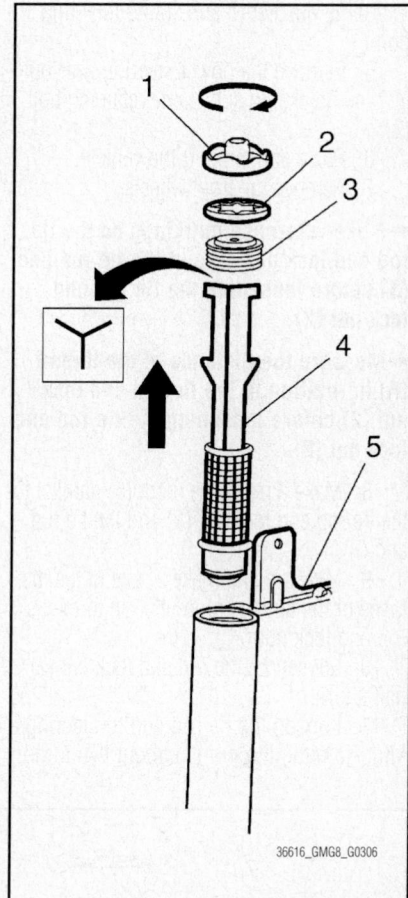

36616_GMG8_G0306

Fig. 283 Replacement of the receiver dehydrator cartridge from the condenser

STEERING

POWER RACK & PINION STEERING GEAR

REMOVAL & INSTALLATION

See Figures 284 through 288.

1. Before servicing the vehicle, refer to the Precautions Section.
2. Remove the engine cover, if necessary
3. Remove the air inlet duct.
4. Remove the power steering gear inlet pipe bracket to sub-frame retaining bolt (1).
5. Remove the power steering gear outlet pipe bracket to sub-frame retaining bolt (2).
6. Raise and support the vehicle.
7. Remove the front wheels.

➡ **Make reference markings on the tie rod end lock nut (2) and the tie rod end (3) before loosening the tie rod end lock nut (2).**

➡ **Measure the distance of the thread (A) in relation to the tie rod end lock nut (2) before loosening the tie rod end lock nut (2).**

8. Make a reference mark (5) parallel to the tie rod end lock nut (2) and the tie rod end (3).
9. Measure and make a note of the distance of the thread (A) in relation to the tie rod end lock nut (2).
10. Loosen the tie rod end lock nut (2) half a turn.
11. Loosen the tie rod end to steering knuckle retaining nut (1) about two turns.

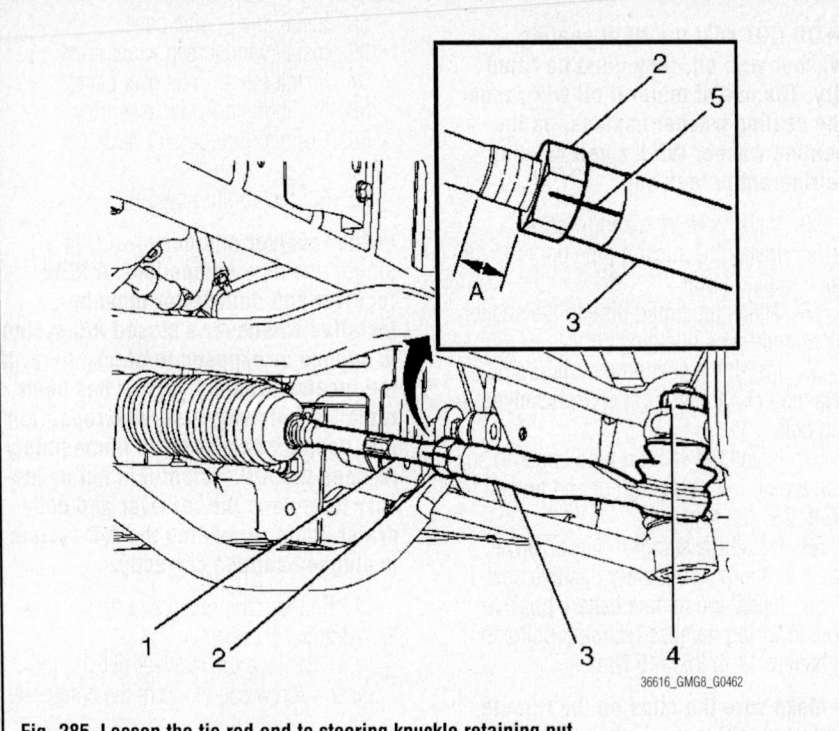

Fig. 285 Loosen the tie rod end to steering knuckle retaining nut

12. Using J-42188-B disconnect the tie rod end from the steering knuckle.
13. Remove and discard the tie rod end to steering knuckle retaining nut.
14. Separate the tie rod end from the steering knuckle.
15. Repeat previous on the opposite side of the vehicle.
16. Remove the engine splash shield.

➡ **Observing the orientation of the intermediate steering shaft with**

reference to the pinion shaft will assist in steering alignment.

17. Make a reference mark parallel to the intermediate steering shaft and the pinion shaft.
18. Remove and discard the intermediate steering shaft to pinion shaft retaining bolt.
19. Disconnect the intermediate shaft from the pinion shaft.
20. Loosen the caster arm to steering knuckle retaining nut about two turns.
21. Using J-42188-B disconnect the driver side caster arm from the steering knuckle.
22. Remove and discard the driver side caster arm to steering knuckle retaining nut.
23. Separate the driver side caster arm from the steering knuckle.
24. Place a suitable container under the vehicle below the power steering gear inlet pipe to power steering gear retaining banjo bolt (2) and the power steering gear outlet pipe to power steering gear retaining banjo bolt (3) to collect draining fluid.
25. Remove the power steering gear inlet pipe to power steering gear retaining banjo bolt (2).
26. Remove and discard the copper sealing washers (1).
27. Plug the steering gear inlet pipe (6) to prevent the entry of foreign particles into the power steering system.

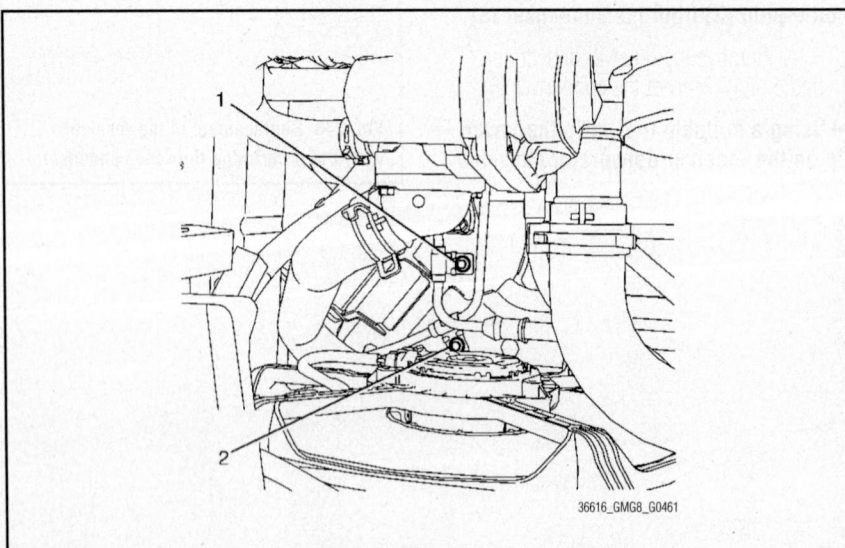

Fig. 284 Power steering gear inlet pipe bracket location

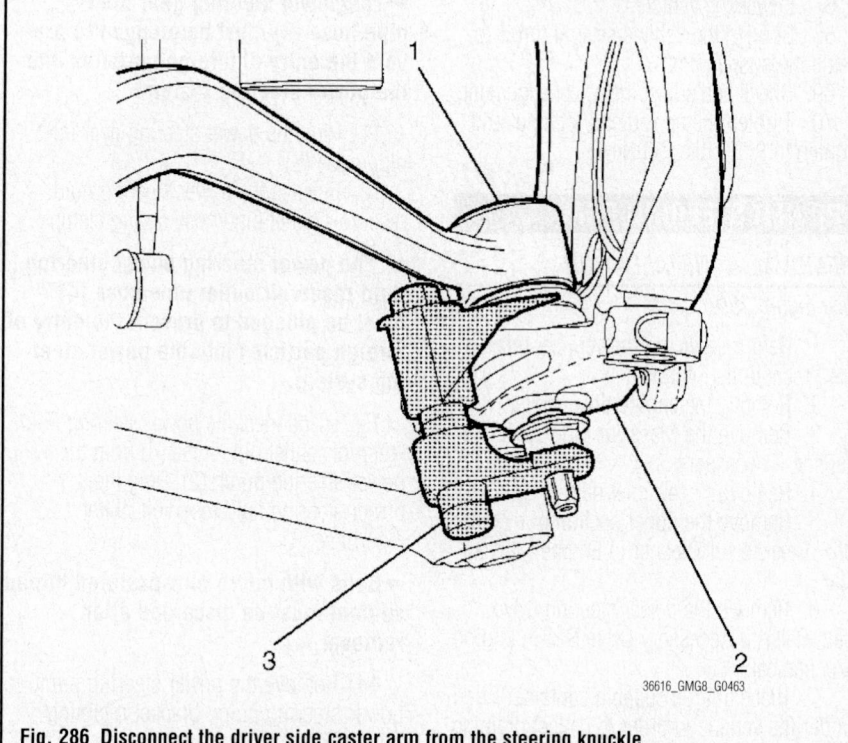

Fig. 286 Disconnect the driver side caster arm from the steering knuckle

28. Remove the power steering gear outlet pipe to power steering gear retaining banjo bolt (3).

29. Remove and discard the copper sealing washers (4).

30. Plug the steering gear outlet pipe (5) to prevent the entry of foreign particles into the power steering system.

31. Remove the and discard the steering gear to sub-frame retaining bolts (1).

32. Remove the steering gear insulator retaining bracket (2) from the steering gear insulator (3).

33. Remove the steering gear insulator (3) from the steering gear.

➡️**The steering gear assembly must be removed from the driver side of the vehicle.**

34. Remove the steering gear assembly from the vehicle.

To install:

➡️**The steering gear must be installed from the driver side of the vehicle.**

35. Install the steering gear to the vehicle.

36. Install the steering gear insulator to the steering gear.

37. Install the steering gear insulator retaining bracket to the steering gear insulator.

38. Install the steering gear to sub-frame retaining bolts and tighten to 48 ft. lbs. (65 Nm).

39. Remove the plug from the steering gear outlet pipe.

40. Install the NEW copper sealing washers.

41. Install the power steering gear outlet pipe to power steering gear retaining banjo bolt and tighten to 43 ft. lbs. (58 Nm).

42. Remove the plug from the steering gear inlet pipe.

43. Install the NEW copper sealing washers.

44. Install the power steering gear inlet pipe to power steering gear retaining banjo bolt and tighten to 43 ft. lbs. (58 Nm).

45. Remove the container with the drained fluid from the vehicle.

46. Install the driver side caster arm to the steering knuckle.

47. Install the driver side front castor arm ball joint to steering knuckle NEW retaining nut.

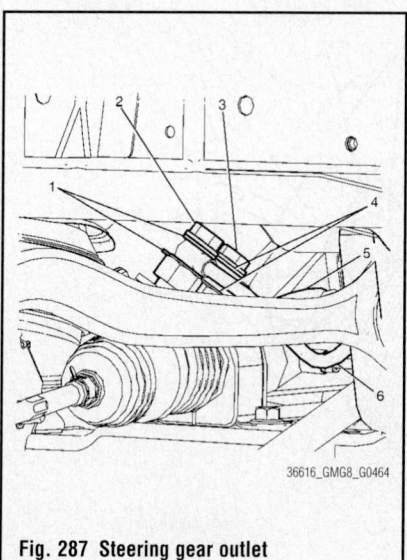

Fig. 287 Steering gear outlet pipe removal

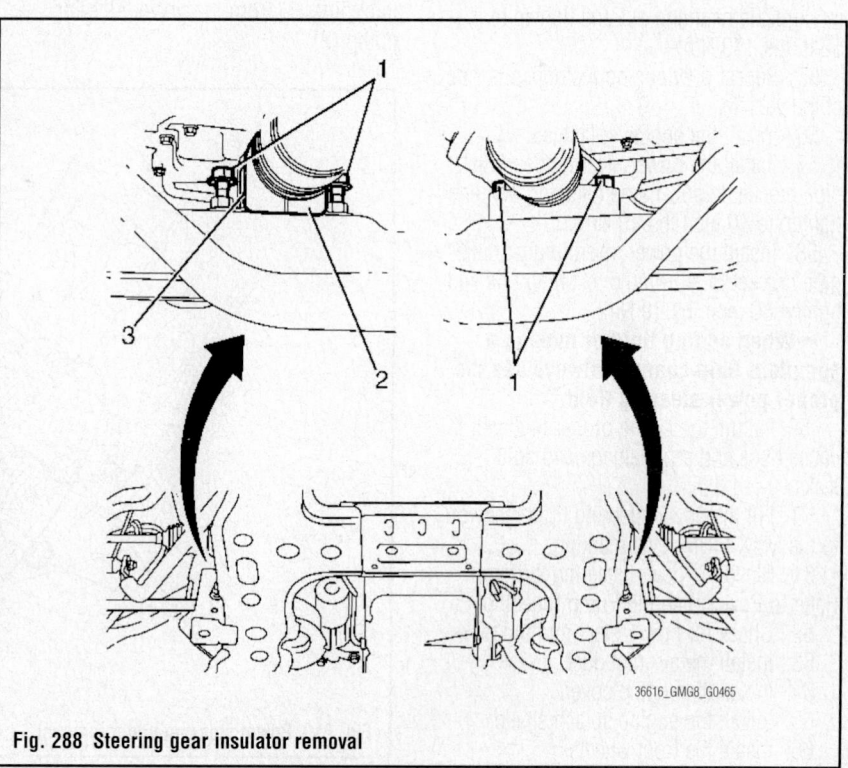

Fig. 288 Steering gear insulator removal

48. Install the NEW driver side caster arm to steering knuckle retaining nut.
   a. Tighten the nut:
   • First Pass: Tighten the nut to 30 ft. lbs. (40 Nm).
   • Final Pass: Tighten the nut an additional 60 degrees using E7115.

➡**Aligning the reference marks will minimize the steering adjustment procedure.**

49. Align the reference mark on the intermediate steering shaft and the reference mark on the pinion shaft.
50. Connect the intermediate steering shaft to the pinion shaft.
51. Install the NEW intermediate steering shaft to pinion shaft retaining bolt and tighten to 18 ft. lbs. (25 Nm).

➡**To minimize the wheel alignment procedure the tie rod end must be installed the distance as was noted in the removal procedure.**

➡**To minimize the wheel alignment procedure align the reference mark on the tie rod end and the reference mark on the tie rod end lock nut.**

➡**The tie rod end lock nut is not to be fully tightened at this stage.**

52. Connect the tie rod end to the steering gear assembly.
53. Connect the tie rod end to the steering knuckle.
54. Install the NEW tie rod end to steering knuckle retaining nut and tighten to 52 ft. lbs. (70 Nm).
55. Repeat previous on the opposite side of the vehicle.
56. Install the engine splash shield.
57. Install the power steering gear inlet pipe bracket to sub-frame retaining bolt and tighten to 80 inch lbs. (9 Nm).
58. Install the power steering gear outlet pipe bracket to sub-frame retaining bolt and tighten 80 inch lbs. (9 Nm).

➡**When adding fluid or making a complete fluid change, always use the proper power steering fluid.**

59. Failure to use the proper fluid will cause hose and seal damage and fluid leaks.
60. Fill the power steering fluid reservoir to the MAXIMUM level marking.
61. Bleed the power steering system. Refer to Power Steering Pump Bleeding.
62. Check for power steering fluid leaks.
63. Install the air inlet duct.
64. Install the engine cover.
65. Install the engine splash shield.
66. Install the front wheels.

67. Lower the vehicle.
68. Bounce the vehicle several times to settle the suspension.
69. Check and adjust the wheel alignment.
70. Tighten the tie rod end lock nut and tighten to 37 ft. lbs. (50 Nm).

POWER STEERING PUMP

REMOVAL & INSTALLATION
See Figure 289.

1. Before servicing the vehicle, refer to the Precautions Section.
2. Remove the engine dress cover.
3. Remove the Mass Air Flow (MAF) sensor, if necessary.
4. Remove the air inlet duct.
5. Remove the upper section of the air box. Refer to Air Cleaner in Engine Mechanical.
6. Remove the power steering drive belt. Refer to Accessory Drive Belt in Engine Mechanical.
7. Place a large suitable container under the vehicle in order to collect draining power steering fluid.

➡**The copper sealing washers (6 and 8) must be discarded after removal.**

8. Remove the power steering gear inlet pipe to power steering pump retaining banjo bolt (3) and copper sealing washers (6 and 8).
9. Discard the washers.
10. Disconnect the power steering gear inlet pipe (5) from the power steering pump (2).

➡**The power steering gear inlet pipe/hose (5) must be plugged to prevent the entry of foreign particles into the power steering system.**

11. Plug the power steering gear inlet pipe/hose (5).
12. Release the power steering fluid reservoir outlet pipe/hose spring clamp (7).

➡ **The power steering power steering fluid reservoir outlet pipe/hose (4) must be plugged to prevent the entry of foreign particles into the power steering system.**

13. Disconnect the power steering fluid reservoir outlet pipe/hose (4) from the power steering pump (2). Plug the power steering fluid reservoir outlet pipe/hose (4).

➡**Bolts with micro-encapsulated thread sealant must be discarded after removal.**

14. Remove the power steering pump to power steering pump bracket retaining bolts (9).
15. Discard the bolts.
16. Remove the power steering pump (2) from the power steering pump bracket (1).

To install:
17. Position the power steering pump to the power steering pump bracket.
18. Install the NEW power steering pump to power steering pump bracket retaining bolts and tighten to 20 ft. lbs. (27 Nm).
19. Remove the plug from the power steering gear inlet pipe/hose.

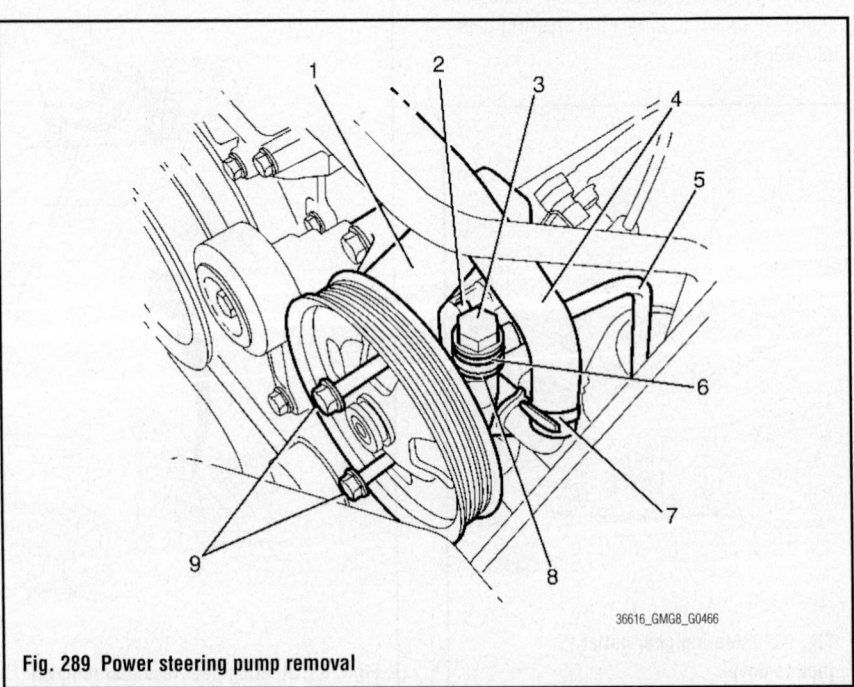

36616_GMG8_G0466

Fig. 289 Power steering pump removal

20. Connect the power steering gear inlet pipe/hose to the power steering pump.

21. Install the power steering gear inlet pipe to power steering pump retaining banjo bolt and NEW copper sealing washers and tighten to 35 ft. lbs. (48 Nm).

22. Remove the plug from the power steering fluid reservoir outlet pipe/hose.

23. Connect the power steering fluid reservoir outlet pipe/hose to the power steering pump.

24. Tighten the power steering fluid reservoir outlet hose spring clamp.

25. Install the power steering drive belt.

26. Install the MAF sensor.

27. Install the upper section of the air box.

28. Install the air inlet duct.

✳✳ WARNING

When adding fluid or making a complete fluid change, always use the proper power steering fluid. Failure to use the proper fluid will cause hose and seal damage and fluid leaks.

29. Fill power steering fluid reservoir with fluid to FULL level mark on the fluid reservoir.

30. Bleed the power steering system. Refer to Power Steering Pump Bleeding.

31. Check for power steering fluid leaks.

32. Remove the container from under the vehicle.

33. Install the engine dress cover.

BLEEDING

1. Before servicing the vehicle, refer to the Precautions Section.

➡**Use approved new power steering fluid from a sealed container. For fluid specifications refer to Fluid and Lubricant Recommendations. Hoses touching the frame, body or engine may cause power steering system noise. Verify that the hoses do not touch any other part of the vehicle.**

➡**Loose connections may not leak, but may allow air into the steering system. Verify that all hose connections are tight.**

✳✳ WARNING

When adding fluid or making a complete fluid change, always use the

proper power steering fluid. Failure to use the proper fluid will cause hose and seal damage and fluid leaks.

➡**Power steering fluid level must be maintained throughout bleed procedure.**

2. Fill power steering fluid reservoir with fluid to the COLD MAX level mark on the reservoir.

3. Raise the vehicle until the front wheels are off the ground. Refer to Lifting and Jacking the Vehicle.

4. With the engine OFF, turn the steering wheel from stop to stop 12 times.

5. Verify power steering fluid level per operating specification.

6. Start the engine and allow to run at idle for three seconds, turn the engine OFF.

7. Repeat steps 5 and 6 until the power steering level remains constant.

8. Start the engine and allow to run at idle.

9. Rotate steering wheel from left to right 8 times. Check for sign of cavitation or fluid aeration (pump noise/whining).

10. Turn the engine OFF. Verify the fluid level.

SUSPENSION

CONTROL LINKS

REMOVAL & INSTALLATION

See Figure 290.

1. Before servicing the vehicle, refer to the Precautions Section.

2. Raise and support the vehicle.

3. Remove the front wheel.

➡**Nuts with micro-encapsulated thread sealant must be discarded after removal.**

4. Remove the stabilizer bar link to stabilizer bar retaining nut.

5. Discard the nut.

6. Disconnect the stabilizer bar link from the stabilizer bar.

7. Remove the stabilizer bar link to strut assembly retaining nut (2).

8. Discard the nut.

9. Remove the stabilizer link bar (1) from the strut assembly bracket (3).

10. Inspect all parts for wear and damage.

To install:

➡**Install the shorter link end to the stabilizer bar.**

11. Install the stabilizer bar link to the stabilizer bar.

12. Install the NEW stabilizer bar link to stabilizer bar retaining nut and tighten to 35 ft. lbs. (48 Nm).

FRONT SUSPENSION

➡**Install the longer link end to the strut.**

13. Install the stabilizer bar link to the strut assembly bracket.

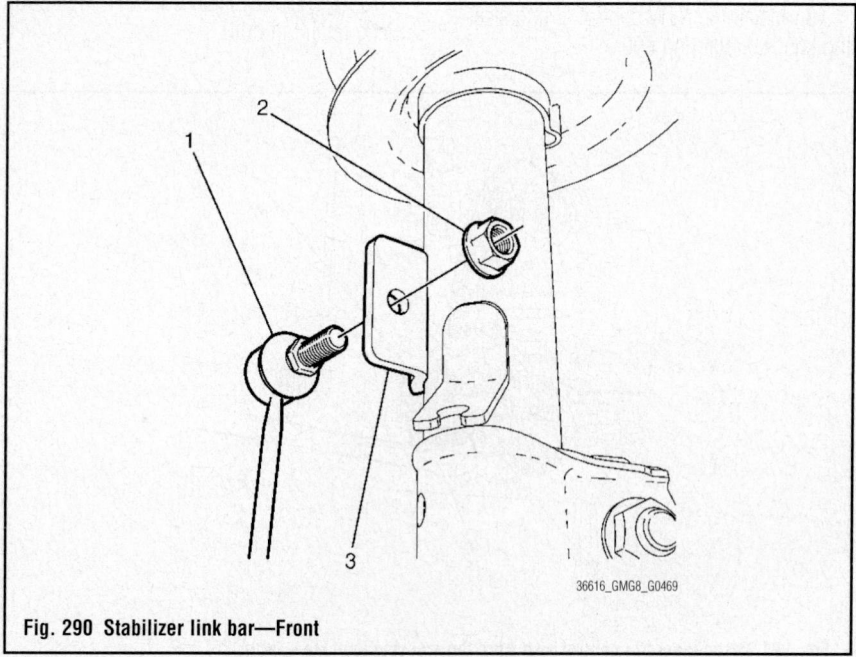

36616_GMG8_G0469

Fig. 290 Stabilizer link bar—Front

14. Install the NEW stabilizer bar link to strut assembly retaining nut and tighten to 35 ft. lbs. (48 Nm).

15. Install the front wheel.

16. Remove the safety stands.

17. Lower the vehicle to the ground.

FRONT CONTROL ARM

REMOVAL & INSTALLATION

See Figures 291 and 292.

1. Before servicing the vehicle, refer to the Precautions Section.

2. Raise and support the vehicle.

3. Remove the front wheel.

4. Loosen the control arm to steering knuckle retaining nut about two turns.

5. Using J-42188-B (1) disconnect the control arm (2) from the steering knuckle (3).

6. Remove and discard the control arm to steering knuckle retaining nut.

7. Separate the control arm from the steering knuckle.

8. Remove and discard the control arm to sub-frame retaining bolt (1).

9. Remove the front control arm (3) from the sub-frame (2).

To install:

10. Install the front control arm to the sub-frame.

➡**The NEW front control arm to sub-frame retaining bolt must not be fully tightened at this stage.**

11. Install the NEW front control arm to sub-frame retaining bolt.

12. Install the front control arm to the steering knuckle.

13. Install the NEW control arm to steering knuckle retaining nut.

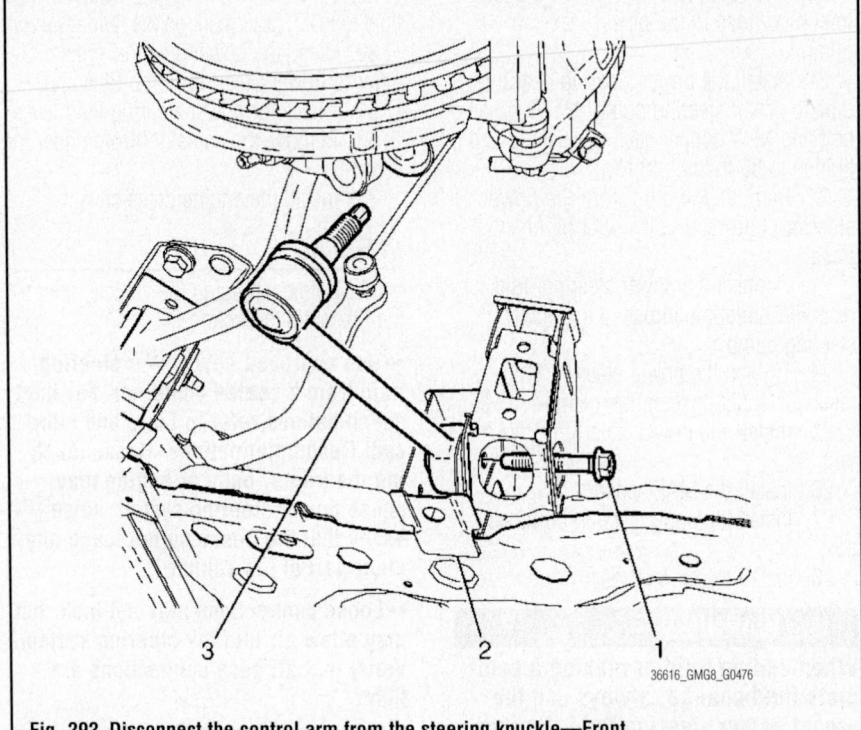

Fig. 292 Disconnect the control arm from the steering knuckle—Front

14. Tighten the nut:
   - First Pass: Tighten the nut to 30 ft. lbs. (40 Nm).
   - Final Pass: Tighten the nut an additional 60 degrees using E7115.

15. Install the front wheel.

16. Lower the vehicle.

17. Bounce the vehicle several times to settle the suspension.

18. Check and adjust the wheel alignment. Refer to Wheel Alignment Measurement.

19. Tighten the NEW control arm to sub-frame retaining bolt.

20. Tighten the nut:
   - First Pass: Tighten the nut to 37 ft. lbs. (50 Nm).
   - Final Pass: Tighten the nut an additional 120 degrees using E7115.

LOWER CONTROL ARM

REMOVAL & INSTALLATION

See Figures 293 through 295.

1. Before servicing the vehicle, refer to the Precautions Section.

2. Raise and support the vehicle.

3. Remove the front wheel.

4. Loosen the caster arm to steering knuckle retaining nut (1) about two turns.

5. Using J-42188-B (1) disconnect the caster arm (1) from the steering knuckle (2).

6. Remove and discard the caster arm to steering knuckle retaining nut.

7. Separate the caster arm from the steering knuckle.

8. Remove and discard the caster arm to sub-frame retaining bolt (2).

9. Remove the offset washer (1).

10. Remove the end plate with encapsulated retaining nut to sub-frame retainer (4).

11. Remove and discard the end plate with encapsulated retaining nut (3).

12. Remove the caster arm from the sub-frame.

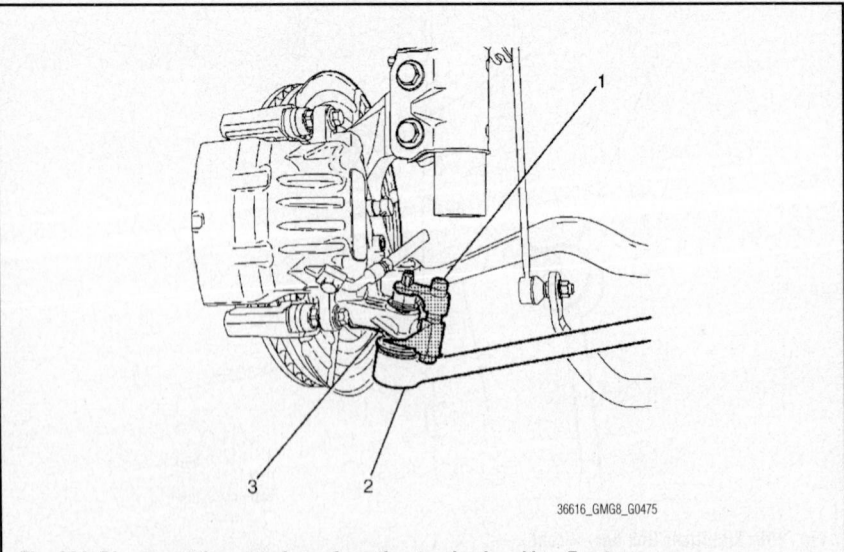

Fig. 291 Disconnect the control arm from the steering knuckle—Front

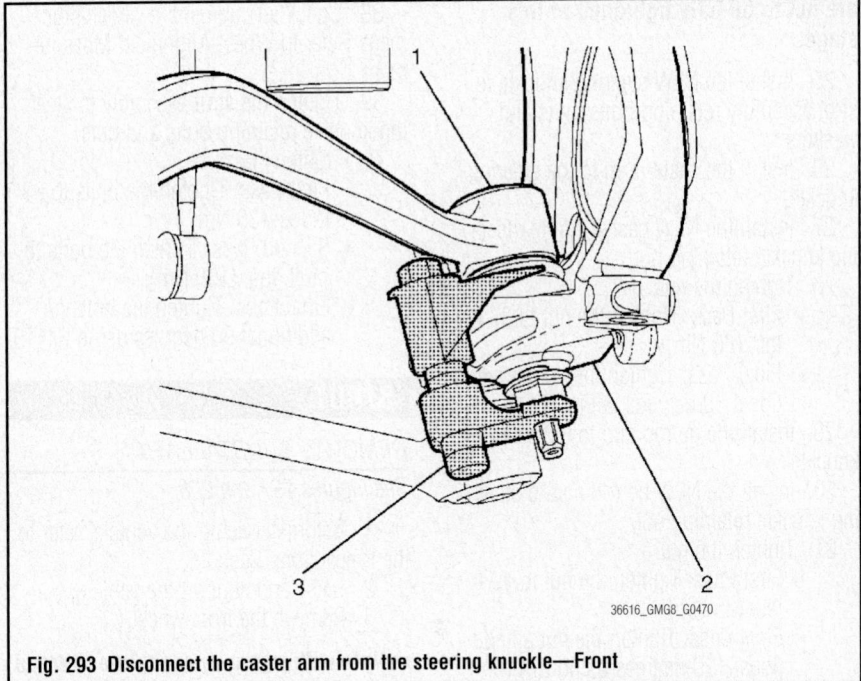

Fig. 293 Disconnect the caster arm from the steering knuckle—Front

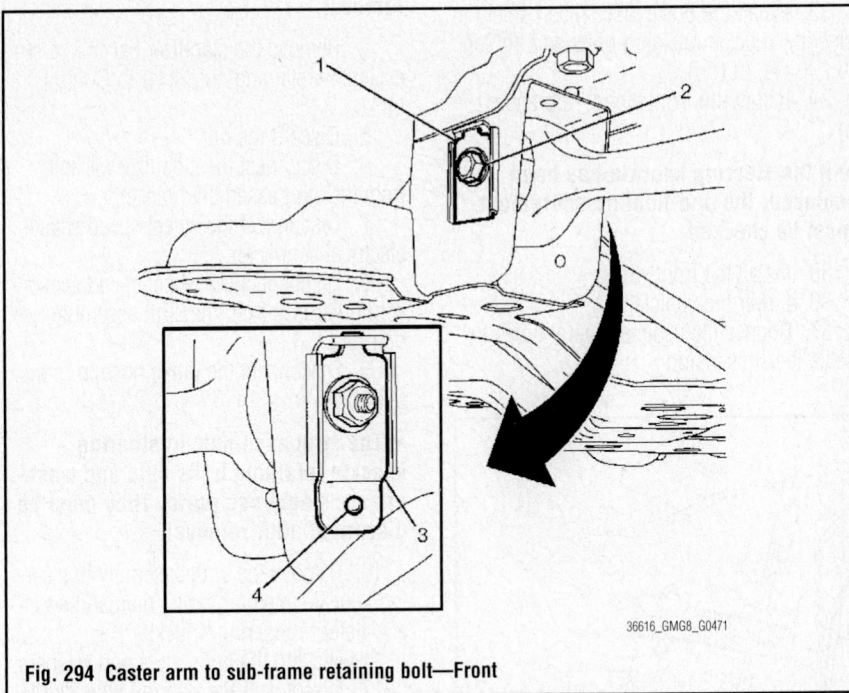

Fig. 294 Caster arm to sub-frame retaining bolt—Front

To install:

13. Install the NEW caster arm to the sub-frame.

➡**The caster arm to sub-frame retaining bolt is not to be fully tightened at this stage.**

14. Install the NEW end plate with encapsulated retaining nut.

15. Install the end plate with encapsulated retaining nut to sub-frame retainer.

16. Install the offset washer.

17. Install the NEW caster arm to sub-frame retaining bolt.

18. Install the caster arm to the steering knuckle.

19. Install the NEW caster arm to steering knuckle retaining nut.

20. Tighten the nut:
- First Pass: Tighten the nut to 30 ft. lbs. (40 Nm).
- Final Pass: Tighten the nut an additional 60 degrees using E7115.

21. Install the front wheel.

22. Lower the vehicle.

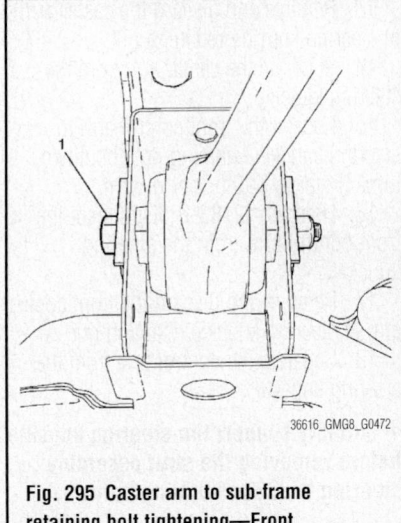

Fig. 295 Caster arm to sub-frame retaining bolt tightening—Front

23. Bounce the vehicle several times to settle the suspension.

24. Check and adjust the wheel alignment.

25. Tighten the caster arm to sub-frame retaining bolt.

26. Tighten the bolts:
- First Pass: Tighten the bolts to 37ft. lbs. (50 Nm).
- Final Pass: Tighten the bolts an additional 120 degrees using E7115

STEERING KNUCKLE

REMOVAL & INSTALLATION

See Figure 296.

1. Before servicing the vehicle, refer to the Precautions Section.

2. Raise and support the vehicle.

3. Remove the front wheel.

4. Remove the front wheel hub assembly. Refer to Wheel Hub and Bearing (sealed unit)

5. Remove the brake disc splash shield to steering knuckle retaining bolts.

6. Remove the brake disc splash shield from the steering knuckle.

7. Loosen the tie rod end to steering knuckle retaining nut about two turns. Refer to Steering Linkage in Steering.

8. Using J-42188-B disconnect the tie rod end from the steering knuckle.

9. Remove and discard the tie rod end to steering knuckle retaining nut.

10. Separate the tie rod end from the steering knuckle.

11. Loosen the caster arm to steering knuckle retaining nut about two turns. Refer to Lower Control Arm.

12. Using J-42188-B disconnect the caster arm from the steering knuckle.

13. Remove and discard the caster arm to steering knuckle retaining nut.

14. Separate the caster arm from the steering knuckle.

15. Loosen the front control arm to steering knuckle retaining nut about two turns. Refer to Front Control Arm.

16. Using J-42188-B disconnect the front control arm from the steering knuckle.

17. Remove and discard the front control arm to steering knuckle retaining nut.

18. Separate the control arm from the steering knuckle.

➡ **Suitably support the steering knuckle before removing the strut assembly to steering knuckle retaining bolts.**

19. Remove and discard the strut assembly to steering knuckle retaining bolts (2), nuts (4) and washers (1).

20. Remove the steering knuckle from the strut assembly.

To install:

21. Install the steering knuckle to the control arm.

22. Install the NEW control arm to steering knuckle retaining nut.

23. Tighten
- First Pass: Tighten the nut to 30 ft. lbs. (40 Nm).
- Final Pass: Tighten the nut an additional 60 degrees using E7115.

24. Install the steering knuckle to strut assembly.

➡ **The steering knuckle to strut assembly retaining bolts, nuts and washers**

are not to be fully tightened at this stage.

25. Install the NEW steering knuckle to strut assembly retaining bolts, nuts and washers.

26. Install the caster arm to the steering knuckle.

27. Install the NEW caster arm to steering knuckle retaining nut.

28. Tighten the nut:
- First Pass: Tighten the nut to 37 ft. lbs. (40 Nm).
- Final Pass: Tighten the nut an additional 60 degrees using E7115 .

29. Install the tie rod end to the steering knuckle.

30. Install the NEW tie rod end to steering knuckle retaining nut.

31. Tighten the nut:
- First Pass: Tighten the nut to 19 ft. lbs. (25 Nm).
- Final Pass: Tighten the nut an additional 120 degrees using E7115.

32. Install the brake disc splash shield.

33. Install the brake disc splash shield to steering knuckle retaining bolts and tighten to 7 ft. lbs. (9 Nm).

34. Install the front wheel hub assembly.

➡ **If the steering knuckle has been replaced, the end-float measurement must be checked.**

35. Install the front wheel.

36. Lower the vehicle.

37. Bounce the vehicle several times to settle the suspension.

38. Check and adjust the wheel alignment. Refer to Wheel Alignment Measurement.

39. Tighten the strut assembly to steering knuckle retaining bolts and nuts.

40. Tighten the bolt:
- First Pass: Tighten the bolts to 63 ft. lbs. (85 Nm).
- Second Pass: Tighten the bolts to 75 ft. lbs. (100 Nm).
- Final Pass: Tighten the bolts an additional 90 degrees using E7115.

STRUT

REMOVAL & INSTALLATION

See Figures 297 and 298.

1. Before servicing the vehicle, refer to the Precautions Section.

2. Raise and support the vehicle.

3. Remove the front wheel.

➡ **Nuts with micro-encapsulated thread sealant must be discarded after removal.**

4. Remove the stabilizer bar link to strut assembly retaining nut. Refer to Control Links.

5. Discard the nut.

6. Disconnect the stabilizer bar link from the strut assembly bracket.

7. Disconnect the wheel speed sensor electrical connector.

8. Disconnect the wheel speed sensor wiring harness from the strut assembly bracket.

9. Disconnect the brake hose from the strut bracket.

➡ **The strut assembly to steering knuckle retaining bolts nuts and washers are single use parts. They must be discarded after removal.**

10. Remove the strut assembly to steering knuckle retaining bolts, nuts and washers. Refer to Steering Knuckle.

11. Discard the bolts, nuts and washers.

12. Disconnect the steering knuckle (1) from the strut assembly (2).

13. Lower the vehicle.

14. Remove the stud dust cover (1) from the strut assembly to body retaining nut (2).

➡ **The strut assembly (4) must be supported from underneath before the strut assembly to body retaining nut (2) is removed.**

15. Remove the strut assembly to body retaining nut (2) while holding the strut piston shaft (4).

16. Discard the nut.

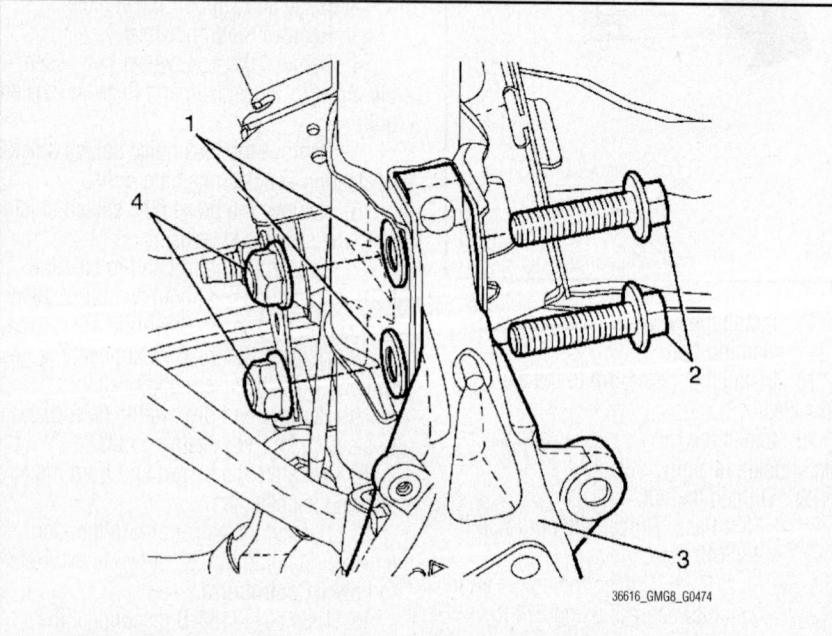

36616_GMG8_G0474

Fig. 296 Strut assembly to steering knuckle retaining bolts—Front

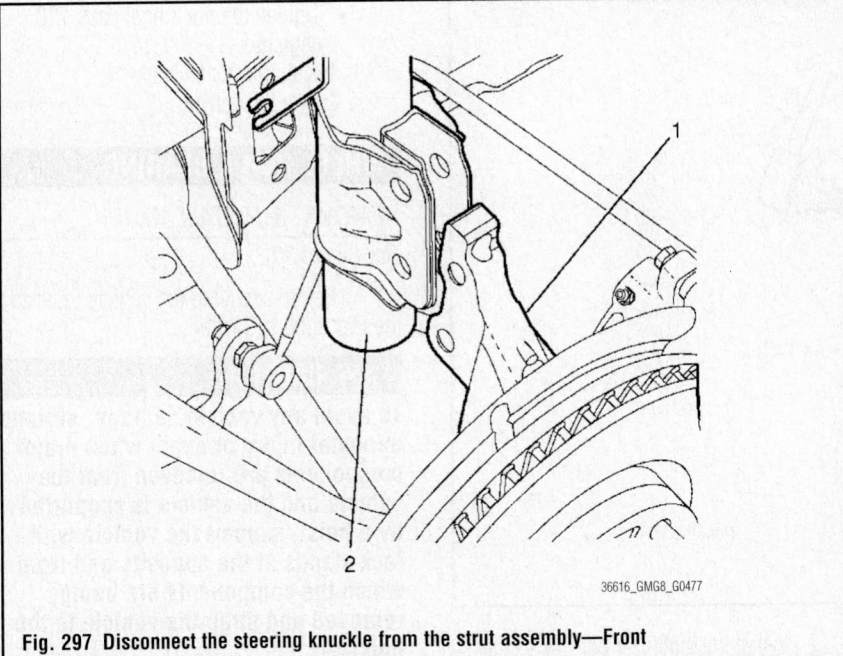

Fig. 297 Disconnect the steering knuckle from the strut assembly—Front

17. Remove the strut assembly to body retaining plate (3).

18. Remove the strut assembly from the vehicle.

19. Inspect all parts for wear and damage.

To install:

➡**The strut assembly retaining nut must be checked for correct torque before installing the strut assembly into the vehicle. The strut assembly retaining nut torque must be 55 ft. lbs. (75 Nm).**

20. Check the torque of the strut assembly retaining nut, correct if necessary.

21. Install the strut assembly to the vehicle.

22. Install strut assembly to body retaining plate.

➡**The strut assembly to body retaining nut must not be fully tightened at this stage.**

23. Install the NEW strut assembly to body retaining nut to the strut assembly.

24. Do not fully tighten at this stage.

25. Raise the vehicle.

26. Install the steering knuckle to the strut assembly.

27. Pivot the hub and steering knuckle assembly sufficiently to line up the bolt holes in the steering knuckle and strut assembly.

28. The strut assembly to steering knuckle retaining bolts and nuts must not be fully tightened at this stage.

29. Install the NEW Strut assembly to steering knuckle retaining bolts, nuts and washers.

30. Do not fully tighten at this stage.

31. Lower the vehicle.

32. Install the NEW strut assembly to the body retaining nut and tighten to 40 ft. lbs. (55 Nm).

33. Install the dust cover to the strut assembly to body retaining nut.

34. Raise the vehicle.

35. Install the brake hose to the strut assembly bracket.

36. Connect the wheel speed sensor electrical connector.

37. Install the wheel speed sensor wiring harness to the strut assembly bracket.

38. Connect the stabilizer bar link to the strut assembly bracket.

39. Install the stabilizer bar link to the strut assembly bracket retaining nut and tighten to 37 ft. lbs. (50 Nm).

40. Install the front wheel.

41. Remove the safety stands.

42. Lower the vehicle to the ground.

43. Bounce the vehicle several times to settle the suspension.

44. Check and adjust the wheel alignment.

45. Install the strut assembly to the steering knuckle retaining bolts and nuts and tighten:

- The nuts a first pass to 63 ft. lbs. (85 Nm)
- The nuts a second pass to 74 ft. lbs.(100 Nm)
- The nuts an additional 90 degrees

STABILIZER SHAFT

REMOVAL & INSTALLATION

See Figures 299 and 300.

1. Before servicing the vehicle, refer to the Precautions Section.

2. Raise and support the vehicle.

3. Remove the driver side front wheel.

4. Remove and discard the stabilizer bar link to stabilizer bar retaining nut (1).

5. Disconnect the stabilizer bar link (2) from the stabilizer bar (3).

6. Repeat steps 4 and 5 for the opposite side of the stabilizer bar.

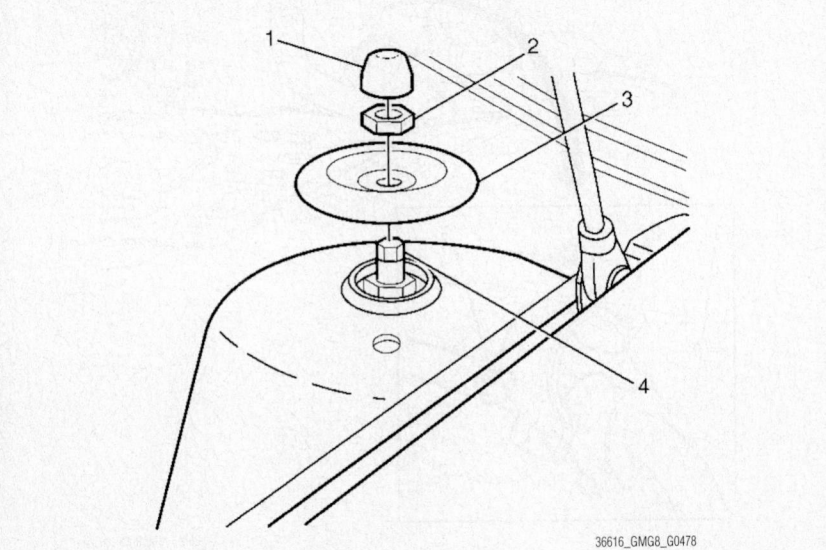

Fig. 298 Disconnect the steering knuckle from the strut assembly—Front

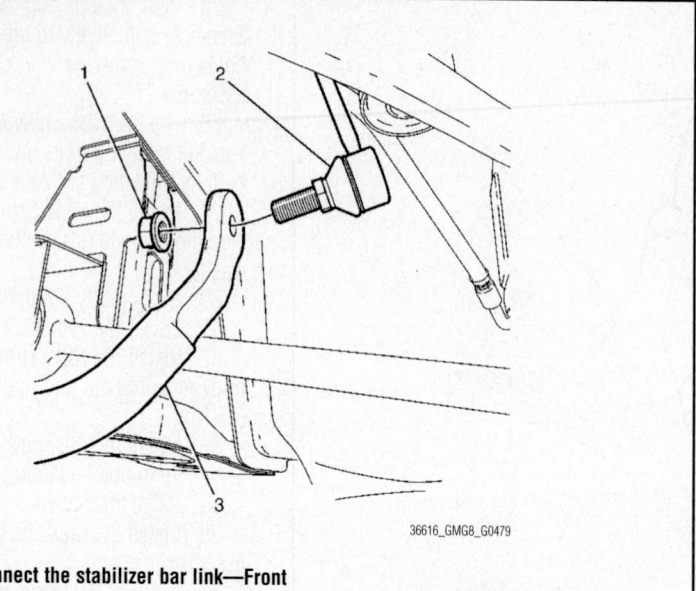

Fig. 299 Disconnect the stabilizer bar link—Front

7. Loosen the tie rod end to steering knuckle retaining nut about two turns. Refer to Steering Linkage in Steering.

8. Using J-42188-B disconnect the driver side tie rod end from the steering knuckle.

9. Remove and discard the driver side tie rod end to steering knuckle retaining nut.

10. Separate the driver side tie rod end from the steering knuckle.

11. Remove the air inlet duct. Refer to Air Cleaner in Engine Mechanical.

12. Remove the power steering gear inlet pipe bracket to sub-frame retaining bolt. Refer to Power Rack & Pinion Steering Gear in Steering.

13. Remove the power steering gear outlet pipe bracket to sub-frame retaining bolt.

14. Remove the stabilizer bar insulators from the stabilizer bar.

15. Remove the stabilizer bar from the vehicle.

To install:

16. Install the NEW stabilizer bar to the vehicle.

17. Install the stabilizer bar insulators.

a. Install the stabilizer bar insulator bracket to the sub-frame retaining nuts on both sides of the stabilizer bar and tighten to 16 ft. lbs. (22 Nm).

18. Install the power steering gear inlet pipe bracket to the sub-frame retaining bolt and tighten to 80 inch lbs. (9 Nm).

19. Install the power steering gear outlet pipe bracket to the sub-frame retaining bolt and tighten to 80 inch lbs. (9 Nm).

20. Install the air inlet duct.

21. Connect the stabilizer bar link to the NEW stabilizer bar.

22. Install the stabilizer bar link to the stabilizer bar retaining nut and tighten to 35 ft. lbs. (48 Nm).

23. Repeat steps 6 and 7 for the opposite side of the stabilizer bar.

24. Install the driver side tie rod end to the steering knuckle.

25. Install the NEW driver side tie rod end to steering knuckle retaining nut and tighten:

- Tighten the nut a first pass to 19 ft. lbs. (25 Nm).

- Tighten the nut a final pass 120 degrees.

26. Install the front wheel.

27. Lower the vehicle.

WHEEL HUB & BEARING

REMOVAL & INSTALLATION

See Figure 301.

1. Before servicing the vehicle, refer to the Precautions Section.

✳✳ CAUTION

To avoid any vehicle damage, serious personal injury or death when major components are removed from the vehicle and the vehicle is supported by a hoist, support the vehicle with jack stands at the opposite end from which the components are being removed and strap the vehicle to the hoist.

2. Raise and support the vehicle.

3. Remove the front wheel.

4. Remove the brake disc. Refer to Front Disc Brakes in Brakes.

5. Disconnect the wheel speed sensor electrical connector.

➡**Before a hub assembly is replaced, the end-float measurement must be checked. Refer to Inspection.**

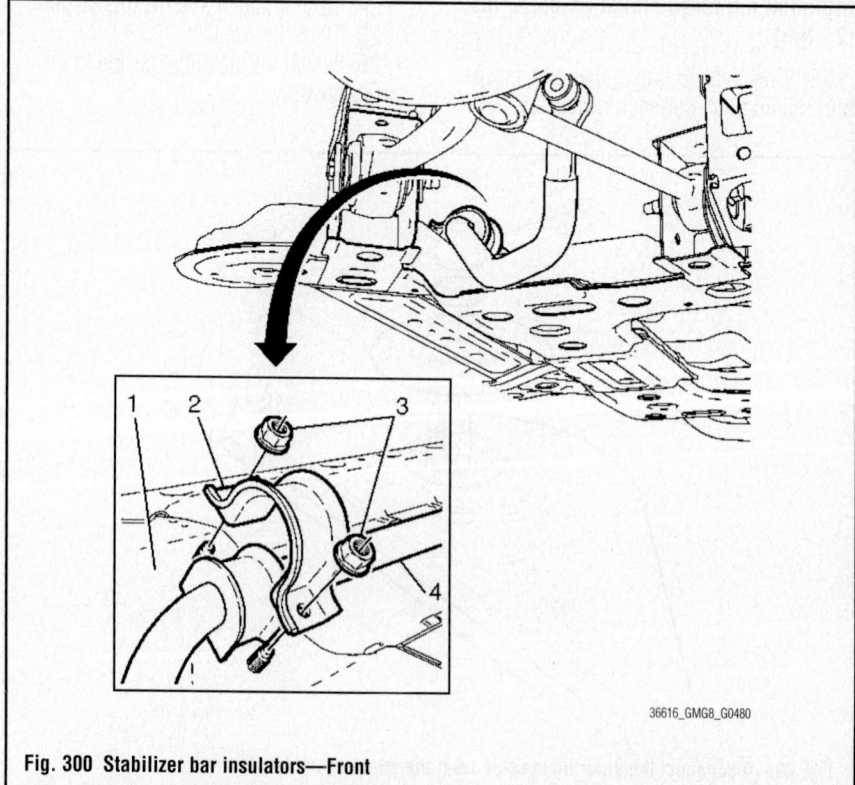

Fig. 300 Stabilizer bar insulators—Front

→Bolts with micro-encapsulated thread sealant must be discarded after removal.

6. Remove the hub assembly to steering knuckle retaining bolts (2).

7. Discard the bolts.

8. Remove the hub assembly (1) from the steering knuckle (3).

To install:

→Wheel studs are the only serviceable item of the front wheel hub assembly.

9. Install the hub assembly to the steering knuckle.

→After a hub assembly is replaced, the end-float measurement must be checked.

10. Install the NEW hub assembly to the steering knuckle retaining bolts and tighten to 79 ft. lbs. (107.5 Nm).

11. Connect the wheel speed sensor electrical connector.

12. Install the brake disc.

13. Install the front wheel.

14. Remove the safety stands.

15. Lower the vehicle to the ground.

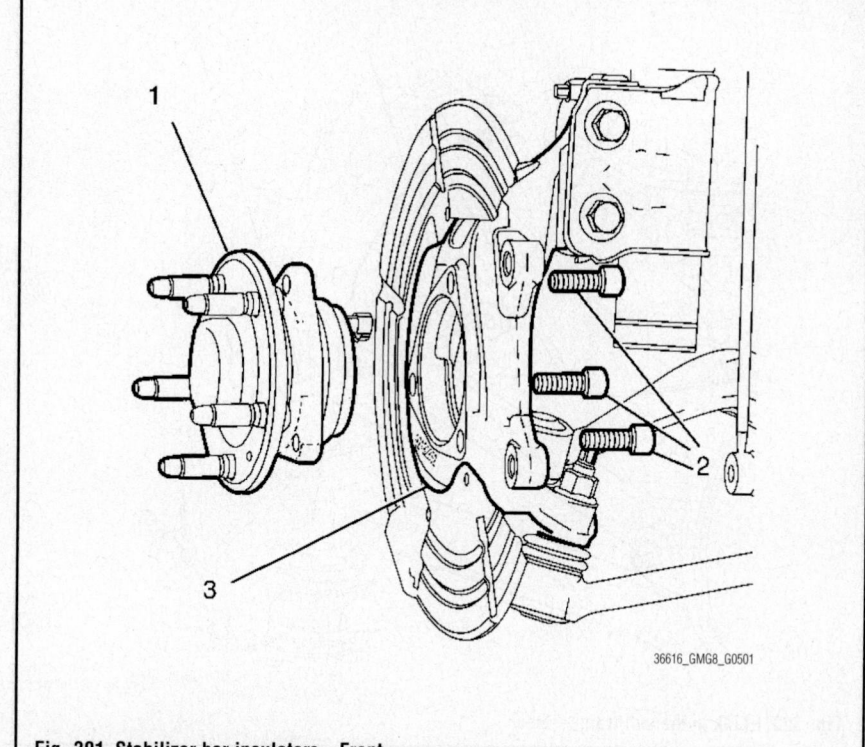

Fig. 301 Stabilizer bar insulators—Front

SUSPENSION

ADJUST LINK (I-LINK)

REMOVAL & INSTALLATION

See Figures 302 and 303.

1. Before servicing the vehicle, refer to the Precautions Section.

2. Raise and support the vehicle.

3. Remove the rear wheel.

4. Disconnect the wheel speed sensor electrical connector.

5. Detach the wheel speed sensor wiring harness retainers.

6. Remove the I-Link to knuckle retaining bolt (1).

→Mark the I-Link to sub-frame retaining bolt (3) in relation to the sub-frame

REAR SUSPENSION

before removing the I-Link to sub-frame retaining nut (1).

7. Remove the I-Link to sub-frame retaining nut (1), eccentric washer (2) and retaining bolt (3).

8. Discard the I-Link to sub-frame retaining nut (1).

9. Remove the I-Link (4) from the sub-frame.

To install:

→The I-Link to sub-frame retaining bolt and nut must not to be fully tightened at this stage.

10. Install the I-Link into the sub-frame.

11. Install the I-Link to sub-frame retaining bolt, eccentric washer and NEW nut.

12. Align the marking of the I-Link to sub-frame retaining bolt in relation to the rear sub-frame marking.

13. The I-Link to knuckle retaining bolt must not to be fully tightened at this stage.

14. Install the I-Link to knuckle retaining bolt.

→The weight of the vehicle must be on a level surface and on all four wheels before fully tightening the nut.

15. Tighten the I-Link to sub-frame retaining nut to 129 ft. lbs. (175 Nm).

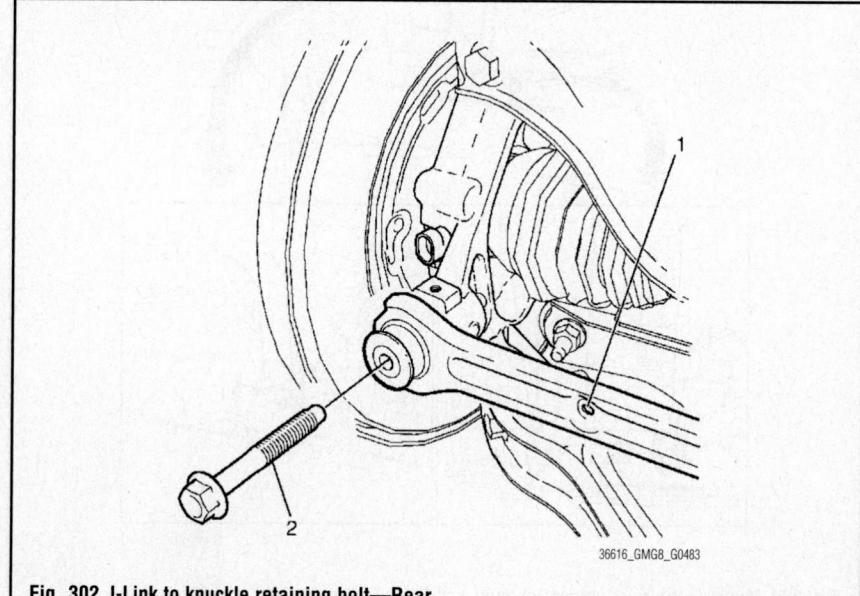

Fig. 302 I-Link to knuckle retaining bolt—Rear

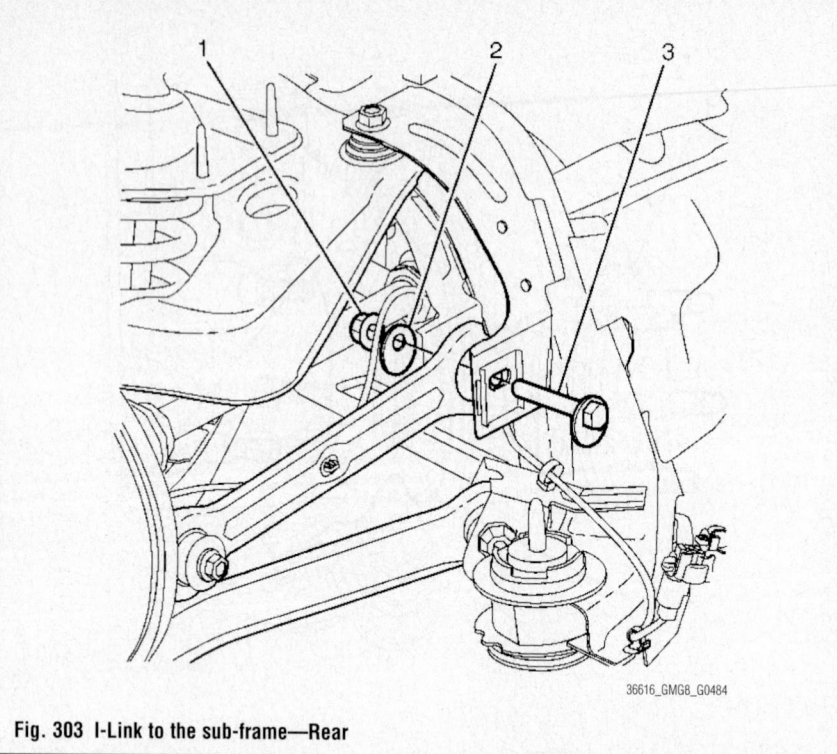

Fig. 303 I-Link to the sub-frame—Rear

16. Connect the wheel speed sensor electrical connector.

17. Attach the wheel speed sensor wiring harness retainers.

18. Tighten the I-Link to knuckle retaining bolt to 103 ft. lbs. (140 Nm).

19. Check the vehicle rear wheel alignment and adjust if necessary.

CONTROL ARMS/LINKS

REMOVAL & INSTALLATION

See Figure 304.

1. Before servicing the vehicle, refer to the Precautions Section.

2. Raise and support the vehicle.

➡ **Nuts with micro-encapsulated thread sealant must be discarded after removal.**

3. Remove the stabilizer bar link to stabilizer bar retaining nut (1).

4. Discard the nut.

5. Disconnect the stabilizer bar link (3) from the stabilizer bar (2).

6. Remove and the stabilizer bar link to lower control arm retaining nut (5).

7. Discard the nut.

8. Remove the stabilizer bar link (3) from the lower control arm (4).

9. Remove the stabilizer bar link (3).

10. Inspect all parts for wear and damage.

To install:

11. Connect the stabilizer bar link to the stabilizer bar.

12. Install the stabilizer bar link to stabilizer bar NEW retaining nut and tighten to 34 ft. lbs. (46 Nm).

13. Install the stabilizer bar link to the lower control arm.

14. Install the stabilizer bar link to lower control arm retaining NEW nut and tighten to 34 ft. lbs. (46 Nm).

15. Remove the safety stands.

16. Lower the vehicle to the ground.

KNUCKLE

REMOVAL & INSTALLATION

See Figures 305 through 308.

1. Before servicing the vehicle, refer to the Precautions Section.

2. Raise and support the vehicle.

3. Remove the rear wheel.

4. Remove the rear brake disc. Refer to Rear Disc Brakes.

5. Install the KM-468 (1) to the wheel hub (2) with two inverted wheel nuts (3).

6. Support the KM-468 (1) outer end on a safety stand.

➡ **The wheel drive shaft retaining nut and washer must be discarded after removal.**

7. Remove the wheel drive shaft retaining nut and washer.

8. Discard the nut and washer.

➡ **The wheel speed sensor cable must be secured to protect it from damage.**

9. Disconnect the wheel speed sensor electrical connector.

10. Detach the wheel speed sensor wiring harness mounting clips.

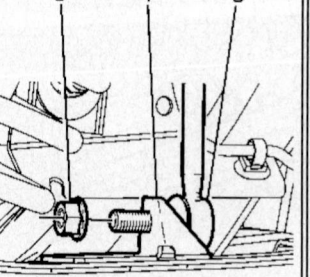
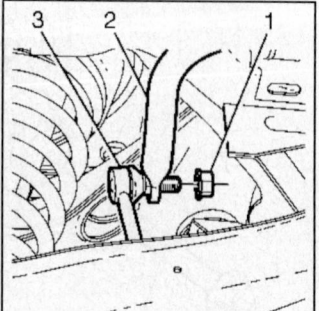

Fig. 304 Measure the total amount of axial end float—Rear

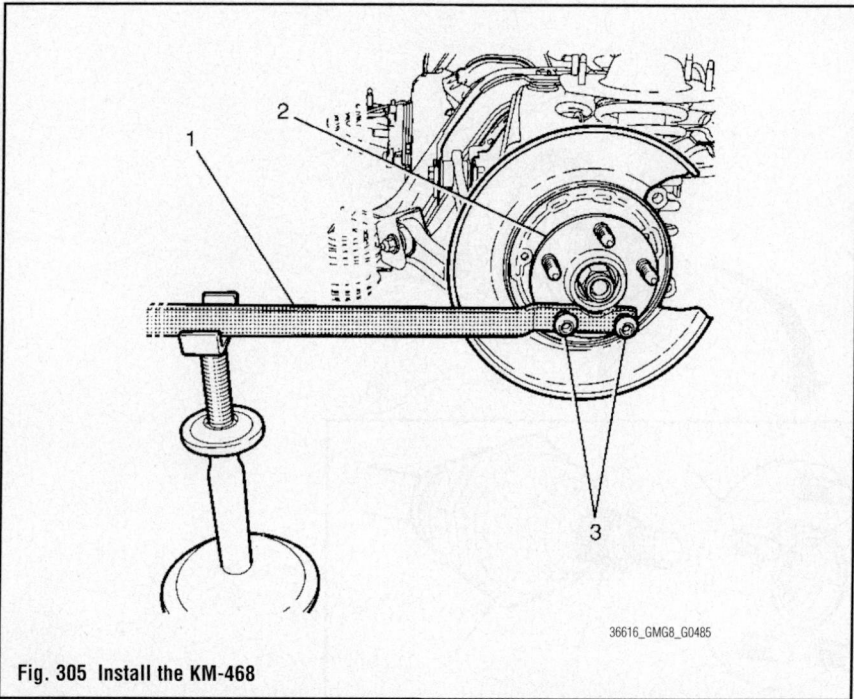

Fig. 305 Install the KM-468

→**Prevailing torque nuts must be discarded after removal.**

11. Remove the lower control arm to knuckle retaining bolt and nut. Refer to Lower Control Arm

12. Discard the nut.

13. Remove the I-Link to knuckle retaining bolt. Refer to Adjust Link.

14. Mark the location of the Y-Link to knuckle retaining bolt and nut relative to the Y-Link for correct re-assembly. Refer to Trailing Arm.

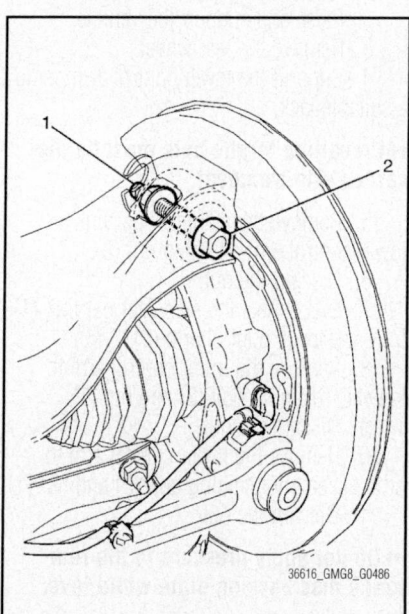

Fig. 306 Upper control arm to knuckle retaining bolt location—Rear

→**Prevailing torque nuts must be discarded after removal.**

15. Remove the Y-Link to knuckle retaining bolt and nut.

16. Discard the nut.

17. Mark the location of the bolt and nut relative to the upper control arm for correct assembly.

→**Do not remove the upper control arm to knuckle retaining bolt and nut.**

18. Loosen the upper control arm to knuckle retaining bolt (2) and nut (1).

19. Install the 7208 (1) to the wheel hub (2).

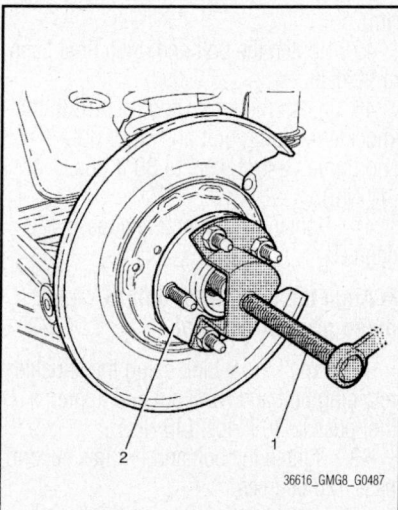

Fig. 307 Tool 7208 to the wheel hub—Rear

20. Press the wheel drive shaft from the wheel hub using the 7208 (1).

21. Remove the 7208 (1) from the wheel hub (2).

→**Prevailing torque nuts must be discarded after removal.**

22. Remove the upper control arm to knuckle retaining bolt and nut.

23. Discard the nut.

24. Remove the wheel hub and knuckle assembly.

To install:

25. Install the wheel hub and knuckle assembly to the upper control arm.

→**The upper control arm to knuckle retaining bolt and NEW nut must not to be fully tightened at this stage.**

26. Install the upper control arm to knuckle retaining bolt and NEW nut.

→**Lightly lubricate the wheel drive shaft outer splined end with the recommended differential lubricant.**

→**Do not excessively push the wheel drive shaft (2) through the wheel hub (1).**

27. Push the wheel drive shaft outer splined end (3) into the splined cavity (4) of the wheel hub (1).

28. Remove the wire used to support the wheel drive shaft.

→**The lower control arm to knuckle retaining bolt and NEW nut must not to be fully tightened at this stage.**

29. Install the lower control arm to knuckle retaining bolt and NEW nut.

30. Install the Y-Link to the knuckle.

→**The Y-Link to knuckle retaining bolt and NEW nut must not to be fully tightened at this stage.**

31. Install the Y-Link to knuckle retaining bolt and NEW nut.

→**The I-Link to knuckle retaining bolt must not to be fully tightened at this stage.**

32. Install the I-Link to knuckle retaining bolt.

33. Connect the wheel speed sensor electrical connector.

34. Attach the wheel speed sensor wiring harness mounting clips.

→**A NEW wheel drive shaft retaining nut and NEW washer must be used when installing the wheel drive shaft.**

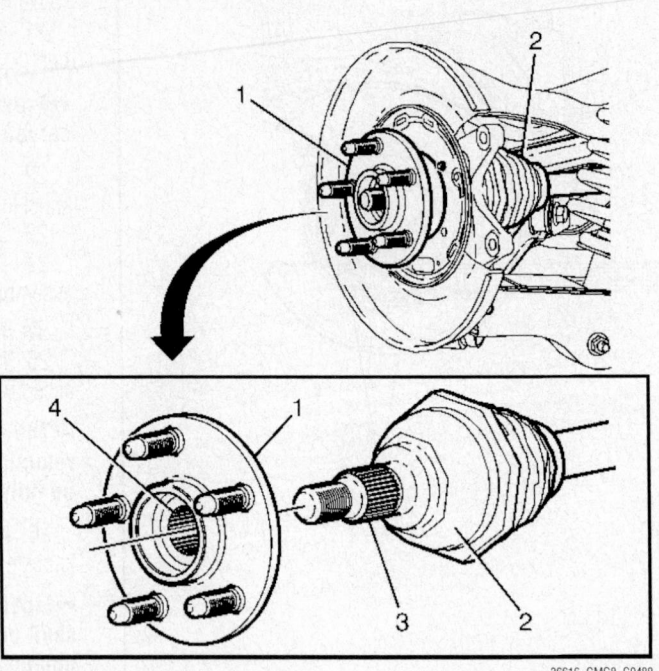

Fig. 308 Installing drive shaft—Rear

35. Install the NEW wheel drive shaft retaining nut and NEW washer.

36. Install the KM-468 to the wheel hub with two inverted wheel nuts and tighten a first pass to 111 ft. lbs. (150 Nm).

37. Support the KM-468 outer end on a safety stand.

➡**Do not exceed the specified tightening values. Premature bearing failure may result.**

38. There are two methods of tightening the wheel drive shaft retaining nut.
   a. Preferred method:
   • Tighten the nut on first pass to 148 ft. lbs. (200 Nm).
   • Loosen the nut on second pass by 180 degrees.
   • Tighten the nut on third pass to 280 ft. lbs. (380 Nm).
   • Crimp nut.
   b. Alternate method:
   • Tighten the nut on first pass to 111 ft. lbs. (150 Nm).
   • Loosen the nut on second pass by 180 degrees.
   • Tighten the nut on the third pass to 111 ft. lbs. (150 Nm).
   • Tighten the nut on the forth pass by 30 degrees.
   • Crimp nut.

39. Install the rear brake disc.

40. Install the rear wheel.

41. Remove the safety stands.

42. Lower the vehicle to the ground.

43. Bounce the vehicle several times to settle the suspension.

➡**The weight of the vehicle must be on a level surface and on all four wheels before fully tightening the nuts and bolts.**

➡**Align the bolt to the mark made prior to removal.**

44. Install the upper control arm using the knuckle retaining bolt and the NEW nut and tighten a first pass to 44 ft. lbs. (60 Nm).

45. Tighten the bolt and nut a final pass to 90 degrees.

46. Install the lower control arm to the knuckle retaining bolt and NEW nut and tighten a first pass to 30 ft. lbs. (40 Nm).

47. Tighten the nut in a final pass 120 degrees.

➡**Align the mark from bolt to Y-Link made prior to removal.**

48. Install the Y-Link using the knuckle retaining bolt and NEW nut and tighten a first pass to 30 ft. lbs. (40 Nm).

49. Tighten the bolt and nut in a second pass 120 degrees.

50. Install the I-Link using the knuckle retaining bolt and tighten to 103 ft. lbs. (140 Nm).

51. Check the vehicle rear wheel alignment and adjust if necessary.

LOWER CONTROL ARM

REMOVAL & INSTALLATION

See Figures 309 through 313.

1. Before servicing the vehicle, refer to the Precautions Section.

2. Raise and support the vehicle.

3. Remove the rear wheel.

4. Support the lower control arm using a suitable jack.

➡**Prevailing torque nuts must be discarded after removal.**

5. Remove the stabilizer bar link to lower control arm retaining nut (3).

6. Discard the nut.

7. Disconnect the stabilizer bar link (1) from the lower control arm (2).

8. Remove the lower control arm to knuckle retaining bolt (2) and nut (1).

9. Discard the nut.

10. Remove the lower control arm to strut assembly retaining bolt (2) and nut (1).

11. Discard the nut.

➡**Do not apply pressure to the rear brake disc backing plate while levering.**

12. Detach the lower control arm using a suitable pry bar.

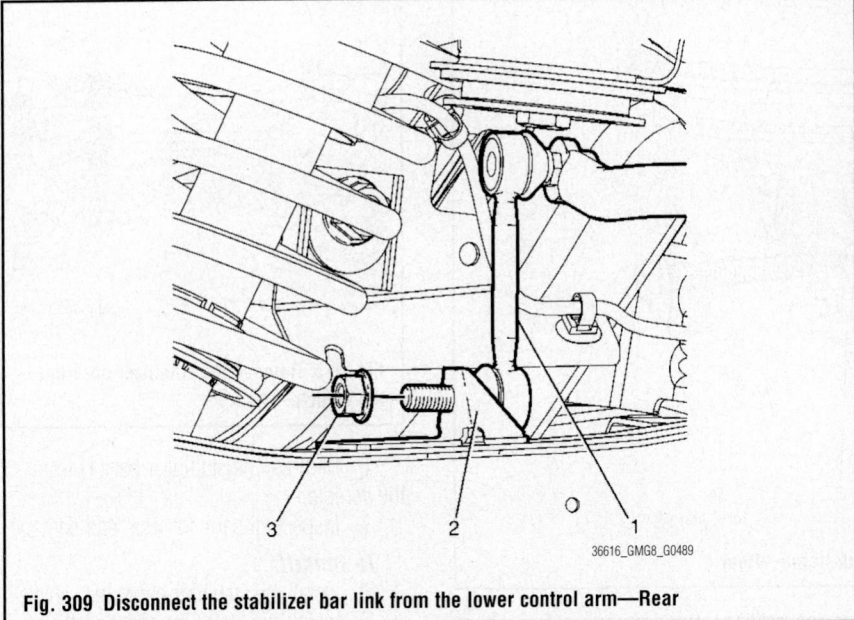

Fig. 309 Disconnect the stabilizer bar link from the lower control arm—Rear

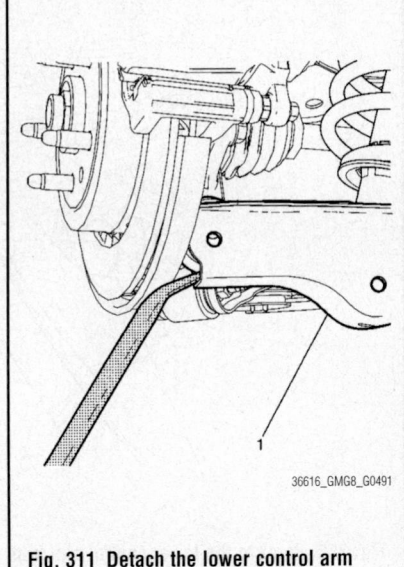

Fig. 311 Detach the lower control arm using a suitable pry bar—Rear

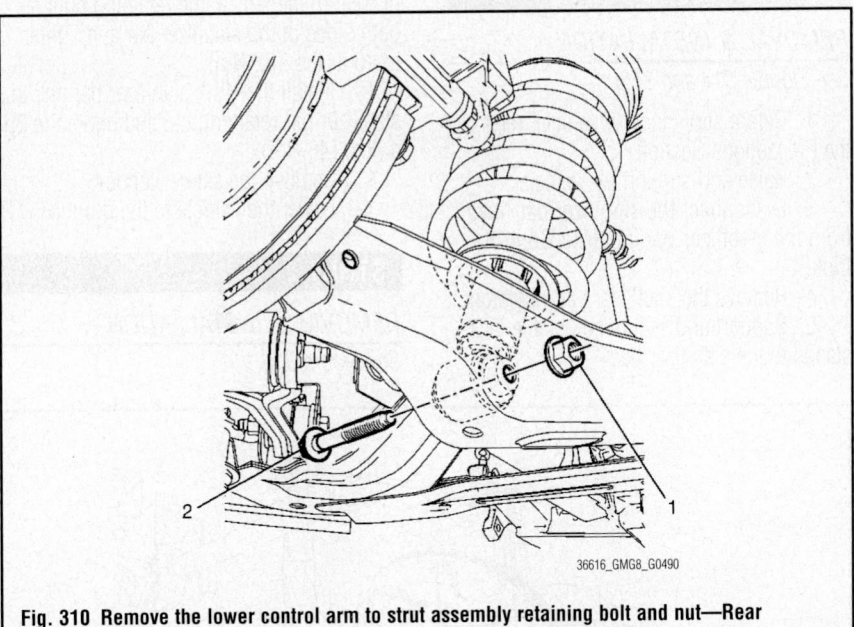

Fig. 310 Remove the lower control arm to strut assembly retaining bolt and nut—Rear

Fig. 312 Scribe the eccentric washers with reference to their seating position relative to the sub-frame—Rear

13. Reposition the jack as necessary.

➡**The lower control arm to sub-frame retaining bolt (1) and nut (2) eccentric washers (3) are used to adjust the rear suspension camber. One eccentric washer (3) is mounted directly to the head of the lower control arm to sub-frame retaining bolt (1).**

14. Scribe the eccentric washers (3) with reference to their seating position relative to the sub-frame.

15. Remove the lower control arm to sub-frame retaining bolt (1) and nut (5).

16. Discard the nut.

17. Remove the lower control arm (4) from the sub-frame (3).

To install:

18. Install the lower control arm into the sub-frame.

➡**The eccentric washers must be fitted correctly in terms of their orientation and alignment marks.**

➡**Do not fully tighten the lower control arm to sub-frame retaining bolt and nut at this stage.**

19. Install the lower control arm to sub-frame retaining bolt.

20. Install the eccentric washer and the NEW nut.

21. Do not fully tighten at this stage.

22. Connect the rear strut assembly to the lower control arm.

➡**Do not fully tighten the lower control arm to strut assembly retaining bolt and nut at this stage.**

23. Install the lower control arm to strut assembly retaining bolt and NEW nut.

24. Do not fully tighten at this stage.

25. Connect the lower control arm to the knuckle using a suitable jack.

➡**Do not fully tighten the lower control arm to knuckle retaining bolt and nut at this stage.**

26. Install the lower control arm to the knuckle retaining bolt and NEW nut.

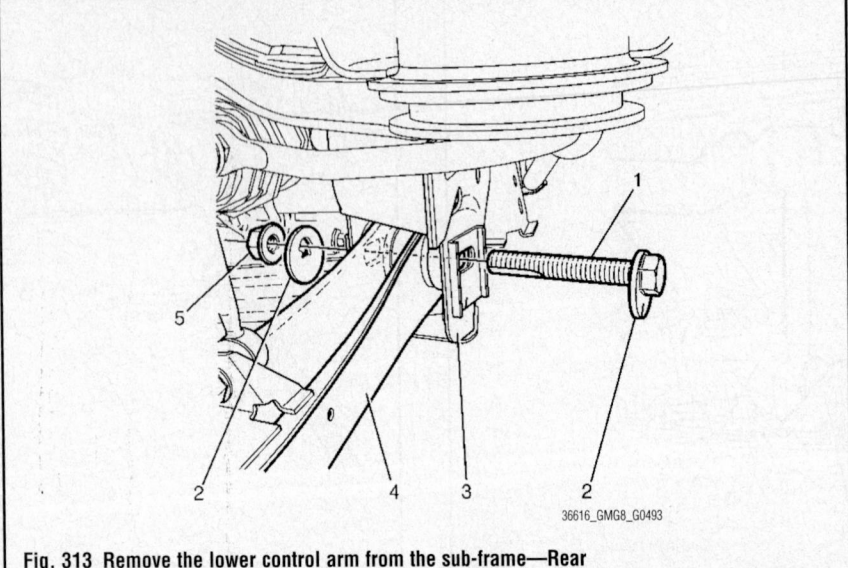

Fig. 313 Remove the lower control arm from the sub-frame—Rear

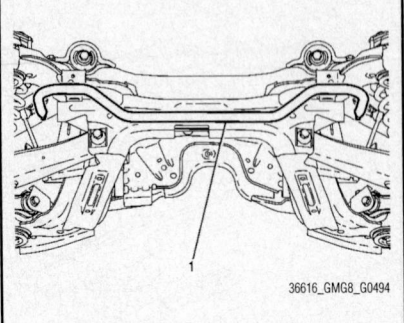

Fig. 315 Remove the stabilizer bar from the vehicle—Rear

27. Do not fully tighten at this stage.

28. Connect the stabilizer bar link to the lower control arm.

29. Install the stabilizer bar link to lower control arm retaining NEW nut and tighten to 34 ft. lbs. (46 Nm).

30. Install the rear wheel.

31. Remove the safety stands.

32. Lower the vehicle to the ground.

33. Bounce the vehicle several times to settle the suspension.

➡The lower control arm to the sub-frame retaining bolt and nut eccentric washers are used to adjust rear suspension camber.

34. Align the marks on the eccentric washers with the marks on the sub-frame.

➡The weight of the vehicle must be on a level surface and on all four wheels before fully tightening the nuts and bolts.

35. Install the lower control arm to sub-frame retaining bolt and nut and tighten to 129 ft. lbs. (175 Nm).

36. Install the lower control arm to strut assembly retaining bolt and nut and tighten to 30 ft. lbs. (40 Nm).

37. Tighten the bolt and nut a final pass 120 degrees.

38. Install the lower control arm to knuckle retaining bolt and nut and tighten a first pass to 30 ft. lbs. (40 Nm).

39. Tighten the bolt and nut a final pass 120 degrees.

40. Check the wheel alignment of the vehicle.

41. Correct the wheel alignment of the vehicle, if necessary.

STABILIZER SHAFT

REMOVAL & INSTALLATION

See Figures 314 and 315.

1. Before servicing the vehicle, refer to the Precautions Section.

2. Raise and support the vehicle.

3. Disconnect the stabilizer bar links from the stabilizer bar. Refer to Control Link.

4. Remove the stabilizer bar insulators.

5. Support and secure adjustable jack stands to the stabilizer bar.

6. Remove the stabilizer bar (1) from the vehicle.

7. Inspect all parts for wear and damage.

To install:

8. Install the stabilizer bar to the vehicle.

9. Install the stabilizer bar insulator bracket to the sub-frame retaining nuts on both sides of the stabilizer bar and tighten to 16 ft. lbs. (22 Nm).

10. Install the NEW stabilizer bar link to stabilizer bar retaining nut and tighten to 35 ft. lbs. (48 Nm).

11. Remove the safety stands.

12. Lower the vehicle to the ground.

STRUT

REMOVAL & INSTALLATION

See Figure 316.

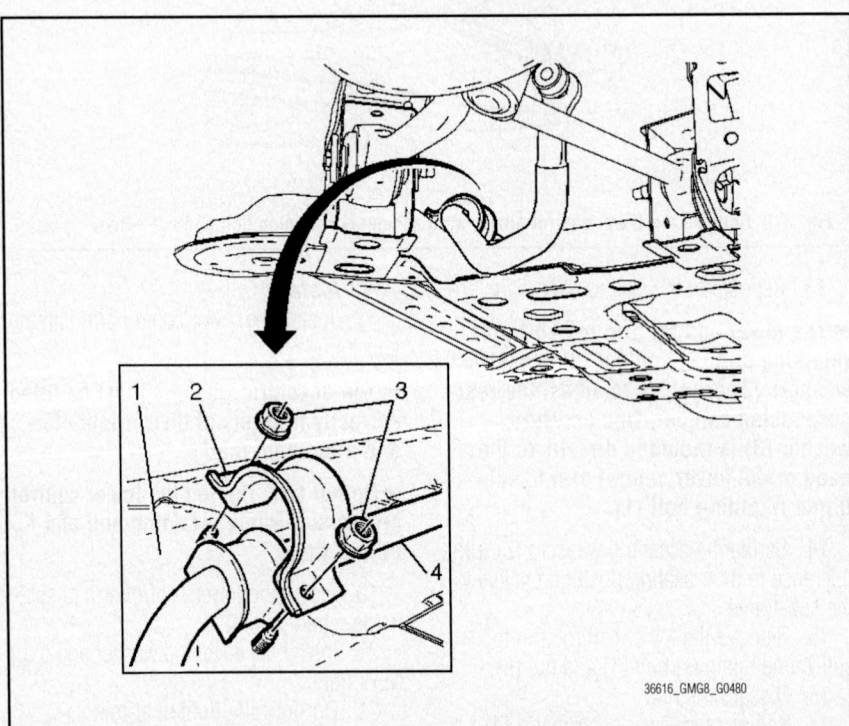

Fig. 314 Remove the lower control arm from the sub-frame—Rear

1. Before servicing the vehicle, refer to the Precautions Section.
2. Raise and support the vehicle.
3. Remove the rear wheel.
4. Support the lower control arm with a suitable jack.

➡**Prevailing torque nuts must be discarded after removal.**

5. Remove the lower control arm to knuckle retaining bolt and nut. Refer to Lower Control Arm.
6. Discard the nut.

➡**Prevailing torque nuts must be discarded after removal.**

7. Remove the lower control arm to rear strut assembly retaining bolt and nut.
8. Discard the nut.

➡**Reposition the jack as necessary.**

9. Detach the lower control arm using a suitable pry bar.

➡**Make sure to support the rear strut assembly during the removal procedure.**

10. Remove the rear strut assembly to body retaining bolts (1).
11. Remove the rear strut assembly from the vehicle.
12. Inspect all parts for wear and damage.

To install:
13. Install the rear strut assembly into the vehicle.
14. Safely support the rear strut assembly.
15. Install the rear strut assembly to body retaining bolts and tighten to 43 ft. lbs. (58 Nm).
16. Connect the rear strut assembly to the lower control arm.

➡**Do not fully tighten the lower control arm to strut assembly retaining bolt and nut at this stage.**

17. Install the lower control arm to strut assembly retaining bolt and NEW nut.
18. Do not fully tighten at this stage.
19. Connect the lower control arm to the knuckle using a suitable jack.

➡**Do not fully tighten the lower control arm to knuckle retaining bolt and nut at this stage.**

20. Install the lower control arm to the knuckle retaining bolt and NEW nut.

➡**Do not fully tighten at this stage.**

21. Install the rear wheel.
22. Remove the safety stands.
23. Lower the vehicle to the ground.
24. Bounce the vehicle several times to settle the suspension.

➡**The weight of the vehicle must be on a level surface and on all four wheels before fully tightening the nuts and bolts.**

25. Install the lower control arm to strut assembly retaining bolt and NEW nut and tighten a first pass to 30 ft. lbs. (40 Nm).
26. Tighten the bolt and nut a final pass 120 degrees.
27. Tighten the lower control arm to knuckle retaining bolt and NEW nut and tighten a first pass to 30 ft. lbs. (40 Nm).
28. Tighten the bolt and nut a final pass 120 degrees.

29. Check the wheel alignment of the vehicle.
30. Correct the wheel alignment of the vehicle, if necessary.

TRAILING ARM (Y LINK)

REMOVAL & INSTALLATION

See Figure 317.

1. Before servicing the vehicle, refer to the Precautions Section.
2. Raise and support the vehicle.
3. Remove the rear wheel.

➡**Mark the location of the bolt and nut relative to the Y-Link for correct reassembly.**

➡**Prevailing torque nuts must be discarded after removal.**

4. Remove the Y-Link to knuckle retaining bolt (1) and nut (2).
5. Discard the nut.
6. Remove the Y-Link to sub-frame retaining bolt (3) and nut (4).
7. Discard the nut.
8. Remove the Y-Link (5).
9. Inspect all parts for wear and damage.

To install:
10. Install the Y-Link into the sub-frame.

➡**The Y-Link to sub-frame retaining bolt and nut must not to be fully tightened at this stage.**

11. Install the Y-Link to sub-frame retaining bolt and NEW nut.

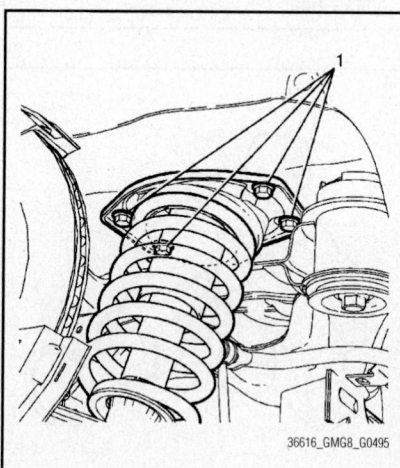

Fig. 316 Remove the rear strut assembly to body retaining bolts—Rear

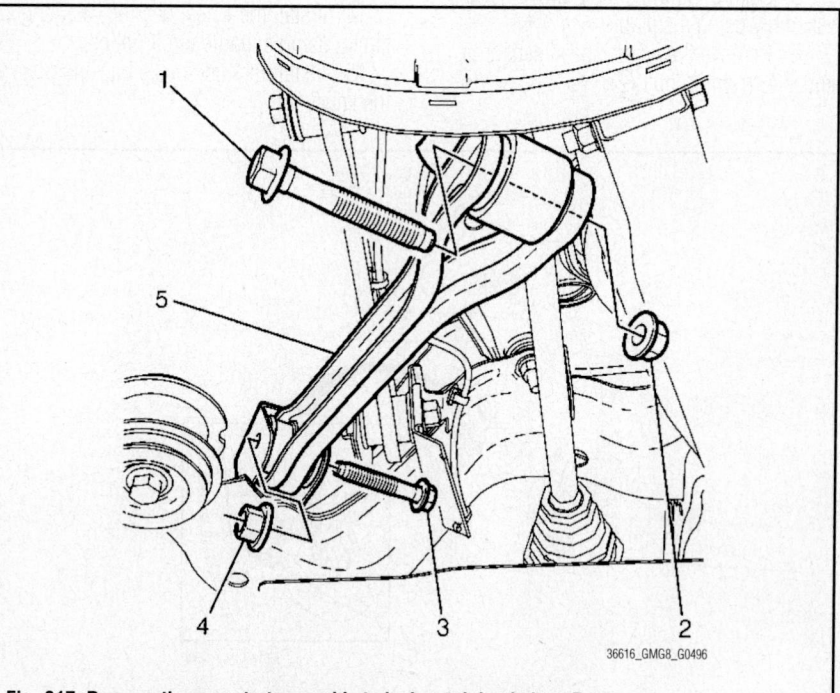

Fig. 317 Remove the rear strut assembly to body retaining bolts—Rear

➥**Do not fully tighten at this stage.**

➥**The Y-Link to knuckle retaining bolt and nut must not to be fully tightened at this stage.**

12. Install the Y-Link to knuckle retaining bolt and NEW nut.

➥**Do not fully tighten at this stage.**

13. Lower the vehicle to the ground.
14. Bounce the vehicle several times to settle the suspension.
15. Check the vehicle rear wheel alignment and adjust if necessary.

➥**The weight of the vehicle must be on a level surface and on all four wheels before fully tightening the nuts and bolts.**

16. Install the Y-Link to the sub-frame retaining bolt and NEW nut and tighten to 74 ft. lbs. (100 Nm).
17. Install the Y-Link to the knuckle retaining bolt and NEW nut and tighten a first pass to 30 ft. lbs. (40 Nm).
18. Tighten the bolt and nut a final pass 120 degrees.

WHEEL HUB & BEARING

REMOVAL & INSTALLATION

See Figures 318 through 320.

1. Before servicing the vehicle, refer to the Precautions Section.
2. Remove the wheel hub and knuckle assembly. Refer to Knuckle.
3. Secure the wheel hub and knuckle assembly using a suitable vice.
4. Remove the wheel speed sensor to knuckle retaining bolt (2).

5. Remove the wheel speed sensor (1).

➥**The wheel bearing will be damaged when pressing out the wheel hub flange. The wheel bearing must be replaced every time the wheel hub is removed.**

6. Remove the wheel hub flange using a suitable workshop press.
7. Remove the park brake shoes. Refer to Parking Brake in Brakes.
8. Remove the disc brake backing plate to knuckle retaining bolts (3 and 4).
9. Remove the disc brake backing plate (2) from the knuckle (1).
10. Remove the wheel bearing retaining circlip (3) using suitable circlip pliers.

➥**The wheel bearing will be damaged when pressing out the wheel hub flange. The wheel bearing must be replaced every time the wheel hub is removed.**

11. Press the wheel bearing (2) from the knuckle (1) using a suitable workshop press.
12. Discard the wheel bearing.

To install:

➥**Prior to installing the NEW wheel bearing it is essential that the correct orientation is attained, the wheel speed sensor decoder ring MUST face inboard, towards the wheel speed sensor. Failure to install in the correct orientation will result in ABS/ESP faults.**

13. Install the NEW wheel bearing to the knuckle using a workshop press.
14. Install the wheel bearing retaining circlip using suitable circlip pliers.
15. Install the disc brake backing plate to the knuckle.

16. Install the upper disc brake backing plate using the knuckle retaining bolt and tighten to 43 ft. lbs. (58 Nm).
17. Install the lower disc brake backing plate using the knuckle retaining bolts and tighten to 44 ft. lbs. (60 Nm).
18. Tighten the bolts a final pass 120 degrees
19. Install the park brake shoes.

➥**The wheel hub flange must be fully seated against the wheel bearing.**

20. Install the wheel hub flange using a suitable press.
21. Install the wheel speed sensor.
22. Install the wheel speed sensor using the knuckle retaining bolt and tighten to 62 inch lbs. (7 Nm).
23. Remove the hub and knuckle assembly from the vice.
24. Install the wheel hub and knuckle assembly.

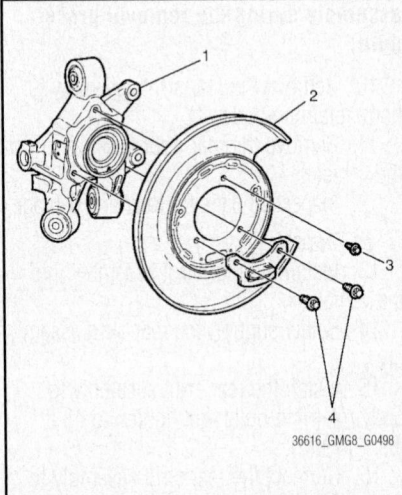

36616_GMG8_G0498

Fig. 319 Remove the disc brake backing plate—Rear

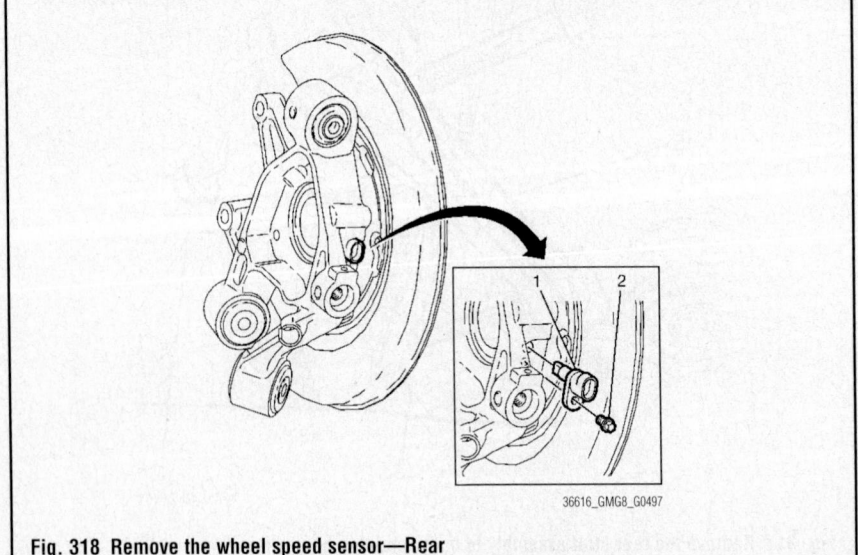

36616_GMG8_G0497

Fig. 318 Remove the wheel speed sensor—Rear

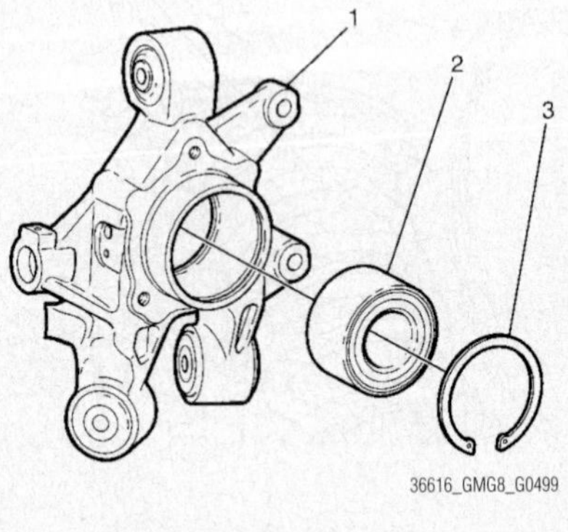

36616_GMG8_G0499

Fig. 320 Remove the wheel bearing—Rear

CHEVROLET

HHR

SPECIFICATIONS AND MAINTENANCE CHARTS

ENGINE AND VEHICLE IDENTIFICATION

Engine							Model Year	
Code ①	Liters	Cu. In.	Cyl.	Fuel Sys.	Engine Type	Eng. Mfg.	Code ②	Year
A. M	2.0	122	4	DI ③	DOHC	GM	9	2009
F	2.2	134	4	MFI	DOHC	GM		
B	2.4	146	4	MFI	DOHC	GM		

DI: Direct Injection

MFI: Multi-port Fuel Injection

DOHC: Double Overhead Camshafts

① 8th digit of VIN

② 10th digit of VIN

③ Turbo

36616_CHHR_C0001

GENERAL ENGINE SPECIFICATIONS

All measurements are given in inches.

Year	Model	Engine Displacement Liters	Engine Series VIN	Net Horsepower @ rpm	Net Torque @ rpm (ft. lbs.)	Bore x Stroke (in.)	Compression Ratio	Oil Pressure @ rpm
2009	HHR SS	2.0	A, M	260@5300	260@5250	3.388x3.388	9.2:1	50-80@1000
	HHR LS, 1LT	2.2	F	148@5600	152@4200	3.386x3.727	10.0:1	50-80@1000
	HHR 2LT	2.4	B	173@6200	163@4800	3.467x3.861	10.0:1	50-80@1000

NA: Not Available

36616_CHHR_C0002

GASOLINE ENGINE TUNE-UP SPECIFICATIONS

Year	Engine Displacement Liters	Engine VIN	Spark Plug Gap (in.)	Ignition Timing (deg.)		Fuel Pump (psi)	Idle Speed (rpm)		Valve Clearance	
				MT	AT		MT	AT	In.	Ex.
2009	2.0	A, M	0.030-0.035	①	①	57-67	②	②	HYD	HYD
	2.2	F	0.037-0.043	①	①	50-60	②	②	HYD	HYD
	2.4	B	0.037-0.043	①	①	50-60	②	②	HYD	HYD

NOTE: The Vehicle Emission Control Information label reflects specification changes made during production.

Follow the figures on the label if they differ from those in this chart.

HYD: Hydraulic

① Ignition timing is preset and cannot be adjusted

② Idle speed is maintained by the PCM

36616_CHHR_C0003

CAPACITIES

Year	Model	Engine Displacement Liters	Engine VIN	Engine Oil with Filter (qts.)	Transmission (pts.) Manual	Transmission (pts.) Auto. ①	Fuel Tank (gal.)	Cooling System (qts.)
2009	HHR SS	2.0	A, M	5.0	②	13.8	16.2	9.2
	HHR LS, 1LT	2.2	F	5.0	②	13.8	16.2	7.4
	HHR 2LT	2.4	B	5.0	②	13.8	16.2	③

NOTE: All capacities are approximate. Add fluid gradually and check to be sure a proper fluid level is obtained.

① Drain and refill

② Getrag 5-Speed: 3.4 pts.; MU3: 4.0 pts.

③ With M/T: 8.7 qts.; with A/T: 8.5 pts.

36616_CHHR_C0004

FLUID SPECIFICATIONS

Year	Model	Engine Displacement Liters	Engine ID/VIN	Engine Oil	Auto. Trans.	Manual Trans.	Power Steering Fluid	Clutch System	Brake Master Cylinder
2009	HHR SS	2.0	A, M	②	Dexron®-VI	GM Part No. 88862472	①	DOT 3	DOT 3
	HHR LS, 1LT	2.2	F	5W-30	Dexron®-VI	GM Part No. 88861800	①	DOT 3	DOT 3
	HHR 2LT	2.4	B	5W-30	Dexron®-VI	GM Part No. 88861800	①	DOT 3	DOT 3

DOT: Department Of Transportation

① These vehicles utilize an Electronic Power Steering (EPS) system

② Mobil 1® 5W-30 or equivalent synthetic oil meeting GM standard GM4718M.

36616_CHHR_C0005

VALVE SPECIFICATIONS

Year	Engine Displacement Liters	Engine VIN	Seat Angle (deg.)	Face Angle (deg.)	Spring Test Pressure (lbs. @ in.)	Spring Installed Height (in.)	Stem-to-Guide Clearance (in.) Intake	Stem-to-Guide Clearance (in.) Exhaust	Stem Diameter (in.) Intake	Stem Diameter (in.) Exhaust
2009	2.0	A, M	NA	NA	118-129 @0.905	1.279	0.0012-0.0022	0.0020-0.0026	0.2344-0.2355	0.2337-0.2343
	2.2	F	NA	NA	118-129 @0.905	1.279	0.0012-0.0022	0.0020-0.0026	0.2344-0.2355	0.2337-0.2343
	2.4	B	NA	NA	118-129 @0.905	1.279	0.0012-0.0022	0.0020-0.0026	0.2344-0.2355	0.2337-0.2343

NA: Not Available

36616_CHHR_C0006

CAMSHAFT AND BEARING SPECIFICATIONS CHART

All measurements are given in inches.

Year	Engine Displacement Liters	Engine ID/VIN	Journal Dia.	Journal dia. Front	Shaft End-play	Thrust Surface	Journal Bore	Lobe Height	
								Intake	Exhaust
2009	2.0	A, M	1.0604-1.0614	1.3774-1.3764	0.0016-0.0121	1.1828-1.1889	NA	NA	NA
	2.2	F	1.0604-1.0614	NA	0.0016-0.0057	0.8268-0.8252	NA	NA	NA
	2.4	B	1.0604-1.0614	NA	0.0016-0.0057	0.8268-0.8252	NA	NA	NA

NA: Not Available

36616_CHHR_C0007

CRANKSHAFT AND CONNECTING ROD SPECIFICATIONS

All measurements are given in inches.

Year	Engine Displacement Liters	Engine VIN	Crankshaft				Connecting Rod		
			Main Brg. Journal Dia.	Main Brg. Oil Clearance	Shaft End-play	Thrust on No.	Journal Diameter	Oil Clearance	Side Clearance
2009	2.0	A, M	2.2045-2.2050	0.0012-0.0026	0.0012-0.0150	2	1.9291-1.9297	0.0011-0.0029	0.0028-0.0146
	2.2	F	2.2045-2.2050	0.0012-0.0026	0.0012-0.0150	2	1.9291-1.9297	0.0011-0.0029	0.0028-0.0146
	2.4	B	2.2045-2.2050	0.0012-0.0026	0.0012-0.0150	2	1.9291-1.9297	0.0011-0.0029	0.0028-0.0146

36616_CHHR_C0008

PISTON AND RING SPECIFICATIONS

All measurements are given in inches.

Year	Engine Displ. Liters	Engine VIN	Piston Clearance	Ring Gap			Ring Side Clearance		
				Top Compression	Bottom Compression	Oil Control	Top Compression	Bottom Compression	Oil Control
2009	2.0	A, M	0.0004-0.0016	0.0078-0.0138	0.0140-0.0220	0.0100-0.0300	0.0016-0.0031	0.0001-0.0027	0.0009-0.0069
	2.2	F	0.0004-0.0016	0.0080-0.0140	0.0140-0.0220	0.0100-0.0300	0.0015-0.0031	0.0012-0.0027	0.0023-0.0081
	2.4	B	0.0004-0.0016	0.0060-0.0012	0.0080-0.0180	0.0060-0.0260	0.0015-0.0031	0.0012-0.0030	0.0023-0.0081

36616_CHHR_C0009

TORQUE SPECIFICATIONS

All readings in ft. lbs.

Year	Engine Displacement Liters	Engine VIN	Cylinder Head Bolts	Main Bearing Bolts	Rod Bearing Bolts	Crankshaft Damper Bolts	Flywheel Bolts	Manifold		Spark Plugs	Oil Pan Drain Plug
								Intake	Exhaust		
2009	2.0	A, M	①	②	③	④	⑤	⑥	⑦	13-17	18
	2.2	F	①	⑧	③	④	⑤	⑨	⑩	15	18
	2.4	B	①	⑧	③	④	⑤	⑨	⑩	15	18

① Step 1: 22 ft. lbs.
Step 2: plus 155 degrees

② Step 1: 15 ft. lbs.
Step 2: plus 77 degrees

③ Step 1: 18 ft. lbs.
Step 2: plus 100 degrees

④ Step 1: 74 ft. lbs.
Step 2: plus 125 degrees

⑤ Step 1: 39 ft. lbs.
Step 2: plus 25 degrees

⑥ Intake Manifold to Cylinder Head Bolt or Nut 18 ft. lbs.
Intake manifold to Cylinder Head Stud 11 ft. lbs.

⑦ Exhaust Manifold to Turbocharger Stud: 15 ft. lbs.
Exhaust Manifold to Cylinder Head Nut 10 ft. lbs.
Exhaust Manifold to Cylinder Head Stud 15 ft. lbs.

⑧ Step 1: 15 ft. lbs.
Step 2: plus 70 degrees

⑨ Intake Manifold to Cylinder Head Bolt or Nut 89 INCH lbs.
Intake Manifold to Cylinder Head Stud 53 INCH lbs.

⑩ Exhaust Manifold to Cylinder Head Nut 124 INCH lbs., in 2 passes
Exhaust Manifold to Cylinder Head Stud 89 INCH lbs.

36616_CHHR_C0010

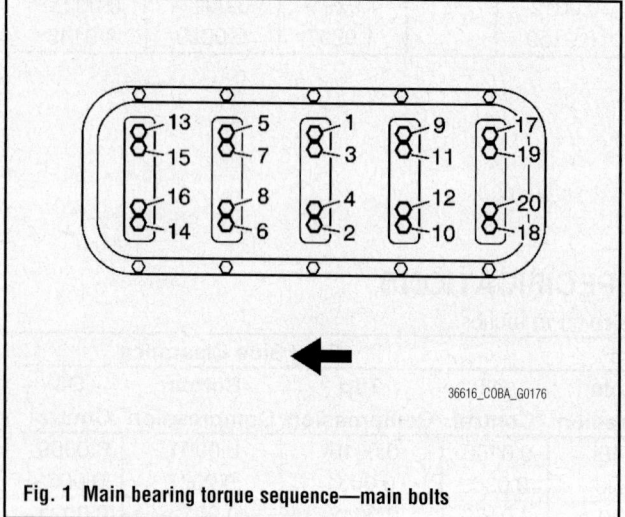

36616_COBA_G0176

Fig. 1 Main bearing torque sequence—main bolts

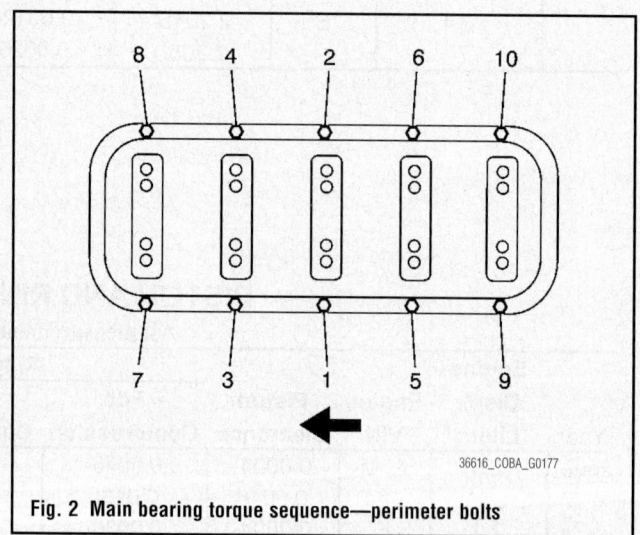

36616_COBA_G0177

Fig. 2 Main bearing torque sequence—perimeter bolts

WHEEL ALIGNMENT

			Caster		Camber		
			Range (+/-Deg.)	Preferred Setting (Deg.)	Range (+/-Deg.)	Preferred Setting (Deg.)	Toe-in (Deg.)
Year	Model						
2009	HHR LS, 1LT ①	Front	0.75	+3.70	0.75	-0.95	0.20+/-0.20
		Rear	—	—	0.75	-0.80	0.25+/-0.30
	HHR 2LT ②	Front	0.75	+3.70	0.75	-0.95	0.20+/-0.20
		Rear	—	—	0.75	-0.80	0.25+/-0.30
	HHR SS ③	Front	0.75	+3.70	0.75	-1.05	0.20+/-0.20
		Rear	—	—	0.75	-0.80	0.25+/-0.30

① FE1 suspension

② FE3 suspension

③ FE5 suspension

36616_CHHR_C0011

TIRE, WHEEL AND BALL JOINT SPECIFICATIONS

		OEM Tires		Tire Pressures (psi)		Wheel Size	Ball Joint Inspection	Lug Nut Torque (ft. lbs.)
		Standard	Optional	Front	Rear			
Year	Model							
2009	HHR LS, 1LT	P215/55R16	NA	①	①	16 in.	NA	100
	HHR 2LT	P215/50R17	NA	①	①	17 in.	NA	100
	HHR SS	P225/45R18	NA	①	①	18 in.	NA	100

NA: Not Available

① Refer to placard on vehicle for proper inflation pressure

36616_CHHR_C0012

BRAKE SPECIFICATIONS

All measurements in inches unless noted

			Brake Disc			Brake Drum Diameter			Minimum Lining Thickness	Brake Caliper	
			Original Thickness	Minimum Thickness	Maximum Runout	Original Inside Diameter	Max. Wear Limit	Maximum Machine Diameter		Bracket Bolts (ft. lbs.)	Guide Pin Bolts (ft. lbs.)
Year	Model										
2009	HHR LS, 1LT	F	1.023	0.898	0.002	NA	NA	NA	0.039	85	26
		R	NA	NA	NA	①	9.079	9.059	0.020	NA	NA
	HHR 2LT	F	1.023	0.898	0.002	NA	NA	NA	0.039	85	26
		R	NA	NA	NA	①	9.079	9.059	0.020	NA	NA
	HHR SS	F	1.023	0.898	0.002	NA	NA	NA	0.039	96	26
		R	0.551	0.465	0.002	NA	NA	NA	0.039	85	26

NA: Not Applicable

NS: Information not specified by OEM

① 8.996-9.004

36616_CHHR_C0013

MAINTENANCE I AND II SERVICE SCHEDULES
Chevrolet HHR

When the CHANGE ENGINE OIL light appears, certain services and inspections are required.
Required services are described as Maintenance I and Maintenance II.
The first service on a vehicle should be Maintenance I, and the second service should be Maintenance II.
Alternate between the 2 thereafter. However, in some cases, Maintenance II may be required more often.
Maintenance I: Use Maintenance I if the CHANGE ENGINE OIL light comes on within 10 months since vehicle was purchased or, if Maintenance II was performed.
Maintenance II: Use Maintenance II if the previous service performed was Maintenance I. Always use Maintenance II whenever the CHANGE ENGINE OIL light comes on 10 months or more since the last service, or, if the CHANGE ENGINE OIL light has not come on at all for one year.

Service	Maintenance I	II
Change the engine oil and filter. Reset the oil life system.	✓	✓
Visually inspect the vehicle for leaks or damage. A fluid loss in the vehicle system could indicate a problem. Inspected, repair and add fluid to the system if necessary.	✓	✓
Inspect the engine air cleaner filter. If necessary, replace the filter (2.0L engine).	✓	✓
Inspect the engine air cleaner filter. If necessary, replace the filter (2.2L & 2.4L engines).	--	✓
Rotate the tires. Inspect the tire inflation pressures and the tire wear.	✓	✓
Visually inspect the brake lines and hoses for proper hook-up, binding, leaks, cracks, chafing, etc. Inspect the disc brake pads for wear and the rotors for surface condition. Inspect the drum brake linings for wear or cracks. Inspect other brake parts, including drums, wheel cylinders, calipers, parking brake, etc. Inspect the parking brake	✓	✓
Inspect the engine coolant and the windshield washer fluid levels. Add fluid as needed.	✓	✓
With a 2.0L engine, check the intercooler fluid level. Add as necessary.	✓	✓
Inspect the suspension and steering components. Inspect the front and rear suspension and the steering system for damaged, loose or missing parts, or signs of wear. Inspect the power steering lines and the hoses for proper hook-up, binding, leaks, cracks,	--	✓
Visually inspect the coolant hoses and replace the hoses if they are cracked, swollen or deteriorated. Inspect all pipes, fittings and clamps; replace with GM parts as needed. To help ensure proper operation, a pressure test of the cooling system and pressure cap and cleaning the outside of the radiator and air conditioning condenser is recommended at least once a year.	--	✓
Inspect the wiper blades for wear or cracking. Clean the windshield and wiper blades, if contaminated. Replace wiper blades that are worn or damaged.	--	✓
Inspect the restraint system components. Ensure the safety belt reminder light and all the belts, buckles, latch plates, retractors and anchorages are working properly. Look for any other loose or damaged safety belt system parts. If you see anything that might keep a safety belt system from working correctly, repair or replaced the damaged part. Replace torn or frayed safety belts, refer to Operational and Functional Checks in Seat Belts. Inspect for any opened or broken air bag coverings, and repair or replace as needed. The air bag system does require regular maintenance	--	✓
Lubricate the body components. Lubricate all key lock cylinders, hood latch assemblies, secondary latches, pivots, spring anchor and release pawl, hood and door hinges, rear folding seats and liftgate hinges. Frequent lubrication may be required when exposed to a corrosive environment, refer to Fluid and Lubricant Recommendations . Applying dielectric silicone grease GM P/N 12345579 (Canadian P/N 1974984) or equivalent on the weatherstrips with a clean cloth.	--	✓
Inspect the transaxle fluid level and add fluid as needed.	--	✓
Inspect the suspension and steering components.		

36616_CHHR_C0014

ADDITIONAL MAINTENANCE SERVICES
Chevrolet HHR

TO BE SERVICED	TYPE OF SERVICE	VEHICLE MILEAGE INTERVAL (x1000)					
		25	50	75	100	125	150
Air cleaner filter	R	✓	✓	✓	✓	✓	✓
Accessory drive belt	I						✓
Auto. Trans. Fluid ①	R		✓		✓		✓
Cooling system hoses and clamps	S/I						✓
Engine coolant	R						✓
Fuel system	I	✓	✓	✓	✓	✓	✓
Exhaust system & heat shields	S/I	✓	✓	✓	✓	✓	✓
Spark plugs	R				✓		

R: Replace   S/I: Inspect and service, if necessary

① Replace if any of the following conditions are met:

Heavy city traffic where the outside temperature regularly reaches 32°C (90°F) or higher

Hilly or mountainous terrain

Frequent trailer towing

Taxi, police or delivery service

Otherwise, change every 100,000 miles

36616_CHHR_C0015

PRECAUTIONS

Before servicing any vehicle, please be sure to read all of the following precautions, which deal with personal safety, prevention of component damage, and important points to take into consideration when servicing a motor vehicle:

• Never open, service or drain the radiator or cooling system when the engine is hot; serious burns can occur from the steam and hot coolant.

• Observe all applicable safety precautions when working around fuel. Whenever servicing the fuel system, always work in a well-ventilated area. Do not allow fuel spray or vapors to come in contact with a spark, open flame, or excessive heat (a hot drop light, for example). Keep a dry chemical fire extinguisher near the work area. Always keep fuel in a container specifically designed for fuel storage; also, always properly seal fuel containers to avoid the possibility of fire or explosion. Refer to the additional fuel system precautions later in this section.

• Fuel injection systems often remain pressurized, even after the engine has been turned **OFF**. The fuel system pressure must be relieved before disconnecting any fuel lines. Failure to do so may result in fire and/or personal injury.

• Brake fluid often contains polyglycol ethers and polyglycols. Avoid contact with the eyes and wash your hands thoroughly after handling brake fluid. If you do get brake fluid in your eyes, flush your eyes with clean, running water for 15 minutes. If eye irritation persists, or if you have taken

brake fluid internally, IMMEDIATELY seek medical assistance.

• The EPA warns that prolonged contact with used engine oil may cause a number of skin disorders, including cancer. You should make every effort to minimize your exposure to used engine oil. Protective gloves should be worn when changing oil. Wash your hands and any other exposed skin areas as soon as possible after exposure to used engine oil. Soap and water, or waterless hand cleaner should be used.

• All new vehicles are now equipped with an air bag system, often referred to as a Supplemental Restraint System (SRS) or Supplemental Inflatable Restraint (SIR) system. The system must be disabled before performing service on or around system components, steering column, instrument panel components, wiring and sensors. Failure to follow safety and disabling procedures could result in accidental air bag deployment, possible personal injury and unnecessary system repairs.

• Always wear safety goggles when working with, or around, the air bag system. When carrying a non-deployed air bag, be sure the bag and trim cover are pointed away from your body. When placing a non-deployed air bag on a work surface, always face the bag and trim cover upward, away from the surface. This will reduce the motion of the module if it is accidentally deployed. Refer to the additional air bag system precautions later in this section.

• Clean, high quality brake fluid from a sealed container is essential to the safe and

proper operation of the brake system. You should always buy the correct type of brake fluid for your vehicle. If the brake fluid becomes contaminated, completely flush the system with new fluid. Never reuse any brake fluid. Any brake fluid that is removed from the system should be discarded. Also, do not allow any brake fluid to come in contact with a painted surface; it will damage the paint.

• Never operate the engine without the proper amount and type of engine oil; doing so WILL result in severe engine damage.

• Timing belt maintenance is extremely important. Many models utilize an interference-type, non-freewheeling engine. If the timing belt breaks, the valves in the cylinder head may strike the pistons, causing potentially serious (also time-consuming and expensive) engine damage. Refer to the maintenance interval charts for the recommended replacement interval for the timing belt, and to the timing belt section for belt replacement and inspection.

• Disconnecting the negative battery cable on some vehicles may interfere with the functions of the on-board computer system(s) and may require the computer to undergo a relearning process once the negative battery cable is reconnected.

• When servicing drum brakes, only disassemble and assemble one side at a time, leaving the remaining side intact for reference.

• Only an MVAC-trained, EPA-certified automotive technician should service the air conditioning system or its components.

BRAKES
ANTI-LOCK BRAKE SYSTEM (ABS)

GENERAL INFORMATION

PRECAUTIONS

• Certain components within the ABS system are not intended to be serviced or repaired individually.

• Do not use rubber hoses or other parts not specifically specified for and ABS system. When using repair kits, replace all parts included in the kit. Partial or incorrect repair may lead to functional problems and require the replacement of components.

• Lubricate rubber parts with clean, fresh brake fluid to ease assembly. Do not

use shop air to clean parts; damage to rubber components may result.

• Use only DOT 3 brake fluid from an unopened container.

• If any hydraulic component or line is removed or replaced, it may be necessary to bleed the entire system.

• A clean repair area is essential. Always clean the reservoir and cap thoroughly before removing the cap. The slightest amount of dirt in the fluid may plug an orifice and impair the system function. Perform repairs after components have been thoroughly cleaned; use only denatured alcohol

to clean components. Do not allow ABS components to come into contact with any substance containing mineral oil; this includes used shop rags.

• The Anti-Lock control unit is a microprocessor similar to other computer units in the vehicle. Ensure that the ignition switch is **OFF** before removing or installing controller harnesses. Avoid static electricity discharge at or near the controller.

• If any arc welding is to be done on the vehicle, the control unit should be unplugged before welding operations begin.

BLEEDING PROCEDURE

Pressure Bleeding

1. Before servicing the vehicle, refer to the Precautions Section.

WARNING

When adding fluid to the brake master cylinder reservoir, use only GM approved or equivalent DOT-3 brake fluid from a clean, sealed brake fluid container. The use of any type of fluid other than the recommended type of brake fluid may cause contamination which could result in damage to the internal rubber seals and/or rubber linings of hydraulic brake system components.

WARNING

Avoid spilling brake fluid onto painted surfaces, electrical connections, wiring, or cables. Brake fluid will damage painted surfaces and cause corrosion to electrical components. If any brake fluid comes in contact with painted surfaces, immediately flush the area with water. If any brake fluid comes in contact with electrical connections, wiring, or cables, use a clean shop cloth to wipe away the fluid.

2. Place a clean shop cloth beneath the brake master cylinder to catch brake fluid spills.
3. With the ignition OFF and the brakes cool, apply the brakes 3–5 times, or until the brake pedal becomes firm, in order to deplete the brake booster power reserve.
4. If you have performed a brake master cylinder bench bleeding on this vehicle, or if you disconnected the brake pipes from the master cylinder, or if you have disconnected the brake pipes from the proportioning valve assembly or the brake modulator assembly, you must perform the following steps to bleed air at the ports of the hydraulic component:
   a. If removal of the reservoir cap and diaphragm is necessary, clean the outside of the reservoir on and around the cap prior to removal.
   b. With the brake pipes installed securely to the master cylinder, proportioning valve assembly, or brake modulator assembly, loosen and separate one of the brake pipes from the port of the component. For the proportioning valve assembly or the brake modulator assembly, perform these steps in the sequence of system flow; begin with the fluid feed pipes from the master cylinder.
   c. Allow a small amount of brake fluid to gravity bleed from the open port of the component.
   d. Reconnect the brake pipe to the component and tighten securely.
   e. Have an assistant slowly depress the brake pedal fully and maintain steady pressure on the pedal.
   f. Loosen the same brake pipe to purge air from the open port of the component.
   g. Tighten the brake pipe, then have the assistant slowly release the brake pedal.
   h. Wait 15 seconds, then repeat steps 3–7 until all air is purged from the same port of the component.
   i. With the brake pipe installed securely to the master cylinder, proportioning valve assembly, or brake modulator assembly, and after all air has been purged from the first port of the component that was bled, loosen and separate the next brake pipe from the component, then repeat steps 3.3–3.8 until each of the ports on the component has been bled.
   j. After completing the final component port bleeding procedure, ensure that each of the brake pipe-to-component fittings is properly tightened.
5. Clean the outside of the reservoir on and around the reservoir cap prior to removing the cap and diaphragm.
6. Install a pressure bleeder such as J 44894-A to the brake master cylinder reservoir.
7. Connect the J 29532, or equivalent, to the J 44894-A.
8. Charge the J 29532, or equivalent, air tank to 25–30 psi (175–205 kPa).
9. Open the J 29532, or equivalent, fluid tank valve to allow pressurized brake fluid to enter the brake system.
10. Wait approximately 30 seconds, then, inspect the entire hydraulic brake system in order to ensure that there are no existing external brake fluid leaks. Any brake fluid leaks identified require repair prior to completing this procedure.
11. Install a proper box-end wrench onto the RIGHT REAR wheel hydraulic circuit bleeder valve.
12. Install a transparent hose over the end of the bleeder valve.
13. Loosen the bleeder valve to purge air from the wheel hydraulic circuit. Allow fluid to flow until air bubbles stop flowing from the bleeder, then tighten the bleeder valve.
14. With the right rear wheel hydraulic circuit bleeder valve tightened securely, and after all air has been purged from the right rear hydraulic circuit, install a proper box-end wrench onto the LEFT FRONT wheel hydraulic circuit bleeder valve.
15. Install a transparent hose over the end of the bleeder valve, then repeat steps 13–14.
16. With the left front wheel hydraulic circuit bleeder valve tightened securely, and after all air has been purged from the left front hydraulic circuit, install a proper box-end wrench onto the LEFT REAR wheel hydraulic circuit bleeder valve.
17. Install a transparent hose over the end of the bleeder valve, then, repeat steps 13–14.
18. With the left rear wheel hydraulic circuit bleeder valve tightened securely, and after all air has been purged from the left rear hydraulic circuit, install a proper box-end wrench onto the RIGHT FRONT wheel hydraulic circuit bleeder valve.
19. Install a transparent hose over the end of the bleeder valve, then, repeat steps 13–14.
20. After completing the final wheel hydraulic circuit bleeding procedure, ensure that each of the 4 wheel hydraulic circuit bleeder valves is properly tightened.
21. Close the J 29532, or equivalent, fluid tank valve, then disconnect the J 29532, or equivalent, from the J 44894-A.
22. Remove the J 44894-A from the brake master cylinder reservoir.
23. Slowly depress and release the brake pedal. Observe the feel of the brake pedal.
24. If the brake pedal feels spongy perform the following steps:
   a. Inspect the brake system for external leaks.
   b. If equipped with anti-lock brakes, using a scan tool, perform the antilock brake system automated bleeding procedure to remove any air that may have been trapped in the Brake Pressure Modulator Valve (BPMV).

Manual Bleeding

1. Before servicing the vehicle, refer to the Precautions Section.

❋❋ WARNING

When adding fluid to the brake master cylinder reservoir, use only GM approved or equivalent DOT-3 brake fluid from a clean, sealed brake fluid container. The use of any type of fluid other than the recommended type of brake fluid may cause contamination which could result in damage to the internal rubber seals and/or rubber linings of hydraulic brake system components.

❋❋ WARNING

Avoid spilling brake fluid onto painted surfaces, electrical connections, wiring, or cables. Brake fluid will damage painted surfaces and cause corrosion to electrical components. If any brake fluid comes in contact with painted surfaces, immediately flush the area with water. If any brake fluid comes in contact with electrical connections, wiring, or cables, use a clean shop cloth to wipe away the fluid.

2. Place a clean shop cloth beneath the brake master cylinder to catch brake fluid spills.

3. With the ignition OFF and the brakes cool, apply the brakes 3–5 times, or until the brake pedal effort increases significantly, in order to deplete the brake booster power reserve.

4. If you have performed a brake master cylinder bench bleeding on this vehicle, or if you disconnected the brake pipes from the master cylinder, or if you have disconnected the brake pipes from the proportioning valve assembly or the brake modulator assembly, you must perform the following steps to bleed air at the ports of the hydraulic component:

   a. If removal of the reservoir cap and diaphragm is necessary, clean the outside of the reservoir on and around the cap prior to removal.

   b. With the brake pipes installed securely to the master cylinder, proportioning valve assembly, or brake modulator assembly, loosen and separate one of the brake pipes from the port of the component. For the proportioning valve assembly or the brake modulator assembly, perform these steps in the sequence of system flow; begin with the fluid feed pipes from the master cylinder.

   c. Allow a small amount of brake fluid to gravity bleed from the open port of the component.

   d. Reconnect the brake pipe to the component and tighten securely.

   e. Have an assistant slowly depress the brake pedal fully and maintain steady pressure on the pedal.

   f. Loosen the same brake pipe to purge air from the open port of the component.

   g. Tighten the brake pipe, then have the assistant slowly release the brake pedal.

   h. Wait 15 seconds, then repeat steps 3–7 until all air is purged from the same port of the component.

   i. With the brake pipe installed securely to the master cylinder, proportioning valve assembly, or brake modulator assembly, and after all air has been purged from the first port of the component that was bled, loosen and separate the next brake pipe from the component, then repeat steps 3–8 until each of the ports on the component has been bled.

   j. After completing the final component port bleeding procedure, ensure that each of the brake pipe-to-component fittings is properly tightened.

5. Ensure the brake master cylinder reservoir remains at least half-full during this bleeding procedure. Add fluid as needed to maintain the proper level. Clean the outside of the reservoir on and around the reservoir cap prior to removing the cap and diaphragm.

6. Install a proper box-end wrench onto the RIGHT REAR wheel hydraulic circuit bleeder valve.

7. Install a transparent hose over the end of the bleeder valve.

8. Have an assistant slowly depress the brake pedal fully and maintain steady pressure on the pedal.

9. Loosen the bleeder valve to purge air from the wheel hydraulic circuit.

10. Tighten the bleeder valve, then have the assistant slowly release the brake pedal.

11. Wait 15 seconds, then repeat steps 8–10 until all air is purged from the same wheel hydraulic circuit.

12. With the right rear wheel hydraulic circuit bleeder valve tightened securely, and after all air has been purged from the right rear hydraulic circuit, install a proper box-end wrench onto the LEFT FRONT wheel hydraulic circuit bleeder valve.

13. Install a transparent hose over the end of the bleeder valve, then repeat steps 7–11.

14. With the left front wheel hydraulic circuit bleeder valve tightened securely, and after all air has been purged from the left front hydraulic circuit, install a proper box-end wrench onto the LEFT REAR wheel hydraulic circuit bleeder valve.

15. Install a transparent hose over the end of the bleeder valve, then repeat steps 7–11.

16. With the left rear wheel hydraulic circuit bleeder valve tightened securely, and after all air has been purged from the left rear hydraulic circuit, install a proper box-end wrench onto the RIGHT FRONT wheel hydraulic circuit bleeder valve.

17. Install a transparent hose over the end of the bleeder valve, then repeat steps 7–11.

18. After completing the final wheel hydraulic circuit bleeding procedure, ensure that each of the 4 wheel hydraulic circuit bleeder valves is properly tightened.

19. Slowly depress and release the brake pedal. Observe the feel of the brake pedal.

20. If the brake pedal feels spongy, repeat the bleeding procedure again. If the brake pedal still feels spongy after repeating the bleeding procedure, perform the following steps:

   a. Inspect the brake system for external leaks.

   b. Pressure bleed the hydraulic brake system in order to purge any air that may still be trapped in the system.

21. Turn the ignition key ON, with the engine OFF. Check to see if the brake system warning lamp remains illuminated.

❋❋ WARNING

DO NOT allow the vehicle to be driven until it is diagnosed and repaired.

BLEEDING THE ABS SYSTEM

1. Before servicing the vehicle, refer to the Precautions Section.

❋❋ WARNING

The Auto Bleed Procedure may be terminated at any time during the process by pressing the EXIT button. No further Scan Tool prompts pertaining to the Auto Bleed procedure will be given. After exiting the bleed procedure, relieve bleed pressure and disconnect bleed equipment per manufacturer's instructions. Failure to properly relieve pressure may result in spilled brake fluid causing damage to components and painted surfaces.

2. Raise and support the vehicle.

3. Remove all four tire and wheel assemblies.

4. Inspect the brake system for leaks and visual damage. Repair or replace components as needed.

5. Lower the vehicle.

6. Inspect the battery state of charge.

7. Install a scan tool.

8. Turn the ignition ON, with the engine OFF.

9. With the scan tool, establish communications with the ABS system. Select Special Functions. Select Automated Bleed from the Special Functions menu.

10. Raise and support the vehicle.

11. Following the directions given on the scan tool, pressure bleed the base brake system. Refer to Bleeding the Brake System.

12. Follow the scan tool directions until the desired brake pedal height is achieved.

13. If the bleed procedure is aborted, a malfunction exists. Perform the following steps before resuming the bleed procedure:

a. If a Diagnostic Trouble Code (DTC) is detected, diagnose the appropriate DTC.

b. If the brake pedal feels spongy, perform the conventional brake bleed procedure again.

14. When the desired pedal height is achieved, press the brake pedal to inspect for firmness.

15. Lower the vehicle.

16. Remove the scan tool.

17. Install the tire and wheel assemblies.

18. Inspect the brake fluid level.

19. Road test the vehicle while inspecting that the pedal remains high and firm.

20. Turn the ignition key ON, with the engine OFF. Check to see if the brake system warning lamp remains illuminated.

> ### ✳✳ WARNING
>
> **If there is a brake malfunction exists, DO NOT allow the vehicle to be driven until it is diagnosed and repaired.**

BRAKES
FRONT DISC BRAKES

> ### ✳✳ CAUTION
>
> **Dust and dirt accumulating on brake parts during normal use may contain asbestos fibers from production or aftermarket brake linings. Breathing excessive concentrations of asbestos fibers can cause serious bodily harm. Exercise care when servicing brake parts. Do not sand or grind brake lining unless equipment used is designed to contain the dust residue. Do not clean brake parts with compressed air or by dry brushing. Cleaning should be done by dampening the brake components with a fine mist of water, then wiping the brake components clean with a dampened cloth. Dispose of cloth and all residue containing asbestos fibers in an impermeable container with the appropriate label. Follow practices prescribed by the Occupational Safety and Health Administration (OSHA) and the Environmental Protection Agency (EPA) for the handling, processing, and disposing of dust or debris that may contain asbestos fibers.**

BRAKE CALIPER

REMOVAL & INSTALLATION

See Figures 3 and 4.

1. Before servicing the vehicle, refer to the Precautions Section.

2. Inspect the fluid level in the brake master cylinder reservoir.

3. If the brake fluid level is midway between the maximum-full point and the minimum allowable level, no brake fluid

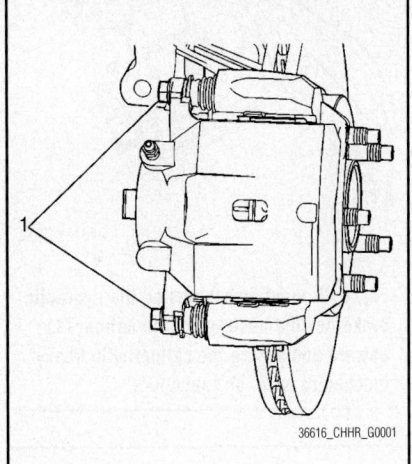

Fig. 3 View of the brake caliper guide pin bolts (1)

36616_CHHR_G0001

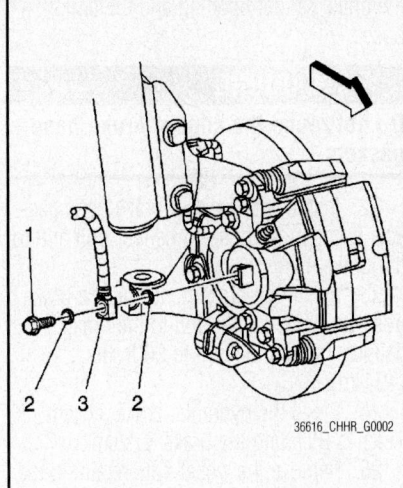

Fig. 4 Install the brake hose fitting bolt (1) and gaskets (2) to the brake hose (3)

36616_CHHR_G0002

needs to be removed from the reservoir before proceeding.

4. If the brake fluid level is higher than midway between the maximum-full point and the minimum allowable level, remove brake fluid to the midway point before proceeding.

5. Raise and support the vehicle.

6. Remove the tire and wheel assembly.

7. Install and firmly hand tighten 2 wheel nuts to opposite wheel studs in order to retain the rotor to the hub.

8. Install a large C-clamp over the body of the brake caliper with the C-clamp ends against the rear of the caliper body and against the outer brake pad.

9. Tighten the C-clamp until the caliper piston is compressed into the caliper bore enough to allow the caliper to slide past the brake rotor.

10. Remove the C-clamp from the caliper.

11. Remove the brake hose-to-caliper bolt from the brake caliper.

12. Remove the brake hose from the brake caliper.

13. Remove and discard the 2 copper brake hose gaskets. These gaskets may be stuck to the brake caliper and/or the brake hose end.

14. Cap or plug the opening in the brake caliper and the brake hose to prevent fluid loss and contamination.

15. Remove the brake caliper guide pin bolts.

16. Remove the brake caliper from the caliper bracket.

17. Inspect the brake caliper guide pins for freedom of movement, and inspect the condition of the guide pin boots. Move the guide pins inboard and outboard within the

bracket bores, without disengaging the slides from the boots, and observe for the following:

- Restricted caliper guide pin movement
- Looseness in the brake caliper mounting bracket
- Seized or binding caliper guide pins
- Split or torn boots

18. If any of the conditions listed are found, the brake caliper guide pins and/or boots require replacement.

To install:

19. Install the brake caliper to the brake caliper bracket.

20. Install the brake caliper guide pin bolts. Tighten the bolts to 26 ft. lbs. (35 Nm).

21. Remove the caps or plugs from the brake caliper opening and the brake hose.

✸✸ WARNING

Do not reuse the copper brake hose gaskets.

22. Install NEW copper brake hose gaskets to the brake hose-to-caliper bolt and to the brake hose.

23. Install the brake hose and the brake hose-to-brake caliper bolt to the brake caliper. Tighten the bolt to 30 ft. lbs. (40 Nm).

24. Bleed the hydraulic brake system. Refer to Bleeding the Brake System.

25. Remove the wheel nuts retaining the brake rotor to the wheel hub.

26. Install the tire and wheel assembly.

27. Lower the vehicle.

28. With the engine OFF, gradually apply the brake pedal to approximately ⅔ of its travel distance.

29. Slowly release the brake pedal.

30. Wait 15 seconds, then gradually apply the brake pedal approximately ⅔ of its travel distance again until a firm brake pedal is obtained. This will properly seat the brake caliper pistons and brake pads.

DISC BRAKE PADS

REMOVAL & INSTALLATION

See Figures 5 through 7.

1. Before servicing the vehicle, refer to the Precautions Section.

2. Inspect the fluid level in the brake master cylinder auxiliary reservoir.

3. If the brake fluid level is midway between the maximum-full point and the minimum allowable level, no brake fluid

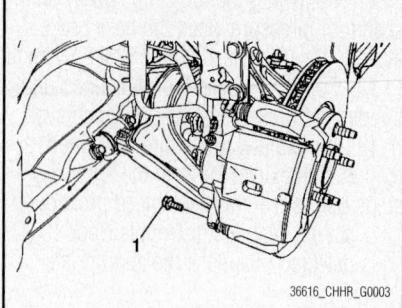

36616_CHHR_G0003

Fig. 5 Remove the lower brake caliper guide pin bolt (1)

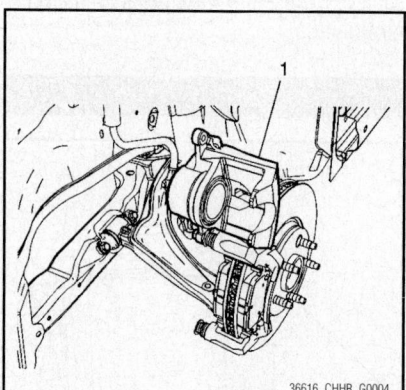

36616_CHHR_G0004

Fig. 6 Without disconnecting the hydraulic brake flexible hose, pivot the caliper (1) upward and secure the caliper with heavy mechanics wire, or equivalent

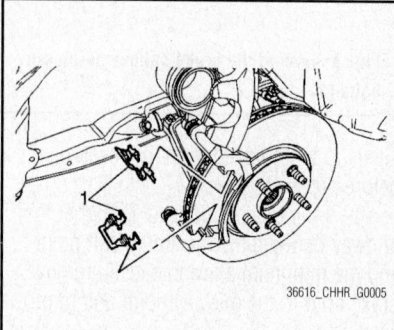

36616_CHHR_G0005

Fig. 7 Remove the brake pad retainers (1) from the caliper bracket

needs to be removed from the reservoir before proceeding.

4. If the brake fluid level is higher than midway between the maximum-full point and the minimum allowable level, remove brake fluid to the midway point before proceeding.

5. Raise and support the vehicle.

6. Remove the tire and wheel assembly.

7. Install and firmly hand tighten 2

wheel nuts to opposite wheel studs in order to retain the rotor to the hub.

8. Using a piston compressing tool, the caliper piston is compressed into the caliper bore enough to allow the caliper to slide past the brake rotor. Or, install a large C-clamp over the body of the brake caliper with the C-clamp ends against the rear of the caliper body and against the outboard brake pad.

9. Tighten the C-clamp evenly until the caliper piston is compressed into the caliper bore enough to allow the caliper to slide past the brake rotor.

10. Remove the C-clamp from the caliper.

11. Remove the brake caliper lower guide pin bolt.

✸✸ WARNING

Support the brake caliper with heavy mechanic's wire, or equivalent, whenever it is separated from its mount and the hydraulic flexible brake hose is still connected. Failure to support the caliper in this manner will cause the flexible brake hose to bear the weight of the caliper, which may cause damage to the brake hose and in turn may cause a brake fluid leak.

12. Without disconnecting the hydraulic brake flexible hose, pivot the caliper upward and secure the caliper with heavy mechanics wire, or equivalent.

13. Remove the brake pads from the caliper mounting bracket.

14. Remove the brake pad retainers from the caliper bracket.

15. Fully compress the piston in its bore.

16. Thoroughly clean the brake pad hardware mating surfaces of the caliper bracket (2), of any debris and corrosion.

17. Inspect the brake caliper guide pins for freedom of movement, and inspect the condition of the guide pin boots. Move the guide pins inboard and outboard within the bracket bores, without disengaging the slides from the boots, and observe for the following:

- Restricted caliper guide pin movement
- Looseness in the brake caliper mounting bracket
- Seized or binding caliper guide pins
- Split or torn boots

18. If any of the conditions listed are found, the brake caliper guide pins and/or boots require replacement.

To install:

19. Apply a very thin coating of high temperature silicone brake lubricant to the pad hardware mating surfaces of the caliper bracket only.

20. Install the brake pad retainers to the brake caliper bracket.

➡ **The wear sensor equipped disc brake pad must be mounted inboard of the rotor with the leading edge of the sensor facing the brake rotor during forward wheel rotation, or at the top of the pad when installed in vehicle position.**

21. Install the brake pads to the caliper bracket.

22. Remove the support, and rotate the brake caliper into position over the disc brake pads and to the caliper mounting bracket.

23. Install the lower brake caliper guide pin bolt. Tighten the bolt to 26 ft. lbs. (35 Nm).

24. Remove the wheel nuts retaining the brake rotor to the hub.

25. Install the tire and wheel assembly.
26. Lower the vehicle.
27. With the engine OFF, gradually apply the brake pedal approximately ⅔ of its travel distance.
28. Slowly release the brake pedal.
29. Wait 15 seconds, then gradually apply the brake pedal approximately ⅔ of its travel distance again until a firm brake pedal apply is obtained. This will properly seat the brake caliper pistons and brake pads.
30. Fill the master cylinder auxiliary reservoir to the proper level.
31. Burnish the pads and rotors.

✳✳ CAUTION

Road test a vehicle under safe conditions and while obeying all traffic laws. Do not attempt any maneuvers that could jeopardize vehicle control. Failure to adhere to these precautions could lead to serious personal injury and vehicle damage.

➡ **Burnishing the brake pads and brake rotors is necessary in order to ensure that the braking surfaces are properly prepared after service has been performed on the disc brake system. This procedure should be performed whenever the disc brake rotors have been refinished or replaced, and/or whenever the disc brake pads have been replaced.**

a. Select a smooth road with little or no traffic.

b. Accelerate the vehicle to 48 km/h (30 mph).

➡ **Use care to avoid overheating the brakes while performing this step.**

c. Using moderate to firm pressure, apply the brakes to bring the vehicle to a stop. Do not allow the brakes to lock.

d. Repeat steps 2 and 3 until approximately 20 stops have been completed. Allow sufficient cooling periods between stops in order to properly burnish the brake pads and rotors.

BRAKES

✳✳ CAUTION

Dust and dirt accumulating on brake parts during normal use may contain asbestos fibers from production or aftermarket brake linings. Breathing excessive concentrations of asbestos fibers can cause serious bodily harm. Exercise care when servicing brake parts. Do not sand or grind brake lining unless equipment used is designed to contain the dust residue. Do not clean brake parts with compressed air or by dry brushing. Cleaning should be done by dampening the brake components with a fine mist of water, then wiping the brake components clean with a dampened cloth. Dispose of cloth and all residue containing asbestos fibers in an impermeable container with the appropriate label. Follow practices prescribed by the Occupational Safety and Health Administration (OSHA) and the Environmental Protection Agency (EPA) for the handling, processing, and disposing of dust or debris that may contain asbestos fibers.

BRAKE CALIPER

REMOVAL & INSTALLATION

See Figures 8 through 10.

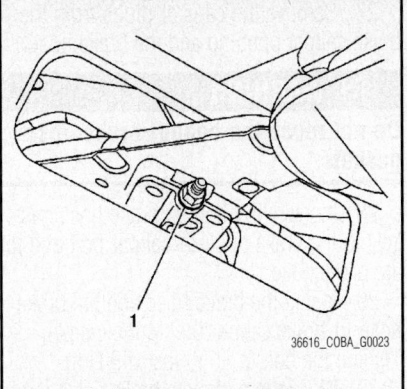

36616_COBA_G0023

Fig. 8 Park brake tension adjustment nut (1)

1. Before servicing the vehicle, refer to the Precautions Section.

2. Inspect the fluid level in the brake master cylinder auxiliary reservoir.

3. If the brake fluid level is midway between the maximum-full point and the minimum allowable level, no brake fluid needs to be removed from the reservoir before proceeding.

4. If the brake fluid level is higher than midway between the maximum-full point and the minimum allowable level, remove brake fluid to the midway point before proceeding.

5. Release the park brake lever boot from the floor console by applying light

REAR DISC BRAKES

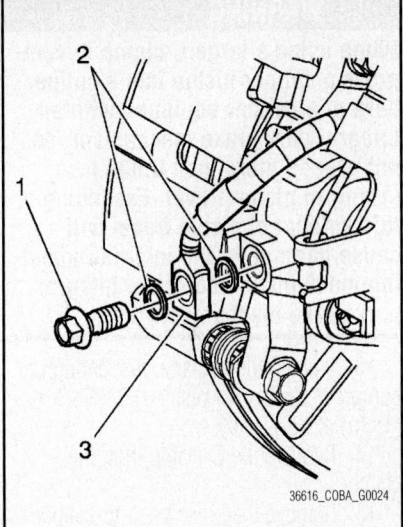

36616_COBA_G0024

Fig. 9 View of the brake hose-to-caliper bolt (1), brake hose gaskets (2) and brake hose (3)

pressure inward on the sides of the boot retainer, and pull the boot back.

6. Release the tension from the park brake cables. With the park brake lever in the released position, using ONLY HAND TOOLS, loosen the adjusting nut completely to the end of the front cable threaded rod.

7. Raise and support the vehicle.

8. Remove the tire and wheel assembly.

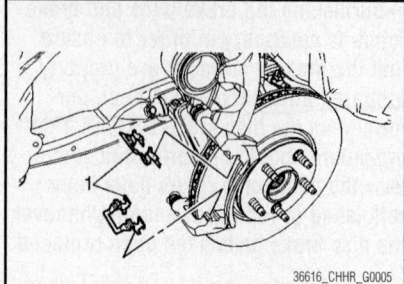

Fig. 10 While using a wrench on the flats of the caliper guide pins (1), install the brake caliper guide pin bolts (2)

9. Install and firmly hand tighten 2 wheel nuts to opposite wheel studs in order to retain the rotor to the hub.

10. Release the park brake cable end from the lever on the caliper.

11. Release the retaining tabs securing the park brake cable to the bracket on the caliper.

12. Install a large C-clamp, over the body of the brake caliper with the C-clamp ends against the rear of the caliper body and against the outer brake pad.

✳✳ WARNING

When using a large C-clamp to compress a caliper piston into a caliper bore of a caliper equipped with an integral park brake mechanism, do not exceed more than 0.039 inch (1mm) of piston travel. Exceeding this amount of piston travel will cause damage to the internal adjusting mechanism and/or the integral park brake mechanism.

13. Tighten the C-clamp just enough to compress the caliper piston 0.039 inch (1mm) of travel only.

14. Remove the C-clamp from the caliper.

15. Remove the brake hose-to-caliper bolt from the brake caliper.

16. Remove the brake hose from the brake caliper.

17. Remove and discard the 2 copper brake hose gaskets. These gaskets may be stuck to the brake caliper and/or the brake hose end.

18. Cap or plug the opening in the brake caliper and the brake hose to prevent fluid loss and contamination.

19. While using a wrench on the flats of the caliper guide pins, remove the brake caliper guide pin bolts.

20. Remove the brake caliper from the caliper bracket.

21. Inspect the brake caliper guide pins for freedom of movement, and inspect the condition of the guide pin boots. Move the guide pins inboard and outboard within the bracket bores, without disengaging the slides from the boots, and observe for the following:

- Restricted caliper guide pin movement
- Looseness in the brake caliper mounting bracket
- Seized or binding caliper guide pins
- Split or torn boots

22. If any of the conditions listed are found, the brake caliper guide pins and/or boots require replacement.

To install:

23. Install the brake caliper to the caliper bracket.

24. While using a wrench on the flats of the caliper guide pins, install the brake caliper guide pin bolts. Tighten the bolts to 26 ft. lbs. (35 Nm).

25. Press the park brake cable end fitting into the bracket on the caliper to secure the retaining tabs.

26. Secure the park brake cable end to the lever on the caliper.

27. Remove the caps or plugs from the brake caliper opening and the brake hose.

✳✳ WARNING

Do not reuse the copper brake hose gaskets.

28. Install NEW copper brake hose gaskets to the brake hose-to-caliper bolt and to the brake hose.

29. Install the brake hose and the brake hose-to-brake caliper bolt to the caliper. Tighten the bolt to 35 ft. lbs. (48 Nm).

30. Bleed the hydraulic brake system. Refer to Bleeding the Brake System.

31. Remove the wheel nuts retaining the brake rotor to the wheel hub.

32. Install the tire and wheel assembly.

33. Lower the vehicle.

34. With the engine OFF, gradually apply the brake pedal to approximately ⅔ of its travel distance.

35. Slowly release the brake pedal.

36. Wait 15 seconds, then gradually apply the brake pedal approximately ⅔ of its travel distance again until a firm brake pedal is obtained. This will properly seat the brake caliper pistons and brake pads.

37. Adjust the park brake cable tension. Refer to Parking Braked Cable Adjustment.

38. Position the park brake lever boot to the floor console and press the boot retainer into place to secure.

DISC BRAKE PADS

REMOVAL & INSTALLATION

See Figures 7, 11 and 12.

1. Before servicing the vehicle, refer to the Precautions Section.

2. Inspect the fluid level in the brake master cylinder auxiliary reservoir.

3. If the brake fluid level is midway between the maximum-full point and the minimum allowable level, no brake fluid needs to be removed from the reservoir before proceeding.

4. If the brake fluid level is higher than midway between the maximum-full point and the minimum allowable level, remove brake fluid to the midway point before proceeding.

5. Raise and support the vehicle.

6. Remove the tire and wheel assembly.

7. Install and firmly hand tighten 2 wheel nuts to opposite wheel studs in order to retain the rotor to the hub.

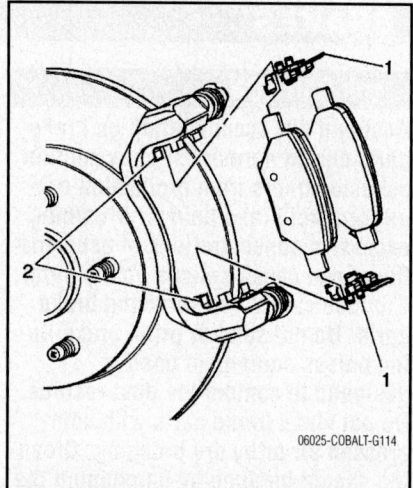

Fig. 11 Rear brake pads and retainers

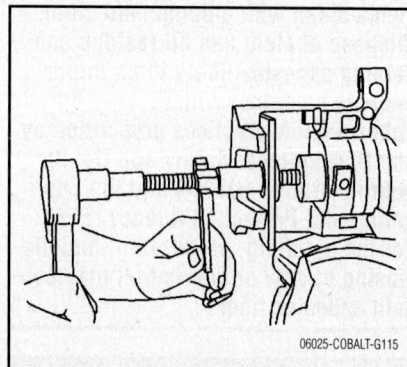

Fig. 12 Using a spanner wrench type caliper piston installer, fully retract the piston into the rear caliper bore

8. Install a large C-clamp, over the body of the brake caliper with the C-clamp ends against the rear of the caliper body and against the outer brake pad.

❋❋ WARNING

When using a large C-clamp to compress a caliper piston into a caliper bore of a caliper equipped with an integral park brake mechanism, do not exceed more than 1mm (0.039 in.) of piston travel. Exceeding this amount of piston travel will cause damage to the internal adjusting mechanism and/or the integral park brake mechanism.

9. Tighten the C-clamp just enough to compress the caliper piston 0.039 inch (1mm) of travel only.
10. Remove the C-clamp from the caliper.
11. While using a wrench on the flats of the caliper guide pins, remove the brake caliper guide pin bolts.

❋❋ WARNING

Support the brake caliper with heavy mechanic's wire, or equivalent, whenever it is separated from its mount and the hydraulic flexible brake hose is still connected. Failure to support the caliper in this manner will cause the flexible brake hose to bear the weight of the caliper, which may cause damage to the brake hose and in turn may cause a brake fluid leak.

12. Without disconnecting the hydraulic brake flexible hose, remove the caliper from the mounting bracket and secure the caliper with heavy mechanics wire, or equivalent.
13. Remove the brake pads from the caliper mounting bracket.
14. Remove the brake pad retainers (1) from the caliper bracket.
15. Thoroughly clean the brake pad hardware mating surfaces of the caliper bracket (2), of any debris and corrosion.

16. Inspect the brake caliper guide pins for freedom of movement, and inspect the condition of the guide pin boots. Move the guide pins inboard and outboard within the bracket bores, without disengaging the slides from the boots, and observe for the following:

- Restricted caliper guide pin movement
- Looseness in the brake caliper mounting bracket
- Seized or binding caliper guide pins
- Split or torn boots

17. If any of the conditions listed are found, the brake caliper guide pins and/or boots require replacement.
18. Using a spanner wrench type caliper piston installer, fully retract the piston into the caliper bore.

To install:

19. Apply a very thin coating of high temperature silicone brake lubricant to the pad hardware mating surfaces of the caliper bracket only.
20. Install the brake pad retainers to the brake caliper bracket.

➡**The wear sensor equipped disc brake pad must be mounted inboard of the rotor with the leading edge of the sensor facing the brake rotor during forward wheel rotation, or at the bottom of the pad when installed in vehicle position.**

21. Install the brake pads to the caliper bracket.
22. Remove the support, and install the caliper into position over the disc brake pads and to the caliper mounting bracket.
23. While using a wrench on the flats of the caliper guide pins, install the brake caliper guide pin bolts. Tighten the bolts to 25 ft. lbs. (34 Nm).
24. Remove the wheel nuts retaining the brake rotor to the hub.
25. Install the tire and wheel assembly.
26. Lower the vehicle.

27. With the engine OFF, gradually apply the brake pedal approximately ⅔ of its travel distance.
28. Slowly release the brake pedal.
29. Wait 15 seconds, then gradually apply the brake pedal approximately ⅔ of its travel distance again until a firm brake pedal apply is obtained. This will properly seat the brake caliper pistons and brake pads.
30. Fill the master cylinder auxiliary reservoir to the proper level.
31. Burnish the pads and rotors.

❋❋ CAUTION

Road test a vehicle under safe conditions and while obeying all traffic laws. Do not attempt any maneuvers that could jeopardize vehicle control. Failure to adhere to these precautions could lead to serious personal injury and vehicle damage.

➡**Burnishing the brake pads and brake rotors is necessary in order to ensure that the braking surfaces are properly prepared after service has been performed on the disc brake system. This procedure should be performed whenever the disc brake rotors have been refinished or replaced, and/or whenever the disc brake pads have been replaced.**

a. Select a smooth road with little or no traffic.
b. Accelerate the vehicle to 48 km/h (30 mph).

➡**Use care to avoid overheating the brakes while performing this step.**

c. Using moderate to firm pressure, apply the brakes to bring the vehicle to a stop. Do not allow the brakes to lock.
d. Repeat steps 2 and 3 until approximately 20 stops have been completed. Allow sufficient cooling periods between stops in order to properly burnish the brake pads and rotors.

BRAKE DRUM

REMOVAL & INSTALLATION

See Figure 13.

1. Before servicing the vehicle, refer to the Precautions Section.

2. Check to ensure that the park brake is fully released.

3. Raise and safely support the vehicle.

4. Remove the tire and wheel assembly.

5. Remove and discard the brake drum retainers (1), if equipped.

6. Remove the brake drum.

7. If the brake drum is to be reinstalled to the vehicle, use the J 41013 to clean any rust or corrosion from the hub/flange mating surface of the brake drum. If necessary, carefully remove any corrosion from the edge of the drum braking surface in order to ease installation.

8. Use the J 42450-A tool to clean the wheel hub flange.

To install:

9. If installing a new brake drum, use denatured alcohol or an equivalent approved brake cleaner and a clean shop towel to remove the protective coating from the friction surface of the drum.

10. Install the brake drum.

11. Install the tire and wheel assembly. Tighten lug nuts to 100 ft. lbs (140 Nm).

12. Apply the brakes approximately three times in order to seat and center the brake shoes within the drum.

13. Lower the vehicle.

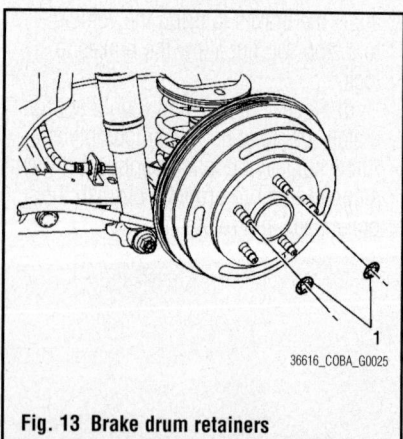

Fig. 13 Brake drum retainers

BRAKE SHOES

REMOVAL & INSTALLATION

See Figures 14 through 21.

1. Remove the brake drum. Refer to Brake Drum Replacement.

2. Remove the brake adjuster actuator lever spring (1).

3. Remove the brake adjuster actuator lever (1).

4. Remove the brake shoe hold down spring and cup (1) assemblies by compressing the spring and rotating the assembly ¼-turn.

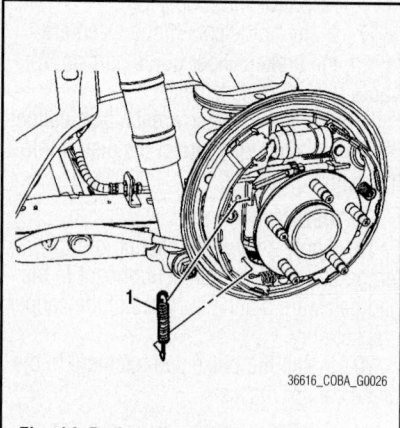

Fig. 14 Brake adjuster actuator lever spring (1)

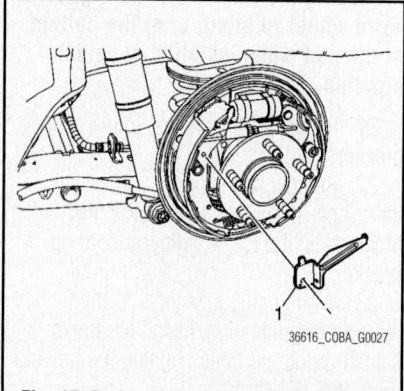

Fig. 15 Brake adjuster actuator lever (1)

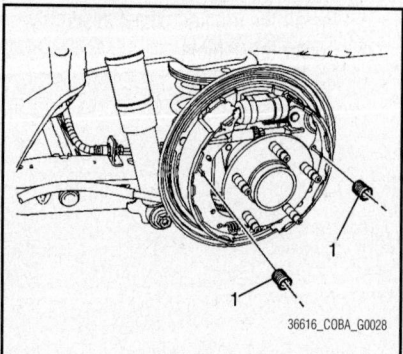

Fig. 16 Brake shoe hold down spring and cup (1)

5. Remove the 2 hold down spring and cup assembly pins.

6. Spread the top of the brake shoes apart slightly and remove the brake shoe adjuster (1).

7. Inspect the drum brake adjusting hardware and replace any components, as necessary. Refer to Drum Brake Adjusting Hardware Inspection.

8. Remove the upper brake shoe return spring (1).

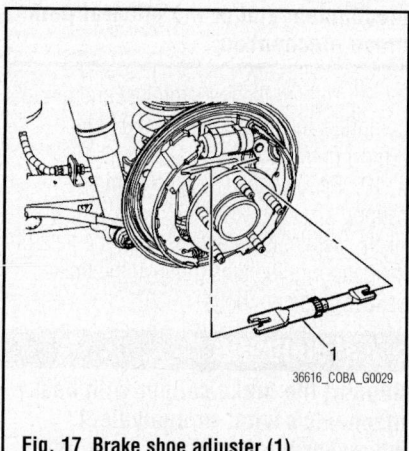

Fig. 17 Brake shoe adjuster (1)

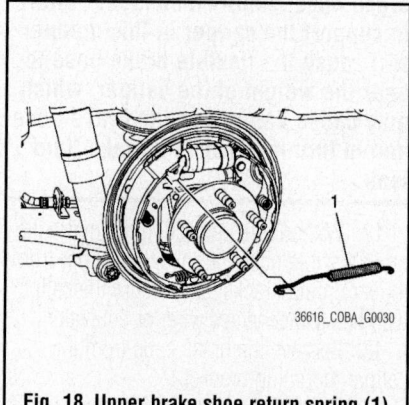

Fig. 18 Upper brake shoe return spring (1)

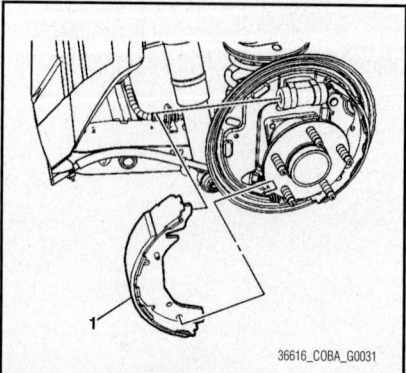

Fig. 19 Primary brake shoe

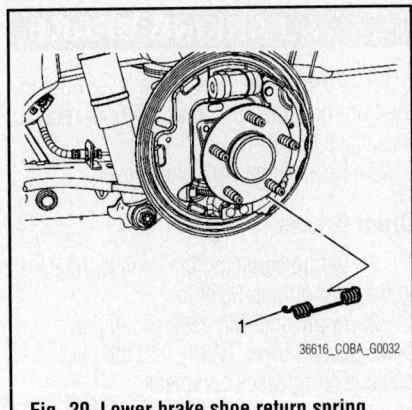

Fig. 20 **Lower brake shoe return spring**

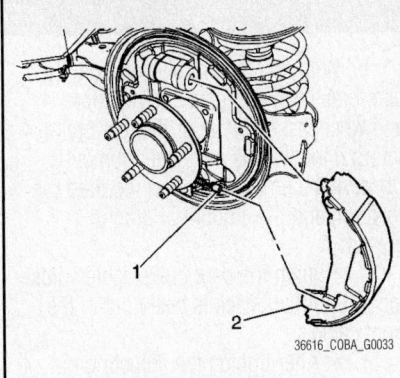

Fig. 21 **Secondary brake shoe**

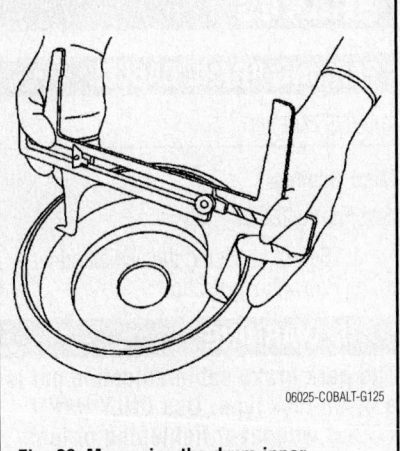

Fig. 22 **Measuring the drum inner diameter**

9. Rotate the primary brake shoe (1) toward the wheel hub assembly and release the brake shoe from the lower brake shoe return spring.

10. Remove the lower brake shoe return spring (1).

11. Inspect the drum brake hardware and replace any components, as necessary. Refer to Drum Brake Hardware Inspection.

12. Compress the park brake cable return spring and release the park brake cable fitting (1) from the park brake apply lever and remove the brake shoe (2).

To install:

13. Clean the drum brake backing plate of any dirt and debris.

14. Apply a light coat of high temperature brake lubricant to the drum brake backing plate brake shoe contact surfaces.

15. Compress the park brake cable return spring and install the park brake cable fitting to the park brake apply lever and position the brake shoe to the drum brake backing plate.

16. Install the lower brake shoe return spring.

17. Position the primary brake shoe to the drum brake backing plate and connect the brake shoe to the lower brake shoe return spring.

18. Install the upper brake shoe return spring.

19. Spread the top of the brake shoes apart slightly and install the brake shoe adjuster.

20. Install the 2 hold down spring and cup assembly pins.

Install the brake shoe hold down spring and cup assemblies by compressing the spring and rotating the assembly 1/4 turn.

21. Install the brake adjuster actuator lever.

22. Install the brake adjuster actuator lever spring.

23. Adjust the drum brakes. Refer Drum Brake Adjustment.

24. Install the brake drum.

DRUM BRAKE ADJUSTMENT

See Figure 22.

1. Before servicing the vehicle, refer to the Precautions Section.

2. Ensure that the park brake lever is in the fully released position.

3. Release the park brake lever boot from the floor console by applying light pressure inward on the sides of the boot retainer.

4. Pull the boot away from the console to expose the front park brake cable adjusting nut.

5. Release the tension from the park brake cable system at the front cable adjusting nut. Using ONLY HAND TOOLS, loosen the adjusting nut completely to the end of the front cable threaded rod.

6. Raise and support the vehicle.

7. Remove the rear tire and wheel assemblies.

8. Remove the brake drums.

9. Measure the inner diameter of the drum with a caliper such as tool J 21177-A at its widest point.

10. Firmly hand tighten the set screw on the tool.

11. Remove the tool from the brake drum and position it over the corresponding brake shoe assembly at its widest point.

12. While holding the tool in position, insert a 0.025 inch (0.635mm) (2008), insert a 0.015 inch (0.375mm) (2009) feeler gage between one side of the tool, and the corresponding brake shoe lining.

13. Rotate the brake shoe adjuster screw until the brake shoe linings contact the tool, and the feeler gage.

14. Repeat the above steps for the opposite brake drum and brake shoe assembly.

15. Install the brake drums.

16. Adjust the park brake.

17. Install the rear tire and wheel assemblies.

18. Lower the vehicle.

19. Position the park brake lever boot to the floor console and press the boot retainer into place to secure.

PARKING BRAKE CABLES

ADJUSTMENT

Disc Brakes

See Figure 23.

1. Before servicing the vehicle, refer to the Precautions Section.

✳✳ WARNING

The park brake cable adjusting nut is a nylon lock type. Use ONLY HAND TOOLS whenever tightening or loosening the adjusting nut.

2. Apply and fully release the park brake several times. Verify that the park brake lever releases completely.

3. Turn ON the ignition. Verify the red BRAKE warning lamp is not illuminated.

4. If the red BRAKE warning lamp is illuminated, verify the following:
- The park brake lever is in the fully released position and against the stop
- There is no slack in the park brake cables

5. Turn OFF the ignition.

6. Release the park brake lever boot from the floor console by applying light pressure inward on the sides of the boot retainer, and pull the boot back.

7. With the park brake lever in the released position, loosen the adjusting nut (1) enough to completely relieve tension on the front cable.

8. Raise and support the vehicle. Raise the vehicle just enough to observe the rear calipers and rotate the rear tire and wheel assemblies.

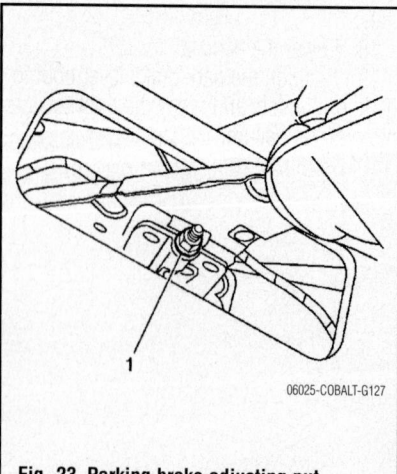

06025-COBALT-G127

Fig. 23 Parking brake adjusting nut

9. With all tension relieved from the park brake cables, rotate the rear tire and wheel assemblies, or the rear brake rotors if the wheels have been removed. Observe the amount of effort required for rotation, and the amount of drag if present.

10. Tighten the park brake cable adjusting nut until all slack is taken out of the front cable.

11. Further tighten the adjusting nut until one of the park brake levers on the rear calipers is just lifted off the stop on the caliper housing.

12. Slowly back off the adjusting nut until the park brake lever just rests on the stop.

13. Back off the adjusting nut one full turn.

14. Fully apply and release the park brake lever 3–5 times.

15. Raise the park brake lever 3 detent positions and attempt to rotate the rear tire and wheel assemblies, or the rear brake rotors.

➡️**If rotating the tire and wheel assemblies, they should be difficult to rotate, but should not be locked. If rotating the brake rotors, they should be locked.**

16. Raise the park brake lever one additional detent position and attempt to rotate the rear tire and wheel assemblies, or the rear brake rotors. The tire and wheel assemblies, or the rear brake rotors should be locked.

17. Fully release the park brake lever.

18. Verify the park brake is released by rotating the rear tire and wheel assemblies, or the rear brake rotors. The rotors should rotate freely and exhibit no brake shoe drag from the park brake system.

19. With the lever released, if the rotors required more effort to rotate, or exhibited more drag than noted previously when all cable tension was relieved, check the park brake levers on the rear calipers. The levers should be on the stops.

20. If the levers are not against the stops, loosen the adjusting nut just until the levers rest against the stops, then repeat steps 14–18.

21. If the rotors still do not rotate freely, with the park lever fully released, park brake adjustment is not the cause of any drag in the brake system.

22. Lower the vehicle.

23. Position the park brake lever boot to the floor console and press the boot retainer into place to secure.

24. Release the park brake lever.

Drum Brakes

1. Before servicing the vehicle, refer to the Precautions Section.

2. Apply and fully release the park brake several times. Verify that the park brake lever releases completely.

3. Turn ON the ignition. Verify the red BRAKE warning lamp is not illuminated.

4. If the red BRAKE warning lamp is illuminated, verify the following:
- The park brake lever is in the fully released position and against the stop
- There is no slack in the park brake cables

5. Turn OFF the ignition.

6. Release the park brake lever boot from the floor console by applying light pressure inward on the sides of the boot retainer, and pull the boot back.

7. With the park brake lever in the released position, loosen the adjusting nut enough to completely relieve tension on the front cable.

8. Raise and support the vehicle. Raise the vehicle just enough to allow rear tire and wheel assembly removal and rear drum adjustment.

9. Remove the rear tire and wheel assemblies.

10. Adjust the rear drum brakes. Refer to Drum Brake Adjustment.

11. Ensure there is no brake shoe drag after adjustment by rotating the brake drums. If drag exists, re-center the brake shoes and perform the brake shoe adjustment again.

12. Install 2 wheel nuts to the wheel studs and firmly hand-tighten in order to retain the brake drums.

13. Raise the park brake lever 6 detent positions.

14. Tighten the park brake cable adjusting nut. Tighten the nut to 35 inch lbs. (4 Nm).

15. Attempt to rotate the rear brake drums. There should be no rotation forward or rearward.

16. Fully release the park brake lever.

17. Verify the park brake is released by rotating the rear brake drums. The drums should rotate freely and exhibit no brake shoe drag.

18. If the drums do not rotate freely, repeat the park brake cable adjustment procedure.

19. Raise the park brake lever 3 detent positions and attempt to rotate the rear brake drums. One of the brake drums should not rotate forward or rearward. The other brake drum should not rotate forward or rearward, or should require substantial effort to rotate.

20. Raise the park brake lever one additional detent position and attempt to rotate the rear brake drums.

21. Verify that the left and right brake drums cannot be rotated.

22. Remove the wheel nuts retaining the brake drums.

23. Install the rear tire and wheel assemblies.

24. Lower the vehicle.

25. Position the park brake lever boot to the floor console and press the boot retainer into place to secure.

26. Release the park brake lever.

PARKING BRAKE SHOES

REMOVAL & INSTALLATION

The rear drum brake shoes and disc brake pads serve as the parking brakes. Refer to the procedures under Rear Drum Brakes and Rear Disc Brakes.

ADJUSTMENT

Refer to parking brake cables, adjustment.

CHASSIS ELECTRICAL

GENERAL INFORMATION

❋❋ CAUTION

These vehicles are equipped with an air bag system. The system must be disarmed before performing service on, or around, system components, the steering column, instrument panel components, wiring and sensors. Failure to follow the safety precautions and the disarming procedure could result in accidental air bag deployment, possible injury and unnecessary system repairs.

SERVICE PRECAUTIONS

❋❋ CAUTION

When performing service on or near the SIR components or the SIR wiring, the SIR system must be disabled. Refer to SIR Disabling and Enabling . Failure to observe the correct procedure could cause deployment of the SIR components, personal injury, or unnecessary SIR system repairs.

The inflatable restraint sensing and diagnostic module (SDM) maintains a reserved energy supply. The reserved energy supply provides deployment power for the air bags. Deployment power is available for as much as 1 minute after disconnecting the vehicle power. Disabling the SIR system prevents deployment of the air bags from the reserved energy supply.

General Service Instructions

1. The following are general service instructions which must be followed in order to properly repair the vehicle and return it to its original integrity:

a. Do not handle the inflatable restraint vehicle rollover sensor when connected to vehicle power.

AIR BAG (SUPPLEMENTAL RESTRAINT SYSTEM)

b. Do not expose inflator modules to temperatures above 65°C (150°F).

c. Verify the correct replacement part number. Do not substitute a component from a different vehicle.

d. Use only original GM replacement parts available from your authorized GM dealer. Do not use salvaged parts for repairs to the SIR system.

2. Discard any of the following components if it has been dropped from a height of 3 ft (91cm) or greater:

- Inflatable restraint front end sensor
- Inflatable restraint instrument panel (I/P) module
- Inflatable restraint passenger presence system (PPS)
- Inflatable restraint roof rail module
- Inflatable restraint SDM
- Inflatable restraint side impact sensor (SIS)
- Inflatable restraint steering wheel module
- Inflatable restraint steering wheel module coil
- Inflatable restraint vehicle rollover sensor
- Seat belt pretensioner

When carrying an undeployed inflator module:

- Do not carry the inflator module by the wires or connector.
- Make sure the air bag opening points away from you.

When storing an undeployed inflator module:

- Make sure the air bag opening points away from the surface on which the inflator module rests.
- Provide free space for the air bag to expand in case of an accidental deployment.
- When storing a steering column, do not rest the column with the air bag opening facing down and the column vertical. Lay the column on its side.

- Failure to observe these guidelines may result in personal injury.

DISABLING THE SYSTEM

Air Bag Fuse

❋❋ CAUTION

If you are performing service on or near the SIR components or the SIR wiring, observe all SIR System Precautions. Failure to follow the correct procedure could cause air bag deployment, unnecessary SIR system repairs, or personal injury or death.

1. Turn the steering wheel so that the vehicles wheels are pointing straight ahead.

2. Place the ignition in the OFF position.

➡**The SDM may have more than one fused power input. To ensure there is no unwanted SIR deployment, personal injury, or unnecessary SIR system repairs, remove all fuses supplying power to the SDM. With all SDM fuses removed and the ignition switch in the ON position, the AIR BAG warning indicator illuminates. This is normal operation, and does not indicate a SIR system malfunction.**

3. Locate and remove the fuse(s) supplying power to the SDM. Refer to Fuses & Flashers.

4. Wait 1 minute before working on the system.

Negative Battery Cable

1. Turn the steering wheel so that the vehicles wheels are pointing straight ahead.

2. Place the ignition in the OFF position.

3. Disconnect the negative battery cable from the battery.

4. Wait 1 minute before working on system.

ENABLING THE SYSTEM

Air Bag Fuse

1. Place the ignition in the OFF position.
2. Install the fuse(s) supplying power to the SDM. Refer to Fuses & Flashers.
3. Turn the ignition switch to the ON position. The AIR BAG indicator will flash then turn OFF.
4. Perform the Diagnostic System Check—Vehicle if the AIR BAG warning indicator does not operate as described. Refer to Diagnostic Trouble Codes.

Negative Battery Cable

1. Place the ignition in the OFF position.
2. Connect the negative battery cable to the battery.
3. Turn the ignition switch to the ON position. The AIR BAG indicator will flash then turn OFF.
4. Perform the Diagnostic System Check—Vehicle if the AIR BAG warning indicator does not operate as described.

CLOCKSPRING CENTERING

See Figures 24 and 25.

1. Before servicing the vehicle, refer to the Precautions Section.

✴✴ CAUTION

If you are performing service on or near the SIR components or the SIR wiring, observe all SIR System Precautions. Failure to follow the correct procedure could cause air bag deployment, unnecessary SIR system repairs, or personal injury or death.

2. Disable the SIR system. Refer to SIR Disabling and Enabling in Chassis Electrical.

✴✴ CAUTION

The new Supplemental Inflatable Restraint (SIR) coil assembly will be centered. Improper alignment of the SIR coil assembly may damage the unit, causing an inflatable restraint malfunction.

3. Verify the following conditions before centering the SIR steering wheel module coil ("clockspring"):
- The wheels on the vehicle are straight ahead
- The block tooth and the centering mark (1) of the steering shaft must be in the 12 o'clock position

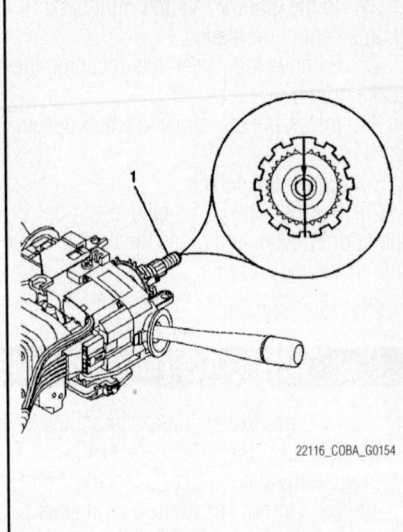

Fig. 24 The block tooth and the centering mark (1) of the steering shaft must be in the 12 o'clock position

4. If available, remove the yellow retaining tab (1) from the SIR steering wheel module coil and save the tab for reassembly.
5. Hold the SIR steering wheel module coil face up by the casing (2).
6. Slowly turn the SIR steering wheel module coil hub (3) in a clockwise direction until the coil ribbon stops.
7. Slowly rotate the SIR steering wheel module coil hub (3) counterclockwise 2½ revolutions until the centering window (4) turns yellow. This indicates the **CENTER** position.

➡**If the retaining tab is not available, the use of tape to secure the SIR steering wheel module coil is recommended for installation to the steering column.**

8. Install the yellow retaining tab (1) to the SIR steering wheel module coil.
9. Slide the centered SIR steering wheel module coil onto the steering shaft.

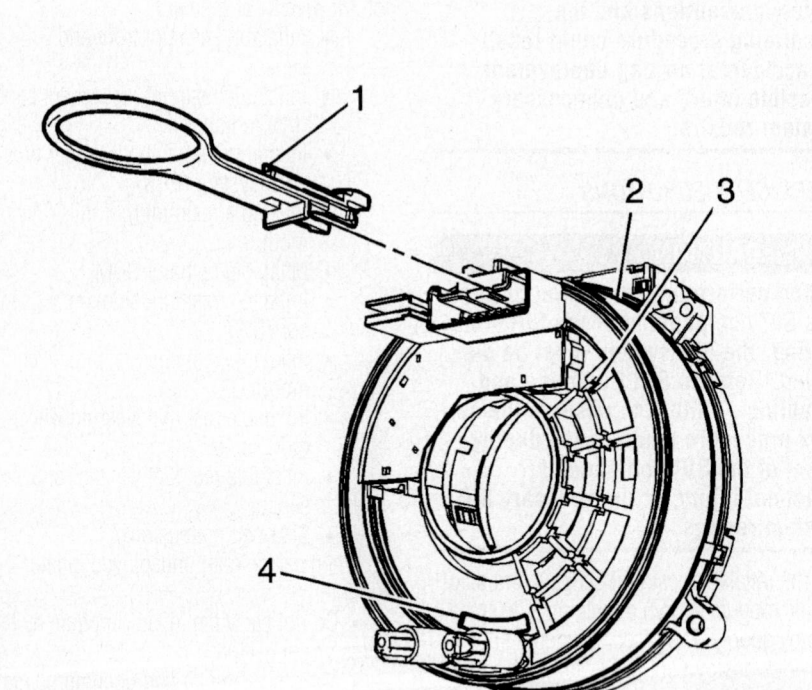

1. SIR steering wheel module coil centering: yellow retaining tab
2. Casing
3. Coil hub
4. Centering window

Fig. 25 SIR steering wheel module coil centering: yellow retaining tab, casing, coil hub, and centering window

DRIVE TRAIN

AUTOMATIC TRANSAXLE ASSEMBLY

REMOVAL & INSTALLATION

See Figures 26 through 28.

1. With the wheels in the straight ahead position, remove the key from the ignition switch.

2. Remove the underhood electrical center cover.

3. Disconnect the negative battery cable.

4. Disconnect the engine and transmission control module harness connectors and remove the modules.

➡ **It may be necessary to remove the positive cable retainer near the bottom of the powertrain control module (PCM) bracket.**

5. Disconnect the positive battery cables from the underhood electrical center.

6. Remove the underhood electrical center tray nuts and bolt.

7. Remove the electrical center tray from the base and disconnect the wiring harnesses from the center tray.

8. Lift the electrical center up and swing it back and out of the way.

9. Remove the electrical center bracket from the vehicle.

10. Disconnect the shift cable from the Park Neutral Position (PNP) switch.

11. Disconnect the electrical connector from the PNP switch.

12. Remove the shift cable with bracket from the transmission.

13. Disconnect the transmission wire harness electrical connector from the transaxle.

14. Remove the upper transmission to engine bolt (2) and stud (1).

15. Install a suitable engine support fixture.

16. Secure the air conditioning (A/C) condenser and radiator cooling module to the upper body structure.

17. Remove the left transmission mount bolts.

18. Raise and support the vehicle.

19. Remove the oil pan to drain the transmission.

20. Remove the front wheel and tire assemblies.

21. Remove the frame. Refer to Frame in Engine Mechanical.

22. Disconnect the wheel driveshafts from the transaxle. Refer to Halfshafts in Front Drive Axle.

23. Remove the transmission brace to transmission bolts.

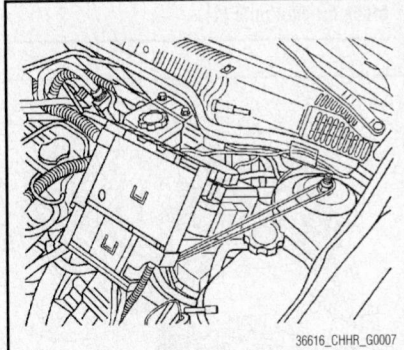

36616_CHHR_G0007

Fig. 26 Lift the electrical center up and swing it back and out of the way

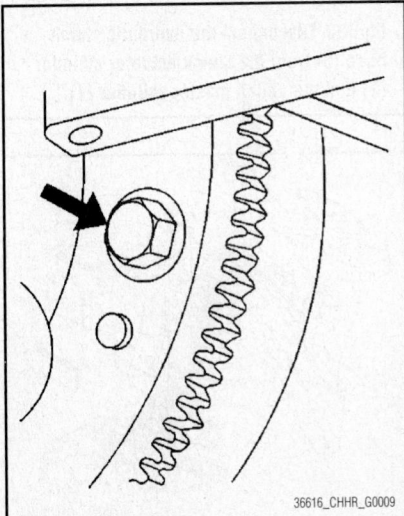

36616_CHHR_G0009

Fig. 27 Use J 43653 to remove the torque converter to flywheel bolts

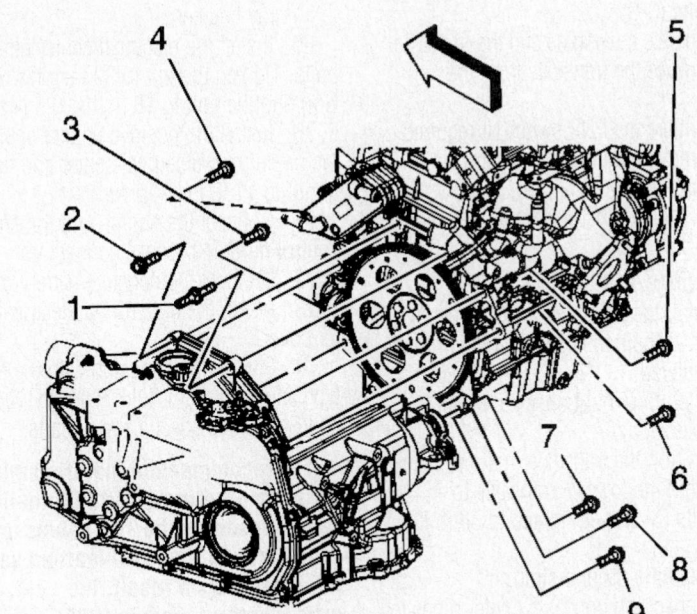

1. Upper transmission-to-engine stud
2. Upper transmission-to-engine bolt
3. Lower transaxle-to-engine bolt
4. Lower transaxle-to-engine bolt
5. Lower transaxle-to-engine bolt
6. Lower transaxle-to-engine bolt
7. Lower transaxle-to-engine bolt
8. Lower transaxle-to-engine bolt
9. Lower transaxle-to-engine bolt

36616_CHHR_G0008

Fig. 28 Transaxle mounting

24. Remove the starter, as outlined in the Engine Electrical Section.

25. Mark the relationship of the flywheel to the torque converter for reassembly.

26. Use the J 43653, or equivalent Flywheel Holding tool to keep the crankshaft from rotating.

27. Use J 43653 to remove the torque converter to flywheel bolts.

28. Remove the transaxle oil cooler pipes retaining nut from the transaxle.

29. Remove the transaxle oil cooler pipes from the transaxle.

30. Disconnect the Vehicle Speed Sensor (VSS) wiring harness from the sensor and harness retainer.

31. Remove the rear O2 wiring harness from the rear transmission mount bracket.

32. Remove the front transmission mount.

33. Lower the transmission with the engine support fixture enough to remove the transmission.

34. Raise the vehicle.

35. Support the transaxle with a suitable jack.

36. Remove the lower 6 transaxle to engine bolts (3-9).

37. Separate the engine and the transaxle.

38. Remove the transaxle from the vehicle.

39. Remove the PNP switch, if required.

40. Remove the transaxle electrical ground stud, if required.

41. Flush the transmission cooler and lines.

To install:

42. Install the PNP switch, if removed.

43. Install the transaxle electrical ground stud, if removed.

44. Install the front transaxle mount to the transaxle.

45. Position the transaxle in the vehicle.

46. Install the lower 6 transaxle to engine bolts (3-9), and tighten to 66 ft. lbs. (90 Nm).

47. Install the ground strap.

48. Connect the transaxle cooler pipes to the transaxle and install the retaining nut. Tighten to 66 ft. lbs. (90 Nm).

49. Connect the VSS wiring harness to the sensor.

50. Connect the rear O2 wiring harness to the rear transaxle bracket.

51. Use the J 43653 to prevent the crankshaft from rotating.

52. Install the torque converter to flywheel bolts and tighten to 46 ft. lbs. (62 Nm).

53. Install the starter.

54. Install the transmission brace to transmission bolts, and tighten to 53 ft. lbs. (72 Nm).

55. Install the rear transaxle mount and bracket, if removed.

56. Install the wheel driveshafts to the transaxle, as outlined in the Drive Train Section.

57. Remove the transmission jack.

58. Install the frame, as outlined in the Engine Mechanical Section.

59. Install the front wheel and tire assemblies.

60. Lower the vehicle.

61. Install the upper transaxle to engine bolt (2) and stud (1) to 66 ft. lbs. (90 Nm).

62. Remove the engine support fixture.

63. Connect the transmission wire harness electrical connector to the transaxle.

64. Connect the electrical connector to the PNP switch.

65. Install the shift cable with bracket to the transaxle. Tighten the bolts to 15 ft. lbs. (20 Nm).

66. Connect the shift cable to the PNP switch.

67. Reposition the underhood electrical center.

68. Connect the wiring harness retainer to the tray bracket.

69. Install the electrical center nuts and bolts. Tighten the nut to 89 inch lbs. (10 Nm) and the bolt to 18 ft. lbs. (25 Nm).

70. Install the positive battery cables to the underhood electrical center and tighten to nut to 11 ft. lbs. (15 Nm).

71. Connect the engine and transmission control module harness connectors.

72. Connect the negative battery cable.

73. Install the underhood electrical center cover.

74. Fill the transmission with the proper type and amount of fluid. Refer to the Fluid and Capacities specification charts.

➡ **It is recommended that transmission adaptive pressure (TAP) information be reset. Resetting the TAP values using a scan tool will erase all learned values in all cells. As a result, the ECM, powertrain control module (PCM), or TCM will need to relearn TAP values. Transmission performance may be affected as new TAP values are learned.**

MANUAL TRANSAXLE ASSEMBLY

REMOVAL & INSTALLATION

MU3 Transaxle

See Figures 29 through 33.

1. Disconnect the negative battery cable.

2. Remove the positive battery post from the underhood junction block.

3. Disconnect the positive cables from the underhood junction block.

4. Remove the underhood junction block bracket nuts.

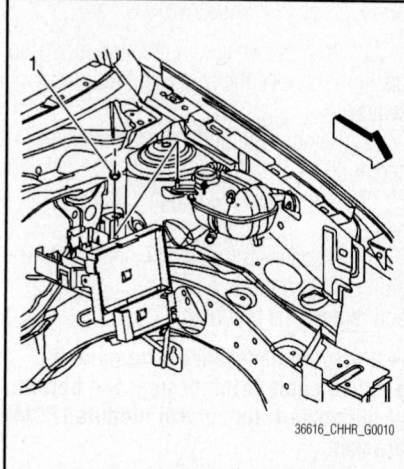

Fig. 29 Remove the underhood junction block bracket nuts (1).

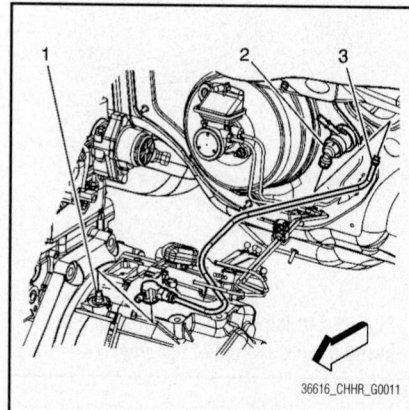

Fig. 30 Disconnect the hydraulic clutch hose (3) from the clutch actuator cylinder (2) and the clutch master cylinder (1).

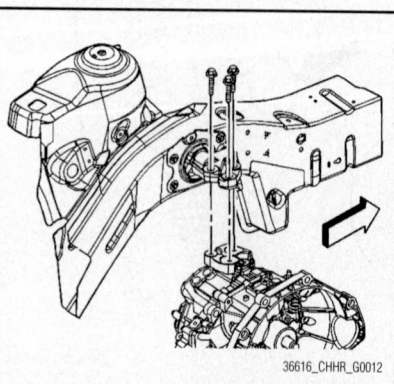

Fig. 31 Remove the upper transmission to mount bolts

5. Loosen the underhood junction block bracket bolt.

6. Disconnect the front wiring harness from the underhood junction block bracket.

7. Reposition the underhood junction block bracket aside.

8. Disconnect the hydraulic clutch hose (3) from the clutch actuator cylinder (2) and the clutch master cylinder (1).

9. Install a suitable engine support fixture.

10. Secure the cooling module to the upper body structure.

11. Remove the upper transmission to mount bolts.

12. Disconnect the wiring harness retainer from the transmission stud.

13. Remove the upper transmission to engine stud and bolt.

14. Remove the frame, as outlined in the Engine Mechanical Section.

15. Drain the transaxle.

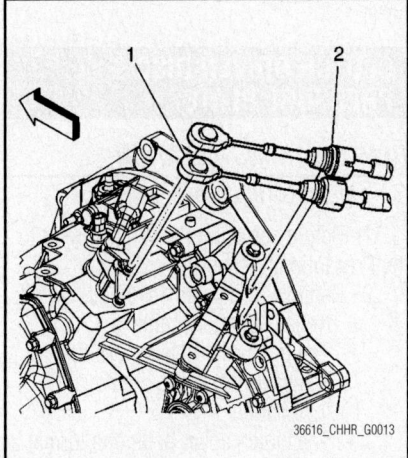

Fig. 32 Disconnect the shift cables (1, 2) from the transmission

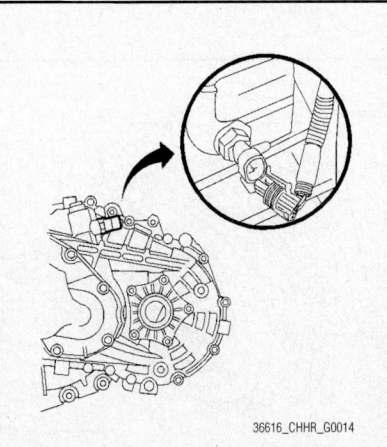

Fig. 33 Disconnect the backup lamp switch harness connector

16. Disconnect the drive axle and intermediate shaft from the transmission and secure out of the way.

17. Remove the starter, as outlined in the Engine Electrical Section.

18. Disconnect the shift cables (1, 2) from the transmission.

19. Disconnect the backup lamp switch harness connector.

20. Lower the vehicle.

21. Use the engine support fixture rear hook to lower the powertrain enough to allow clearance between the side rail and powertrain.

22. Raise the vehicle.

23. Use a transmission jack to secure the transmission, and remove the transmission to engine bolts.

24. Remove the transmission from the vehicle.

25. Remove the front transmission mount from the transmission.

26. Remove the rear transmission mount and bracket from the transmission.

To install:

27. Install the rear transmission mount to the transmission.

28. Install the front transmission mount to the transmission.

29. Use a transmission jack to position the transmission to the vehicle.

30. Secure the transmission to the engine and tighten the bolts to 55 ft. lbs. (75 Nm).

31. Connect the backup lamp switch harness connector.

32. Connect the shift cables to the transmission.

33. Connect the drive axle and intermediate shaft to the transmission.

34. Lower the vehicle.

35. Use the engine support fixture in order to raise the powertrain assembly.

36. Install the left transmission mount.

37. Install the frame.

38. Remove the engine support fixture.

39. Release the cooling module from the upper body structure.

40. Install the top engine to transmission bolt and tighten to 55 ft. lbs. (75 Nm).

41. Install the top engine to transmission stud and tighten to 55 ft. lbs. (75 Nm).

42. Connect the wiring harness retainer to the transmission stud.

43. Connect the hydraulic clutch hose to the clutch actuator cylinder.

44. Bleed the clutch hydraulic system.

45. Connect the front wiring harness to the underhood junction block bracket.

46. Install the junction block bracket, bolt and nuts. Tighten the nuts to 89 inch

lbs. (10 Nm) and the bolt to 18 ft. lbs. (25 Nm).

47. Install the front wiring harness to the junction block bracket.

48. Connect the positive battery cables to the junction block bracket.

49. Install the positive battery post to the junction block bracket.

50. Connect the negative battery cable.

51. Fill the transaxle to the proper level.

M86 Transaxle

See Figures 29, 34 through 38.

1. Disconnect the negative battery cable.

2. Remove the positive battery post from the underhood junction block.

3. Disconnect the positive cables from the underhood junction block.

4. Remove the underhood junction block bracket nuts.

5. Loosen the underhood junction block bracket bolt.

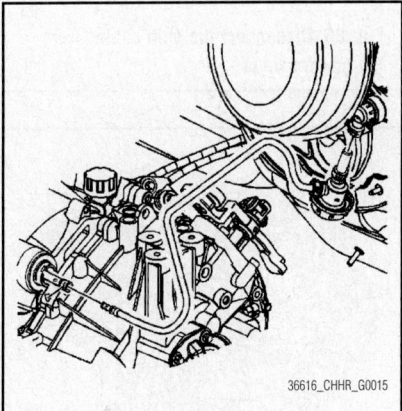

Fig. 34 Disconnect the hydraulic clutch hose from the clutch actuator cylinder

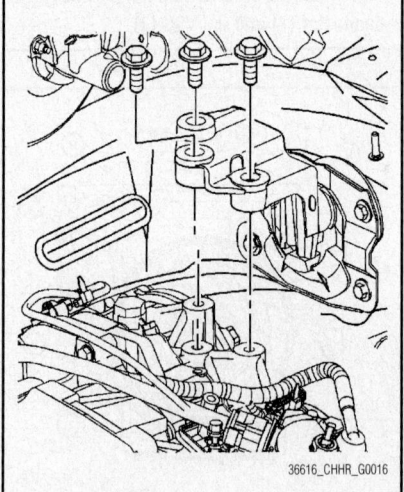

Fig. 35 Remove the upper transmission to mount bolts

6. Disconnect the front wiring harness from the underhood junction block bracket.

7. Reposition the underhood junction block bracket aside.

8. Disconnect the hydraulic clutch hose from the clutch actuator cylinder.

9. Install a suitable engine support fixture.

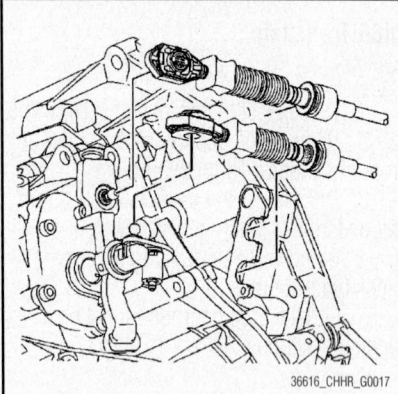

Fig. 36 Disconnect the shift cables from the transmission

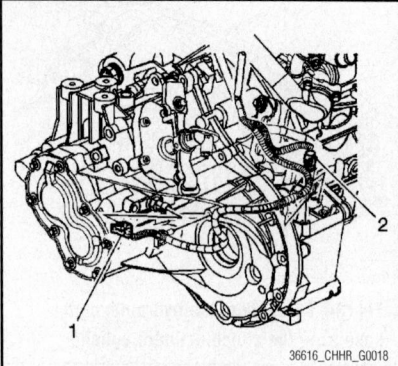

Fig. 37 Detach the backup lamp switch connector (1) and the VSS (2)

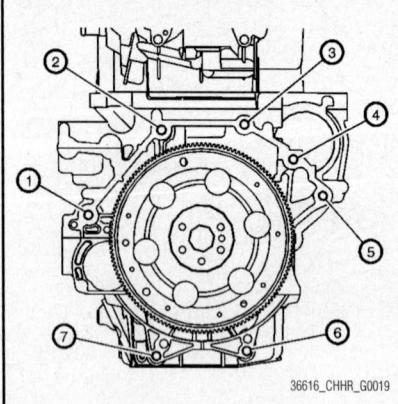

Fig. 38 Transaxle bolt locations & tightening sequence

10. Secure the cooling module to the upper body structure.

11. Remove the upper transmission to mount bolts.

12. Remove the upper transmission to engine bolt.

13. Remove the frame, as outlined in the Engine Mechanical section.

14. Drain the transaxle.

15. Disconnect the drive axles from the transmission and secure out of the way. Refer to Halfshaft in the Drive Train Section.

16. Remove the starter, as outlined in the Engine Electrical Section.

17. Disconnect the shift cables from the transmission.

18. Disconnect the backup lamp switch harness connector.

19. Disconnect the Vehicle Speed Sensor (VSS).

20. Lower the vehicle.

21. Use the engine support fixture rear hook to lower the powertrain enough to allow clearance between the side rail and powertrain.

22. Raise the vehicle.

23. Use a transmission jack to secure the transmission, and remove the transmission to engine bolts.

24. Remove the transmission from the vehicle.

25. Remove the front transmission mount from the transmission.

26. Remove the rear transmission mount and bracket from the transmission.

To install:

27. Install the rear transmission mount to the transmission.

28. Install the front transmission mount to the transmission.

29. Use a transmission jack to position the transmission to the vehicle.

➡ **The number 3 position does not require a bolt.**

30. Secure the transmission to the engine and tighten the bolts, the sequence shown, 55 ft. lbs. (75 Nm).

31. Connect the VSS.

32. Connect the backup lamp switch harness connector .

33. Connect the shift cable to the transmission.

34. Install the starter.

35. Connect the drive axles to the transmission.

36. Lower the vehicle.

37. Use the engine support fixture in order to raise the powertrain assembly.

38. Install the transmission side mount.

39. Position the underhood junction block to the original position.

40. Install the front wiring harness to the junction block bracket.

41. Connect the positive battery cables to the junction block bracket .

42. Install the positive battery post to the junction block bracket.

43. Install the junction block bracket, bolt and nuts. Tighten the bolt to 18 ft. lbs. (25 Nm) and the nuts to 89 inch lbs. (10 Nm).

44. Install the frame.

45. Remove the engine support fixture.

46. Install the top engine to transmission bolt and tighten to 55 ft. lbs. (75 Nm).

47. Connect the hydraulic clutch hose to the clutch actuator cylinder.

48. Bleed the clutch hydraulic system.

49. Release the cooling module from the upper body structure.

50. Connect the negative battery cable.

51. Fill the transmission to the proper level.

CLUTCH DRIVEN DISC & PRESSURE PLATE

REMOVAL & INSTALLATION

See Figures 39 through 42.

1. Before servicing the vehicle, refer to the Precautions Section.

2. Remove or disconnect the following:
   - Negative battery cable
   - The transaxle. Refer to Manual Transaxle Assembly Removal & Installation
   - The clutch cover bolts one turn at a time, until spring pressure is relieved
   - The clutch cover
   - The clutch driven disc and pressure plate

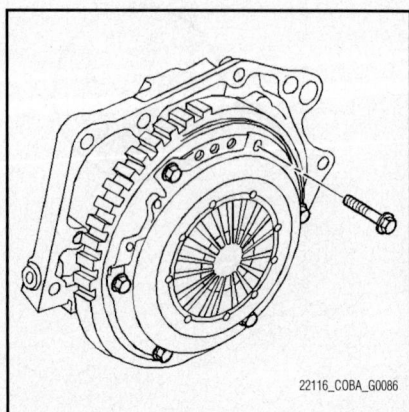

Fig. 39 Remove the clutch cover bolts one turn at a time

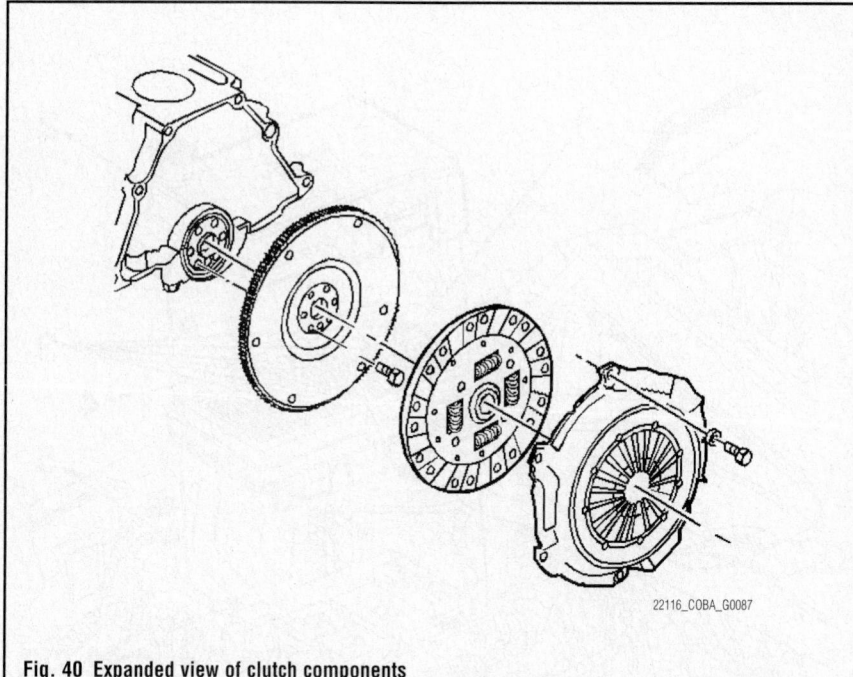

Fig. 40 Expanded view of clutch components

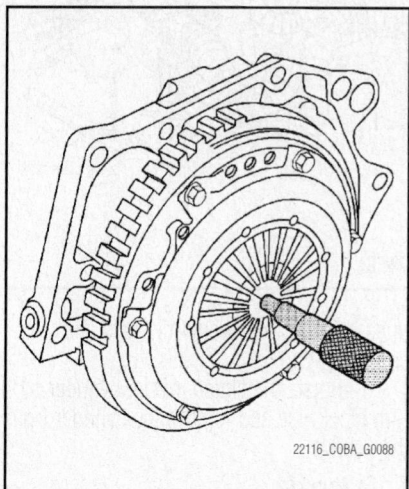

Fig. 41 Install the J 43482 in order to support the clutch cover to the flywheel assembly

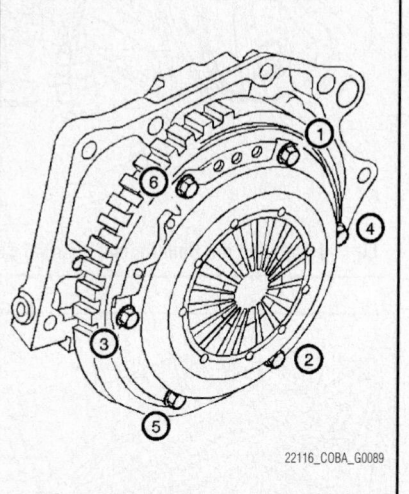

Fig. 42 Torque sequence for clutch cover to flywheel bolts

To install:

3. For the Getrag transaxle, align the machined side of the flywheel assembly, with the machined side of the cover.

4. Install the clutch disc and the clutch cover.

5. Hand start the clutch cover to flywheel bolts, leaving the clutch cover loose enough to reposition for alignment.

6. Install the J 43482 in order to support the clutch cover to the flywheel assembly.

✳✳ WARNING

Use the correct fastener in the correct location. Replacement fasteners

must be the correct part number for that application. Fasteners requiring replacement or fasteners requiring the use of thread locking compound or sealant are identified in the service procedure. Do not use paints, lubricants, or corrosion inhibitors on fasteners or fastener joint surfaces unless specified. These coatings affect fastener torque and joint clamping force and may damage the fastener. Use the correct tightening sequence and specifications when installing fasteners in order to avoid damage to parts and systems.

7. Tighten the clutch cover to flywheel bolts in the sequence shown. Tighten the bolts to 22 ft. lbs. (30 Nm).

8. Recheck each bolt torque using the tightening sequence.

9. Remove the J 43482.

➡**Excessive amounts of lubricant on the input shaft splines may contaminate the clutch disc and cause clutch shudder.**

10. Lubricate the inside diameter of the bearing.

11. Install the transaxle. Refer to Manual Transaxle Assembly Removal & Installation.

12. Bleed the hydraulic system. Refer to Clutch, Hydraulic System Bleeding.

13. Connect the negative battery cable.

ADJUSTMENTS

1. Before servicing the vehicle, refer to the Precautions Section.

The clutch has an automatic adjusting mechanism to compensate for normal wear on clutch plates no adjustment is possible, or necessary. However, clutch pedal position sensor learn is possible and necessary

✳✳ CAUTION

Replacement or reprogramming of the ECM, or replacement of the clutch pedal position sensor (CPPS) or clutch pedal requires that a CPPS learn procedure be performed. Failure to perform the CPPS learn procedure may result in personal injury or damage to the vehicle or its components if the vehicle is in gear and the starter motor is accidentally engaged.

➡**The clutch pedal position (CPP) sensor learn procedure is required when the following service procedures have been performed regardless of whether DTC P080A is set:**

- An engine control module (ECM) replacement
- A CPP sensor replacement
- Any repairs which affect the CPP sensor relationship

Clutch Pedal Position Sensor Learn

1. Before servicing the vehicle, refer to the Precautions Section.

2. Install a scan tool.

3. Monitor the ECM for DTCs with a scan tool. If other DTCs are set, except DTC P080A, refer to Diagnostic Trouble Codes.

4. With a scan tool, select Clutch Pedal Position Learn under Module Setup in Manual Transmission, and perform the following instructions displayed on the scan tool screen.

➡ **The CPP sensor learn procedure cannot be performed more than once per ignition cycle. The clutch pedal needs to be fully depressed and held steady throughout this procedure in order to perform a correct learning.**

5. The scan tool will display under CPP Learn Status: Not Learned, In Process, Complete, Fail—Low Volt, Fail—High Volt, or Fail Moving. The scan tool will display under CPP Learn Status Complete if the process was successful.

6. If the scan tool indicates that DTC P080A ran and passed this ignition the CPP sensor learn procedure is complete. If the scan tool indicates DTC P080A failed or did not run this ignition, refer to DTC P080A.

7. If any other DTC is set, refer to Diagnostic Trouble Codes. If any other DTC is set, refer to Diagnostic Trouble Codes.

8. Turn OFF the ignition for 30 seconds after the learn procedure has successfully completed in order to store the CPP sensor variation values in ECM history.

CLUTCH MASTER CYLINDER

REMOVAL & INSTALLATION

See Figures 43 and 44.

1. Before servicing the vehicle, refer to the Precautions Section.

2. Remove the clutch pedal retainer from the front of the clutch pedal assembly.

3. Pull the clutch pedal upward in order to disengage the clutch master cylinder pushrod from the clutch pedal.

4. Remove the Underhood Electrical Center (UBEC). Refer to Underhood Electrical Center in Chassis Electrical

✳✳ WARNING

Avoid spilling brake fluid onto painted surfaces, electrical connections, wiring, or cables. Brake fluid will damage painted surfaces and cause corrosion to electrical components. If any brake fluid comes in contact with painted surfaces, immediately flush the area with water. If any brake fluid comes in contact with electrical connections, wiring, or cables, use a clean shop cloth to wipe away the fluid.

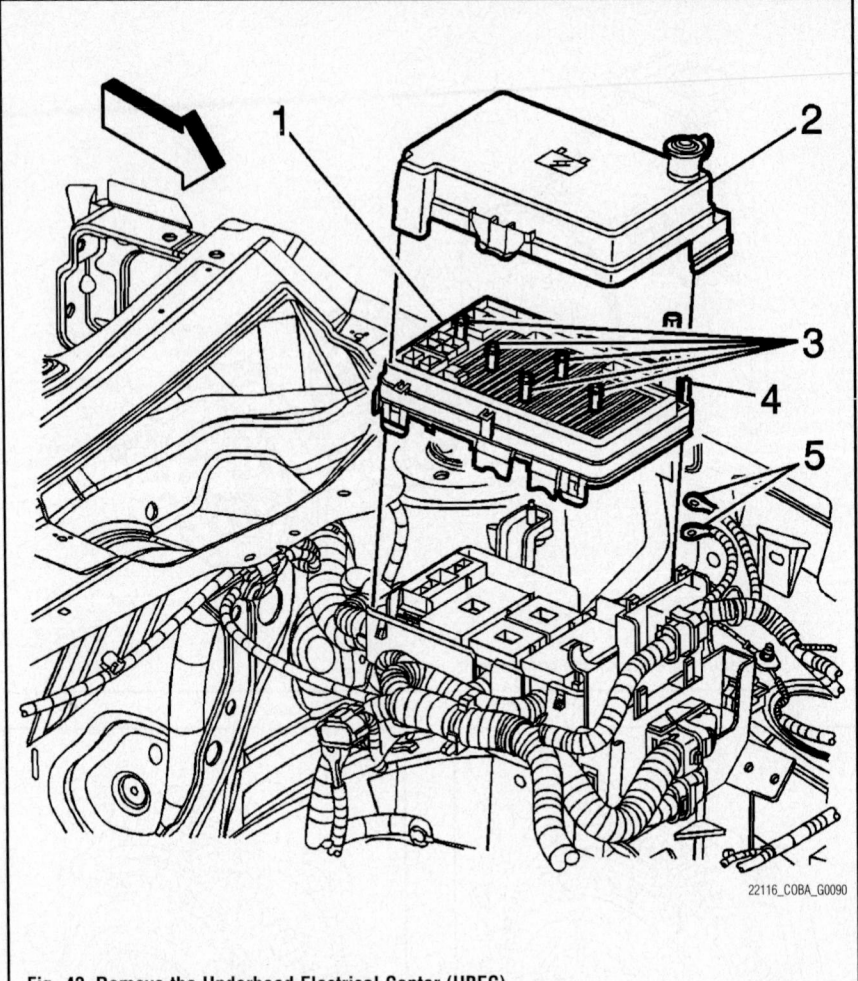

Fig. 43 Remove the Underhood Electrical Center (UBEC)

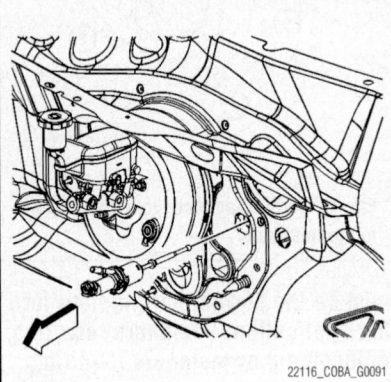

Fig. 44 Rotate the clutch master cylinder ¼ turn clockwise to remove

5. Place a shop towel under the clutch master cylinder in order to catch any fluid loss.

6. Disconnect the clutch hose from the clutch master cylinder.

7. Disconnect the clutch line from the clutch master cylinder.

8. Cap the reservoir and hydraulic lines in order to prevent fluid loss and contamination.

9. Rotate the clutch master cylinder ¼ turn clockwise and remove the cylinder from the vehicle.

To install:

➡ **While installing, ensure that the clutch master cylinder pushrod is aligned with the clutch pedal.**

10. Install the clutch master cylinder while rotating ¼ turn counterclockwise.

11. Uncap the reservoir and hydraulic lines.

12. Connect the clutch line to the clutch master cylinder.

13. Connect the clutch hose to the clutch master cylinder.

14. Install the Underhood Electrical Center UBEC.

15. Connect the negative battery cable.

16. Connect the clutch master cylinder pushrod to the clutch pedal.

17. Install the clutch pedal retainer.

18. Bleed the clutch hydraulic system. Refer to Hydraulic System Bleeding.

CLUTCH ACTUATOR CYLINDER

REMOVAL & INSTALLATION

See Figures 45 through 47.

1. Before servicing the vehicle, refer to the Precautions Section.
2. Disconnect the negative battery cable.

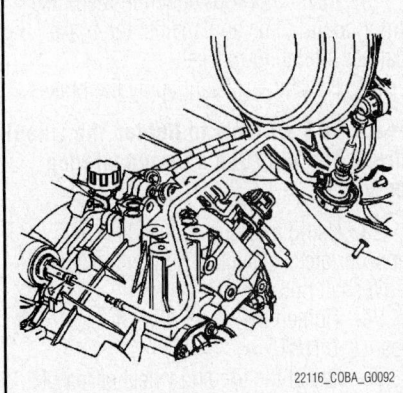

Fig. 45 Disconnect the clutch actuator cylinder line

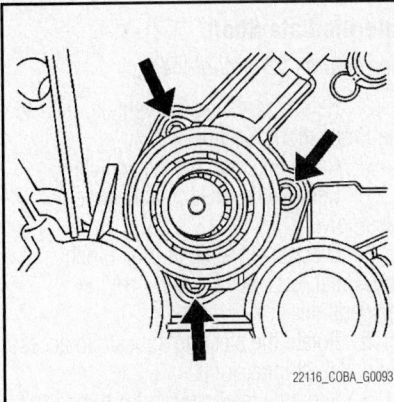

Fig. 46 Remove the clutch actuator cylinder bolts from the transmission

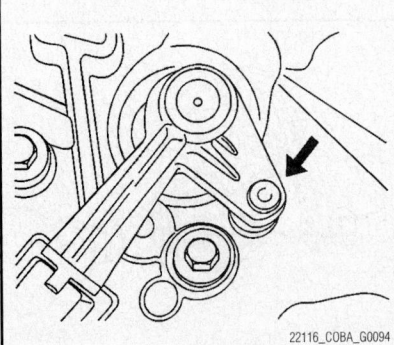

Fig. 47 Remove the upper bolt and the clutch actuator cylinder from the transaxle

3. Disconnect the clutch actuator cylinder line.
4. Remove the transaxle. Refer to Manual Transaxle Assembly Removal & Installation.
5. Remove the clutch actuator cylinder bolts from the transaxle.
6. Remove the following components from the transaxle:
   a. The upper bolt.
   b. The clutch actuator cylinder.

To install:

> ✳✳ **WARNING**
>
> **Excessive amounts of lubricant on the input shaft splines can contaminate the clutch disc and cause clutch shudder.**

7. Lubricate the inside diameter of the bearing.
8. Install the clutch actuator cylinder to the transaxle.
9. Install the clutch actuator cylinder bolts. Tighten the bolts to 89 inch lbs. (10 Nm).
10. Install the upper line release bolt. Tighten the bolt to 89 inch lbs. (10 Nm).
11. Install the transaxle. Refer to Manual Transaxle Assembly Removal & Installation.
12. Connect the clutch actuator cylinder line.
13. Connect the negative battery cable.
14. Bleed the hydraulic system. Refer to Hydraulic System Bleeding.

CLUTCH HYDRAULIC SYSTEM BLEEDING

VACUUM BLEEDING

1. Before servicing the vehicle, refer to the Precautions Section.
2. Verify that all the hydraulic lines are dry and secure.
3. Clean dirt and grease from the reservoir cap in order to ensure that no foreign substances enter the system.
4. Remove the reservoir cap.
5. Fill the reservoir using DOT 3 hydraulic fluid.

> ✳✳ **WARNING**
>
> **Brake fluid will deteriorate the rubber on the adapter, use a clean shop towel to wipe away all fluid after each use.**

6. Install a vacuum pump such as adapter J 43485 and pump J 35555 to the reservoir.

7. Hold the adapter to position while applying 51–68 kPa (15–20 hg) of vacuum.
8. Remove the adapter and refill the reservoir
9. Repeat previous steps.
10. If needed, refill the reservoir and continue to pull a vacuum until no more bubbles can be seen in the reservoir or until the fluid level no longer drops.

> ✳✳ **CAUTION**
>
> **The vehicle will move if started in gear before the Actuator Cylinder is refilled and operational. Start the vehicle the first time in neutral to help prevent personal injury from vehicle movement and see if the transmission will shift easily into gear.**

11. Pump the clutch pedal until firm (to refill actuator cylinder).
12. Add additional fluid if needed.
13. Test drive the vehicle to ensure proper operation.

FRONT HALFSHAFTS

REMOVAL & INSTALLATION

See Figures 48 through 51.

1. Before servicing the vehicle, refer to the Precautions Section.

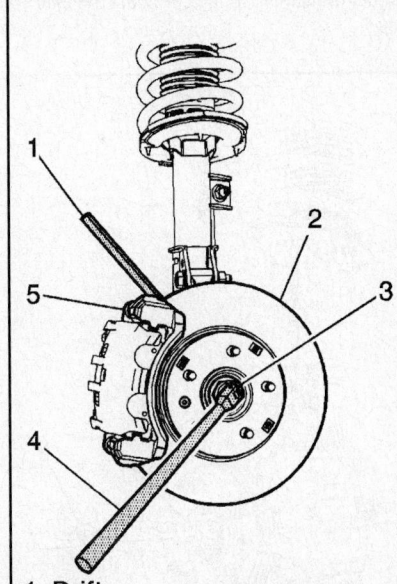

1. Drift
2. Brake rotor
3. Halfshaft (driveshaft) nut
4. Socket
5. Caliper mounting bracket

Fig. 48 Removing the halfshaft (driveshaft) nut

2. Raise and support the vehicle.

3. Remove the tire and wheel assembly.

4. Insert a punch or drift (1) in the cooling fins of the brake rotor (2).

5. Position the punch or drift (1) against the brake caliper mounting bracket (5).

6. Using a breaker bar and the appropriate size socket (4), loosen the wheel driveshaft nut (3).

7. Have an assistant apply the brakes.

8. Remove the wheel driveshaft nut (2) from the wheel driveshaft (1) and discard. DO NOT re-use the wheel driveshaft nut. Use NEW nut only.

9. Using the J 28733-B (or an equivalent suitable puller) separate the wheel driveshaft from the steering knuckle.

10. Remove the lower ball joint from the steering knuckle. Refer to Lower Control Arm in Suspension.

➡**The transmission stub staff may still be attached to the right wheel driveshaft and be removed at the same time as the wheel driveshaft. If this occurs, refer to Stub Shaft.**

11. Using the J-2619-A and the J 45341, remove the wheel driveshaft.

To install:

12. For the left wheel driveshaft, position the J 44394 in the transaxle.

13. Install the wheel driveshaft until the wheel driveshaft splines are past the axle seal.

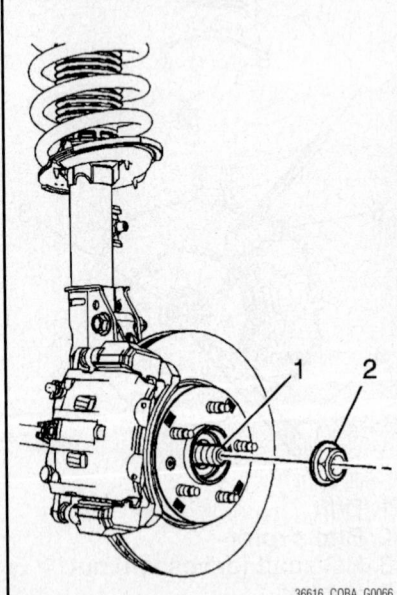

Fig. 49 Remove the wheel driveshaft nut (2) from the wheel driveshaft (1) and discard. DO NOT re-use the wheel driveshaft nut. Use NEW nut only

14. Remove the J 44394 from the wheel driveshaft.

➡**The following service procedure is for those vehicles equipped with an intermediate shaft.**

15. For the right wheel driveshaft, apply a very small amount of grease, GM P/N 1051344 (Canadian P/N 993037), or equivalent to the splines of the wheel driveshaft inner joint.

16. Install the wheel driveshaft into the intermediate driveshaft.

17. Install the wheel driveshaft until it is fully seated in the transaxle.

➡**In the following step, DO NOT pull on the wheel driveshaft. Pull only on the tripod.**

18. With the wheel driveshaft installed, grasp the inner tripot housing and pull the tripot outward to ensure that the wheel drive-

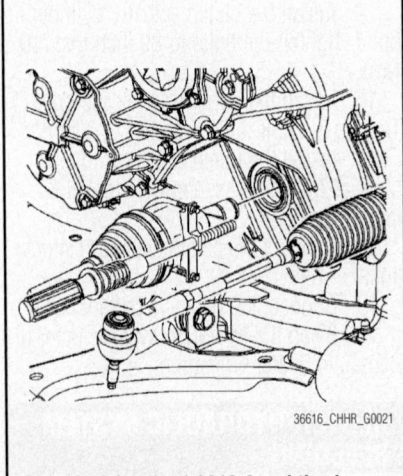

Fig. 50 Using the J-2619-A and the J 45341, remove the wheel driveshaft

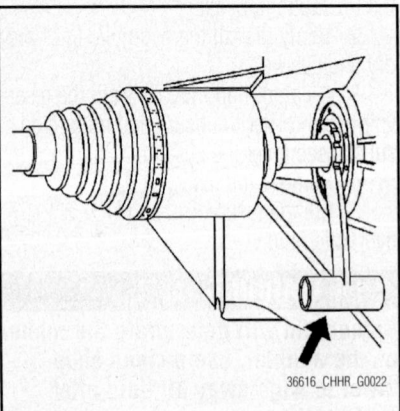

Fig. 51 For the left wheel driveshaft, position the J 44394 in the transaxle. Install the wheel driveshaft until the wheel driveshaft splines are past the axle seal

shaft is properly engaged. The wheel driveshaft will remain in place if properly installed.

19. Install the lower ball joint in the steering knuckle.

20. Hand tighten the NEW wheel driveshaft nut on the wheel driveshaft.

➡**Step 10 is for standard disc brakes only, proceed to step 16 if the vehicle has Brembo brakes.**

21. Insert a drift or punch in the brake rotor cooling fins and against the brake caliper mounting bracket.

22. Have an assistant apply the brakes.

➡**DO NOT air tools to tighten the wheel driveshaft nut. Use a torque wrench only.**

23. Using a torque wrench and the appropriate size socket, tighten the wheel driveshaft nut.

24. Tighten the wheel drive nut to 155 ft. lbs. (210 Nm).

25. Install the tire and wheel assembly.

26. Remove the support and lower the vehicle.

27. Inspect the fluid level of the transaxle.

Intermediate Shaft

See Figures 52 through 54.

1. Before servicing the vehicle, refer to the Precautions Section.

2. Raise and support the vehicle.

3. Remove the RH tire and wheel assembly.

4. Disconnect the ball joint pinch bolt. Refer to Lower Control Arm in Suspension.

5. Rotate the steering knuckle to access the halfshaft inner joint.

6. Separate the halfshaft from the intermediate driveshaft.

7. Reposition and support the halfshaft from the intermediate driveshaft.

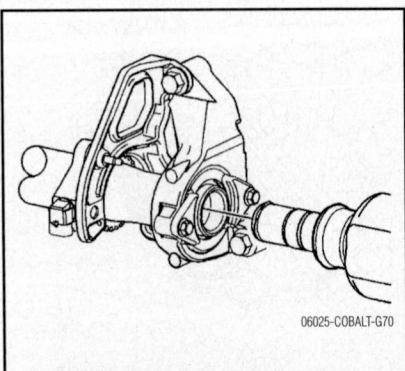

Fig. 52 Separate the halfshaft from the intermediate driveshaft

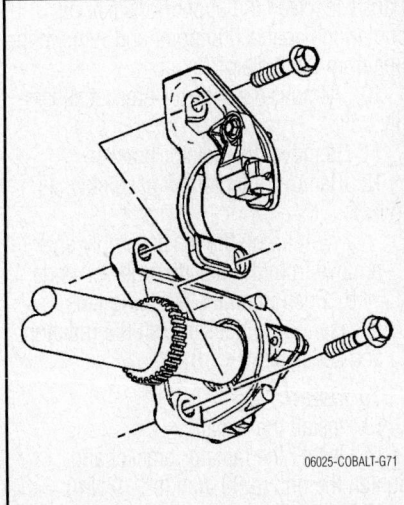

Fig. 53 Remove the remaining intermedi-ate shaft bracket-to-engine block bolts

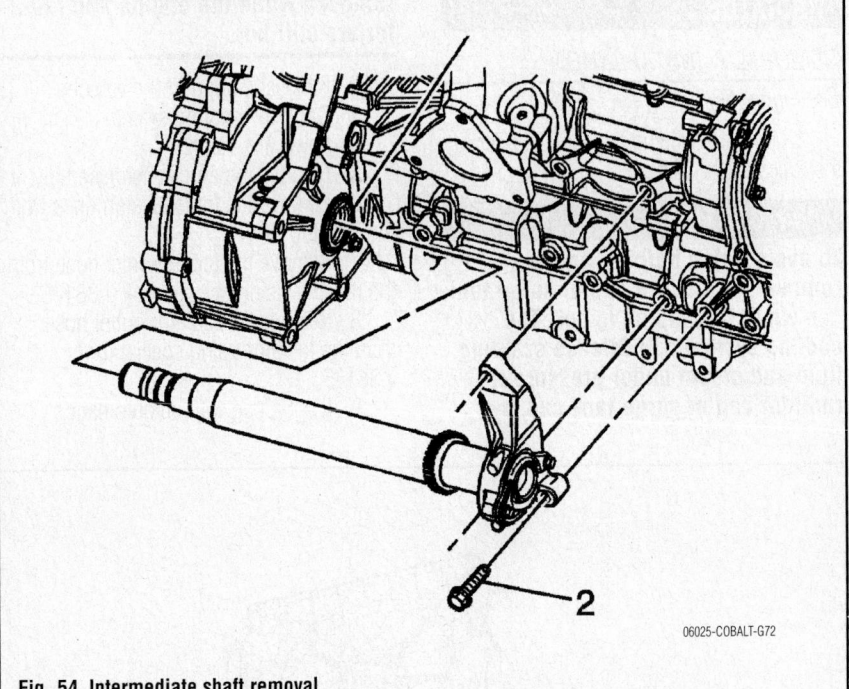

Fig. 54 Intermediate shaft removal

8. Inspect the halfshaft-to-intermediate driveshaft seal for excessive wear, damage, and/or contamination and replace if necessary.

9. Remove the rear, or LH intermediate driveshaft bracket-to-engine block bolts.

10. Remove the remaining intermediate shaft bracket-to-engine block bolts.

11. Using care to not damage the transaxle output shaft seal, remove the intermediate driveshaft assembly.

12. Inspect the transaxle output shaft seal for damage and/or contamination and replace if necessary.

To install:

13. Install tool J 44394 into the transaxle output shaft seal.

14. Install the intermediate driveshaft

into the transaxle until the driveshaft splines are past the seal, remove the tool, then fully install the driveshaft.

15. Install, but do NOT tighten the inter-mediate driveshaft bracket-to-engine block forward, or RH bolt.

16. Tighten the intermediate driveshaft bracket-to-engine block bolts, beginning with the upper bolt. Tighten the bolts to 37 ft. lbs. (50 Nm).

17. Apply a very small amount of grease, GM P/N 1051344 (Canadian P/N 993037), or equivalent to the splines of the halfshaft inner joint.

18. Install the halfshaft into the interme-diate driveshaft.

19. Verify that the halfshaft is properly engaged:

a. Grasp the inner tripod housing and pull the inner housing outward. Do NOT pull on the wheel drive axle shaft.

b. The halfshaft will remain firmly in place when properly engaged.

20. Install the tire and wheel assembly.

21. Lower the vehicle.

22. Inspect the transaxle fluid level.

ENGINE COOLING

ENGINE FAN

REMOVAL & INSTALLATION

2.0L Engine

See Figure 55.

1. Remove the charge air cooler inlet pipe.

2. Remove the coolant recovery reser-voir.

3. Remove the hood latch from the tie bar and set aside.

4. Remove the radiator inlet hose from the radiator.

5. Remove the upper radiator air baffle.

6. Remove the radiator support brack-ets.

7. Disconnect the cooling fan motor electrical connector.

8. Remove the transmission line con-nector from the fan shroud.

9. Lift the radiator out of the support bracket and pull toward the front of the vehicle.

10. Lift up on the fan shroud assembly to release from the radiator.

11. Installation is the reverse of the removal procedure.

2.2L & 2.4L Engines

See Figure 55.

1. Remove the air cleaner assembly.

2. Remove the coolant recovery reser-voir.

3. Remove the hood latch from the tie bar and set aside.

4. Remove the radiator inlet hose from the radiator.

5. Remove the upper radiator air baffle.

6. Remove the radiator support brackets

7. Disconnect the cooling fan motor electrical connector.

8. Remove the transmission line con-nector from the fan shroud.

9. Lift the radiator out of the support bracket and pull toward the front of the vehicle.

10. Lift up on the fan shroud assembly to release from the radiator.

11. Installation is the reverse of the removal procedure.

RADIATOR

REMOVAL & INSTALLATION

See Figure 56.

1. Before servicing the vehicle, refer to the Precautions Section.

✳✳ CAUTION

To avoid being burned, do not remove the radiator cap or surge tank cap while the engine is hot. The cooling system will release scalding fluid and steam under pressure if radiator cap or surge tank cap is removed while the engine and radiator are still hot.

2. Raise and support the vehicle.
3. Drain the cooling system.
4. Lower the vehicle.
5. Remove the air cleaner assembly.
6. Remove the transmission lines from the radiator.
7. Remove the radiator inlet hose from the radiator using special tool, J 38185.
8. Remove the radiator outlet hose from the radiator using special tool, J 38185.
9. If equipped with an automatic transaxle, clean the upper transaxle oil cooler line connection point and remove the line from the radiator.
10. Remove the radiator bracket assembly bolt.
11. Remove the radiator bracket.
12. Remove the radiator assembly, as follows:

   a. Lift up on the fan assembly and remove from the radiator and set aside.

   b. Push in on the retaining tabs to release the condenser from the radiator and set aside.

To install:

13. Install the radiator.
14. Install the radiator bracket and tighten the bolt to 80 inch lbs. (9 Nm).
15. Install the radiator outlet hose to the radiator.
16. Reposition the hose clamp to secure the hose using special tool, J 38185.
17. Install the radiator inlet hose to the radiator.
18. Reposition the hose clamp to secure the hose using special tool, J 38185.
19. Install the transmission lines to the radiator.
20. Install the air cleaner.
21. Fill the cooling system.
22. If equipped with an automatic transaxle, add fluid to the transaxle as necessary.

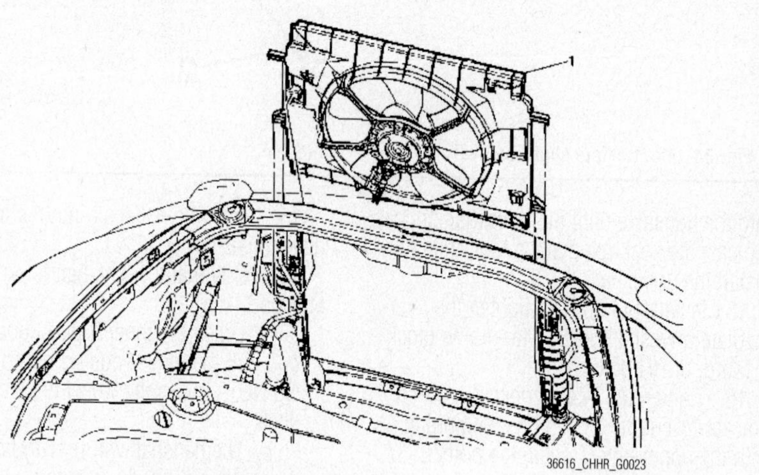

THERMOSTAT

REMOVAL & INSTALLATION

See Figure 57.

1. Before servicing the vehicle, refer to the Precautions Section.
2. Drain the cooling system.
3. Reposition the radiator outlet hose clamp at the thermostat housing.

Fig. 55 View of the engine cooling fan and shroud (1)

36616_CHHR_G0023

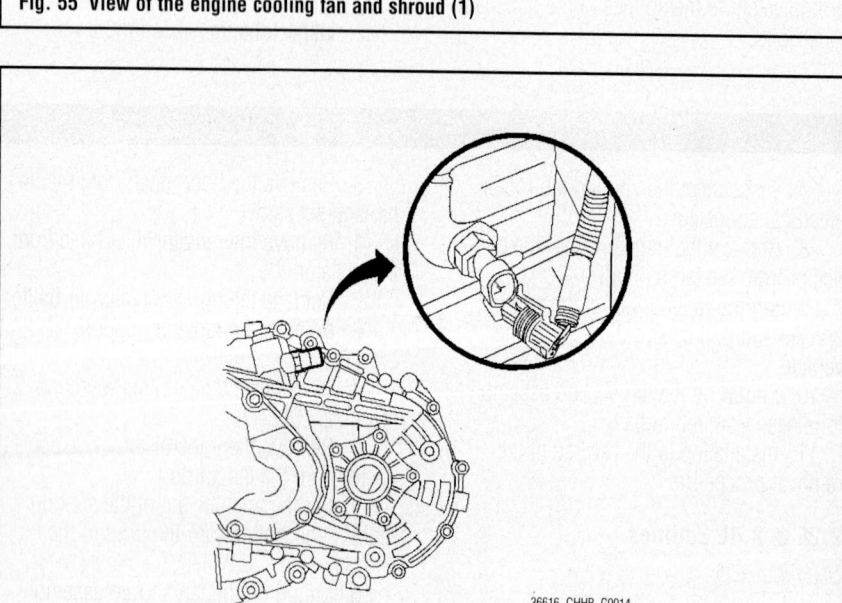

Fig. 56 View of the radiator bracket bolt (1), bracket (2) and radiator assembly (3)

36616_CHHR_G0014

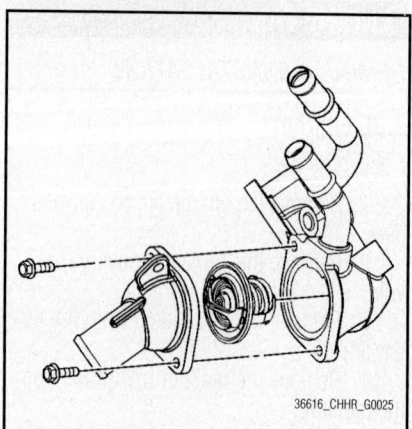

Fig. 57 Exploded view of the thermostat mounting

36616_CHHR_G0025

4. Remove the radiator outlet hose from the thermostat housing.

5. Remove the thermostat housing cover bolts and cover.

6. Remove the thermostat.

7. Remove and discard the thermostat housing O-ring seal.

To install:

8. Install a NEW thermostat housing cover O-ring seal.

9. Install the thermostat.

10. Install the thermostat housing cover bolts and tighten the bolts to 89 inch lbs. (10 Nm).

11. Install the radiator outlet hose to the thermostat housing.

12. Position the radiator outlet hose clamp at the thermostat housing.

13. Fill the cooling system.

WATER PUMP

REMOVAL & INSTALLATION

2.0L Engine

See Figures 58 through 62.

1. Remove the air cleaner assembly.

2. Remove the thermostat housing, as follows:

   a. Partially drain the coolant system.

   b. Remove the thermostat, as outlined earlier in this section.

   c. Disconnect the inlet and outlet heater hoses.

   d. Remove the turbocharger coolant return pipe.

➡ **If replacing the engine coolant thermostat housing, transfer the coolant temperature sensor.**

e. Disconnect the coolant temperature sensor harness connector.

   f. Unfasten the thermostat housing bolts.

   g. Remove the thermostat housing and seal. Discard the seal.

3. Remove the water pump access plate from the front cover.

➡ **A drain plug has been provided at the bottom of the water pump assembly for additional coolant drainage from the engine block and water pump.**

4. Drain the coolant from the water pump using the plug at the bottom of the pump.

➡ **The water pump holding tool supports the sprocket and chain during water pump service. The tool must be used or the balance shaft must be re-timed.**

Fig. 59 A drain plug has been provided at the bottom of the water pump assembly for additional coolant drainage from the engine block and water pump

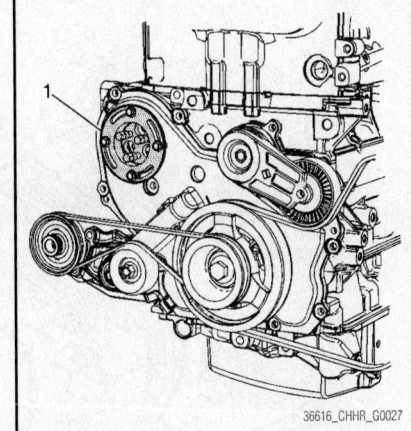

Fig. 60 View of the water pump holding tool (1)

5. Install the J 43651, or equivalent water pump holding tool, into position.

6. Tighten the bolts on the water pump holding tool into the threads on the water pump sprocket.

7. Install the access cover bolts that were removed earlier to secure the water pump holding tool to the front cover assembly.

8. Remove the 3 inner water pump sprocket to water pump bolts.

➡ **Be sure to remove both water pump bolts from the front of the engine block.**

9. Remove the 2 water pump bolts.

10. Remove the rear 2 water pump bolts.

11. Remove the water pump. Remove and discard the water pump O-ring seal.

To install:

➡ **Before installing the water pump, read the entire procedure. This will help avoid balance shaft chain re-timing and ensure proper sealing.**

Fig. 58 Thermostat housing bolts (1), housing (2) and seal (3)—2.0L engine

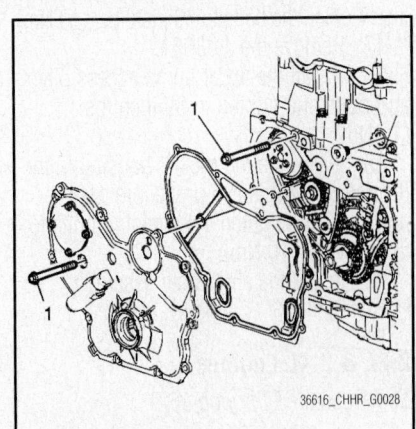

Fig. 61 Remove the 2 water pump bolts (1).

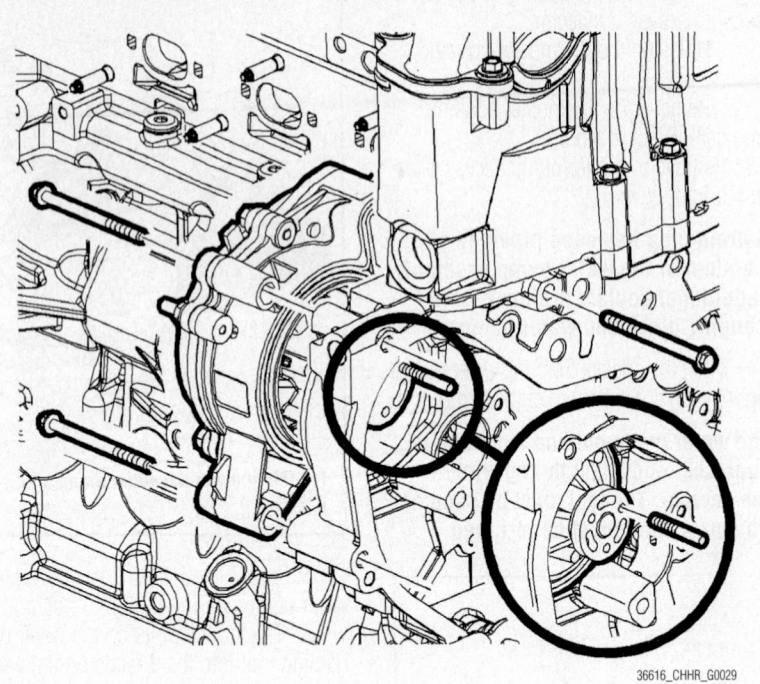

36616_CHHR_G0029

Fig. 62 A guide pin can be created to aid in water pump alignment. Use a M 6 m x 6 mm stud. Thread the pin into the water pump sprocket

12. Install a NEW water pump O-ring seal.

➡ **A guide pin can be created to aid in water pump alignment. Use a M 6 m x 6 mm stud. Thread the pin into the water pump sprocket.**

13. Using the guide pin, align the pin with the water pump holding tool.

14. Position the water pump against the engine block and hand tighten the water pump bolts.

15. Install the inner water pump sprocket bolts. After 2 are snug, remove the guide pin and install the 3rd bolt. Tighten the bolts to 18 ft. lbs. (25 Nm).

16. Tighten the water pump sprocket bolts last. Tighten the bolts to 89 inch lbs. (10 Nm).

17. Remove the J 43651.

18. Install the water pump access plate and bolts and tighten to 89 inch lbs. (10 Nm)

19. Install the thermostat housing in the reverse of the removal procedure. Use a new seal, and tighten the retaining bolts to 89 inch lbs. (10 Nm).

20. Install the air cleaner assembly.

21. Refill the cooling system.

2.2L & 2.4L Engines

See Figures 63 through 66.

1. Drain the cooling system.

2. Remove the thermostat housing, as follows:

a. Remove the air cleaner assembly.

b. Remove the air cleaner bracket nuts.

c. Remove the air cleaner bracket.

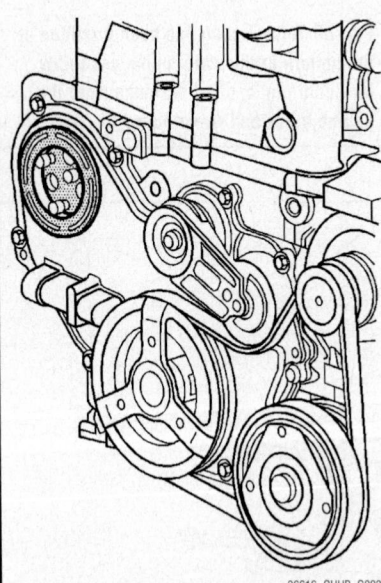

36616_CHHR_G0031

Fig. 63 Install the water pump holding tool into position The water pump holding tool supports the sprocket and chain during water pump service. The tool must be used or the balance shaft must be re-timed

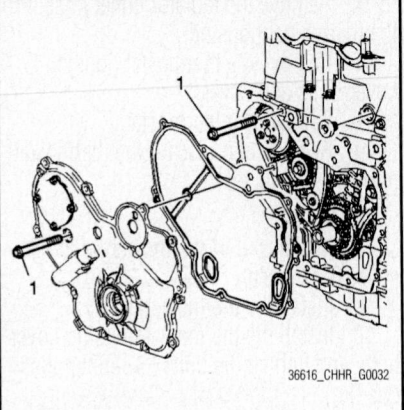

36616_CHHR_G0032

Fig. 64 Remove the 2 water pump bolts (1)

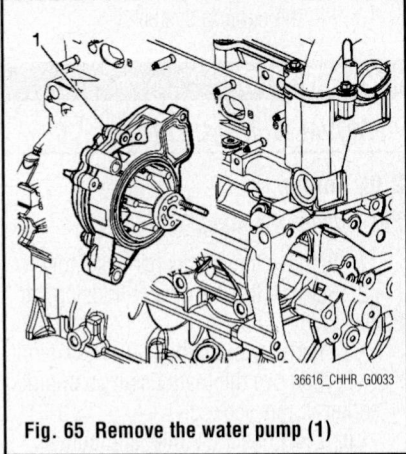

36616_CHHR_G0033

Fig. 65 Remove the water pump (1)

d. Remove the exhaust heat shield studs.

e. Remove the exhaust heat shield.

➡ **A drain has been provided at the bottom of the water pump for engine block coolant drainage.**

f. Drain the coolant from the engine block at the water pump drain. After the coolant has drained, tighten the drain bolt.

g. Lower the vehicle.

h. If equipped with a automatic transaxle, disconnect the Engine Coolant Temperature (ECT) sensor electrical connector. Disconnect the heated oxygen sensor (HO2S) electrical connector clip from the thermostat housing.

i. If equipped with a manual transaxle, disconnect the ECT sensor electrical connector.

j. Remove the ECT sensor.

k. Reposition the radiator outlet hose clamp at the thermostat housing.

l. Remove the radiator outlet hose from the thermostat housing.

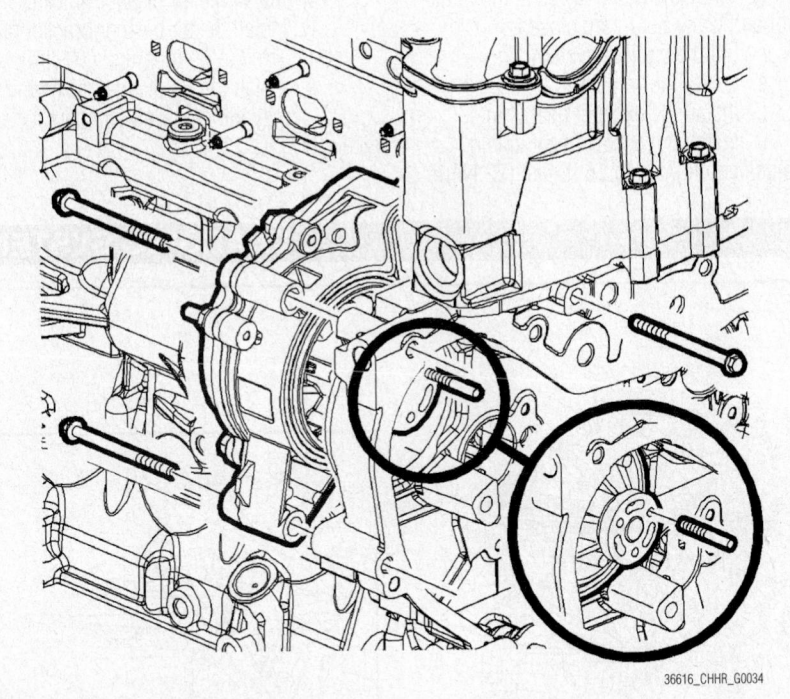

Fig. 66 A guide pin can be created using a M6 m x 6 mm stud to aid in water pump alignment. Thread the pin into the water pump sprocket

m. Reposition the heater inlet and outlet hose clamps at the thermostat housing pipes.

n. Disconnect the heater inlet and outlet hoses from the thermostat housing pipes.

o. Raise and support the vehicle.

p. Remove the thermostat housing bolts.

➡ **Twist the water transfer pipe while pulling in order to remove it from the water pump.**

q. Remove the thermostat housing from the vehicle.

3. Remove the coolant heater.

4. Remove the windshield washer solvent container.

5. Remove the water pump access plate from the front cover.

➡ **The water pump holding tool supports the sprocket and chain during water pump service. The tool must be used or the balance shaft must be re-timed.**

6. Install the J 43651 into position.

7. Tighten the bolts on the water pump holding tool into the threads on the water pump sprocket.

8. Install the access cover bolts that were removed earlier to secure the water pump holding tool to the front cover assembly.

9. Remove the 3 inner water pump sprocket to water pump bolts.

➡ **Be sure to remove both water pump bolts from the front of the engine block.**

10. Remove the 2 water pump bolts.

11. Remove the rear 2 water pump bolts.

12. Remove the engine harness clip nut from the water pump stud.

13. Remove the engine harness clip from the stud.

14. Remove the water pump.

To install:

15. Apply sealant to the water pump drain plug. Install the water pump drain plug and tighten to 16 ft. lbs. (22 Nm).

➡ **Prior to installing the water pump, read the entire procedure. This will help avoid balance shaft chain re-timing and ensure proper sealing.**

➡ **A guide pin can be created using a M6 m x 6 mm stud to aid in water pump alignment. Thread the pin into the water pump sprocket.**

16. Using the J 25025-5 or the guide pin that was created, align the pin with the water pump holding tool.

17. Position the water pump against the

engine block and hand tighten the water pump bolts.

18. Install the inner water pump sprocket bolts. After 2 are snug, remove the guide pin and install the 3rd bolt. Tighten the water pump bolts to 18 ft. lbs. (25 Nm).

Tighten the water pump sprocket bolts last. Tighten the water pump sprocket bolts to 89 inch lbs. (10 Nm).

19. Remove the J 43651 .

20. Install the water pump access plate and bolts and tighten to 89 inch lbs. (10 Nm).

21. Install the coolant heater.

22. Install the windshield washer solvent container.

23. Install the thermostat housing:

a. Install a NEW thermostat housing to engine gasket onto the thermostat housing.

b. Load the thermostat housing assembly into position.

➡ **The water feed pipe seals can be lightly lubricated with coolant to aid during installation.**

c. Install NEW O-ring seals onto the water feed pipe.

➡ **Lubricate the O-rings with coolant ONLY.**

d. Install the water feed pipe into the thermostat housing aligning locator tab.

e. Align the water pipe to water pump.

f. Seat the water feed O-ring seal by pushing inward toward the water pump. Take care not to tear or damage the O-ring.

g. Position the thermostat housing against the engine. Install the thermostat housing bolts and tighten to 89 inch lbs. (10 Nm).

h. Lower the vehicle.

i. Connect the heater inlet and outlet hoses to the thermostat housing pipes.

j. Position the heater inlet and outlet hose clamps at the thermostat housing pipes.

k. Install the radiator outlet hose to the thermostat housing.

l. Position the radiator outlet hose clamp at the thermostat housing.

m. If reinstalling the old sensor, coat the threads with sealant.

n. Install the ECT sensor and tighten to 15 ft. lbs. (20 Nm).

o. If equipped with a manual transaxle, connect the ECT sensor electrical connector (1).

p. If equipped with a automatic transaxle, perform the following steps, connect the ECT sensor electrical connector and connect the HO2S electrical connector clip to the thermostat housing.

→ **The vehicle must be level when filling the cooling system.**

q. Verify the drain valves at the radiator and water pump are closed.
r. Fill the cooling system.
s. Lower the vehicle.
t. Install the exhaust heat shield.
u. Install the exhaust heat shield studs and tighten to 16 ft. lbs. (22 Nm).

v. Install the air cleaner bracket.
w. Install the air cleaner bracket nuts and tighten to 89 inch lbs. (10 Nm).
x. Install the air cleaner assembly.
24. Verify the repair and inspect for any leaks

ENGINE ELECTRICAL

ALTERNATOR

REMOVAL & INSTALLATION

See Figure 67.

1. Before servicing the vehicle, refer to the Precautions Section.
2. Disconnect negative battery cable.
3. Remove the accessory drive belt. Refer to Accessory Drive Belt in Engine Mechanical
4. Remove the air cleaner outlet resonator.
5. Disconnect the alternator connectors.
6. Remove the alternator bolts.
7. Remove the alternator from the vehicle.

To install:

8. Position the alternator on the engine.
9. Install the alternator bolts. Tighten the alternator bolts to 16 ft. lbs. (22 Nm).
10. Connect the positive battery harness to the alternator battery terminal. Tighten the alternator terminal nut to 15 ft. lbs. (20 Nm).
11. Connect the alternator harness connectors.
12. Install the air cleaner outlet resonator.
13. Install the accessory drive belt.
14. Connect the battery negative cable.

CHARGING SYSTEM

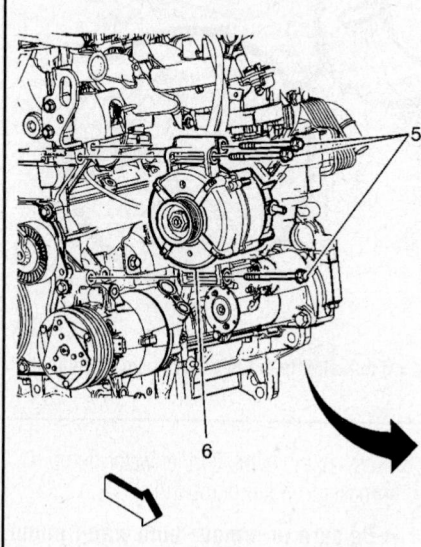
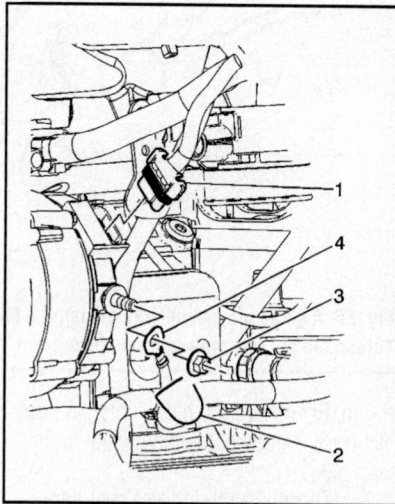

1. Engine harness alternator connector
2. Engine harness alternator terminal boot
3. Alternator terminal nut
4. Engine harness alternator connector
5. Alternator bolts
6. Alternator

36616_CHHR_G0035

Fig. 67 Alternator mounting

ENGINE ELECTRICAL

FIRING ORDERS

The 2.0L, 2.2L and 2.4L engines fire in this cylinder order:
- 1–3–4–2

IGNITION COIL

REMOVAL & INSTALLATION

2.0L Engine

See Figure 68.

1. Before servicing the vehicle, refer to the Precautions Section.
2. Check stored fault messages.
3. Switch off ignition.
4. Remove or disconnect the following:

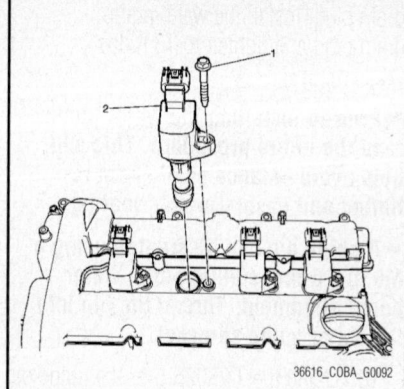

36616_COBA_G0092

Fig. 68 Ignition coil bolt locations— 2.0L engine

IGNITION SYSTEM

- The negative battery cable
- The ignition coil connectors from the ignition coils
- The retaining bolts from the ignition coils
- The ignition coils from the engine

To install:

→ **Make sure that the ignition coil seals are properly seated to the valve cover.**

5. Install or connect the following:
- The ignition coil
- The ignition coil retaining bolts, tighten to 89 inch lbs. (10 Nm)
- the ignition coil connectors

2.2L & 2.4L Engines

See Figures 69 through 71.

1. Before servicing the vehicle, refer to the Precautions Section.
2. Check stored fault messages.
3. Switch off ignition.
4. Remove or disconnect the following:
   - The negative battery cable
   - The engine oil fill cap
   - Grasp the intake manifold cover by the lower right inboard corner and pull up to disengage the cover from the stud
   - Grasp the intake manifold cover by the upper left corner and pull up to disengage the cover from the stud
   - Remove the intake manifold cover

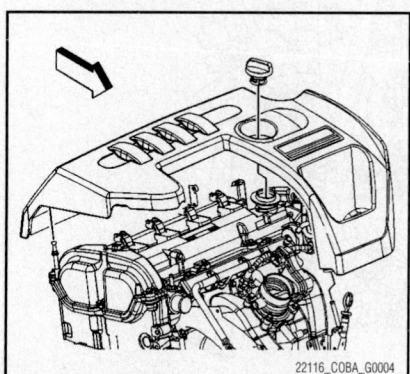

Fig. 69 Intake manifold cover removal— 2.2L and 2.4L engines

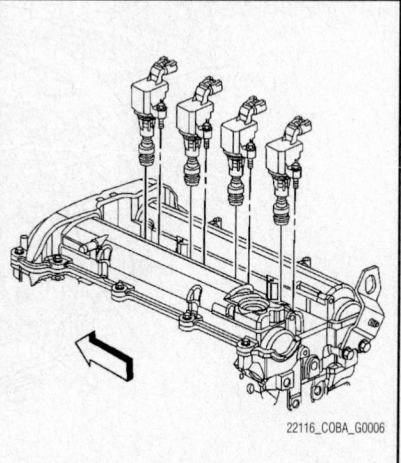

Fig. 71 Removing the ignition coils—2.2L and 2.4L engines

5. Disconnect the ignition coil electrical connectors (1).
6. Remove the ignition coil bolts.
7. Remove the ignition coils.

To install:

8. Install or connect the following:
   - The ignition coils into position over the spark plugs
   - The ignition coil bolts and tighten to 89 inch lbs (10 Nm)
   - The ignition coil electrical connectors
9. Install the intake manifold cover:
   a. Place the intake manifold cover onto the engine over the studs.
   b. Push down on the intake manifold cover directly over the lower right stud in order to engage the cover to the stud.
   c. Push down on the intake manifold cover directly over the upper left stud in order to engage the cover to the stud.
   d. Install the engine oil fill cap.

IGNITION TIMING

ADJUSTMENT

The ignition timing is controlled by the Powertrain Control Module (PCM). No adjustment is necessary or possible.

SPARK PLUGS

REMOVAL & INSTALLATION

1. Before servicing the vehicle, refer to the Precautions Section.
2. Remove ignition coils. Refer to Ignition Coil Pack Removal & Installation.
3. Remove spark plug connector from the spark plug.
4. Clean loose debris away from area of spark plug to keep contaminants from entering engine when spark plug is removed.
5. Remove the spark plug using a spark plug socket and wrench.

To install:

6. Be sure the spark plugs are set to the proper gap:
   - 2.0L engine—0.035 inch (0.90mm)
   - 2.2L and 2.4L engines—0.042 (1.06mm)
7. Carefully install the spark plugs and tighten to 15 ft. lbs. (20 Nm).
8. Apply dielectric compound to the spark plug boots and make sure no corrosion is present.
9. Install the ignition coils. Refer to Ignition Coil Pack Removal & Installation.

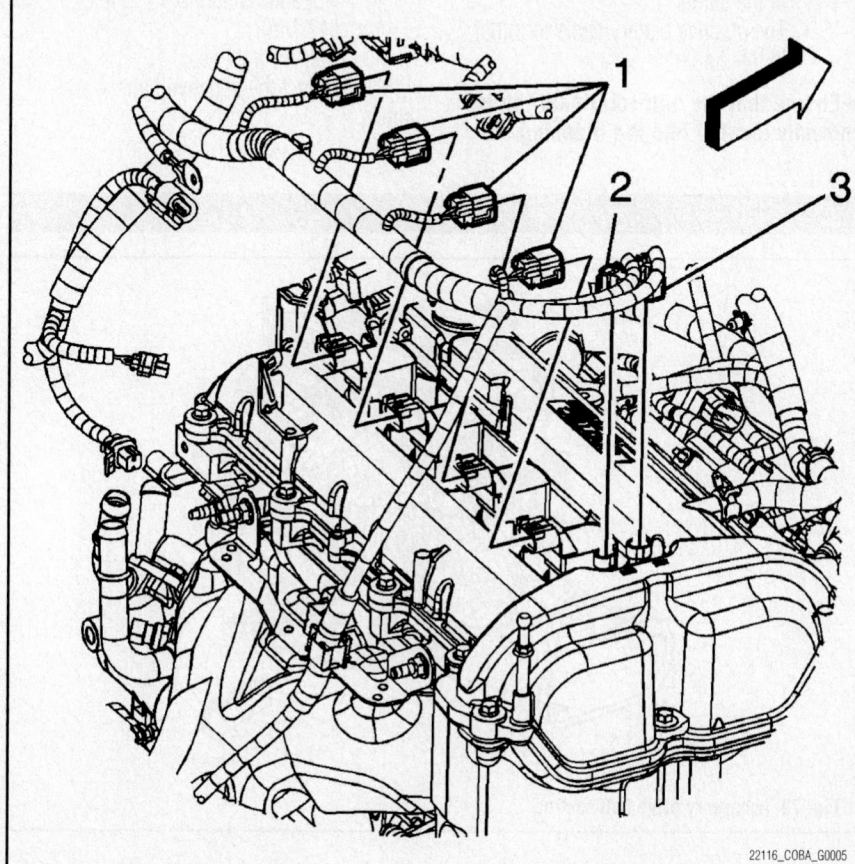

Fig. 70 Removing ignition coil electrical connectors (1)—2.2L and 2.4L engines

ENGINE ELECTRICAL

STARTER

REMOVAL & INSTALLATION

See Figure 72.

1. Before servicing the vehicle, refer to the Precautions Section.
2. Disconnect the negative battery cable.
3. Raise and support the vehicle.
4. Remove or disconnect the following:
   - The starter solenoid terminal nut (5)
   - The positive battery cable terminal (4) from the starter
   - The starter solenoid wire terminal (3) from the starter
   - The starter solenoid "S" terminal nut (2)
   - The engine harness terminal (1) from the starter
   - The starter bolts
   - The starter

To install:

5. Position the starter to the engine.
6. Install or connect the following:
   - The starter bolts and tighten to 30 ft. lbs. (40 Nm).
   - The engine harness terminal to the starter
   - The starter solenoid "S" terminal nut and tighten to 27 inch lbs. (3 Nm)

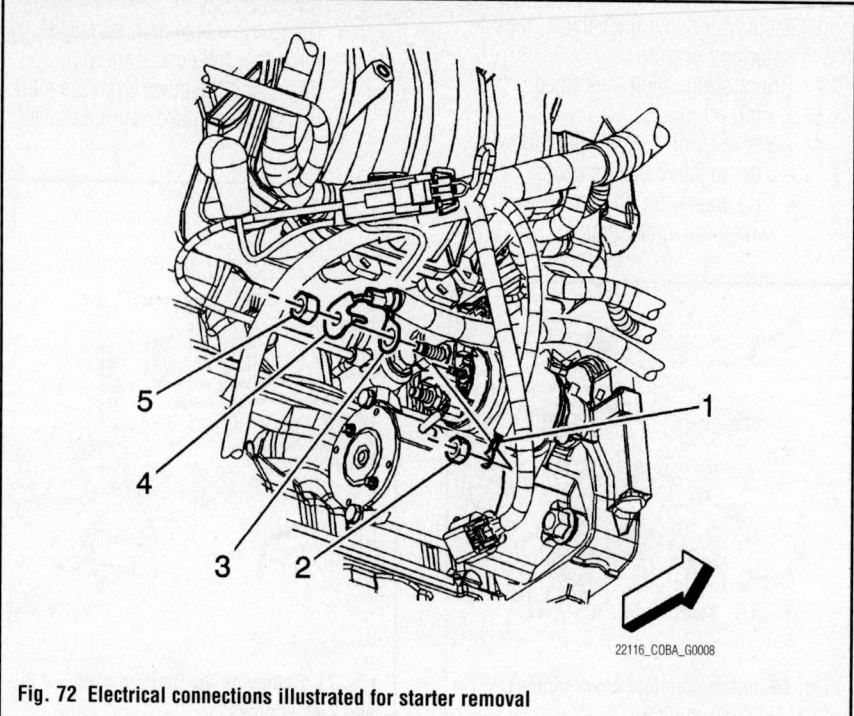

Fig. 72 Electrical connections illustrated for starter removal

- The starter solenoid wire terminal to the starter
- The positive battery cable terminal to the starter

➡ **Ensure that the anti-rotational tab is correctly located into the indexing slot.**

- The starter solenoid terminal nut and tighten to 13 ft. lbs. (17 Nm)

7. Lower the vehicle.
8. Connect the negative battery cable.

ENGINE MECHANICAL

ACCESSORY DRIVE BELTS

ACCESSORY BELT ROUTING

See Figure 73.

INSPECTION

Inspect the drive belt for signs of glazing or cracking. A glazed belt will be perfectly smooth from slippage, while a good belt will have a slight texture of fabric visible. Cracks will usually start at the inner edge of the belt and run outward. All worn or damaged drive belts should be replaced immediately.

ADJUSTMENT

The accessory drive belt adjustment is maintained by an automatic tensioner.

REMOVAL & INSTALLATION

See Figures 73 and 74.

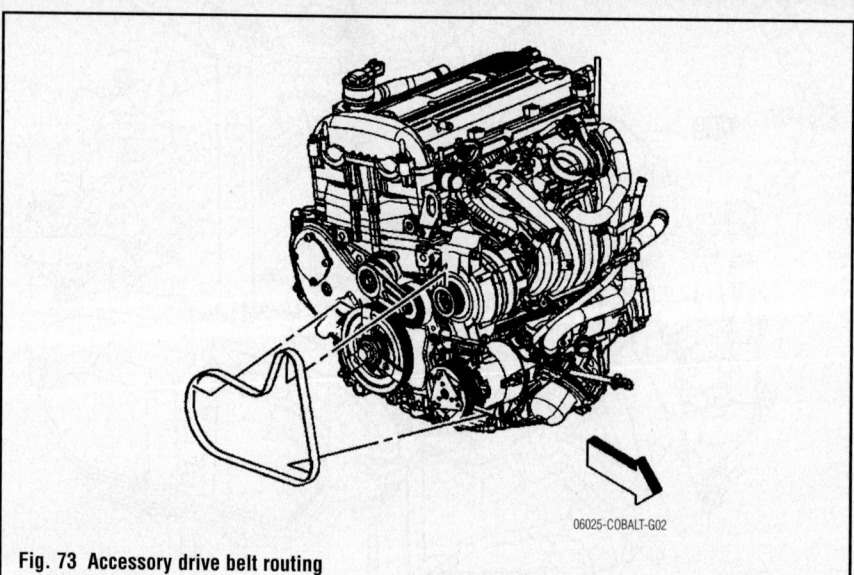

Fig. 73 Accessory drive belt routing

1. Before servicing the vehicle, refer to the Precautions Section.
2. Remove the engine splash shield.

3. Install the special tool J 44811 to the accessory drive belt tensioner.
4. Rotate the tensioner counterclock-

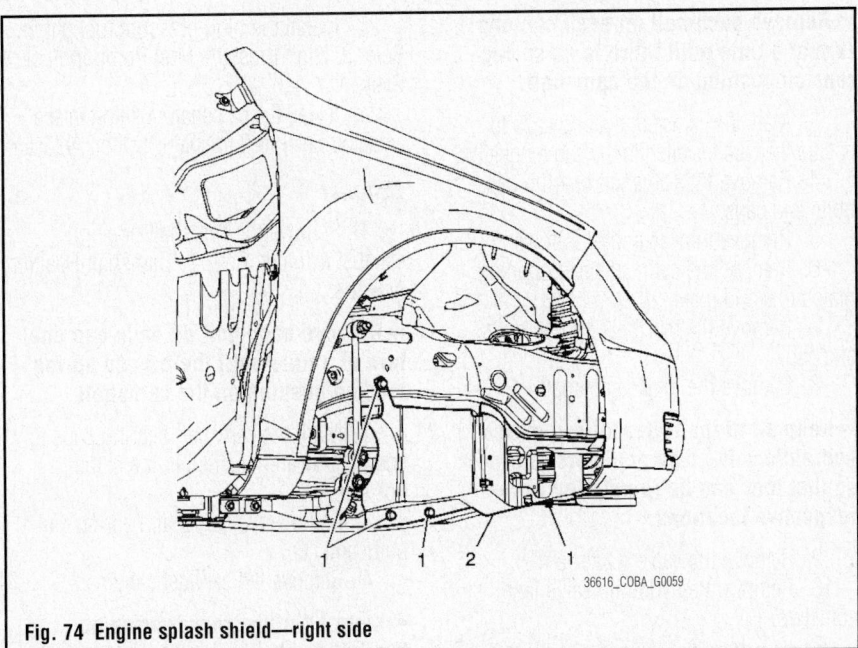

Fig. 74 Engine splash shield—right side

wise in order to release the tension from the accessory drive belt.

5. Remove the accessory drive belt.

6. Slowly rotate special tool J 44811 and the tensioner clockwise in order to allow the tensioner to rest.

7. Remove special tool J 44811 from the drive belt tensioner.

To install:

8. Install and position the drive belt around all of the pulleys except for the drive belt tensioner.

9. Install special tool J 44811 to the drive belt tensioner.

10. Using special tool J 44811, rotate the tensioner counterclockwise.

11. Position the drive belt under the tensioner pulley.

12. Using special tool J 44811 rotate the tensioner clockwise in order to seat the tensioner pulley onto the drive belt.

13. Install the engine splash shield.

BALANCE SHAFT

REMOVAL & INSTALLATION

See Figures 75 through 77.

1. Before servicing the vehicle, refer to the Precautions Section.

2. Remove the balance shaft bearing carrier bolts.

❋❋ WARNING

It is possible to install the intake side balance shaft into the exhaust side and vice versa. Please use care not to install the balance shafts into the wrong bores. Engine vibration will

result. Do not remove the bolt holding the sprocket.

3. Remove the balance shaft assemblies.

❋❋ WARNING

Proper centering of the tool is required on the balance shaft bushing. If the tool is not properly centered, then damage to the bearing bore and block will occur.

4. Install tool J 43650 into the balance shaft hole. Insert the tool with the foot parallel to the shaft.

5. When the J 43650 is inserted in the block turn the tool so that the foot becomes perpendicular to the shaft.

6. Center the foot of the tool on the balance shaft bushing.

7. Once the tool is centered on the balance shaft bushing, then insert the centering guide into the front balance shaft bore and

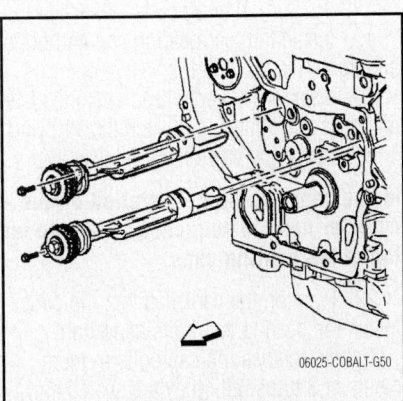

Fig. 75 Balance shaft assemblies

tighten the nut with an appropriate wrench. When the tool is properly installed, before removing the bushing, the end of the tool should be 4.6 inches (116mm) (a) from the block face. If the tool is less than approximately 4.5 inches (114mm) (a), recheck the tool alignment.

8. Tighten the nut on the tool until the tension releases. When the tension releases, remove the tool and the balance shaft bushing.

To install:

9. Install the balance shaft bushing using the J 43650.

10. Seat the balance shaft bushing into the bore using the J 43650 and a wrench.

11. When the J 43650 is fully seated in the engine block, remove it with a wrench.

❋❋ WARNING

If the balance shafts are not properly timed to the engine, the engine may vibrate or make noise.

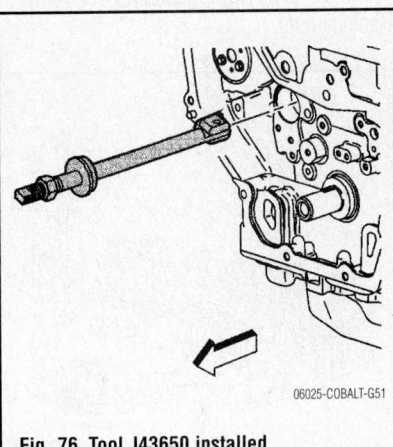

Fig. 76 Tool J43650 installed

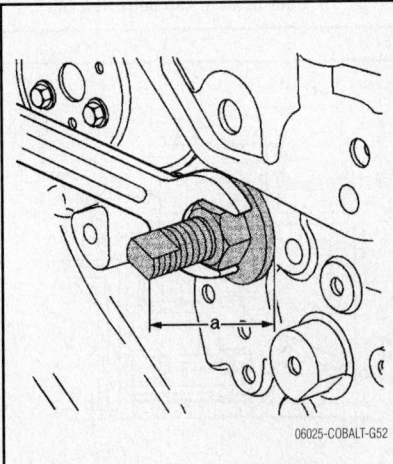

Fig. 77 When the J 43650 is inserted in the block turn the tool so that the foot becomes perpendicular to the shaft

12. Install the balance shaft assemblies to the engine using the following steps:

a. Place the number one piston at Top Dead Center (TDC).

b. Lubricate the balance shaft lobes with engine oil.

c. Install the balance shafts into their bores.

d. Install the balance shaft retaining bolts. Tighten the balance shaft retaining bolts to 89 inch lbs. (10 Nm).

CAMSHAFT AND VALVE LIFTERS

REMOVAL & INSTALLATION

2.0L Engine

Intake

See Figures 78 and 79.

1. Remove the camshaft position intake actuator. Refer to Camshaft Position Actuator.

2. Remove the high pressure fuel pump. Refer to High Pressure Fuel Pump Replacement.

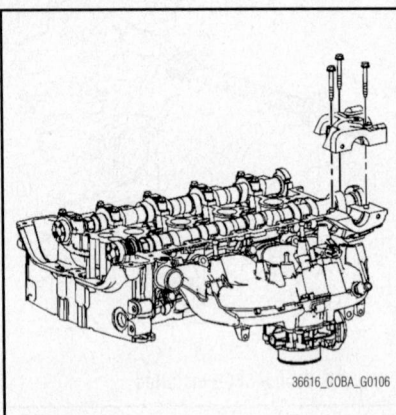

Fig. 78 Rear bearing cap bolts and cap

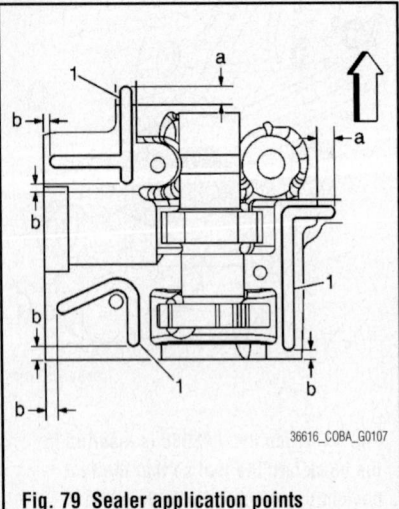

Fig. 79 Sealer application points

➡ **Remove each bolt on each cap one turn at a time until there is no spring tension pushing on the camshaft.**

3. Mark the camshaft bearing caps to ensure they are installed in the same position.

4. Remove the camshaft bearing cap bolts and caps.

5. Remove the valve lifter follower.

6. Remove the cylinder head opening plate bolts and plate.

7. Remove the rear bearing cap bolts and cap.

8. Remove the intake camshaft.

➡ **Keep all of the roller followers and hydraulic valve lash adjusters in order so that they can be reinstalled in their respective locations.**

9. Remove the valve rocker arms.

10. Remove the hydraulic valve lash adjusters.

To install:

11. Install the hydraulic valve lash adjusters into their bores in the cylinder head.

12. Lubricate the hydraulic lash adjusters. Refer to Adhesives, Fluids, Lubricants, and Sealers.

13. Lubricate the valve tips.

➡ **Used valve rocker arms MUST be returned to their original position on the camshaft. If the camshaft is being replaced, the rocker arms MUST also be replaced.**

14. Position the valve rocker arms on the tip of the valve stem and on the valve lash adjuster. Lubricate the rocker arms.

15. Install the intake camshaft. Lubricate the camshaft.

16. Apply a 0.138 inches (3.5 mm) bead of sealer (1) to the cylinder head.

17. In areas were the rear bearing cap ends on the perimeter rail, extend the bead of sealer 0.1575 inches (4.0 mm) beyond the edge of the cap (a).

18. Run the bead of sealer to within 4.0 mm (0.1575 in) of end points (b).

19. Install the rear bearing cap and bolts and tighten to 89 inch lbs. (10 Nm).

20. Install the cylinder head opening plate and bolts and tighten to 89 inch lbs. (10 Nm).

21. Install the valve lifter follower.

➡ **The caps should be installed on the cylinder head in sequence as shown on top of the bearing caps.**

22. Position the camshaft bearing caps. Install the bearing cap bolts hand tight.

Tighten the bearing cap bolts in increments of 3 turns until they are seated and tighten to 89 inch lbs. (10 Nm).

23. Install the high pressure fuel pump. Refer to High Pressure Fuel Pump in Fuel Systems.

24. Install the camshaft position intake actuator. Refer to Camshaft Position Actuator.

Exhaust

1. Remove the camshaft position exhaust actuator. Refer to Camshaft Position Actuator.

➡ **Remove each bolt on each cap one turn at a time until there is no spring tension pushing on the camshaft.**

2. Mark the camshaft bearing caps to ensure they are installed in the same position.

3. Remove the camshaft bearing cap bolts and cap.

4. Remove the exhaust camshaft.

➡ **Keep all of the rocker arms and hydraulic valve lash adjusters in order so that they can be reinstalled in their respective locations.**

5. Remove the valve rocker arms.

6. Remove the hydraulic valve lash adjusters.

To install:

7. Install the hydraulic valve lash adjusters into their bores in the cylinder head.

8. Lubricate the hydraulic valve lash adjusters.

9. Lubricate the valve tips.

➡ **Used rocker arms MUST be returned to the original position on the camshaft. If the camshaft is being replaced, the rocker arms MUST also be replaced.**

10. Position the rocker arms on the tip of the valve stem and on the valve lash adjuster. Lubricate the rocker arms.

11. Install the exhaust camshaft. Lubricate the camshaft.

➡ **The caps should be installed on the cylinder head in sequence as shown on top of the bearing caps.**

12. Position the camshaft bearing caps. Install the bearing cap bolts hand tight.

13. Tighten the bearing cap bolts in increments of 3 turns until they are seated and tighten to 89 inch lbs. (10 Nm).

14. Install the camshaft position exhaust actuator. Refer to Camshaft Position Actuator.

2.2L & 2.4L Engines

Intake

1. Remove the intake camshaft position actuator. Refer to Camshaft Position Actuator.

➡**Remove each bolt on each cap one turn at a time until there is no spring tension pushing on the camshaft.**

2. Mark the bearing caps to ensure they are installed in the original position.
3. Remove the bearing cap bolts.
4. Remove the bearing caps.
5. Remove the intake camshaft.

➡**Keep all of the roller followers and hydraulic adjusters in order so that they can be reinstalled in their respective locations.**

6. Remove the camshaft roller followers.
7. Remove the hydraulic element lash adjusters.

To install:

8. Install the hydraulic element lash adjusters into their bores in the cylinder head.
9. Lubricate the hydraulic lash adjusters with GM P/N 12345501 (Canadian P/N 992704) or equivalent.
10. Lubricate the valve tips with GM P/N 12345501 (Canadian P/N 992704) or equivalent.

➡**Used roller followers MUST be returned to their original position on the camshaft. If the camshaft is being replaced, the roller followers actuated by the camshaft must also be replaced.**

11. Position the camshaft roller followers on the tip of the valve stem and on the lash adjuster. Lubricate the roller followers with GM P/N 12345501 (Canadian P/N 992704) or equivalent.
12. Install the intake camshaft. Lubricate with GM P/N 12345501 (Canadian P/N 992704) or equivalent.
13. Install the camshaft bearing caps. Hand tighten the cap bolts.
14. Tighten the bearing cap bolts in increments of 3 turns until they are seated. Tighten the bolts to tighten to 89 inch lbs. (10 Nm).
15. Install the intake camshaft position actuator. Refer to Camshaft Position Actuator.

Exhaust

1. Remove the camshaft position exhaust actuator. Refer to Camshaft Position Actuator.

➡**Remove each bolt on each cap one turn at a time until there is no spring tension pushing on the camshaft.**

2. Mark the camshaft bearing caps to ensure they are installed in the same position.
3. Remove the camshaft bearing cap bolts and cap.
4. Remove the exhaust camshaft.

➡**Keep all of the rocker arms and hydraulic valve lash adjusters in order so that they can be reinstalled in their respective locations.**

5. Remove the valve rocker arms.
6. Remove the hydraulic valve lash adjusters.

To install:

7. Install the hydraulic valve lash adjusters into their bores in the cylinder head.
8. Lubricate the hydraulic valve lash adjusters.
9. Lubricate the valve tips.

➡**Used rocker arms MUST be returned to the original position on the camshaft. If the camshaft is being replaced, the rocker arms MUST also be replaced.**

10. Position the rocker arms on the tip of the valve stem and on the valve lash adjuster. Lubricate the rocker arms.
11. Install the exhaust camshaft. Lubricate the camshaft.

➡**The caps should be installed on the cylinder head in sequence as shown on top of the bearing caps.**

12. Position the camshaft bearing caps. Install the bearing cap bolts hand tight.
13. Tighten the bearing cap bolts in increments of 3 turns until they are seated and tighten to 89 inch lbs. (10 Nm).
14. Install the camshaft position exhaust actuator. Refer to Camshaft Position Actuator.

CAMSHAFT COVERS

REMOVAL & INSTALLATION

2.0L Engine

See Figures 80 and 81.

1. Remove the air cleaner.
2. Remove the air cleaner outlet duct.
3. Remove the charge air cooler inlet pipe.
4. Disconnect the engine wiring harness intake and exhaust electrical connectors from the camshaft position actuator solenoid valves.
5. Remove the engine wiring harness clips from the camshaft cover.
6. Disconnect the engine wiring harness electrical connector from the evaporative emission (EVAP) canister purge solenoid valve.
7. Remove the ignition coils. Refer to Ignition Coil.

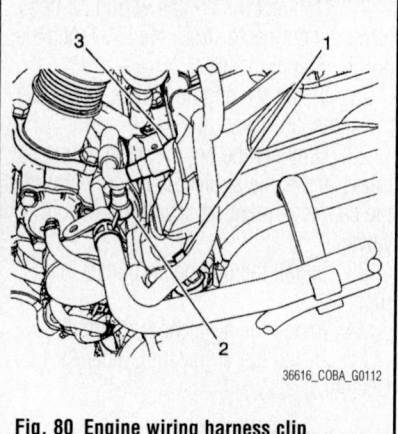

Fig. 80 Engine wiring harness clip

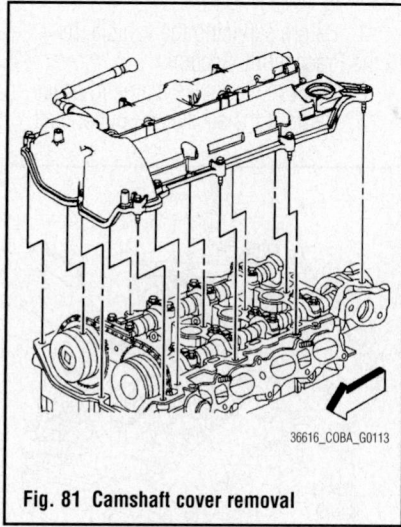

Fig. 81 Camshaft cover removal

8. Remove the engine wiring harness clip (1) from the turbocharger.
9. Disconnect the PCV hose.
10. Remove the engine wiring harness clips from the camshaft cover.
11. Disconnect the fuel line from the camshaft cover.

➡**The PCV hose should NOT be disconnected from the camshaft cover as damage to the hose connection will result.**

12. Remove the camshaft cover bolts.
13. Remove the camshaft cover.

To install:

14. Install the camshaft cover and bolts and tighten to 89 inch lbs. (10 Nm).
15. Connect the fuel line to the valve cover.
16. Install the engine wiring harness clips from the camshaft cover.
17. Connect the PCV hose.
18. Install the engine wiring harness clip to the turbocharger.
19. Install the ignition coils. Refer to Ignition Coil Replacement.

20. Connect the engine wiring harness electrical connector from the EVAP canister purge solenoid valve.

21. Install the engine harness clips to the camshaft cover.

22. Connect the engine wiring harness intake and exhaust electrical connectors to the camshaft position actuator solenoid valves.

23. Install the charge air cooler inlet pipe.

24. Install the air cleaner outlet duct.

25. Install the air cleaner. Refer to Air Cleaner.

2.2L & 2.4L Engines

See Figures 82 and 83.

1. Before servicing the vehicle, refer to the Precautions Section.

2. Remove the intake manifold cover.

3. Remove the air cleaner outlet duct.

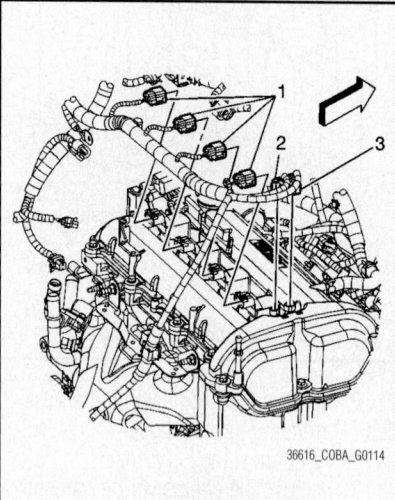

36616_COBA_G0114

Fig. 82 Camshaft position actuator solenoid valve electrical connectors

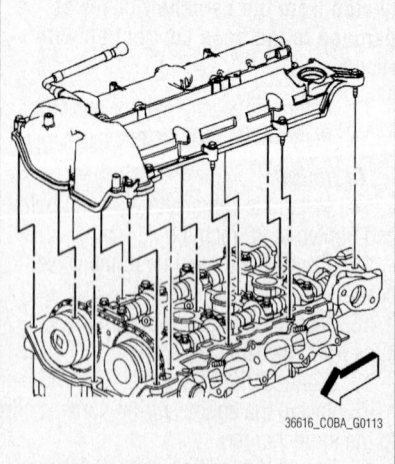

36616_COBA_G0113

Fig. 83 Camshaft cover removal

4. Disconnect the intake (3) and exhaust (2) camshaft position actuator solenoid valve electrical connectors.

5. Remove the ignition coils. Refer to Ignition Coil Replacement.

6. Remove the engine harness clips from the cover.

7. Remove the fuel feed line retainers from the engine brackets.

8. Remove the camshaft cover bolts.

9. Remove the camshaft cover.

To install:

10. Install or connect the following:
   • The camshaft cover and bolts. Tighten the bolts to 89 inch lbs. (10 Nm)

11. Install the ignition coils. Refer to Ignition Coil Replacement.

12. Install the engine harness clips to the cover.

13. Install the feed line retainers to the engine brackets.

14. Connect the intake and exhaust camshaft position actuator solenoid valve electrical connectors.

15. Install the air cleaner outlet duct.

16. Install the intake manifold cover.

CATALYTIC CONVERTER

REMOVAL & INSTALLATION

2.0L Engine

1. Raise and support the vehicle.

2. Remove the Heated Oxygen (HO2S) sensor from the Catalytic Converter.

3. Disconnect any electrical connectors.

4. Remove turbocharger exhaust pipe nuts.

5. Remove catalytic converter nuts.

6. Remove catalytic converter.

To install:

7. Installation is reverse of removal.

8. Tighten turbocharger exhaust pipe nuts to 37 ft. lbs. (50 Nm).

9. Tighten catalytic converter nuts to 34 ft. lbs. (46 Nm).

2.2L & 2.4L Engines

1. Raise and support the vehicle.

2. Remove the wheel driveshaft heat shield.

3. Remove the Heated Oxygen (HO2S) sensor from the Catalytic Converter.

4. Disconnect any electrical connectors.

5. Remove catalytic converter to resonator nuts.

6. Remove catalytic converter to exhaust manifold nuts.

7. Remove catalytic converter.

8. Discard the exhaust gaskets.

9. Clean the flange mating surfaces of any remaining gasket material.

To install:

10. Installation is reverse of removal.

11. Install a NEW gasket onto the resonator pipe studs.

12. Install the catalytic converter to the resonator pipe nuts and tighten to 22 ft. lbs. (30 Nm).

13. Install the wheel driveshaft heat shield.

CRANKSHAFT DAMPER

REMOVAL & INSTALLATION

See Figure 84.

1. Before servicing the vehicle, refer to the Precautions Section.

2. Remove the accessory drive belt. Refer to Accessory Drive Belt Removal & Installation.

3. Use tool J 38122-A, or equivalent, to prevent the crankshaft from rotating while loosening the crankshaft damper bolt.

4. Remove the crankshaft damper bolt. Discard the bolt.

5. Remove the crankshaft damper.

To install:

6. Install the crankshaft damper.

7. Install a NEW crankshaft damper bolt.

8. Use J 38122-A to prevent the crankshaft from rotating while tightening the crankshaft damper bolt. Tighten the bolt to 74 ft. lbs. (100 Nm) plus 75°.

9. Install the accessory drive belt. Refer to Accessory Drive Belts Removal & Installation.

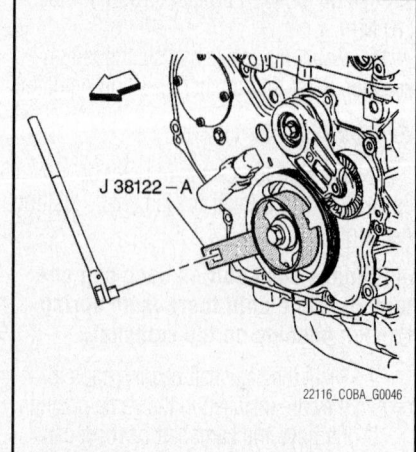

J 38122 – A

22116_COBA_G0046

Fig. 84 Crankshaft damper holding tool installed

CRANKSHAFT FRONT SEAL

REMOVAL & INSTALLATION

See Figures 85 and 86.

1. Before servicing the vehicle, refer to the Precautions Section.
2. Remove the crankshaft damper. Refer to Crankshaft Damper.
3. Use a flat-bladed tool to remove the seal from the front cover.

To install:

4. Use the J 35268-A to install the crankshaft front oil seal to the engine front cover.
5. Install the crankshaft damper. Refer to Crankshaft Damper.

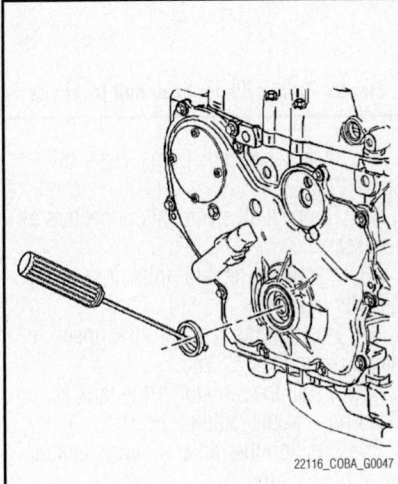

22116_COBA_G0047

Fig. 85 Using a flat-bladed tool to remove the front seal

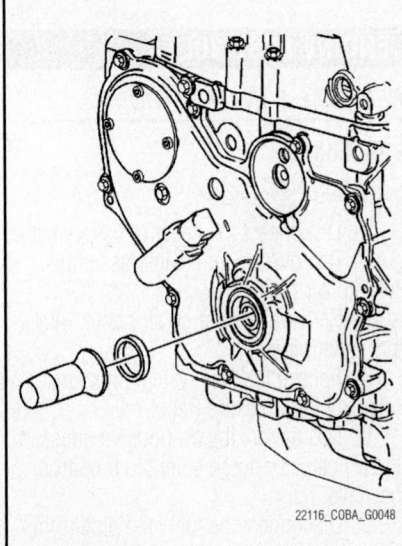

22116_COBA_G0048

Fig. 86 Using the J 35268-A to install the crankshaft front oil seal

CYLINDER HEAD

REMOVAL & INSTALLATION

See Figures 87 through 93.

1. Drain the cooling system.
2. Remove the exhaust manifold. Refer to Exhaust Manifold.

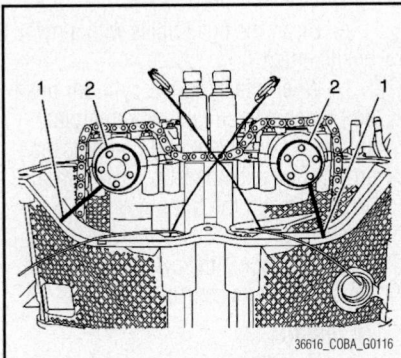

36616_COBA_G0116

Fig. 87 Marking the cylinder head—2.0L and 2.4L Engine

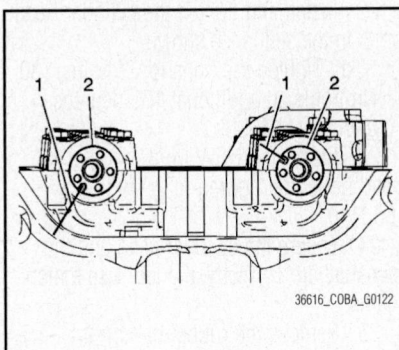

36616_COBA_G0122

Fig. 88 Marking the cylinder head—2.2L Engine

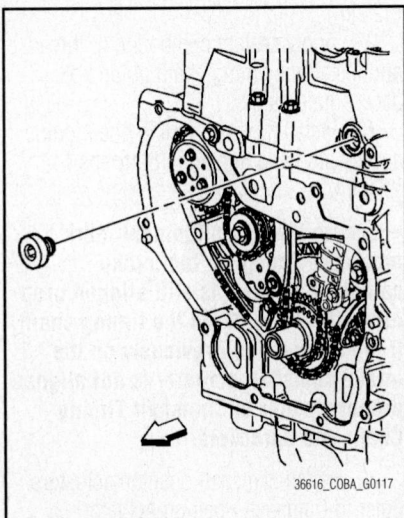

36616_COBA_G0117

Fig. 89 Fixed timing chain guide access plug

3. Remove the intake manifold. Refer to Intake Manifold.
4. Reposition the radiator surge tank air bleed hose clamp.
5. Remove the radiator surge tank air bleed hose from the cylinder head.
6. Reposition the radiator inlet hose clamp using the J 38185.
7. Remove the radiator inlet hose from the cylinder head.
8. Disconnect all electrical connectors as necessary.
9. Remove the spark plugs. Refer to Spark Plugs
10. Remove the camshaft cover.

➡ If the intake camshaft actuator is moving independently of the camshaft, this means the camshaft is not locked to the actuator. Rotate the camshaft counter-clockwise while the holding tool is installed and this will lock the camshaft to the actuator.

11. Remove camshaft position actuators, Refer to Camshaft Position Actuator.
12. Mark the cylinder head (1) in relationship to the camshaft actuator notch is on the camshaft (2).
Remove the fixed timing chain guide access plug.
Remove the upper fixed timing chain guide bolt.

➡ The threaded rod from the timing chain retention tool can be used to help feed the rubber band around the chain guides.

13. Install a rubber band (1) around the top of the upper timing chain guides (2) in order to pull the guides together.
14. Remove the cylinder head bolts in the sequence shown. Discard the bolts.

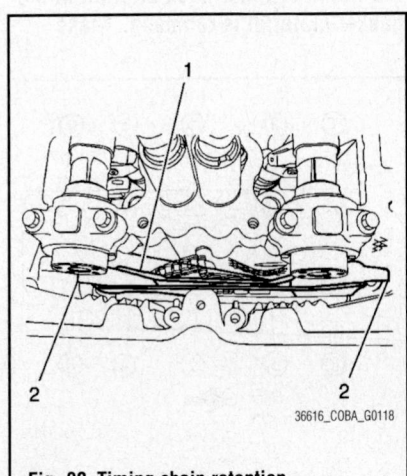

36616_COBA_G0118

Fig. 90 Timing chain retention

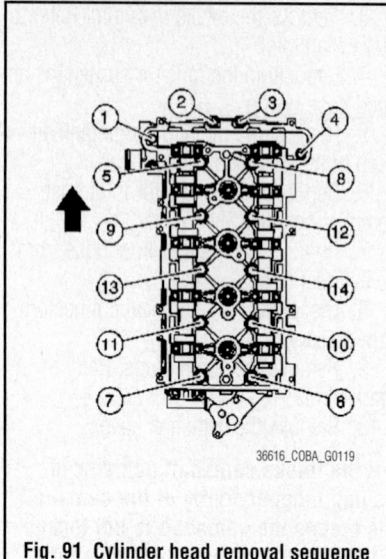

Fig. 91 Cylinder head removal sequence

15. Remove the cylinder head.
16. Remove the cylinder head gasket.
17. Clean all of the gasket surfaces.
18. Use the following steps when cleaning the cylinder head and cylinder block surfaces:
   a. Use a razor blade gasket scraper to clean the cylinder head and cylinder block gasket surfaces. Do not scratch or gouge either surface.

➡ **DO NOT use any other method or technique to clean these gasket surfaces.**

   b. Use a NEW razor blade on the cylinder head and a NEW blade on the cylinder block.

➡ **Be careful not to gouge or scratch the gasket surfaces. DO NOT gouge or scrape the combustion chamber surfaces. The feel of the gasket surface is important, not the appearance. There will be indentations from the gasket left in the cylinder head after all of the gasket material is removed. These**

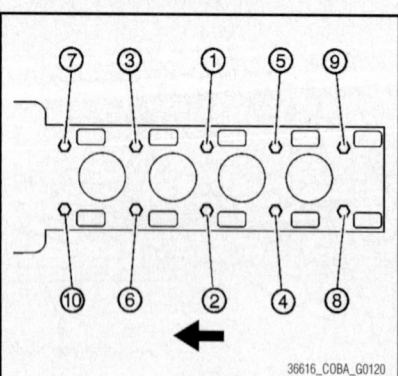

Fig. 92 Cylinder head tightening sequence

small indentations will be filled in by the NEW gasket.

   c. Hold the razor blade as parallel to the gasket surface as possible.
   d. Clean the old sealer/lube and any dirt from around the bolt holes.

➡ **DO NOT use a tap to clean the cylinder head bolt holes.**

   e. Clean the bolts holes with a nylon bristle brush.
   f. When cleaning the cylinder head bolt holes use suitable commercial spray liquid solvent and compressed air from an extended-tip blow gun in order to reach the bottom of the holes.
   g. If replacing the cylinder head, transfer all parts as necessary.

To install:

➡ **DO NOT use any sealing material.**

19. Install the cylinder head gasket.
20. Install the cylinder head.
21. Install NEW cylinder head bolts.
22. Install and tighten the cylinder head bolts in the sequence shown.
   a. Tighten the bolts to 22 ft. lbs. (30 Nm) plus an additional 155 degrees using the J 45059 .
23. Install the NEW front cylinder head bolts and tighten to 26 ft. lbs. (35 Nm).
24. Ensure the cylinder head and the camshaft are correctly aligned. Use matchmarks.
25. Remove the rubber band from around the top of the upper timing chain guides.
26. Install the fixed guide bolt into the cylinder head and tighten to 106 inch lbs. (12 Nm).
27. Apply sealant compound to thread and install the timing chain guide bolt access hole plug.
28. Install the fixed timing chain guide access plug and tighten to 59 ft. lbs. (90 Nm).

➡ **Ensure that the alignment mark made previously on the intake camshaft actuator is still aligned properly with the mark on the timing chain. If the mark made previously on the intake camshaft actuator is not aligned properly, refer to Camshaft Timing Chain and Sprockets.**

29. Install camshaft position actuators, Refer to Camshaft Position Actuator.
30. Install the camshaft cover. Refer to Camshaft Cover.

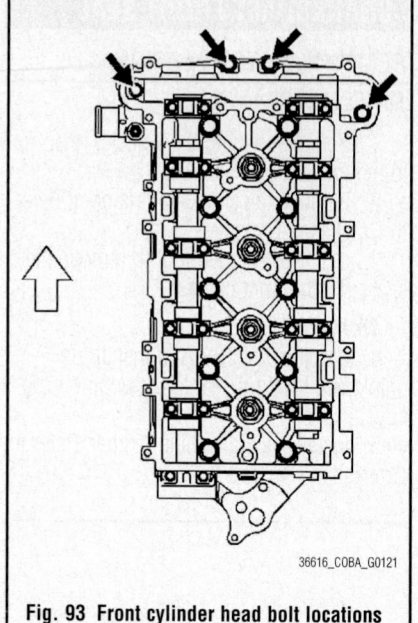

Fig. 93 Front cylinder head bolt locations

31. Install the spark plugs. Refer to Spark Plug.
32. Connect all electrical connectors as necessary.
33. Install the radiator inlet hose to the cylinder head.
34. Position the radiator inlet hose clamp using the J 38185 .
35. Install the radiator surge tank air bleed hose to the cylinder head.
36. Position the radiator surge tank air bleed hose clamp.
37. Install the exhaust manifold. Refer to Exhaust Manifold.
38. Install the intake manifold. Refer to Intake Manifold.
39. Fill the cooling system.

ENGINE ASSEMBLY

REMOVAL & INSTALLATION

2.0L Engine

See Figures 94 through 99.

1. Disconnect the negative battery cable.
2. Remove the air cleaner assembly. Refer to Air Cleaner.
3. Remove the charge air cooler inlet and outlet pipes.
4. Relieve the fuel system pressure. Refer to Fuel Pressure Relief.
5. Disconnect the evaporative emission (EVAP) canister purge solenoid tube from the valve.
6. Disconnect the fuel feed pipe from the fuel line.
7. Remove the turbocharger heat shield bolts and shield.

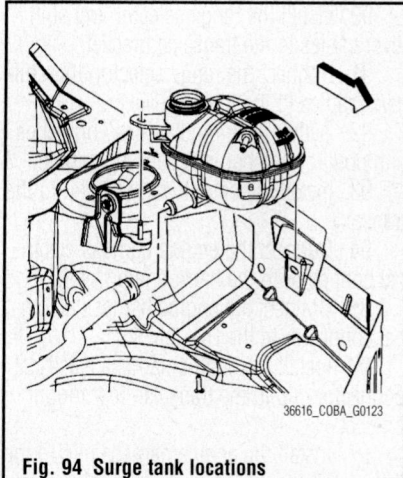

Fig. 94 Surge tank locations

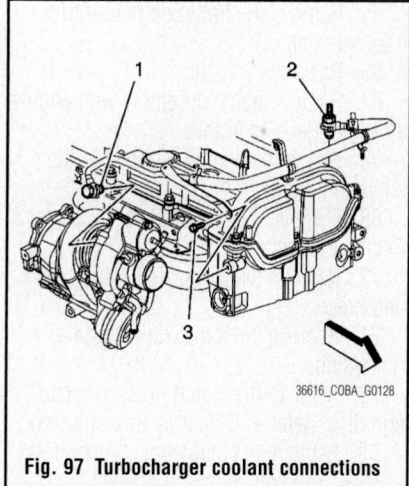

Fig. 97 Turbocharger coolant connections

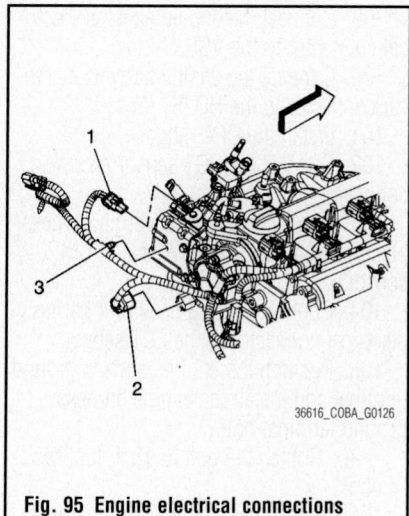

Fig. 95 Engine electrical connections

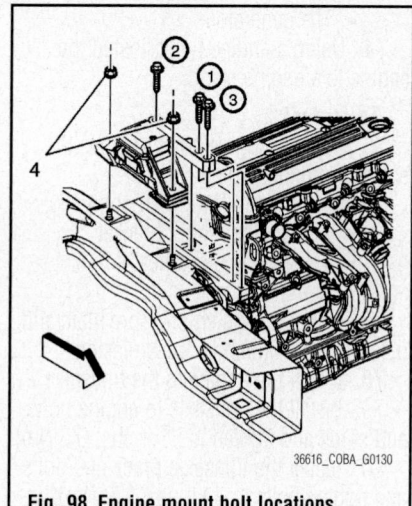

Fig. 98 Engine mount bolt locations

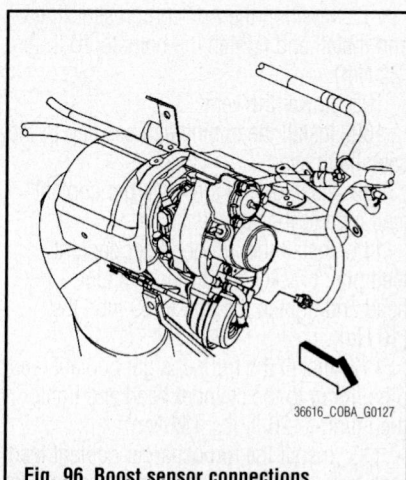

Fig. 96 Boost sensor connections

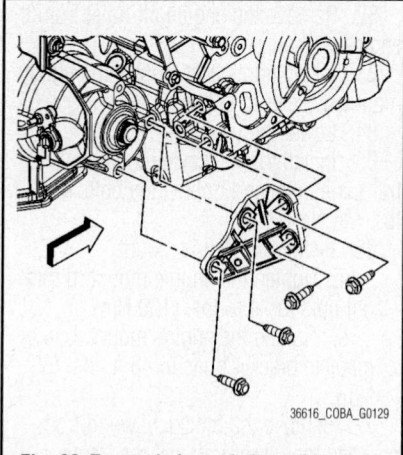

Fig. 99 Transaxle brace bolts and brace

8. Secure the cooling module to the upper body structure.

9. Remove the engine drive belt. Refer to Accessory Drive Belt.

10. Remove the charge air cooler pipe to turbocharger bolts.

11. Remove the charge air cooler pipe and gasket from the turbocharger.

12. Cap or plug the turbocharger opening.

13. Remove the radiator inlet hose. Refer to Radiator.

14. Remove the radiator outlet hose. Refer to Radiator.

15. Lower the vehicle.

16. Reposition the surge tank outlet hose clamp at the surge tank.

17. Remove the surge tank outlet hose from the surge tank.

18. Reposition the heater inlet and outlet hose clamps at the thermostat housing. Remove the heater inlet and outlet hoses from the thermostat housing.

19. Disconnect the engine wiring harness electrical connector from the Crankshaft Position (CKP) sensor.

20. Disconnect the engine wiring harness electrical connector (2) from the oil pressure sensor.

21. Disconnect the engine wiring harness electrical connector from the generator. Refer to Alternator in Engine Electrical.

22. Reposition the positive battery cable terminal boot.

23. Remove the generator terminal nut.

24. Remove the positive battery cable terminal from the generator.

25. Disconnect the engine wiring harness electrical connector from the A/C compressor.

26. Disconnect the engine wiring harness electrical connector from the fuel injector jumper electrical connector.

27. Disconnect the engine wiring harness electrical connector from the knock sensor. Refer to Knock Sensor in Engine Performance & Emission Controls.

28. Disconnect the engine wiring harness electrical connector (2) from the intake camshaft position (CMP) sensor.

29. Disconnect the engine wiring harness electrical connector (1) from the high pressure fuel pump.

30. Remove the engine wiring harness clip (3) from the high pressure fuel pump bracket.

31. Disconnect the engine wiring harness electrical connector from the intake CMP actuator.

32. Disconnect the engine wiring harness electrical connector from the exhaust CMP actuator.

33. Disconnect the ignition coil electrical connectors from the ignition coils.

34. Disconnect the engine harness clips from the camshaft cover.

35. Disconnect the engine harness clip from the camshaft cover.

36. Disconnect the engine wiring harness electrical connector from the boost sensor.

37. Remove the turbocharger coolant feed pipe bolt at the turbocharger.

38. Remove the turbocharger coolant feed pipe fitting from the cylinder head.

39. Remove the turbocharger coolant feed pipe bracket bolt from the cylinder head.

40. Remove the turbocharger coolant feed pipe bracket from the vehicle.

41. Remove the A/C compressor line bolt and reposition the line off to the side.

42. Remove the engine harness clip from the camshaft cover.

43. Raise and suitably support the vehicle.

44. Disconnect the engine wiring harness electrical connector from the heated oxygen sensor (HO2S).

45. Disconnect the engine wiring harness electrical connector from the exhaust CMP sensor.

46. Remove the engine harness ground terminal bolt and reposition the engine harness ground terminal.

47. Disconnect the engine wiring harness electrical connector from the engine coolant temperature (ECT) sensor.

48. Disconnect the ECT sensor electrical connector. Refer to Engine Coolant Temperature Sensor in Engine Performance & Emission Controls.

49. Remove the CPA retainer.

50. Disconnect the engine harness electrical connector from the HO2S.

51. Disconnect the engine harness electrical connector from the VSS. Refer to Vehicle Speed sensor in Engine Performance & Emission Controls.

52. Remove the engine harness clip from the transaxle.

53. Remove the CPA retainer.

54. Remove the engine harness electrical connector clip from the transaxle rear mount bracket.

55. Disconnect the engine harness electrical connector from the HO2S.

56. Disconnect the engine harness electrical connector from the back up lamp switch.

57. Remove the engine harness clip from the transaxle.

58. Gather all engine harness branches are reposition the harness off to the side, out of the way.

59. Disconnect the range selector and shift lever cables from the transaxle levers.

60. Remove the range selector and shift lever cables from the transaxle bracket.

61. Remove the catalytic converter. Refer to Catalytic Converter.

62. Lower the vehicle.

63. Insert blocks of wood between the powertrain and the frame, in order to support the powertrain.

64. Remove the engine mount.

65. Remove the transaxle mount to transaxle bolts.

66. Raise the vehicle.

67. Remove frame assembly with engine attached. Refer to Frame.

68. Attach the engine lift hoist to the engine lift hooks.

69. Remove the starter. Refer to Starter in Engine Electrical.

70. Remove the transaxle brace bolts and brace.

71. Remove the transaxle to engine bolts/stud.

72. Remove the clutch pressure plate and disc. Refer to Clutch in Transmission.

73. Remove the following components:
   - The engine mount bracket
   - The engine block heater
   - The generator

74. Using a engine hoist, install the engine to a engine stand.

To install:

75. Using a engine hoist, remove the engine from the engine stand.

76. Install the following components:
   - The engine mount bracket
   - The engine block heater
   - The generator

77. Install the clutch pressure plate and disc. Refer to Clutch in Transmission.

78. Install the engine to the transaxle.

79. Install the transaxle to engine bolts and studs and tighten to 55 ft. lbs. (75 Nm).

80. Install the transaxle brace and bolts and tighten bolts to 37 ft. lbs. (50 Nm).

81. Install the starter. Refer to Starter in Engine Electrical.

82. Remove the engine lift hoist from the engine lift hooks.

83. Install frame assembly with engine mounted. Refer to Frame.

84. Lower the vehicle.

85. Install the transaxle mount to transaxle bolts and tighten the bolts to 33 ft. lbs. (45 Nm).

86. Install the engine mount.
   a. Tighten the engine mount to mid-rail nuts to 74 ft. lbs. (100 Nm).
   b. Tighten the engine mount to intermediate bracket bolts to 48 ft. lbs. (65 Nm).

87. Remove the blocks of wood from between the powertrain and the frame.

88. Install the catalytic converter. Refer to Catalytic Converter.

89. Lower the vehicle.

➡ **Ensure that the black cable is installed in the top notch of the transaxle bracket and the white cable in installed in the bottom notch of the transaxle bracket.**

90. Install the range selector and shift lever cables to the transaxle bracket.

91. Connect the range selector and shift lever cables to the transaxle levers.

92. Gather all engine harness branches and position the harness over the engine.

93. Install the engine harness clip to the transaxle.

94. Connect the engine harness electrical connector to the backup lamp switch.

95. Connect the engine harness electrical connector to the HO2S.

96. Install the engine harness electrical connector clip to the transaxle rear mount bracket.

97. Install the engine harness clip to the transaxle.

98. Install the CPA retainer.

99. Connect the engine harness electrical connector to the VSS.

100. Connect the engine harness electrical connector to the HO2S.

101. Install the CPA retainer.

102. Connect the ECT sensor electrical connector.

103. Connect the engine wiring harness electrical connector to the exhaust CMP sensor.

104. Connect the engine wiring harness electrical connector to the ECT sensor.

105. Position the engine harness ground terminal and install the engine harness ground terminal bolt.
   a. Tighten the bolt to 18 ft. lbs. (25 Nm).

106. Connect the engine wiring harness electrical connector to the HO2S.

107. Position the A/C compressor line and install and tighten the bolts to 16 ft. lbs. (22 Nm).

108. Lower the vehicle.

109. Install the engine harness clip to the camshaft cover.

110. Position the turbocharger coolant feed pipe to the vehicle.

111. Install the turbocharger coolant feed pipe bracket bolt to the cylinder head and tighten the bolt to 89 inch lbs. (10 Nm).

112. Install the turbocharger coolant feed pipe fitting to the cylinder head and tighten the fitting to 26 ft. lbs. (35 Nm).

113. Install the turbocharger coolant feed pipe bolt (1) at the turbocharger and tighten to 26 ft. lbs. (35 Nm)

114. Install the charge air bypass valve vacuum solenoid.

115. Install the charge air bypass valve vacuum hose to the turbocharger coolant feed pipe clips.

116. Position the charge air bypass valve vacuum hose clamp at the turbocharger.

117. Place the charge air bypass valve solenoid out of the way.

118. Connect the engine wiring harness electrical connector to the boost sensor.

119. Connect the engine harness clips to the camshaft cover.

120. Connect the engine harness clip to the camshaft cover.

121. Connect the engine wiring harness electrical connectors to the ignition coils.

122. Connect the engine wiring harness electrical connector to the intake CMP actuator.

123. Connect the engine wiring harness electrical connector to the exhaust CMP actuator.

124. Connect the engine wiring harness electrical connector to the high pressure fuel pump.

125. Install the engine wiring harness clip to the high pressure fuel pump bracket.

126. Connect the engine wiring harness electrical connector to the knock sensor.

127. Connect the engine wiring harness electrical connector to the fuel injector jumper electrical connector.

128. Install the positive battery cable terminal to the generator.

129. Install the generator terminal nut and tighten the nut to 15 ft. lbs. (20 Nm).

130. Position the positive battery cable terminal boot.

131. Connect the engine wiring harness electrical connector to the A/C compressor.

132. Connect the engine wiring harness electrical connector to the generator.

133. Install the catalytic converter. Refer to Catalytic Converter.

134. Connect the engine wiring harness electrical connector to the CKP sensor.

135. Connect the engine wiring harness electrical connector to the oil pressure sensor.

136. Lower the vehicle.

137. Install the heater inlet and outlet hoses to the thermostat housing.

138. Position the heater inlet and outlet hose clamps at the thermostat housing.

139. Install the surge tank outlet hose to the surge tank.

140. Position the surge tank outlet hose clamp at the surge tank.

141. Install the radiator outlet hose.

142. Install the radiator inlet hose.

143. Remove the cap or plug from the turbocharger opening.

144. Install the charge air cooler pipe to the turbocharger.

145. Install the charge air cooler pipe to turbocharger bolts and tighten the bolts to 16 ft. lbs. (22 Nm).

146. Install the engine drive belt. Refer to Accessory Drive Belt.

147. Un-secure the cooling module from the upper body structure.

148. Fill the cooling system.

149. Install the turbocharger heat shield and bolts and tighten the bolts to 89 inch lbs. (10 Nm).

150. Connect the fuel feed pipe to the fuel line.

151. Connect the EVAP canister purge solenoid tube to the valve.

152. Install the charge air cooler inlet and outlet pipes.

153. Install the air cleaner assembly. Refer to Air Cleaner.

154. Connect the negative battery cable.

155. Fill the engine with oil.

2.2L Engine

See Figures 100 and 101.

1. Before servicing the vehicle, refer to the Precautions Section.

2. With the tires in the straight forward position, remove the key from the ignition.

3. Disconnect the negative battery cable.

4. Remove the air inlet duct and resonator.

5. Secure the cooling module to the upper body structure.

6. Relieve the fuel system pressure. Refer to Fuel System.

7. Disconnect the fuel lines from the fuel rail.

8. Drain the cooling system.

9. Remove the radiator inlet hose.

10. Remove the surge tank to cylinder head hose.

11. Remove the radiator outlet hose.

12. Remove the inlet and outlet heater hoses.

13. Disconnect the following harness connectors:

- Idle Air Control (IAC) motor
- TPS
- Manifold Absolute Pressure (MAP) sensor
- Crankshaft sensor
- Oil pressure sensor
- Purge solenoid
- Ignition coil and module assembly
- Oxygen (O_2) sensor
- Vehicle speed sensor
- Engine temperature sensor
- Backup lamp switch

14. Raise and suitably support the vehicle.

15. Remove the engine accessory drive belt. Refer to Accessory Drive Belt.

16. Remove the front fender liner.

17. Rotate the drive belt tensioner counterclockwise to release the spring tension.

18. Remove the drive belt.

19. Disconnect the electrical connector from the A/C compressor.

20. Remove the A/C compressor bolts and set the compressor aside.

21. Disconnect the starter harness connectors. Refer to Starter in Engine Electrical.

22. Disconnect the generator harness connectors. Refer to Alternator in Engine Electrical.

23. Drain the engine oil.

24. Disconnect the front exhaust pipe

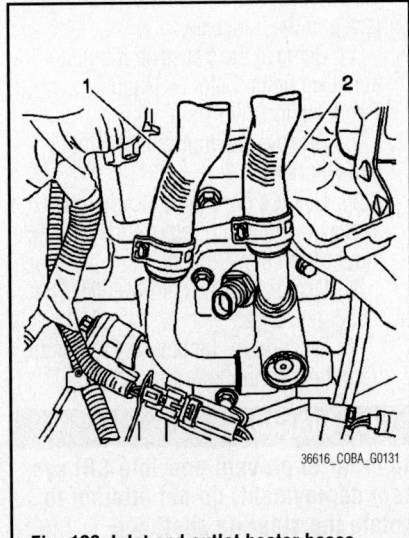

Fig. 100 Inlet and outlet heater hoses

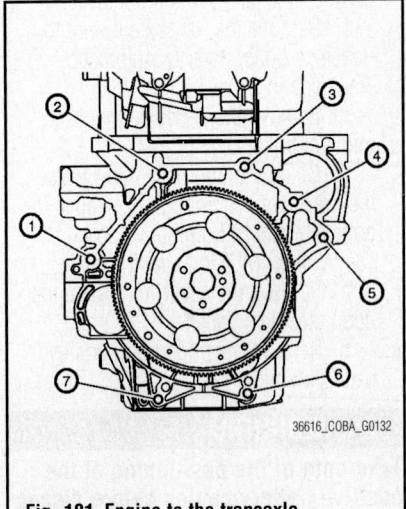

Fig. 101 Engine to the transaxle bolt locations

from the exhaust manifold. Refer to Catalytic Converter.

25. Disconnect the transaxle harness connectors.

26. Disconnect the transaxle shift cable from the transaxle.

27. Use blocks of wood to support the powertrain assembly between the frame and the powertrain.

28. Support the engine with a hydraulic floor jack. Use a piece of wood between the jack and the oil pan.

29. Remove the engine mount to intermediate bracket bolts.

30. Remove the engine mount to mid-rail nuts.

31. Remove the engine mount from the engine compartment.

32. With an automatic transaxle:

   a. Remove the front transaxle mount thru bolt.

   b. Remove the rear transaxle mount thru bolt.

   c. Lower the vehicle.

   d. Remove the under hood electrical center cover.

   e. Disconnect the engine control module harness connector.

   f. Disconnect the positive battery cables from the underhood electrical center. Refer to Underhood Electrical Center in Chassis Electrical.

   g. Disconnect the surge tank inlet hose from the surge tank.

   h. Remove the under hood electrical center tray bracket nuts and bolt.

   i. Disconnect the wiring harness retainer from the tray bracket.

   j. Lift the electrical center up and swing it back and out of the way.

   k. Support the transaxle with a hydraulic floor jack. Use a block of wood between the jack and the transaxle.

   l. Remove the transaxle mount to transaxle bolts. Refer to Automatic Transaxle in Drive Train.

   m. Remove the transaxle mount to mid-rail bolts.

   n. Using the floor jack, slowly lower the transaxle just enough to remove the transaxle mount from the vehicle.

33. With an MU3 manual transaxle:

   a. Remove the cover from the underhood electrical center.

   b. Remove the underhood positive battery terminal lug.

   c. Disconnect the positive battery cables from the underhood electrical center.

   d. Loosen all of the underhood electrical bolts.

   e. Remove the underhood electrical center bracket from the vehicle and reposition the electrical center.

   f. Support the transaxle with a floor jack. Use a piece of wood between the jack and the transaxle.

   g. Remove the transaxle mount-to-transaxle bracket bolts. Refer to Manual Transaxle in Drive Train.

   h. Remove the transaxle mount to mid-rail bolts.

   i. Using a floor jack, slowly lower the transaxle enough to remove the transaxle mount from the vehicle.

34. With a Getrag 5-speed manual transaxle:

   a. Remove the underhood electrical center cover.

   b. Disconnect the Engine Control Module (ECM) harness connector.

   c. Disconnect the positive battery cables from the underhood electrical center.

   d. Disconnect the surge tank inlet hose from the surge tank.

   e. Remove the underhood electrical center tray bracket nuts and bolt.

   f. Disconnect the wiring harness retainer from the tray bracket.

   g. Lift the electrical center up and swing it back and out of the way.

   h. Support the transaxle with a floor jack. Use a piece of wood between the jack and the transaxle.

   i. Remove the transaxle mount to transaxle bolts. Refer to Manual Transaxle in Drive Train

   j. Remove the transaxle mount to mid-rail bolts.

   k. Using a floor jack, slowly lower the transaxle enough to remove the transaxle mount from the vehicle.

   l. Disconnect the control links from the stabilizer bar.

   m. Disconnect the outer tie rod ends from the steering knuckles.

   n. Disconnect the intermediate shaft from the steering gear.

   o. Disconnect the lower control arms from the steering knuckles.

   p. Disconnect the drive axles from the steering knuckle.

   q. Use a paint pen or magic marker in order to mark the frame to body position.

   r. Lower the vehicle to about 3 feet off the ground in order to position the lift table under the frame.

   s. Use wood blocks as necessary between the lift table and the frame to support the assembly.

35. Slowly remove the frame bolts using the following sequence:

   a. Remove the front frame bolts.

   b. Partially unscrew the rear frame bolts until 1.5 inches of bolt shank is exposed.

36. Slowly lower the table to the floor with the cradle and powertrain assembly.

37. Attach the engine lift hoist to the engine lift hooks.

38. Remove the starter.

39. If applicable, remove the torque converter to flywheel bolts.

40. Remove the transaxle to engine bolts.

41. Separate the engine from the transaxle.

42. If applicable, remove the clutch pressure plate and disk.

43. Remove the following components:

44. Remove the exhaust manifold

45. Remove the exhaust manifold studs

46. Remove the engine mount bracket

47. Remove the engine block heater

48. Remove the thermostat housing and feed pipe

49. Remove the generator

50. Remove the engine from the engine lift.

To install:

51. Attach the engine lift hoist to the engine lift hooks.

52. Install the exhaust manifold.

53. Install the intermediate bracket to the engine.

54. Hand tighten the engine mount intermediate bracket bolts in the following locations:

   • The long bolts in the forward and front lower holes

   • The short bolt in the rear upper hole

55. Tighten the intermediate bracket bolts to 74 ft. lbs. (100 Nm).

56. Install the fuel rail.

57. Install the engine block heater, if equipped.

58. Install the drive belt tensioner.
59. Install the thermostat and retaining sleeve with the dimple placed into the housing slot.

> ⁜ **WARNING**
>
> **Lubricate the O-ring with soapy water or coolant before installing the O-ring in the water pump.**

60. Install the feed pipe that connects the thermostat housing to the water pump.
61. Install the bolt that secures the water pump feed pipe. Tighten the bolt to 88 inch lbs. (10 Nm).
62. Install the generator.
63. Install the flywheel. Tighten the flywheel bolts to 39 ft. lbs. (53 Nm) plus 25°.
64. If applicable, install the clutch pressure plate and disk.
65. Align the engine to the transaxle.

> ⁜ **WARNING**
>
> **The number 3 bolt location is not used.**

66. Secure the engine to the transaxle. Tighten the transaxle to engine bolts to 55 ft. lbs. (75 Nm).

➡ **The number 3 bolt location is not used.**

67. If applicable, install the torque converter bolts. Tighten the bolts to 44 ft. lbs. (60 Nm).
68. Install the starter.
69. Remove the engine lift from the engine.
70. Raise and position the frame and powertrain assembly to the vehicle.
71. Hand start all the frame bolts while aligning the frame to the paint marks.
72. Tighten the frame bolts. Tighten the frame bolts to 74 ft. lbs. (100 Nm) plus 180°.
73. Remove the lift table.
74. Connect the drive axles to the steering knuckles.
75. Connect the lower control arm to the steering knuckle.
76. Connect the intermediate steering shaft to the steering gear.
77. Connect the outer tie rod ends to the steering knuckles.
78. Connect the control links to the stabilizer bar.
79. With an automatic transaxle:
   a. Install the transaxle mount to the mid-rail.
   b. Hand start the transaxle mount to mid-rail bolts. Tighten the bolts to 25 ft. lbs. (34 Nm).
   c. Using a hydraulic jack, raise the transaxle until it contacts the transaxle mount.

> ⁜ **WARNING**
>
> **The transaxle mount to transaxle bolts must be hand started. Do not pry the transaxle or mount to align the holes.**

   d. Hand start the transaxle mount to transaxle bolts using the following sequence:
   • Rear Bolt
   • Middle Bolt
   • Front Bolt
   e. Using the previous sequence, tighten the transaxle mount bolts. Tighten the bolts to 37 ft. lbs. (50 Nm).
   f. Reposition the under hood electrical center.
   g. Connect the wiring harness retainer to the tray bracket.
   h. Install the electrical center nuts and bolts. Tighten the nut to 89 inch lbs. (10 Nm). Tighten the bolt to 18 ft. lbs. (25 Nm).
   i. Connect the surge tank inlet hose to the surge tank.
   j. Install the positive battery cables to the under hood electrical center. Tighten the positive cable nut to 11 ft. lbs. (15 Nm).
   k. Connect the engine control module harness connectors.
   l. Install the under hood electrical center cover.
   m. Raise the vehicle.
   n. Hand tighten the front transaxle mount thru bolt
   o. Hand tighten the rear transaxle mount thru bolt.
   p. Tighten the front transaxle mount thru bolt. Tighten the bolt to 74 ft. lbs. (100 Nm).
   q. Tighten the rear transaxle mount thru bolt. Tighten the bolt to 74 ft. lbs. (100 Nm).
80. With an MU3 manual transaxle:
   a. Install the transaxle mount to the mid-rail.
   b. Install the transaxle mount to mid-rail bolts. Tighten the bolts to 20 ft. lbs. (27 Nm).
   c. Using a floor jack, raise the transaxle until it contacts the transaxle mount.

> ⁜ **WARNING**
>
> **The transaxle mount to transaxle bolts must be hand started. Do not pry the transaxle or mount to align the holes.**

   d. Hand start the transaxle mount to bracket bolts using the following sequence:
   • Rear bolt
   • Middle bolt
   • Front bolt
   e. Using the previous sequence, tighten the transaxle mount bolts. Tighten the bolts to 37 ft. lbs. (50 Nm).
   f. Install the underhood electrical center bracket to the vehicle and install the electrical center into position on the bracket.
81. With a Getrag 5-speed:
   a. Install the transaxle mount to the mid-rail.
   b. Hand start the transaxle mount to mid-rail bolts. Tighten the bolts to.
   c. Using a floor jack, raise the transaxle until it contacts the transaxle mount.

> ⁜ **WARNING**
>
> **The transaxle mount to transaxle bolts must be hand started. Do not pry the transaxle or mount to align the holes.**

   d. Hand start the transaxle mount to transaxle bolts using the following sequence:
   • Rear bolt
   • Middle bolt
   • Front bolt
   e. Using the previous sequence, tighten the transaxle mount bolts. Tighten the bolts to 33 ft. lbs. (45 Nm).
82. Reposition the underhood electrical center.
83. Connect the wiring harness to the tray bracket.
84. Install the electrical center nuts and bolt. Tighten the nuts to 89 inch lbs. (10 Nm). Tighten the bolt to 18 ft. lbs. (25 Nm).
85. Connect the surge tank inlet hose to the surge tank.
86. Install the positive battery cables to the underhood electrical center. Tighten the positive cable nut to 11 ft. lbs. (15 Nm).
87. Connect the engine control module harness connectors.
88. Install the underhood electrical center cover.
89. Place the engine mount onto the mid rail and hand start the nuts.
90. Tighten the engine mount to mid-rail nuts. Tighten the nuts to 74 ft. lbs. (100 Nm).

> ⁜ **WARNING**
>
> **The engine mount to intermediate bracket bolts must be hand started. Do not pry the engine mount to align the holes.**

91. Hand start the engine mount to intermediate bracket bolts.

92. Tighten the engine mount to intermediate bracket bolts. Tighten the bolts to 37 ft. lbs. (50 Nm).

93. Remove the hydraulic floor jack.

94. Install the air cleaner assembly.

95. Remove the wood blocks between the powertrain and frame.

96. Connect the transaxle shift cable to the transaxle.

97. Connect the transaxle harness connector.

98. Connect the exhaust takedown pipe to the exhaust manifold. Tighten the nuts to 22 ft. lbs. (30 Nm).

99. Connect the generator harness connectors. Tighten the generator terminal nut to 15 ft. lbs. (20 Nm).

100. Connect the starter harness connectors. Tighten the battery terminal nut to 13 ft. lbs. (17 Nm). Tighten the S-terminal nut to 27 inch lbs. (3 Nm).

101. Install the A/C compressor to the engine. Tighten the bolts to 18 ft. lbs. (25 Nm).

102. Install the engine drive belt.

103. Connect the following harness connectors:
- IAC motor
- TPS
- MAP sensor
- Crankshaft sensor
- Oil pressure sensor
- Purge solenoid
- Ignition coil and module assembly
- O_2 sensor
- Vehicle speed sensor
- Engine temperature sensor

104. Install the inlet heater hose and outlet heater hose.

105. Install the radiator outlet hose.

106. Connect the fuel line to the fuel rail.

107. Connect the brake booster hose at the brake booster.

108. Release the cooling module from the upper body structure.

109. Install the air inlet duct and resonator.

110. Connect the negative battery cable.

111. Fill the engine with engine oil to the proper level.

112. Fill the cooling system.

113. Road test the vehicle.

2.4L Engine

See Figures 102 through 111.

1. Before servicing the vehicle, refer to the Precautions Section.

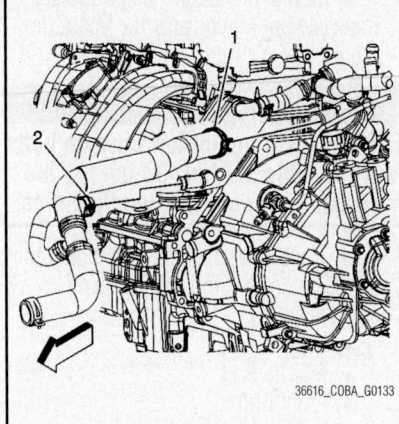

Fig. 102 Radiator outlet hose locations

2. With the tires in the straight forward position, remove the key from the ignition.

3. Disconnect the negative battery cable.

4. Relieve fuel system pressure.

5. Disconnect the fuel feed line quick connect fitting from the fuel rail.

6. Disconnect the Evaporative Emission (EVAP) line quick connect fitting from the EVAP purge solenoid.

7. Remove the fuel line clips from the engine brackets.

8. Drain the cooling system.

9. Secure the cooling module to the upper body structure.

10. Remove the accessory drive belt. Refer to Accessory Drive Belts.

11. Disconnect the cooling fan electrical connector.

12. Reposition the radiator inlet hose clamp at the engine.

13. Remove the radiator inlet hose from the engine.

14. If the vehicle is equipped with an

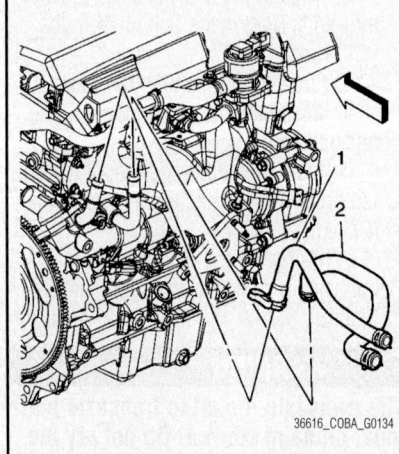

Fig. 103 Heater inlet and outlet hoses

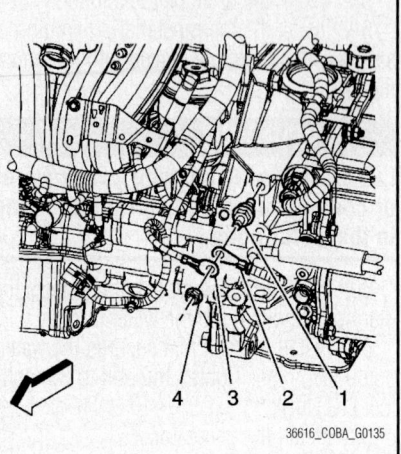

Fig. 104 Negative battery cable ground terminal location

engine oil cooler, perform the following steps, otherwise proceed to step 19.

15. Reposition the radiator outlet hose clamp at the water outlet.

16. Reposition the radiator outlet hose clamp at the oil cooler.

17. Remove the radiator outlet hose from the water outlet.

18. Remove the radiator outlet hose from the oil cooler. Proceed to step 23.

19. If the vehicle is not equipped with an engine oil cooler, reposition the surge tank outlet hose clamp at the surge tank.

20. Remove the surge tank outlet hose from the surge tank.

21. Reposition the radiator outlet hose clamp at the thermostat cover.

22. Remove the radiator outlet hose from the thermostat cover.

23. Reposition the heater inlet and outlet hose clamps at the thermostat housing.

24. Remove the heater inlet and outlet hoses from the thermostat housing.

25. Reposition the brake booster vacuum hose clamp at the intake manifold.

26. Remove the brake booster vacuum hose from the intake manifold. Reposition the hose.

27. Disconnect the following electrical connectors:
- Throttle Actuator Control (TAC)
- Manifold Absolute Pressure (MAP) sensor
- Fuel injector harness
- Alternator

28. Remove or disconnect the following:
- The engine harness clip from the oil level indicator tube
- The engine harness clips from the intake manifold
- The ignition coils electrical connectors

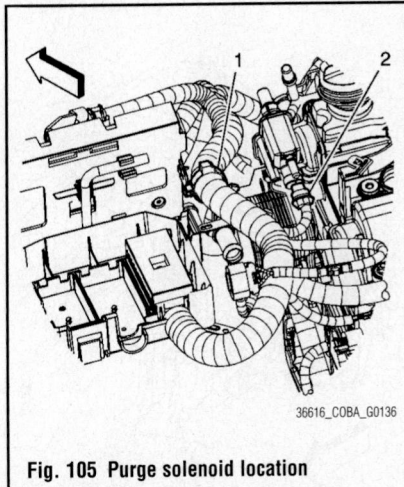

Fig. 105 Purge solenoid location

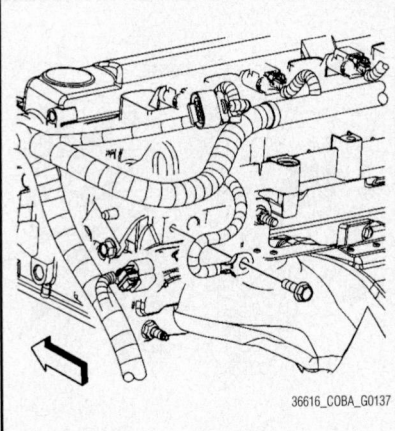

Fig. 106 Engine harness ground location

- The intake and exhaust camshaft position actuator electrical connectors
- The engine harness clips from the camshaft cover
- The negative battery cable ground nut
- The engine harness ground terminal from the stud
- The negative battery cable ground terminal from the stud

29. Disconnect the following engine harness electrical connectors:
- Oil pressure sensor
- Crankshaft Position (CKP) sensor
- Knock sensor
- The EVAP purge solenoid electrical connector

30. Remove the engine harness clip from the purge solenoid bracket.

31. Remove the engine harness ground bolt.

32. Reposition the engine harness ground terminal.

33. Disconnect the engine harness electrical connector from the Air Conditioning (A/C) pressure switch.

34. Disconnect the engine harness electrical connector from A/C compressor.

35. Unbolt and reposition the A/C compressor to one side.

36. Raise and suitably support the vehicle.

37. Drain the engine oil.

38. Remove the transaxle fluid cooler bracket nut.

39. Remove the transaxle fluid cooler lines from the transaxle.

40. Remove the engine harness clip nut from the engine stud.

41. Remove the engine harness clip from the stud.

42. If equipped with an automatic transaxle, disconnect the engine harness electrical connector from the Vehicle Speed Sensor (VSS).

43. Remove the engine harness clip from the speed sensor.

44. Remove the positive battery cable lead nut from the starter solenoid. Refer to Starter in Engine Electrical.

45. Remove the positive battery cable terminal from the starter.

46. Remove the engine harness terminal from the starter.

47. Remove the engine harness to starter solenoid "S" terminal nut.

48. Remove the engine harness lead terminals from the starter solenoid.

49. Lower the vehicle.

50. If equipped with an automatic transaxle, disconnect the engine harness from the transaxle.

51. If equipped with a automatic transaxle, perform the following steps.

   a. Disconnect the engine harness electrical connector (2) from the engine coolant temperature (ECT) sensor.

   b. Remove the heated oxygen sensor (HO2S) connector position assurance (CPA) retainers.

   c. Disconnect the engine harness electrical connectors (2, 4) from the HO2S.

   d. Remove the HO2S connector clips from the thermostat housing and engine bracket.

   e. Disconnect the engine harness electrical connector (1) from the park neutral position switch.

52. If equipped with a manual transaxle, disconnect the engine harness electrical connector (6) from the VSS.

   a. Disconnect the engine harness electrical connector (7) from the back up lamp switch.

   b. Remove the HO2S CPA retainers (2, 4).

   c. Disconnect the engine harness

electrical connectors (1, 5) from the HO2S.

   d. Remove the HO2S clips from the engine brackets.

   e. Gather all engine harness branches are reposition the harness off to the side, out of the way.

53. If equipped with an automatic transaxle:

   a. Disconnect the range selector lever cable from the transaxle lever.

   b. Remove the range selector lever cable from the transaxle bracket.

54. If equipped with a manual transaxle:

   a. Disconnect the range selector and shift lever cables from the transaxle levers.

   b. Remove the range selector and shift lever cables from the transaxle bracket.

55. Remove the catalytic converter.

56. Lower the vehicle.

57. Insert blocks of wood between the powertrain and the frame, in order to support the powertrain.

58. Remove the engine mount.

59. Remove the transaxle mount to transaxle bolts.

60. Raise the vehicle.

61. Disconnect the control links from the stabilizer bar.

62. Disconnect the outer tie rod ends from the steering knuckles.

63. Disconnect the intermediate shaft from the steering gear.

64. Disconnect the lower control arms from the steering knuckles.

65. Using a paint pen or magic marker, mark the frame to body position.

66. Lower the vehicle to about 3 feet off the ground.

67. Position a engine lift table under the frame.

68. Place wood blocks on top of the lift table between the table and the frame.

69. Lower the vehicle until the frame is resting on the blocks of wood.

70. Slowly loosen/remove the frame bolts using the following sequence:

   a. Loosen/remove the front frame bolts.

   b. Loosen/remove the rear frame bolts.

71. Slowly raise the vehicle away from the powertrain assembly.

72. Slide the lift table out from under the vehicle.

73. Attach the engine lift hoist to the engine lift hooks.

74. Remove the starter bolts and starter.

75. If equipped with an automatic transaxle:

   a. Remove the torque converter housing access plug.

   b. Remove the torque converter bolts.

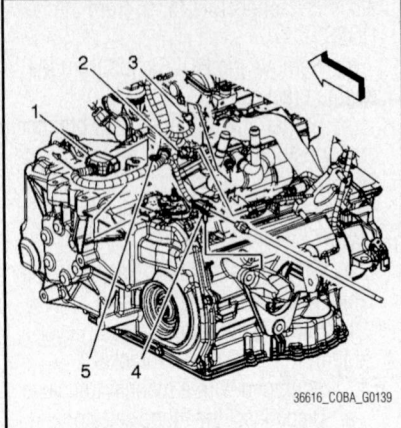

Fig. 107 Automatic Transaxle harness locations

36616_COBA_G0139

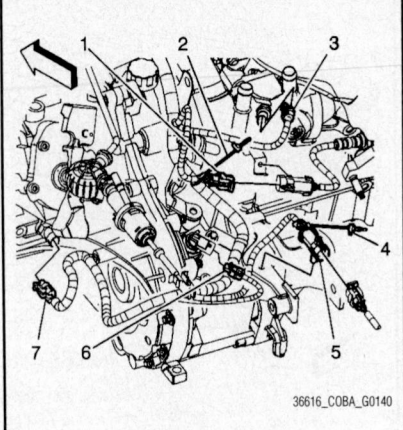

Fig. 108 Manual Transaxle harness locations

36616_COBA_G0140

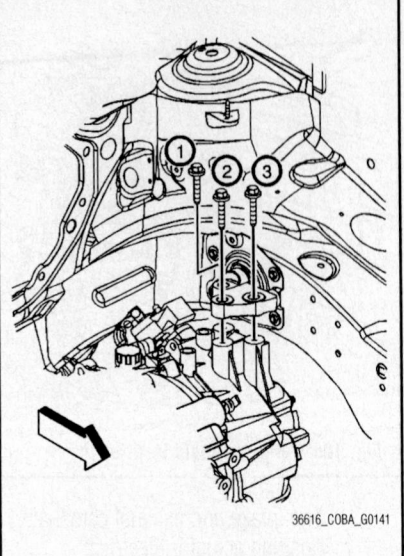

36616_COBA_G0141

Fig. 109 Transaxle mount to transaxle bolt locations

76. Remove the transaxle brace bolts and brace.

77. If equipped with a manual transaxle, remove the transaxle to engine bolts/stud.

78. If equipped with an automatic transaxle, remove the transaxle to engine bolts/stud.

79. Separate the engine from the transaxle.

80. If equipped with a manual transaxle, remove the clutch pressure plate and disc.

81. Remove the following components:
   • The engine mount bracket
   • The engine block heater
   • The alternator

82. Using an engine hoist, install the engine onto an engine stand.

To install:

83. Using an engine hoist, remove the engine from the engine stand.

84. Install the following components:
   • The engine mount bracket
   • The engine block heater
   • The alternator

85. If equipped with a manual transaxle, install the clutch pressure plate and disc.

86. Install the engine to the transaxle.

87. If equipped with an automatic transaxle, install the transaxle to engine bolts/stud. Tighten the bolts/stud to 55 ft. lbs. (75 Nm).

88. If equipped with a manual transaxle, install the transaxle to engine bolts/stud. Tighten the bolts/stud to 55 ft. lbs. (75 Nm).

89. Install the transaxle brace and bolts. Tighten the bolts to 37 ft. lbs. (50 Nm).

90. If equipped with an automatic transaxle:
   a. Install the torque converter bolts. Tighten the bolts to 46 ft. lbs. (62 Nm).
   b. Install the torque converter housing access plug.

91. Install the starter and bolts. Tighten the bolts to 30 ft. lbs. (40 Nm).

92. Remove the engine lift hoist from the engine lift hooks.

93. Slide the lift table under the vehicle.

94. Slowly lower the vehicle until it aligns with the alignment marks made during the removal.

95. Tighten/install the frame bolts. Tighten the bolts to 74 ft. lbs. (100 Nm) plus and additional 180°.

96. Raise the vehicle until the lift table can be removed from under the vehicle.

97. Remove the lift table.

98. Install the transaxle fluid cooler lines to the transaxle.

99. Install the transaxle fluid cooler bracket nut. Tighten the nut to 62 inch lbs. (7 Nm).

100. Connect the lower control arms to the steering knuckles. Refer to Lower Control Arm in Suspension.

101. Connect the intermediate shaft to the steering gear. Refer to Intermediate Shaft in Suspension.

102. Connect the outer tie rod ends to the steering knuckles. Refer to Tie Rod Ends in Steering.

103. Connect the control links to the stabilizer bar. Refer to Stabilizer Bar in Suspension.

104. Lower the vehicle.

105. Install the transaxle mount to transaxle bolts. Tighten the bolts to 33 ft. lbs. (45 Nm).

106. Install the engine mount.

107. Remove the blocks of wood from between the powertrain and the frame.

108. Install the catalytic converter.

109. Lower the vehicle.

➡**Ensure that the black cable is installed in the top notch of the transaxle bracket and the white cable**

is installed in the bottom notch of the transaxle bracket.

110. If equipped with a manual transaxle:
   a. Install the range selector and shift lever cables to the transaxle bracket.
   b. Connect the range selector and shift lever cables to the transaxle levers.

111. If equipped with an automatic transaxle:
   a. Install the range selector lever cable to the transaxle bracket.
   b. Connect the range selector lever cable to the transaxle lever.

112. Gather all engine harness branches and position the harness over the engine.

113. If equipped with a manual transaxle, perform the following steps:
   a. Install the HO2S clips to the engine brackets.
   b. Connect the engine harness electrical connectors to the HO2S.
   c. Install the HO2S CPA retainers.

114. Connect the engine harness electrical connector to the backup lamp switch.

115. Connect the engine harness electrical connector to the VSS.

116. If equipped with an automatic transaxle, perform the following steps:
   a. Connect the engine harness electrical connector to the park neutral position switch.
   b. Install the engine harness clips to the thermostat housing and engine brackets.
   c. Connect the engine harness electrical connectors to the HO2S.
   d. Install the HO2S CPA retainers.

117. Connect the ECT sensor electrical connector.

118. If equipped with an automatic transaxle, connect the engine harness to the transaxle.

119. Raise the vehicle.

120. Install the engine harness lead terminal to the starter solenoid.

121. Install the engine harness to starter solenoid "S" terminal nut. Tighten the nut to 27 inch lbs. (3 Nm).

122. Install the engine harness terminal to the starter.

123. Install the positive battery cable terminal to the starter.

124. Install the positive/negative battery cable lead nut to the starter solenoid. Tighten the nut to 13 ft. lbs. (17 Nm).

125. Install the engine harness clip to the speed sensor.

126. Connect the engine harness electrical connector to the VSS.

127. Install the engine harness clip to the stud.

128. Install the engine harness clip nut to the engine stud. Tighten the nut to 37 ft. lbs. (50 Nm).

129. Lower the vehicle.

130. Reposition and install the A/C compressor. Tighten the bolts to 37 ft. lbs. (50 Nm).

131. Connect the engine harness electrical connector to the A/C compressor.

132. Connect the engine harness electrical connector to the A/C pressure switch.

133. Position the engine harness ground terminal to the engine block.

134. Install the engine harness ground bolt. Tighten the bolt to 18 ft. lbs. (25 Nm).

135. Connect the EVAP purge solenoid electrical connector.

136. Install the engine harness clip to the EVAP purge solenoid bracket.

137. Connect the following electrical connectors:
- Knock sensor
- CKP sensor
- Oil pressure sensor

138. Install the negative battery cable ground terminal to the stud.

139. Install the engine harness ground terminal to the stud.

140. Install the negative battery cable ground nut. Tighten the nut to 89 inch lbs. (10 Nm).

141. Install the engine harness clips to the camshaft cover.

142. Connect the intake and exhaust camshaft position actuator electrical connectors.

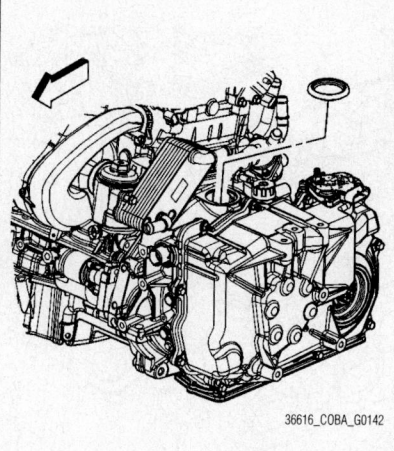

Fig. 110 Torque converter housing access plug location

143. Connect the ignition coils electrical connectors.

144. Connect the engine harness clips to the intake manifold.

145. Connect the engine harness clip to the oil level indicator tube.

146. Connect the following electrical connectors:
- TAC
- MAP sensor
- Fuel injector harness
- Alternator

147. Install the brake booster vacuum hose to the intake manifold.

148. Position the brake booster vacuum hose clamp at the intake manifold.

149. Install the heater inlet and outlet hoses to the thermostat housing.

150. Position the heater inlet and outlet hose clamps at the thermostat housing.

151. If the vehicle is not equipped with a engine oil cooler, perform the following steps:

   a. Install the surge tank outlet hose to the surge tank.

   b. Position the surge tank outlet hose clamp at the surge tank.

   c. Install the radiator outlet hose to the thermostat cover.

   d. Position the radiator outlet hose clamp at the thermostat cover.

152. If the vehicle is equipped with a engine oil cooler, perform the following steps:

   a. Install the radiator outlet hose to the oil cooler.

   b. Install the radiator outlet hose to the water outlet.

   c. Position the radiator outlet hose clamp at the oil cooler.

   d. Position the radiator outlet hose clamp at the water outlet.

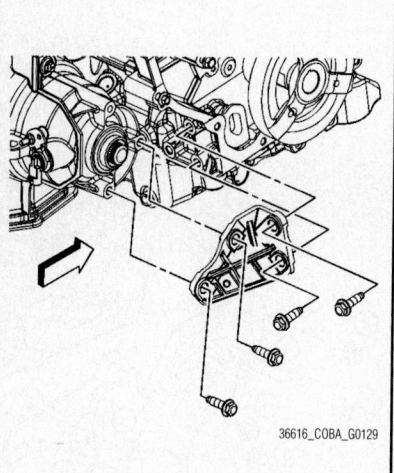

Fig. 111 Transaxle brace bolts and brace location

153. Install the radiator inlet hose to the engine.

154. Position the radiator inlet hose clamp at the engine.

155. Connect the cooling fan electrical connector.

156. Install the accessory drive belt. Refer to Accessory Drive Belt.

157. Remove the cooling module from the upper body structure.

158. Fill the cooling system.

159. Check and fill the transaxle fluid as needed.

160. Connect the EVAP line quick connect fitting to the EVAP purge solenoid.

161. Connect the fuel feed line quick connect fitting to the fuel rail.

162. Install the fuel line clips to the engine brackets.

163. Fill the engine with oil.

164. Connect the negative battery cable.

165. Road test the vehicle.

EXHAUST MANIFOLD

REMOVAL & INSTALLATION

2.0L Engine

See Figure 112.

1. Before servicing the vehicle, refer to the Precautions Section.

2. Remove the turbo charger. Refer to Turbocharger.

3. Remove the exhaust manifold heat shield.

4. Remove the exhaust manifold nuts and manifold.

5. Clean and inspect all gasket mating surfaces.

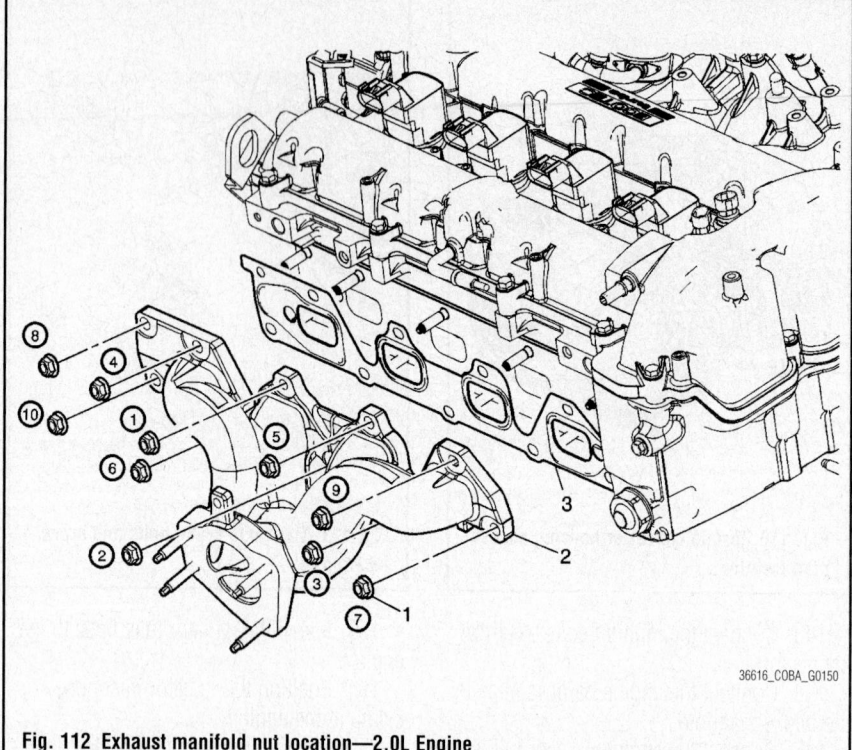

Fig. 112 Exhaust manifold nut location—2.0L Engine

To install:

6. Install new gasket.
7. Install exhaust manifold.
8. Install NEW exhaust manifold nuts.
9. Tighten nuts to 12 ft. lbs. (14 Nm).
10. Install heat shield.
11. Install turbocharger. Refer to Turbocharger.

2.2L & 2.4L Engines

See Figure 113.

1. Remove the intake manifold cover. Refer to Intake Manifold Cover Replacement.
2. If equipped with RPO NU3, remove the secondary air injection (AIR) check valve. Refer to Secondary Air Injection

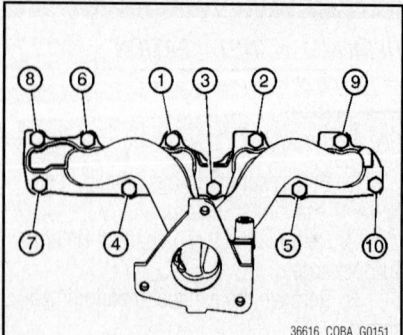

Fig. 113 Exhaust manifold nut tightening sequence—2.2L and 2.4L Engines

Check Valve in Engine Performance & Emission Controls.

3. Remove the exhaust manifold heat shield.
4. Remove the heated oxygen sensor (HO2S). Refer to Heated Oxygen Sensor in Engine Performance & Emission Controls.
5. Raise and support the vehicle.
6. Remove the catalytic converter assembly. Refer to Catalytic Converter.
7. Lower the vehicle.
8. Remove the exhaust manifold nuts.
9. Remove the exhaust manifold and discard the exhaust manifold gasket.
10. Clean and inspect all gasket mating surfaces.

To install:

11. Install a NEW exhaust manifold gasket onto the studs.
12. Install the exhaust manifold to the engine.
13. Install NEW exhaust manifold nuts and tighten the exhaust manifold nuts in sequence to 10 ft. lbs. (14 Nm).
14. Raise and support the vehicle.
15. Install the catalytic converter assembly. Refer to Catalytic Converter.
16. Lower the vehicle.
17. Install the heated oxygen sensor HO2S. Refer to Heated Oxygen Sensor in Engine Performance & Emission Controls.
18. If equipped, install the AIR check valve. Refer to Secondary Air Injection

Check Valve in Engine Performance & Emission Controls.

19. Install the intake manifold cover.
20. Inspect the exhaust system for leaks.

FLYWHEEL

REMOVAL & INSTALLATION

See Figures 114 and 115.

1. Before servicing the vehicle, refer to the Precautions Section.
2. Remove the transaxle:
   a. If automatic transaxle, refer to Automatic Transaxle Assembly in Drive Train.
   b. If manual transaxle, refer to Manual Transaxle Assembly in Drive Train.
3. Using the J 38122-A, hold the crankshaft damper.

➡ It may be necessary to remove the chamfer (bevel) from the edge of an 18mm socket in order to get full engagement on the thin-headed flywheel bolts.

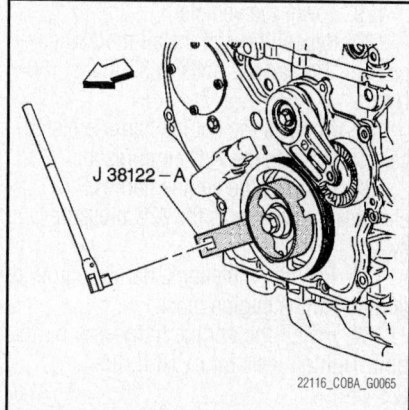

Fig. 114 Using tool J 38122-A to hold the crankshaft damper

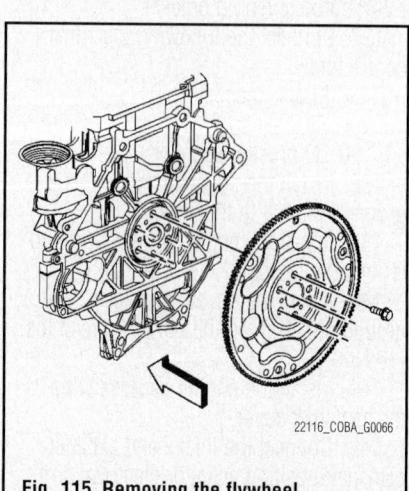

Fig. 115 Removing the flywheel

4. Remove and discard the flywheel bolts.

➡**Do not orientate the flywheel to the crankshaft. It is balanced separately from the engine.**

5. Remove the flywheel.

6. Clean the thread adhesive from the flywheel bolt holes. Use a nylon bristle brush to clean the holes in the crankshaft.

To install:

7. Install the flywheel.

8. Install the NEW flywheel bolts. Tighten the bolts to 39 ft. lbs. (53 Nm) plus an additional 25° using the J 45059.

9. Remove the J 38122-A tool from holding the crankshaft damper.

10. Install the transaxle:

    a. If automatic transaxle, refer to Automatic Transaxle Assembly in Drive Train.

    b. If manual transaxle, refer to Manual Transaxle Assembly in Drive Train.

FRAME

REMOVAL & INSTALLATION

See Figures 116 through 121.

1. With the wheels in the straight ahead position, remove the key from the ignition switch.

2. Secure the cooling module to the upper body structure.

3. Raise and support the vehicle.

4. Remove the front wheels from the vehicle.

5. Remove the left and right splash shields and the 3 screws in the inner fenders.

    a. Remove front wheelhouse liner fasteners.

    b. Remove rocker panel screws.

    c. Lift the fender liner from the rocker molding.

6. Remove engine splash shield retainer.

7. Remove the lower radiator air deflector from the frame.

8. Remove the front transaxle mount to frame through bolt.

9. Remove the rear transaxle mount to frame bolts.

10. Remove both stabilizer link to stabilizer shaft nuts. Refer to Stabilizer Bar in Suspension.

11. Remove both tie rod to steering knuckle nuts. Refer to Tie Rod Ends in Steering.

12. Use the J 24319-B to separate the outer tie rods from the steering knuckles.

13. Remove the intermediate steering shaft to steering gear pinch bolt and

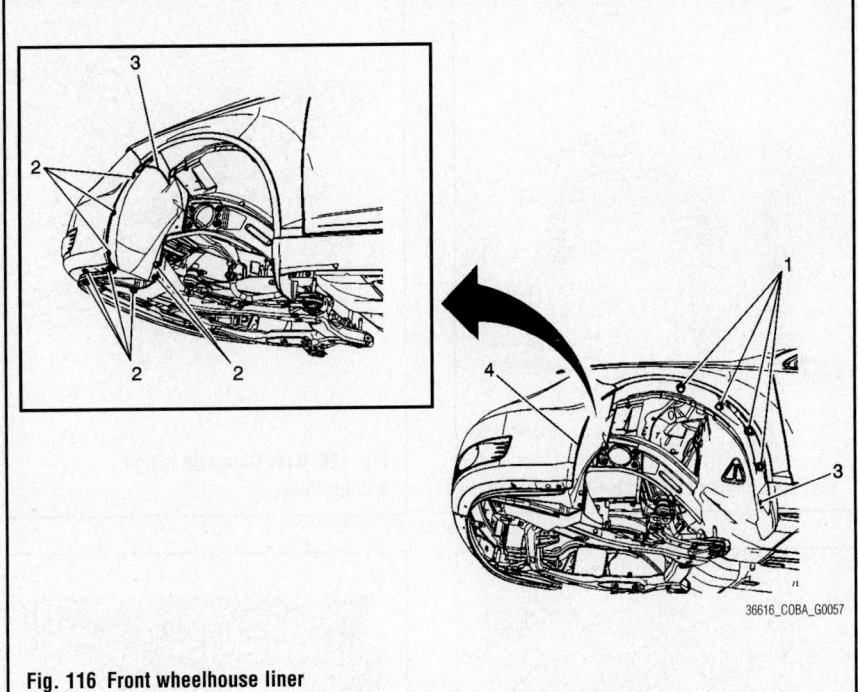

Fig. 116 Front wheelhouse liner

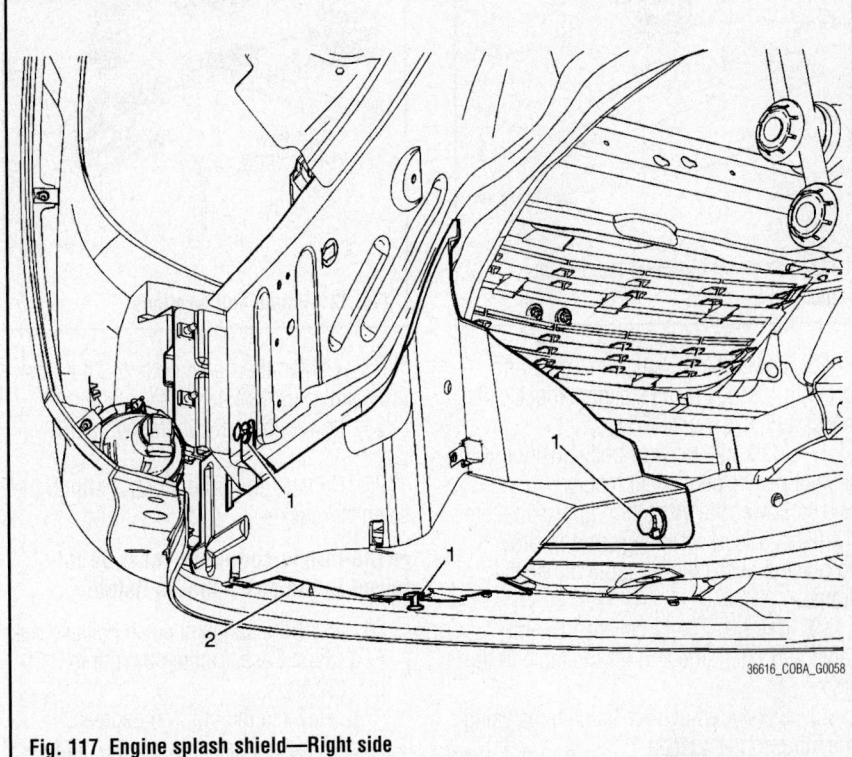

Fig. 117 Engine splash shield—Right side

discard. Refer to Intermediate Shaft in Steering.

➡**DO NOT rotate the intermediate shaft once separated from the gear. Possible damage or a malfunction could occur.**

14. Disconnect the intermediate steering shaft from the steering gear.

15. Remove both lower control arm ball

stud to steering knuckle pinch bolts. Refer to Lower Control Arm in Suspension.

✲✲ WARNING

Do not free the ball stud by using a pickle fork or a wedge-type tool. Damage to the seal or bushing may result.

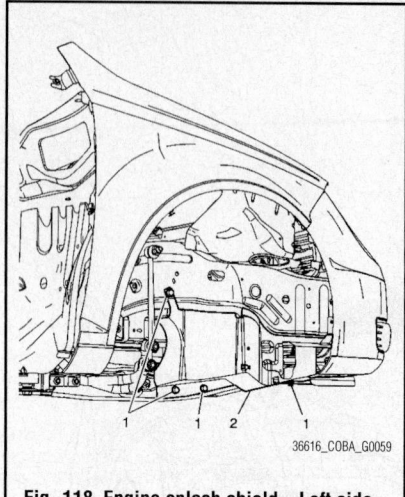

Fig. 118 Engine splash shield—Left side

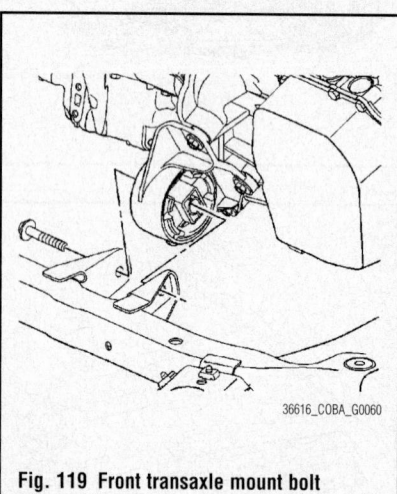

Fig. 119 Front transaxle mount bolt location

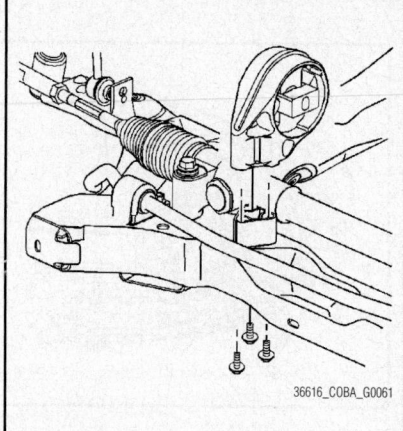

Fig. 120 Rear transaxle mount bolt location

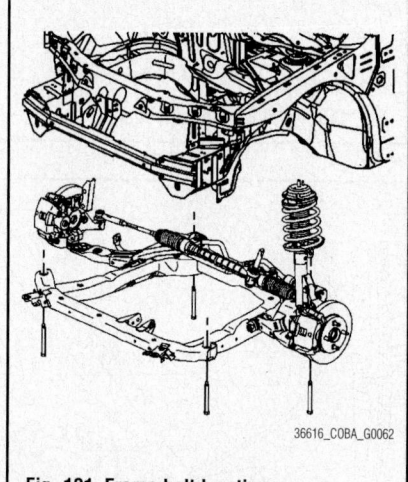

Fig. 121 Frame bolt locations

16. Lower the lower control arms in order to disengage the steering knuckle. If necessary, use the J43631.

17. Mark the frame to body position with a paint pen or permanent marker.

18. Lower the vehicle to approximately 1 meter (3 feet) off the ground in order to place a hydraulic lift table under the frame.

19. Use two 2 x 4s between the lift table and the frame and lift the table to the frame.

20. Slowly remove the frame bolts using the following sequence:
- Remove the front frame bolts.
- Remove the rear frame bolts.
- Slowly lower the lift table and frame to the floor.

To install:

21. With the frame on the lift table, raise the frame to the vehicle.

22. Hand start all the frame bolts while aligning the frame to the paint marks.

23. Tighten the frame bolts to 74 ft. lbs. (100 Nm) plus 180 degrees.

24. Lower and remove the hydraulic table.

25. Connect the lower control arm to the steering knuckle.

➡The torque sequence must be followed in the order that is listed.

26. Install the ball joint pinch bolt and nut.
a. First Pass: Tighten the nut to 37 ft. lbs. (50 Nm).
b. Reverse the nut 270 degrees.
c. Second Pass: Tighten the nut to 37 ft. lbs. (50 Nm) plus 30 degrees.

27. The front and rear transmission mounts must be allowed to settle with the through bolts loosened.

28. Hand start the front transaxle mount through bolt.

29. Loosen the rear transmission mount through bolt.

30. Tighten the rear transaxle mount to frame bolts to 37 ft. lbs. (50 Nm).

31. Tighten the front and rear transaxle mount through bolts in the following order.
a. Tighten the rear bolt to 74 ft. lbs. (100 Nm).
b. Tighten the front bolt to 74 ft. lbs. (100 Nm).

32. Install the outer tie rods to the steering knuckles.

33. Install the new outer tie rod to the knuckle nuts and tighten to 18 ft. lbs. (25 Nm) plus 90 degrees.

34. Connect the stabilizer links to the stabilizer shaft. Refer to Stabilizer Shaft Link Replacement.

35. Connect the intermediate shaft to the steering gear.

36. Install a new intermediate shaft pinch bolt and tighten to 25 ft. lbs. (34 Nm).

37. Install the left and right splash shields and the 3 inner fender screws, by reversing removal procedure.

38. Install the lower radiator air deflector to the frame.

39. Install the front wheels

40. Lower the vehicle.

41. Road test the vehicle in order to test for the following conditions:
a. Steering leads or pulls. Realign if necessary.
b. Abnormal powertrain noise or vibration at idle, if symptoms are present; Inspect the engine and transmission mounts for proper alignment and torque.

INTAKE MANIFOLD

REMOVAL & INSTALLATION

2.0L Engine

See Figures 122 through 126.

1. Disconnect the charge air cooler outlet pipe from the throttle body.

2. Remove the oil level indicator tube.

3. Disconnect the fuel feed line quick connect fitting to the fuel rail.

4. Disconnect the charge air valve solenoid vacuum lines.

5. Mark the lines to ease installation.

6. Disconnect the charge air valve solenoid vacuum electrical connector.

7. Disconnect the evaporative emission (EVAP) electrical connector from the EVAP purge solenoid.

8. Disconnect the evaporative emission (EVAP) line quick connect fitting from the EVAP purge solenoid.

9. Disconnect the manifold absolute pressure (MAP) sensor electrical connector.

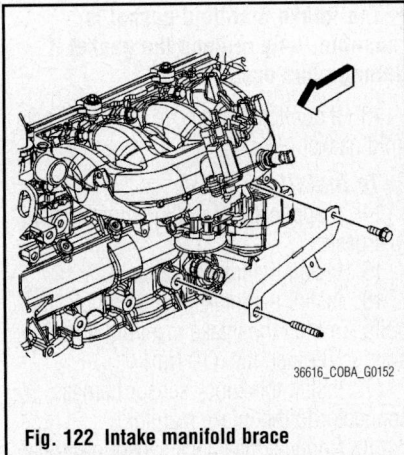

Fig. 122 Intake manifold brace

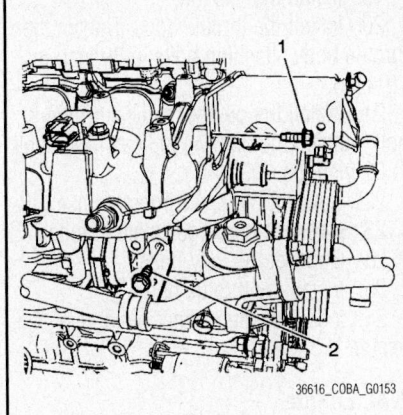

Fig. 123 Fuel pump and A/C pipe bracket bolt locations

Refer to Manifold Absolute Pressure sensor in Engine Performance & Emission Controls.

10. Reposition the brake booster vacuum hose clamp at the intake manifold.

11. Remove the brake booster hose from the intake manifold.

12. Remove the knock sensor electrical

connector clip from the intake manifold brace.

13. Disconnect the engine wiring harness electrical connector from the Throttle Actuator Control (TAC). Refer to Throttle Actuator Control module in Engine Performance & Emission Controls.

14. Remove the engine wiring harness clip from the intake manifold brace.

15. Reposition the surge tank air bleed hose clamp at the engine.

16. Reposition the surge tank air bleed hose out of the way.

17. Reposition the charge air bypass valve vacuum hose clamp at the intake manifold.

18. Remove the charge air bypass valve vacuum hose from the intake manifold.

19. Remove the charge air bypass valve solenoid bolts.

20. Reposition the charge air bypass valve solenoid assembly out of the way.

21. Disconnect the metal quick connect fitting from the fuel feed pipe.

22. Disconnect the fuel feed pipe fitting from the fuel pump.

23. Remove the fuel feed pipe bolts.

24. Remove the fuel feed pipe.

25. Inspect the fuel feed pipe nut for damaged threads.

26. Inspect the fuel feed pipe sealing bail for damage or debris.

27. Replace the fuel feed pipe if any damage is found.

28. Remove the charge air bypass valve vacuum tank.

29. Remove the intake manifold brace bolt.

30. Remove the intake manifold brace. Remove the fuel pump bracket bolt (1). Remove the A/C pipe bracket bolt (2) and reposition the bracket.

31. Remove the intake manifold nuts (1) and bolts (2).

32. Remove the intake manifold and place on a clean work surface.

33. Remove the intake manifold gasket and discard.

34. If replacing the intake manifold perform the following steps, otherwise proceed to step 2 in the installation procedure.

   a. Remove the MAP sensor bolts (1).

   b. Remove the MAP sensor (2), ensure that the O-ring seal (3) is still attached on the sensor, if not remove the O-ring seal from the intake manifold.

   c. Remove the EVAP purge solenoid bolt (6).

   d. Remove the EVAP purge solenoid (5), ensure that the O-ring seal (4) is still attached on the sensor, if not remove the O-ring seal from the intake manifold.

   e. Turn the intake manifold upside down.

   f. Remove the throttle body bolts.

   g. Remove the throttle body and seal.

To install:

35. If replacing the intake manifold perform the following steps, otherwise proceed to step 2.

   a. Inspect the throttle body seal and replace if necessary.

   b. Install the throttle body seal and position the throttle body.

   c. Install the throttle body bolts and tighten the bolts to 89 inch lbs. (10 Nm).

   d. Turn the intake manifold right side up.

   e. Inspect the EVAP purge solenoid and MAP sensor O-ring seals, replace if necessary.

   f. Ensure that the EVAP purge solenoid O-ring seal is installed on the EVAP purge solenoid.

   g. Install the EVAP purge solenoid and bolt and tighten the bolts to 89 inch lbs. (10 Nm).

   h. Ensure that the MAP sensor O-ring seal is installed on the MAP sensor.

   i. Install the MAP sensor and bolts and tighten the bolts to 89 inch lbs. (10 Nm).

36. Install a NEW intake manifold gasket.

37. Install the intake manifold to the studs.

38. Install the intake manifold nuts and bolts.

   • Tighten the bolts (2) to 18 ft. lbs. (25 Nm).

   • Tighten the nuts (1) to 15 ft. lbs. (20 Nm).

39. Install the fuel pump bracket bolt and tighten the bolt to 89 inch lbs. (10 Nm).

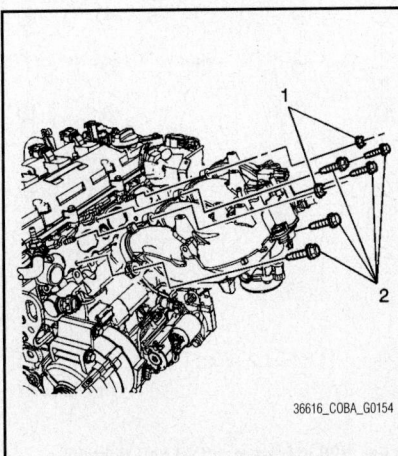

Fig. 124 Intake manifold bolt locations

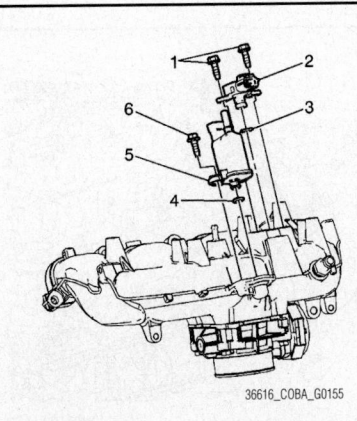

Fig. 125 Intake manifold component disassembly

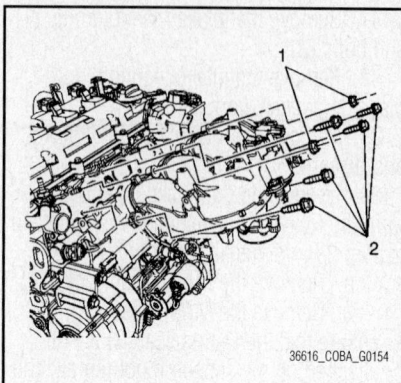

Fig. 126 Intake manifold bolt locations

40. Install the A/C pipe bracket bolt and tighten the bolt to 89 inch lbs. (10 Nm).

41. Install the intake manifold brace.

42. Loosely install the intake manifold brace bolt.

43. Tighten the intake manifold brace bolt and tighten the bolt to 16 ft lbs. (22 Nm).

44. Install the charge air bypass valve vacuum tank.

45. Lubricate the high pressure fuel pump fuel feed pipe connection threads with silicon free engine oil GM P/N 12345610 (Canadian P/N 993193) or equivalent.

46. Place the fuel feed pipe on top of the intake manifold.

47. Connect the fuel feed pipe fitting to the high pressure fuel pump.

48. Install the fuel feed pipe bolts and tighten the bolt to 89 inch lbs. (10 Nm) and the fittings to 22 ft. lbs. (30 Nm).

49. Connect the metal quick connect fitting to the fuel feed pip.

50. Position the charge air bypass valve solenoid assembly to the intake manifold.

51. Install the charge air bypass valve solenoid bolts and tighten the bolt to 89 inch lbs. (10 Nm).

52. Install the charge air bypass valve vacuum hose to the intake manifold.

53. Position the charge air bypass valve vacuum hose clamp at the intake manifold.

54. Position the surge tank air bleed hose to the engine.

55. Connect the engine wiring harness electrical connector to the TAC module.

56. Install the engine wiring harness clip to the intake manifold brace.

57. Install the knock sensor electrical connector clip to the intake manifold brace.

58. Install the brake booster hose to the intake manifold.

59. Position the brake booster vacuum hose clamp at the intake manifold.

60. Connect the EVAP line quick connect fitting to the EVAP purge solenoid.

61. Connect the charge air valve solenoid vacuum electrical connector.

62. Connect the charge air valve solenoid vacuum lines.

63. Connect the fuel feed line quick connect fitting to the fuel rail.

64. Install the oil level indicator tube.

65. Install the charge air cooler outlet pipe to the throttle body.

66. Install the air cleaner assembly. Refer to Air Cleaner Assembly.

2.2L Engine

See Figure 127.

1. Before servicing the vehicle, refer to the Precautions Section.

2. Remove the air cleaner outlet resonator.

3. Remove the throttle body. Refer to Throttle Body in Engine Performance & Emission Controls.

4. Disconnect the Positive Crankcase Ventilation (PCV) hose. Refer to Positive Crankcase Ventilation in Engine Performance & Emission Controls.

5. Disconnect the purge solenoid tube.

6. Disconnect the brake booster hose.

7. Remove the oil level indicator tube bolt.

8. Remove the fuel rail. Refer to Fuel Rail and Injectors in Fuel System.

9. Disconnect the knock sensor electrical connector. Refer to Knock Sensor in Engine Performance & Emission Controls.

10. Remove the knock sensor harness connector from the intake manifold.

11. Remove the intake manifold nuts and bolts.

12. Remove the intake manifold.

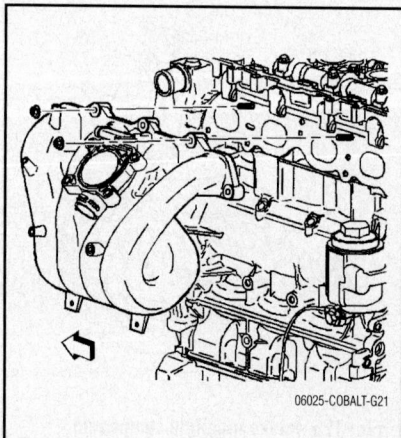

Fig. 127 Intake manifold—2.2L Engines

➡ **The intake manifold gasket is reusable, only replace the gasket if damage has occurred.**

13. If applicable, remove the intake manifold gasket.

To install:

14. If applicable, install the intake manifold gasket.

15. Install the intake manifold.

16. Install the intake manifold nuts and bolts. Tighten the intake manifold nuts and bolts to 89 inch lbs. (10 Nm).

17. Install the knock sensor harness connector to the intake manifold.

18. Connect the knock sensor electrical connector.

19. Install the fuel rail.

20. Install the throttle body. Tighten the throttle body attaching bolts to 89 inch lbs. (10 Nm).

21. Install the oil level indicator tube bolt. Tighten the oil level indicator tube bolt to 89 inch lbs. (10 Nm).

22. Connect the brake booster hose.

23. Connect the purge solenoid tube.

24. Connect the PCV hose.

25. Install the throttle body.

26. Install the air cleaner outlet resonator.

2.4L Engine

See Figure 128.

1. Before servicing the vehicle, refer to the Precautions Section.

➡ **Never attempt to remove the intake manifold from a hot engine, allow the engine to cool to ambient temperature. The intake manifold can be damaged if it is removed when the engine is hot.**

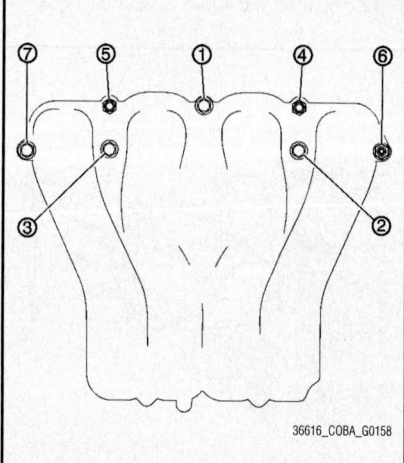

Fig. 128 Intake manifold bolt tightening sequence

2. Remove the evaporative emission (EVAP) canister valve tube.

3. Remove the EVAP canister valve.

4. Remove the throttle body bolts.

5. Remove the throttle body.

6. Remove fuel pipes and clip.

7. Remove the fuel rail assembly.

8. Remove the fuel injector tip insulators and discard.

9. Remove the intake manifold retaining nuts and bolts.

10. Remove the intake manifold.

11. Remove the intake manifold gasket, if necessary. The gasket can be used again if it is not damaged.

12. If the intake manifold needs to be replaced, transfer the throttle body to the new intake manifold.

To install:

13. Install the intake manifold studs in the manifold face and tighten the intake manifold studs to 53 inch lbs. (6 Nm).

14. Install a new intake manifold gasket on the intake manifold.

15. Install the intake manifold.

16. Install the intake manifold bolts and nuts finger tight.

Tighten the intake manifold bolts and nuts in sequence and tighten the bolts and nuts to 89 inch lbs. (10 Nm).

17. Lubricate NEW fuel injector tip insulators with engine oil.

18. Install NEW fuel injector tip insulators.

19. Lubricate the fuel injector oil rings with engine oil.

20. Install the fuel rail assembly.

21. Install the fuel rail stud and tighten the bolts to 89 inch lbs. (10 Nm).

22. Install a new throttle body gasket.

23. Install the throttle body.

24. Install the throttle body bolts and tighten the bolts to 89 inch lbs. (10 Nm).

25. Install the EVAP canister valve and tighten the bolts and nuts to 16 ft. lbs. (22 Nm).

26. Install the EVAP canister valve tube.

OIL PAN

REMOVAL & INSTALLATION

See Figures 129 through 131.

1. Install the engine support fixture.

2. Remove the engine mount.

3. Raise the engine enough to allow clearance for the oil pan removal.

4. Raise and support the vehicle.

5. Place a drain pan under the oil pan drain plug.

6. Remove the oil pan drain plug.

7. Drain the engine oil.

8. Remove the engine drive belt. Refer to Accessory Drive Belt.

9. Remove the lower A/C compressor bolt and loosen the upper bolts.

10. Remove the 4 oil pan to transaxle bolts (1).

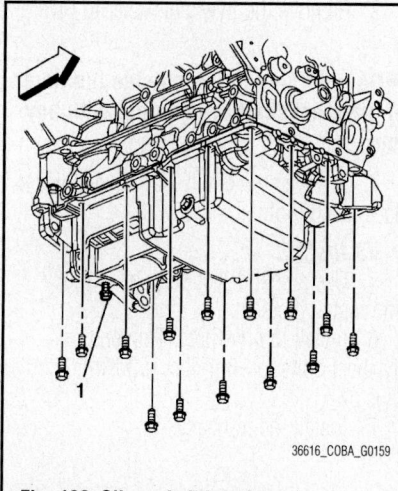
Fig. 129 Oil pan bolt location

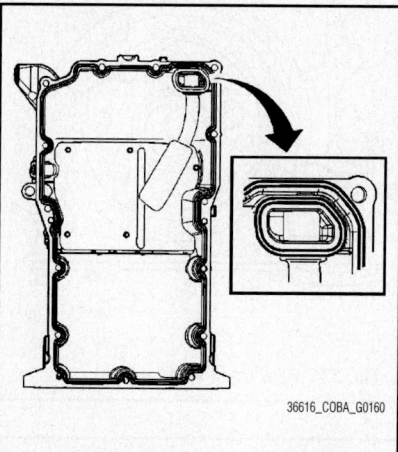
Fig. 130 Oil pan bolt sealant application

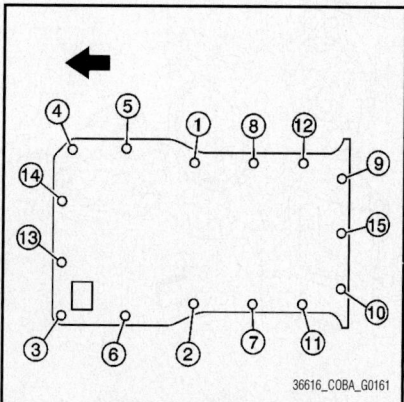
Fig. 131 Oil pan bolt tightening sequence

11. Remove the oil pan bolts.

12. Remove the oil pan

13. Remove any old oil pan sealant.

To install:

14. Make sure that the oil pan and mounting surface on the lower crankcase are free of all oil and debris.

15. Apply a 2 mm bead of GM P/N 123785251 (Canadian P/N 88901148) around the perimeter of the oil pan and the oil suction port opening. Do not over apply the RTV. More than a 2 mm bead is not required.

16. Install the oil pan.

17. Install the oil pan bolts in sequence. Tighten the oil pan bolts to 18 ft. lbs. (25 Nm).

18. Install the A/C compressor bolts. Tighten the bolts to 18 ft. lbs. (25 Nm).

19. Install the engine drive belt. Refer to Accessory Drive Belt.

20. Lower the vehicle.

21. Fill the engine oil to the proper level.

OIL PUMP

REMOVAL & INSTALLATION

See Figure 132.

1. Before servicing the vehicle, refer to the Precautions Section.

2. Remove the timing chain front cover. Refer to Timing Chain Cover and Seal Removal & Installation.

3. Disassemble the pressure relief valve.

4. Remove the oil pump gerotor cover and bolts.

To assemble:

5. Lubricate all oil pump parts with engine oil.

6. Install the inner gear into the outer gear.

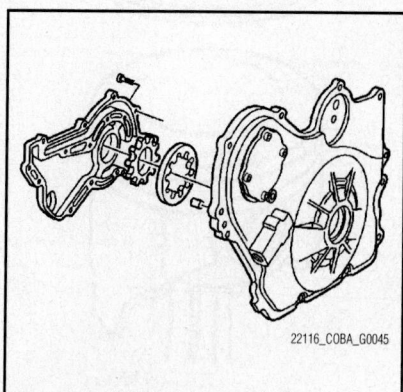
Fig. 132 Exploded view of the disassembled oil pump

✳✳ WARNING

If gears are improperly installed in the front cover, the gerotor cover will not bolt on.

7. Install the gears together into the front cover with the hub of the center gear facing the front cover.

8. Install the oil pump gerotor cover and bolts. Tighten the oil pump gerotor bolts to 53 inch lbs. (6 Nm).

9. Install the pressure relief valve piston.

10. Install the pressure relief valve spring. Tighten the pressure relief valve plug to 30 ft. lbs. (40 Nm).

11. Install the timing chain front cover. Refer to Timing Chain Cover and Seal Removal & Installation.

PISTON AND RING

POSITIONING

See Figure 133.

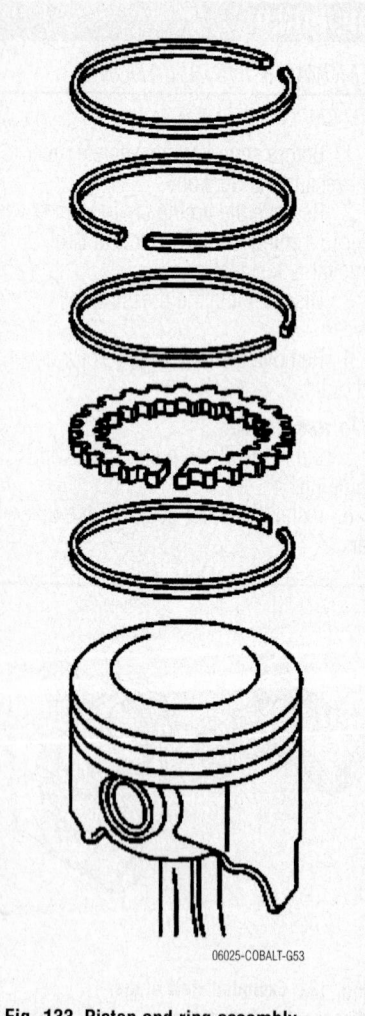

06025-COBALT-G53

Fig. 133 Piston and ring assembly

REAR MAIN SEAL

REMOVAL & INSTALLATION

See Figures 134 and 135.

1. Before servicing the vehicle, refer to the Precautions Section.

2. Remove the transaxle. Refer to Transaxle in Drive Train.

3. Remove the flywheel. Refer to Flywheel.

➡ **Do not damage the outside diameter of the crankshaft or chamber with any tool.**

4. Pry the crankshaft rear oil seal with a flat-bladed tool.

To install:

5. Use a seal driver such as J 42067 and install the seal.

6. Install the flywheel. Tighten the flywheel bolts to 39 ft. lbs. (53 Nm) plus 25°.

7. Install the transaxle.

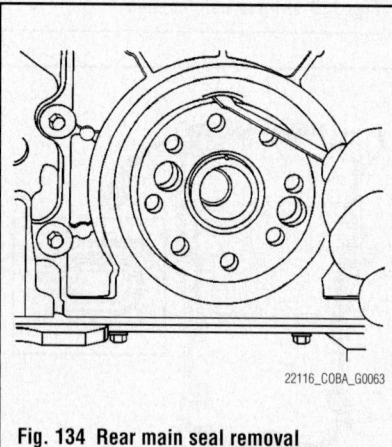

22116_COBA_G0063

Fig. 134 Rear main seal removal

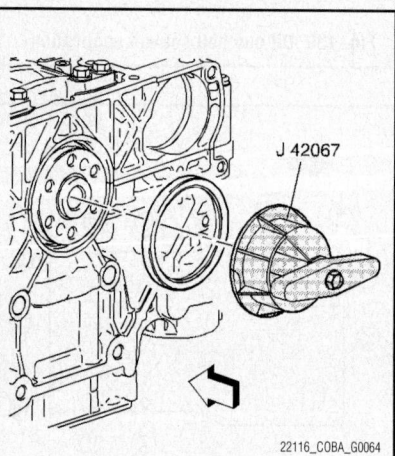

22116_COBA_G0064

Fig. 135 Rear main seal installation using tool J 42067

TIMING CHAIN COVER AND SEAL

REMOVAL & INSTALLATION

See Figures 136 through 144.

1. Before servicing the vehicle, refer to the Precautions Section.

2. Remove or disconnect the following:
- The drive belt tensioner
- The crankshaft damper
- The air cleaner assembly.
- The windshield washer solvent reservoir

3. Install the engine support fixture:

a. Place the engine support fixture legs (1) from the J 28467-B across the engine compartment.

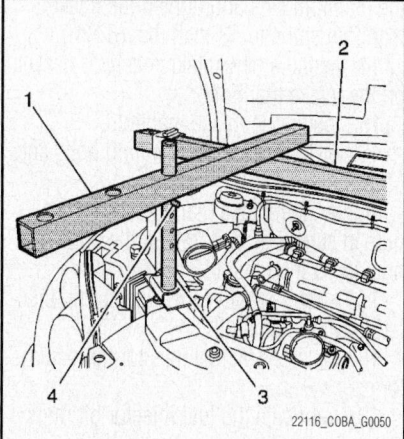

22116_COBA_G0050

Fig. 136 Place the engine support fixture legs (1) from the J 28467-B across the engine compartment and install the engine support fixture legs (1) from the J 28467-500 on the engine support fixture long bar.

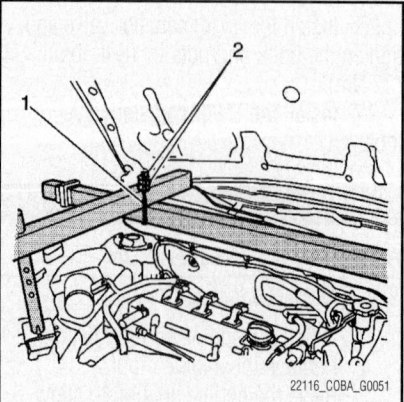

22116_COBA_G0051

Fig. 137 Install the J-28467-1A cross bracket assembly (1) and hand tighten the J-28467-1A cross bracket wing nuts (2).

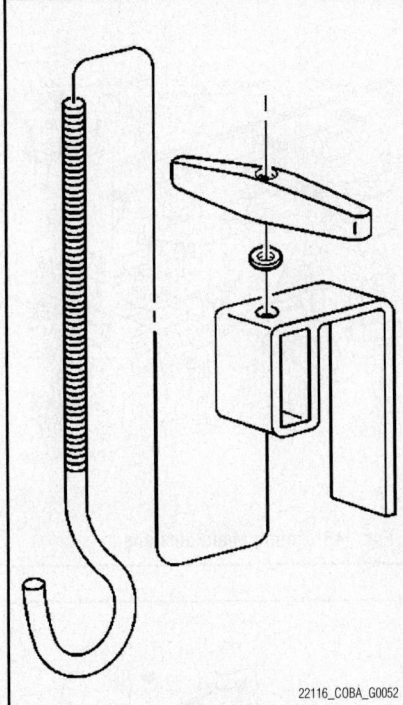

Fig. 138 View of the J-28467-7A bolt hook and the J-28467-34 lift hook wing nut and washer for installing the engine support fixture.

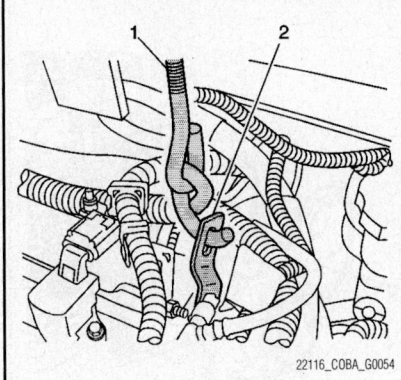

Fig. 140 Install the lift hook J-28467-7A through the engine rear lift bracket (2)

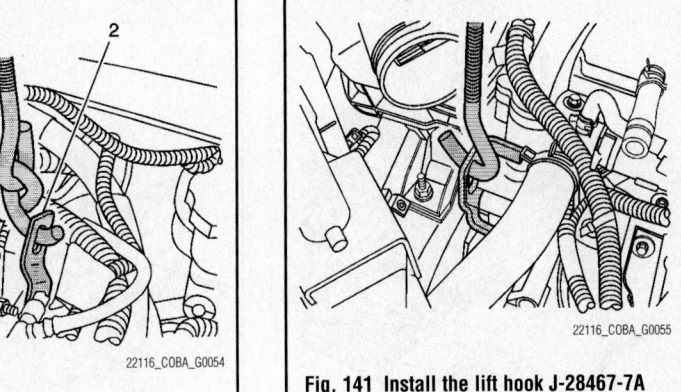

Fig. 141 Install the lift hook J-28467-7A (3) through the engine front lift bracket (4)

b. Install the engine support fixture legs (1) from the J 28467-500 on the engine support fixture long bar (2).

c. Install the radiator shelf tube J-28467-2A (1) on top of the strut tower tube J-28467-3 (2) above the engine front (right back) lift hook bracket.

d. Install the round tube of the front support assembly J-28467-4A (3) through the large hole in the radiator shelf tube J-28467-2A.

e. Position the J-28467-4A front support assembly on to the upper tie bar.

f. Install the J-28467-9 $7/16$ inch x 2.0 inch quick-release pin (4) through the top hole in the J-28467-4A front support assembly.

g. Install the J-28467-1A cross bracket assembly (1).

h. Hand tighten the J-28467-1A cross bracket wing nuts (2).

i. Install the J-28467-7A bolt hook through the J-28467-6A bracket.

j. Install the J-28467-34 lift hook wing nut and washer to the J-28467-7A lift hook.

k. Repeat the previous 2 steps in order to assemble 2 lift hooks and brackets.

l. Install one of the lift hook and bracket assemblies (1) to the engine support fixture long bar (2).

m. Install the other lift hook and bracket assembly (3) to the J-28467-2A radiator shelf tube (4) above the engine front lift bracket.

n. Install the lift hook J-28467-7A through the engine rear lift bracket (2).

o. Install the lift hook J-28467-7A (3) through the engine front lift bracket (4).

p. Hand tighten the lift hook wing nuts J-28467-34 in order to remove all slack from the engine support fixture assembly.

4. Remove or disconnect the following:
- The engine mount to bracket bolts
- The engine mount to side rail nuts
- The engine mount from the engine compartment
- The engine mount bracket to engine bolts
- The engine mount bracket
- The engine front cover to water pump bolt

5. Raise and suitably support the vehicle.

6. Remove the timing chain cover bolts.

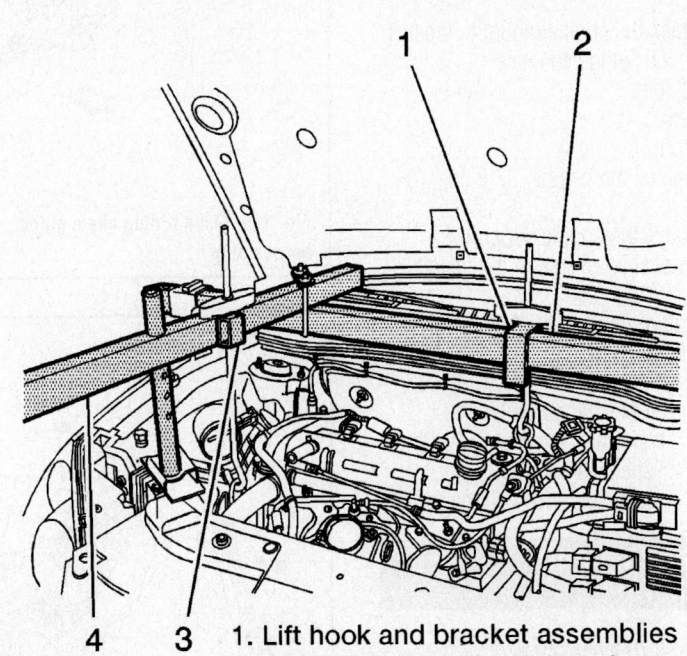

1. Lift hook and bracket assemblies
2. Engine support fixture long bar
3. Lift hook and bracket assembly
4. J-28467-2A radiator shelf tube

Fig. 139 Installing lift hook and bracket assemblies to the engine support fixture long bar, lift hook, and bracket assembly to the J-28467-2A radiator shelf tube.

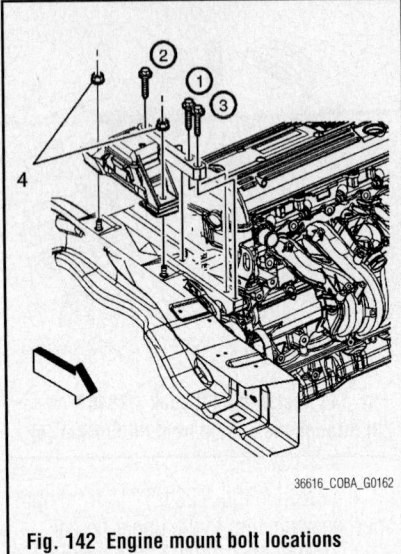

Fig. 142 Engine mount bolt locations

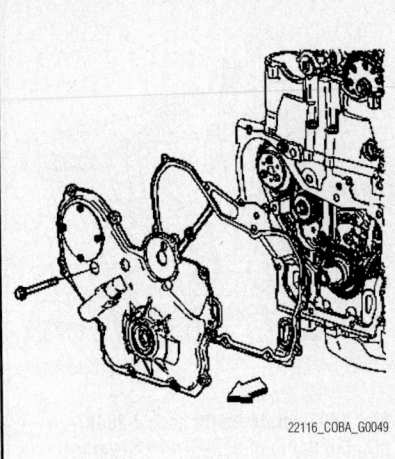

Fig. 144 Removing long water pump bolt and remaining cover bolts

Fig. 145 Timing chain tensioner

7. Remove the timing chain cover.

8. Remove and discard the timing chain cover seal.

To install:

9. Install a NEW timing chain cover seal.

10. Install the timing chain cover.

11. Install the timing chain cover bolts. Tighten the bolts to 18 ft. lbs. (25 Nm).

12. Lower the vehicle.

13. Install the timing chain cover to water pump bolt. Tighten the bolt to 18 ft. lbs. (25 Nm).

14. Position the engine mount bracket to the engine.

15. Install the engine mount bracket bolts in the following locations:

    a. The long bolts in the forward and lower rear holes.

    b. The short bolt in the upper rear hole.

16. Tighten the engine mount bracket bolts in the following sequence:

    a. Upper rear

    b. Lower rear

    c. Forward

    d. Tighten the bolts to 37 ft. lbs. (50 Nm).

17. Install the engine mount to the engine compartment.

18. Install the engine mount to side rail nuts. Tighten the nuts to 74 ft. lbs. (100 Nm).

19. Install the engine mount to bracket bolts.

20. Tighten the engine mount to bracket bolts in the following sequence:

    a. Middle.

    b. Rear.

    c. Front.

    d. Tighten the bolts to 37 ft. lbs. (50 Nm).

21. Remove the engine support fixture. Removal is reverse of the installation.

22. Install or connect the following:

- The windshield washer solvent reservoir
- The air cleaner assembly
- The crankshaft damper. Refer to Crankshaft Damper.
- The accessory drive belt tensioner

TIMING CHAIN AND SPROCKETS

REMOVAL & INSTALLATION

2.0L Engine

See Figures 145 through 158.

1. Before servicing the vehicle, refer to the Precautions Section.

2. Remove the camshaft cover.

3. Raise and support the vehicle.

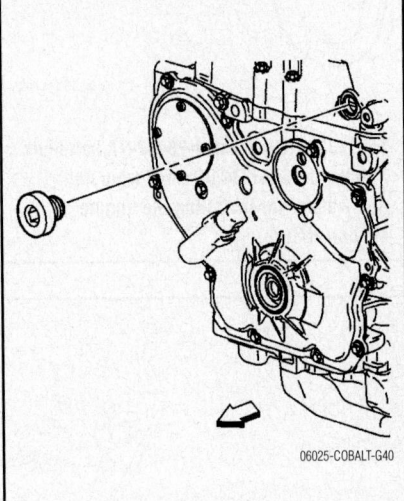

Fig. 146 Fixed timing chain guide access plug

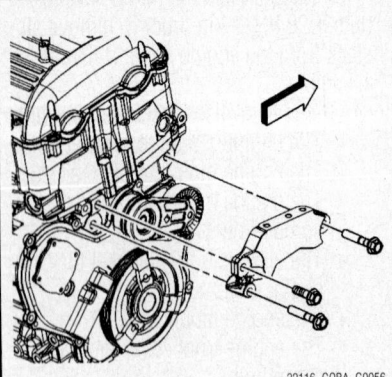

Fig. 143 Removing the engine mount bracket to engine bolts

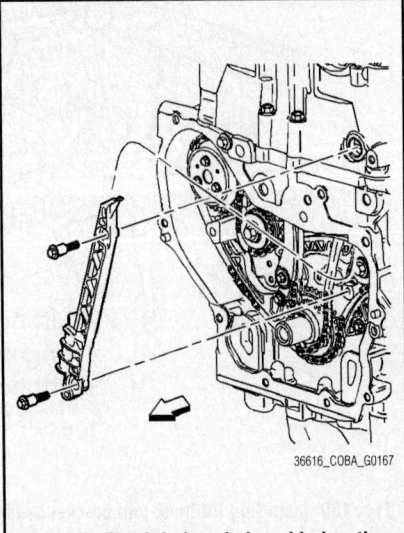

Fig. 147 Fixed timing chain guide location

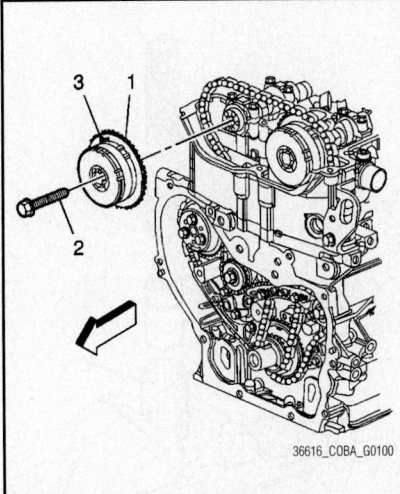

Fig. 148 Exhaust camshaft actuator location

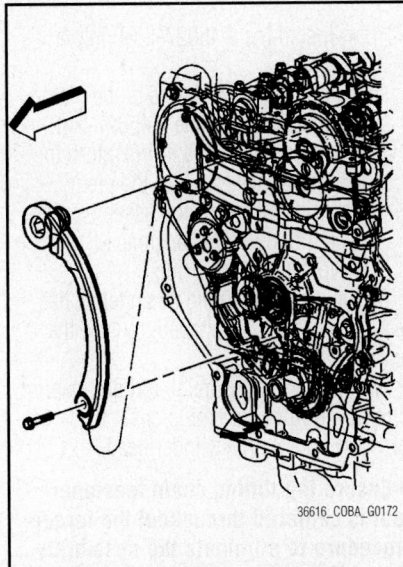

Fig. 149 Timing chain tensioner guide

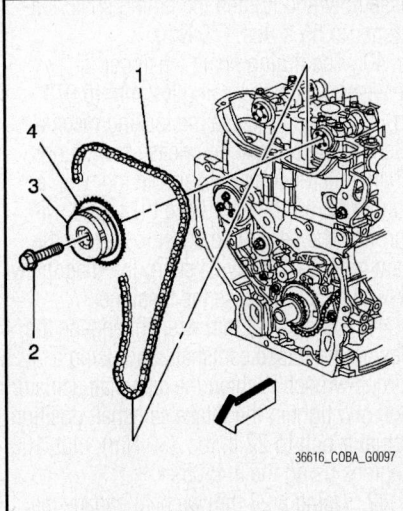

Fig. 150 Intake camshaft actuator location

4. Remove the timing chain cover. Refer to Timing Chain Cover & Seal.
5. Lower the vehicle.

➡ **To rotate the camshaft, use a 24 mm open-end wrench on the camshaft flats. Camshaft should be rotated in a clockwise direction only, facing camshaft sprockets from the passenger side of the vehicle.**

6. Locate the No. 1 piston to top dead center.
7. Remove the spark plugs. This will ease the rotation effort.
8. Remove the timing chain tensioner.
9. Remove the fixed timing chain guide access plug.
10. Remove the fixed timing chain guide.
11. Remove the upper timing chain guide.
12. Use a 24mm wrench to hold the camshafts from turning.
13. Remove the exhaust camshaft actuator bolt and discard.
14. Remove the exhaust camshaft actuator.
15. Remove the timing chain tensioner guide.
16. Remove the intake camshaft actuator bolt and discard.
17. Remove the intake camshaft actuator.
18. Remove the timing chain through the top of the cylinder head.
19. Remove the crankshaft sprocket.

To install:
20. Ensure the intake camshaft notch is in the 5 o'clock position (2) and the exhaust camshaft notch is in the 7 o'clock position (1). The number 1 piston should be at top dead center (TDC), crankshaft key at 12 o'clock.
21. Install the timing chain drive sprocket to the crankshaft with the timing mark in the 5 o'clock position and the front of the sprocket facing out.

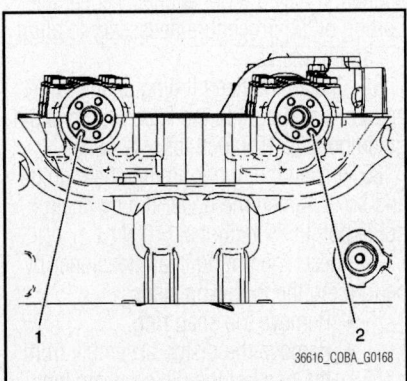

Fig. 151 Camshaft notch positioning

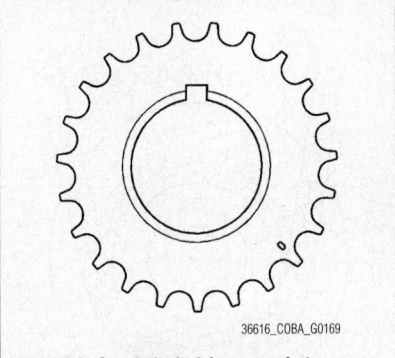

Fig. 152 Crankshaft drive sprocket positioning

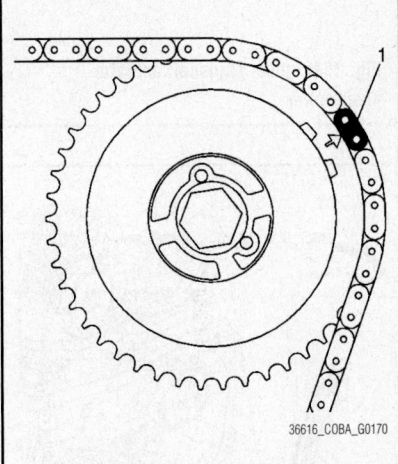

Fig. 153 Intake camshaft actuator positioning

➡ **There are 3 colored links on the timing chain. 2 links are of matching color, and 1 link is of a unique color. Use the following procedure to line up the links with the actuators. Orient the chain so that the colored links are visible.**

➡ **Always use new actuator bolts.**

22. Assemble the intake camshaft actuator into the timing chain with the timing mark lined up with the uniquely colored link (1).
23. Lower the timing chain through the opening in the cylinder head. Use care to ensure that the chain goes around both sides of the cylinder block bosses.
24. Install the intake camshaft actuator onto the intake camshaft while aligning the dowel pin into the camshaft slot.
25. Hand tighten the new intake camshaft actuator bolt.
26. Route the timing chain around the crankshaft sprocket and line up the first matching colored link with the timing mark on the crankshaft sprocket, in approximately the 5 o'clock position.

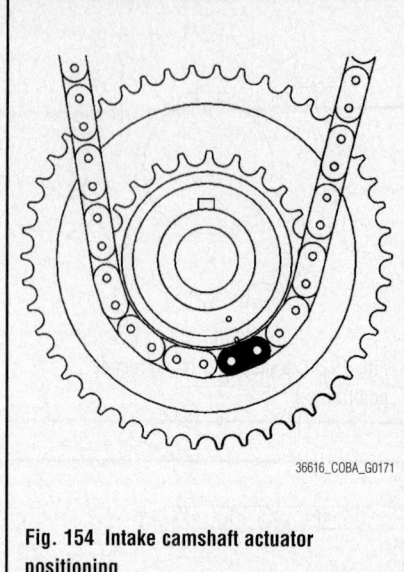

Fig. 154 Intake camshaft actuator positioning

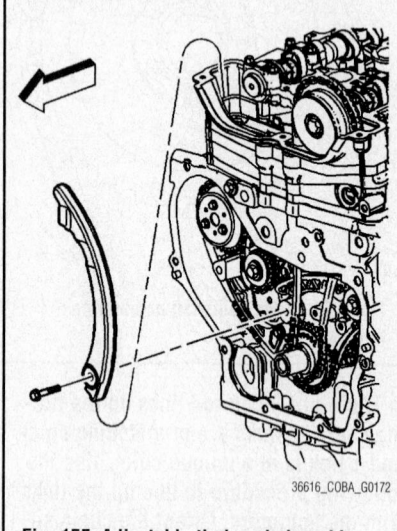

Fig. 155 Adjustable timing chain guide positioning

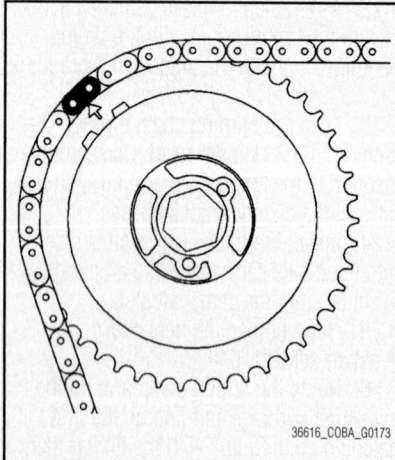

Fig. 156 Exhaust camshaft actuator positioning

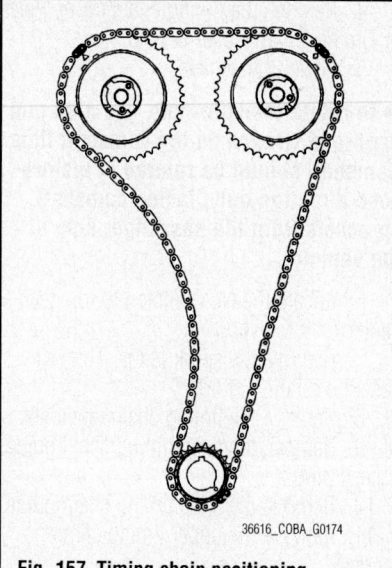

Fig. 157 Timing chain positioning

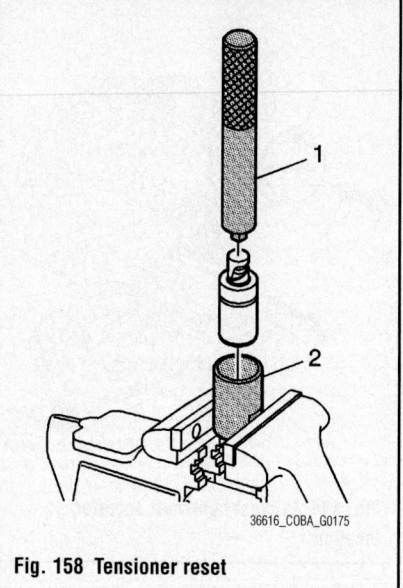

Fig. 158 Tensioner reset

27. Rotate the crankshaft clockwise to remove all chain slack. Do not rotate the intake camshaft.

28. Install the adjustable timing chain guide down through the opening in the cylinder head and install the adjustable timing chain bolt and tighten the adjustable timing chain guide bolt to 89 inch lbs. (10 Nm).

29. Install the exhaust camshaft actuator into the timing chain with the timing mark lined up with the second matching colored link.

30. Install the exhaust camshaft actuator onto the exhaust camshaft, aligning the dowel pin into the camshaft slot.

31. Using a 23 mm open end wrench, rotate the exhaust camshaft approximately 45 degrees until the dowel pin in the camshaft actuator goes into the camshaft slot.

32. When the actuator seats on the cam, tighten the new exhaust camshaft actuator bolt hand tight.

33. Verify that all of the colored links and the appropriate timing marks are still aligned. If they are not aligned, repeat the portion of the procedure necessary to align the timing marks.

34. Install the fixed timing chain guide and bolts and tighten the fixed timing chain guide bolts to 106 inch lbs. (12 Nm).

35. Install the upper timing chain guide and bolts tighten the upper timing chain guide bolt to 89 inch lbs. (10 Nm).

36. Reset the timing chain tensioner by performing the following steps:
- Remove the snap ring.
- Remove the piston assembly from the body of the timing chain tensioner.

- Install the J 45027-2 (2) into a vise.
- Install the notch end of the piston assembly into the J 45027-2 (2).
- Using the J 45027-1 (1), turn the ratchet cylinder into the piston.
- Reinstall the piston assembly into the body of the tensioner.
- Install the snap ring.

37. Inspect the timing chain tensioner seal for damage. If damaged, replace the seal.

38. Inspect to ensure all dirt and debris is removed from the timing chain tensioner threaded hole in the cylinder head.

➡**Ensure the timing chain tensioner seal is centered throughout the torque procedure to eliminate the possibility of an oil leak.**

39. Install the timing chain tensioner assembly and tighten the timing chain tensioner to 55 ft. lbs. (75 Nm).

40. The timing chain tensioner is released by compressing it 2 mm (0.079 in), which will release the locking mechanism in the ratchet. To release the timing chain tensioner, use a suitable tool with a rubber tip on the end. Feed the tool down through the cam drive chest to rest on the cam chain. Then give a sharp jolt diagonally downwards to release the tensioner.

41. Using a 23 mm wrench, engage the hex on the intake camshaft, and using a torque wrench, tighten the camshaft actuator bolt and tighten the intake camshaft position actuator bolt to 22 ft. lbs. (30 Nm), plus 100 degrees using the J 45059.

42. Using a 23 mm wrench, engage the hex on the exhaust camshaft, and using a

torque wrench, tighten the camshaft actuator bolt and tighten the intake camshaft position actuator bolt to 22 ft. lbs. (30 Nm), plus 100 degrees using the J 45059.

43. Install the camshaft cover.
44. Raise the vehicle.
45. Install the engine front cover. Refer to Timing Chain Cover and Seal.
46. Lower the vehicle.

2.2L & 2.4L Engines

See Figures 159 through 166.

1. Before servicing the vehicle, refer to the Precautions Section.
2. Remove the camshaft cover.
3. Raise and support the vehicle.
4. Remove the timing chain cover. Refer to Timing Chain Cover & Seal.
5. Lower the vehicle.

Fig. 159 Timing chain tensioner

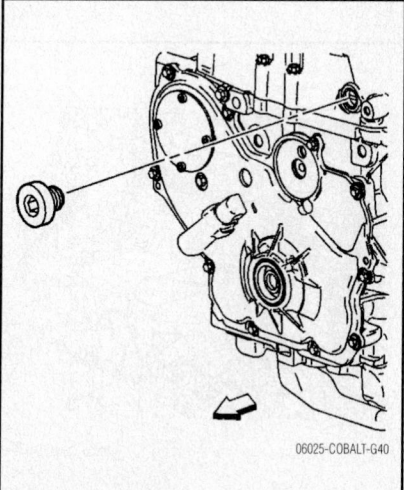

Fig. 160 Fixed timing chain guide access plug

➡To rotate the camshaft, use a 24 mm open-end wrench on the camshaft flats. Camshaft should be rotated in a clockwise direction only, facing camshaft sprockets from the passenger side of the vehicle.

6. Locate the No. 1 piston to top dead center.
7. Remove the spark plugs. This will ease the rotation effort.
8. Remove the timing chain tensioner.
9. Remove the fixed timing chain guide access plug.
10. Remove the fixed timing chain guide.
11. Remove the upper timing chain guide.
12. Use a 24mm wrench to hold the camshafts from turning.
13. Remove the exhaust camshaft sprocket bolt and discard.
14. Remove the exhaust camshaft sprocket.
15. Remove the timing chain tensioner guide.
16. Remove the intake camshaft sprocket bolt and discard.
17. Remove the intake camshaft sprocket.
18. Remove the timing chain through the top of the cylinder head.
19. Remove the crankshaft sprocket.
20. Remove the oil nozzle and bolt.

To install:

21. Install the oil nozzle and bolt. Tighten the oil nozzle bolt to 89 inch lbs. (10 Nm).
22. Install the crankshaft sprocket with timing mark at the 5 o'clock position.
23. Lower the timing chain through the opening in the top of the cylinder head.

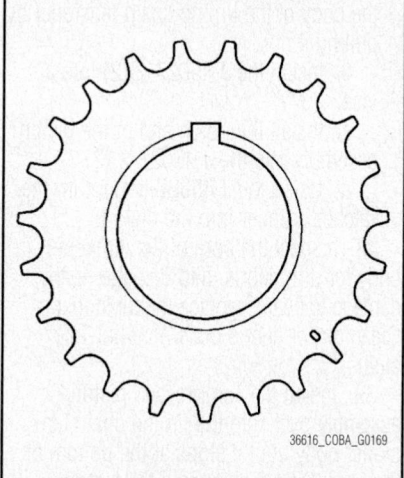

Fig. 161 Install the crankshaft sprocket with timing mark at the 5 o'clock position

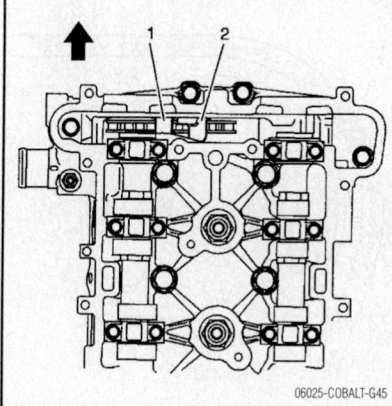

Fig. 162 Lower the timing chain through the opening in the top of the cylinder head. Carefully ensure that the chain goes around both sides of the cylinder block bosses (1, 2)

Carefully ensure that the chain goes around both sides of the cylinder block bosses (1, 2).

24. Install the intake camshaft sprocket with the INT diamond at the 2 o'clock position.

➡Always install NEW sprocket bolts.

25. Hand tighten a NEW intake camshaft sprocket bolt.
26. Route the timing chain around the crankshaft sprocket with the matching colored link aligning with the timing mark.
27. Route the timing chain around the intake camshaft sprocket with the uniquely colored link (1) aligning with the INT diamond.
28. Install the timing chain tensioner guide through the opening in the top of

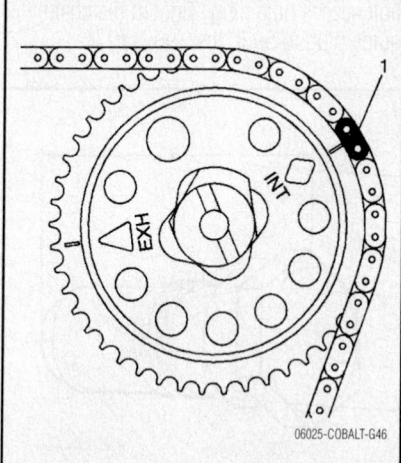

Fig. 163 Install the intake camshaft sprocket with the INT diamond at the 2 o'clock position

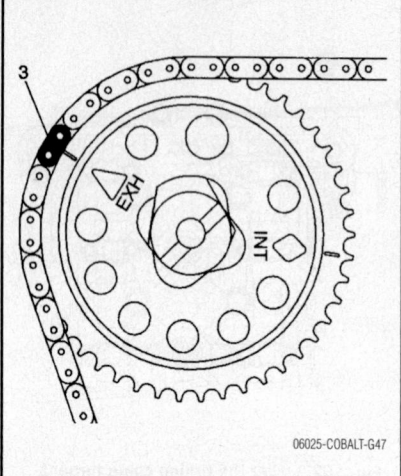

Fig. 164 Install the exhaust camshaft sprocket with the timing chain matching colored link (3) at EXH triangle aligned at the 10 o'clock position

the cylinder head. Tighten the timing chain tensioner guide bolt to 89 inch lbs. (10 Nm).

29. Install the exhaust camshaft sprocket with the timing chain matching colored link (3) at EXH triangle aligned at the 10 o'clock position.

30. Use a 24mm wrench to rotate the camshaft slightly, until exhaust sprocket aligns with the camshaft.

➡**Always install NEW sprocket bolts.**

31. Hand-tighten the NEW exhaust camshaft sprocket bolt.

32. Install the fixed timing chain guide. Tighten the fixed timing chain bolts to 89 inch lbs. (10 Nm).

33. Apply sealant, GM P/N 12378521 (Canadian P/N 88901148) compound to thread and install the timing chain guide bolt access hole plug. Tighten the chain guide plug to 59 ft. lbs. (90 Nm).

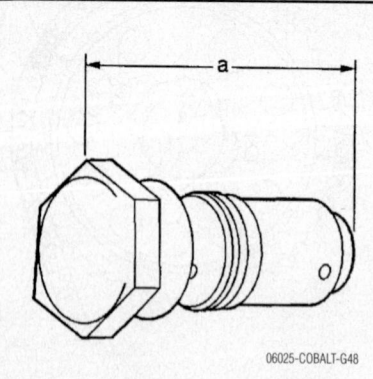

Fig. 165 Measure the timing chain tensioner assembly from end to end

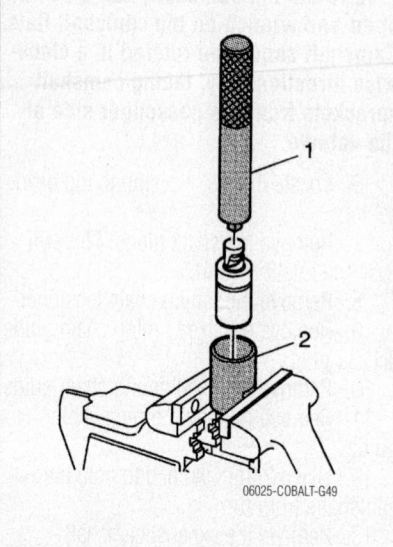

Fig. 166 Compressing the timing chain tensioner

34. Install the timing chain upper guide. Tighten the timing chain upper guide bolts to 89 inch lbs. (10 Nm).

35. Inspect the timing chain tensioner. If the timing chain tensioner, O-ring seal, or washer is damaged, replace the timing chain tensioner.

36. Measure the timing chain tensioner assembly from end to end. A new tensioner should be supplied in the fully compressed non-active state. A tensioner in the compressed state will measure approximately 3 inches (72mm) (a) from end to end. A tensioner in the active state will measure 3 5/16 inches (85mm) (a) from end to end.

37. If the timing chain tensioner is not in the compressed state, perform the following steps:

    a. Remove the piston assembly from the body of the timing chain tensioner by pulling it out.

    b. Install the J 45027-2 (2) into a vise.

    c. Install the notch end of the piston assembly into the J 45027-2 (2).

    d. Using the J 45027-1 (1), turn the ratchet cylinder into the piston.

38. Inspect the bore of the tensioner body for dirt, debris, and damage. If any damage appears, replace the tensioner. Clean dirt or debris out with a lint-free cloth.

39. Install the compressed piston assembly back into the timing chain tensioner body until it stops at the bottom of the bore. Do not compress the piston assembly against the bottom of the bore. If the piston assembly is compressed against

the bottom of the bore, it will activate the tensioner, which will then need to be reset again.

40. At this point the tensioner should measure approximately 3 inches (72mm) (a) from end to end. If the tensioner does not read approximately 3 inches (72mm) (a) from end to end repeat steps 26.1 through 26.4.

41. Install the timing chain tensioner. Tighten the timing chain tensioner to 55 ft. lbs. (75 Nm).

42. Use a suitable tool with a rubber tip on the end. Feed the tool down through the camshaft drive chain to rest on the timing chain. Then give a sharp jolt diagonally downwards to release the tensioner.

43. Use a 24mm wrench to hold the camshaft. Tighten the NEW camshaft bolts to 63 ft. lbs. (85 Nm) plus 30°.

44. Install the camshaft cover.

45. Raise the vehicle.

46. Install the engine front cover.

47. Lower the vehicle.

TURBOCHARGER

REMOVAL & INSTALLATION

See Figures 167 through 173.

1. Drain the cooling system.

2. Remove the charge air cooler inlet pipe.

3. Remove the air cleaner outlet duct.

4. Remove the charge air cooler pipe bolts at the turbocharger.

5. Remove the charge air cooler pipe from the turbocharger.

6. Remove the air conditioning (A/C) evaporator hose assembly.

7. Remove the A/C rear condenser tube.

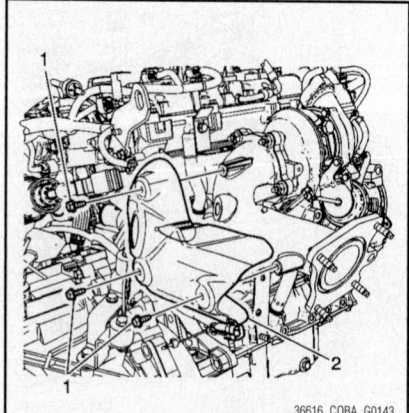

Fig. 167 Turbocharger exhaust pipe heat shield

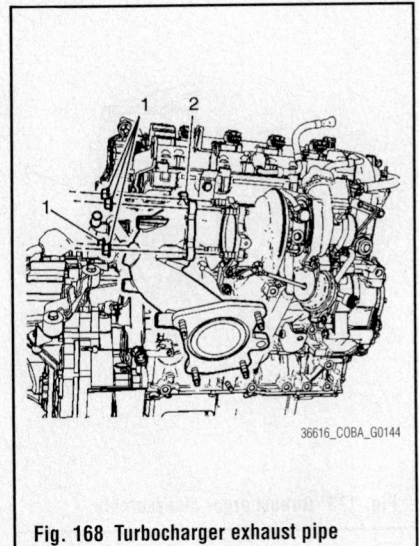

Fig. 168 Turbocharger exhaust pipe

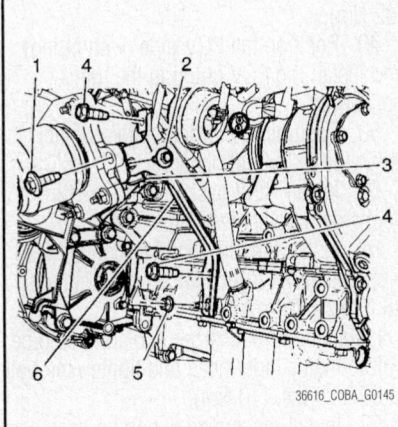

Fig. 169 Turbocharger brace and bracket bolt locations

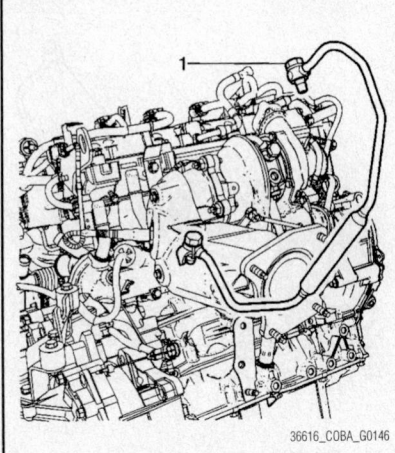

Fig. 170 Turbocharger oil feed pipe bolts and pipe locations

8. Remove the brake vacuum booster vacuum hose from the booster.

9. Unbolt the transmission shifter bracket from the transmission and leave cables attached and position aside.

10. Remove the turbocharger heat shield bolts and shield.

11. Remove the catalytic converter. Refer to Catalytic Converter.

12. Remove the heated oxygen sensor. Refer to Heated Oxygen Sensor in Engine Performance and Emission Control.

13. Remove the turbocharger exhaust pipe heat shield bolts (1).

14. Remove the turbocharger exhaust pipe heat shield (2).

15. Raise and support the vehicle. Remove the turbocharger exhaust pipe nuts (1).
Remove the turbocharger exhaust pipe (2).

16. Remove the turbocharger bracket bolt (1).

17. Remove the turbocharger bracket bolt (2) and bracket (3).

18. Remove the turbocharger brace bolts (4).

19. Remove the turbocharger brace nut (5) and brace (6).

20. Lower the vehicle.

21. Disconnect the engine wiring harness electrical connector from the turbocharger wastegate solenoid valve.

22. Reposition the vacuum hose clamp at the turbocharger.

23. Remove the vacuum hose from the turbocharger.

24. Remove the engine wiring harness clip from the turbocharger coolant feed pipe.

25. Remove the turbocharger coolant feed pipe bolt at the turbocharger.

26. Remove and discard the turbocharger coolant feed pipe gasket.

27. Remove the turbocharger coolant feed pipe bolt from the cylinder head.

28. Reposition the turbocharger coolant feed pipe out of the way.

29. Remove the positive crankcase ventilation (PCV) pipe from the turbocharger. Reposition the PCV pipe (with fitting) out of the way.

30. Remove the thermostat outlet housing and pipe. Refer to Thermostat in Engine Cooling.

➡ **Do not twist the turbocharger oil feed pipe. Twisting of the feed pipe will result in the collapse and deformation of the plastic pipe, restricting oil flow and causing turbocharger damage. During turbocharger replacement, gently push the oil feed pipe towards the front of the engine to clear the turbocharger. Assistance may be required to keep the pipes clear of the turbocharger during removal or installation.**

31. Remove the turbocharger oil feed pipe bolts and pipe (1).

32. Remove and discard the turbocharger oil feed pipe gaskets.

33. Remove the turbocharger coolant return pipe bolts and pipe (1).

34. Remove and discard the turbocharger coolant return pipe gaskets.

35. Remove the turbocharger nuts (2).

36. Remove the turbocharger from the exhaust manifold studs while also removing the turbocharger oil return hose from the engine block.

37. Remove and discard the turbocharger gasket (1) and oil return hose O-ring seal (3).

38. If replacing the turbocharger, perform the following steps otherwise proceed to the step 2 in the Installation Procedure.

a. Remove the turbocharger oil return hose bolts and hose from the turbocharger.

b. Remove and discard the turbocharger oil return hose gasket.

c. Reposition the vacuum hose clamps (1, 2, and 3) at the turbocharger wastegate solenoid valve.

d. Remove the vacuum hoses from the turbocharger wastegate solenoid valve.

e. Gently push back the turbocharger wastegate solenoid valve retainer (4) and remove the turbocharger wastegate solenoid valve from the bracket.

To install:

39. If replacing the turbocharger, perform the following steps otherwise proceed to step 7.

a. Install the turbocharger wastegate solenoid valve to the bracket until the retainer clips into place.

b. Install the vacuum hoses to the turbocharger wastegate solenoid valve.

c. Position the vacuum hose clamps at the turbocharger wastegate solenoid valve.

d. Position a NEW turbocharger oil return hose gasket on the turbocharger oil return hose.

e. Install the turbocharger oil return hose and bolts and tighten the bolts to 89 inch lbs. (10 Nm).

40. Install NEW gaskets onto the turbocharger coolant return pipe fittings.

41. Install the turbocharger coolant return pipe and bolts tighten the bolts to 26 ft. lbs. (35 Nm).

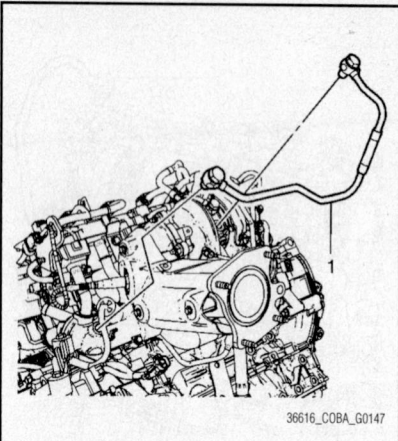

Fig. 171 Turbocharger coolant return pipe bolts and pipe locations

42. Install the thermostat outlet housing and pipe. Refer to Thermostat in Engine Cooling.

43. Install a NEW turbocharger gasket onto the exhaust manifold studs.

44. Lubricate and install a NEW turbocharger oil return hose O-ring seal.

45. Install the turbocharger oil return hose to the engine block while also installing the turbocharger to the exhaust manifold studs.

46. Install the turbocharger nuts and tighten the nuts to 26 ft. lbs. (35 Nm).

47. Install NEW gaskets onto the turbocharger oil feed pipe fittings.

48. Install the turbocharger oil feed pipe

and bolts and tighten the bolts to 24 ft. lbs. (32 Nm).

49. Position the PCV pipe (with fitting) and install the PCV fitting to the turbocharger.

50. Position the turbocharger coolant feed pipe to the turbocharger.

51. Install NEW gaskets onto the turbocharger coolant feed pipe fitting.

52. Install the turbocharger coolant feed pipe bolt at the turbocharger and tighten to 26 ft lbs. (35 Nm).

Install the turbocharger coolant feed pipe bolt to the cylinder head and tighten the bolt to 89 inch lbs. (10 Nm).

53. Install the engine wiring harness clip to the turbocharger coolant feed pipe.

54. Install the vacuum hose to the turbocharger.

55. Position the vacuum hose clamp at the turbocharger.

56. Connect the engine wiring harness electrical connector to the turbocharger wastegate solenoid valve.

57. Install the turbocharger brace and brace nut and tighten the nut to 37 ft. lbs. (50 Nm).

58. Install the turbocharger brace bolts and tighten the nut to 37 ft. lbs. (50 Nm).

59. Install the turbocharger bracket and bracket bolt and tighten the nut to 18 ft. lbs. (25 Nm).

60. Install the turbocharger bracket bolt and tighten to 18 ft. lbs. (25 Nm).

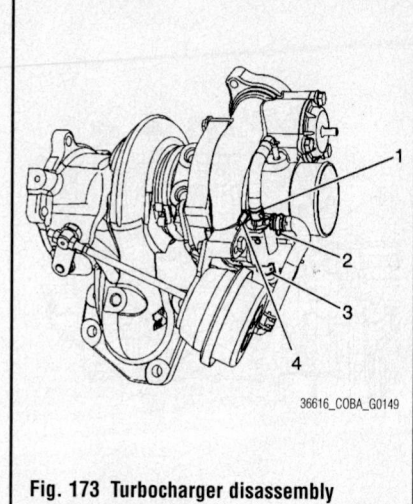

Fig. 173 Turbocharger disassembly

61. Install the turbocharger exhaust pipe.

62. Install the turbocharger exhaust pipe nuts and tighten to 37 ft. lbs. (50 Nm).

63. Install the turbocharger exhaust pipe heat shield.

64. Install the turbocharger exhaust pipe heat shield and tighten bolts to 89 inch lbs. (10 Nm).

65. Install the transmission shiftier bracket with the cables to the transmission.

66. Install the brake vacuum booster vacuum hose to the booster.

67. Install the A/C rear condenser tube.

68. Install the A/C evaporator hose assembly.

69. Raise and suitably support the vehicle.

70. Install the heated oxygen sensor.

71. Install the catalytic converter. Refer to Catalytic Converter.

72. Lower the vehicle.

73. Install the turbocharger heat shield and bolts and tighten bolts to 89 inch lbs. (10 Nm).

74. Install the charge air cooler pipe and gasket to the turbocharger.

75. Install the charge air cooler pipe bolts at the turbocharger and tighten the bolts to 16 ft. lbs. (22 Nm).

76. Install the air cleaner outlet duct.

77. Install the charge air cooler inlet pipe.

78. Fill the cooling system.

VALVE LASH

ADJUSTMENT

Valve lash is maintained by hydraulic valve lash adjusters.

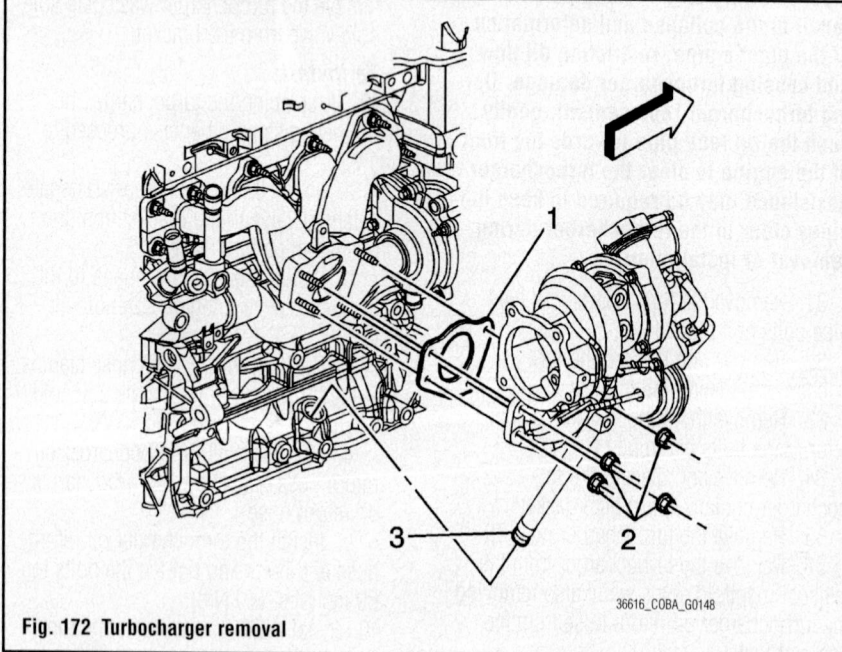

Fig. 172 Turbocharger removal

ENGINE PERFORMANCE & EMISSION CONTROLS

ACCELERATOR PEDAL POSITION (APP) SENSOR

LOCATION

See Figure 174.

REMOVAL & INSTALLATION

See Figure 174.

1. Disconnect the Connector Position Assurance (CPA) from the Accelerator Pedal Position (APP) sensor connector.

2. Disconnect the APP sensor harness connector.

3. Remove the APP assembly attachment bolts from the brake pedal assembly.

4. Remove the APP assembly from the vehicle.

To install:

5. Install the upper attachment bolt into the APP assembly.

6. Install the APP assembly into the vehicle.

7. Install the attachment bolts into the APP assembly. Tighten the APP assembly—to—brake bracket bolt to 80 inch lbs. (9 Nm).

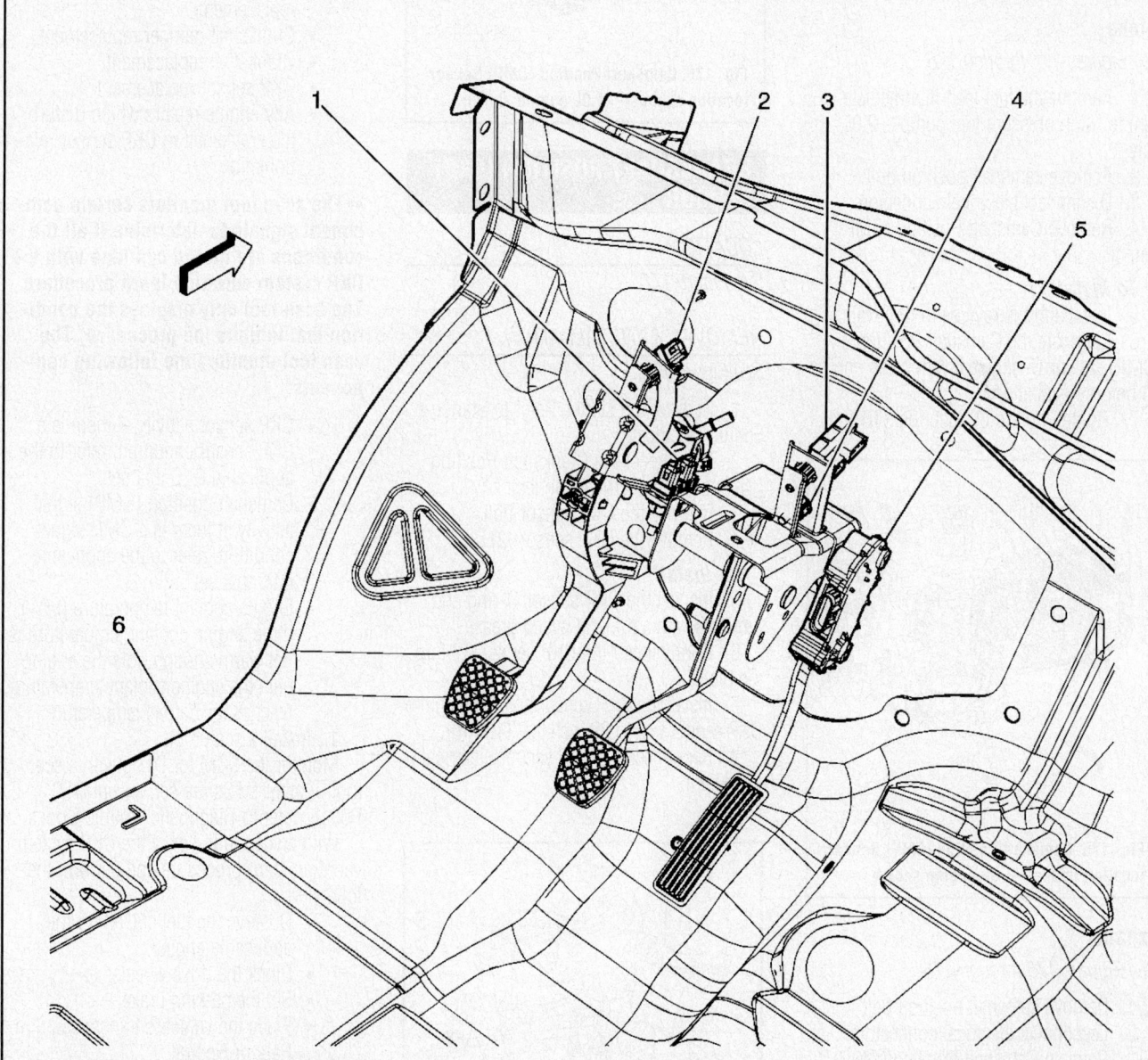

1. Clutch Pedal Position (CCP) Switch (M86)
2. Clutch Start Switch (M86)
3. Stop Lamp/TCC Switch
4. Cruise Control Cancel Switch
5. Accelerator Pedal Position (APP) Sensor
6. Floor Pan

22116_COBA_G0165

Fig. 174 Accelerator Pedal Position (APP) sensor and related components

8. Connect the APP sensor harness connector. Push the CPA connector in until the lock position is felt, then pull back to confirm engagement.

CAMSHAFT POSITION (CMP) SENSOR

LOCATION

See Figures 175 and 176.

REMOVAL & INSTALLATION

Intake

See Figures 175 through 176.

1. Remove the fuel feed intermediate pipe for high pressure fuel pump—2.0L only.
2. Remove camshaft position bolt.
3. Disconnect electrical connectors.
4. Remove Camshaft Position (CMP) sensor.

To install:

5. Installation is reverse of removal.
6. Lubricate the Camshaft Position (CMP) sensor O-ring seal with clean engine oil before installation.
7. Tighten bolt to 89 inch lbs. (10 Nm).

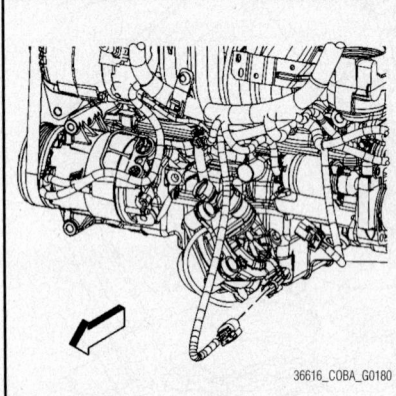

Fig. 175 Camshaft Position (CMP) Sensor location intake—2.0L engine shown

Exhaust

See Figures 175 through 176.

1. Remove camshaft position bolt.
2. Disconnect electrical connectors.
3. Remove Camshaft Position (CMP) sensor.

To install:

4. Installation is reverse of removal.
5. Lubricate the Camshaft Position (CMP) sensor O-ring seal with clean engine oil before installation.
6. Tighten bolt to 89 inch lbs. (10 Nm).

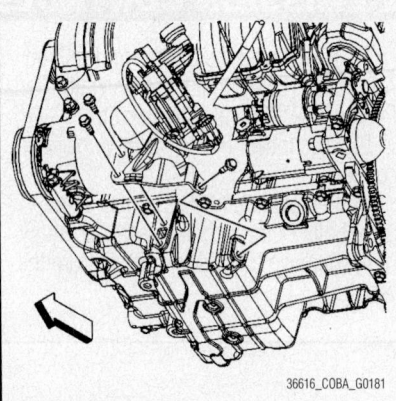

36616_COBA_G0181

Fig. 176 Camshaft Position (CMP) Sensor location exhaust—2.0L engine shown

CRANKSHAFT POSITION (CKP) SENSOR

LOCATION

See Figure 177.

REMOVAL & INSTALLATION

See Figure 177.

1. Remove the starter. Refer to Starter in Engine Electrical.
2. Disconnect the Crankshaft Position (CKP) sensor electrical connector.
3. Remove the CKP sensor bolt.
4. Remove the CKP sensor (2).

To install:

5. Inspect the CKP sensor O-ring and lubricate with a mineral based grease.
6. Gently insert the CKP sensor (2) into the block.
7. Install the CKP sensor bolt. Tighten the CKP sensor bolt to 89 inch lbs. (10 Nm).
8. Reconnect the CKP sensor electrical connector.

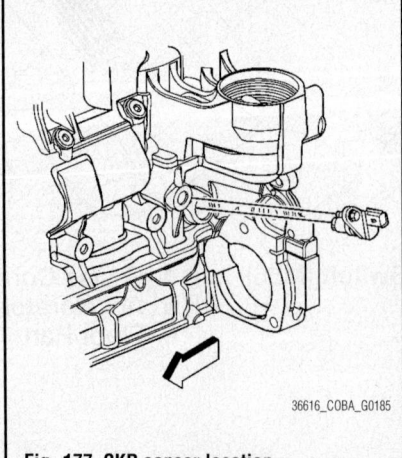

36616_COBA_G0185

Fig. 177 CKP sensor location

9. Install the starter. Tighten starter bolts to 37 ft. lbs. (50 Nm).

RELEARN PROCEDURE

➡The Crankshaft Position (CKP) system variation learn procedure is required when the following service procedures have been performed, regardless of whether DTC P0315 is set:

- Engine replacement
- Engine control module (ECM) replacement
- Crankshaft damper replacement
- Crankshaft replacement
- CKP sensor replacement
- Any engine repairs which disturb the crankshaft to CKP sensor relationship

➡The scan tool monitors certain component signals to determine if all the conditions are met to continue with the CKP system variation learn procedure. The scan tool only displays the condition that inhibits the procedure. The scan tool monitors the following components:

- CKP sensor activity, if there is a CKP sensor condition, refer to the applicable DTC that set.
- Camshaft position (CMP) signal activity, if there is a CMP signal condition, refer to the applicable DTC that set.
- Engine coolant temperature (ECT), if the engine coolant temperature is not warm enough, idle the engine until the engine coolant temperature reaches the correct temperature.

1. Install a scan tool.
Monitor the ECM for DTCs with a scan tool. If other DTCs are set, except DTC P0315, refer to Diagnostic Trouble Codes.

With a scan tool, select the CKP system variation learn procedure and perform the following:

- Observe the fuel cut-off for the applicable engine.
- Block the drive wheels.
- Set the parking brake.
- Place the vehicle's transmission in Park or Neutral.
- Turn the air conditioning (A/C) OFF.
- Cycle the ignition from OFF to ON.
- Apply and hold the brake pedal for the duration of the procedure.
- Start and idle the engine.
- Accelerate to wide open throttle (WOT). The engine should not

accelerate beyond the calibrated fuel cut-off RPM value noted in step 3.1. Release the throttle immediately if the value is exceeded.

➡️ While the learn procedure is in progress, release the throttle immediately when the engine starts to decelerate. The engine control is returned to the operator and the engine responds to throttle position after the learn procedure is complete.

• Release the throttle when fuel cut-off occurs.

2. The scan tool displays Learn Status: Learned this Ignition. If the scan tool indicates that DTC P0315 ran and passed, the CKP variation learn procedure is complete. If the scan tool indicates DTC P0315 failed or did not run, refer to DTC P0315 . If any other DTCs set, refer to Diagnostic Trouble Codes.

3. Turn OFF the ignition for 30 seconds after the learn procedure is completed successfully.

ELECTRONIC CONTROL MODULE (ECM)

LOCATION
See Figure 178.

REMOVAL & INSTALLATION
See Figure 178.

➡️ In order to prevent any possible electrostatic discharge damage to the ECM, do not touch the connector pins or the

soldered components on the circuit board. Always turn the ignition off when installing or removing the ECM connectors in order to prevent damage to the components. It is necessary to record the remaining engine oil life. If the replacement module is not programmed with the remaining engine oil life, the engine oil life will default to 100 percent. If the replacement module is not programmed with the remaining engine oil life, the engine oil will need to be changed at 5 000 km (3,000 mi) from the last oil change.

✳✳ CAUTION
Replacement or reprogramming of the ECM, or replacement of the clutch pedal position sensor (CPPS) or clutch pedal requires that a CPPS learn procedure be performed. Failure to perform the CPPS learn procedure may result in personal injury or damage to the vehicle or its components if the vehicle is in gear and the starter motor is accidentally engaged. Refer to Clutch Pedal Position Sensor Learn in Clutch.

➡️ Service of the ECM should normally consist of either replacement of the ECM or electrically erasable programmable read only memory (EEPROM) programming. If the diagnostic procedures call for ECM replacement, inspect the ECM first to see if the replacement is the correct part. If the ECM is faulty, remove the ECM and

install the new service ECM. The new service ECM will not be programmed. You must program the new ECM. DTC P0602 indicates the EEPROM is not programmed or has malfunctioned.

➡️ Replacement of the ECM requires a proprietary Service Programming System to reprogram.

1. Disconnect the negative battery cable.
2. Disconnect the electrical connectors.
3. Pull back the plastic locking tabs on both sides and lift straight up.

To install:
4. Installation is reverse of removal.
5. Reprogram ECM.

RESET
Replacement of the ECM requires a proprietary Service Programming System to reprogram.

ENGINE COOLANT TEMPERATURE (ECT) SENSOR

REMOVAL & INSTALLATION

✳✳ WARNING
Use care when handling the coolant sensor. Damage to the coolant sensor will affect the operation of the fuel control system.

1. Turn OFF the ignition.
2. Drain the coolant system to below the Engine Coolant Temperature (ECT) sensor.
3. Disconnect the ECT sensor electrical connector.
4. Carefully remove the ECT sensor.

To install:
5. If you are reinstalling the original sensor, or if you are installing a new sensor without a sealer, coat the threads with sealer GM P/N 12346004 (Canadian P/N 10953480) or Saturn P/N 21485278 or an equivalent.
6. Install the ECT sensor. Tighten the ECT sensor to 89 inch lbs. (10 Nm).
7. Connect the ECT sensor electrical connector.
8. Refill the engine coolant system.
9. Run the engine to normal operating temperature and check for leaks.

EVAPORATIVE EMISSIONS (EVAP) CANISTER

LOCATION
See Figure 179.

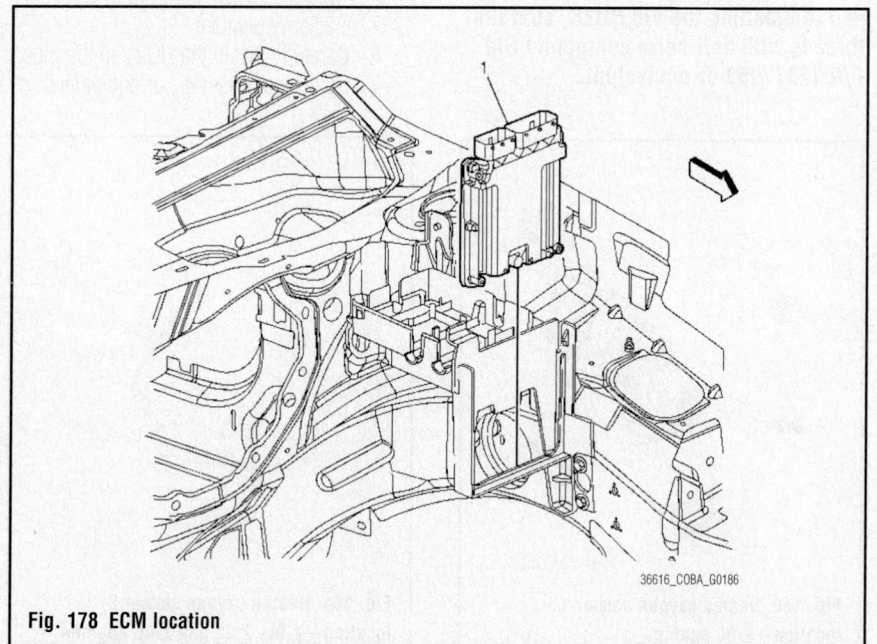
36616_COBA_G0186

Fig. 178 ECM location

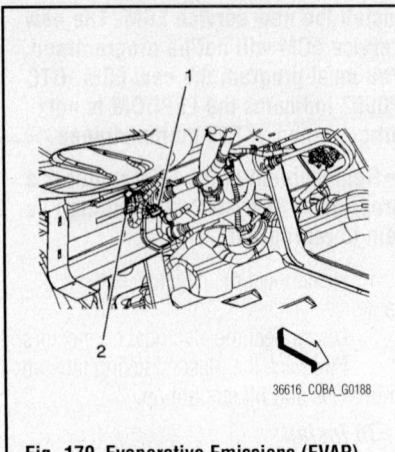

Fig. 179 Evaporative Emissions (EVAP) Canister location

REMOVAL & INSTALLATION

See Figure 179.

1. Raise and suitably support the vehicle.

2. Disconnect the evaporative emission (EVAP) canister harness electrical connector from the fuel tank pressure sensor.

3. Disconnect the EVAP canister harness electrical connector from the EVAP canister vent solenoid valve.

4. Disconnect the fuel fill vent pipe quick connect fitting from the EVAP canister.

5. Disconnect the fuel tank EVAP line quick connect fittings from the EVAP canister.

6. Remove the EVAP canister bolt.

Slide the EVAP canister assembly toward the driver side of the vehicle in order to remove.

➡The EVAP canister may have released carbon particles which caused this part to fail and may cause damage to other components. Check the EVAP canister for loose carbon before returning the vehicle to service. If reusing the EVAP canister, inspect the canister for loose carbon particles.

To install:

7. Insert the retaining tab on the EVAP canister into the slotted bracket on the vehicle underbody.

8. Install the EVAP canister bolt and tighten to 89 inch lbs. (10 Nm).

9. Connect the fuel tank EVAP line quick connect fittings to the EVAP canister.

10. Connect the fuel fill vent pipe quick connect fitting to the EVAP canister. Connect the EVAP canister harness electrical connector to the fuel tank pressure sensor.

11. Connect the EVAP canister harness electrical connector to the EVAP canister vent solenoid valve.

12. Lower the vehicle.

HEATED OXYGEN (HO2S) SENSOR

LOCATION
See Figures 180 through 182.

REMOVAL & INSTALLATION

2.0L Engine

Heated Oxygen Sensor—1
See Figure 180.

1. Open the hood.

2. Remove the underhood junction block bracket. Refer to Underhood Electrical Center in Chassis Electrical.

3. Remove the connector position assurance (CPA) retainer.

4. Disconnect the engine wiring harness electrical connector from the HO2S electrical connector.

5. Remove the HO2S electrical connector clip from the camshaft cover.

6. Using the J 39194 , remove the HO2S.

To install:

➡A special anti-seize compound is used on the HO2S threads. The compound consists of a liquid graphite and glass beads. The graphite will burn away, but the glass beads will remain, making the sensor easier to remove. New or service sensors will have the compound applied to the threads. If a sensor is removed and is to be reinstalled, the threads must have an anti-seize compound applied before installation.

➡If reinstalling the old HO2S, coat the threads with anti-seize compound GM P/N 12377953 or equivalent.

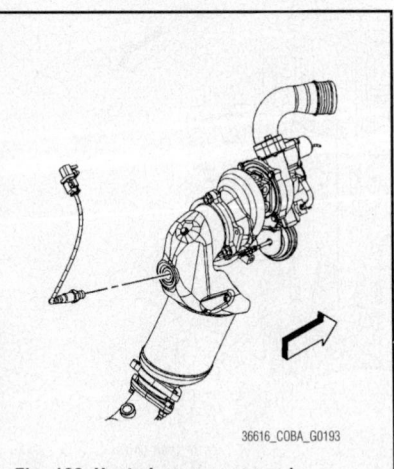

Fig. 180 Heated oxygen sensor 1 location—2.0L engine

7. Using the J 39194 , install the position 1 HO2S and tighten the sensor to 31 ft. lbs. (42 Nm).

8. Connect the engine wiring harness electrical connector (1) to the HO2S electrical connector (3).

9. Install the HO2S electrical connector clip to the camshaft cover.

10. Install the CPA retainer.

11. Install the underhood junction block bracket. Refer to Underhood Electrical Center in Chassis Electrical.

12. Close the hood.

Heated Oxygen Sensor—2
See Figure 181.

1. Disconnect the electrical connector.

2. Un-crimp the heat shield from the O2 sensor wiring harness.

3. Remove the oxygen sensor using the oxygen sensor wrench, J 39194.

4. Lower the HO2S electrical harness away from the underbody.

To install:

➡A special anti-seize compound is used on the oxygen sensor threads. The compound consists of a liquid graphite and glass beads. The graphite will burn away, but the glass beads will remain, making the sensor easier to remove. New or service sensors will have the compound applied to the threads. If a sensor is removed and is to be reinstalled, the threads must have an anti-seize compound applied before installation.

5. If reinstalling the old HO2S, coat the threads with anti-seize compound, GM P/N 12377953, or equivalent.

6. Carefully install the HO2S to the pipe.

7. Using the J 39194 , or equivalent,

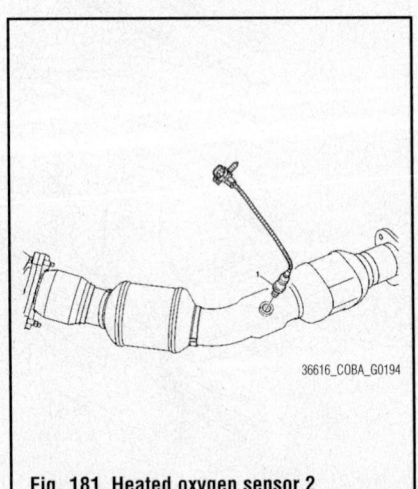

Fig. 181 Heated oxygen sensor 2 location—2.0L. 2.2L and 2.4L engines

tighten the HO2S. Tighten the HO2S to 30 ft. lbs. (41 Nm).

8. Install the HO2S electrical harness into position as noted before removal.

> ✱✱ **WARNING**
>
> **Use care when securing the HO2S electrical harness into the channel on the exhaust heat shield, to not pinch the wires.**

9. Carefully bend the edge of the channel on the LH side of the exhaust heat shield inboard, just enough to secure the HO2S electrical harness in the channel.

10. Connect the HO2S electrical connector.

11. Install the wheel driveshaft heat shield into position on the vehicle, if necessary.

12. Lower the vehicle.

2.2L & 2.4L Engines

Heated Oxygen Sensor—1

See Figure 182.

> ✱✱ **WARNING**
>
> **The oxygen sensor uses a permanently attached pigtail and connector. Do not remove the pigtail from the oxygen sensor. Damage to or removal of the pigtail connector could affect proper operation of the oxygen sensor.**

> ✱✱ **WARNING**
>
> **The use of excessive force may damage the threads in the exhaust manifold/pipe.**

➡ **The in-line connector and louvered end must be kept clear of grease, dirt or other contaminants. Avoid using cleaning solvents of any type. DO NOT drop or roughly handle the oxygen sensor.**

➡ **The oxygen sensor may be difficult to remove when the engine temperature is less than 120°F (48°C).**

1. Remove the exhaust manifold heat shield.

2. Disconnect the oxygen sensor harness connector.

3. Remove the oxygen sensor using the oxygen sensor wrench, J 39194-C.

To install:

➡ **A special anti-seize compound is used on the oxygen sensor threads. The compound consists of a liquid graphite and glass beads. The graphite will burn away, but the glass beads will**

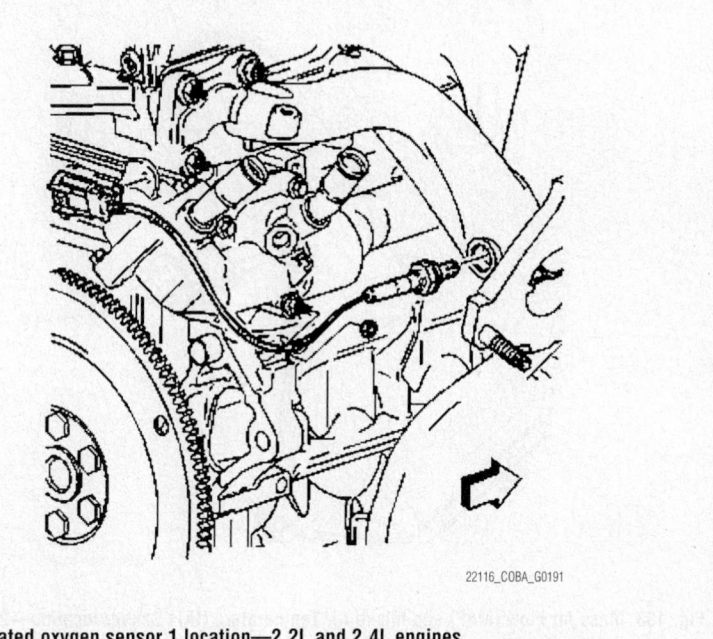

Fig. 182 Heated oxygen sensor 1 location—2.2L and 2.4L engines

remain, making the sensor easier to remove. New or service sensors will have the compound applied to the threads. If a sensor is removed and is to be reinstalled, the threads must have an anti-seize compound applied before installation.

4. Coat the threads of the oxygen sensor with anti-seize compound GM P/N 12377953, or equivalent, if necessary.

5. Install the oxygen sensor. Tighten the oxygen sensor to 30 ft. lbs. (41 Nm).

6. Connect the oxygen sensor harness connector.

7. Install the exhaust manifold heat shield. Tighten the heat shield studs to 16 ft. lbs. (22 Nm).

Heated Oxygen Sensor—2

See Figure 181.

1. Disconnect the electrical connector.

2. Un-crimp the heat shield from the O2 sensor wiring harness.

3. Remove the oxygen sensor using the oxygen sensor wrench, J 39194.

4. Lower the HO2S electrical harness away from the underbody.

To install:

➡ **A special anti-seize compound is used on the oxygen sensor threads. The compound consists of a liquid graphite and glass beads. The graphite will burn away, but the glass beads will remain, making the sensor easier to remove. New or service sensors will have the compound applied to the**

threads. If a sensor is removed and is to be reinstalled, the threads must have an anti-seize compound applied before installation.

5. If reinstalling the old HO2S, coat the threads with anti-seize compound, GM P/N 12377953, or equivalent.

6. Carefully install the HO2S to the pipe.

7. Using the J 39194 , or equivalent, tighten the HO2S. Tighten the HO2S to 30 ft. lbs. (41 Nm).

8. Install the HO2S electrical harness into position as noted before removal.

> ✱✱ **WARNING**
>
> **Use care when securing the HO2S electrical harness into the channel on the exhaust heat shield, to not pinch the wires.**

9. Carefully bend the edge of the channel on the LH side of the exhaust heat shield inboard, just enough to secure the HO2S electrical harness in the channel.

10. Connect the HO2S electrical connector.

11. Install the wheel driveshaft heat shield into position on the vehicle, if necessary.

12. Lower the vehicle.

INTAKE AIR TEMPERATURE (IAT) SENSOR

LOCATION

See Figures 183 and 184.

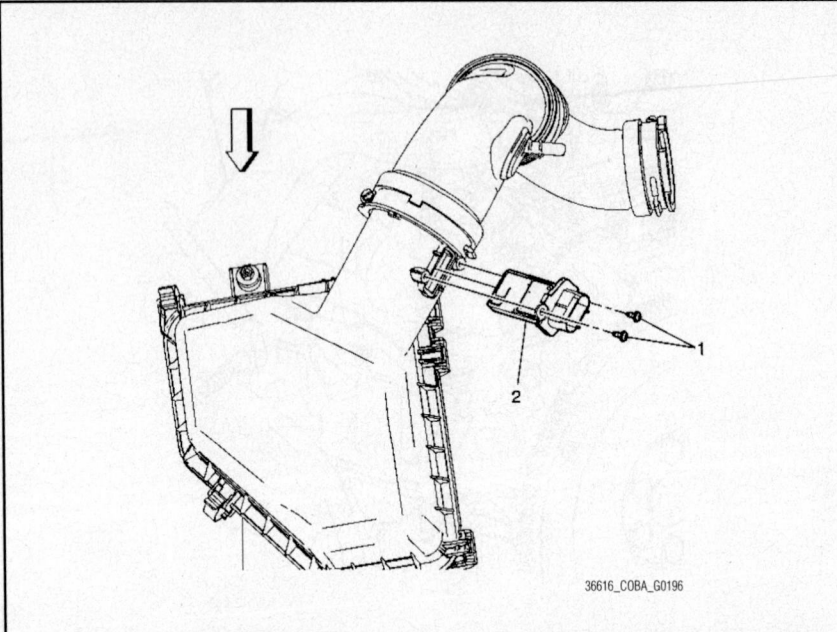

Fig. 183 Mass Air Flow (MAF) and Intake Air Temperature (IAT) Sensor location—2.0L engine

36616_COBA_G0196

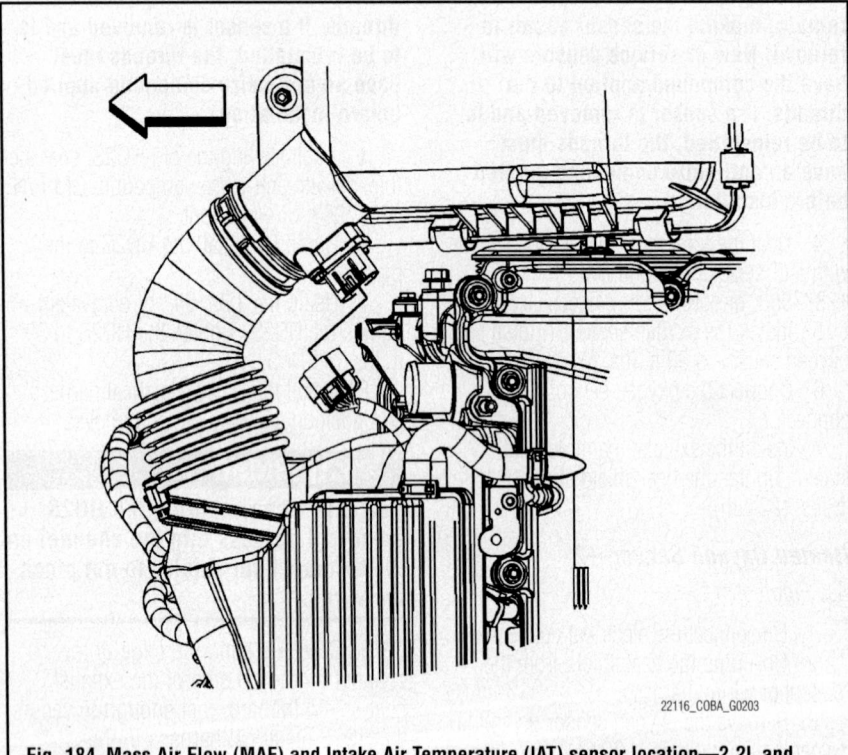

Fig. 184 Mass Air Flow (MAF) and Intake Air Temperature (IAT) sensor location—2.2L and 2.4L engines

22116_COBA_G0203

REMOVAL & INSTALLATION

2.0L Engine
See Figure 183.

1. Disconnect the Intake Air Temperature (IAT) sensor harness connector.
2. Remove the IAT sensor bolt.
3. While twisting the IAT sensor, pull the sensor from the engine.

To install:
4. Press the IAT sensor into the engine.
5. Install the IAT sensor bolt. Tighten the bolt to 5 inch lbs. (0.6 Nm).
6. Connect the IAT sensor harness connector.

2.2L & 2.4L Engines
See Figure 184.

1. Disconnect the engine harness electrical connector from the Mass Air Flow (MAF)/Intake Air Temperature (IAT) sensor.
2. Remove the MAF/IAT sensor screws.
3. Remove the MAF/IAT sensor.

To install:
4. Install the MAF/IAT sensor.
5. Install the MAF/IAT sensor screws. Tighten the screws to 5 inch lbs. (0.6 Nm).
6. Connect the engine harness electrical connector to the MAF/IAT sensor.

KNOCK SENSOR (KS)

LOCATION
See Figures 185 and 186.

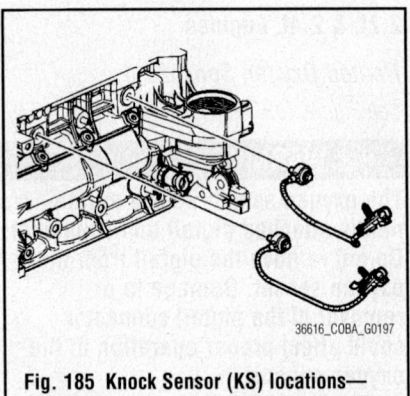

Fig. 185 Knock Sensor (KS) locations— 2.0L engine

36616_COBA_G0197

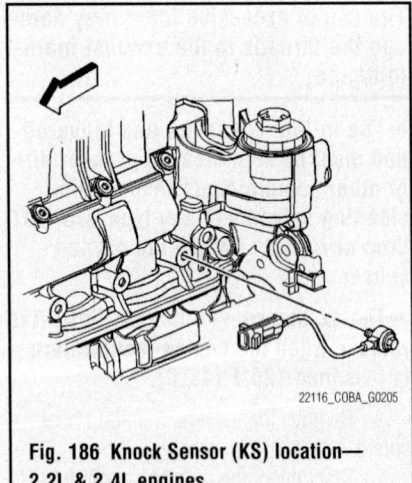

Fig. 186 Knock Sensor (KS) location— 2.2L & 2.4L engines

22116_COBA_G0205

REMOVAL & INSTALLATION

2.0L Engine
See Figure 185.

1. Remove the charge air bypass tank.
2. Disconnect the engine wiring

harness electrical connector from the front knock sensor, if required.

3. Disconnect the engine wiring harness electrical connector from the rear knock sensor, if required.

4. Remove the front knock sensor clip from the oil level indicator tube, if required.

5. Remove the rear knock sensor clip from the intake manifold brace, if required.

6. Loosen the appropriate knock sensor bolt.

7. Remove the appropriate knock sensor.

To install:

➡**Rotate the pigtail 90 degrees from vertical before securing the fastener.**

8. Position the appropriate knock sensor to the engine block.

9. Tighten the appropriate knock bolt and tighten the bolt to 18 ft. lbs. (25 Nm).

10. Install the front knock sensor clip to the oil level indicator tube, if required.

11. Install the rear knock sensor clip to the intake manifold brace, if required.

12. Connect the engine wiring harness electrical connector to the rear knock sensor.

13. Connect the engine wiring harness electrical connector to the front knock sensor.

14. Install the charge air bypass tank.

2.2L & 2.4L Engines

See Figure 186.

1. Disconnect the negative battery cable.

2. Remove the starter. Refer to Starter in Engine Electrical.

3. Disconnect the Knock Sensor (KS) harness connector.

4. Remove the KS retaining bolt.

5. Remove the KS.

To install:

❈❈ WARNING

Use the correct fastener in the correct location. Replacement fasteners must be the correct part number for that application. Fasteners requiring replacement or fasteners requiring the use of thread locking compound or sealant are identified in the service procedure. Do not use paints, lubricants, or corrosion inhibitors on fasteners or fastener

joint surfaces unless specified. These coatings affect fastener torque and joint clamping force and may damage the fastener. Use the correct tightening sequence and specifications when installing fasteners in order to avoid damage to parts and systems.

➡**The KS threaded surfaces must be clean before installation.**

6. Install the KS. Tighten the KS retaining bolt to 18 ft. lbs. (25 Nm).

7. Connect the KS harness connector.

8. Install the starter. Refer to Starter in Engine Electrical.

9. Connect the negative battery cable.

MALFUNCTION INDICATOR LIGHT (MIL)

RESET PROCEDURE

1. Proper operation of the Malfunction Indicator Lamp (MIL):
   - The MIL will illuminate with the ignition switch ON and the engine OFF
   - The MIL will turn OFF when the engine is started
   - The MIL will remain ON if the self-diagnostic system has detected a malfunction
   - The MIL may turn OFF if the malfunction is no longer present
   - If the MIL is illuminated and then the engine stalls, the MIL will remain illuminated as long as the ignition switch is ON
   - If the MIL is not illuminated and the engine stalls, the MIL will not illuminate until the ignition switch is cycled OFF, then ON
2. Resetting the MIL:
   - The control module turns OFF the MIL after 3 consecutive ignition cycles that the diagnostic system runs and does not fail
   - A current Diagnostic Trouble Code (DTC) clears when the diagnostic cycle runs and passes
   - There may still be a history of DTC's stored in the system. These will clear after 40 consecutive warm-up cycles, if no failures are reported by any other related diagnostic system
   - Manual resetting of the MIL and any DTC stored in the system, requires the use of an OBD2 scan tool connected to the data link connector for communication with the

vehicle. Follow the instructions of the scan tool for both retrieval and resetting of DTC's.

➡**If the error symptoms causing the MIL to illuminate have been corrected, the MIL will return to normal operation.**

MASS AIR FLOW (MAF) SENSOR

LOCATION

See Figures 183 and 184.

REMOVAL & INSTALLATION

2.0L Engine

See Figure 183.

1. Disconnect the Intake Air Temperature (IAT) sensor harness connector.

2. Remove the IAT sensor bolt.

3. While twisting the IAT sensor, pull the sensor from the engine.

To install:

4. Press the IAT sensor into the engine.

5. Install the IAT sensor bolt. Tighten the bolt to 5 inch lbs. (0.6 Nm).

6. Connect the IAT sensor harness connector.

2.2L & 2.4L Engines

See Figure 184.

1. Disconnect the engine harness electrical connector from the Mass Air Flow (MAF)/Intake Air Temperature (IAT) sensor.

2. Remove the MAF/IAT sensor screws.

3. Remove the MAF/IAT sensor.

To install:

4. Install the MAF/IAT sensor.

5. Install the MAF/IAT sensor screws. Tighten the screws to 5 inch lbs. (0.6 Nm).

6. Connect the engine harness electrical connector to the MAF/IAT sensor.

MANIFOLD ABSOLUTE PRESSURE (MAP) SENSOR

LOCATION

See Figures 187 and 188.

REMOVAL & INSTALLATION

2.0L Engine

See Figure 187.

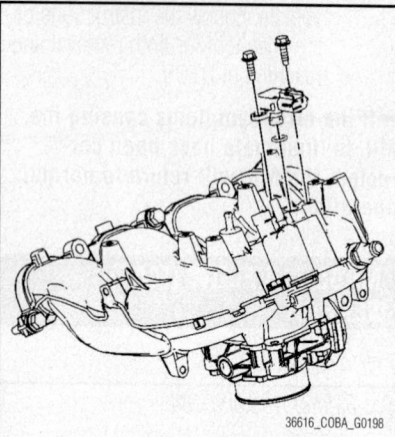

Fig. 187 Manifold Absolute Pressure (MAP) sensor location—2.0L engine

1. Disconnect the engine wiring harness electrical connector from the manifold absolute pressure (MAP) sensor.
2. Remove the MAP sensor bolts.
3. Remove the MAP sensor and O-ring seal from the intake manifold.

To install:

4. Lubricate the O-ring seal with clean engine oil.
5. Install the MAP sensor to the intake manifold.
6. Install the MAP sensor bolts and tighten the bolts to 89 inch lbs. (10 Nm).
7. Connect the engine wiring harness electrical connector to the MAP sensor.

2.2L & 2.4L Engines

See Figure 188.

1. Remove the throttle body. Refer to Throttle Body in Fuel System.
2. Disconnect the engine harness electrical connector from the manifold absolute pressure (MAP) sensor.

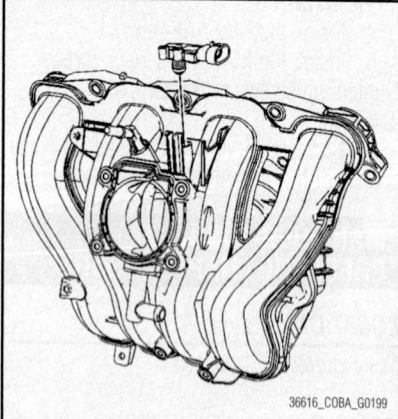

Fig. 188 Manifold Absolute Pressure (MAP) sensor location—2.2L and 2.4L engines

3. Remove the MAP sensor and seal.

To install:

4. Lubricate the NEW MAP sensor seal with clean engine oil.
5. Install the MAP sensor into the intake manifold.
6. Connect the engine harness electrical connector to the MAP sensor.
7. Install the throttle body.

POSITIVE CRANKCASE VENTILATION (PCV) VALVE

LOCATION

For the 2.2L and 2.4L engines, the PCV orifice is an integral part of the camshaft cover. For the 2.0L engine, it is located in the intake manifold.

REMOVAL & INSTALLATION

1. Cleaning the orifice is possible, replacement is not specified.

THROTTLE POSITION SENSOR (TPS)

LOCATION

The Throttle Position Sensor (TPS) is integrated with the Throttle Control Actuator.

REMOVAL & INSTALLATION

2.0L Engine

❊❊ WARNING

Do not use solvent of any type when cleaning the gasket surfaces on the intake manifold and the throttle body assembly, as damage to the gasket surfaces and throttle body assembly may result. Use care in cleaning the gasket surfaces on the intake manifold and the throttle body assembly, as sharp tools may damage the gasket surfaces. Do not use any solvent that contains Methyl Ethyl Ketone (MEK). This solvent may damage fuel system components.

1. Remove the charge air cooler outlet pipe.
2. Disconnect the engine wiring harness electrical connector from the electronic throttle control (ETC).
3. Remove the throttle body bolts.
4. Remove the throttle body and seal from the intake manifold.

To install:

5. Inspect the throttle body seal, and replace if necessary.

6. Position the throttle body to the intake manifold.
7. Install the throttle body bolts and tighten to 89 inch lbs. (10 Nm).
8. Connect the engine wiring harness electrical connector to the ETC.
9. Install the charge air cooler outlet pipe.

2.2L & 2.4L Engines

1. Remove the air cleaner outlet duct.
2. Remove the intake manifold cover.
3. Disconnect the Throttle Actuator Control (TAC) electrical connector.
4. Remove the throttle body bolts.
5. Remove the throttle body.
6. Inspect the throttle body gasket, and replace if necessary.

To install:

7. Install the throttle body.
8. Install the throttle body bolts and tighten the bolts to 89 inch lbs. (10 Nm).
9. Connect the TAC electrical connector.
10. Install the intake manifold cover.
11. Install the air cleaner outlet duct.

VEHICLE SPEED SENSOR (VSS)

LOCATION

See Figures 189 through 191.

REMOVAL & INSTALLATION

Automatic Transaxle 4T45–E

See Figure 189.

❊❊ WARNING

Unless directed otherwise, the ignition and start switch must be in the OFF or LOCK position, and all electrical loads must be OFF before servicing any electrical component. Disconnect the negative battery cable to prevent an electrical spark

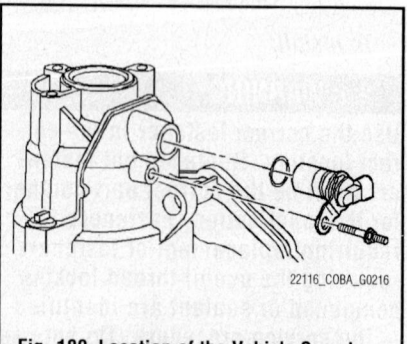

Fig. 189 Location of the Vehicle Speed Sensor (VSS) on automatic transaxle 4T45–E

should a tool or equipment come in contact with an exposed electrical terminal. Failure to follow these precautions may result in personal injury and/or damage to the vehicle or its components.

1. Disconnect the negative battery cable.
2. Raise and support the vehicle.
3. Remove the electrical connector at the Vehicle Speed Sensor (VSS).
4. Remove the retaining stud and the sensor. Pull straight out in order to avoid damage to the case.

To install:
5. Clean and dry the VSS.

➡Use the correct fastener in the correct location. Replacement fasteners must be the correct part number for that application. Fasteners requiring replacement or fasteners requiring the use of thread locking compound or sealant are identified in the service procedure. Do not use paints, lubricants, or corrosion inhibitors on fasteners or fastener joint surfaces unless specified. These coatings affect fastener torque and joint clamping force and may damage the fastener. Use the correct tightening sequence and specifications when installing fasteners in order to avoid damage to parts and systems.

6. Install the VSS and the retaining bolt. Tighten the stud to 97 inch lbs. (12 Nm).
7. Install the electrical connector at the sensor.
8. Lower the vehicle.
9. Connect the negative battery cable. Tighten the terminal bolt to 11 ft. lbs. (15 Nm).

Manual Transaxle—MU3
See Figure 190.

1. Remove or disconnect the following:
- The left front wheel
- The Vehicle Speed Sensor (VSS) electrical connector (2)
- The retainer bolt
- The retainer
- The VSS
- Discard the O—ring

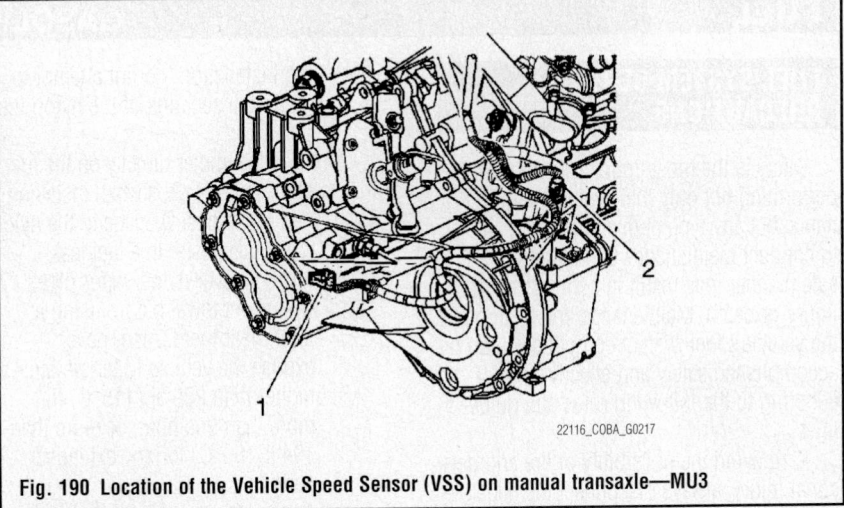

Fig. 190 Location of the Vehicle Speed Sensor (VSS) on manual transaxle—MU3

To install:
2. Lubricate a new O—ring with transmission fluid.
3. Install or connect the following:
- The new O-ring
- The VSS retainer
- The VSS assembly
- The VSS retainer bolt. Tighten the bolt to 80 inch lbs. (9 Nm)
- The VSS connector to the VSS
- The left front wheel. Tighten the lug nuts to 100 ft. lbs. (140 Nm)

Manual Transaxle—M86
See Figure 191.

1. Raise and safely support the vehicle.
2. Disconnect the Vehicle Speed Sensor (VSS) electrical connector.
3. Remove the retainer bolt.
4. Remove the retainer.
5. Pull up on the VSS in order to remove the VSS from the transaxle.
6. Remove the O-ring.

To install:
7. Lubricate a new O-ring with DEXRON III transmission fluid.
8. Install or connect the following:
- The new O—ring
- The VSS assembly
- The VSS retainer

➡Use the correct fastener in the correct location. Replacement fasteners must be the correct part number for that application. Fasteners requiring replacement or fasteners requiring the

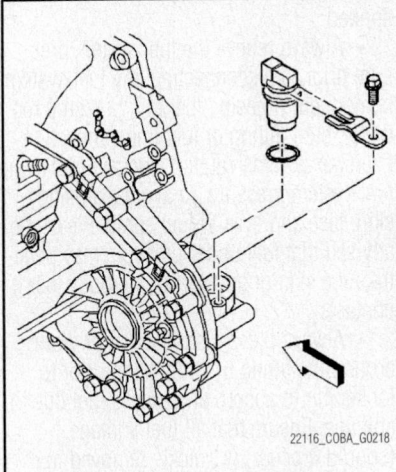

Fig. 191 Location of the Vehicle Speed Sensor (VSS) on manual transaxle—Getrag 5—speed

use of thread locking compound or sealant are identified in the service procedure. Do not use paints, lubricants, or corrosion inhibitors on fasteners or fastener joint surfaces unless specified. These coatings affect fastener torque and joint clamping force and may damage the fastener. Use the correct tightening sequence and specifications when installing fasteners in order to avoid damage to parts and systems.

- The VSS retainer bolt. Tighten the bolt to 96 inch lbs. (12 Nm)
- The VSS connector to the VSS
9. Lower the vehicle.

FUEL SYSTEM SERVICE PRECAUTIONS

Safety is the most important factor when performing not only fuel system maintenance but any type of maintenance. Failure to conduct maintenance and repairs in a safe manner may result in serious personal injury or death. Maintenance and testing of the vehicle's fuel system components can be accomplished safely and effectively by adhering to the following rules and guidelines.

• To avoid the possibility of fire and personal injury, always disconnect the negative battery cable unless the repair or test procedure requires that battery voltage be applied.

• Always relieve the fuel system pressure prior to disconnecting any fuel system component (injector, fuel rail, pressure regulator, etc.), fitting or fuel line connection. Exercise extreme caution whenever relieving fuel system pressure, to avoid exposing skin, face and eyes to fuel spray. Please be advised that fuel under pressure may penetrate the skin or any part of the body that it contacts.

• Always place a shop towel or cloth around the fitting or connection prior to loosening to absorb any excess fuel due to spillage. Ensure that all fuel spillage (should it occur) is quickly removed from engine surfaces. Ensure that all fuel soaked cloths or towels are deposited into a suitable waste container.

• Always keep a dry chemical (Class B) fire extinguisher near the work area.

• Do not allow fuel spray or fuel vapors to come into contact with a spark or open flame.

• Always use a back-up wrench when loosening and tightening fuel line connection fittings. This will prevent unnecessary stress and torsion to fuel line piping. Always follow the proper torque specifications.

• Always replace worn fuel fitting O-rings with new ones. Do not substitute fuel hose, or equivalent, where fuel pipe is installed.

✳✳ CAUTION

In order to reduce the risk of fire and personal injury observe the following items:

• Replace all nylon fuel pipes that are nicked, scratched or damaged during installation, do not attempt to repair the sections of the nylon fuel pipes

• Do not hammer directly on the fuel harness body clips when installing new fuel pipes. Damage to the nylon pipes may result in a fuel leak.

• Always cover nylon vapor pipes with a wet towel before using a torch near them. Also, never expose the vehicle to temperatures higher than 239°F (115°C) for more than one hour, or more than 194°F (90°C) for any extended period.

• Apply a few drops of clean engine oil to the male pipe ends before connecting fuel pipe fittings. This will ensure proper reconnection and prevent a possible fuel leak. (During normal operation, the O-rings located in the female connector will swell and may prevent proper reconnection if not lubricated.)

RELIEVING FUEL SYSTEM PRESSURE

2.0L Engine

High Pressure Side

1. Install a scan tool to the vehicle and command the fuel pump relay OFF, allowing the low pressure fuel pump to shut off.

2. Start the vehicle and allow the engine to idle until the engine stops. The engine will stop in approximately 20–30 seconds.

3. Turn the ignition OFF.

4. Using the scan tool, verify that there is little to no fuel pressure, if there still is fuel pressure repeat step 2.

➡ **If a scan tool is not available, WAIT at LEAST 2 hours after the engine has been run, before removing the high pressure fuel line.**

5. Remove the high pressure fuel line.

Low Pressure Side

✳✳ CAUTION

Remove the fuel tank cap and relieve the fuel system pressure before servicing the fuel system in order to reduce the risk of personal injury. After you relieve the fuel system pressure, a small amount of fuel may be released when servicing the fuel lines, the fuel injection pump, or the connections. In order to reduce the risk of personal injury, cover the fuel system components with a shop towel before disconnection. This will catch any fuel that may leak out. Place the towel in an approved container when the disconnection is complete.

1. If the fuel system requires repair, prevent fuel spillage by removing the fuel pump fuse.

2. Loosen the fuel fill cap in order to relieve the fuel tank vapor pressure.

3. Remove the engine cover, if required.

4. Remove the fuel feed pipe service port cap.

5. Wrap a shop towel around the fuel rail service port and using a small flat-bladed tool, depress (open) the fuel feed pipe test port valve.

6. Remove the shop towel from around the fuel service port, and place in an approved gasoline container.

7. Install the fuel feed pipe service port cap.

8. Install the engine cover, if required.

9. Tighten the fuel fill cap.

2.2L & 2.4L Engines

✳✳ CAUTION

Remove the fuel tank cap and relieve the fuel system pressure before servicing the fuel system in order to reduce the risk of personal injury. After you relieve the fuel system pressure, a small amount of fuel may be released when servicing the fuel lines, the fuel injection pump, or the connections. In order to reduce the risk of personal injury, cover the fuel system components with a shop towel before disconnection. This will catch any fuel that may leak out. Place the towel in an approved container when the disconnection is complete.

1. If the fuel system requires repair, prevent fuel spillage by removing the fuel pump fuse.

2. Loosen the fuel fill cap in order to relieve the fuel tank vapor pressure.

3. Remove the engine cover, if required.

4. Remove the fuel feed pipe service port cap.

5. Wrap a shop towel around the fuel rail service port and using a small flat-

bladed tool, depress (open) the fuel feed pipe test port valve.

6. Remove the shop towel from around the fuel service port, and place in an approved gasoline container.

7. Install the fuel feed pipe service port cap.

8. Install the engine cover, if required.

9. Tighten the fuel fill cap.

FUEL PUMP MODULE

REMOVAL & INSTALLATION

See Figures 192 through 194.

✳ CAUTION

To reduce the risk of fire and personal injury that may result from a fuel leak, always replace the fuel sender gasket when reinstalling the fuel sender assembly.

1. Before servicing the vehicle, refer to the Precautions Section.

2. Relieve the fuel system pressure.

3. Drain the fuel tank.

4. Remove the fuel tank, as outlined in this section

5. Disconnect the fuel pressure sensor and fuel pump module electrical connectors (1, 4).

6. Disconnect the fuel tank vent pipe quick connect fittings (2, 3).

7. Disconnect the fuel tank feed pipe quick connect fitting (5).

8. Install the J 45722 , or equivalent Fuel Sender Lock Ring Wrench to the lock ring.

✳ WARNING

Avoid damaging the lock ring. Use only J-45722 to prevent damage to the lock ring.

✳ WARNING

Do Not handle the fuel sender assembly by the fuel pipes. The amount of leverage generated by handling the fuel pipes could damage the joints.

➡ **Do NOT use impact tools. Significant force will be required to release the lock ring. The use of a hammer and screwdriver is not recommended. Secure the fuel tank in order to prevent fuel tank rotation.**

9. Use the J 45722 and a long breaker-bar in order to unlock the fuel sender lock ring. Turn the fuel sender lock ring in a counterclockwise direction.

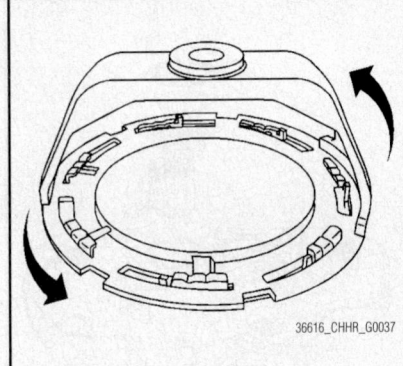

Fig. 193 Turn the fuel sender lock ring in a counterclockwise direction.

10. Remove the module lock ring.

11. Slowly raise the module until the fuel level sensor float arm is just visible. Ensure that the fuel level sensor harness connector clears the tank opening.

➡ **When removing the module from the fuel tank, be aware that the module reservoir bowl is full of fuel. The module must be tipped slightly during removal to avoid bending the fuel level sensor float arm.**

12. Tilt the module toward the rear of the fuel tank to allow the level sensor float arm to clear the tank opening. Remove the module from the tank.

13. Carefully discard the fuel in the module reservoir bowl into an approved fuel container.

➡ **DO NOT reuse the old fuel pump module seal.**

14. Remove and discard the fuel pump module seal.

➡ **Some lock ring were manufactured with DO NOT REUSE stamped into them. These lock rings may be reused if they are not damaged or warped. Inspect the lock ring for damage due to improper removal or installation procedures. If damage is found, install a NEW lock ring. Check the lock ring for flatness.**

15. Place the lock ring on a flat surface. Measure the clearance between to lock ring and the flat surface using a feeler gauge at 7 points.

a. If the warpage is less than 0.41 mm (0.016 in), the lock ring does not require replacement.

b. If the warpage is greater than 0.41 mm (0.016 in), the lock ring must be replaced.

16. If only replacing the module, remove the fuel level sensor.

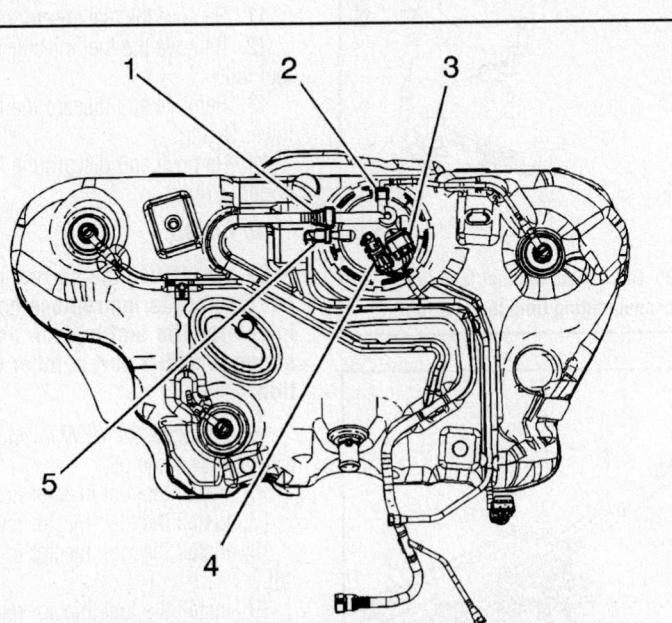

1. Fuel pump module electrical connector
2. Fuel tank vent pipe quick connect fitting
3. Fuel pump module electrical connector
4. Fuel tank vent pipe quick connect fitting
5. Fuel tank feed pip quick connect fitting

Fig. 192 View of the connectors and fittings

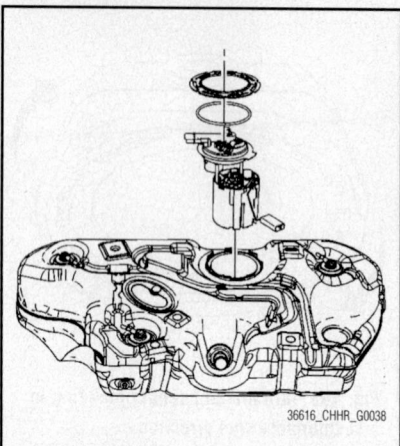

Fig. 194 Exploded view of the fuel pump module and related components

To install:

17. Install a NEW fuel pump module seal onto the fuel tank.

18. If installing only the module, install the fuel level sensor.

➡**The reservoir must be tipped slightly during installation to avoid bending the fuel level sensor float arm.**

19. Tilt the module toward the rear of the fuel tank to allow the fuel level sensor float arm to clear the tank opening. Install the module into the fuel tank.

20. Lower the module assembly into the tank. Ensure that the fuel level sensor harness connector is positioned properly.

21. Install the module lock ring over the module pipes and electrical harness, and into position on the top of the module.

➡**Always replace the fuel sender seal when installing the fuel sender assembly. Replace the lock ring if necessary. Do not apply any type of lubrication in the seal groove.**

22. Ensure the lock ring is installed with the correct side facing upward. A correctly installed lock ring will only turn in a clockwise direction.

23. Use the J 45722 in order to install the fuel sender lock ring. Turn the fuel sender lock ring in a clockwise direction. Remove the J 45722 from the lock ring.

24. Connect the fuel tank feed pipe quick connect fitting.

25. Connect the fuel tank vent pipe quick connect fittings.

26. Connect the fuel pressure sensor and fuel pump module electrical connectors.

27. Install the fuel tank.

FUEL RAIL & INJECTORS

REMOVAL & INSTALLATION

See Figures 195 through 197.

1. Relieve the fuel system pressure.
2. Remove the air cleaner assembly.
3. Disconnect the fuel feed line quick connect fitting from the fuel rail.
4. Disconnect the Evaporative emission (EVAP) purge tube from the intake manifold.
5. Disconnect the fuel injector harness electrical connector.
6. Disconnect the Manifold Absolute Pressure (MAP) sensor electrical connector.
7. Remove the fuel injector harness electrical connector clips from the intake manifold.
8. Remove the fuel rail studs.

➡**Use care when removing the fuel rail assembly in order to prevent damage to the fuel injectors electrical connector terminals and spray tips.**

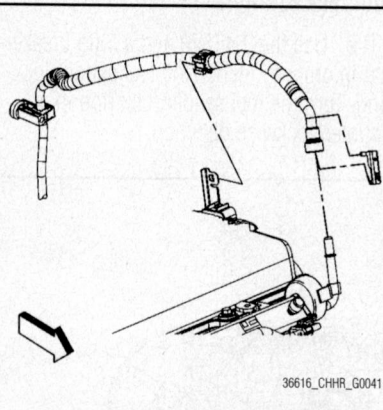

Fig. 195 Disconnect the fuel feed line quick connect fitting from the fuel rail

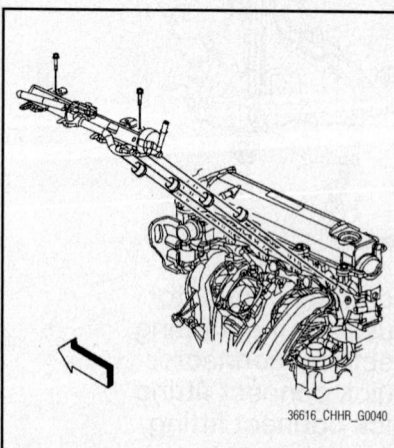

Fig. 196 Fuel rail removal—2.0L engine

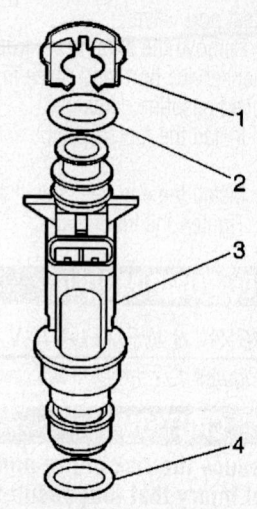

1. Fuel injector retaining clip
2. Fuel injector upper O-ring
3. Fuel injector
4. Fuel injector lower O-ring

Fig. 197 Exploded view of a fuel injector—2.0L engine

9. Pull the fuel rail back and upward in order to release the fuel injectors from the cylinder head ports.

10. Remove the fuel rail.

11. Remove the fuel injector retaining clip.

12. Remove the fuel injector from the fuel rail.

13. Remove and discard the fuel injector lower O-ring.

14. Remove and discard the fuel injector upper O-ring.

To install:

➡**Be sure to use the correct part number when ordering replacement fuel injectors. The fuel injector assembly is stamped with a part number identification.**

15. Lubricate the NEW injector O-rings with clean engine oil.

16. Install the fuel injector upper O-ring.

17. Install the fuel injector lower O-ring.

18. Install the fuel injector to the fuel rail.

19. Install the fuel injector retaining clip.

➡**If reusing the fuel injectors, you must still install new lower O-rings. Lubricate the injector tip O-rings prior to installing the injectors into the intake manifold.**

20. With the fuel injectors positioned downward, lower the fuel injectors into the cylinder head ports.

21. Carefully push the fuel injectors into the cylinder head ports.

22. Install the fuel rail bolts and tighten to 89 inch lbs. (10 Nm).

23. Connect the fuel injector harness electrical connector.

24. Connect the MAP sensor electrical connector.

25. Install the fuel injector harness electrical connector clips to the intake manifold.

26. Connect the EVAP purge tube to the intake manifold.

27. Connect the fuel feed line quick connect fitting to the fuel rail.

28. Install the air cleaner assembly.

29. Connect the negative battery cable.

30. Inspect for fuel leaks using the following procedure:

　a. Turn ON the ignition, with the engine OFF for 2 seconds.

　b. Turn OFF the ignition for 10 seconds.

　c. Turn ON the ignition.

　d. Inspect for fuel leaks.

FUEL TANK

REMOVAL & INSTALLATION

See Figures 198 through 200.

1. Before servicing the vehicle, refer to the Precautions Section.

2. Disconnect the negative battery cable.

3. Relieve the fuel system pressure. Refer to Relieving Fuel System Pressure.

4. Drain the fuel tank:

✻✻ CAUTION

Never drain or store fuel in an open container. Always use an approved

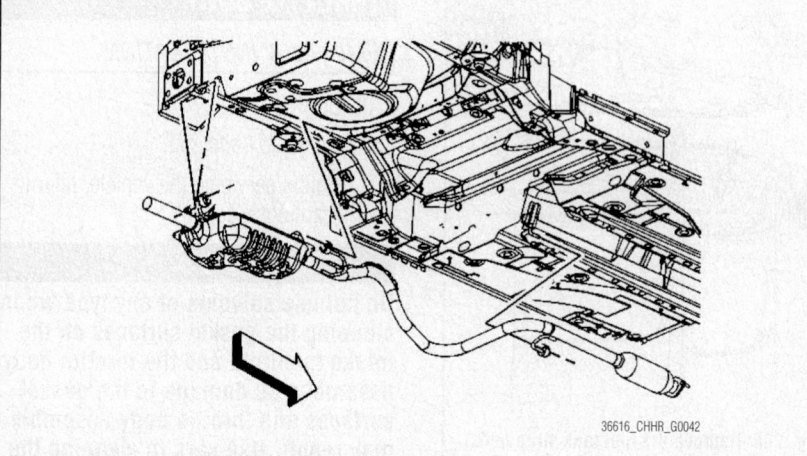

Fig. 199 Remove the muffler insulators from the underbody hanger and slowly lower the exhaust in order to allow it to rest on the rear axle beam

36616_CHHR_G0042

fuel storage container in order to reduce the chance of fire or explosion. Place a dry chemical (Class B) fire extinguisher nearby before performing any on-vehicle service procedures. Failure to follow these precautions may result in personal injury.

　a. Remove the fuel filler cap.

　b. Install J 42960-2, or equivalent, into the fuel fill pipe in order to hold the door open.

　c. Insert J 43290 (2) through the J 42960-2 (1) and into the filler pipe.

　d. Continue to insert the J 43290 (2) into the filler pipe until the hose exits the valve (1) and reaches the bottom of the tank.

　e. Use an air operated pump device in order to drain as much fuel through the J 43290 (1) as possible.

5. Raise and support the vehicle.

6. Disconnect the fuel tank vent pipe quick connect fittings.

7. Loosen the fuel fill pipe hose clamp at the fuel tank.

8. Remove the fuel fill pipe hose from the fuel tank.

9. Disconnect the fuel tank electrical connector from the pass thru connector.

10. Remove the exhaust pipe insulators from the underbody hangers.

11. Remove the muffler insulators from the underbody hanger and slowly lower the exhaust in order to allow it to rest on the rear axle beam.

12. Place an adjustable jack under the fuel tank.

13. Remove the fuel tank strap bolts, then remove the fuel tank straps.

14. Using the adjustable jack, carefully lower the fuel tank away from the vehicle.

15. With the aid of an assistant, place the fuel tank on a suitable work surface.

16. If replacing the fuel tank perform the following steps

　a. Remove the fuel tank vent pipe.

　b. Remove the fuel feed intermediate pipe.

　c. Remove the fuel tank vent pipe

　d. Disconnect and remove the fuel tank electrical harness.

　e. Remove the fuel pump module, as outlined in this section.

To install:

17. If the fuel tank was replaced, install the fuel pump module and pipes as necessary. Attach the fuel tank electrical harness.

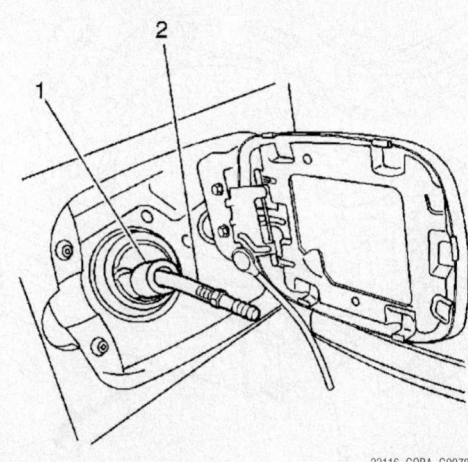

22116_COBA_G0078

Fig. 198 Insert J 43290 (2) through the J 42960-2 (1) and into the filler pipe. Continue to insert the J 43290 (2) into the filler pipe until the hose exits the valve (1) and reaches the bottom of the tank

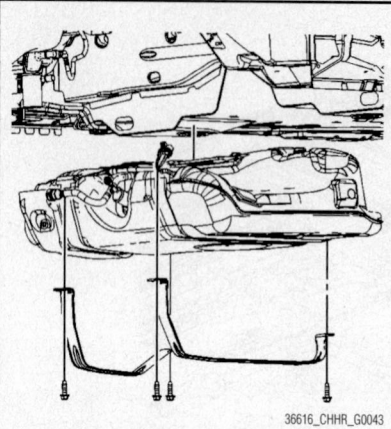

Fig. 200 Remove the fuel tank strap bolts, then remove the fuel tank straps

18. With the aid of an assistant, place the fuel tank on the suitable jack.

19. Using the adjustable jack, carefully raise the fuel tank into position.

20. Position the fuel tank straps.

21. Install the fuel tank strap bolts and tighten the bolts to 33 ft. lbs. (45 Nm).

22. Remove adjustable jack from under the fuel tank.

23. Raise the exhaust and install the muffler insulators to the underbody hangers.

24. Install the exhaust pipe insulators to the underbody hangers.

25. Connect the fuel tank electrical connector to the pass thru connector.

26. Install the fuel fill pipe hose to the fuel tank.

27. Tighten the fuel fill pipe hose clamp at the fuel tank to 40 inch lbs. (4.5 Nm).

28. Connect the fuel tank vent pipe quick connect fittings.

29. Lower the vehicle.

30. Refill the fuel tank.

31. Connect the negative battery cable.

32. Inspect for fuel leaks using the following procedure:

   a. Turn the ignition switch ON, but do not start the engine. Wait 2 seconds.

   b. Turn the ignition switch OFF and wait 10 seconds.

   c. Turn the ignition switch ON, but do not start the engine.

   d. Inspect for fuel leaks.

IDLE SPEED

ADJUSTMENT

Idle speed is maintained by the Powertrain Control Module (PCM). No adjustment is necessary or possible.

THROTTLE BODY

REMOVAL & INSTALLATION

2.0L Engine

See Figures 201 and 202.

1. Before servicing the vehicle, refer to the Precautions Section.

✳✳ WARNING

Do not use solvents of any type when cleaning the gasket surfaces on the intake manifold and the throttle body assembly, as damage to the gasket surfaces and throttle body assembly may result. Use care in cleaning the gasket surfaces on the intake manifold and the throttle body assembly, as sharp tools may damage the gasket surfaces. Solvents that contain Methyl Ethyl Ketone (MEK) may damage fuel system components.

2. Remove the charge air cooler outlet pipe, as follows:

   a. Remove the upper baffle deflector.

   b. Loosen the charge air cooler outlet pipe clamp at the intake manifold.

   c. Remove the front bumper fascia extension.

   d. Disconnect the engine wiring harness electrical connector from the intake air pressure and temperature sensor.

   e. Disconnect the vacuum hose from the outlet pipe.

   f. Loosen the charge air cooler outlet pipe clamp (1) at the charge air cooler assembly (2).

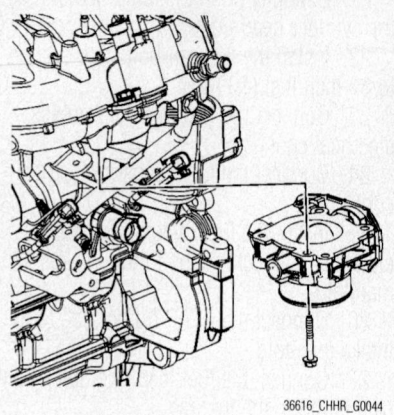

Fig. 202 Throttle body mounting—2.0L engine

   g. Remove the right radiator support in order to reposition the radiator and allow the pipe to be removed.

   h. Remove the charge air cooler outlet pipe (3).

3. Disconnect the engine wiring harness electrical connector from the electronic throttle control (ETC).

4. Remove the throttle body bolts, then remove the throttle body and seal from the intake manifold.

To install:

5. Inspect the throttle body seal, and replace if necessary.

6. Position the throttle body to the intake manifold. Install the throttle body bolts and tighten to 89 inch lbs. (10 Nm).

7. Connect the engine wiring harness electrical connector to the ETC.

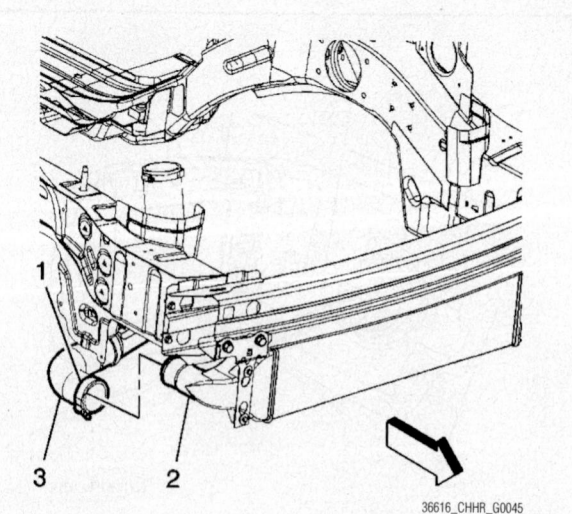

Fig. 201 View of the charge air cooler outlet pipe clamp (2), charge air cooler assembly (2) and charge air cooler pipe (3)

8. Install the charge air cooler outlet pipe in the reverse of the removal procedure.

2.2L & 2.4L Engines

See Figures 203 and 204.

1. Before servicing the vehicle, refer to the Precautions Section.

❋❋ WARNING

Do not use solvents of any type when cleaning the gasket surfaces on the intake manifold and the throttle body assembly, as damage to the gasket surfaces and throttle body assembly may result. Use care in cleaning the gasket surfaces on the intake manifold and the throttle body assembly, as sharp tools may damage the gasket surfaces. Solvents that contain Methyl Ethyl Ketone (MEK) may damage fuel system components.

➡**DO NOT prop open the throttle blade with the ignition key in the ON position as it may set a Diagnostic Trouble Code (DTC).**

2. Remove the air cleaner outlet duct.

3. Remove the intake manifold cover:

a. Remove the engine oil fill cap.

b. Grasp the intake manifold cover by the lower right inboard corner and pull up to disengage the cover from the stud.

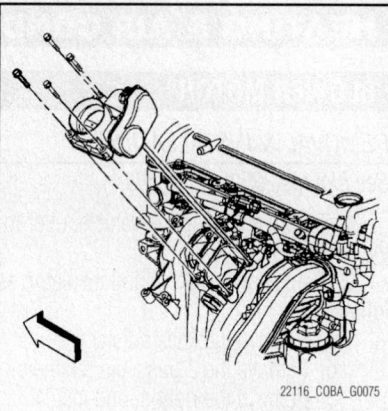

Fig. 204 Removing the throttle body—2.2L and 2.4L Engines

c. Grasp the intake manifold cover by the upper left corner and pull up to disengage the cover from the stud.

d. Remove the intake manifold cover.

4. Disconnect the Throttle Actuator Control (TAC) electrical connector (1).

5. Remove the throttle body bolts.

6. Remove the throttle body.

To install:

7. Inspect the throttle body gasket, and replace if necessary.

8. Install the throttle body.

9. Install the throttle body bolts. Tighten the bolts to 89 inch lbs. (10 Nm).

10. Connect the TAC electrical connector (1).

11. Install the intake manifold cover:

a. Place the intake manifold cover onto the engine over the studs.

b. Push down on the intake manifold cover directly over the lower right stud in order to engage the cover to the stud.

c. Push down on the intake manifold cover directly over the upper left stud in order to engage the cover to the stud.

d. Install the engine oil fill cap.

12. Install the air cleaner outlet duct.

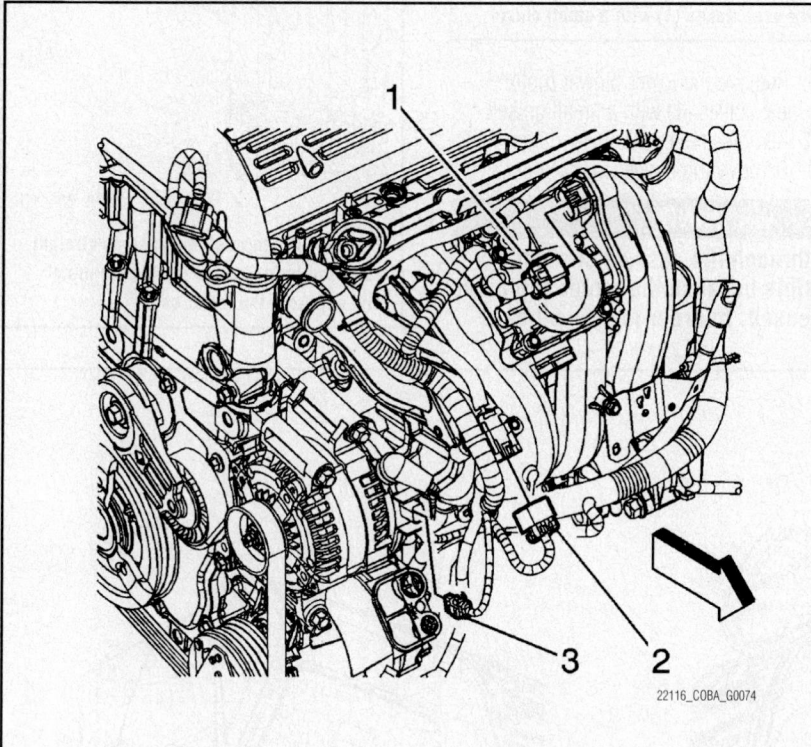

Fig. 203 Location of the Throttle Actuator Control (TAC) electrical connector (1)

HEATING & AIR CONDITIONING SYSTEM

BLOWER MOTOR

REMOVAL & INSTALLATION

See Figures 205 through 208.

1. Before servicing the vehicle, refer to the Precautions Section.

2. Remove the right sound insulator, as follows:

    a. Remove the knee bolster.

    b. Remove the 2 push-pin retainers.

    c. Remove the right sound insulator/closeout panel.

3. Remove the instrument panel (I/P) compartment, as follows:

    a. Unfasten the instrument panel compartment dampener screw

    b. Squeeze the sides of the compartment and pull the compartment out of the instrument panel opening past the stops.

    c. Pull outward on the compartment assembly releasing the 3 hinge points from the instrument panel assembly

4. Disconnect the negative battery cable.

5. Disconnect the blower motor electrical connector.

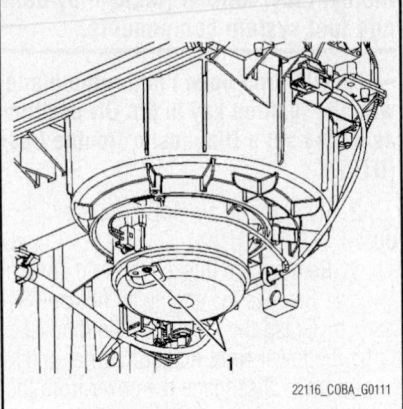

Fig. 206 Remove the lower blower motor cover heat stakes (1) with a small chisel

6. Remove the lower blower motor cover heat stakes (1) with a small chisel.

7. Remove the lower blower motor cover.

8. Remove the blower motor nuts.

✳✳ WARNING

Cut through the case as straight as possible because the motor cup must be reused. In order to prevent damage to the component, do not cut any deeper than necessary to remove the motor cup.

9. Remove the blower motor and cup from the lower case by cutting through the case between the circular ribs around the motor with a sharp utility knife.

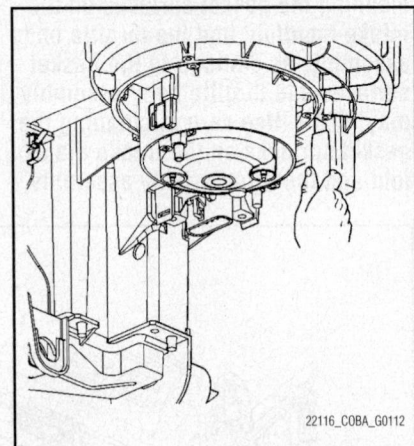

Fig. 207 Cut through the case as straight as possible to remove the blower motor and cup from the lower case

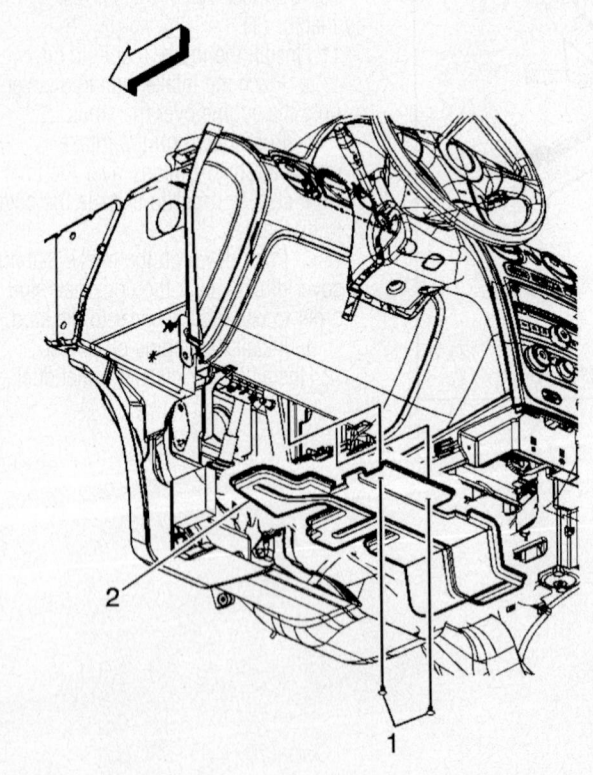
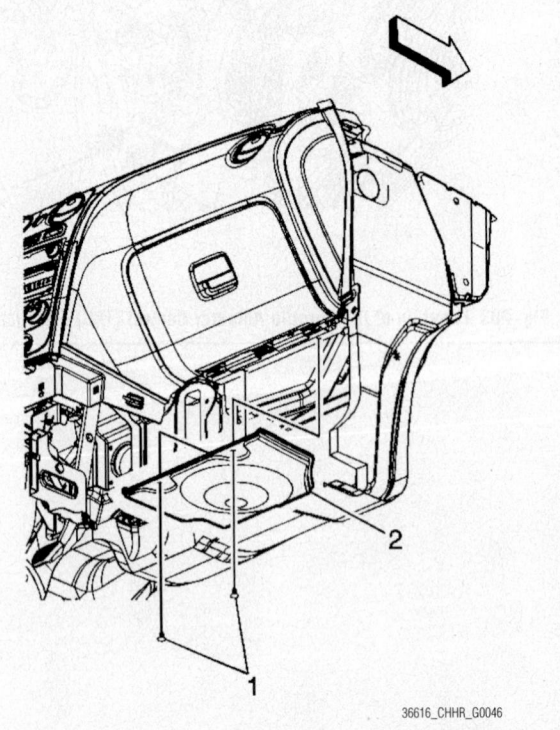

Fig. 205 View of the push pin retainers (1) and insulator/closeout panel (2)

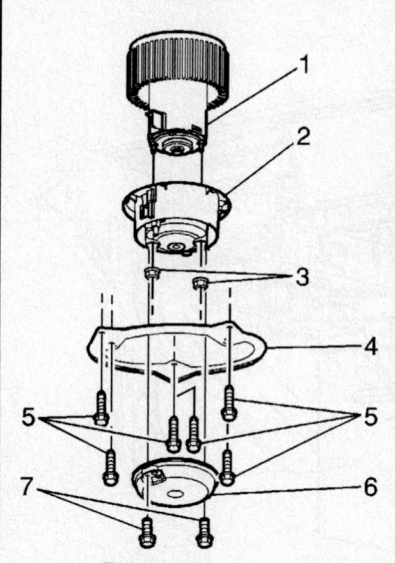

1. Blower motor
2. Motor cup
3. Blower motor nuts
4. Service ring
5. Blower motor screws

22116_COBA_G0113

Fig. 208 Expanded view of the blower motor

10. Release the blower motor retaining tab and remove the motor from the cup.

To install:

11. Install the blower motor (1) into the motor cup (2) that was cut out of the lower case.

12. Install the blower motor nuts (3). Tighten the nuts to 21 inch lbs. (2 Nm).

13. Attach the service ring (4) to the motor cup (2) with the screws (5). Tighten the screws to 15 inch lbs. (2 Nm).

14. Install the blower motor and service ring into the HVAC module using the screws (5). Make certain the blower motor electrical connector is pointing rearward in the vehicle. Tighten the screws to 15 inch lbs. (2 Nm).

15. Install the lower blower motor cover.

16. Install the lower blower motor cover retaining screws and tighten to 15 inch lbs. (2 Nm).

17. Connect the blower motor electrical connector.

18. Install the I/P compartment in the reverse of the removal procedure.

19. Install the right sound insulator in the reverse of the removal procedure.

20. Connect the negative battery cable.

HEATER CORE

REMOVAL & INSTALLATION
See Figures 209 and 210.

✳✳ CAUTION

With a pressurized cooling system, the coolant temperature in the radiator can be considerably higher than the boiling point of the solution at atmospheric pressure. Removal of the surge tank cap, while the cooling system is hot and under high pressure, causes the solution to boil instantaneously with explosive force. This will cause the solution to spew out over the engine, the fenders, and the person removing the cap. Serious bodily injury may result.

1. Before servicing the vehicle, refer to the Precautions Section.

2. Drain the cooling system.

3. Raise and support the vehicle.

4. Place a drain pan under the water pump drain port.

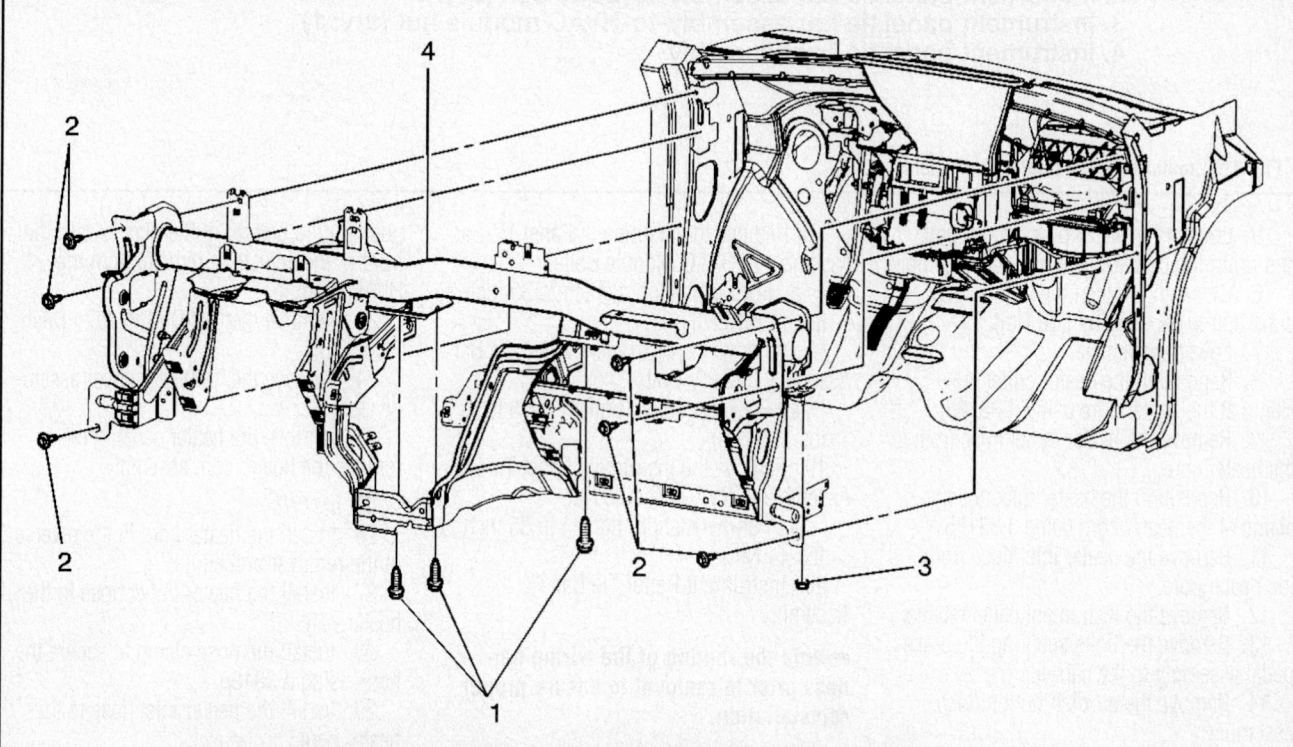

1. Instrument panel tie bar assembly-to-HVAC module bolt (qty: 3)
2. Instrument panel tie bar assembly-to-body bolt (qty: 6)
3. Instrument panel tie bar assembly-to-HVAC module nut (qty: 1)
4. Instrument panel tie bar assembly

36616_CHHR_G0047

Fig. 209 Instrument panel tie bar replacement

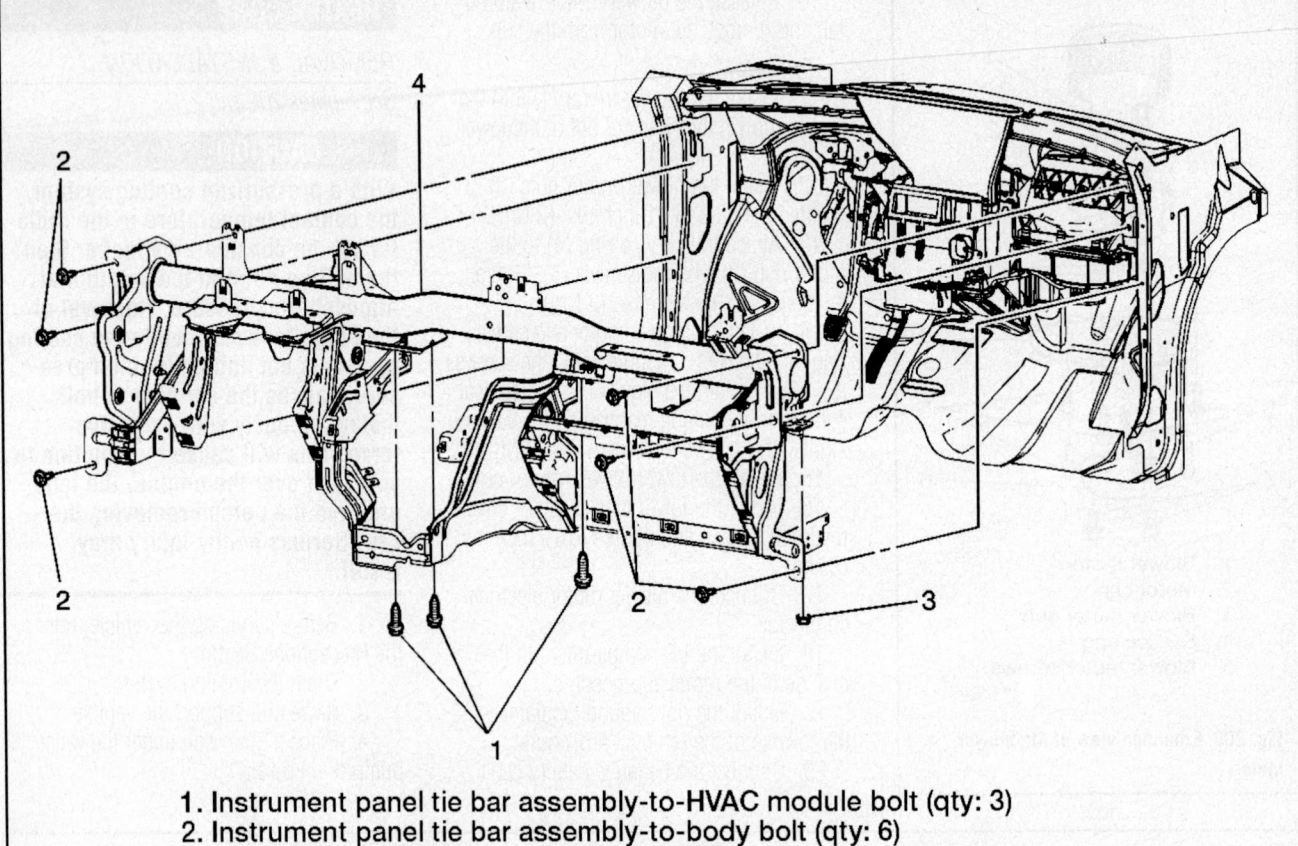

1. Instrument panel tie bar assembly-to-HVAC module bolt (qty: 3)
2. Instrument panel tie bar assembly-to-body bolt (qty: 6)
3. Instrument panel tie bar assembly-to-HVAC module nut (qty: 1)
4. Instrument panel tie bar assembly

36616_CHHR_G0047

Fig. 210 Heater core and related components

5. Loosen the water pump drain bolt and drain the coolant from the water pump.

6. Close and tighten the water pump drain bolt to 88 inch lbs. (10 Nm).

7. Lower the vehicle.

8. Reposition the heater outlet hose clamp at the heater core using J 38185.

9. Remove the heater outlet hose from the heater core.

10. Reposition the heater inlet hose clamp at the heater core using J 38185.

11. Remove the heater inlet hose from the heater core.

12. Remove the instrument panel retainer.

13. Remove the bolts securing the brake pedal assembly to the carrier.

14. Remove the air distribution duct assembly.

15. Remove the right defogger outlet duct assembly.

16. Remove the left defogger outlet duct assembly.

17. Remove the instrument Panel Tie Bar Assembly to HVAC Module Bolts.

a. For installation, tighten to 35 inch lbs. (4 Nm).

18. Remove the instrument Panel Tie Bar Assembly to Body Bolts.

a. For installation, tighten to 18 ft. lbs. (25 Nm).

19. Remove the instrument Panel Tie Bar Assembly to HVAC Module Nut.

a. For installation, tighten to 35 inch lbs. (4 Nm).

20. Instrument Panel Tie Bar Assembly

➡Note the routing of the wiring harness prior to removal to ensure proper reinstallation.

21. With the aid of an assistant, remove the carrier from the vehicle.

22. Remove the center rear floor air duct, by lifting up on the rear floor air duct and

pushing the bottom of the duct toward the front of the vehicle to remove from the HVAC module.

23. Remove the HVAC Module to Dash Panel Nuts.

24. Remove the 12 heater cover assembly screw

25. Remove the heater cover, then remove the heater core assembly.

To install:

26. Install the heater core in the reverse of the removal procedure.

27. Install the heater outlet hose to the heater core.

28. Install the hose clamp to secure the hose using J 38185.

29. Install the heater inlet hose to the heater core.

30. Install the hose clamp to secure the hose using J 38185.

31. Fill the cooling system.

STEERING

POWER RACK & PINION STEERING GEAR

REMOVAL & INSTALLATION

See Figures 211 and 212.

1. Before servicing the vehicle, refer to the Precautions Section.

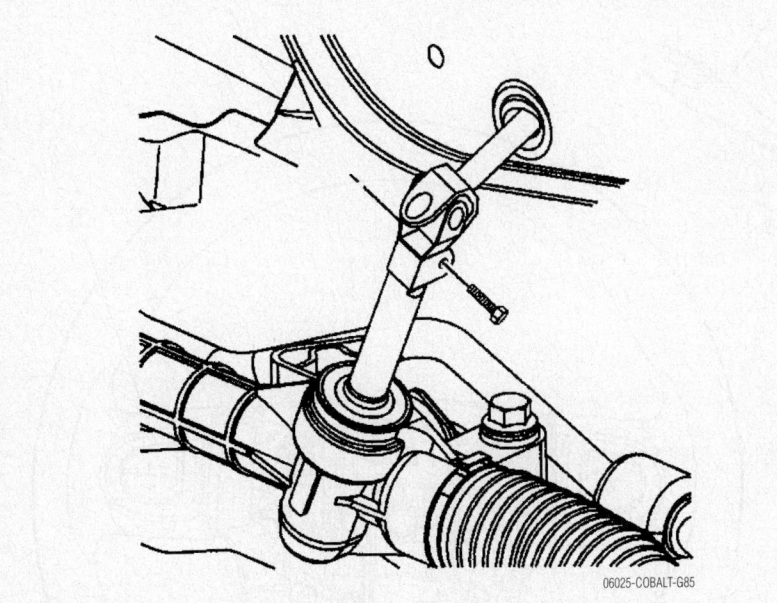

Fig. 211 Intermediate Steering shaft pinch bolt (discard and replace with a new bolt during installation)

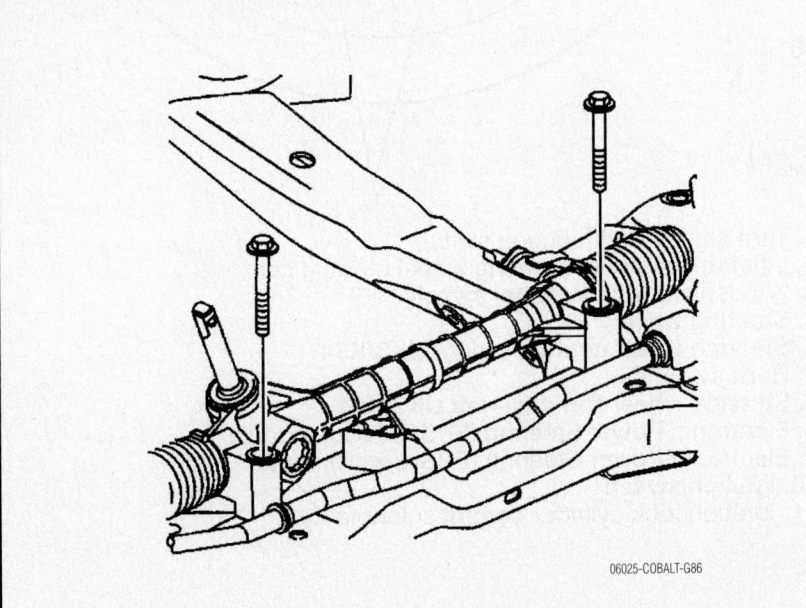

Fig. 212 Steering gear mounting

2. Turn the steering wheel to the straight ahead position and lock it in place.

✳✳ WARNING

With wheels of the vehicle facing straight ahead, secure the steering wheel utilizing steering column anti-rotation pin, steering column lock, or a strap to prevent rotation. Locking of the steering column will prevent damage and a possible malfunction of the SIR system. The steering wheel must be secured in position before disconnecting the following components: the steering column, the intermediate shaft(s), and the steering gear. After disconnecting these components, do not rotate the steering wheel or move the front tires and wheels. Failure to follow this procedure may cause the SIR coil assembly to become un-centered and cause possible damage to the SIR coil. If you think the SIR coil has became un-centered, refer to your specific SIR coil's centering procedure to re-center SIR Coil.

3. Raise and support the vehicle.
4. Remove the front wheels.
5. Remove both rack and pinion outer tie rod end nuts and discard them.

➡ **Do not attempt to separate the rack and pinion outer tie rod ends using a wedge type tool.**

6. Use the J 24319-B Puller in order to separate the rack and pinion outer tie rod ends from the steering knuckles.
7. Remove the intermediate steering shaft bolt at the steering gear and discard it.
8. Separate the intermediate steering shaft from the steering gear.
9. Remove the catalytic converter.
10. Remove the transmission rear mount.
11. Remove the steering gear bolts.
12. Remove the steering gear from the vehicle through the left wheelhouse opening.

To install:

13. Install the steering gear to the vehicle through the left wheelhouse opening.
14. Install the steering gear bolts and tighten to 81 ft. lbs. (110 Nm).
15. Install the rear transaxle mount. Refer to Transaxle, in the Drive Train section.
16. Install the catalytic converter.
17. Connect the intermediate steering shaft to the steering gear.
18. Install a new intermediate steering shaft bolt and tighten to 25 ft. lbs. (34 Nm).
19. Install the rack and pinion outer tie rod ends to the steering knuckles.
20. Install new rack and pinion outer tie

rod end nuts. Tighten the bolts to 18 ft. lbs. (25 Nm) plus 90°.

21. Install the front wheels.
22. Lower the vehicle.
23. Inspect the front toe.
24. If equipped with RPO JL4, calibrate the steering angle sensor:

a. Keep the steering wheel centered and the wheels facing forward.
b. With a scan tool, perform the special functions steering position sensor calibration and follow the on screen instructions.

POWER STEERING PUMP

REMOVAL & INSTALLATION

See Figure 213.

This vehicle uses electronic power steering.

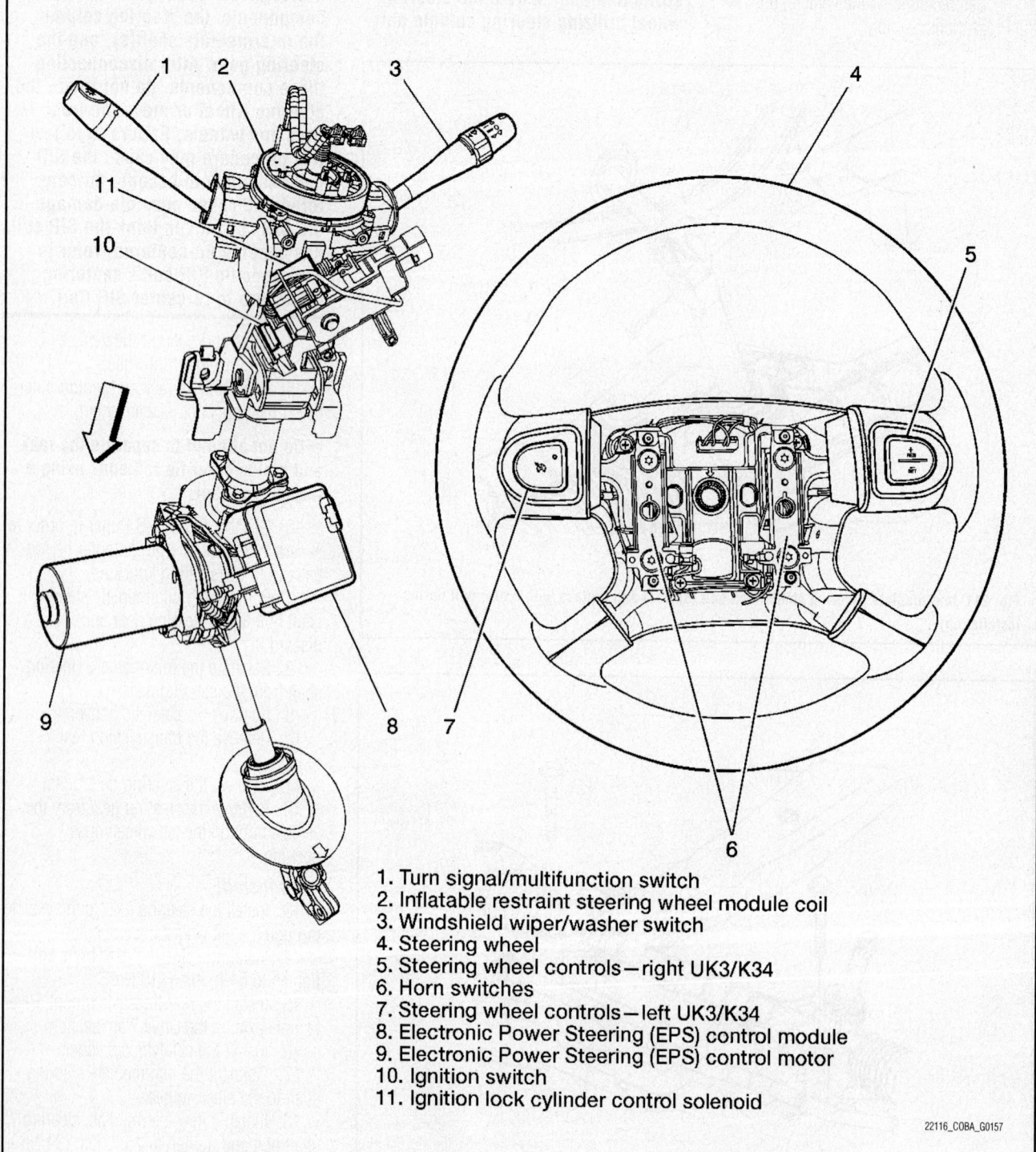

1. Turn signal/multifunction switch
2. Inflatable restraint steering wheel module coil
3. Windshield wiper/washer switch
4. Steering wheel
5. Steering wheel controls—right UK3/K34
6. Horn switches
7. Steering wheel controls—left UK3/K34
8. Electronic Power Steering (EPS) control module
9. Electronic Power Steering (EPS) control motor
10. Ignition switch
11. Ignition lock cylinder control solenoid

22116_COBA_G0157

Fig. 213 Expanded view of power steering and related components

LOWER CONTROL ARM

REMOVAL & INSTALLATION

See Figure 214.

1. Raise and support the vehicle.
2. Remove the tire and wheel assembly.
3. Remove the front lower control arm ball stud nut.
4. Remove the front lower control arm ball stud bolt from the steering knuckle.
5. Remove the drivetrain and front suspension frame bolt (4) from the drivetrain and front suspension frame (6).
6. Remove the front lower control arm bolts (2), and the front lower control arm brackets (5).
7. Remove the front lower control arm (3) from the steering knuckle (1) and the drivetrain and front suspension frame (6).

To install:

8. Position the front lower control arm on the drivetrain and front suspension frame.
9. Install the drivetrain and front suspension frame bolt in the frame.
10. Tighten the frame bolt to 74 ft. lbs. (100 Nm), plus an additional 180 degrees, using a torque angle meter.
11. Install the front lower control arm brackets and the lower control arm bolts and tighten to 41 ft. lbs. (55 Nm).
12. Install the front lower control arm in the steering knuckle.
13. Install the lower control arm ball stud bolt in the steering knuckle.

14. Install the lower control arm ball stud bolt nut.
15. Tighten the lower control arm ball stud nut to 37 ft. lbs. (50 Nm), plus an additional 30 degrees using a torque angle meter.
16. Install the wheel and tire assembly, then carefully lower the vehicle.

STEERING KNUCKLE

REMOVAL & INSTALLATION

See Figure 215.

1. Raise and support the vehicle.
2. Remove the wheel bearing and hub assembly, as outlined later in this section.
3. Remove the outer tie rod end from the knuckle.

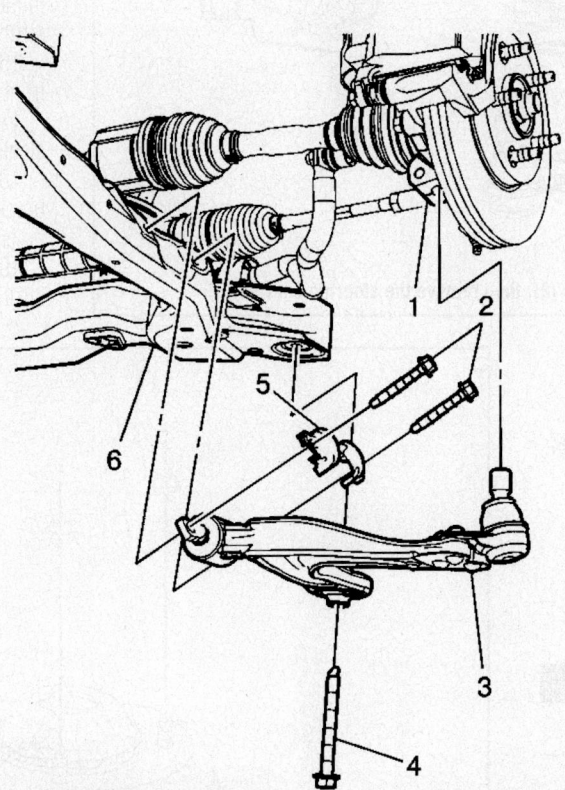

1. Steering knuckle
2. Lower control arm bolts
3. Lower control arm
4. Drivetrain and front suspension frame bolt
5. Lower control arm brackets
6. drivetrain and front suspension frame

36616_CHHR_G0049

Fig. 214 Exploded view of the lower control arm mounting

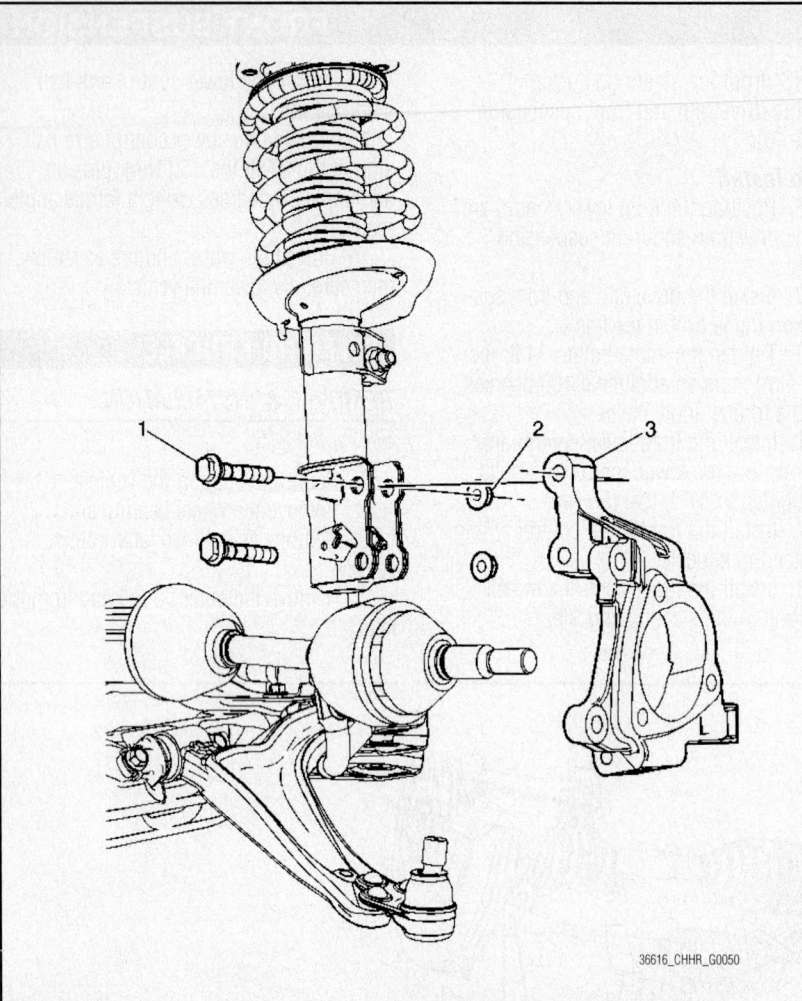

Fig. 215 View of the 2 bolts (1) and 2 nuts (2), then remove the steering knuckle (3)

4. Remove the lower control arm from the knuckle, as outlined in this section.

5. Unfasten the 2 bolts and 2 nuts, then remove the steering knuckle.

6. Install the steering knuckle in the reverse of the removal procedure. Tighten the steering knuckle nuts to 89 ft. lbs. (120 Nm).

7. Check the wheel alignment.

STRUT

REMOVAL & INSTALLATION

See Figures 216 and 217.

1. Before servicing the vehicle, refer to the Precautions Section.

2. Raise the vehicle just enough to remove the tire and wheel assembly.

3. Remove the tire and wheel.

4. Disconnect the stabilizer bar link from the strut assembly.

5. Lower the vehicle enough to access the upper strut mounting nuts.

6. Remove the front suspension strut

mounting nut (1) from the front suspension strut stud (2).

7. Raise the vehicle high enough to access the lower strut bolts.

8. Support the lower control arm with a suitable adjustable jackstand.

9. Remove the front suspension strut nut (2) from the front suspension strut bolts (5).

10. Disconnect the wheel speed sensor electrical connectors (3) and (4).

11. Remove the wheel speed sensor bracket (1), and relocate to the side.

12. Remove the strut bolts, from the strut, then remove the strut from the vehicle.

To install:

13. Position the strut in the vehicle.

14. Install the upper mounting nuts on the front suspension strut studs and tighten to 15 ft. lbs. (20 Nm).

15. Using the adjustable jack stand, lift the lower control arm to allow the installation of the front suspension strut.

16. Install the lower strut bolts in the front suspension strut.

17. Reconnect the wheel speed sensor electrical connectors.

18. Position the wheel speed sensor bracket on the front suspension strut bolts.

19. Install the front suspension strut nuts on the front suspension

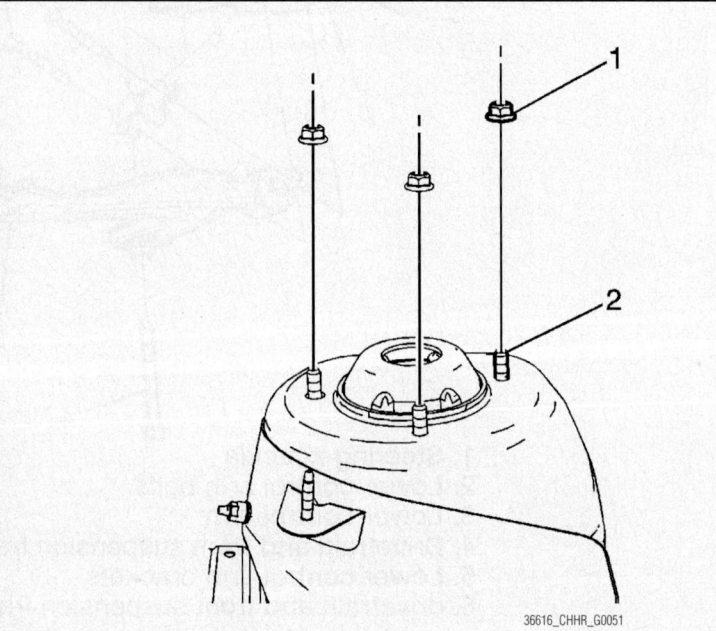

Fig. 216 Remove the front suspension strut mounting nut (1) from the front suspension strut stud (2)

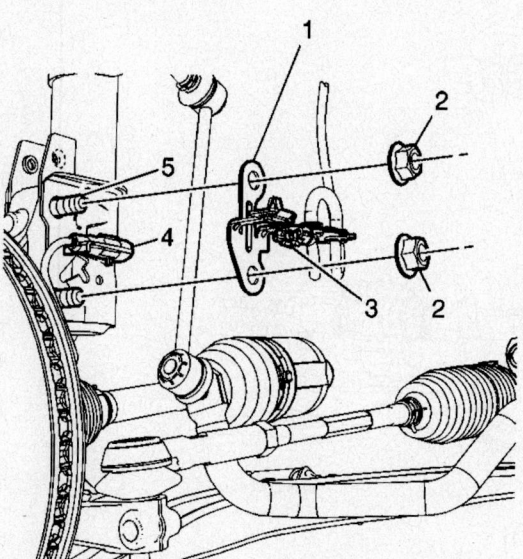

1. Wheel speed sensor bracket
2. Strut nut
3. Wheel speed sensor electrical connector
4. Wheel speed sensor electrical connector
5. Strut bolts

36616_CHHR_G0052

Fig. 217 View of the lower strut nuts and bolts and wheel speed sensor bracket

strut bolts and tighten to 89 ft. lbs.
(120 Nm).
  20. Install the stabilizer shaft link the
front suspension strut.
  21. Install the tire and wheel.
  22. Lower the vehicle.
  23. Inspect the front wheel alignment.

STABILIZER SHAFT LINK

REMOVAL & INSTALLATION

See Figure 218.

  1. Before servicing the vehicle, refer to
the Precautions Section.
  2. Raise and safely support the
vehicle.
  3. Remove the wheel and tire assembly.
  4. Remove the 2 stabilizer shaft link
nuts.
  5. Remove the stabilizer shaft link.

To install:

➡**Some models are equipped with a
washer/spacer between the stabilizer
link and the shock strut. It will be necessary to transfer the washer/spacer
when replacing the stabilizer shaft or
the stabilizer link**

  6. Install the stabilizer shaft link and 2
retaining nuts. Tighten the nuts to 59 ft. lbs.
(80 Nm).

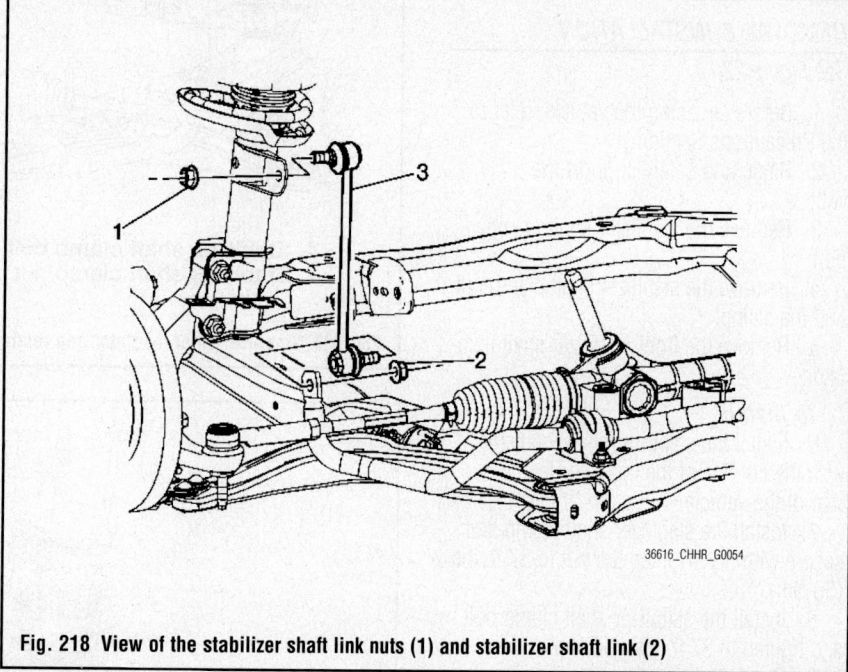

36616_CHHR_G0054

Fig. 218 View of the stabilizer shaft link nuts (1) and stabilizer shaft link (2)

  7. Install the wheel and tire assembly,
then carefully lower the vehicle.

STABILIZER SHAFT

REMOVAL & INSTALLATION

See Figure 219.

  1. Before servicing the vehicle, refer to
the Precautions Section.
  2. Raise and support the vehicle.
  3. Remove the front wheels.
  4. Remove the stabilizer shaft link from
the stabilizer shaft, as outlined in this
section.

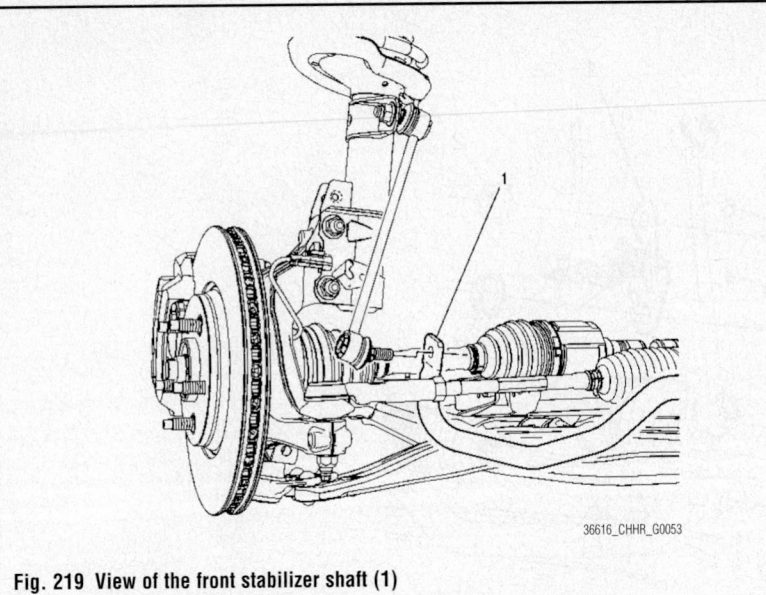

Fig. 219 View of the front stabilizer shaft (1)

5. Remove the stabilizer shaft insulators from the stabilizer shaft, as outlined in this section.

6. Remove the stabilizer shaft from the right side of the vehicle.

7. Installation is the reverse of the removal procedure.

STABILIZER SHAFT INSULATOR

REMOVAL & INSTALLATION

See Figure 220.

1. Before servicing the vehicle, refer to the Precautions Section.

2. Raise and safely support the vehicle.

3. Remove the stabilizer shaft clamp bolt.

4. Remove the stabilizer shaft clamp nut and the clamp.

5. Remove the front stabilizer shaft insulator.

To install:

6. Install the stabilizer shaft insulator with the cut line of the insulator facing the rear of the vehicle.

7. Install the stabilizer shaft clamp and secure with nut. Tighten the nut to 37 ft. lbs. (50 Nm).

8. Install the stabilizer shaft clamp bolt and tighten to 37 ft. lbs. (50 Nm).

9. Carefully lower the vehicle.

WHEEL HUB & BEARING

REMOVAL & INSTALLATION

See Figure 221.

1. Before servicing the vehicle, refer to the Precautions Section.

2. Raise and support the vehicle.

3. Remove the tire and wheel assembly.

4. Remove the front brake rotor.

5. Remove the wheel hub and bearing bolts.

6. Remove the wheel hub and bearing assembly.

7. Remove the wheel hub and bearing spacer.

To install:

8. Installation is the reverse of removal. Tighten the wheel hub and bearing bolts to 85 ft. lbs. (115 Nm).

ADJUSTMENT

All models use sealed wheel bearings that are pre-adjusted. If the bearing needs replacing, replace the front wheel hub/bearing assembly.

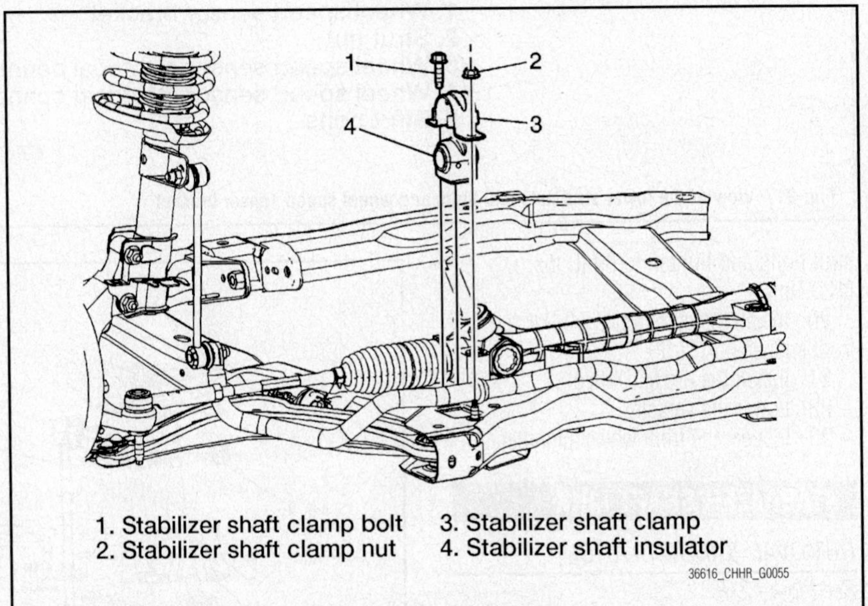

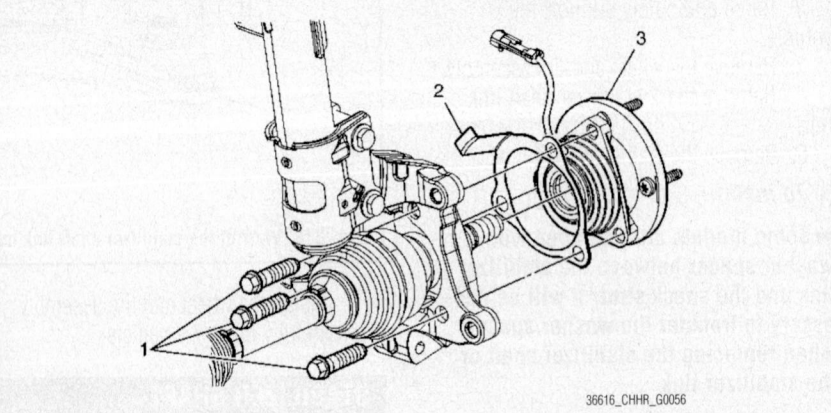

1. Stabilizer shaft clamp bolt
2. Stabilizer shaft clamp nut
3. Stabilizer shaft clamp
4. Stabilizer shaft insulator

Fig. 220 Stabilizer shaft insulator and related components

Fig. 221 View of the wheel hub and bearing mounting bolts (1), hub and bearing assembly (2) and steering knuckle bearing spacer (4)

COIL SPRING

REMOVAL & INSTALLATION

See Figure 222.

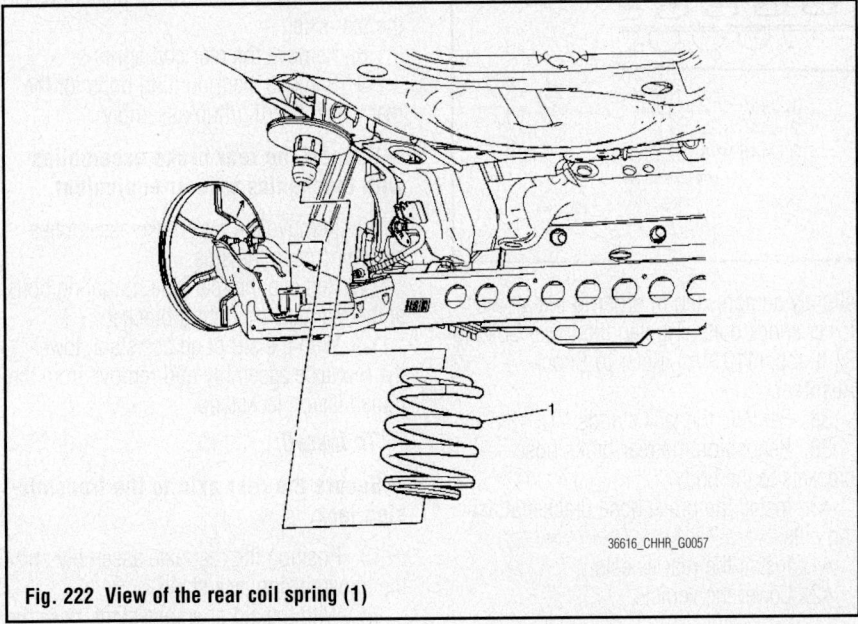

Fig. 222 View of the rear coil spring (1)

1. Before servicing the vehicle, refer to the Precautions Section.
2. Raise and support the vehicle.
3. Remove the tires and wheels.
4. Support the rear axle with a adjustable jack stand.
5. Remove the lower shock absorber bolt. Refer to the procedure in this section.
6. Using the adjustable jack stands, lower the rear axle to remove the rear coil spring
7. Installation is the reverse of the removal procedure.

CONTROL ARMS/LINKS

CONTROL ARM BUSHING REPLACEMENT

See Figures 223 and 224.

1. Before servicing the vehicle, refer to the Precautions Section.
2. Raise and support the vehicle.
3. Remove the rear wheels.
4. Place 2 screw type jack stands under both ends of the rear axle.
5. Remove the rear brake hose bracket attaching nuts from the body.
6. Detach the rear brake hose brackets from the body allowing the lines to hang free.
7. Remove the lower shock bolts.

✳✳ WARNING

Do not kink the brake pipes while lowering the axle.

8. Lower the jacks in order to remove the coil springs.
9. Temporarily re-install the lower shock bolts to support the axle.
10. Remove the bushing bracket to body bolts from both ends of the rear axle.
11. Using the jackstands, raise the rear of the axle until the bushing brackets pivot away from the body.
12. Remove the axle bushing through bolts and remove the bushing brackets.

→ Note the depth and orientation of the old bushing before removal.

13. Using tool J 44570 , install tool J 44570-1 with the lip between the axle sleeve and bushing flange. It may require tapping with a hammer to fully seat the tool.
14. Insert J 44570-3 through tool J 44570-1 and the axle bushing.
15. Install the washer and nut by hand, tightening until the tool is snug.
16. Using a hammer, drive the bushing from the axle sleeve.
17. Disassemble the tool and remove the bushing.

To install:

18. Slide the new bushings into the axle sleeve in the same orientation noted during removal. Make sure the rubber end is facing inboard and the largest void is in line with the wheel hub center.
19. Place the J 44570-1 onto the bushing. Make sure the bushing is still oriented correctly.
20. Insert the J 44570-3 through the J 44570-1 and the axle bushing.
21. Install the J 44570-2 bearing, washer, and nut.
22. Pull the bushing into the axle sleeve by holding the hex end of the threaded shaft while turning the nut.
23. Disassemble and remove the bushing installation tool from the axle.
24. Install the axle brackets to the axle bushings with the alignment slot on the outboard side.

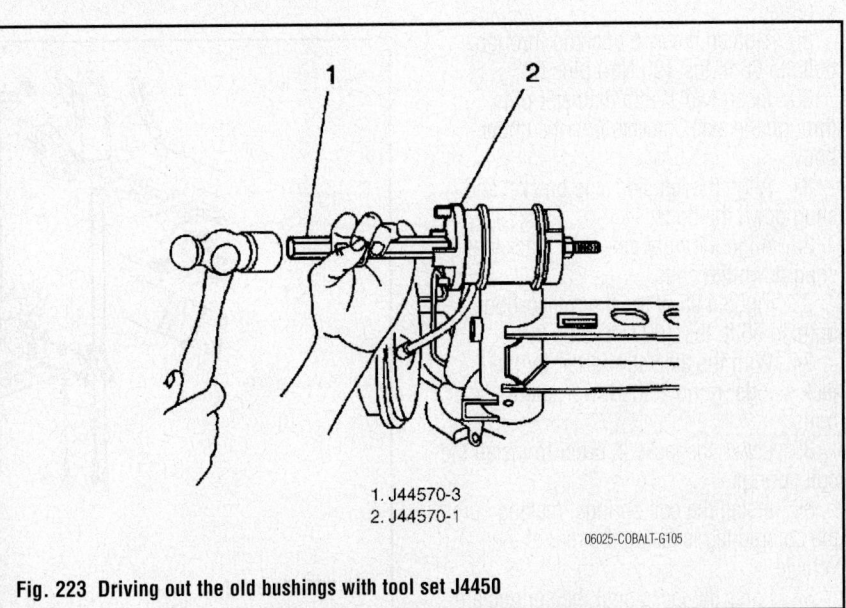

1. J44570-3
2. J44570-1

Fig. 223 Driving out the old bushings with tool set J4450

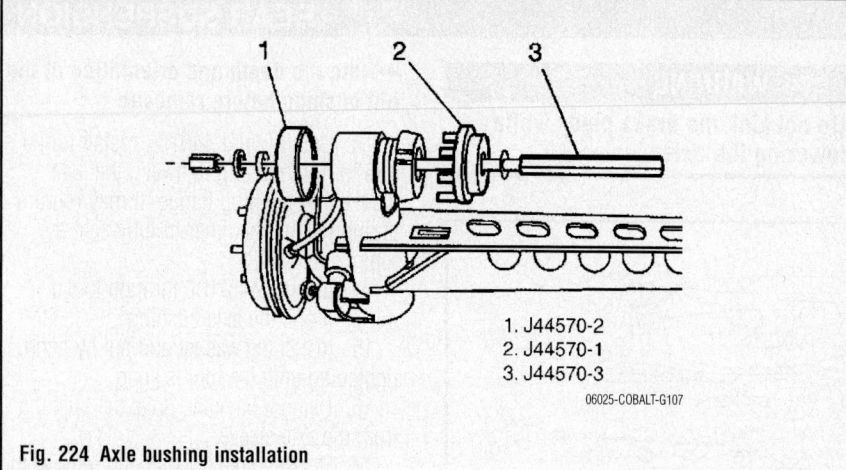

1. J44570-2
2. J44570-1
3. J44570-3

06025-COBALT-G107

Fig. 224 Axle bushing installation

➡**The axle bushing through bolts must be installed with the bolt head facing inboard.**

25. Loosely install the bushing bolts, park brake cable brackets and nuts .

26. Using the jack stands, lower the rear of the axle until the bushing brackets contact the body.

27. Hand tighten the axle bracket to body bolts just enough to hold the brackets flush to the body.

➡**The axle through bolts must be tightened with the axle at the correct trim height and prior to tightening the axle bracket to body bolts.**

28. Using the jack stands, raise the axle to the proper trim height specification by measuring the vertical distance between the bottom edge of the upper spring seat and the bottom of the notch in the lower spring seat. Refer to Rear Axle Beam for the D height measurement.

29. Tighten the axle bushing through bolts to 66 ft. lbs. (90 Nm) plus 60°

30. Insert two 12mm diameter pins through the axle brackets into the underbody.

31. Align the left side axle bracket and snug down the bolts.

32. Align the right side axle bracket and snug down the bolts.

33. Tighten all of the bracket-to-body bolts to 66 ft. lbs. (90 Nm) plus 30°.

34. With the axle supported by the jack stands, remove the lower shock bolts.

35. Lower the jacks in order to install the coil springs.

36. Install the coil springs, making sure the colored tag is facing the rear of the vehicle.

37. Raise the jacks until the springs are slightly compressed in order to install the lower shock bolts. Tighten the lower bolts to 81 ft. lbs. (110 Nm). Refer to Shock Absorber.

38. Remove the jack stands.

39. Reposition the rear brake hose brackets to the body.

40. Install the brake hose bracket attaching nuts.

41. Install the rear wheels.

42. Lower the vehicle.

REAR AXLE

REMOVAL & INSTALLATION

See Figure 225.

1. Before servicing the vehicle, refer to the Precautions Section.

2. Raise and support the vehicle.

3. Remove the rear wheels.

➡**Secure the rear axle to the transmission jack.**

4. Support the rear axle with a transmission jack stand.

5. Disconnect the rear wheel speed sensor electrical connector, if equipped.

6. Remove the rear park brake cables from the retaining clips at the rear axle mounting bracket.

7. Remove the rear brake hoses from the rear axle.

8. Remove the rear coil springs.

9. Remove the mounting bolts for the rear wheel bearing/hub assembly.

➡**Support the rear brake assemblies with mechanics wire or equivalent.**

10. Remove the rear brake assemblies and relocate to the side.

11. Remove the rear axle mounting bolts at the rear axle mounting bracket.

12. With the aid of an assistant, lower the rear axle assembly and remove from the transmission jackstand.

To install:

➡**Secure the rear axle to the transmission jack.**

13. Position the rear axle assembly on the transmission jack stand.

14. With the aid of an assistant, raise the rear axle assembly.

15. Install the rear axle mounting bolts in the rear axle mounting bracket. Tighten to 66 ft. lbs. (90 Nm).

16. Install the rear coil springs, as outlined in this section.

17. Remove the transmission jack stand.

18. Position the rear brake assemblies on the rear axle.

19. Install the mounting bolts for the rear wheel bearing/hub assembly.

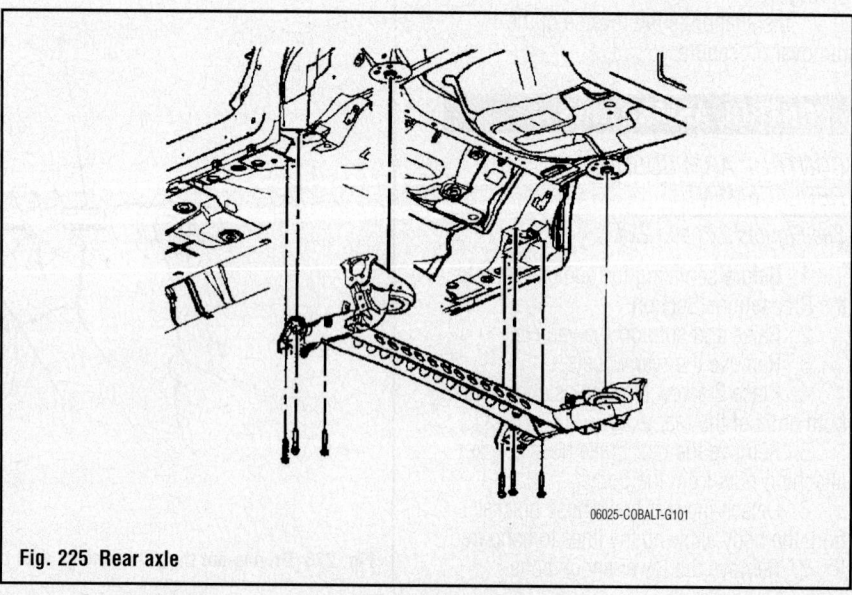

06025-COBALT-G101

Fig. 225 Rear axle

20. Reconnect the rear wheel speed sensor electrical connector, if equipped.

21. Install the rear brake hoses to the rear axle.

22. Install the rear park brake cables retaining clips at the rear axle mounting bracket.

23. Install the tires and wheels.

24. Remove the support and lower the vehicle

SHOCK ABSORBER

REMOVAL & INSTALLATION

See Figures 226 and 227.

1. Before servicing the vehicle, refer to the Precautions Section.

2. Raise and support the vehicle.

3. Remove the wheel.

4. Support the rear axle with a tall jackstand near the shock absorber.

5. Remove the upper and lower shock bolts.

6. Remove the shock from the vehicle.

To install:

7. Position the shock absorber to the vehicle.

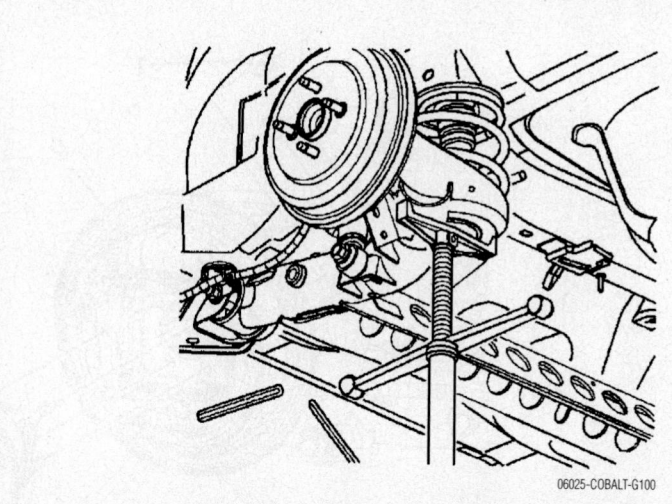

06025-COBALT-G100

Fig. 226 Support the rear axle with a tall jackstand near the shock absorber

8. Install NEW upper and lower shock bolts. Tighten the upper bolt to 66 ft. lbs. (90 Nm). Tighten the lower bolt to 92 ft. lbs. (125 Nm).

9. Remove the jackstand.

10. Install the wheel.

11. Lower the vehicle.

WHEEL HUB & BEARING

REMOVAL & INSTALLATION

See Figure 228.

1. Before servicing the vehicle, refer to the Precautions Section.

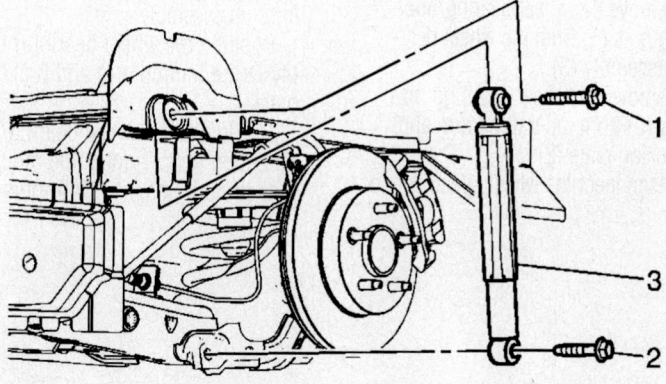

36616_CHHR_G0058

Fig. 227 View of the upper shock absorber bolt (2), lower bolt (2) and shock absorber (3)

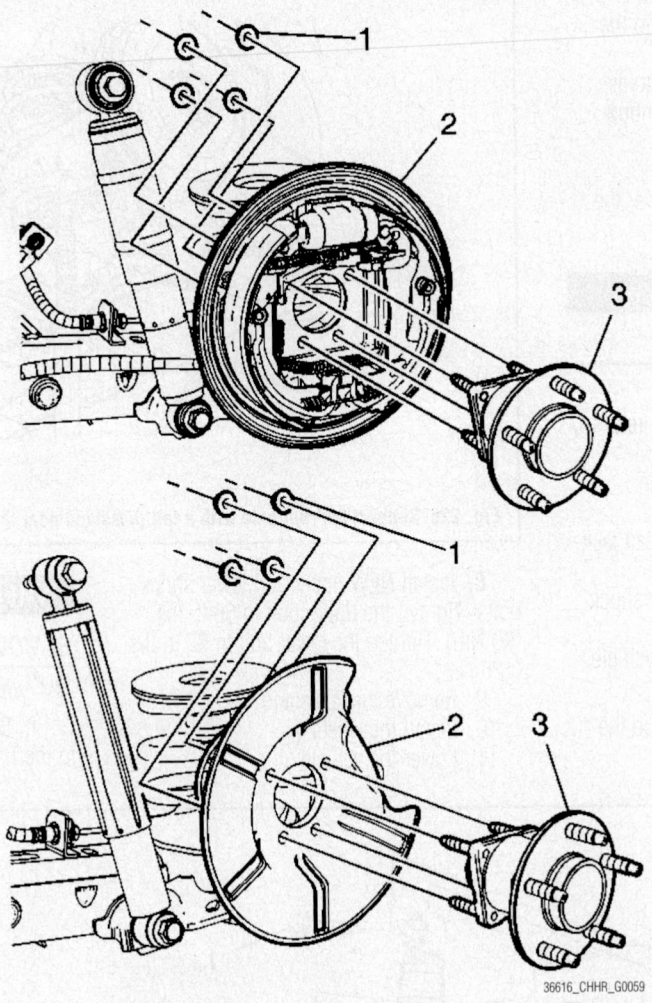

Fig. 228 Remove the wheel bearing/hub mounting nuts (1) from the wheel bearing/hub (3), then remove the wheel bearing/hub assembly (3) from the trailing arm and brake backing plate (2)

2. Raise and support the vehicle.
3. Remove the tire and wheel assembly.
4. Remove the brake rotor or drum, as applicable.
5. Remove the wheel bearing/hub mounting nuts (1) from the wheel bearing/hub assembly (3).
6. Remove the wheel bearing/hub assembly (3) from the trailing arm and brake backing plate (2).
7. Disconnect the wheel speed sensor electrical connector from the wheel bearing/hub assembly.

To install:
8. Reconnect the wheel speed sensor electrical connector to the wheel bearing/hub assembly.
Position the wheel bearing/hub assembly in the trailing arm and brake backing plate.
9. Install the wheel bearing/hub mounting nuts. Tighten the mounting nuts to 33 ft. lbs. (45 Nm), plus and additional 30 degrees with a torque angle meter.
10. Install the brake rotor or drum, as applicable.
11. Install the tire and wheel assembly.
12. Lower the vehicle.

ADJUSTMENT

All models use sealed wheel bearings that are pre-adjusted. If the bearing needs replacing, replace the rear wheel hub/bearing assembly.

SPECIFICATIONS AND MAINTENANCE CHARTS

ENGINE AND VEHICLE IDENTIFICATION

Engine Code							Model Year	
Code ①	Liters (cc)	Cu. In.	Cyl.	Fuel Sys.	Engine Type	Eng. Mfg.	Code ②	Year
N	3.5 (3510)	214	6	MFI	OHV	GM	9	2009
M	3.9 (3880)	238	6	MFI	OHV	GM		
C	5.3 (5327)	325	8	MFI	OHV	GM		

MFI: Multi-point Fuel Injection

OHV: Overhead Valves

① 8th position of VIN

② 10th position of VIN

36616_IMPA_C0001

GENERAL ENGINE SPECIFICATIONS

Year	Model	Engine Displacement Liters	Engine Series VIN	Net Horsepower @ rpm	Net Torque @ rpm (ft. lbs.)	Bore x Stroke (in.)	Compression Ratio	Oil Pressure @ rpm
2009	Impala	3.5	N	211@5800	214@4000	3.90x2.99	9.8:1	30-45@1850
	Impala	3.9	M	233@5600	240@4000	3.90x3.31	9.8:1	30-45@1850
	Impala	5.3	C	303@5600	323@4400	3.78x3.622	9.9:1	18@2000

36616_IMPA_C0002

ENGINE TUNE-UP SPECIFICATIONS

Year	Engine Displacement Liters	Engine VIN	Spark Plug Gap (in.)	Ignition Timing (deg.)	Fuel Pump (psi)	Idle Speed (rpm)	Valve Clearance In.	Valve Clearance Ex.
2009	3.5	N	0.04	①	55-62	②	HYD	HYD
	3.9	M	0.04	①	55-62	②	HYD	HYD
	5.3	C	0.04	①	55-62	②	HYD	HYD

NOTE: The Vehicle Emission Control Information label often reflects specification changes made during production.

The label figures must be used if they differ from those in this chart.

HYD: Hydraulic

① Distributorless Ignition System (DIS) timing is not adjustable

② Idle speed is maintained by the Engine Control Module (ECM). There is no recommended adjustment procedure.

36616_IMPA_C0003

CAPACITIES

Year	Model	Engine Displacement Liters	Engine VIN	Engine Oil with Filter (qts.)	Transmission (pts.) *	Fuel Tank (gal.)	Cooling System (qts.)
2009	Impala	3.5	N	4.0	13.4	17.0	10.1
	Impala	3.9	M	4.0	13.4	17.0	10.1
	Impala	5.3	C	6.0	13.4	17.5	13.3

NOTE: All capacities are approximate. Add fluid gradually and ensure a proper fluid is obtained.

* Drain and refill

36616_IMPA_C0004

FLUID SPECIFICATIONS

Year	Model	Engine Displacement Liters	Engine Oil	Auto. Trans. ①	Drive Axle	Power Steering Fluid	Brake Master Cylinder
2009	Impala	3.5	5W-30	Dexron VI	NA	GM Part No. 89021184	DOT 3
	Impala	3.9	5W-30	Dexron VI	NA	GM Part No. 89021184	DOT 3
	Impala	5.3	5W-30	Dexron VI	NA	GM Part No. 89021184	DOT 3

NA: Not Available

DOT: Department Of Transpotation

36616_IMPA_C0005

VALVE SPECIFICATIONS

Year	Engine Displacement Liters	Engine VIN	Seat Angle (deg.)	Face Angle (deg.)	Spring Test Pressure (lbs. @ in.)	Spring Installed Height (in.)	Stem-to-Guide Clearance (in.) Intake	Stem-to-Guide Clearance (in.) Exhaust	Stem Diameter (in.) Intake	Stem Diameter (in.) Exhaust
2009	3.5	N	46	45	76.4@1.70	1.84	0.0009-0.0025	NA	NA	NA
	3.9	M	46	45	76.4@1.70	1.84	0.0009-0.0025	NA	NA	NA
	5.3	C	46	45	76@1.8	1.800	0.0010-0.0026	0.0010-0.0026	0.3130-0.3140	0.3130-0.3140

NA: Not Available

36616_IMPA_C0006

CAMSHAFT AND BEARING SPECIFICATIONS CHART

All measurements are given in inches.

Year	Engine Displacement Liters	Engine ID/VIN	Journal Dia.	Brg. Oil Clearance	Shaft End-play	Runout	Journal Bore	Lobe Height Intake	Lobe Height Exhaust
2009	3.5	N	2.024-2.0250	NA	NA	NA	NA	0.2727	0.2727
	3.9	M	2.024-2.0250	NA	NA	NA	NA	0.2727	0.2727
	5.3	C	2.164-2.1660	0.0009-0.0038	0.001-0.0120	0.002	NA	①	②

NA: Not Available

① Non Active Fuel Management Cylinders:

Intake: 0.283

Exhaust: 0.283

② Active Fuel Management Cylinders:

Intake: 0.289

Exhaust: 0.289

36616_IMPA_C0007

CRANKSHAFT AND CONNECTING ROD SPECIFICATIONS

All measurements are given in inches.

Year	Engine Displacement Liters	Engine VIN	Crankshaft Main Brg. Journal Dia.	Crankshaft Main Brg. Oil Clearance	Crankshaft Shaft End-play	Thrust on No.	Connecting Rod Journal Diameter	Connecting Rod Oil Clearance	Connecting Rod Side Clearance
2009	3.5	N	2.6473-2.6483	0.0008- ① 0.0025	0.0024-0.0083	3	2.2489-2.2495	0.0007-0.017	0.008-0.0090
	3.9	M	2.6473-2.6483	0.0008- ① 0.0025	0.0024-0.0083	3	2.248-2.2490	0.0007-0.024	0.008-0.0090
	5.3	C	2.5580-2.5590	0.0008-0.0021	0.0015-0.0078	3	2.0991-2.0999	0.0009-0.0025	0.0043-0.0200

① Thrust bearing: 0.0012 - 0.0030

36616_IMPA_C0008

PISTON AND RING SPECIFICATIONS

All measurements are given in inches.

Year	Engine Displacement Liters	Engine VIN	Piston Clearance	Ring Gap Top Compression	Ring Gap Bottom Compression	Ring Gap Oil Control	Ring Side Clearance Top Compression	Ring Side Clearance Bottom Compression	Ring Side Clearance Oil Control
2009	3.5	N	0.0011-0.011	0.007-0.015	0.019-0.029	0.010-0.029	0.001-0.003	0.002-0.003	0.0004
	3.9	M	0.0011-0.011	0.007-0.015	0.019-0.029	0.010-0.029	0.001-0.003	0.002-0.003	0.0004
	5.3	C	0.00008-0.0006	0.0090-0.0170	0.0170-0.0270	0.0070-0.0290	0.0016-0.0034	0.0016-0.0031	0.0005-0.0078

36616_IMPA_C0009

TORQUE SPECIFICATIONS
All readings in ft. lbs.

| Year | Engine Displacement Liters | Engine VIN | Cylinder Head Bolts | Main Bearing Bolts | Rod Bearing Bolts | Crankshaft Damper Bolts | Flywheel Bolts | Manifold | | Spark Plug | Oil Pan Drain Plug |
								Intake	Exhaust		
2009	3.5	N	①	②	③	④	⑤	⑥	15	11	18
	3.9	M	①	②	③	④	⑤	⑥	15	11	18
	5.3	C	⑦	⑧	③	⑨	⑩	⑪	⑫	11	18

① Step 1: 44 ft. lbs.
   Step 2: plus 95 degrees

② 37 ft. lbs. plus 77 degrees

③ 15 ft. lbs. plus 75 degrees

④ Step 1: Use the old bolt to ensure the damper is installed
   to 92 ft. lbs.
   Step 2: Install a NEW bolt after installing the old bolt and
   tighten to 92 ft. lbs., plus 130 degrees

⑤ A/T: 52 ft. lbs.
   M/T: 37 ft. lbs. plus 70 degrees

⑥ Lower intake manifold center bolt:
   Step 1: 62 inch lbs.
   Step 2: 115 inch. lbs.
   Lower intake manifold corner bolt:
   Step 1: 62 inch lbs.
   Step 2: 18 ft. lbs.

⑦ M11 bolts
   Step 2: plus 90 degrees
   Step 3: plus 70 degrees
   M8 bolts: 22 ft. lbs.

⑧ M10 bolts
   Step 1: 15 ft. lbs
   Step 2: plus 80 degrees
   M10 studs
   Step 1: 15 ft. lbs
   Step 2: plus 51 degrees
   M8 bolts: 18 ft. lbs.

⑨ Step 1: install the old bolt and tighten to 240 ft. lbs.
   Step 2: install a NEW bolt and tighten to 37 ft. lbs.
   Step 3: plus 140 degrees

⑩ Step 1: 15 ft. lbs.
   Step 2: 37 ft. lbs.
   Step 3: 74 ft. lbs.

⑪ Step 1: 44 inch lbs.
   Step 2: 89 inch lbs.

⑫ Step 1: 11 ft. lbs.
   Step 2: 15 ft. lbs.

36616_IMPA_C0010

WHEEL ALIGNMENT

| Year | Model | | Caster | | Camber | | Toe-in |
			Range (Deg.)	Preferred Setting (Deg.)	Range (Deg.)	Preferred Setting (Deg.)	(Deg.)
2009	Impala w/ RPO FE1 (LS, LT)	F	+/-0.75	2.90 +/- 0.75	+/-0.75	-0.80	0.10 +/- 0.20
		R	NA	NA	NA	-0.65	-0.10 +/- 0.20
	Impala w/ RPO FE3 (SS)	F	+/-0.75	3.15 +/- 0.75	+/-0.75	-0.70	-0.10 +/- 0.20
		R	NA	NA	NA	-0.90	-0.10 +/- 0.20
	Impala w/ Police Pkg. RPO 7B3	F	+/-0.75	3.15 +/- 0.75	+/-0.75	-0.50	-0.10 +/- 0.20
		R	NA	NA	NA	-0.70	-0.10 +/- 0.20

NA: Not Available

36616_IMPA_C0012

TIRE, WHEEL AND BALL JOINT SPECIFICATIONS

Year	Model	OEM Tires		Tire Pressures (psi)		Wheel Size	Ball Joint Inspection	Lug Nut Torque (ft. lbs.)
		Standard	Optional	Front	Rear			
2009	Impala	P245/50R16	—	①	①	—	②	100
			—	①	①	—		

OEM: Original Equipment Manufacturer

PSI: Pounds Per Square Inch

① See placard on vehicle

② Remove all load from the joint. Vertical and horizontal movement is 0.125 in. max.

36616_IMPA_C0016

BRAKE SPECIFICATIONS
All measurements in inches unless noted

Year	Model		Brake Disc			Brake Drum Diameter			Minimum Lining Thickness		Brake Caliper	
			Original Thickness	Minimum Thickness	Maximum Runout	Original Inside Diameter	Max. Wear Limit	Maximum Machine Diameter	Front	Rear	Bracket Bolts (ft. lbs.)	Mounting Bolts (ft. lbs.)
2009	Impala	F	1.181	1.142	0.001	NA	NA	NA	NA	NA	133	26
		R	0.433	0.368	0.001	NA	NA	NA	NA	NA	88	32

F: Front

R: Rear

NA: Information not available

36616_IMPA_C0018

MAINTENANCE I AND II SERVICE SCHEDULES
Chevrolet Impala

When the CHANGE ENGINE OIL light appears, certain services and inspections are required.

Required services are described as Maintenance I and Maintenance II.

The first service on a vehicle should be Maintenance I, and the second service should be Maintenance II.

Alternate between the 2 thereafter. However, in some cases, Maintenance II may be required more often.

Maintenance I: Use Maintenance I if the CHANGE ENGINE OIL light comes on within 10 months since vehicle was purchased or, if Maintenance II was performed.

Maintenance II: Use Maintenance II if the previous service performed was Maintenance I. Always use Maintenance II whenever the CHANGE ENGINE OIL light comes on 10 months or more since the last service, or, if the CHANGE ENGINE OIL light has not come on at all for one year.

Service	Maintenance I	Maintenance II
Change the engine oil and filter. Reset the oil life system.	✓	✓
Visually inspect the vehicle for leaks or damage. A fluid loss in the vehicle system could indicate a problem. Inspected, repair and add fluid to the system if necessary.	✓	✓
Inspect the engine air cleaner filter. If necessary, replace the filter.		✓
Rotate the tires. Inspect the tire inflation pressures and the tire wear.	✓	✓
Visually inspect the brake lines and hoses for proper hook-up, binding, leaks, cracks, chafing, etc. Inspect the disc brake pads for wear and the rotors for surface condition. Inspect the drum brake linings for wear or cracks. Inspect other brake parts, including drums, wheel cylinders, calipers, parking brake, etc. Inspect the parking brake adjustment.	✓	✓
Inspect the engine coolant and the windshield washer fluid levels. Add fluid as needed.	✓	✓
Inspect the suspension and steering components. Inspect the front and rear suspension and the steering system for damaged, loose or missing parts, or signs of wear. Inspect the power steering lines and the hoses for proper hook-up, binding, leaks, cracks, chafing, etc.	--	✓
Visually inspect the coolant hoses and replace the hoses if they are cracked, swollen or deteriorated. Inspect all pipes, fittings and clamps; replace with GM parts as needed. To help ensure proper operation, a pressure test of the cooling system and pressure cap and cleaning the outside of the radiator and air conditioning condenser is recommended at least once a year.	--	✓
Inspect the transaxle fluid level and add fluid as needed.	--	✓
Inspect the wiper blades and replace as necessary	✓	✓
Inspect the restraint system components.		✓
Inspect the throttle system.	--	✓
Replace the passenger compartment air filter.		✓

To reset the CHANGE ENGINE OIL LIGHT:
1. Turn the ignition key to RUN with the engine off.
2. Fully press and release the accelerator pedal three times within five seconds. The change engine oil light will flash while the system is resetting
3. Turn the key to OFF. The oil life will change to 100%.

If the change engine oil light comes back on and stays on when you start your vehicle, the engine oil life system has not reset, repeat the procedure

36616_IMPA_C0021

PRECAUTIONS

Before servicing any vehicle, please be sure to read all of the following precautions, which deal with personal safety, prevention of component damage, and important points to take into consideration when servicing a motor vehicle:

• Never open, service or drain the radiator or cooling system when the engine is hot; serious burns can occur from the steam and hot coolant.

• Observe all applicable safety precautions when working around fuel. Whenever servicing the fuel system, always work in a well-ventilated area. Do not allow fuel spray or vapors to come in contact with a spark, open flame, or excessive heat (a hot drop light, for example). Keep a dry chemical fire extinguisher near the work area. Always keep fuel in a container specifically designed for fuel storage; also, always properly seal fuel containers to avoid the possibility of fire or explosion. Refer to the additional fuel system precautions later in this section.

• Fuel injection systems often remain pressurized, even after the engine has been turned **OFF**. The fuel system pressure must be relieved before disconnecting any fuel lines. Failure to do so may result in fire and/or personal injury.

• Brake fluid often contains polyglycol ethers and polyglycols. Avoid contact with the eyes and wash your hands thoroughly after handling brake fluid. If you do get brake fluid in your eyes, flush your eyes with clean, running water for 15 minutes. If eye irritation persists, or if you have taken brake fluid internally, IMMEDIATELY seek medical assistance.

• The EPA warns that prolonged contact with used engine oil may cause a number of skin disorders, including cancer. You should make every effort to minimize your exposure to used engine oil. Protective gloves should be worn when changing oil. Wash your hands and any other exposed skin areas as soon as possible after exposure to used engine oil. Soap and water, or waterless hand cleaner should be used.

• All new vehicles are now equipped with an air bag system, often referred to as a Supplemental Restraint System (SRS) or Supplemental Inflatable Restraint (SIR) system. The system must be disabled before performing service on or around system components, steering column, instrument panel components, wiring and sensors. Failure to follow safety and disabling procedures could result in accidental air bag deployment, possible personal injury and unnecessary system repairs.

• Always wear safety goggles when working with, or around, the air bag system. When carrying a non-deployed air bag, be sure the bag and trim cover are pointed away from your body. When placing a non-deployed air bag on a work surface, always face the bag and trim cover upward, away from the surface. This will reduce the motion of the module if it is accidentally deployed. Refer to the additional air bag system precautions later in this section.

• Clean, high quality brake fluid from a sealed container is essential to the safe and proper operation of the brake system. You should always buy the correct type of brake fluid for your vehicle. If the brake fluid becomes contaminated, completely flush the system with new fluid. Never reuse any brake fluid. Any brake fluid that is removed from the system should be discarded. Also, do not allow any brake fluid to come in contact with a painted surface; it will damage the paint.

• Never operate the engine without the proper amount and type of engine oil; doing so WILL result in severe engine damage.

• Timing belt maintenance is extremely important. Many models utilize an interference-type, non-freewheeling engine. If the timing belt breaks, the valves in the cylinder head may strike the pistons, causing potentially serious (also time-consuming and expensive) engine damage. Refer to the maintenance interval charts for the recommended replacement interval for the timing belt, and to the timing belt section for belt replacement and inspection.

• Disconnecting the negative battery cable on some vehicles may interfere with the functions of the on-board computer system(s) and may require the computer to undergo a relearning process once the negative battery cable is reconnected.

• When servicing drum brakes, only disassemble and assemble one side at a time, leaving the remaining side intact for reference.

• Only an MVAC-trained, EPA-certified automotive technician should service the air conditioning system or its components.

BRAKES

GENERAL INFORMATION

PRECAUTIONS

• Certain components within the ABS system are not intended to be serviced or repaired individually.

• Do not use rubber hoses or other parts not specifically specified for and ABS system. When using repair kits, replace all parts included in the kit. Partial or incorrect repair may lead to functional problems and require the replacement of components.

• Lubricate rubber parts with clean, fresh brake fluid to ease assembly. Do not use shop air to clean parts; damage to rubber components may result.

• Use only DOT 3 brake fluid from an unopened container.

• If any hydraulic component or line is removed or replaced, it may be necessary to bleed the entire system.

• A clean repair area is essential. Always clean the reservoir and cap thoroughly before removing the cap. The slightest amount of dirt in the fluid may plug an orifice and impair the system function. Perform repairs after components have been thoroughly cleaned; use only denatured alcohol to clean components. Do not allow ABS components to come into contact with any substance containing mineral oil; this includes used shop rags.

• The Anti-Lock control unit is a microprocessor similar to other computer units in the vehicle. Ensure that the ignition switch is **OFF** before removing or installing controller harnesses. Avoid static electricity discharge at or near the controller.

ANTI-LOCK BRAKE SYSTEM (ABS)

• If any arc welding is to be done on the vehicle, the control unit should be unplugged before welding operations begin.

WHEEL SPEED SENSORS

REMOVAL & INSTALLATION

See Figures 1 and 2.

1. Raise and support the vehicle.
2. Remove the right front tire and wheel.
3. Disconnect the Vehicle Speed Sensor (VSS) electrical connector.
4. Remove the VSS bolt.
5. Remove the VSS from the extension case.
6. Remove the O-ring from the VSS.

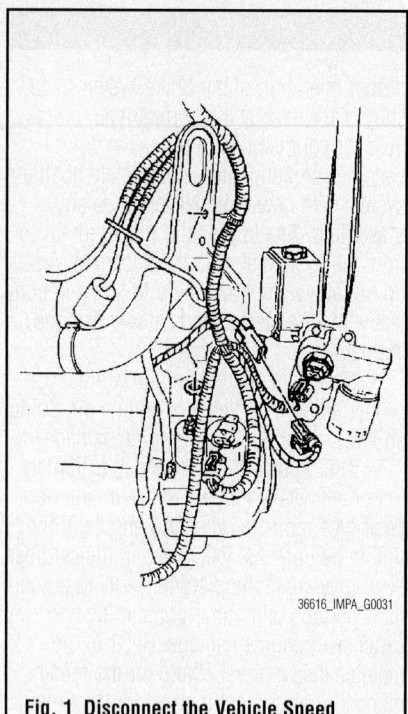

Fig. 1 Disconnect the Vehicle Speed Sensor (VSS) electrical connector

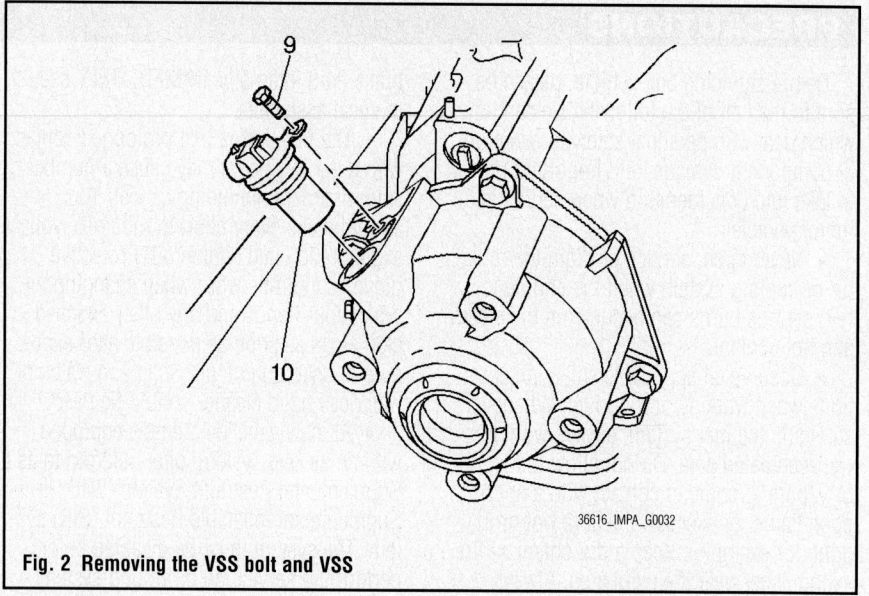

36616_IMPA_G0032

Fig. 2 Removing the VSS bolt and VSS

To install:

7. Install the O-ring to the VSS and install the VSS

8. Install the VSS bolt and tighten to 106 inch lbs. (12 Nm).

9. Connect the VSS electrical connector.

10. Install the right front tire and wheel.

11. Lower the vehicle.

BRAKES

BLEEDING THE BRAKE SYSTEM

BLEEDING PROCEDURE

※※ CAUTION

Use only GM SUPREME 11 (GM no. 1052542) or equivalent DOT 3 brake fluid from a clean, sealed container. Do not use fluid from an open container that may be contaminated with water. Improper or contaminated fluid could result in damage to components or loss of braking, with possible personal injury.

※※ WARNING

Overfilling the brake fluid reservoir must be avoided due to the potential for overflow onto the nearby catalytic converters in the exhaust system. Brake fluid is flammable, and contact with hot exhaust components could result in a fire and possible personal injury. Do NOT allow brake fluid to spill on or come in contact with the vehicle's finish as it will remove the paint. In case of a spill, immediately flush the area with water.

➡ **If any brake component is repaired or replaced such that air is allowed to enter the brake system, the entire bleeding procedure MUST be followed.**

Prior to bleeding the brakes, the front and rear displacement cylinder pistons must be returned to the topmost position. The preferred method uses a Tech 1® or equivalent scan tool to perform the rehoming procedure. If a scan tool is not available, a second procedure may be used, but it is extremely important that the procedure be followed exactly as outlined.

A bleeding operation is necessary to remove air when it has been introduced into the hydraulic brake system (by disconnecting brake lines or if the brake fluid reservoir has been allowed to run dry).

It is necessary to bleed the system at all four brakes. If a brake hose or steel brake line has been disconnected at one wheel, only that wheel caliper (or wheel cylinder, as equipped) needs to be bled. If brake lines or hoses are disconnected at any fitting located between the master cylinder and the brakes, then the brake system served by the disconnected brake line must be bled.

BLEEDING THE ABS SYSTEM

Before bleeding the ABS brake system, the front and rear displacement cylinder pistons must be returned to the topmost position. The preferred method uses a Tech 1® or T-100® scan tool to perform the rehom-

ing procedure. If a Tech 1® is not available, the second procedure may be used, but it must be followed EXACTLY.

Re-home Procedure

With Tech 1® or T-100® or Equivalent Scan Tools

1. Using a Tech 1® or T-100® (CAMS), select "Motor Rehome." The motor rehome function cannot be performed if current DTCs are present. If DTCs are present, the vehicle must be repaired and the codes cleared before performing the motor rehome function.

2. The entire brake system should now be bled using the pressure or manual bleeding procedures.

Wthout Tech 1® or T-100® or Equivalent Scan Tools

➡ **Do not place your foot on the brake pedal through this entire procedure unless specifically instructed to do so.**

This method can only be used if the ABS warning lamp is not illuminated and no DTCs are present.

1. Remove your foot from the brake pedal.

2. Start the engine and allow it to run for at least 10 seconds while observing the amber ABS warning lamp.

3. If the ABS warning lamp turned ON and stayed ON after about 10 seconds, the bleeding procedure must be stopped and a Tech 1 ® or equivalent scan tool must be used to diagnose the ABS function.

4. If the ABS warning lamp turned ON for about 3 seconds, then turned OFF and stayed OFF, turn the ignition switch to the **OFF** position.

5. Repeat Steps 1 – 4 one more time.

6. The entire brake system should now be bled by following the manual or pressure bleeding procedure.

Pressure Bleeding

See Figures 3 and 4.

➡ **The pressure bleeding equipment must be of the diaphragm type. It must have a rubber diaphragm between the air supply and the brake fluid to prevent air, moisture and other contaminants from entering the hydraulic system.**

1. Clean the master cylinder fluid reservoir cover and surrounding area, then remove the cover.

2. Add fluid, if necessary to obtain a proper fluid level.

3. Connect bleeder adapter J 35589, or equivalent, to the brake fluid reservoir, then connect the bleeder adapter to the pressure bleeding equipment.

4. Adjust the pressure bleed equipment to 5 – 10 psi (35 – 70 kPa) and wait about 30 seconds to be sure there is no leakage.

5. Adjust the pressure bleed equipment to 30 – 35 psi (205 – 240 kPa).

✷✷ WARNING

Use a shop rag to catch the escaping brake fluid. Be careful not to let any fluid run down the motor pack base or into the electrical connector.

6. With the pressure bleeding equipment connected and pressurized, proceed as follows:

a. Attach a clear plastic bleeder hose to the rearward bleeder valve on the hydraulic modulator.

b. Slowly open the bleeder valve and allow fluid to flow until no air is seen in the fluid.

c. Close the valve when fluid flows out without any air bubbles.

d. Repeat Steps 6b and 6c until no air bubbles are present.

e. Relocate the bleeder hose on the forward hydraulic modulator bleed valve and repeat Steps 6a through 6d.

7. Tighten the bleeder valve to 80 inch lbs. (9 Nm).

8. Proceed to bleed the hydraulic modulator brake pipe connections as follows with the pressure bleeding equipment connected and pressurized:

a. Slowly open the forward brake pipe tube nut on the hydraulic modulator and check for air in the escaping fluid.

b. When the air flow ceases, immediately tighten the tube nut. Tighten the tube nut to 18 ft. lbs. (24 Nm).

9. Repeat Steps 8a and 8b for the remaining three brake pipe connections moving from the front to the rear.

10. Raise and safely support the vehicle.

11. Proceed, as outlined in the following steps, to bleed the wheel brakes in the following sequence: right rear, left rear, right front, then left front.

a. Attach a clear plastic bleeder hose to the bleeder valve at the wheel, then submerge the opposite hose end in a clean container partially filled with clean brake fluid.

b. Slowly open the bleeder valve and allow the fluid to flow.

c. Close the valve when fluid begins to flow without any air bubbles. Tap lightly on the caliper or backing plate to dislodge any trapped air bubbles.

12. Repeat Step 11 on the other brakes using the earlier sequence.

13. Remove the pressure bleeding equipment, including bleeder adapter J 35589, or equivalent.

14. Carefully lower the vehicle, then check the brake fluid and add if necessary. Secure the reservoir cap onto the reservoir.

15. With the ignition switch turned to the **RUN** position, apply the brake pedal with moderate force and hold it. Note the pedal travel and feel. If the pedal feels firm and constant and the pedal travel is not excessive, start the engine. With the engine running, recheck the pedal travel. If it's still firm and constant and pedal travel is not excessive, go to Step 17.

16. If the pedal feels soft or has excessive

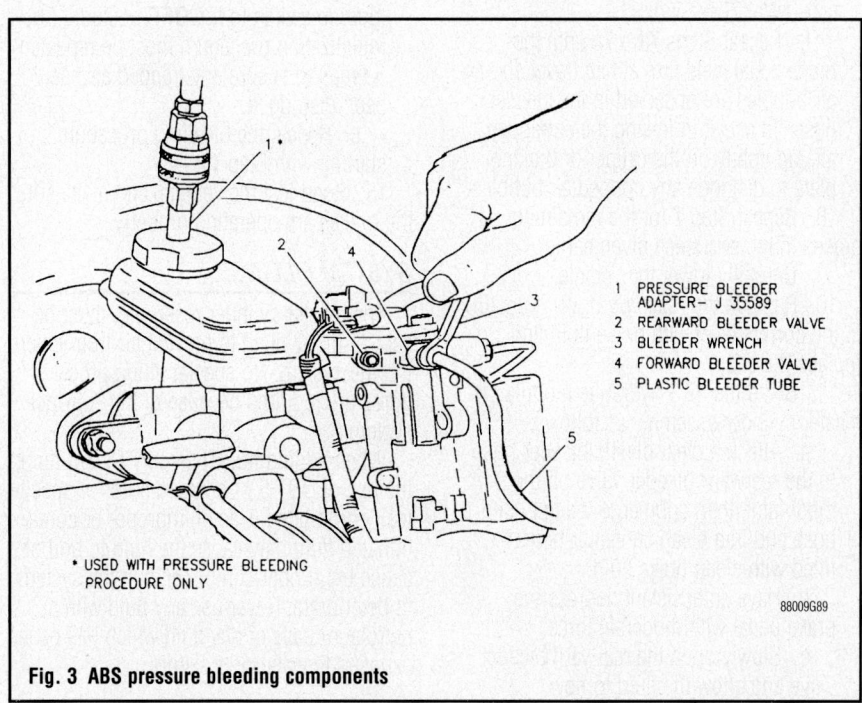

1 PRESSURE BLEEDER
  ADAPTER– J 35589
2 REARWARD BLEEDER VALVE
3 BLEEDER WRENCH
4 FORWARD BLEEDER VALVE
5 PLASTIC BLEEDER TUBE

* USED WITH PRESSURE BLEEDING
  PROCEDURE ONLY

88009G89

Fig. 3 ABS pressure bleeding components

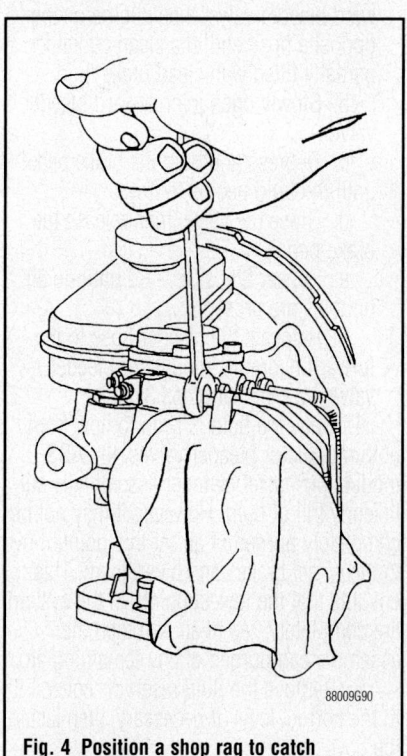

88009G90

Fig. 4 Position a shop rag to catch escaping brake fluid

travel either initially or after the engine is started, the following procedure may be used:

a. With the Tech 1® or equivalent scan tool, RELEASE then APPLY each motor 2 – 3 times and cycle each solenoid 5 – 10 times. When finished, be sure to APPLY the front and rear motors to ensure the pistons are in the upmost position. DO NOT DRIVE THE VEHICLE.

b. If a Tech 1® or equivalent scan tool is not available, remove your foot from the brake pedal, start the engine and allow it run for at least 10 seconds to initialize the ABS. DO NOT DRIVE THE VEHICLE. After 10 seconds, turn the ignition switch to the **OFF** position. The initialization procedure most be repeated 5 times to ensure any trapped air has been dislodged.

c. Repeat the bleeding procedure, starting with Step 1.

17. Road test the vehicle, and make sure the brakes are operating properly.

Manual Bleeding

See Figure 5.

1. Clean the master cylinder fluid reservoir cover and surrounding area, then remove the cover.

2. Add fluid, if necessary to obtain a proper fluid level, then put the reservoir cover back on.

3. Prime the ABS hydraulic modulator/master cylinder assembly as follows:

a. Attach a bleeder hose to the rearward bleeder valve, then submerge the opposite hose end in a clean container partially filled with clean brake fluid.

b. Slowly open the rearward bleeder valve.

c. Depress and hold the brake pedal until the fluid begins to flow.

d. Close the valve, then release the brake pedal.

e. Repeat Steps 3b – 3d until no air bubbles are present.

f. Relocate the bleeder hose to the forward hydraulic modulator bleeder valve, then repeat Steps 3a – 3e.

4. Once the fluid is seen to flow from both modulator bleeder valves, the ABS modulator/master cylinder assembly is sufficiently full of fluid. However, it may not be completely purged of air. At this point, move to the wheel brakes and bleed them. This ensures that the lowest points in the system are completely free of air and then the assembly can purged of any remaining air.

5. Remove the fluid reservoir cover. Fill to the correct level, if necessary, then fasten the cover.

6. Raise and safely support the vehicle.

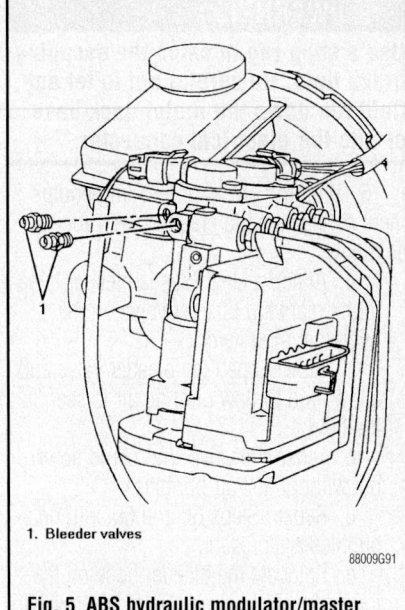

1. Bleeder valves

88009G91

Fig. 5 ABS hydraulic modulator/master cylinder bleeder locations

7. Proceed, as outlined in the following steps, to bleed the wheel brakes in the following sequence: right rear, left rear, right front, then left front.

a. Attach a clear plastic bleeder hose to the bleeder valve at the wheel, then submerge the opposite hose end in a clean container partially filled with clean brake fluid.

b. Open the bleeder valve.

c. Have an assistant slowly depress the brake pedal.

d. Close the valve and slowly release the release the brake pedal.

e. Wait 5 seconds.

f. Repeat Steps 7a – 7e until the brake pedal feels firm at half travel and no air bubbles are observed in the bleeder hose. To assist in freeing the entrapped air, tap lightly on the caliper or braking plate to dislodge any trapped air bubbles.

8. Repeat Step 7 for the remaining brakes in the sequence given earlier.

9. Carefully lower the vehicle.

10. Remove the reservoir cover, then fill to the correct level with brake fluid and replace the cap.

11. Bleed the ABS hydraulic modulator/master cylinder assembly as follows:

a. Attach a clear plastic bleeder hose to the rearward bleeder valve on the modulator, then submerge the opposite hose end in a clean container partially filled with clean brake fluid.

b. Have an assistant depress the brake pedal with moderate force.

c. Slowly open the rearward bleeder valve and allow the fluid to flow.

d. Close the valve, then release the brake pedal.

e. Wait 5 seconds.

f. Repeat Steps 11a – 11e until no air bubbles are present.

g. Relocate the bleeder hose to the forward hydraulic modulator bleeder valve, then repeat Steps 11a – 11f.

12. Carefully lower the vehicle, then check the brake fluid and add if necessary. Secure the reservoir cap to the reservoir.

13. With the ignition switch placed in the **RUN** position, apply the brake pedal with moderate force and hold it. Note the pedal travel and feel. If the pedal feels firm and constant and the pedal travel is not excessive, start the engine. With the engine running, recheck the pedal travel. If it's still firm and constant and pedal travel is not excessive, road test the vehicle and make sure the brakes are operating properly.

14. If the pedal feels soft or has excessive travel either initially or after the engine is started, the following procedure may be used:

a. With the Tech 1 ® or equivalent scan tool, RELEASE then APPLY each motor 2 – 3 times and cycle each solenoid 5 – 10 times. When finished, be sure to APPLY the front and rear motors to ensure the pistons are in the upmost position. DO NOT DRIVE THE VEHICLE.

b. If a Tech 1 ® or equivalent scan tool is not available, remove your foot from the brake pedal, start the engine and allow it run for at least 10 seconds to initialize the ABS. DO NOT DRIVE THE VEHICLE. After 10 seconds, turn the ignition switch to the **OFF** position. The initialization procedure most be repeated 5 times to ensure any trapped air has been dislodged.

c. Repeat the bleeding procedure, starting with Step 1.

15. Road test the vehicle, and make sure the brakes are operating properly.

SYSTEM FILLING

The master cylinder reservoirs must be kept properly filled to prevent air from entering the system. No special filling procedures are required because of the anti-lock system.

When adding fluid, use only DOT 3 fluid; the use of DOT 5 or silicone fluids is specifically prohibited. Use of improper or contaminated fluid may cause the fluid to boil or cause the rubber components in the system to deteriorate. Never use any fluid with a petroleum base or any fluid which has been exposed to water or moisture.

✳✳ CAUTION

Dust and dirt accumulating on brake parts during normal use may contain asbestos fibers from production or aftermarket brake linings. Breathing excessive concentrations of asbestos fibers can cause serious bodily harm. Exercise care when servicing brake parts. Do not sand or grind brake lining unless equipment used is designed to contain the dust residue. Do not clean brake parts with compressed air or by dry brushing. Cleaning should be done by dampening the brake components with a fine mist of water, then wiping the brake components clean with a dampened cloth. Dispose of cloth and all residue containing asbestos fibers in an impermeable container with the appropriate label. Follow practices prescribed by the Occupational Safety and Health Administration (OSHA) and the Environmental Protection Agency (EPA) for the handling, processing, and disposing of dust or debris that may contain asbestos fibers.

BRAKE CALIPER

REMOVAL & INSTALLATION

See Figure 6.

1. Raise and support the vehicle
2. Remove the tire and wheel.
3. Remove the brake hose fitting bolt and the two gaskets. Use new gaskets for installation.
4. Remove the brake hose and cap brake hose fitting to prevent brake fluid loss and contamination.
5. Remove the two guide pin bolts.

To install:

6. To install reverse removal procedure.
7. Tighten the guide pin bolts to 26 ft. lbs. (36 Nm).
8. Use new brake hose fitting gaskets and tighten the bolt to 40 ft. lbs (54 Nm).
9. Bleed the hydraulic brake system.
10. With the engine OFF, gradually apply the brake pedal to approximately ⅔ of its travel distance.
11. Slowly release the brake pedal.
12. Wait 15 seconds, then repeat steps 2 – 3 until a firm brake pedal is obtained. This will properly seat the brake caliper pistons and brake pads.

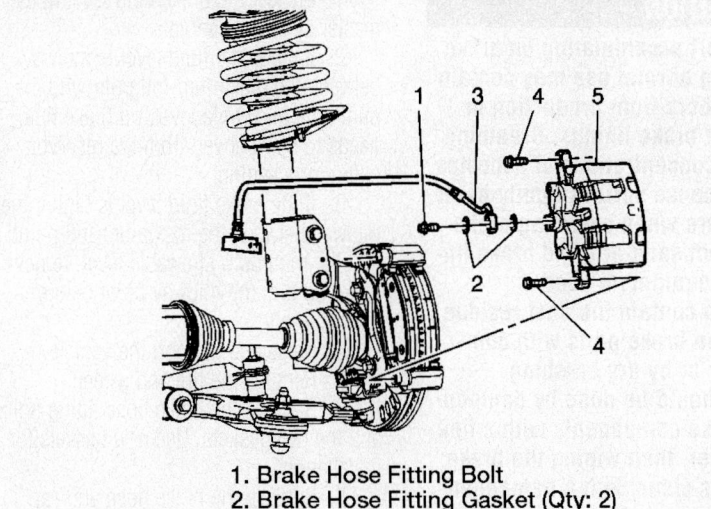

1. Brake Hose Fitting Bolt
2. Brake Hose Fitting Gasket (Qty: 2)
3. Brake Hose
4. Guide Pin Bolt (Qty: 2)
5. Brake Caliper

36616_IMPA_G0033

Fig. 6 Front brake components

13. Fill the master cylinder reservoir to the proper level.
14. Burnish the pads and rotors.

DISC BRAKE PADS

REMOVAL & INSTALLATION

See Figure 6.

✳✳ CAUTION

Support the brake caliper with heavy mechanic wire, or equivalent, whenever it is separated from its mount and the hydraulic flexible brake hose is still connected. Failure to support the caliper in this manner will cause the flexible brake hose to bear the weight of the caliper, which may cause damage to the brake hose and in turn may cause a brake fluid leak.

1. Inspect the fluid level in the brake master cylinder reservoir.
2. If the brake fluid level is midway between the maximum-full point and the minimum allowable level, no brake fluid needs to be removed before proceeding.
3. If the brake fluid level is higher than midway between the maximum-full point and the minimum allowable level, remove brake fluid to the midway point before proceeding.
4. Raise and support the vehicle.
5. Remove the tire and wheel.
6. Remove the guide pin bolt.
7. Rotate the brake caliper up and to

the rear until it rests on the mounting bracket and support with heavy mechanics wire or equivalent.
8. Place a block of wood or an old disc brake pad against the brake caliper pistons.
9. Using a brake pad spreader or a C clamp, slowly compress the brake caliper pistons squarely into the caliper bores.
10. If installing the original brake pads, note the brake pad location for proper installation.
11. When replacing the brake pads, ensure the brake pad with the wear indicator is positioned inboard of the brake rotor and the wear indicator is pointing down.
12. Clean the friction surfaces of the brake rotor with denatured alcohol.

To install:

13. To install, reverse removal procedure.
14. Tighten the guide pin bolt to 26 ft. lbs. (36 Nm).
15. If replacing the brake pads, DO NOT reuse the spring retainers. Install NEW spring retainers.
16. With the engine OFF, gradually apply the brake pedal to approximately 2/3 of its travel distance.
17. Slowly release the brake pedal.
18. Wait 15 seconds, then repeat steps 2-3 until a firm brake pedal is obtained. This will properly seat the brake caliper pistons and the brake pads.
19. Fill the master cylinder reservoir to the proper level.
20. Burnish the pads and rotors.

✳✳ CAUTION

Dust and dirt accumulating on brake parts during normal use may contain asbestos fibers from production or aftermarket brake linings. Breathing excessive concentrations of asbestos fibers can cause serious bodily harm. Exercise care when servicing brake parts. Do not sand or grind brake lining unless equipment used is designed to contain the dust residue. Do not clean brake parts with compressed air or by dry brushing. Cleaning should be done by dampening the brake components with a fine mist of water, then wiping the brake components clean with a dampened cloth. Dispose of cloth and all residue containing asbestos fibers in an impermeable container with the appropriate label. Follow practices prescribed by the Occupational Safety and Health Administration (OSHA) and the Environmental Protection Agency (EPA) for the handling, processing, and disposing of dust or debris that may contain asbestos fibers.

BRAKE CALIPER

REMOVAL & INSTALLATION

See Figure 7.

1. Inspect the brake fluid level in the master cylinder reservoir.

2. If the brake fluid level is midway between the maximum-full point and the minimum allowable level, no brake fluid needs to be removed from the reservoir before proceeding.

3. If the brake fluid level is higher than midway between the maximum-full point and the minimum allowable level, remove brake fluid to the midway point before proceeding.

4. Raise and support the vehicle.

5. Remove the tire and wheel.

6. Remove the brake hose fitting bolt and the two gaskets. Use new gaskets for installation.

7. Remove the brake hose and cap brake hose fitting to prevent brake fluid loss and contamination.

8. Remove the two guide pin bolts.

To install:

9. To install reverse removal procedure.

10. Tighten the guide pin bolts to 32 ft. lbs. (44 Nm).

11. Use new brake hose fitting gaskets and tighten the bolt to 40 ft. lbs (54 Nm).

12. Bleed the hydraulic brake system.

13. With the engine OFF, gradually apply the brake pedal to approximately ⅔ of its travel distance.

14. Slowly release the brake pedal.

15. Wait 15 seconds, then repeat steps

2 – 3 until a firm brake pedal is obtained. This will properly seat the brake caliper pistons and brake pads.

16. Fill the master cylinder reservoir to the proper level.

DISC BRAKE PADS

REMOVAL & INSTALLATION

See Figure 8.

1. Before servicing the vehicle, refer to the Precautions Section.

2. Siphon ⅔ of the brake fluid out of the master cylinder.

3. Remove the tire and wheel assembly.

4. Install 2 lug nuts to secure the rotor in place when the caliper is removed.

5. Remove bolt and washer attaching cable support bracket to caliper body assembly. It is not necessary to disconnect the parking brake lever or disconnect the brake hose.

6. Remove the caliper retaining bolt.

7. Pivot the caliper body assembly up from the rotor and remove from the bracket. Do not completely remove the caliper assembly body.

8. Remove the outboard and inboard shoe and linings from the caliper support assembly.

9. Remove 2 brake lining clips from the caliper support.

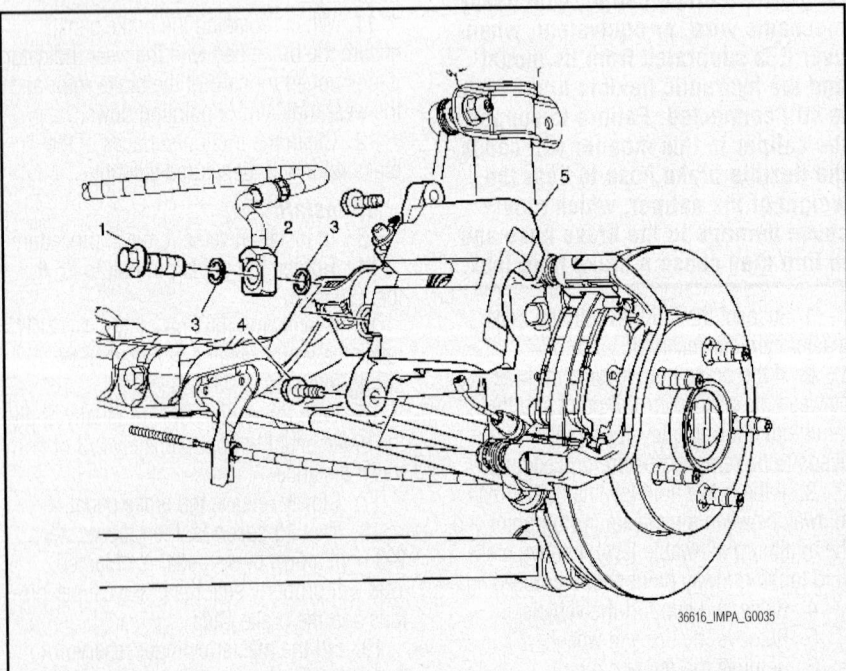

36616_IMPA_G0035

Fig. 7 Removing the rear brake caliper

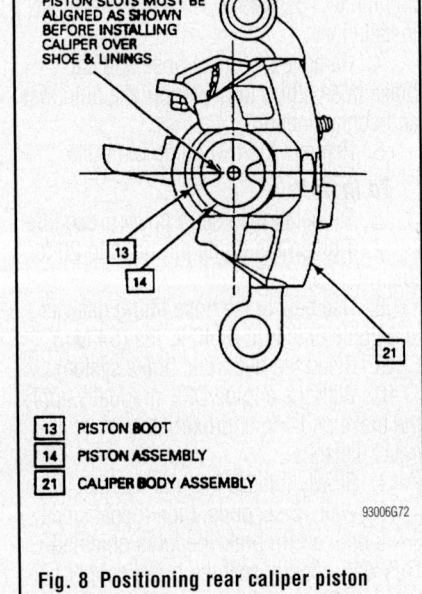

PISTON SLOTS MUST BE ALIGNED AS SHOWN BEFORE INSTALLING CALIPER OVER SHOE & LININGS

13	PISTON BOOT
14	PISTON ASSEMBLY
21	CALIPER BODY ASSEMBLY

93006G72

Fig. 8 Positioning rear caliper piston slots

To install:

➡ **In order for the rear pads to seat in the caliper properly, the cut outs in the caliper piston must be at the 6 and 12 o'clock positions. Failure to align the piston correctly can lead to brake drag, premature brake wear and possible brake failure.**

10. Using a suitable type spanner tool turn the piston in to bottom the piston fully into the caliper bore. Once the caliper is fully seated make sure the cutouts in the piston are at the 6 and 12 o'clock positions.

11. After bottoming the piston into the caliper bore, lift the inner edge of boot next to the piston assembly and press out any trapped air.

12. Install 2 pad clips in the caliper support.

13. Lubricate the inner pad where it contacts the piston and mounting surfaces.

14. Install outboard and inboard shoe and linings in caliper support. Position the wear sensors downward at the leading edge of the rotor during forward wheel rotation.

15. Hold the metal shoe edge against the spring end of clips in the caliper support. Push brake pad in towards the hub, bending spring ends slightly and engage shoe notches with support abutments.

16. Pivot the caliper body assembly down over the brake pad.

➡ **After the caliper body assembly is in position, recheck installation of the**

brake pad clips. If necessary, use a small prying tool to reseat or center the pad clip on the support abutments.

17. Install the bolts.

18. Install the cable support bracket with the cable attached and bolt washer. Torque bolt to 32 ft. lbs. (43 Nm).

19. Remove the 2 lug nuts securing the rotor.

20. Install the tire and wheel assembly and tighten to specification.

21. Pump the brake pedal several times to seat the pads against the rotor.

22. Check the brake fluid level and top off as necessary.

23. Adjust parking brake as necessary.

24. Road test the vehicle for proper brake performance.

BRAKES

PARKING BRAKE CABLES

ADJUSTMENT

See Figure 9.

1. Apply the parking brake pedal three times with heavy force of about 175 lbs. (778 N).

➡ **Do not apply the main/service brake pedal during the next step.**

2. Fully apply and release the parking brake three times.

3. Raise the vehicle and safely support the vehicle with safety stands.

4. Matchmark the position of the wheel to the hub and bearing assembly.

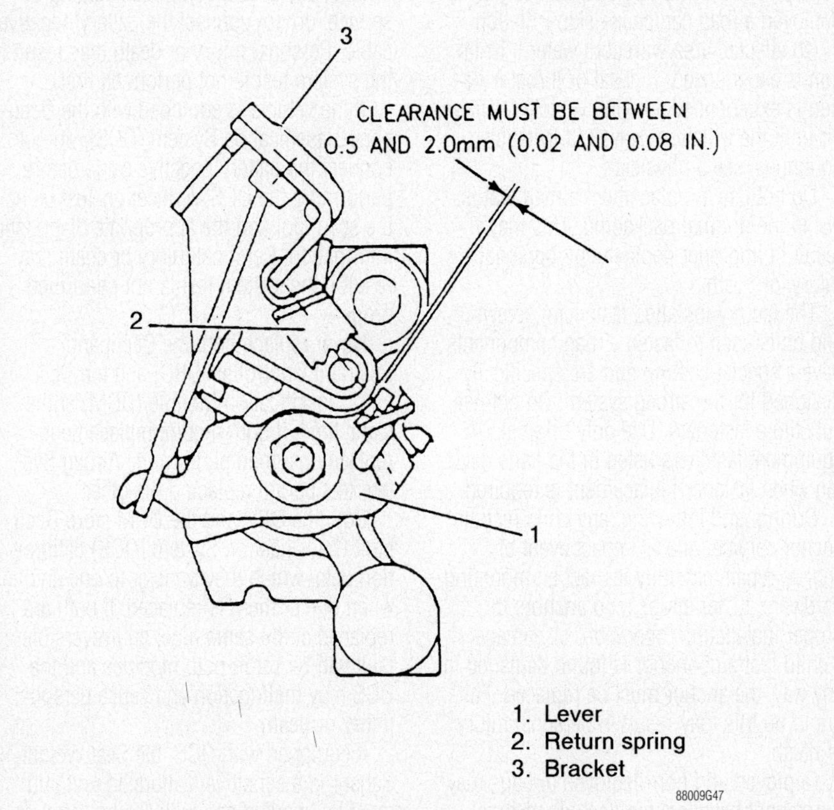

CLEARANCE MUST BE BETWEEN 0.5 AND 2.0mm (0.02 AND 0.08 IN.)

1. Lever
2. Return spring
3. Bracket

88009G47

Fig. 9 Parking brake cable adjustment specifications

PARKING BRAKE

5. Make sure the parking brake is fully released. Turn the ignition switch to the **ON** position. The BRAKE warning lamp should be off. If the BRAKE warning light is still on, pull downward on the front parking brake to remove the slack from the pedal assembly.

6. Remove the rear wheel and tire assemblies, then reinstall two lug nuts to retain the rotors.

7. The parking brake levers on both calipers should be against the lever stops on the caliper housing. If not against the stops, check for binding in the rear cables and/or loosen the cables at the adjuster until both left and right levers are against their stops.

8. Tighten the parking brake cable at the adjuster until either the right or left lever reaches the dimensions shown in the accompanying figure.

➡ **Do not apply the main/service brake pedal during the next step.**

9. Operate the parking brake several times to check adjustments. A firm pedal should be present. The rear wheels should not rotate forward when the parking brake is fully applies. If necessary, repeat steps 8 and 9.

10. Remove the two wheel lug nuts, then install the rear wheel and tire assemblies.

11. Carefully lower the vehicle.

PARKING BRAKE SHOES

REMOVAL & INSTALLATION

On vehicles equipped with rear disc brake calipers without built-in parking brake adjusters, the parking brake assembly is contained inside the rear disc brake rotor. Two small brake shoes press against the inside diameter of the rear brake rotor.

1. Raise and safely support the vehicle with safety stands.

2. Remove the rear caliper. It is not necessary to disconnect the brake line. Use wire to hang the caliper out of the way. Do not allow the caliper to hang by the brake hose.

3. Remove the caliper bracket bolts and remove the caliper. It may take considerable force to remove the bolts. They were factory installed with a thread-locking compound.

4. Remove the rear rotor.

5. Disconnect the parking brake actuator.

6. Remove the rear wheel hub.

7. Remove the shoes from the parking brake support plate.

8. Installation is the reverse of the removal process. Note that when the caliper bracket is installed, use thread-locking compound on the bolts. Torque the caliper bracket bolts to 92 ft. lbs. (125 Nm).The parking brake brakes should be adjusted before the rotor is installed.

ADJUSTMENT

➡ **The factory recommends using a Drum To Brake Shoe Clearance Gauge to setup and adjust the parking brake shoes on vehicles equipped with rear disc brake calipers without a built-in parking brake adjuster.**

1. Remove the caliper, caliper bracket and rear disc brake rotor. Slowly turn the rotor while pulling away from the hub.

2. Loosen the parking brake cable adjusting nut until the lever is at its "rest" position.

3. Using a Drum To Brake Shoe Clearance Gauge such as GM's J 41713, or equivalent:

   a. Set the tool so that it contacts the inside diameter of the rotor.

   b. Position the Clearance Gauge over the parking brake shoes at its widest point.

   c. Turn the adjuster nut until the brake shoe lining just touches the Clearance Gauge.

   d. Repeat the procedure for the opposite side.

4. Tighten the parking brake cable adjusting nut.

5. Slowly turn the rotor while installing onto the bearing assembly.

6. Assemble the remaining components.

CHASSIS ELECTRICAL

AIR BAG (SUPPLEMENTAL RESTRAINT SYSTEM)

GENERAL INFORMATION

✳✳ CAUTION

Some vehicles are equipped with an air bag system. The system must be disarmed before performing service on, or around, system components, the steering column, instrument panel components, wiring and sensors. Failure to follow the safety precautions and the disarming procedure could result in accidental air bag deployment, possible injury and unnecessary system repairs.

SERVICE PRECAUTIONS

Disconnect and isolate the battery negative cable before beginning any airbag system component diagnosis, testing, removal, or installation procedures. Allow system capacitor to discharge for two minutes before beginning any component service. This will disable the airbag system. Failure to disable the airbag system may result in accidental airbag deployment, personal injury, or death.

Do not place an intact undeployed airbag face down on a solid surface. The airbag will propel into the air if accidentally deployed and may result in personal injury or death.

When carrying or handling an undeployed airbag, the trim side (face) of the airbag should be pointing towards the body to minimize possibility of injury if accidental deployment occurs. Failure to do this may result in personal injury or death.

Replace airbag system components with OEM replacement parts. Substitute parts may appear interchangeable, but internal differences may result in inferior occupant protection. Failure to do so may result in occupant personal injury or death.

Wear safety glasses, rubber gloves, and long sleeved clothing when cleaning powder residue from vehicle after an airbag deployment. Powder residue emitted from a deployed airbag can cause skin irritation. Flush affected area with cool water if irritation is experienced. If nasal or throat irritation is experienced, exit the vehicle for fresh air until the irritation ceases. If irritation continues, see a physician.

Do not use a replacement airbag that is not in the original packaging. This may result in improper deployment, personal injury, or death.

The factory installed fasteners, screws and bolts used to fasten airbag components have a special coating and are specifically designed for the airbag system. Do not use substitute fasteners. Use only original equipment fasteners listed in the parts catalog when fastener replacement is required.

During, and following, any child restraint anchor service, due to impact event or vehicle repair, carefully inspect all mounting hardware, tether straps, and anchors for proper installation, operation, or damage. If a child restraint anchor is found damaged in any way, the anchor must be replaced. Failure to do this may result in personal injury or death.

Deployed and non-deployed airbags may or may not have live pyrotechnic material within the airbag inflator.

Do not dispose of driver/passenger/curtain airbags or seat belt tensioners unless you are sure of complete deployment. Refer to the Hazardous Substance Control System for proper disposal.

Dispose of deployed airbags and tensioners consistent with state, provincial, local, and federal regulations.

After any airbag component testing or service, do not connect the battery negative cable. Personal injury or death may result if the system test is not performed first.

If the vehicle is equipped with the Occupant Classification System (OCS), do not connect the battery negative cable before performing the OCS Verification Test using the scan tool and the appropriate diagnostic information. Personal injury or death may result if the system test is not performed properly.

Never replace both the Occupant Restraint Controller (ORC) and the Occupant Classification Module (OCM) at the same time. If both require replacement, replace one, then perform the Airbag System test before replacing the other.

Both the ORC and the OCM store Occupant Classification System (OCS) calibration data, which they transfer to one another when one of them is replaced. If both are replaced at the same time, an irreversible fault will be set in both modules and the OCS may malfunction and cause personal injury or death.

If equipped with OCS, the Seat Weight Sensor is a sensitive, calibrated unit and must be handled carefully. Do not drop or handle roughly. If dropped or damaged, replace with another sensor. Failure to do so may result in occupant injury or death.

If equipped with OCS, the front passenger seat must be handled carefully as well. When removing the seat, be careful when setting on floor not to drop. If dropped, the sensor may be inoperative, could result in occupant injury, or possibly death.

If equipped with OCS, when the passenger front seat is on the floor, no one should sit in the front passenger seat. This uneven force may damage the sensing ability of the seat weight sensors. If sat on and damaged, the sensor may be inoperative, could result in occupant injury, or possibly death.

DISARMING AND ARMING THE SYSTEM

Zone 1

See Figures 10 and 11.

1. Before servicing the vehicle, refer to the Precautions Section.
2. Turn the steering wheel so that the vehicle wheels are pointing straight ahead.
3. Turn OFF the ignition.
4. Remove the key from the ignition switch.
5. Remove the instrument panel (I/P) fuse block cover.

➡ **With the SIR fuse removed and the ignition ON, the AIR BAG indicator illuminates. This is normal operation, and does not indicate an SIR system malfunction.**

6. Remove the SDM fuse.
7. Remove the radiator upper air baffle and deflector.
8. Remove the connector position assurance (CPA) (2) from the front end sensor harness connector (3).
9. Disconnect the front end sensor har-

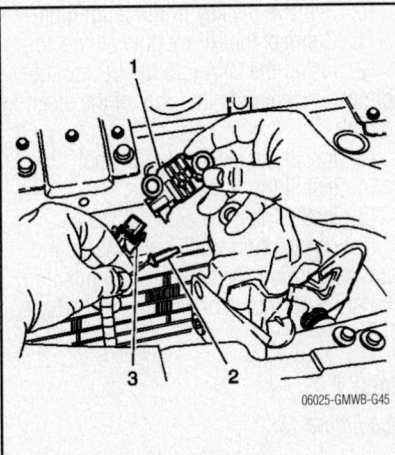

Fig. 11 Front end sensor harness

ness connector (3) from the front end sensor (1).

Enabling Procedure:
10. Remove the key from the ignition.
11. Connect the front end sensor harness connector (3) to the front end sensor (1).
12. Install the CPA (2) into the front end sensor harness connector (3).
13. Install the radiator upper air baffle and deflector.
14. Install the SDM fuse.
15. Install the I/P fuse block cover.
16. Use caution while reaching in and turn the ignition switch to the ON position. The AIR BAG indicator will flash then turn OFF.

Zone 2

1. Before servicing the vehicle, refer to the Precautions Section.
2. Turn the steering wheel so that the vehicle wheels are pointing straight ahead.
3. Turn OFF the ignition.
4. Remove the key from the ignition switch.
5. Remove the instrument panel (I/P) fuse block cover.

➡ **With the SIR fuse removed and the ignition ON, the AIR BAG indicator illuminates. This is normal operation, and does not indicate an SIR system malfunction.**

6. Remove the SDM fuse.
7. Remove the connector position assurance (CPA) from the left side impact sensor (SIS) connector.
8. Disconnect the left SIS connector from the left SIS.

Enabling Procedure:
9. Remove the key from the ignition.
10. Connect the left SIS connector to the left SIS.
11. Install the CPA to the left SIS connector.
12. Install the SDM fuse.
13. Install the fuse block access cover.
14. Use caution while reaching in and turn the ignition switch to the ON position. The AIR BAG indicator will flash then turn OFF.

Zone 3

1. Before servicing the vehicle, refer to the Precautions Section.
2. Turn the steering wheel so that the vehicle wheels are pointing straight ahead.
3. Turn OFF the ignition.
4. Remove the key from the ignition switch.

10A PCM/BCM	??A FUTURE	25A WSW
10A PCM	10A CIG/AUX	10A BCM
??A FUTURE	??A FUTURE	10A SDM
10A ABS	10A STOP	15A EXT LP
2A CRUISE	10A A/C	20A A/C BLO
??A FUTURE	??A FUTURE	2A STR COL
??A FUTURE	??A FUTURE	??A FUTURE
20A DR LK	10A PWR MIR	10A CSTR/BCM
15A HTD ST		
??A FUTURE		

10A SDM

85 87
30 86
RAP

06025-GMWB-G44

Fig. 10 SDM fuse

5. Remove the instrument panel (I/P) fuse block cover.

➡ **With the SIR fuse removed and the ignition ON, the AIR BAG indicator illuminates. This is normal operation, and does not indicate an SIR system malfunction.**

6. Remove the SDM fuse.
7. Remove the LH insulator panel.
8. Remove the connector position assurance (CPA) from the steering wheel module coil connector located at the base of the steering column.
9. Disconnect the steering wheel module coil connector.

Enabling Procedure:
10. Remove the key from the ignition.
11. Connect the steering wheel module coil connector.
12. Install the CPA to the steering wheel module coil connector located at the base of the steering column.
13. Install the LH insulator panel.
14. Install the SDM fuse.
15. Install the I/P fuse block cover.
16. Use caution while reaching in and turn the ignition switch to the ON position. The AIR BAG indicator will flash then turn OFF.

Zone 5

See Figure 12.

1. Before servicing the vehicle, refer to the Precautions Section.
2. Turn the steering wheel so that the vehicle wheels are pointing straight ahead.
3. Turn OFF the ignition.
4. Remove the key from the ignition switch.
5. Remove the instrument panel (I/P) fuse block cover.

➡ **With the SIR fuse removed and the ignition ON, the AIR BAG indicator illu-**

minates. This is normal operation, and does not indicate an SIR system malfunction.

6. Remove the SDM fuse.
7. Remove the RH I/P access hole cover.
8. Remove the connector position assurance (CPA) from the I/P module connector located to the right of the steering column.
9. Disconnect the I/P module connector.

Enabling Procedure:
10. Remove the key from the ignition.
11. Connect the I/P module connector.
12. Install the CPA into the I/P module connector located to the right of the steering column.
13. Install the LH insulator panel.
14. Install the SDM fuse.
15. Install the I/P fuse block cover.
16. Use caution while reaching in and turn the ignition switch to the ON position. The AIR BAG indicator will flash then turn OFF.

Zone 7

See Figure 13.

1. Before servicing the vehicle, refer to the Precautions Section.
2. Turn the steering wheel so that the vehicle's wheels are pointing straight ahead.
3. Turn OFF the ignition.
4. Remove the key from the ignition switch.
5. Remove the fuse block access cover.

➡ **With the SIR fuse removed and the ignition ON, the AIR BAG indicator illuminates. This is normal operation, and does not indicate an SIR system malfunction.**

6. Remove the SDM fuse.
7. Remove the connector position

assurance (CPA) from the side impact module LF connector (1) located under the driver seat.
8. Disconnect the side impact module LF connector (1).

Enabling Procedure:
9. Remove the key from the ignition.
10. Connect the side impact module LF connector (1) located under the driver seat.
11. Install the CPA to the side impact module LF connector (1).
12. Remove the SDM fuse.
13. Install the fuse block access cover.
14. Use caution while reaching in and turn the ignition switch to the ON position. The AIR BAG indicator will flash then turn OFF.

Zone 9

1. Before servicing the vehicle, refer to the Precautions Section.
2. Turn the steering wheel so that the vehicle wheels are pointing straight ahead.
3. Turn OFF the ignition.
4. Remove the key from the ignition switch.
5. Remove the instrument panel (I/P) fuse block cover.

➡ **With the SIR fuse removed and the ignition ON, the AIR BAG indicator illuminates. This is normal operation, and does not indicate an SIR system malfunction.**

6. Remove the SDM fuse.
7. Remove the RH I/P access hole cover.
8. Remove the connector position assurance (CPA) from the I/P module connector, located at the RH side of the I/P.
9. Disconnect the I/P module connector.
10. Remove the LH insulator panel.
11. Remove the CPA from the steering wheel module coil connector located at the base of the steering column.
12. Disconnect the steering wheel module coil connector.
13. Remove the CPA from the side impact module LF connector (1), located under the driver seat.
14. Disconnect the side impact module LF connector.

Enabling Procedure:
15. Remove the key from the ignition.
16. Connect the side impact module LF connector (1), located under the driver seat.
17. Install the CPA to the side impact module LF connector.
18. Connect the steering wheel module coil connector.

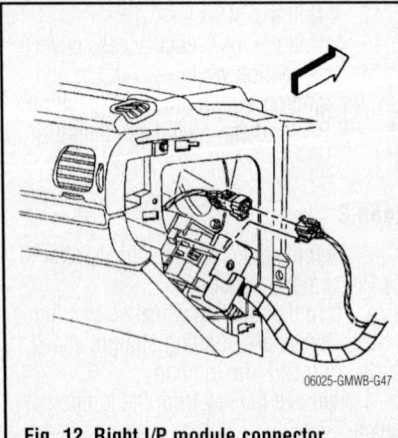

06025-GMWB-G47

Fig. 12 Right I/P module connector

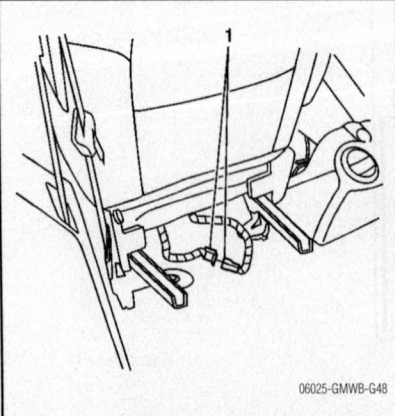

06025-GMWB-G48

Fig. 13 Side impact module

19. Install the CPA to the steering wheel module coil connector located at the base of the steering column.

20. Install the LH insulator panel.

21. Connect the I/P module connector, located at the RH side of the I/P.

22. Install the CPA to the I/P module connector.

23. Install the RH I/P access hole cover.

24. Install the SDM fuse.

25. Install the LH I/P access hole cover.

26. Use caution while reaching in and turn the ignition switch to the ON position. The AIR BAG indicator will flash then turn OFF.

WHEEL MODULE COIL CENTERING

See Figures 14 through 17.

⁕ CAUTION

The new SIR coil assembly will be centered. Improper alignment of the SIR coil assembly may damage the unit, causing an inflatable restraint malfunction.

➡ **If double wire harness strap is installed onto the wire harness assembly and column, you must reuse the holder for the wire straps during installation.**

1. Verify the following conditions before centering the SIR coil:

  a. The wheels on the vehicle are straight ahead.

  b. The block tooth of the steering shaft assembly is in the 12 o'clock position.

  c. The ignition switch is in the LOCK position.

2. If the front of the SIR coil has a centering window and the back side includes a spring service lock, perform the following steps:

  a. Hold the SIR coil with the face up.

  b. While depressing the spring service lock, rotate the coil hub clockwise until the coil ribbon stops.

  c. Rotate the coil hub slowly, counterclockwise, until the centering window appears yellow and both arrows line up.

  d. Release spring service lock between the locking tab. The SIR coil is now centered.

  e. Align the centered SIR coil with the horn tower and slide onto the steering shaft assembly.

3. If the front of the SIR coil has a centering window, and the back side includes NO spring service lock, perform the following steps:

  a. Hold the SIR coil with the face up.

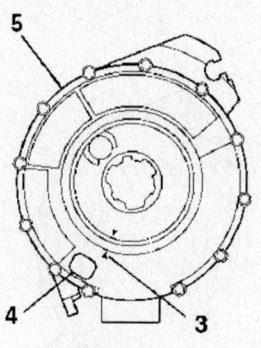
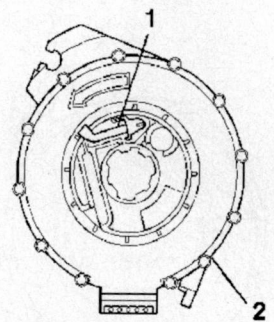

1. Spring service lock
2. Back side
3. Arrows
4. Centering window
5. Front

36616_IMPA_G0047

Fig. 14 Front of SIR coil with centering window – With a spring service lock

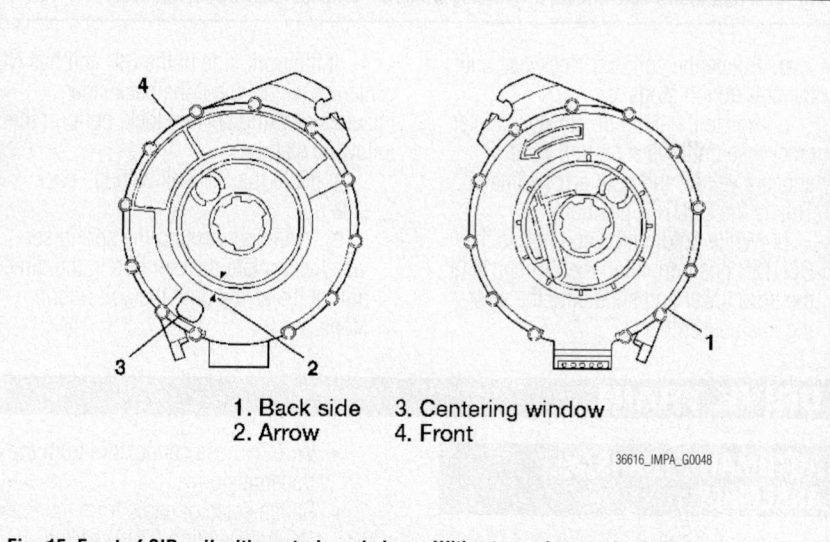

1. Back side
2. Arrow
3. Centering window
4. Front

36616_IMPA_G0048

Fig. 15 Front of SIR coil with centering window – Without a spring service lock

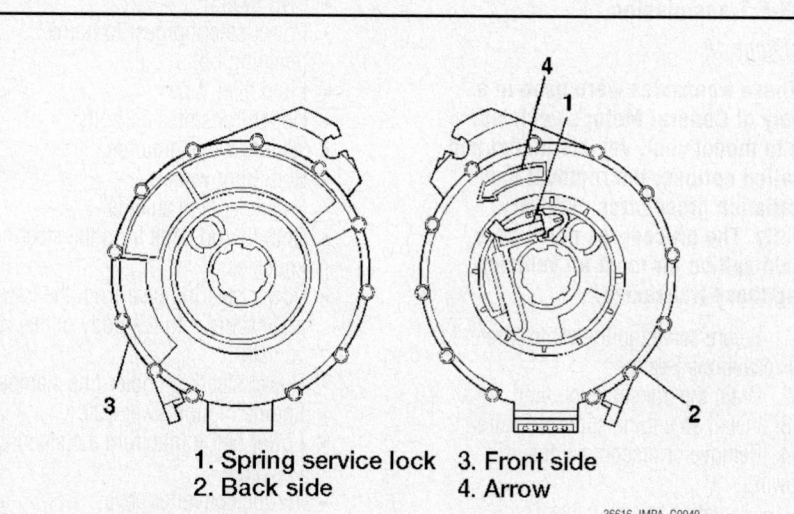

1. Spring service lock
2. Back side
3. Front side
4. Arrow

36616_IMPA_G0049

Fig. 16 Front of SIR coil without a centering window – With a spring service lock

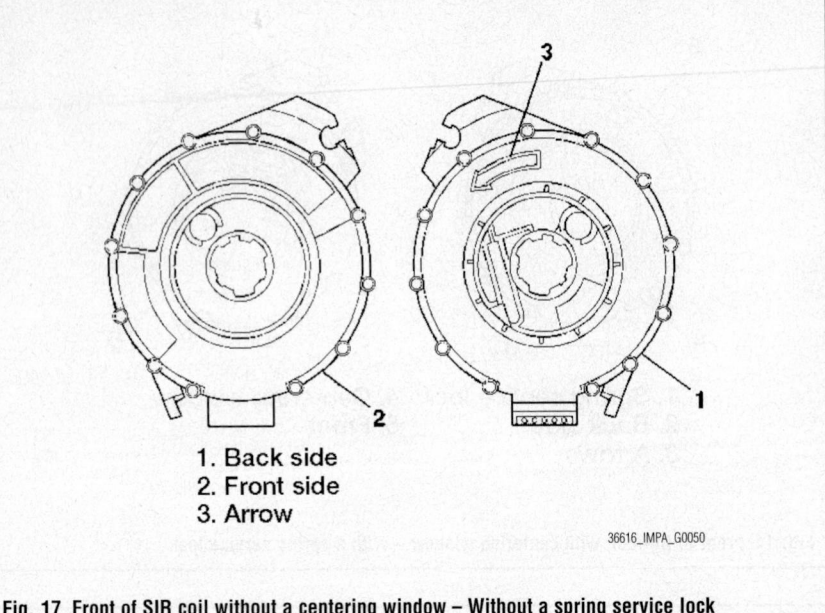

1. Back side
2. Front side
3. Arrow

36616_IMPA_G0050

Fig. 17 Front of SIR coil without a centering window – Without a spring service lock

b. Rotate the coil hub clockwise until the coil ribbon stops.

c. Rotate the coil hub slowly, counter-clockwise until the centering window appears yellow and both arrows line up. This is the CENTER position.

d. While holding the coil hub in the CENTER position, align the SIR coil with the horn tower and slide onto the steering shaft assembly.

4. If the front side of the SIR coil has NO centering window, but the back side includes a spring service lock, perform the following steps:

a. Hold the SIR coil with the back side up.

b. While depressing the spring service lock, rotate the coil hub in the direction of the arrow until the coil ribbon stops.

c. Still pressing the spring service lock, rotate the coil hub in the opposite direction 2½ revolutions.

d. Release the spring service lock between locking tabs. The SIR coil is now centered.

e. Align the centered SIR coil with the horn tower and slide onto the steering shaft assembly.

5. If the front side of the SIR coil has NO centering window, and the back side includes NO spring service lock, perform the following steps:

a. Hold the SIR coil with the face up.

b. Rotate the coil hub in the direction of the arrow until the coil ribbon stops.

c. Rotate the coil hub, slowly, counterclockwise, for 2½ revolutions. This is the CENTER position.

d. While maintaining the coil hub in the CENTER position, align the centered SIR coil with the horn tower and slide onto the steering shaft assembly.

6. If double wire harness strap is installed onto the wire harness assembly and column, you must route the wires up against the steering column. One wire harness strap will surround one lead from the coil to the steering column. The other wire harness strap will surround all leads to the steering column.

DRIVE TRAIN

AUTOMATIC TRANSAXLE ASSEMBLY

REMOVAL & INSTALLATION

4T65-E Transmission
See Figure 18.

➡ **These transaxles were used in a variety of General Motor's vehicles. Due to model year, vehicle model and installed options, the removal and installation procedures may vary slightly. The procedures given here should suffice for most all vehicles using these transaxles.**

1. Before servicing the vehicle, refer to the Precautions Section.
2. Drain the transmission fluid.
3. Install an engine support fixture.
4. Remove or disconnect the following:
   - Negative battery cable
   - Throttle body air inlet duct
   - Engine mount struts
   - Wire harness connectors from the transmission
   - Range selector cable from the Park Neutral Position (PNP) switch
   - Range selector cable and bracket
   - PNP switch
   - Power steering gear to frame retaining bolts
   - Fluid filler tube
   - Upper transmission bolts
   - Wire harness grounds
   - Both front wheels
   - Engine splash shields
   - Both tie rod ends from the steering knuckles
   - Power steering gear from the frame and secure it to the body of the vehicle
   - Power steering cooler line clamps
   - Engine mount lower nuts
   - Lower ball joints from the steering knuckles
   - Torque converter cover
   - Starter motor
   - Torque converter bolts
   - Oil cooler hoses
   - Drive axles and secure them to the steering knuckles
   - Wheel Speed Sensor (WSS) electrical connectors
   - Vehicle Speed Sensor (VSS) electrical connectors

5. Use a transmission table to support the transmission.
   - Engine mount lower nuts
   - Transmission brace
   - Lower transmission bolts
   - Frame-to-body bolts

6. Separate the transmission from the engine.
7. Lower the transmission and frame from the vehicle.
8. Remove the transmission.

To install:
9. Install or connect the following:
   - Transmission to the frame and raise the assembly into position
   - New frame-to-body bolts and torque them to 133 ft. lbs. (180 Nm)

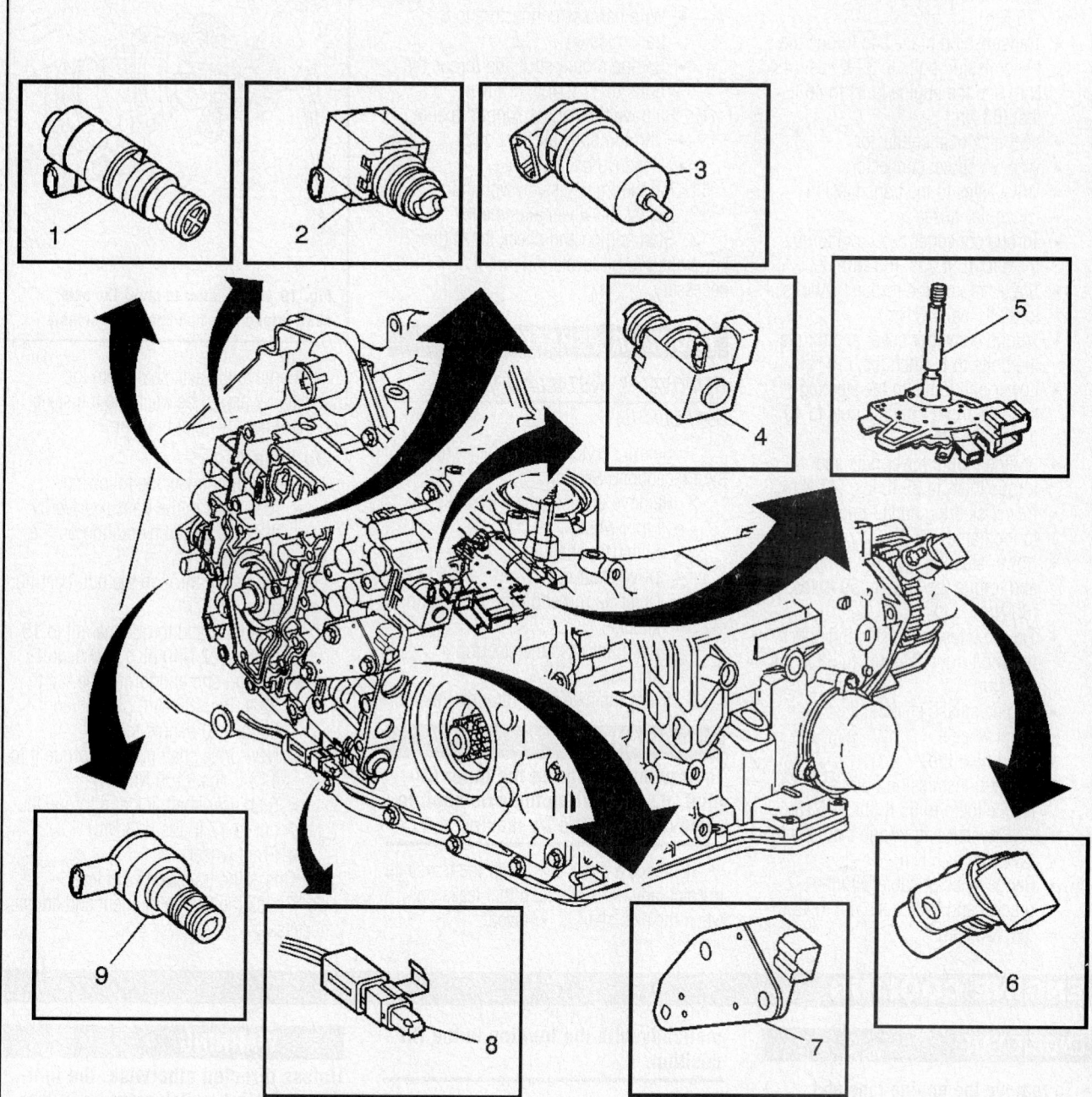

1. Pressure Control (PC) Solenoid Valve
2. Pressure Control (PC) Solenoid Valve
3. Automatic Transmission Input Shaft Speed (ISS) Sensor
4. 2-3 Shift Solenoid (SS) Valve
5. Automatic Transmission Internal Mode Switch (IMS)
6. Vehicle Speed Sensor (VSS)
7. Automatic Transmission Fluid Pressure (TFP) Manual Valve Position Switch
8. Automatic Transmission Fluid Temperature (TFT)Sensor
9. Torque Converter Clutch (TCC) Solenoid Valve

36616_IMPA_G0053

Fig. 18 Removing the transmission

- Lower transmission-to-engine bolts and torque them to 55 ft. lbs. (75 Nm)
- Transmission brace and torque the transmission bolts to 32 ft. lbs. (43 Nm) and the engine bolts to 46 ft. lbs. (63 Nm)
- VSS electrical connector
- WSS electrical connectors
- Drive axles to the transmission
- Oil cooler hoses
- Torque converter bolts and torque them to 46 ft. lbs. (63 Nm)
- Starter motor and torque the bolts to 32 ft. lbs. (43 Nm)
- Torque converter cover and torque the bolts to 89 inch lbs. (10 Nm).
- Lower ball joints to the steering knuckle and torque the nuts to 40 ft. lbs. (55 Nm)
- Engine mount lower nuts and torque them to 35 ft. lbs. (47 Nm)
- Power steering cooler line clamps to the frame
- Power steering gear to the frame and torque the bolts to 59 ft. lbs. (80 Nm)
- Tie rod ends to the steering knuckles and torque the nuts to 63 ft. lbs. (85 Nm)
- Engine splash shields
- Front wheels
- Fluid filler tube
- Upper transmission bolts and torque them to 55 ft. lbs. (75 Nm)
- PNP switch and torque the bolts to 18 ft. lbs. (25 Nm)
- Range selector cable with the bracket and torque the nut to 15 ft. lbs. (20 Nm)
- Range selector cable to the PNP switch
- Wire harness connectors to the transmission
- Engine mount strut and torque the bolts to 37 ft. lbs. (50 Nm)

10. Remove the engine support fixture.
    - Throttle body air inlet duct
    - Negative battery cable
11. Fill the transmission with fluid.
12. Adjust the wheel alignment.
13. Start engine and check the engine and transaxle oil levels. Add oil if necessary.

FRONT HALFSHAFTS

REMOVAL & INSTALLATION

See Figure 19.

1. Before servicing the vehicle, refer to the Precautions Section.
2. Remove or disconnect the following:
    - Front wheel
    - Stabilizer shaft link
    - Drive shaft nut
    - Outer tie rod end from the steering knuckle
    - Ball joint from the steering knuckle
3. Press the axle shaft through the hub.

**** WARNING**

To prevent damage to the inner CV-joint, do not pull on the axle shaft to remove it from the transaxle.

4. Place a drain pan under the transaxle to catch any transaxle fluid that leaks out when the axle shaft is removed.

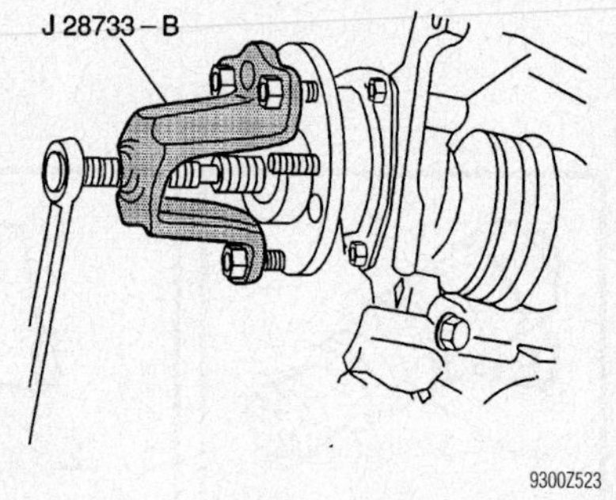

Fig. 19 Use a puller to press the axle shaft through the hub/bearing assembly

5. Remove the axle shaft from the transaxle by prying between the transaxle and the inner CV-joint housing.

To install:

6. Install or connect the following:
    - Axle shaft in the transaxle. Verify that it is seated by pulling on the housing
    - Axle shaft through the hub/bearing assembly
    - Ball joint and torque the nut to 15 ft. lbs. (22 Nm) plus 120 degrees
    - Tie rod end and torque the nut to 22 ft. lbs. (30 Nm) plus an additional 120 degree turn
    - New drive shaft nut and torque it to 118 ft. lbs. (160 Nm)
    - Stabilizer shaft link and torque the nut to 17 ft. lbs. (23 Nm)
    - Front wheel
7. Check the transaxle fluid level.
8. Check the front alignment and adjust, if necessary.

ENGINE COOLING

ENGINE FAN

➡ To remove the engine fans and motors, the engine fan shroud assembly must be removed first.

REMOVAL & INSTALLATION

Fan Shroud

See Figure 20.

**** WARNING**

Keep hands, tools, and clothing away from the electric engine coolant fans in order to help prevent personal injury. These fans are electric and can turn on whether or not the engine is running. The fans can start automatically with the ignition in the ON position.

**** WARNING**

An electric fan under the hood can start up even when the engine is not running and can injure you. Keep hands, clothing and tools away from any underhood electric fan.

**** WARNING**

To help avoid personal injury or damage to the vehicle, a bent, cracked, or damaged fan blade or housing should always be replaced.

**** WARNING**

Unless directed otherwise, the ignition and start switch must be in the OFF or LOCK position, and all electrical loads must be OFF before servicing any electrical component. Disconnect the negative battery cable to prevent an electrical spark should a tool or equipment come in contact with an exposed electrical terminal. Failure to follow these precautions may result in personal injury and/or damage to the vehicle or its components.

1. Before servicing the vehicle, refer to the Precautions Section.
2. Disconnect the negative battery cable.

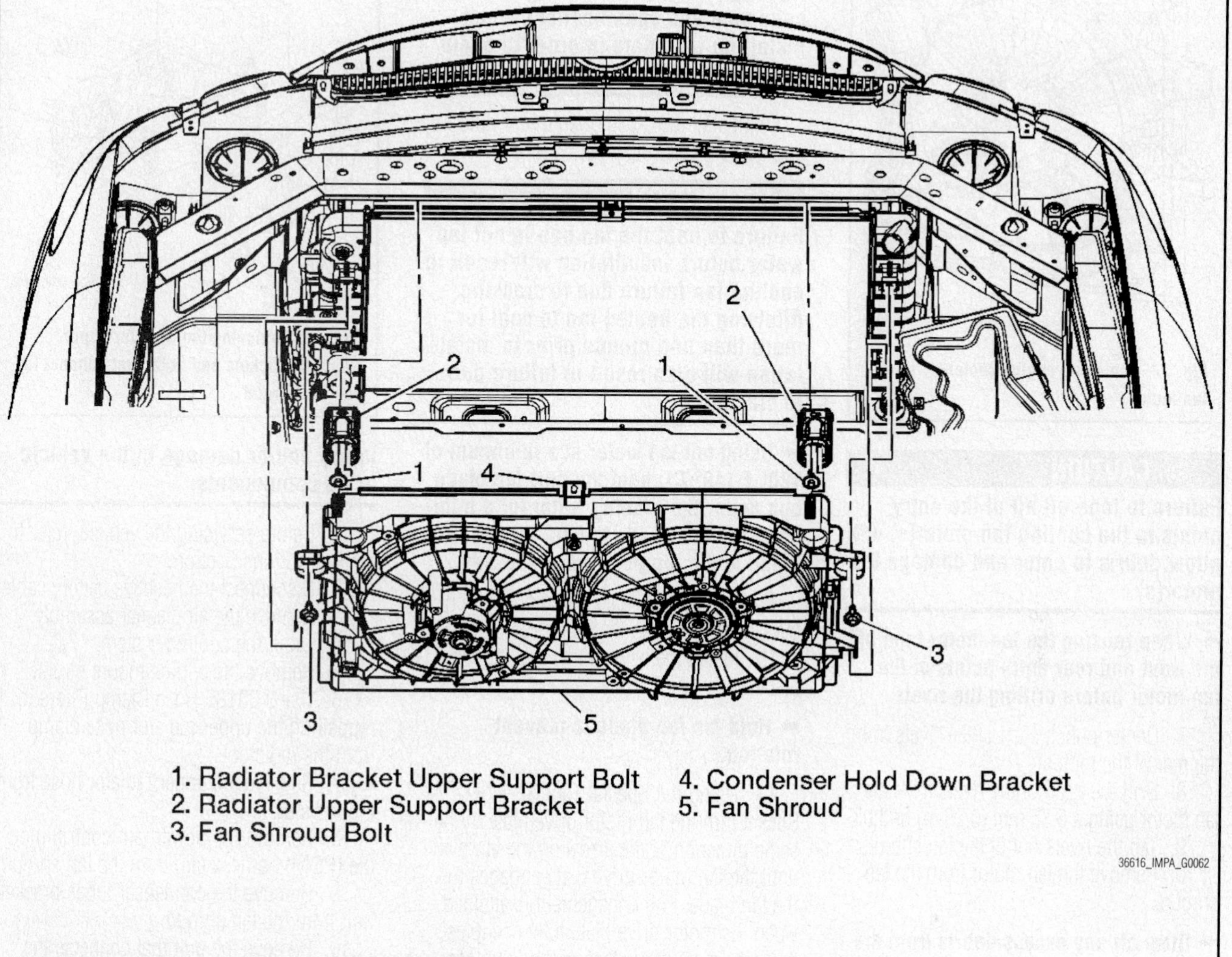

1. Radiator Bracket Upper Support Bolt
2. Radiator Upper Support Bracket
3. Fan Shroud Bolt
4. Condenser Hold Down Bracket
5. Fan Shroud

36616_IMPA_G0062

Fig. 20 Removing the engine coolant fan shroud assembly

3. Remove the air cleaner assembly.

4. Remove the engine mount struts.

5. Remove the coolant reservoir hose from the fan shroud (LS4 only).

6. Disconnect the upper transaxle oil cooler pipe from the radiator.

7. Remove the radiator bracket upper support bolt and radiator upper support bracket.

8. Remove the fan shroud bolt.

9. Remove the bolt that connects the fan shroud to the condenser hold down bracket.

10. Remove the fan shroud.

To install:

11. Install the fan assembly(s) to the vehicle. Install the mounting bolts and tighten to 53 inch lbs. (6 Nm).

12. Connect the wiring harness to the fan motors and the clips.

13. Install the air clean and duct assembly, as required.

14. Connect the negative battery cable.

Engine Coolant Fan Motor Replacement

See Figures 21 and 22.

1. Before servicing the vehicle, refer to the Precautions Section.

2. Disconnect the negative battery cable.

3. Remove the fan shroud assembly from the vehicle.

4. Hold the fan blade to prevent rotation.

5. Using Special Tool GE-47827 socket turn the fan motor drive plate in the opposite direction of the arrow on the fan blade until the motor drive plate disengages from the fan blade.

6. Remove and discard the fan blade.

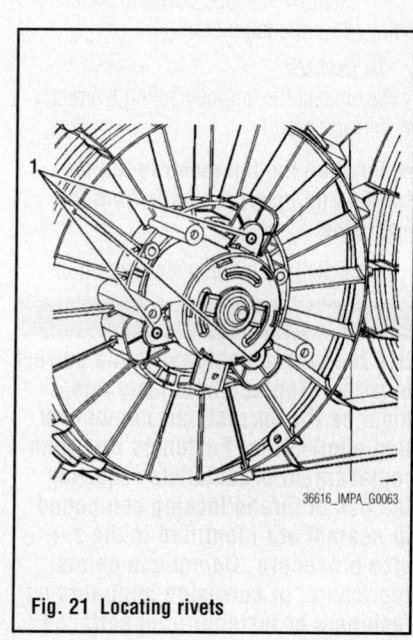

36616_IMPA_G0063

Fig. 21 Locating rivets

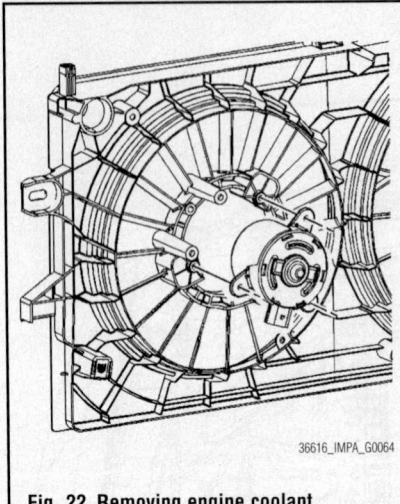

Fig. 22 Removing engine coolant fan motor

✳✳ CAUTION

Failure to tape off all of the entry points to the cooling fan motor(s) will allow debris to enter and damage the motor(s).

➡ When reusing the fan motor tape off the front and rear entry points of the fan motor before drilling the rivets.

7. Center punch each of the rivets from the rear of the motor.

8. Drill the head of the rivets from the fan motor using a 6.35 mm (0.25 in) drill bit.

9. Tap the rivets out of the fan shroud.

10. Remove the fan motor from the fan shroud.

➡ Blow off any excess debris from the fan motor.

11. Remove the tape covering the entry points from the fan motor.

To install:

12. Install the engine cooling fan motor to the fan shroud.

➡ Position the fan motor to the fan shroud and insert the bolts from the front side.

13. Install the cooling fan motor bolts.

✳✳ CAUTION

Use the correct fastener in the correct location. Replacement fasteners must be the correct part number for that application. Fasteners requiring replacement or fasteners requiring the use of thread locking compound or sealant are identified in the service procedure. Do not use paints, lubricants, or corrosion inhibitors on fasteners or fastener joint surfaces

unless specified. These coatings affect fastener torque and joint clamping force and may damage the fastener. Use the correct tightening sequence and specifications when installing fasteners in order to avoid damage to parts and systems.

14. Install the cooling fan motor nuts and tighten to 53 inch lbs. (6 Nm).

✳✳ CAUTION

Failure to heat the fan hub in hot tap water before installation will result in cooling fan failure due to cracking. Allowing the heated fan to cool for more than one minute prior to installation will also result in failure due to cracking.

➡ Using hot tap water at a minimum of 120° F (49° C), hold the new fan blade hub under the running water for a minimum of 60 seconds to heat the fan blade to the temperature of the water.

15. Immediately after heating, position the fan blade on the fan motor drive plate.

16. Install the new engine cooling fan blade.

➡ Hold the fan blade to prevent rotation.

17. Using the Special Tool GE-47827 Socket turn the fan motor drive plate in the same direction of the arrow on the fan blade until the fan motor drive plate engages to the fan blade. Full engagement is attained when the motor drive plate fully occupies the three slots in the face of the fan blade.

18. Rotate the cooling fan blade to ensure proper rotation.

19. Install the fan shroud assembly to the vehicle.

RADIATOR

REMOVAL & INSTALLATION
See Figure 23.

✳✳ WARNING

Unless directed otherwise, the ignition and start switch must be in the OFF or LOCK position, and all electrical loads must be OFF before servicing any electrical component. Disconnect the negative battery cable to prevent an electrical spark should a tool or equipment come in contact with an exposed electrical terminal. Failure to follow these precautions may result in personal

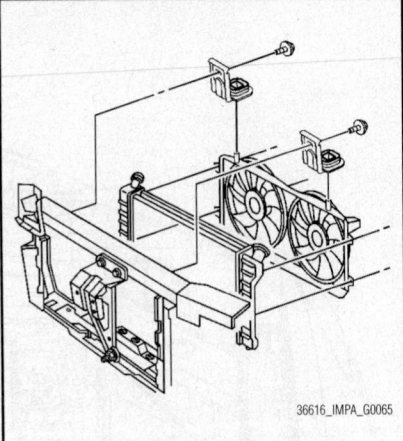

Fig. 23 Removing the radiator upper support brackets and bolts that connect to the fan shroud

injury and/or damage to the vehicle or its components.

1. Before servicing the vehicle, refer to the Precautions Section.

2. Disconnect the negative battery cable.

3. Remove the air cleaner assembly.

4. Drain the cooling system.

5. Remove the engine mount struts.

6. Use J 38185 Hose Clamp Pliers to reposition the upper radiator hose clamp from the radiator.

7. Remove the upper radiator hose from the radiator.

8. Remove the powertrain control module (PCM) harness clip from the fan shroud.

9. Remove the condenser tubes bracket bolt from the fan shroud.

10. Remove the bolt that connects the fan shroud to the condenser hold down bracket.

11. Remove the condenser hold down bracket from the radiator and condenser.

12. Remove the cooling fan shroud bolts.

13. Remove the coolant reservoir hose from the fan shroud, LS4 only.

14. Remove the radiator vent hose from the right upper radiator tank LS4 only.

15. Remove the radiator upper support brackets and bolts that connect to the fan shroud.

16. Disconnect the engine cooling fan motors electrical connectors.

17. Remove the cooling fan motors electrical harness from the fan shroud clips.

18. Remove the cooling fan shroud.

19. Use J 38185 Hose Clamp Pliers to reposition the lower radiator hose clamp from the radiator.

20. Remove the lower radiator hose from the radiator.

21. Disconnect the transaxle oil cooler pipes from the radiator.

22. Tilt the top of the radiator rearward.

23. Lift the condenser from the mounting tabs on the radiator. Position the condenser aside.

24. Remove the radiator.

To install:

25. Install the radiator to the lower mounts.

➡ **Verify that the condenser is fully seated in the radiator mounting tabs.**

26. Install the condenser to the mounting tabs on the radiator.

27. Install the condenser hold down bracket (1) to the radiator and condenser.

28. Install the lower radiator hose to the radiator.

29. Use J 38185 Hose Clamp Pliers to install the lower radiator hose clamp to the radiator.

➡ **Ensure the right and left edge of the fan shroud engages the radiator slots.**

30. Install the cooling fan shroud.

❋ CAUTION

Use the correct fastener in the correct location. Replacement fasteners must be the correct part number for that application. Fasteners requiring replacement or fasteners requiring the use of thread locking compound or sealant are identified in the service procedure. Do not use paints, lubricants, or corrosion inhibitors on fasteners or fastener joint surfaces unless specified. These coatings affect fastener torque and joint clamping force and may damage the fastener. Use the correct tightening sequence and specifications when installing fasteners in order to avoid damage to parts and systems.

31. Install the condenser tubes bracket bolt to the fan shroud.

32. Install the cooling fan motors electrical harness to the fan shroud clips.

33. Connect the engine cooling fan motors electrical connectors.

34. Install the cooling fan shroud bolts.

35. Connect the transaxle oil cooler pipes to the radiator.

36. Install the radiator upper support brackets and bolts that connect to the fan shroud.

37. Install the bolt that connects the fan shroud to the condenser hold down bracket.

38. Install the PCM harness clip on to the fan shroud.

39. Install the upper radiator hose to the radiator.

40. Use J 38185 Hose Clamp Pliers to install the upper radiator hose clamp to the radiator.

41. Install the air cleaner assembly.

42. Install the coolant reservoir hose to the fan shroud.

43. Install the radiator vent hose to the right upper radiator tank and fill neck.

44. Install the engine mount struts.

45. Fill the cooling system.

46. Connect the negative battery cable.

47. When refilling the cooling system, use the proper mix of DEX-COOL® and water. Check for leaks.

THERMOSTAT

REMOVAL & INSTALLATION

3.5L & 3.9L Engines

See Figure 24.

➡ **This engine uses a combination water inlet housing and thermostat assembly. If replacement is required, the entire assembly must be replaced.**

1. Partially drain the cooling system into a suitable container.

2. Using hose clamp pliers, remove the hose clamps from the water inlet housing.

3. Disconnect the radiator hose and the heater hose from the water inlet housing.

4. Remove the surge tank inlet hose clamp and disconnect the surge tank inlet hose from the water inlet housing.

5. Remove the water inlet housing bolts and remove the water inlet/thermostat assembly

To install:

6. Clean all parts well. Make sure there are no traces of dirt or debris on the sealing surfaces.

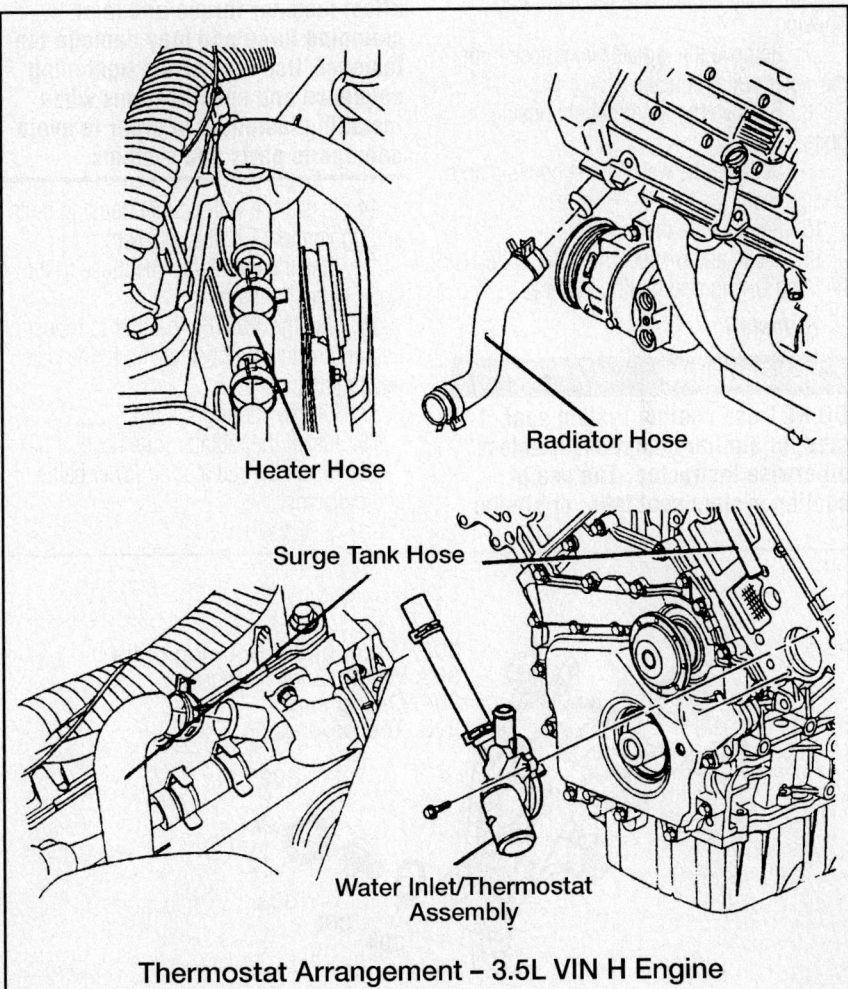

Thermostat Arrangement – 3.5L VIN H Engine

93173G22

Fig. 24 The thermostat and water inlet assembly are combined in one assembly and must be serviced together

7. Install the inlet/thermostat assembly to the engine. Install the housing bolts using RTV Sealer GM no. 1052366, or equivalent. Torque the housing bolts to 80 inch lbs. (9 Nm). Do not over-torque.

8. Connect the surge tank hose, heater hose and radiator hose to the inlet housing.

9. Refill the cooling system with the correct mix of DEX-COOL® and water.

10. Inspect for leaks.

5.3L Engines

See Figure 25.

1. Before servicing the vehicle, refer to the Precautions Section.

2. Disconnect the negative battery cable.

3. Remove the radiator air lower baffle and deflector.

4. Reposition the radiator inlet hose.

5. Partially drain the cooling system.

6. Use the J 38185 in order to reposition the hose clamp from the water outlet housing.

7. Remove the radiator inlet hose from the water outlet housing.

8. Remove the water outlet housing bolts.

9. Remove the water outlet housing and O-ring seal.

10. Remove the thermostat.

11. Clean and inspect the water outlet housing O-ring seal mating surfaces.

To install:

✳ CAUTION

DO NOT use cooling system seal tabs, or similar compounds, unless otherwise instructed. The use of cooling system seal tabs, or similar compounds, may restrict coolant flow through the passages of the cooling system or the engine components. Restricted coolant flow may cause engine overheating and/or damage to the cooling system or the engine components/assembly.

12. Install the thermostat.

13. Install the O-ring seal and water outlet housing.

✳ CAUTION

Use the correct fastener in the correct location. Replacement fasteners must be the correct part number for that application. Fasteners requiring replacement or fasteners requiring the use of thread locking compound or sealant are identified in the service procedure. Do not use paints, lubricants, or corrosion inhibitors on fasteners or fastener joint surfaces unless specified. These coatings affect fastener torque and joint clamping force and may damage the fastener. Use the correct tightening sequence and specifications when installing fasteners in order to avoid damage to parts and systems.

14. Install the water outlet housing bolts and tighten to 11 ft. lbs. (15 Nm).

15. Install the radiator inlet hose to the water outlet housing.

16. Use the J 38185 in order to reposition and install the hose clamp to the water outlet housing.

17. Fill the cooling system.

18. Install the radiator inlet hose.

19. Install the radiator air lower baffle and deflector.

WATER PUMP

REMOVAL & INSTALLATION

3.5L & 3.9L Engines

See Figures 26 and 27.

1. Before servicing the vehicle, refer to the Precautions Section.

2. Partially drain the cooling system.

3. Remove or disconnect the following:
- Surge tank outlet hose
- Drive belt
- Idler pulley
- Water pump pulley

➡ The water pump is attached to the engine with both long and short bolts, be sure to note their locations.

- Water pump

To install:

4. Install or connect the following:
- Water pump using a new gasket and torque the bolts to 124 inch lbs. (14 Nm)

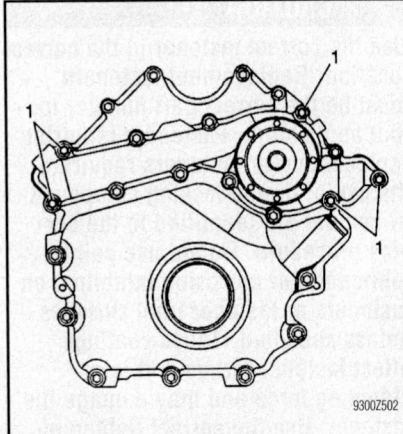

Fig. 26 Be sure to install the 5 long water pump bolts in the correct locations — 3.5L engine

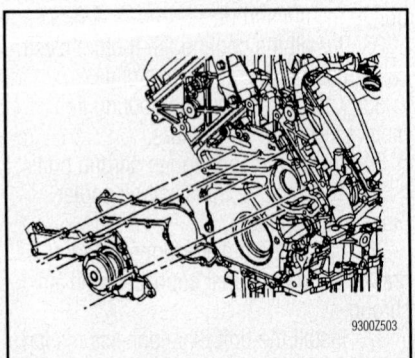

Fig. 27 Water pump mounting — 3.5L engine

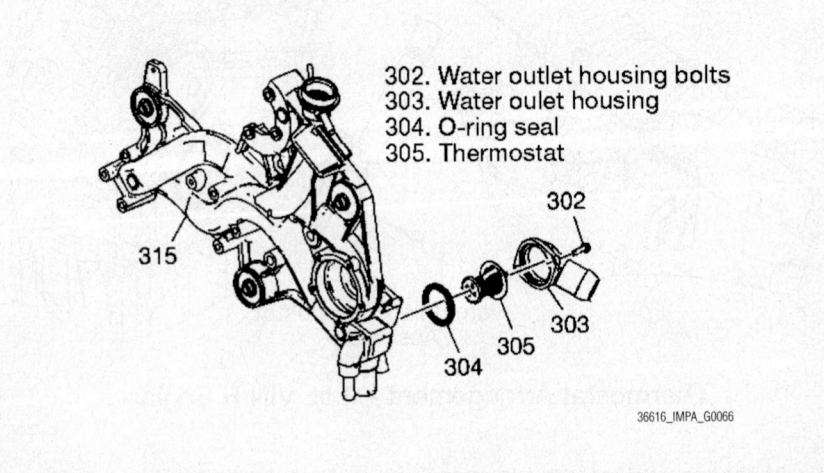

302. Water outlet housing bolts
303. Water oulet housing
304. O-ring seal
305. Thermostat

Fig. 25 Removing the thermostat — 5.3L Engines

- Water pump pulley and torque the bolts to 106 inch lbs. (12 Nm)
- Idler pulley and torque the bolt to 37 ft. lbs. (50 Nm)
- Drive belt
- Surge tank hose
5. Refill the cooling system.
6. Start the engine and check for leaks.

5.3L Engine

See Figure 28.

1. Before servicing the vehicle, refer to the Precautions Section.
2. Drain the cooling system.
3. Remove the battery and battery tray.
4. Remove the drive belt.
5. Remove the water pump bolts (3).
6. Remove the water pump (1) and gasket (2). Discard the gasket.
7. Clean and inspect the water pump gasket mating surfaces.

To install:

8. Install the water pump (1) and a NEW gasket (2).
9. Tighten the water pump bolts (3). Tighten the bolts to 89 inch lbs. (10 Nm).
10. Install the drive belt.
11. Install the battery tray and battery.
12. Fill the cooling system.

Fig. 28 Water pump mounting — 5.3L engine

ENGINE ELECTRICAL

ALTERNATOR

REMOVAL & INSTALLATION

3.5L and 3.9L Engine

See Figure 29.

1. Before servicing the vehicle, refer to the Precautions Section.
2. Drain the cooling system.
3. Remove or disconnect the following:
- Battery and tray
- Drive belt
- Engine cooling fan assembly
- Thermostat housing and radiator hose
- Outboard/inboard alternator bolts
- Idler pulley bolt and pulley
- Alternator electrical connectors
- Alternator bolts and the alternator

To install:

4. Install or connect the following:
- Alternator
- Alternator electrical connectors. Torque the positive battery terminal to 15 ft. lbs. (20 Nm).

- Idler pulley and torque the bolt to 37 ft. lbs. (50 Nm)
- Alternator bolts and torque them to 37 ft. lbs. (50 Nm)
- Thermostat housing with radiator hose and torque the bolts to 80 inch lbs. (9 Nm)

CHARGING SYSTEM

- Engine cooling fan assembly
- Drive belt
- Battery tray and torque the bolts to 44 inch lbs. (5 Nm)
- Battery
5. Refill the cooling system.

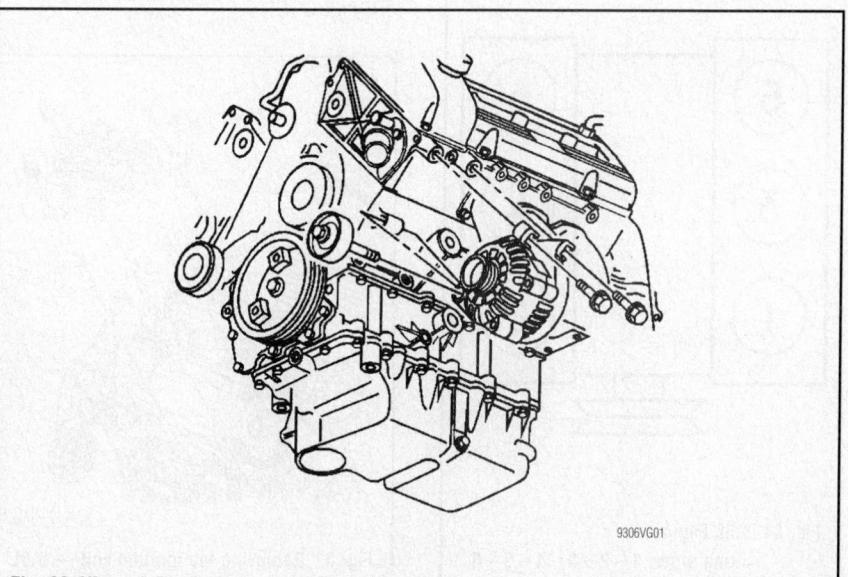

Fig. 29 View of the alternator — 3.5L engine

5.3L Engine

See Figure 30.

1. Before servicing the vehicle, refer to the Precautions Section.

2. Disconnect the negative battery cable.

3. Remove the engine sight shield.

4. Remove the drive belt.

5. Disconnect the generator electrical connector (2).

6. Position aside the protective boot (1) from the generator output BAT terminal for access.

7. Remove the generator output BAT terminal nut (4) and remove the positive battery lead (3) from the generator.

8. Remove the generator bolts and generator.

To install:

9. Install the generator and bolts. Tighten the bolts to 37 ft. lbs. (50 Nm).

10. Install the positive battery lead (3) and generator output BAT terminal nut (4) to the generator. Tighten the nut to 15 ft. lbs. (20 Nm).

11. Position the protective boot (1) to the generator output BAT terminal.

12. Connect the generator electrical connector (2).

13. Install the drive belt.

14. Install the engine sight shield.

15. Connect the negative battery cable.

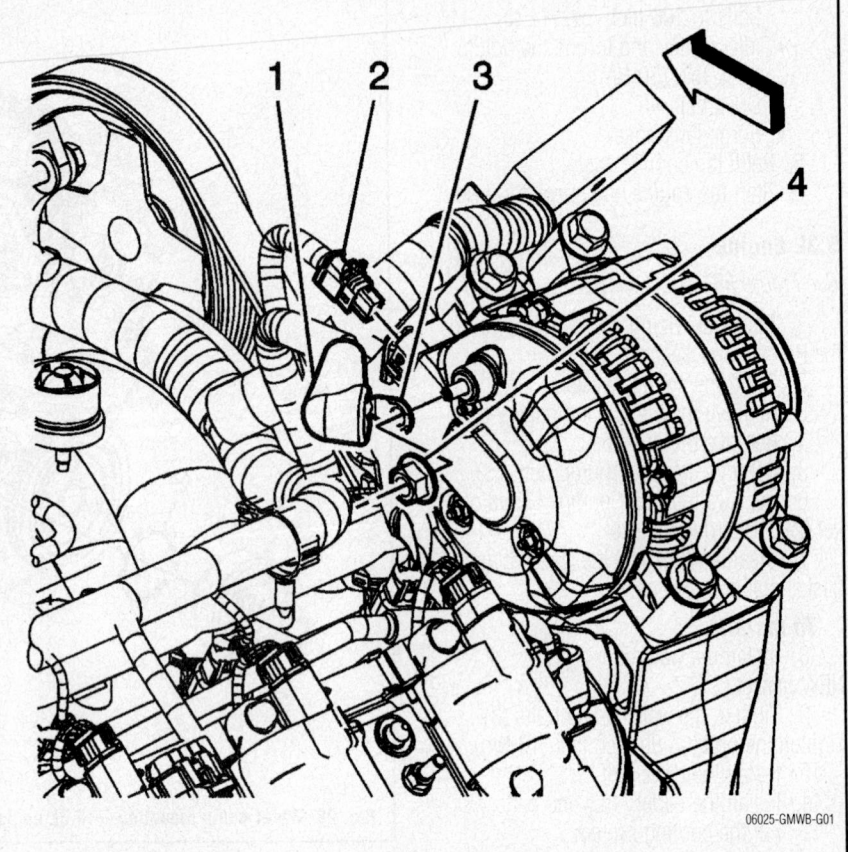

06025-GMWB-G01

Fig. 30 Alternator mounting — 5.3L engine

ENGINE ELECTRICAL

IGNITION SYSTEM

FIRING ORDERS

See Figure 31.

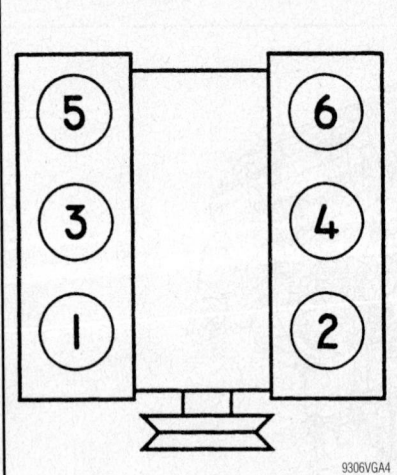

9306VGA4

Fig. 31 3.5L Engine
Firing order: 1 – 2 – 3 – 4 – 5 – 6
Distributorless ignition system

IGNITION COIL

REMOVAL & INSTALLATION

3.5L & 3.9L Engines

See Figure 32.

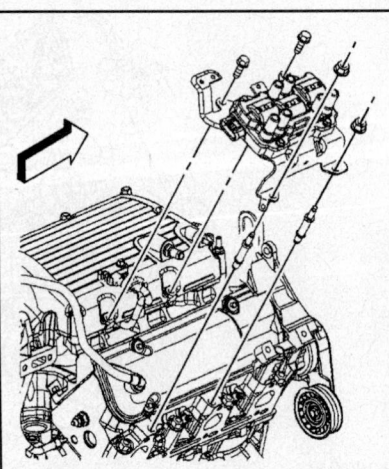

36616_IMPA_G0084

Fig. 32 Removing the ignition coil — 3.5L and 3.9L Engines

1. Before servicing the vehicle, refer to the Precautions Section.

2. Disconnect the negative battery cable.

3. Remove the intake manifold cover.

4. Disconnect the manifold absolute pressure (MAP) sensor electrical connector.

5. Disconnect the ignition coil electrical connector.

6. Disconnect the left side spark plug wires from the ignition coil.

7. Disconnect the right side spark plug wires from the ignition coil.

8. Remove the ignition coil bolts/nuts.

9. Remove the ignition coil.

10. Remove the ignition coil studs, if necessary.

11. To install, reverse removal procedure.

12. Tighten all ignition coil fasteners to 15 ft. lbs. (25 Nm).

5.3L Engine

See Figures 33 and 34.

➡ The following procedure shows the left side service procedure, the right side service procedure is similar.

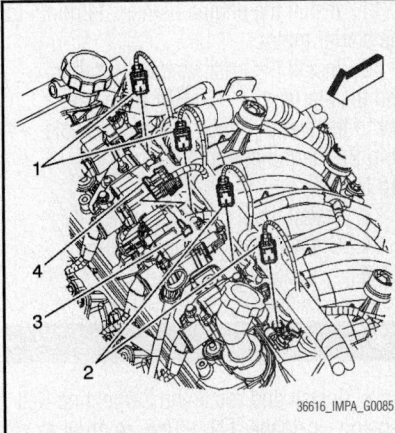

Fig. 33 Removing the CPA retainer (3) and disconnecting the ignition coil main connector (4) — 5.3L Engines

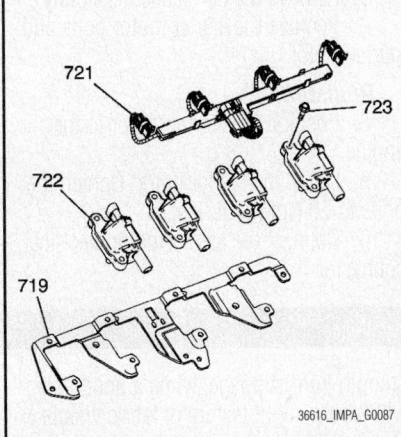

Fig. 34 Removing the ignition coil bolts and ignition coils — 5.3L Engines

1. Before servicing the vehicle, refer to the Precautions Section.
2. Disconnect the negative battery cable.
3. Remove the engine sight shield.
4. Remove the Connector Position Assurance (CPA) retainer.
5. Disconnect the ignition coil main electrical connector.
6. Remove the spark plug wire(s) from the ignition coil, as necessary.
7. Remove the ignition coil bolts, as necessary.
8. Remove the ignition coil(s), as necessary.
9. To install, reverse removal procedure.
10. Apply threadlock GM P/N 12345382 (Canadian P/N 10953489) or equivalent to the threads of the ignition coil bolts.

ENGINE ELECTRICAL

STARTER

REMOVAL & INSTALLATION

3.5L & 3.9L Engines

See Figure 35.

1. Before servicing the vehicle, refer to the Precautions Section.

➡ **The starter motors used in these vehicles are of varying lengths, make sure to use the correct size starter motor.**

2. Remove or disconnect the following:
- Negative battery cable
- Radiator lower air deflector
- Torque converter cover
- Electrical connections from the starter
- Starter motor

To install:

3. Install or connect the following:
- Starter motor and torque the bolts to 32 ft. lbs. (43 Nm) on all models except Intrigue. On Intrigue models, tighten the bolts to 37 ft. lbs. (50 Nm).
- Starter solenoid BAT terminal

STARTING SYSTEM

- Starter solenoid S terminal
- Torque converter cover and torque the bolts to 89 inch lbs. (10 Nm)
- Radiator lower air deflector and torque the bolts to 15 ft. lbs. (20 Nm)
- Negative battery cable

5.3L Engine

See Figure 36.

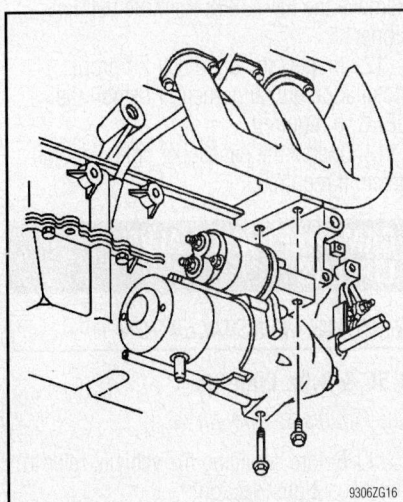

Fig. 35 Exploded view of the starter — 3.5L and 3.9L engines

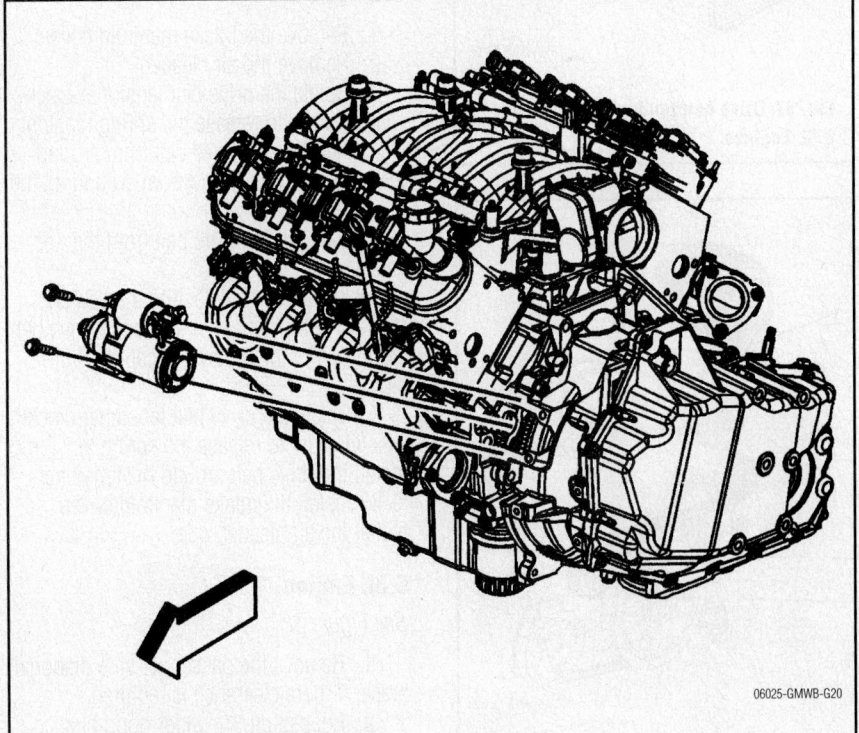

Fig. 36 Starter mounting — 5.3L engine

1. Before servicing the vehicle, refer to the Precautions Section.

2. Disconnect the negative battery cable.

3. Remove the starter solenoid BAT terminal nut and remove the positive battery cable from the starter motor.

4. Remove the engine harness terminal from the starter motor.

5. Disconnect the starter motor electrical connector.

6. Remove the air cleaner assembly.

7. Remove the starter motor bolts and starter motor.

To install:

8. Position the starter motor to the engine.

9. Install the starter bolts. Tighten the bolts to 50 Nm (37 ft. lbs).

10. Connect the starter motor electrical connector.

11. Install the engine harness terminal to the starter motor.

12. Install the positive battery cable and the starter solenoid BAT terminal nut to the starter motor. Tighten the solenoid BAT terminal nut to 89 inch lbs. (10 Nm).

13. Install the air cleaner assembly.

14. Connect the negative battery cable.

ENGINE MECHANICAL

ACCESSORY DRIVE BELTS

ACCESSORY BELT ROUTING

See Figures 37 and 38.

INSPECTION

Inspect the drive belt for signs of glazing or cracking. A glazed belt will be perfectly smooth from slippage, while a good belt will have a slight texture of fabric visible. Cracks will usually start at the inner edge of the belt and run outward. All worn or damaged drive belts should be replaced immediately.

Inspect the drive belt for signs of glazing or cracking. A glazed belt will be perfectly smooth from slippage, while a good belt will have a slight texture of fabric visible. Cracks will usually start at the inner edge of the belt and run outward. All worn or damaged drive belts should be replaced immediately.

ADJUSTMENT

No adjustment is possible or necessary.

REMOVAL & INSTALLATION

3.5L & 3.9L Engines

See Figure 37.

1. Remove the intake manifold cover.

2. Remove the air cleaner.

3. Rotate the drive belt tensioner clockwise in order to release the spring tension.

4. Remove the drive belt from around the tensioner pulley and from around all the other pulleys.

5. Remove the drive belt from the vehicle.

6. Install the drive belt to the vehicle. Starting at the generator, route the drive belt around all of the pulleys, except for tensioner.

7. Rotate the drive belt tensioner clockwise in order to release the spring tension. Install the drive belt around the tensioner.

8. Install the intake manifold cover. Install the air cleaner.

5.3L Engine

See Figure 38.

1. Remove the passenger side diagonal brace, if more clearance is required.

2. Reposition the under-hood bussed electrical center (UBEC), if more clearance is required.

3. Install and rotate the Serpentine Belt Tension Un-loader EN-47988, in order to relieve the tension on the belt tensioner.

4. Remove the drive belt from over the power steering pump pulley. Slowly release the EN-47988 and remove from the belt tensioner.

5. Remove the drive belt from around all the other pulleys. Clean and inspect the belt surfaces of all the pulleys.

6. Install and route the drive belt around all the pulleys except for the power steering pump pulley.

7. Ensure that when installing the EN-47988, to the belt tensioner that the EN-47988 is NOT installed above the drive belt.

8. Ensure that when installing the EN-47988, to the belt tensioner that the EN-47988 is installed below the drive belt.

9. Rotate the EN-47988 clockwise in order to relieve the tension on the belt tensioner.

10. Ensure that the drive belt is still properly routed around all the other pulleys, then install the drive belt over the power steering pump pulley.

11. Slowly release the EN-47988. Remove the EN-47988 from the belt tensioner.

12. Inspect the drive belt for proper installation and alignment. Position the UBEC, if required.

13. Install the passenger side diagonal brace, if required.

CAMSHAFT AND VALVE LIFTERS

REMOVAL & INSTALLATION

3.5L & 3.9L Engines

See Figures 39 through 42.

1. Before servicing the vehicle, refer to the Precautions Section.

2. Drain the cooling system.

3. Remove or disconnect the following:
   • Negative battery cable

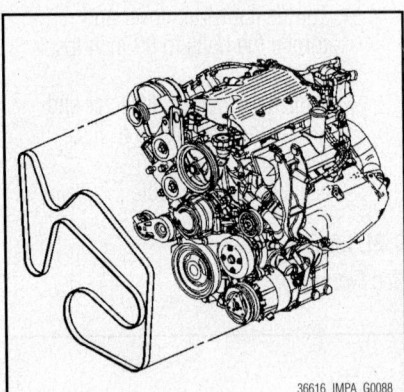

Fig. 37 Drive belt routing — 3.5L and 3.9L Engines

36616_IMPA_G0088

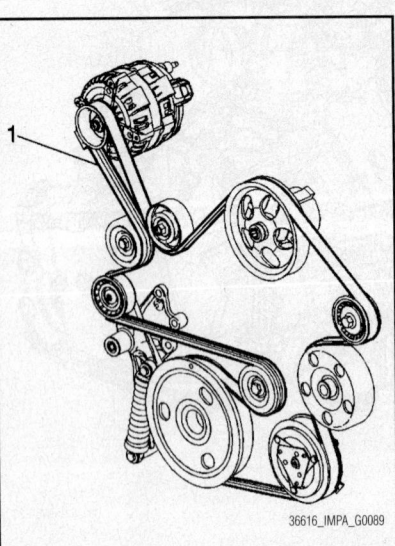

Fig. 38 Drive belt routing — 5.3L Engines

36616_IMPA_G0089

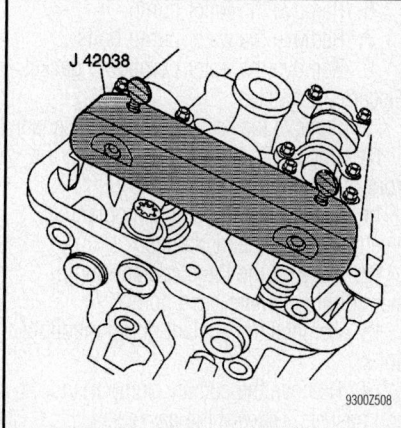

Fig. 39 Camshaft holding fixture installed on the camshafts — 3.5L engine

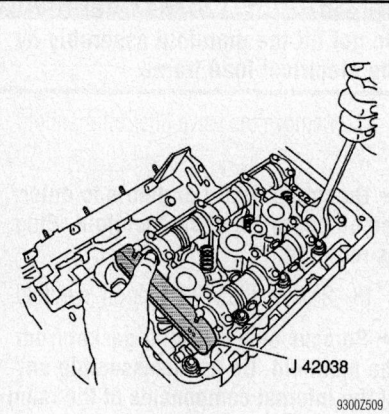

Fig. 40 Timing chain/sprocket holding fixture installed on the cylinder head; use the flats on the camshaft if rotation is necessary for installation of the holding tool — 3.5L engine

1. Left intake
2. Left exhaust
3. Right intake
4. Right exhaust

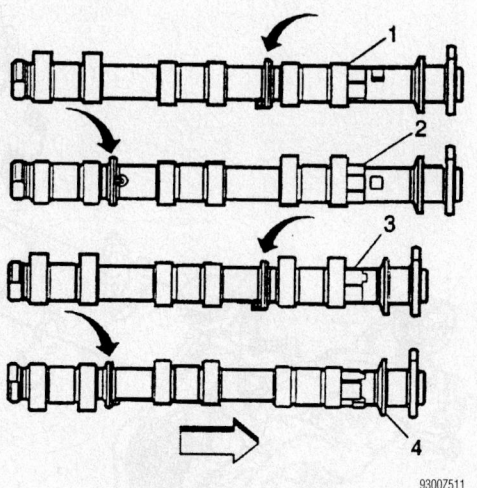

Fig. 41 Camshaft identification — 3.5L engine

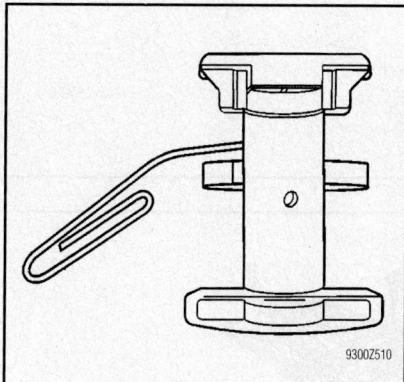

Fig. 42 Before installation, compress the tensioner and lock it in place with a piece of wire — 3.5L engine

- Fuel injector sight shield
- Thermostat housing for clearance when installing the Camshaft Holding Fixture
- Camshaft cover

4. Rotate the crankshaft so the camshaft flats are parallel to the camshaft's sealing surface, then install a camshaft holding fixture.

5. Remove the camshaft sprocket bolts.

6. Install a timing chain/sprocket holding fixture J 42042.

7. Evenly slide the camshaft sprocket and chain from the camshafts onto the holding tool.

➡ The camshaft bearing caps are marked. Be sure the raised portion of the cap faces the outside of the engine. They must always be installed in their original positions.

8. Remove or disconnect the following:

- Camshaft bearing caps
- Camshaft holding fixture
- Camshafts

To install:

9. Coat the rocker arms with engine oil and place them in their original positions.

➡ Be sure to install the rounded end on the lash adjuster and the flat end on the tip of the valve.

10. Install or connect the following:

- Camshafts, lubricated with engine oil, with the sprocket drive pin notch located at the top
- Bearing caps and torque the bolts to 71 inch lbs. (8 Nm) plus an additional 22 degree turn
- Camshaft Holding Fixture tool onto the camshaft(s) at the rear of the cylinder head

➡ Use the camshaft flats to turn the camshaft.

11. Compress the secondary timing chain tensioner by hand and insert a wire into the access hole to lock it in place.

12. Slide the camshaft sprockets/timing chain off the tool and onto the camshafts. Be sure to align the drive pins.

13. Remove the timing chain/sprocket holder from the front of the cylinder head. Torque the sprocket bolts to 18 ft. lbs. (25 Nm); then, an additional 45 degree turn.

14. Remove the wire from the chain tensioner and allow the tensioner to apply pressure to the chain.

15. Remove the camshaft holding fixture.

16. Install or connect the following:

- Camshaft cover and torque the bolts to 80 inch lbs. (9 Nm)
- Thermostat housing, if removed
- Fuel injector sight shield and torque the nuts to 27 inch lbs. (3 Nm)
- Negative battery cable

17. Refill the cooling system.

18. Start the vehicle and check for leaks, repair if necessary.

5.3L Engine

See Figures 43 through 47.

1. Before servicing the vehicle, refer to the Precautions Section.

2. Remove the engine.

3. Remove the crankshaft balancer. Refer to Crankshaft Front Seal.

4. Remove the oil level indicator.

5. Remove the left and right exhaust manifolds.

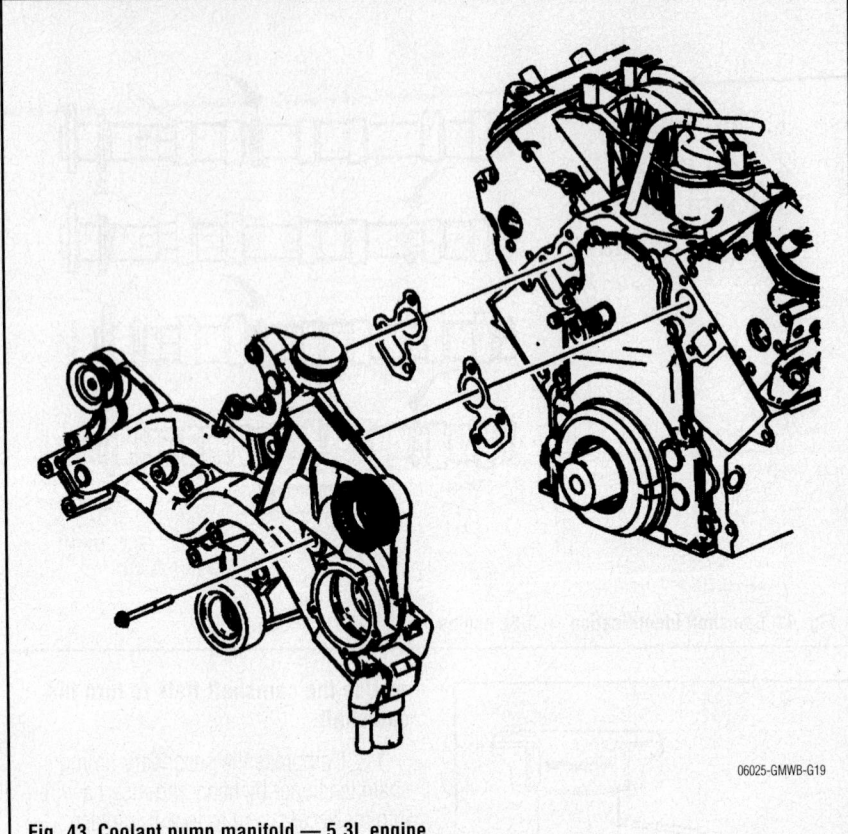

Fig. 43 Coolant pump manifold — 5.3L engine

06025-GMWB-G19

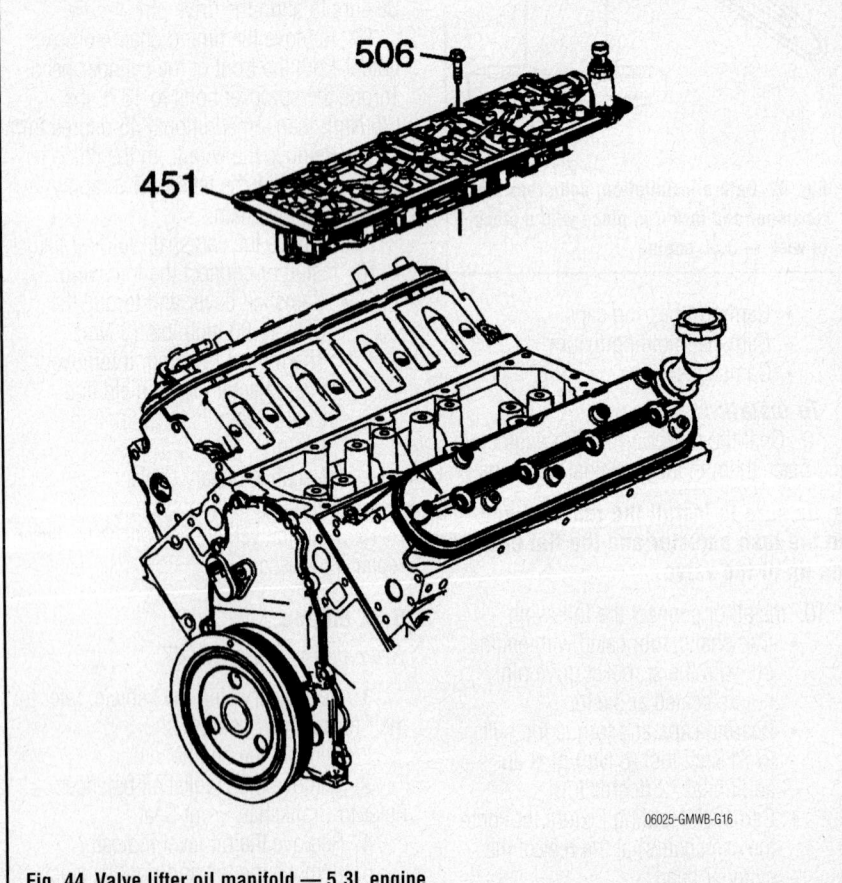

Fig. 44 Valve lifter oil manifold — 5.3L engine

06025-GMWB-G16

6. Remove the water pump.

7. Remove the water pump bolts.

8. Remove the water pump and gasket. Discard the gasket.

9. Remove the camshaft position sensor.

10. Unclip the wiring harness from the front of the engine.

11. Disconnect the engine coolant air bleed pipe hoses and clamps.

12. Remove the three coolant pump manifold to cylinder head bolts.

13. Remove the coolant pump manifold bolts.

14. Remove the coolant pump manifold and gaskets. Discard the gaskets.

15. Clean and inspect the water pump manifold mounting surfaces.

16. Remove the intake manifold.

✳ WARNING

Do not lift the manifold assembly by the electrical lead frame.

17. Remove the valve lifter oil manifold bolts.

➡ **Do not allow dirt or debris to enter the oil passages of the manifold. Plug, as required.**

18. Remove the valve lifter oil manifold.

➡ **Remove only the outer gasket from the manifold. Do not disassemble any of the internal components of the manifold in an attempt to remove the 8 inner sealing gaskets. If the inner gaskets are cut or damaged, replace the manifold as an assembly. Only use a wire-cutter type tool in order to minimize the amount of debris. Do not use a rotary-type cutting tool on the retaining straps.**

19. Identify the 8 gasket retaining strap locations.

20. Using a wire-cutter type tool, snip the 8 retaining straps of the outer gasket.

21. Remove the outer gasket from the manifold.

22. Remove the coolant air bleed pipe.

23. Remove the left and right valve rocker arm covers. Refer to Rocker Arm Removal & Installation.

24. Remove the valve rocker arms and pushrods. Refer to Rocker Arm Removal & Installation.

25. Remove the bolts.

26. Remove the guides (2) with the lifters. Note the installed position of the guides. The notched area of the guide is to align with the locating tab of the block.

27. Remove the valve lifters (1, 3 [on-demand lifter]) from the guide.

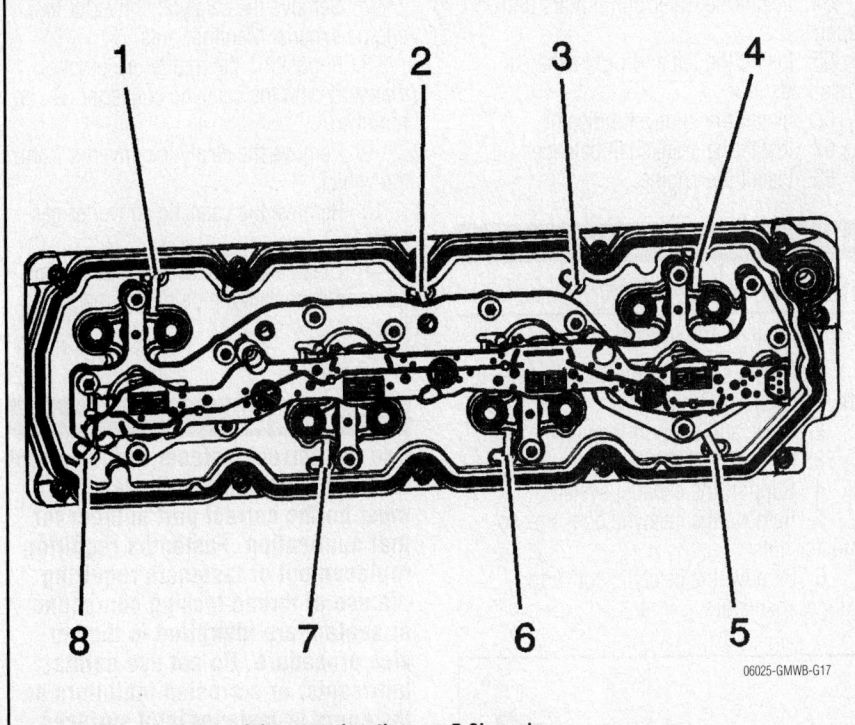

Fig. 45 The 8 gasket retaining strap locations — 5.3L engine

28. Organize or mark the components so they can be installed in the same location from which they were removed. The displacement on demand lifters are installed into the guide by aligning the notched area of the guide with the raised surface on the side of the lifter.

29. Remove the oil pan-to-front cover bolts.

30. Remove the front cover bolts.

31. Remove the front cover and gasket.

32. Rotate the crankshaft in order to align the timing marks (1, 2).

33. Remove the camshaft sprocket bolts.

34. Remove the camshaft sprocket and timing chain.

35. Remove the camshaft retainer bolts and retainer.

36. Remove the camshaft.

    a. Install 3 M8-125 x 100 mm bolts in the camshaft front bolt holes.

    b. Using the bolts as a handle, carefully rotate and pull the camshaft out of the engine block.

    c. Remove the bolts from the camshaft.

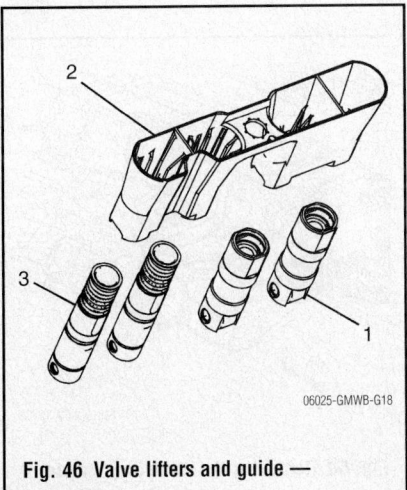

Fig. 46 Valve lifters and guide — 5.3L engine

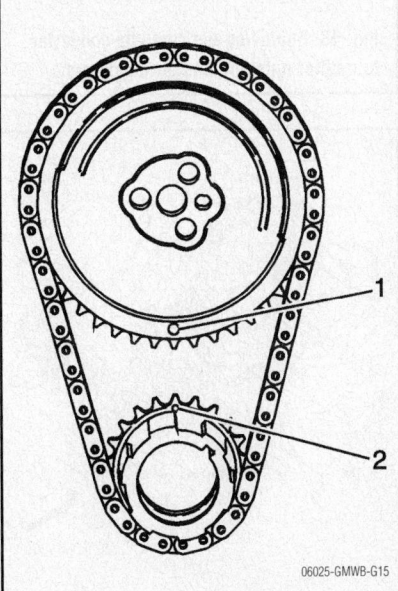

Fig. 47 Timing mark alignment — 5.3L engine

To install:

➡ **If camshaft replacement is required, the valve lifters must also be replaced.**

37. Lubricate the camshaft journals and the bearings with clean engine oil.

38. Install 3 M8-125 x 100 mm bolts in the NEW camshaft front bolt holes.

39. Using the bolts as a handle, carefully install the NEW camshaft into the engine block.

40. Remove the 3 bolts from the camshaft.

➡ **Install the retainer plate with the sealing gasket facing the engine block. The gasket surface on the engine block should be clean and free of dirt or debris.**

41. Install the camshaft retainer and bolts. Tighten the bolts to 18 ft. lbs. (25 Nm).

➡ **Properly locate the camshaft sprocket onto the locating pin of the camshaft. The sprocket teeth and timing chain teeth must mesh. The camshaft and crankshaft sprocket alignment marks MUST be aligned properly. Position the camshaft sprocket alignment mark in the 6 o'clock position.**

42. Install the camshaft sprocket and timing chain. If necessary, rotate the camshaft or crankshaft sprocket in order to align the timing marks.

43. Install the camshaft sprocket bolts. Tighten the bolts to 18 ft. lbs. (25 Nm).

44. Inspect the camshaft and crankshaft sprockets for proper timing mark alignment.

45. Install the front cover.

46. Install the oil pan-to-front cover bolts. Tighten the bolts to 18 ft. lbs. (25 Nm).

➡ **When using the valve lifters again, install the lifters to their original locations. If camshaft replacement is required, the valve lifters must also be replaced. Each of the 4 valve guide assemblies will contain 2 displacement on demand valve lifters and 2 non-displacement on demand valve lifters. With the lifters and guides properly installed, cylinders 1, 4, 6, and 7 lifter bores will each contain 2 displacement on demand valve lifters.**

47. Lubricate the valve lifters and engine block valve lifter bores with clean engine oil.

48. Insert the valve lifters into the lifter guides. Align the flat area on the top of the

non displacement on demand lifter with the flat area in the lifter guide bore. Push the lifter completely into the guide bore. The displacement on demand lifters are to be installed into the guide, with the notch in the guide aligned with the raised area of the lifter.

49. Install the valve lifters and guide assembly to the engine block.

50. Install the valve lifter guide bolts. Tighten the valve lifter guide bolts to 12 Nm (106 inch lbs.).

51. Install the valve rocker arms and pushrods.

52. Install the left and right valve rocker arm covers.

53. Install the coolant air bleed pipe.

➡ All gasket surfaces should be free of oil or other foreign material during assembly. Do not allow dirt or debris to enter the oil passages of the manifold. Plug as required.

54. Install the service gasket onto the manifold.

55. Install the valve lifter oil manifold with gasket.

56. Install the manifold bolts. Tighten the manifold bolts to 18 ft. lbs. (25 Nm).

57. Install the intake manifold.

❋❋ WARNING

DO NOT use cooling system seal tabs, or similar compounds, unless otherwise instructed. The use of cooling system seal tabs, or similar compounds, may restrict coolant flow through the passages of the cooling system or the engine components. Restricted coolant flow may cause engine overheating and/or damage to the cooling system or the engine components/assembly.

➡ All gasket surfaces are to be free of oil and other foreign material during assembly.

58. Install the water pump manifold and NEW gaskets. Tighten the M10 bolts to 44 ft. lbs. (60 Nm). Tighten the M8 bolts to 22 ft. lbs. (30 Nm).

59. Install the water pump manifold bolts.

60. Install the camshaft position sensor.

61. Install the cylinder head to coolant pump manifold bolts.

62. Connect the engine coolant air bleed pipe hose and clamp.

63. Install the water pump and a NEW gasket.

64. Install the water pump bolts until sung.

65. Install the left and right exhaust manifolds.

66. Install the oil level indicator.

67. Install the crankshaft balancer.

68. Install the engine.

CATALYTIC CONVERTER

REMOVAL & INSTALLATION

See Figures 48 through 50.

1. Before servicing the vehicle, refer to the Precautions Section.

2. Raise and support the vehicle.

3. Remove the HO2S, sensor 2.

4. Support the exhaust system.

5. Remove the catalytic converter to muffler nuts.

6. Remove the catalytic converter hanger insulators.

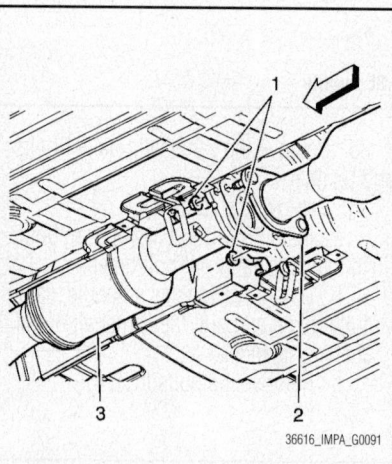

Fig. 48 Removing the catalytic converter to muffler nuts and hanger insulators

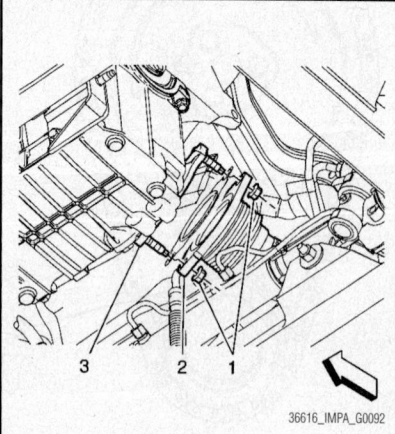

Fig. 49 Removing the catalytic converter to exhaust manifold nuts

7. Remove the catalytic converter to engine exhaust Manifold nuts

8. Reposition the muffler assembly rearward until the catalytic converter can be removed.

9. Remove the catalytic converter from the vehicle.

10. Remove the catalytic converter gaskets.

11. Clean and inspect the exhaust manifold and the exhaust pipe gasket mating surfaces.

To install:

❋❋ CAUTION

Use the correct fastener in the correct location. Replacement fasteners must be the correct part number for that application. Fasteners requiring replacement or fasteners requiring the use of thread locking compound or sealant are identified in the service procedure. Do not use paints, lubricants, or corrosion inhibitors on fasteners or fastener joint surfaces unless specified. These coatings affect fastener torque and joint clamping force and may damage the fastener. Use the correct tightening sequence and specifications when installing fasteners in order to avoid damage to parts and systems.

12. Install new gaskets to the catalytic converter and muffler assembly.

13. Reposition the muffler assembly rearward in order to position the catalytic converter to the exhaust Manifold and muffler assembly.

14. Install the catalytic converter (1) to muffler assembly nuts and tighten to 44 ft. lbs. (60 Nm).

15. Install the catalytic converter (3) hanger insulators

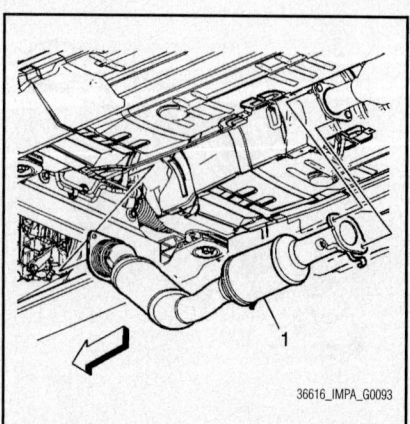

Fig. 50 Removing the catalytic converter and gaskets

16. Install the catalytic converter (3) to muffler nuts (1) and tighten to 26 ft. lbs. (35 Nm).

17. Remove the support from the exhaust system.

18. Install the HO2S sensor 2.

19. Lower the vehicle.

CRANKSHAFT DAMPER

REMOVAL & INSTALLATION

3.5L & 3.9L Engines

See Figures 51 and 52.

❋❋ WARNING

The factory recommended procedure for removing the crankshaft balancer is a lengthy and difficult procedure requiring special lifting and support equipment. The steering shaft must be separated and the vehicle subframe must be loosened and lowered for access to the crankshaft balancer. Careful work is required for reassembly. This is not a job for the inexperienced or ill-equipped.

1. Disconnect the negative battery cable.
2. Remove the accessory drive belt.
3. Raise and safely support the vehicle.
4. Remove the right front tire assembly. Locate and remove the right engine splash shield.
5. Place adjustable safety stands on the right side of the frame.
6. Remove the two right side frame bolts.
7. Lower the right side of the frame and engine using the adjustable safety stands to allow access to attach the three-legged puller to the crankshaft balancer.

8. GM recommends a device be used to lock the flywheel to keep the crankshaft from turning when the balancer center bolt is being removed. Their tool, J 43442 is a toothed device that, after removing the torque converter cover, bolts to the block with its teeth engaging the teeth of the flywheel, effectively locking the crankshaft in place. Use care if using substitutes.

9. Loosen and remove the crankshaft balancer bolt.

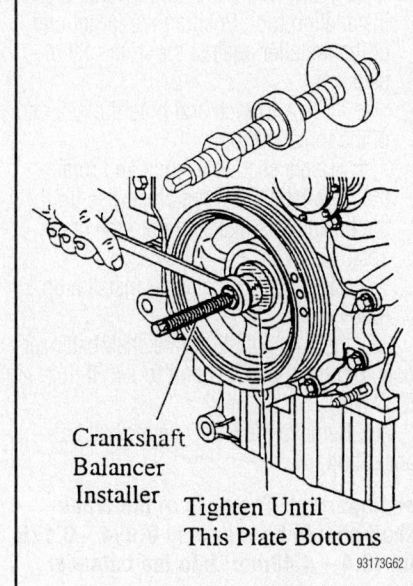

Fig. 52 This tool installs the balancer by threading into the crankshaft then by turning the nut, the tool presses the balancer into place — 3.5L (VIN H) engine

10. Mount a three-legged puller into the recesses cast into the backside of the balancer inner hub. The factory recommended tool, J 41816, has an accessory piece J 43010 which goes into the nose of the crankshaft to protect the retainer bolt threads. Use care if using substitutes. If the crankshaft threads are damaged, repairs will be lengthy and expensive. Tighten the center screw on the puller until the balancer is drawn clear of the crankshaft end. Remove the balancer from the puller.

To install:

11. Clean all parts well. Inspect the balancer for signs of damage. Do not lubricate the crankshaft front oil seal or the crankshaft balancer sealing surfaces. The crankshaft balancer is installed into a dry seal.

12. Place the balancer in position on the crankshaft. A special tool, J 4201, is recommended to thread into the end of the crankshaft and then draw the balancer back into position. GM recommends engaging at least ten threads of the tool to the crankshaft, before pressing the balancer in place by tightening the nut on the tool until the large washer bottoms out on the crankshaft end. Use care if using substitutes.

❋❋ WARNING

DO NOT attempt to hammer the balancer into place. It will be damaged.

13. Install the crankshaft balancer bolt. Using a torque angle meter, tighten to 37 ft. lbs. (50 Nm), plus as additional 125 degrees.

14. Remove the flywheel locking tool and install the torque converter cover.

15. Raise the right side of the frame with the engine, using the adjustable safety stands.

16. Install the two right side frame bolts.

17. Remove the adjustable safety stands.

18. Install the engine splash shield and right tire assembly. Lower the vehicle.

19. Install the remainder of the components in the reverse order of removal.

5.3L Engine

This procedure requires the following special tools, or their equivalents:
- Flywheel Holding Tool, EN 47699
- Crankshaft Balance and Sprocket Installer, J 41665
- Crankshaft Balancer Remover, J 41816
- Crankshaft End Protector, J 41816-2
- Steering Column Anti-Rotation Pin, J 42640
- Torque Angle Meter, J 45059

1. Install Steering Column Anti-Rotation Pin, tool no. J 42640 or equivalent.

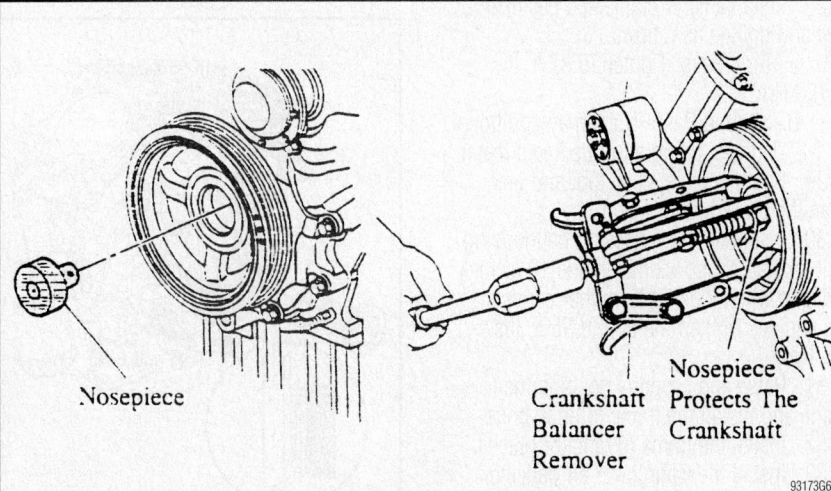

Fig. 51 Use care when rigging a puller on the balancer. Note the nosepiece to protect the balancer bolt threads in the end of the crankshaft — 3.5L (VIN H) engine

2. Remove the accessory drive belt.

3. Remove the air cleaner upper housing.

4. Remove the engine mount strut.

5. Remove the starter motor.

6. Remove the front fender splash shield.

7. Remove the transmission bellhousing bolt located at approximately the 10 o'clock position when looking from the rear of the engine.

8. Disconnect the transaxle cooler lines at the transaxle.

9. Remove the stabilizer shaft link lower nuts.

10. Remove the intermediate steering shaft pinch bolt and separate the shaft from the steering gear.

11. Remove the front lower air deflector braces and the deflector.

12. Remove the radiator to frame braces.

13. Install the engine support fixture.

14. Raise and support the vehicle.

15. Remove the frame to body bolts.

16. Install Flywheel Holding Tool No. EN 47699, or equivalent, and bolt to the block and flywheel. Tighten the bolt to 44 ft. lbs. (60 Nm).

17. Remove the right front tire and wheel assembly.

18. Lower the engine approximately 4 in. (100mm).

19. Remove the crankshaft balancer bolt. Do not discard the crankshaft balancer bolt. The balancer bolt will be used during the balancer installation procedure.

20. Install the Crankshaft Balancer Remover, J 41816 and Crankshaft End Protector, J 41816-2, to the crankshaft balancer.

21. Remove the crankshaft balancer.

22. Remove the tools from the crankshaft balancer.

To install:

➡ The used crankshaft balancer bolt will be used only during the first pass of the balancer installation procedure. Install a NEW bolt and tighten as described in the second, third and forth passes of the balancer bolt tightening procedure. The crankshaft balancer installation and bolt tightening involves a four stage tightening process. The first pass ensures that the balancer is installed completely onto the crankshaft. The second, third, and forth passes tighten the new bolt to the proper torque.

➡ The balancer should be positioned onto the end of the crankshaft as straight as possible prior to tool installation.

23. Position the crankshaft balancer onto the end of the crankshaft.

24. Using the Crankshaft Balance and Sprocket Installer, J 41665, install the crankshaft balancer:

a. Assemble the threaded rod, nut, washer and installer. Insert the smaller end of the installer into the front of the balancer.

b. Use a wrench and hold the hex end of the threaded rod.

c. Use a second wrench and rotate the installation tool nut clockwise until the balancer is started onto the crankshaft.

d. Remove the tool and reverse the installation tool. Position the larger end of the installer against the front of the balancer.

e. Use a wrench and hold the hex end of the threaded rod.

f. Use a second wrench and rotate the installation tool nut clockwise until the balancer is installed onto the crankshaft.

g. Remove the balancer installation tool.

25. Install the USED crankshaft balancer bolt. Tighten the USED bolt to 240 ft. lbs. (330 Nm).

26. Remove the USED crankshaft balancer bolt.

➡ **Important: The nose of the crankshaft should be recessed 0.094 – 0.176 in. (2.4 – 4.48mm) into the balancer bore.**

27. Measure for a correctly installed balancer. If the balancer is not installed to the proper dimensions, install the special tool, J 41665, and repeat the installation procedure.

28. Install a NEW crankshaft balancer bolt and tighten as follows:

a. First Pass: Tighten to 37 ft. lbs. (50 Nm)

b. Second Pass: Tighten an additional 140 degrees, using a torque angle meter.

29. Remove the special tool and bolt from the block and flywheel.

30. Install the transmission bellhousing bolt located at approximately the 10 o'clock position when looking from the rear of the engine. Tighten the bolt to 55 ft. lbs. (75 Nm).

31. Raise and properly position the frame and install the frame to body bolts.

32. Install the frame to radiator braces.

33. Install the front lower air deflector.

34. Connect the intermediate steering shaft to the steering gear.

35. Install the stabilizer shaft link lower nuts.

36. Connect the transaxle cooler lines to the transaxle.

37. Remove the engine support fixture.

38. Install the front fender splash shield.

39. Install the starter motor.

40. Install the air cleaner upper housing.

41. Install the accessory drive belt.

42. Install the engine mount strut.

43. Install the right front tire and wheel assembly.

44. Use a scan tool to perform the Crankshaft Position (CKP) system variation learn procedure.

CRANKSHAFT FRONT SEAL

REMOVAL & INSTALLATION

3.5L & 3.9L Engines

See Figures 53 and 54.

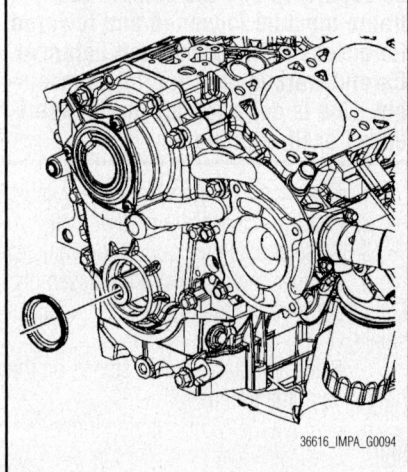

36616_IMPA_G0094

Fig. 53 Removing the crankshaft front seal

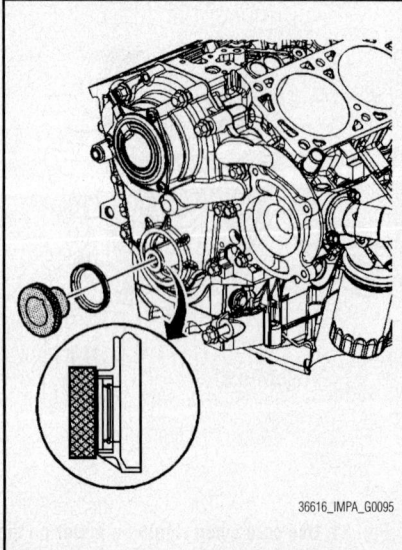

36616_IMPA_G0095

Fig. 54 Installing the crankshaft front seal

1. Before servicing the vehicle, refer to the Precautions Section.

2. Remove the crankshaft damper.

3. Remove the crankshaft key from the keyway.

4. Pry out the crankshaft front oil seal using a suitable tool. Use care not to damage the engine front cover or the crankshaft.

To install:

5. Lubricate the NEW oil seal with clean engine oil

6. Align Special Tool EN-48869 and the crankshaft front oil seal with the engine front cover and crankshaft.

7. Install the crankshaft front oil seal using EN-48869 and a suitable tool.

8. Install the crankshaft key into the keyway.

9. Install the crankshaft balancer.

5.3L Engine

See Figures 55 and 56.

1. Before servicing the vehicle, refer to the Precautions Section.

2. Remove the crankshaft balancer.

3. Remove and discard the crankshaft oil seal.

To install:

➡ **Do not lubricate the oil seal sealing surface. Do not reuse the crankshaft oil seal.**

4. Lubricate the outer edge of the oil seal with clean engine oil.

5. Lubricate the front cover oil seal bore with clean engine oil.

6. Install the crankshaft front oil seal onto the J 41478.

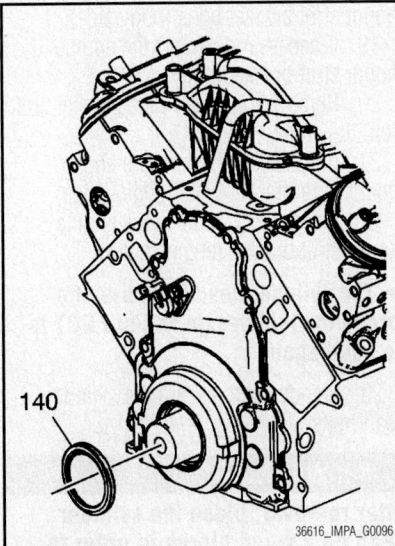

Fig. 55 Removing the crankshaft front seal — 5.3L Engines

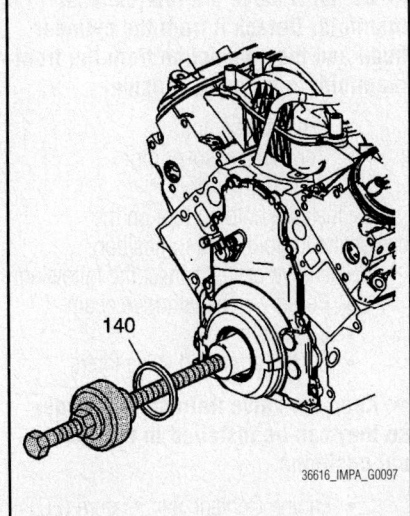

Fig. 56 Installing the crankshaft front seal

7. Install the J 41478 threaded rod with nut, washer, guide, and oil seal into the end of the crankshaft.

8. Using the J 41478 , install the oil seal into the cover bore.

a. Use a wrench and hold the hex on the installer bolt.

b. Use a second wrench and rotate the installer nut clockwise until the seal bottoms in the cover bore.

c. Remove the J 41478.

d. Inspect the oil seal for proper installation. The oil seal should be installed evenly and completely into the front cover bore.

9. Install the crankshaft balancer.

CYLINDER HEAD

REMOVAL & INSTALLATION

3.5L and 3.9L Engine

Front

See Figures 57 and 58.

1. Before servicing the vehicle, refer to the Precautions Section.

2. Drain the engine oil.

3. Drain the cooling system.

4. Remove or disconnect the following:
- Negative battery cable
- Intake manifold
- Water outlet housing
- Engine mount strut bracket
- Coolant crossover pipe
- Front exhaust manifold
- Camshaft cover

5. Install a holding tool on the camshafts to hold them in position.

6. Remove or disconnect the following:
- Camshaft primary chain

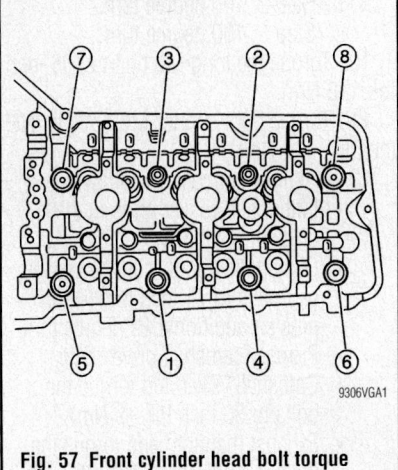

Fig. 57 Front cylinder head bolt torque sequence — 3.5L engine

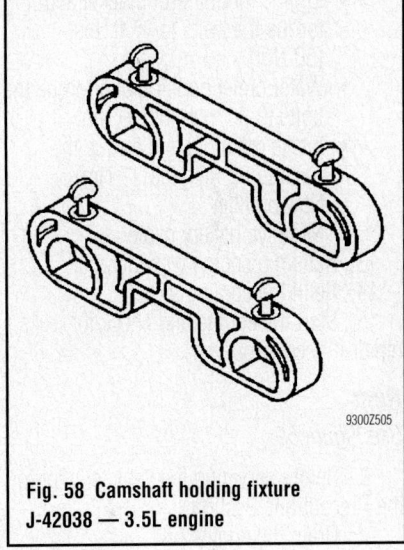

Fig. 58 Camshaft holding fixture J-42038 — 3.5L engine

- Camshafts from the front cylinder head
- Rocker arms and valve lifters

➡ **Be sure to keep the arms and lifters in order so they can be installed the their original locations.**

- M6 bolts from the front of the cylinder head
- M11 cylinder head bolts and discard
- Cylinder head

To install:

7. Be sure the dowels are securely mounted in the engine block.

8. Install or connect the following:
- New gasket
- Cylinder head
- New M11 bolts
- M6 bolts in the front of the cylinder head

9. Torque the M11 bolts in sequence to:
a. Step 1: 22 ft. lbs. (30 Nm).

b. Step 2: 100 degree turn.

c. Step 3: 100 degree turn.

10. Torque the long M6 bolt to 106 inch lbs. (12 Nm).

11. Torque both shorter M6 bolts to 106 inch lbs. (12 Nm).

12. Install or connect the following:
- Lifters and rocker arms in their original positions
- Camshafts and torque the bearing cap bolts to 71 inch lbs. (8 Nm) plus an additional 22 degree turn
- Primary camshaft drive chain
- Camshaft cover and torque the bolts to 80 inch lbs. (9 Nm)
- Exhaust manifold and torque the bolts to 18 ft. lbs. (25 Nm)
- Coolant crossover pipe and torque the bolts to 18 ft. lbs. (25 Nm)
- Engine mount strut bracket and torque the bolts to 37 ft. lbs. (50 Nm)
- Water outlet housing and torque the bolts to 80 inch lbs. (9 Nm)
- Intake manifold and torque the bolts to 62 inch lbs. (7 Nm)
- New oil filter
- Negative battery cable

13. Refill the engine with clean oil.

14. Refill the cooling system.

15. Start the engine and check for leaks, repair if necessary.

Rear

See Figure 59.

1. Before servicing the vehicle, refer to the Precautions Section.

2. Drain the engine oil.

3. Drain the cooling system.

4. Remove or disconnect the following:
- Negative battery cable
- Intake manifold

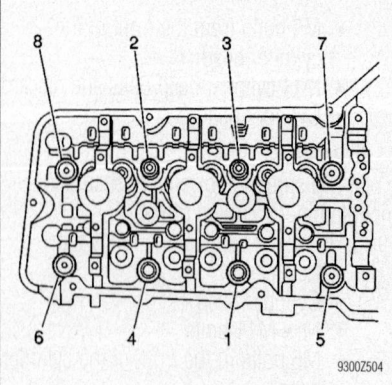

Fig. 59 Rear cylinder head bolt torque sequence — 3.5L engine

➡ **Do not remove the rear exhaust manifold. Detach it from the cylinder head and the connection from the front manifold; then, move it aside.**

- Exhaust manifold
- Coolant crossover pipe
- Camshaft cover

5. Install a holding tool on the camshafts to hold them in position.

6. Remove or disconnect the following:
- Primary camshaft drive chain
- Camshafts
- Rocker arms and valve lifters

➡ **Keep the valve train parts in order so they can be installed in their original positions.**

- Engine Coolant Temperature (ECT) sensor from the cylinder head
- M6 bolts from the front of the cylinder head, note the location of the longer bolt
- M11 cylinder head bolts and discard the bolts
- Cylinder head

To install:

7. Be sure the dowels are securely mounted in the engine block.

8. Install or connect the following:
- New gasket
- Cylinder head
- New M11 bolts
- M6 bolts in the front of the cylinder head

9. Torque the M11 bolts in sequence to:
a. Step 1: 22 ft. lbs. (30 Nm).

b. Step 2: 100 degree turn.

c. Step 3: 100 degree turn.

10. Torque the long M6 bolt to 106 inch lbs. (12 Nm).

11. Torque both shorter M6 bolts to 106 inch lbs. (12 Nm).

12. Install or connect the following:
- ECT sensor and torque the fastener to 15 ft. lbs. (20 Nm)
- Lifters and rocker arms in their original positions
- Camshafts and torque the bearing cap bolts to 71 inch lbs. (8 Nm) plus an additional 22 degree turn
- Primary camshaft drive chain
- Camshaft cover and torque the bolts to 80 inch lbs. (9 Nm)
- Coolant crossover pipe and torque the bolts to 18 ft. lbs. (25 Nm)
- Exhaust manifold and torque the bolts to18 ft. lbs. (25 Nm)
- Intake manifold and torque the bolts to 62 inch lbs. (7 Nm)
- New oil filter
- Negative battery cable

13. Refill the engine with clean oil.

14. Refill the cooling system.

15. Start the engine and check for leaks, repair if necessary.

5.3L Engine

Left Side

See Figures 60 and 61.

1. Before servicing the vehicle, refer to the Precautions Section.

2. Remove the intake manifold.

3. Disconnect the hose clamp and hose from the coolant fill neck.

4. Remove the coolant air bleed pipe bolts.

5. Remove the coolant air bleed pipe (1) with hose and seals.

6. Remove the hose (2) and clamps (3) from the coolant air bleed pipe as required.

7. Remove the engine coolant air bleed cover bolts.

8. Remove the covers with seals.

9. Remove the seals from the pipe and covers. Discard the seals.

10. Remove the left exhaust manifold.

11. Remove the pushrods.

12. Remove the power steering pump pulley.

13. Remove the 3 coolant manifold bolts to the cylinder head.

14. Remove the forward engine mount strut bolt and nut.

15. Remove the rear engine mount strut bolt and nut.

16. Remove the engine mount strut.

17. Inspect the rubber in the engine mount strut for the following conditions:

18. If necessary, remove the engine mount strut bracket bolts (body side).

19. If necessary, remove the engine mount strut bracket (body side).

20. Remove the heater pipe bracket bolt from the engine mount.

21. If necessary, remove the engine mount strut bracket bolts (engine side).

22. If necessary, remove the engine mount strut bracket (engine side).

➡ **The cylinder head bolts are of a torque to yield design and are NOT to be used again.**

23. Remove and discard the cylinder head bolts.

✳✳ WARNING

After removal, place the cylinder head on 2 wood blocks in order to prevent damage to the sealing surfaces.

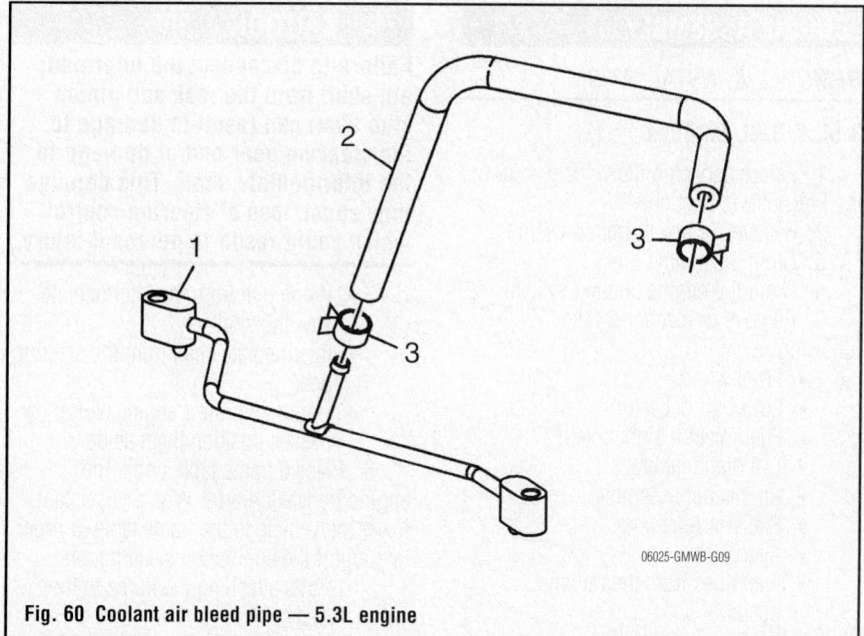

Fig. 60 Coolant air bleed pipe — 5.3L engine

06025-GMWB-G09

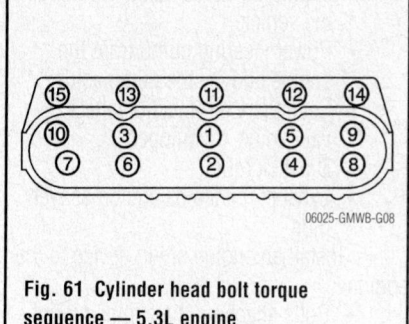

06025-GMWB-G08

Fig. 61 Cylinder head bolt torque sequence — 5.3L engine

24. Remove the cylinder head.
25. Remove and discard the cylinder head gasket.
26. Clean and inspect the cylinder head.

To install:

✲✲ CAUTION

Wear safety glasses in order to avoid eye damage.

✲✲ WARNING

Clean all dirt, debris, and coolant from the engine block cylinder head bolt holes. Failure to remove all foreign material may result in damaged threads, improperly tightened fasteners or damage to components.

➡ **Do not reuse the cylinder head bolts. Install NEW cylinder head bolts during assembly. Do not use any type of sealant on the cylinder head gasket (unless specified). The cylinder head gaskets must be installed in the proper direction and position.**

27. Clean the cylinder head bolt holes, if required.
28. Clean the engine block bolt holes, if required.
29. Use spray cleaner GM P/N 12346139 or P/N 12377981, Canadian P/N 10953463), or equivalent into the hole.
30. Clean the cylinder head bolt holes with compressed air.
31. Check the cylinder head locating pins for proper installation.
32. Inspect the displacement markings on the cylinder head gasket, for the proper usage.
33. Install the NEW cylinder head gasket onto the locating pins.
34. Install the cylinder head onto the locating pins.
35. Install the NEW cylinder head bolts.
36. Tighten the cylinder head bolts. Tighten the M11 bolts (1-10) a first pass in sequence to 22 ft. lbs. (30 Nm).
   a. Tighten the M11 bolts (1-10) a second pass in sequence to 90 degrees.
   b. Tighten the M11 bolts (1-10) a final pass in sequence to 70 degrees.
   c. Tighten the M8 bolts (11-15) to 22 ft. lbs. (30 Nm). Begin with the center bolt (11) and alternating side-to-side, work outward tightening all of the bolts.
37. If necessary, position the engine mount strut bracket (engine side) to the cylinder head.
38. If necessary, install the engine mount strut bracket bolts (engine side). Tighten the bolts to 48 Nm (35 ft. lbs.).

39. Install the heater pipe bracket bolt. Tighten the bolt to 12 ft. lbs. (16 Nm).
40. If necessary, position the engine mount strut bracket (body side) to the vehicle.
41. If necessary, install the engine mount strut bracket bolts (body side). Tighten the bolt to 35 ft. lbs. (48 Nm).
42. Install the engine mount strut.
43. Install the rear engine mount strut bolt and nut. Tighten the bolt/nut to 35 ft. lbs. (48 Nm).
44. Install the forward engine mount strut bolt and nut. Tighten the bolt/nut to 35 ft. lbs. (48 Nm).
45. Install the 3 coolant manifold bolts to the cylinder head. Tighten the bolts to 37 ft. lbs. (50 Nm).
46. Install the power steering pump pulley.
47. Install the pushrods.
48. Install the left exhaust manifold.
49. Install the coolant air bleed pipe.
50. Install the intake manifold.

Right Side

1. Before servicing the vehicle, refer to the Precautions Section.
2. Remove the intake manifold.
3. Disconnect the hose clamp and hose from the coolant fill neck.
4. Remove the coolant air bleed pipe bolts.
5. Remove the coolant air bleed pipe with hose and seals.
6. Remove the hose and clamps from the coolant air bleed pipe as required.
7. Remove the engine coolant air bleed cover bolts.
8. Remove the covers with seals.
9. Remove the seals from the pipe and covers. Discard the seals.
10. Remove the generator bracket.
11. Remove the right exhaust manifold.
12. Remove the pushrods.

➡ **The cylinder head bolts are of a torque to yield design and are NOT to be used again.**

13. Remove and discard the cylinder head bolts.

✲✲ WARNING

After removal, place the cylinder head on 2 wood blocks in order to prevent damage to the sealing surfaces.

14. Remove the cylinder head.
15. Remove and discard the cylinder head gasket.
16. Clean and inspect the cylinder head.

To install:

✷✷ CAUTION

Wear safety glasses in order to avoid eye damage.

✷✷ WARNING

Clean all dirt, debris, and coolant from the engine block cylinder head bolt holes. Failure to remove all foreign material may result in damaged threads, improperly tightened fasteners or damage to components.

➡ Do not reuse the cylinder head bolts. Install NEW cylinder head bolts during assembly. Do not use any type of sealant on the cylinder head gasket (unless specified). The cylinder head gaskets must be installed in the proper direction and position.

17. Clean the cylinder head bolt holes, if required.
18. Clean the engine block bolt holes, if required.
19. Use spray cleaner GM P/N 12346139 or P/N 12377981, Canadian P/N 10953463), or equivalent into the hole.
20. Clean the cylinder head bolt holes with compressed air.
21. Check the cylinder head locating pins for proper installation.
22. Inspect the displacement markings on the cylinder head gasket, for the proper usage.
23. Install the NEW cylinder head gasket onto the locating pins.
24. Install the cylinder head onto the locating pins.
25. Install the NEW cylinder head bolts.
26. Tighten the cylinder head bolts.
   a. Tighten the M11 bolts (1-10) a first pass in sequence to 22 ft. lbs. (30 Nm).
   b. Tighten the M11 bolts (1-10) a second pass in sequence to 90 degrees.
   c. Tighten the M11 bolts (1-10) a final pass in sequence to 70 degrees.
   d. Tighten the M8 bolts (11-15) to 22 ft. lbs. (30 Nm). Begin with the center bolt (11) and alternating side-to-side, work outward tightening all of the bolts.
27. Install the pushrods.
28. Install the right exhaust manifold.
29. Install the generator bracket.
30. Install the coolant air bleed pipe.
31. Install the intake manifold.

ENGINE ASSEMBLY

REMOVAL & INSTALLATION

3.5L & 3.9L Engines

1. Before servicing the vehicle, refer to the Precautions Section.
2. Relieve the fuel system pressure.
3. Drain the engine oil.
4. Drain the engine cooling system.
5. Remove or disconnect the following:
   - Front wheels
   - Lower air deflector
   - Fuel injector sight shield
   - Left diagonal brace
   - Air cleaner assembly
   - Radiator inlet hose
   - Alternator
   - Fuel lines from the rail and position
   - Fuel vapor line
   - Throttle and cruise cables with the mounting bracket from the throttle body
   - Automatic range selector cable from the Park/Neutral Position (PNP) switch
   - Vacuum brake booster hose from the booster
   - Transaxle oil cooler lines from the radiator
   - Heater hoses from the engine
   - Right side AIR control valve, if equipped
   - Upper engine electrical connectors, including grounds
   - Lower AIR hose from the elbow, if equipped and discard the clamp
   - Lower electrical connectors, including grounds and the harness retainer
   - Fog lamp electrical connectors, if equipped
   - Torque converter cover
   - Starter
   - Bolts attaching the engine flywheel to the torque converter
   - Engine splash shields from the inner fender
   - A/C compressor and position aside without disconnecting the lines
   - Catalytic converter pipe from the rear exhaust manifold
   - Bolts attaching the lower transaxle to the engine
   - Connectors from the Wheel Speed Sensors, and unclip the harnesses from the lower control arms
   - Drive axles from the steering knuckles

✷✷ CAUTION

Failure to disconnect the intermediate shaft from the rack and pinion stub shaft can result in damage to the steering gear and/or damage to the intermediate shaft. This damage may cause loss of steering control which could result in personal injury.

   - Pinch bolt from the intermediate steering shaft
   - Intermediate shaft from the steering gear
   - Upper and lower engine wiring harnesses position them aside
6. Place a frame table under the engine/transaxle/frame. With an assistant, lower the vehicle to the frame table in order to support the engine/transaxle/frame.
   - Bolts attaching the frame to the body
   - Frame table with the engine/transaxle/frame from under the vehicle
   - Power steering pump from the engine and lay the pump aside
   - Secondary air injection check valve/pipe, if equipped
   - Dipstick tube
   - Exhaust manifolds and crossover pipe
7. Install an engine lifting device to the engine.
   - Bolts attaching the engine mount bracket to the engine
   - Transaxle brace
   - Bolts attaching the upper transmission to the engine
   - Engine from the transaxle/frame

To install:
8. Installation is the reverse of removal, please note the following torques:
9. Install or connect the following:
   - Bolts attaching the transmission to the engine to 55 ft. lbs. (75 Nm)
   - Frame bolts to 133 ft. lbs. (180 Nm)
10. Center the steering angle sensor.
11. Fill the engine with new oil.

➡ A filter change is recommended.

12. Fill the cooling system.
13. Perform the Crankshaft Position (CKP) system variation learn procedure.
14. Start the engine and check for leaks, repair if necessary.

5.3L Engine

See Figure 62.

1. Before servicing the vehicle, refer to the Precautions Section.

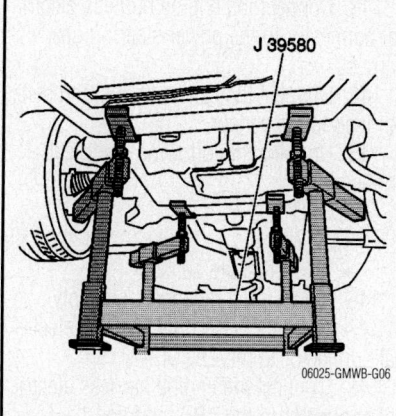

J 39580

06025-GMWB-G06

Fig. 62 Engine holding fixture J39580 — 5.3L engine

2. Disconnect the negative battery cable.

3. Remove the engine sight shield.

4. Evacuate the air conditioning (A/C) system and recover the refrigerant.

5. Remove the front tires and wheels.

6. Drain the cooling system.

7. Drain the engine oil.

8. Lower the vehicle.

9. Reposition the inlet hose clamp at the radiator.

10. Remove the inlet hose from the radiator.

11. Reposition the outlet hose clamp at the radiator.

12. Disengage the outlet hose clips from the fan shroud.

13. Remove the outlet hose from the radiator.

14. Remove the A/C compressor hose nut at the A/C receiver/dehydrator tube.

15. Remove the A/C compressor hose.

16. Remove the A/C compressor hose nut at the A/C condenser.

17. Remove the A/C compressor hose.

18. Remove the brake booster vacuum hose from the brake booster.

19. Remove the brake booster vacuum hose from the intake manifold.

20. Disconnect the engine harness electrical connectors from the instrument panel (I/P) harness electrical connectors.

21. Disconnect the brake fluid level switch electrical connector from the master cylinder.

22. Remove brake fluid from the master cylinder.

23. Disconnect the from brake pipe fittings from the master cylinder.

24. Disconnect the brake pipe fittings from the antilock brake (ABS) module.

25. Remove the master cylinder nuts.

26. Position the master cylinder to the engine. Hold the master cylinder in place using mechanic's wire.

27. Relieve the fuel system pressure.

28. Disconnect the fuel feed line from the fuel rail.

29. Disconnect the evaporative emission (EVAP) line from the purge solenoid.

30. Remove the right front fender diagonal brace.

31. Remove the underhood electrical center cover.

32. Loosen the 4 integral bolts attaching the fuse block. Reposition the fuse block.

33. Loosen the engine harness connector bolt. Remove the engine harness connector from the bracket.

34. Disconnect the camshaft position sensor lead.

35. Disconnect the engine harness electrical connector from the ABS module.

36. Disconnect the engine harness electrical connector from the electronic brake control module (EBCM).

37. Remove the air cleaner assembly.

38. Disconnect the following electrical connectors:

- Transmission control module (TCM)
- Engine control module (ECM)
- A/C pressure sensor

39. Disconnect the engine harness electrical connector from the Crankshaft Position (CKP) sensor harness.

40. Disconnect the engine harness electrical connector from the power steering gear harness.

41. Remove the clip attaching the power steering gear harness to the bracket.

42. Remove the shift cable clip.

43. Disconnect the shift cable from the transaxle selector lever stud.

44. Remove the shift cable from the bracket.

45. Remove the Vehicle Speed Sensor (VSS) shield nut and bolt. Remove the shield.

46. Disconnect the engine harness electrical connector from the VSS.

47. Set all branches of the engine wiring harness on top of the engine.

48. Reposition the intermediate shaft lower boot.

49. Remove the intermediate shaft to steering gear bolt.

50. Separate the intermediate shaft from the steering gear.

51. Disconnect both front wheel speed sensors.

52. Unclip the ABS wire harness from the lower control arm.

53. Reposition the heater inlet and outlet hose clamps.

54. Remove the heater inlet and outlet hoses from the heater inlet/outlet pipe.

55. Raise and support the vehicle.

56. Disconnect the stabilizer links from the stabilizer shaft.

57. Disconnect the ball joints from the steering knuckles.

58. Disconnect the power steering pressure hose from the steering gear.

59. Disconnect the power steering pressure line clips from the frame.

60. Disconnect the outer tie rod ends from the steering knuckles.

61. Loosen the power steering hose clamp at the inlet pipe.

62. Remove the power steering hose from the inlet pipe.

63. Remove the left and right halfshafts from the transaxle.

64. Support the halfshafts using mechanic's wire.

65. Remove the transaxle oil cooler line bracket bolt/stud.

66. Disconnect the transaxle oil cooler lines from the transaxle.

67. Remove the positive battery cable nut from the starter.

68. Remove the cable terminal from the starter.

69. Remove the battery cable ground nut.

70. Remove the cable ground terminal from the stud.

71. Remove the battery cable retainers from the engine frame.

72. Disconnect the exhaust system.

73. Disconnect the O_2 sensor harness pigtail.

74. Remove the transaxle converter cover bolt/stud.

75. Remove the converter cover.

76. Remove the flywheel bolts.

77. Remove the front air deflectors.

78. Raise the vehicle enough to place engine holding fixture J39580 under the engine, frame, and front suspension.

79. Support the rear of the vehicle with suitable jackstand.

80. Strap the front of the vehicle to the hoist.

81. Raise the engine holding fixture, or lower the vehicle to preload the weight of the engine, frame, and front suspension.

82. Remove the radiator to frame brackets.

83. Remove the engine frame front bolts.

84. Remove the engine frame rear bolts.

85. With the aid of an assistant, lower the engine holding fixture and/or raise the vehicle to remove the engine and the frame from the vehicle.

86. Ensure that all hoses, wires, and pipes clear the vehicle during the removal process.

87. Use a suitable engine lift to support the engine.

88. Remove the front engine mount to frame nuts.

89. Remove the rear engine mount to frame nuts.

90. Remove the transaxle to engine bolts and stud.

91. Separate the engine from the transaxle.

92. Using a suitable engine lift, remove the engine from the frame.

93. Install the engine onto a suitable engine stand.

To install:

94. Using a suitable engine lift, remove the engine from the engine stand.

95. Position and install the engine to the frame and the transaxle.

96. Install the transaxle to engine bolts and stud. Tighten the bolts/stud to 75 Nm (55 ft. lbs.).

97. Install the rear engine mount to frame nuts. Tighten the nuts to 37 ft. lbs. (50 Nm).

98. Install the front engine mount to frame nuts. Tighten the nuts to 37 ft. lbs. (50 Nm).

99. Ensure that all hoses, wires, and pipes clear the vehicle during the installation process.

100. With the aid of an assistant, raise the engine holding fixture and/or lower the vehicle to install the engine and frame to the vehicle.

101. Install the engine frame rear bolts. Tighten the bolts to 160 Nm (118 ft. lbs.).

102. Install the engine frame front bolts. Tighten the bolts to 145 Nm (107 ft. lbs.).

103. Install radiator to front frame brackets.

104. Lower the engine holding fixture or raise the vehicle to preload the weight of the engine, frame, and front suspension.

105. Remove the support from under the rear of the vehicle.

106. Raise the vehicle enough to remove the engine holding fixture from under the engine, frame, and front suspension.

107. Connect the exhaust system and connect the O2 sensor harness pigtail.

108. Install the flywheel bolts. Tighten the bolts to 63 Nm (47 ft. lbs.).

109. Install the converter cover.

110. Install the transaxle converter cover bolt/stud. Tighten the bolt/stud to 89 inch lbs. (10 Nm).

111. Install the left and right halfshafts into the transaxle.

112. Install the battery cable retainers to the engine frame.

113. Install the front air deflector.

114. Install the cable ground terminal to the stud.

115. Install the battery cable ground nut. Tighten the nut to 22 ft. lbs. (30 Nm).

116. Install the cable terminal to the starter.

117. Install the positive battery cable nut to the starter. Tighten the nut to 89 inch lbs. (10 Nm).

118. Connect the transaxle oil cooler lines to the transaxle.

119. Install the transaxle oil cooler line bracket bolt/stud. Tighten the bolt/stud to 18 ft. lbs. (25 Nm).

120. Install the power steering hose to the inlet pipe.

121. Tighten the power steering hose clamp at the inlet pipe. Tighten the clamp to 6 Nm (53 inch lbs.).

122. Connect the power steering pipe to the steering gear.

123. Connect the power steering pipe to the frame clips.

124. Lower the vehicle.

125. Position and install the ball joint nuts.

126. Install the sway links to the stabilizer shaft.

127. Install the tie rod ends to the steering knuckles.

128. Connect the wheel speed sensor electrical connectors.

129. Connect the wheel speed sensor wiring harness to the lower control arm.

130. Install the heater inlet and outlet hoses to the heater inlet/outlet pipe.

131. Reposition the heater inlet and outlet hose clamps.

132. Install the intermediate shaft to the steering gear.

133. Install the intermediate shaft to steering gear bolt. Tighten the bolt to 48 Nm (35 ft. lbs.).

134. Position the intermediate shaft lower boot.

135. Route all branches of the engine wiring harness to their correct locations.

136. Connect the engine harness electrical connector to the VSS.

137. Install the VSS shield. Install the VSS shield nut and bolt. Tighten the bolt/nut to 18 ft. lbs. (25 Nm).

138. Install the shift cable to the bracket.

139. Connect the shift cable to the transaxle selector lever stud.

140. Install the shift cable clip.

141. Install the clip attaching the power steering gear harness to the bracket.

142. Connect the engine harness electrical connector to the CKP sensor harness.

143. Connect the engine harness electrical connector to the power steering gear harness.

144. Connect the camshaft position sensor lead to the sensor.

145. Connect the following electrical connectors:
- ECM
- TCM
- A/C pressure sensor

146. Install the air cleaner assembly.

147. Connect the engine harness electrical connector to the EBCM.

148. Connect the engine harness electrical connector to the ABS module.

149. Install the engine harness connector to the bracket. Tighten the engine harness connector bolt. Tighten the bolt to 89 inch lbs. (10 Nm).

150. Position the fuse block. Tighten the 4 integral bolts attaching the fuse block. Tighten the bolts to 89 inch lbs. (10 Nm).

151. Install the electrical center cover.

152. Connect the fuel feed line to the fuel rail.

153. Connect the EVAP line to the purge solenoid.

154. Remove the mechanic's wire holding the master cylinder. Position the master cylinder to the brake booster.

155. Install the master cylinder nuts. Tighten the nuts to 33 Nm (24 ft. lbs.).

156. Connect the brake pipe fittings to the ABS module. Tighten the fittings to 15 Nm (11 ft. lbs.).

157. Connect the from brake pipe fittings to the master cylinder. Tighten the fittings to 22 ft. lbs. (30 Nm).

158. Connect the brake fluid level switch electrical connector to the master cylinder.

159. Connect the engine harness electrical connectors to the I/P harness electrical connectors.

160. Install the brake booster vacuum hose to the intake manifold.

161. Install the brake booster vacuum hose to the brake booster.

162. Install the A/C compressor hose.

163. Install the A/C compressor hose nut at the A/C condenser. Tighten the nut to 16 Nm (12 ft. lbs.).

164. Install the A/C compressor hose.

165. Install the A/C compressor hose nut at the A/C receiver/dehydrator tube. Tighten the nut to 16 Nm (12 ft. lbs.).

166. Install the outlet hose to the radiator.

167. Connect the outlet hose clips to the fan shroud.

168. Reposition the outlet hose clamp at the radiator.

169. Install the inlet hose to the radiator.

170. Reposition the inlet hose clamp at the radiator.

171. Install the front tires and wheels.

172. Connect the negative battery cable.

173. Install the right fender diagonal brace.

174. Refill the engine with oil.

175. Recharge the A/C system.

176. Refill the cooling system.

177. Bleed the brake system.

178. Check the transaxle fluid level, add fluid if necessary.

179. Install the engine sight shield.

180. Run the engine and inspect for leaks.

EXHAUST MANIFOLD

REMOVAL & INSTALLATION

3.5L & 3.9L Engines

Left Side

1. Before servicing the vehicle, refer to the Precautions Section.

2. Drain the cooling system.

3. Remove or disconnect the following:
- Negative battery cable
- Fuel injector sight shield
- Engine mount strut and bracket
- Cooling fans
- Upper and lower radiator hoses
- Transaxle oil cooler lines from the radiator
- Radiator
- Alternator
- Exhaust manifold heat shield
- Oil level indicator tube
- Secondary Air Injection (AIR) control valve assembly from the engine mount strut bracket
- Exhaust manifold-to-crossover pipe studs
- Exhaust manifold

To install:

4. Install or connect the following:
- Manifold to the crossover pipe using a new gasket and torque the studs to 18 ft. lbs. (25 Nm)
- Exhaust manifold with a new gasket and torque the bolts to 18 ft. lbs. (25 Nm)
- AIR valve and torque the pipe nut to 44 ft. lbs. (60 Nm) and the bolt to 80 inch lbs. (9 Nm)
- Oil level indicator tube and torque the bolt to 80 inch lbs. (9 Nm)
- Exhaust manifold heat shield and torque the bolts to 80 inch lbs. (9 Nm)
- Alternator and torque the bolts to 37 ft. lbs. (50 Nm)

- Radiator and torque the bolts to 89 inch lbs. (10 Nm)
- Transaxle oil cooler lines and torque the fitting to 17 ft. lbs. (23 Nm)
- Upper and lower radiator hoses
- Cooling fans and torque the bolts to 89 inch lbs. (10 Nm)
- Engine mount strut bracket and torque the bolts to 37 ft. lbs. (50 Nm)
- Engine mount strut and torque the bolts to 35 ft. lbs. (48 Nm)
- Fuel injector sight shield and torque the nuts to 27 inch lbs. (3 Nm)
- Negative battery cable

5. Fill the cooling system.

6. Start the vehicle and check for leaks, repair if necessary.

Right Side

See Figure 63.

1. Before servicing the vehicle, refer to the Precautions Section.

2. Relieve the fuel system pressure.

3. Drain the cooling system.

4. Remove or disconnect the following:
- Negative battery cable
- Fuel injector cover
- Air intake duct
- Engine mount strut
- Fuel lines from the supply rail
- Cruise control and accelerator cables from the throttle body
- Transaxle selector range cable and cable brackets
- Transaxle shift cable from the shift module
- Brake booster vacuum hose from the engine
- Wiring harness connectors from the engine and transaxle

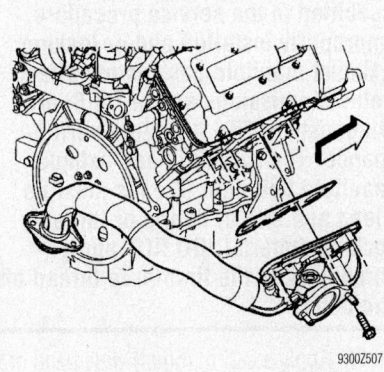

Fig. 63 Exploded view of the right exhaust manifold — 3.5L engine

- Upper radiator hose
- Transaxle oil cooler lines from the radiator
- Surge tank inlet hose
- Heater hoses from the engine
- Lower radiator air deflector
- Battery cables from the retainers
- Lower radiator hose
- A/C compressor without disconnecting the lines and move it aside
- Starter wiring
- Catalytic converter from the manifold
- Front wheels and splash shields
- Wheel Speed Sensor (WSS) wiring from the lower control arms
- Tie rod ends from the steering knuckles
- Lower ball joints from the knuckles
- Halfshafts
- Intermediate shaft from the steering rack

5. Secure the vehicle to the lift in preparation for engine removal.

6. Position an engine/frame support table under the vehicle and lower the vehicle to meet the table.

7. Remove or disconnect the following:
- Frame-to-body bolts
- Crossover pipe from the front manifold
- Exhaust Gas Recirculation (EGR) pipe from the crossover pipe
- Right exhaust manifold from the engine

To install:

8. Install or connect the following:
- Right exhaust manifold with a new gasket and torque the bolts to 18 ft. lbs. (25 Nm)
- Crossover pipe to the front exhaust manifold and torque the bolts to 18 ft. lbs. (25 Nm)
- EGR pipe to the crossover pipe and torque the pipe nut to 44 ft. lbs. (60 Nm)

9. Position the engine/transaxle assembly under the vehicle.

10. Coat the sub-frame bushings with rubber lubricant.

11. Lower the vehicle onto the assembly. Align the sub-frame on the vehicle using 2 bolts or drill bits, ¾ inches thick by 8 inches long through the alignment holes on the right side of the frame.

12. Install new frame-to-body bolts. Torque the bolts to 133 ft. lbs. (180 Nm) starting with the rear bolts and then the front bolts.

13. Raise the vehicle and remove the frame table.

14. Install or connect the following:
- Intermediate shaft to the steering rack and torque the bolts to 35 ft. lbs. (48 Nm)

➡ **Be sure the shaft is fully seated on the stub before installing the pinch bolt.**

- Halfshafts
- Ball joints and torque the nuts to 40 ft. lbs. (55 Nm)
- Tie rod ends and torque the nuts to 22 ft. lbs. (30 Nm) plus an additional 120 degree turn
- WSS wiring harness
- Splash shields and front wheels
- Catalytic converter and torque the nuts to 53 inch lbs. (6 Nm)
- Starter wiring
- A/C compressor and torque the bolts to 37 ft. lbs. (50 Nm)
- Lower radiator hose
- Battery cables in their retainers
- Lower radiator air deflector and torque the bolts to 15 ft. lbs. (20 Nm)

15. Remove the straps securing the vehicle to the lift.
- Heater hoses
- Surge tank hose
- Transaxle oil cooler lines to the radiator and torque the fittings to 17 ft. lbs. (23 Nm)
- Upper radiator hose
- Wiring harness connectors to the engine and transaxle
- Transaxle shift cable to the shift module and bracket
- Transaxle range selector cable
- Cruise control and accelerator cables to the throttle body
- Fuel lines to the supply rail
- Engine mount strut and torque the bolts to 35 ft. lbs. (48 Nm)
- Air inlet duct
- Fuel injector sight shield
- Negative battery cable

16. Refill the cooling system.
17. Start the engine and check for leaks, repair if necessary.

5.3L Engine

Left Side

See Figure 64.

1. Before servicing the vehicle, refer to the Precautions Section.
2. Remove the engine sight shield.
3. Remove the exhaust crossover pipe heat shield in order to access the cross pipe to the exhaust manifold nuts.
4. Remove the exhaust crossover pipe nuts from the left exhaust manifold.

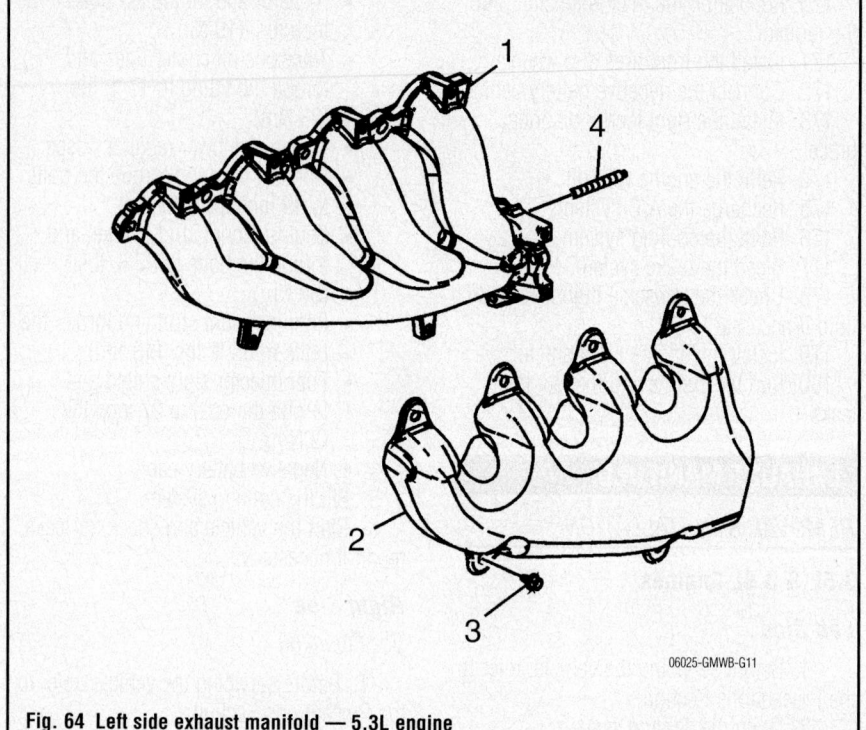

Fig. 64 Left side exhaust manifold — 5.3L engine

06025-GMWB-G11

5. Remove the left side spark plugs.
6. Remove the oil level indicator tube.
7. Remove the exhaust manifold heat shield bolts (3).
8. Remove the exhaust manifold heat shield (2).
9. Remove the heater hose retainer bolts in order to be able to remove the manifold.
10. Remove the exhaust manifold bolts.
11. Remove the exhaust manifold (1).
12. Remove and discard the exhaust manifold gasket.
13. Clean and inspect the left exhaust manifold.

To install:

❊❊ WARNING

Tighten the exhaust manifold bolts as specified in the service procedure. Improperly installed and/or leaking exhaust manifold gaskets my affect vehicle emissions and/or On Board Diagnostic (OBD) II system performance. The cylinder head exhaust manifold bolt hole threads must be clean and free of debris or threadlocking material. DO NOT apply threadlock to the first three thread of the bolts.

14. Apply a 0.2 in. (5mm) wide band of threadlock GM P/N 12345493 (Canadian P/N 10953488) or equivalent to the threads of the exhaust manifold bolts.

15. Install a NEW exhaust manifold gasket, the exhaust manifold and bolts. Tighten as follows:
- Tighten the bolts a first pass to 15 Nm (11 ft. lbs.). Tighten the bolts beginning with the center 2 bolts. Alternate from side to side, and work toward the outside.
- Tighten the bolts a final pass to 15 ft. lbs. (20 Nm). Tighten the bolts beginning with the center 2 bolts. Alternate from side to side, and work toward the outside.

16. Using a flat punch, bend over the exposed edge of the exhaust manifold gasket at the rear of the left cylinder head.
17. Install the exhaust manifold heat shield (2).
18. Install the exhaust manifold heat shield bolts (3). Tighten the bolts to 9 Nm (80 inch lbs.).
19. Install the oil level indicator tube.
20. Install the left side spark plugs.
21. Install the exhaust crossover pipe nuts from the left exhaust manifold. Tighten the nuts to 18 ft. lbs. (25 Nm).
22. Install the exhaust crossover pipe heat shield.
23. Install the heater pipe retainer bolts. Tighten the bolts to 16 Nm (12 ft. lbs.).
24. Install the engine sight shield.

Right Side

1. Before servicing the vehicle, refer to the Precautions Section.

2. Remove the engine sight shield.

3. Remove the spark plugs.

4. Remove the exhaust crossover pipe nuts from the right exhaust manifold.

✳✳ WARNING

To prevent internal damage to the flexible coupling of the catalytic converter assembly, the converter must be supported. The vertical movement at the rear of the catalytic converter assembly must not exceed 6 degrees up or down.

5. Disconnect the catalytic converter from the exhaust manifold. Support the catalytic converter and exhaust system with the mechanics wire.

6. Lower the vehicle.

7. Remove the ignition coil.

✳✳ WARNING

Do not remove the pigtail from either the heated oxygen sensor (HO2S) or the oxygen sensor (O2S). Removing the pigtail or the connector will affect sensor operation. Handle the oxygen sensor carefully. Do not drop the HO2S. Keep the in-line electrical connector and the louvered end free of grease, dirt, or other contaminants. Do not use cleaning solvents of any type Do not repair the wiring, connector or terminals. Replace the oxygen sensor if the pigtail wiring, connector, or terminal is damaged. This external clean air reference is obtained by way of the oxygen sensor signal and heater wires. Any attempt to repair the wires, connectors, or terminals could result in the obstruction of the air reference and degraded sensor performance. The following guidelines should be used when servicing the heated oxygen sensor:

- Do not apply contact cleaner or other materials to the sensor or vehicle harness connectors. These materials may get into the sensor causing poor performance.
- Do not damage the sensor pigtail and harness wires in such a way that the wires inside are exposed. This could provide a path for foreign materials to enter the sensor and cause performance problems.
- Ensure the sensor or vehicle lead wires should not be bent sharply or kinked. Sharp bends or kinks could

block the reference air path through the lead wire.

- Do not remove or defeat the oxygen sensor ground wire (where applicable). Vehicles that utilize the ground wired sensor may rely on this ground as the only ground contact to the sensor. Removal of the ground wire will cause poor engine performance.
- Ensure that the peripheral seal remains intact on the vehicle harness connector in order to prevent damage due to water intrusion. The engine harness may be repaired using Packard's Crimp and Splice Seals Terminal Repair Kit. Under no circumstances should repairs be soldered since this could result in the air reference being obstructed.

8. Remove the O2 sensors.

9. Remove the exhaust manifold heat shield bolts.

10. Remove the exhaust manifold heat shield.

11. Remove the exhaust manifold bolts.

12. Remove the exhaust manifold.

13. Remove and discard the exhaust manifold gasket.

14. Clean and inspect the left exhaust manifold.

To install:

✳✳ WARNING

Tighten the exhaust manifold bolts as specified in the service procedure. Improperly installed and/or leaking exhaust manifold gaskets my affect vehicle emissions and/or On Board Diagnostic (OBD) II system performance. The cylinder head exhaust manifold bolt hole threads must be clean and free of debris or thread-locking material. DO NOT apply threadlock to the first three threads of the bolts.

15. Apply a 0.2 in. (5mm) wide band of threadlock GM P/N 12345493 (Canadian P/N 10953488) or equivalent to the threads of the exhaust manifold bolts.

16. Install a NEW exhaust manifold gasket, the exhaust manifold and bolts. Tighten as follows:

- Tighten the bolts a first pass to 15 Nm (11 ft. lbs.). Tighten the bolts beginning with the center 2 bolts. Alternate from side to side, and work toward the outside.
- Tighten the bolts a final pass to 15 ft. lbs. (20 Nm). Tighten the bolts

beginning with the center 2 bolts. Alternate from side to side, and work toward the outside.

17. Using a flat punch, bend over the exposed edge of the exhaust manifold gasket at the rear of the right cylinder head.

18. Install the exhaust manifold heat shield.

19. Install the exhaust manifold heat shield bolts. Tighten the bolts to 9 Nm (80 inch lbs.).

➡ **A special anti-seize compound is used on the HO2S threads. The compound consists of liquid graphite and glass beads. The graphite tends to burn away, but the glass beads remain, making the sensor easier to remove. New or service replacement sensors already have the compound applied to the threads. If the sensor is removed from an exhaust component and if for any reason the sensor is to be reinstalled, the threads must have anti-seize compound applied before reinstallation.**

20. If re-installing the old sensor, coat the threads with anti-seize compound P/N 12377953, or equivalent.

21. Install the bank 1 sensor 1 to the exhaust manifold. Tighten the sensor to 42 Nm (31 ft. lbs.).

22. Connect the bank 1 sensor 1 electrical connector.

23. Install the CPA retainer.

24. Raise the vehicle.

25. Install NEW gaskets to the exhaust manifold and muffler studs.

26. Position the catalytic converter into place.

27. Install the catalytic converter hangers to the converter.

28. Install the catalytic converter pipe stud nuts. Tighten the nuts to 35 Nm (26 ft. lbs.).

29. Install the catalytic converter nuts. Tighten the nuts to 44 ft. lbs. (60 Nm).

30. Remove the exhaust system support.

31. Install the exhaust crossover pipe nuts to the right exhaust manifold. Tighten the nuts to 18 ft. lbs. (25 Nm).

32. Apply threadlock GM P/N 12345382 (Canadian P/N 10953489) or equivalent to the threads of the ignition coil bolts.

33. Install the ignition coil(s), as necessary.

34. Install the ignition coil bolts, as necessary. Tighten the bolts to 8 Nm (71 inch lbs.).

35. Install the spark plug wire(s) to the ignition coil(s), as necessary.

36. Connect the left ignition coil main electrical connector.

37. Install the CPA retainer.
38. Install the spark plugs.
39. Install the fuel injector sight shield.

FLYWHEEL/FLEXPLATE

REMOVAL & INSTALLATION

See Figure 65.

Please note that the entire transaxle assembly must be removed to perform this procedure. Make very sure of the diagnosis before beginning work. New service replacement flywheel bolts are recommended.

1. Remove the transaxle from the vehicle.
2. A flywheel locking tool may be helpful to keep the crankshaft from rotating when the flywheel bolts are loosened.
3. Remove 5 of the 6 flywheel bolts leaving one bolt at the top of the crankshaft.
4. Grip the flywheel and remove the remaining bolt. Do not drop the flywheel when removing the final bolt.
5. Remove the flywheel bolts. New service replacement bolts are recommended.
6. Remove the flywheel from the vehicle.
7. Clean the engine flywheel bolt threads and bolt holes.

To install:

❋❋ CAUTION

Use the correct fastener in the correct location. Replacement fasteners must be the correct part number for that application. Fasteners requiring replacement or fasteners requiring the use of thread locking compound or sealant are identified in the service procedure. Do not use paints, lubricants, or corrosion inhibitors on fasteners or fastener joint surfaces unless specified. These coatings affect fastener torque and joint clamping force and may damage the fastener. Use the correct tightening sequence and specifications when installing fasteners in order to avoid damage to parts and systems.

8. Clean all parts well. If there is evidence of oil leaking past the rear crankshaft oil seal, replace the oil seal. Examine the teeth around the other edge of the wheel where the starter engages. If they are worn or damaged, replace the flywheel.
9. Flywheel bolts may have thread-locking adhesive on the threads. If the bolts must be reused, clean the threads on the bolts and in the crankshaft.
10. Apply fresh thread-locking compound to all of the flywheel-to-crankshaft bolts.
11. The remaining installation steps are the reverse of the removal procedure. Tighten the flywheel bolts evenly. Final torque should be: 52 ft. lbs. (70 Nm).
12. Install the transaxle.

FRONT COVER AND SEAL, TIMING CHAIN, AND SPROCKETS

REMOVAL & INSTALLATION

3.5L & 3.9L Engines

Primary Chain

See Figures 66 through 68.

1. Before servicing the vehicle, refer to the Precautions Section.
2. Drain the engine oil.
3. Drain the cooling system.
4. Disconnect the negative battery cable.
5. Remove the camshaft covers.
6. Rotate the crankshaft so the No. 1 piston is at Top Dead Center (TDC) and the flats on the rear of the camshafts are parallel with the camshaft cover sealing surface.
7. Install camshaft holding fixtures on both sets of camshafts. Turn the hex portion of the camshaft to align them for tool installation.

➡ **When installed, the flats on the rear of the camshafts will be parallel with the camshaft cover sealing surface.**

8. Remove or disconnect the following:
   - Right diagonal brace
   - Battery and tray
   - Coolant reservoir
   - Underhood accessory wiring junction block, move it aside
   - Drive belt
   - Power steering pump pulley
   - Idler pulley and belt tensioner
   - Water pump pulley
   - Water pump drive belt shield
   - Water pump
9. Support the engine cradle.
10. Remove the right side engine cradle bolts.
11. Lower the cradle.

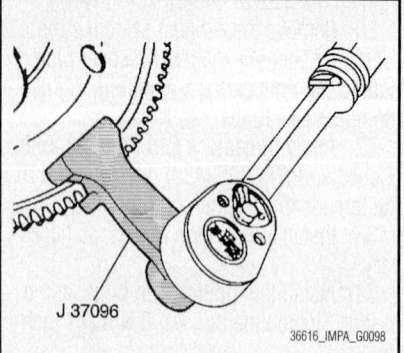

Fig. 65 This typical flywheel locking tool keeps the flywheel from turning when the bolts are loosened or tightened

J 37096

36616_IMPA_G0098

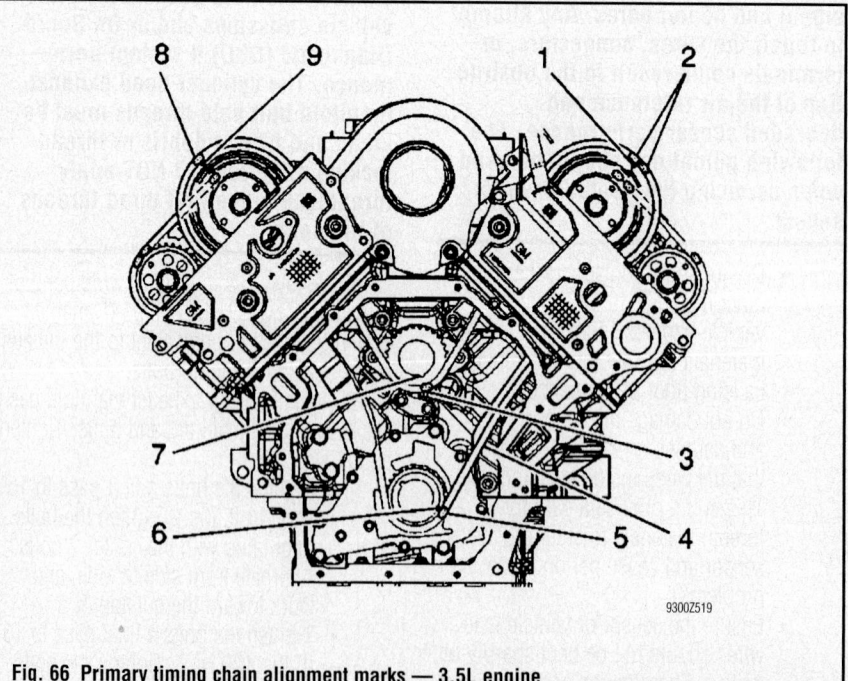

Fig. 66 Primary timing chain alignment marks — 3.5L engine

9300Z519

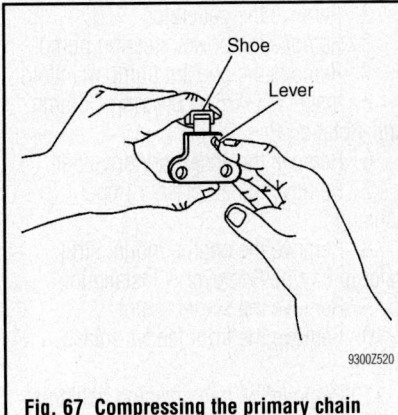

Fig. 67 Compressing the primary chain tensioner — 3.5L engine

12. Remove or disconnect the following:

- Crankshaft balancer
- Front cover
- Engine lift bracket from the front of the engine
- Camshaft Position (CMP) sensor
- Sprocket bolt from the exhaust camshaft on the right cylinder head to allow for clearance of the chain guide
- Four chain guide access plugs from the cylinder heads

➡ Note that each plug has an O-ring.

- Primary chain tensioner

➡ Remove the lower bolt allowing the tensioner to swing down and expand.

- Primary chain tensioner shoe, by removing the bolt, pushing the guide downward slightly and pulling it up through the cylinder head
- Primary chain from the right camshaft, allowing it to fall into the oil pump area
- Primary chain

To install:

13. Rotate the crankshaft so the No. 1 piston is at Top Dead Center (TDC) and the mark on the crankshaft is at the 4 o'clock position.

14. Rotate the balance shaft so the timing mark is at the 5 o'clock position.

➡ Be sure the painted links are facing the front of the engine.

15. Install the timing chain on the sprockets.

16. Center the mark on the left intake camshaft sprocket between the 2 painted links.

17. Verify that all of the timing marks are aligned.

18. Install the primary chain tensioner shoe. Torque the bolt to 22 ft. lbs. (30 Nm).

19. Compress the primary chain tensioner using the following sub-steps:

a. Step 1: Rotate the ratchet release lever counterclockwise and hold it.

b. Step 2: Press the tensioner shoe in and hold it.

c. Step 3: Release the ratchet lever and slowly release the pressure on the shoe.

d. Step 4: Insert a pin through the hole in the lever as the lever moves to the first click. The ratchet should hold the shoe in the compressed position.

➡ Be sure the lever on the tensioner is facing you when installed.

20. Install or connect the following:

- Primary chain tensioner and torque the bolts to 18 ft. lbs. (25 Nm); then, remove the chain tensioner pin
- Four chain guide access plugs and torque the plugs to 44 inch lbs. (5 Nm)
- Front engine lift bracket and torque the hex head bolt to 37 ft. lbs. (50 Nm) and the internal drive bolt to 18 ft. lbs. (25 Nm)
- CMP sensor and torque the bolts to 80 inch lbs. (9 Nm)

21. Remove the camshaft holding tools.

22. Install the rocker arm covers. Torque the bolts to 80 inch lbs. (9 Nm).

23. Place a small bead of RTV sealant on the 3 areas indicated in the diagram.

24. Install or connect the following:

- Front cover with a new gasket and torque the bolts to 124 inch lbs. (14 Nm) and the coolant drain plug to 89 inch lbs. (10 Nm)
- Crankshaft balancer and torque the bolt to 37 ft. lbs. (50 Nm) plus an additional 120 degree turn

25. Raise the engine cradle and install new bolts loosely.

26. Coat the sub-frame bushings with rubber lubricant.

27. Lower the vehicle onto the assembly. Align the sub-frame on the vehicle using 2 bolts or drill bits, ¾ inches thick by 8 inches long through the alignment holes on the right side of the frame.

28. Install or connect the following:

- New frame-to-body bolts and torque the bolts to 133 ft. lbs. (180 Nm)
- Water pump with a new gasket and torque the bolts to 124 inch lbs. (14 Nm)
- Water pump pulley and torque the bolts to 106 inch lbs. (12 Nm)
- Belt tensioner and torque the bolt to 37 ft. lbs. (50 Nm)
- Power steering pump pulley
- Drive belt
- Underhood accessory wiring junction
- Coolant reservoir and torque the nuts to 30 inch lbs. (3 Nm)
- Battery and tray
- Right diagonal brace and torque the bolts to 35 ft. lbs. (47 Nm)

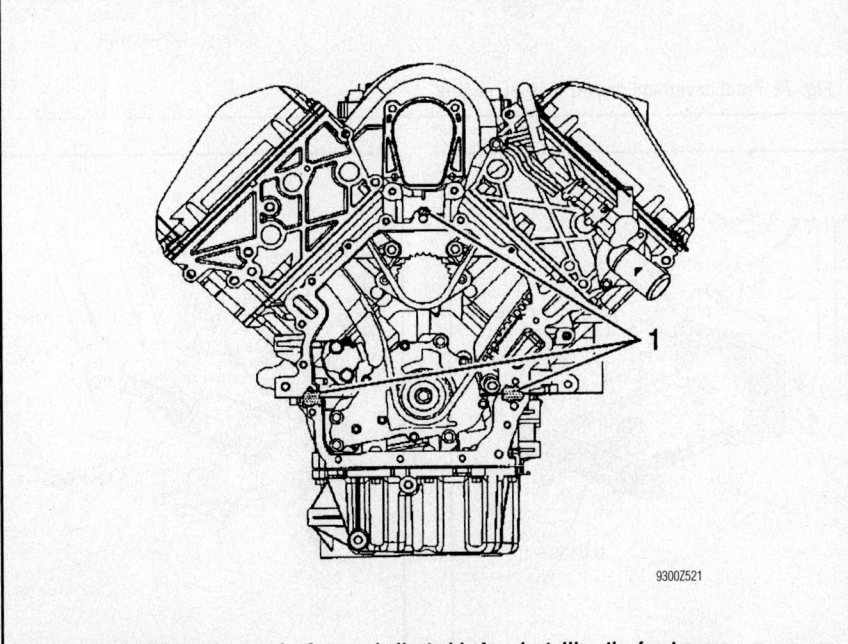

Fig. 68 Apply RTV sealant to the 3 areas indicated before installing the front cover and gasket — 3.5L engine

- Camshaft covers and torque the bolts to 80 inch lbs. (9 Nm)
- Negative battery cable

29. Refill the engine cooling system.

30. Refill the engine with new oil.

31. Start the vehicle and check for leaks, repair if necessary.

Secondary Timing Chain

See Figure 69.

1. Before servicing the vehicle, refer to the Precautions Section.

2. Drain the cooling system.

3. Remove or disconnect the following:

- Negative battery cable
- Thermostat housing for clearance (when working on the front cylinder head)
- Rocker arm cover and install a Camshaft Holding Fixture
- Camshaft Position (CMP) sensor
- Camshaft sprocket bolts

4. Install the timing chain/sprocket holding fixture on the cylinder head.

5. Evenly slide the secondary drive chain and sprockets off the camshafts.

To install:

6. Install the secondary timing chain on the sprockets, with the drive pins at the 12 o'clock positions.

7. Install the sprockets/chain assembly onto the camshafts, with the chain properly aligned on the tensioner.

8. Remove the sprocket holding fixture from the cylinder head.

9. Install the sprocket bolts and torque the bolts to 18 ft. lbs. (25 Nm) plus an additional 45 degree turn.

10. Remove the camshaft holding fixture.

11. Install or connect the following:

- Rocker arm cover and torque the bolts to 80 inch lbs. (9 Nm)
- Thermostat housing (if removed) and torque the bolts to 80 inch lbs. (9 Nm)
- CMP sensor and torque the bolts to 80 inch lbs. (9 Nm)
- Negative battery cable

12. Refill the cooling system.

13. Start the vehicle and check for leaks, repair if necessary.

5.3L Engine

See Figures 70 through 75.

1. Before servicing the vehicle, refer to the Precautions Section.

2. Remove the generator.

3. Remove the power steering pump.

4. Remove the coolant pump manifold.

5. Install a J 42640 Steering Column Anti-Rotation Pin.

6. Remove the accessory drive belt.

7. Remove the air cleaner upper housing.

8. Remove the engine mount strut. Refer to Engine Removal & Installation.

9. Remove the starter motor.

10. Remove the front fender splash shield.

11. Remove the transmission bellhousing bolt located at approximately the 10 o'clock position when looking from the rear of the engine.

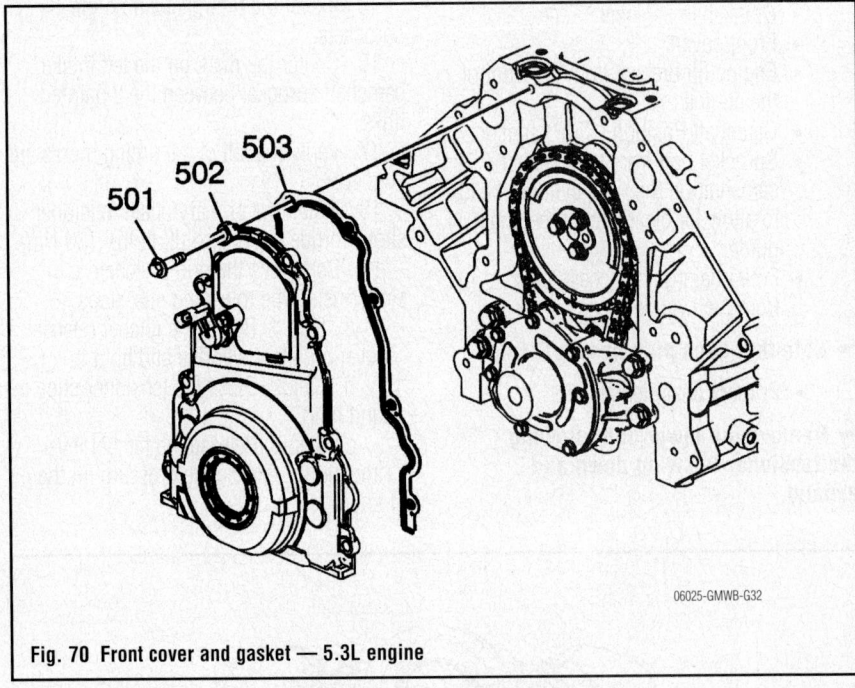

Fig. 70 Front cover and gasket — 5.3L engine

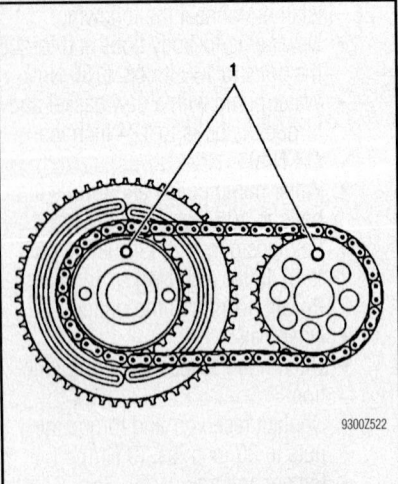

Fig. 69 Correct sprocket alignment for secondary timing chain — 3.5L engine

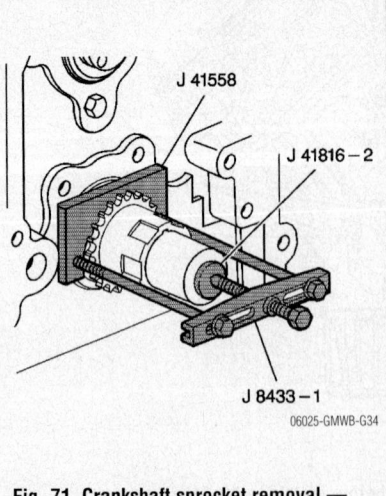

Fig. 71 Crankshaft sprocket removal — 5.3L engine

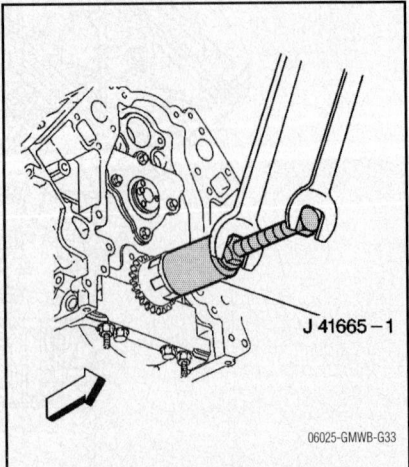

Fig. 72 Using the J 41665, install the crankshaft sprocket — 5.3L engine

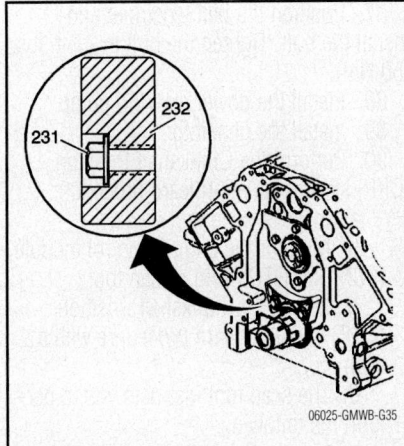

Fig. 73 With the chain dampener properly installed, the heads of the bolts (231) should install to flush or below the face of the guide (232) — 5.3L engine

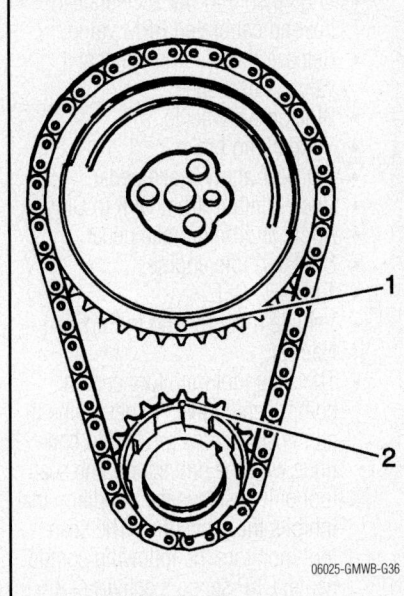

Fig. 74 Timing mark alignment — 5.3L engine

12. Disconnect the transaxle cooler lines at the transaxle.

13. Remove the stabilizer shaft link lower nuts.

14. Remove the intermediate steering shaft pinch bolt and separate the shaft from the steering gear.

15. Remove the front lower air deflector braces and the deflector.

16. Remove the radiator to frame braces.

17. Install the engine support fixture. Refer to Engine Removal & Installation.

18. Raise and support the vehicle. .

19. Remove the frame to body bolts.

20. Install a flywheel holding tool to the block and flywheel.

21. Remove the right front tire and wheel assembly.

22. Lower the engine approximately 100 mm (4 in.).

23. Remove the crankshaft balancer bolt. Do not discard the crankshaft balancer bolt. The balancer bolt will be used during the balancer installation procedure.

24. Install a puller to the crankshaft balancer.

25. Remove the crankshaft balancer.

26. Remove the belt tensioner bolt and reposition the tensioner (which blocks the front cover bolt).

27. Remove the oil pan-to-front cover bolts.

28. Remove the front cover bolts (501).

29. Remove the front cover (502) and gasket (503).

30. Discard the front cover gasket.

31. Remove the oil seal, if necessary.

32. Remove the Camshaft Position (CMP) sensor bolt and sensor, if necessary.

33. Remove the O-ring seal from the sensor, if necessary.

34. Clean and inspect the engine front cover.

35. Rotate the crankshaft until the timing marks on the crankshaft and the camshaft sprockets are aligned.

✲✲ WARNING

Do not turn the crankshaft assembly after the timing chain has been removed in order to prevent damage to the piston assemblies or the valves.

36. Remove the camshaft sprocket bolts.

37. Remove the camshaft sprocket and timing chain.

38. Remove the timing chain dampener and bolts.

39. Using a puller, remove the crankshaft sprocket.

40. Remove the crankshaft sprocket.

41. Remove the crankshaft sprocket key, if required.

Clean and inspect the timing chain and sprockets.

To install:

42. Install the key into the crankshaft keyway, if previously removed.

43. Tap the key into the keyway until both ends of the key bottom onto the crankshaft.

44. Install the crankshaft sprocket onto the front of the crankshaft. Align the crankshaft key with the crankshaft sprocket keyway.

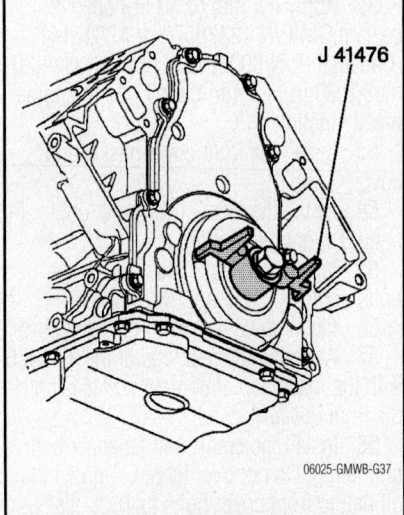

Fig. 75 Install the J 41476 to the front cover — 5.3L engine

45. Using the J 41665, install the crankshaft sprocket onto the crankshaft until fully seated against the crankshaft flange.

46. Rotate the crankshaft sprocket until the alignment mark is in the 12 o'clock position.

47. Install the timing change guide and bolts. Tighten the bolts to 18 ft. lbs. (25 Nm).

➡ Properly locate the camshaft sprocket locating pin with the camshaft sprocket alignment hole. The sprocket teeth and timing chain must mesh. The camshaft and the crankshaft sprocket alignment marks MUST be aligned properly. Position the camshaft sprocket alignment mark in the 6 o'clock position.

48. Install the camshaft sprocket and timing chain. If necessary, rotate the camshaft or crankshaft sprockets in order to align the timing marks.

49. Install the camshaft sprocket bolts. Tighten the bolts to 18 ft. lbs. (25 Nm).

50. Inspect the camshaft and crankshaft sprockets for proper timing mark alignment.

51. Install the oil pump.

➡ Do not reuse the crankshaft oil seal or front cover gasket. Do not apply any type of sealant to the front cover gasket (unless specified). The special tool in this procedure is used to properly center the front crankshaft front oil seal. All gasket surfaces should be free of oil or other foreign material during assembly. The crankshaft front oil seal MUST be centered in relation to the crankshaft. An improperly aligned front cover may cause premature front oil seal wear and/or engine oil leaks.

52. Apply a 5 mm (0.20 in.) bead of sealant GM P/N 12378577 or 12346141 (Canadian P/N 89022195) or equivalent 20 mm (0.80 in.) long to the oil pan to engine block junction.

53. Install the front cover gasket and cover.

54. Install the front cover bolts until snug. Do not overtighten.

55. Install the oil pan-to-front cover bolts until snug. Do not over tighten.

56. Install the J 41476 to the front cover.

57. Align the tapered legs of the J 41476 with the machined alignment surfaces on the front cover.

58. Install the crankshaft balancer bolt until snug. Do not overtighten. Tighten the oil pan to front cover bolts to 18 ft. lbs. (25 Nm). Tighten the engine front cover bolts to 18 ft. lbs. (25 Nm).

59. Remove the J 41476.

60. Install a NEW crankshaft front oil seal.

➡ **The used crankshaft balancer bolt will be used only during the first pass of the balancer installation procedure. Install a NEW bolt and tighten as described in the second, third and forth passes of the balancer bolt tightening procedure. The crankshaft balancer installation and bolt tightening involves a four stage tightening process. The first pass ensures that the balancer is installed completely onto the crankshaft. The second, third, and forth passes tighten the new bolt to the proper torque.**

➡ **The balancer should be positioned onto the end of the crankshaft as straight as possible prior to tool installation.**

61. Position the crankshaft balancer onto the end of the crankshaft.

62. Using tool J 41665, install the crankshaft balancer.

  a. Assemble the threaded rod, nut, washer and installer. Insert the smaller end of the installer into the front of the balancer.

  b. Use a wrench and hold the hex end of the threaded rod.

  c. Use a second wrench and rotate the installation tool nut clockwise until the balancer is started onto the crankshaft.

  d. Remove the tool and reverse the installation tool. Position the larger end of the installer against the front of the balancer.

  e. Use a wrench and hold the hex end of the threaded rod.

  f. Use a second wrench and rotate the installation tool nut clockwise until the balancer is installed onto the crankshaft.

  g. Remove the balancer installation tool.

63. Install the USED crankshaft balancer bolt. Tighten the USED bolt to 330 Nm (240 ft. lbs.).

64. Remove the USED crankshaft balancer bolt.

➡ **The nose of the crankshaft should be recessed 2.4-4.48 mm (0.094-0.176 in.) into the balancer bore.**

65. Measure for a correctly installed balancer. If the balancer is not installed to the proper dimensions, install the J 41665 and repeat the installation procedure.

66. Install a NEW crankshaft balancer bolt. Tighten the bolt a first pass to 37 ft. lbs. (50 Nm). Tighten the bolt a second pass to 140 degrees.

67. Remove the flywheel holding tool from the block and flywheel.

68. Install the transmission bellhousing bolt located at approximately the 10 o'clock position when looking from the rear of the engine. Tighten the bolt to 75 Nm (55 ft. lbs.).

69. Raise and properly position the frame and install the frame to body bolts. Refer to Engine Removal & Installation.

70. Install the frame to radiator braces.

71. Install the front lower air deflector.

72. Connect the intermediate steering shaft to the steering gear.

73. Install the stabilizer shaft link lower nuts.

74. Connect the transaxle cooler lines to the transaxle.

75. Remove the engine support fixture.

76. Install the front fender splash shield.

77. Install the starter motor.

78. Install the air cleaner upper housing.

79. Install the accessory drive belt.

80. Install the engine mount strut. Refer to Engine Removal & Installation.

81. Install the right front tire and wheel assembly.

82. Install the coolant pump manifold.

83. Inspect the CMP sensor O-ring seal for cuts or damage. If the seal is not cut or damaged, it may be reused.

84. Lubricate the O-ring seal with clean engine oil.

85. Install the O-ring seal onto the CMP sensor.

86. Install the CMP sensor and bolt from the front cover. Tighten the bolt to 12 Nm (106 inch lbs.).

87. Position the belt tensioner and install the bolt. Tighten the bolt to 37 ft. lbs. (50 Nm).

88. Install the power steering pump.

89. Install the generator.

90. Perform the Crankshaft Position (CKP) system variation learn procedure.

  a. Install a scan tool.

  b. Monitor the engine control module (ECM) for DTCs with a scan tool.

  c. Select the Crankshaft Position (CKP) variation learn procedure with a scan tool.

  d. The scan tool instructs you to perform the following:

  • Accelerate to wide open throttle (WOT).
  • Release throttle when fuel cut-off occurs.
  • Observe fuel cut-off for applicable engine.
  • Engine should not accelerate beyond calibrated RPM value.
  • Release throttle immediately if value is exceeded.
  • Block drive wheels.
  • Set parking brake.
  • DO NOT apply brake pedal.
  • Cycle ignition from OFF to ON.
  • Apply and hold brake pedal.
  • Start and idle engine.
  • Turn A/C OFF.
  • Vehicle must remain in Park or Neutral.
  • The scan tool monitors certain component signals to determine if all the conditions are met to continue with the procedure. The scan tool only displays the condition that inhibits the procedure. The scan tool monitors the following components: CKP sensors activity—If there is a CKP sensor condition, refer to the applicable DTC that set. Camshaft Position (CMP) sensor activity—If there is a CMP sensor condition, refer to the applicable DTC that set. Engine coolant temperature (ECT)—If the ECT is not warm enough, idle the engine until the engine coolant temperature reaches the correct temperature.

  e. Enable the CKP system variation learn procedure with a scan tool.

➡ **While the learn procedure is in progress, release the throttle immediately when the engine starts to decelerate. The engine control is returned to the operator and the engine responds to throttle position after the learn procedure is complete.**

f. Accelerate to WOT.

g. Release when the fuel cut-off occurs.

h. Test in progress

i. The scan tool displays Learn Status: Learned this ignition.

j. Turn OFF the ignition for 30 seconds after the learn procedure is completed successfully.

k. The CKP system variation learn procedure is also required when the following service procedures have been performed, regardless of whether DTC P0315 is set:

- A CKP sensor replacement
- An engine replacement
- An ECM replacement
- A harmonic balancer replacement
- A crankshaft replacement
- Any engine repairs which disturb the CKP sensor relationship

INTAKE MANIFOLD

REMOVAL & INSTALLATION

3.5L & 3.9L Engines

See Figure 76.

1. Before servicing the vehicle, refer to the Precautions Section.

2. Partially drain the engine coolant.

3. Remove or disconnect the following:

- Negative battery cable
- Throttle body air inlet duct
- Fuel injector sight shield
- Throttle and cruise control cables from the throttle body with the bracket
- Coolant hoses from the throttle body
- Fuel lines from the fuel supply rail

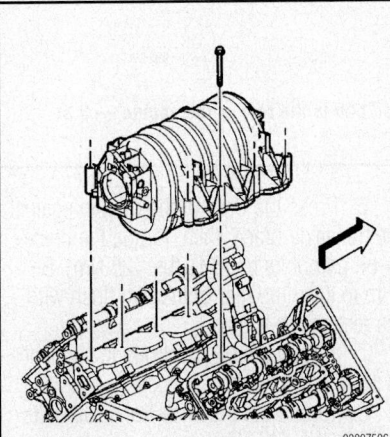

Fig. 76 Intake manifold assembly — 3.5L and 3.9L engines

93002506

- Fuel vapor line from the Evaporative Emission (EVAP) canister purge solenoid
- Brake booster vacuum hose
- Air conditioning vacuum hose from the engine
- Surge tank inlet pipe retainer from the fuel supply rail
- Fuel injector electrical connectors
- Throttle Position Sensor (TPS) electrical connectors
- Idle Air Control (IAC) valve electrical connector
- EVAP canister purge solenoid connector
- Manifold Absolute Pressure (MAP) sensor connector
- Wiring harness channels from the camshaft covers
- Vacuum tube from the fuel pressure regulator
- Positive Crankcase Ventilation (PCV) valve and both feed tubes
- Exhaust Gas Recirculation (EGR) valve outlet pipe
- Fuel supply rail with injectors

➡ **Disengage the snap-lock retainers by pushing toward the camshaft covers and lifting.**

- Throttle body coolant hose
- Intake manifold

➡ **The manifold-to-cylinder head seals are reusable unless cut or damaged.**

To install:

4. Install or connect the following:

- New intake manifold-to-cylinder head seals
- Intake manifold and torque the bolts, in a circular pattern, starting from the center to 62 inch lbs. (7 Nm)
- Throttle body heater hose
- New O-rings on the fuel injectors
- Fuel supply rail with injectors
- EGR pipe and torque the intake manifold bolt to 89 inch lbs. (10 Nm) and the coolant crossover bolt to 18 ft. lbs. (24 Nm)
- PCV valve and related tubing
- Brake booster vacuum hose
- Fuel pressure regulator vacuum hose
- Air conditioning vacuum hose
- Engine wiring harness with channel to the camshaft covers and torque the bolts to 89 inch lbs. (10 Nm)
- Surge tank pipe retainer to the fuel supply rail
- TPS electrical connector
- IAC electrical connector

- EVAP solenoid electrical connector
- MAP sensor electrical connector
- Fuel injector electrical connectors
- Coolant hoses to the throttle body
- Throttle and cruise control cables to the throttle body
- Fuel lines to the fuel supply rail
- Fuel vapor line to the purge solenoid
- Fuel injector sight shield
- Throttle body air inlet duct
- Negative battery cable

5. Refill the cooling system.

6. Start the engine and check for leaks, repair if necessary.

5.3L Engine

See Figure 77.

1. Before servicing the vehicle, refer to the Precautions Section.

➡ **The intake manifold, throttle body, fuel rail, and injectors may be removed as an assembly. If not servicing the individual components, remove the manifold as a complete assembly.**

2. Remove the throttle body.

3. Remove the fuel injectors.

4. Remove the brake booster vacuum hose from the intake manifold and the booster check valve.

5. Remove the Positive Crankcase Ventilation (PCV) clean air tube from the air intake duct and valve rocker arm cover.

6. Remove the PCV foul air tube from the intake manifold and valve rocker arm cover.

7. Remove the evaporative emission (EVAP) purge solenoid tube (2) from the solenoid and reposition.

8. Disconnect the following electrical connectors:

- EVAP purge solenoid
- Manifold absolute pressure (MAP) sensor
- Oil pressure sensor
- Valve lifter oil manifold

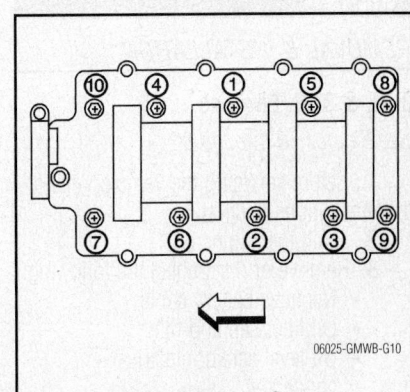

Fig. 77 Intake manifold bolt torque sequence — 5.3L engine

06025-GMWB-G10

9. Remove the MAP sensor from the intake manifold.

10. Remove the EVAP purge solenoid valve and bracket.

11. Remove the intake manifold bolts.

12. Remove the intake manifold.

13. Remove and discard the intake manifold gaskets.

To install:

14. Install the NEW intake manifold gaskets.

15. Install the intake manifold.

16. Apply a band of threadlock GM P/N 12345382 (Canadian P/N 10953489) or equivalent to the threads of the intake manifold bolts.

17. Install the intake manifold bolts. Tighten the bolts a first pass in sequence to 5 Nm (44 inch lbs.). Tighten the bolts a second pass in sequence to 89 inch lbs. (10 Nm).

18. Install the EVAP purge solenoid bracket and solenoid.

19. Install the MAP sensor to the intake manifold.

20. Connect the following electrical connectors:
   • EVAP purge solenoid
   • MAP sensor
   • Oil pressure sensor
   • Valve lifter oil manifold

21. Position and install the EVAP purge solenoid tube to the solenoid.

22. Install the PCV foul air tube to the intake manifold and valve rocker arm cover.

23. Install the PCV clean air tube to the air intake duct and valve rocker arm cover.

24. Install the brake booster vacuum hose to the intake manifold and the booster check valve.

25. Install the fuel injectors.

26. Install the throttle body.

OIL PAN

REMOVAL & INSTALLATION

3.5L & 3.9L Engines

See Figures 78 through 80.

1. Before servicing the vehicle, refer to the Precautions Section.

2. Drain the engine oil.

3. Remove or disconnect the following:
   • Negative battery cable
   • Oil filter cap and filter
   • Oil level sensor electrical connector
   • Transaxle brace
   • Oil pan

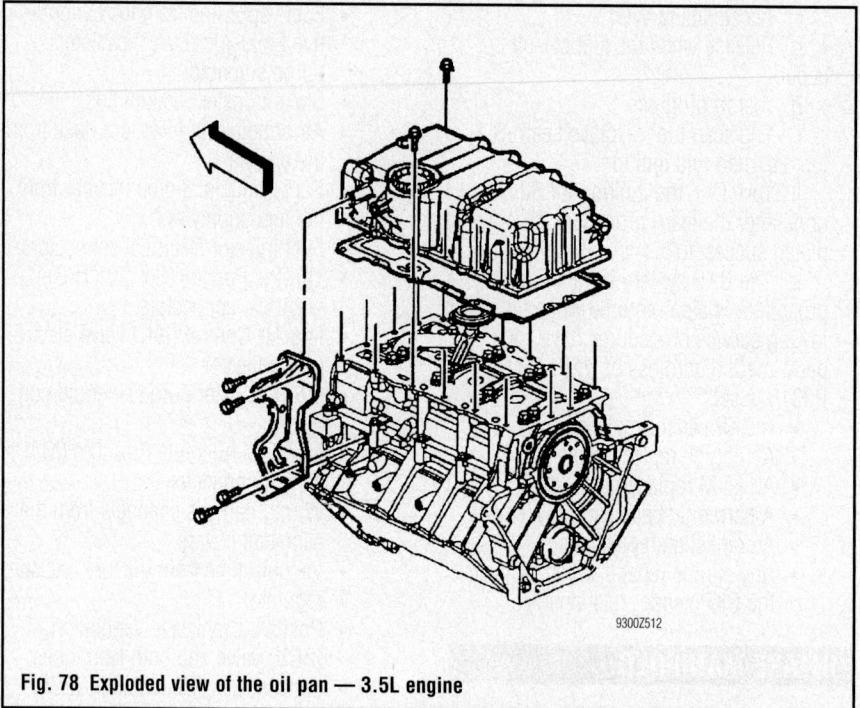

Fig. 78 Exploded view of the oil pan — 3.5L engine

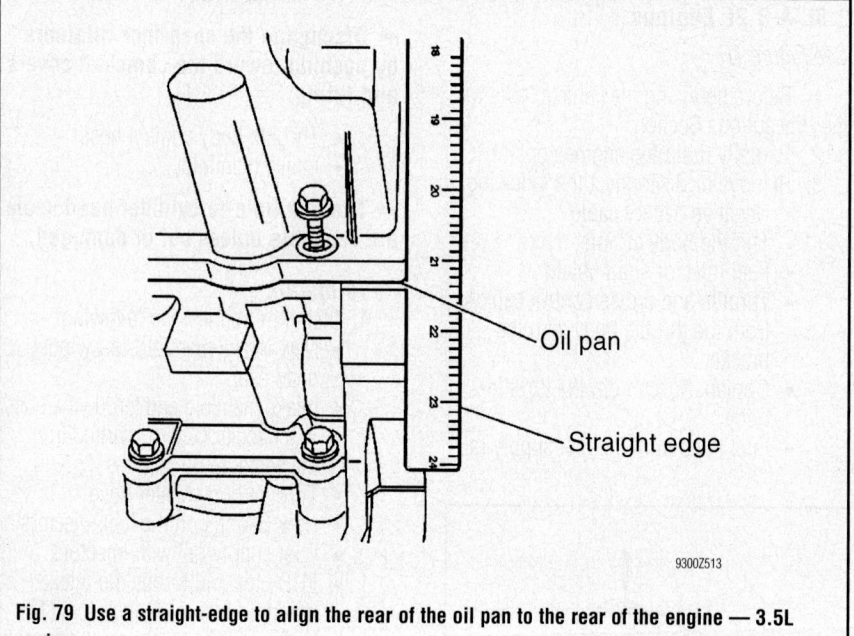

Fig. 79 Use a straight-edge to align the rear of the oil pan to the rear of the engine — 3.5L engine

To install:

4. Install or connect the following:
   • Oil pan with a new gasket, DO NOT tighten the bolts
   • Transaxle brace on the engine block only and torque the bolts to 18 ft. lbs. (25 Nm)
   • Brace-to-oil pan bolts, loosely install them

5. Align the rear of the oil pan flush with the rear of the engine block. Use a straight edge for reference.

6. Press the front of the oil pan against the transaxle brace; then, torque the brace-to-oil pan bolts to 18 ft. lbs. (25 Nm). Be sure to keep the rear of the pan flush with the rear of the engine.

7. Torque the oil pan bolts in sequence to 18 ft. lbs. (25 Nm).

8. Torque the brace-to-transaxle bolts to 32 ft. lbs. (43 Nm).

9. Install or connect the following:
   • Oil level sensor electrical connection

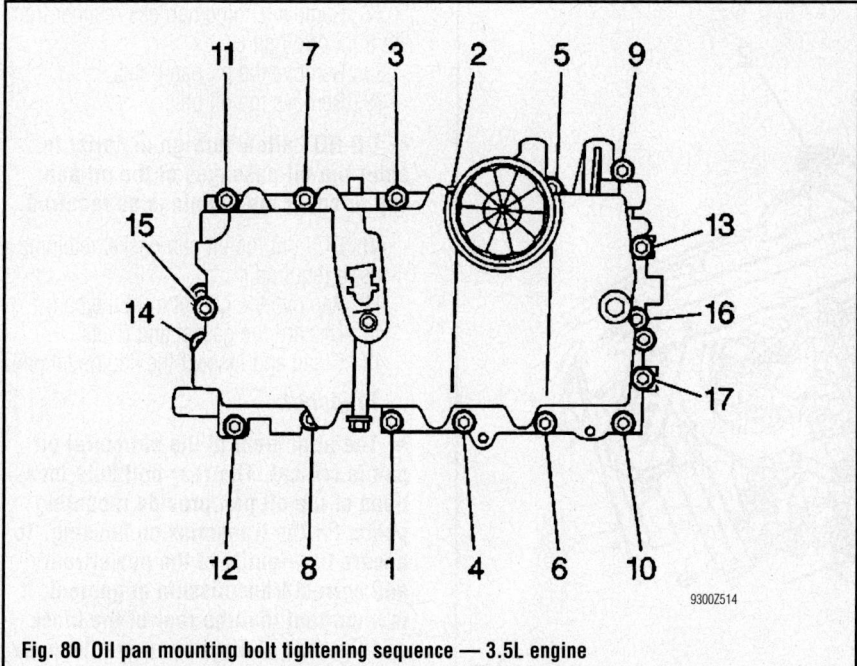

Fig. 80 Oil pan mounting bolt tightening sequence — 3.5L engine

- Drain plug and torque it to 15 ft. lbs. (20 m)
- New oil filter and torque the cap to 18 ft. lbs. (25 Nm)
- Negative battery cable

10. Refill the engine with clean oil.

11. Start the vehicle and check for leaks, repair if necessary.

5.3L Engine

See Figures 81 through 87.

1. Before servicing the vehicle, refer to the Precautions Section.

2. Disconnect the negative battery cable.

3. Remove the left engine mount strut and the bracket from the upper radiator support.

4. Assemble the J-28467-501 (2) to the J 28467-B cross bar (1).

5. Install the J 28467-B (1) and the J-28467-501 (2) to the fender rails.

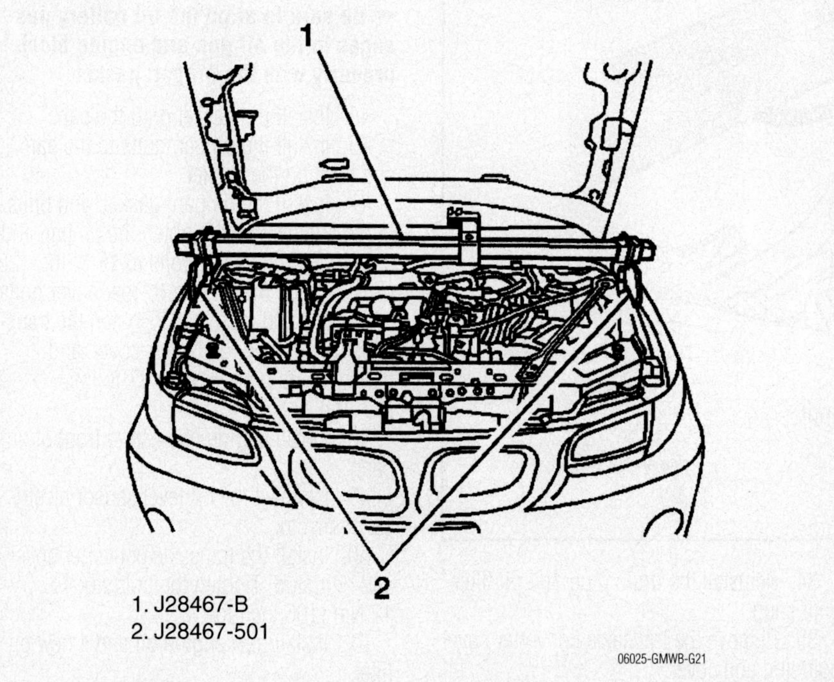

6. Install the J 36462-A (1) to the cross bar (2).

7. Install the support lift hook (2) to the cross bar (1).

8. Install the support hook (1) to the right engine lift hook (3).

9. Install the support hook (1) to the J 36462-A (2).

10. Install the support hook (1) to the left engine lift hook (3).

11. Raise the engine to release the pressure off of the engine mounts.

12. Raise and support the vehicle.

13. Remove the front tires and wheels.

14. Remove and discard the 2 plastic braces from the front of the radiator lower air deflector. The plastic braces are directly below the front cradle bolts.

15. Remove the positive battery cable and the retainers from the frame and position aside.

16. Disconnect the power steering return hose from the frame.

17. Secure the power steering return hose.

18. Remove the stabilizer shaft links and rotate the stabilizer shaft upward to gain access to the mounting bolts in the power steering gear.

19. Remove the mounting bolts from the power steering gear.

20. Secure the power steering gear.

21. Remove the nuts that secure the engine mount to the frame.

22. Remove the nuts which secure the transaxle mount to the frame.

23. If applicable, disconnect the front wheel speed sensor harness connectors.

24. If applicable, disconnect the wheel speed sensor harness from the frame and lower control arms.

25. If applicable, remove the retainers at the front wheel speed harness from the frame and from the lower control arms.

26. Separate both of the lower ball joints from the steering knuckle.

27. Remove both front drivetrain reinforcements using the following procedure.

   a. Remove the drivetrain reinforcement to support brace bolts.

   b. Remove the drivetrain reinforcement to front frame mounting stud nut.

   c. Remove the drivetrain reinforcement from the vehicle.

28. Lower the vehicle until the frame contacts the J 39580.

29. Remove the radiator to front frame brackets.

30. Remove the bolts which secure the front frame to the body.

1. J28467-B
2. J28467-501

06025-GMWB-G21

Fig. 81 Assemble the J-28467-501 (2) to the J 28467-B cross bar (1) — 5.3L engine

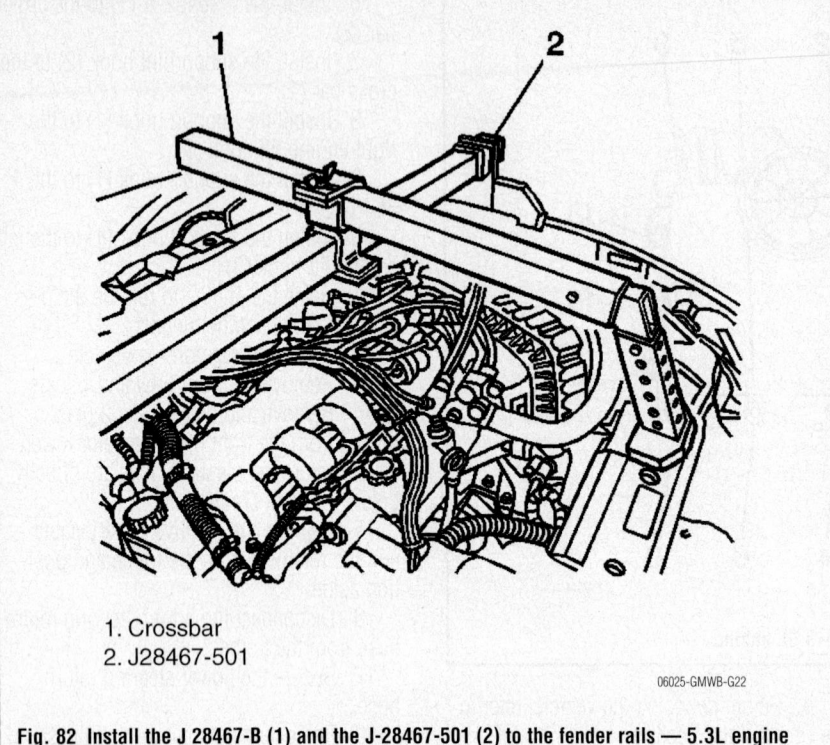

1. Crossbar
2. J28467-501

06025-GMWB-G22

Fig. 82 Install the J 28467-B (1) and the J-28467-501 (2) to the fender rails — 5.3L engine

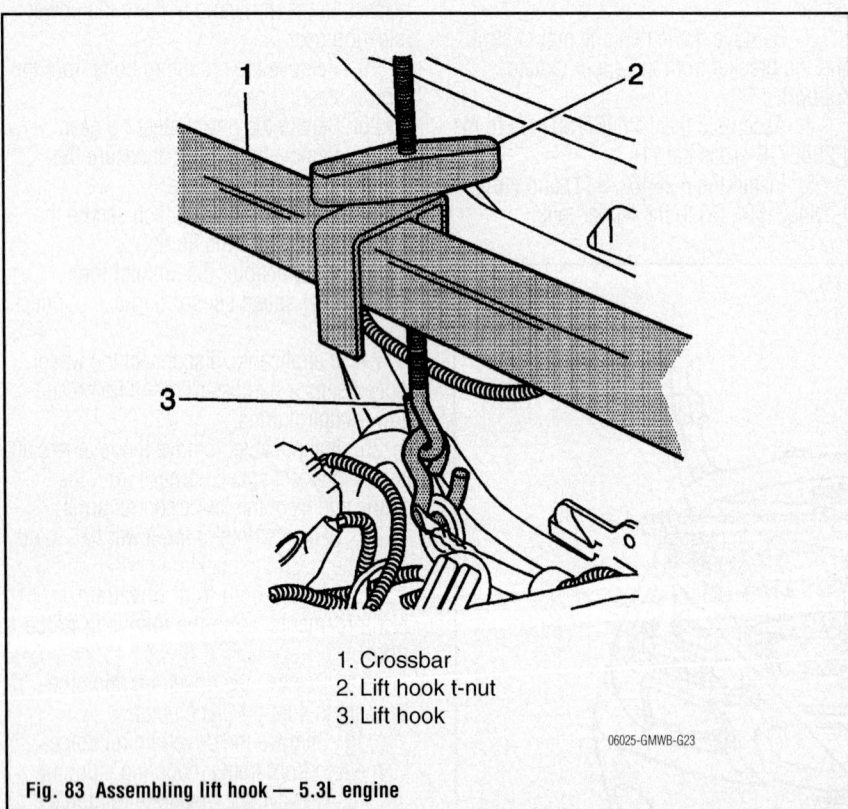

1. Crossbar
2. Lift hook t-nut
3. Lift hook

06025-GMWB-G23

Fig. 83 Assembling lift hook — 5.3L engine

31. Remove the bolts which secure the rear frame to the body.

32. Raise the vehicle in order to separate the frame from the body.

33. Drain the engine oil and remove the engine oil filter.

34. Reinstall the drain plug and oil filter until snug.

35. Remove the transaxle converter cover bolt/stud and cover.

36. Disconnect the oil level sensor electrical connector.

37. Remove engine harness retainer from the front of oil pan.

38. Remove the oil pan bolts.

39. Remove the oil pan.

➡ **DO NOT allow foreign material to enter the oil passages of the oil pan, cap or cover the openings as required.**

40. Drill out the oil pan gasket retaining rivets, if required.

41. Remove the gasket from the pan.

42. Discard the gasket and rivets.

43. Clean and inspect the engine oil pan.

To install:

➡ **The alignment of the structural oil pan is critical. The rear bolt hole locations of the oil pan provide mounting points for the transmission housing. To ensure the rigidity of the powertrain and correct transmission alignment, it is important that the rear of the block and the rear of the oil pan are flush, or even. The rear of the oil pan must NEVER protrude beyond the engine block and transmission housing plane. Do NOT reuse the oil pan gasket. It is NOT necessary to rivet the NEW gasket to the oil pan.**

44. Apply a 5 mm (0.20 in.) bead of sealant GM P/N 12346141 or 12378577 (Canadian P/N 89022195), or equivalent 20 mm (0.80 in.) long to the engine block. Apply the sealant directly onto the tabs of the front/rear cover gasket that protrudes into the oil pan surface.

➡ **Be sure to align the oil gallery passages in the oil pan and engine block properly with the oil pan gasket.**

45. Install the gasket onto the pan.

46. Install the oil pan bolts to the pan and through the gasket.

47. Install the oil pan, gasket, and bolts to the engine block. Tighten the oil pan and oil pan-to-front cover bolts to 18 ft. lbs. (25 Nm). Tighten the oil pan-to-rear cover bolts to 12 Nm (106 inch lbs.). Tighten the transmission housing, converter cover, and transmission bolts/stud to 37 ft. lbs. (50 Nm).

48. Install engine harness to front of oil pan.

49. Connect the oil level sensor electrical connector.

50. Install the transaxle converter cover and bolt/stud. Tighten the bolt/stud to 12 Nm (106 inch lbs.).

51. Install new engine oil and a new oil filter.

52. Position the engine support table with the frame under the vehicle.

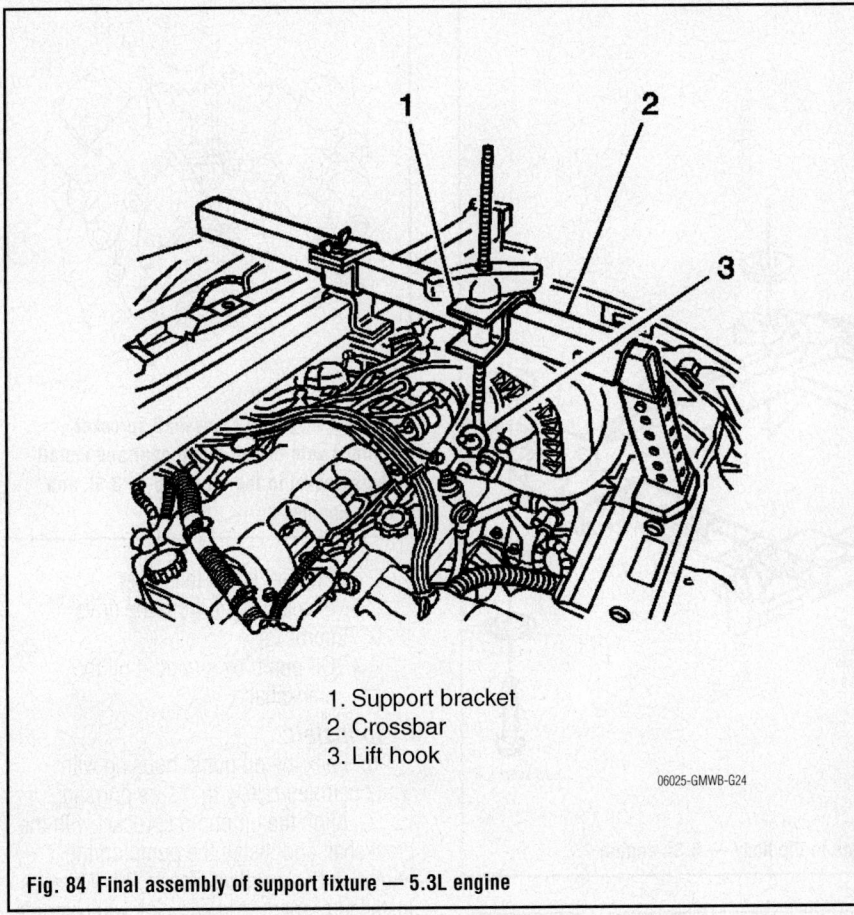

1. Support bracket
2. Crossbar
3. Lift hook

06025-GMWB-G24

Fig. 84 Final assembly of support fixture — 5.3L engine

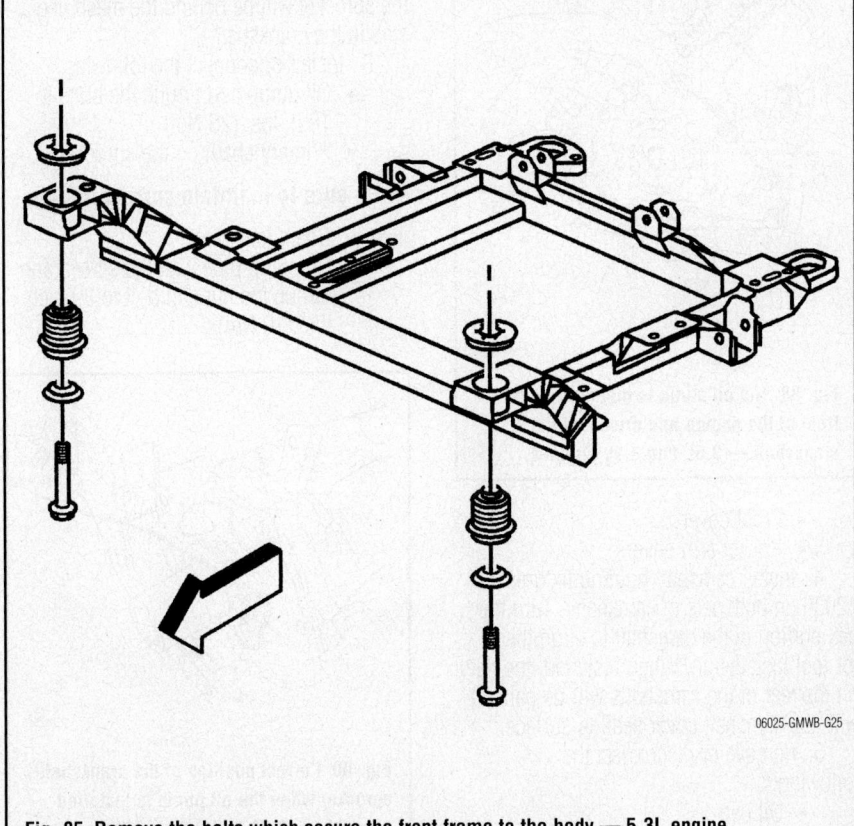

06025-GMWB-G25

Fig. 85 Remove the bolts which secure the front frame to the body — 5.3L engine

53. Lower the vehicle to the frame.
54. Loosely install the bolts to secure the rear frame to the body.
55. Loosely install the bolts to secure the front frame to the body.
56. Align the frame to the body by inserting two 19 X 203 mm (0.74 X 8 in) pins in the alignment holes on the right side of the frame.
57. Install the front and rear frame bolts. Tighten the front bolts to 107 ft. lbs. (145 Nm). Tighten the rear bolts to 118 ft. lbs. (160 Nm).
58. Install the drivetrain reinforcements using the following procedure:
    a. Position the drivetrain reinforcements to the front frame mount stud to the support brace.
    b. Loosely install the drivetrain reinforcement to support brace bolts.
    c. Install the drivetrain reinforcement to cradle mount nut. Tighten the drivetrain reinforcement brace nut to 37 ft. lbs. (50 Nm). Tighten the drivetrain reinforcement brace bolts to 18 ft. lbs. (25 Nm).
59. Install the radiator to front frame brackets.
60. Connect both the lower ball joints to the steering knuckle.
61. Install the nuts that secure the engine mount to the frame. Install the lower engine mount nuts. Tighten the nuts to 37 ft. lbs. (50 Nm).
62. Install the engine mount bracket bolts. Tighten the bolts to 37 ft. lbs. (50 Nm).
63. Install the nuts which secure the transaxle mount to the frame. Tighten the transaxle mount lower nuts to 35 ft. lbs. (47 Nm).
64. Install the steering gear mounting bolts.
65. Install the stabilizer shaft links.
66. If applicable, connect the wheel speed sensor wiring harness to the frame and lower control arm.
67. If applicable, connect the front wheel speed sensor connectors.
68. If applicable, install the front wheel speed harness retainers to the frame and to the lower control arm.
69. Install the positive battery cable and retainers to the frame.
70. Install the power steering cooler pipe.
71. Connect the fog lamp harness connectors.
72. Install the front tires and wheels.
73. Lower the vehicle.
74. Remove the engine support fixture.
75. Inspect the front wheel alignment.

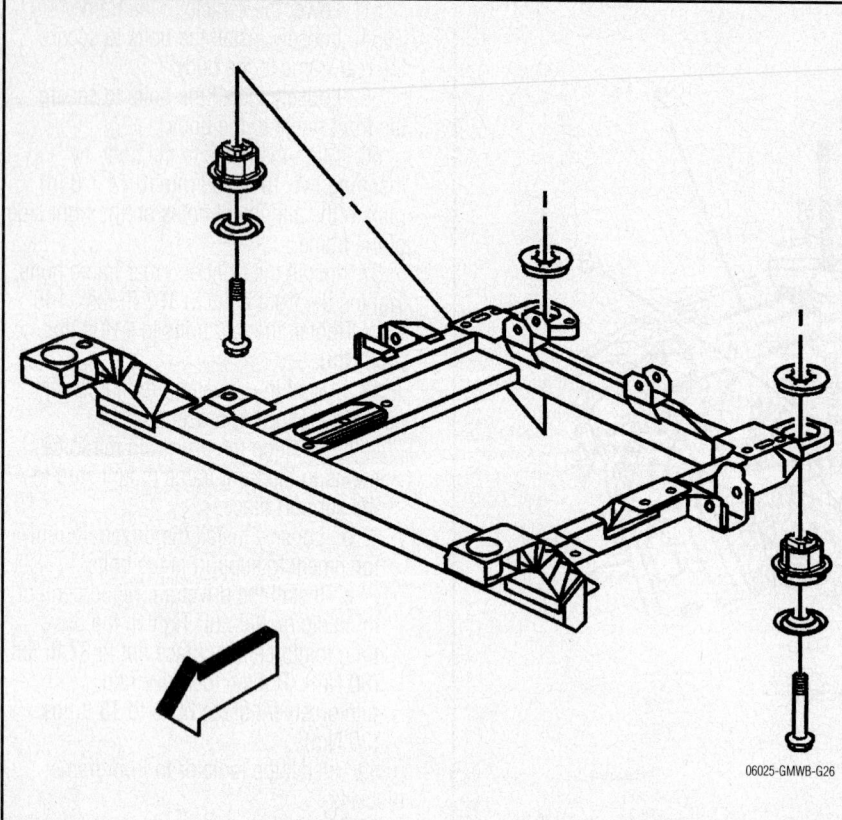

Fig. 86 Remove the bolts which secure the rear frame to the body — 5.3L engine

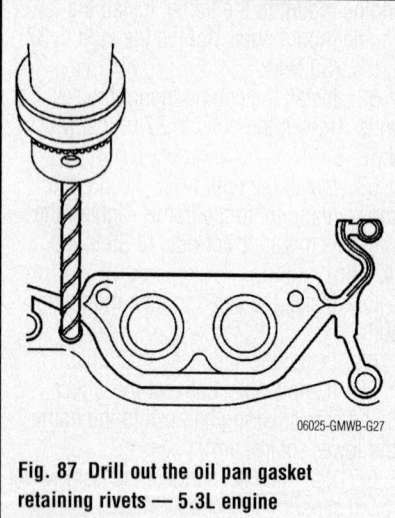

Fig. 87 Drill out the oil pan gasket retaining rivets — 5.3L engine

OIL PUMP

REMOVAL & INSTALLATION

3.5L & 3.9L Engines

See Figures 88 through 90.

1. Before servicing the vehicle, refer to the Precautions Section.
2. Drain the engine oil.
3. Remove or disconnect the following:
   • Negative battery cable

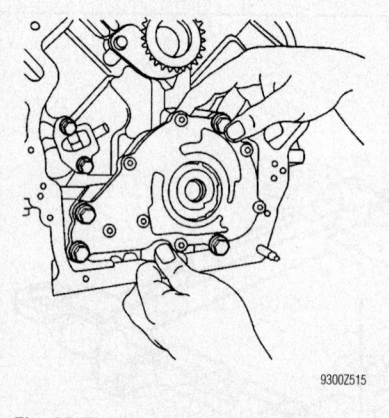

Fig. 88 The oil pump is mounted on the front of the engine and driven by the crankshaft — 3.5L and 3.9L engines

   • Front cover
   • Rocker arm covers
4. Install camshaft holding fixtures J 42038 on both sets of camshafts. Turn the hex portion of the camshaft to align them for tool installation. When installed, the flats on the rear of the camshafts will be parallel with the camshaft cover sealing surface.
5. Remove or disconnect the following:
   • Oil pan
   • Oil pump pipe and screen

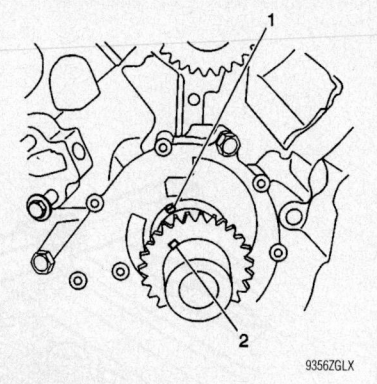

Fig. 89 Align the crankshaft sprocket splines with the oil pump gear and install the sprocket in the oil pump — 3.5L and 3.9L Engines

   • Primary chain tensioner
   • Primary chain from the drive sprocket
   • Oil pump by sliding it off the crankshaft

To install:

6. Pack the oil pump housing with white petroleum jelly to insure priming.
7. Align the oil pump sprocket with the crankshaft and install the pump on the engine until a positive stop is felt. When installed properly, the sprocket will protrude slightly from the oil pump and the face of the sprocket will be behind the machined step in the crankshaft.
8. Install or connect the following:
   • Oil pump and torque the bolts to 18 ft. lbs. (25 Nm)
   • Primary chain on the sprocket

➡ **Be sure to maintain correct timing.**

   • Chain tensioner
   • Oil pump pipe with the screen and torque the nut and bolt to 89 inch lbs. (10 Nm)

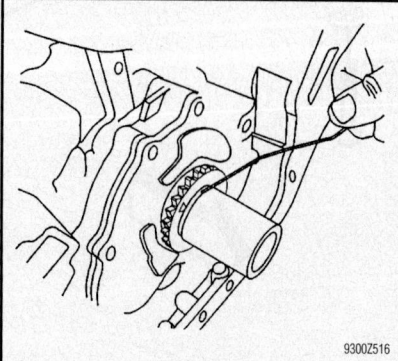

Fig. 90 Correct position of the crankshaft sprocket when the oil pump is installed correctly — 3.5L and 3.9L engine

- Oil pan and torque the bolts to 18 ft. lbs. (25 Nm)
9. Remove the camshaft holding tools.
10. Install or connect the following:
    - Camshaft covers and torque the bolts to 80 inch lbs. (99 Nm)
    - Engine front cover and torque the bolts to 124 inch lbs. (14 Nm)
    - Negative battery cable
11. Fill the engine with new oil.
12. Start the vehicle and check for leaks, repair if necessary.

5.3L Engine

See Figure 91.

1. Before servicing the vehicle, refer to the Precautions Section.
2. Remove the oil pan.
3. Remove the engine front cover.
4. Remove the oil pump screen bolt and nuts.
5. Remove the oil pump screen with O-ring seal.

6. Remove the O-ring seal from the pump screen.
7. Discard the O-ring seal.
8. Remove the remaining crankshaft oil deflector nuts.
9. Remove the crankshaft oil deflector.
10. Remove the oil pump bolts.

➡ **Do not allow dirt or debris to enter the oil pump assembly, cap end as necessary.**

11. Remove the oil pump.
12. Clean and inspect the oil pump.

To install:

13. Align the splined surfaces of the crankshaft sprocket and the oil pump drive gear and install the oil pump.
14. Install the oil pump onto the crankshaft sprocket until the pump housing contacts the face of the engine block.
15. Install the oil pump bolts. Tighten the bolts to 18 ft. lbs. (25 Nm).
16. Install the crankshaft oil deflector and nuts until snug.

17. Lubricate a NEW oil pump screen O-ring seal with clean engine oil.
18. Install the NEW O-ring seal onto the oil pump screen.

➡ **Push the oil pump screen tube completely into the oil pump prior to tightening the bolt. Do not allow the bolt to pull the tube into the pump.**

19. Align the oil pump screen mounting brackets with the correct crankshaft bearing cap studs.
20. Install the oil pump screen.
21. Install the oil pump screen bolt and nuts. Tighten the bolt to 12 Nm (106 lb in). Tighten the nuts to 18 ft. lbs. (25 Nm).
22. Install the engine front cover.
23. Install the oil pan.

PISTON AND RING

POSITIONING

See Figures 92 through 97.

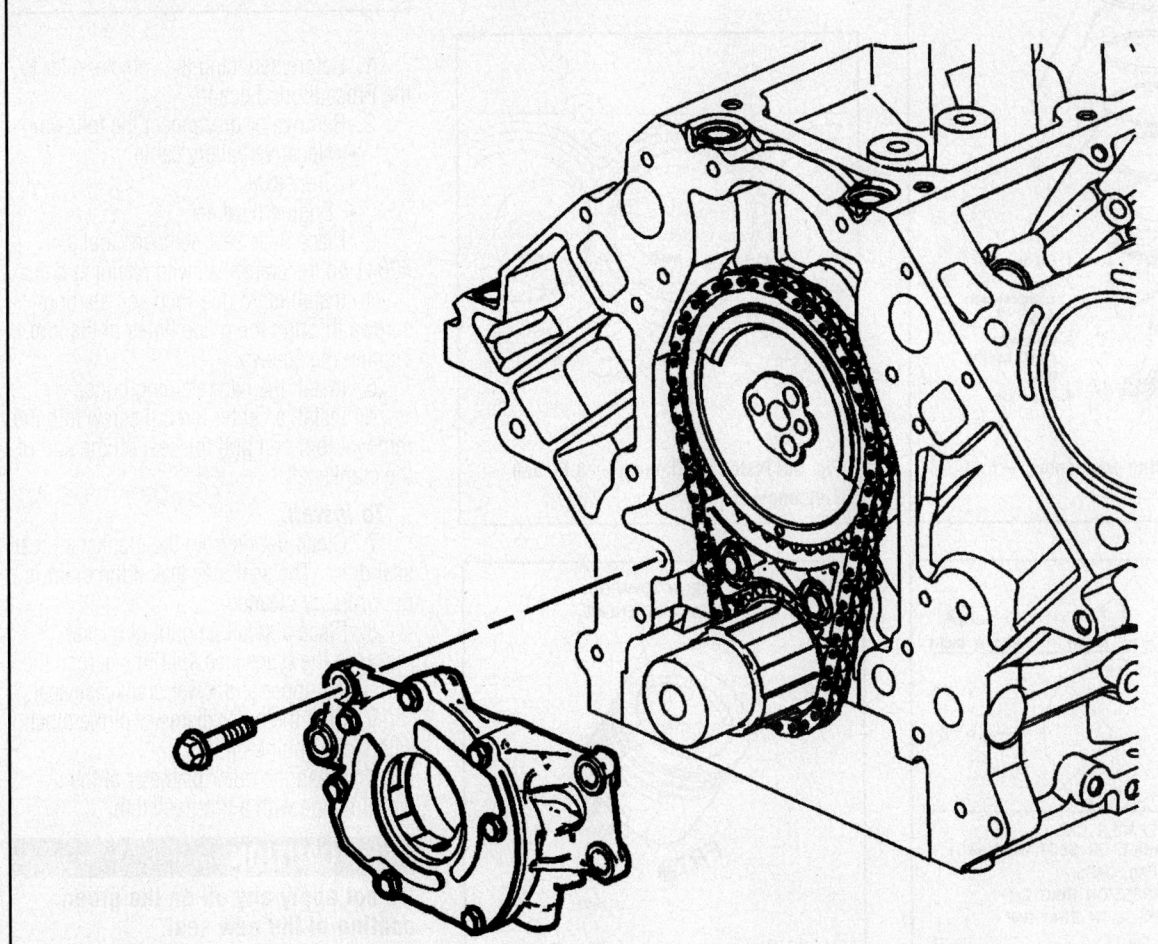

06025-GMWB-G28

Fig. 91 Oil pump — 5.3L engine

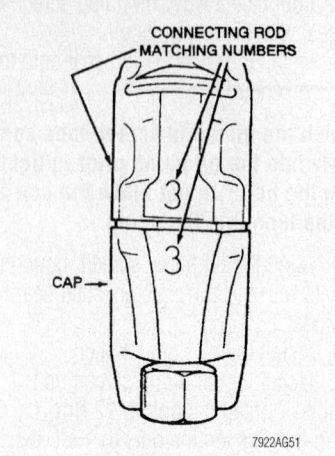

Fig. 92 Connecting rod and cap installation. Be sure to matchmark the cap and rod prior to disassembly, as shown — 5.3L engines

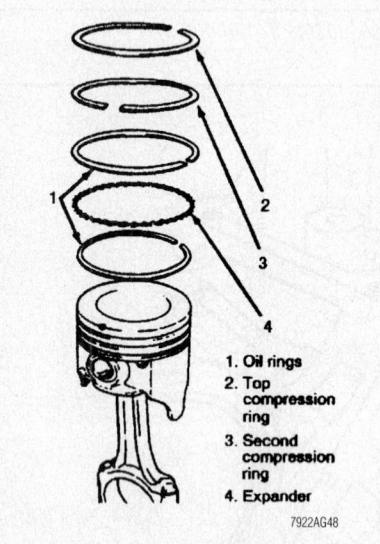

1. Oil rings
2. Top compression ring
3. Second compression ring
4. Expander

Fig. 93 Piston ring positioning — 5.3L engines

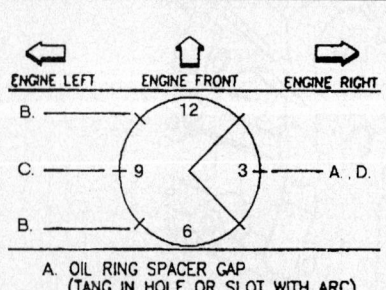

A. OIL RING SPACER GAP (TANG IN HOLE OR SLOT WITH ARC)
B. OIL RING RAIL GAPS
C. 2ND COMPRESSION RING GAP
D. TOP COMPRESSION RING GAP

Fig. 94 Piston ring end-gap spacing — 5.3L engines

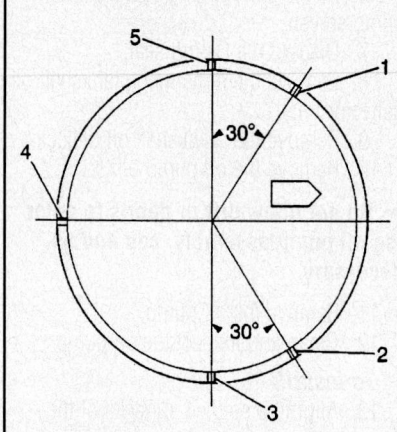

1. Lower oil control ring
2. Upper oil control ring
3. Top Ring
4. Oil control ring expander
5. Second ring

Fig. 95 Piston ring end-gap positioning — 3.5L and 3.9L engines

Fig. 96 Piston positioning — 3.5L and 3.9L engines

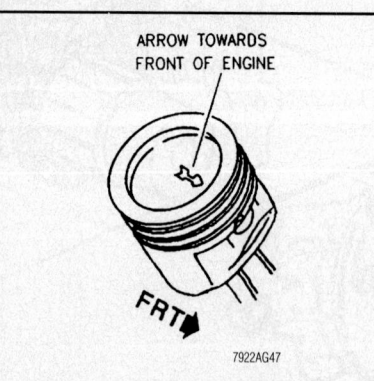

Fig. 97 Piston positioning. Often the arrow is replaced by a notch, which also must face toward the front of the engine — 5.3L engines

REAR MAIN SEAL

REMOVAL & INSTALLATION

3.5L & 3.9L Engines

See Figures 98 and 99.

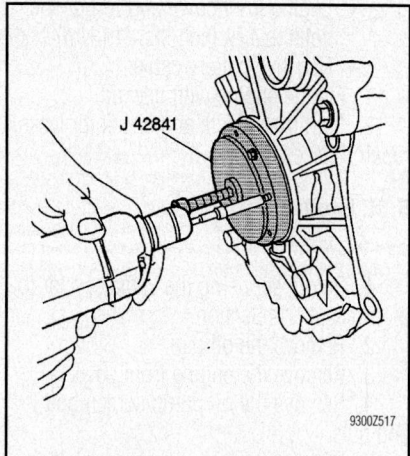

Fig. 98 Use the guide holes in Tool J 42841 to install the screws in the seal — 3.5L engine

1. Before servicing the vehicle, refer to the Precautions Section.
2. Remove or disconnect the following:
   - Negative battery cable
   - Transaxle
   - Engine flywheel
3. Place Rear Seal Remover Tool J 42841 on the crankshaft with retaining bolts.
4. Install eight one-inch self starting screws through the guide holes of the tool. Tighten the screws.
5. Install the two retaining bolts.
6. Install a center forcing screw into the removal tool and pull the seal off the end of the crankshaft.

To install:

7. Clean debris from the crankshaft rear seal drain. The seal may leak if the drain is not properly cleaned.
8. Place a small amount of gasket maker to the crankcase split line across the end of the upper and lower crankcase seal.
9. Coat the outer diameter of the block with clean engine oil.
10. Clean the outer diameter of the flywheel flange with a lint-free cloth.

✳✳ CAUTION

Do not apply any oil on the green coating of the new seal.

11. Loosen the center bolt of the seal installer tool until the hub protrudes past the outer plate (approximately ½ inch).

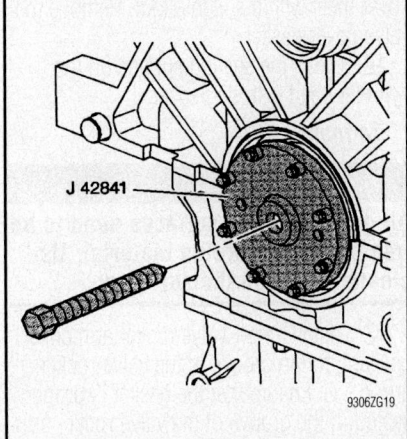

Fig. 99 Install a center forcing screw into the removal tool — 3.5L engine

12. Install or connect the following:
- Three mounting bolts into the crankshaft flange until the tool is fully seated on the crankshaft
- New seal by tightening the center bolt until the tool bottoms out against the crankshaft

13. Remove the removal/installer tool and make certain the seal is installed properly

14. Install or connect the following:
- Flywheel. Torque the bolts to 11 ft. lbs. (15 Nm) plus an additional 50 degrees with a torque angle meter.
- Transaxle
- Negative battery cable

15. Top off the engine oil if needed.

16. Start the vehicle and check for leaks, repair if necessary.

5.3L Engine

See Figures 100 through 102.

1. Before servicing the vehicle, refer to the Precautions Section.

2. Remove the automatic transmission.

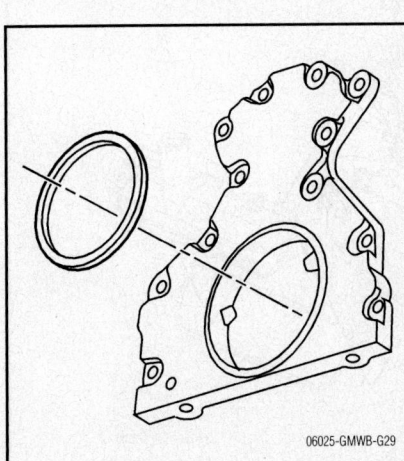

Fig. 100 Rear main seal — 5.3L engine

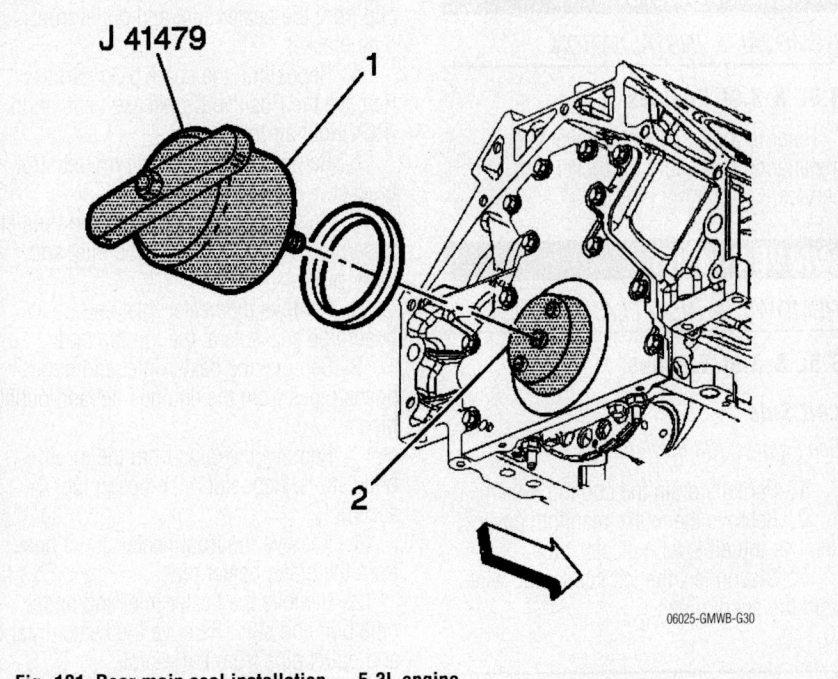

Fig. 101 Rear main seal installation — 5.3L engine

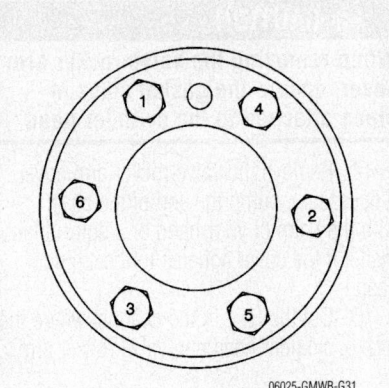

Fig. 102 Flywheel torque sequence — 5.3L engine

3. Remove the flywheel bolts and flywheel.

4. Remove and discard the crankshaft rear oil seal.

To install:

➡ **Do not lubricate the oil seal inside diameter (ID) or the crankshaft surface.**

5. Lubricate the outside diameter (OD) of the oil seal with clean engine oil. DO NOT allow oil or other lubricants to contact the seal surface.

6. Lubricate the rear cover oil seal bore with clean engine oil. DO NOT allow oil or other lubricants to contact the crankshaft surface.

7. Install the J 41479 tapered cone (2) and bolts onto the rear of the crankshaft.

8. Tighten the bolts until snug. Do not overtighten.

9. Install the rear oil seal onto the tapered cone (2) and push the seal to the rear cover bore.

10. Thread the J 41479 threaded rod into the tapered cone until the tool (1) contacts the oil seal.

11. Align the oil seal into the tool (1).

12. Rotate the handle of the tool (1) clockwise until the seal enters the rear cover and bottoms into the cover bore.

13. Remove the J 41479.

➡ **The flywheel does not use a locating pin for alignment and will not initially seat against the crankshaft flange or spacer if applicable, but will be pulled onto the crankshaft by the engine flywheel bolts. This procedure requires a 3-stage tightening process.**

14. Install the flywheel to the crankshaft.

15. Apply threadlock GM P/N 12345382 (Canadian P/N 10953489), or equivalent to the threads of the flywheel bolts.

16. Install the engine flywheel bolts:
- First pass in sequence: 15 ft. lbs. (20 Nm).
- Second pass in sequence: 37 ft. lbs. (50 Nm).
- Third pass in sequence: 74 ft. lbs. (100 Nm).

17. Install the automatic transmission.

ROCKER ARMS/SHAFTS

REMOVAL & INSTALLATION

3.5L & 3.9L Engines

Refer to the camshaft removal and installation procedure for rocker arm service.

VALVE COVERS

REMOVAL & INSTALLATION

3.5L & 3.9L Engines

Left Side

See Figures 103 through 105.

1. Partially drain the cooling system.
2. Remove the intake manifold cover. Remove the oil level indicator tube.
3. Disconnect the left spark plug wires from the spark plugs.

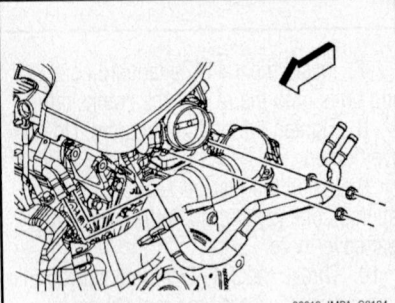

Fig. 103 Repositioning heater inlet and outlet hose/pipe clamps at the engine inlet and outer pipes

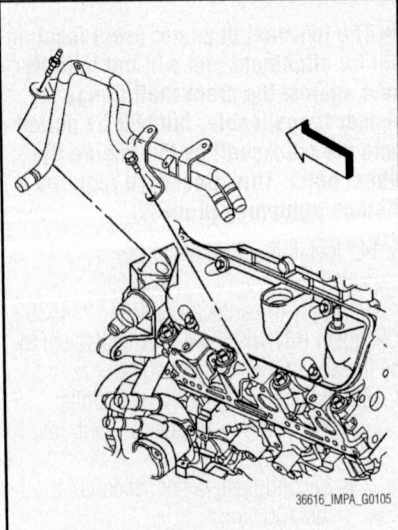

Fig. 104 Removing the front heater outlet hose from the outlet heater pipe

4. Remove the spark plug wire harness clip from the heater inlet and outlet front pipe bracket.
5. Reposition the spark plug harness. Remove the Positive Crankcase Ventilation (PCV) foul air tube.
6. Remove the left engine mount strut bracket.
7. Reposition the heater inlet and outlet hose/pipe clamps at the engine inlet and outer pipes.
8. Remove the heater inlet and outlet hose/pipe clip nuts at the throttle body.
9. Remove the heater inlet and outer hoses/pipes from the engine inlet and outlet pipes.
10. Remove the clips from the throttle body studs. Reposition the hose/pipe assembly.
11. Remove the front heater outlet hose from the outlet heater pipe.
12. Remove the heater inlet and outlet pipe bolt and stud. Remove the heater inlet and outlet pipe from the vehicle.
13. Loosen the valve rocker arm cover bolts.

✴✴ CAUTION

When removing the valve rocker arm cover, ensure the gasket stays in place attached to the cylinder head.

14. Remove the valve rocker arm cover. If necessary, bump the end of the cover with the palm of your hand or a soft rubber mallet if the cover adheres to the cylinder head.
15. Cut the RTV in the channel where the intake, cylinder head and valve rocker arm

cover meet with a suitable tool. Remove the valve cover gasket.
16. Clean the sealing surface on the cylinder head with degreaser.

To install:

✴✴ CAUTION

All gasket mating surfaces need to be free of oil and foreign material. Use cleaner to clean the surfaces.

17. Install a new valve rocker arm cover gasket into the groove in the valve rocker arm cover. Ensure that the gasket is properly seated in the groove of the valve rocker arm cover.
18. Apply sealant at the cylinder head to the surfaces where the cylinder head and intake manifold meet.

➡ **Use the correct fastener in the correct location. Replacement fasteners must be the correct part number for that application. Fasteners requiring replacement or fasteners requiring the use of thread locking compound or sealant are identified in the service procedure. Do not use paints, lubricants, or corrosion inhibitors on fasteners or fastener joint surfaces unless specified. These coatings affect fastener torque and joint clamping force and may damage the fastener. Use the correct tightening sequence and specifications when installing fasteners in order to avoid damage to parts and systems.**

19. Install the valve rocker arm cover. Tighten the bolts to 89 inch lbs. (10 Nm).

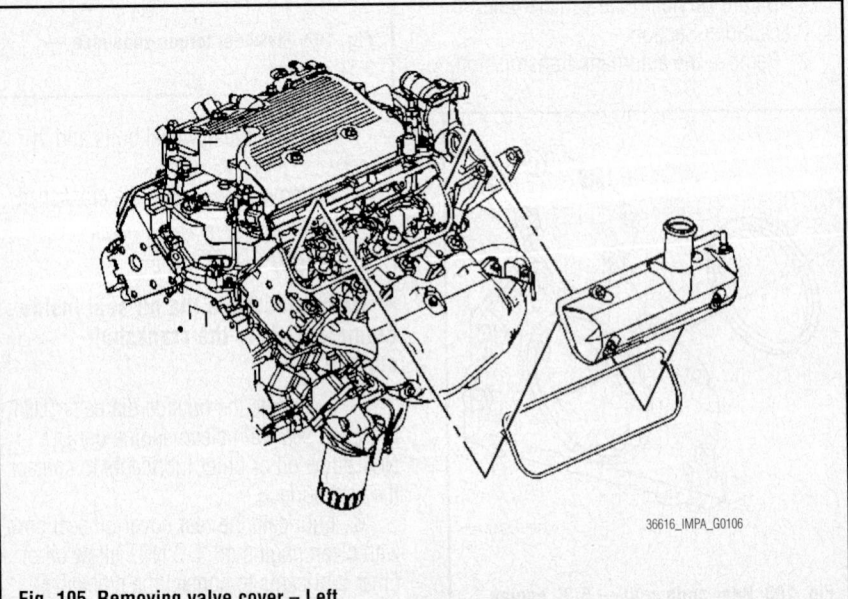

Fig. 105 Removing valve cover – Left

20. Install the heater inlet and outlet pipe to the vehicle. Install the heater inlet and outlet pipe bolt to 18 ft. lbs. (25 Nm) and stud to 89 inch lbs (10 Nm).

21. Install the front heater outlet hose to the outlet heater pipe. Position the hose/pipe assembly. Install the clips to the throttle body studs.

22. Install the heater inlet and outer hoses/pipes to the engine inlet and outlet pipes. Install the heater inlet and outlet hose/pipe clip nuts at the throttle body.

23. Position the heater inlet and outlet hose/pipe clamps at the engine inlet and outer pipes. Install the left engine mount strut bracket.

24. Install the PCV foul air tube. Position the spark plug harness.

25. Install the spark plug wire harness clip to the heater inlet and outlet front pipe bracket.

26. Connect the left spark plug wires to the spark plugs. Install the oil level indicator tube.

27. Install the intake manifold cover. Fill the cooling system.

Right Side

See Figure 106.

1. Remove the engine coolant crossover pipe. Disconnect the Positive Crankcase Ventilation (PCV) fresh air tube from the air cleaner outlet duct.

2. Remove the PCV fresh air tube from the right side valve rocker arm cover.

3. Disconnect the right side spark plug wires from the spark plugs.

4. Remove the right side spark plug harness clip from the ignition coil bracket.

5. Remove the spark plug harness.

6. Disconnect the manifold absolute pressure (MAP) sensor electrical connector.

7. Disconnect the ignition coil electrical connector. Remove the engine harness clip from the ignition coil bracket.

8. Remove the heated oxygen sensor (HO2S) electrical connector clip from the ignition coil bracket.

9. Remove the ignition coil bracket nuts. Remove the ignition coil bracket bolts. Remove the ignition coil.

10. Loosen the valve rocker arm cover bolts.

✳✳ CAUTION

When removing the valve rocker arm cover, ensure the gasket stays in place attached to the cylinder head.

11. Remove the valve rocker arm cover. Bump the end of the cover with the palm of your hand or a soft rubber mallet if the cover adheres to the cylinder head.

12. Cut the room temperature vulcanizing (RTV) sealer in the channel where the intake, cylinder head and valve rocker arm cover meet with a suitable tool.

13. Remove the valve cover gasket. Clean the sealing surface on the cylinder head with degreaser.

To install:

✳✳ CAUTION

All gasket mating surfaces need to be free of oil and foreign material. Use cleaner to clean the surfaces.

14. Install a new valve rocker arm cover gasket into the groove in the valve rocker arm cover. Ensure that the gasket is properly seated in the groove of the valve rocker arm cover.

15. Apply sealant at the cylinder head to the surfaces where the cylinder head and intake manifold meet.

16. Install a new gasket to the valve rocker arm cover. Ensure that the gasket is properly seated in the groove of the valve rocker arm cover.

17. Install the right valve rocker arm cover.

➡ **Use the correct fastener in the correct location. Replacement fasteners must be the correct part number for that application. Fasteners requiring replacement or fasteners requiring the use of thread locking compound or sealant are identified in the service procedure. Do not use paints, lubricants, or corrosion inhibitors on fasteners or fastener joint surfaces unless specified. These coatings affect fastener torque and joint clamping force and may damage the fastener. Use the correct tightening sequence and specifications when installing fasteners in order to avoid damage to parts and systems.**

✳✳ CAUTION

Use an alternating criss-cross pattern when tightening the valve rocker cover bolts. Failure to do so may result in oil leakage from the valve cover due to improper seating of the gasket.

18. Tighten the valve rocker arm cover bolts to 89 inch lbs. (10 Nm).

19. Install the ignition coil. Install the ignition coil bracket bolts. Install the ignition coil bracket nuts and tighten to 18 ft. lbs. (25 Nm).

20. Install the HO2S electrical connector clip to the ignition coil bracket.

21. Install the engine harness clip to the ignition coil bracket. Connect the ignition coil electrical connector . Connect the MAP sensor electrical connector.

22. To complete installation, reverse removal procedure.

5.3L Engine

Left Side (Front)

See Figure 107.

1. Remove the engine sight shield, if required.

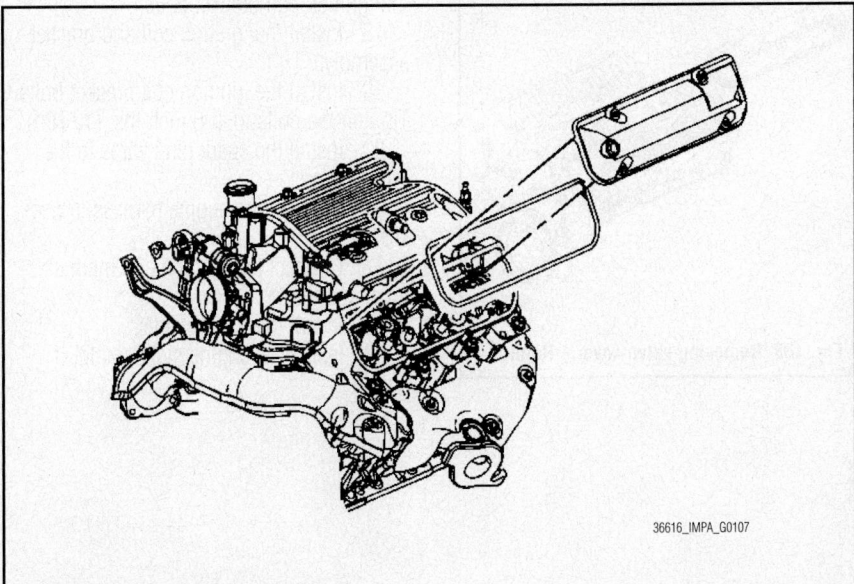

36616_IMPA_G0107

Fig. 106 Removing valve cover – Right

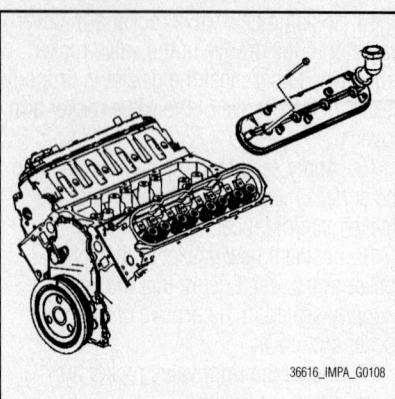

Fig. 107 Removing valve cover – Left

2. Remove the Connector Position Assurance (CPA) retainer.

3. Disconnect the ignition coil main electrical connector.

4. Reposition the engine harness, as necessary.

5. Remove the spark plug wires from the ignition coils:

  a. Twist each plug wire 1/2 turn.

  b. Pull only on the boot in order to remove the wire from the ignition coil.

6. Remove the ignition coil bracket bolts. Remove the ignition coil and bracket assembly.

7. Remove the Positive Crankcase Ventilation (PCV) clean air tube from the valve rocker arm cover.

8. Remove the valve rocker arm cover bolts and cover.

9. Remove and discard the old the gasket from the valve rocker arm cover.

10. Remove the valve rocker arm cover bolt grommets, if cut or damaged.

➡ **Do not remove the oil fill tube from the rocker cover unless service is required. If the oil fill tube has been removed, install a NEW tube during assembly.**

11. Remove the oil fill cap from the oil fill tube, if necessary.

12. Remove the oil fill tube, if necessary.

13. Discard the oil fill tube, if necessary.

To install:

➡ **All gasket surfaces should be free of oil and/or other foreign material during assembly. DO NOT reuse the valve rocker arm cover gasket. The valve**

rocker arm cover bolt grommets may be reused.

14. Install a NEW gasket into the groove of the valve rocker arm cover.

15. Install a NEW oil fill tube to the valve rocker arm cover, if necessary.

16. Install NEW valve rocker arm cover bolt grommets, if necessary.

17. Install the valve rocker arm cover and bolts. Tighten to 106 inch lbs. (12 Nm).

18. Install the PCV clean air tube from the valve rocker arm cover.

19. Apply threadlock to the threads of the ignition coil bracket bolts.

20. Install the ignition coil and bracket assembly.

21. Install the ignition coil bracket bolts. Tighten to 106 inch lbs. (12 Nm).

22. Install the spark plug wires to the ignition coils.

23. Position the engine harness, as necessary.

24. Connect the ignition coil main electrical connector.

25. Install the CPA retainer.

26. Install the engine sight shield, if required.

Right Side (Rear)

See Figure 108.

1. Remove the engine sight shield, if required.

2. Remove the connector position assurance (CPA) retainer.

3. Disconnect the ignition coil main electrical connector.

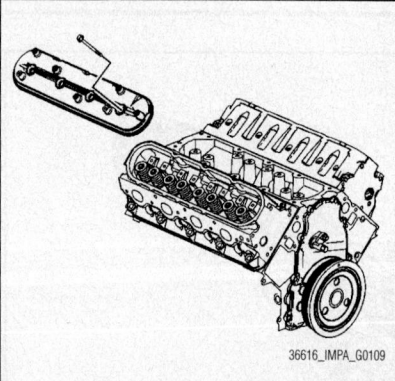

Fig. 108 Removing valve cover – Right

4. Reposition the engine harness, if necessary.

5. Remove the spark plug wires from the ignition coils:

  a. Twist each plug wire 1/2 turn.

  b. Pull only on the boot in order to remove the wire from the ignition coil.

6. Remove the ignition coil bracket bolts.

7. Remove the ignition coil and bracket assembly.

8. Remove the Positive Crankcase Ventilation (PCV) foul air hose from the intake manifold and valve rocker arm cover.

9. Remove the valve rocker arm cover bolts and cover.

10. Remove and discard the old the gasket from the valve rocker arm cover.

11. Remove the valve rocker arm cover bolt grommets, if cut or damaged.

To install:

➡ **All gasket surfaces should be free of oil and/or other foreign material during assembly. DO NOT reuse the valve rocker arm cover gasket. The valve rocker arm cover bolt grommets may be reused.**

12. Install a NEW gasket into the groove of the valve rocker arm cover.

13. Install NEW valve rocker arm cover bolt grommets, if necessary.

14. Install the valve rocker arm cover and bolts.

15. Install the rocker arm cover bolts and grommets. Tighten the bolts to 106 inch lbs. (12 Nm).

16. Install the PCV foul air hose to the intake manifold and valve rocker arm cover.

17. Apply threadlock to the threads of the ignition coil bracket bolts.

18. Install the ignition coil and bracket assembly.

19. Install the ignition coil bracket bolts. Tighten the bolts to 106 inch lbs. (12 Nm).

20. Install the spark plug wires to the ignition coils.

21. Position the engine harness, if necessary.

22. Connect the ignition coil main electrical connector.

23. Install the CPA retainer.

24. Install the engine sight shield, if required.

ENGINE PERFORMANCE & EMISSION CONTROLS

ACCELERATOR PEDAL POSITION (APP) SENSOR

LOCATION

The APP sensor is located on the accelerator pedal assembly.

REMOVAL & INSTALLATION

See Figures 109 and 110.

1. Before servicing the vehicle, refer to the Precautions Section.
2. Disconnect the negative battery cable.
3. Remove the left instrument panel sound insulator.
4. Disconnect the APP sensor electrical connector.
5. Remove the APP sensor assembly bolts.
6. Remove the APP sensor assembly from the vehicle.
7. To install, reverse removal procedure.

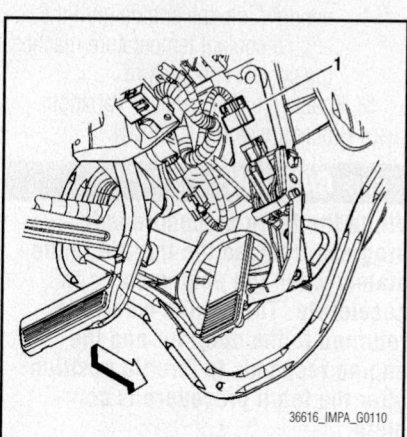

Fig. 109 Disconnecting the APP sensor electrical connector (1)

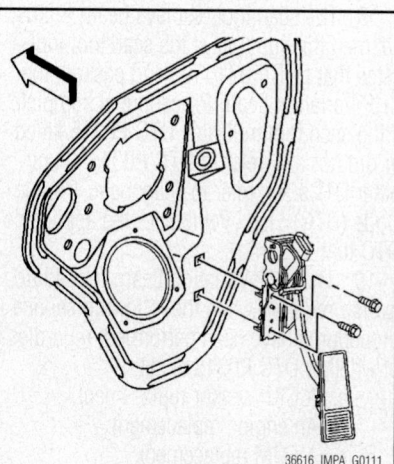

36616_IMPA_G0111

Fig. 110 Removing the APP sensor

CAMSHAFT POSITION (CMP) SENSOR

LOCATION

Refer to the illustrations under Removal and Installation to locate the Camshaft Position Sensor (CMP) sensor.

REMOVAL & INSTALLATION

3.5L & 3.9L Engines

See Figure 111.

36616_IMPA_G0119

Fig. 111 Removing the CMP sensor

1. Disconnect the negative battery cable.
2. Remove the power steering pump.
3. Disconnect the Camshaft Position (CMP) sensor electrical connector.
4. Remove the CMP sensor bolt.
5. Remove the CMP sensor.
6. Inspect the sensor O-ring for wear, cracks, or leakage if the sensor is not being replaced.
7. To install, reverse removal procedure.
8. Lubricate the CMP sensor O-ring with clean engine oil. Tighten the bolt to 89 inch. Lbs (10 Nm).

5.3L Engines

See Figures 112 and 113.

1. Disconnect the negative battery cable.
2. Disconnect the Camshaft Position (CMP) sensor electrical connector.
3. Remove the CMP sensor bolt.
4. Remove the CMP sensor.
5. Inspect the CMP sensor O-ring seal for cuts or damage. If the seal is not cut or damaged, it may be reused.
6. Remove the CMP sensor O-ring seal, if necessary.
7. To install, reverse removal procedure.
8. Lubricate the CMP sensor O-ring with clean engine oil. Tighten the bolt to 106 inch. Lbs (12 Nm).

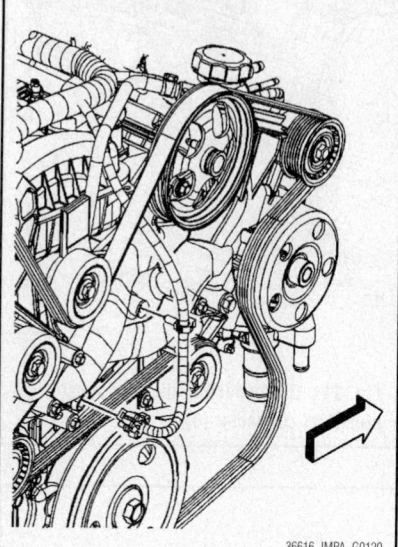

36616_IMPA_G0120

Fig. 112 Disconnecting the CMP sensor electrical connector

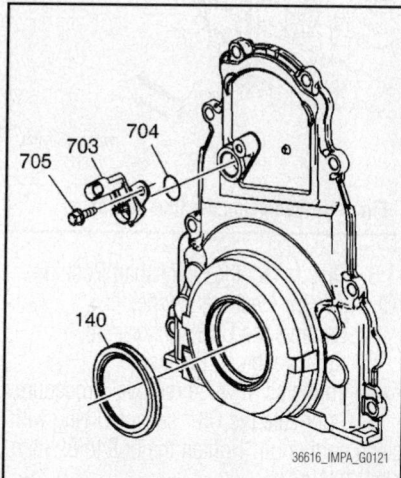

36616_IMPA_G0121

Fig. 113 Removing the CMP sensor — 5.3L Engines

CRANKSHAFT POSITION (CKP) SENSOR

LOCATION

Refer to the illustrations under Removal and Installation to locate the Crankshaft Position (CKP) sensor.

REMOVAL & INSTALLATION

3.5L & 3.9L Engines

See Figures 114 and 115.

1. Disconnect the negative battery cable.
2. Raise and support the vehicle.

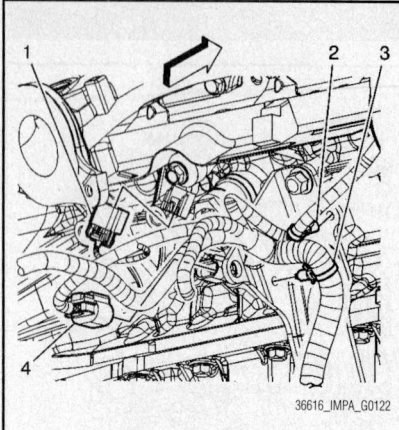

Fig. 114 Disconnecting the CKP sensor electrical connector (4)

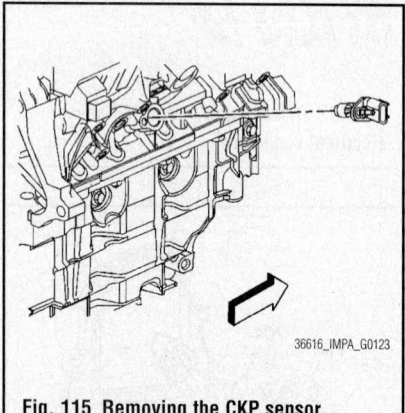

Fig. 115 Removing the CKP sensor

3. Disconnect the Crankshaft Position (CKP) sensor electrical connector.
4. Remove the CKP sensor stud.
5. Remove the CKP sensor.
6. To install, reverse removal procedure.
7. Lubricate the CKP sensor O-ring with clean engine oil. Tighten the bolt to 89 inch. Lbs (10 Nm).

5.3L Engines

See Figures 116 and 117.

✳✳ WARNING

To avoid any vehicle damage, serious personal injury or death when major components are removed from the vehicle and the vehicle is supported by a hoist, support the vehicle with jack stands at the opposite end from which the components are being removed and strap the vehicle to the hoist.

1. Disconnect the negative battery cable.
2. Remove the right exhaust manifold.
3. Disconnect the Crankshaft Position (CKP) sensor electrical connector.

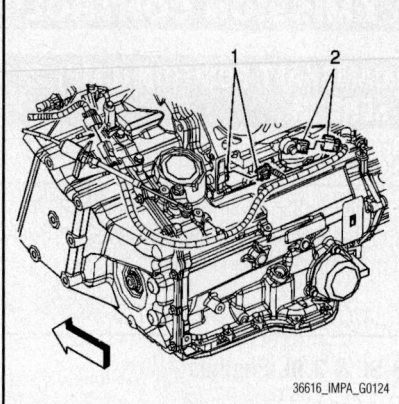

Fig. 116 Disconnecting the CKP sensor electrical connector (1)

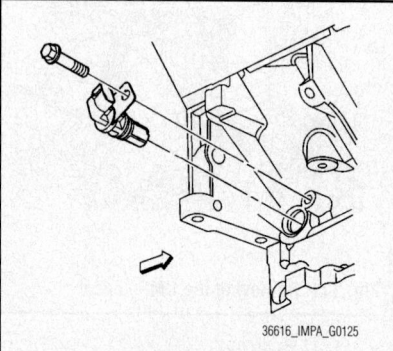

Fig. 117 Removing the CKP sensor — 5.3L Engines

➥ Clean the area around the CKP before removal in order to avoid debris from entering the engine.

4. Remove the CKP sensor bolt.
5. Remove the CKP sensor.
6. To install, reverse removal procedure.
7. Tighten the bolt to 89 Ft. Lbs. (10 Nm).

Crankshaft Position System Variation Learn Procedure

1. Install a scan tool.
2. Monitor the engine control module (ECM) for DTCs with a scan tool. If other DTC's are set, except DTC P0315, refer to the Diagnostic Trouble Code list.
3. Select the Crankshaft Position (CKP) variation learn procedure with a scan tool.
4. The scan tool instructs you to perform the following:
   a. Accelerate to wide open throttle (WOT).
   b. Release throttle when fuel cut-off occurs.
   c. Observe fuel cut-off for applicable engine.
   d. Engine should not accelerate beyond calibrated RPM value.

e. Release throttle immediately if value is exceeded.
   f. Block drive wheels.
   g. Set parking brake.
   h. DO NOT apply brake pedal.
   i. Cycle ignition from OFF to ON.
   j. Apply and hold brake pedal.
   k. Start and idle engine.
   l. Turn A/C OFF.
   m. Vehicle must remain in Park or Neutral.
   n. The scan tool monitors certain component signals to determine if all the conditions are met to continue with the procedure. The scan tool only displays the condition that inhibits the procedure. The scan tool monitors the following components:
   - CKP sensors activity – If there is a CKP sensor condition, refer to the applicable DTC that set
   - CMP sensor activity – If there is a CMP sensor condition, refer to the applicable DTC that set
   - ECT – If the ECT is not warm enough, idle the engine until the engine coolant temperature reaches the correct temperature
5. Enable the CKP System Variation Learn Procedure with a scan tool.

✳✳ CAUTION

While the learn procedure is in progress, release the throttle immediately when the engine starts to decelerate. The engine control is returned to the operator and the engine responds to throttle position after the learn procedure is complete.

6. Accelerate to WOT.
7. Release when the fuel cut-off occurs.
8. Test in progress.
9. The scan tool displays Learn Status: Learned this ignition. If the scan tool indicates that DTC P0315 ran and passed, the CKP Variation Learn Procedure is complete. If the scan tool indicates DTC P0315 failed or did not run, refer to DTC P0315. If any other DTCs set, refer to Diagnostic Trouble Code (DTC) List - Vehicle for the applicable DTC that set.
10. The CKP Variation Learn Procedure is also required when the following service procedures have been performed, regardless of whether DTC P0315 is set:
   a. A CKP sensor replacement.
   b. An engine replacement.
   c. A ECM replacement.
   d. A harmonic balancer replacement.
   e. A crankshaft replacement.

f. Any engine repairs which disturb the CKP sensor relationship.

ENGINE CONTROL MODULE (ECM)

LOCATION

Refer to the illustrations under Removal and Installation to locate the Crankshaft Position (CKP) sensor.

REMOVAL & INSTALLATION

See Figures 118 through 120.

Service of the engine control module (ECM) should normally consist of either replacement of the ECM or electrically erasable programmable read only memory (EEPROM) programming. If the diagnostic procedures call for ECM replacement, inspect the ECM first to see if the replacement is the correct part. If the ECM is faulty, remove the ECM and install the new service ECM.

The new service ECM will not be programmed. You must program the new ECM. DTC P0602 indicates the EEPROM is not programmed or has malfunctioned.

⁑ **CAUTION**

In order to prevent any possible electrostatic discharge damage to the ECM, do not touch the connector pins or the soldered components on the circuit board.

⁑ **CAUTION**

Always turn the ignition off when installing or removing the ECM connectors in order to prevent damage to the components.

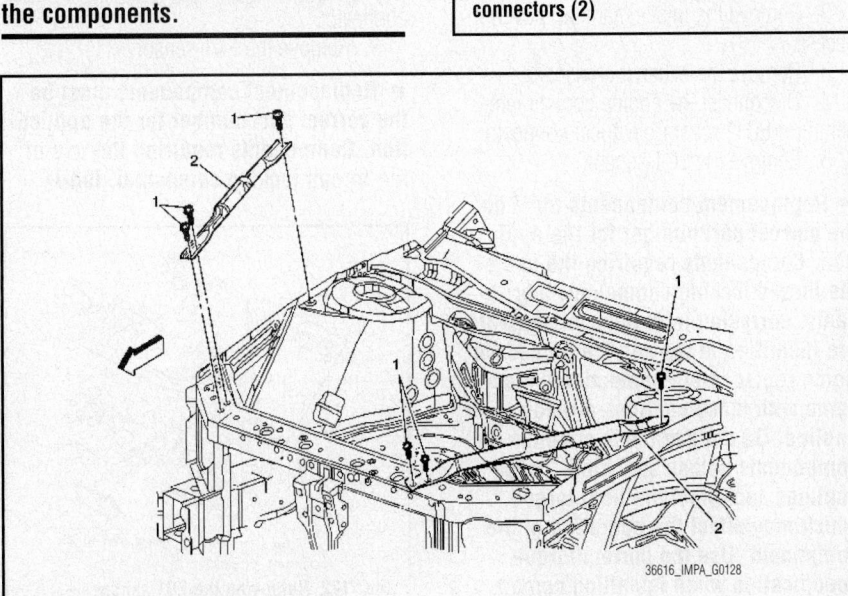

Fig. 118 Removing the fender braces

➡ **It is necessary to record the remaining engine oil life. If the replacement module is not programmed with the remaining engine oil life, the engine oil life will default to 100 percent. If the replacement module is not programmed with the remaining engine oil life, the engine oil will need to be changed at 5 000 km (3,000 mi) from the last engine oil change.**

1. Using a scan tool, retrieve the percentage of remaining engine oil. Record the remaining engine oil life, if required.
2. Disconnect the negative battery cable.
3. Remove the left front inner fender brace.
4. Remove the air cleaner assembly.
5. Disconnect the ECM electrical connectors.
6. Remove the ECM from the air cleaner lower housing.
7. To install, reverse removal procedure.
8. Program the new ECM.

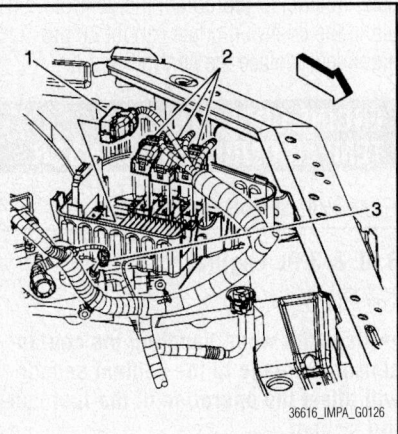

Fig. 119 Disconnecting the ECM electrical connectors (2)

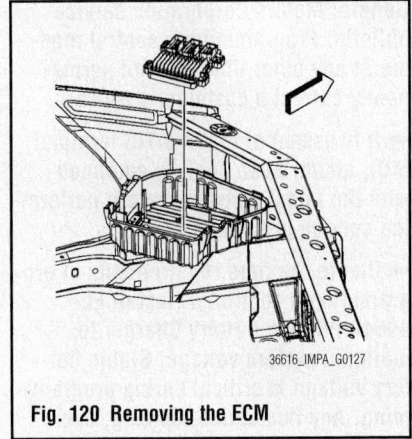

Fig. 120 Removing the ECM

ECM REPLACEMENT PROCEDURES

If the ECM is replaced, the following procedures must be performed:

1. ECM Reprogramming.
2. The CKP System variation learn.
3. The Throttle/Idle learn procedure.
4. Fuel Composition Diagnosis.
5. Engine Oil Life Remaining. When available, use a scan tool to reset the engine oil life remaining back to the original percentage recorded before the module was replaced.
6. Transmission Fluid Life Remaining. When available, use the scan tool to reset the Transmission Fluid Life Remaining back to the original percentage recorded before the module was replaced.
7. Theft Deterrent reprogramming.
8. Refer to the appropriate sections for these procedures.

ECM REPROGRAMMING

If the ECM needs to be reprogrammed, perform the following below.

Engine Oil Life Remaining – When available, use a scan tool to reset the Engine Oil Life Remaining back to the original percentage recorded before the module was reprogrammed.

⁑ **CAUTION**

After programming, perform the following to avoid future misdiagnosis:

a. Turn the ignition OFF for 30 seconds.
b. Turn the ignition ON with the engine OFF.
c. Use the scan tool in order to retrieve history DTCs from all modules.
d. Clear all history DTCs.

Review the information below to ensure proper programming protocol.

➡ **DO NOT program a control module unless you are directed by a service procedure or you are directed by a**

General Motors Corporation service bulletin. Programming a control module at any other time will not permanently correct a customer's concern.

→ It is essential that the TIS terminal, MDI, and/or Scan Tool, is equipped with the latest software before performing service programming.

→ Due to the time requirements of programming a controller, install EL-49642 PSC550 Battery Charger to maintain system voltage. Stable battery voltage is critical during programming. Any fluctuation, spiking, over voltage or loss of voltage will interrupt programming. If the above tool is not available, connect a fully charged 12V jumper or booster pack disconnected from the AC voltage supply.

→ Some modules will require additional programming/setup events to be performed before or after programming.

→ Some vehicles may require the use of a CANDi or MDI module for programming.

→ Review the appropriate service information for these procedures. DTCs may set during programming. Clear DTCs after programming is complete. Clearing powertrain DTCs will set the Inspection/Maintenance (I/M) system status indicators to NO.

Ensure the following conditions are met before programming a control module:
1. Vehicle system voltage:
   a. There is not a charging system concern. All charging system concerns must be repaired before programming a control module.
   b. Battery voltage is greater than 12 volts but less than 16 volts. The battery must be fully charged before programming the control module.
   c. Turn OFF or disable any system that may put a load on the vehicles battery, such as the following components:
   • Twilight sentinel
   • Daytime running lights (DRL) – Applying the parking brake, on most vehicles, disables the DRL system
   • Heating, Ventilation, And Air Conditioning (HVAC) systems
   • Engine cooling fans, radio, etc
2. The ignition switch must be in the proper position. SPS prompts you to turn ON the ignition, with the engine OFF. DO NOT change the position of the ignition switch during the programming procedure, unless instructed to do so.

3. Make certain all tool connections are secure, including the following components and circuits:
   a. Scan Tool.
   b. The RS-232 communication cable port.
   c. The connection at the Data Link Connector (DLC).
   d. The voltage supply circuits (MDI).
   e. The USB, Ethernet or Wireless communication port
   f. The connection at the Data Link Connector (DLC)
4. DO NOT disturb the tool harnesses while programming. If an interruption occurs during the programming procedure, programming failure or control module damage may occur.
5. DO NOT turn OFF the ignition if the programming procedure is interrupted or unsuccessful. Ensure that all control module and DLC connections are secure and the TIS terminal operating software is up to date. Attempt to reprogram the control module. If the control module cannot be programmed, replace the control module.

ENGINE COOLANT TEMPERATURE (ECT) SENSOR

REMOVAL & INSTALLATION

3.5L & 3.9L Engines
See Figure 121.

→ Use care when handling the coolant sensor. Damage to the coolant sensor will affect the operation of the fuel control system.

1. Drain the cooling system.
2. Remove the intake manifold cover, if necessary.
3. Remove the exhaust crossover.
4. Disconnect the engine coolant temperature (ECT) sensor electrical connector.
5. Remove the ECT sensor.

→ Replacement components must be the correct part number for the application. Components requiring the use of the thread locking compound, lubricants, corrosion inhibitors, or sealants are identified in the service procedure. Some replacement components may come with these coatings already applied. Do not use these coatings on components unless specified. These coatings can affect the final torque, which may affect the operation of the component. Use the correct torque specification when installing components in order to avoid damage.

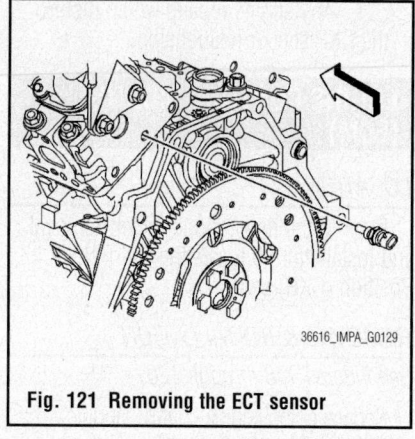
36616_IMPA_G0129

Fig. 121 Removing the ECT sensor

→ Use care when handling the coolant sensor. Damage to the coolant sensor will affect the operation of the fuel control system.

6. To install, coat the threads with sealer GM P/N 12346004 (Canadian P/N 10953480) or equivalent.
7. Install the ECT sensor. Tighten the sensor to 15 ft. lbs. (20 Nm). Connect the ECT electrical connector.
8. To complete installation, reverse removal procedure. Fill the cooling system.

5.3L Engine
See Figure 122.

→ Use care when handling the coolant sensor. Damage to the coolant sensor will affect the operation of the fuel control system.

1. Drain the cooling system below the level of the engine coolant temperature (ECT) sensor.
2. Disconnect the ECT sensor electrical connector.
3. Remove the ECT sensor.

→ Replacement components must be the correct part number for the application. Components requiring the use of the thread locking compound, lubri-

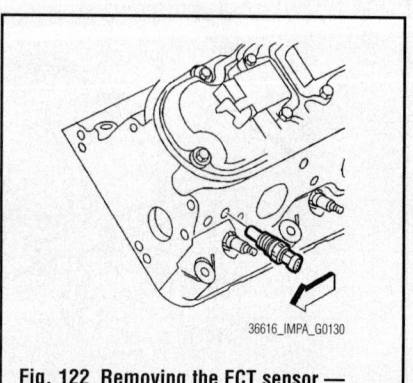
36616_IMPA_G0130

Fig. 122 Removing the ECT sensor — 5.3L Engines

cants, corrosion inhibitors, or sealants are identified in the service procedure. Some replacement components may come with these coatings already applied. Do not use these coatings on components unless specified. These coatings can affect the final torque, which may affect the operation of the component. Use the correct torque specification when installing components in order to avoid damage.

→ Use care when handling the coolant sensor. Damage to the coolant sensor will affect the operation of the fuel control system.

4. To install, coat the threads with sealer GM P/N 12346004 (Canadian P/N 10953480) or equivalent.

5. Install the ECT sensor. Tighten the sensor to 15 ft. lbs. (20 Nm). Connect the ECT electrical connector.

6. Fill the cooling system.

EVAPORATIVE EMISSIONS (EVAP) CANISTER

LOCATION

The Evaporative Emissions (EVAP) Canister is located on the fuel tank.

REMOVAL & INSTALLATION

See Figures 123 through 125.

✳✳ CAUTION

Observe all applicable safety precautions when working around fuel. Whenever servicing the fuel system, always work in a well ventilated area. Do not allow fuel spray or vapors to come in contact with a spark or open flame. Keep a dry chemical fire extinguisher near the

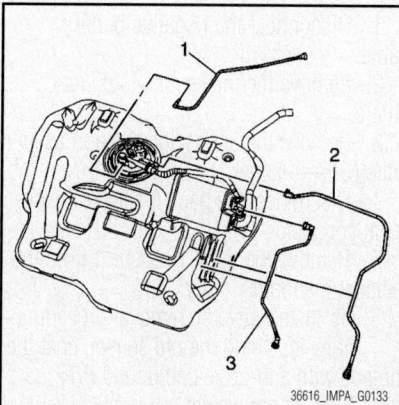

Fig. 123 Disconnecting the EVAP line (3) from the canister

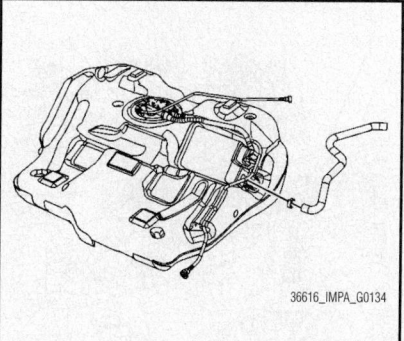

Fig. 124 Removing the EVAP canister hose

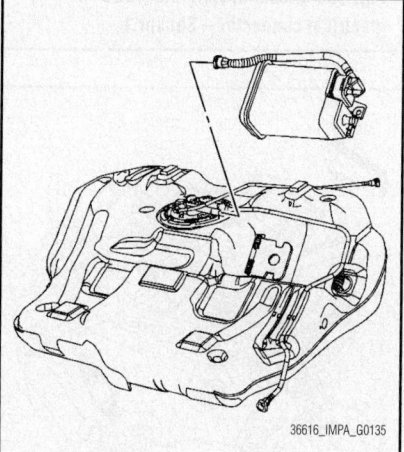

Fig. 125 Disconnecting the EVAP line from the from the fuel sender and remove the EVAP canister

work area. Always keep fuel in a container specifically designed for fuel storage; also, always properly seal fuel containers to avoid the possibility of fire or explosion.

✳✳ CAUTION

Do not attempt to straighten kinked nylon pipes. Replace any kinked nylon pipes in order to prevent damage to the vehicle. Do not attempt to repair sections of nylon pipes. Replace damaged nylon pipes. Replace the vapor pipes with original equipment or parts that meet GM specifications. Replace the vapor hoses with original equipment or parts meeting GM specifications. Use only reinforced fuel resistant hose identified with the word Fluoroelastomer or GM 6163M on the hose.

1. Disconnect the negative battery cable.

2. Remove the fuel tank.

3. Disconnect the EVAP line from the canister.

4. Reposition the EVAP canister hose clamp

5. Remove the EVAP canister hose.

6. Disconnect the canister EVAP line from the fuel sender.

7. Squeeze the small retainer in front of the canister in order to disengage the canister.

8. Remove the EVAP canister.

HEATED OXYGEN SENSOR (HO2S)

LOCATION

To locate the Heated Oxygen Sensors (HO2S), refer to the illustrations below.

REMOVAL & INSTALLATION

✳✳ CAUTION

Do not remove the pigtail from either the Heated Oxygen Sensor (HO2S) or the Oxygen Sensor (O2S). Removing the pigtail or the connector will affect sensor operation. Handle the oxygen sensor carefully. Do not drop the HO2S. Keep the in-line electrical connector and the louvered end free of grease, dirt, or other contaminants. Do not use cleaning solvents of any type. Do not repair the wiring, connector or terminals. Replace the oxygen sensor if the pigtail wiring, connector, or terminal is damaged. This external clean air reference is obtained by way of the oxygen sensor signal and heater wires. Any attempt to repair the wires, connectors, or terminals could result in the obstruction of the air reference and degraded sensor performance.

✳✳ CAUTION

The following guidelines should be used when servicing the heated oxygen sensor:

- Do not apply contact cleaner or other materials to the sensor or vehicle harness connectors. These materials may get into the sensor causing poor performance.
- Do not damage the sensor pigtail and harness wires in such a way that the wires inside are exposed. This could provide a path for foreign materials to enter

the sensor and cause performance problems.

- Ensure the sensor or vehicle lead wires are not bent sharply or kinked. Sharp bends or kinks could block the reference air path through the lead wire.
- Do not remove or defeat the oxygen sensor ground wire, where applicable. Vehicles that utilize the ground wired sensor may rely on this ground as the only ground contact to the sensor. Removal of the ground wire will cause poor engine performance.
- Ensure that the peripheral seal remains intact on the vehicle harness connector in order to prevent damage due to water intrusion. The engine harness may be repaired using Packard's Crimp and Splice Seals Terminal Repair Kit. Under no circumstances should repairs be soldered since this could result in the air reference being obstructed.

➡ A special anti-seize compound is used on the HO2S threads. The compound consists of liquid graphite and glass beads. The graphite tends to burn away, but the glass beads remain, making the sensor easier to remove. New or service replacement sensors already have the compound applied to the threads. If the sensor is removed from an exhaust component and if for any reason the sensor is to be reinstalled, the threads must have anti-seize compound applied before reinstallation.

3.5L & 3.9L Engines

Sensor 1

See Figures 126 and 127.

1. Disconnect the negative battery cable.
2. Remove the CPA retainer.
3. Disconnect the HO2S electrical connector.
4. Remove the oxygen sensor electrical connector from the ignition coil bracket.
5. Remove the HO2S from the exhaust manifold.
6. To install, reverse removal procedure.
7. If re-installing the old sensor, coat the threads with anti-seize compound P/N 12377953, or equivalent.
8. Tighten the sensor to 31 ft. lbs. (42 Nm).

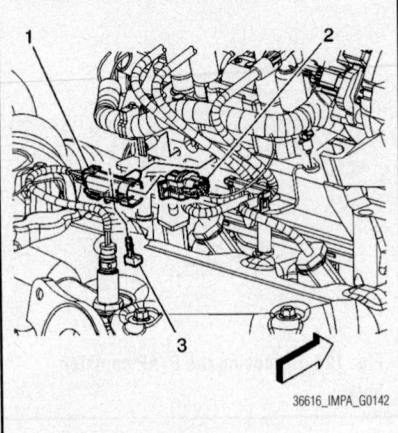

Fig. 126 Disconnecting the HO2S electrical connector – Sensor 1

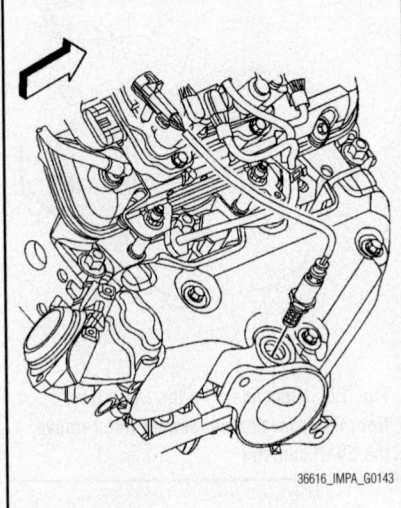

Fig. 127 Removing the HO2S from the exhaust manifold

Sensor 2

See Figures 128 and 129.

1. Disconnect the negative battery cable.
2. Raise and support the vehicle.
3. Remove the Connector Position Assurance (CPA) retainer.
4. Disconnect the Heated Oxygen Sensor (HO2S) electrical connector.
5. Remove the HO2S electrical connector clip from the heat shield.
6. Remove the HO2S from the catalytic converter.
7. To install, reverse removal procedure.
8. If re-installing the old sensor, coat the threads with anti-seize compound P/N 12377953, or equivalent.
9. Tighten the sensor to 31 ft. lbs. (42 Nm).

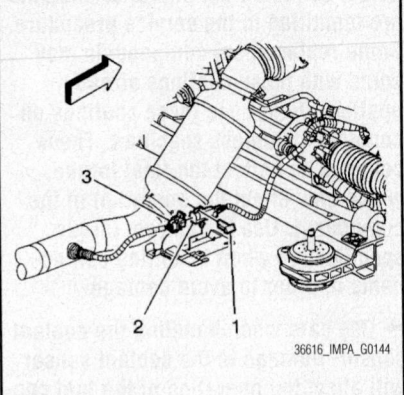

Fig. 128 Removing the CPA retainer (1) and Disconnecting the HO2S electrical connector (3) — Sensor 2

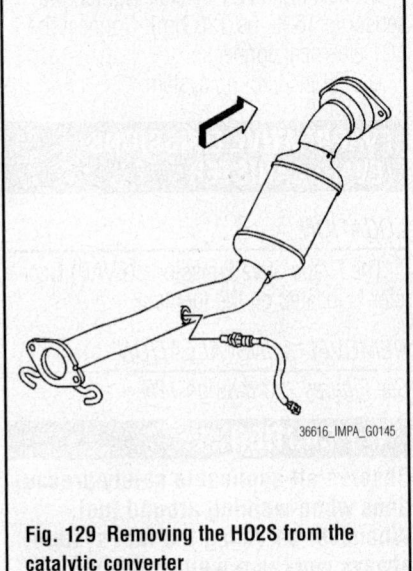

Fig. 129 Removing the HO2S from the catalytic converter

5.3L Engines

Bank 1, Sensor 1

See Figures 130 and 131.

1. Disconnect the negative battery cable.
2. Remove the intake manifold sight shield.
3. Remove the connector position assurance (CPA) retainer.
4. Disconnect the bank 1 sensor 1 electrical connector.
5. Remove the bank 1 sensor 1 from the exhaust manifold.
6. To install, reverse removal procedure.
7. If re-installing the old sensor, coat the threads with anti-seize compound P/N 12377953, or equivalent.
8. Tighten the sensor to 31 ft. lbs. (42 Nm).

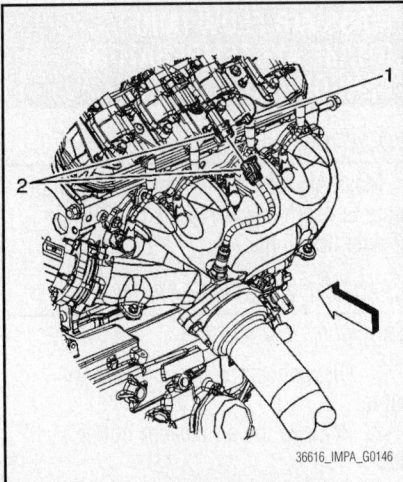

Fig. 130 Removing the CPA retainer (1) and Disconnecting the HO2S electrical connector (2) — Bank 1, Sensor 1

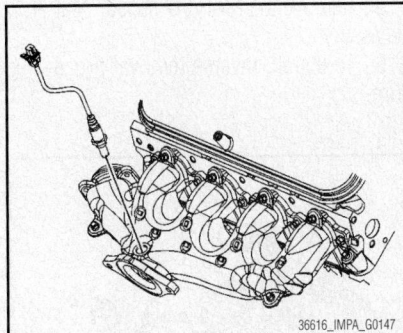

Fig. 131 Removing the HO2S from the exhaust manifold — Bank 1, Sensor 1

Bank 1, Sensor 2

See Figures 132 and 133.

1. Disconnect the negative battery cable.
2. Remove the CPA retainer.
3. Disconnect the bank 2 sensor 2 electrical connector

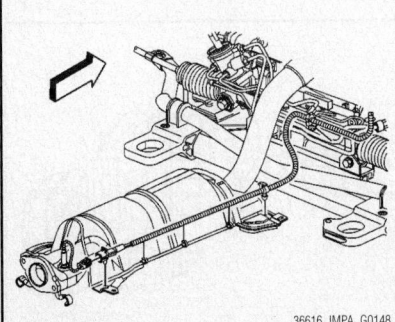

Fig. 132 Removing the CPA retainer and Disconnecting the HO2S electrical connector — Bank 1, Sensor 2

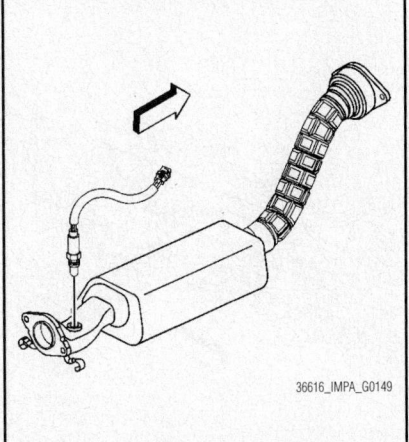

Fig. 133 Removing the HO2S from the exhaust manifold — Bank 1, Sensor 2

4. Remove the bank 2 sensor 2 from the catalytic converter.
5. To install, reverse removal procedure.
6. If re-installing the old sensor, coat the threads with anti-seize compound P/N 12377953, or equivalent.
7. Tighten the sensor to 31 ft. lbs. (42 Nm).

INTAKE AIR TEMPERATURE (IAT) SENSOR

LOCATION

The Intake Air Temperature (IAT) Sensor is integrated with the Mass Airflow Sensor (MAF).

REMOVAL & INSTALLATION

To remove and install the IAT sensor, refer to the MAF sensor.

KNOCK SENSOR (KS)

LOCATION

Refer to the illustrations below to locate the Knock Sensor (KS)

REMOVAL & INSTALLATION

3.5L & 3.9L Engines

See Figures 134 through 137.

1. Disconnect the negative battery cable.
2. Raise and support the vehicle.
3. Disconnect the left knock sensor electrical connector.
4. Loosen and remove the knock sensor.
5. To install, reverse removal procedure.

➡ **DO NOT apply thread sealant to the sensor threads. The sensor threads**

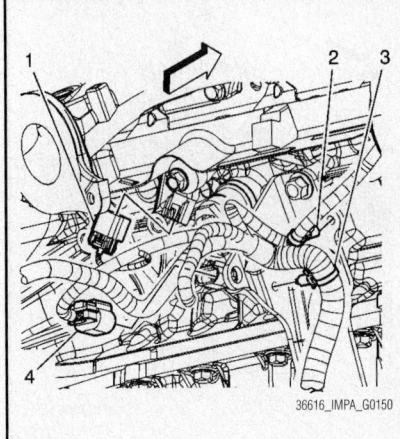

Fig. 134 Disconnecting the left knock sensor electrical connector (1) — Bank 1

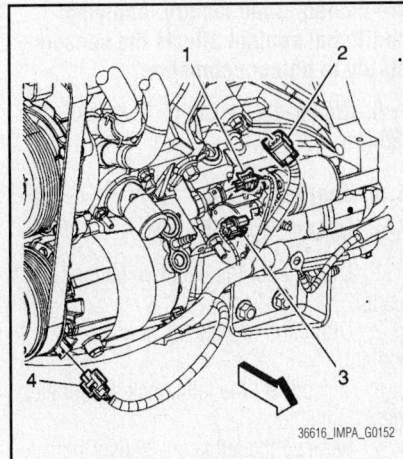

Fig. 135 Disconnecting the right knock sensor electrical connector (2) — Bank 2

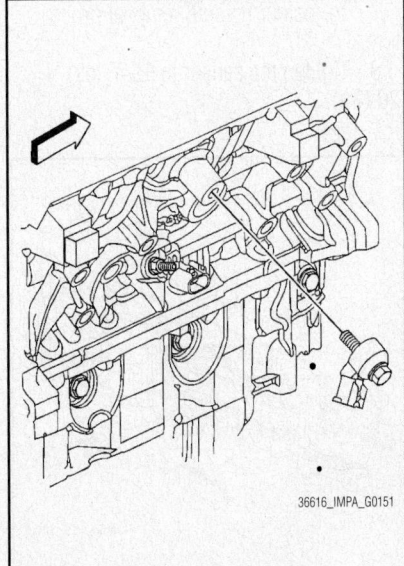

Fig. 136 Removing the left knock sensor — Bank 1

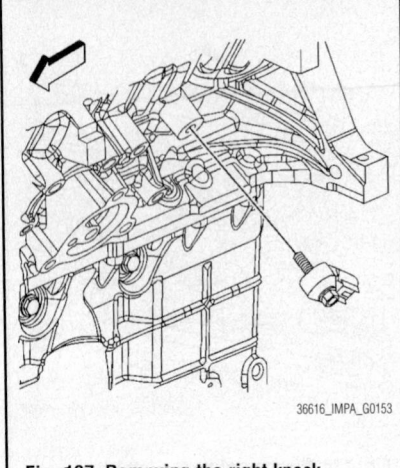

Fig. 137 Removing the right knock sensor — Bank 2

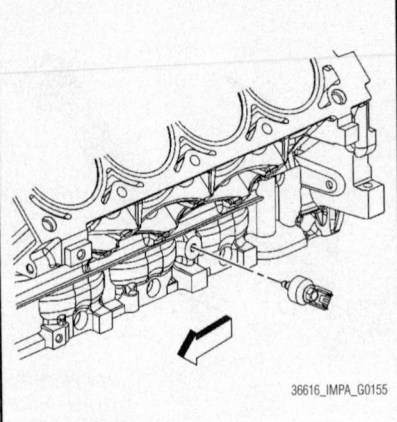

Fig. 139 Removing the left knock sensor — 5.3L Engine

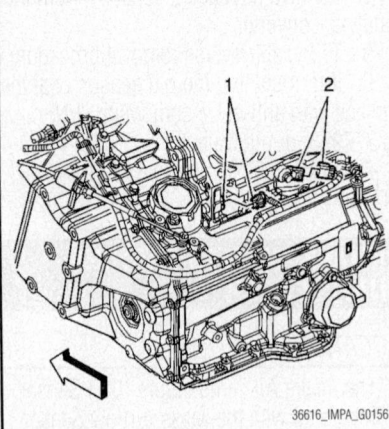

Fig. 140 Disconnecting the right knock sensor electrical connector (2) — 5.3L Engine

are coated at the factory. Applying additional sealant affects the sensors ability to detect detonation.

6. Tighten the sensor to 18 ft. lbs. (25 Nm).

5.3L Engines

See Figures 138 through 141.

1. Disconnect the negative battery cable.
2. Drain and recycle the engine coolant.
3. Disconnect the left knock sensor electrical connector.
4. Remove the left knock sensor bolt.
5. Disconnect the right knock sensor electrical connector.
6. Remove the right knock sensor and bolt.
7. To install, reverse removal procedure.
8. Tighten the sensor to 15 ft. lbs. (20 Nm).

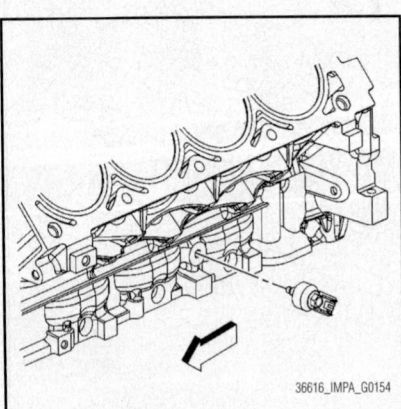

Fig. 138 Disconnecting the left knock sensor electrical connector — 5.3L Engine

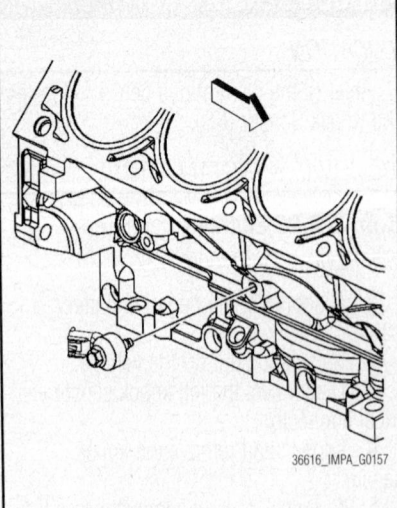

Fig. 141 Removing the right knock sensor — 5.3L Engine

MASS AIR FLOW (MAF)/ INTAKE AIR TEMPERATURE SENSOR (IAT)

LOCATION

Mass Air Flow (MAF)/ Intake Air Temperature Sensor (IAT) are located on the air cleaner housing.

REMOVAL & INSTALLATION

See Figures 142 and 143.

1. Disconnect the negative battery cable.
2. Remove the air cleaner outlet duct.
3. Disconnect the Mass Air Flow (MAF)/Intake Air Temperature (IAT) sensor electrical connector.
4. Remove the MAF/IAT sensor and bolts from the housing.
5. Remove the MAF/IAT sensor seal, if necessary.
6. To install, reverse removal procedure.

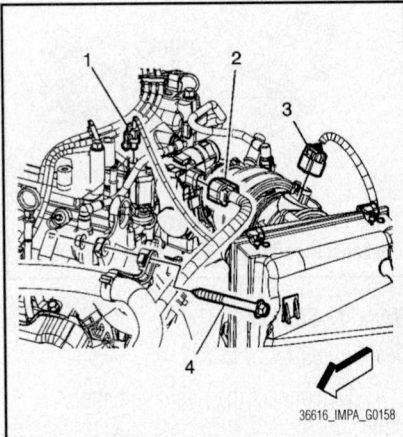

Fig. 142 Disconnecting the Mass Air Flow (MAF)/Intake Air Temperature (IAT) sensor electrical connector (3)

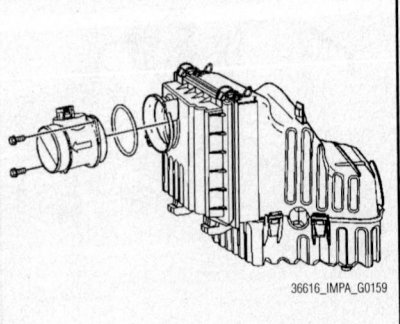

Fig. 143 Removing the MAF/IAT sensor and bolts from the housing

MANIFOLD ABSOLUTE PRESSURE (MAP) SENSOR

REMOVAL & INSTALLATION

3.5L & 3.9L Engines

See Figures 144 and 145.

1. Disconnect the negative battery cable.
2. Remove the intake manifold cover.
3. Disconnect the MAP sensor electrical connector.
4. Remove the spark plug wire clip from the intake manifold bracket, if necessary.

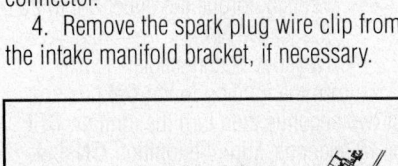
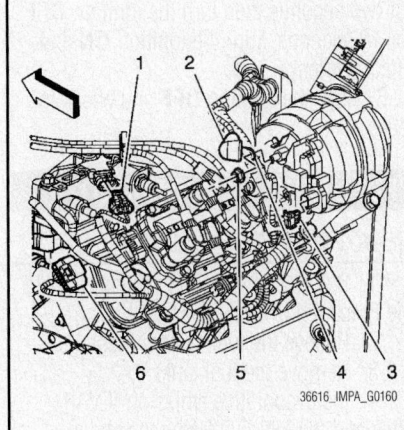

Fig. 144 Disconnect the MAP sensor electrical connector (1)

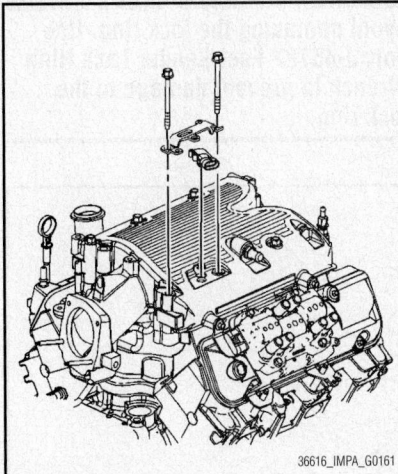

Fig. 145 Removing the MAP sensor and bracket

5. Remove the upper intake manifold bolts.
6. Remove the MAP sensor and bracket.
7. Remove the MAP sensor seal from the upper intake manifold.
8. To install, reverse removal procedure.
9. Tighten the upper intake manifold bolts to 18 ft. lbs. (25 Nm).

5.3L Engines

See Figures 146 and 147.

1. Disconnect the negative battery cable.
2. Remove the engine sight shield.

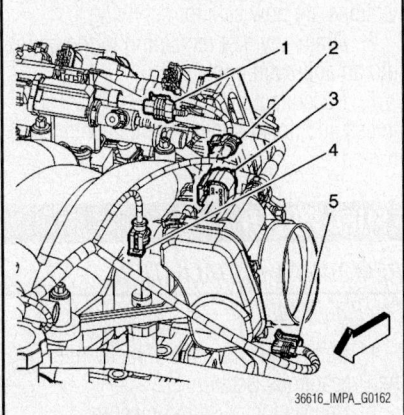

Fig. 146 Disconnect the MAP sensor electrical connector (2) — 5.3L Engines

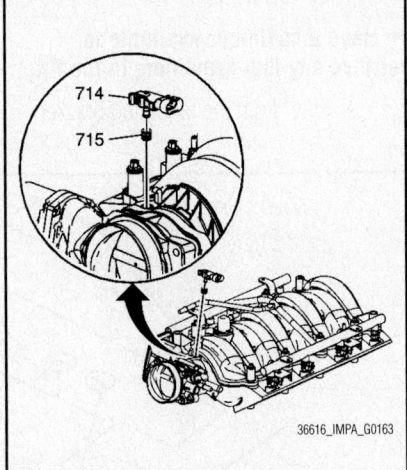

Fig. 147 Removing the MAP sensor (714) and grommet (715) — 5.3L Engines

3. Disconnect the MAP sensor electrical connector.
4. Remove the MAP sensor from the intake manifold.
5. Remove the MAP sensor grommet, if required.
6. To install, reverse removal procedure.
7. Lubricate the MAP sensor grommet with clean engine oil.

THROTTLE POSITION SENSOR (TPS)

LOCATION

The Throttle Position Sensor (TPS) is located in the throttle body.

REMOVAL & INSTALLATION

Refer to Throttle Body for removal and installation.

VEHICLE SPEED SENSOR (VSS)

REMOVAL & INSTALLATION

See Figure 148.

1. Remove the transmission.
2. Position the transmission so that the VSS is facing up
3. Remove the VSS bolt.
4. Remove the VSS.
5. To install, reverse removal procedure.

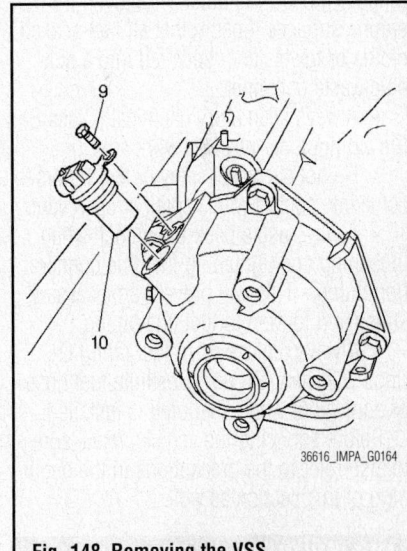

Fig. 148 Removing the VSS

FUEL SYSTEM SERVICE PRECAUTIONS

Safety is the most important factor when performing not only fuel system maintenance but any type of maintenance. Failure to conduct maintenance and repairs in a safe manner may result in serious personal injury or death. Maintenance and testing of the vehicle's fuel system components can be accomplished safely and effectively by adhering to the following rules and guidelines.

- To avoid the possibility of fire and personal injury, always disconnect the negative battery cable unless the repair or test procedure requires that battery voltage be applied.
- Always relieve the fuel system pressure prior to disconnecting any fuel system component (injector, fuel rail, pressure regulator, etc.), fitting or fuel line connection. Exercise extreme caution whenever relieving fuel system pressure to avoid exposing skin, face and eyes to fuel spray. Please be advised that fuel under pressure may penetrate the skin or any part of the body that it contacts.
- Always place a shop towel or cloth around the fitting or connection prior to loosening to absorb any excess fuel due to spillage. Ensure that all fuel spillage (should it occur) is quickly removed from engine surfaces. Ensure that all fuel soaked cloths or towels are deposited into a suitable waste container.
- Always keep a dry chemical (Class B) fire extinguisher near the work area.
- Do not allow fuel spray or fuel vapors to come into contact with a spark or open flame.
- Always use a back-up wrench when loosening and tightening fuel line connection fittings. This will prevent unnecessary stress and torsion to fuel line piping.
- Always replace worn fuel fitting O-rings with new. Do not substitute fuel hose or equivalent where fuel pipe is installed.

Before servicing the vehicle, make sure to also refer to the precautions in the beginning of this section as well.

RELIEVING FUEL SYSTEM PRESSURE

1. Before servicing the vehicle, refer to the Precautions Section.
2. Disconnect the negative battery cable to prevent possible discharge of fuel if an accidental attempt is made to start the engine.

3. Loosen the fuel filler cap to relieve tank pressure.
4. This procedure calls for a fuel pressure test gauge with a line equipped with a fitting to connect to the to the fuel pressure test connection and another hose to discharge into an approved gasoline container. Wrap a shop towel around the pressure test fitting connection while connecting gauge to avoid spillage.
5. Install the bleed hose into an approved container and open the valve to bleed fuel system pressure. The fuel connections are now safe for servicing.
6. Drain any fuel remaining in the gauge into an approved container.
7. Reconnect the negative battery cable unless additional service work is being performed.

FUEL FILTER

REMOVAL & INSTALLATION

See Figure 149.

1. Before servicing the vehicle, refer to the Precautions Section.
2. Relieve fuel system pressure.
3. Remove or disconnect the following:
- Quick-connect fitting at the inlet of the fuel filter
- Threaded fitting at the outlet side of the fuel filter.

➡ **Have a container available to retrieve any fuel remaining in the filter.**

- Filter from the mounting bracket

To install:

4. Install or connect the following:
- Fuel filter into the mounting bracket and torque the bolt to 15 ft. lbs. (20 Nm)
- Quick-connect fitting on the inlet side of the filter
- Threaded fitting to the outlet side of the filter and using a back up wrench, torque the outlet nut to 22 ft. lbs. (30 Nm)
- Negative battery cable
5. Turn the ignition to the **ON** position for two seconds then turn the ignition **OFF** for 10 seconds. Turn the ignition **ON** and check for leaks.
6. Turn the ignition **OFF** and check for leaks.

FUEL LEVEL SENDING UNIT

REMOVAL & INSTALLATION

1. Before servicing the vehicle, refer to the Precautions Section.
2. Relieve the fuel system pressure.
3. Remove the fuel tank.
4. the evaporative emission (EVAP) lines and the fuel line from the sender.
5. Reposition the fuel feed and EVAP lines in order to access the lock ring.

✳✳ CAUTION

Avoid damaging the lock ring. Use only J-45722 Fuel Sender Lock Ring Wrench to prevent damage to the lock ring.

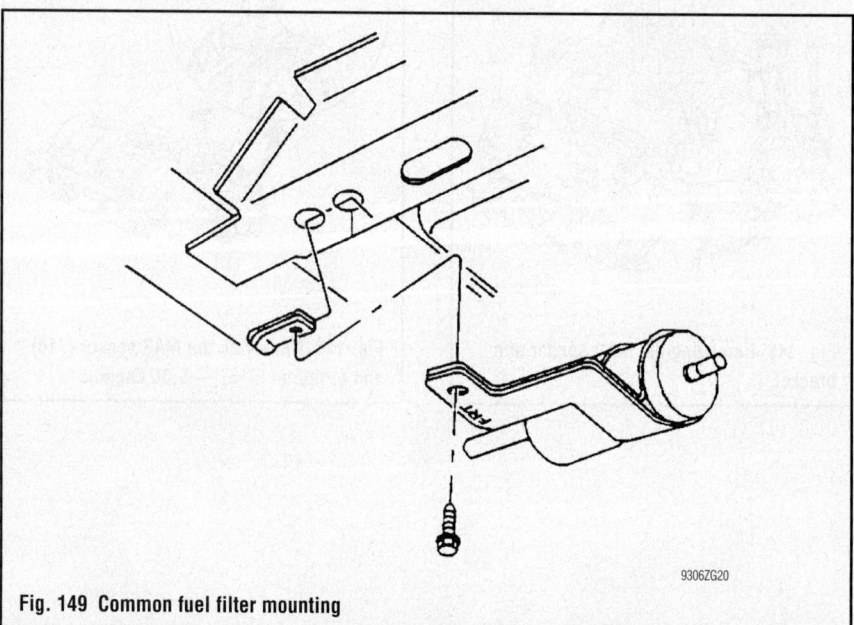

9306ZG20

Fig. 149 Common fuel filter mounting

Do Not handle the fuel sender assembly by the fuel pipes. The amount of leverage generated by handling the fuel pipes could damage the joints.

➡ **Do NOT use impact tools. Significant force will be required to release the lock ring. The use of a hammer and screwdriver is not recommended. Secure the fuel tank in order to prevent fuel tank rotation.**

6. Use the J 45722 and a long breaker-bar in order to unlock the fuel sender lock ring. Turn the fuel sender lock ring in a counterclockwise direction.

7. Remove the fuel sender from the fuel tank.

8. Remove and discard the fuel sender O-ring seal.

9. Clean and inspect the fuel sender assembly O-ring seal sealing surfaces.

➡ **Some lock ring were manufactured with DO NOT REUSE stamped into them. These lock rings may be reused if they are not damaged or warped.**

➡ **Inspect the lock ring for damage due to improper removal or installation procedures. If damage is found, install a NEW lock ring.**

➡ **Check the lock ring for flatness.**

10. Place the lock ring on a flat surface. Measure the clearance between to lock ring and the flat surface using a feeler gage at 7 points.

11. If the warpage is less than 0.41 mm (0.016 in), the lock ring does not require replacement.

12. If the warpage is greater than 0.41 mm (0.016 in), the lock ring must be replaced.

To install:

13. Position the NEW fuel sender O-ring seal onto the fuel tank.

14. Install the fuel sender (2) into the fuel tank. Ensure that the align tab is in the proper location.

15. Push down the fuel sender and position the lock ring (1) onto the fuel tank.

➡ **Always replace the fuel sender seal when installing the fuel sender assembly. Replace the lock ring if necessary. Do not apply any type of lubrication in the seal groove. Ensure the lock ring is installed with the correct side facing upward. A correctly installed lock ring will only turn in a clockwise direction.**

16. Use the J 45722 in order to install the fuel sender lock ring. Turn the fuel sender lock ring in a clockwise direction.

17. Connect the fuel line and the EVAP lines to the sender.

18. Install the fuel tank.

FUEL PUMP

REMOVAL & INSTALLATION

See Figures 150 and 151.

1. Before servicing the vehicle, refer to the Precautions Section.

2. Relieve the fuel system pressure.

3. Drain the fuel tank with a hand held siphon until the level is less than ¼ full.

4. Remove or disconnect the following:
   - Negative battery cable
   - Spare tire and jack
   - Floor trunk liner by pulling it back
   - Fuel sender access panel
   - Fuel tank pressure sensor electrical connector
   - Fuel sender electrical connector
   - Fuel sender assembly quick connect fittings
   - Retaining lock-ring from the fuel sender

When the lock-ring is removed from the fuel sender, the sender assembly will spring up. Downward pressure should be kept on the assembly and slowly released to ensure the sender assembly does not get damaged.

   - Modular fuel sender assembly

To install:

5. Install or connect the following:
   - New O-ring on the fuel tank
   - Fuel sender
   - Lockring on the fuel sender
   - Fuel sender electrical connector
   - Fuel tank pressure sensor electrical connector
   - Quick connect fittings at the fuel sender
   - Negative battery cable

6. Add a small amount of fuel to the fuel tank.

7. Turn the ignition to the **ON** position for 2 seconds then turn the ignition **OFF** for 10 seconds. Turn the ignition **ON** and check for leaks.

8. Turn the ignition **OFF** and check for leaks.

9. Install or connect the following:
   - Fuel sender access panel and torque the nuts to 89 inch lbs. (10 Nm)
   - Trunk liner
   - Spare tire, jack and spare tire cover

10. Refill the fuel tank.

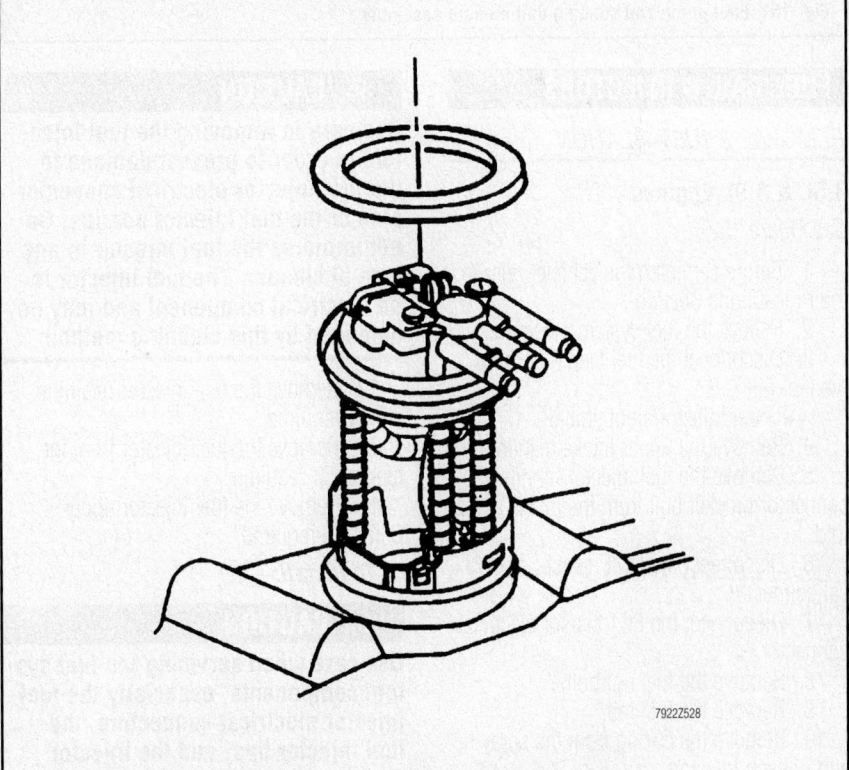

79222528

Fig. 150 Remove the fuel pump from the tank after removing the locking ring

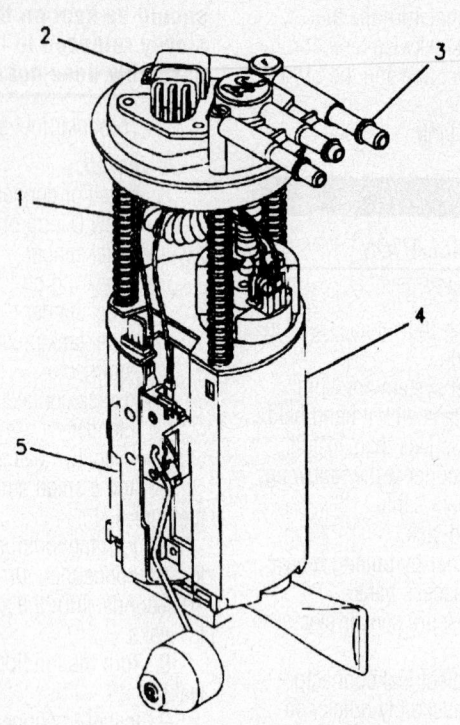

1 SUPPORT ASSEMBLY – FUEL SENDER
2 COVER ASSEMBLY – FUEL SENDER
3 FUEL PIPES (ABOVE COVER)
4 RESERVOIR – FUEL PUMP FUEL
5 SENSOR ASSEMBLY – FUEL LEVEL

7922XG19

Fig. 151 Fuel pump and sending unit module assembly

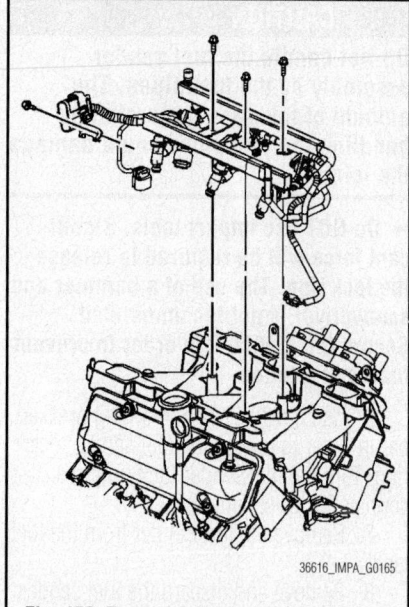

36616_IMPA_G0165

Fig. 152 Removing the fuel rail and injector assembly

FUEL RAIL & INJECTORS

REMOVAL & INSTALLATION

3.5L & 3.9L Engines

See Figure 152.

1. Before servicing the vehicle, refer to the Precautions Section.
2. Relieve the fuel system pressure.
3. Disconnect the fuel feed pipe from the fuel rail
   • Fuel injector sight shield
4. Remove the upper intake manifold
5. Remove the fuel injector harness connector bracket bolt from the intake manifold.
6. Disconnect the CMP sensor electrical connector.
7. Disconnect the ECT sensor electrical connector.
8. Remove the fuel rail bolts.
9. Remove the fuel rail.
10. Remove the O-ring from the spray tip end of each injector.
11. Discard the O-rings if damaged.

✳✳ CAUTION

Use care in removing the fuel injectors in order to prevent damage to the fuel injector electrical connector pins or the fuel injector nozzles. Do not immerse the fuel injector in any type of cleaner. The fuel injector is an electrical component and may be damaged by this cleaning method

12. Remove the fuel injector retaining clip, if required.
13. Remove the fuel injector from the fuel rail, if required.
14. Remove the fuel injector upper O-ring, if required.

To install:

✳✳ CAUTION

Use care when servicing the fuel system components, especially the fuel injector electrical connectors, the fuel injector tips, and the injector O-rings. Plug the inlet and the outlet

ports of the fuel rail in order to prevent contamination.

✳✳ CAUTION

Do not use compressed air to clean the fuel rail assembly as this may damage the fuel rail components.

✳✳ CAUTION

Do not immerse the fuel rail assembly in a solvent bath in order to prevent damage to the fuel rail assembly.

➡ Ensure to use the correct part number when ordering the replacement fuel injectors.

15. Coat the new fuel injector O-rings with clean engine oil.
16. Install or connect the following:
    • Lower backup O-ring
    • Upper O-ring
    • Lower O-ring
    • Fuel injector
    • Fuel injector retaining clips
    • Fuel rail and torque the bolts to 7 ft. lbs. (10 Nm) if equipped with bolt retainers. If equipped with snap-lock tab retainers, push down until the retainers snap into place.
    • Fuel injector electrical connectors
    • Ignition coil wires to the coil
    • Fuel pressure regulator vacuum connection

- Fuel feed and return lines
- Negative battery cable

17. Start the vehicle and check for leaks, repair if necessary.

18. Install the fuel injector sight shield and torque the nuts to 27 inch lbs. (3 Nm).

5.3L Engine

See Figure 153.

1. Before servicing the vehicle, refer to the Precautions Section.

➡ **Clean the fuel and evaporative emission (EVAP) connections and surrounding areas prior to disconnecting the lines in order to avoid possible system contamination.**

2. Relieve the fuel system pressure.

3. Remove the air cleaner outlet duct.

4. Disconnect the following electrical connectors:

- EVAP purge solenoid
- Manifold absolute pressure (MAP) sensor
- Electronic throttle control (ETC)
- Oil pressure sensor
- Valve lifter oil manifold

5. Disconnect the generator electrical connector.

6. Remove the connector position assurance (CPA) retainer.

7. Disconnect the main ignition coil harness electrical connector.

➡ **Mark the injector connectors to their corresponding injectors to ensure correct reassembly.**

8. Disconnect the fuel injector electrical connectors.

9. Remove the CPA retainer.

10. Disconnect the main ignition coil harness electrical connector.

➡ **Mark the injector connectors to their corresponding injectors to ensure correct reassembly.**

11. Disconnect the fuel injector electrical connectors.

12. Remove the engine wiring harness retainers from the tabs on the fuel rail.

13. Reposition the harness out of the way.

14. Disconnect the fuel feed and EVAP lines.

15. Note the location of the fuel rail ground strap.

16. Remove the intake manifold bolt and ground strap.

17. Remove the fuel rail bolts.

18. Remove the fuel rail with injectors.

Lift evenly on both sides of the fuel rail until all injectors have been removed from their bores.

➡ **Do not separate the fuel injectors from the fuel rail unless component service is required.**

19. Remove the fuel injector retaining clip, as required.

20. Remove the fuel injector, as required.

21. Remove and discard the fuel injector O-ring seals, as required.

To install:

➡ **Do not reuse the fuel injector O-ring seals. Install NEW O-ring seals during assembly.**

22. Note the installed location of the fuel rail ground strap.

23. Lubricate the NEW O-ring seals with clean engine oil.

24. Install the NEW fuel injector O-ring seals (532, 534) onto the injector, as required.

25. Install the fuel injector (533), as required

26. Install the fuel injector retaining clip (521), as required.

27. If necessary, lubricate the NEW O-ring seals with clean engine oil.

28. If necessary, install NEW O-ring seals to the fuel injectors.

29. Install the fuel rail (510) with injectors. Push firmly on both sides of the rail until all the injectors have been seated into their bores.

30. Apply a 0.2 in. (5mm) band of threadlock GM P/N 12345382 (Canadian P/N 10953489) or equivalent to the threads of the fuel rail bolts.

31. Install the fuel rail bolts. Tighten the bolts to 89 inch lbs. (10 Nm).

32. Install the ground strap and intake manifold bolt. Tighten the bolt to 89 inch lbs. (10 Nm).

33. Connect the fuel feed and EVAP lines.

34. Position the harness to the engine. Install the engine wiring harness retainers to the tabs on the fuel rail.

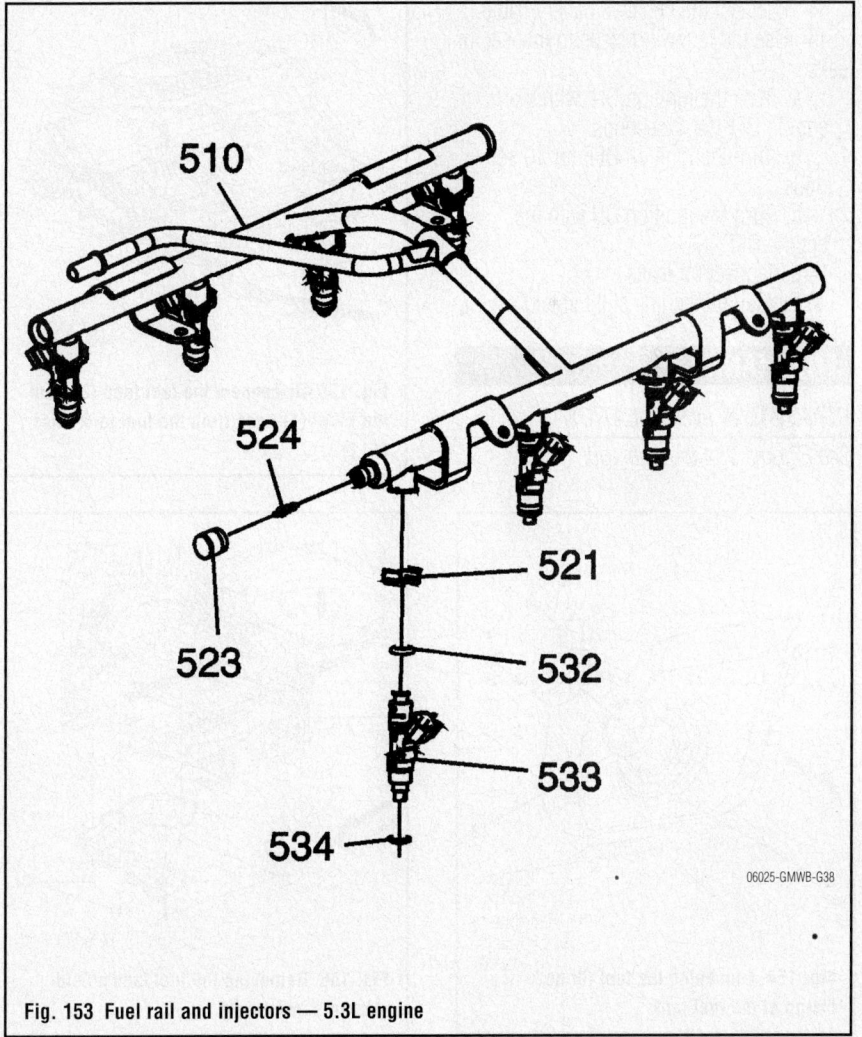

Fig. 153 Fuel rail and injectors — 5.3L engine

06025-GMWB-G38

➡ **Install the marked injector connectors to their corresponding injectors.**

35. Connect the fuel injector electrical connectors.

36. Connect the main ignition coil harness electrical connector.

37. Install the CPA retainer.

➡ **Install the marked injector connectors to their corresponding injectors.**

38. Connect the fuel injector electrical connectors.

39. Connect the main ignition coil harness electrical connector.

40. Install the CPA retainer.

41. Connect the generator electrical connector.

42. Connect the following electrical connectors:

- EVAP purge solenoid
- MAP sensor
- ETC
- Oil pressure sensor
- Valve lifter oil manifold

43. Install the air cleaner outlet duct.

44. Connect the negative battery cable.

45. Use the following steps to inspect for leaks:

a. Turn the ignition ON, with the engine OFF, for 2 seconds.

b. Turn the ignition OFF for 10 seconds.

c. Turn the ignition ON with the engine OFF.

d. Inspect for leaks.

46. Install the engine sight shield.

FUEL TANK

REMOVAL & INSTALLATION

See Figures 154 through 160.

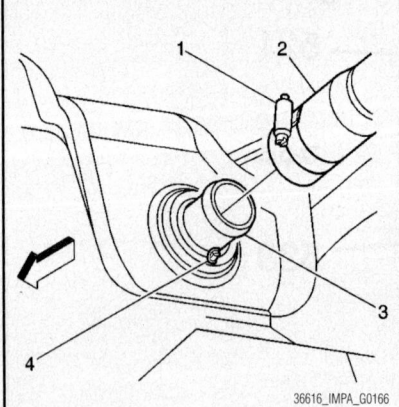

Fig. 154 Loosening the fuel fill hose clamp at the fuel tank

✳✳ **CAUTION**

Clean the fuel and evaporative emission (EVAP) connections and surrounding areas prior to disconnecting the lines in order to avoid possible system contamination.

1. Relieve the fuel system fuel pressure.

2. Drain the fuel tank.

3. Raise and support the vehicle.

4. Loosen the fuel fill hose clamp at the fuel tank.

5. Remove the fuel tank fill hose from the fuel tank.

6. Disconnect the EVAP vent solenoid hose on the tank from the EVAP vent valve solenoid hose.

7. Disconnect the EVAP vent pipe quick connect fitting from the fill pipe EVAP vent pipe quick connect fitting.

8. Disconnect the fuel feed, and the EVAP lines from the fuel tank lines.

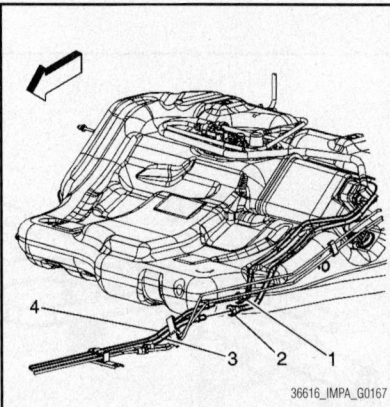

Fig. 155 Disconnect the fuel feed (3), and the EVAP (4) lines from the fuel tank lines (1, 2)

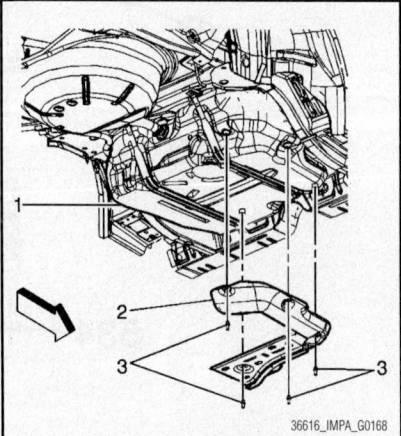

Fig. 156 Removing the fuel tank shield retainers and shield

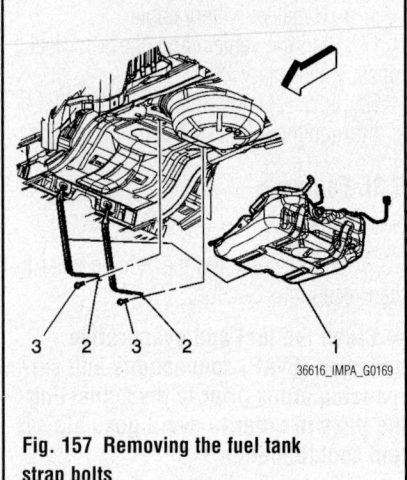

Fig. 157 Removing the fuel tank strap bolts

9. Support the exhaust system.

10. Remove the rubber exhaust pipe hangers in order to allow the exhaust system to drop slightly.

11. Remove the fuel tank shield retainers.

12. Remove the fuel tank shield.

➡ **Do not bend the fuel tank straps as this may damage the straps.**

13. Support the fuel tank with a suitable adjustable jack.

✳✳ **CAUTION**

Do not bend the fuel tank straps as this may damage the straps.

14. Remove the fuel tank strap bolts.

15. Using the jack, lower the fuel tank.

16. Disconnect the fuel sender jumper harness electrical connector.

17. Remove the fuel tank and place the tank in a suitable work area.

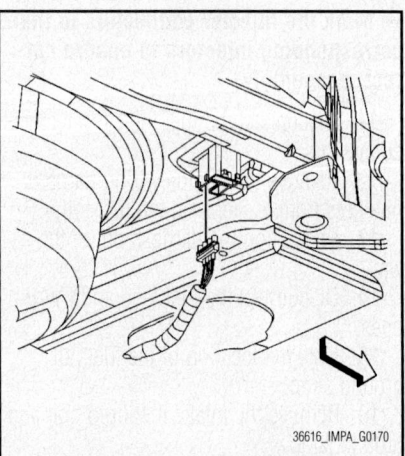

Fig. 158 Disconnecting the fuel sender jumper harness electrical connector

18. Disconnect and remove the fuel pressure sensor and fuel sender jumper harness electrical connectors.

❈❈ CAUTION

Note the routing of the lines for installation.

19. Disconnect and remove the fuel feed line and the EVAP lines.
20. Remove the EVAP canister.
21. Remove the insulator pads from the fuel tank. Note the location of the insulator pads for installation.

To install:

➡ **Do not attempt to straighten kinked nylon pipes. Replace any kinked nylon pipes in order to prevent damage to the vehicle. Do not attempt to repair sections of nylon pipes. Replace damaged nylon pipes. Replace the vapor pipes with original equipment or parts that**

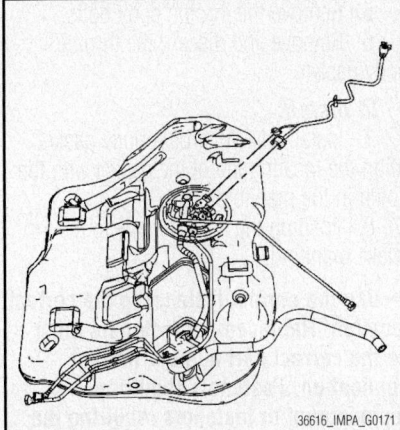

36616_IMPA_G0171

Fig. 159 Disconnecting and removing the fuel pressure sensor and fuel sender jumper harness electrical connectors

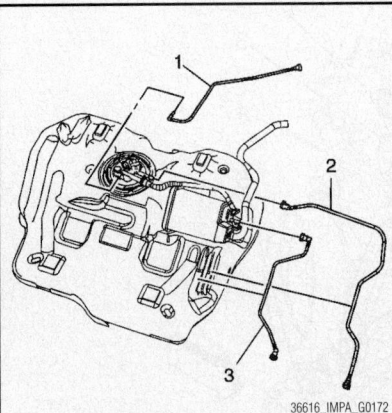

36616_IMPA_G0172

Fig. 160 Disconnect and remove the fuel feed line (3) and the EVAP lines (1, 2)

meet GM specifications. Replace the vapor hoses with original equipment or parts meeting GM specifications. Use only reinforced fuel-resistant hose identified with the word Fluoroelastomer or GM 6163M on the hose.

22. Install the insulator pads to the fuel tank.
23. Install the EVAP canister.
24. Install and connect the fuel feed line and the EVAP lines.
25. Install and connect the fuel pressure sensor and fuel sender jumper harness electrical connectors.
26. Install the fuel tank onto a suitable jack.
27. Partially raise the fuel tank until the electrical connections can be made.
28. Connect the fuel sender jumper harness electrical connector.
29. Completely raise the tank.

➡ **Use the correct fastener in the correct location. Replacement fasteners must be the correct part number for that application. Fasteners requiring replacement or fasteners requiring the use of thread locking compound or sealant are identified in the service procedure. Do not use paints, lubricants, or corrosion inhibitors on fasteners or fastener joint surfaces unless specified. These coatings affect fastener torque and joint clamping force and may damage the fastener. Use the correct tightening sequence and specifications when installing fasteners in order to avoid damage to parts and systems.**

30. Install the fuel tank strap bolts to 35 ft. lbs. (48 Nm).
31. Remove the jack from the fuel tank.
32. Position the fuel tank shield to the fuel tank.
33. Install the shield retainers.
34. Install the rubber exhaust pipe hangers.
35. Remove the support from the exhaust system.
36. Connect the fuel feed and EVAP lines to the fuel tank lines.
37. Connect the EVAP vent pipe quick connect fitting to the fill pipe EVAP vent pipe quick connect fitting.
38. Connect the EVAP vent solenoid hose on the tank to the EVAP vent valve solenoid hose.
39. Install the fuel tank fill hose onto the fuel tank. Install the hose over the orientation feature on the tank until fully seated to the tank. Tighten the clamp at the tank to 22 inch lbs. (2.5 Nm).

40. Lower the vehicle.
41. Add fuel and install the fuel fill cap.
42. Connect the negative battery cable.
43. Inspect the fuel system for leaks by performing the following steps:
   - Turn ON the ignition for 2 seconds
   - Turn OFF the ignition for 10 seconds
   - Turn ON the ignition
   - Inspect for fuel leaks
44. Install the fuel injector sight shield.

IDLE SPEED

ADJUSTMENT

Idle speed is maintained by the Powertrain Control Module (PCM). No adjustment is necessary or possible.

THROTTLE BODY

REMOVAL & INSTALLATION

3.5L & 3.9L Engines

See Figure 161.

➡ **Handle the electronic throttle control components carefully. Use cleanliness in order to prevent damage. Do not drop the electronic throttle control components. Do not roughly handle the electronic throttle control components. Do not immerse the electronic throttle control components in cleaning solvents of any type.**

❈❈ CAUTION

DO NOT for any reason, insert a screwdriver or other small hand tool into the throttle body to hold open the throttle plate as a wedge, as the inside of the throttle body could be damaged. An 8-digit part identification number is stamped on the throttle body casting. Refer to this number, if servicing or part replacement is required.

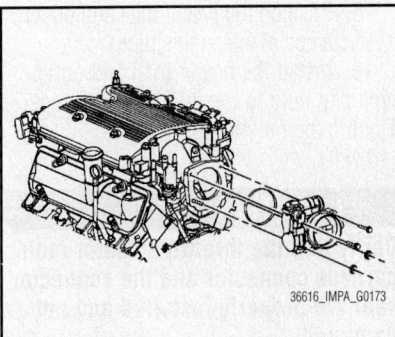

36616_IMPA_G0173

Fig. 161 Remove the throttle body bolts/studs, throttle body and gasket

1. Remove the intake manifold cover.
2. Drain the engine cooling.
3. Remove the air cleaner outlet duct.
4. Disconnect the electronic throttle control (ETC) electrical connector.
5. Remove the heater inlet and outlet pipe clip nuts from the throttle body studs.
6. Reposition the heater inlet and outlet hose clamps at the engine pipes.
7. Reposition the heater inlet and outlet hose/pipe.
8. Remove the throttle body bolts/studs.
9. Remove the throttle body. Remove and discard the throttle body gasket.

To install:

> ※※ **CAUTION**
>
> **DO NOT reuse the throttle body gasket. Install a NEW gasket during assembly.**

10. Install a NEW throttle body gasket. Align the locating tab of the gasket with the notch in the manifold.
11. Position the throttle body to the intake manifold.
12. Use the correct fastener in the correct location. Replacement fasteners must be the correct part number for that application. Fasteners requiring replacement or fasteners requiring the use of thread locking compound or sealant are identified in the service procedure. Do not use paints, lubricants, or corrosion inhibitors on fasteners or fastener joint surfaces unless specified. These coatings affect fastener torque and joint clamping force and may damage the fastener. Use the correct tightening sequence and specifications when installing fasteners in order to avoid damage to parts and systems.
13. Install the throttle body bolts. Tighten the bolts to 89 inch lbs. (10 Nm).
14. Position the heater inlet and outlet hose/pipe.
15. Position the heater inlet and outlet hose clamps at the engine pipes.
16. Install the heater inlet and outlet pipe clip nuts to the throttle body studs. Tighten the nuts to 89 inch lbs. (10 Nm).

> ※※ **CAUTION**
>
> **Verify that the throttle actuator motor harness connector and the connector seal are properly installed and not damaged.**

17. Connect the ETC electrical connector. Install the air cleaner outlet duct.

18. Fill the engine cooling. Install the intake manifold cover.
19. Connect a scan tool in order to test for proper throttle opening and throttle closing ranges.
20. Operate the accelerator pedal and monitor the throttle angles. The accelerator pedal should operate freely, without binding, between closed throttle, and wide open throttle (WOT).
21. Verify that the vehicle meets the following conditions:
   - The vehicle is not in a reduced engine power mode
   - The ignition is ON
   - The engine is OFF

5.3L Engine

See Figures 162 and 163.

➡ **Handle the electronic throttle control components carefully. Use cleanliness in order to prevent damage. Do not drop the electronic throttle control components. Do not roughly handle the electronic throttle control components. Do not immerse the electronic throttle control components in cleaning solvents of any type.**

> ※※ **CAUTION**
>
> **DO NOT for any reason, insert a screwdriver or other small hand tool into the throttle body to hold open the throttle plate as a wedge, as the inside of the throttle body could be damaged. An 8 digit part identification number is stamped on the throttle body casting. Refer to this number if servicing, or part replacement is required.**

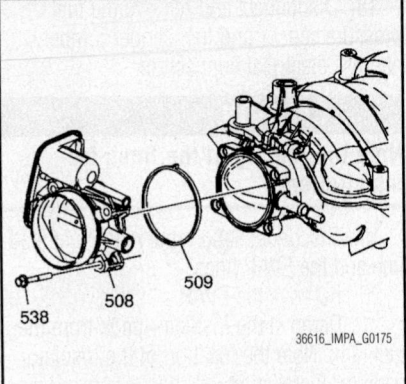

Fig. 163 Remove the throttle body bolts, throttle body and gasket — 5.3L Engine

1. Remove the engine sight shield.
2. Remove the air cleaner outlet duct.
3. Disconnect the throttle actuator control motor electrical connector.
4. Disconnect the evaporative emission (EVAP) canister purge tube from the throttle body.
5. Remove the throttle body bolts.
6. Remove and discard the throttle body gasket.

To install:

7. Install a NEW throttle body gasket. Align the locating tab of the gasket with the notch in the manifold.
8. Position the throttle body to the intake manifold.

➡ **Use the correct fastener in the correct location. Replacement fasteners must be the correct part number for that application. Fasteners requiring replacement or fasteners requiring the use of thread locking compound or**

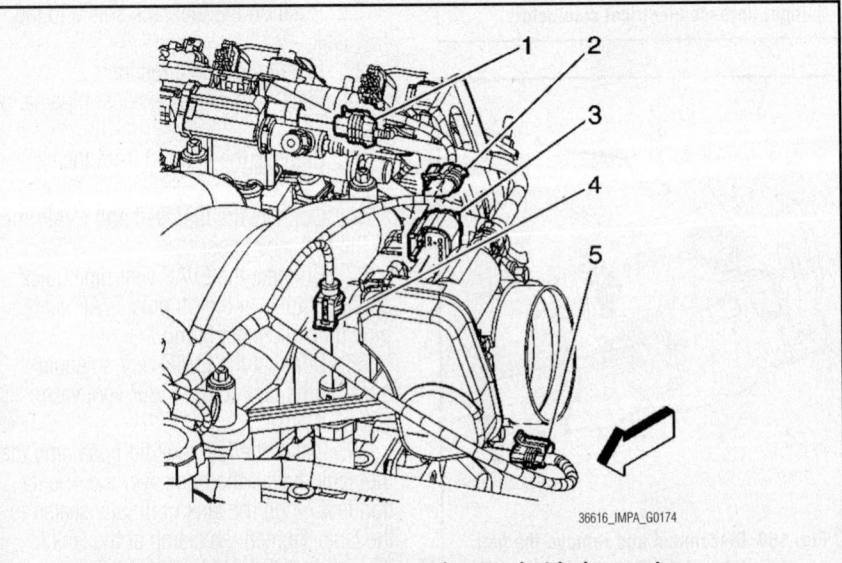

Fig. 162 Disconnecting the throttle actuator control motor electrical connector

sealant are identified in the service procedure. **Do not use paints, lubricants, or corrosion inhibitors on fasteners or fastener joint surfaces unless specified. These coatings affect fastener torque and joint clamping force and may damage the fastener. Use the correct tightening sequence and specifications when installing fasteners in order to avoid damage to parts and systems.**

9. Install the bolts and tighten to 89 inch lbs. (10 Nm).
10. To complete installation, reverse remaining removal procedure.
11. Connect a scan tool in order to test for proper throttle opening and throttle closing ranges.
12. Operate the accelerator pedal and monitor the throttle angles. The accelerator pedal should operate freely, without binding, between closed throttle, and wide open throttle (WOT).
13. Verify that the vehicle meets the following conditions:
- The vehicle is not in a reduced engine power mode
- The ignition is ON
- The engine is OFF

HEATING & AIR CONDITIONING SYSTEM

BLOWER MOTOR

REMOVAL & INSTALLATION

See Figure 164.

1. Disconnect the negative battery cable.

2. Remove the right closeout insulator.
   a. Remove the two push pin retainers.
   b. Remove the Instrument panel closeout/insulator panel.
   c. Remove the courtesy lamp, if equipped.

3. Disconnect the blower motor electrical connector.
4. Remove the blower motor screws.
5. Remove the blower motor.
6. To install, reverse removal procedure.

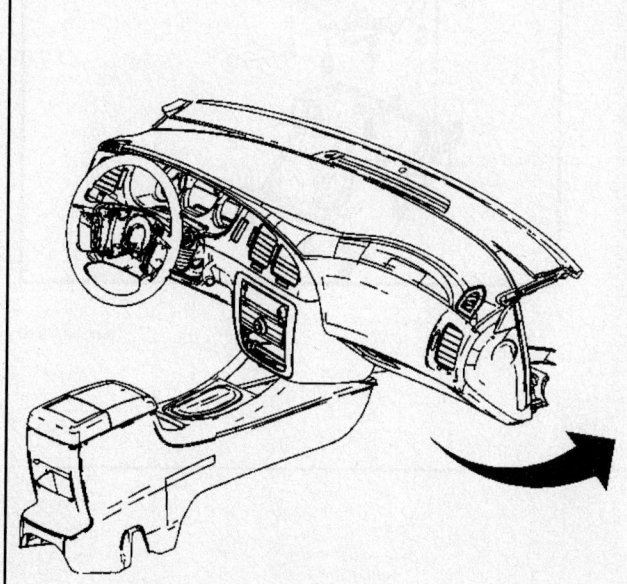
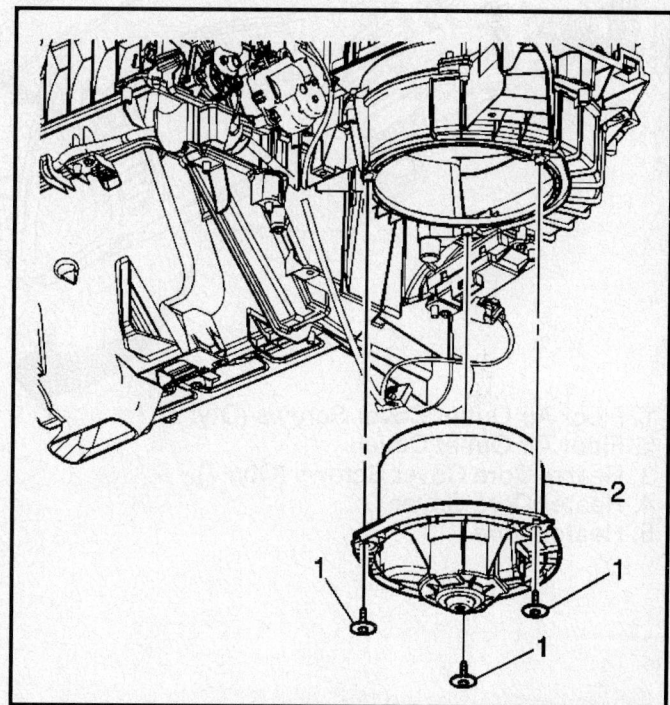

Fig. 164 Removing the blower motor screws (1) and blower motor (2)

36616_IMPA_G0180

HEATER CORE

REMOVAL & INSTALLATION

See Figure 165.

1. Before servicing the vehicle, refer to the Precautions Section.
2. Disconnect the negative battery cable.
3. Remove the right closeout panel.
4. Remove the left closeout panel.
5. Remove the rear floor air outlet duct:
    a. Remove the rear floor air outlet duct from the holes in the floor reinforcement.
    b. Disconnect the rear floor air outlet duct from the heater outlet cover.
    c. Remove the rear floor air outlet duct.
6. Remove the heat stakes that secure the HVAC module assembly upper case to the HVAC module lower case using a small chisel and remove the floor air outlet cover screws.
7. Remove the floor outlet cover.
8. Remove the heat stakes that secure the HVAC module assembly upper case to the HVAC module lower case using a small chisel and remove the heater core cover screws.
9. Remove the heater core cover.
10. Remove the heater core.
11. To install, reverse removal procedure.

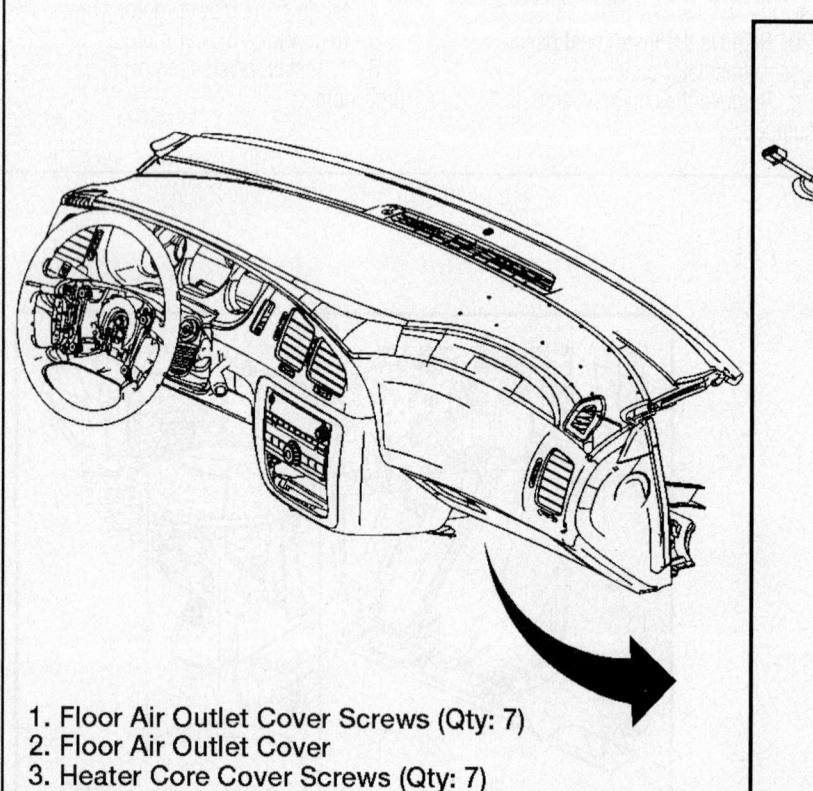
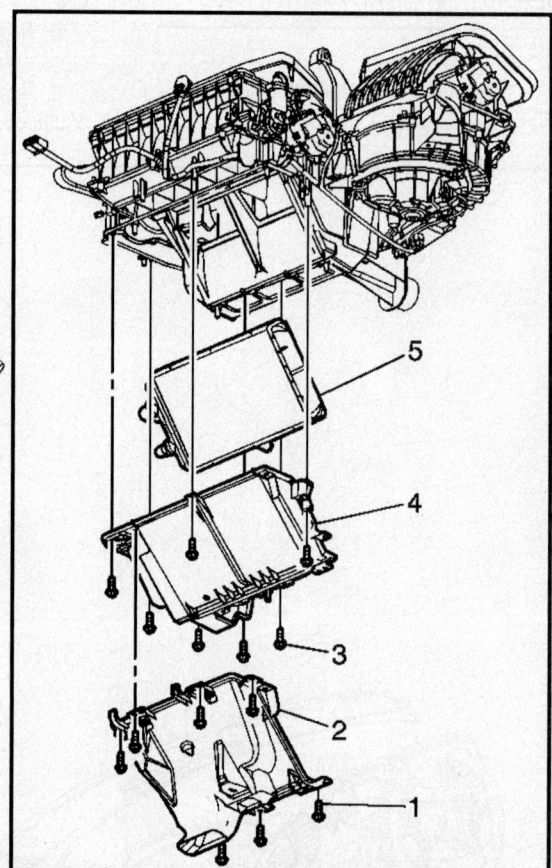

1. Floor Air Outlet Cover Screws (Qty: 7)
2. Floor Air Outlet Cover
3. Heater Core Cover Screws (Qty: 7)
4. Heater Core Cover
5. Heater Core

36616_IMPA_G0192

Fig. 165 Removing the heater core assembly

STEERING

POWER RACK & PINION STEERING GEAR

REMOVAL & INSTALLATION
See Figure 166.

❋❋ CAUTION

With wheels of the vehicle facing straight ahead, secure the steering wheel utilizing steering column anti-rotation pin, steering column lock, or a strap to prevent rotation. Locking of the steering column will prevent damage and a possible malfunction of the SIR system. The steering wheel must be secured in position before disconnecting the following components:

- The steering column
- The intermediate shaft(s)
- The steering gear

After disconnecting these components, do not rotate the steering wheel or move the front tires and wheels. Failure to follow this procedure may cause the SIR coil assembly to become un-centered and cause possible damage to the SIR coil. If you think the SIR coil has became un-centered, refer to your specific SIR coil's centering procedure to re-center SIR Coil.

1. Before servicing the vehicle, refer to the Precautions Section.
2. Disconnect the negative battery cable.
3. Insert J-42640 pin into the steering column access hole in order to lock the steering column.
4. Raise and support the vehicle.
5. Remove the tire and wheel assemblies.

❋❋ WARNING

Failure to disconnect the intermediate shaft from the rack and pinion steering gear stub shaft can result in damage to the steering gear and/or intermediate shaft. This damage may cause loss of steering control which could result in an accident and possible personal injury.

6. Remove the lower pinch bolt from the power steering gear stub shaft.
7. Remove the intermediate steering shaft from the power steering gear stub shaft.
8. Remove both of the tie rod ends from the steering knuckles.

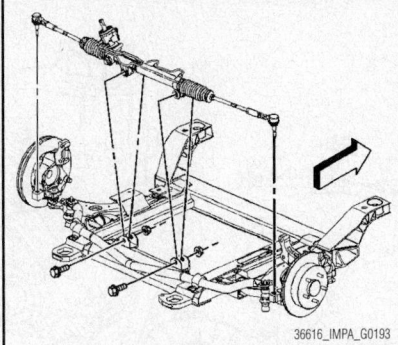

36616_IMPA_G0193

Fig. 166 Removing the power steering gear

9. Support the rear of the frame using jackstands.
10. Remove the frame bolts from the rear of the frame.

❋❋ CAUTION

Do not lower the rear of the frame too far as damage to the engine components nearest to the cowl may result.

11. Lower the rear of the frame
12. Remove the power steering pressure hose from the power steering gear.
13. Remove the power steering return hose from the power steering gear.
14. Remove the power steering gear mounting bolts and nuts.
15. Remove the power steering gear through the left wheel opening.

To install:
16. Install the power steering gear through the left wheel opening.
17. Install the power steering gear mounting bolts (1) and nuts (4). Tighten the power steering gear mounting bolts to 66 ft. lbs. (90 Nm).
18. Inspect the threads on the power steering pressure hose and the power steering return hose.
19. Inspect the O-ring seals on the power steering hoses.
20. Replace the seals if damaged, lubricate the seals before installation.
21. Install the clamp that holds the power steering hoses to the power steering gear.
22. Install the power steering pressure hose to the power steering gear.
23. Install the power steering return hose to the power steering gear.
24. Raise the frame into position.
25. Install rear frame bolts.

26. Remove the jackstands.
27. Install the tie rod ends to the steering knuckles.
28. Raise and support the vehicle.

POWER STEERING PUMP

REMOVAL & INSTALLATION
See Figures 167 and 168.

1. Place a drain pan under the vehicle.
2. Remove the cosmetic/acoustic engine cover.
3. Remove the accessory drive belt.
4. Remove the power steering pump pulley from the pump noting the following:
   a. Use the J 25034-C pulley remover to remove the pulley from the pump.
   b. Use the J 25033-C power steering pump pulley installer to install the pulley to the pump.
   c. Ensure the axial tolerance of the pulley on the pump shaft is within 0.010 in (0.25 mm).
5. Remove the three power steering pump bolts. Use an appropriate tool to remove the power steering fluid from the reservoir before removing the hoses from the pump.
6. Remove the power steering high pressure hose fitting.
7. Remove the power steering return hose clamp (at pump).
8. To install, reverse removal procedure.
9. Tighten the power steering pump bolts to 18 ft. lbs. (25 Nm).
10. Tighten the power steering high pressure hose fitting 24 ft. lbs. (32 Nm).

To install:
11. Install the pump to the engine. Install the bolts and tighten to 25 ft. lbs. (34 Nm).
12. Connect the power steering return line.
13. Connect the power steering pressure line. Using a "crows foot" adapter and a torque wrench, torque the pressure line fitting to 20 ft. lbs. (27 Nm).
14. Install the power steering pump pulley noting the following.
   a. Use a power steering pump pulley installer such as J 36015, or equivalent. This type of installer threads into the end of the pump shaft. A nut is then turned to press the pulley onto the pump shaft.

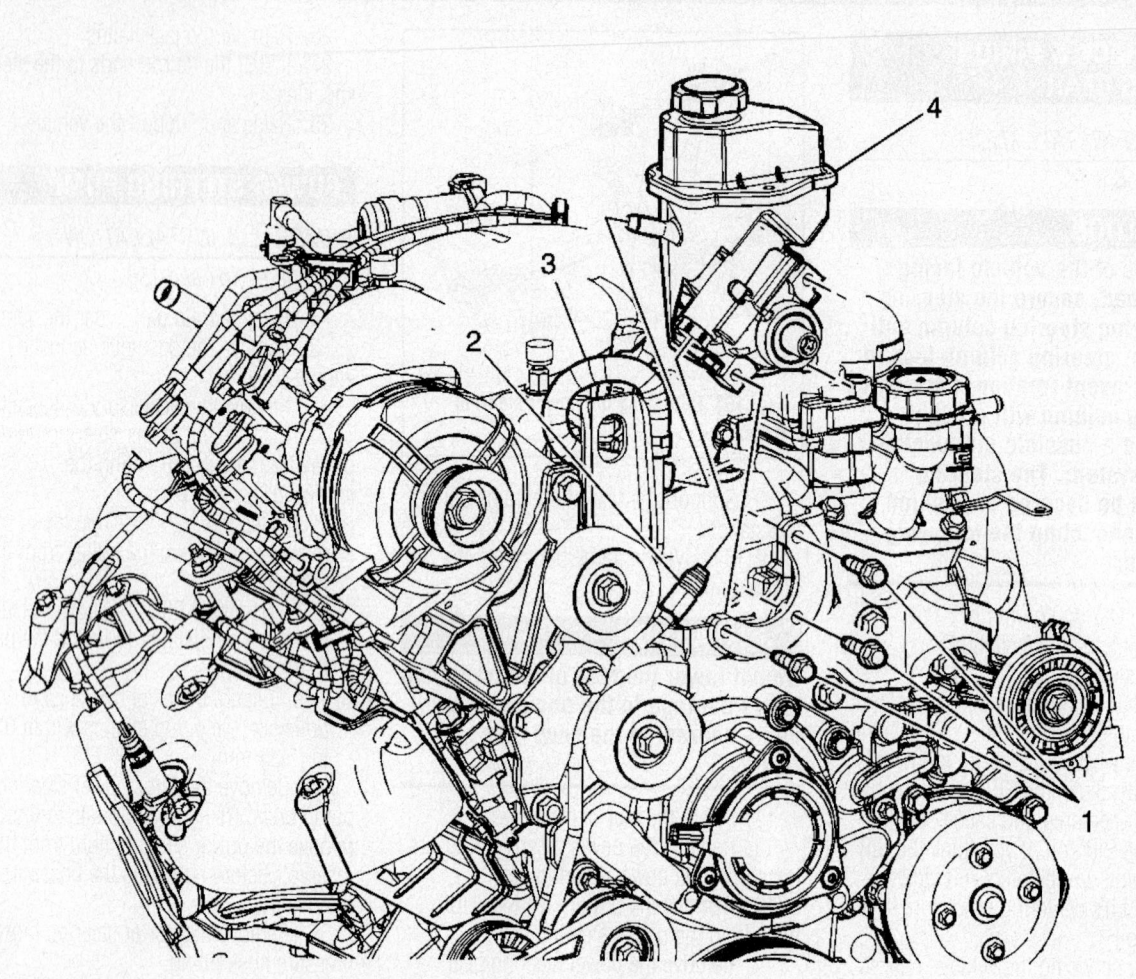

1. Power Steering Pump Bolt (Qty: 3)
2. Power Steering High Pressure Hose Fitting
3. Power Steering Return Hose Clamp (at pump)
4. Power Steering Pump

36616_IMPA_G0194

Fig. 167 Removing the power steering pump — 3.5L and 3.9L Engines

b. The face of the pulley hub must be flush with the end of the pump shaft.

⁂ WARNING

Do not attempt to use a shop press to install a pump pulley.

15. Install the accessory wiring junction block.

16. Install the accessory drive belt, making sure it is properly routed and seated in all pulley grooves.

17. Install the coolant surge tank.

18. Install the engine cover.

19. Fill the power steering system and bleed the system. Check for leaks.

BLEEDING

See Figure 169.

The power steering fluid replacement procedure is a two-stage process: first, flushing the old fluid from the system with new fluid and second, bleeding the system to remove any trapped air. The following sequences outline these procedures.

1. Raise and safely support the front end of the vehicle off the ground until the front wheels are free to turn.

2. Remove the fluid return line at the pump reservoir inlet connector.

3. Plug the inlet connector port on the pump reservoir.

4. Position the fluid return line toward a container (several quart capacity) to catch the draining fluid.

5. When an assistant fills the reservoir with either the standard power steering fluid or optional cold weather power steering fluid, start and run the engine at idle.

6. Turn the steering wheel from stop-to-stop.

⁂ WARNING

Do not hold the steering wheel against the stops while flushing the system. Holding the steering wheel against the stops will cause high system pressure, overheating and

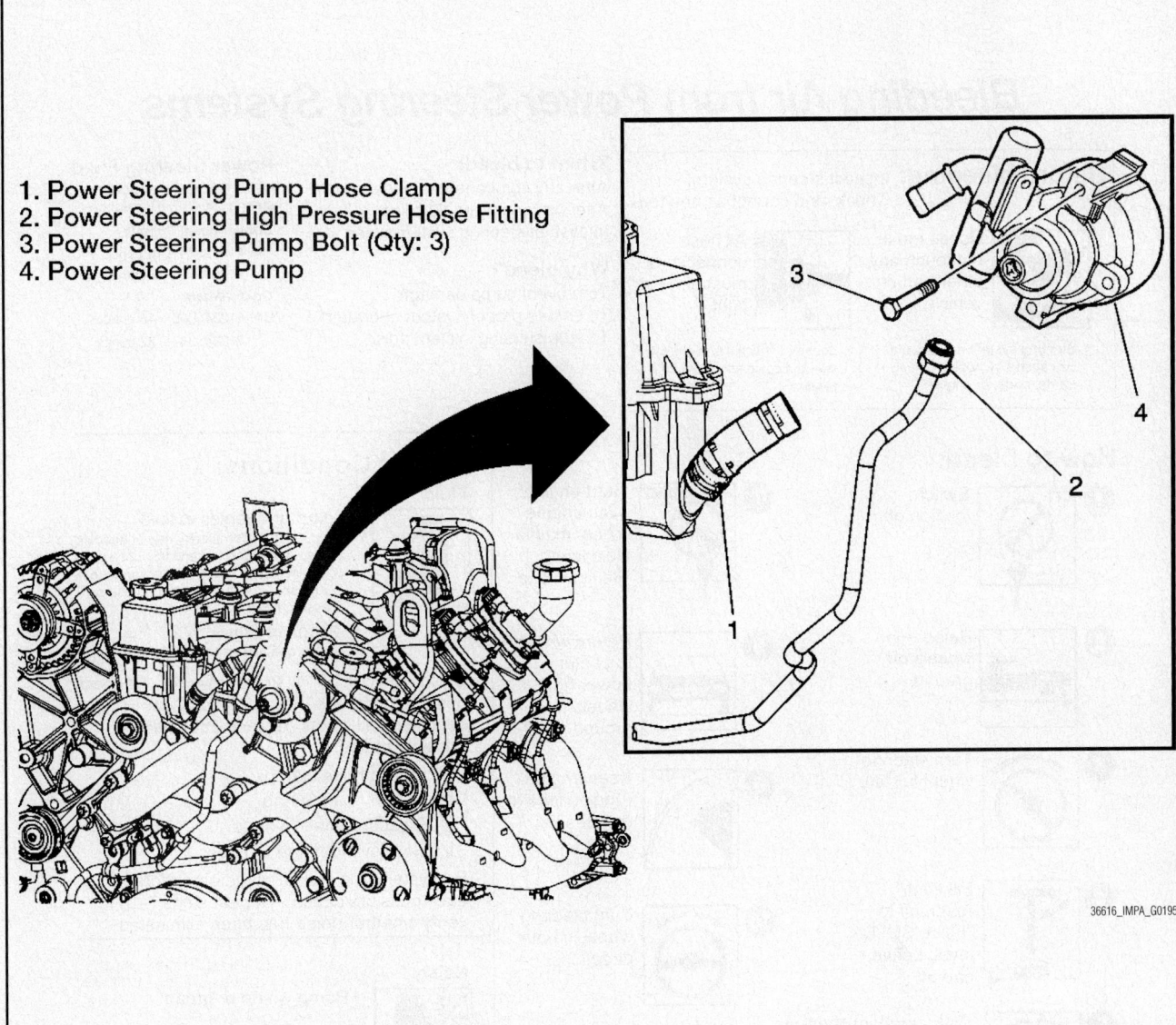

1. Power Steering Pump Hose Clamp
2. Power Steering High Pressure Hose Fitting
3. Power Steering Pump Bolt (Qty: 3)
4. Power Steering Pump

36616_IMPA_G0195

Fig. 168 Removing the power steering pump — 5.3L engine

damage to the pump and/or the steering gear assembly.

7. Continue draining until all of the old fluid is cleared from the power steering system. The addition of another quart of fresh fluid will be required to flush the system.

8. Turn the engine **OFF**. Unplug the pump reservoir inlet and reconnect the return line.

9. Fill the reservoir to the FULL COLD mark.

After replacing the fluid or servicing the power steering hydraulic system, you must bleed air from the system. Air in the system prevents an accurate fluid level reading, causes pump cavitation noise and over time could damage the pump. To bleed the power steering system, proceed as follows.

10. Begin with the engine **OFF**, front wheels off the ground and the wheels turned all the way to the left.

11. Add either standard power steering fluid or optional cold climate fluid to the FULL COLD mark on the fluid level indicator.

12. With the engine still **OFF**, bleed the system by turning the wheels from stop-to-stop, but without hitting the stops.

➡ **This may require turning the wheels from side to side up to 40 times. Keep the fluid level at the FULL COLD mark. Fluid with air in it may have a light tan appearance. This air must be eliminated from the fluid before normal steering action can be obtained.**

13. Start the engine. With the engine idling, recheck the fluid level. If necessary,

add fluid to bring the level to the FULL COLD mark.

14. Return the front wheels to the center position. Verify that the transaxle is in PARK and that the parking brake had been firmly set. Lower the front wheels to the ground. Continue running the engine for two or three minutes.

15. Test drive the vehicle to be sure the power steering functions normally and is free from noise.

➡ **Inspect for fluid leakage at the connection points along the power steering system.**

16. Recheck the fluid level. The fluid level should now be up to the FULL HOT mark after the system has stabilized at operating temperature.

Bleeding Air from Power Steering Systems

Before bleeding: Inspect steering system. Check, and correct as needed:

Hoses must not touch any other part of vehicle.

- Steering system noise could be caused by hose touching frame, body, or engine

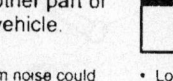

All hose connections must be tight.

- Loose connections might not leak but could allow air into system

When to bleed:
After any component replacement
After disconnecting fluid line
In case of steering system noise

Why bleed?
To prevent pump damage
To ensure proper system operation
To stop steering system noise

Power Steering Fluid
Use only clean, new power steering fluid. Fluid must be

Conventional Climate
GM #1052884 – 16 ounce
   #1050017 – 32 ounce
Cold Climate
GM #12345866 – 16 ounce
   #12345867 – 32 ounce

How to bleed:

1  Switch ignition off.

2 Raise front wheels off ground.

3  Turn steering wheel full left.

4  Fill fluid reservoir to "FULL COLD" level. Leave cap off

5  With assistant checking fluid level and condition, turn steering wheel lock-to-lock at least 20 times. Engine remains off.

- On systems with long return lines or fluid coolers, turn steering wheel lock-to-lock at least 40 times
- Trapped air may cause fluid to overflow. Thoroughly clean any spilled fluid to allow for leak check
- Keep fluid level at "FULL COLD"

6  While turning wheel, check fluid constantly

- No bubbles are allowed
- For any sign of bubbles, recheck connections. Repeat step 5

7 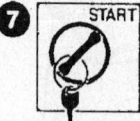 Start engine. With engine idling, maintain fluid level. Reinstall cap

8 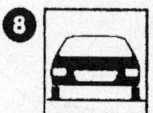 Return wheels to center Lower front wheels to ground.

9  Keep engine running for two minutes

10  Turn steering wheel in both directions

Verify
- ☑ Smooth power assist
- ☑ Noiseless operation
- ☑ Proper fluid level
- ☑ No system leaks
- ☑ Proper fluid condition
- No bubbles, no foam, no discoloration

11 If all proper conditions apply, procedure is complete

12 If any problem remains, see "Special Conditions"

Special Conditions:
Fluid

- Foam or bubbles in fluid
  Fluid must be completely free of bubbles. In step 5, be alert to periodic bubbles that could indicate a loose connection or leak. O-ring seal in either the return hose or pressure hose
- Discolored fluid
  (milky, opaque, or light tan color)

Switch ignition off. Wait two minutes. Recheck hose connections. Repeat steps 7-10. If condition still exists, replace and check a possible cause

- ☑ Return hose clamps
- ☑ Return hose O-ring
- ☑ Pressure hose O-rings
- ☑ Gear cylinder line O-rings

Fill system and repeat bleed procedure for each possible cause. Repeat steps 7-10 to verify whether noise has been eliminated

Noise

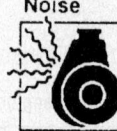

- Pump whine or groan

With engine running, recheck hoses for possible contact with frame, body or engine. If no contact is found, follow either method below to cool down fluid and repressurize system

Method 1:
Normal Cool Down

Switch engine off
Wait for system to cool
Install reservoir cap

Method 2:
Partial Fluid Replacement

Switch engine off
Use a suction device to remove fluid from reservoir
Refill with cool, clean fluid
Install reservoir cap

After either method of cooling, start engine and allow engine to come up to operating temperature. If noise persists, remove and replace power steering pump. Repeat bleed procedure following pump replacement

88008G73

Fig. 169 Power steering system bleeding

SUSPENSION

COIL SPRING

REMOVAL & INSTALLATION

See Figure 170.

➡ **Special Tools: J 42991 Strut Rod Nut Socket. J 45400 Strut Spring Compressor.**

1. Before servicing the vehicle, refer to the Precautions Section.
2. Remove the strut from the vehicle.
3. Install the strut in the J 45400.

➡ **The spring is compressed when the strut moves freely.**

4. Turn the spring compressor forcing screw until the coil spring is compressed.
5. Use a 45 TORX® socket in order to hold the strut shaft. Remove the upper strut mount nut by turning with J 42991.
6. Remove the strut from the J 45400.
7. Loosen the compressor forcing screw until the upper strut mount and coil spring may be removed.
8. To install, reverse removal procedure.
9. Tighten the strut mount nut to 52 ft. lbs. (70 Nm).

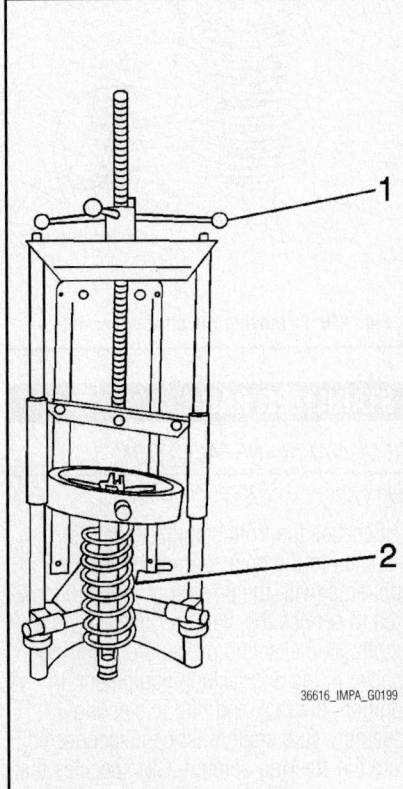

Fig. 170 Removing the coil spring

LOWER BALL JOINT

REMOVAL & INSTALLATION

See Figure 171.

1. Before servicing the vehicle, refer to the Precautions Section.
2. Remove the wheel.
3. Remove the lower control arm from the vehicle.
4. Remove the ball joint from the lower control arm by drilling out the 3 rivets retaining the ball joint to the control arm.
5. Remove the ball joint.

To install:

6. Install or connect the following:
   - Ball joint to the control arm
   - Bolts with the heads facing down and torque them to 50 ft. lbs. (68 Nm)
   - Lower control arm to the vehicle
   - Wheel

➡ **A 4-wheel alignment is recommended after any steering/suspension repairs are performed.**

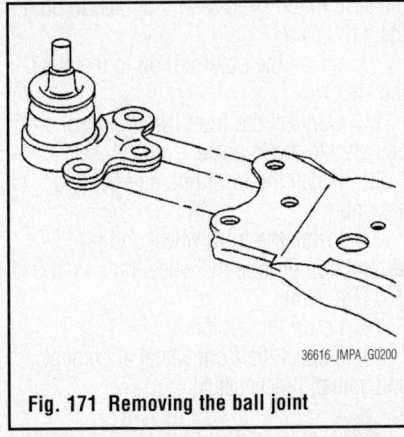

Fig. 171 Removing the ball joint

LOWER CONTROL ARM

REMOVAL & INSTALLATION

See Figures 172 through 174.

✳✳ CAUTION

Use only the recommended tools for separating the ball joint from the knuckle. Do NOT hammer or pry the ball joint from the knuckle. Failure to use the recommended tools may cause damage to the ball joint and seal.

➡ **Use the ignition key in order to unlock the steering column.**

FRONT SUSPENSION

1. Before servicing the vehicle, refer to the Precautions Section.
2. Turn the steering wheel in order to move the front of the applicable wheel to the outboard most position.

➡ **Use ONLY a frame-contact type vehicle lift or a floor jack at the recommended lift points. Do NOT use a suspension-contact type vehicle lift. Do NOT lift the vehicle by the lower control arms.**

3. Raise and support the vehicle.
4. Remove the tire and wheel.
5. Disconnect the ABS wheel speed sensor connector, if equipped.
6. Disconnect the ABS wheel speed sensor jumper harness from the harness retainer clips, if equipped.
7. Remove the stabilizer shaft link.
8. Remove the cotter pin from the ball stud.
9. Loosen the ball stud nut.
10. Install the J 41820 over the ball stud and lower control arm.
11. Rotate the ball stud nut counterclockwise in order to separate the ball stud from the steering knuckle.
12. Remove the J 41820.
13. Remove the ball stud nut.
14. Remove the lower control arm bolts and nuts.
15. Remove the lower control arm.

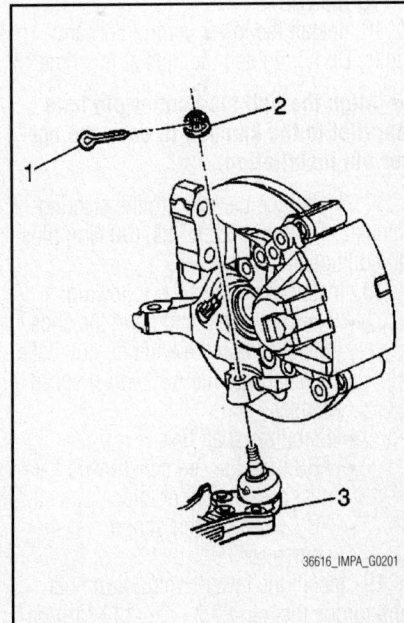

Fig. 172 Removing the cotter pin (1) from the ball stud (3) and Loosen the ball stud nut (2)

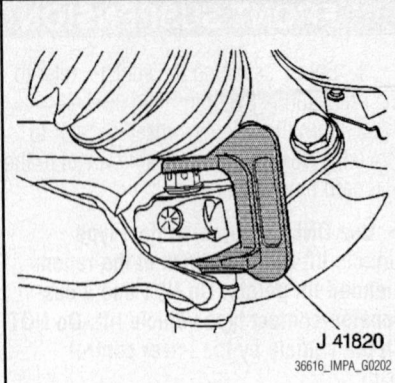

Fig. 173 Install the J 41820 over the ball stud and lower control arm as shown

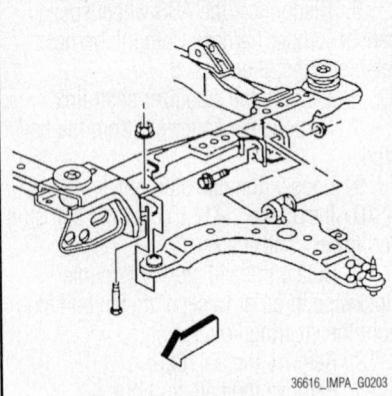

Fig. 174 Remove the lower control arm, bolts and nuts

To install:

16. Install the lower control arm and bolts. Do not tighten the nuts at this time.

➡ **Align the ball stud cotter pin hole parallel to the knuckle to ease the cotter pin installation.**

17. Install the ball stud to the steering knuckle. Tighten to 22 ft. lbs. (30 Nm) plus an additional 120 degrees.
18. Install or connect the following:
   - New cotter pin and bend the ends. Make certain the ends do not make contact with the ABS wheel speed sensor
   - Stabilizer shaft link
   - ABS wheel speed sensor wire harness to the retainer clips
   - ABS wheel speed sensor connector
19. Install the lower control arm nuts and torque them to 83 ft. lbs. (113 Nm) on all models except Lumina. On Lumina models tighten the control arm-to-frame nuts to 52 ft. lbs. (70 Nm).
   - Front wheel

STEERING KNUCKLE

REMOVAL & INSTALLATION

See Figure 175.

➡ **The steering knuckle is a machined aluminum casting. Do not use a hammer to loosen suspension components from the knuckle.**

1. Raise and safely support the vehicle.
2. Remove the wheel and tire assembly.
3. Remove the front hub and bearing assembly.
4. Disconnect the front lower control arm ball stud.
5. Remove the outer tie rod end.
6. If the knuckle is to be reused, scribe a mark around the strut bracket to the knuckle. This will help align the strut at assembly.
7. Remove the bolts connecting the strut to the knuckle and remove the knuckle from the vehicle.

To install:

8. Install the knuckle to the vehicle.
9. Install the bolts and nuts attaching the strut to the knuckle and tighten to 96 ft. lbs. (130 Nm).
10. Install the outer tie rod to the steering knuckle.
11. Connect the front lower control arm ball stud to the knuckle.
12. Install the front hub and bearing assembly.
13. Install the front wheel and tire assemblies. Torque the wheel nuts to 100 ft. lbs. (140 Nm).
14. Lower the vehicle.
15. Inspect the front wheel alignment and adjust, if necessary.

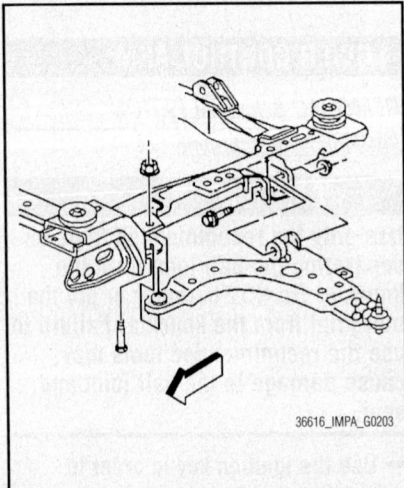

Fig. 175 Removing the steering knuckle

STRUT

REMOVAL & INSTALLATION

See Figure 176.

1. Before servicing the vehicle, refer to the Precautions Section.
2. Remove the strut upper nuts.
3. Raise and support the vehicle.
4. Remove the tire and wheel.
5. Scribe the strut to the steering knuckle for proper installation.
6. Remove the strut to steering knuckle lower bolts and nuts.
7. Remove the strut.

To install:

8. Install or connect the following:
   - Strut
   - Three upper strut nuts and torque them to 24 ft. lbs. (33 Nm)
   - Lower strut bolts
9. Align the strut to the scribe mark on the steering knuckle. Torque the lower bolts to 90 ft. lbs. (123 Nm).
10. Install the front wheel.
11. Road test the vehicle and check the front end alignment, adjust if necessary.

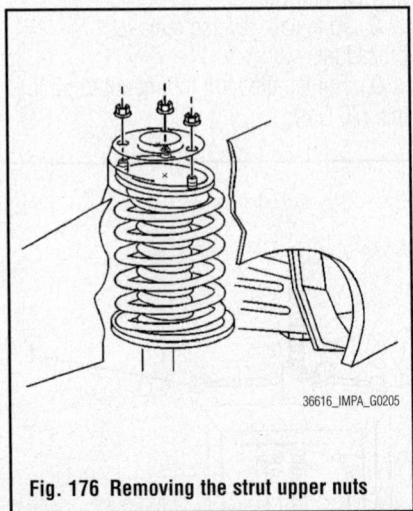

Fig. 176 Removing the strut upper nuts

STABILIZER BAR

REMOVAL & INSTALLATION

See Figures 177 through 179.

Because the front stabilizer shaft is mounted to the powertrain subframe, the subframe (with the powertrain) must be lowered to service the stabilizer bar. This is a lengthy and exacting procedure requiring special lifting and jacking equipment. In addition, the rack and pinion steering assembly stub shaft must be disconnected from the steering column. GM specifies that the subframe-to-body bolts, once disturbed,

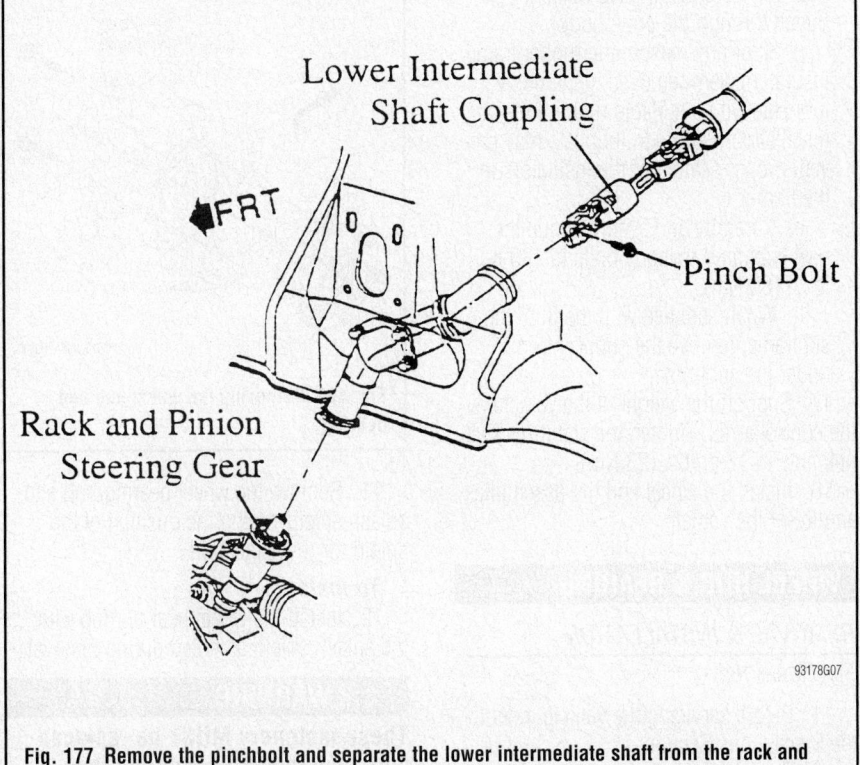

Fig. 177 Remove the pinchbolt and separate the lower intermediate shaft from the rack and pinion stub shaft

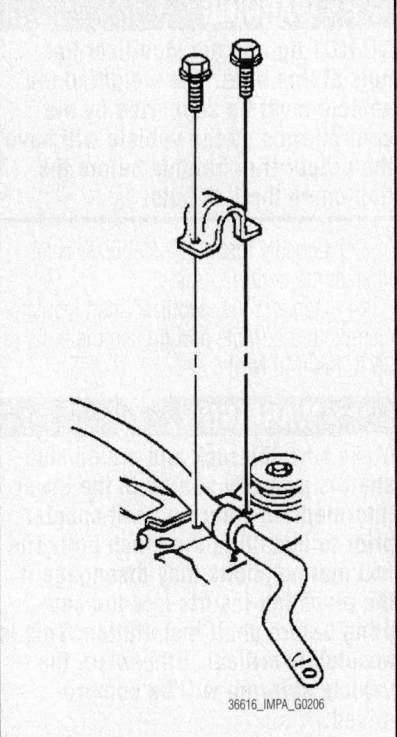

Fig. 178 Removing the stabilizer shaft insulator clamps and insulators

must be replaced with new service replacement parts. Procure the necessary hardware before beginning this procedure. This is not a job for the inexperienced or ill-equipped.

1. Center the front wheels to the straight ahead position and lock the steering column. This is important because it protects the steering wheel airbag coil from damage.

2. Raise and safely support the vehicle.

3. Remove the front wheel and tire assemblies.

4. Locate the steering shaft dust seal and move it back to gain access to the pinch bolt that joins the steering column intermediate shaft to the rack and pinion input shaft (stub shaft).

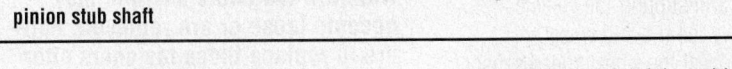

Failure to disconnect the intermediate shaft from the rack and pinion stub shaft can result in damage to the rack and pinion steering gear assembly and/or the steering intermediate shaft. The damage can cause loss of steering control which could result in personal injury.

5. Remove the pinch bolt from the lower intermediate steering shaft, noting the following:

a. The wheels of the vehicle must be in the straight ahead position and the steering column in the **LOCK** position before disconnecting the steering column or the intermediate shaft from the rack and pinion steering gear.

b. Failure to do this will cause the SIR (airbag) coil, which feeds power to the steering wheel airbag module, to become uncentered, which will cause damage to the airbag coil.

6. Loosen the stabilizer shaft insulator clamp attaching nuts and bolts.

7. Place an adjustable safety stand or hydraulic jack under the center of the rear subframe crossmember.

8. Locate the large subframe-to-body retaining bolts. Remove the two rear frame-to-body bolts.

9. Carefully lower the rear of the subframe just enough to access the stabilizer shaft.

10. Remove the stabilizer shaft insulator clamps and insulators from the subframe.

11. Remove the stabilizer shaft links from the control arms and pull the stabilizer shaft rearward. Swing the stabilizer shaft down and remove from the left side of the vehicle.

To install:

12. Insert the stabilizer shaft from the left side of the vehicle.

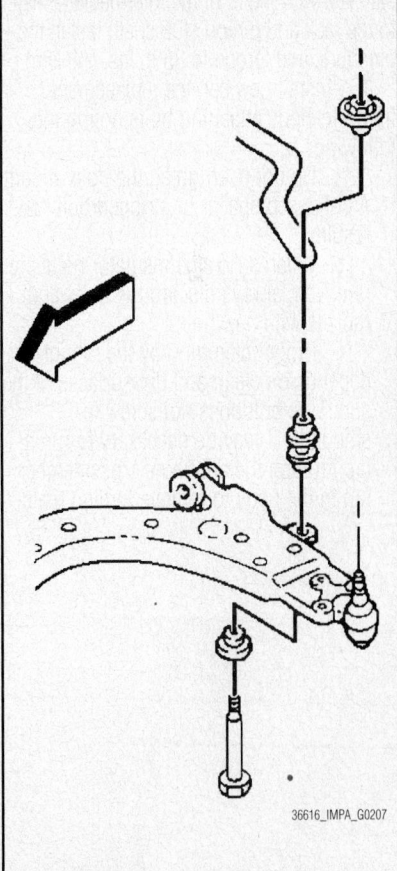

Fig. 179 Remove the stabilizer shaft links from the control arms

13. Loosely install the stabilizer shaft links at the control arms.

14. Connect the stabilizer shaft insulator clamps to the frame and tighten the bolts to 35 ft. lbs. (48 Nm).

15. Raise the subframe back into position, while guiding the intermediate steering shaft onto the rack and pinion stub shaft. When satisfied with the fit of the intermediate shaft to the rack and pinion stub shaft, install the pinchbolt and torque to 35 ft. lbs. (48 Nm).

16. Install new service replacement frame-to-body attaching bolts noting the following:

a. Do not overtighten the body mount. A collapsed spacer or stripped bolt may result.

b. When subframe insulator bolts are removed, always discard the bolts and replace with new bolts.

c. Proper clamping by the mount depends on clean and dry surfaces. If the subframe bolt does not screw in smoothly, it may be necessary to run a tap through the subframe crossmember nut in the body to remove foreign mate-

rial. Take care that the tap does not punch through the underbody.

d. If for any reason, the rubber frame insulators were removed, generously lubricate with a suitable rubber lube, at installation. Failure to lubricate may prevent proper seating of the insulators in the frame.

e. Carefully and evenly torque the new subframe-to-body bolts to 133 ft. lbs. (180 Nm).

f. When satisfied with the fit of the subframe, remove the support from under the subframe.

17. Support the weight of the vehicle by the control arms. Tighten the stabilizer shaft link nuts to 17 ft. lbs. (23 Nm).

18. Install the wheel and tire assemblies and lower the vehicle.

WHEEL HUB & BEARING

REMOVAL & INSTALLATION

See Figure 180.

1. Before servicing the vehicle, refer to the Precautions Section.

2. Raise and support the vehicle.

3. Remove the tire and wheel.

4. Disconnect the wheel speed sensor electrical connector , if equipped.

5. Remove the wheel speed sensor electrical connector from the bracket, if equipped.

6. Remove the front wheel drive shaft nut.

7. Remove the brake rotor.

8. Use 3 wheel nuts in order to attach the J 42129 to the wheel bearing/hub.

9. Use the J 42129 in order to push the wheel drive shaft out of the wheel bearing/hub.

10. Remove and DISCARD the wheel bearing/hub bolts. Remove the J 42129 from the hub.

➡ **Ensure that the wheel drive shaft outer seal/boot is not damaged.**

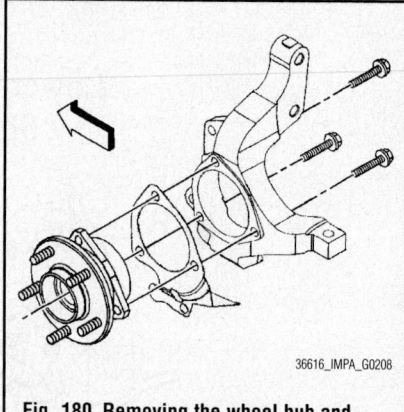

Fig. 180 Removing the wheel hub and bearing

11. Remove the wheel bearing/hub and splash shield-noting the position of the shield for re-installation.

To install:

12. Install the wheel bearing/hub with the splash shield as noted during removal.

13. Install NEW wheel bearing/hub bolts and tighten to 96 ft. lbs. (130 Nm).

14. Install the brake rotor and caliper.

15. Install the front wheel drive shaft nut.

➡ **Ensure that the connector clip engages the bracket properly.**

16. Install the wheel speed sensor electrical connector to the bracket, if equipped.

17. Connect the wheel speed sensor electrical connector, if equipped.

18. Install the tire and wheel.

19. Lower the vehicle.

SUSPENSION

REAR SUSPENSION

COIL SPRING

REMOVAL & INSTALLATION

To remove the rear coil spring, refer to Coil Spring under Front Suspension.

CONTROL ARMS/LINKS

REMOVAL & INSTALLATION

See Figure 181.

➡ **Use the correct fastener in the correct location. Replacement fasteners must be the correct part number for that application. Fasteners requiring replacement or fasteners requiring the use of thread locking compound or sealant are identified in the service procedure. Do not use paints, lubricants, or corrosion inhibitors on fasteners or fastener joint surfaces unless specified. These coatings affect fastener torque and joint clamping force and may damage the fastener. Use the correct tightening sequence and specifications when installing fasteners in order to avoid damage to parts and systems.**

1. Raise and support the vehicle.
2. Remove the stabilizer shaft link nut from the stabilizer shaft link and the stabilizer shaft.
3. Remove the stabilizer shaft link nut from the stabilizer shaft link and the strut.
4. Remove the stabilizer shaft link from the vehicle.
5. To install, reverse removal procedure.
6. Tighten the following to specification:
   • Stabilizer shaft link nut to the stabilizer shaft link and stabilizer shaft: 37 ft .lbs. (50 Nm).

• Stabilizer shaft link nut to the stabilizer shaft link and the strut: 37 ft .lbs. (50 Nm).

STRUTS

REMOVAL & INSTALLATION

See Figure 182.

1. Before servicing the vehicle, refer to the Precautions Section.
2. Remove or disconnect the following:
   • Negative battery cable
   • Three strut-to-body nuts
   • Rear tire and wheel
   • Stabilizer shaft link from the strut
3. Scribe the strut to the knuckle.

➡ **The knuckle must be retained after the strut to knuckle bolts have been removed. Damage may occur to the ball joint or drive axle if the knuckle is not retained.**

4. Remove or disconnect the following:
   • Strut to knuckle bolts
   • Strut

To install:
5. Install or connect the following:
   • Strut
   • Strut to knuckle bolts and

torque the bolts to 90 ft. lbs. (122 Nm)
   • Stabilizer shaft link to the strut
   • Rear tire and wheel
   • Three strut to body mount nuts and torque them to 30 ft. lbs. (41 Nm)
6. Road test the vehicle and adjust the rear wheel alignment if needed.

WHEEL HUB & BEARING

REMOVAL & INSTALLATION

See Figures 183 and 184.

The rear wheel bearing/hub is integrated into one unit. The unit is non-serviceable. If the hub or bearing is damaged, the complete hub and bearing unit must be replaced.

1. Before servicing the vehicle, refer to the Precautions Section.
2. Remove or disconnect the following:
   • Rear wheel
   • Brake drum, if equipped
   • Rear caliper and bracket, if equipped
   • Brake rotor, if equipped
   • Antilock Brake System (ABS) Wheel Speed Sensor (WSS) electrical connector
   • Rear wheel hub to knuckle bolts

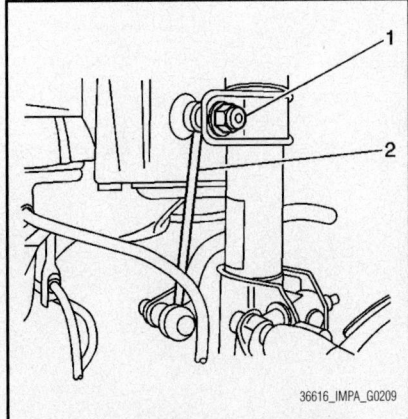

36616_IMPA_G0209

Fig. 181 Removing the stabilizer shaft link from the vehicle

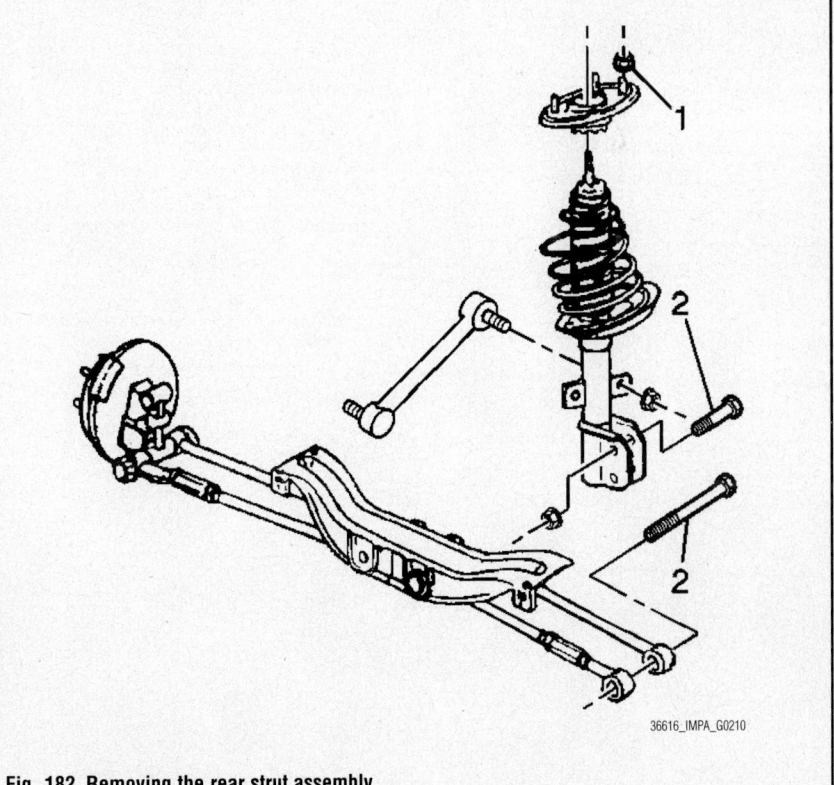

36616_IMPA_G0210

Fig. 182 Removing the rear strut assembly

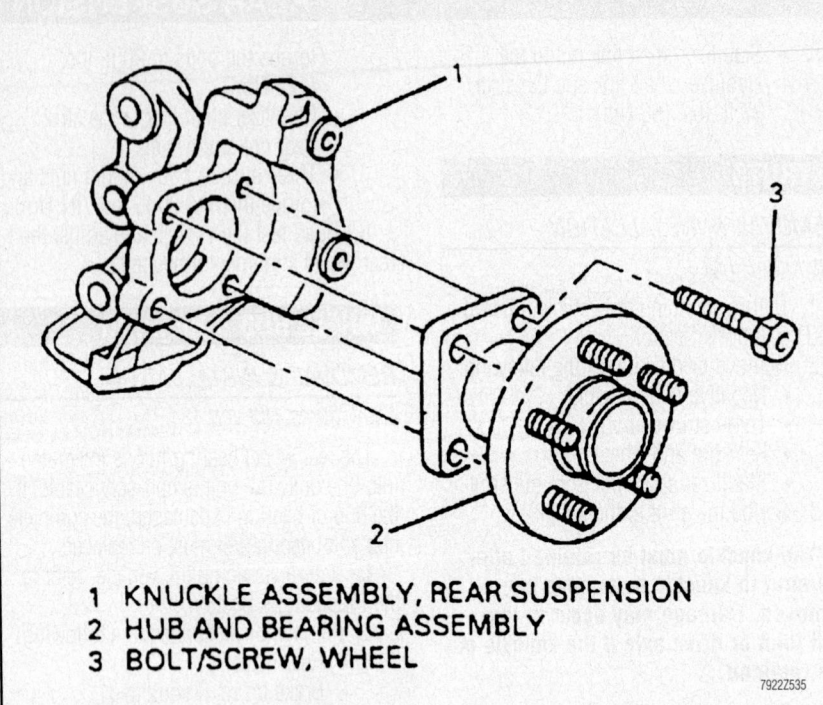

1 KNUCKLE ASSEMBLY, REAR SUSPENSION
2 HUB AND BEARING ASSEMBLY
3 BOLT/SCREW, WHEEL

7922Z535

Fig. 183 The rear hub/bearing assembly is bolted to the knuckle

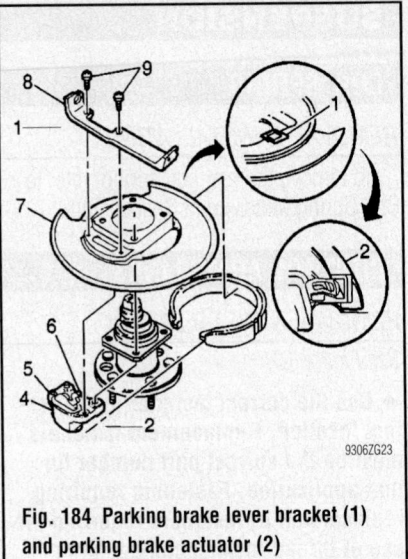

9306ZG23

Fig. 184 Parking brake lever bracket (1)
and parking brake actuator (2)

- Parking brake lever bracket and
  parking brake actuator
- Rear wheel hub from the knuckle

To install:

3. Install or connect the
following:

- Parking brake lever bracket and
  actuator
- Hub and bearing assembly and
  torque the bolts to 55 ft. lbs. (75 Nm)
- WSS electrical connector
- Brake rotor, if equipped
- Brake caliper with the bracket
- Brake drum, if equipped
- Rear wheel

4. A 4-wheel alignment is recommended
after any steering/suspension repairs have
been performed.

SPECIFICATIONS AND MAINTENANCE CHARTS

ENGINE AND VEHICLE IDENTIFICATION

			Engine					Model Year	
Code ①	Liters	Cu. In.	Cyl.	Fuel Sys.	Engine Type	Eng. Mfg.		Code ②	Year
2	3.9	238	6	SFI	OHV	GM		9	2009
Y	4.6	279	8	SFI	DOHC	GM			
9	4.6	279	8	SFI	DOHC	GM			

SFI: Sequential Fuel Injection

DOHC: Dual overhead camshafts

OHV: Overhead Valves

① 8th position of VIN

② 10th position of VIN

36616_LUCE_C0001

GENERAL ENGINE SPECIFICATIONS

Year	Model	Engine Displacement Liters	Engine Series VIN	Net Horsepower @ rpm	Net Torque @ rpm (ft. lbs.)	Bore x Stroke (in.)	Compression Ratio	Oil Pressure @ rpm
2009	Lucerne	3.9	2	227@5700	237@3200	3.90x3.31	9.8:1	30-45@1850
		4.6	Y	275@5600	300@4000	3.66x3.31	10.0:1	35@2000
		4.6	9	275@5600	300@4000	3.66x3.31	10.0:1	35@2000

36616_LUCE_C0002

GASOLINE ENGINE TUNE-UP SPECIFICATIONS

Year	Engine Displacement Liters	Engine VIN	Spark Plug Gap (in.)	Ignition Timing (deg.)	Fuel Pump (psi)	Idle Speed (rpm)	Valve Clearance Intake	Valve Clearance Exhaust
2009	3.9	2	0.040	①	NA	②	HYD	HYD
	4.6	Y	0.050	①	NA	②	HYD	HYD
	4.6	9	0.050	①	NA	②	HYD	HYD

NOTE: The Vehicle Emission Control Information label often reflects specification changes made during production.

The label figures must be used if they differ from those in this chart.

NA: Not Available

HYD: Hydraulic

① Timing not adjustable

② Idle speed maintained by PCM. There is no recommended adjustment procedure.

36616_LUCE_C0003

CAPACITIES

Year	Model	Engine Displacement Liters	Engine VIN	Engine Oil with Filter (qts.)	Transmission (pts.)	Fuel Tank (gal.)	Cooling System (qts.)
2009	Lucerne	3.9	2	4.0	①	18.3	9.7
		4.6	Y	7.5	①	18.6	12.7
		4.6	9	7.5	①	18.6	12.7

NOTE: All capacities are approximate. Add fluid gradually and ensure a proper fluid level is obtained.

① 4T65-E transaxle: bottom pan removal: 14.8 pts.; complete overhaul: 20.0 pts.

4T80-E transaxle: bottom pan removal (requires drain plug removal): 14 pts.; complete overhaul (with existing converter): 25.2 pts

36616_LUCE_C0004

FLUID SPECIFICATIONS

Year	Model	Engine Displacement Liters	Engine ID/VIN	Engine Oil	Auto. Trans.	Manual Trans.	Power Steering Fluid	Brake Master Cylinder
2009	Lucerne	3.9	2	5W-30	Dexron VI	—	GM Part No. 89021184	DOT 3
		4.6	Y	5W-30	Dexron VI	—	GM Part No. 89021184	DOT 3
		4.6	9	5W-30	Dexron VI	—	GM Part No. 89021184	DOT 3

DOT: Department Of Transportation

36616_LUCE_C0005

VALVE SPECIFICATIONS

Year	Engine Displacement Liters	Engine VIN	Seat Angle (deg.)	Face Angle (deg.)	Spring Test Pressure (lbs. @ in.)	Spring Installed Height (in.)	Stem-to-Guide Clearance (in.) Intake	Stem-to-Guide Clearance (in.) Exhaust	Stem Diameter (in.) Intake	Stem Diameter (in.) Exhaust
2009	3.9	2	45	46	NA	1.840	0.0009-0.0025	0.0009-0.0025	NA	NA
	4.6	Y	45.75	45	130-142@ 0.9646	1.378	0.0011-0.0027	0.0020-0.0039	0.2331-0.2339	0.2331-0.2339
	4.6	9	45.75	45	130-142@ 0.9646	1.378	0.0011-0.0027	0.0020-0.0039	0.2331-0.2339	0.2331-0.2339

NA: Not Available

36616_LUCE_C0006

CAMSHAFT AND BEARING SPECIFICATIONS CHART
All measurements are given in inches.

Year	Engine Displ. Liters	Engine ID/VIN	Journal Dia.	Brg. Oil Clearance	Shaft End-play	Runout	Journal-to-Bore Clearance	Lobe Lift Intake	Lobe Lift Exhaust
2009	3.8	K	2.0240-2.0250	NA	NA	NA	NA	0.2727	0.2727
	4.6	Y	1.0610-1.0619	NA	0.0050-0.0087	0.0020	①	0.2421	0.2339
	4.6	9	1.0610-1.0619	NA	0.0050-0.0087	0.0020	①	0.2421	0.2339

NA: Not Available
① Production: 0.0020 - 0.0030 in.
   Service: 0.0016-0.0035 in.

36616_LUCE_C0007

CRANKSHAFT AND CONNECTING ROD SPECIFICATIONS
All measurements given in inches

Year	Engine Displacement Liters	Engine VIN	Main Brg. Journal Dia.	Main Brg. Oil Clearance	Shaft End-play	Thrust on No.	Journal Diameter	Oil Clearance	Side Clearance
2009	3.9	2	2.4988-2.4998	①	0.0024-0.0083	3	2.2480-2.2490	NA	0.0080-0.0090
	4.6	Y	2.5335-2.5341	0.0006-0.0022	0.0020-0.0197	3	2.1239-2.1245	0.0010-0.0030	0.0079-0.0197
	4.6	9	2.5335-2.5341	0.0006-0.0022	0.0020-0.0197	3	2.1239-2.1245	0.0010-0.0030	0.0079-0.0197

NA: Not Available
① Except #3: 0.0008 - 0.0025
   #3: 0.0012 - 0.0030

36616_LUCE_C0008

PISTON AND RING SPECIFICATIONS
All measurements given in inches

Year	Engine Displacement Liters	Engine VIN	Piston Clearance	Ring Gap Top Compression	Ring Gap Bottom Compression	Ring Gap Oil Control	Ring Side Clearance Top Compression	Ring Side Clearance Bottom Compression	Ring Side Clearance Oil Control
2009	3.9	2	①	0.0060-0.0110	0.0090-0.0170	0.0600-0.0250	NA	NA	NA
	4.6	Y	0.0008-0.0020	0.0098-0.0157	0.0020-0.0138	0.0098-0.0299	0.0016-0.0037	0.0016-0.0037	②
	4.6	9	0.0008-0.0020	0.0098-0.0157	0.0020-0.0138	0.0098-0.0299	0.0016-0.0037	0.0016-0.0037	②

NA: Not Available
① Piston-to-bore clearance (Production): 0.0003 - 0.0018 in.
   Piston-to-bore clearance (Service limit): 0.003 in.
② None - side sealing

36616_LUCE_C0009

TORQUE SPECIFICATIONS

All measurements given in ft. lbs. unless otherwise noted

Year	Engine Displacement Liters	Engine VIN	Cylinder Head Bolts	Main Bearing Bolts	Rod Bearing Bolts	Crankshaft Damper Bolts	Flywheel Bolts	Manifold		Spark Plugs	Oil Pan Drain Plug
								Intake	Exhaust		
2009	3.9	2	①	②	③	④	⑤	⑥	⑦	11	18
	4.6	Y	⑧	⑨	⑩	⑪	⑫	7.5	18	11	15
	4.6	9	⑧	⑨	⑩	⑪	⑫	7.5	18	11	15

① Step 1: Tighten all bolts to 44 ft. lbs.

   Step 2: Turn all bolts 140 degrees

② Cap bolts: 37 ft. lbs. plus 77 degrees

③ 18 ft. lbs. plus 110 degrees

④ 92 ft. lbs. plus 130 degrees

⑤ 52 ft. lbs.

⑥ Upper manifold: 18 ft. lbs.

   Lower manifold (center): 10 ft. lbs. then 15 ft. lbs.

   Lower manifold (corner): 10 ft. lbs. then 18 ft. lbs.

⑦ Exhaust manifold bolt: 15 ft. lbs.

   Heat shield: 89 in. lbs

⑧ M11 bolts:

   Step 1: 30 ft. lbs.

   Step 2: +70 degrees

   Step 3: +60 degrees

   Step 4: +45 degrees

   Do not exceed 175 degrees total

   M6 bolts: 106 inch lbs.

⑨ Lower crankcase

   M10x1.5

   Step 1: 15 ft. lbs.

   Step 2: +65 degrees

   M8x1.25: 22 ft. lbs.

⑩ Step 1: 22 ft. lbs.

   Step 2: back off to zero

   Step 3: 18 ft. lbs.

   Step 4: +110 degrees

⑪ Step 1: 37 ft. lbs.

   Step 2: +120 degrees

⑫ Step 1: 11 ft. lbs.

   Step 2: +50 degrees

36616_LUCE_C0010

WHEEL ALIGNMENT SPECIFICATIONS

Year	Model		Caster		Camber		Toe-in (in.)
			Range (+/-Deg.)	Preferred Setting (Deg.)	Range (+/-Deg.)	Preferred Setting (Deg.)	
2009	Lucerne	F	0.75	+5.40	0.75	-0.00	0.20 +/- 0.20
		R	—	—	0.75	-0.05	0.10 +/- 0.20

36616_LUCE_C0011

TIRE, WHEEL AND BALL JOINT SPECIFICATIONS

Year	Model	OEM Tires		Tire Pressures (psi)		Wheel Size	Ball Joint Inspection	Lug Nut Torque (ft. lbs.)
		Standard	Optional	Front	Rear			
2009	Lucerne CX	P235/55R17	None	①	①	17 in.	0.063 in. ②	100
	Lucerne CXL	P235/55R17	None	①	①	17 in.	0.063 in. ②	100
	Lucerne Super	P245/50R18	None	①	①	18 in.	0.063 in. ②	100

OEM: Original Equipment Manufacturer

PSI: Pounds Per Square Inch

① See placard on vehicle.

② Support the lower control arm with a floor stand. Gently lift or pry the suspension to induce ball joint movement.

36616_LUCE_C0012

BRAKE SPECIFICATIONS
All measurements given in inches unless otherwise noted

Year	Model		Original Thickness	Brake Disc Minimum Thickness	Maximum Runout	Minimum Lining Thickness	Caliper Bracket Bolts (ft. lbs.)	Caliper Guide Pin Bolts (ft. lbs.)
2009	Lucerne	F	1.181	1.126	0.002	NA	133	27
		R	0.472	0.413	0.002	NA	94	25

NA: Not Available

36616_LUCE_C0013

MAINTENANCE I AND II SERVICE SCHEDULES
2009 Buick Lucerne

When the CHANGE ENGINE OIL light appears, certain services and inspections are required.
Required services are described as Maintenance I and Maintenance II.
The first service on a vehicle should be Maintenance I, and the second service should be Maintenance II.

Alternate between the 2 thereafter. However, in some cases, Maintenance II may be required more often.
Maintenance I: Use Maintenance I if the CHANGE ENGINE OIL light comes on within 10 months since vehicle was purchased or, if Maintenance II was performed.
Maintenance II: Use Maintenance II if the previous service performed was Maintenance I. Always use Maintenance II whenever the CHANGE ENGINE OIL light comes on 10 months or more since the last service, or, if the CHANGE ENGINE OIL light has not come on at all for one year.

Service	Maintenance I	II
Change the engine oil and filter. Reset the oil life system.	✓	✓
Visually inspect the vehicle for leaks or damage. A fluid loss in the vehicle system could indicate a problem. Inspect, repair, and add fluid to the system if necessary.	✓	✓
Inspect the engine air cleaner filter. If necessary, replace the filter.	--	✓
Rotate the tires. Inspect the tire inflation pressures and the tire wear.	✓	✓
Visually inspect the brake lines and hoses for proper hook-up, binding, leaks, cracks, chafing, etc. Inspect the disc brake pads for wear and the rotors for surface condition. Inspect the drum brake linings for wear or cracks. Inspect other brake parts, including drums, wheel cylinders, calipers, parking brake, etc. Inspect the parking brake adjustment.	✓	✓
Inspect the engine coolant and the windshield washer fluid levels. Add fluid as needed.	✓	✓
Inspect the suspension and steering components. Inspect the front and rear suspension and the steering system for damaged, loose or missing parts, or signs of wear. Inspect the power steering lines and the hoses for proper hook-up, binding, leaks, cracks, chafing, etc.	--	✓
Visually inspect the coolant hoses and replace the hoses if they are cracked, swollen, or deteriorated. Inspect all pipes, fittings and clamps; replace with GM parts as needed. To help ensure proper operation, a pressure test of the cooling system and pressure cap and cleaning the outside of the radiator and air conditioning condenser is recommended at least once a year.	--	✓
Inspect the front and rear suspension and the steering system for damaged, loose, or missing parts, or signs of wear. Inspect power steering lines and hoses for proper hook-up, binding, leaks, cracks, chafing, etc.	--	✓
Inspect the throttle system for interference or binding and for damaged or missing parts. Replace the parts as needed. Replace any components that have high effort or excessive wear. Do not lubricate the accelerator or the cruise control cables.	--	✓
Replace the passenger compartment air filter.	--	✓

To reset the CHANGE ENGINE OIL LIGHT:
1. Press the option button on the DIC until ENGINE OIL MONITOR appears on the DIC screen.
2. Press the set/reset button to reset the system. The next screen indicates that the CHANGE OIL SOON message has been reset. If the vehicle has the uplevel DIC, when the gages button is pressed and the OIL LIFE REMAINING mode appears, it should read 100 percent OIL LIFE REMAINING.
3. Turn the key to OFF.

Vehicles without Driver Information Center (DIC)
1. With the engine off, turn the ignition key to RUN.
2. Fully press and release the accelerator pedal slowly three times within five seconds.
3. Turn the key to OFF, then start the vehicle.

If the light or message comes back on when you start your vehicle, the oil life system has not reset. Repeat the procedure.

36616_LUCE_C0014

ADDITIONAL MAINTENANCE SERVICES
2009 Buick Lucerne

TO BE SERVICED	TYPE OF	VEHICLE MILEAGE INTERVAL (x1000)					
		25	50	75	100	125	150
Air cleaner filter	R	✓	✓	✓	✓	✓	✓
Accessory drive belt	I						✓
Auto. Trans. Fluid ①	R		✓		✓		✓
Cooling system hoses and clamps	S/I						✓
Engine coolant	R						✓
Fuel system	I	✓	✓	✓	✓	✓	✓
Exhaust system & heat shields	S/I	✓	✓	✓	✓	✓	✓
Spark plugs	R				✓		

R: Replace   S/I: Inspect and service, if necessary

① Replace if any of the following conditions are met:

Heavy city traffic where the outside temperature regularly reaches 32°C (90°F) or higher

Hilly or mountainous terrain

Frequent trailer towing

Taxi, police, or delivery service

Otherwise, change every 100,000 miles

36616_LUCE_C0015

PRECAUTIONS

Before servicing any vehicle, please be sure to read all of the following precautions, which deal with personal safety, prevention of component damage, and important points to take into consideration when servicing a motor vehicle:

• Never open, service or drain the radiator or cooling system when the engine is hot; serious burns can occur from the steam and hot coolant.

• Observe all applicable safety precautions when working around fuel. Whenever servicing the fuel system, always work in a well-ventilated area. Do not allow fuel spray or vapors to come in contact with a spark, open flame, or excessive heat (a hot drop light, for example). Keep a dry chemical fire extinguisher near the work area. Always keep fuel in a container specifically designed for fuel storage; also, always properly seal fuel containers to avoid the possibility of fire or explosion. Refer to the additional fuel system precautions later in this section.

• Fuel injection systems often remain pressurized, even after the engine has been turned **OFF**. The fuel system pressure must be relieved before disconnecting any fuel lines. Failure to do so may result in fire and/or personal injury.

• Brake fluid often contains polyglycol ethers and polyglycols. Avoid contact with the eyes and wash your hands thoroughly after handling brake fluid. If you do get brake fluid in your eyes, flush your eyes with clean, running water for 15 minutes. If eye irritation persists, or if you have taken brake fluid internally, IMMEDIATELY seek medical assistance.

• The EPA warns that prolonged contact with used engine oil may cause a number of skin disorders, including cancer. You should make every effort to minimize your exposure to used engine oil. Protective gloves should be worn when changing oil. Wash your hands and any other exposed skin areas as soon as possible after exposure to used engine oil. Soap and water, or waterless hand cleaner should be used.

• All new vehicles are now equipped with an air bag system, often referred to as a Supplemental Restraint System (SRS) or Supplemental Inflatable Restraint (SIR) system. The system must be disabled before performing service on or around system components, steering column, instrument panel components, wiring and sensors. Failure to follow safety and disabling procedures could result in accidental air bag deployment, possible personal injury and unnecessary system repairs.

• Always wear safety goggles when working with, or around, the air bag system. When carrying a non-deployed air bag, be sure the bag and trim cover are pointed away from your body. When placing a non-deployed air bag on a work surface, always face the bag and trim cover upward, away from the surface. This will reduce the motion of the module if it is accidentally deployed. Refer to the additional air bag system precautions later in this section.

• Clean, high quality brake fluid from a sealed container is essential to the safe and proper operation of the brake system. You should always buy the correct type of brake fluid for your vehicle. If the brake fluid becomes contaminated, completely flush the system with new fluid. Never reuse any brake fluid. Any brake fluid that is removed from the system should be discarded. Also, do not allow any brake fluid to come in contact with a painted surface; it will damage the paint.

• Never operate the engine without the proper amount and type of engine oil; doing so WILL result in severe engine damage.

• Timing belt maintenance is extremely important. Many models utilize an interference-type, non-freewheeling engine. If the timing belt breaks, the valves in the cylinder head may strike the pistons, causing potentially serious (also time-consuming and expensive) engine damage. Refer to the maintenance interval charts for the recommended replacement interval for the timing belt, and to the timing belt section for belt replacement and inspection.

• Disconnecting the negative battery cable on some vehicles may interfere with the functions of the on-board computer system(s) and may require the computer to undergo a relearning process once the negative battery cable is reconnected.

• When servicing drum brakes, only disassemble and assemble one side at a time, leaving the remaining side intact for reference.

• Only an MVAC-trained, EPA-certified automotive technician should service the air conditioning system or its components.

BRAKES

GENERAL INFORMATION

PRECAUTIONS

• Certain components within the ABS system are not intended to be serviced or repaired individually.

• Do not use rubber hoses or other parts not specifically specified for and ABS system. When using repair kits, replace all parts included in the kit. Partial or incorrect repair may lead to functional problems and require the replacement of components.

• Lubricate rubber parts with clean, fresh brake fluid to ease assembly. Do not use shop air to clean parts; damage to rubber components may result.

• Use only DOT 3 brake fluid from an unopened container.

• If any hydraulic component or line is removed or replaced, it may be necessary to bleed the entire system.

• A clean repair area is essential. Always clean the reservoir and cap thoroughly before removing the cap. The slightest amount of dirt in the fluid may plug an orifice and impair the system function. Perform repairs after components have been thoroughly cleaned; use only denatured alcohol

ANTI-LOCK BRAKE SYSTEM (ABS)

to clean components. Do not allow ABS components to come into contact with any substance containing mineral oil; this includes used shop rags.

• The Anti-Lock control unit is a microprocessor similar to other computer units in the vehicle. Ensure that the ignition switch is **OFF** before removing or installing controller harnesses. Avoid static electricity discharge at or near the controller.

• If any arc welding is to be done on the vehicle, the control unit should be unplugged before welding operations begin.

BLEEDING PROCEDURE

BRAKE LINE BLEEDING

WARNING

When adding fluid to the brake master cylinder reservoir, use only Delco Supreme 11®, GM P/N 12377967 (Canadian P/N 992667), or equivalent DOT-3 brake fluid from a clean, sealed brake fluid container. The use of any type of fluid other than the recommended type of brake fluid may cause contamination which could result in damage to the internal rubber seals and/or rubber linings of hydraulic brake system components.

1. Before servicing the vehicle, refer to the Precautions Section.
2. Place a clean shop cloth beneath the brake master cylinder to prevent brake fluid spills.
3. With the ignition OFF and the brakes cool, apply the brakes 3–5 times, or until the brake pedal effort increases significantly, in order to deplete the brake booster power reserve.
4. If you have performed a brake master cylinder bench bleeding on this vehicle, or if you disconnected the brake pipes from the master cylinder, you must perform the following steps:
   a. Ensure that the brake master cylinder reservoir is full to the maximum-fill level. If necessary, add Delco Supreme 11®, GM P/N 12377967 (Canadian P/N 992667), or equivalent DOT-3 brake fluid from a clean, sealed brake fluid container. If removal of the reservoir cap and diaphragm is necessary, clean the outside of the reservoir on and around the cap prior to removal.
   b. With the rear brake pipe installed securely to the master cylinder, loosen and separate the front brake pipe from the front port of the brake master cylinder.
   c. Allow a small amount of brake fluid to gravity bleed from the open port of the master cylinder.
   d. Reconnect the brake pipe to the master cylinder port and tighten securely.
   e. Have an assistant slowly depress the brake pedal fully and maintain steady pressure on the pedal.
   f. Loosen the same brake pipe to purge air from the open port of the master cylinder.
   g. Tighten the brake pipe, then have the assistant slowly release the brake pedal.
   h. Wait 15 seconds, then repeat steps 3–7 until all air is purged from the same port of the master cylinder.
   i. With the front brake pipe installed securely to the master cylinder, after all air has been purged from the front port of the master cylinder, loosen and separate the rear brake pipe from the master cylinder, then repeat steps 3–8.
   j. After completing the final master cylinder port bleeding procedure, ensure that both of the brake pipe to master cylinder fittings are properly tightened.
5. Fill the brake master cylinder reservoir with Delco Supreme 11®, GM P/N 12377967 (Canadian P/N 992667), or equivalent DOT-3 brake fluid from a clean, sealed brake fluid container. Ensure that the brake master cylinder reservoir remains at least half-full during this bleeding procedure. Add fluid as needed to maintain the proper level. Clean the outside of the reservoir on and around the reservoir cap prior to removing the cap and diaphragm.
6. Install a proper box-end wrench onto the RIGHT REAR wheel hydraulic circuit bleeder valve.
7. Install a transparent hose over the end of the bleeder valve.
8. Submerge the open end of the transparent hose into a transparent container partially filled with Delco Supreme 11®, GM P/N 12377967 (Canadian P/N 992667), or equivalent DOT-3 brake fluid from a clean, sealed brake fluid container.
9. Have an assistant slowly depress the brake pedal fully and maintain steady pressure on the pedal.
10. Loosen the bleeder valve to purge air from the wheel hydraulic circuit.
11. Tighten the bleeder valve, then, have the assistant slowly release the brake pedal.
12. Wait 15 seconds, then repeat steps 8–10 until all air is purged from the same wheel hydraulic circuit.
13. With the right rear wheel hydraulic circuit bleeder valve tightened securely, after all air has been purged from the right rear hydraulic circuit, install a proper box-end wrench onto the LEFT FRONT wheel hydraulic circuit bleeder valve.
14. Install a transparent hose over the end of the bleeder valve, then, repeat steps 7–11.
15. With the left front wheel hydraulic circuit bleeder valve tightened securely, after all air has been purged from the left front hydraulic circuit, install a proper box-end wrench onto the LEFT REAR wheel hydraulic circuit bleeder valve.
16. Install a transparent hose over the end of the bleeder valve, then, repeat steps 7–11.
17. With the left rear wheel hydraulic circuit bleeder valve tightened securely, after all air has been purged from the left rear hydraulic circuit, install a proper box-end wrench onto the RIGHT FRONT wheel hydraulic circuit bleeder valve.
18. Install a transparent hose over the end of the bleeder valve, then, repeat steps 7–11.
19. After completing the final wheel hydraulic circuit bleeding procedure, ensure that each of the 4 wheel hydraulic circuit bleeder valves is properly tightened.
20. Fill the brake master cylinder reservoir to the maximum-fill level with Delco Supreme 11®, GM P/N 12377967 (Canadian P/N 992667), or equivalent DOT-3 brake fluid from a clean, sealed brake fluid container.
21. Slowly depress and release the brake pedal. Observe the feel of the brake pedal.
22. If the brake pedal feels spongy, repeat the bleeding procedure again. If the brake pedal still feels spongy after repeating the bleeding procedure, perform the following steps:
   a. Inspect the brake system for external leaks.
   b. Pressure bleed the hydraulic brake system in order to purge any air that may still be trapped in the system.
23. Turn the ignition key ON, with the engine OFF. Check to see if the brake system warning lamp remains illuminated.

BLEEDING THE ABS SYSTEM

➡The Auto Bleed Procedure may be terminated at any time during the process by pressing the EXIT button. No further Scan Tool prompts pertaining to the Auto Bleed procedure will be given. After exiting the bleed procedure, relieve bleed pressure and disconnect bleed equipment per manufacturer's instructions. Failure to properly relieve pressure may result in spilled brake fluid causing damage to components and painted surfaces.

1. Raise and support the vehicle.
2. Remove all four tire and wheel assemblies.

3. Inspect the brake system for leaks and visual damage.

4. Lower the vehicle.

5. Inspect the battery state of charge.

6. Install a scan tool.

7. Turn the ignition ON, with the engine OFF.

8. With the scan tool, establish communications with the ABS system. Select Special Functions. Select Automated Bleed from the Special Functions menu.

9. Raise and support the vehicle.

10. Following the directions given on the scan tool, pressure bleed the base brake system.

11. Follow the scan tool directions until the desired brake pedal height is achieved.

12. If the bleed procedure is aborted, a malfunction exists. Perform the following steps before resuming the bleed procedure:

a. If a DTC is detected, diagnose the appropriate DTC.

b. If the brake pedal feels spongy, perform the conventional brake bleed procedure again.

13. When the desired pedal height is achieved, press the brake pedal to inspect for firmness.

14. Lower the vehicle.

15. Remove the scan tool.

16. Install the tire and wheel assemblies.

17. Inspect the brake fluid level.

18. Road test the vehicle while inspecting that the pedal remains high and firm.

BRAKES   FRONT DISC BRAKES

✳✳ CAUTION

Dust and dirt accumulating on brake parts during normal use may contain asbestos fibers from production or aftermarket brake linings. Breathing excessive concentrations of asbestos fibers can cause serious bodily harm. Exercise care when servicing brake parts. Do not sand or grind brake lining unless equipment used is designed to contain the dust residue. Do not clean brake parts with compressed air or by dry brushing. Cleaning should be done by dampening the brake components with a fine mist of water, then wiping the brake components clean with a dampened cloth. Dispose of cloth and all residue containing asbestos fibers in an impermeable container with the appropriate label. Follow practices prescribed by the Occupational Safety and Health Administration (OSHA) and the Environmental Protection Agency (EPA) for the handling, processing, and disposing of dust or debris that may contain asbestos fibers.

BRAKE CALIPER

REMOVAL & INSTALLATION

See Figure 1.

1. Before servicing the vehicle, refer to the Precautions Section.

2. Raise and safely support the vehicle.

3. Remove the wheel and tire assembly.

4. Disconnect the brake hose from the brake caliper. Cap or plug the brake hose to prevent the contamination of the brake system and fluid leaks. Remove and discard the copper brake hose gaskets.

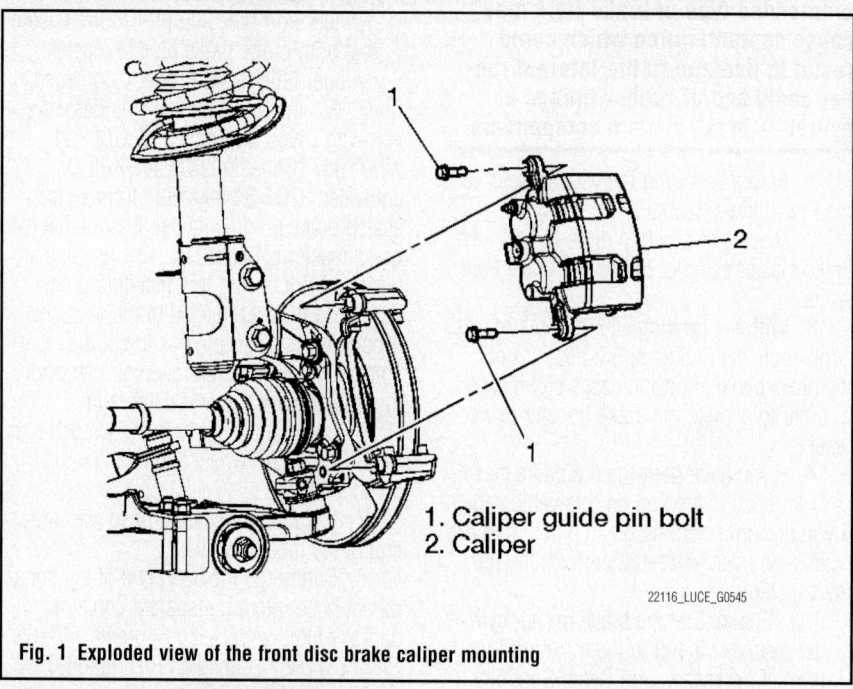

1. Caliper guide pin bolt
2. Caliper

22116_LUCE_G0545

Fig. 1 Exploded view of the front disc brake caliper mounting

✳✳ WARNING

DO NOT re-use the gaskets for the brake hose bolt. Use NEW gaskets only.

➡Hold the guide pin stationary when removing the guide pin bolt.

5. Use an open-ended wrench to hold the caliper guide pin, then unfasten the caliper guide pin bolts, and remove the caliper.

✳✳ WARNING

Do NOT let the open end of the wrench contact the brake caliper.

To install:

6. Install the caliper and secure with the guide pin bolts. Tighten to 27 ft. lbs. (36 Nm). Hold the guide pin stationary when installing the guide pin bolt.

7. Install the brake hose, using NEW gaskets, and tighten to 30 ft. lbs. (40 Nm).

8. Bleed the brake system.

9. With the engine **OFF**, gradually apply the brake pedal to approximately ⅔ of its travel distance.

10. Slowly release the brake pedal.

11. Wait 15 seconds, then repeat the previous 2 steps until a firm brake pedal is obtained. This will properly seat the brake caliper pistons and brake pads.

12. Fill the master cylinder reservoir to the proper level with the correct type of fluid.

DISC BRAKE PADS

REMOVAL & INSTALLATION

See Figure 2.

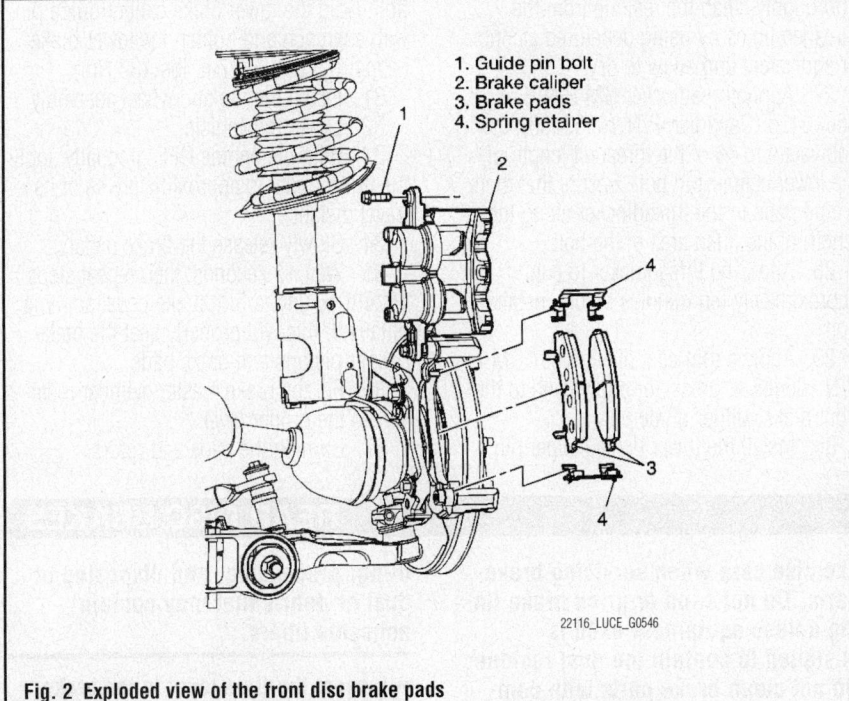

1. Guide pin bolt
2. Brake caliper
3. Brake pads
4. Spring retainer

22116_LUCE_G0546

Fig. 2 Exploded view of the front disc brake pads

✳ CAUTION

Dust and dirt accumulating on brake parts during normal use may contain asbestos fibers from production or aftermarket brake linings. Breathing excessive concentrations of asbestos fibers can cause serious bodily harm. Exercise care when servicing brake parts. Do not sand or grind brake lining unless equipment used is designed to contain the dust residue. Do not clean brake parts with compressed air or by dry brushing. Cleaning should be done by dampening the brake components with a fine mist of water, then wiping the brake components clean with a dampened cloth. Dispose of cloth and all residue containing asbestos fibers in an impermeable container with the appropriate label. Follow practices prescribed by the Occupational Safety and Health Administration (OSHA) and the Environmental Protection Agency (EPA) for the handling, processing, and disposing of dust or debris that may contain asbestos fibers.

➡**Two different designs of the front brake rotors and front brake pads are used on this vehicle. Do NOT interchange first design and second design parts, or a loss of braking and personal injury could occur.**

1. Before servicing the vehicle, refer to the Precautions Section.
2. Inspect the fluid level in the brake master cylinder reservoir.
3. If the brake fluid level is midway between the maximum-full point and the minimum allowable level, no brake fluid needs to be removed from the reservoir before proceeding.
4. If the brake fluid level is higher than midway between the maximum-full point and the minimum allowable level, remove brake fluid to the midway point before proceeding.
5. Raise and suitably support the vehicle.
6. Remove the tire and wheel assembly.
7. Install large C-clamp over the body of the brake caliper with the C-clamp ends against the rear of the caliper body and against the outboard brake pad.
8. Tighten the C-clamp evenly until the caliper pistons are compressed into the caliper bores enough to allow the caliper to slide past the brake rotor.
9. Remove the C-clamp from the caliper.
10. To loosen the brake caliper lower pin bolt, hold the brake caliper guide pin with a wrench.
11. Remove the brake caliper pin bolt.

✳ WARNING

Support the brake caliper with heavy mechanic's wire, or equivalent,

whenever it is separated from its mount and the hydraulic flexible brake hose is still connected. Failure to support the caliper in this manner will cause the flexible brake hose to bear the weight of the caliper, which may cause damage to the brake hose and in turn may cause a brake fluid leak.

12. Pivot the brake caliper body upward and secure the caliper out of the way with heavy mechanic's wire or equivalent. Ensure that there is no tension on the hydraulic brake flexible hose. Do NOT disconnect the hydraulic brake flexible hose from the caliper.
13. Remove the brake pads from the caliper bracket.
14. Remove and inspect the brake pad retainers from the caliper bracket.

To install:

➡**Ensure that the caliper guide pin boots are fully seated to the caliper guide pin retaining seat of the caliper pin. Ensure that the caliper guide pin boots are fully seated to the caliper boot seal retaining seat of the brake caliper mounting bracket.**

15. Inspect the brake caliper guide pin bolts. If damaged or corroded replace the brake caliper guide bolts.
16. Inspect the brake caliper guide pins. If damaged, or corroded replace the brake caliper guide pin. Do not attempt to clean away any corrosion.
17. Inspect the brake caliper guide pin boots for cuts, tears, or deterioration. If damaged, replace the brake caliper guide pin boots.
18. Carefully pull outward on the caliper guide pin to ensure that the caliper guide pin retaining seat is fully seated to the caliper guide pin boot.
19. Inspect the brake caliper piston boot for deterioration, replace if damaged.
20. Install a large C-clamp over the body of the brake caliper, with the C-clamp ends against the rear of the caliper body and against an old inboard brake pad or a wood block installed against the caliper pistons.
21. Tighten the C-clamp evenly until the caliper pistons are compressed completely into the caliper bores.
22. Remove the C-clamp and the old brake pad or wood block from the caliper.
23. Install the brake pad retainers to the caliper bracket.
24. Install the brake pads to the caliper bracket.

25. Pivot the brake caliper downward, over the brake pads and into the caliper bracket.

➡If reusing the lower caliper pin bolt, the threads of the lower caliper pin bolt and the threads of the caliper bracket mounting holes must be free of residue and debris prior to application of threadlocker in order to ensure proper adhesion and fastener retention.

26. If reusing the caliper pin bolts prepare the bolt and the threaded hole for assembly: Thoroughly clean the residue from the bolt threads by using denatured alcohol or equivalent and allow to dry.

Thoroughly clean the residue from the threaded holes by using denatured alcohol or equivalent and allow to dry.

27. Apply threadlocker GM P/N 36616493 (Canadian P/N 10953488), or equivalent to ⅔ of the threaded length of the lower caliper pin bolt. Ensure that there are no gaps in the threadlocker along the length of the filled area of the bolt.

28. Allow the threadlocker to cure approximately ten minutes before installation.

29. Apply a thin coat of Niglube® GM P/N 18046532 grease or equivalent, to the front brake caliper guide pin.

30. Install the lower brake caliper pin

bolt. Hold the lower brake caliper guide pin with a wrench and tighten the lower brake caliper pin bolt to 27 ft. lbs. (36 Nm).

31. Install the tire and wheel assembly.

32. Lower the vehicle.

33. With the engine OFF, gradually apply the brake pedal to approximately ⅔ of its travel distance.

34. Slowly release the brake pedal.

35. Wait 15 seconds, then repeat steps 15 and 16 until a firm brake pedal apply is obtained; this will properly seat the brake caliper pistons and brake pads.

36. Fill the brake master cylinder reservoir to the proper level.

37. Burnish the pads and rotors.

BRAKES   REAR DISC BRAKES

❊❊ CAUTION

Dust and dirt accumulating on brake parts during normal use may contain asbestos fibers from production or aftermarket brake linings. Breathing excessive concentrations of asbestos fibers can cause serious bodily harm. Exercise care when servicing brake parts. Do not sand or grind brake lining unless equipment used is designed to contain the dust residue. Do not clean brake parts with compressed air or by dry brushing. Cleaning should be done by dampening the brake components with a fine mist of water, then wiping the brake components clean with a dampened cloth. Dispose of cloth and all residue containing asbestos fibers in an impermeable container with the appropriate label. Follow practices prescribed by the Occupational Safety and Health Administration (OSHA) and the Environmental Protection Agency (EPA) for the handling, processing, and disposing of dust or debris that may contain asbestos fibers.

BRAKE CALIPER

REMOVAL & INSTALLATION
See Figure 3.

❊❊ CAUTION

Dust and dirt accumulating on brake parts during normal use may contain asbestos fibers from production or aftermarket brake linings. Breathing excessive concentrations of asbestos fibers can cause serious bodily harm.

Exercise care when servicing brake parts. Do not sand or grind brake lining unless equipment used is designed to contain the dust residue. Do not clean brake parts with compressed air or by dry brushing. Cleaning should be done by dampening the brake components with a fine mist of water, then wiping the brake components clean with a dampened cloth. Dispose of cloth and all residue containing asbestos fibers in an impermeable container with the appropriate label. Follow practices prescribed by the Occupational Safety and Health Administration (OSHA) and the Environmental Protection Agency (EPA) for the handling, processing, and disposing of dust or debris that may contain asbestos fibers.

➡Inspect the fluid level in the brake master cylinder reservoir. If the brake fluid level is midway between the maximum-full point and the minimum allowable level, no brake fluid needs to be removed from the reservoir before proceeding. If the brake fluid level is higher than midway between the maximum-full point and the minimum allowable level, remove brake fluid to the midway point before proceeding.

1. Before servicing the vehicle, refer to the Precautions Section.

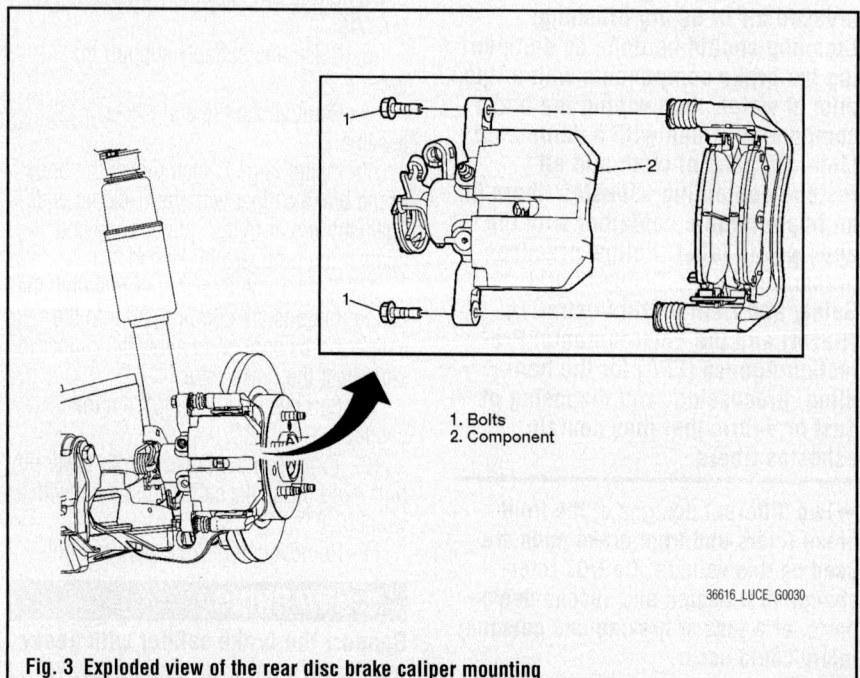

1. Bolts
2. Component

36616_LUCE_G0030

Fig. 3 Exploded view of the rear disc brake caliper mounting

2. Raise the vehicle and suitably support.

3. Remove the tire and wheel assembly.

4. Pull down on the front park brake cable.

5. Remove the front park brake cable from the park brake cable connector.

✳✳ WARNING

When using a large C-clamp to compress a caliper piston into a caliper bore of a caliper equipped with an integral park brake mechanism, do not exceed more than 0.039 in. (1mm) of piston travel. Exceeding this amount of piston travel will cause damage to the internal adjusting mechanism and/or the integral park brake mechanism.

6. Install a large C-clamp over the top of the brake caliper housing and against the back of the outboard brake pad. Compress the brake caliper piston into brake caliper bore to allow the piston enough clearance to slide the brake caliper off the brake rotor.

7. Remove the C-clamp.

➡**Be sure to plug the opening in the brake caliper and brake hose to prevent fluid loss and/or contamination.**

8. Remove brake hose to caliper bolt attaching the brake hose to the brake caliper.

9. Remove the brake hose from the brake caliper.

10. Remove and discard the two copper brake hose gaskets. These gaskets may be stuck to the brake caliper and/or the brake hose end.

11. Remove the park brake cable bracket from the brake caliper. Leave the park brake cable attached to the cable bracket.

12. Disconnect the park brake cable from the park brake lever on the brake caliper.

13. Remove the lower brake caliper pin bolt.

14. Rotate the brake caliper up.

15. Remove the brake caliper from the upper brake caliper pin bolt.

To install:

16. If reusing the brake caliper retainers, clean the sleeves using denatured alcohol, or equivalent.

17. Lubricate the brake caliper pin bolts with a thin coat of high temperature silicone lube.

18. Install the brake caliper to the upper caliper pin bolt.

19. Rotate the brake caliper down over the brake pads into the brake caliper bracket.

20. Install the brake caliper pin bolts. Tighten the brake caliper pin bolts to 27 ft. lbs. (36 Nm).

21. Remove the plugs in the brake hose end.

➡**Install NEW copper brake hose gaskets.**

22. Assemble the brake hose bolt and the NEW copper brake hose gaskets to the brake hose.

23. Install the brake hose to caliper bolt to the brake caliper. Tighten the brake hose to caliper bolt to 33 ft. lbs. (44 Nm).

24. Connect the park brake cable to the park brake lever on the brake caliper.

25. Install the park brake cable bracket to the brake caliper. Tighten the park brake cable bracket bolt to 32 ft. lbs. (43 Nm).

26. Install the front park brake cable to the park brake cable connector.

27. Bleed the brake system.

28. With the engine OFF, gradually apply the brake pedal to approximately ⅔ of its travel distance.

29. Slowly release the brake pedal.

30. Wait 15 seconds, then repeat until a firm brake pedal is obtained. This will properly seat the brake caliper pistons and brake pads.

31. Install the tire and wheel assembly. Tighten the wheel lug nuts to 100 ft. lbs. (136 Nm).

32. Lower the vehicle.

DISC BRAKE PADS

REMOVAL & INSTALLATION

See Figure 4.

✳✳ CAUTION

Dust and dirt accumulating on brake parts during normal use may contain asbestos fibers from production or aftermarket brake linings. Breathing excessive concentrations of asbestos fibers can cause serious bodily harm. Exercise care when servicing brake parts. Do not sand or grind brake lining unless equipment used is designed to contain the dust residue. Do not clean brake parts with compressed air or by dry brushing. Cleaning should be done by dampening the brake components with a fine mist of water, then wiping the brake components clean with a dampened cloth. Dispose of cloth and all residue containing asbestos fibers in an impermeable container with the appropriate label. Follow practices prescribed by the Occupational Safety and Health Administration (OSHA) and the Environmental Protection Agency (EPA) for the handling, processing, and disposing of dust or debris that may contain asbestos fibers.

➡**Inspect the fluid level in the brake master cylinder reservoir. If the brake fluid level is midway between the maximum-full point and the minimum allowable level, no brake fluid needs to be removed from the reservoir before proceeding. If the brake fluid level is higher than midway between the maximum-full point and the minimum allowable level, remove brake fluid to the midway point before proceeding.**

1. Before servicing the vehicle, refer to the Precautions Section.

2. Raise and safely support the vehicle.

3. Remove the tire and wheel assembly.

➡**When using a large C-clamp to compress a caliper piston into a caliper bore of a caliper equipped with an integral park brake mechanism, do not exceed more than 0.039 in. (1mm) of piston travel. Exceeding this amount of piston travel will cause damage to the internal adjusting mechanism and/or the integral park brake mechanism.**

4. Using a large C clamp, compress the brake caliper piston into the brake caliper bore to gain enough clearance to allow the brake caliper to pivot off the brake caliper bracket.

5. Compress the piston until resistance is felt.

6. Remove the park brake cable guide bolt from the lower control arm.

7. Remove the bottom brake caliper pin bolt.

➡**Support the brake caliper with heavy mechanic's wire, or equivalent, whenever it is separated from its mount and the hydraulic flexible brake hose is still connected. Failure to support the caliper in this manner will cause the flexible brake hose to bear the weight of the caliper, which may cause damage to the brake hose and in turn may cause a brake fluid leak.**

8. Pivot the brake caliper body upward and secure out of the way with heavy mechanic's wire. Do NOT disconnect the hydraulic brake flexible hose from the caliper.

9. Remove the inboard and outboard brake pads from the brake caliper bracket.

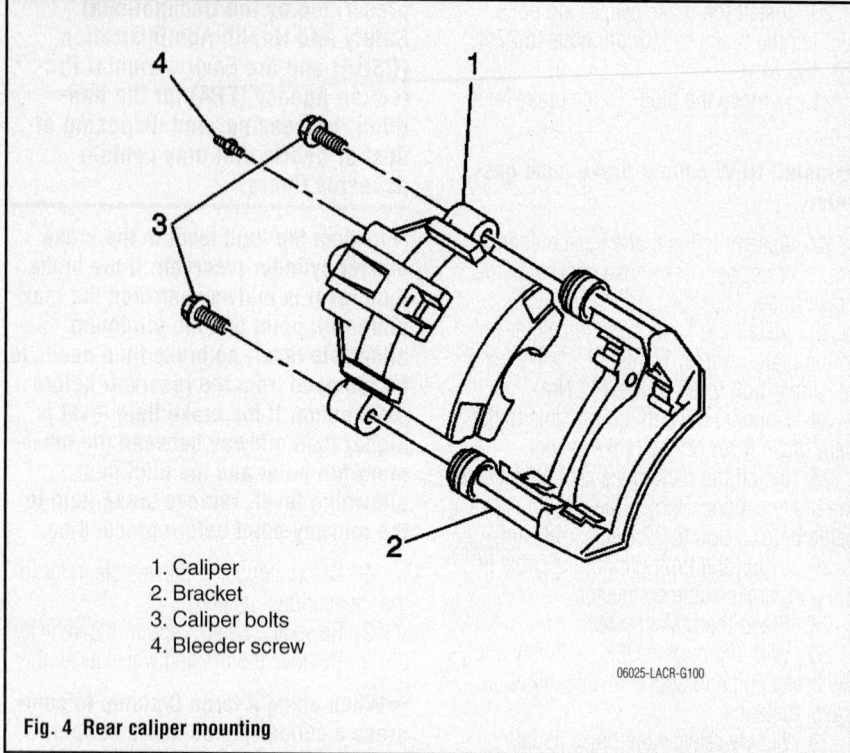

1. Caliper
2. Bracket
3. Caliper bolts
4. Bleeder screw

06025-LACR-G100

Fig. 4 Rear caliper mounting

10. Remove and inspect the brake pad retainers.

To install:

11. Inspect the brake caliper bolt suspension boots for cuts, tears, or deterioration. If damaged, replace the brake caliper pin boots.

12. Inspect the brake caliper pin bolts for damage or corrosion. Replace if damaged or corroded. Do not attempt to clean away corrosion. Corrosion is typically caused by damaged pin boots.

13. Inspect the brake caliper piston boot for deterioration, repair or replace the brake caliper if damaged.

14. Retract the brake caliper piston into the brake caliper bore. Use a spanner type wrench to turn the piston clockwise until it bottoms in the brake caliper bore and align the piston.

15. Align the cutouts in the brake caliper piston to the alignment pins on the brake pads.

16. Apply a thin coat of high temperature silicone lube to the rear brake caliper bolts.

17. Install the brake pad retainers into the brake caliper bracket.

18. Install the inboard and outboard brake pads into the brake caliper bracket.

19. Pivot the brake caliper down over the brake pads and into the brake caliper bracket.

20. Insert the lower brake caliper pin bolt. Tighten the brake caliper pin bolt to 27 ft. lbs. (36 Nm).

21. Install the park brake cable guide bolt to the lower control arm. Tighten the park brake cable guide bolt to 18 ft. lbs. (24 Nm).

22. Install the tire and wheel assembly. Tighten the wheel lug nuts to 100 ft. lbs. (136 Nm).

23. Lower the vehicle.

24. With the engine OFF, gradually apply the brake pedal to approximately ⅔ of its travel distance.

25. Slowly release the brake pedal.

26. Wait 15 seconds, then repeat until a firm brake pedal is obtained. This will properly seat the brake caliper pistons and brake pads.

27. Fill the brake master cylinder reservoir to the proper level.

28. Burnish the pads and rotors.

BRAKES

PARKING BRAKE

PARKING BRAKE CABLES

ADJUSTMENT

The plastic coated park brake cables do not require periodic lubrication. Coated park brake cables are used to reduce apply effort and increase corrosion protection. The cables are coated with a plastic material which slides against nylon seals inside the conduit end fittings.

The park brake lever has an indicator switch which closes when the park brake is set, thus illuminating the red BRAKE lamp.

The park brake lever/cable adjustment is automatic. Cycling the lever two to three times should result in properly adjusting the park brake after disabling it for service. The park brake application is completely independent of the hydraulic brake system. The park brake system is a mechanical system which operates the rear disc brakes through the calipers. The system is activated by depressing the park brake pedal, which applies the rear disc brakes via cables. When the park brake is set and the ignition switch is on, the BRAKE warning lamp on the instrument panel will be on. The park brake is released by pushing the pedal down until a click is heard and then releasing. The pedal will click again and the BRAKE lamp in the instrument panel should go out when the park brake system is fully released.

Manual adjustment may be necessary when the rear brake cables have been disconnected. A need for park brake cable adjustment is indicated if the hydraulic brake system operates with good reserve, but a firm park brake pedal feel cannot be achieved with less than one full stroke of the park brake pedal.

1. Before servicing the vehicle, refer to the Precautions Section.

2. Apply and release the park brake four times.

3. The park brake light should be illuminated after park brake has been depressed slightly.

4. Check the parking brake pedal assembly for full release by turning the ignition on and inspecting the PARK BRAKE warning light. The light should be off. If the PARK BRAKE warning light is on and the park brake appears to be fully released, pull the pedal back by hand and continue with the adjustment procedure.

5. Raise the vehicle and suitably support.

6. Check the park brake levers on rear calipers. The levers should be against the stops on the caliper housing. If the levers are not against the stops, check for binding in the rear brake cables and position levers against stops.

7. Tighten the park brake cable at the equalizer until either the left or right lever begins to move off the stop.

8. Loosen the adjustment at the equalizer until the lever which has moved off the stop, as in step 5, is again resting fully against the stops. Loosen the tension at the equalizer until the cables feel slightly loose to the touch. The cables should not sag under their own weight.

9. Operate the park brake several times to check adjustment. A firm pedal feel should be obtained by depressing the pedal less than one full stroke.

10. Inspect the left and right caliper levers. Both levers must be resting on the stops after the adjustment of the parking brake.

11. Check the operation of the park brake.

12. To achieve optimal performance, ensure the cables are not over-tensioned at the equalizer.

CHASSIS ELECTRICAL

AIR BAG (SUPPLEMENTAL RESTRAINT SYSTEM)

GENERAL INFORMATION

※※ CAUTION

These vehicles are equipped with an air bag system. The system must be disarmed before performing service on, or around, system components, the steering column, instrument panel components, wiring and sensors. Failure to follow the safety precautions and the disarming procedure could result in accidental air bag deployment, possible injury and unnecessary system repairs.

SERVICE PRECAUTIONS

Disconnect and isolate the battery negative cable before beginning any airbag system component diagnosis, testing, removal, or installation procedures. Allow system capacitor to discharge for two minutes before beginning any component service. This will disable the airbag system. Failure to disable the airbag system may result in accidental airbag deployment, personal injury, or death.

Do not place an intact undeployed airbag face down on a solid surface. The airbag will propel into the air if accidentally deployed and may result in personal injury or death.

When carrying or handling an undeployed airbag, the trim side (face) of the airbag should be pointing towards the body to minimize possibility of injury if accidental deployment occurs. Failure to do this may result in personal injury or death.

Replace airbag system components with OEM replacement parts. Substitute parts may appear interchangeable, but internal differences may result in inferior occupant protection. Failure to do so may result in occupant personal injury or death.

Wear safety glasses, rubber gloves, and long sleeved clothing when cleaning powder residue from vehicle after an airbag deployment. Powder residue emitted from a deployed airbag can cause skin irritation. Flush affected area with cool water if irritation is experienced. If nasal or throat irritation is experienced, exit the vehicle for fresh air until the irritation ceases. If irritation continues, see a physician.

Do not use a replacement airbag that is not in the original packaging. This may result in improper deployment, personal injury, or death.

The factory installed fasteners, screws and bolts used to fasten airbag components have a special coating and are specifically designed for the airbag system. Do not use substitute fasteners. Use only original equipment fasteners listed in the parts catalog when fastener replacement is required.

During, and following, any child restraint anchor service, due to impact event or vehicle repair, carefully inspect all mounting hardware, tether straps, and anchors for proper installation, operation, or damage. If a child restraint anchor is found damaged in any way, the anchor must be replaced. Failure to do this may result in personal injury or death.

Deployed and non-deployed airbags may or may not have live pyrotechnic material within the airbag inflator.

Do not dispose of driver/passenger/curtain airbags or seat belt tensioners unless you are sure of complete deployment. Refer to the Hazardous Substance Control System for proper disposal.

Dispose of deployed airbags and tensioners consistent with state, provincial, local, and federal regulations.

After any airbag component testing or service, do not connect the battery negative cable. Personal injury or death may result if the system test is not performed first.

If the vehicle is equipped with the Occupant Classification System (OCS), do not connect the battery negative cable before performing the OCS Verification Test using the scan tool and the appropriate diagnostic information. Personal injury or death may result if the system test is not performed properly.

Never replace both the Occupant Restraint Controller (ORC) and the Occupant Classification Module (OCM) at the same time. If both require replacement, replace one, then perform the Airbag System test before replacing the other.

Both the ORC and the OCM store Occupant Classification System (OCS) calibration data, which they transfer to one another when one of them is replaced. If both are replaced at the same time, an irreversible fault will be set in both modules and the OCS may malfunction and cause personal injury or death.

If equipped with OCS, the Seat Weight Sensor is a sensitive, calibrated unit and must be handled carefully. Do not drop or handle roughly. If dropped or damaged, replace with another sensor. Failure to do so may result in occupant injury or death.

If equipped with OCS, the front passenger seat must be handled carefully as well. When removing the seat, be careful when setting on floor not to drop. If dropped, the sensor may be inoperative, could result in occupant injury, or possibly death.

If equipped with OCS, when the passenger front seat is on the floor, no one should sit in the front passenger seat. This uneven force may damage the sensing ability of the seat weight sensors. If sat on and damaged, the sensor may be inoperative, could result in occupant injury, or possibly death.

DISARMING THE SYSTEM

➡For vehicles equipped with OnStar (RPO UE1), with battery backup, the backup battery is a redundant power supply to allow limited OnStar functionality in the event of a main battery power disruption to the OnStar module (VCIM). Do not disconnect the main vehicle battery or remove the OnStar fuse with the ignition key in any position other than OFF. Retained accessory power should be allowed to time out or be disabled by opening the driver's side door before disconnecting power. Disconnecting power to the module in any way while the ignition is ON or with the retained accessory power activated may cause activation of the OnStar backup battery system and will discharge and permanently damage the backup battery. Once the backup battery is activated it will stay on until it has completely discharged. The backup battery is not rechargeable

and once it is activated, it must be replaced.

➡The rear seat cushion must be removed to gain access to the battery.

1. Before servicing the vehicle, refer to the Precautions Section.

➡When performing service on or near the SRS components, or SRS wiring the SRS must be disabled. Failure to observe the correct procedure could cause deployment of the SRS components. Serious injury can occur.

2. Position the steering wheel so the front wheels are in the straight ahead position.

3. Be sure the ignition switch is in the OFF position.

4. Disconnect the negative battery cable.

➡The SDM may have more than one fused power input. To ensure that there is no unwanted SRS deployment, personal injury, or unnecessary SRS system repairs, remove all fuses supplying power to the SDM. With all SDM fuses removed and the ignition switch in the ON position, the AIR BAG warning indicator will illuminate. This is normal and does not indicate a SRS system malfunction.

5. Locate and remove the fuses supplying power to the SDM.

6. Wait one minute before working on the vehicle.

ARMING THE SYSTEM

1. Before servicing the vehicle, refer to the Precautions Section.

2. Be sure the ignition switch is in the OFF position.

3. Install the fuses.

4. Connect the negative battery cable.

5. Turn the ignition switch to the ON position.

6. If the system is operating properly the AIR BAG indicator will flash

7. Correct problems as required.

CLOCKSPRING CENTERING

See Figures 5 and 6.

1. Before servicing the vehicle, refer to the Precautions Section.

➡The new SIR coil assembly will be centered. Improper alignment of the

SIR coil assembly may damage the unit, causing an inflatable restraint malfunction.

2. Verify that the front wheels are in the straight ahead position, the tooth block of the steering shaft assembly is in the 12 o'clock position and the ignition switch is in the LOCK position

3. Hold the coil with the face up. Rotate the coil hub in the direction of the arrow (see illustration), until the coil ribbon stops.

4. Rotate the coil hub slowly, counterclockwise for 2 ½ revolutions. This is the center position.

5. While maintaining the coil hub in the center position, align the centered coil with the horn tower and slide the coil onto the steering shaft assembly.

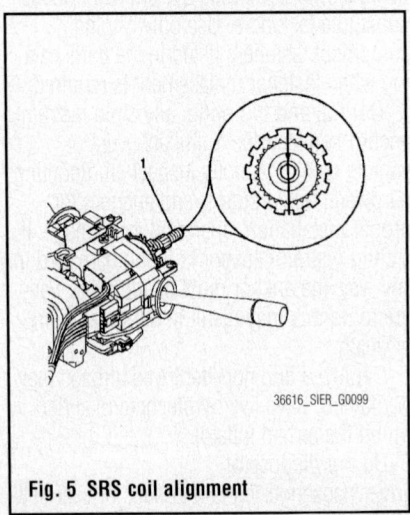

36616_SIER_G0099

Fig. 5 SRS coil alignment

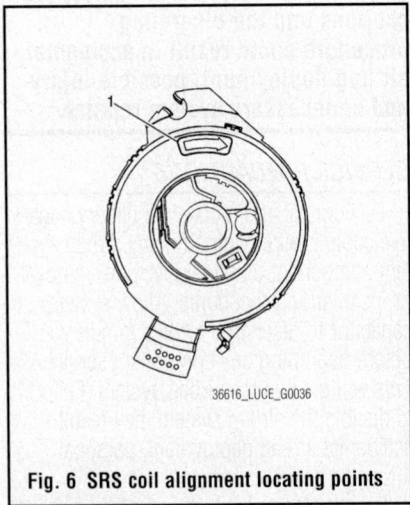

36616_LUCE_G0036

Fig. 6 SRS coil alignment locating points

DRIVE TRAIN

AUTOMATIC TRANSAXLE ASSEMBLY

REMOVAL & INSTALLATION

See Figures 7 and 8.

➡For vehicles equipped with OnStar (RPO UE1), with battery backup, the backup battery is a redundant power supply to allow limited OnStar functionality in the event of a main battery power disruption to the OnStar module (VCIM). Do not disconnect the main vehicle battery or remove the OnStar fuse with the ignition key in any position other than OFF. Retained accessory power should be allowed to time out or be disabled by opening the driver's side door before disconnecting power. Disconnecting power to the

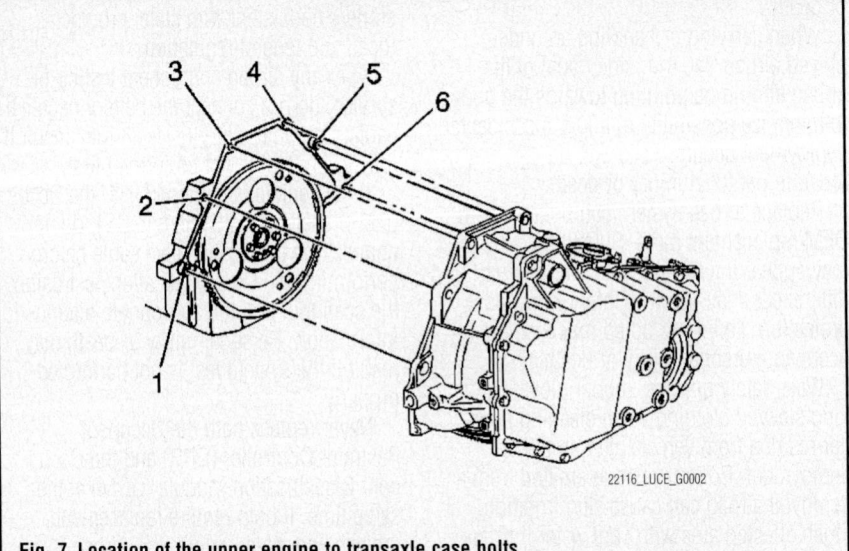

22116_LUCE_G0002

Fig. 7 Location of the upper engine to transaxle case bolts

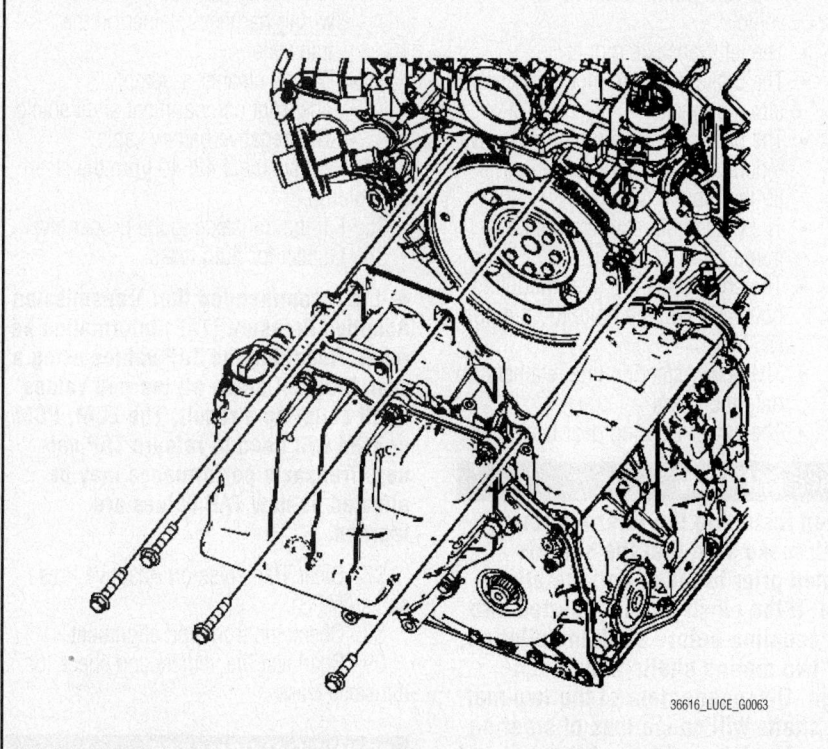

Fig. 8 Location of the upper engine to transaxle case bolts—4T80-E transaxle

module in any way while the ignition is ON or with the retained accessory power activated may cause activation of the OnStar backup battery system and will discharge and permanently damage the backup battery. Once the backup battery is activated it will stay on until it has completely discharged. The backup battery is not rechargeable and once it is activated, it must be replaced.

➡The rear seat cushion must be removed to gain access to the battery.

✳✳ WARNING

The wheels of the vehicle must be straight ahead and the steering column in the LOCK position before disconnecting the steering column or intermediate shaft from the steering gear. Failure to do so will cause the SIR coil assembly to become uncentered, which may cause damage to the coil assembly.

1. Lock the steering column by installing J 42640 into the underside of the steering column.
2. Remove or disconnect the following:
   - The negative battery cable

- The front compartment sight shield
- The air cleaner assembly.
- The range select cable terminal from the transaxle range select lever
- The range selector cable bracket nuts
- The range selector cable with bracket from the transmission case and position aside
- The transaxle electrical connector C100
- The wiring harness from the wiring harness retainer on the transaxle
- The ground cable bolt from the transaxle

3. Install the engine support fixture.
4. Remove the upper engine to transaxle case bolts (2–5).
5. Raise and support the vehicle.
6. Remove or disconnect the following:
   - The front tire and wheel
   - The left front wheelhouse liner
   - The front air deflector
   - The stabilizer shaft links (control links)
7. Swing the stabilizer shaft downward in order to gain access to the power steering gear retaining bolts.

✳✳ WARNING

Failure to disconnect the intermediate shaft from the rack and pinion steering gear stub shaft can result in damage to the steering gear or to the intermediate shaft. This damage may cause loss of steering control, which could result in an accident and possible personal injury.

8. Remove the intermediate shaft lower pinch bolt.
9. Disconnect the intermediate shaft from the power steering gear.
10. Remove the power steering gear heat shield.
11. Remove the power steering gear mounting bolts.
12. Remove the power steering line retainers from the frame.
13. Secure the power steering gear to the exhaust manifold.
14. Remove the mounting bolts in order to allow removal of the brake pressure modulator valve from the bracket.
15. Remove the brake line retainers from the frame.
16. The following are exceptions while following the frame removal procedure:
   a. Do not remove the front stabilizer shaft from the frame.
   b. Do not remove the insulators from the frame.
   c. Do not remove the control arms from the frame.
17. Remove or disconnect the following:
   - The front frame
   - The right and left drive axles from the transaxle. Refer to Halfshafts, removal & installation.
   - The transmission oil cooler hoses from the transaxle using the J 41623-B
   - The transaxle fluid filler tube
   - The torque converter cover
18. Mark the flywheel to converter relationship to ensure proper reassembly. Remove the flywheel to torque converter bolts.
19. Support the transaxle using an appropriate transaxle jack.
20. Remove or disconnect the following:
   - The Vehicle Speed Sensor (VSS) electrical connector.
   - The right engine to transaxle brace bolts
   - The front transaxle to engine brace bolt
   - The engine to transaxle case bolt (6) which is accessible through right wheel opening

- The remaining transaxle to engine bolt (1)
- The transaxle from vehicle using an appropriate transaxle jack
- The rear transaxle mount bracket from the transaxle
- The left transaxle mount bracket from the transaxle

21. Remove the automatic transaxle assembly.

To install:

22. Flush the transmission cooler and lines.

23. Install or connect the following:
- The left transaxle mount bracket to the transaxle
- The left transaxle bracket bolts. Tighten the bolts to 52 ft. lbs. (70 Nm)
- The rear transaxle mount bracket to the transaxle
- The rear transaxle mount bracket bolts. Tighten the bolts to 37 ft. lbs. (50 Nm)
- The transaxle into the vehicle and align the engine alignment dowels
- The Install the transaxle case to engine bolts. Tighten the bolts to 55 ft. lbs. (75 Nm)
- The front transaxle to engine brace bolt. Tighten the bolt to 37 ft. lbs. (50 Nm)
- The right engine to transaxle brace bolts. Tighten the bolts to 37 ft. lbs. (50 Nm)
- The VSS electrical connector

24. Remove the transaxle jack.

➡**Align the mark made on the torque converter with the mark made on the flywheel made in the disassembly unless installing a new converter. Tighten all the torque converter to flywheel bolts twice.**

25. Install or connect the following:
- The flywheel to torque converter bolts. Tighten the bolts to 47 ft. lbs. (63 Nm)
- The torque converter cover
- The transaxle fluid filler tube
- The transmission oil cooler hoses to the transaxle

✱✱ WARNING

Use care when installing the right side drive axle into the transaxle case. The splined shaft of the drive axle can easily damage the seal.

- The left and the right drive axle into the transaxle. Refer to Halfshafts, removal & installation

- The front frame assembly to the vehicle
- The left transaxle mount
- The brake pressure modulator valve into the bracket
- The brake pressure modulator valve mounting bolt. Tighten the bolt to 89 inch lbs. (10 Nm)
- The brake line retainers onto the frame
- The power steering gear mounting bolts. Tighten the bolts to 55 ft. lbs. (75 Nm)
- The power steering line retainers onto the frame
- The power steering gear heat shield

✱✱ CAUTION

When installing the intermediate shaft make sure that the shaft is seated prior to pinch bolt installation. If the pinch bolt is inserted into the coupling before shaft installation, the two mating shafts may disengage. Disengagement of the two mating shafts will cause loss of steering control which could result in personal injury.

- The intermediate shaft to the power steering gear
- The intermediate shaft lower pinch bolt. Tighten the bolt to 33 ft. lbs. (45 Nm)
- The stabilizer shaft links (control links)
- The air deflector extension
- The left front wheelhouse liner
- The front tire and wheel assembly. Tighten the wheel lug nuts to 100 ft. lbs. (136 Nm)

26. Lower the vehicle.

27. Install the upper transaxle case to engine bolts (2–5). Tighten the bolts to 55 ft. lbs. (75 Nm).

28. Remove the engine support fixture.

29. Install the range selector cable with bracket.

30. Install the range selector cable bracket nuts. Tighten the nuts to 18 ft. lbs. (25 Nm).

31. Install the range selector cable onto the range selector lever.

32. Check adjustment of the range selector cable. Re-adjust as needed.

33. Install or connect the following:
- The ground cable and bolt to transaxle. Tighten the bolt to 13 ft. lbs. (17 Nm)
- The transaxle electrical connector C100

- The wiring harness into the wiring harness retainer on the transaxle
- The air cleaner assembly
- The front compartment sight shield
- The negative battery cable

34. Remove the J 42640 from the steering column.

35. Fill the transaxle to the proper level.

36. Inspect for fluid leaks.

➡**It is recommended that Transmission Adaptive Pressure (TAP) information be reset. Resetting the TAP values using a scan tool will erase all learned values in all cells. As a result, The ECM, PCM or TCM will need to relearn TAP values. Transaxle performance may be affected as new TAP values are learned.**

37. Clear Transmission Adaptive Pressures (TAPS).

38. Check the front end alignment.

39. Road test the vehicle and check for transaxle leaks.

FRONT HALFSHAFTS

REMOVAL & INSTALLATION

See Figures 9 and 10.

✱✱ CAUTION

To prevent personal injury and/or component damage, do not allow the weight of the vehicle to load the front wheels, or attempt to operate the vehicle, when the halfshaft(s) or halfshaft nut(s) are removed. To do so may cause the inner bearing race to separate, resulting in damage to brake and suspension components and loss of vehicle control.

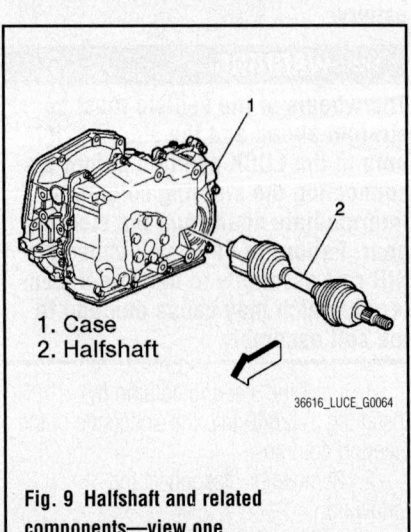

1. Case
2. Halfshaft

36616_LUCE_G0064

Fig. 9 Halfshaft and related components—view one

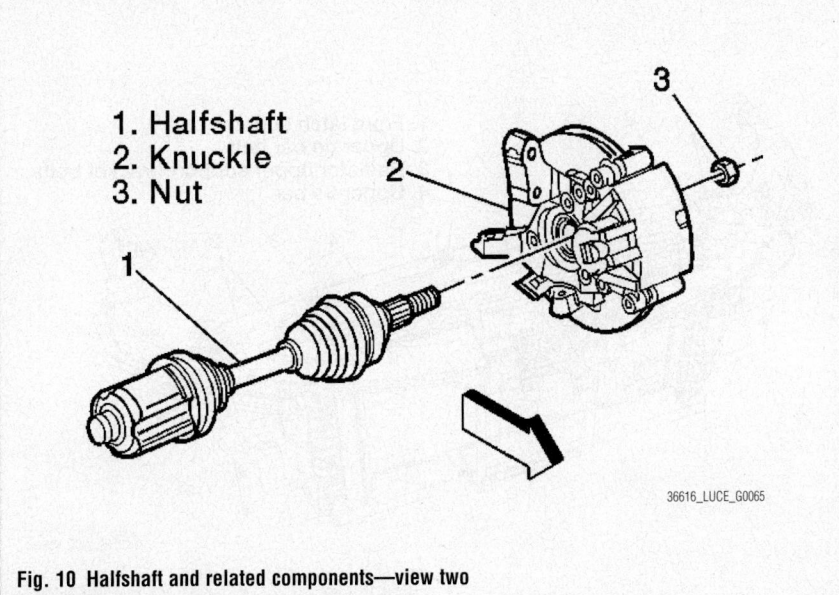

1. Halfshaft
2. Knuckle
3. Nut

36616_LUCE_G0065

Fig. 10 Halfshaft and related components—view two

1. Before servicing the vehicle, refer to the Precautions Section.
2. Raise and suitably support the vehicle.
3. Remove the wheel and the tire.
4. Remove the control link.
5. Remove the front halfshaft nut. Insert a drift or a flat-bladed tool into the caliper and the rotor to prevent the rotor from turning.
6. Disconnect the outer tie rod assembly from the steering knuckle.

7. Separate the ball joint from the steering knuckle.
8. Separate the front halfshaft from the front halfshaft bearing using a slide hammer and adapter.

To install:

9. Install the front wheel drive axle into the transaxle.
10. Verify that the front halfshaft retaining ring is properly seated:
 - Grasp the inner housing and pull the inner housing outward. Do not pull on the front wheel drive axle shaft.
 - The front wheel drive axle will remain in place when the front halfshaft retaining ring is properly seated.
11. Install the front wheel drive axle into the front halfshaft bearing.
12. Connect the ball joint to the steering knuckle.
13. Connect the outer tie rod assembly to the steering knuckle.
14. Install a new front halfshaft nut. Insert a drift or a flat-bladed tool into the caliper and the rotor to prevent the rotor from turning. Tighten the nut to 118 ft. lbs. (160 Nm).
15. Install the control link.
16. Install the wheel and the tire.
17. Lower the vehicle.
18. Inspect the transaxle fluid level.
19. Inspect the wheel alignment.

ENGINE COOLING

ENGINE FAN

REMOVAL & INSTALLATION

➡ For vehicles equipped with OnStar (RPO UE1), with battery backup, the backup battery is a redundant power supply to allow limited OnStar functionality in the event of a main battery power disruption to the OnStar module (VCIM). Do not disconnect the main vehicle battery or remove the OnStar fuse with the ignition key in any position other than OFF. Retained accessory power should be allowed to time out or be disabled by opening the driver's side door before disconnecting power. Disconnecting power to the module in any way while the ignition is ON or with the retained accessory power activated may cause activation of the OnStar backup battery system and will discharge and permanently damage the backup battery. Once the backup battery is activated it will stay on until it has completely discharged.

The backup battery is not rechargeable and once it is activated, it must be replaced.

3.9L Engine

See Figure 11.

➡ The rear seat cushion must be removed to gain access to the battery.

1. Before servicing the vehicle, refer to the Precautions Section.
2. Disconnect the negative battery cable.
3. Properly discharge the air conditioning system.
4. Drain the cooling system.
5. Remove the condenser.
6. Remove the upper tie bar.
7. Raise and safely support the vehicle.
8. Remove the front air deflector.
9. Disconnect and plug the upper and lower radiator hoses at the radiator.
10. Disconnect and plug the transmission fluid lines.

11. Disconnect the fan assembly electrical connectors.
12. Remove the fan shroud mounting bolts. Remove the fan shroud.
13. Remove the cooling fan retaining nut. Remove the cooling fan.

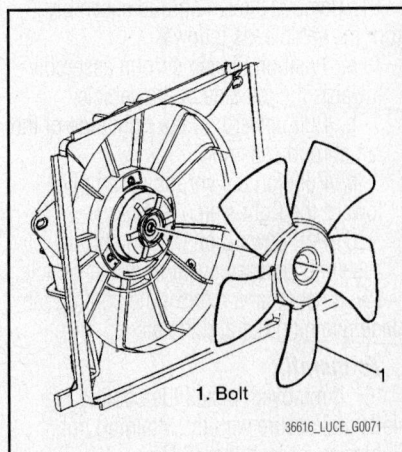

1. Bolt

36616_LUCE_G0071

Fig. 11 Cooling fan and related components

To install:

➡ **Be sure to use new fasteners, as required.**

14. Position the cooling fan blade and secure with the retaining nut. Tighten to 53 inch lbs. (6 Nm).

15. Continue the installation in the reverse order of the removal procedure.

16. Be sure to fill the cooling system with the proper grade and type coolant.

17. Start the engine and check for leaks. Correct, as required.

4.6L Engine

See Figure 12.

➡ **The rear seat cushion must be removed to gain access to the battery.**

1. Before servicing the vehicle, refer to the Precautions Section.

2. Disconnect the negative battery cable.

3. Remove the condenser.

4. Remove the upper tie bar. Refer to accompanying illustration.

5. Drain the coolant into a suitable container.

6. Remove the front air deflector.

7. Reposition the hose clamp at the radiator inlet hose.

8. Remove the radiator inlet hose from the radiator.

9. Remove the transaxle oil cooler pipe retaining bolts from the fan shroud.

10. Remove the transaxle lines from the radiator.

11. Disconnect the wiring harness electrical connectors from the fan motors.

12. Remove the clips securing the harness to the shroud.

13. Remove the fan shroud mounting bolts.

14. Remove the fan shroud assembly from the vehicle, as follows:

a. Position the fan shroud assembly towards the left side of the vehicle.

b. Pull upward on the right side of the fan shroud assembly.

c. Position the shroud assembly toward the right side of the car.

d. Pull upward on the fan shroud assembly and remove it from the vehicle.

15. If necessary, remove the cooling fan blade retaining nut and the blade.

To install:

16. If removed, install the cooling fan blade and secure with the retaining nut. Tighten to 53 inch lbs. (6 Nm).

17. Install the fan shroud assembly to the vehicle, as follows:

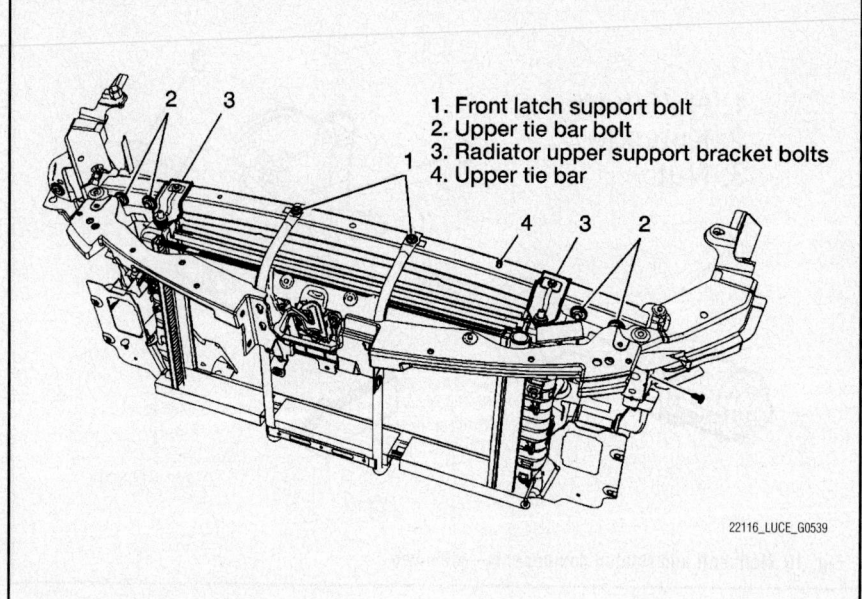

1. Front latch support bolt
2. Upper tie bar bolt
3. Radiator upper support bracket bolts
4. Upper tie bar

22116_LUCE_G0539

Fig. 12 Exploded view of the upper tie bar

a. Position the fan shroud assembly behind the radiator.

b. Position the assembly toward the right side of the car.

c. Push down on the right side of the fan shroud assembly.

d. Move the fan shroud into position, aligning the feet of the fan shroud to the mounting tabs on the radiator.

✳✳ WARNING

The bolts retaining the cooling fan to the radiator end tanks are a special length and should be the ONLY bolts used upon reinstallation. The use of longer bolts will damage the radiator end tanks.

18. Install the fan shroud mounting bolts and tighten to 53 inch lbs. (6 Nm).

19. Connect the wiring harness electrical connectors to the cooling fan motors.

20. Attach the wiring harness retaining clips to the fan shroud.

21. Push the upper transaxle oil cooler pipe into the radiator quick connect fitting, until a "click" is heard. Tug gently on the cooler pipe to ensure proper retention.

22. Slide the plastic cap over the quick connect joint.

23. Install the transmission oil cooler pipe retaining bolts to the fan shroud and tighten the bolts to 53 inch lbs. (6 Nm).

24. Install the radiator inlet hose to the radiator. Reposition the radiator inlet hose clamp.

25. Raise and support the vehicle.

26. Install the front air deflector.

27. Lower the vehicle.

28. Install the upper tie bar.

29. Install the condenser.

30. Fill the cooling system.

31. Connect the negative battery cable.

32. Inspect the engine oil level

RADIATOR

REMOVAL & INSTALLATION

➡ **For vehicles equipped with OnStar (RPO UE1), with battery backup, the backup battery is a redundant power supply to allow limited OnStar functionality in the event of a main battery power disruption to the OnStar module (VCIM). Do not disconnect the main vehicle battery or remove the OnStar fuse with the ignition key in any position other than OFF. Retained accessory power should be allowed to time out or be disabled by opening the driver's side door before disconnecting power. Disconnecting power to the module in any way while the ignition is ON or with the retained accessory power activated may cause activation of the OnStar backup battery system and will discharge and permanently damage the backup battery. Once the backup battery is activated it will stay on until it has completely discharged. The backup battery is not rechargeable and once it is activated, it must be replaced.**

3.9L Engine

See Figure 13.

➡ **The rear seat cushion must be removed to gain access to the battery.**

1. Before servicing the vehicle, refer to the Precautions Section.
2. Disconnect the negative battery cable.
3. Properly discharge the air conditioning system.
4. Drain the cooling system.
5. Remove the condenser.
6. Remove the upper tie bar.
7. Raise and safely support the vehicle.
8. Remove the front air deflector.
9. Disconnect and plug the upper and lower radiator hoses at the radiator.
10. Disconnect and plug the transmission fluid lines.
11. Disconnect the fan assembly electrical connectors.
12. Remove the fan shroud mounting bolts. Remove the fan shroud.
13. Remove the condenser line to radiator retaining bolt.
14. Remove the radiator brackets.
15. Remove the radiator from the vehicle.

To install:

➡ **Be sure to use new fasteners, as required.**

16. Install the radiator to the vehicle.

➡ **Be careful when installing the condenser not to damage the lower attachment points of both the radiator and condenser.**

17. Position the condenser, aligning the lower feet to the lower mounting features located at the front of the radiator.

❊❊ WARNING

The bolts retaining the condenser to the radiator end tanks are a special length and should be the ONLY bolts used upon reinstallation. The use of longer bolts will damage the radiator end tanks.

18. Install the condenser mounting bolts and tighten to 115 inch lbs. (13 Nm).
19. Continue the installation in the reverse order of the removal procedure.
20. Be sure to fill the cooling system with the proper grade and type coolant.
21. Start the engine and check for leaks. Correct, as required.

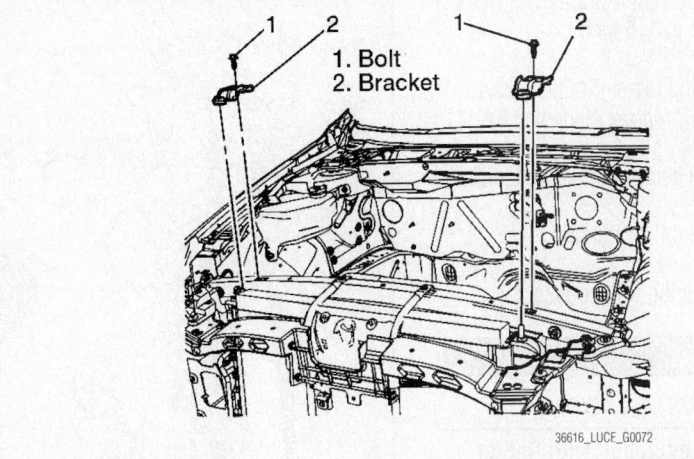

1. Bolt
2. Bracket

36616_LUCE_G0072

Fig. 13 Radiator brackets

4.6L Engine

See Figures 14 and 15.

➡ **The rear seat cushion must be removed to gain access to the battery.**

1. Before servicing the vehicle, refer to the Precautions Section.
2. Disconnect the negative battery cable.
3. Drain the engine coolant.
4. Remove the radiator cooling fan assembly.
5. Remove the condenser line to radiator retaining bolt.
6. Using J 38185 reposition the hose clamps from the radiator outlet hose, then disconnect the radiator outlet hose from the radiator.
7. Remove the condenser mounting bolts.

➡ **Be careful when removing the condenser not to damage the lower attachment points of both the radiator and condenser.**

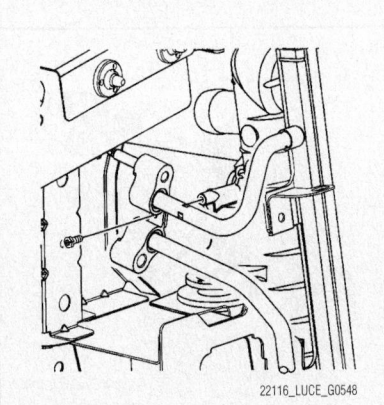

22116_LUCE_G0548

Fig. 14 Remove the condenser line to radiator retaining bolt

8. Lift the condenser upward slightly in order to release the lower feet from the lower mounting features located at the front of the radiator.
9. Lift the radiator up and out the vehicle.

To install:

➡ **Be sure to use new fasteners, as required.**

10. Install the radiator to the vehicle.

➡ **Be careful when installing the condenser not to damage the lower attachment points of both the radiator and condenser.**

11. Position the condenser, aligning the lower feet to the lower mounting features located at the front of the radiator.

❊❊ WARNING

The bolts retaining the condenser to the radiator end tanks are a special length and should be the ONLY bolts used upon reinstallation. The use of longer bolts will damage the radiator end tanks.

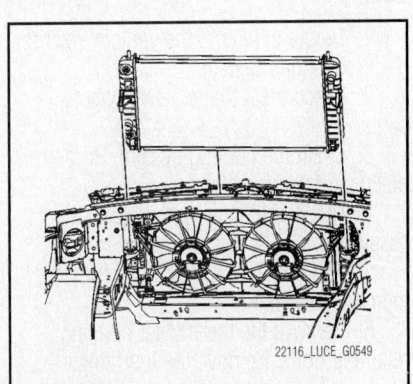

22116_LUCE_G0549

Fig. 15 Lift the radiator up and out the vehicle

12. Install the condenser mounting bolts and tighten to 115 inch lbs. (13 Nm).

13. Connect the radiator outlet hose to the radiator, then properly reposition the hose clamp.

14. Install the condenser line to radiator retaining bolt.

15. Install the radiator cooling fan assembly.

16. Fill the engine with coolant.

THERMOSTAT

REMOVAL & INSTALLATION

➡ For vehicles equipped with OnStar (RPO UE1), with battery backup, the backup battery is a redundant power supply to allow limited OnStar functionality in the event of a main battery power disruption to the OnStar module (VCIM). Do not disconnect the main vehicle battery or remove the OnStar fuse with the ignition key in any position other than OFF. Retained accessory power should be allowed to time out or be disabled by opening the driver's side door before disconnecting power. Disconnecting power to the module in any way while the ignition is ON or with the retained accessory power activated may cause activation of the OnStar backup battery system and will discharge and permanently damage the backup battery. Once the backup battery is activated it will stay on until it has completely discharged. The backup battery is not rechargeable and once it is activated, it must be replaced.

3.9L Engine

See Figure 16.

➡ The rear seat cushion must be removed to gain access to the battery.

1. Before servicing the vehicle, refer to the Precautions Section.

2. Disconnect the negative battery cable.

3. Drain the cooling system. Properly dispose of used coolant.

4. Remove the air cleaner outlet duct assembly.

5. Remove the radiator hose from the thermostat housing.

6. Remove the thermostat housing retaining bolts. Remove the thermostat housing. Remove the thermostat. Discard the gasket.

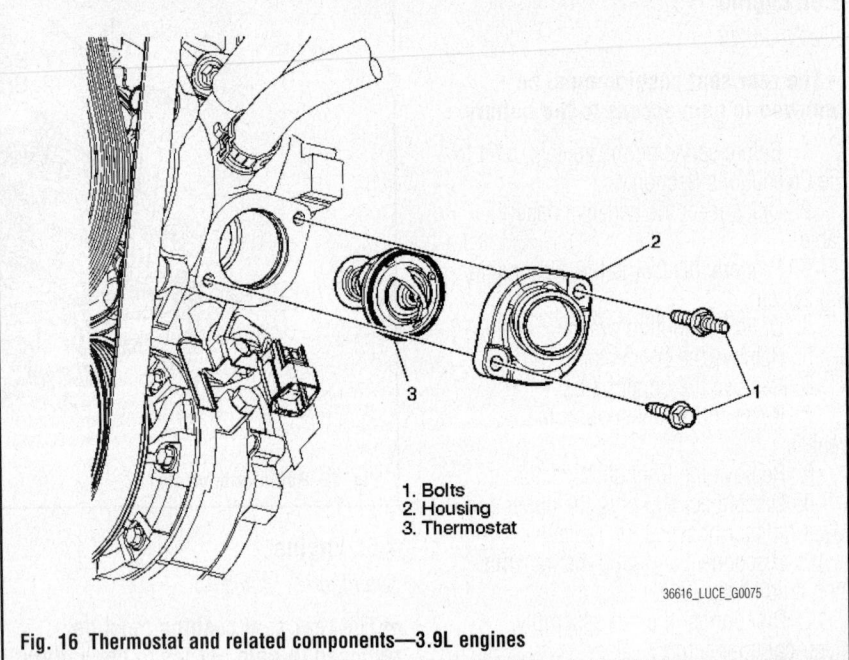

1. Bolts
2. Housing
3. Thermostat

36616_LUCE_G0075

Fig. 16 Thermostat and related components—3.9L engines

To install:

➡ Be sure to use new fasteners, as required.

7. Install the thermostat and a new gasket.

8. Install the thermostat housing.

9. Install the thermostat housing bolts and tighten to 89 inch lbs. (10 Nm).

10. Continue the installation in the reverse order of the removal procedure.

11. Be sure to fill the cooling system with the proper grade and type coolant.

12. Start the engine and check for leaks. Correct, as required.

4.6L Engine

See Figure 17.

➡ The rear seat cushion must be removed to gain access to the battery.

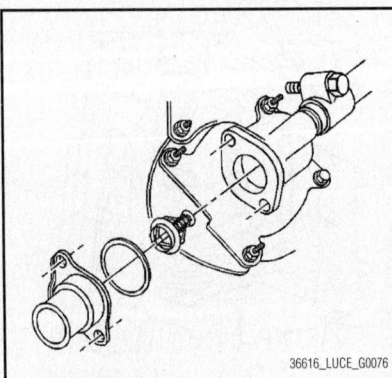

36616_LUCE_G0076

Fig. 17 Thermostat and related components—4.6L engines

1. Before servicing the vehicle, refer to the Precautions Section.

2. Disconnect the negative battery cable.

3. Partially drain the cooling system.

4. Remove the air cleaner assembly.

5. Remove the radiator outlet hose from the thermostat housing.

6. Remove the bolts securing the thermostat housing to the water pump inlet.

7. Remove the thermostat and the gasket from the water pump housing.

To install:

8. Install the thermostat and a new gasket into the water pump housing.

9. Install the thermostat housing.

10. Install the thermostat housing bolts and tighten to 89 inch lbs. (10 Nm).

11. Connect the radiator outlet hose to the thermostat housing.

12. Install the air cleaner assembly.

13. Fill the cooling system.

WATER PUMP

REMOVAL & INSTALLATION

➡ For vehicles equipped with OnStar (RPO UE1), with battery backup, the backup battery is a redundant power supply to allow limited OnStar functionality in the event of a main battery power disruption to the OnStar module (VCIM). Do not disconnect the main vehicle battery or remove the OnStar fuse with the ignition key in any position other than OFF. Retained accessory power should be allowed to time out or be disabled by opening the driver's side door before disconnecting power. Disconnecting power to the module in any way while the ignition is ON or with the retained accessory power activated may cause activation of the OnStar backup battery system and will discharge and permanently damage the backup battery. Once the backup battery is activated it will stay on until it has completely discharged. The backup battery is not rechargeable and once it is activated, it must be replaced.

3.9L Engine

See Figure 18.

➡**The rear seat cushion must be removed to gain access to the battery.**

1. Before servicing the vehicle, refer to the Precautions Section.
2. Disconnect the negative battery cable.
3. Drain the cooling system. Properly dispose of used coolant.
4. Remove the intake manifold cover.
5. Remove the drive belt.

6. Remove the water pump pulley retaining bolts. Remove the water pump pulley.
7. Remove the water pump retaining bolts. Remove the water pump. Discard the gasket.

To install:

➡**Be sure to use new fasteners, as required.**

8. Install a NEW water pump gasket.
9. Install the water pump.
10. Install the water pump bolts and tighten to 18 ft. lbs. (25 Nm).
11. Install the pulley bolts and tighten to 18 ft. lbs. (25 Nm).
12. Continue the installation in the reverse order of the removal procedure.
13. Be sure to fill the cooling system with the proper grade and type coolant.
14. Start the engine and check for leaks. Correct, as required.

4.6L Engine

See Figures 19 through 24.

➡**The rear seat cushion must be removed to gain access to the battery.**

1. Before servicing the vehicle, refer to the Precautions Section.
2. Disconnect the negative battery cable.
3. Drain the cooling system.
4. Remove the water pump housing, as follows:
   a. Remove the air cleaner.
   b. Remove the fuel injector sight shield.
   c. Remove the water pump drive belt by removing the tensioner shield, then inserting a breaker bar into the tensioner to rotate the tensioner and remove the belt.
   d. Reposition the brake booster vacuum hose clamp at the water pump housing.
   e. Remove the brake booster vacuum hose from the water pump housing.
   f. Remove the oil level indicator tube nut.
   g. Reposition the oil level indicator tube.
   h. Remove the transaxle vent hose clip from the bracket
   i. Remove the throttle body bolts.
   j. Remove the bracket.
   k. Remove the throttle body. Remove and discard the throttle body seal.

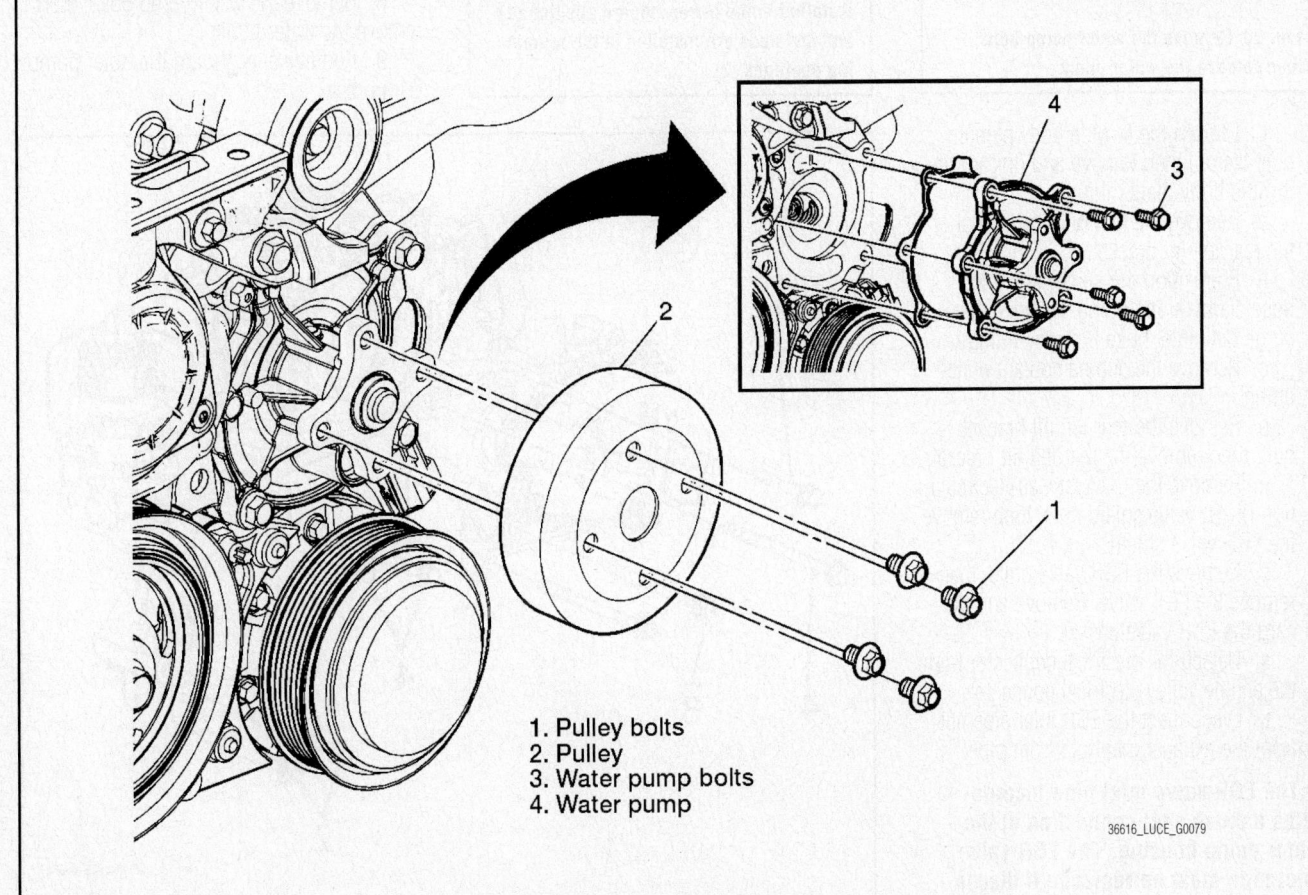

1. Pulley bolts
2. Pulley
3. Water pump bolts
4. Water pump

36616_LUCE_G0079

Fig. 18 Water pump and related components—3.9L engines

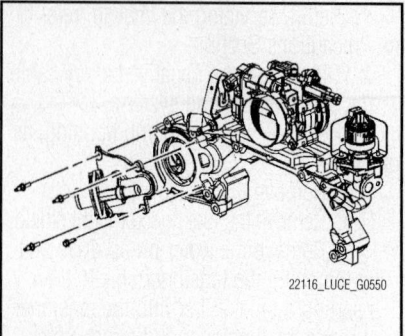

Fig. 19 Exploded view of the water pump housing

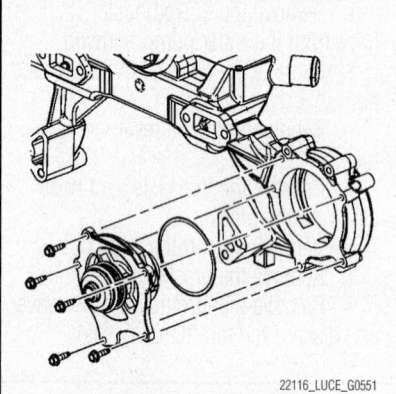

Fig. 20 Remove the water pump bolts, then remove the water pump

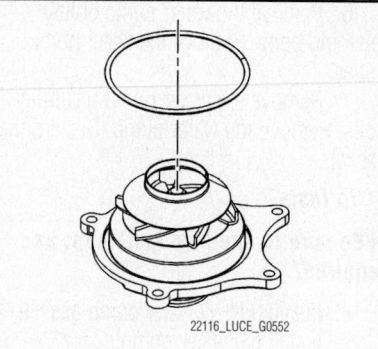

Fig. 21 Remove and discard the water pump O-ring seal

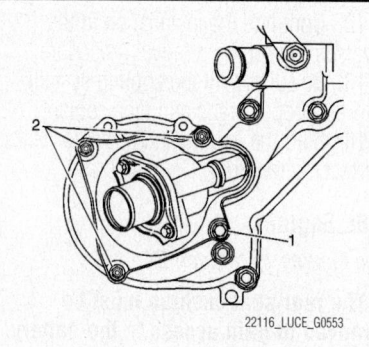

Fig. 22 Make sure that the bolt is installed in the lower inboard position (1) and the studs are installed in the remaining positions (2)

l. Loosen the throttle body plenum duct clamp, then remove and discard the throttle body plenum duct.

m. Remove the fuel rail bracket nut at the rear left lift bracket.

n. Reposition the surge tank inlet hose clamp at the fitting. Remove the surge tank inlet hose from the fitting.

o. Remove the engine coolant outlet fitting.

p. Remove the rear left lift bracket bolt, then remove the rear left lift bracket.

q. Remove the Exhaust Gas Recirculation (EGR) valve shield nuts, then remove the EGR valve shield.

r. Remove the EGR valve bolts, then remove the EGR valve. Remove and discard the EGR valve gasket.

s. Detach the electrical connector from the engine valley electrical connector.

t. Disconnect the EGR inlet pipe nut from the exhaust manifold front pipe.

➡The EGR valve inlet pipe incorporates a crush seal connection at the water pump housing. The EGR valve inlet pipe must be replaced if disconnected from the water pump housing.

u. Remove the EGR inlet pipe bolt from the water pump housing. Remove and discard the EGR inlet pipe.

v. Remove the Evaporative Emission (EVAP) canister purge solenoid valve bolt. Remove the EVAP canister purge solenoid valve.

w. Remove the Manifold Absolute Pressure (MAP) sensor bracket bolt. Remove the MAP sensor bracket and the MAP sensor.

x. Reposition the radiator inlet hose clamp (1) at the water pump housing, then remove the radiator inlet hose (2) from the water pump housing.

y. Reposition the radiator outlet hose clamp (1) at the thermostat housing. Remove the radiator outlet hose (2) from the thermostat housing.

5. Remove the water pump belt tensioner studs. Remove the water pump belt tensioner.

a. Reposition the heater outlet hose clamp at the heater pipe. Remove the heater outlet hose from the heater pipe.

6. Remove the water pump cover bolt/studs.

7. Remove the water pump cover.

8. Remove the water pump bolts, then remove the water pump.

9. Remove and discard the water pump O-ring seal.

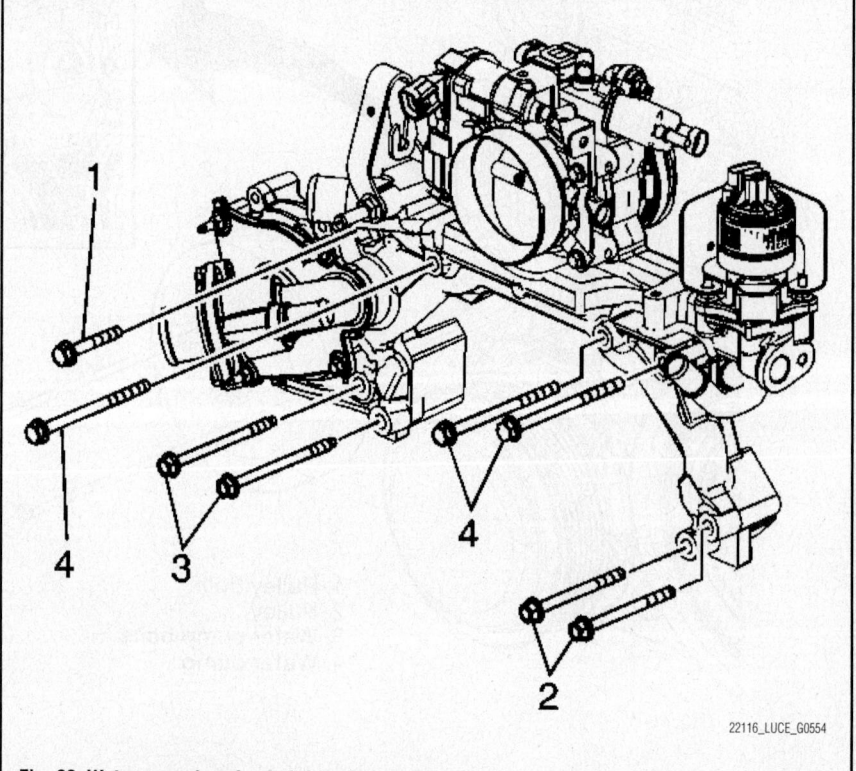

Fig. 23 Water pump housing bolt locations

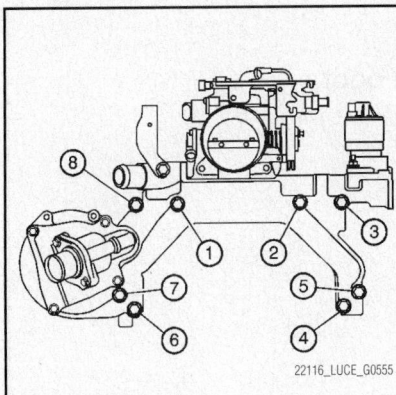

Fig. 24 Water pump housing bolt tightening sequence

To install:

10. Install a NEW water pump O-ring seal.

11. Install the water pump.

12. Install the water pump bolts and tighten to 89 inch lbs. (10 Nm).

13. Install the water pump cover.

> ※ **WARNING**
>
> **Make sure that the bolt is installed in the lower inboard position (1) and the studs are installed in the remaining positions (2).**

14. Install the water pump cover bolt/studs and tighten to 89 inch lbs. (10 Nm).

15. Install the water pump housing in the reverse of the removal procedure, and noting the following:

   a. When installing the housing, with the housing on the bench, install the bolts in the locations shown in the accompanying illustration:

   - Bolt (1) length: 1.6024 in. (40.7mm)
   - Bolts (2) length: 3.6220 in. (92.0mm)
   - Bolts (3) length: 4.2913 in. (109.0mm)
   - Bolts (4) length: 4.5276 in. (115.0mm)

   b. Tighten the water pump housing bolts, in sequence, to 18 ft. lbs. (25 Nm).

16. Fill the cooling system.

ENGINE ELECTRICAL

CHARGING SYSTEM

ALTERNATOR

REMOVAL & INSTALLATION

➡For vehicles equipped with OnStar (RPO UE1), with battery backup, the backup battery is a redundant power supply to allow limited OnStar functionality in the event of a main battery power disruption to the OnStar module (VCIM). Do not disconnect the main vehicle battery or remove the OnStar fuse with the ignition key in any position other than OFF. Retained accessory power should be allowed to time out or be disabled by opening the driver's side door before disconnecting power. Disconnecting power to the module in any way while the ignition is ON or with the retained accessory power activated may cause activation of the OnStar backup battery system and will discharge and permanently damage the backup battery. Once the backup battery is activated it will stay on until it has completely discharged. The backup battery is not rechargeable and once it is activated, it must be replaced.

3.9L Engine

See Figure 25.

➡The rear seat cushion must be removed to gain access to the battery.

1. Before servicing the vehicle, refer to the Precautions Section.

2. Disconnect the negative battery cable.

3. Remove the intake manifold cover.

4. Remove the drive belt.

5. Disconnect the electrical connectors.

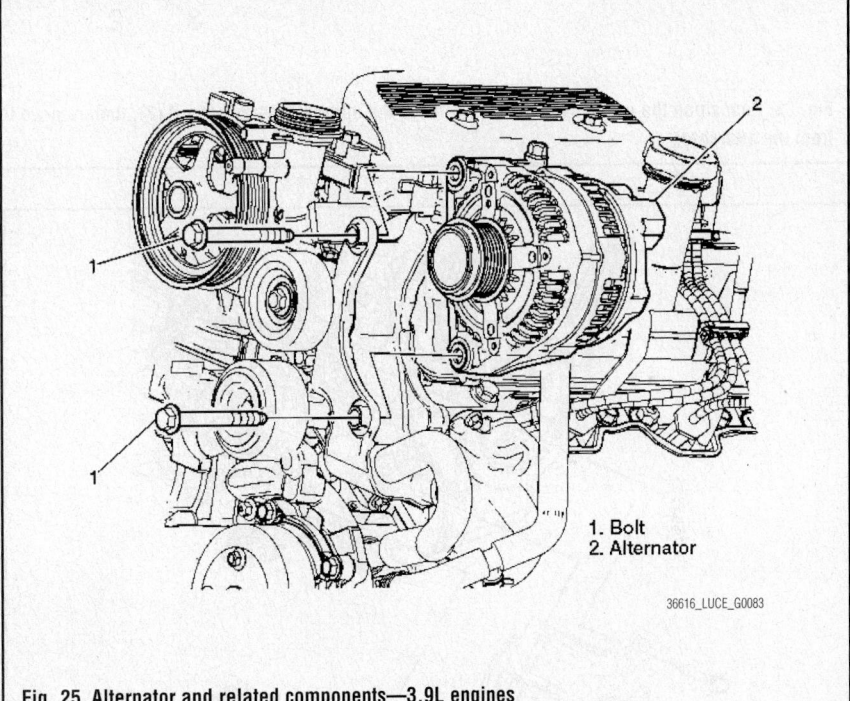

1. Bolt
2. Alternator

Fig. 25 Alternator and related components—3.9L engines

Remove the mounting bolts. 6. Remove the alternator from the vehicle.

To install:

➡Be sure to use new fasteners, as required.

7. Position the alternator to the engine. Install the alternator bolts. Tighten to 37 ft. lbs. (50 Nm).

8. Continue the installation in the reverse order of the removal procedure.

4.6L Engine

See Figures 26 and 27.

➡The rear seat cushion must be removed to gain access to the battery.

1. Before servicing the vehicle, refer to the Precautions Section.

2. Disconnect the negative battery cable.

3. Remove the radiator, as outlined in the Engine Cooling Section.

4. Remove the drive belt, as outlined in the Engine Mechanical Section.

5. Disconnect the engine wiring harness electrical connector from the alternator.

6. Reposition the starter solenoid cable protective boot (1) at the alternator.

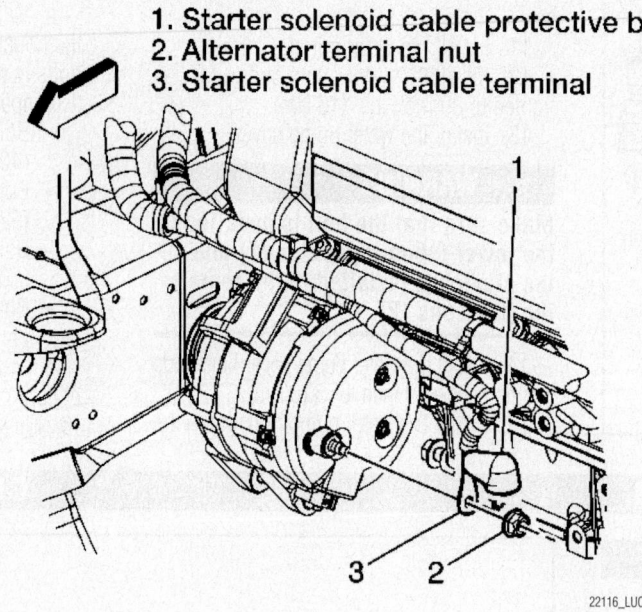

1. Starter solenoid cable protective boot
2. Alternator terminal nut
3. Starter solenoid cable terminal

22116_LUCE_G0556

Fig. 26 Reposition the protective boot (1). Remove the alternator terminal nut (2), then remove the starter solenoid cable terminal (3) from the alternator

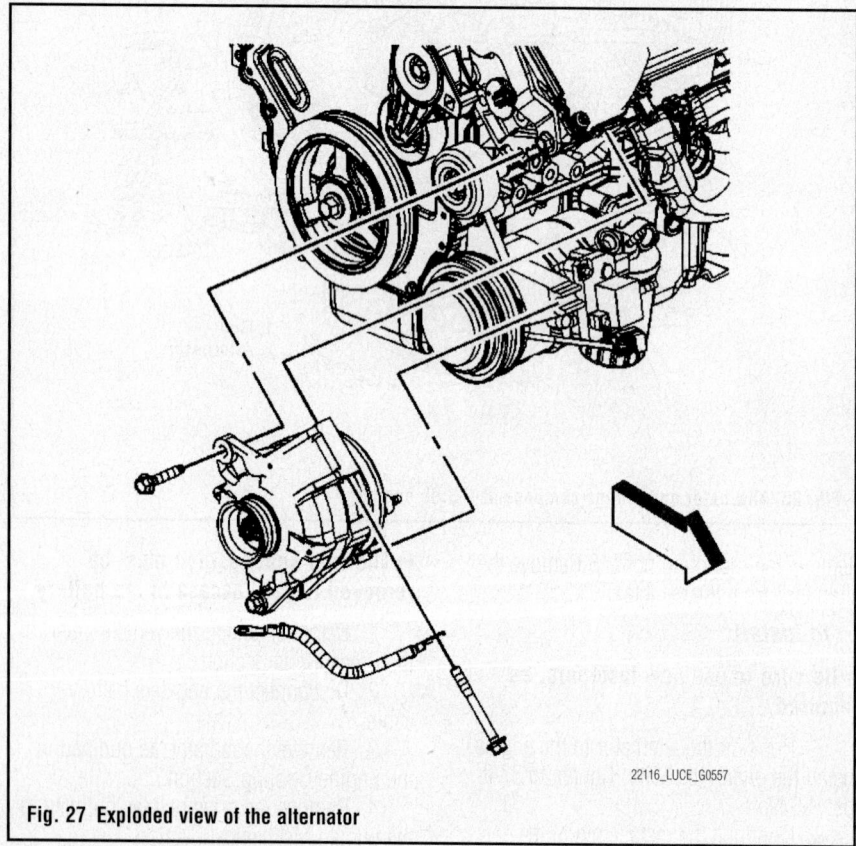

22116_LUCE_G0557

Fig. 27 Exploded view of the alternator

7. Remove the alternator terminal nut (2).

8. Remove the starter solenoid cable terminal (3) from the alternator.

9. Remove the alternator bolts.

10. Reposition the engine ground cable, then remove the alternator.

To install:

11. Position the alternator to the engine. Install the alternator bolts finger-tight in the following sequence.

    a. Upper bolt

    b. Side bolt

    c. Lower bolt

12. Tighten the alternator mounting bolts to 37 ft. lbs. (50 Nm).

13. Install the starter solenoid cable terminal (3) to the alternator.

14. Install the alternator terminal nut (2). Tighten the nut to 106 inch lbs. (12 Nm).

15. Position the starter solenoid cable protective boot (1) at the alternator.

16. Connect the engine wiring harness electrical connector to the alternator.

17. Install the drive belt.

18. Install the radiator.

19. Connect the negative battery cable

ENGINE ELECTRICAL

IGNITION SYSTEM

FIRING ORDER

See Figure 28.

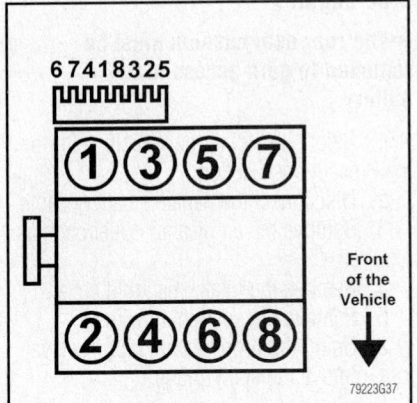

Fig. 28 4.6L (VIN 9 and Y) Engines Firing order: 1—2—7—3—4—5—6—8 Distributorless ignition system

IGNITION COIL

REMOVAL & INSTALLATION

➡For vehicles equipped with OnStar (RPO UE1), with battery backup, the backup battery is a redundant power supply to allow limited OnStar functionality in the event of a main battery power disruption to the OnStar module (VCIM). Do not disconnect the main vehicle battery or remove the OnStar fuse with the ignition key in any position other than OFF. Retained accessory power should be allowed to time out or be disabled by opening the driver's side door before disconnecting power. Disconnecting power to the module in any way while the ignition is ON or with the retained accessory power activated may cause activation of the OnStar backup battery system and will discharge and permanently damage the backup battery. Once the backup battery is activated it will stay on until it has completely discharged. The backup battery is not rechargeable and once it is activated, it must be replaced.

3.9L Engine

See Figure 29.

➡The rear seat cushion must be removed to gain access to the battery.

1. Before servicing the vehicle, refer to the Precautions Section.
2. Disconnect the negative battery cable.
3. Remove the intake manifold cover.
4. Disconnect the MAP sensor electrical connector. Disconnect the ignition coil connector.
5. Disconnect the spark plug wires from the coil assembly.
6. Remove the coil retaining nuts. Remove the coil from its mounting.
7. Remove the coil studs, as required.

To install:

➡Be sure to use new fasteners, as required.

8. Installation is the reverse of the removal procedure.
9. Tighten the retaining nuts to 15 ft. lbs. (25 Nm).

4.6L Engine

➡The rear seat cushion must be removed to gain access to the battery.

1. Before servicing the vehicle, refer to the Precautions Section.
2. Disconnect the negative battery cable.
3. Turn OFF the ignition.
4. Remove the fuel injector sight shield(s).
5. On bank 1, remove the ignition coil

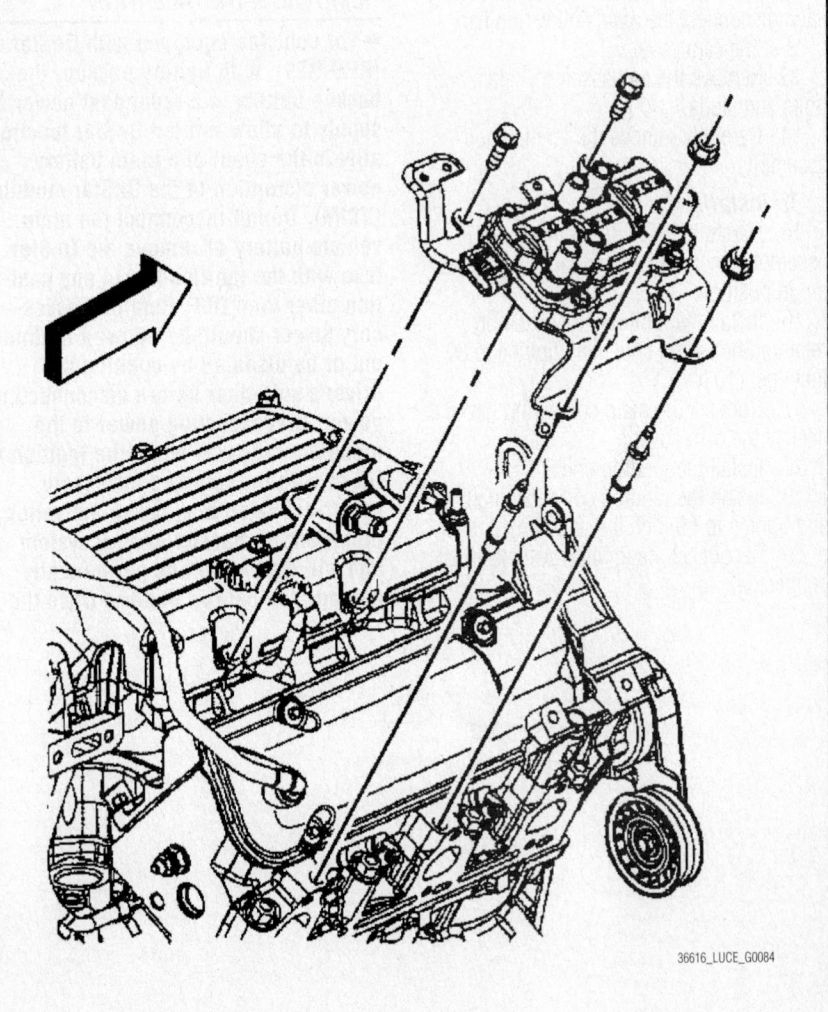

Fig. 29 Ignition coil and related components—3.9L engines

cover from the cam cover by lifting straight up, if equipped.

6. Disconnect the secondary Air Injection (AIR) vent solenoid electrical connector, if necessary, to gain access to the individual coil being serviced.

7. Remove the AIR check valve, if necessary, to gain access to the individual coil being serviced.

8. On bank 2, remove the upper filler panel, if necessary, to gain access to the individual coil being serviced. Remove the ignition coil cover from the cam cover by lifting straight up, if equipped.

9. On both banks, disconnect the ignition coil wiring harness electrical connector from the coil that needs to be replaced.

10. Remove the ignition coil retaining bolt.

11. Carefully remove the ignition coil.

12. If removal of all the coils are necessary, disconnect the main coil wiring harness at the cam cover.

13. Remove the coil assembly retaining bolts and studs.

14. Carefully remove the ignition coil assembly.

To install:

15. Carefully install the ignition coil assembly. Ensure that the spark plug seals are in position.

16. Install the ignition coil assembly retaining bolts and studs and tighten to 89 inch lbs. (10 Nm).

17. Connect the main coil wiring harness at the cam cover.

18. Install the ignition coil.

19. Install the ignition coil retaining bolt and tighten to 89 inch lbs. (10 Nm).

20. Reconnect the ignition coil electrical connector.

21. Install the ignition coil cover to the cam cover.

22. On bank 2, install the upper filler panel, if removed during disassembly.

23. On bank 1, install the AIR check valve.

24. Connect the AIR vent solenoid electrical connector.

25. On both banks, install the fuel injector sight shield.

IGNITION TIMING

ADJUSTMENT

The ignition timing is not adjustable, and is set according to engine demand electronically. The Powertrain Control Module (PCM) controls the ignition timing for all driving conditions.

SPARK PLUGS

REMOVAL & INSTALLATION

➡ **For vehicles equipped with OnStar (RPO UE1), with battery backup, the backup battery is a redundant power supply to allow limited OnStar functionality in the event of a main battery power disruption to the OnStar module (VCIM). Do not disconnect the main vehicle battery or remove the OnStar fuse with the ignition key in any position other than OFF. Retained accessory power should be allowed to time out or be disabled by opening the driver's side door before disconnecting power. Disconnecting power to the module in any way while the ignition is ON or with the retained accessory power activated may cause activation of the OnStar backup battery system and will discharge and permanently damage the backup battery. Once the**

backup battery is activated it will stay on until it has completely discharged. The backup battery is not rechargeable and once it is activated, it must be replaced.

3.9L Engine

➡**The rear seat cushion must be removed to gain access to the battery.**

1. Before servicing the vehicle, refer to the Precautions Section.

2. Disconnect the negative battery cable.

3. Remove the air cleaner outlet duct, as required.

4. Remove the intake manifold cover.

5. Remove the spark plug wires.

6. Using the proper spark plug removal tool, remove the spark plugs.

To install:

➡**Be sure to use new fasteners, as required.**

7. Installation is the reverse of the removal procedure.

8. Tighten the spark plugs to 11 ft. lbs. (15 Nm).

4.6L Engine

➡**The rear seat cushion must be removed to gain access to the battery.**

1. Before servicing the vehicle, refer to the Precautions Section.

2. Disconnect the negative battery cable.

3. Remove the ignition coils. Refer to Ignition Coil, removal and installation.

4. Use a spark plug socket and wrench to remove the spark plugs.

5. To install, reverse the removal procedure. Tighten the spark plugs to 11 ft. lbs. (15 Nm).

ENGINE ELECTRICAL   **STARTING SYSTEM**

STARTER

REMOVAL & INSTALLATION

➡ For vehicles equipped with OnStar (RPO UE1), with battery backup, the backup battery is a redundant power supply to allow limited OnStar functionality in the event of a main battery power disruption to the OnStar module (VCIM). Do not disconnect the main vehicle battery or remove the OnStar fuse with the ignition key in any position other than OFF. Retained accessory power should be allowed to time out or be disabled by opening the driver's side door before disconnecting power. Disconnecting power to the module in any way while the ignition is ON or with the retained accessory power activated may cause activation of the OnStar backup battery system and will discharge and permanently damage the backup battery. Once the backup battery is activated it will stay on until it has completely discharged. The backup battery is not rechargeable and once it is activated, it must be replaced.

3.9L Engine

See Figure 30.

➡ The rear seat cushion must be removed to gain access to the battery.

1. Before servicing the vehicle, refer to the Precautions Section.
2. Disconnect the negative battery cable.
3. Raise and safely support the vehicle.
4. Remove the torque converter cover.

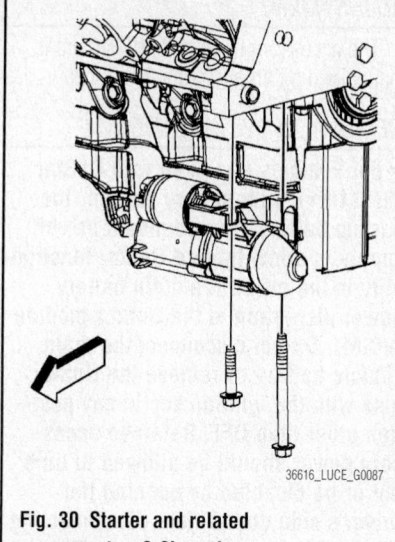

Fig. 30 Starter and related components—3.9L engines

36616_LUCE_G0087

5. Remove the starter retaining bolts. Remove the starter from the vehicle.

To install:

➡ Be sure to use new fasteners, as required.

6. Installation is the reverse of the removal procedure.
7. Tighten the retaining bolts to 32 ft. lbs. (43 Nm).

4.6L Engine

See Figure 31.

➡ The rear seat cushion must be removed to gain access to the battery.

1. Before servicing the vehicle, refer to the Precautions Section.
2. Disconnect the negative battery cable.
3. Remove the intake manifold.

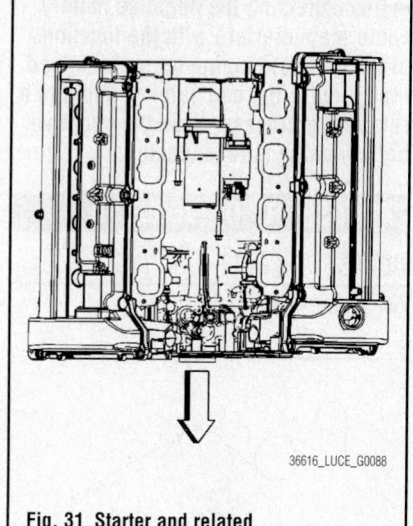

Fig. 31 Starter and related components—4.6L engines

36616_LUCE_G0088

4. Disconnect the BAT cable from the starter.
5. Disconnect the wire from the S terminal on the starter.
6. Remove the 2 starter motor mounting bolts.
7. Remove the starter motor.

To install:

8. Connect the starter motor S terminal wire. Tighten the starter solenoid S terminal nut to 35 inch lbs. (4 Nm).
9. Connect the starter motor BAT terminal wire. Tighten the battery cable to starter terminal nut to 89 inch lbs. (10 Nm).
10. Install the starter motor.
11. Install the starter motor mounting bolts. Tighten the starter motor mounting bolts to 22 ft. lbs. (30 Nm).
12. Install the intake manifold.
13. Connect the negative battery cable.

ENGINE MECHANICAL

➡Disconnecting the negative battery cable may interfere with the functions of the on board computer systems and may require the computer to undergo a relearning process, once the negative battery cable is reconnected.

ACCESSORY DRIVE BELTS

ACCESSORY BELT ROUTING

See Figures 32 and 33.

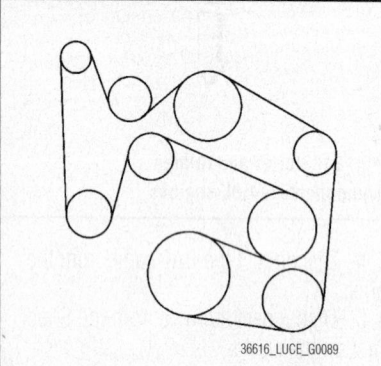

Fig. 32 Accessory drive belt routing— 3.9L engines

36616_LUCE_G0089

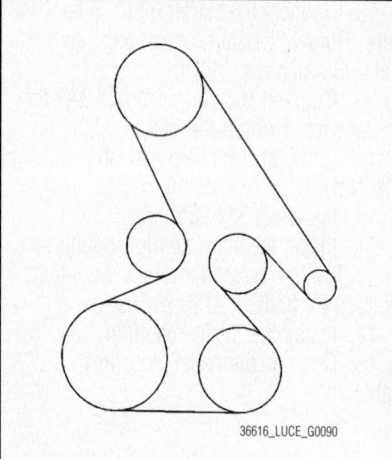

Fig. 33 Accessory drive belt routing— 4.6L engines

36616_LUCE_G0090

INSPECTION

Inspect the accessory drive belt for signs of glazing or cracking. A glazed belt will be perfectly smooth from slippage, while a good belt will have a slight texture of fabric visible. Cracks will usually start at the inner edge of the belt and run outward. All worn or damaged accessory drive belts should be replaced immediately.

ADJUSTMENT

The accessory drive belt adjustment is maintained by an automatic tensioner.

REMOVAL & INSTALLATION

➡For vehicles equipped with OnStar (RPO UE1), with battery backup, the backup battery is a redundant power supply to allow limited OnStar functionality in the event of a main battery power disruption to the OnStar module (VCIM). Do not disconnect the main vehicle battery or remove the OnStar fuse with the ignition key in any position other than OFF. Retained accessory power should be allowed to time out or be disabled by opening the driver's side door before disconnecting power. Disconnecting power to the module in any way while the ignition is ON or with the retained accessory power activated may cause activation of the OnStar backup battery system and will discharge and permanently damage the backup battery. Once the backup battery is activated it will stay on until it has completely discharged. The backup battery is not rechargeable and once it is activated, it must be replaced.

3.9L Engine

See Figure 32.

➡The rear seat cushion must be removed to gain access to the battery.

1. Before servicing the vehicle, refer to the Precautions Section.
2. Disconnect the negative battery cable.
3. Remove the intake manifold cover.
4. Rotate the drive belt tensioner clockwise, in order to release the tension spring tension.
5. Remove the belt from around the tensioner pulley.
6. Release the drive belt tensioner.
7. Remove the belt from the other pulleys.

To install:

➡Be sure to use new fasteners, as required.

8. Position the drive belt around all pulleys except the tensioner pulley.
9. Rotate the tensioner clockwise to release the spring tension.

10. Install the belt around the tensioner pulley. Release the tensioner.
11. Continue the installation in the reverse order of the removal procedure.

4.6L Engine

See Figure 33.

➡The rear seat cushion must be removed to gain access to the battery.

1. Before servicing the vehicle, refer to the Precautions Section.
2. Disconnect the negative battery cable.
3. Raise and safely support the vehicle.
4. Remove the right front wheel and tire assembly.
5. Unfasten the retainers, then remove the right front wheelhouse liner.
6. Lower the vehicle.
7. Install a ½ inch breaker into the drive belt tensioner.
   a. Push down on the breaker bar to relieve the belt tension.
8. Remove the drive belt from the power steering pump.
9. Slowly return the tensioner to the original position.
10. Remove the belt from the lower pulley and idlers.
11. Partially raise the vehicle.

To install:

12. Route the drive belt around all the pulleys except for the power steering pump.
13. Lower the vehicle.
14. Install a ½ inch breaker bar into the drive belt tensioner.
15. Push down on the breaker bar in order to release the tension and route the belt around the power steering pump pulley.
16. Make sure that the belt is seated on all pulleys.
17. Slowly return the tensioner to its original position.
18. After drive belt installation, check the drive belt for the proper routing and correct alignment.
19. Raise and support the vehicle.
20. Install the right front wheelhouse liner.
21. Install the wheel and tire assembly.
22. Lower the vehicle.
23. Start the engine and check for proper belt and accessory operation.

CAMSHAFT AND VALVE LIFTERS

REMOVAL & INSTALLATION

➡️For vehicles equipped with OnStar (RPO UE1), with battery backup, the backup battery is a redundant power supply to allow limited OnStar functionality in the event of a main battery power disruption to the OnStar module (VCIM). Do not disconnect the main vehicle battery or remove the OnStar fuse with the ignition key in any position other than OFF. Retained accessory power should be allowed to time out or be disabled by opening the driver's side door before disconnecting power. Disconnecting power to the module in any way while the ignition is ON or with the retained accessory power activated may cause activation of the OnStar backup battery system and will discharge and permanently damage the backup battery. Once the backup battery is activated it will stay on until it has completely discharged. The backup battery is not rechargeable and once it is activated, it must be replaced.

3.9L Engine

➡️At this time the manufacturer does not provide service information for this component.

4.6L Engine

Left Side

See Figures 34 through 44.

Tools Required
- J 45059 Torque Angle/Meter
- J 44212 Camshaft Holding Tool

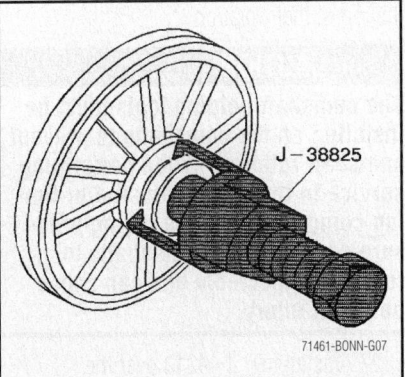

Fig. 34 Remove the water pump drive pulley from the intake camshaft using tool J 38825—4.6L engine

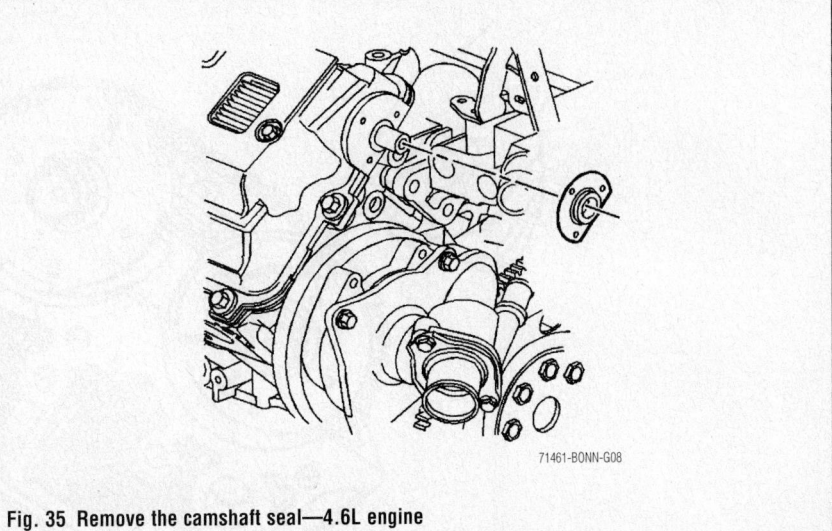

Fig. 35 Remove the camshaft seal—4.6L engine

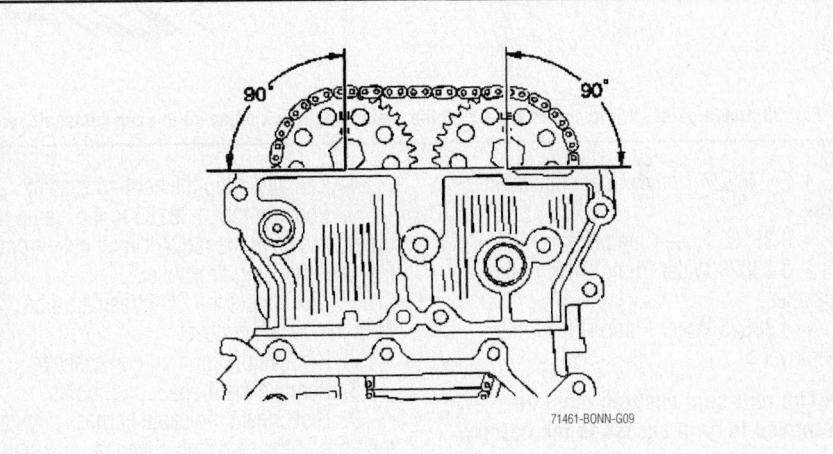

Fig. 36 Rotate the crankshaft to TDC of the no. 1 cylinders compression stroke, both camshaft sprocket drive pins should be at the top of their rotation—4.6L engine

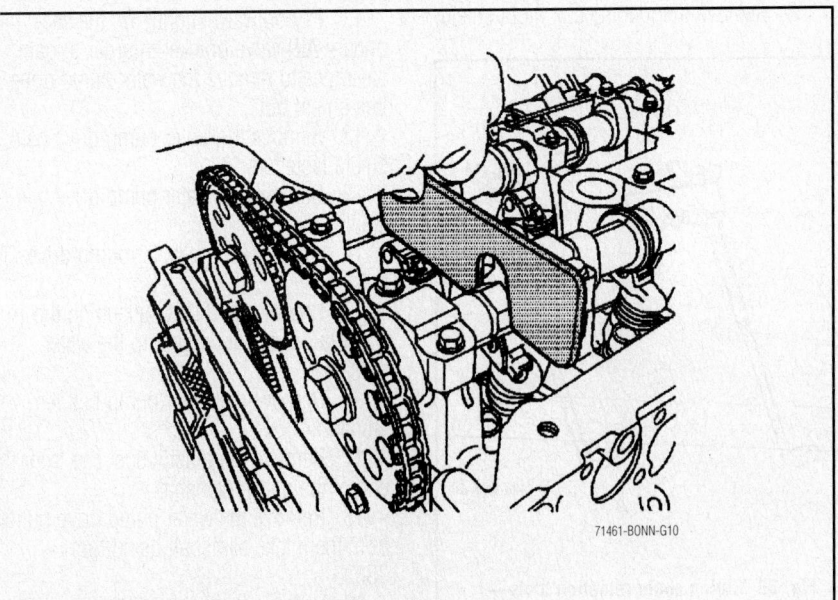

Fig. 37 Install tool J 44212 over the camshafts—4.6L engine

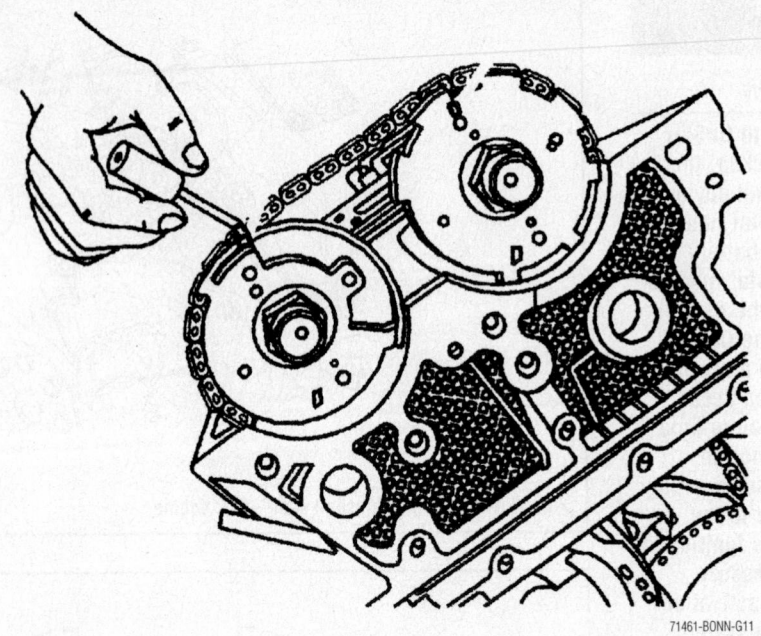

Fig. 38 Use a paint stick to create a mark on the timing chain link adjacent to each camshaft sprocket timing mark—4.6L engine

71461-BONN-G11

• EN 46327 Timing Chain Retention Tool
• J 38185 Hose Clamp Pliers
• J 38823 Water Pump Drive Pulley Installer
• J 38825 Water Pump Drive Pulley Remover

➡The rear seat cushion must be removed to gain access to the battery.

1. Before servicing the vehicle, refer to the Precautions Section.
2. Disconnect the negative battery cable.
3. Remove the fuel injector sight shield.

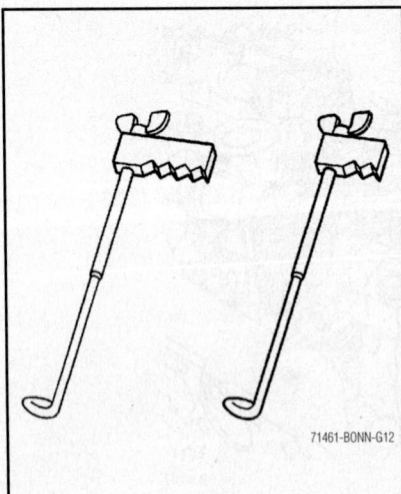

Fig. 39 Timing chain retention tools—4.6L engine

71461-BONN-G12

4. Partially drain the cooling system.
5. Position tool J 38185 to the clamp in order to remove the radiator inlet hose from the water housing crossover.
6. Disconnect the PCV fresh air tube from the camshaft cover.
7. Remove the ignition coil cassette.
8. Remove the 4 spark plug boots.
9. Disconnect the cable harness clips at the front of the camshaft cover and position the cable harness aside.
10. Remove the secondary AIR valve bracket nut closest to the center of the engine.
11. Pry outward slightly on the secondary AIR valve bracket in order to gain clearance to remove the water pump drive belt shield nut.
12. Remove the water pump drive belt shield fasteners.
13. Remove the water pump drive belt shield.
14. Disconnect the water pump drive belt.
15. Loosen the 2 bolts attaching the water pump belt tensioner to the water crossover.
16. Remove the water pump belt tensioner.
17. Remove the plastic dust cap from the end of the intake camshaft.
18. Remove the water pump drive pulley from the intake camshaft using tool J 38825.
19. Remove the 3 camshaft seal retainer bolts.

➡DO NOT reuse the camshaft seal.

20. Remove the camshaft seal.
21. Remove the camshaft cover bolts.
22. Lift the camshaft drive end of the camshaft cover up.
23. Remove the camshaft cover reward to clear the water pump drive shaft.
24. Discard the camshaft cover perimeter seals and spark plug seals if there is any evidence of damage or if the seal comes out of the groove in the cover during removal.
25. Clean and inspect the camshaft cover.
26. Rotate the crankshaft to TDC of the no. 1 1 cylinders compression stroke, both camshaft sprocket drive pins should be at the top of their rotation.

✲✲ CAUTION

The camshaft holding tools must be installed on the camshafts to prevent camshaft rotation. When performing service to the valve train and/or timing components, valve spring pressure can cause the camshafts to rotate unexpectedly and can cause personal injury.

27. Install tool J 44212 over the camshafts.
28. Use a paint stick to create a mark on the timing chain link adjacent to each camshaft sprocket timing mark.

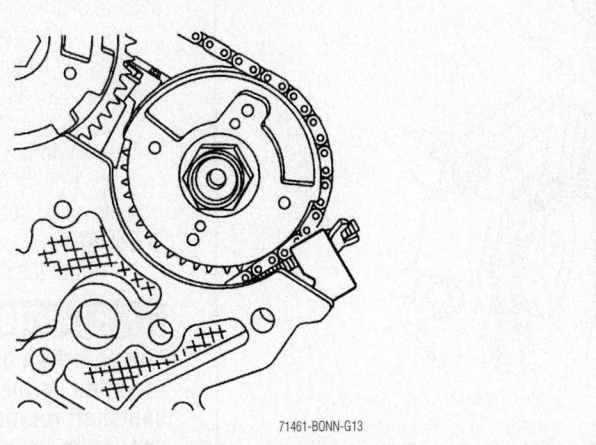

71461-BONN-G13

Fig. 40 Position the bottom retention tool on the cylinder head with the V-notch of the block adjacent to the left exhaust camshaft sprocket and chain—4.6L engine

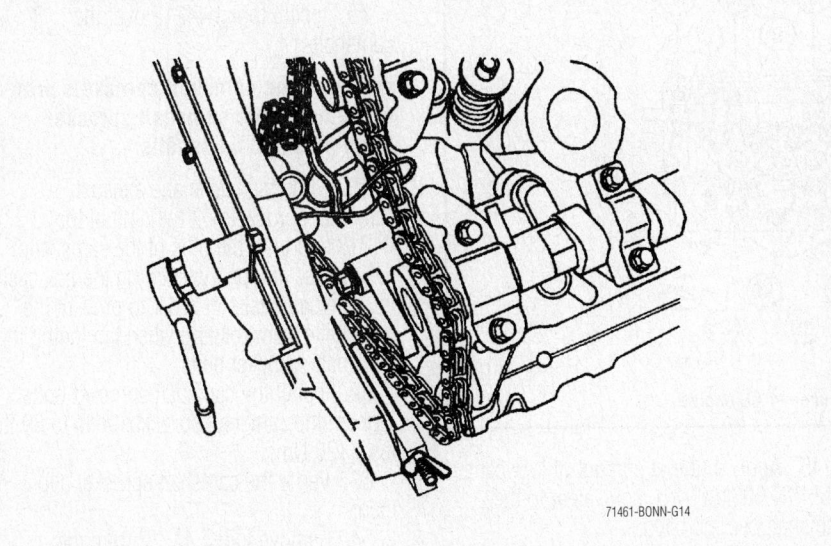

71461-BONN-G14

Fig. 41 Insert the hook end into a secondary timing chain link as shown—4.6L engine

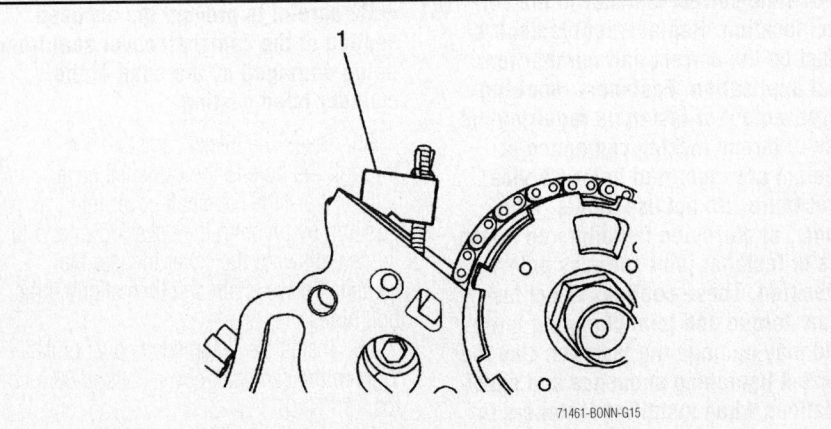

71461-BONN-G15

Fig. 42 Position the top retention tool on the cylinder head with the V-notch of the block adjacent to the left intake camshaft sprocket and chain—4.6L engine

29. Install the timing chain retention tools using the procedure below:

a. Rotate the wing nut to the top of its travel.

b. Position the bottom retention tool on the cylinder head with the V-notch of the block adjacent to the left exhaust camshaft sprocket and chain.

c. Insert the hook end into a secondary timing chain link as shown.

d. Rotate the wing nut until it contacts the retention tool block. DO NOT tighten the wing nut at this time.

e. Rotate the wing nut to the top of its travel.

f. Position the top retention tool on the cylinder head with the V-notch of the block adjacent to the left intake camshaft sprocket and chain.

g. Insert the hook end into a secondary timing chain link as shown.

h. Rotate the wing nut until it contacts the retention tool block. Alternately tighten both wing nuts to retain the chain.

30. Use an open wrench on the hex cast into the camshafts in order to prevent the camshafts from rotating when removing the camshaft sprocket bolts.

31. Remove the camshaft sprocket bolts.

32. Remove the camshaft sprockets.

33. Alternately loosen the camshaft bearing cap bolts a few turns at a time until all valve spring pressure has been released.

34. Remove the camshaft bearing caps.

35. Remove tool J 44212 from the camshafts.

36. Remove the camshafts.

37. Remove the camshaft followers.

38. Clean and inspect the camshafts.

To install:

39. Apply a liberal amount of lubricant GM P/N 36616001 or equivalent to the roller pivot pocket and valve slot areas of the camshaft followers.

➡**The follower must be positioned squarely on the valve tip so that the full width of the roller will completely contact the camshaft lobe. If the followers are being reused you must put them back in their original location.**

40. Place the camshaft followers in position on the valve tip and the Stationary Hydraulic Lash Adjusters (SHLA). The rounded head of the follower goes on the SHLA, while the flat end goes on the valve tip.

41. Clean the camshaft carriers with a clean, lint-free cloth.

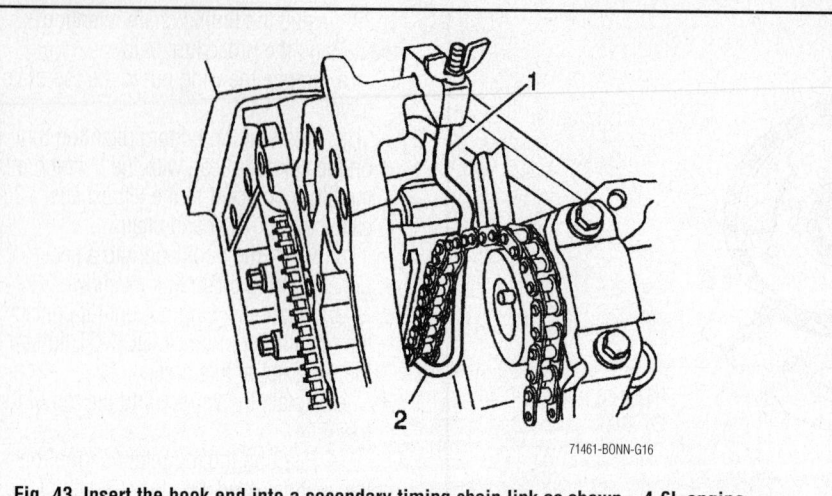

Fig. 43 Insert the hook end into a secondary timing chain link as shown—4.6L engine

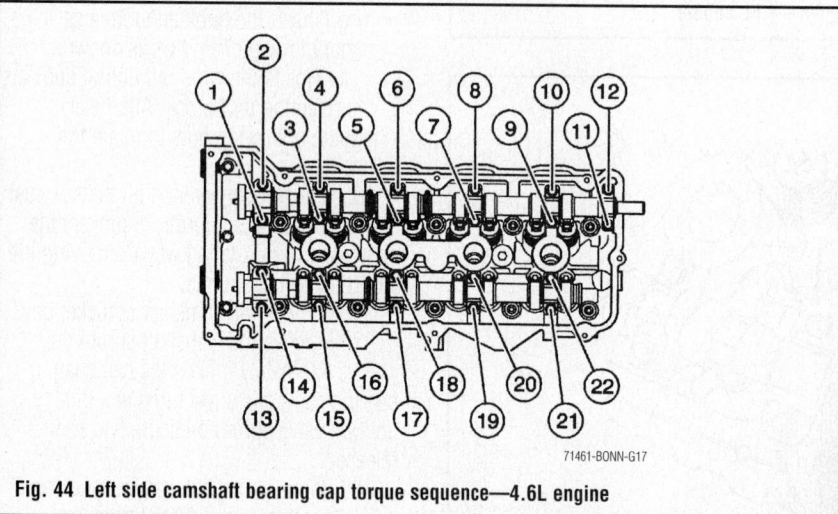

Fig. 44 Left side camshaft bearing cap torque sequence—4.6L engine

42. Apply a liberal amount of lubricant GM P/N 36616001 or equivalent to the camshaft carriers, camshaft lobes and the camshaft journals.

43. Place the camshaft in the camshaft carriers with the camshaft sprocket drive pins near the top of their rotation and the camshaft lobes in a neutral position. The camshafts can be identified by a stamping near the rear journal. For example: L-EXH is defined as Left bank Exhaust.

44. Observe the markings on the camshaft bearing caps. Each camshaft bearing cap is marked in order to identify its location. The markings have the following meanings:

- The arrow should point to the front of the engine.
- The number indicates the position from the front of the engine.
- The "E" indicates the exhaust camshaft.
- The "I" indicates the Intake camshaft.

45. Apply a liberal amount of lubricant GM P/N 36616001 or equivalent to the camshaft bearing caps.

46. Install the camshaft bearing caps according to the identification marks.

➡**Use the correct fastener in the correct location. Replacement fasteners must be the correct part number for that application. Fasteners requiring replacement or fasteners requiring the use of thread locking compound or sealant are identified in the service procedure. Do not use paints, lubricants, or corrosion inhibitors on fasteners or fastener joint surfaces unless specified. These coatings affect fastener torque and joint clamping force and may damage the fastener. Use the correct tightening sequence and specifications when installing fasteners in order to avoid damage to parts and systems.**

47. Install the camshaft bearing cap bolts in sequence.

a. Alternately hand tighten the camshaft bearing cap bolts a few turns at a time until all caps are fully seated.

b. Tighten the camshaft bearing cap bolts to 44 inch lbs. (5 Nm).

c. Tighten the camshaft bearing cap bolts an additional 30° using tool J 36660-A.

48. Align the camshafts.

✳✳ CAUTION

The camshaft holding tools must be installed on the camshafts to prevent camshaft rotation. When performing service to the valve train and/or timing components, valve spring pressure can cause the camshafts to rotate unexpectedly and can cause personal injury.

49. Install tool J 44212 over the camshafts.

➡**Ensure the camshaft sprockets properly engage the camshaft sprocket drive pins and camshafts.**

50. Slide the intake and exhaust camshaft sprockets off the pins of tool J 44213 and onto the pins of the camshafts.

51. Use an open wrench on the hex cast into the camshafts in order to prevent the camshafts from rotating when tightening the camshaft sprocket bolts.

52. Install the camshaft sprocket bolts. Tighten the camshaft sprocket bolts to 89 ft. lbs. (120 Nm).

53. Verify the camshaft sprocket alignment.

54. Remove tool J 44212 from the camshafts.

55. Install the camshaft cover seal as required.

➡**Be careful to prevent the exposed section of the camshaft cover seal from being damaged by the edge of the cylinder head casting.**

56. Insert the intake camshaft end through the hole in the camshaft cover.

57. Work the camshaft cover into position by pivoting the cover down and to the left allowing the cover to clear the camshaft drive chain and then aligning the bolt holes.

58. Install the 9 camshaft cover bolts. Tighten the camshaft cover bolts to 89 inch lbs. (10 Nm).

59. Install the NEW seal as follows:

60. Lubricate the camshaft seal lips with engine oil.

61. Push the camshaft seal into position around the intake camshaft using the protective sleeve supplied with the seal.

62. Coat the bolt threads with sealant GM P/N 1052080 (Canadian P/N 10953480) or equivalent.

63. Install the camshaft seal bolts. Tighten the camshaft seal bolts to 27 inch lbs. (3 Nm).

64. Place the water pump drive pulley in position on the intake camshaft.

65. Install the water pump pulley using tool J 38823. During installation, the tool will bottom out on the camshaft at the proper depth.

66. Install the plastic dust cap into the end of the camshaft.

67. Position the water pump belt tensioner to the water crossover. Tighten the water pump belt tensioner bolts to 89 inch lbs. (10 Nm).

68. Connect the water pump drive belt.

69. Install the water pump drive belt shield.

70. Install the water pump drive belt shield fasteners. Tighten the water pump drive belt shield fasteners to 89 inch lbs. (10 Nm). Tighten the secondary AIR valve bracket nut to 80 inch lbs. (9 Nm).

71. Connect the cable harness clips to the cable harness at the front of the camshaft cover.

72. Install the spark plug boots onto the coil cassette. Ensure that the boots are fully seated against the cassette.

73. Install the ignition coil cassette.

74. Connect the PCV fresh air tube to the left camshaft cover.

75. Position tool J 38185 to the clamp in order to connect the radiator inlet hose to the water housing crossover.

76. Install the fuel injector sight shield.

77. Fill the cooling system.

Right Side

See Figures 45 through 48.

➡The rear seat cushion must be removed to gain access to the battery.

1. Before servicing the vehicle, refer to the Precautions Section.

2. Disconnect the negative battery cable.

3. Remove the 2 nuts from the intake manifold sight shield.

4. Remove the sight shield from the engine.

5. Disconnect the PCV dirty air tube from the camshaft cover.

6. Disconnect the oxygen sensor wire.

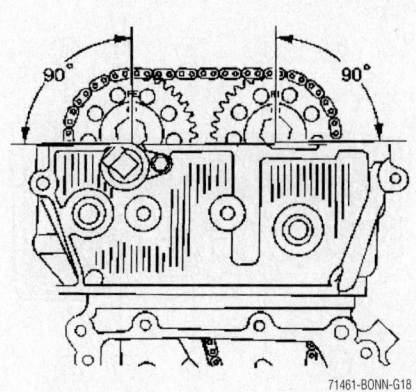

71461-BONN-G18

Fig. 45 Rotate the crankshaft to TDC of the no. 1 cylinders compression stroke, both right side camshaft sprocket drive pins should be at the top of their rotation—4.6L engine

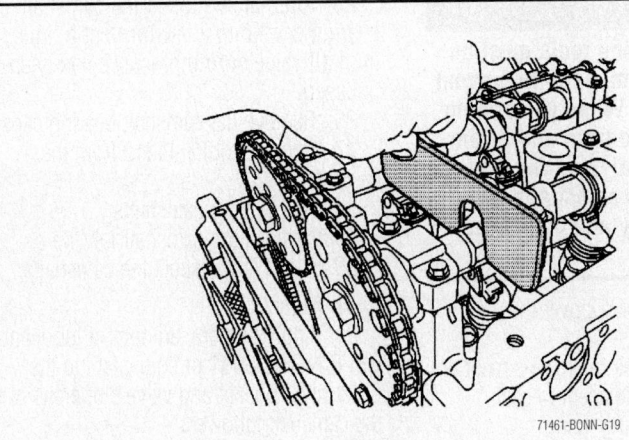

71461-BONN-G19

Fig. 46 Install tool J 44212 over the camshafts

7. Disconnect the vacuum tubes from the secondary AIR vent solenoid.

8. Disconnect the secondary AIR vent solenoid electrical connector.

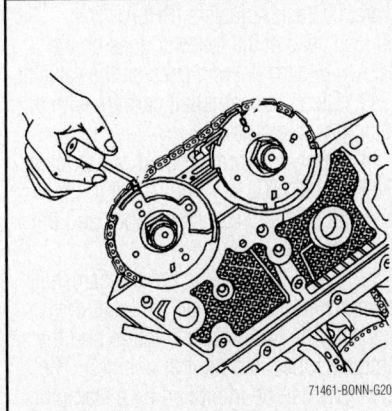

71461-BONN-G20

Fig. 47 Use a paint stick to create a mark on the timing chain link adjacent to each camshaft sprocket timing mark

9. Remove the secondary AIR control valve bracket.

10. Remove the nut securing the secondary AIR tube.

11. Remove the ignition coil cassette.

12. Remove the 4 spark plug boots.

13. Disconnect the cable harness clips at the front of the camshaft cover and position the cable harness aside.

14. Remove the 9 camshaft cover bolts.

15. Remove the camshaft cover.

16. Discard the camshaft cover perimeter seals and spark plug seals if there is any evidence of damage or if the seal comes out of the groove in the cover during removal.

17. Clean and inspect the camshaft cover.

18. Remove the camshaft position sensor.

19. Rotate the crankshaft to TDC of the no. 1 cylinders compression stroke, both camshaft sprocket drive pins should be at the top of their rotation.

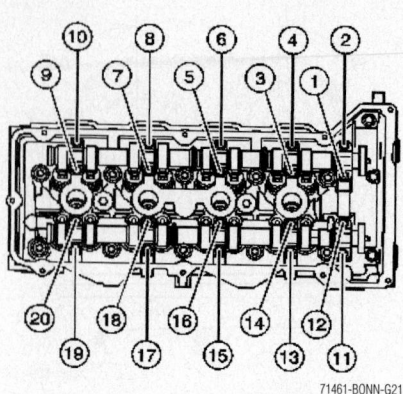

Fig. 48 Right side camshaft bearing cap torque sequence—4.6L engine

71461-BONN-G21

✳✳ WARNING

The camshaft holding tools must be installed on the camshafts to prevent camshaft rotation. When performing service to the valve train and/or timing components, valve spring pressure can cause the camshafts to rotate unexpectedly and can cause personal injury.

20. Install tool J 44212 over the camshafts.

21. Use a paint stick to create a mark on the timing chain link adjacent to each camshaft sprocket timing mark.

22. Install the using the procedure below:

    a. Rotate the wing nut to the top of its travel.

    b. Position the bottom retention tool on the cylinder head with the V-notch of the block adjacent to the right exhaust camshaft sprocket and chain.

    c. Insert the hook end into a secondary timing chain link as shown.

    d. Rotate the wing nut until it contacts the retention tool block. DO NOT tighten the wing nut at this time.

    e. Rotate the wing nut to the top of its travel.

    f. Position the top retention tool on the cylinder head with the V-notch of the block adjacent to the right intake camshaft sprocket and chain.

    g. Insert the hook end into a secondary timing chain link as shown.

    h. Rotate the wing nut until it contacts the retention tool block. Alternately tighten both wing nuts to retain the chain.

23. Use an open wrench on the hex cast into the camshafts in order to prevent the camshafts from rotating when removing the camshaft sprocket bolts.

24. Remove the camshaft sprocket bolts.

25. Alternately loosen the camshaft bearing cap bolts a few turns at a time until all valve spring pressure has been released.

26. Remove the camshaft bearing caps.

27. Remove tool J 44212 from the camshafts.

28. Remove the camshafts.

29. Remove the camshaft followers.

30. Clean and inspect the camshafts.

To install:

31. Apply a liberal amount of lubricant GM P/N 36616001 or equivalent to the roller pivot pocket and valve slot areas of the camshaft followers.

➡**The follower must be positioned squarely on the valve tip so that the full width of the roller will completely contact the camshaft lobe. If the followers are being reused you must put them back in their original location.**

32. Place the camshaft followers in position on the valve tip and the Stationary Hydraulic Lash Adjusters (SHLA). The rounded head of the follower goes on the SHLA, while the flat end goes on the valve tip.

33. Clean the camshaft carriers with a clean, lint-free cloth.

34. Apply a liberal amount of lubricant GM P/N 36616001 or equivalent to the camshaft carriers, camshaft lobes and the camshaft journals.

35. Place the camshaft in the camshaft carriers with the camshaft sprocket drive pins near the top of their rotation and the camshaft lobes in a neutral position. The camshafts can be identified by a stamping near the rear journal. For example: R-EXH is defined as Right Bank Exhaust.

36. Observe the markings on the camshaft bearing caps. Each camshaft bearing cap is marked in order to identify its location. The markings have the following meanings:

- The arrow should point to the front of the engine
- The number indicates the position from the front of the engine
- The **E** indicates the exhaust camshaft
- The **I** indicates the Intake camshaft

37. Apply a liberal amount of lubricant GM P/N 36616001 or equivalent to the camshaft bearing caps.

38. Install the camshaft bearing caps according to the identification marks.

39. Install the camshaft bearing cap bolts in sequence. Alternately hand tighten the camshaft bearing cap bolts a few turns at a time until all caps are fully seated.

    a. Tighten the camshaft bearing cap bolts to 44 inch lbs. (5 Nm).

    b. Tighten the camshaft bearing cap bolts an additional 30 degrees using tool J 36660-A.

40. Align the camshafts.

✳✳ CAUTION

The camshaft holding tools must be installed on the camshafts to prevent camshaft rotation. When performing service to the valve train and/or timing components, valve spring pressure can cause the camshafts to rotate unexpectedly and can cause personal injury.

41. Install tool J 44212 over the camshafts.

➡**Ensure the camshaft sprockets properly engage the camshaft sprocket drive pins and camshafts.**

42. Slide the intake and exhaust camshaft sprockets off the pins of tool J 44213 and onto the pins of the camshafts.

43. Use an open wrench on the hex cast into the camshafts in order to prevent the camshafts from rotating when tightening the camshaft sprocket bolts.

44. Install the camshaft sprocket bolts. Tighten the camshaft sprocket bolts to 89 ft. lbs. (120 Nm).

45. Verify the camshaft sprocket alignment.

46. Remove tool J 44212 from the camshafts.

47. Install the camshaft position sensor.

48. Install the camshaft cover seal as required.

➡**Be careful to prevent the exposed section of the camshaft cover seal from being damaged by the edge of the cylinder head casting.**

49. Install the camshaft cover.
50. Install the 9 camshaft cover bolts. Tighten the camshaft cover bolts to 89 inch lbs. (10 Nm).
51. Install the spark plug boots onto the coil cassette. Ensure that the boots are fully seated against the cassette.
52. Install the ignition coil cassette.
53. Install the secondary AIR control valve bracket.
54. Connect the cable harness clips to the cable harness at the front of the camshaft cover.
55. Connect the secondary AIR vent solenoid electrical connector.
56. Connect the vacuum tubes to the secondary AIR vent solenoid.
57. Connect the oxygen sensor wire.
58. Connect the PCV dirty air tube to the camshaft cover.
59. Position the intake manifold sight shield to the engine.
60. Install the 2 intake manifold sight shield nuts. Tighten the nuts to 27 inch lbs. (3 Nm).

CATALYTIC CONVERTER

REMOVAL & INSTALLATION

➡For vehicles equipped with OnStar (RPO UE1), with battery backup, the backup battery is a redundant power supply to allow limited OnStar functionality in the event of a main battery power disruption to the OnStar module (VCIM). Do not disconnect the main vehicle battery or remove the OnStar fuse with the ignition key in any position other than OFF. Retained accessory power should be allowed to time out or be disabled by opening the driver's side door before disconnecting power. Disconnecting power to the module in any way while the ignition is ON or with the retained accessory power activated may cause activation of the OnStar backup battery system and will discharge and permanently damage the backup battery. Once the backup battery is activated it will stay on until it has completely discharged. The backup battery is not rechargeable and once it is activated, it must be replaced.

3.9L Engine

See Figure 49.

➡The rear seat cushion must be removed to gain access to the battery.

1. Before servicing the vehicle, refer to the Precautions Section.

2. Disconnect the negative battery cable.
3. Raise and support the vehicle safely.
4. Properly support the exhaust system, with a suitable jack, as required.
5. Remove the nuts retaining the converter in place.

➡Move the muffler assembly rearward, in order to clear the studs.

6. Remove the converter from its mounting. Discard the gasket.

To install:

➡Be sure to use new fasteners, as required.

7. Position the converter to its mounting. Use new gaskets.
8. Tighten the retaining nuts to 35 ft. lbs. (50 Nm).
9. Continue the installation in the reverse order of the removal procedure.
10. Lower the vehicle.
11. Start the engine and check for exhaust leaks. Correct, as required.

4.6L Engine

See Figures 50 and 51.

➡The rear seat cushion must be removed to gain access to the battery.

1. Before servicing the vehicle, refer to the Precautions Section.
2. Disconnect the negative battery cable.
3. Raise and support the vehicle safely.
4. Properly support the exhaust system, near the resonator, with a suitable jack.
5. Remove the oxygen sensor. It is not

necessary to disconnect the electrical connector.
6. Remove the nuts securing the converter to the exhaust manifold pipe.

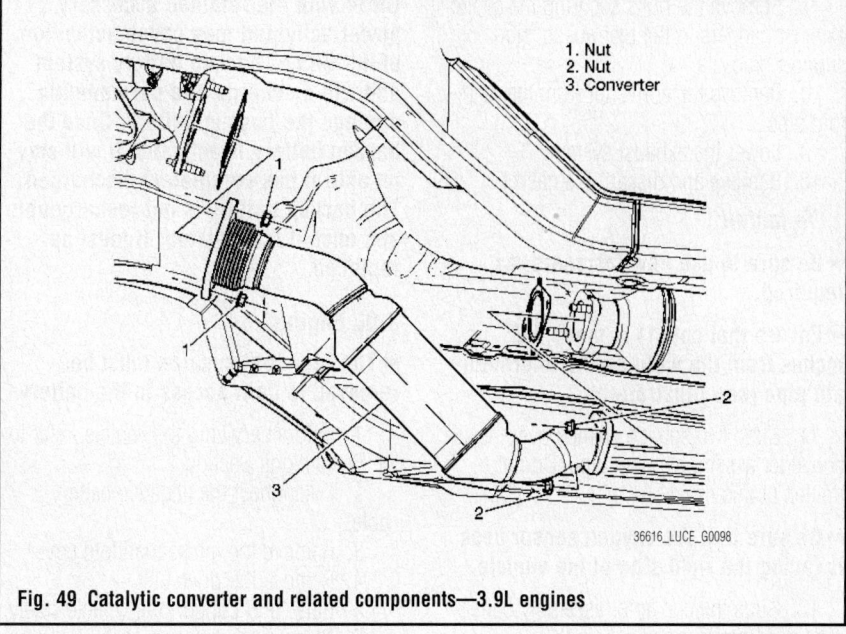
Fig. 49 Catalytic converter and related components—3.9L engines

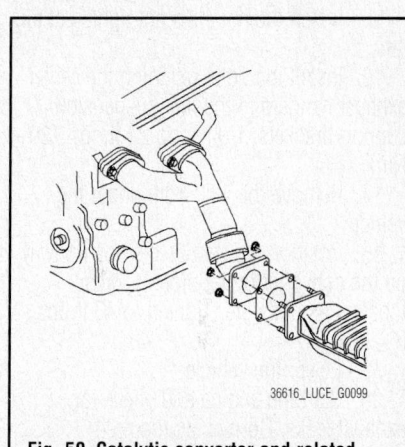
Fig. 50 Catalytic converter and related components—4.6L engines

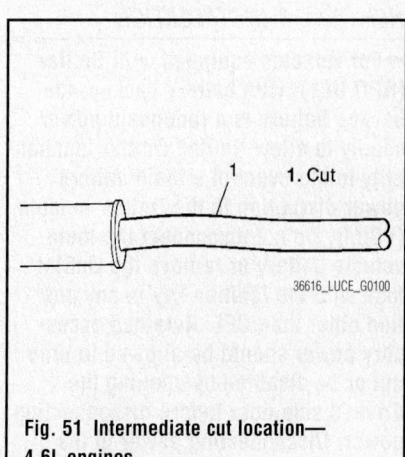
Fig. 51 Intermediate cut location—4.6L engines

7. Remove the bolts securing the center exhaust hangers to the rear suspension support brackets.

8. Remove the converter from the manifold pipe.

9. Lower the exhaust system.

10. Remove and discard the gasket.

To install:

➡ Be sure to use new fasteners, as required.

➡ Ensure that cut (1) is made 1.3 inches from the weld on the intermediate pipe (see illustration).

11. Slide two service clamps over the converter assembly outlet pipe. Do not tighten at this time.

➡ Be sure that the oxygen sensor boss is facing the right side of the vehicle.

12. Slide the converter assembly outlet pipe over the intermediate pipe.

13. Place a new gasket over the converter studs.

14. Raise the exhaust system into position. Align the converter with the manifold pipe.

15. Install the nuts. Do not tighten at this time.

16. Install the bolts retaining the center exhaust hangers to the rear suspension support brackets. Tighten to 22 ft. lbs. (30 Nm).

17. Remove the jack from under the vehicle.

18. Position the service clamps midway on the converter outlet pipe, as close together as possible. Tighten to 40 ft. lbs. (54 Nm).

19. Lower the vehicle.

20. Start the engine and check for exhaust leaks. Correct, as required.

CRANKSHAFT DAMPER

REMOVAL & INSTALLATION

➡ For vehicles equipped with OnStar (RPO UE1), with battery backup, the backup battery is a redundant power supply to allow limited OnStar functionality in the event of a main battery power disruption to the OnStar module (VCIM). Do not disconnect the main vehicle battery or remove the OnStar fuse with the ignition key in any position other than OFF. Retained accessory power should be allowed to time out or be disabled by opening the driver's side door before disconnecting power. Disconnecting power to the module in any way while the ignition is ON or with the retained accessory power activated may cause activation of the OnStar backup battery system and will discharge and permanently damage the backup battery. Once the backup battery is activated it will stay on until it has completely discharged. The backup battery is not rechargeable and once it is activated, it must be replaced.

3.9L Engine

➡ The rear seat cushion must be removed to gain access to the battery.

1. Before servicing the vehicle, refer to the Precautions Section.

2. Disconnect the negative battery cable.

3. Remove the intake manifold cover.

4. Remove the drive belt.

5. Raise and support the vehicle safely.

6. Remove the tire and wheel assembly.

7. Remove the wheelhouse liner.

8. Position jackstands under the frame.

9. Loosen the left side frame bolts. Remove the right side frame bolts.

10. Using the jackstands lower the right side of the frame to gain access to the balancer.

11. Remove the torque converter covers.

12. Install tool J37096, or equivalent, in order to prevent flywheel rotation.

13. Remove the balancer bolt and washer.

➡ Do not use power tools to remove this bolt.

14. Using a balancer removal tool remove the balance from its mounting on the engine.

To install:

➡ Be sure to use new fasteners, as required.

15. Apply sealer to the keyway of the balancer.

16. Position the balancer to its mounting.

17. Thread tool J29113 into the crankshaft. Rotate the hex nut on the tool in order to install the balance on the crankshaft. Remove the tool.

18. Install the old balancer washer and bolt. Tighten to 92 ft. lbs. (125 Nm). Remove the old balancer washer and bolt.

19. Install a new balancer washer and bolt. Tighten to 92 ft. lbs. (125 Nm). Tighten again and additional 130 degrees.

20. Install the old balancer washer and bolt. Tighten to 92 ft. lbs. (125 Nm). Remove the old balancer washer and bolt.

Continue the installation in the reverse order of the removal procedure.

21. Install the old balancer washer and bolt. Tighten to 92 ft. lbs. (125 Nm). Remove the old balancer washer and bolt.

Tighten the frame bolts to 74 ft. lbs, plus an additional 90 degrees.

4.6L Engine

See Figures 52 through 57.

➡ This procedure requires the following special tools, or their equivalents:

- J 45059 Angle Meter
- J 41816 Crankshaft Balancer (Damper) Remover
- J 41998-B Crankshaft Balancer (Damper) Installer
- J 44214 Flywheel Holder

➡ The rear seat cushion must be removed to gain access to the battery.

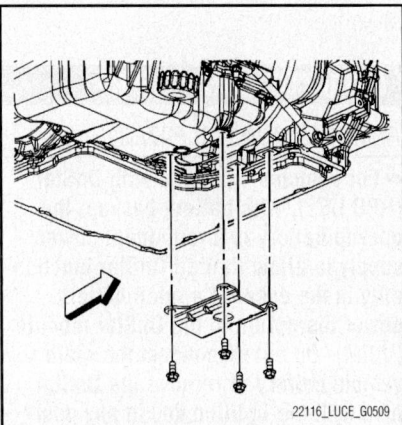

22116_LUCE_G0509

Fig. 52 Remove the transaxle to engine brace bolts, then remove the transaxle to engine brace

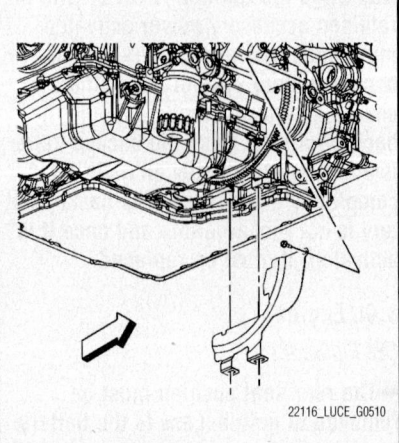

22116_LUCE_G0510

Fig. 53 Unfasten the bolt, and remove the torque converter cover

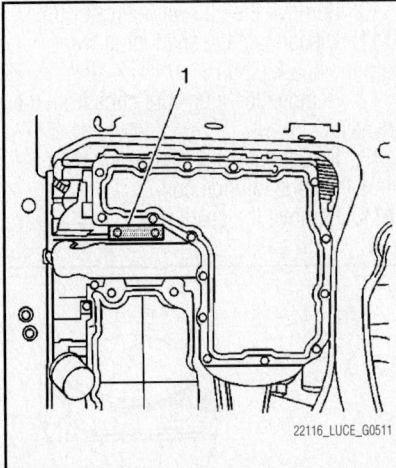

Fig. 54 Install a suitable Flywheel holder tool, special tool J 44214 (1), or its equivalent

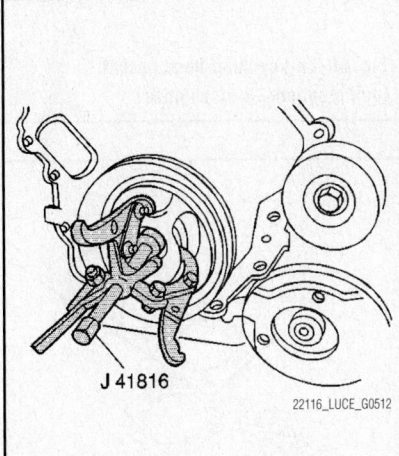

Fig. 55 View of the crankshaft damper removal tool installed on the crankshaft

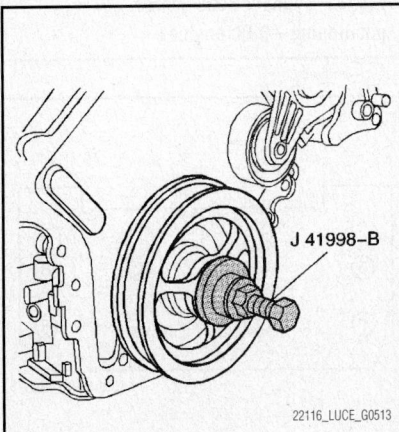

Fig. 56 Position the crankshaft damper on the nose of the crankshaft

1. Before servicing the vehicle, refer to the Precautions Section.

2. Disconnect the negative battery cable.

3. Before servicing the vehicle, refer to the Precautions Section.

4. Disconnect the negative battery cable.

5. Raise and safely support the vehicle.

6. Remove the right front wheel and wheel liner.

7. Remove the accessory drive belt. Refer to the procedure in this section for more information.

8. Raise and support the vehicle.

9. Remove the transaxle to engine brace bolts, then remove the transaxle to engine brace.

10. Remove the torque converter cover bolt and cover.

11. Unfasten the crankshaft damper bolt.

12. Remove the front fascia.

13. Support the frame with a suitable adjustable jack,

14. Loosen the right side frame bolts.

15. Carefully lower the frame to obtain clearance for Crankshaft Damper removal tool J 41816, or equivalent, below the body rail.

16. Place the remover pilot into the end of the crankshaft.

17. Use the Crankshaft Damper removal tool J 41816 to remove the crankshaft damper.

To install:

18. Position the crankshaft damper on the nose of the crankshaft.

19. Press the crankshaft damper in place using the Damper (Balancer) Installer J-41998-B.

Fig. 57 Press the crankshaft damper in place using the Damper (Balancer) Installer J-41998-B

20. Clean the crankshaft damper bolt threads, then apply clean engine oil to the crankshaft damper bolt threads.

21. Install the crankshaft damper bolt, and tighten as follows:

   a. Step 1: Tighten the bolt to 37 ft. lbs. (50 Nm).

   b. Step 2: Tighten the crankshaft damper bolt an additional 120°.

22. Raise the frame into position.

23. Install the right side frame bolts and tighten to 133 ft. lbs. (181 Nm).

24. Install the front fascia.

25. Remove the supports from the frame.

26. Remove the flywheel lock (tool J 44214).

27. Install the torque converter cover. Tighten the bolt to 106 inch lbs. (12 Nm).

28. Install the transaxle-to-engine brace. Tighten the bolts to 37 ft. lbs. (50 Nm).

29. Install the accessory drive belt.

30. Install the right front wheel liner and wheel.

31. Lower the vehicle.

CRANKSHAFT FRONT SEAL

REMOVAL & INSTALLATION

➡For vehicles equipped with OnStar (RPO UE1), with battery backup, the backup battery is a redundant power supply to allow limited OnStar functionality in the event of a main battery power disruption to the OnStar module (VCIM). Do not disconnect the main vehicle battery or remove the OnStar fuse with the ignition key in any position other than OFF. Retained accessory power should be allowed to time out or be disabled by opening the driver's side door before disconnecting power. Disconnecting power to the module in any way while the ignition is ON or with the retained accessory power activated may cause activation of the OnStar backup battery system and will discharge and permanently damage the backup battery. Once the backup battery is activated it will stay on until it has completely discharged. The backup battery is not rechargeable and once it is activated, it must be replaced.

3.9L Engine

See Figure 58.

➡The rear seat cushion must be removed to gain access to the battery.

1. Before servicing the vehicle, refer to the Precautions Section.

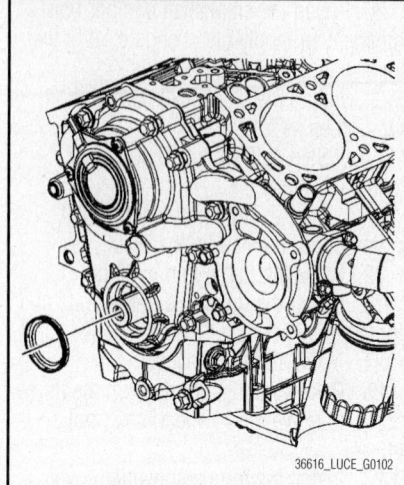

Fig. 58 Crankshaft front oil seal and related components—3.9L engines

2. Disconnect the negative battery cable.
3. Remove the crankshaft balancer.
4. Pry the seal from its mounting, using a suitable tool. Use care not to damage the engine front cover or the crankshaft.

To install:

→Be sure to use new fasteners, as required.

5. Lubricate the new seal with clean engine oil.
6. Using tool EN48869, or equivalent, align the seal with the front cover and the crankshaft. Install the seal.
7. Continue the installation in the reverse order of the removal procedure.

4.6L Engine

Do not remove the crankshaft front oil seal. The crankshaft front oil seal is not serviced as an individual component. When replacing the crankshaft front oil seal, install a **NEW** engine front cover. In order to precisely align the crankshaft front oil seal to the crankshaft damper and crankshaft damper dust shield, the engine front cover and the crankshaft front oil seal are sold as an assembly.

CYLINDER HEAD

REMOVAL & INSTALLATION

→For vehicles equipped with OnStar (RPO UE1), with battery backup, the backup battery is a redundant power supply to allow limited OnStar functionality in the event of a main battery power disruption to the OnStar module (VCIM). Do not disconnect the main vehicle battery or remove the OnStar

fuse with the ignition key in any position other than OFF. Retained accessory power should be allowed to time out or be disabled by opening the driver's side door before disconnecting power. Disconnecting power to the module in any way while the ignition is ON or with the retained accessory power activated may cause activation of the OnStar backup battery system and will discharge and permanently damage the backup battery. Once the backup battery is activated it will stay on until it has completely discharged. The backup battery is not rechargeable and once it is activated, it must be replaced.

3.9L Engine

Left Side

See Figures 59 through 62.

→The rear seat cushion must be removed to gain access to the battery.

1. Before servicing the vehicle, refer to the Precautions Section.
2. Disconnect the negative battery cable.
3. Drain the cooling system. Properly dispose of used coolant.
4. Drain the engine oil. Properly dispose of used oil.
5. Remove the alternator.
6. Remove the lower intake manifold.
7. Remove the valve cover.
8. Remove the rocker arms and pushrods.
9. Remove the exhaust manifold.

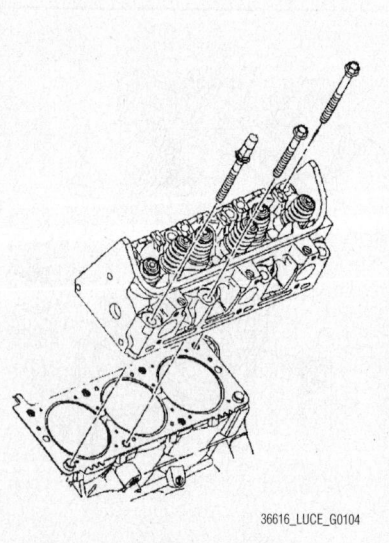

Fig. 59 Cylinder head and related components—3.9L engines

10. Remove the oil level indicator tube.
11. Disconnect the spark plug wires from the spark plugs.
12. Remove the plug wire clips from the brackets.
13. Disconnect and remove the plug wires from the ignition coil.
14. Remove the spark plugs.

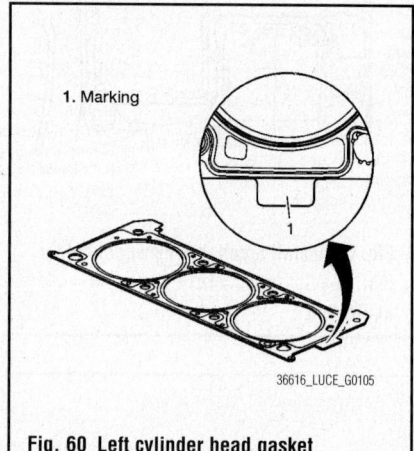

Fig. 60 Left cylinder head gasket identification—3.9L engines

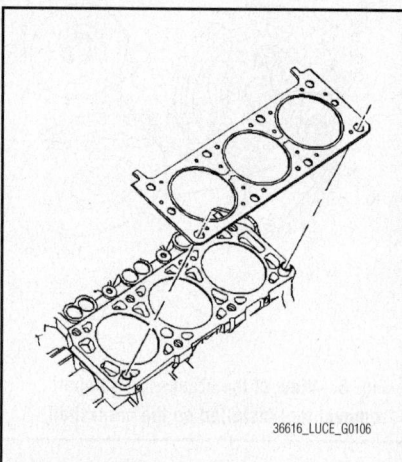

Fig. 61 Cylinder head gasket positioning—3.9L engines

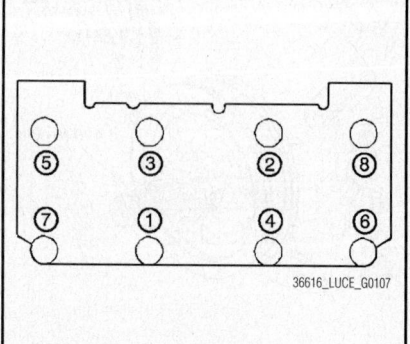

Fig. 62 Cylinder head bolt tightening sequence—3.9L engines

15. Remove the cylinder head retaining bolts.

16. Remove the cylinder head. Discard the gasket.

To install:

→Be sure to use new fasteners, as required.

→Cylinder head gaskets are specific for right and left side applications. Gaskets must also be installed with the correct side facing upward. Note the markings on the gasket for proper installation. Failure to properly install the gasket could result in engine damage.

17. Inspect the cylinder head dowel pins for proper installation.

18. Position the gasket on the block.

19. Install the cylinder head.

→This component uses torque-to-yield bolts. When servicing, do not reuse the old bolts. New bolts must be used. Failure to use new bolts may result in engine damage.

20. Install the new cylinder head bolts, finger tight. Install the new small hex cylinder head bolts (5 and 8). Install the new large hex cylinder head bolts (1, 2, 3, 4, 6, and 7).

21. Tighten the bolts in sequence to 44 ft. lbs. (60 Nm), first pass. Tighten the bolts an additional 140 degrees, second pass.

22. Continue the installation in the reverse order of the removal procedure.

Right Side

See Figure 63.

→The rear seat cushion must be removed to gain access to the battery.

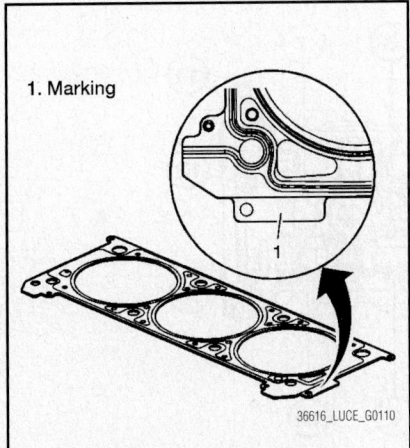

1. Marking

36616_LUCE_G0110

Fig. 63 Right cylinder head gasket identification—3.9L engines

1. Before servicing the vehicle, refer to the Precautions Section.

2. Disconnect the negative battery cable.

3. Drain the cooling system. Properly dispose of used coolant.

4. Drain the engine oil. Properly dispose of used oil.

5. Remove the lower intake manifold.

6. Remove the valve cover.

7. Remove the rocker arms and pushrods.

8. Remove the exhaust manifold.

9. Disconnect the spark plug wires from the spark plugs.

10. Remove the power steering pump reservoir.

11. Remove the intake manifold cover. Remove the drive belt. Remove the drive belt tensioner.

12. Remove the cylinder head retaining bolts.

13. Remove the cylinder head. Discard the gasket.

To install:

→Be sure to use new fasteners, as required.

→Cylinder head gaskets are specific for right and left side applications. Gaskets must also be installed with the correct side facing upward. Note the markings on the gasket for proper installation. Failure to properly install the gasket could result in engine damage.

14. Inspect the cylinder head dowel pins for proper installation.

15. Position the gasket on the block.

16. Install the cylinder head.

→This component uses torque-to-yield bolts. When servicing, do not reuse the old bolts. New bolts must be used. Failure to use new bolts may result in engine damage.

17. Install the new cylinder head bolts, finger tight. Install the new small hex cylinder head bolts (5 and 8). Install the new large hex cylinder head bolts (1, 2, 3, 4, 6, and 7).

18. Tighten the bolts in sequence to 44 ft. lbs. (60 Nm), first pass. Tighten the bolts an additional 140 degrees, second pass.

19. Continue the installation in the reverse order of the removal procedure.

4.6L Engine

Left Side

See Figure 64.

→The rear seat cushion must be removed to gain access to the battery.

1. Before servicing the vehicle, refer to the Precautions Section.

2. Disconnect the negative battery cable.

3. Remove the following subassemblies:

- The left exhaust manifold
- The engine mount strut bracket
- The alternator
- The water crossover
- The intake manifold
- The camshaft cover
- The engine front cover
- The left secondary camshaft drive chain

4. Remove the 3 M6 external drive bolts from the front portion of the cylinder head.

→DO NOT reuse the M11 cylinder head bolts.

5. Remove and discard the ten M11 internal drive cylinder head bolts.

6. Remove the left cylinder head. Make sure that no dowel guide pins are stuck in the cylinder head.

→You must clean the thread sealant material from the cylinder head bolt holes in the cylinder block. Failure to do so could cause false torque readings during reassembly.

7. After removing the cylinder head, remove any remaining bolt thread sealant material from the threaded cylinder block holes.

→DO NOT reuse the cylinder head gasket.

8. Remove the left cylinder head gasket.

9. Remove all remaining gasket material from the cylinder head and cylinder block using tool J 28410.

10. Place the cylinder head on a flat, clean surface with the combustion chamber side face-up in order to prevent damage to the deck face.

11. Clean and inspect the cylinder head.

To install:

12. Make sure all the cylinder head locating pins are securely mounted in the cylinder block deck face.

→Failure to remove all the old thread sealant material from the cylinder block could cause false torque readings.

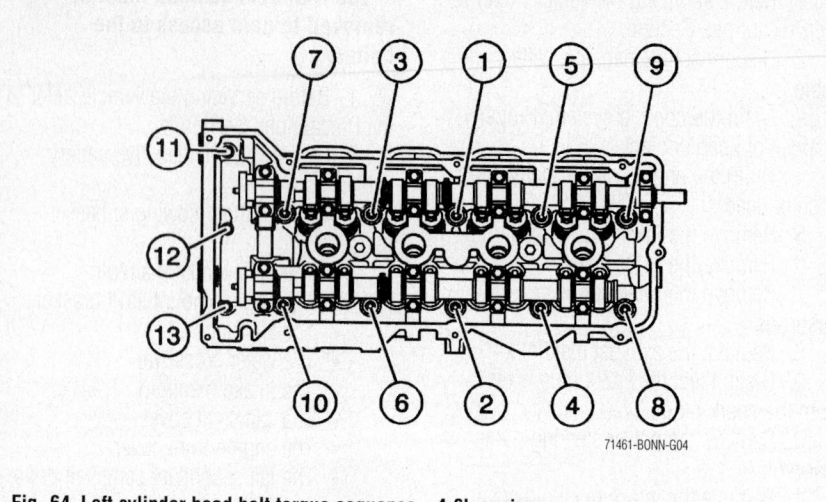

Fig. 64 Left cylinder head bolt torque sequence—4.6L engine

13. Make sure any old thread sealant material is removed from the cylinder head bolt holes in the cylinder block.

14. Install a new left cylinder head gasket using the deck face locating pins for retention.

15. Align the cylinder head with the deck face locating pins.

16. Place the cylinder head in position on the deck face.

➡**DO NOT reuse the old M11 cylinder head bolts.**

17. Install new M11 cylinder head bolts in the cylinder head.

18. Install the M6 cylinder head bolts at the front of the cylinder head.

19. Tighten the left cylinder head bolts in the sequence shown:

  a. First Pass: Tighten the left cylinder head M11 cylinder head bolts to 22 ft. lbs. (30 Nm) in the sequence shown.

  b. Second Pass: Tighten the left cylinder head M11 cylinder head bolts an additional 70° in the sequence shown.

  c. Third Pass: Repeat the sequence turning each bolt another 60°.

  d. Final Pass: Repeat the sequence again turning each bolt a final 45°.

➡**The total degrees of torque must not exceed 175°.**

20. Tighten the M6 bolts at the front of the cylinder head to 106 inch lbs. (12 Nm).

21. Install the following subassemblies:
  • The left secondary camshaft drive chain
  • The engine front cover
  • The camshaft cover
  • The intake manifold
  • The water crossover
  • The alternator

  • The engine mount strut bracket
  • The left exhaust manifold

Right Side
See Figure 65.

➡**The rear seat cushion must be removed to gain access to the battery.**

1. Before servicing the vehicle, refer to the Precautions Section.

2. Disconnect the negative battery cable.

3. Remove the following subassemblies:
  • The right exhaust manifold
  • The water crossover
  • The intake manifold
  • The camshaft cover
  • The engine front cover
  • The right secondary camshaft drive chain

4. Disconnect the electrical connector from the Engine Coolant Temperature (ECT) sensor.

5. Remove the nut securing the coil cassette ground wire to the cylinder head.

6. Remove the bolt securing the exhaust crossover pipe to the cylinder head.

7. Raise and support the vehicle.

8. Remove the bolt securing the front transaxle brace to the cylinder head.

9. Loosen the bolts attaching the transaxle brace to the transaxle.

10. Remove the bolt securing the rear transaxle brace to the transaxle.

11. Lower the vehicle.

12. Remove the nuts securing the rear transaxle brace to the cylinder head.

13. Remove the rear transaxle brace.

14. Remove the 3 M6 external drive bolts from the front portion of the cylinder head.

➡**DO NOT reuse the M11 cylinder head bolts.**

15. Remove and discard the ten M11 internal drive cylinder head bolts.

16. Remove the right cylinder head. Make sure that no dowel guide pins are stuck in the cylinder head.

➡**You must clean the thread sealant material from the cylinder head bolt holes in the cylinder block. Failure to do so could cause false torque readings during reassembly.**

17. After removing the cylinder head, remove any remaining bolt thread sealant material from the threaded cylinder block holes.

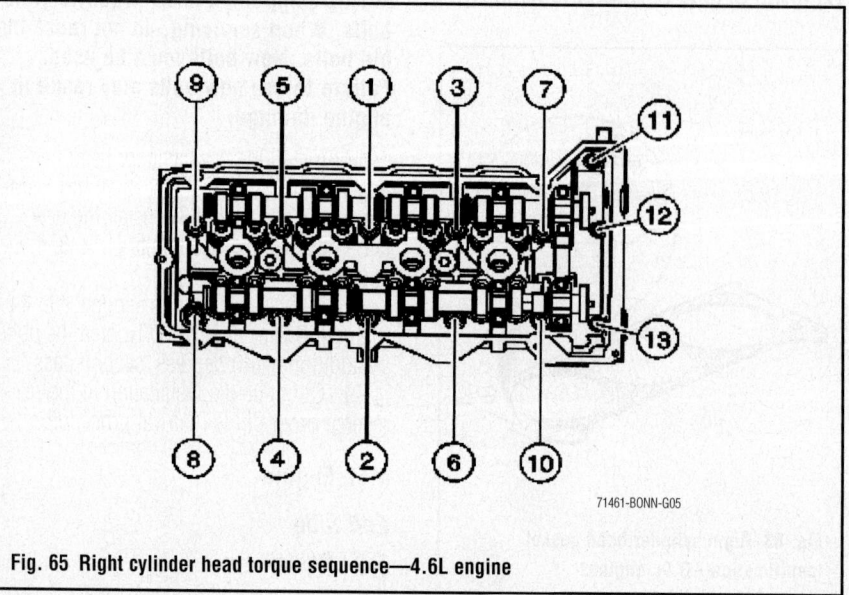

Fig. 65 Right cylinder head torque sequence—4.6L engine

➡**DO NOT reuse the cylinder head gasket.**

18. Remove the right cylinder head gasket.

19. Remove all remaining gasket material from the cylinder head and cylinder block.

20. Place the cylinder head on a flat, clean surface with the combustion chambers face-up in order to prevent damage to the deck face.

21. Clean and inspect the cylinder head.

To install:

22. Make sure all the cylinder head locating pins are securely mounted in the cylinder block deck face.

➡**Failure to remove all the old thread sealant material from the cylinder block could cause false torque readings.**

23. Make sure any old thread sealant material is removed from the cylinder head bolt holes in the cylinder block.

24. Install a new right cylinder head gasket using the deck face locating pins for retention.

25. Align the cylinder head with the deck face locating pins.

26. Place the cylinder head in position on the deck face.

➡**DO NOT reuse the old M11 cylinder head bolts.**

27. Install new M11 cylinder head bolts in the cylinder head.

28. Install the M6 cylinder head bolts at the front of the cylinder head.

29. Tighten the right cylinder head bolts in the sequence shown:

a. First Pass: Tighten the right cylinder head M11 cylinder head bolts to 30 ft. lbs. (40 Nm) in the sequence shown.

b. Second Pass: Tighten the right cylinder head M11 cylinder head bolts an additional 70° in the sequence shown.

c. Third Pass: Repeat the sequence turning each bolt another 60°.

d. Final Pass: Repeat the sequence again turning each bolt a final 45°.

➡**The total degrees of torque must not exceed 175°.**

30. Tighten the M6 bolts at the front of the cylinder head to 106 inch lbs. (12 Nm).

31. Position the rear transaxle brace over the studs located at the rear of the right cylinder head.

32. Loosely install the nuts securing the rear transaxle brace to the cylinder head.

33. Raise and support the vehicle.

34. Install the bolt securing the rear transaxle brace to the transaxle. Tighten the rear transaxle brace bolt to 37 ft. lbs. (50 Nm).

35. Install the bolt securing the front transaxle brace to the cylinder head. Tighten the front transaxle brace bolts to 37 ft. lbs. (50 Nm).

36. Lower the vehicle.

37. Tighten the rear transaxle brace to the cylinder head nuts to 37 ft. lbs. (50 Nm).

38. Connect the electrical connector to the ECT sensor.

39. Install the bolt securing the exhaust crossover pipe to the cylinder head. Tighten the exhaust crossover pipe to cylinder head bolt to 18 ft. lbs. (25 Nm).

40. Install the nut securing the coil cassette ground wire to the cylinder head. Tighten the coil cassette ground wire nut to 13 ft. lbs. (17 Nm).

41. Install the following subassemblies:
- The right secondary camshaft drive chain
- The engine front cover
- The camshaft cover
- The intake manifold
- The water crossover
- The right exhaust manifold

ENGINE ASSEMBLY

REMOVAL & INSTALLATION

3.9L Engine

➡**For vehicles equipped with OnStar (RPO UE1), with battery backup, the backup battery is a redundant power supply to allow limited OnStar functionality in the event of a main battery power disruption to the OnStar module (VCIM). Do not disconnect the main vehicle battery or remove the OnStar fuse with the ignition key in any position other than OFF. Retained accessory power should be allowed to time out or be disabled by opening the driver's side door before disconnecting power. Disconnecting power to the module in any way while the ignition is ON or with the retained accessory power activated may cause activation of the OnStar backup battery system and will discharge and permanently damage the backup battery. Once the backup battery is activated it will stay on until it has completely discharged. The backup battery is not rechargeable and once it is activated, it must be replaced.**

➡**The rear seat cushion must be removed to gain access to the battery.**

1. Before servicing the vehicle, refer to the Precautions Section.

2. Disconnect the negative battery cable.

3. Properly relieve the fuel system pressure.

4. Remove the hood.

5. Remove the intake manifold cover. Remove the air cleaner assembly.

6. Remove the engine strut mounts.

7. Remove the drive belt.

8. Drain the cooling system. Properly dispose of used coolant.

9. Raise and safely support the vehicle.

10. Drain the engine oil. Properly dispose of used oil.

11. Remove the oil pressure sensor heat shield. Disconnect the electrical connector.

12. Disconnect the knock sensor electrical connector, starter motor electrical connector and A/C compressor electrical connector.

13. Disconnect the oil level sensor electrical connector. Remove the engine harness clips from the transaxle brace and oil pan.

14. Lower the vehicle.

15. Disconnect the EVAP electrical connector. Disconnect the ETC electrical connector. Disconnect the MAP sensor electrical connector.

16. Disconnect the alternator electrical connectors. Disconnect the ignition coil electrical connector.

17. Disconnect the fuel injector inline electrical connector. Remove the engine harness clips from the brackets.

18. Disconnect the camshaft sensor electrical connector. Remove the engine harness clip.

19. Remove the CPA retainer. Disconnect the oxygen sensor electrical connector.

20. Disconnect the CKP electrical connector. Remove the harness clips from the transaxle bracket.

21. Remove the engine harness ground terminals from the transaxle. Reposition out of the way.

22. Remove the catalytic converter.

23. Remove the engine mount lower nuts.

24. Remove the torque converter cover. Remove the starter.

25. Remove the torque converter retaining bolts.

26. Remove the A/C compressor retaining bolts. Reposition the compressor out of the way. Do not discharge the A/C system.

27. Remove the transaxle brace to transaxle bolts. Remove the transaxle brace to engine bolts. Remove the transaxle brace.

28. Remove the transaxle to engine lower rear bolt.

29. Disconnect and reposition the lower radiator hose assembly.

30. Lower the vehicle and properly support the transaxle.

31. Remove the brake booster vacuum hose. Disconnect and reposition the heater hoses.

32. Remove the exhaust crossover pipe.

33. Disconnect the fuel line from the fuel rail.

34. Remove the upper radiator hose.

35. Remove the power steering pump bolts. Reposition the pump to the side.

36. Install a suitable engine lifting device to the engine.

37. Remove the transaxle to engine bolts and nuts.

38. Check to be sure that all lines, wires and hoses have been removed so that the engine can be removed from the vehicle freely.

39. Carefully remove the engine from the vehicle.

To install:

➡ **Be sure to use new fasteners, as required.**

40. Installation is the reverse of the removal procedure.

41. Be sure to fill the cooling system with the proper grade and type coolant.

42. Be sure to fill the engine with the proper grade and type oil.

43. Start the engine and check for leaks. Correct as required.

44. Roadtest the vehicle.

4.6L Engine

See Figures 66 through 81.

➡ **For vehicles equipped with OnStar (RPO UE1), with battery backup, the backup battery is a redundant power supply to allow limited OnStar functionality in the event of a main battery power disruption to the OnStar module (VCIM). Do not disconnect the main vehicle battery or remove the OnStar fuse with the ignition key in any position other than OFF. Retained accessory power should be allowed to time out or be disabled by opening the driver's side door before disconnecting power. Disconnecting power to the module in any way while the ignition is ON or with the retained accessory power activated may cause activation of the OnStar backup battery system and will discharge and permanently damage the backup battery. Once the**

backup battery is activated it will stay on until it has completely discharged. The backup battery is not rechargeable and once it is activated, it must be replaced.

➡ **This procedure requires the use of the following special tools, or their equivalents:**

- J 37097-A Hose Clamp Remover/Installer
- J 38185 Hose Clamp Pliers
- J 39580 Universal Engine Support Table
- J 41623-B Cooler Quick Connect Tool
- J 42640 Steering Column Lock Pin

➡ **The rear seat cushion must be removed to gain access to the battery.**

1. Before servicing the vehicle, refer to the Precautions Section.

2. Disconnect the negative battery cable.

3. Recover the A/C refrigerant system.

➡ **Only a MVAC-trained, EPA-certified, automotive technician should service the A/C system or its components.**

4. Remove or disconnect the following:
- The battery negative cable
- Fuel injector sight shield.
- Reposition the brake booster vacuum hose at the engine port
- The vacuum brake booster hose from the vacuum connection and position aside
- The fuel feed and Evaporative emission (EVAP) line quick-connect fittings

- Front compartment sight shield
- The air cleaner assembly
- Junction block cover lock tabs, and cover
- The nut securing the starter cable to the Bussed Electric Center (BEC)
- Starter cable clip from the BEC terminal, and secure it to the top of the engine

5. Disengage the lever lock.

6. Disconnect the electrical connector from the Transaxle Control Module (TCM).

7. Disengage the lever lock.

8. Disconnect the engine harness electrical connect from the body harness electrical connector.

9. Secure the TCM and engine harness wiring branches to the engine.

10. Disengage the lever locks, then detach the electrical connectors from the Engine Control Module (ECM).

11. Unfasten the junction block bolts, then remove the junction block.

12. Remove the engine harness from the BEC.

13. Unfasten the engine ground strap bolt from the right side frame rail, and secure the ground strap to the engine.

14. Remove the transaxle shift cable clip from the shift cable bracket.

15. Remove the transaxle shift cable retainer.

16. Disconnect the transaxle shift cable end from the range selector lever.

17. Remove the transaxle shift cable from the bracket, then position the cable aside.

18. Drain the cooling system into a suitable container.

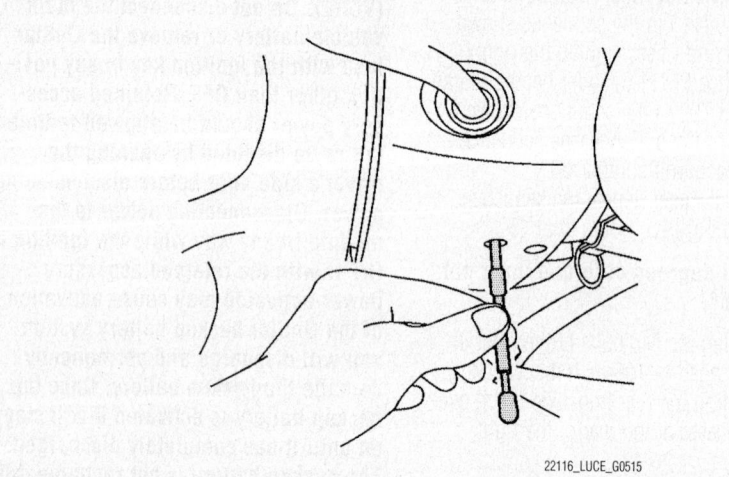

22116_LUCE_G0515

Fig. 66 Lock the steering column by installing the J 42640 into the underside of the steering column

19. Using tool J 37097-A, reposition the radiator inlet hose clamp, then remove the radiator inlet hose from the water pump housing and position it aside.

20. Using tool J 38185, reposition the radiator outlet hose clamp. Disconnect the outlet hose from the thermostat housing and position it aside.

21. Reposition the radiator surge tank inlet hose clamp at the surge tank, then disconnect the surge tank inlet hose from the tank.

22. Reposition the heater inlet and outlet hose clamps at the heater pipes. Disconnect the heater inlet and outlet hoses from the heater pipes.

23. Remove the master cylinder nuts and master cylinder from the brake booster.

24. Reposition the master cylinder and secure the master cylinder to the engine.

25. Loosen the upper transaxle oil cooler pipe bolt (1) from the fan shroud.

26. Slide the plastic caps off the transaxle oil cooler pipe quick connect fittings.

27. Remove the right front engine mount strut bolt.

28. Disconnect the transaxle oil cooler pipes from the radiator using the J 41623-B .

➥With wheels of the vehicle facing straight ahead, secure the steering wheel utilizing steering column anti-rotation pin, steering column lock, or a strap to prevent rotation. Locking of the steering column will prevent damage and a possible malfunction of the SIR system. The steering wheel must be secured in position before disconnecting the following components:

- The steering column
- The intermediate shaft(s)
- The steering gear

✳✳ WARNING

After disconnecting these components, do not rotate the steering wheel or move the front tires and wheels. Failure to follow this procedure may cause the SIR coil assembly to become un-centered and cause possible damage to the SIR coil. If you think the SIR coil has became un-centered, refer to your specific SIR coil's centering procedure to re-center SIR Coil, found in the Chassis Electrical Section..

29. Lock the steering column by installing the J 42640 into the underside of the steering column.

30. Remove the left and right side strut tower bolts.

31. Raise and safely support the vehicle.

32. Remove the rear exhaust manifold pipe.

33. Remove the front wheel and tire assemblies.

34. Remove the engine harness grommet from the frame rail bracket.

35. Remove the engine harness clip from the ride lever sensor bracket.

36. If equipped, disconnect the electronic suspension front position sensor link from the lower control arms ball stud.

37. Loosen the nut securing the left front brake pipe bracket to the body frame rail. Remove the front brake pipe bracket from the body frame rail.

38. Loosen the nut securing the right front brake pipe bracket to the body frame rail. Remove the front brake pipe bracket from the body frame rail.

39. Disconnect the rear brake pipes from the front brake pipes. Make sure to plug or tape the open brake lines in order to prevent fluid loss and/or system contamination.

40. Unfasten the A/C compressor discharge hose bolt at the condenser. Remove the A/C compressor discharge hose from the condenser and secure to the engine. Make sure to plug the A/C condenser discharge port.

41. Remove the A/C compressor suction hose nut at the condenser. Remove the A/C compressor suction hose from the condenser and secure to the engine. Make sure to plug the A/C condenser suction port.

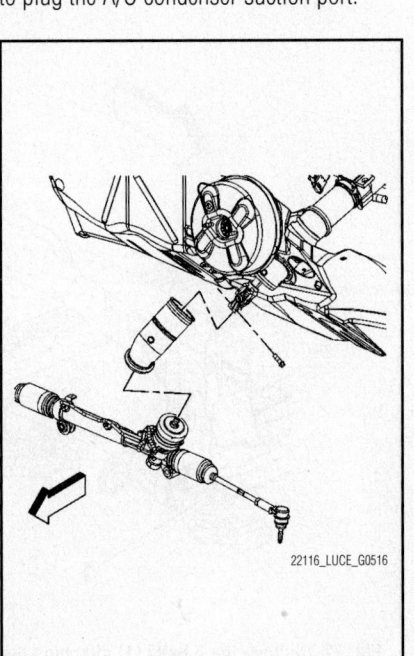

Fig. 67 View of the steering gear

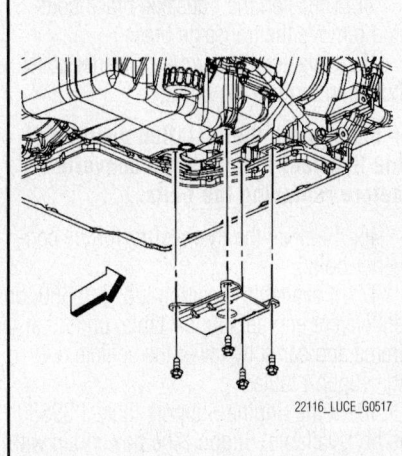

22116_LUCE_G0517

Fig. 68 Unfasten the transaxle brace bolts and remove the transaxle brace

✳✳ CAUTION

Failure to disconnect the intermediate shaft from the rack and pinion stub shaft can result in damage to the steering gear and/or damage to the intermediate shaft. This damage may cause loss of steering control which could result in personal injury.

42. Remove the intermediate steering shaft cover, then remove the intermediate shaft pinch bolt and remove the intermediate shaft from the steering gear.

43. Remove the oxygen sensor wiring harness heat shield, then disconnect the engine harness electrical connector from the Heated Oxygen Sensor (HO2S).

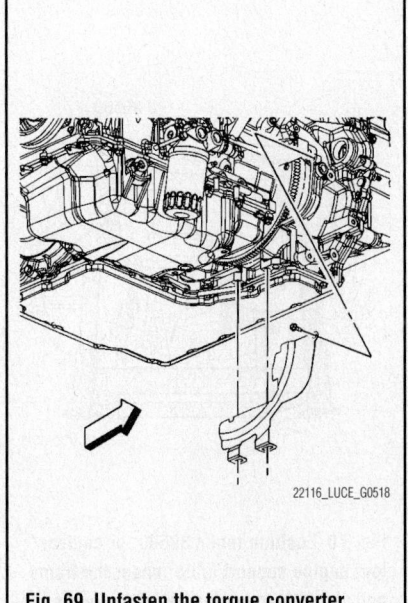

22116_LUCE_G0518

Fig. 69 Unfasten the torque converter cover bolt, and remove the cover

44. Unfasten the transaxle brace bolts and remove the transaxle brace.

45. Unfasten the torque converter cover bolt, and remove the cover.

➡**Matchmark the installed position of the flywheel to the torque converter before removing the bolts.**

46. Remove the flywheel-to-torque converter bolts.

47. If available, position tool J 39580, or equivalent engine support table, under the frame and carefully lower the vehicle onto the support table.

48. If the Engine Support Table J 39580 is not available. Support the powertrain with four suitable jackstands.

49. Place a 2 in x 4 in block of wood between the front of the engine oil pan and the engine frame.

✳✳ CAUTION

To avoid any vehicle damage, serious personal injury or death when major components are removed from the vehicle and the vehicle is supported by a hoist, support the vehicle with jackstands at the opposite end from which the components are being removed and strap the vehicle to the hoist.

50. Secure the front hoist pads to the vehicle.

51. Remove the front fascia.

52. Remove the 6 bolts (1) attaching the frame to the body. (Left side shown, right side similar).

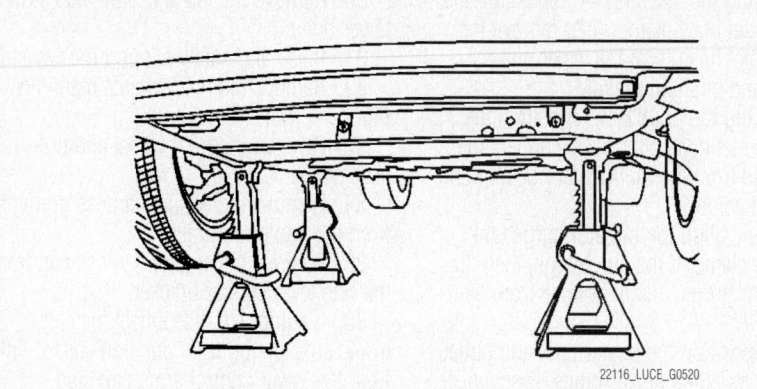

Fig. 71 If the Engine Support Table J 39580 is not available. Support the powertrain with four suitable jackstands

➡**Ensure clearance is maintained between the engine/transaxle assembly and the following:**

- A/C compressor components
- Brake pipes
- Heater hoses
- Radiator hoses
- Wheel Speed Sensor (WSS) leads
- Wiring harnesses

53. Carefully raise the vehicle in order to clear the supported engine/transaxle assembly.

54. Drain the engine oil into a suitable container.

55. Remove the heater outlet pipe nut from the transaxle stud.

56. Reposition the heater outlet pipe clamp from the water pump housing and remove the heater outlet pipe.

57. Remove the secondary Air Injection (AIR) inlet hose retainer from the transaxle stud.

58. Disconnect the AIR inlet hose quick connect fitting from the AIR pump.

59. Remove the AIR inlet hose.

60. Reposition the AIR outlet hose clamp at the AIR outlet pipe, then separate the AIR outlet hose from the outlet pipe.

61. Remove the AIR pipe outlet pipe nut from the transaxle stud.

62. Remove the AIR pipe outlet pipe nut from the check valve bracket stud.

63. Disconnect the AIR outlet pipe quick connect fitting from the check valve. Remove the AIR outlet pipe from the studs.

64. Remove the Ignition Control module (ICM) ground strap bolt from the right cylinder head, then remove the ICM ground strap from the head.

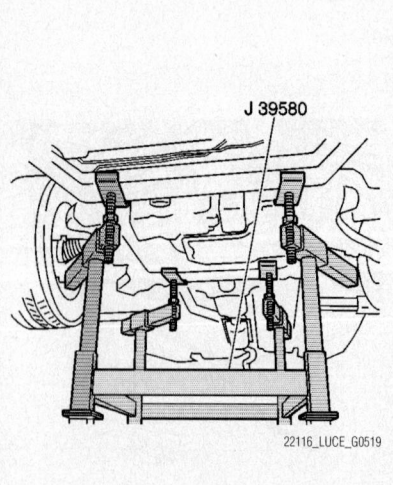

Fig. 70 Position tool J 39580, or equivalent engine support table, under the frame and carefully lower the vehicle onto the support table

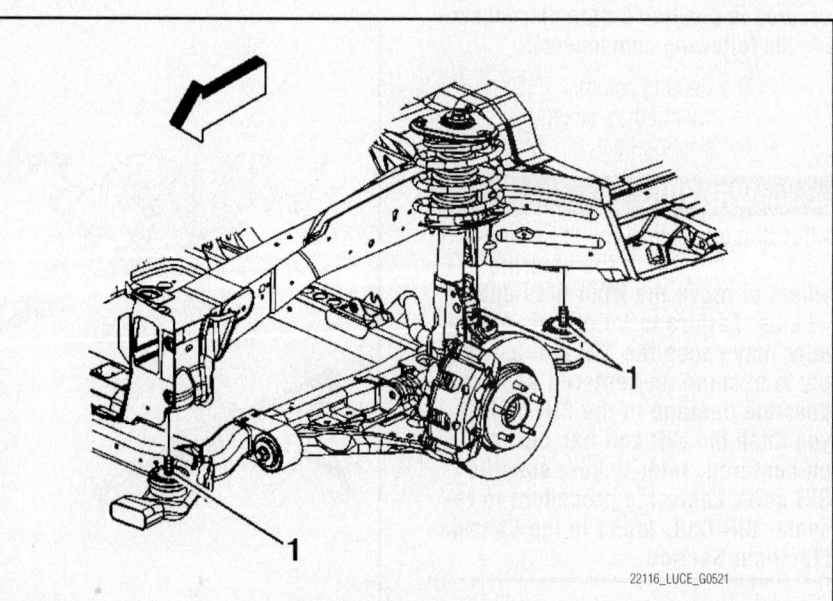

Fig. 72 Remove the 6 bolts (1) attaching the frame to the body. (Left side shown, right side similar)

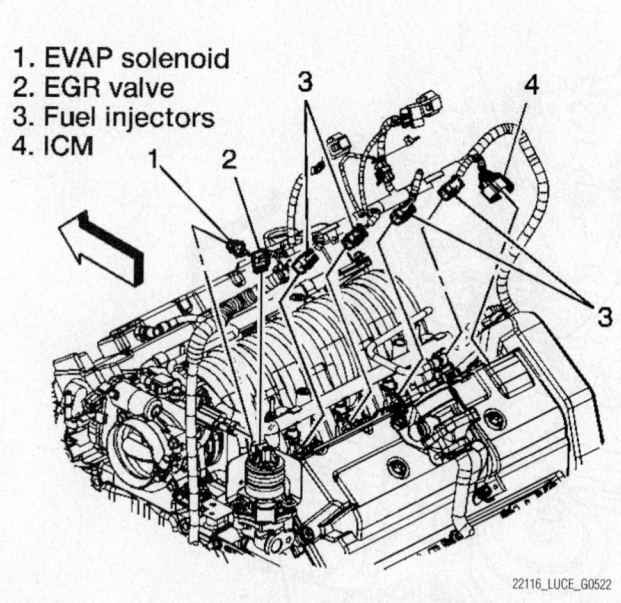

1. EVAP solenoid
2. EGR valve
3. Fuel injectors
4. ICM

22116_LUCE_G0522

Fig. 73 Detach the electrical connectors from the rear of the engine

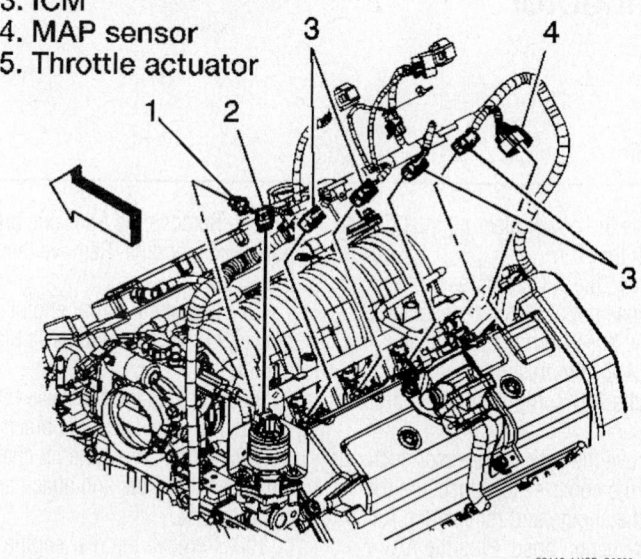

1. Fuel injectors
2. Engine harness clip
3. ICM
4. MAP sensor
5. Throttle actuator

22116_LUCE_G0523

Fig. 74 Detach the electrical connectors from the front of the engine, then remove the engine harness clip from the fuel rail stud

65. Detach the following electrical connectors from the rear of the engine:
   - EVAP solenoid (1)
   - Exhaust Gas Recirculation (EGR) valve (2)
   - Fuel injectors (3)
   - ICM (4)

66. Detach the following electrical connectors from the front of the engine:
   - Fuel injectors (1)
   - ICM (3)
   - Manifold Absolute Pressure (MAP) sensor (4)
   - Throttle actuator (5)

67. Remove the engine harness clip from the fuel rail stud.

68. Disconnect the starter inline and the AIR check valve following engine harness electrical connectors from the top of the engine:

69. Disconnect the engine harness electrical connector (1) from the engine valley jumper harness electrical connector.

70. Disconnect the engine harness electrical connector (3) from the power steering sensor.

71. Remove the engine harness clip (2) from the steering gear shield.

72. Remove the engine harness ground nut (4).

73. Remove the engine harness ground (5).

74. Disconnect the engine harness electrical connector (6) from the engine coolant temperature (ECT) sensor.

75. Disconnect the engine harness electrical connector from the Vehicle Speed Sensor (VSS).

76. Remove the engine harness clips from the rear engine mount bracket and steering gear shield.

77. Disconnect the engine harness electrical connector from the A/C pressure sensor.

78. Remove the engine harness clip (1) from the boss on the engine block.

79. Disconnect the following engine harness electrical connectors:
   - Oil pressure sensor (2)
   - Oil level sensor (3)
   - A/C compressor (4)
   - Alternator (5)

80. Disconnect the engine harness electrical connectors from the following:
   - AIR Pump
   - Brake modulator

81. Remove the engine harness clip from the engine bracket.

82. Remove the Connector Position Assurance (CPA) retainer.

83. Disconnect the engine harness electrical connector from the HO2S.

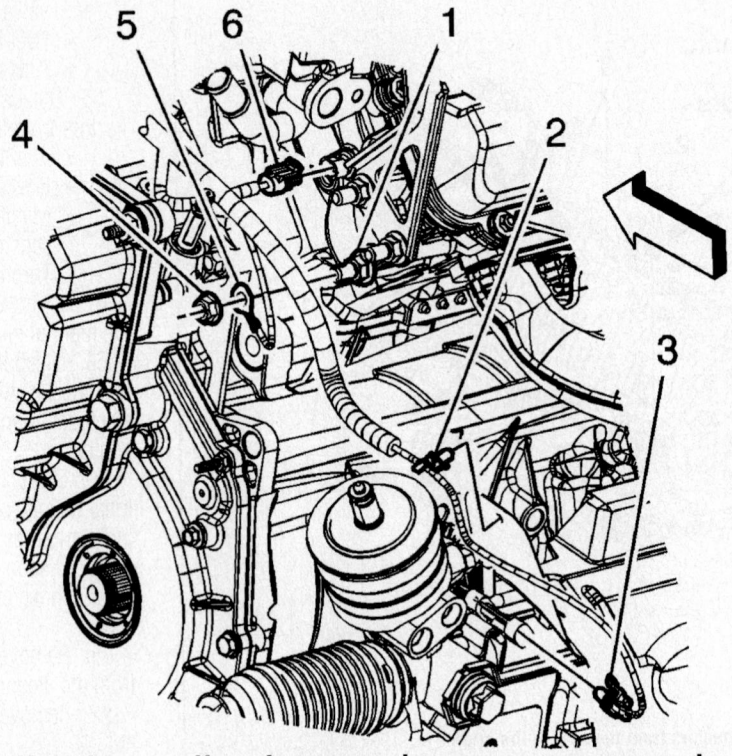

1. Engine valley jumper harness connector
2. Engine harness clip
3. Power steering sensor electrical connector
4. Engine harness ground nut
5. Engine harness ground
6. ECT sensor connector

22116_LUCE_G0524

Fig. 75 Location of electrical connectors

84. Disconnect the engine harness electrical connector from the transaxle.

85. Remove the engine harness ground bolts.

86. Gather all the branches of the engine harness and remove the engine harness from the engine.

87. Reposition the power steering outlet hose clamp at the pump reservoir.

88. Remove the power steering outlet hose from the reservoir.

89. Remove the power steering outlet pipe bolt from the engine mount strut bracket.

90. Remove the power steering inlet pipe fitting from the power steering pump.

91. Remove the power steering inlet pipe nut from the rear engine mount bracket stud. Remove the power steering inlet pipe bracket from the stud.

92. Remove the A/C compressor discharge hose nut at the compressor. Unsecure the hose from the engine and remove the A/C compressor discharge hose. Plug the A/C compressor discharge port.

93. Remove the A/C compressor suction hose nut at the compressor. Unsecure the hose from the engine and remove the A/C compressor suction hose. Plug the A/C compressor suction port.

94. Remove the transaxle brace bolt and nuts, then remove the transaxle brace.

95. Remove the transaxle brace bolt/stud to the transaxle.

96. Remove the transaxle brace bolts to the engine. Remove the transaxle brace.

97. Loosen the front engine mount bracket nut with the transaxle brace behind it.

98. Remove the transaxle brace bolt, then remove the transaxle brace.

99. Install an engine lift chain to the engine lift brackets and attach an engine lifting device.

100. Remove the rear engine mount to frame nut.

101. Remove the rear engine mount bracket bolts and stud.

102. Remove the rear engine mount bracket.

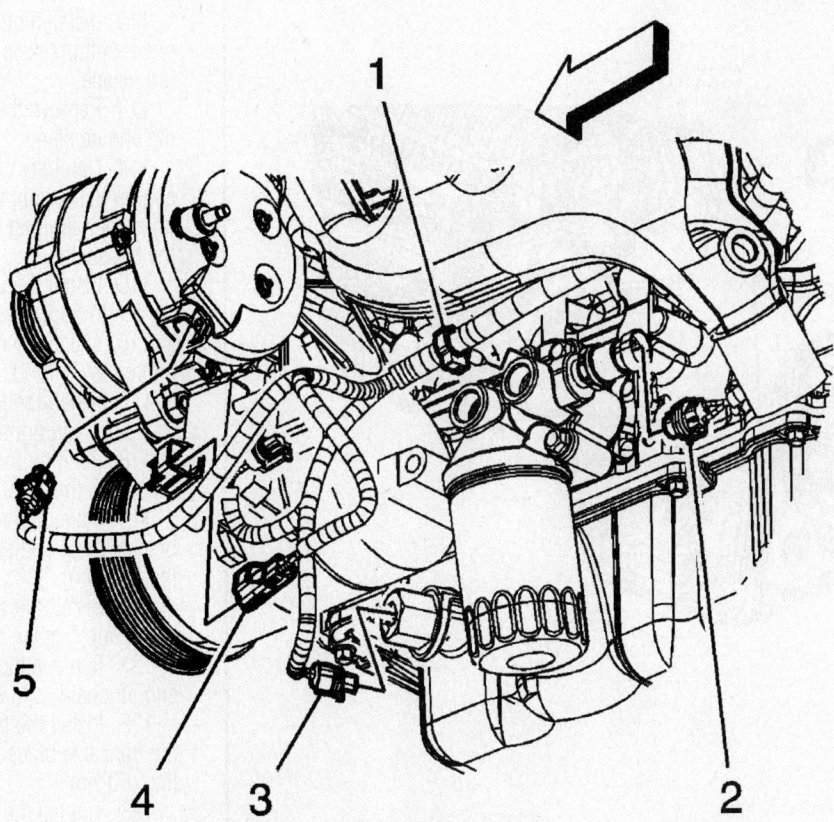

1. Engine harness clip
2. Oil pressure sensor connector
3. Oil level sensor connector
4. A/C compressor connector
5. Alternator connector

22116_LUCE_G0525

Fig. 76 Electrical connectors

103. Remove the front engine mount to frame nut.

104. Remove the rear transaxle bolt.

105. Remove the upper transaxle bolts.

106. Separate the engine from the transaxle.

107. Raise the engine from the supported frame and transaxle assembly.

108. Remove the front engine mount bracket bolts/nuts.

109. Remove the front engine mount bracket.

110. Install the engine assembly to a suitable engine stand.

To install:

111. Install the front engine mount bracket. Install the front engine mount

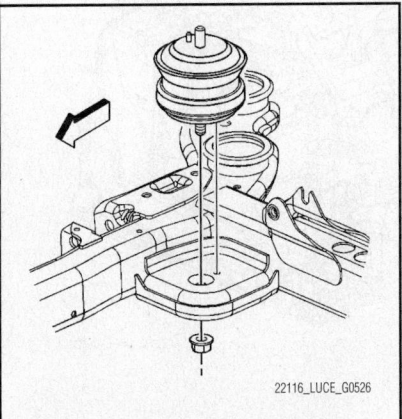

22116_LUCE_G0526

Fig. 77 Remove the rear engine mount to frame nut

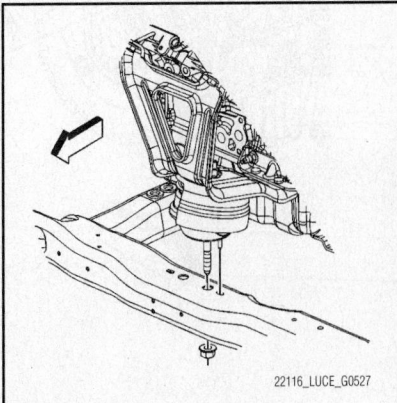

22116_LUCE_G0527

Fig. 78 Remove the front engine mount to frame nut

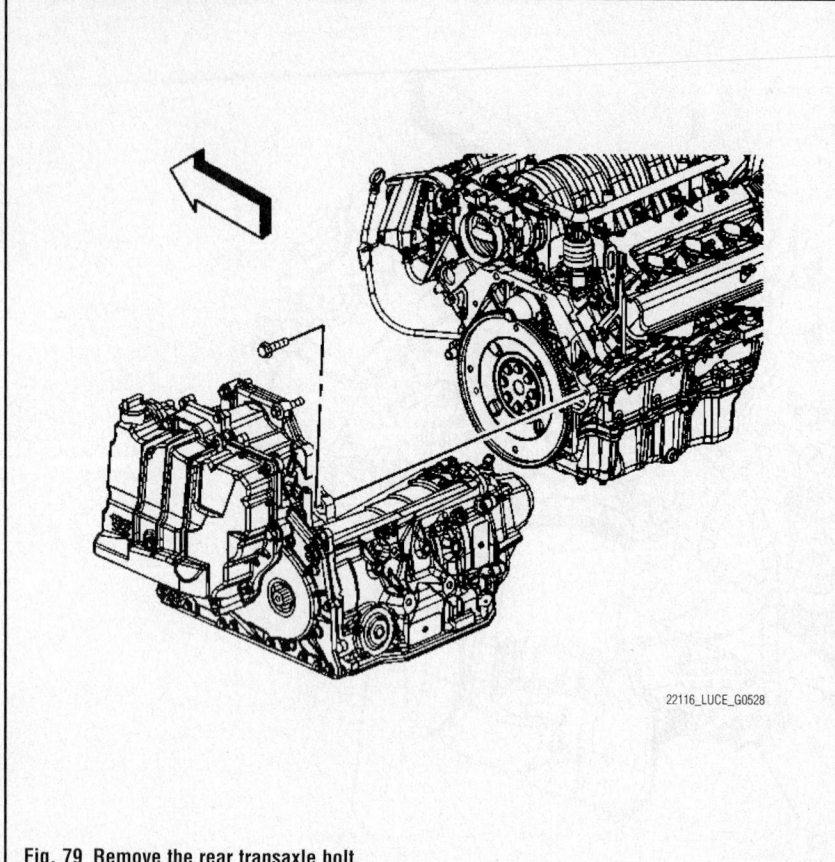

Fig. 79 Remove the rear transaxle bolt.

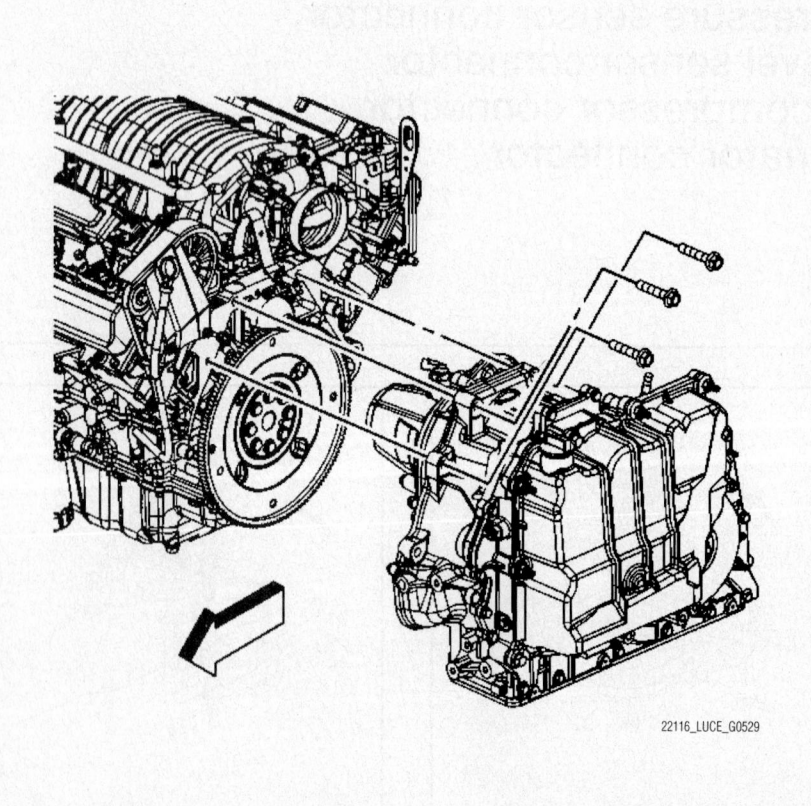

Fig. 80 Remove the upper transaxle bolts

bracket bolts/nuts and tighten to 37 ft. lbs. (50 Nm).

112. Install an engine lift chain to the engine lift brackets and attach an engine lifting device.

113. Remove the engine assembly from the engine stand.

114. Carefully position and install the engine to the supported frame and transaxle, aligning the engine dowel pins to the transaxle.

115. Install the upper transaxle bolts and tighten to 55 ft. lbs. (75 Nm).

116. Install the rear transaxle bolt and tighten to 55 ft. lbs. (75 Nm).

117. Install the front engine mount to frame nut and tighten to 59 ft. lbs. (80 Nm).

118. Position the rear engine mount bracket to the engine and transaxle.

119. Install the rear engine mount bracket bolts and stud and tighten to 54 ft. lbs. (73 Nm).

120. Install the rear engine mount to frame nut. Tighten to 59 ft. lbs. (80 Nm).

121. Remove the engine lifting device and lift chain.

122. Install the transaxle brace. Install the transaxle brace bolt and tighten to 37 ft. lbs. (50 Nm).

123. Tighten the front engine mount bracket nut with the transaxle brace behind it. Tighten the nut to 37 ft. lbs. (50 Nm).

124. Position the transaxle brace to the engine and transaxle. Install the transaxle brace bolts to the engine and tighten to 37 ft. lbs. (50 Nm).

125. Install the transaxle brace bolt/stud to the transaxle. Tighten the bolt/stud to 37 ft. lbs. (50 Nm).

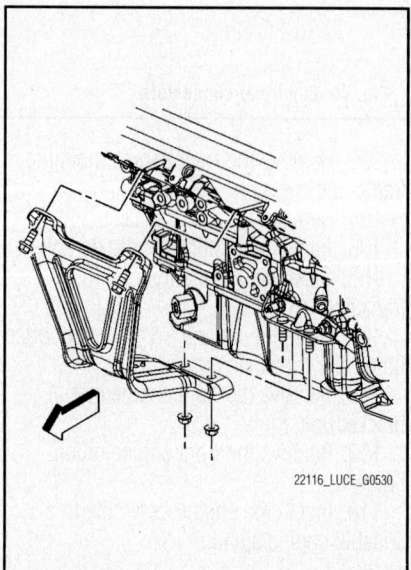

Fig. 81 Remove the front engine mount bracket bolts/nuts

126. Install the transaxle brace to the lift bracket studs. Install the transaxle brace bolt and tighten to 37 ft. lbs. (50 Nm).

127. Install the transaxle brace nuts and tighten to 37 ft. lbs. (50 Nm).

128. Remove the plug from the A/C compressor suction port. Remove and discard the old sealing washer from the compressor end of the suction hose. Install a NEW sealing washer to the compressor end of the suction hose.

129. Install the A/C compressor suction hose the compressor. Install the A/C compressor suction hose nut at the compressor and tighten to 12 ft. lbs. (16 Nm).

130. Secure the suction hose to the engine.

131. Remove the plug from the A/C compressor discharge port. Remove and discard the old sealing washer from the compressor end of the discharge hose. Install a NEW sealing washer to the compressor end of the discharge hose.

132. Install the A/C compressor discharge hose the compressor. Install the A/C compressor discharge hose nut at the compressor and tighten to 12 ft. lbs. (16 Nm).

133. Secure the discharge hose to the engine.

134. Install the power steering inlet pipe fitting to the power steering pump. Tighten the fitting to 20 ft. lbs. (27 Nm).

135. Install the power steering inlet pipe bracket to the stud. Install the power steering inlet pipe nut to the rear engine mount bracket stud and tighten to 80 inch lbs. (9 Nm).

136. Install the power steering outlet hose to the reservoir. Position the power steering outlet hose clamp at the pump reservoir.

137. Install the power steering outlet pipe bolt to the engine mount strut bracket. Tighten the bolt to 80 inch lbs. (9 Nm).

138. Install the engine harness to the engine.

139. Position the engine harness grounds to the engine block. Install the engine harness ground bolts and tighten to 18 ft. lbs. (25 Nm).

140. Connect the engine harness electrical connector to the transaxle.

141. Connect the engine harness electrical connector to the HO2S. Install the CPA retainer.

142. Install the engine harness clip to the engine bracket.

143. Connect the engine harness electrical connectors to the AIR pump and brake modulator.

144. Install the engine harness clip to the boss on the engine block.

145. Attach the following engine harness electrical connectors:
- Oil pressure sensor
- Oil level sensor
- A/C compressor
- Alternator

146. Connect the engine harness electrical connector to the A/C pressure sensor.

147. Connect the engine harness electrical connector to the VSS.

148. Install the engine harness clips to the rear engine mount bracket and steering gear shield.

149. Connect the engine harness electrical connector to the ECT sensor.

150. Install the engine harness ground to the stud. Install the engine harness ground nut and tighten to 18 ft. lbs. (25 Nm).

151. Install the engine harness clip to the steering gear shield.

152. Connect the electrical connector to the power steering sensor.

153. Connect the electrical connector to the engine valley jumper harness electrical connector.

154. Attach the following engine harness electrical connectors to the top of the engine:
- Starter inline
- AIR check valve

155. Attach the following electrical connectors to the front of the engine:
- Fuel injectors
- ICM
- MAP sensor
- Throttle actuator

156. Install the engine harness clip to the fuel rail stud.

157. Attach the following electrical connectors to the rear of the engine:
- EVAP solenoid
- EGR valve
- Fuel injectors
- ICM

158. Position the ICM ground strap to the cylinder head. Install the ICM ground strap bolt (3) to the right cylinder head and tighten to 18 ft. lbs. (25 Nm).

159. Install the AIR pipe over the studs.

160. Connect the AIR outlet pipe quick connect fitting to the check valve.

161. Install the AIR pipe outlet pipe nut to the check valve bracket stud and tighten the nut to 80 inch lbs. (9 Nm).

162. Install the AIR pipe outlet pipe nut to the transaxle stud and tighten the nut to 80 inch lbs. (9 Nm).

163. Connect the AIR outlet hose to the AIR outlet pipe. Position the AIR outlet hose clamp at the AIR outlet pipe.

164. Install the AIR inlet hose. Connect the AIR inlet hose quick connect fitting to the AIR pump.

165. Install the AIR inlet hose retainer to the transaxle stud.

166. Install the heater outlet pipe to the engine and stud.

167. Install the heater outlet pipe nut to the transaxle stud. Tighten the nut to 18 ft. lbs. (25 Nm).

168. Position the heater outlet pipe clamp at the water pump housing.

169. Position the engine/transaxle assembly under the vehicle.

➡ **Make sure clearance is maintained between the engine/transaxle assembly and the following:**

- A/C compressor components
- Brake pipes
- Heater and radiator hoses
- WSS leads
- Wiring harnesses

170. Carefully lower the vehicle over the engine/transaxle assembly, aligning the struts to the strut towers.

171. Install the 6 bolts attaching the frame to the body. Tighten the bolts to 141 ft. lbs. (191 Nm).

172. Install the front fascia.

173. Raise the vehicle off of the J 39580 or the jackstands.

174. Remove the J 39580 or jackstands from under the frame.

175. Align the flywheel with the marks made during the removal. Install the flywheel to torque converter bolts. Tighten the bolts to 44 ft. lbs. (60 Nm).

176. Position the torque converter cover. Install the torque converter cover bolt and tighten to 106 inch lbs. (12 Nm).

177. Install the transaxle brace. Install the transaxle brace bolts and tighten to 35 ft. lbs. (47 Nm).

178. Connect the engine harness electrical connector to the HO2S.

179. Install the oxygen sensor wiring harness heat shield.

✷✷ CAUTION

When installing the intermediate shaft make sure that the shaft is seated prior to pinch bolt installation. If the pinch bolt is inserted into the coupling before shaft installation, the two mating shafts may disengage. Disengagement of the two mating shafts will cause loss of steering control which could result in personal injury.

180. Install the intermediate shaft to the steering gear. Install the intermediate shaft pinch bolt.
Tighten to 33 ft. lbs. (45 Nm).

181. Install the intermediate steering shaft cover.

182. Remove the plug from the A/C condenser suction port. Unsecure the A/C compressor suction hose from the engine. Remove and discard the old sealing washer from the condenser end of the suction hose. Install a NEW sealing washer to the condenser end of the suction hose.

183. Install the A/C compressor suction hose to the condenser. Install the A/C compressor suction hose nut and tighten to 12 ft. lbs. (16 Nm).

184. Remove the plug from the A/C condenser discharge port. Unsecure the A/C compressor discharge hose from the engine. Remove and discard the old sealing washer from the condenser end of the discharge hose. Install a NEW sealing washer to the condenser end of the discharge hose.

185. Install the A/C compressor discharge hose to the condenser. Install the A/C compressor discharge hose nut and tighten to 12 ft. lbs. (16 Nm).

186. Remove the plugs from the open brake lines. Connect the rear brake pipes to the front brake pipes. Tighten the fittings to 15 ft. lbs. (20 Nm).

187. Install the front brake pipe bracket to the body frame rail. Tighten the nut securing the right front brake pipe bracket to the body frame rail and tighten to 80 inch lbs. (9 Nm).

188. Install the front brake pipe bracket to the body frame rail. Tighten the nut securing the left front brake pipe bracket to the body frame rail to 80 inch lbs. (9 Nm).

189. Install the front air deflector.

190. Connect the electronic suspension front position sensor link to the lower control arms ball stud, if equipped.

191. Install the engine harness clip to the ride lever sensor bracket.

192. Install the engine harness grommet to the frame rail bracket.

193. Install the front wheels.

194. Install the rear exhaust manifold pipe.

195. Lower the vehicle.

196. Install the left and right side strut tower bolts and tighten to 30 ft. lbs. (40 Nm).

197. Remove the J 42640 from the steering column.

198. Connect the transaxle oil cooler pipes to the radiator.

199. Slide the plastic caps onto the transaxle oil cooler pipe quick connect fittings.

200. Tighten the upper transaxle oil cooler pipe bolt (1) to the fan shroud and tighten the bolt to 53 inch lbs. (6 Nm).

201. Unsecure the master cylinder from the engine and position the master cylinder the brake booster. Install the master cylinder nuts and tighten to 22 ft. lbs. (30 Nm).

202. Install the heater inlet and outlet hoses to the heater pipes. Position the heater inlet and outlet hose clamps at the heater pipes.

203. Install the surge tank inlet hose to the surge tank. Position the radiator surge tank inlet hose clamp at the surge tank.

204. Install the radiator outlet hose to the thermostat housing. Using the J 38185 position the radiator outlet hose clamp.

205. Install the radiator inlet hose to the water pump housing. Using the J 37097-A position the radiator inlet hose clamp.

206. Install the transaxle shift cable to the bracket. Connect the transaxle shift cable end to the range selector lever.

207. Install the transaxle shift cable retainer.

208. Install the transaxle shift cable clip to the shift cable bracket.

209. Position the ground strap to the frame rail. Install the engine ground strap bolt to the right side frame rail and tighten to 18 ft. lbs. (25 Nm).

210. Install the engine harness to the BEC.

211. Install the junction block. Install the junction block bolts and tighten to 58 inch lbs. (6 Nm).

212. Connect the engine harness electrical connectors to the ECM. Engage the lever locks.

213. Connect the engine harness electrical connector to the body harness electrical connector. Engage the lever lock.

214. Connect the engine harness electrical connector to the TCM. Engage the lever lock.

215. Install the starter cable to the BEC terminal. Install the starter cable clip to the BEC. Install the nut securing the starter cable to the BEC and tighten to 11 ft. lbs. (15 Nm).

216. Install the junction block cover.

217. Install the air cleaner.

218. Install the front compartment sight shield.

219. Connect the fuel feed and EVAP line quick-connect fittings.

220. Connect the brake booster vacuum hose to the vacuum connection.

221. Position the brake booster vacuum hose clamp at the engine port.

222. Connect the negative battery cable.

223. Fill the engine with oil.

224. Fill the cooling system.

225. Bleed the brake system. Refer to the Brake System Section.

226. Recharge the A/C refrigerant system.

227. Bleed the power steering system. Refer to the Steering Section.

228. Check the wheel alignment.

229. Pre-lube the engine.

230. Install the fuel injector sight shield.

231. With the ignition **OFF** or disconnected, crank the engine several times. Listen for any unusual noises or evidence that any parts are binding.

232. Start the engine and listen for abnormal conditions.

233. Check the vehicle oil pressure gauge or light and confirm that the engine has acceptable oil pressure.

234. Run the engine at approximately 1000 RPM until the engine reaches normal operating temperature.

235. While the engine continues to idle raise and support the vehicle.

236. Inspect for oil, coolant and exhaust leaks while the engine is idling.

237. Lower the vehicle.

238. Perform the crankshaft position (CKP) system variation learn procedure, using a suitable scan tool.

239. Perform a final inspection for the proper engine oil and coolant levels.

240. Road test the vehicle.

EXHAUST MANIFOLD

REMOVAL & INSTALLATION

➡ **For vehicles equipped with OnStar (RPO UE1), with battery backup, the backup battery is a redundant power supply to allow limited OnStar functionality in the event of a main battery power disruption to the OnStar module (VCIM). Do not disconnect the main vehicle battery or remove the OnStar fuse with the ignition key in any position other than OFF. Retained accessory power should be allowed to time out or be disabled by opening the driver's side door before disconnecting power. Disconnecting power to the module in any way while the ignition is ON or with the retained accessory power activated may cause activation of the OnStar backup battery system and will discharge and permanently damage the backup battery. Once the backup battery is activated it will stay on until it has completely discharged. The backup battery is not rechargeable and once it is activated, it must be replaced.**

3.9L Engine

Left Side (Front)

See Figure 82.

➡ **The rear seat cushion must be removed to gain access to the battery.**

1. Before servicing the vehicle, refer to the Precautions Section.
2. Disconnect the negative battery cable.
3. Remove the intake manifold cover. Remove the air cleaner outlet duct.
4. Remove the exhaust crossover pipe heat shield retaining bolts. Remove the shield.
5. Remove the exhaust manifold heat shield retaining bolts. Remove the shield.
6. Remove the crossover to manifold retaining nuts.
7. Remove the exhaust manifold retaining bolts. Remove the exhaust manifold from its mounting. Discard the gasket.

To install:

➡ **Be sure to use new fasteners, as required.**

8. Position the exhaust manifold on its mounting. Be sure to use a new gasket.
9. Tighten the retaining bolts and nuts to 15 ft. lbs. (20 Nm).
10. Continue the installation in the reverse order of the removal procedure.
11. Start the engine and check for exhaust leaks, correct as required.

Right Side (Rear)

See Figure 83.

➡ **The rear seat cushion must be removed to gain access to the battery.**

1. Before servicing the vehicle, refer to the Precautions Section.
2. Disconnect the negative battery cable.
3. Remove the CPA assurance retainer.
4. Disconnect the oxygen sensor electrical connector.
5. Remove the sensor clip from the coil bracket.

➡ **The sensor uses a permanently attached pigtail and connector. This pigtail should not be removed from the sensor. Damage or removal of the pigtail or connector will affect proper operation of the sensor.**

6. Remove the sensor.
7. Remove the exhaust crossover pipe heat shield retaining bolts. Remove the shield.

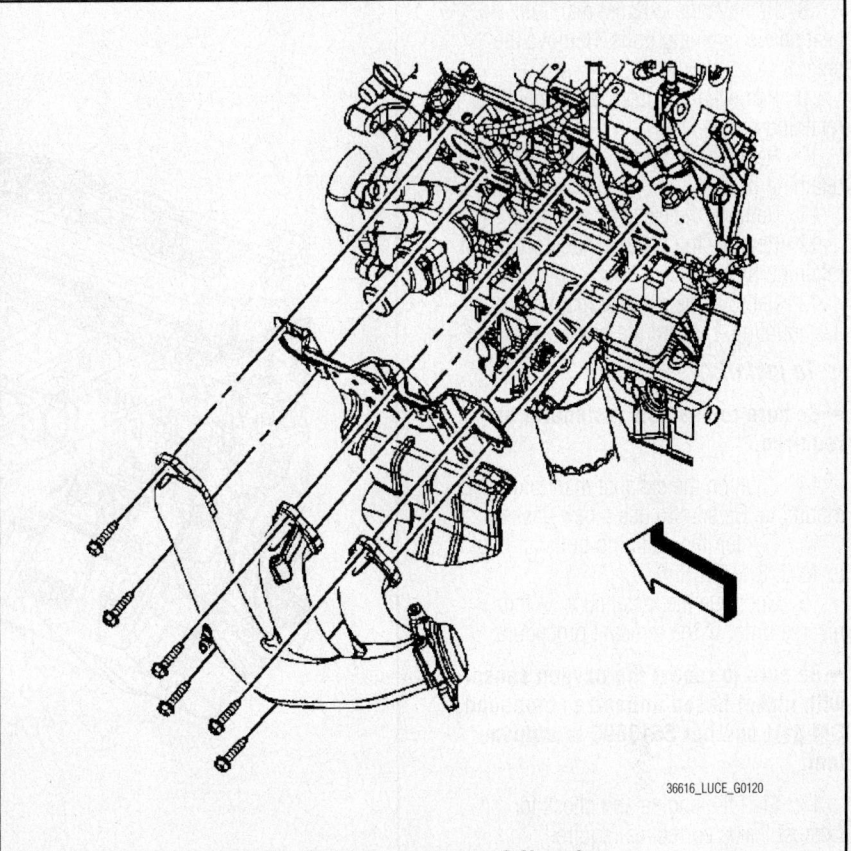

36616_LUCE_G0120

Fig. 82 Left exhaust manifold and related components—3.9L engines

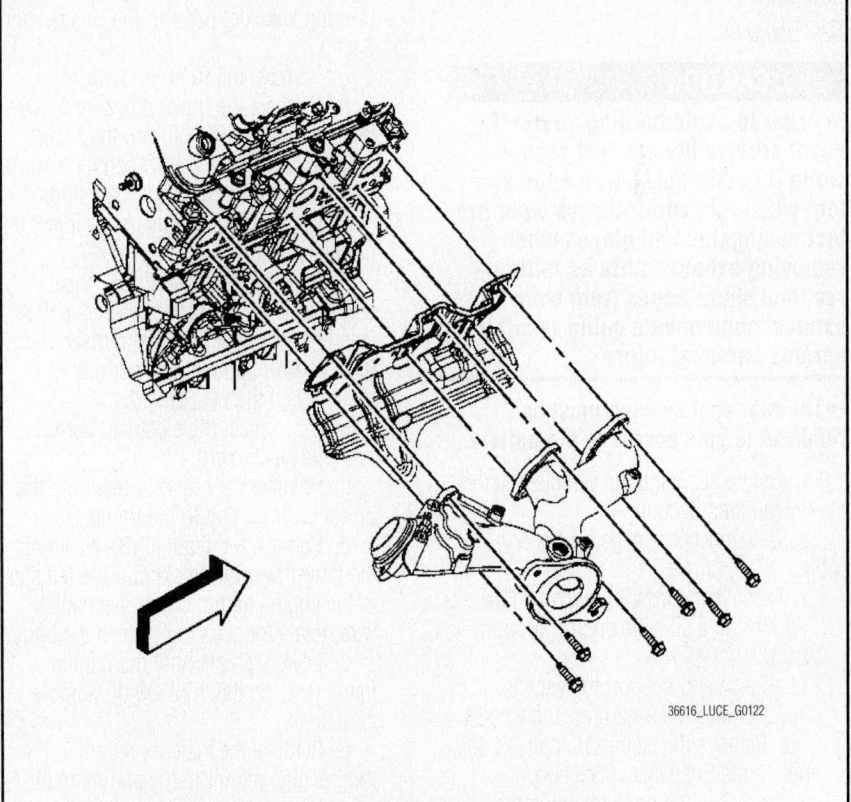

36616_LUCE_G0122

Fig. 83 Right exhaust manifold and related components—3.9L engines

8. Remove the exhaust manifold heat shield retaining bolts. Remove the shield.

9. Remove the crossover to manifold retaining nuts.

10. Remove the upper exhaust manifold retaining bolts.

11. Remove the catalytic converter.

12. Remove the lower exhaust manifold retaining bolts.

13. Remove the exhaust manifold from its mounting. Discard the gasket.

To install:

➡ **Be sure to use new fasteners, as required.**

14. Position the exhaust manifold on its mounting. Be sure to use a new gasket.

15. Tighten the retaining bolts and nuts to 15 ft. lbs. (20 Nm).

16. Continue the installation in the reverse order of the removal procedure.

➡ **Be sure to recoat the oxygen sensor with nickel based antiseize compound, GM part number 5613695 or equivalent.**

17. Start the engine and check for exhaust leaks, correct as required.

4.6L Engine

Left Side (Front)

See Figure 84.

> ❄❄ **CAUTION**
>
> **In order to avoid burning yourself, never service the exhaust system while it is still hot. Service the system when it is cool. Always wear protective goggles and gloves when removing exhaust parts as falling rust and sharp edges from worn exhaust components could result in serious personal injury.**

➡ **The rear seat cushion must be removed to gain access to the battery.**

1. Before servicing the vehicle, refer to the Precautions Section.

2. Disconnect the negative battery cable.

3. Remove the front frame, as follows:

   a. Install a suitable engine support fixture.

   b. Raise and support the vehicle.

   c. Remove the front tires and wheels.

   d. Remove the stabilizer shaft, as outlined in the Suspension Section.

   e. Remove the bolts retaining the steering gear to the engine frame.

   f. Remove the ball joints from the steering knuckle. Refer to the Suspension Section.

   g. Remove the front air deflector.

   h. Remove the brake pressure modulator valve and bracket from the frame.

   i. Disconnect the ESC sensor links from the lower control arm ball studs.

   j. Remove the secondary air injection pump assembly.

   k. Remove the steering gear heat shield fasteners in order to remove the steering gear heat shield and disconnect the electrical harness retainer that is mounted on the heat shield.

   l. Disconnect the electrical harness from the heat shield.

   m. Remove the brackets retaining the power steering line to the frame.

   n. Remove the retainer (3), retaining the power steering line along the left side of the engine frame. Using mechanics wire, retain the steering gear to the body.

   o. Lower vehicle until the engine frame rests on the J 39580 or suitable jackstands.

   p. Remove the fastener retaining the front engine mount to the engine frame.

   q. Remove the fasteners retaining the rear transaxle mount to the engine frame.

   r. Remove the engine frame insulator bolts retaining the engine frame to the vehicle.

   s. Raise vehicle away from engine frame.

   t. Remove the control arms

4. Remove the front engine mount bracket, as follows:

   a. Remove the engine mount bracket to cylinder head bolts.

   b. Remove the upper engine mount bracket to lower engine mount bracket nuts.

   c. Remove the upper engine mount bracket.

   d. Remove the transaxle brace bolt.

   e. Remove the lower engine mount bracket to engine stud nuts.

   f. Remove the transaxle brace.

   g. Remove the lower engine mount bracket.

5. Remove the Connector Position Assurance (CPA) retainer.

6. Disconnect the engine harness electrical connector from the Heated Oxygen Sensor (HO2S).

7. Remove the HO2S.

8. Remove the exhaust manifold front pipe bolts.

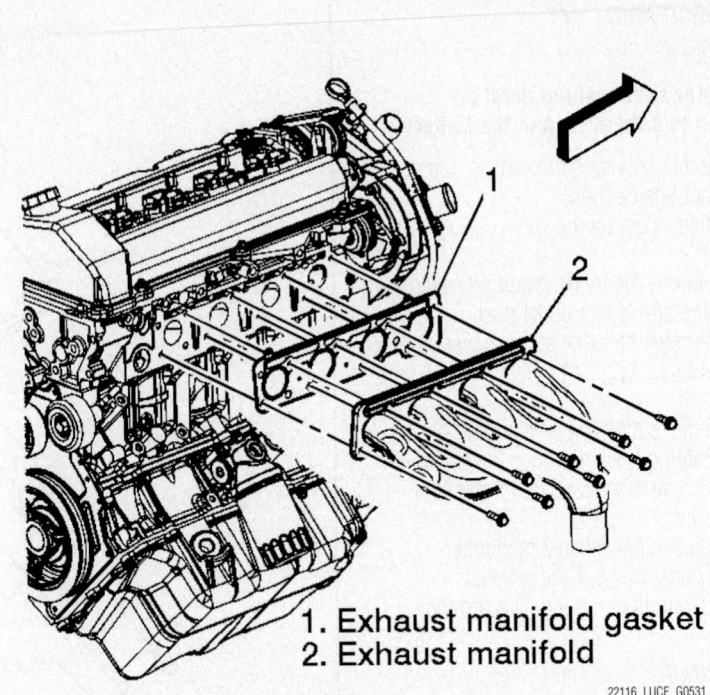

1. Exhaust manifold gasket
2. Exhaust manifold

22116_LUCE_G0531

Fig. 84 Exploded view of the left exhaust manifold—4.6L engine

9. Remove the exhaust manifold bolts.

10. Remove the exhaust manifold (2).

11. Remove and discard the exhaust manifold gasket (1).

12. Remove and discard the front exhaust manifold pipe seal.

13. Remove the front exhaust manifold pipe flange.

To install:

14. Install the front exhaust manifold pipe flange and a NEW seal onto the exhaust manifold.

15. Insert the upper right exhaust manifold bolt to the manifold in this location (2).

16. Place the NEW exhaust manifold gasket over the bolt and against the manifold.

17. Insert the exhaust manifold into the front exhaust manifold pipe and against the cylinder head.

18. Finger start the exhaust manifold bolt.

19. Install the remaining exhaust manifold bolts and tighten all exhaust manifold bolts starting from right to left beginning with the bolt in this location (2). Tighten the bolts to 18 ft. lbs. (25 Nm).

20. Install the exhaust manifold front pipe bolts.

21. If reusing the old HO2S, coat the threads with anti-seize compound, GM P/N 12377953 or equivalent.

22. Install the HO2S. Tighten to 30 ft. lbs. (41 Nm).

23. Attach the electrical connector to the HO2S and install the CPA retainer.

24. Install the front engine mount bracket, as follows:

   a. Install the lower engine mount bracket onto the engine studs.

   b. Install the transaxle brace.

   c. Install the lower engine mount bracket to engine stud nuts finger-tight.

   d. Install the transaxle brace bolt, and tighten the retainers as follows:

   • Tighten the transaxle brace bolt to 37 ft. lbs. (50 Nm).

   • Tighten the lower engine mount bracket-to-engine stud nuts to 37 ft. lbs. (50 Nm).

   e. Install the upper engine mount bracket onto the studs.

   f. Install the engine mount bracket to cylinder head bolts. Tighten to 37 ft. lbs. (50 Nm).

   g. Install the upper engine mount bracket to lower engine mount bracket nuts and tighten to 37 ft. lbs. (50 Nm).

25. Install the front frame, as follows:

   a. Install the control arms. Refer to the Suspension Section.

   b. Lower the vehicle onto the engine frame.

   c. Using dowel pins in the alignment holes, align the engine frame with the vehicle.

   d. Install the engine frame insulator retainer bolts in order to retain the engine frame to the vehicle. Tighten to 133 ft. lbs. (181 Nm).

   e. Check the front wheel alignment.

   f. Raise the vehicle away from the jack stands supporting the engine frame.

   g. Install the fasteners in order to retain the rear transaxle mount to the bracket. Tighten the retainers to 37 ft. lbs. (50 Nm).

   h. Install the fastener in order to retain the front engine mount to the engine frame. Tighten to 52 ft. lbs. (70 Nm).

   i. Install the fasteners in order to retain the steering gear to the engine frame. Tighten to 70 ft. lbs. (95 Nm).

   j. Install the bracket to retain the power steering line to the engine frame. Install the clips retaining power steering line along engine frame rail.

   k. Connect the wiring harness to the heat shield.

   l. Install the steering gear heat shield to the vehicle. Tighten the retainers to 80 inch lbs. (9 Nm).

   m. Install the secondary air injection pump to the vehicle.

   n. Install the brake pressure modulator valve.

   o. Install the ESC sensor links to the lower control arm ball studs.

   p. Install the front air deflector.

   q. Install the ball joints to the steering knuckle.

   r. Install the front tires and wheels.

   s. Install the stabilizer shaft.

   t. Lower the vehicle.

   u. Remove the engine support fixture.

   v. Check the front wheel alignment

Right Side (Rear)

See Figure 85.

➡This procedure requires the use of special tool J 42640, or equivalent Steering Column Anti-Rotation Pin.

➡The rear seat cushion must be removed to gain access to the battery.

1. Before servicing the vehicle, refer to the Precautions Section.

2. Disconnect the negative battery cable.

3. Remove the Connector Position Assurance (CPA) retainer.

4. Disconnect the engine harness electrical connector (2) from the Heated Oxygen Sensor.

5. Remove the HO2S clip from the secondary air injection (AIR) valve hose bracket.

➡Notice: With wheels of the vehicle facing straight ahead, secure the steering wheel utilizing steering column anti-rotation pin, steering column lock, or a strap to prevent rotation. Locking of the steering column will prevent damage and a possible malfunction of the SIR system. The steering wheel must be secured in position before disconnecting the following components:

• Steering column
• Intermediate shaft(s)
• Steering gear

➡After disconnecting these components, do not rotate the steering wheel or move the front tires and wheels. Failure to follow this procedure may cause the SIR coil assembly to become un-centered and cause possible damage to the SIR coil. If you think the SIR coil has became un-centered, refer to your specific SIR coil's centering procedure to re-center SIR Coil.

6. Lock the steering column by installing the J 42640 into the underside of the steering column.

7. Raise and support the vehicle.

8. Remove the rear exhaust manifold pipe.

9. Remove the AIR check valve.

10. Disconnect the engine harness clips from the steering gear heat shield.

11. Remove the steering gear heat shield bolts and remove the steering gear heat shield.

12. Disconnect the electronic suspension position sensor link ball studs from the lower control arms.

✳✳ CAUTION

Failure to disconnect the intermediate shaft from the rack and pinion stub shaft can result in damage to the steering gear and/or damage to the intermediate shaft. This damage may cause loss of steering control which could result in personal injury.

13. Unsnap and remove the intermediate shaft seal. Remove the intermediate shaft pinch bolt. Separate the intermediate shaft from the steering gear.

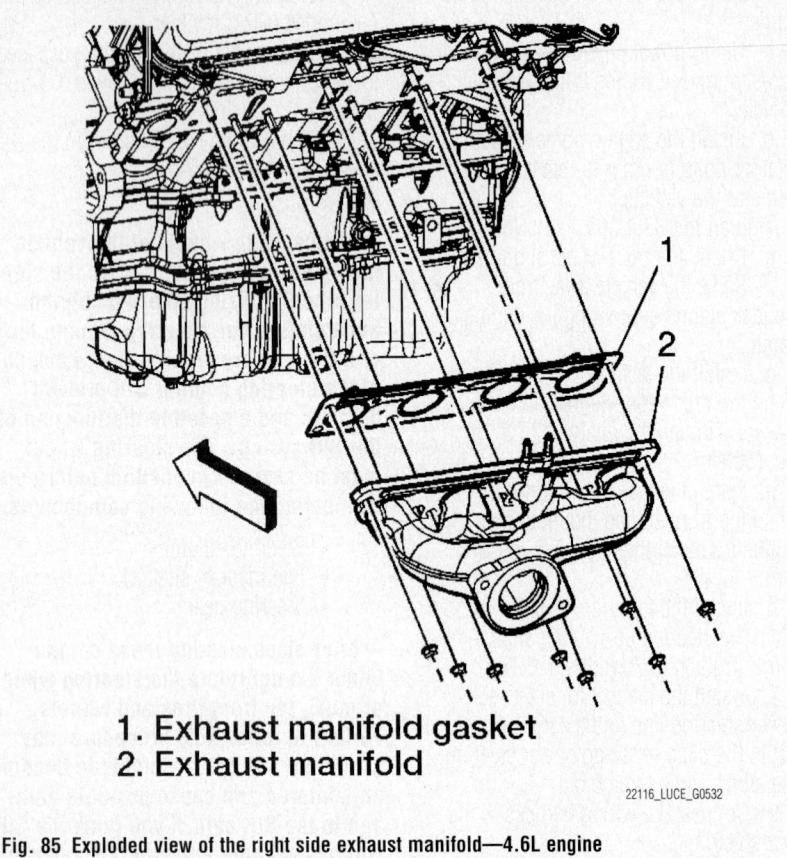

1. Exhaust manifold gasket
2. Exhaust manifold

22116_LUCE_G0532

Fig. 85 Exploded view of the right side exhaust manifold—4.6L engine

14. Remove the right engine mount to frame nut.

15. Remove the left engine mount to frame nut.

16. Remove the transaxle mount to frame nuts.

17. Support the rear of the frame with a tall screw type jack.

18. Remove the 4 rearward engine frame-to-body bolts.

19. Lower the screw type jack approximately 4 cm (1.5 in) allowing the rear of the engine frame to lower.

20. Remove the HO2S.

21. Remove the exhaust manifold nuts.

22. Remove the exhaust manifold (2).

23. Remove and discard the exhaust manifold gasket (1).

To install:

24. Install a NEW exhaust manifold gasket (1) onto the cylinder head studs.

25. Install exhaust manifold (2).

26. Install the exhaust manifold nuts and tighten to 18 ft. lbs. (25 Nm).

27. If reusing the old HO2S, coat the threads with anti-seize compound, GM P/N 12377953 or equivalent.

28. Install the HO2S and tighten to 30 ft. lbs. (41 Nm).

29. Raise the engine frame into position.

30. Install the 4 rearward engine frame-to-body bolts (1) (left side shown, right side similar). Tighten to 141 ft. lbs. (191 Nm).

31. Remove the screw-type jack.

32. Install the transaxle mount to frame nuts and tighten to 37 ft. lbs. (50 Nm).

33. Install the left engine mount to frame nut, tighten to 59 ft. lbs. (80 Nm).

34. Install the right engine mount to frame nut, tighten to 59 ft. lbs. (80 Nm).

✳✳ CAUTION

Failure to disconnect the intermediate shaft from the rack and pinion stub shaft can result in damage to the steering gear and/or damage to the intermediate shaft. This damage may cause loss of steering control which could result in personal injury.

35. Connect the intermediate shaft to the steering gear.

36. Install the intermediate shaft pinch bolt and tighten to 33 ft. lbs. (45 Nm).

37. Install the intermediate shaft seal.

38. Connect the electronic suspension position sensor link ball studs to the lower control arms.

39. Install the steering gear heat shield. Install the steering gear heat shield bolts and tighten to 80 inch lbs. (9 Nm).

40. Connect the engine harness clips to the steering gear heat shield.

41. Install the AIR check valve.

42. Install the rear exhaust manifold pipe.

43. Carefully lower the vehicle.

44. Remove the Steering column anti-rotation pin.

45. Connect the engine harness electrical connector to the HO2S.

46. Install the HO2S clip to the AIR valve hose bracket.

47. Install the CPA retainer.

INTAKE MANIFOLD

REMOVAL & INSTALLATION

➡**For vehicles equipped with OnStar (RPO UE1), with battery backup, the backup battery is a redundant power supply to allow limited OnStar functionality in the event of a main battery power disruption to the OnStar module (VCIM). Do not disconnect the main vehicle battery or remove the OnStar fuse with the ignition key in any position other than OFF. Retained accessory power should be allowed to time out or be disabled by opening the driver's side door before disconnecting power. Disconnecting power to the module in any way while the ignition is ON or with the retained accessory power activated may cause activation of the OnStar backup battery system and will discharge and permanently damage the backup battery. Once the backup battery is activated it will stay on until it has completely discharged. The backup battery is not rechargeable and once it is activated, it must be replaced.**

3.9L Engine

Upper

See Figure 86.

➡**The rear seat cushion must be removed to gain access to the battery.**

1. Before servicing the vehicle, refer to the Precautions Section.

2. Disconnect the negative battery cable.

3. Remove the intake manifold cover.

4. Drain the cooling system. Properly dispose of used engine coolant.

5. Remove the PCV fresh air tube. Remove the PCV foul air tube.

6. Remove the brake booster vacuum hose. Reposition the heater hoses.

7. Remove the heater hoses inlet and outlet pipe clamp nuts and throttle body studs. Reposition, out of the way.

8. Remove the EVAP line clip and the MAP sensor bracket. Disconnect the MAP sensor electrical connector.

9. Disconnect the EVAP canister purge solenoid electrical connector. Disconnect the ECT electrical connector.

10. Remove the air cleaner outlet duct.

11. Remove the left side spark plug wires.

12. Remove the throttle body bolts and nuts.

13. Remove the throttle body. Discard the gasket.

➡ **If installing a new manifold, remove the throttle body to manifold studs.**

14. Remove the EVAP canister purge solenoid valve.

15. Remove the ignition coil bracket to intake manifold bolts.

16. Loosen the power steering reservoir to intake manifold bolt, and reposition.

17. Remove the alternator to intake manifold bracket bolt.

18. Remove the intake manifold cover ball stud nut from the intake manifold stud.

19. Remove the upper intake manifold bolts and stud.

20. Separate and remove the upper intake manifold from the lower intake manifold.

21. Remove and discard the lower intake manifold gaskets.

To install:

➡ **Be sure to use new fasteners, as required.**

22. Position the upper intake manifold on to the lower intake. Be sure to use new gaskets.

➡ **Apply threadlock to the upper intake manifold bolts/stud threads.**

23. Install the upper intake manifold bolts and stud. Tighten to 18 ft. lbs. (25 Nm).

24. Install the intake manifold cover ball stud nut to the intake manifold stud. Tighten to 44 inch lbs. (5 NM).

25. Install the coil bracket to intake manifold bolts. Tighten to 18 ft. lbs. 25 Nm).

26. Continue the installation in the reverse order of the removal procedure.

27. Tighten the throttle body retaining bolts and nuts to 89 inch lbs. (10 Nm).

28. Tighten the throttle body studs to 53 inch lbs. (6 Nm), as required.

Lower

See Figures 87 through 90.

➡ **The rear seat cushion must be removed to gain access to the battery.**

1. Before servicing the vehicle, refer to the Precautions Section.

2. Disconnect the negative battery cable.

3. Properly relieve the fuel system pressure.

4. Remove the intake manifold cover.

5. Drain the cooling system. Properly dispose of used engine coolant.

6. Remove the air cleaner outlet duct.

7. Remove the throttle body. Discard the gasket.

8. Remove the upper intake manifold.

9. Remove the left and right valve covers. Discard the gaskets.

10. Disconnect the fuel feed line from the fuel rail. Disconnect the fuel injector inline connector.

11. Remove the fuel injector harness connector bracket. Disconnect the engine coolant temperature electrical connector.

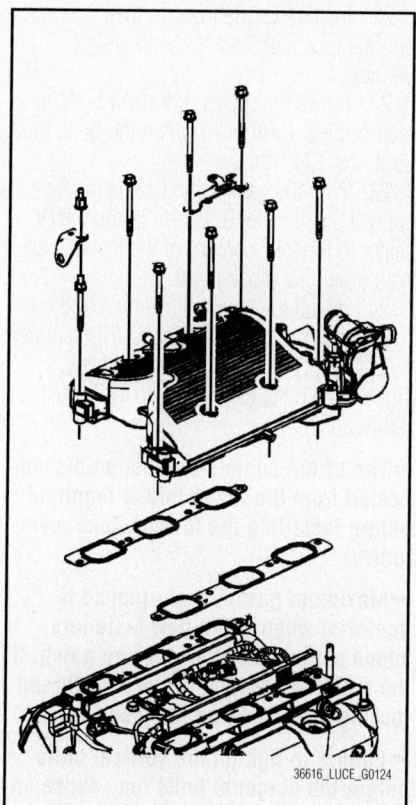

36616_LUCE_G0124

Fig. 86 Upper intake manifold and related components—3.9L engines

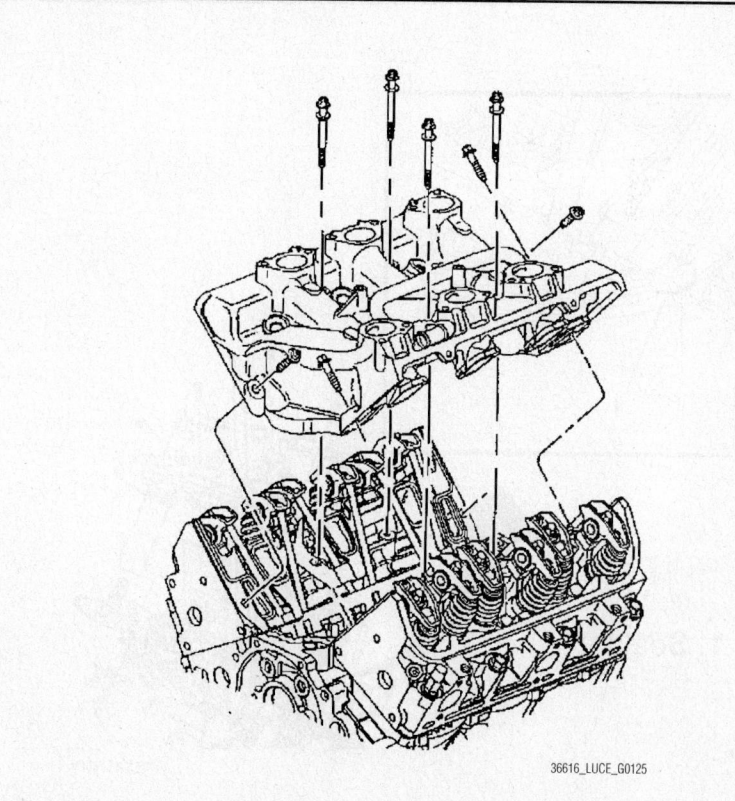

36616_LUCE_G0125

Fig. 87 Lower intake manifold and related components—3.9L engines

Fig. 88 Lower intake manifold gaskets and seals—3.9L engines

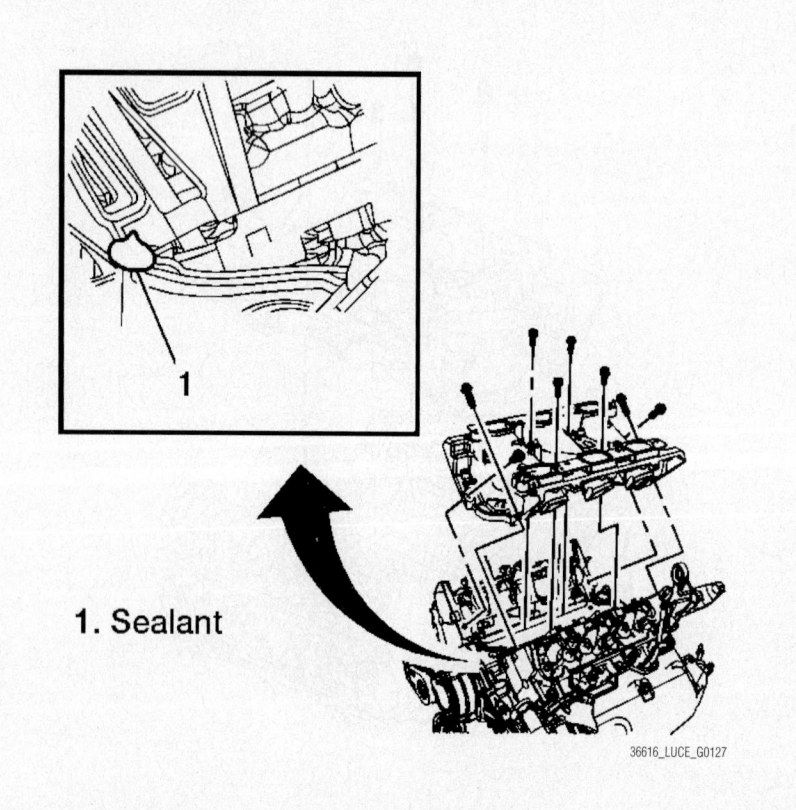

1. Sealant

Fig. 89 Sealant installation and location points—3.9L engines

12. Disconnect the CMP sensor electrical connector.

13. Remove the two Lifter Oil Manifold Assembly (LOMA) electrical connector bolts from the lower intake manifold, if equipped.

14. Remove the fuel injector rail bolts.

15. Remove the power steering pump.

16. Remove the fuel rail and LOMA.

17. Remove the lower intake manifold retaining bolts. Remove the manifold from its mounting.

18. Loosen the valve rocker arm bolts. Remove the rocker arms and pushrods. Be sure that the removed components are reinstalled in their same location.

➡The intake pushrods measure 5.81 inch. The exhaust pushrods measure 6.1 inch.

19. Remove and discard the lower intake manifold gaskets and seals.

To install:

➡Be sure to use new fasteners, as required.

20. Position the intake manifold gaskets and seals in position.

➡RTV sealant is not to be placed under the lower intake manifold gaskets.

21. Install the pushrods in their original location. Coat the ends using prelube.

22. Install the rocker arms and bolts in their original location. Tighten the bolts to 25 ft. lbs. (34 Nm).

23. With the gaskets and seals in place apply a small drop, 0.031–0.39 inch, RTV sealer to the four corners of the intake manifold to engine block joints.

24. Install the lower intake manifold. Apply sealer to the bolt threads. Tighten the bolts (1, 2, 3, 4) to 15 ft. lbs. (20 Nm). Tighten the bolts (5, 6, 7, 8) to 18 ft. lbs. (25 Nm).

➡The LOMA connector must be disconnected from the lower intake manifold before installing the lower intake manifold.

➡Maximum gasket performance is achieved when using new fasteners, which contain a thread locking patch. If the fasteners are not replaced a thread locking chemical must be used.

➡Failure to tighten the vertical bolts before the diagonal bolts may cause an oil leak.

25. Continue the installation in the reverse order of the removal procedure.

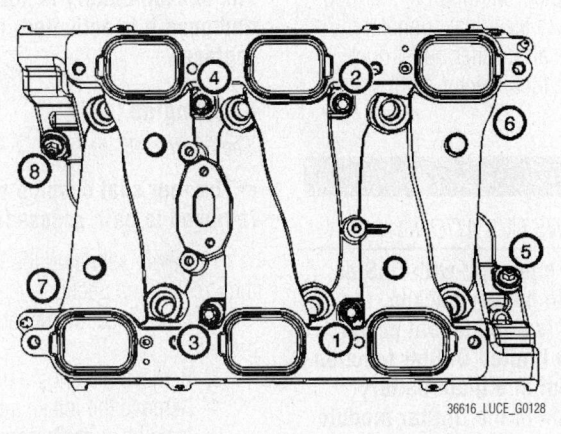

Fig. 90 Lower intake manifold tightening sequence—3.9L engines

4.6L Engine

See Figures 91 and 92.

➡ **The rear seat cushion must be removed to gain access to the battery.**

1. Before servicing the vehicle, refer to the Precautions Section.
2. Disconnect the negative battery cable.
3. Remove the fuel injector sight shield cover.
4. Remove the air cleaner outlet duct.
5. Disconnect the front ignition coil module engine harness electrical connector.
6. Disconnect the front fuel injectors engine harness electrical connectors.
7. Disconnect the rear ignition coil module engine harness electrical connector.
8. Disconnect the rear fuel injectors engine harness electrical connectors.
9. Disconnect the Positive Crankcase Ventilation (PCV) foul air tube quick connect fitting from the right camshaft cover.
10. Disconnect the PCV fresh air tube quick connect fitting from the camshaft cover.
11. Disconnect the fuel feed line quick connect fitting at the fuel rail.
12. Reposition the radiator surge tank inlet hose/pipe clamp at the surge tank.
13. Remove the surge tank inlet hose/pipe from the surge tank.
14. Reposition the radiator surge tank inlet hose/pipe clamp at the engine.
15. Remove the surge tank inlet hose/pipe from the engine fitting.
16. Remove the 2 push nuts securing the surge tank inlet hose/pipe to the fuel rail studs.
17. Remove the surge tank inlet hose/pipe from the fuel rail studs.
18. Remove the engine harness retainer from the fuel rail stud.

19. Remove the coolant heater cord tabs from the fuel rail studs, if equipped.
20. Remove the fuel rail bracket nut at the rear left lift bracket.
21. Remove the fuel rail studs, then remove the fuel rail.
22. Loosen the plenum duct clamp screw at the water pump housing.
23. Remove intake manifold bolts.
24. Unbolt and position the power steering aside. Do not disconnect the fluid lines.
25. Remove the intake manifold.
26. Disconnect the PCV foul air tube quick connect fitting at the intake manifold.
27. Remove the PCV foul air tube from the retaining features on the intake manifold.

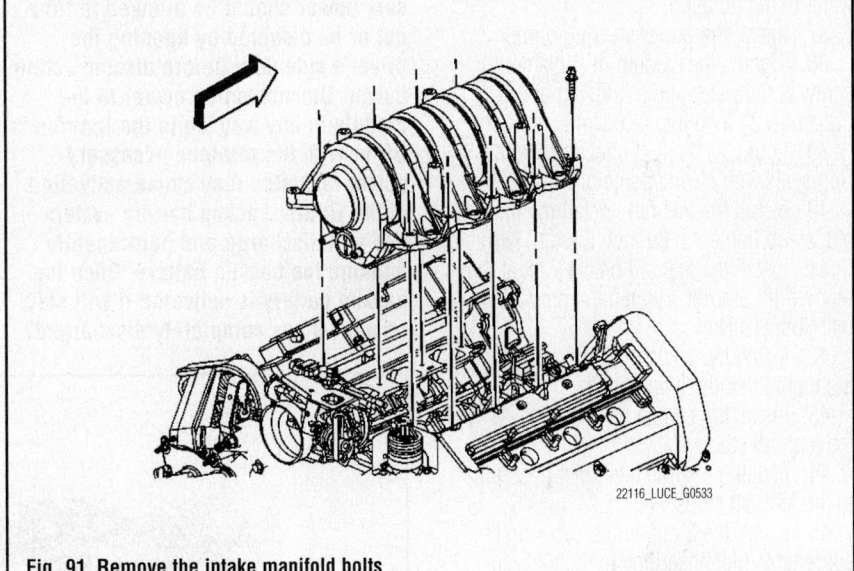

Fig. 91 Remove the intake manifold bolts

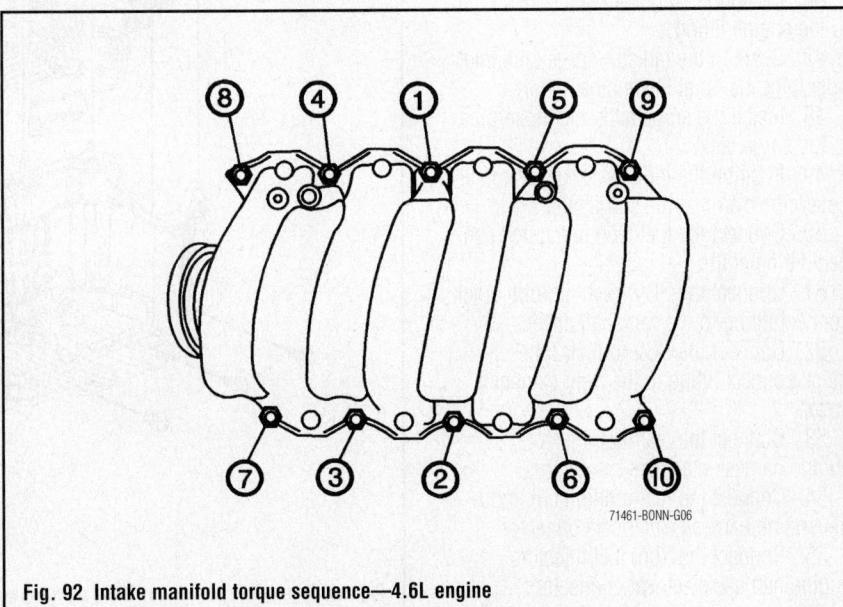

Fig. 92 Intake manifold torque sequence—4.6L engine

28. Remove and discard the old seals.

29. Clean and inspect the intake manifold.

To install:

30. Install the new intake manifold seals.

31. Connect the PCV foul air tube quick connect fitting at the intake manifold.

32. Install the PCV foul air tube to the retaining features on the intake manifold.

33. Lightly grease the inside edge of the rubber plenum duct on the water pump housing.

34. Install the intake manifold. Install intake manifold bolts until snug.

35. Tighten the intake manifold bolts, in the sequence shown in the accompanying illustration, to 89 inch lbs. (10 Nm).

36. Ensure that the intake manifold is fully installed into the plenum duct on the water pump housing.

37. Install the power steering pump.

38. Tighten the plenum duct clamp screw at the water pump housing and tighten to 24 inch lbs. (2.8 Nm).

39. Lubricate the fuel injector lower O-ring seals with clean engine oil.

40. Install the fuel rail. Install the fuel rail studs and tighten to 89 inch lbs. (10 Nm).

41. Install the fuel rail bracket nut at the rear left lift bracket. Tighten the nut to 89 inch lbs. (10 Nm).

42. Install the coolant heater cord tabs to the fuel rail studs, if equipped.

43. Install the engine harness retainer to the fuel rail stud.

44. Install the surge tank inlet hose/pipe to the fuel rail studs.

45. Install the 2 push nuts securing the surge tank inlet hose/pipe to the fuel rail studs.

46. Install the surge tank inlet hose/pipe to the engine fitting.

47. Position the radiator surge tank inlet hose/pipe clamp at the engine.

48. Install the surge tank inlet hose/pipe to the surge tank.

49. Position the radiator surge tank inlet hose/pipe clamp at the surge tank.

50. Connect the fuel feed line quick connect fitting at the fuel rail.

51. Connect the PCV fresh air tube quick connect fitting to the camshaft cover.

52. Connect the PCV foul air tube quick connect fitting to the right camshaft cover.

53. Connect the rear fuel injectors engine harness electrical connectors.

54. Connect the rear ignition coil module engine harness electrical connector.

55. Connect the front fuel injectors engine harness electrical connectors.

56. Connect the front ignition coil module engine harness electrical connector.

57. Install the air cleaner outlet duct.

58. Install the fuel injector sight shield cover

OIL PAN

REMOVAL & INSTALLATION

➡For vehicles equipped with OnStar (RPO UE1), with battery backup, the backup battery is a redundant power supply to allow limited OnStar functionality in the event of a main battery power disruption to the OnStar module (VCIM). Do not disconnect the main vehicle battery or remove the OnStar fuse with the ignition key in any position other than OFF. Retained accessory power should be allowed to time out or be disabled by opening the driver's side door before disconnecting power. Disconnecting power to the module in any way while the ignition is ON or with the retained accessory power activated may cause activation of the OnStar backup battery system and will discharge and permanently damage the backup battery. Once the backup battery is activated it will stay on until it has completely discharged.

The backup battery is not rechargeable and once it is activated, it must be replaced.

3.9L Engine

See Figures 93 and 94.

➡The rear seat cushion must be removed to gain access to the battery.

1. Before servicing the vehicle, refer to the Precautions Section.

2. Disconnect the negative battery cable.

3. Remove the engine mount strut.

4. Remove the intake manifold cover.

5. Install a suitable engine support tool. Use tool J28467B, J36462 and J 36857, or equivalents. Be sure to follow the manufacturer's instructions when setting up the tool.

6. Raise and safely support the vehicle.

7. Remove the catalytic converter.

8. Drain the engine oil. Properly dispose of used engine oil.

9. Remove the tire and wheel assembly.

10. Remove the front wheelhouse.

11. Remove the drivebelt.

12. Remove the oil filter. Remove the oil filter adapter.

13. Remove the starter.

14. Remove the air conditioning

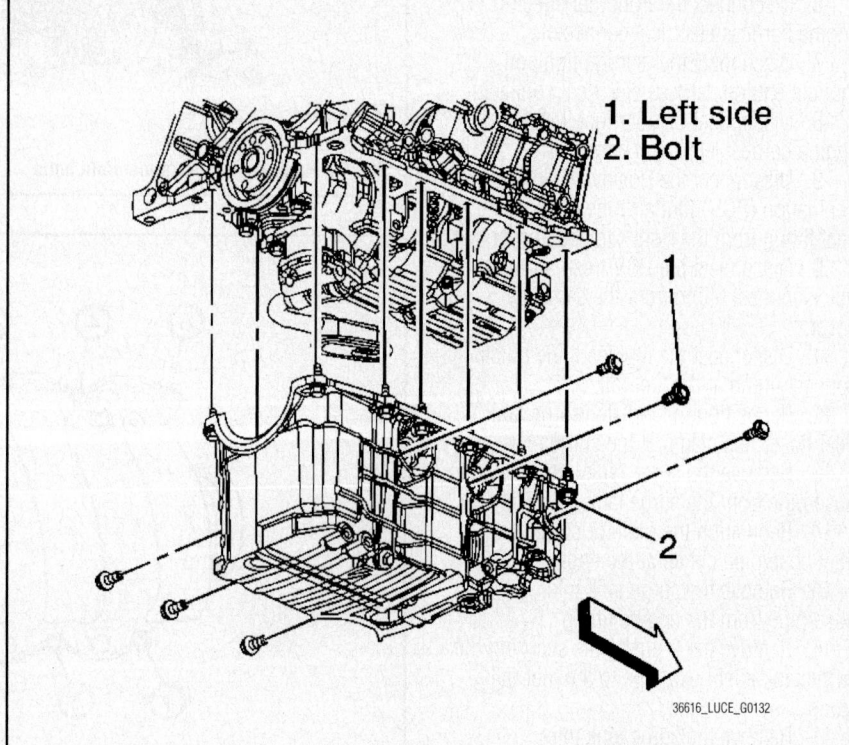

1. Left side
2. Bolt

36616_LUCE_G0132

Fig. 93 Engine oil pan and related components—3.9L engines

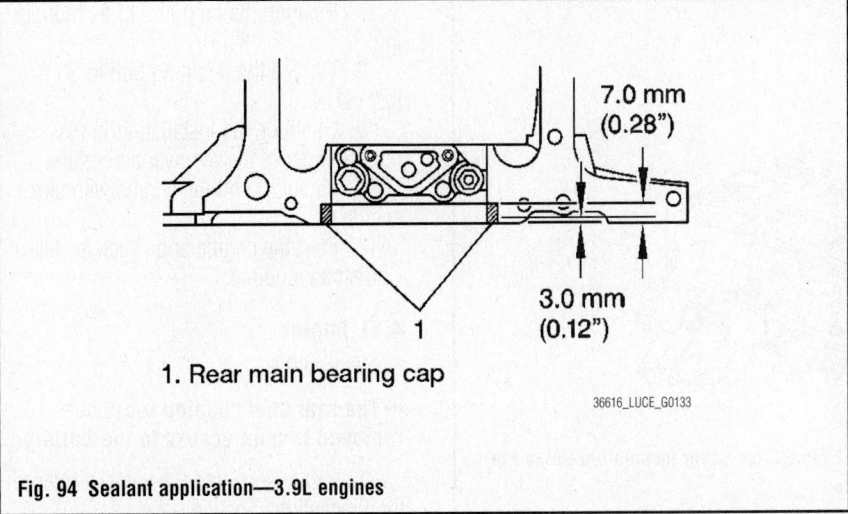

Fig. 94 Sealant application—3.9L engines

compressor retaining bolts. Position the compressor to the side.

15. Disconnect the oil level sensor electrical connector. Remove the engine harness clips from the oil pan and the transaxle brace.

16. Remove the front transaxle brace to lower engine bolts and the brace.

17. Loosen the transaxle mount lower nuts.

18. Remove the rear transaxle brace to engine/oil pan bolts. Lower the vehicle.

19. Using the engine support tool, raise the engine.

20. Remove the right side oil pan side bolts.

21. Remove the left side oil pan side bolts.

22. Remove the oil pan bolts. Remove the oil pan. Discard the gasket.

To install:

➡**Be sure to use new fasteners, as required.**

23. Apply sealer to both sides of the crankshaft rear main bearing cap and the front cover/block mating area. Press the sealer into the gap using a putty knife.

24. Position the oil pan to its mounting, using a new gasket.

25. Tighten the retaining bolts to 18 ft. lbs. (25 Nm).

26. Install the left side oil pan side bolts.

27. Install the right side oil pan side bolts. Tighten to 37 ft. lbs. (50 Nm), plus an additional 50 degrees.

28. Continue the installation in the reverse order of the removal procedure.

29. Be sure to fill the engine with clean engine oil.

30. Start the engine and check for leaks. Correct as required.

4.6L Engine

See Figures 95 through 97.

➡**The rear seat cushion must be removed to gain access to the battery.**

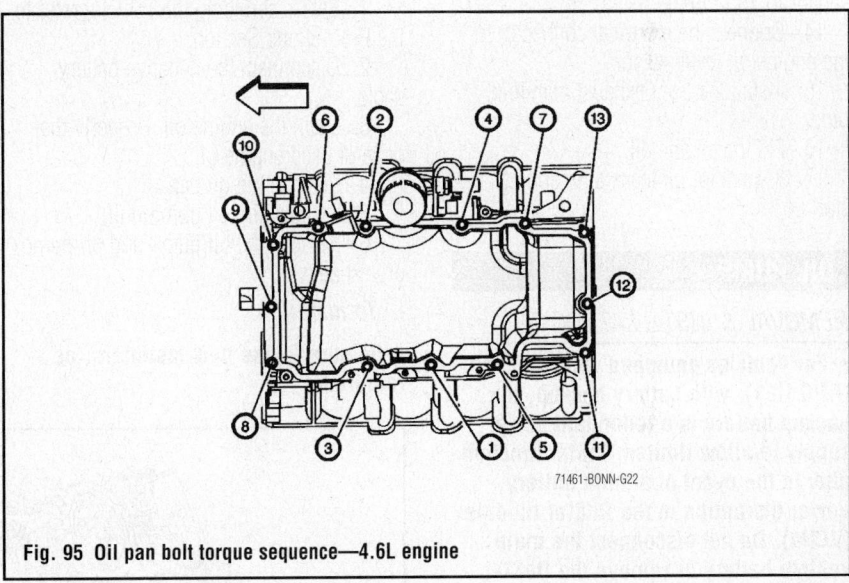

Fig. 95 Oil pan bolt torque sequence—4.6L engine

Fig. 96 Ensure the RTV sealant is higher than the oil pan sealing surface (1) by 3 mm (0.118 in)

1. Before servicing the vehicle, refer to the Precautions Section.

2. Disconnect the negative battery cable.

3. Raise and safely support the vehicle. Drain the engine oil.

4. Remove the front exhaust manifold pipe.

5. Disconnect the electrical connector from the engine oil level sensor.

6. Remove the engine oil level sensor from the oil pan.

7. Remove the oil pan bolts.

➡**The oil pan gasket is reusable unless damaged. Do not remove the gasket from the oil pan groove unless replacement is required.**

8. Remove the oil pan.

9. Clean and inspect the oil pan.

To install:

10. If required, install a new oil pan seal using the following procedure:

a. Clean any residual oil from the seal groove.

b. Completely fill and slightly overfill the oil pan seal groove with a continuous bead of RTV sealant.

c. Ensure the RTV sealant is higher than the oil pan sealing surface (1) by 3 mm (0.118 in).

11. To prevent shifting of the oil pan, install one Engine Front Cover Installation Guide Pin, special tool EN 46109, or equivalent, into the bolt hole in each side of the lower crankcase.

12. Position the oil pan to the crankcase. Install the oil pan retaining bolts. Tighten the oil pan bolts, in the sequence shown, as follows:

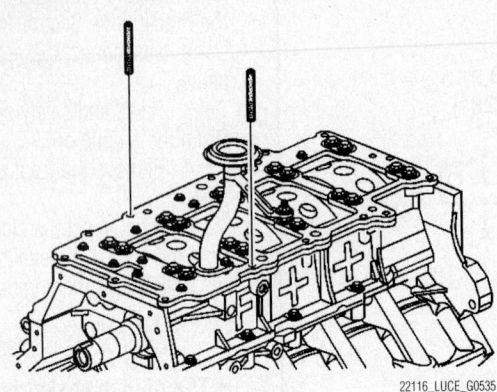

Fig. 97 To prevent shifting of the oil pan, install an Engine Front Cover Installation Guide Pin into the bolt hole in each side of the lower crankcase

a. First pass: 71 inch lbs. (8 Nm)
b. Final pass: 106 inch lbs. (12 Nm)
13. Install the engine oil level sensor into the oil pan. Tighten the engine oil level sensor to 15 ft. lbs. (20 Nm).
14. Connect the electrical connector to the engine oil level sensor.
15. Install the front exhaust manifold pipe.
16. Fill the engine oil.
17. Inspect for oil leaks after engine start up.

OIL PUMP

REMOVAL & INSTALLATION

➡For vehicles equipped with OnStar (RPO UE1), with battery backup, the backup battery is a redundant power supply to allow limited OnStar functionality in the event of a main battery power disruption to the OnStar module (VCIM). Do not disconnect the main vehicle battery or remove the OnStar fuse with the ignition key in any position other than OFF. Retained accessory power should be allowed to time out or be disabled by opening the driver's side door before disconnecting power. Disconnecting power to the module in any way while the ignition is ON or with the retained accessory power activated may cause activation of the OnStar backup battery system and will discharge and permanently damage the backup battery. Once the backup battery is activated it will stay on until it has completely discharged. The backup battery is not rechargeable and once it is activated, it must be replaced.

3.9L Engine

See Figure 98.

➡**The rear seat cushion must be removed to gain access to the battery.**

1. Before servicing the vehicle, refer to the Precautions Section.
2. Disconnect the negative battery cable.
3. Drain the engine oil. Properly dispose of used engine oil.
4. Remove the oil pan.
5. Remove the oil pump bolt.
6. Remove the oil pump and oil pump driveshaft.

To install:

➡**Be sure to use new fasteners, as required.**

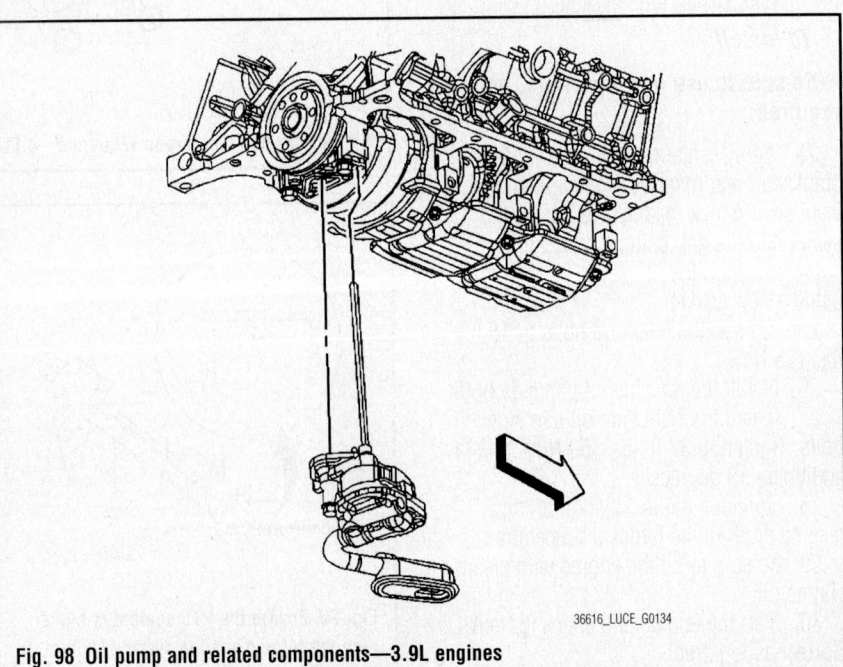

Fig. 98 Oil pump and related components—3.9L engines

7. Position the oil pump to its mounting.
8. Tighten the retaining bolt to 30 ft. lbs. (41 Nm).
9. Continue the installation in the reverse order of the removal procedure.
10. Be sure to fill the engine with clean engine oil.
11. Start the engine and check for leaks. Correct as required.

4.6L Engine

See Figure 99.

➡**The rear seat cushion must be removed to gain access to the battery.**

1. Before servicing the vehicle, refer to the Precautions Section.
2. Disconnect the negative battery cable.
3. Remove the engine front cover.
4. Remove the 3 oil pump assembly retaining bolts identified by the larger head size.
5. Slide the oil pump assembly off the nose of the crankshaft with the drive collar in place.
6. Clean and inspect the oil pump.

To install:

7. Install the oil pump drive spacer into the oil pump so that the drive flat engages the pump rotor.
8. Position the oil pump on the crankshaft.
9. Install the retaining bolts.
10. Apply upward pressure on the pump while tightening the 3 retaining bolts. Tighten the bolts in the sequence shown:

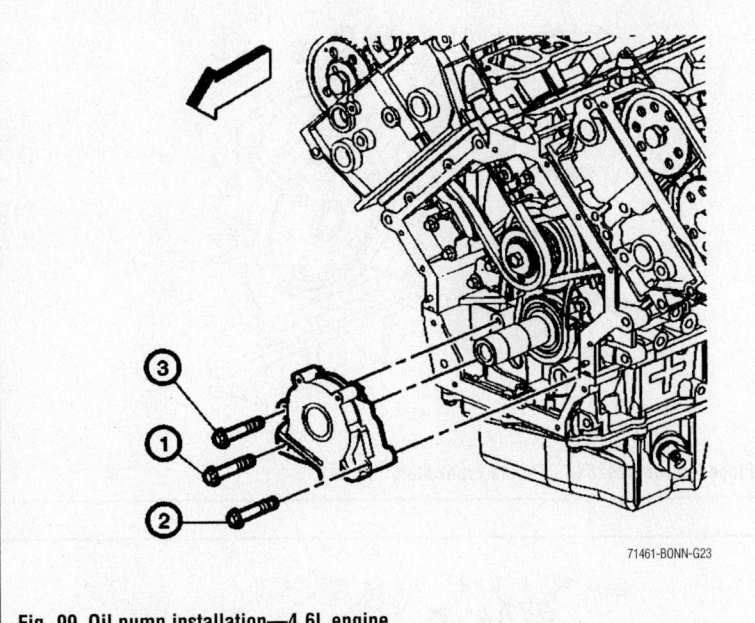

Fig. 99 Oil pump installation—4.6L engine

a. First Pass: Tighten the oil pump mounting bolts in sequence to 89 inch lbs. (10 Nm).

b. Final Pass: Tighten the oil pump mounting bolts in sequence an additional 35°.

11. Install the engine front cover.

PISTON AND RING

POSITIONING

See Figures 100 through 102.

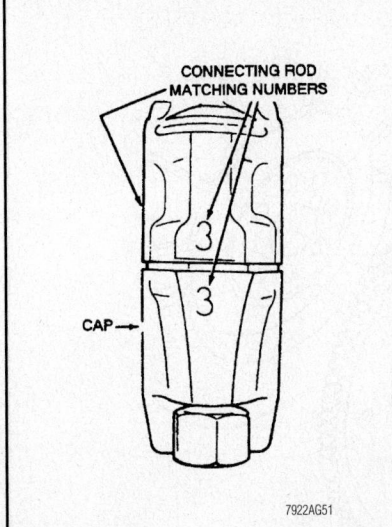

Fig. 100 Engine connecting rod and cap installation. Be sure to matchmark the cap and rod prior to disassembly, as shown—4.6L engine

REAR MAIN SEAL

REMOVAL & INSTALLATION

➡For vehicles equipped with OnStar (RPO UE1), with battery backup, the backup battery is a redundant power supply to allow limited OnStar functionality in the event of a main battery power disruption to the OnStar module (VCIM). Do not disconnect the main vehicle battery or remove the OnStar fuse with the ignition key in any position other than OFF. Retained accessory power should be allowed to time out or be disabled by opening the driver's side door before disconnecting power. Disconnecting power to the module in any way while the ignition is ON or with the retained accessory power activated may cause activation of the OnStar backup battery system and will discharge and permanently

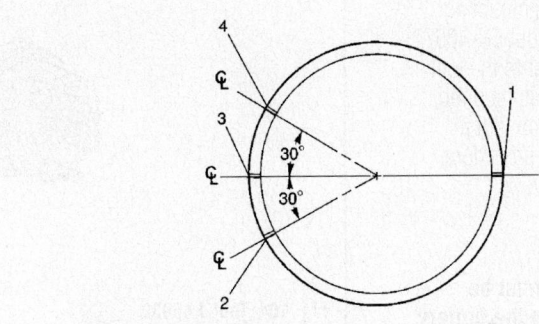

1. Oil control ring and expander, and 2nd compression ring gaps
2. Upper oil control ring gap
3. Top compression ring gap
4. Lower oil control ring gap

Fig. 101 Piston ring positioning—4.6L engine

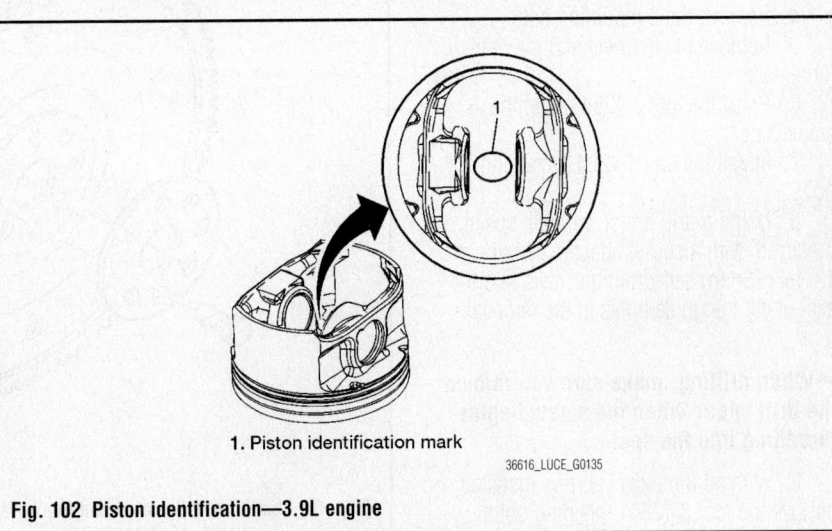

1. Piston identification mark

Fig. 102 Piston identification—3.9L engine

damage the backup battery. Once the backup battery is activated it will stay on until it has completely discharged. The backup battery is not rechargeable and once it is activated, it must be replaced.

3.9L Engine

➡The rear seat cushion must be removed to gain access to the battery.

1. Before servicing the vehicle, refer to the Precautions Section.
2. Disconnect the negative battery cable.
3. Remove the transaxle.
4. Remove the flywheel.
5. Install tool EN-48672, or equivalent, onto the crankshaft. Be sure to refer to the tool manufacturer's instructions, as required.
6. Remove the seal from the crankshaft.

To install:

➡Be sure to use new fasteners, as required.

7. Position the seal to its mounting.
8. Install the seal using tool EN-48672, or equivalent. Be sure to refer to the tool manufacturer's instructions, as required.
9. Continue the installation in the reverse order of the removal procedure.

4.6L Engine

See Figures 103 through 105.

➡The rear seat cushion must be removed to gain access to the battery.

1. Before servicing the vehicle, refer to the Precautions Section.
2. Disconnect the negative battery cable.
3. Remove the transaxle assembly.

➡Do not reuse the flywheel bolts.

4. Remove the 8 mounting bolts.
5. Remove the flywheel and the reinforcement.
6. Place the tool J 42841 onto the crankshaft.
7. Install the tool J 42841 retaining bolts.
8. Using a drill motor, variable speed preferred, with a socket adapter, install eight 1.0 in. (25mm) self-drilling screws into the seal using the guide holes in the removal tool.

➡When drilling, make sure you reduce the drill speed when the screw begins threading into the seal.

9. With all 8 removal screws installed, remove the tool J 42841 retaining bolts.

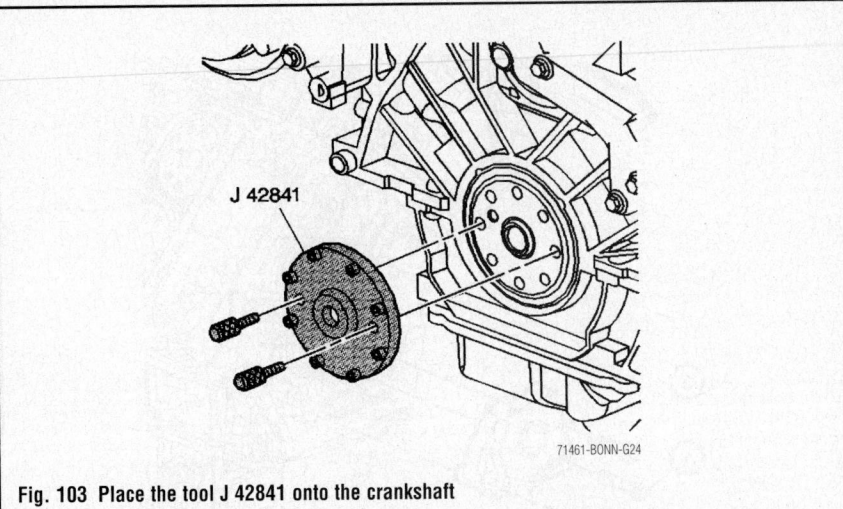

Fig. 103 Place the tool J 42841 onto the crankshaft

71461-BONN-G24

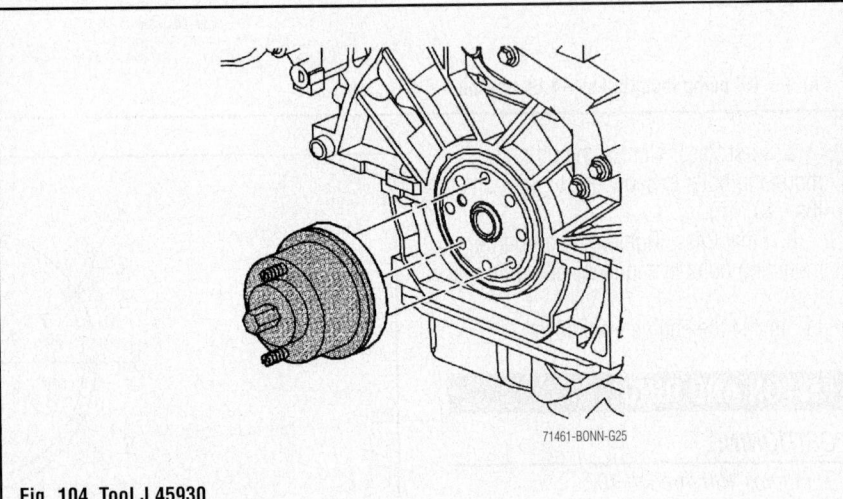

Fig. 104 Tool J 45930

71461-BONN-G25

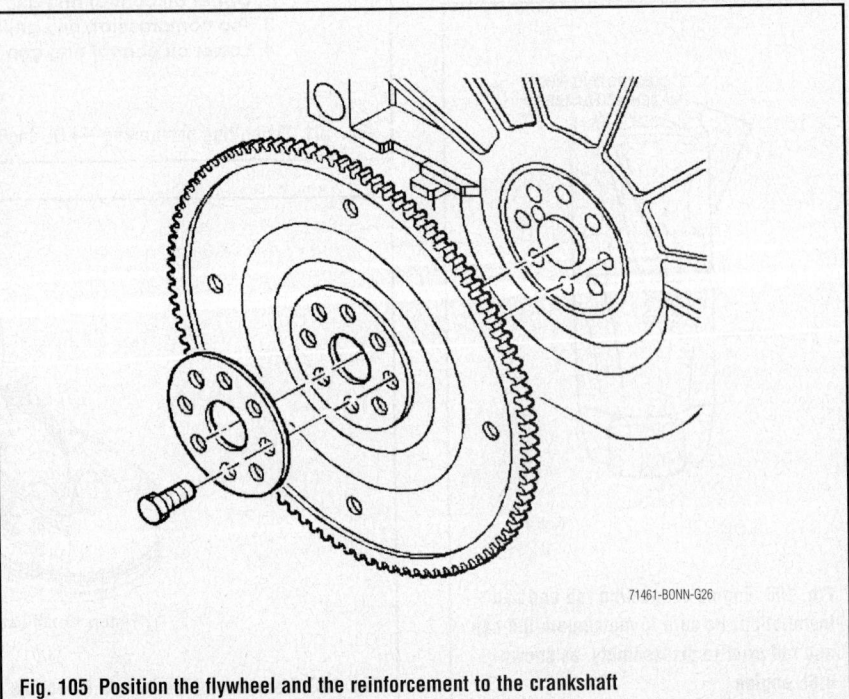

Fig. 105 Position the flywheel and the reinforcement to the crankshaft

71461-BONN-G26

10. Install the center forcing screw.

11. Tighten the center screw on the tool J 42841 to pull the seal assembly off the end of the crankshaft.

To install:

Make sure the drain is clear before installing the new crankshaft rear oil seal. Failure to clear the drain could cause the crankshaft rear oil seal to leak.

12. Clean any debris from the crankshaft rear oil seal drain using wire or an unbound plastic tie-wrap.

13. Place a small amount of Gasket Maker, GM P/N 1052942 (Canadian P/N 10953466), or equivalent, at the crankcase split line across the end of the upper/lower crankcase seal.

14. Coat the outer diameter of the cylinder block crankshaft rear oil seal area with clean engine oil GM P/N 36616501 (Canadian P/N 992704), or equivalent.

➡ **DO NOT allow any engine oil on the area where the crankshaft rear oil seal is to be pressed onto the crankshaft. The green coating is a sealant preapplied to the inner diameter of the crankshaft rear oil seal and must not be contaminated.**

15. Wipe the outer diameter of the flywheel flange clean with a lint-free cloth.

16. Lubricate the outer rubber surface of the crankshaft rear oil seal with clean engine oil GM P/N 36616501 (Canadian P/N 992704), or equivalent.

17. Loosen the center bolt of the tool J 45930 until the center hub protrudes approximately ½ in. (13mm) beyond the outer plate. It is not necessary to completely unthread the center bolt and separate the 2 pieces of the tool J 45930.

18. Install the tool J 45930 to the rear of the crankshaft.

19. Thread the 2 mounting bolts into the crankshaft flange.

20. Tighten the bolts until the tool J 45930 is firmly mounted on the crankshaft.

21. Install the crankshaft rear oil seal by tightening the center bolt until the tool J 45930 bottoms against the crankcase.

22. Loosen the center bolt to release pressure on the crankcase.

23. Loosen the 2 mounting bolts.

24. Remove the tool J 45930 from the crankshaft flange.

25. Inspect to ensure the installation depth is equal around the crankshaft rear oil

seal's circumference. If the depth is not equal reinstall the tool J 45930 and repeat the installation procedures.

26. Position the flywheel and the reinforcement to the crankshaft.

27. Apply sealant, GM P/N 12346004 (Canadian P/N 10953480) or equivalent, to the flywheel mounting bolts.

28. Install the 8 NEW mounting bolts.
    a. First Pass: Tighten the flywheel mounting bolts to 11 ft. lbs. (15 Nm).
    b. Final Pass: Tighten the flywheel mounting bolts an additional 50° using the tool J 36660-A .

29. Install the transaxle assembly.

TIMING CHAIN COVER AND SEAL

REMOVAL & INSTALLATION

➡ **For vehicles equipped with OnStar (RPO UE1), with battery backup, the backup battery is a redundant power**

supply to allow limited OnStar functionality in the event of a main battery power disruption to the OnStar module (VCIM). Do not disconnect the main vehicle battery or remove the OnStar fuse with the ignition key in any position other than OFF. Retained accessory power should be allowed to time out or be disabled by opening the driver's side door before disconnecting power. Disconnecting power to the module in any way while the ignition is ON or with the retained accessory power activated may cause activation of the OnStar backup battery system and will discharge and permanently damage the backup battery. Once the backup battery is activated it will stay on until it has completely discharged. The backup battery is not rechargeable and once it is activated, it must be replaced.

3.9L Engine
See Figures 106 and 107.

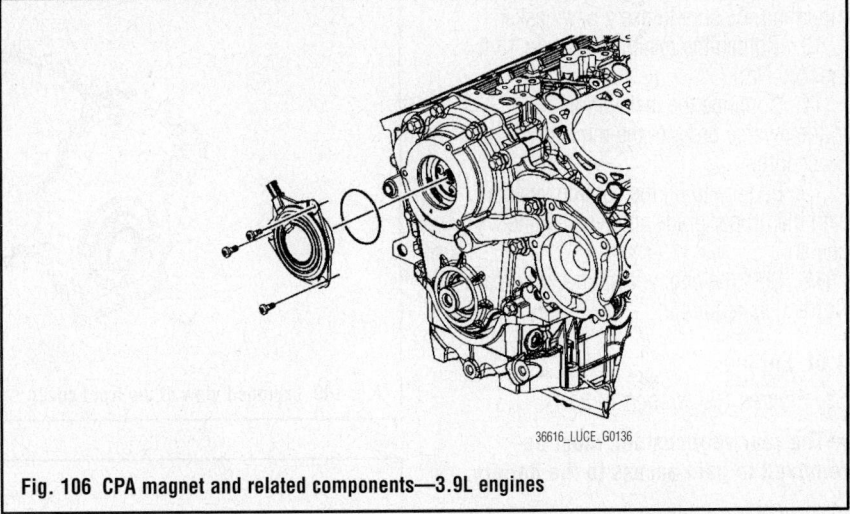
36616_LUCE_G0136
Fig. 106 CPA magnet and related components—3.9L engines

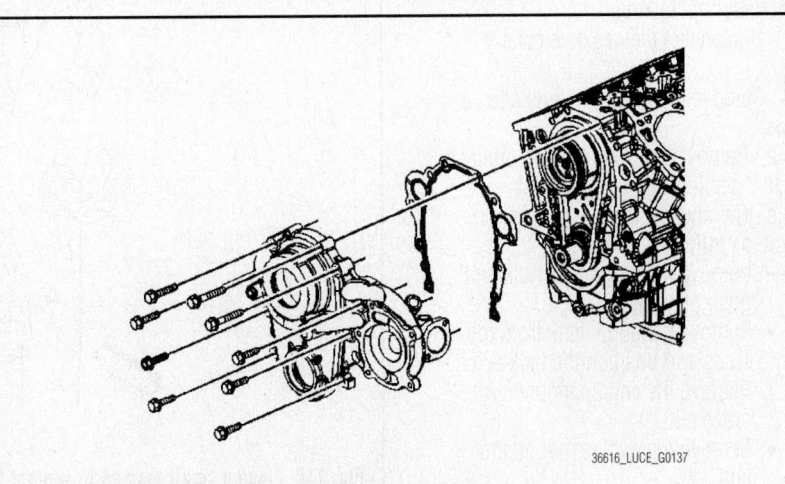
36616_LUCE_G0137
Fig. 107 Front cover and related components—3.9L engines

➡The rear seat cushion must be removed to gain access to the battery.

1. Before servicing the vehicle, refer to the Precautions Section.

2. Disconnect the negative battery cable.

3. Drain the cooling system. Properly dispose of used engine coolant.

4. Remove the drive belt tensioner.

5. Remove the oil pan.

6. Remove the crankshaft balancer.

7. Remove the CPA actuator magnet.

8. Remove the thermostat. Remove the water pump.

9. Remove the front cover retaining bolts.

10. Remove the coolant hose from the cover.

11. Remove the front cover. Discard the gasket.

To install:

➡Be sure to use new fasteners, as required.

12. Position the component to its mounting. Be sure to use a new gasket.

13. Tighten the retaining bolts to 18 ft. lbs. (25 Nm).

14. Continue the installation in the reverse order of the removal procedure.

15. Be sure to fill the cooling system with the proper grade and type engine coolant.

16. Start the engine and check for leaks. Correct, as required.

4.6L Engine

See Figures 108 through 111.

➡The rear seat cushion must be removed to gain access to the battery.

1. Before servicing the vehicle, refer to the Precautions Section.

2. Disconnect the negative battery cable.

3. Remove the drive belt tensioner, as follows:

   a. Remove the drive belt, as outlined in this section.

   b. Remove the right engine mount strut, as follows:

- Remove the surge tank nuts and push pin retainer.
- Remove the surge tank from the studs and position the tank aside.
- Remove the engine mount strut brace nut.
- Remove the engine mount strut bolt.
- Remove the engine mount strut.

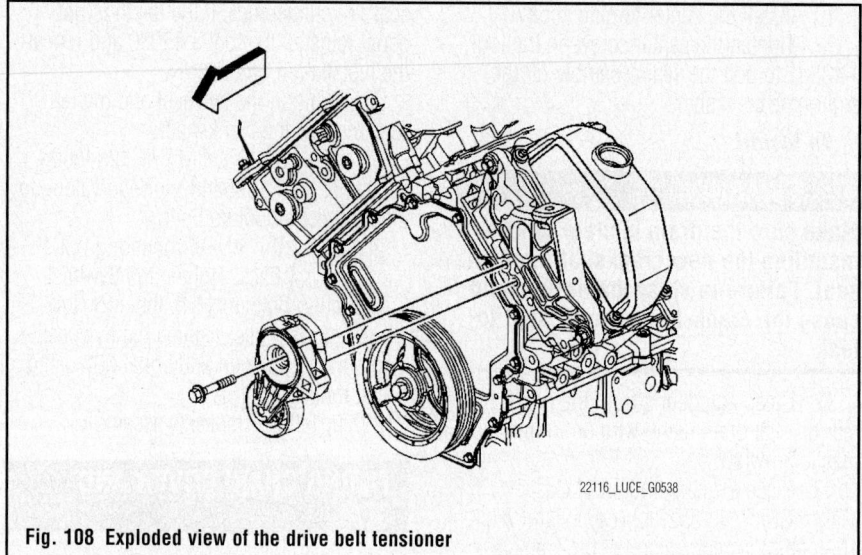

Fig. 108 Exploded view of the drive belt tensioner

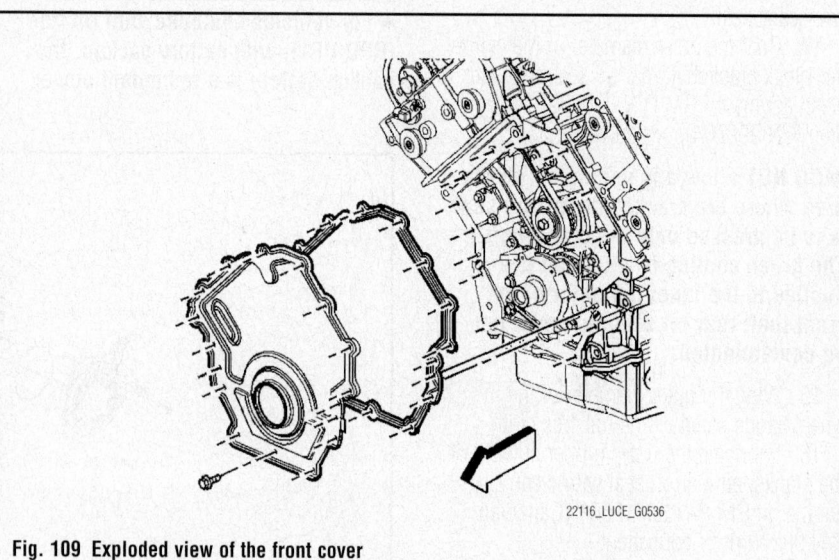

Fig. 109 Exploded view of the front cover

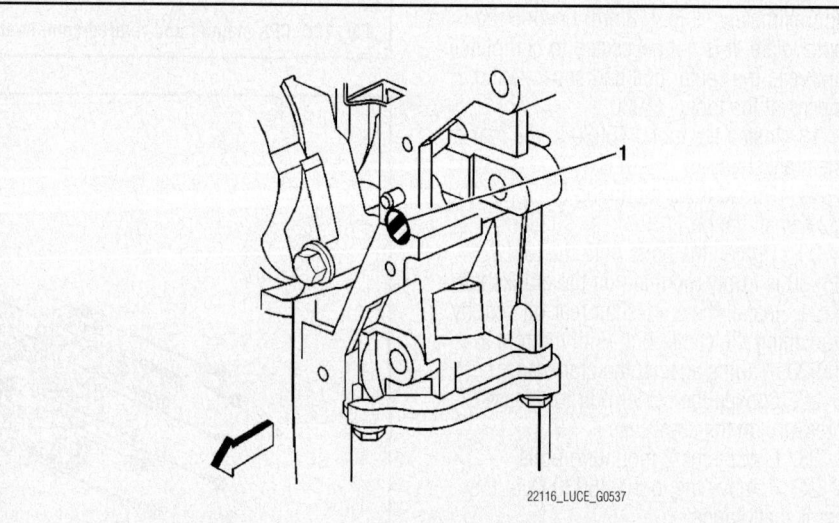

Fig. 110 Place a small amount of sealant GM P/N 36616739, (Canadian P/N 10953541), or equivalent at the split line of the upper and lower crankcases (1)

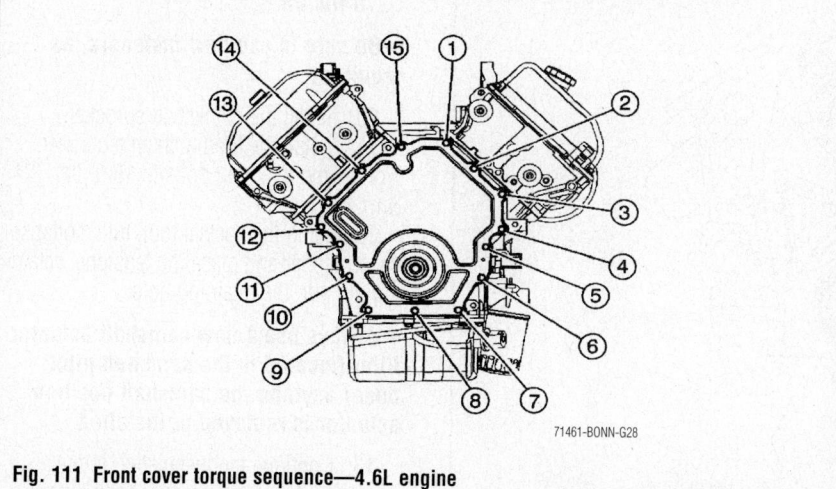

Fig. 111 Front cover torque sequence—4.6L engine

c. Discharge the Air Conditioning (A/C) system, as outlined in the Heating & Air Conditioning Section.

d. Disconnect the A/C compressor suction hose from the A/C evaporator hose. Discard seal and reposition hose.

e. Remove the drive belt tensioner bolt.

f. Remove the drive belt tensioner

4. Remove the drive belt idler pulley, as follows:.

5. Remove the crankshaft damper (balancer), as outlined in this section.

6. Remove the engine front cover bolts.

7. Remove the engine front cover and gasket. The gasket is reusable. Do not discard unless it is damaged.

To install:

8. Place a small amount of sealant GM P/N 36616739, (Canadian P/N 10953541), or equivalent at the split line of the upper and lower crankcases.

9. Place the front cover gasket over the crankcase dowel pins.

10. Place the front cover in position on the crankcase.

11. Apply a suitable threadlock on the front cover retaining bolts, then install the bolts until just snug.

12. Tighten the front cover retaining bolts, in the sequence shown, to 89 inch lbs. (10 Nm).

13. Install the crankshaft damper (balancer), as outlined in this section.

14. Position the drive belt idler pulley to the engine and finger starter the pulley bolt. Tighten the drive belt idler pulley bolt to 37 ft. lbs. (50 Nm).

15. Install the drive belt tensioner, as follows:

a. Position the drive belt tensioner to the left cylinder head. Ensure the anti-rotation pin is in the hole.

b. Install the drive belt tensioner bolt and tighten to 37 ft. lbs. (50 Nm).

c. Install the drive belt, as outlined in this section.

d. Install new seal, then connect the A/C compressor suction hose to the A/C evaporator hose.

e. Recharge the A/C system, as outlined in the Heating & Air Conditioning Section.

f. Install the right engine mount strut in the reverse of the removal procedure. Tighten the strut nut and bolt to 52 ft. lbs. (70 Nm).

16. Connect the negative battery cable

TIMING CHAIN AND SPROCKETS

REMOVAL & INSTALLATION

➡**For vehicles equipped with OnStar (RPO UE1), with battery backup, the backup battery is a redundant power supply to allow limited OnStar functionality in the event of a main battery power disruption to the OnStar module (VCIM). Do not disconnect the main vehicle battery or remove the OnStar fuse with the ignition key in any position other than OFF. Retained accessory power should be allowed to time out or be disabled by opening the driver's side door before disconnecting power. Disconnecting power to the module in any way while the ignition is ON or with the retained accessory power activated may cause activation of the OnStar backup battery system and will discharge and permanently damage the backup battery. Once the backup battery is activated it will stay on until it has completely discharged. The backup battery is not rechargeable and once it is activated, it must be replaced.**

3.9L Engine

See Figures 112 through 115.

➡**The rear seat cushion must be removed to gain access to the battery.**

1. Before servicing the vehicle, refer to the Precautions Section.

2. Disconnect the negative battery cable.

3. Remove the engine front cover.

4. Align the crankshaft timing mark to the timing mark on the bottom of the timing chain tensioner.

5. Align the timing mark on the camshaft gear with the timing mark on top of the timing chain tensioner.

6. Using tool EN47719, collapse the tensioner and place the tensioner retaining pin into the retaining hole.

7. Remove the camshaft sprocket/actuator bolts.

8. Remove the timing chain, camshaft sprocket/actuator and crankshaft sprockets.

9. Remove the timing chain tensioner bolts. Remove the timing chain tensioner.

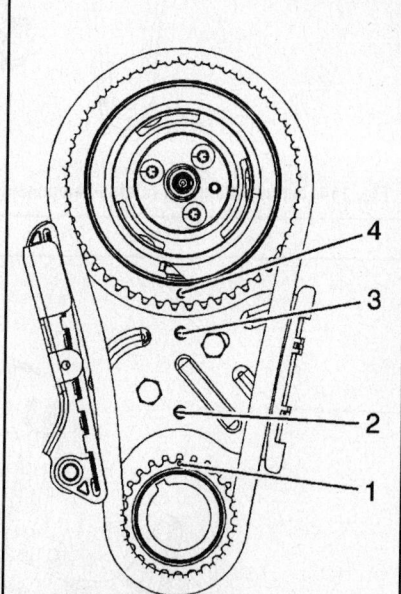

1. Crankshaft alignment mark
2. Tensioner bottom
3. Tensioner Top
4. Camshaft alignment mark

Fig. 112 Timing mark alignment— 3.9L engines

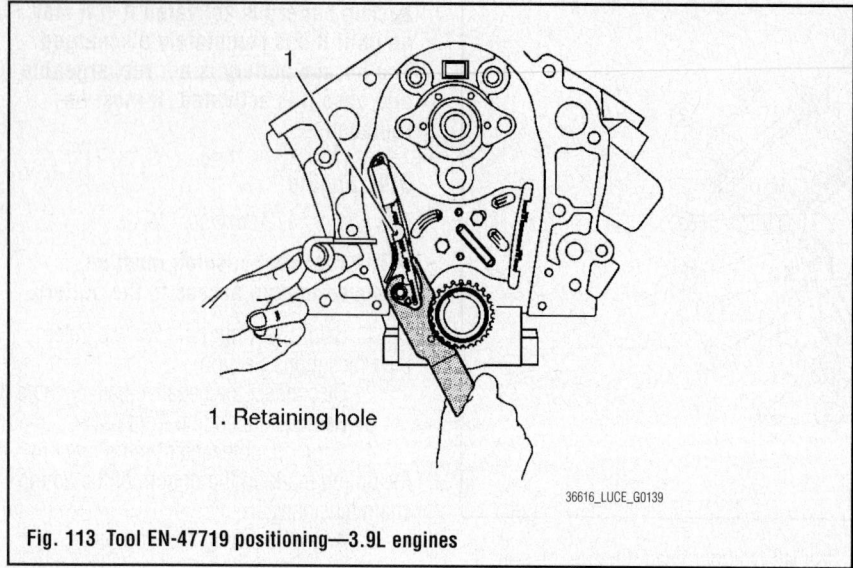

1. Retaining hole

36616_LUCE_G0139

Fig. 113 Tool EN-47719 positioning—3.9L engines

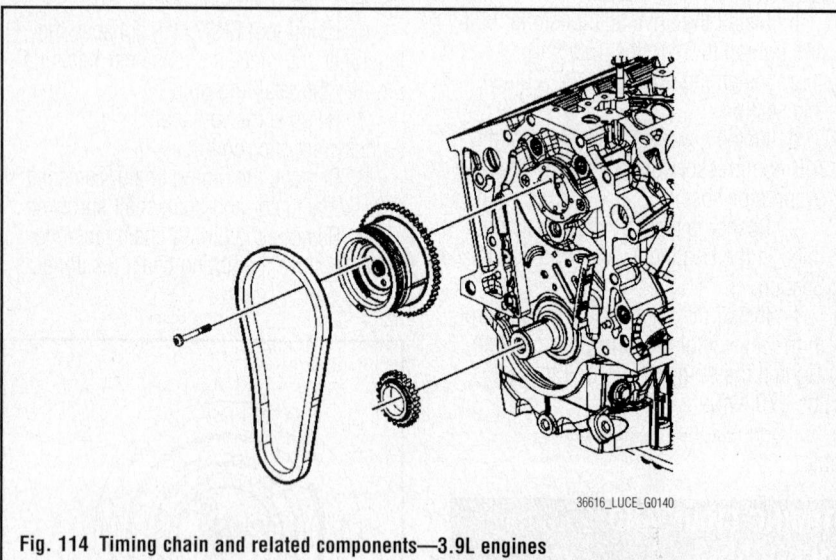

36616_LUCE_G0140

Fig. 114 Timing chain and related components—3.9L engines

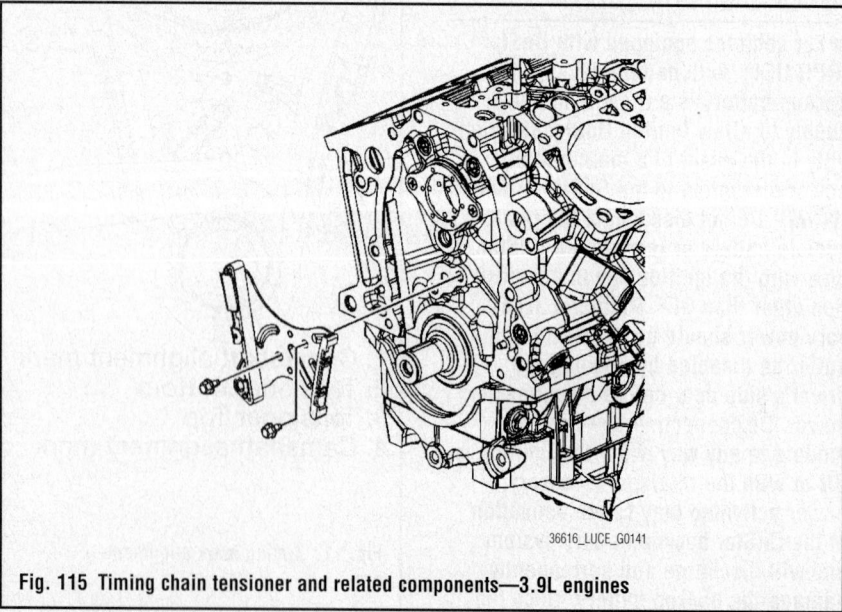

36616_LUCE_G0141

Fig. 115 Timing chain tensioner and related components—3.9L engines

To install:

➡**Be sure to use new fasteners, as required.**

10. Install the crankshaft sprocket.

11. Install the timing chain tensioner. Tighten the retaining bolts to 15 ft. lbs. (21 Nm).

12. using the special tool, fully collapse the tensioner and place the tensioner retaining pin into the retaining hole.

➡**Always use a new camshaft actuator filter (located in the camshaft pilot nose) anytime the camshaft position actuator is removed or installed.**

13. Continue the installation in the reverse order of the removal procedure.

4.6L Engine

See Figures 116 and 117.

➡**The rear seat cushion must be removed to gain access to the battery.**

1. Before servicing the vehicle, refer to the Precautions Section.

2. Disconnect the negative battery cable.

3. Remove the front cover perimeter bolts.

4. Remove the front cover and the gasket. Ensure that you do not damage the sealing surface.

➡**Do not remove the crankshaft front oil seal.**

The crankshaft front oil seal is not serviced as an individual component. When replacing the crankshaft front oil seal, install a NEW engine front cover. In order to precisely align the crankshaft front oil seal to the crankshaft damper and crankshaft damper dust shield, the engine front cover and the crankshaft front oil seal are sold as an assembly.

5. Primary camshaft drive chain removal:

    a. Remove the camshaft intermediate drive shaft sprocket bolt.

    b. Remove the primary camshaft drive chain tensioner bolts.

    c. Remove the primary camshaft drive chain tensioner.

    d. Remove the primary camshaft drive chain guide bolts.

    e. Remove the primary camshaft drive chain guide.

    f. Remove the camshaft intermediate drive shaft sprocket, primary camshaft drive chain and crankshaft sprocket as an assembly.

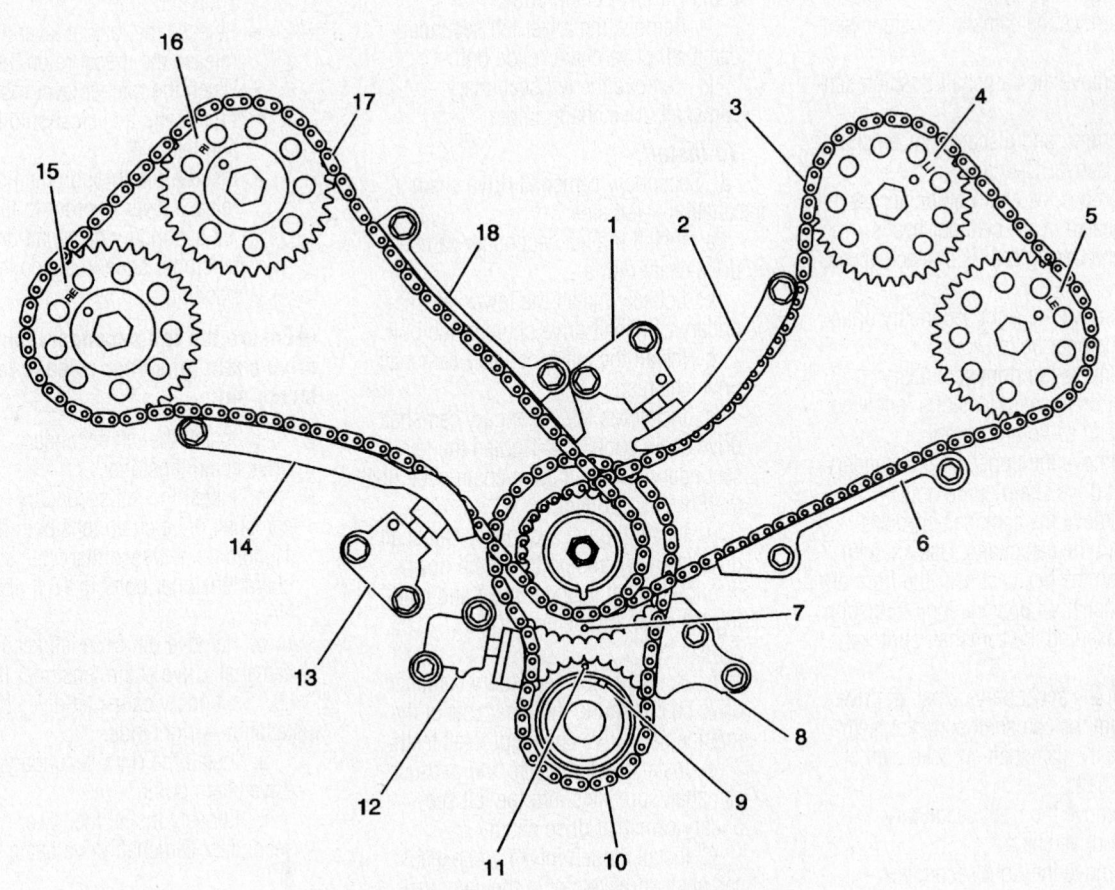

(1) Left Secondary Timing Chain Tensioner
(2) Left Secondary Timing Chain Shoe
(3) Left Secondary Timing Chain
(4) Left Intake Camshaft Sprocket Timing Mark
(5) Left Exhaust Camshaft Sprocket Timing Mark
(6) Left Secondary Timing Chain Guide
(7) Intermediate Sprocket Timing Mark
(8) Primary Timing Chain Guide
(9) Crankshaft Sprocket Pin Alignment Slot
(10) Primary Timing Chain
(11) Crankshaft Sprocket Timing Mark
(12) Primary Timing Chain Tensioner
(13) Right Secondary Timing Chain Tensioner
(14) Right Secondary Timing Chain Shoe
(15) Right Exhaust Camshaft Sprocket Timing Mark
(16) Right Intake Camshaft Sprocket Timing Mark
(17) Right Secondary Timing Chain
(18) Right Secondary Timing Chain Guide

71461-BONN-G27

Fig. 116 Correct alignment of the primary and secondary timing chains—4.6L engine

6. Secondary camshaft drive chain removal—right side:

a. Remove the camshaft position sensor bolt.

b. Remove the camshaft position sensor.

c. Remove and discard the camshaft position sensor O-ring.

d. Remove the chain guide access plugs located in the cylinder heads. Ensure the O-ring seal is on each access plug.

e. Remove the right secondary drive chain tensioner bolts.

f. Remove the right secondary camshaft drive chain tensioner allowing it to expand as you remove it.

g. Remove the upper right secondary camshaft drive chain guide bolt.

h. Remove the camshaft sprocket bolts from the camshafts. Use an open wrench on the hex cast near the front of each camshaft to prevent engine rotation when loosening the camshaft sprocket bolts.

i. Lift the secondary camshaft drive chain from the camshaft sprocket teeth and slide the camshaft sprockets off of the camshafts.

j. Remove the right secondary camshaft drive chain.

k. Remove the right secondary camshaft drive chain shoe bolt.

l. Remove the right secondary camshaft drive chain shoe.

m. Remove the lower right secondary camshaft drive chain guide bolt.

n. Remove the right secondary camshaft drive chain guide.

7. Secondary camshaft drive chain removal—left side:

a. Remove the left secondary camshaft drive chain tensioner bolts.

b. Remove the left secondary camshaft drive chain tensioner allowing it to expand as you remove it.

c. Remove the upper left secondary camshaft drive chain guide bolt.

d. Remove the camshaft sprocket bolts from the camshafts. Use an open wrench on the hex cast near the front of each camshaft to prevent engine rotation when loosening the camshaft sprocket bolts.

e. Lift the secondary camshaft drive chain from the camshaft sprocket teeth and slide the camshaft sprockets off of the camshafts.

f. Remove the left secondary drive chain.

g. Remove the left secondary camshaft drive lchain shoe bolt.

h. Remove the left secondary camshaft drive chain shoe.

i. Remove the lower left secondary camshaft drive chain guide bolt.

j. Remove the left secondary camshaft drive chain guide.

To install:

8. Secondary camshaft drive chain installation—left side:

a. Install the left secondary camshaft drive chain guide.

b. Loosely install the lower left secondary camshaft drive chain guide bolt.

c. Install the left secondary camshaft drive chain shoe.

d. Install the left secondary camshaft drive chain shoe bolt. Tighten the left secondary camshaft drive chain shoe bolt to 18 ft. lbs. (25 Nm).

e. Install the left secondary camshaft drive chain by sliding the chain down through the left cylinder head and placing the chain on the end of the camshafts.

f. Route the left secondary camshaft drive chain around the inner row of the intermediate drive chain sprocket teeth.

g. Install the left intake and exhaust camshaft sprockets into the left secondary camshaft drive chain.

h. Install the left intake and exhaust camshaft sprockets onto the camshafts. The camshaft sprocket notch marked "LI" which indicates left intake, engages the intake camshaft pin and the camshaft sprocket notch marked "LE" which indicates left exhaust, engages the exhaust camshaft pin.

i. If necessary, use an open wrench on the hex cast near the front of each camshaft to help align the sprocket notch to the camshaft pin.

j. Loosely install the left intake and exhaust camshaft sprocket bolts.

k. Ensure the perpendicular alignment of the left intake and exhaust camshaft sprocket notches and camshaft pins to the cylinder head.

l. Install tool J 44212 to the left cylinder head camshafts.

m. Install the upper left secondary camshaft drive chain guide bolt. Tighten BOTH the upper and lower left secondary camshaft drive chain guide bolts to 18 ft. lbs. (25 Nm).

n. Collapse the left secondary camshaft drive chain tensioner using the following procedure:

- Rotate the ratchet release lever counterclockwise and hold
- Collapse the left secondary camshaft drive chain tensioner shoe and hold
- Release the ratchet lever and slowly release the pressure on the shoe
- When the ratchet lever moves to the first detent a click should be heard and felt
- Insert a pin through the hole in the release lever in order to lock the left secondary camshaft drive chain tensioner shoe in the collapsed position

➡**Ensure the left secondary camshaft drive chain tensioner release lever is facing out.**

o. Install the left secondary camshaft drive chain tensioner.

p. Install the left secondary camshaft drive chain tensioner bolts. Tighten the left secondary camshaft drive chain tensioner bolts to 18 ft. lbs. (25 Nm).

q. Remove pin from left secondary camshaft drive chain tensioner lever.

9. Secondary camshaft dive chain installation—right side:

a. Install the right secondary camshaft drive chain guide.

b. Loosely install the lower right secondary camshaft drive chain guide bolt.

c. Install the right secondary camshaft drive chain shoe.

d. Install the right secondary camshaft drive chain shoe bolt. Tighten the right secondary camshaft drive chain shoe bolt to 18 ft. lbs. (25 Nm).

e. Install the right secondary camshaft drive chain by sliding the chain down through the right cylinder head and placing the chain on the end of the camshafts.

f. Route the right secondary camshaft drive chain around the outer row of the intermediate drive chain sprocket teeth.

g. Install the right intake and exhaust camshaft sprockets into the right secondary camshaft drive chain.

h. Install the right intake and exhaust camshafts onto the camshafts. The camshaft sprocket notch marked "RI" which indicates right intake, engages the intake camshaft pin and the camshaft sprocket notch marked "RE" which indicates right exhaust, engages the exhaust camshaft pin.

i. If necessary, use an open wrench on the hex cast near the front of each camshaft to help align the sprocket notch to the camshaft pin.

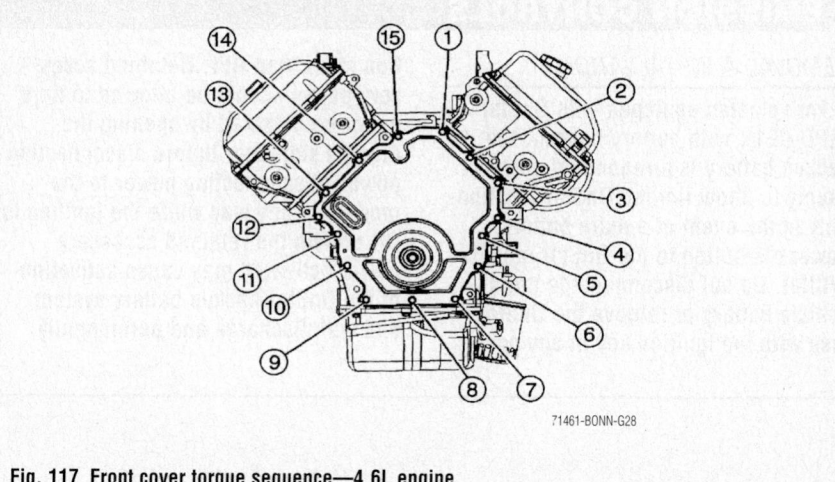

71461-BONN-G28

Fig. 117 Front cover torque sequence—4.6L engine

j. Loosely install the right intake and exhaust camshaft sprocket bolts.

k. Ensure the perpendicular alignment of the right intake and exhaust camshaft sprocket notches and camshaft pins to the cylinder head.

l. Install tool J 44212 to the right cylinder head camshafts.

m. Install the upper right secondary camshaft drive chain guide bolt. Tighten BOTH the upper and lower right secondary camshaft drive chain guide bolts to 18 ft. lbs. (25 Nm).

n. Collapse the right secondary camshaft drive chain tensioner using the following procedure:

- Rotate the ratchet release lever counter-clockwise and hold.
- Collapse the right secondary camshaft drive chain tensioner shoe and hold.
- Release the ratchet lever and slowly release the pressure on the shoe.
- When the ratchet lever moves to the first detent a click should be heard and felt.
- Insert a pin through the hole in the release lever in order to lock the right secondary camshaft drive chain tensioner shoe in the collapsed position.

➡**Ensure the right secondary camshaft drive chain tensioner release lever is facing out.**

o. Install the right secondary drive chain tensioner.

p. Install the right secondary drive chain tensioner bolts. Tighten the right secondary camshaft drive chain tensioner bolts to 18 ft. lbs. (25 Nm).

q. Remove pin from right secondary camshaft drive chain tensioner lever.

r. Ensure the correct alignment of all secondary timing components.

s. Ensure the correct alignment of all primary timing components.

t. Tighten ALL camshaft sprocket bolts. Use the hex cast into each camshaft to prevent engine rotation and provide leverage. Tighten ALL camshaft sprocket bolts to 90 ft. lbs. (120 Nm).

u. Install the chain guide access plugs located in the cylinder heads. Ensure the O-ring seal is on each access plug. Tighten the chain guide access plugs to 39 inch lbs. (5 Nm).

v. Install a NEW O-ring on the camshaft position sensor.

w. Lubricate the O-ring with clean engine oil.

x. Install the camshaft position sensor.

y. Install the camshaft position sensor bolt. Tighten the camshaft position sensor bolt to 89 inch lbs. (10 Nm).

10. Primary camshaft drive chain installation:

a. Install the primary camshaft drive chain on the camshaft intermediate drive shaft sprocket and crankshaft sprocket.

b. Align the timing marks of the camshaft intermediate drive shaft sprocket and crankshaft sprocket. Ensure the marks are aligned vertically.

c. Ensure the number one piston is at Top Dead Center (TDC) and the crankshaft pin is approximately at the one o'clock position using tool J 39946.

d. Install the primary camshaft drive chain, camshaft intermediate drive shaft sprocket and crankshaft sprocket as an assembly onto the camshaft intermediate drive shaft and the crankshaft.

e. Install the camshaft intermediate drive shaft sprocket bolt. Tighten the

camshaft intermediate drive shaft sprocket bolt to 44 ft. lbs. (60 Nm).

f. Install the primary camshaft drive chain guide.

g. Install the primary camshaft drive chain guide bolts. Tighten the primary camshaft drive chain guide bolts to 18 ft. lbs. (25 Nm).

h. Collapse the primary camshaft drive chain tensioner using the following procedure:

- Rotate the ratchet release lever counterclockwise and hold
- Collapse the primary camshaft drive chain tensioner shoe and hold
- Release the ratchet lever and slowly release the pressure on the shoe
- When the ratchet lever moves to the first detent a click should be heard and felt
- Insert a pin through the hole in the release lever in order to lock the primary camshaft drive chain tensioner shoe in the collapsed position

➡**Ensure the primary camshaft drive chain tensioner release lever is facing out.**

i. Install the primary camshaft drive chain tensioner.

j. Install the primary camshaft drive chain tensioner bolts. Tighten the primary camshaft drive chain tensioner bolts to 18 ft. lbs. (25 Nm).

k. Remove the pin in the release lever locking the primary camshaft drive chain tensioner.

l. Ensure the timing marks are aligned vertically.

m. Place a small amount of sealant GM P/N 36616739, (Canadian P/N 10953541), or equivalent at the split line of the upper and lower crankcases.

n. Place the front cover gasket over the crankcase dowel pins.

o. Place the front cover in position on the crankcase.

p. Install the front cover retaining bolts.

q. Tighten the front cover retaining bolts in the sequence shown. Tighten the front cover retaining bolts in proper sequence to 89 inch lbs. (10 Nm).

VALVE LASH

ADJUSTMENT

The valve clearance cannot be adjusted on these engines. The engine is equipped with hydraulic lifters, and adjustment is not necessary.

ENGINE PERFORMANCE & EMISSION CONTROLS

COMPONENT LOCATIONS

See Figures 118 through 121.

CAMSHAFT POSITION (CMP) SENSOR

LOCATION

See Figures 122 and 123.

REMOVAL & INSTALLATION

➡For vehicles equipped with OnStar (RPO UE1), with battery backup, the backup battery is a redundant power supply to allow limited OnStar functionality in the event of a main battery power disruption to the OnStar module (VCIM). Do not disconnect the main vehicle battery or remove the OnStar fuse with the ignition key in any position other than OFF. Retained accessory power should be allowed to time out or be disabled by opening the driver's side door before disconnecting power. Disconnecting power to the module in any way while the ignition is ON or with the retained accessory power activated may cause activation of the OnStar backup battery system and will discharge and permanently

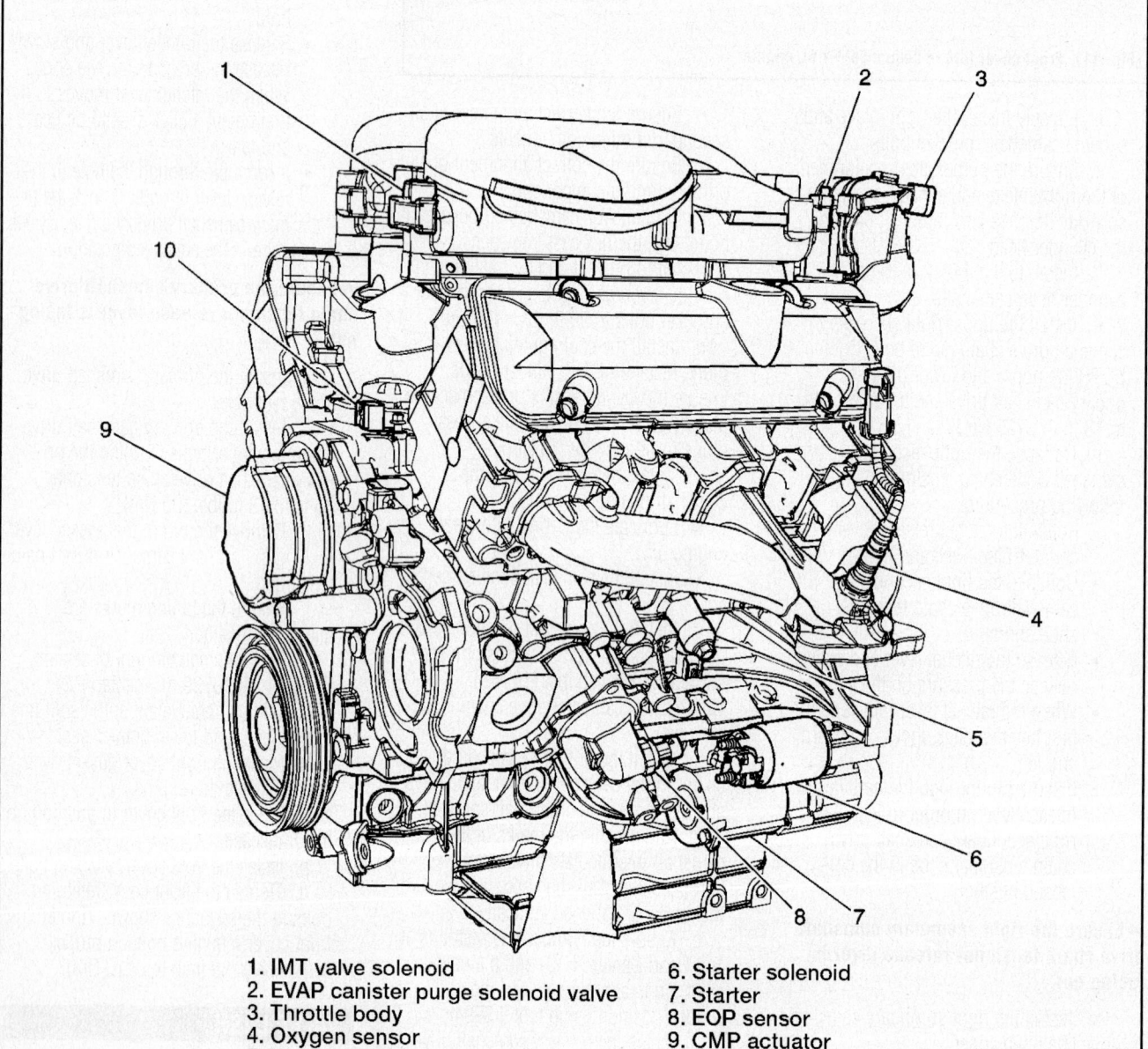

1. IMT valve solenoid
2. EVAP canister purge solenoid valve
3. Throttle body
4. Oxygen sensor
5. Knock sensor
6. Starter solenoid
7. Starter
8. EOP sensor
9. CMP actuator
10. CMP sensor

36616_LUCE_G0143

Fig. 118 Engine control component locations (front) —3.9L engines

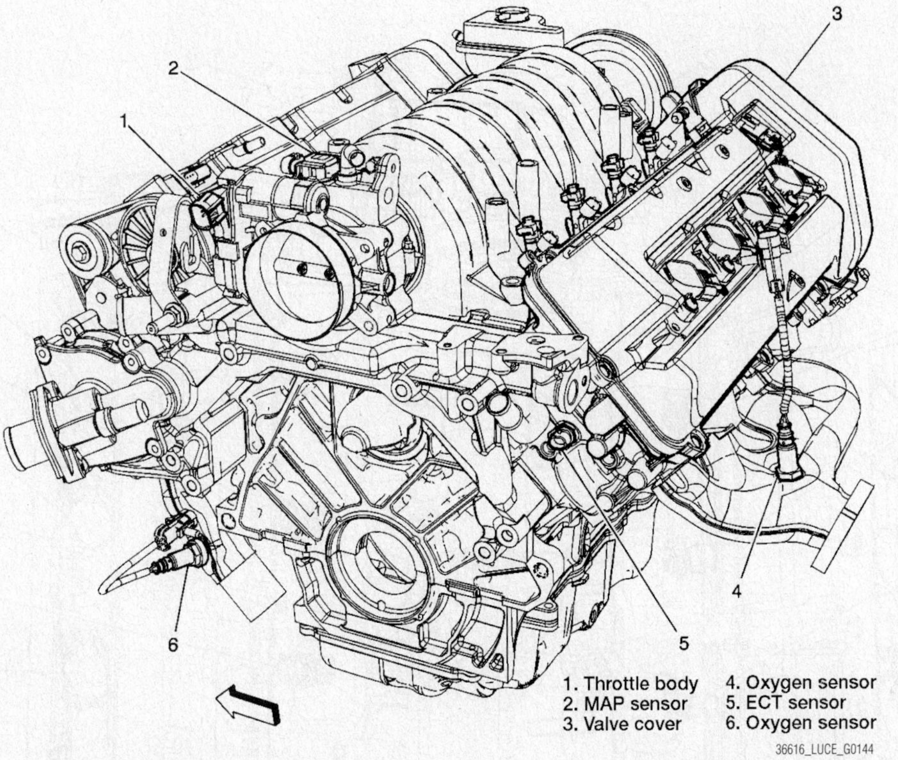

1. Throttle body
2. MAP sensor
3. Valve cover
4. Oxygen sensor
5. ECT sensor
6. Oxygen sensor

36616_LUCE_G0144

Fig. 119 Engine control component locations (left rear) —3.9L engines

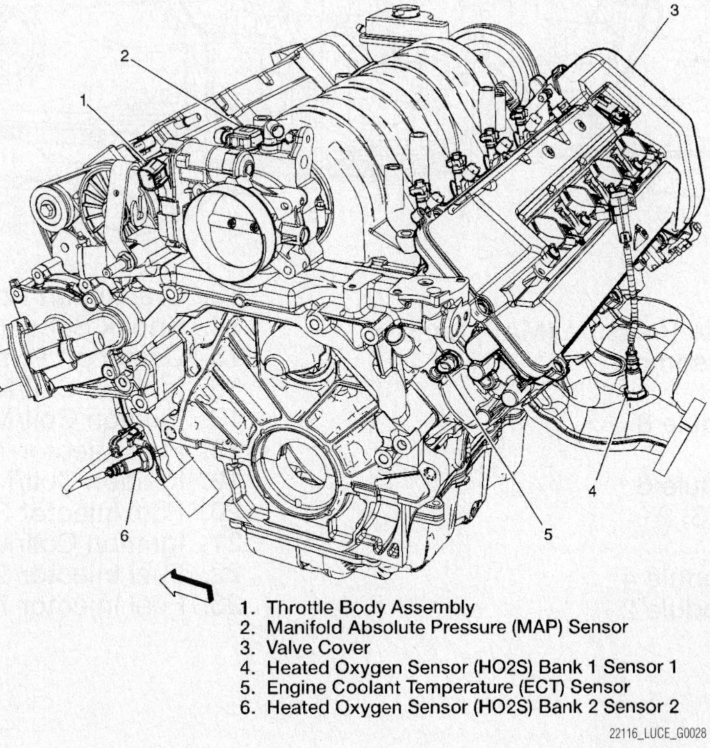

1. Throttle Body Assembly
2. Manifold Absolute Pressure (MAP) Sensor
3. Valve Cover
4. Heated Oxygen Sensor (HO2S) Bank 1 Sensor 1
5. Engine Coolant Temperature (ECT) Sensor
6. Heated Oxygen Sensor (HO2S) Bank 2 Sensor 2

22116_LUCE_G0028

Fig. 120 Engine control component locations (rear)—4.6L

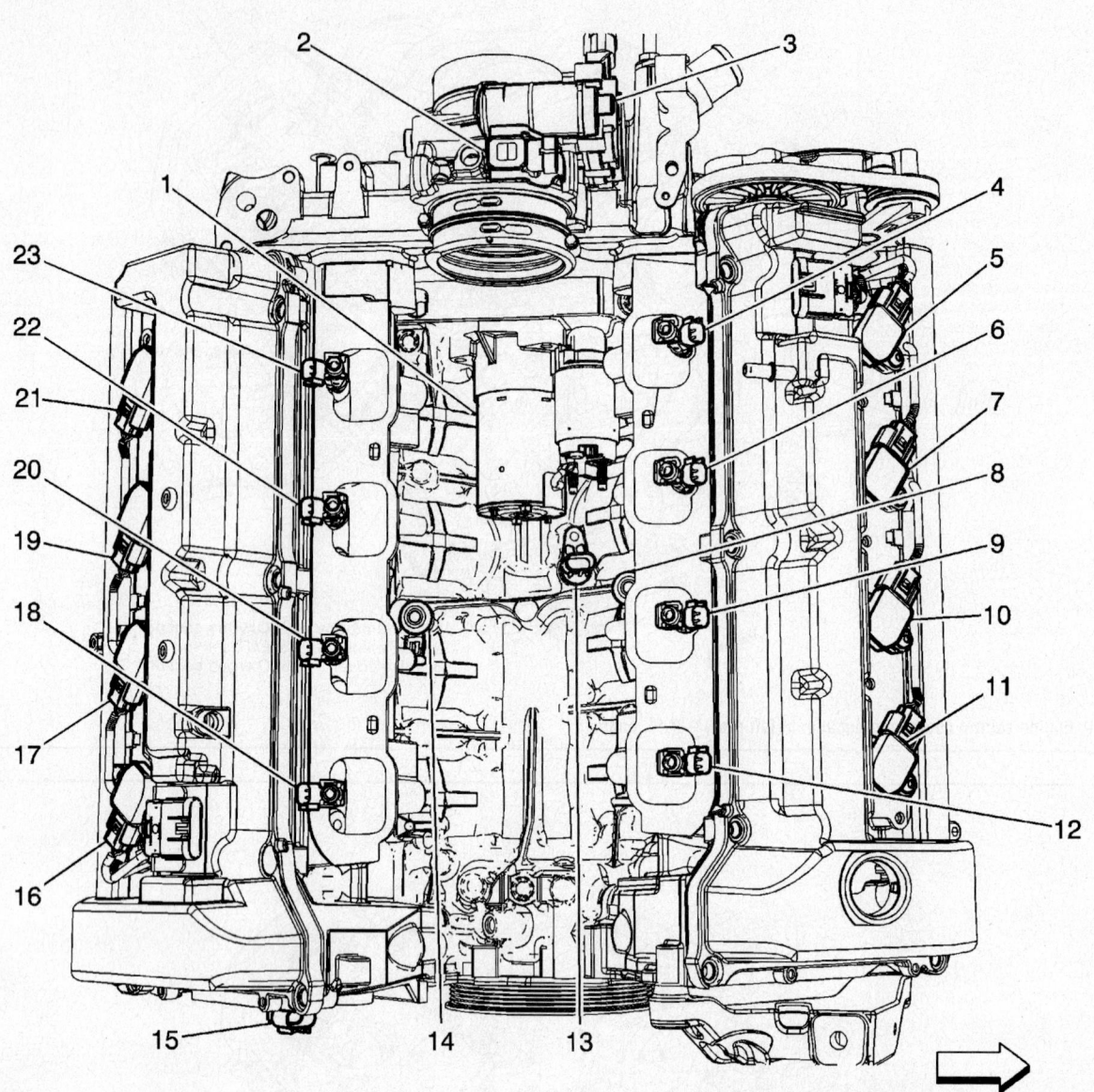

1. Starter
2. Manifold Absolute Pressure (MAP) Sensor
3. Throttle Body Assembly
4. Fuel Injector 8
5. Ignition Coil/Module 8
6. Fuel Injector 6
7. Ignition Coil/Module 6
8. Knock Sensor (KS) 2
9. Fuel Injector 4
10. Ignition Coil/Module 4
11. Ignition Coil/Module 2
12. Fuel Injector 2
13. Crankshaft Position (CKP) Sensor
14. Knock Sensor (KS) 1
15. Camshaft Position (CMP) Sensor
16. Ignition Coil/Module 1
17. Ignition Coil/Module 3
18. Fuel Injector 1
19. Ignition Coil/Module 5
20. Fuel Injector 3
21. Ignition Coil/Module 7
22. Fuel Injector 5
23. Fuel Injector 7

22116_LUCE_G0029

Fig. 121 Engine control component locations (top)—4.6L

Fig. 122 Camshaft Position (CMP) sensor location—3.9L engine

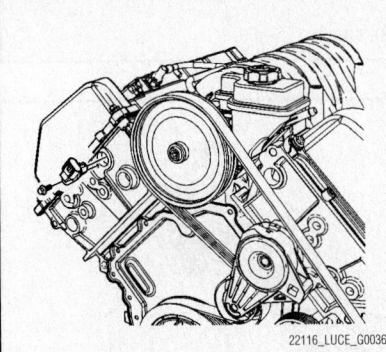

Fig. 123 Camshaft Position (CMP) sensor location—4.6L engine

damage the backup battery. Once the backup battery is activated it will stay on until it has completely discharged. The backup battery is not rechargeable and once it is activated, it must be replaced.

3.9L Engine

➡The rear seat cushion must be removed to gain access to the battery.

1. Before servicing the vehicle, refer to the Precautions Section.
2. Disconnect the negative battery cable.
3. Remove the power steering pump.
4. Disconnect the sensor electrical connector.
5. Remove the sensor retaining bolt. Remove the sensor from its mounting.
6. Inspect the O-ring for damage and replace as required.

To install:

➡Be sure to use new fasteners, as required.

7. Using a new O-ring, as required, position the sensor to its mounting.

➡Be sure to coat the O-ring with clean engine oil prior to installation.

8. Tighten the retaining bolt to 89 inch lbs. (10 Nm).
9. Continue the installation in the reverse order of the removal procedure.

4.6L Engine

1. Before servicing the vehicle, refer to the Precautions Section.
2. Disconnect the electrical connector from the Camshaft Position (CMP) sensor.
3. Remove the CMP sensor bolt.
4. Remove the CMP sensor.

To install:

5. Lubricate the CMP sensor O-ring seal with clean engine oil.
6. Install the CMP sensor.
7. Install the CMP sensor bolt. Tighten the bolt to 89 inch lbs. (10 Nm).
8. Connect the electrical connector to the CMP sensor.

CRANKSHAFT POSITION (CKP) SENSOR

LOCATION

See Figures 124 and 125.

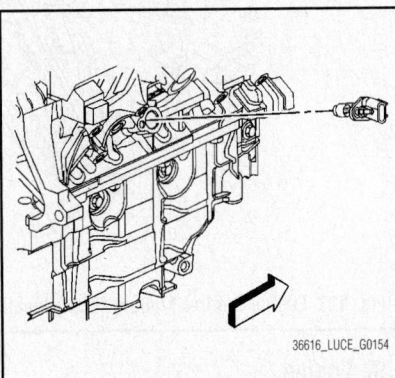

Fig. 124 Crankshaft Position (CKP) sensor location—3.9L engine

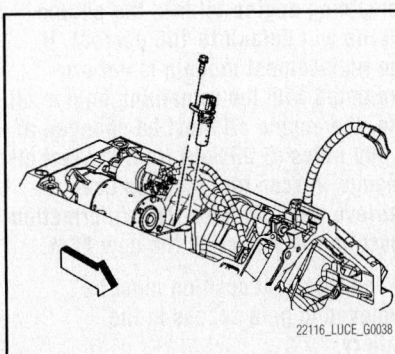

Fig. 125 Crankshaft Position (CKP) sensor location—4.6L engine

REMOVAL & INSTALLATION

➡For vehicles equipped with OnStar (RPO UE1), with battery backup, the backup battery is a redundant power supply to allow limited OnStar functionality in the event of a main battery power disruption to the OnStar module (VCIM). Do not disconnect the main vehicle battery or remove the OnStar fuse with the ignition key in any position other than OFF. Retained accessory power should be allowed to time out or be disabled by opening the driver's side door before disconnecting power. Disconnecting power to the module in any way while the ignition is ON or with the retained accessory power activated may cause activation of the OnStar backup battery system and will discharge and permanently damage the backup battery. Once the backup battery is activated it will stay on until it has completely discharged. The backup battery is not rechargeable and once it is activated, it must be replaced.

3.9L Engine

➡The rear seat cushion must be removed to gain access to the battery.

1. Before servicing the vehicle, refer to the Precautions Section.
2. Disconnect the negative battery cable.
3. Raise and safely support the vehicle.
4. Remove the catalytic converter.
5. Disconnect the sensor electrical connector.
6. Remove the sensor stud. Remove sensor from its mounting.
7. Discard the O-ring.

To install:

➡Be sure to use new fasteners, as required.

8. Using a new O-ring, position the sensor to its mounting.

➡Be sure to coat the O-ring with clean engine oil prior to installation.

9. Tighten the retaining stud to 89 inch lbs. (10 Nm).
10. Continue the installation in the reverse order of the removal procedure.

4.6L Engine

1. Before servicing the vehicle, refer to the Precautions Section.

2. Remove the intake manifold. Refer to Intake Manifold, removal & installation.

3. Disconnect the Crankshaft Position (CKP) sensor wiring harness electrical connector from the CKP sensor.

4. Remove the CKP sensor bolt. (The cylinder heads are shown removed, for clarity).

5. Remove the CKP sensor.

To install:

6. Lubricate the crankshaft sensor O-ring seal with clean engine oil.

7. Install the CKP sensor.

8. Install the CKP sensor bolt. Tighten the bolt to 89 inch lbs. (10 Nm).

9. Connect the CKP sensor wiring harness electrical connector to the CKP sensor.

10. Install the intake manifold. Refer to Intake Manifold, removal & installation.

11. Perform the CKP System Variation Learn Procedure.

ELECTRONIC CONTROL MODULE (ECM)

LOCATION

See Figures 126 and 127.

The Electronic Control Module (ECM) may also be referred to as the Engine Control Module (ECM).

REMOVAL & INSTALLATION

➡For vehicles equipped with OnStar (RPO UE1), with battery backup, the backup battery is a redundant power supply to allow limited OnStar functionality in the event of a main battery power disruption to the OnStar module (VCIM). Do not disconnect the main vehicle battery or remove the OnStar fuse with the ignition key in any position other than OFF. Retained accessory power should be allowed to time out or be disabled by opening the driver's side door before disconnecting power. Disconnecting power to the module in any way while the ignition is ON or with the retained accessory power activated may cause activation of the OnStar backup battery system and will discharge and permanently damage the backup battery. Once the backup battery is activated it will stay on until it has completely discharged. The backup battery is not rechargeable and once it is activated, it must be replaced.

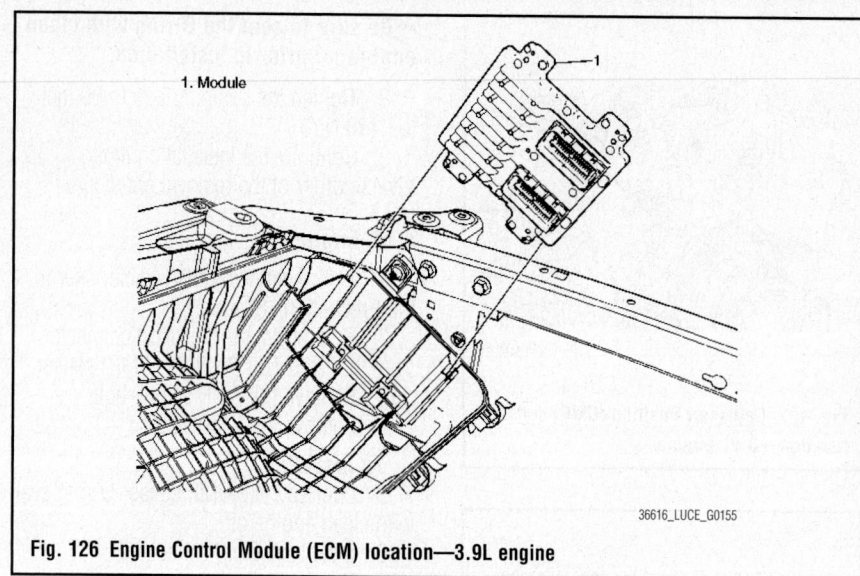

1. Module

36616_LUCE_G0155

Fig. 126 Engine Control Module (ECM) location—3.9L engine

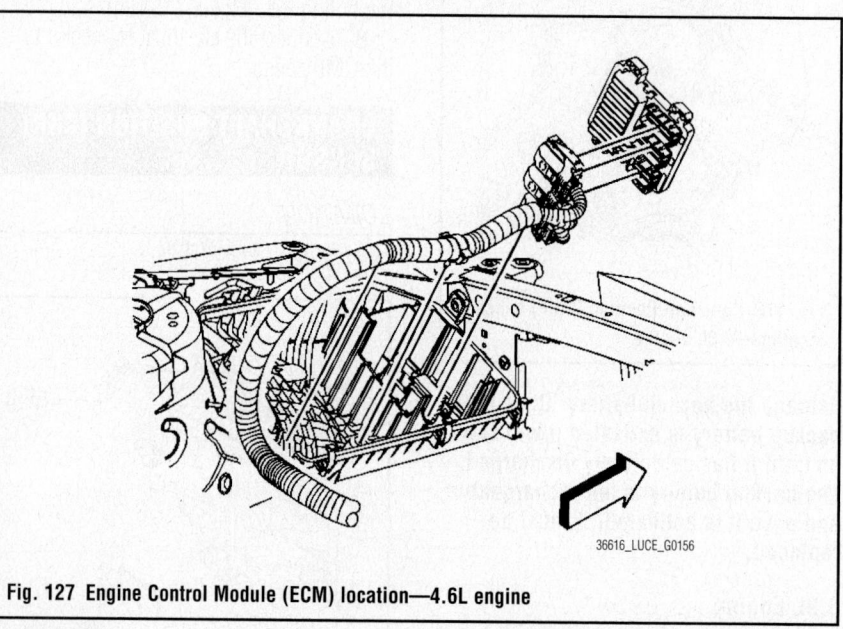

36616_LUCE_G0156

Fig. 127 Engine Control Module (ECM) location—4.6L engine

3.9L Engine

➡It is necessary to record the remaining engine oil life. If the replacement module is not programmed with the remaining engine oil life, the engine oil life will default to 100 percent. If the replacement module is not programmed with the remaining engine oil life, the engine oil must be changed at 3,000 miles (5,000km) from the last oil change. A scan tool must be used to retrieve the ECM data. This information must be transferred to the new ECM.

➡The rear seat cushion must be removed to gain access to the battery.

1. Before servicing the vehicle, refer to the Precautions Section.

2. Disconnect the negative battery cable.

3. Remove the air cleaner assembly upper housing.

4. Disconnect the electrical connectors.

5. Pull straight up to release the component from its mounting.

6. Remove the component from its mounting.

To install:

➡Be sure to use new fasteners, as required.

7. Installation is the reverse of the removal procedure.

8. Using the GM diagnostic scan tool, or equivalent, refer to the on-screen reprogramming directions and reprogram the component.

4.6L Engine

✳✳ WARNING

Turn the ignition OFF when installing or removing the control module connectors and disconnecting or reconnecting the power to the control module (battery cable, Powertrain Control Module (PCM)/Engine Control Module (ECM)/Transaxle Control Module (TCM) pigtail, control module fuse, jumper cables, etc.) in order to prevent internal control module damage.

✳✳ WARNING

Control module damage may result when the metal case contacts battery voltage. DO NOT contact the control module metal case with battery voltage when servicing a control module, using battery booster cables, or when charging the vehicle battery.

✳✳ WARNING

In order to prevent any possible electrostatic discharge damage to the control module, do not touch the connector pins or the soldered components on the circuit board.

➡Remove any debris from around the control module connector surfaces before servicing the control module. Inspect the control module connector gaskets when diagnosing or replacing the control module. Ensure that the gaskets are installed correctly. The gaskets prevent contaminant intrusion into the control module.

➡The replacement control module must be programmed.

➡It is necessary to record the remaining engine oil life. If the replacement engine control module (ECM) is not programmed with the remaining engine oil life, the engine oil life will default to 100 percent. If the replacement ECM is not programmed with the remaining engine oil life, the engine oil will need to be changed at 3,000 miles (5,000 km) from the last oil change.

➡It is necessary to record the remaining automatic transaxle fluid life. If the replacement ECM is not programmed with the remaining transaxle fluid life, the transaxle fluid life will default to 100 percent. If the replacement ECM is not programmed with the remaining

transaxle fluid life, the transaxle fluid will need to be changed at 50,000 miles (83,000 km) from the last transaxle fluid change.

➡The rear seat cushion must be removed to gain access to the battery.

1. Before servicing the vehicle, refer to the Precautions Section.
2. Disconnect the negative battery cable.
3. Using a scan tool, retrieve the percentage of remaining engine oil and automatic transaxle fluid life. Record the remaining engine oil and transaxle fluid life.
4. Ensure that the ignition is in the OFF position.
5. Disconnect the negative battery cable.
6. Disconnect the engine harness electrical connector from the Mass Air Flow/Intake Air Temperature (MAF/IAT) sensor.
7. Disconnect the Positive Crankcase Ventilation (PCV) fresh air tube quick connect fitting from the air duct.
8. Disconnect the secondary Air Injection (AIR) pump inlet tube quick connect fitting from the air cleaner upper housing.
9. Loosen the air cleaner outlet duct clamp at the throttle body.
10. Remove the air cleaner outlet duct from the throttle body.
11. Disengage the lower housing clips.
12. Disengage the upper housing front tabs from the lower housing.
13. Remove the air cleaner upper housing.
14. Disengage the engine harness electrical connector lever locks at the ECM.
15. Remove the engine harness electrical connectors from the ECM.
16. Remove the ECM from the air cleaner lower housing.

To install:

17. Inspect the following areas prior to installing the ECM:
   - Ensure there is no debris in the air filter/ECM housing assembly, or the MAF/IAT sensor inlet screen that may distort the air flow
   - Ensure there are no signs of damage to the air filter/ECM housing assembly, or the intake air duct. If a problem is found, replace the components as necessary.
18. Install the ECM to the lower air cleaner housing.
19. Install the engine harness electrical connectors to the ECM.

20. Engage the engine harness electrical connector lever locks at the ECM.
21. Install the air cleaner upper housing.
22. Engage the upper housing front tabs to the lower housing.
23. Engage the lower housing clips.

➡Properly install the air cleaner outlet duct to the throttle body. An improperly installed, distorted, or damaged air duct may cause a Diagnostic Trouble Code (DTC) to set.

24. Install the air cleaner outlet duct to the throttle body.
25. Tighten the air cleaner outlet duct clamp at the throttle body. Tighten the clamp to 27 inch lbs. (3 Nrm).
26. Connect the AIR pump inlet tube quick connect fitting to the air cleaner upper housing.
27. Connect the PCV fresh air tube quick connect fitting to the air duct.
28. Connect the engine harness electrical connector to the MAF/IAT sensor.
29. Connect the negative battery cable.
30. Program the ECM.

ENGINE COOLANT TEMPERATURE (ECT) SENSOR

LOCATION

See Figures 128 and 129.

REMOVAL & INSTALLATION

3.9L Engine

➡The rear seat cushion must be removed to gain access to the battery.

1. Before servicing the vehicle, refer to the Precautions Section.
2. Disconnect the negative battery cable.
3. Drain the cooling system. Be sure to properly dispose of used coolant.

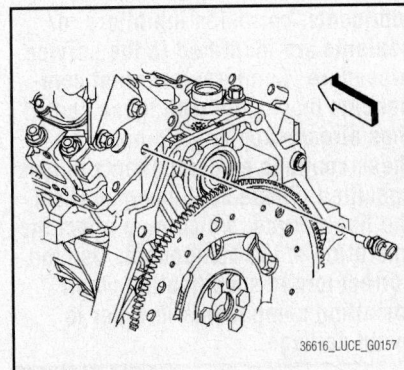

36616_LUCE_G0157

Fig. 128 Engine Coolant Temperature (ECT) sensor location—3.9L engine

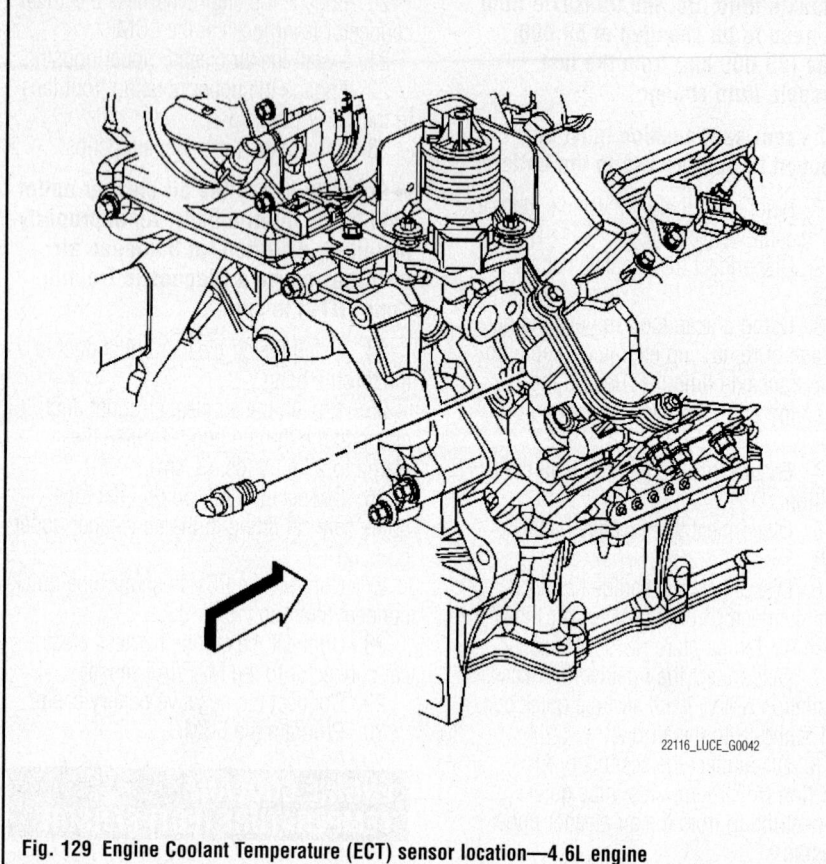

Fig. 129 Engine Coolant Temperature (ECT) sensor location—4.6L engine

4. Remove the intake manifold cover, as necessary.

5. Disconnect the sensor electrical connector.

6. Remove the sensor from its mounting.

To install:

→Be sure to use new fasteners, as required.

✳✳ WARNING

Replacement components must be the correct part number for the application. Components requiring the use of the thread locking compound, lubricants, corrosion inhibitors, or sealants are identified in the service procedure. Some replacement components may come with these coatings already applied. Do not use these coatings on components unless specified. These coatings can affect the final torque, which may affect the operation of the component. Use the correct torque specification when installing components in order to avoid damage.

7. Apply sealant GM P/N 12346004 (Canadian P/N 10953480) or equivalent to the threads of the ECT sensor.

8. Install the ECT sensor. Tighten the sensor to 15 ft. lbs. (20 Nm).

9. Connect the engine harness electrical connector to the ECT sensor.

10. Fill the cooling system.

11. Install the intake manifold cover, if necessary.

12. Inspect and fill the cooling system as necessary.

4.6L Engine

✳✳ CAUTION

Allow sufficient time for the engine to cool before removing the Engine Coolant Temperature (ECT) sensor. A hot engine may cause excessive coolant loss and/or personal injury.

✳✳ WARNING

Use care when handling the ECT. Damage to the coolant sensor will affect the operation of the fuel control system.

1. Before servicing the vehicle, refer to the Precautions Section.

2. Remove the fuel injector sight shield.

3. Drain the cooling system.

4. Disconnect the engine harness electrical connector from the Engine Coolant Temperature (ECT) sensor.

5. Remove the ECT sensor.

To install:

✳✳ WARNING

Replacement components must be the correct part number for the application. Components requiring the use of the thread locking compound, lubricants, corrosion inhibitors, or sealants are identified in the service procedure. Some replacement components may come with these coatings already applied. Do not use these coatings on components unless specified. These coatings can affect the final torque, which may affect the operation of the component. Use the correct torque specification when installing components in order to avoid damage.

6. Apply sealant GM P/N 12346004 (Canadian P/N 10953480) or equivalent to the threads of the ECT sensor.

7. Install the ECT sensor. Tighten the sensor to 15 ft. lbs. (20 Nm).

8. Connect the engine harness electrical connector to the ECT sensor.

9. Fill the cooling system.

10. Install the fuel injector sight shield.

11. Inspect and fill the cooling system as necessary.

HEATED OXYGEN (HO2S) SENSOR

LOCATION

See Figures 130 through 134.

REMOVAL & INSTALLATION

→For vehicles equipped with OnStar (RPO UE1), with battery backup, the backup battery is a redundant power supply to allow limited OnStar functionality in the event of a main battery power disruption to the OnStar module (VCIM). Do not disconnect the main vehicle battery or remove the OnStar fuse with the ignition key in any position other than OFF. Retained accessory power should be allowed to time out or be disabled by opening the driver's side door before disconnecting power. Disconnecting power to the module in any way while the ignition is ON or with the retained accessory power activated may cause activation of the OnStar backup battery system

3.9L Engine

Heated Oxygen Sensor—1

➡The rear seat cushion must be removed to gain access to the battery.

1. Before servicing the vehicle, refer to the Precautions Section.
2. Disconnect the negative battery cable.
3. Remove the CPA retainer.
4. Disconnect the sensor electrical connector.
5. Remove the sensor electrical connector from the coil bracket.
6. Remove the sensor from the exhaust manifold.

To install:

➡Be sure to use new fasteners, as required.

✳✳ WARNING

Handle the oxygen sensors carefully in order to prevent damage to the component. Keep the electrical connector and the exhaust inlet end free of contaminants. Do not use cleaning solvents on the sensor. Do not drop or mishandle the sensor.

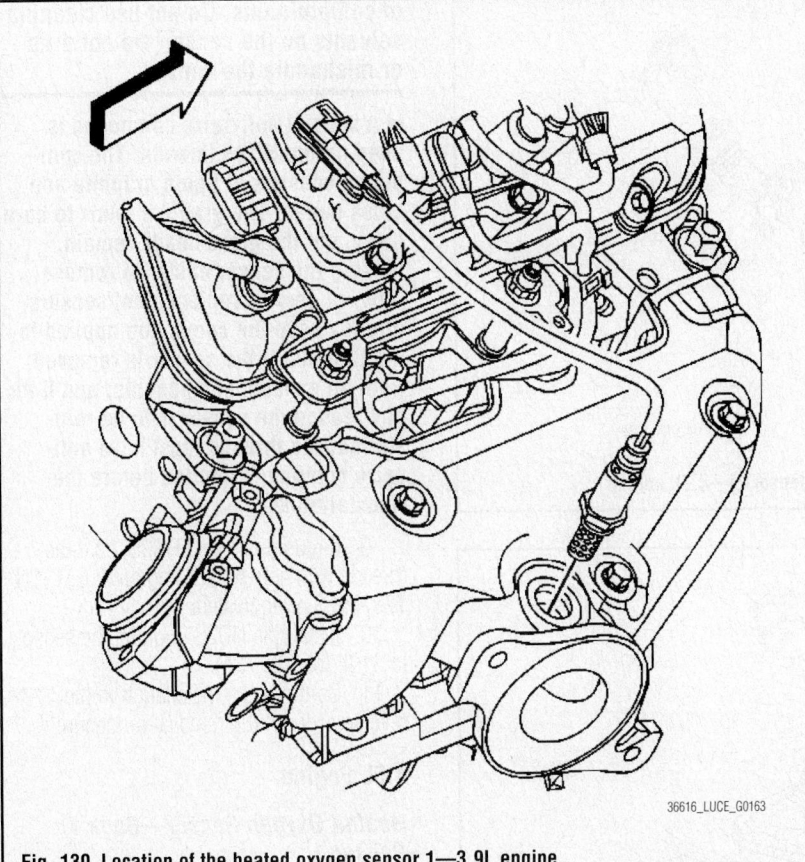

Fig. 130 Location of the heated oxygen sensor 1—3.9L engine

and will discharge and permanently damage the backup battery. Once the backup battery is activated it will stay on until it has completely discharged. The backup battery is not rechargeable and once it is activated, it must be replaced.

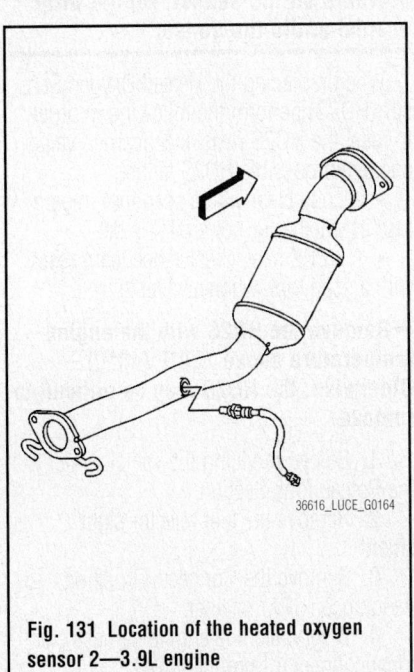

Fig. 131 Location of the heated oxygen sensor 2—3.9L engine

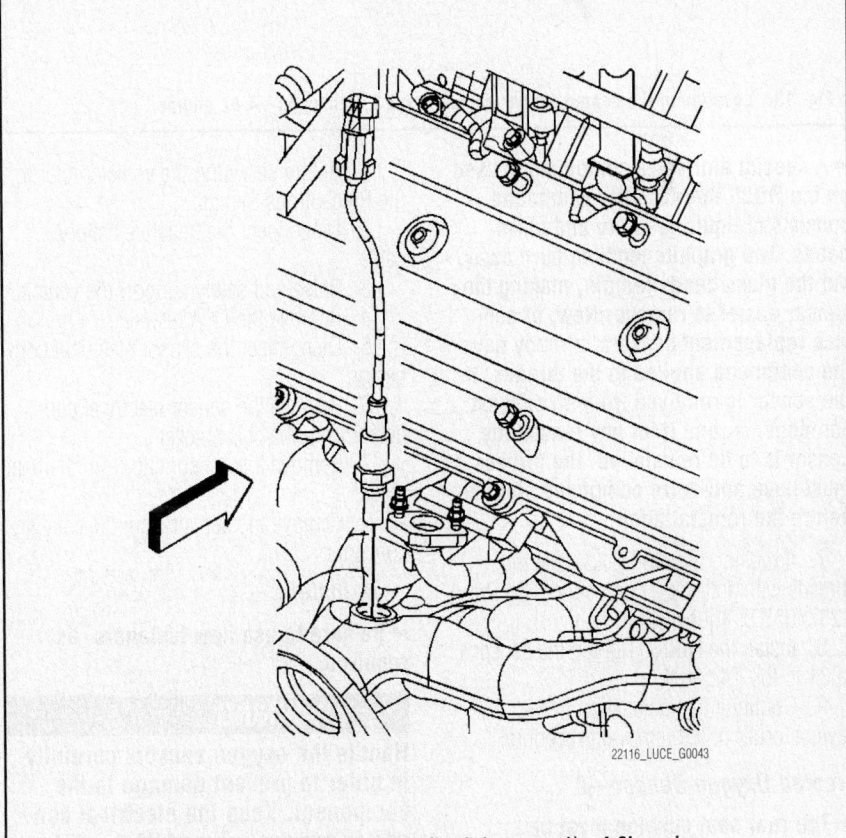

Fig. 132 Location of the heated oxygen sensor (bank 1, sensor 1)—4.6L engine

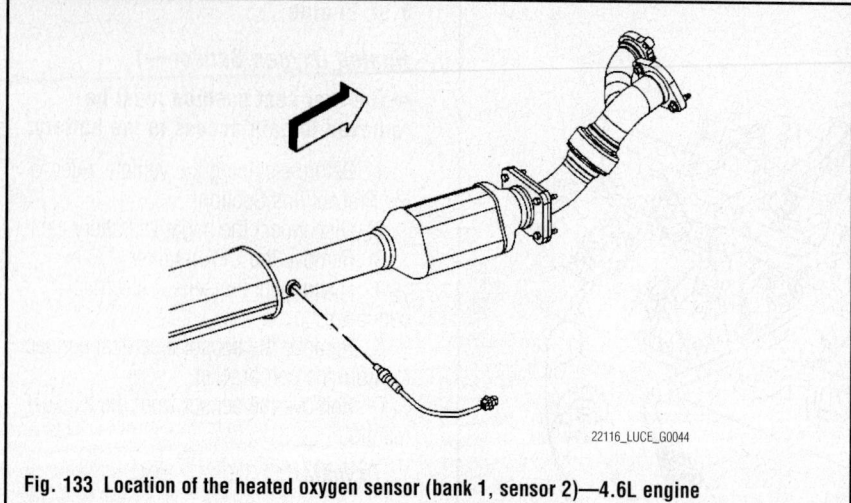

22116_LUCE_G0044

Fig. 133 Location of the heated oxygen sensor (bank 1, sensor 2)—4.6L engine

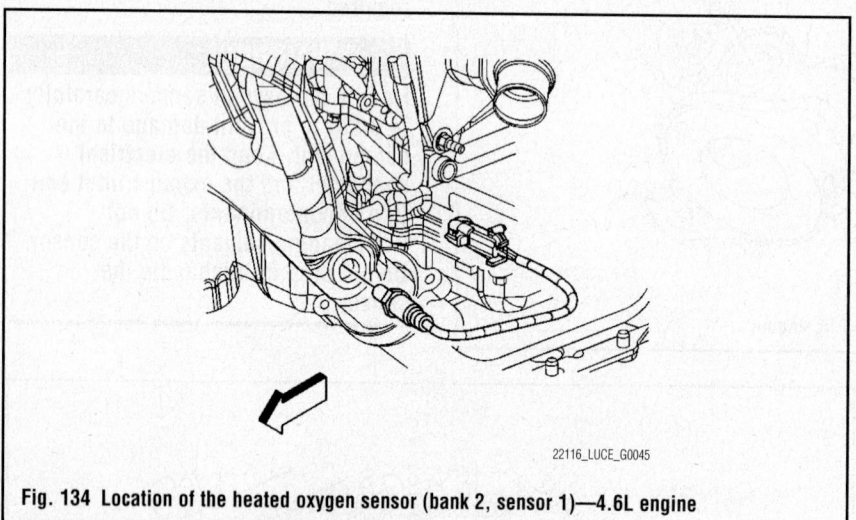

22116_LUCE_G0045

Fig. 134 Location of the heated oxygen sensor (bank 2, sensor 1)—4.6L engine

➡A special anti-seize compound is used on the HO2S threads. The compound consists of liquid graphite and glass beads. The graphite tends to burn away, but the glass beads remain, making the sensor easier to remove. New, or service replacement sensors, already have the compound applied to the threads. If the sensor is removed from an exhaust components, and if for any reason the sensor is to be reinstalled, the threads must have anti-seize compound applied before the reinstallation.

7. If reusing the old HO2S, coat the threads with anti-sieze compound, GM P/N 12377953 or equivalent.

8. Install the HO2S. Tighten the sensor to 31 ft. lbs. (42 Nm).

9. Continue the installation in the reverse order of the removal procedure.

Heated Oxygen Sensor—2

➡The rear seat cushion must be removed to gain access to the battery.

1. Before servicing the vehicle, refer to the Precautions Section.

2. Disconnect the negative battery cable.

3. Raise and safely support the vehicle.

4. Remove the CPA retainer.

5. Disconnect the sensor electrical connector.

6. Remove the sensor electrical connector from the coil bracket.

7. Remove the sensor clip from the heat shield.

8. Remove the sensor from the catalytic converter.

To install:

➡Be sure to use new fasteners, as required.

✸✸ WARNING

Handle the oxygen sensors carefully in order to prevent damage to the component. Keep the electrical connector and the exhaust inlet end free

of contaminants. Do not use cleaning solvents on the sensor. Do not drop or mishandle the sensor.

➡A special anti-seize compound is used on the HO2S threads. The compound consists of liquid graphite and glass beads. The graphite tends to burn away, but the glass beads remain, making the sensor easier to remove. New, or service replacement sensors, already have the compound applied to the threads. If the sensor is removed from an exhaust components, and if for any reason the sensor is to be reinstalled, the threads must have anti-seize compound applied before the reinstallation.

9. If reusing the old HO2S, coat the threads with anti-seize compound, GM P/N 12377953 or equivalent.

10. Install the HO2S. Tighten the sensor to 31 ft. lbs. (42 Nm).

11. Continue the installation in the reverse order of the removal procedure.

4.6L Engine

Heated Oxygen Sensor—Bank 1, Sensor 1

See Figure 135.

✸✸ WARNING

Handle the oxygen sensors carefully in order to prevent damage to the component. Keep the electrical connector and the exhaust inlet end free of contaminants. Do not use cleaning solvents on the sensor. Do not drop or mishandle the sensor.

When replacing the Heated Oxygen Sensor (HO2S) perform the following in order to reset the HO2S resistance learned value and avoid possible HO2S failure:

• A code clear with a scan tool, regardless of whether or not a DTC is set

• A HO2S heater resistance learn reset with a scan tool, where available

➡Remove the HO2S with the engine temperature above 120°F (48°C). Otherwise, the HO2S may be difficult to remove.

1. Before servicing the vehicle, refer to the Precautions Section.

2. Remove the fuel injector sight shield.

3. Remove the Connector Position Assurance (CPA) retainer.

4. Disconnect the engine harness electrical connector from the HO2S.

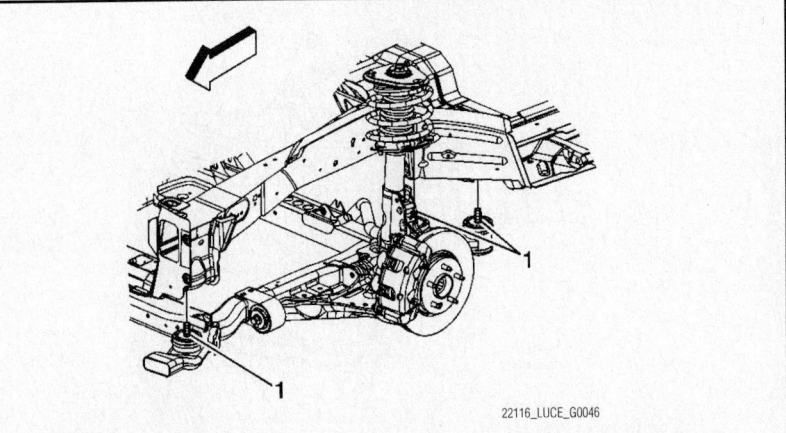

Fig. 135 Remove the 4 rearward frame to body bolts (left side shown, right side similar) (bank 1, sensor 1)—4.6L engine

5. Remove the HO2S clip from the secondary Air Injection (AIR) check valve hose bracket.

6. Raise and support the vehicle.

7. Support the rear of the frame with a tall screw type jack.

8. Remove the 4 rearward frame to body bolts (1) (left side shown, right side similar).

9. Lower the screw type jack approximately 1 ½ inches (4 cm) but not more than 3 inches (76mm), allowing the rear of the frame to lower.

10. Remove the HO2S.

To install:

➡A special anti-seize compound is used on the HO2S threads. The compound consists of liquid graphite and glass beads. The graphite tends to burn away, but the glass beads remain, making the sensor easier to remove. New, or service replacement sensors, already have the compound applied to the threads. If the sensor is removed from an exhaust components, and if for any reason the sensor is to be reinstalled, the threads must have anti-seize compound applied before the reinstallation.

11. If reusing the old HO2S, coat the threads with anti-seize compound, GM P/N 12377953 or equivalent.

12. Install the HO2S. Tighten the sensor to 30 ft. lbs. (41 Nm).

13. Raise the engine frame into position.

14. Install the 4 rearward frame to body bolts (1) (left side shown, right side similar). Tighten the bolts to 141 ft. lbs. (191 Nm).

15. Remove the screw type jack.

16. Install the HO2S clip to the AIR check valve hose bracket.

17. Connect the engine harness electrical connector to the HO2S.

18. Install the CPA retainer.

19. Install the fuel injector sight shield.

Heated Oxygen Sensor—Bank 1, Sensor 2

✵✵ WARNING

Handle the oxygen sensors carefully in order to prevent damage to the component. Keep the electrical connector and the exhaust inlet end free of contaminants. Do not use cleaning solvents on the sensor. Do not drop or mishandle the sensor.

When replacing the Heated Oxygen Sensor (HO2S) perform the following in order to reset the HO2S resistance learned value and avoid possible HO2S failure:

• A code clear with a scan tool, regardless of whether or not a DTC is set

• A HO2S heater resistance learn reset with a scan tool, where available

➡Remove the HO2S with the engine temperature above 120°F (48°C). Otherwise, the HO2S may be difficult to remove.

1. Before servicing the vehicle, refer to the Precautions Section.

2. Remove the oxygen sensor wiring harness heat shield.

3. Disconnect the engine harness electrical connector from the Heated Oxygen Sensor (HO2S).

4. Remove the HO2S.

To install:

➡A special anti-seize compound is used on the HO2S threads. The compound consists of liquid graphite and glass beads. The graphite tends to burn away, but the glass beads remain, making the sensor easier to remove. New, or service replacement sensors, already have the compound applied to the threads. If the sensor is removed from an exhaust components, and if for any reason the sensor is to be reinstalled, the threads must have anti-seize compound applied before the reinstallation.

5. If reusing the old HO2S, coat the threads with anti-seize compound, GM P/N 12377953 or equivalent.

6. Install the HO2S. Tighten the sensor to 30 ft. lbs. (41 Nm).

7. Connect the engine harness electrical connector to the HO2S.

8. Install the oxygen sensor wiring harness heat shield.

Heated Oxygen Sensor—Bank 2, Sensor 1

✵✵ WARNING

Handle the oxygen sensors carefully in order to prevent damage to the component. Keep the electrical connector and the exhaust inlet end free of contaminants. Do not use cleaning solvents on the sensor. Do not drop or mishandle the sensor.

When replacing the Heated Oxygen Sensor (HO2S) perform the following in order to reset the HO2S resistance learned value and avoid possible HO2S failure:

• A code clear with a scan tool, regardless of whether or not a DTC is set

• A HO2S heater resistance learn reset with a scan tool, where available

➡Remove the HO2S with the engine temperature above 120°F (48°C). Otherwise, the HO2S may be difficult to remove.

1. Before servicing the vehicle, refer to the Precautions Section.

2. Remove the front air deflector.

3. Remove the Connector Position Assurance (CPA) retainer.

4. Disconnect the engine harness electrical connector from the HO2S.

5. Remove the HO2S clip from the engine bracket.

6. Remove the HO2S.

To install:

→A special anti-seize compound is used on the HO2S threads. The compound consists of liquid graphite and glass beads. The graphite tends to burn away, but the glass beads remain, making the sensor easier to remove. New, or service replacement sensors, already have the compound applied to the threads. If the sensor is removed from an exhaust components, and if for any reason the sensor is to be reinstalled, the threads must have anti-seize compound applied before the reinstallation.

7. If reusing the old HO2S, coat the threads with anti-seize compound, GM P/N 12377953 or equivalent.

8. Install the HO2S. Tighten the sensor to 30 ft. lbs. (41 Nm).

9. Connect the engine harness electrical connector to the HO2S.

10. Install the CPA retainer.

11. Install the HO2S clip to the engine bracket.

12. Install the front air deflector.

INTAKE AIR TEMPERATURE (IAT) SENSOR

LOCATION

See Figures 136 and 137.

REMOVAL & INSTALLATION

→For vehicles equipped with OnStar (RPO UE1), with battery backup, the backup battery is a redundant power supply to allow limited OnStar functionality in the event of a main battery power disruption to the OnStar module (VCIM). Do not disconnect the main vehicle battery or remove the OnStar fuse with the ignition key in any position other than OFF. Retained accessory power should be allowed to time out or be disabled by opening the driver's side door before disconnecting power. Disconnecting power to the module in any way while the ignition is ON or with the retained accessory power activated may cause activation of the OnStar backup battery system and will discharge and permanently damage the backup battery. Once the backup battery is activated it will stay on until it has completely discharged. The backup battery is not rechargeable and once it is activated, it must be replaced.

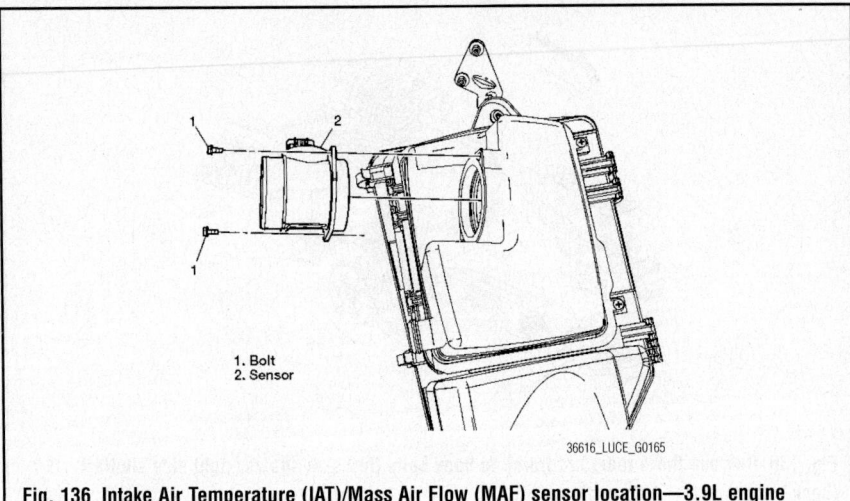

1. Bolt
2. Sensor

36616_LUCE_G0165

Fig. 136 Intake Air Temperature (IAT)/Mass Air Flow (MAF) sensor location—3.9L engine

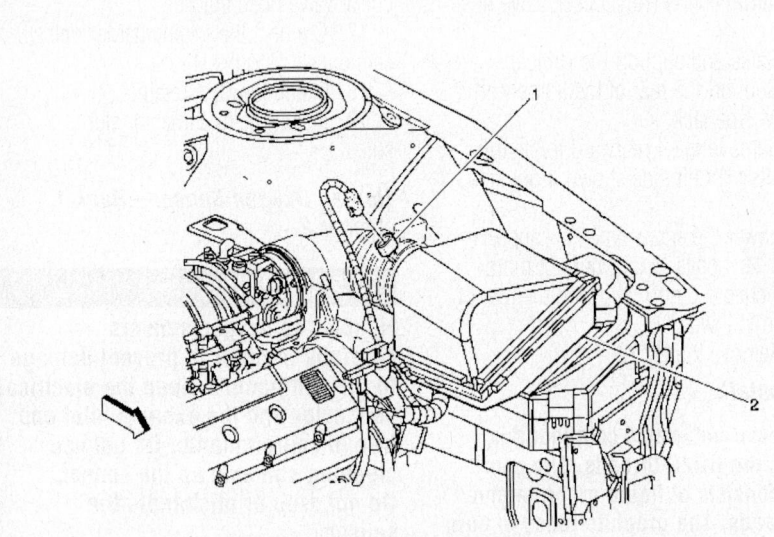

1. Mass Air Flow (MAF) / Intake Air Temperature (IAT) Sensor
2. Engine Control Module (ECM), in the Air Cleaner Assembly

22116_LUCE_G0031

Fig. 137 Intake Air Temperature (IAT)/Mass Air Flow (MAF) sensor location—4.6L engine

3.9L Engine

→The rear seat cushion must be removed to gain access to the battery.

1. Before servicing the vehicle, refer to the Precautions Section.

2. Disconnect the negative battery cable.

3. Remove the air cleaner outlet assembly.

4. Remove the sensor retaining bolts.

5. Remove the sensor from its mounting.

6. Disconnect the electrical connectors.

To install:

→Be sure to use new fasteners, as required.

✵ WARNING

Handle the Intake Air Temperature (IAT)/Mass Air Flow (MAF) sensor carefully. Do not drop the sensor. Do not damage the screen located on the air inlet end of the sensor. Do not touch the sensing elements. Do not allow solvents and lubricants to come in contact with the sensing elements. Use a small amount of a soap-based solution in order to aid in the installation.

7. Position the sensor to its mounting.

8. Tighten the retaining bolts to 89 inch lbs. (10 Nm).

9. Continue the installation in the reverse order of the removal procedure.

4.6L Engine

✳ WARNING

Handle the Intake Air Temperature (IAT)/Mass Air Flow (MAF) sensor carefully. Do not drop the sensor. Do not damage the screen located on the air inlet end of the sensor. Do not touch the sensing elements. Do not allow solvents and lubricants to come in contact with the sensing elements. Use a small amount of a soap-based solution in order to aid in the installation.

1. Before servicing the vehicle, refer to the Precautions Section.

2. Disconnect the engine harness electrical connector from the Intake Air Temperature (IAT)/Mass Air Flow (MAF) sensor.

3. Loosen the air cleaner outlet duct clamp at the throttle body.

4. Loosen the air cleaner outlet duct clamp at the MAF/IAT sensor.

5. Remove the air cleaner outlet duct.

6. Remove the MAF/IAT sensor bolts.

7. Remove the MAF/IAT sensor.

To install:

8. Install the MAF/IAT sensor.

9. Install the MAF/IAT sensor bolts. Tighten the bolts to 35 inch lbs. (4 Nm).

10. Install the air cleaner outlet duct.

11. Tighten the air cleaner outlet duct clamp at the MAF/IAT sensor. Tighten the clamp to 35 inch lbs. (4 Nm).

12. Tighten the air cleaner outlet duct clamp at the throttle body. Tighten the clamp to 35 inch lbs. (4 Nm).

13. Connect the engine harness electrical connector to the MAF/IAT sensor.

KNOCK SENSOR (KS)

LOCATION

See Figures 138 and 139.

REMOVAL & INSTALLATION

➡For vehicles equipped with OnStar (RPO UE1), with battery backup, the backup battery is a redundant power supply to allow limited OnStar functionality in the event of a main battery power disruption to the OnStar module (VCIM). Do not disconnect the main vehicle battery or remove the OnStar fuse with the ignition key in any posi-

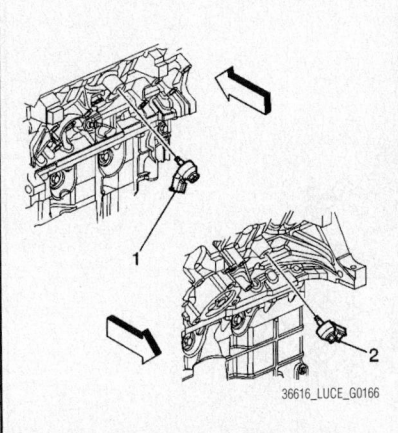

Fig. 138 Knock Sensor (KS) location bank 1 & 2—3.9L engine

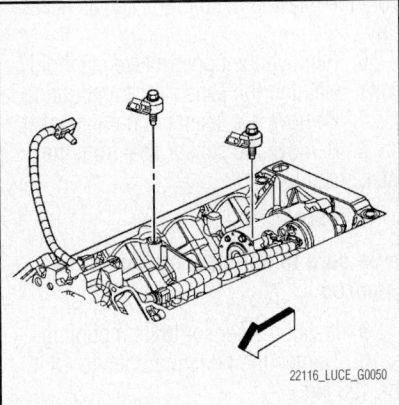

Fig. 139 Knock Sensor (KS) location bank 1 & 2—4.6L engine

tion other than OFF. Retained accessory power should be allowed to time out or be disabled by opening the driver's side door before disconnecting power. Disconnecting power to the module in any way while the ignition is ON or with the retained accessory power activated may cause activation of the OnStar backup battery system and will discharge and permanently damage the backup battery. Once the backup battery is activated it will stay on until it has completely discharged. The backup battery is not rechargeable and once it is activated, it must be replaced.

3.9L Engine

➡The rear seat cushion must be removed to gain access to the battery.

1. Before servicing the vehicle, refer to the Precautions Section.

2. Disconnect the negative battery cable.

3. Raise and support the vehicle safely.

4. Remove the catalytic converter, Bank 1 sensor.

5. Disconnect the sensor electrical connector.

6. Loosen and remove the sensor.

To install:

➡Be sure to use new fasteners, as required.

7. Do not apply thread sealant to the sensor. The sensor threads are coated at the factory.

8. Install the sensor to its mounting.

9. Tighten the sensor to 18 ft. lbs. (25 Nm).

10. Continue the installation in the reverse order of the removal procedure.

4.6L Engine

1. Before servicing the vehicle, refer to the Precautions Section.

2. Remove the intake manifold.

3. Disconnect the electrical connector from the right knock sensor, if required.

4. Disconnect the electrical connector from the left knock sensor, if required.

5. Remove the appropriate knock sensor. (The cylinder heads are shown removed for clarity).

To install:

6. Install the appropriate knock sensor. Tighten the sensor to 18 ft. lbs. (25 Nm).

7. Connect the electrical connector to the left knock sensor, if required.

8. Connect the electrical connector to the right knock sensor, if required.

9. Install the intake manifold.

MANIFOLD ABSOLUTE PRESSURE (MAP) SENSOR

LOCATION

See Figures 140 and 141.

REMOVAL & INSTALLATION

➡For vehicles equipped with OnStar (RPO UE1), with battery backup, the backup battery is a redundant power supply to allow limited OnStar functionality in the event of a main battery power disruption to the OnStar module (VCIM). Do not disconnect the main vehicle battery or remove the OnStar fuse with the ignition key in any position other than OFF. Retained accessory power should be allowed to time out or be disabled by opening the driver's side door before disconnecting

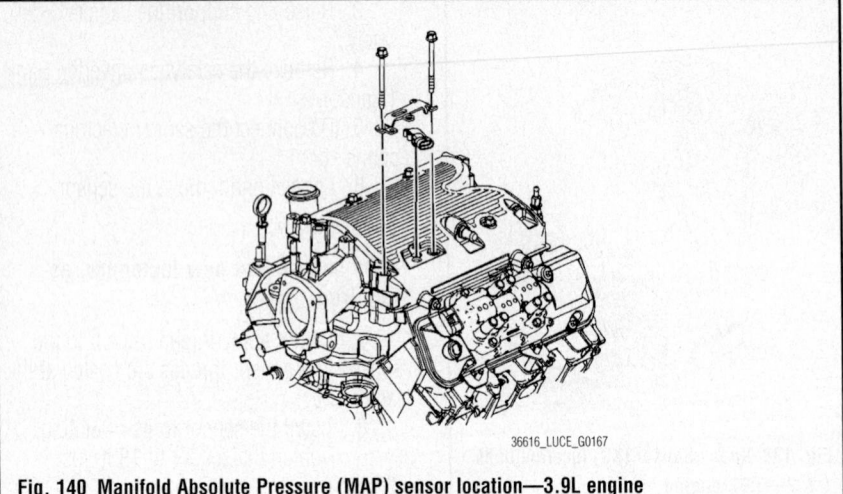

Fig. 140 Manifold Absolute Pressure (MAP) sensor location—3.9L engine

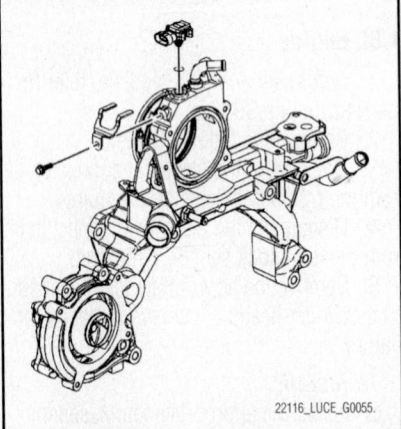

Fig. 141 Manifold Absolute Pressure (MAP) sensor location—4.6L engine

power. Disconnecting power to the module in any way while the ignition is ON or with the retained accessory power activated may cause activation of the OnStar backup battery system and will discharge and permanently damage the backup battery. Once the backup battery is activated it will stay on until it has completely discharged. The backup battery is not rechargeable and once it is activated, it must be replaced.

3.9L Engine

➡The rear seat cushion must be removed to gain access to the battery.

1. Before servicing the vehicle, refer to the Precautions Section.
2. Disconnect the negative battery cable.
3. Remove the intake manifold cover.
4. Disconnect the sensor electrical connector.
5. Remove the spark plug wire clip

from the intake manifold bracket, as necessary.
6. Remove the upper intake manifold bolts, retaining the sensor to its mounting.
7. Remove the sensor and the bracket.
8. Remove the sensor seal from the intake manifold.

To install:

➡Be sure to use new fasteners, as required.

9. Install the sensor to its mounting.
10. Tighten the retaining bolts to 18 ft. lbs. (25 Nm).
11. Continue the installation in the reverse order of the removal procedure.

4.6L Engine

1. Remove the fuel injector sight shield, if necessary.
2. Disconnect the engine harness electrical connector from the Manifold Absolute Pressure (MAP) sensor.

3. Remove the MAP sensor bracket bolt.
4. Remove the MAP sensor bracket.
5. Remove the MAP sensor.

To install:

6. Install the MAP sensor.
7. Install the MAP sensor bracket.
8. Install the MAP sensor bracket bolt. Tighten the bolt to 89 inch lbs. (10 Nm).
9. Connect the engine harness electrical connector to the MAP sensor.
10. Install the fuel injector sight shield, if necessary.

MASS AIR FLOW (MAF) SENSOR

LOCATION

See Figures 142 and 143.

REMOVAL & INSTALLATION

3.9L Engine

➡For vehicles equipped with OnStar (RPO UE1), with battery backup, the backup battery is a redundant power supply to allow limited OnStar functionality in the event of a main battery power disruption to the OnStar module (VCIM). Do not disconnect the main vehicle battery or remove the OnStar fuse with the ignition key in any position other than OFF. Retained accessory power should be allowed to time out or be disabled by opening the driver's side door before disconnecting power. Disconnecting power to the module in any way while the ignition is ON or with the retained accessory power activated may cause activation of the OnStar backup battery system

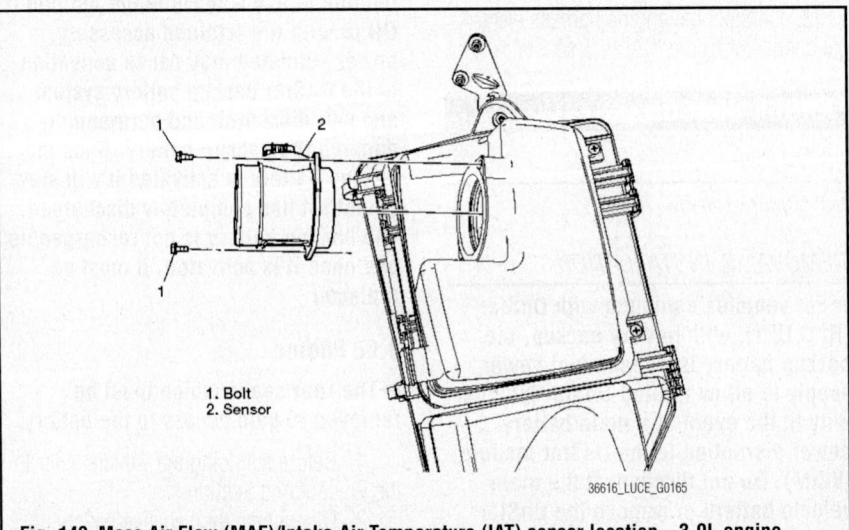

1. Bolt
2. Sensor

Fig. 142 Mass Air Flow (MAF)/Intake Air Temperature (IAT) sensor location—3.9L engine

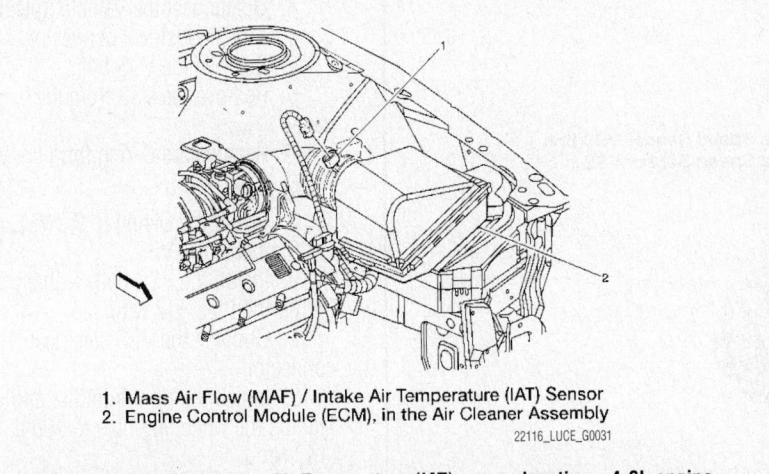

1. Mass Air Flow (MAF) / Intake Air Temperature (IAT) Sensor
2. Engine Control Module (ECM), in the Air Cleaner Assembly

22116_LUCE_G0031

Fig. 143 Mass Air Flow (MAF)/Intake Air Temperature (IAT) sensor location—4.6L engine

and will discharge and permanently damage the backup battery. Once the backup battery is activated it will stay on until it has completely discharged. The backup battery is not rechargeable and once it is activated, it must be replaced.

3.9L Engine

➡The rear seat cushion must be removed to gain access to the battery.

1. Before servicing the vehicle, refer to the Precautions Section.
2. Disconnect the negative battery cable.
3. Remove the air cleaner outlet assembly.
4. Remove the sensor retaining bolts.
5. Remove the sensor from its mounting.
6. Disconnect the electrical connectors.

To install:

➡Be sure to use new fasteners, as required.

✱✱ WARNING

Handle the Intake Air Temperature (IAT)/Mass Air Flow (MAF) sensor carefully. Do not drop the sensor. Do not damage the screen located on the air inlet end of the sensor. Do not touch the sensing elements. Do not allow solvents and lubricants to come in contact with the sensing elements. Use a small amount of a soap-based solution in order to aid in the installation.

7. Position the sensor to its mounting.
8. Tighten the retaining bolts to 89 inch lbs. (10 Nm).

9. Continue the installation in the reverse order of the removal procedure.

4.6L Engine

✱✱ WARNING

Handle the Intake Air Temperature (IAT)/Mass Air Flow (MAF) sensor carefully. Do not drop the sensor. Do not damage the screen located on the air inlet end of the sensor. Do not touch the sensing elements. Do not allow solvents and lubricants to come in contact with the sensing elements. Use a small amount of a soap-based solution in order to aid in the installation.

1. Before servicing the vehicle, refer to the Precautions Section.
2. Disconnect the engine harness

electrical connector from the Intake Air Temperature (IAT)/Mass Air Flow (MAF) sensor.
3. Loosen the air cleaner outlet duct clamp at the throttle body.
4. Loosen the air cleaner outlet duct clamp at the MAF/IAT sensor.
5. Remove the air cleaner outlet duct.
6. Remove the MAF/IAT sensor bolts.
7. Remove the MAF/IAT sensor.

To install:

8. Install the MAF/IAT sensor.
9. Install the MAF/IAT sensor bolts. Tighten the bolts to 35 inch lbs. (4 Nm).
10. Install the air cleaner outlet duct.
11. Tighten the air cleaner outlet duct clamp at the MAF/IAT sensor. Tighten the clamp to 35 inch lbs. (4 Nm).
12. Tighten the air cleaner outlet duct clamp at the throttle body. Tighten the clamp to 35 inch lbs. (4 Nm).
13. Connect the engine harness electrical connector to the MAF/IAT sensor.

VEHICLE SPEED SENSOR (VSS)

LOCATION

See Figures 144 and 145.

REMOVAL & INSTALLATION

See Figures 144 and 145.

1. Raise and support the vehicle.
2. Remove the right front tire and wheel, as necessary.
3. On the 4T80-E transaxle, remove the transaxle brace.

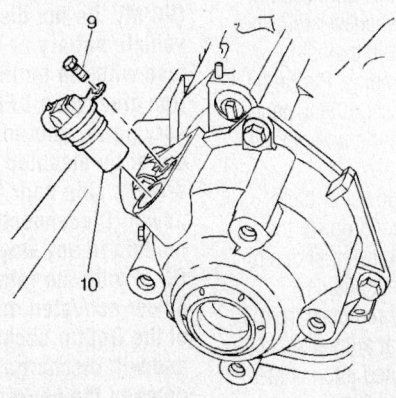

9. Vehicle Speed Sensor bolt
10. Vehicle Speed Sensor

22116_LACR_G0127

Fig. 144 Location of the Vehicle Speed Sensor (VSS) on automatic transaxle 4T65–E

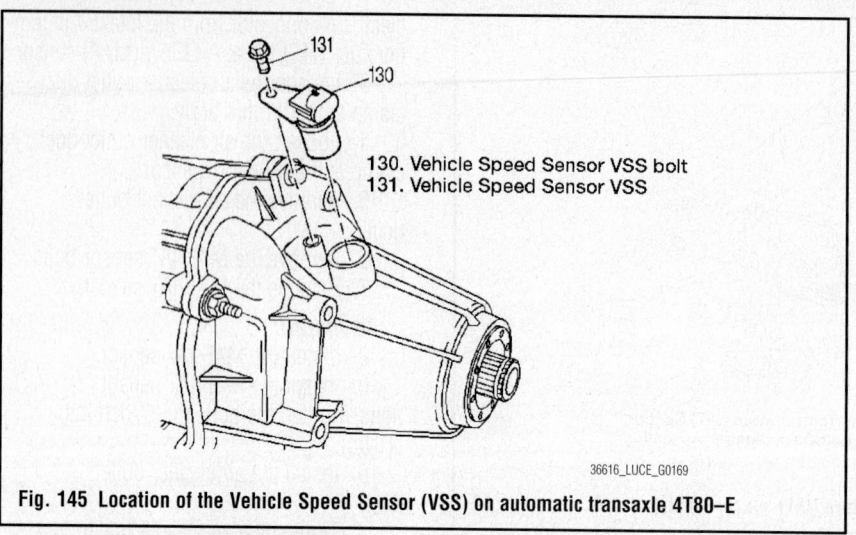

130. Vehicle Speed Sensor VSS bolt
131. Vehicle Speed Sensor VSS

36616_LUCE_G0169

Fig. 145 Location of the Vehicle Speed Sensor (VSS) on automatic transaxle 4T80-E

4. Disconnect the Vehicle Speed Sensor (VSS) electrical connector.
5. Remove the VSS bolt.
6. Remove the VSS from the extension case.
7. Remove the O-ring from the VSS.

To install:

8. Install the O-ring to the VSS.
9. Install the VSS.
10. Install the VSS bolt. Tighten the bolt to 106 inch lbs. (12 Nm).
11. Connect the VSS electrical connector.
12. Install the right front tire and wheel. Tighten the wheel lug nuts to 100 ft. lbs. (140 Nm).
13. Lower the vehicle.

FUEL   GASOLINE FUEL INJECTION SYSTEM

FUEL SYSTEM SERVICE PRECAUTIONS

Safety is the most important factor when performing not only fuel system maintenance but any type of maintenance. Failure to conduct maintenance and repairs in a safe manner may result in serious personal injury or death. Maintenance and testing of the vehicle's fuel system components can be accomplished safely and effectively by adhering to the following rules and guidelines.

• To avoid the possibility of fire and personal injury, always disconnect the negative battery cable unless the repair or test procedure requires that battery voltage be applied.

• Always relieve the fuel system pressure prior to disconnecting any fuel system component (injector, fuel rail, pressure regulator, etc.), fitting or fuel line connection. Exercise extreme caution whenever relieving fuel system pressure to avoid exposing skin, face and eyes to fuel spray. Please be advised that fuel under pressure may penetrate the skin or any part of the body that it contacts.

• Always place a shop towel or cloth around the fitting or connection prior to loosening to absorb any excess fuel due to spillage. Ensure that all fuel spillage (should it occur) is quickly removed from engine surfaces. Ensure that all fuel soaked cloths or towels are deposited into a suitable waste container.

• Always keep a dry chemical (Class B) fire extinguisher near the work area.

• Do not allow fuel spray or fuel vapors to come into contact with a spark or open flame.

• Always use a back-up wrench when loosening and tightening fuel line connection fittings. This will prevent unnecessary stress and torsion to fuel line piping.

• Always replace worn fuel fitting O-rings with new. Do not substitute fuel hose or equivalent where fuel pipe is installed.

Before servicing the vehicle, make sure to also refer to the precautions in the beginning of this section as well.

RELIEVING FUEL SYSTEM PRESSURE

➡**For vehicles equipped with OnStar (RPO UE1), with battery backup, the backup battery is a redundant power supply to allow limited OnStar functionality in the event of a main battery power disruption to the OnStar module (VCIM). Do not disconnect the main vehicle battery or remove the OnStar fuse with the ignition key in any position other than OFF. Retained accessory power should be allowed to time out or be disabled by opening the driver's side door before disconnecting power. Disconnecting power to the module in any way while the ignition is ON or with the retained accessory power activated may cause activation of the OnStar backup battery system and will discharge and permanently damage the backup battery. Once the backup battery is activated it will stay on until it has completely discharged. The backup battery is not rechargeable and once it is activated, it must be replaced.**

➡**The rear seat cushion must be removed to gain access to the battery.**

1. Before servicing the vehicle, refer to the Precautions Section.
2. Disconnect the negative battery cable.
3. Remove the fuel pump fuse.
4. Loosen the fuel tank cap, to relieve system pressure.
5. Remove the fuel tank cap. Do not tighten until the service procedure has been completed.
6. Remove the fuel rail service port cap.
7. Wrap a shop towel around the fuel rail service port and using a small flat blade tool, depress (open) the fuel rail test port valve.
8. Remove the shop towel. Install the service cap.
9. Install the fuel tank cap.

FUEL FILTER

REMOVAL & INSTALLATION

A fuel strainer is attached to the lower end of the fuel sender. The fuel strainer is made of woven plastic. The functions of the fuel strainer are to filter contaminants and to wick fuel. The fuel strainer is self-cleaning and normally requires no maintenance. Fuel stoppage at this point indicates that the fuel tank contains an abnormal amount of sediment, water, or contamination.

To service this filter, remove the fuel pump. Refer to Fuel Pump, removal & installation.

FUEL PUMP

REMOVAL & INSTALLATION

See Figures 146 and 147.

Fig. 146 The fuel pump service cover is located in the luggage compartment under the spare tire

→For vehicles equipped with OnStar (RPO UE1), with battery backup, the backup battery is a redundant power supply to allow limited OnStar functionality in the event of a main battery power disruption to the OnStar module (VCIM). Do not disconnect the main vehicle battery or remove the OnStar fuse with the ignition key in any position other than OFF. Retained accessory power should be allowed to time out or be disabled by opening the driver's side door before disconnecting power. Disconnecting power to the module in any way while the ignition is ON or with the retained accessory power activated may cause activation of the OnStar backup battery system and will discharge and permanently damage the backup battery. Once the backup battery is activated it will stay on until it has completely discharged. The backup battery is not rechargeable

and once it is activated, it must be replaced.

→**The rear seat cushion must be removed to gain access to the battery.**

1. Before servicing the vehicle, refer to the Precautions Section.
2. Disconnect the negative battery cable.
3. Relieve the fuel system pressure.
4. Drain the fuel tank.
5. Remove the rear compartment trim panel.
6. Remove or disconnect the following:
   • The spare tire and jack
   • The trunk lining
   • The fuel sender access panel
   • The sender and quick connect fittings from the sender
   • The electrical connector from the sender and position harness and hoses aside

✳✳ CAUTION

When removing the fuel sender from the tank, the reservoir bucket is full of fuel. Use caution in containing the fuel.

   • The sender retaining ring
   • The sender (take note of its position)
   • The fuel sender O-ring and discard it

→**Take note of the direction that the strainer is pointing.**

   • The strainer from the pump by pulling it down and twisting
   • The pump electrical wires and hoses
   • The pump assembly out of the rubber connectors

To install:

7. Transfer any insulators and grommets from the old pump to the new one.
8. Connect the pump to the fuel hose and tilt the bottom of the pump into the mounting bracket.
9. Install or connect the following:
   • The new strainer on the pump so it points in the same direction as noted during removal
   • The electrical connectors and fuel lines to the pump
   • The new O-ring on top of the fuel tank
   • The fuel sender assembly into the tank
   • The lockring
   • The fuel line quick connectors
   • The sender electrical connector
   • The fuel sender access cover
   • The trunk liner
   • The spare tire and jack
10. Refill with fuel and check for leaks.

FUEL RAIL & INJECTORS

REMOVAL & INSTALLATION

→For vehicles equipped with OnStar (RPO UE1), with battery backup, the backup battery is a redundant power supply to allow limited OnStar functionality in the event of a main battery power disruption to the OnStar module (VCIM). Do not disconnect the main vehicle battery or remove the OnStar fuse with the ignition key in any position other than OFF. Retained accessory power should be allowed to time out or be disabled by opening the driver's side door before disconnecting power. Disconnecting power to the module in any way while the ignition is ON or with the retained accessory power activated may cause activation of the OnStar backup battery system and will discharge and permanently damage the backup battery. Once the backup battery is activated it will stay on until it has completely discharged. The backup battery is not rechargeable and once it is activated, it must be replaced.

3.9L Engine

See Figures 148 and 149.

→**The rear seat cushion must be removed to gain access to the battery.**

1. Before servicing the vehicle, refer to the Precautions Section.
2. Disconnect the negative battery cable.

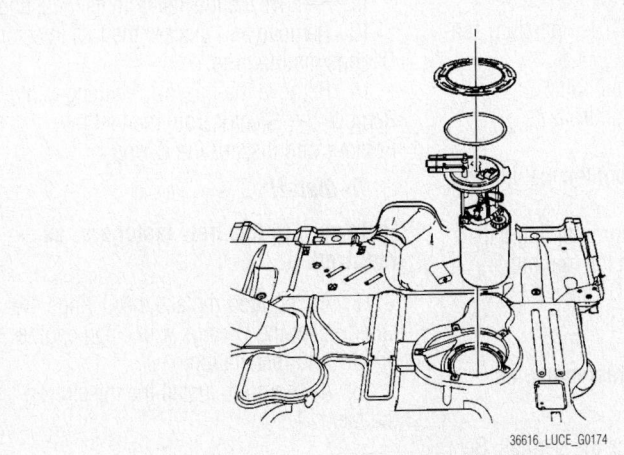

Fig. 147 Fuel pump assembly and related components

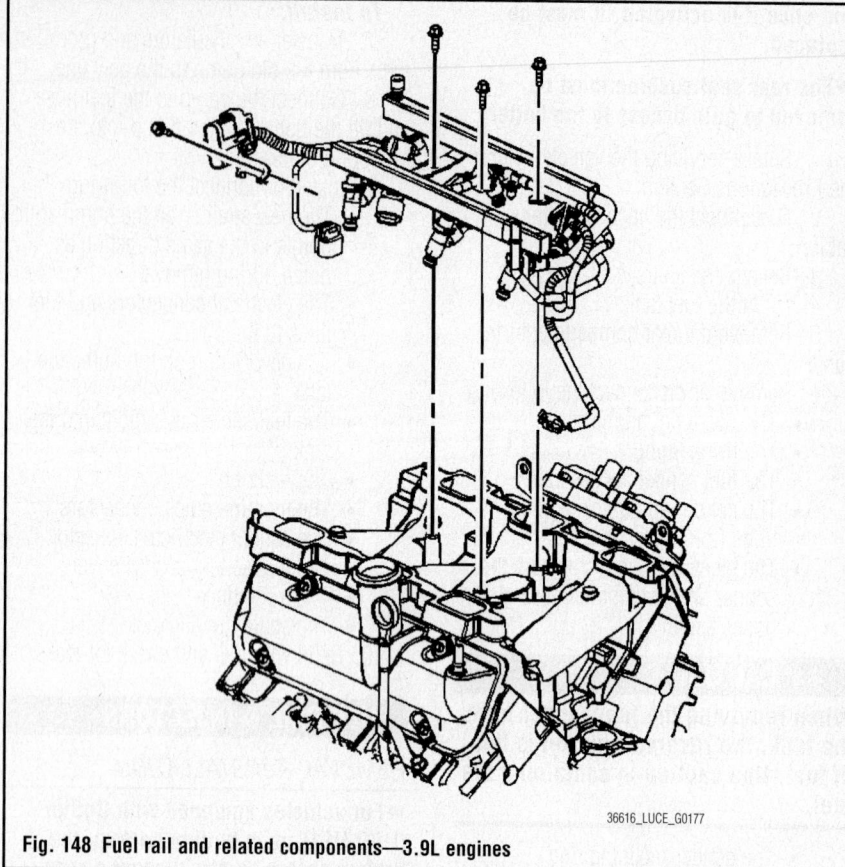

Fig. 148 Fuel rail and related components—3.9L engines

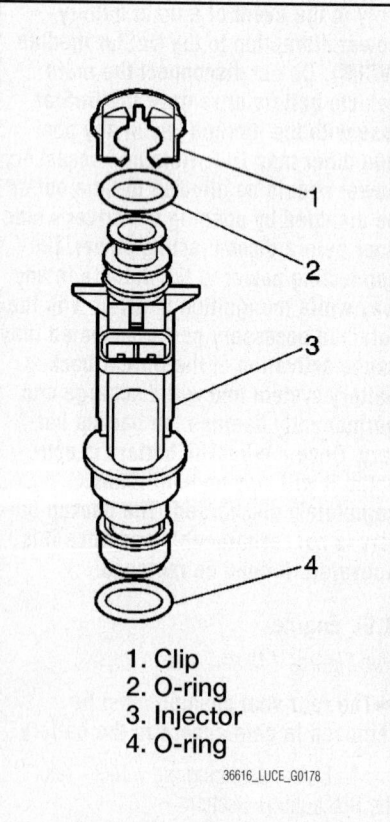

1. Clip
2. O-ring
3. Injector
4. O-ring

Fig. 149 Fuel injector—3.9L engines

3. Properly relieve the fuel system pressure.

➡ **If the fuel injectors are leaking, the engine oil may be contaminated with fuel.**

4. Disconnect the fuel feed pipe from the fuel rail.
5. Disconnect the electrical connectors.
6. Remove the upper intake manifold.
7. Remove the fuel injector harness connector bracket bolt from the manifold.
8. Disconnect the CMP sensor electrical connector.
9. Disconnect the ECT temperature sensor electrical connector.
10. Remove the fuel rail bolts.
11. Remove the fuel rail from its mounting.
12. Remove and discard the fuel injector O-rings, as required.
13. Remove the injector retaining clip. Remove the injector from the fuel rail. Remove and discard the O-ring.

To install:

➡ **Be sure to use new fasteners, as required.**

14. As required replace the O-rings. Be sure to coat the O-rings with clean engine oil, prior to installation.

15. As required, install the injector on the fuel rail.

➡ **Be sure to use the correct part number when replacing a fuel injector.**

16. Position the fuel rail assembly on its mounting.
17. Tighten the retaining bolts to 71 inch lbs. (8 Nm).
18. Continue the installation in the reverse order of the removal procedure.
19. To inspect for fuel leaks, turn ON the ignition for two seconds. Turn OFF the ignition for ten seconds. Turn ON the ignition.
20. Inspect for fuel leaks, correct as required.

4.6L Engine

See Figure 150.

➡ **The rear seat cushion must be removed to gain access to the battery.**

1. Before servicing the vehicle, refer to the Precautions Section.
2. Disconnect the negative battery cable.
3. Remove the fuel injector sight shield.
4. Properly relieve the fuel system pressure.

➡ **If the fuel injectors are leaking, the engine oil may be contaminated with fuel.**

5. Disconnect the fuel feed pipe from the fuel rail.
6. Disconnect the electrical connectors.
7. Disconnect the PCV valve.
8. Reposition the surge tank inlet pipe hose clamp at the tank.
9. Remove the inlet pipe hose from the tank.
10. Disconnect the required electrical connectors.
11. Remove the fuel rail bracket retainer nut. Remove the fuel rail studs.
12. Remove the fuel rail from its mounting.
13. Remove and discard the fuel injector O-rings, as required.
14. Remove the injector retaining clip. Remove the injector from the fuel rail. Remove and discard the O-ring.

To install:

➡ **Be sure to use new fasteners, as required.**

15. As required replace the O-rings. Be sure to coat the O-rings with clean engine oil, prior to installation.
16. As required, install the injector on the fuel rail.

➡ **Be sure to use the correct part number when replacing a fuel injector.**

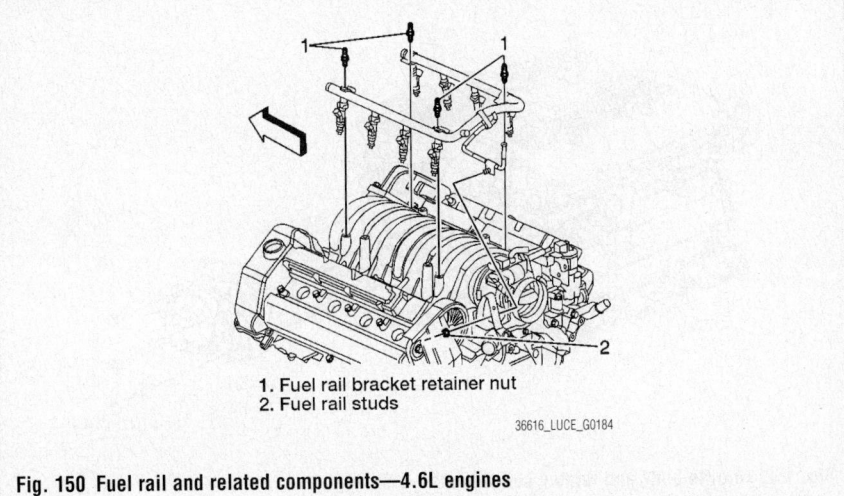

1. Fuel rail bracket retainer nut
2. Fuel rail studs

36616_LUCE_G0184

Fig. 150 Fuel rail and related components—4.6L engines

17. Position the fuel rail assembly on its mounting.

18. Tighten the retaining bolts to 89 inch lbs. (10 Nm).

19. Continue the installation in the reverse order of the removal procedure.

20. To inspect for fuel leaks, turn ON the ignition for two seconds. Turn OFF the ignition for ten seconds. Turn ON the ignition.

21. Inspect for fuel leaks, correct as required.

FUEL TANK

REMOVAL & INSTALLATION

See Figure 151.

➡For vehicles equipped with OnStar (RPO UE1), with battery backup, the backup battery is a redundant power supply to allow limited OnStar functionality in the event of a main battery power disruption to the OnStar module (VCIM). Do not disconnect the main vehicle battery or remove the OnStar fuse with the ignition key in any position other than OFF. Retained accessory power should be allowed to time out or be disabled by opening the driver's side door before disconnecting power. Disconnecting power to the module in any way while the ignition is ON or with the retained accessory power activated may cause activation of the OnStar backup battery system and will discharge and permanently damage the backup battery. Once the backup battery is activated it will stay on until it has completely discharged. The backup battery is not rechargeable and once it is activated, it must be replaced.

➡The rear seat cushion must be removed to gain access to the battery.

1. Before servicing the vehicle, refer to the Precautions Section.

2. Disconnect the negative battery cable.

3. Properly relieve the fuel system pressure.

4. Raise and safely support the vehicle.

5. Drain the fuel tank.

6. Remove the tire and wheel assembly.

7. Remove the left wheelhouse assembly.

➡Clean the fuel and Evaporative Emission (EVAP) connections and surrounding areas prior to disconnecting the lines in order to avoid possible system contamination.

➡Always maintain cleanliness when servicing the fuel system components.

8. Disconnect the fuel fill hose from the fuel fill pipe.

9. Disconnect the EVAP quick connect fitting.

10. Disconnect the left and right electronic position sensor links from the ball studs.

11. Disconnect the fill pipe vent line and the vapor tank line quick connect fittings.

12. Remove the EVAP line retainer from the side rail.

13. Disconnect the body harness electrical connector from the fuel tank harness electrical connector.

14. Remove the fuel tank harness clips from the rear compartment side rail.

15. Remove the exhaust system.

16. Loosen the left and right brake hose bracket nut and slide the stud out of the keyhole slot in the side rail.

17. Remove the rear shock bolts.

18. Support the front of the vehicle using a jack stand and engine cradle.

19. Support the rear suspension crossmember with a suitable adjustable jack.

20. Remove the rear suspension crossmember bolts.

21. Using the adjustable jack, slowly lower the rear suspension crossmember allowing the crossmember to pivot at the front bolts, until the rear springs can be removed.

22. Remove the rear coil springs.

23. Check to ensure that nothing is still attached that will interfere with the removal of the fuel tank (wires, hoses, lines etc.)

24. Remove the fuel tank strap bolts. Remove the straps.

25. Carefully remove the fuel tank from the vehicle.

To install:

➡Be sure to use new fasteners, as required.

26. Position the fuel tank to its mounting.

27. Install the retaining straps.

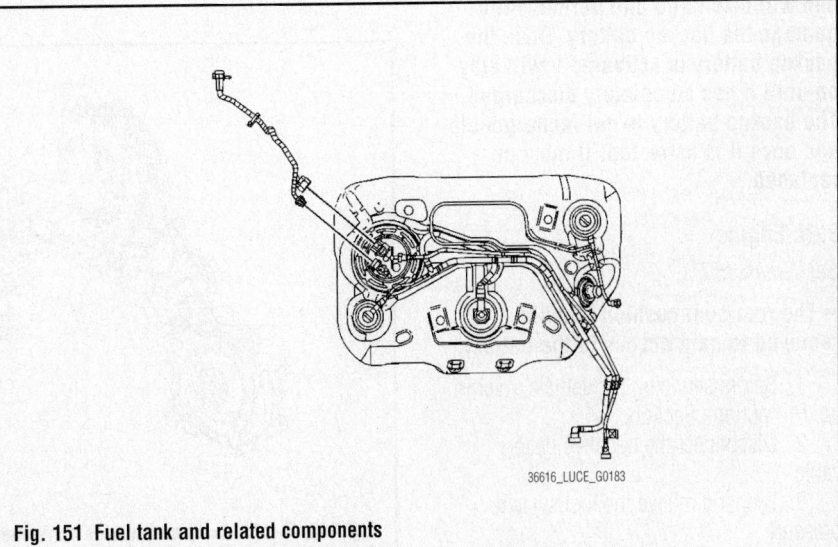

36616_LUCE_G0183

Fig. 151 Fuel tank and related components

28. Tighten the bolts to 34 ft. lbs (46 Nm).

Continue the installation in the reverse order of the removal procedure.

29. Tighten the rear suspension cross-member bolts to 141 ft. lbs. (191 Nm).

30. Tighten the rear shock bolts to 18 ft. lbs. (25 Nm).

31. To inspect for fuel leaks, turn ON the ignition for two seconds. Turn OFF the ignition for ten seconds. Turn ON the ignition.

32. Inspect for fuel leaks, correct as required.

IDLE SPEED

ADJUSTMENT

Idle speed is maintained by the Engine Control Module (ECM). No adjustment is necessary or possible.

THROTTLE BODY

REMOVAL & INSTALLATION

➡For vehicles equipped with OnStar (RPO UE1), with battery backup, the backup battery is a redundant power supply to allow limited OnStar functionality in the event of a main battery power disruption to the OnStar module (VCIM). Do not disconnect the main vehicle battery or remove the OnStar fuse with the ignition key in any position other than OFF. Retained accessory power should be allowed to time out or be disabled by opening the driver's side door before disconnecting power. Disconnecting power to the module in any way while the ignition is ON or with the retained accessory power activated may cause activation of the OnStar backup battery system and will discharge and permanently damage the backup battery. Once the backup battery is activated it will stay on until it has completely discharged. The backup battery is not rechargeable and once it is activated, it must be replaced.

3.9L Engine

See Figure 152.

➡The rear seat cushion must be removed to gain access to the battery.

1. Before servicing the vehicle, refer to the Precautions Section.
2. Disconnect the negative battery cable.
3. Properly relieve the fuel system pressure.

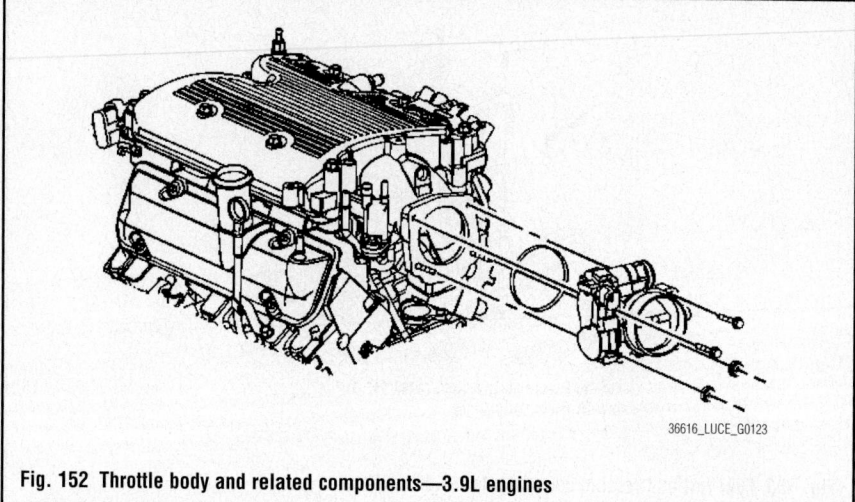

Fig. 152 Throttle body and related components—3.9L engines

36616_LUCE_G0123

4. Remove the intake manifold cover.
5. Remove the air cleaner outlet duct assembly.
6. Disconnect the ECT electrical connector.
7. Remove the heater inlet and outlet clips from the throttle body. Reposition the inlet and outlet hose/pipe.
8. Remove the throttle body retaining bolts/studs.
9. Remove the throttle body. Discard the gasket.

To install:

➡Be sure to use new fasteners, as required.

10. Using a new gasket position the throttle body to its mounting.
11. Tighten the retaining bolts/studs to 89 inch lbs. (10 Nm).
12. Continue the installation in the reverse order of the removal procedure.
13. Operate the accelerator pedal and monitor the throttle angles. The accelerator pedal should operate freely, without binding, between closed throttle and wide open throttle.
14. Verify that the vehicle meets the following conditions.
15. The vehicle is not in reduced power mode. The ignition is ON. The engine is OFF.
16. Using the GM diagnostic scan tool, or equivalent, refer to the on-screen reprogramming directions and perform the throttle learn procedure.

4.6L Engine

See Figure 153.

➡The rear seat cushion must be removed to gain access to the battery.

1. Before servicing the vehicle, refer to the Precautions Section.
2. Disconnect the negative battery cable.
3. Relieve the fuel system pressure.
4. Remove the air cleaner intake duct.
5. Remove the PCV valve fresh air tube.

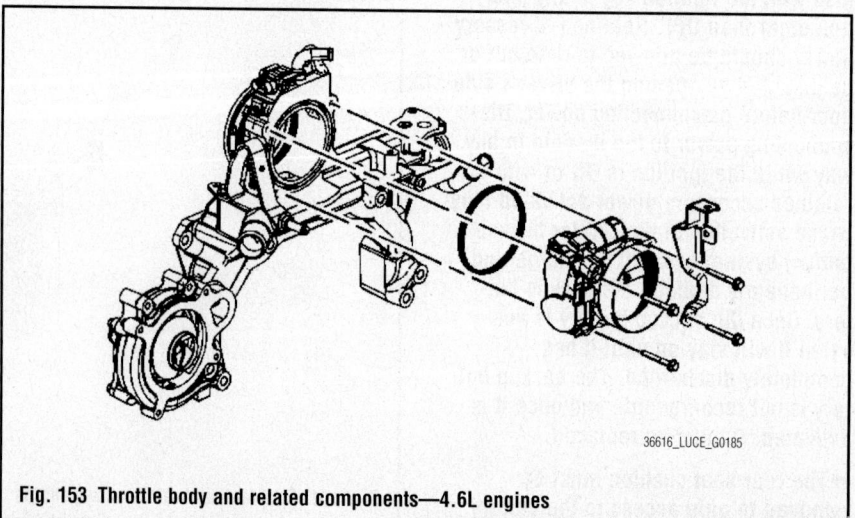

Fig. 153 Throttle body and related components—4.6L engines

36616_LUCE_G0185

6. Remove the cruise control cable from the accelerator controls cable bracket.

7. Remove the accelerator cable from the accelerator controls cable bracket.

8. Remove the cruise control cable from the throttle body lever.

9. Remove the accelerator control cable from the throttle body lever.

10. Remove the Idle Air Control (IAC) valve electrical connector from the IAC valve.

11. Remove the Throttle Position (TP) sensor electrical connector from the TP sensor.

12. Remove the fuel feed and return lines from the retainer on the accelerator controls cable bracket.

13. Remove the transaxle shift cable clip from the accelerator controls cable bracket.

14. Remove the throttle body from the water crossover.

15. Remove the accelerator controls cable bracket from the throttle body.

To install:

➡The outlet of the air cleaner assembly and the Mass Air Flow (MAF) sensor inlet duct must line up when completely installed. Misalignment

may cause incorrect airflow readings resulting in Malfunction Indicator Light (MIL) illumination or a drivability concern. An improperly installed inlet duct assembly or air cleaner assembly may cause misalignment.

16. Install the accelerator cable bracket to the throttle body and tighten to 106 inch lbs. (12 Nm).

17. Position the new throttle body gasket on to the throttle body.

18. Install bolts from the throttle body to throttle body spacer and finger tighten 2 lower bolts.

19. Tighten all the bolts to 106 inch lbs. (12 Nm).

20. Install the IAC valve electrical connector to the IAC valve.

21. Install the TP sensor electrical connector to the TP sensor.

22. Install the accelerator control cable at the throttle body lever.

23. Install the cruise control cable at the throttle body lever.

24. Install the accelerator cable to the accelerator controls cable bracket.

25. Install the cruise control cable to accelerator controls cable bracket.

26. Install the transaxle shift cable clip to the accelerator controls cable bracket.

27. Install the fuel feed and return lines from the retainer on to the accelerator controls cable bracket.

28. Install the air cleaner intake duct clamp to the air cleaner intake air duct.

29. Install the PCV valve fresh air tube.

30. Install the fuel injector sight shield.

31. Connect the negative battery cable.

32. Perform the TP sensor learn procedure as follows:

   a. Turn ignition switch to the RUN/ON position.

   b. Wait 1 minute.

   c. Turn ignition switch to the LOCK/OFF position.

   d. Wait 15 seconds.

33. Perform the IAC valve learn procedure as follows:

   a. Start and idle the engine for 15 seconds.

   b. Turn the ignition switch to the LOCK/OFF position.

   c. Wait 15 seconds,

   d. Restart the engine and check for proper idle operation.

HEATING & AIR CONDITIONING SYSTEM

BLOWER MOTOR

REMOVAL & INSTALLATION

See Figure 154.

➡For vehicles equipped with OnStar (RPO UE1), with battery backup, the backup battery is a redundant power supply to allow limited OnStar functionality in the event of a main battery power disruption to the OnStar module (VCIM). Do not disconnect the main vehicle battery or remove the OnStar fuse with the ignition key in any position other than OFF. Retained accessory power should be allowed to time out or be disabled by opening the driver's side door before disconnecting power. Disconnecting power to the module in any way while the ignition is ON or with the retained accessory power activated may cause activation of the OnStar backup battery system and will discharge and permanently damage the backup battery. Once the backup battery is activated it will stay on until it has completely discharged. The backup battery is not rechargeable and once it is activated, it must be replaced.

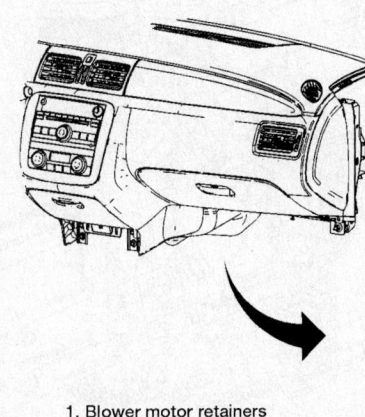
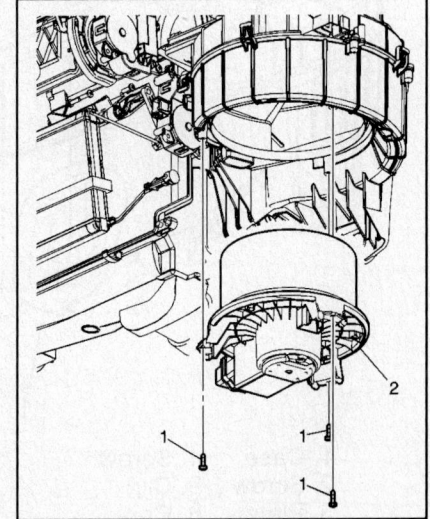

1. Blower motor retainers
2. Blower motor

36616_LUCE_G0187

Fig. 154 Blower motor and related components

➡The rear seat cushion must be removed to gain access to the battery.

1. Before servicing the vehicle, refer to the Precautions Section.
2. Disconnect the negative battery cable.
3. Remove the right side sound insulator in the passenger compartment.
4. Disconnect the electrical connector from the blower motor.
5. Disconnect the blower ventilation tube from the module.
6. Remove the blower motor screws.
7. Remove the blower motor from the housing.
8. Install the blower motor into the housing.

To install:

➡Be sure to use new fasteners, as required.

9. Install the blower motor screws and tighten to 9 inch lbs. (1 Nm).
10. Install the blower ventilation tube to the module.

11. Connect the blower motor electrical connector.
12. Install the right side sound insulator.

HEATER CORE

REMOVAL & INSTALLATION

See Figure 155.

➡For vehicles equipped with OnStar (RPO UE1), with battery backup, the backup battery is a redundant power supply to allow limited OnStar functionality in the event of a main battery power disruption to the OnStar module (VCIM). Do not disconnect the main vehicle battery or remove the OnStar fuse with the ignition key in any position other than OFF. Retained accessory power should be allowed to time out or be disabled by opening the driver's side door before disconnecting power. Disconnecting power to the module in any way while the ignition is ON or with the retained accessory power activated may cause activation

of the OnStar backup battery system and will discharge and permanently damage the backup battery. Once the backup battery is activated it will stay on until it has completely discharged. The backup battery is not rechargeable and once it is activated, it must be replaced.

➡The rear seat cushion must be removed to gain access to the battery.

1. Before servicing the vehicle, refer to the Precautions Section.
2. Disconnect the negative battery cable.
3. Disable the SRS system.
4. Drain the cooling system. Properly dispose of used coolant.
5. Discharge the air conditioning system.
6. Remove the HVAC module assembly.
7. Remove the blower motor assembly from the HVAC module.
8. Remove the left hand floor air outlet duct.
9. Remove the TXV pass thru seal. Remove the heater and A/C pipe cover.

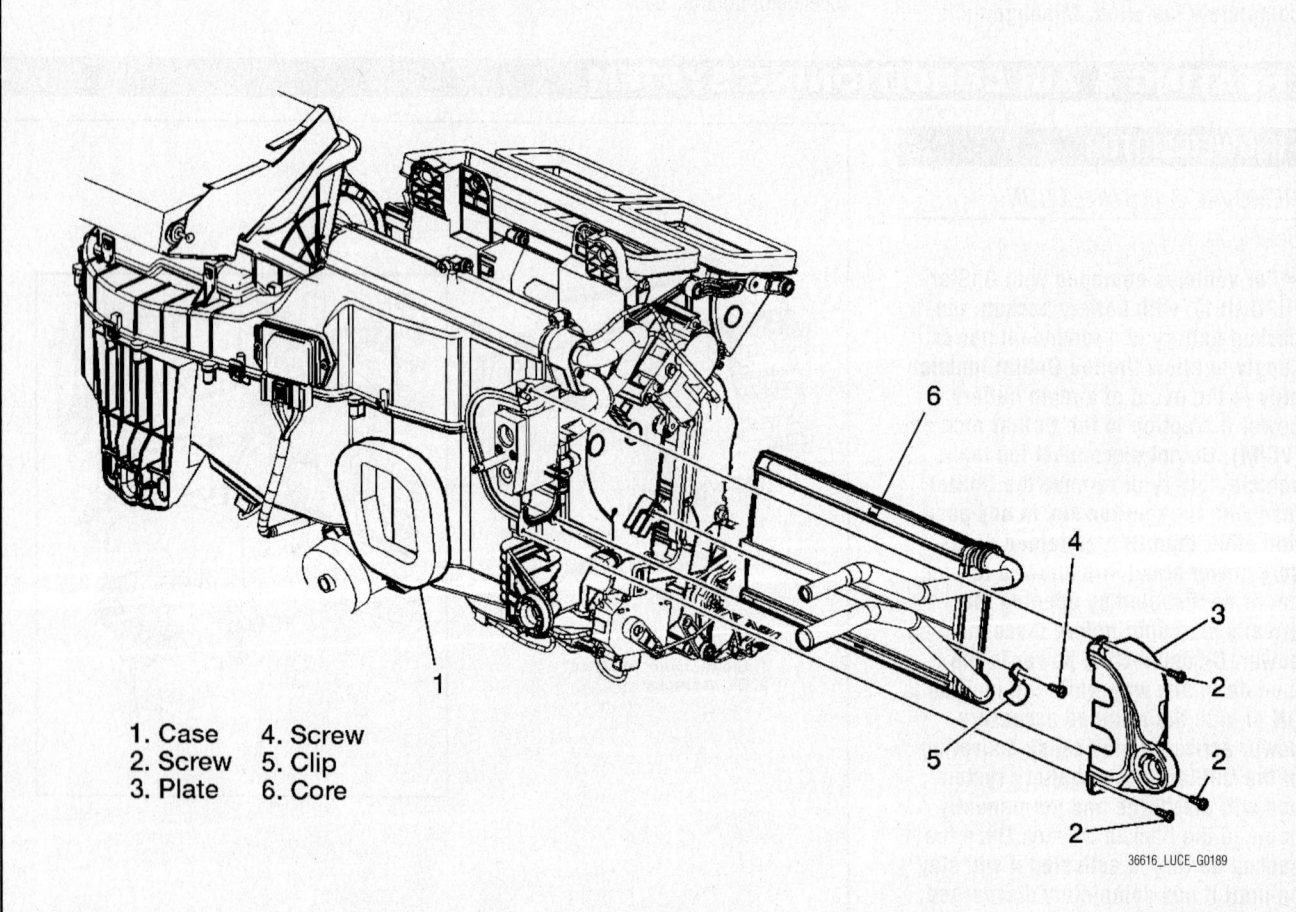

1. Case
2. Screw
3. Plate
4. Screw
5. Clip
6. Core

36616_LUCE_G0189

Fig. 155 Heater core and related components

10. Remove the heater core clamp screw.
11. Remove the heater core tube clamp.
12. Remove the heater core.

To install:

➡**Be sure to use new fasteners, as required.**

13. Installation is the reverse of the removal procedure.
14. Be sure to fill the cooling system with the proper grade and type engine coolant.
15. Properly recharge the air conditioning system.
16. Start the engine and check for proper air conditioning operation.
17. Check for coolant leaks. Correct, as required.

HVAC CONTROL MODULE ASSEMBLY

REMOVAL & INSTALLATION

See Figure 156.

➡**For vehicles equipped with OnStar (RPO UE1), with battery backup, the backup battery is a redundant power supply to allow limited OnStar functionality in the event of a main battery power disruption to the OnStar module (VCIM). Do not disconnect the main vehicle battery or remove the OnStar**

fuse with the ignition key in any position other than OFF. Retained accessory power should be allowed to time out or be disabled by opening the driver's side door before disconnecting power. Disconnecting power to the module in any way while the ignition is ON or with the retained accessory power activated may cause activation of the OnStar backup battery system and will discharge and permanently damage the backup battery. Once the backup battery is activated it will stay on until it has completely discharged. The backup battery is not rechargeable and once it is activated, it must be replaced.

➡**The rear seat cushion must be removed to gain access to the battery.**

1. Before servicing the vehicle, refer to the Precautions Section.
2. Disconnect the negative battery cable.
3. Disable the SRS system.
4. Drain the cooling system. Properly dispose of used coolant.
5. Discharge the air conditioning system.
6. Remove the evaporator tube from the thermal expansion valve.
7. Remove the heater hoses from the heater core.

8. Remove the brake pedal bracket assembly.
9. Remove the lower instrument panel support brace.
10. Reposition the auxiliary air distribution duct.
11. Remove the instrument panel carrier assembly.
12. Disconnect the HVAC module assembly electrical connectors.
13. Remove the component retaining nuts and bolts.
14. Carefully remove the component from its mounting.

To install:

➡**Be sure to use new fasteners, as required.**

15. Position the component to its mounting.
16. Tighten the retaining bolts and nuts to 80 inch lbs. (9 Nm) in sequence.

➡**See illustration for tightening sequence.**

17. Continue the installation in the reverse order of the removal procedure.
18. Be sure to fill the cooling system with the proper grade and type engine coolant.
19. Properly recharge the air conditioning system.

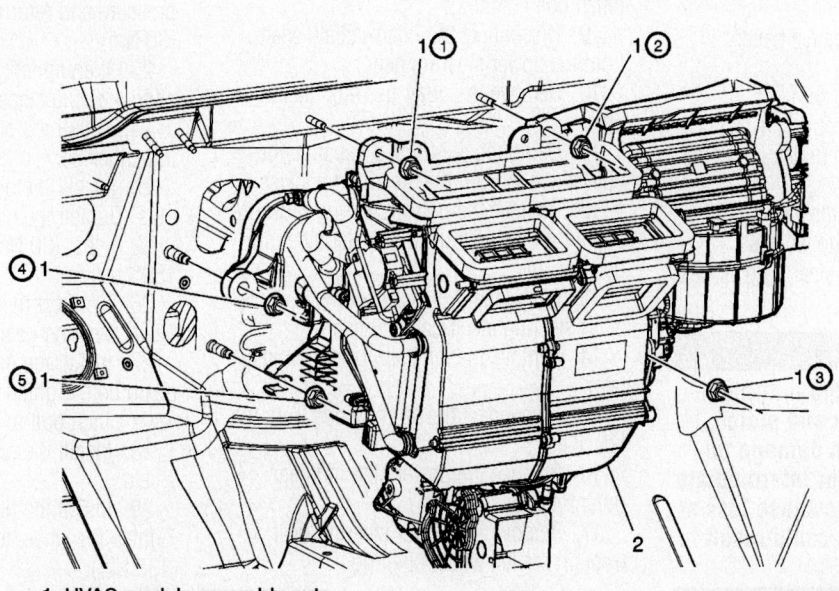

1. HVAC module assembly nuts
2. HVAC module

36616_LUCE_G0186

Fig. 156 Air conditioning and heater module assembly (HVAC module)

STEERING

POWER RACK & PINION STEERING GEAR

REMOVAL & INSTALLATION

See Figure 157.

➡ For vehicles equipped with OnStar (RPO UE1), with battery backup, the backup battery is a redundant power supply to allow limited OnStar functionality in the event of a main battery power disruption to the OnStar module (VCIM). Do not disconnect the main vehicle battery or remove the OnStar fuse with the ignition key in any position other than OFF. Retained accessory power should be allowed to time out or be disabled by opening the driver's side door before disconnecting power. Disconnecting power to the module in any way while the ignition is ON or with the retained accessory power activated may cause activation of the OnStar backup battery system and will discharge and permanently damage the backup battery. Once the backup battery is activated it will stay on until it has completely discharged. The backup battery is not rechargeable and once it is activated, it must be replaced.

➡ The rear seat cushion must be removed to gain access to the battery.

1. Before servicing the vehicle, refer to the Precautions Section.
2. Disconnect the negative battery cable.
3. Disable the SRS system.
4. Lock the steering column by installing J 42640 into the underside of the steering column.
5. Raise and support the vehicle.
6. Remove the tires and wheels.
7. Remove the power steering gear heat shield.

✳✳ CAUTION

Failure to disconnect the intermediate shaft from the rack and pinion stub shaft can result in damage to the steering gear and/or intermediate shaft. This damage can cause loss of steering control which could result in personal injury.

✳✳ WARNING

The wheels of the vehicle must be straight ahead and the steering column in the LOCK position before disconnecting the steering column or intermediate shaft from the steering gear. Failure to do so will cause the coil assembly in the steering column to become uncentered which will cause damage to the coil assembly.

8. Remove the intermediate shaft lower pinch bolt coupling.
9. Disconnect the intermediate shaft from the power steering gear.
10. Remove the outer tie rods retaining nuts.
11. Using the J 24319-B separate the outer tie rods from the steering knuckles.
12. Remove the power steering pressure and return hoses from the power steering gear.
13. If equipped, disconnect the variable effort steering electrical connector.
14. Remove the left stabilizer shaft insulator.
15. Disconnect the tie rod ends from the knuckles.
16. Remove the power steering gear mounting bolts.
17. Remove the power steering gear through the left wheel opening.

To install:
18. Transfer the outer tie rods if replacing the power steering gear.
19. Install the power steering gear through the left wheel opening.

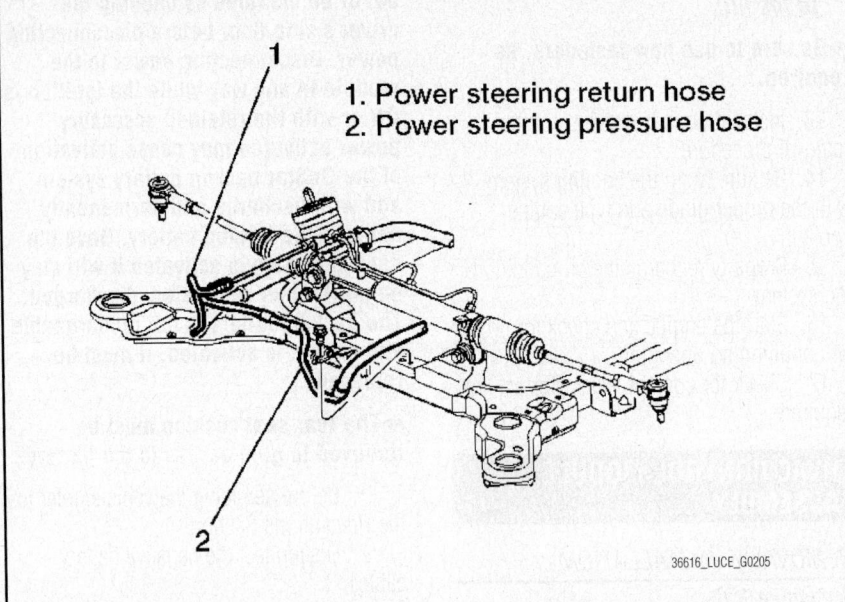

1. Power steering return hose
2. Power steering pressure hose

36616_LUCE_G0205

Fig. 157 Remove the power steering pressure and return hoses from the power steering gear

20. Install the power steering gear mounting bolts. Tighten the power steering gear mounting bolts to 70 ft. lbs. (95 Nm).
21. Install the left stabilizer shaft insulator.
22. Install the power steering pressure and return hoses to the power steering gear. Tighten the power steering pressure and return hoses to 22 ft. lbs. (30 Nm).
23. If equipped, connect the variable effort steering electrical connector.
24. Install the outer tie rod to the steering knuckles.
25. Install the outer tie rod retaining nuts. Tighten the outer tie rod retaining nuts to 22 ft. lbs. (30 Nm), plus an additional 180°.
26. Connect the intermediate shaft to the power steering gear.
27. Install the intermediate shaft lower pinch bolt. Tighten the intermediate shaft lower pinch bolt to 37 ft. lbs. (47 Nm).
28. Install the power steering gear heat shield.
29. Install the tires and wheels. Tighten the wheel lug nuts to 100 ft. lbs. (136 Nm).
30. Lower the vehicle.
31. Remove the J 42640 from the steering column.
32. Bleed the power steering system:

⁂ WARNING

When adding fluid or making a complete fluid change, always use the proper power steering fluid. Failure to use the proper fluid will cause hose and seal damage and fluid leaks.

➡ Use clean, new power steering fluid type only. Hoses touching the frame, body, or engine may cause system noise. Verify that the hoses do not touch any other part of the vehicle. Loose connections may not leak, but could allow air into the steering system. Verify that all hose connections are tight.

➡ Maintain the fluid level throughout the bleed procedure.

    a. Remove the pump reservoir cap.
    b. Fill the pump reservoir with fluid to the FULL COLD level.
    c. Attach a vacuum pump and adapter to the reservoir.
    d. Apply a vacuum of 68 kPa (20 in Hg) maximum.
    e. Wait 5 minutes. Typical vacuum drop is 7–10 kPa (2–3 in Hg).
    f. Remove the vacuum pump and adapter.
    g. Reinstall the pump reservoir cap.
    h. Start the engine. Allow the engine to idle.
    i. Turn OFF the engine.
    j. Verify the fluid level. Repeat steps 8–10 until the fluid stabilizes.

➡ Do NOT turn the steering wheel to LOCK.

    k. Start the engine. Allow the engine to idle.
    l. Turn the steering wheel 180–360° in both directions 5 times.
    m. Turn OFF the ignition.
    n. Verify the fluid level.
    o. Remove the pump reservoir cap.
    p. Attach a vacuum pump and adapter to the reservoir.
    q. Apply a vacuum of 68 kPa (20 in. Hg) maximum.
    r. Wait 5 minutes.
    s. Remove the vacuum pump and adapter.
    t. Verify the fluid level.
    u. Reinstall the pump reservoir cap.
33. Inspect the power steering system for leaks.
34. Adjust the front toe as necessary.

POWER STEERING PUMP

REMOVAL & INSTALLATION

➡ For vehicles equipped with OnStar (RPO UE1), with battery backup, the backup battery is a redundant power supply to allow limited OnStar functionality in the event of a main battery power disruption to the OnStar module (VCIM). Do not disconnect the main vehicle battery or remove the OnStar fuse with the ignition key in any position other than OFF. Retained accessory power should be allowed to time out or be disabled by opening the driver's side door before disconnecting power. Disconnecting power to the module in any way while the ignition is ON or with the retained accessory power activated may cause activation of the OnStar backup battery system and will discharge and permanently damage the backup battery. Once the backup battery is activated it will stay on until it has completely discharged. The backup battery is not rechargeable and once it is activated, it must be replaced.

3.9L Engine

See Figure 158.

➡ The rear seat cushion must be removed to gain access to the battery.

1. Before servicing the vehicle, refer to the Precautions Section.
2. Disconnect the negative battery cable.
3. Remove the intake manifold cover.
4. Remove the upper intake manifold cover nut.
5. Remove the power steering fluid reservoir bracket bolt.
6. Remove the remote power steering reservoir.
7. Place a drain pan under the vehicle. Disconnect the inlet hose from the reservoir. Remove as much fluid as possible from the reservoir.
8. Remove the power steering pump retaining bolts.
9. Remove the pump from its mounting.

To install:

➡ Be sure to use new fasteners, as required.

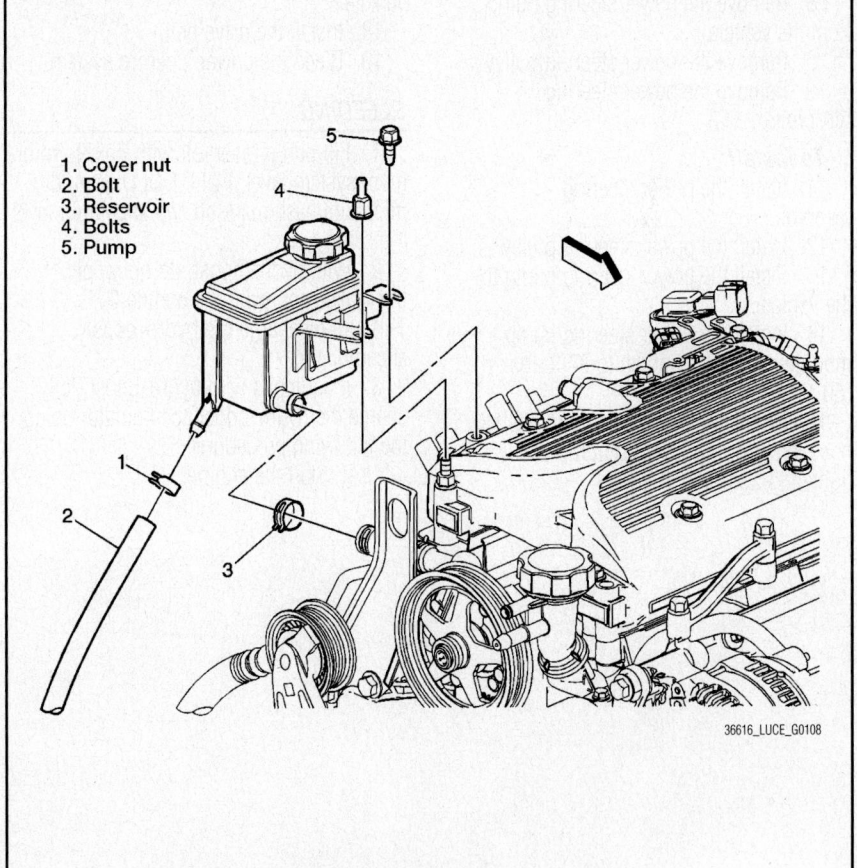

1. Cover nut
2. Bolt
3. Reservoir
4. Bolts
5. Pump

36616_LUCE_G0108

Fig. 158 Power steering pump and related components—3.9L engines

10. Position the pump to its mounting.

11. Tighten the retaining bolts to 18 ft. lbs. (25 Nm).

12. Continue the installation in the reverse order of the removal procedure.

13. Fill the reservoir with the proper grade and type power steering fluid.

14. Bleed the system.

4.6L Engine

See Figure 159.

➡ **The rear seat cushion must be removed to gain access to the battery.**

1. Before servicing the vehicle, refer to the Precautions Section.

2. Disconnect the negative battery cable.

3. Remove the accessory drive belt.

4. Install a drain pan under the vehicle.

5. Disconnect the power steering return hose from the power steering reservoir.

6. Remove the power steering pressure hose from the power steering pump.

7. Remove the power steering pump mounting bolt.

8. Remove the power steering pump from the vehicle.

9. Remove the power steering pulley.

10. Remove the power steering reservoir.

To install:

11. Install the power steering reservoir.

12. Install the power steering pulley.

13. Install the power steering pump to the vehicle.

14. Install the power steering pump mounting bolt and tighten to 37 ft. lbs. (50 Nm).

15. Install the power steering pressure hose to the power steering pump and tighten to 20 ft. lbs. (27 Nm).

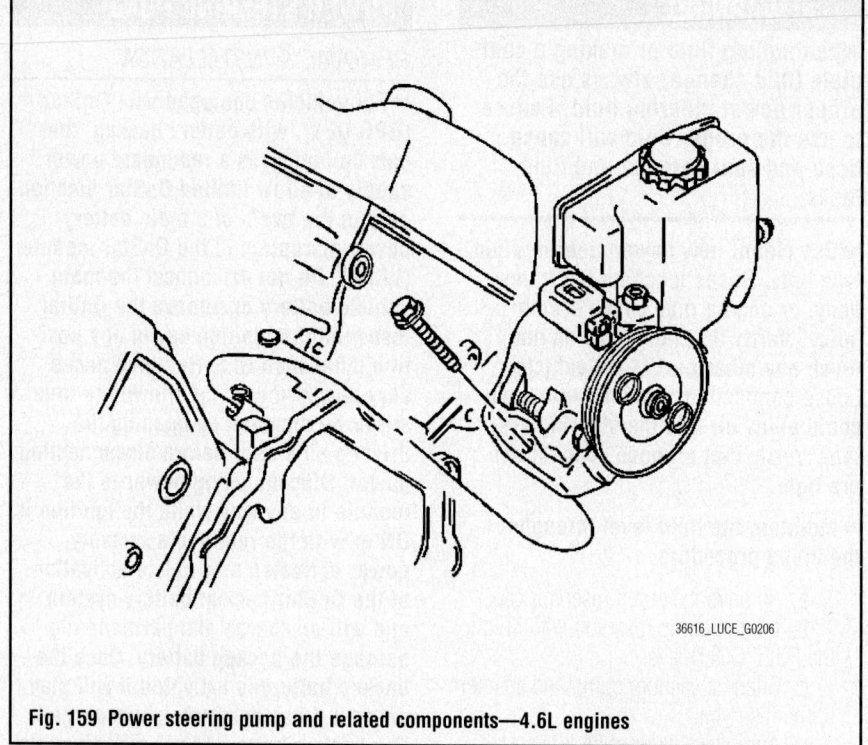

Fig. 159 Power steering pump and related components—4.6L engines

36616_LUCE_G0206

16. Install the power steering return hose to the power steering reservoir.

17. Remove the drain pan from under vehicle.

18. Install the drive belt.

19. Bleed the power steering system.

BLEEDING

1. Fill pump reservoir with fluid to minimum system level, FULL COLD level, or middle of hash mark on cap stick fluid level indicator.

2. With hydro-boost, do not apply the brake pedal with the engine OFF. This will discharge the hydro-boost accumulator.

3. If equipped with hydro-boost, fully charge the hydro-boost accumulator using the following procedure:

a. Start the engine.

b. Firmly apply the brake pedal 10–15 times.

c. Turn the engine OFF.

4. Raise the vehicle until the front wheels are off the ground.

5. With the key ON engine OFF, turn the steering wheel from stop to stop 12 times. Vehicles equipped with hydro-boost systems, or longer length power steering hoses, may require turning up to 15–20 times from stop to stop.

6. Verify power steering fluid level per operating specification.

7. Start the engine. Rotate steering wheel from left to right. Check for signs of cavitation or fluid aeration (pump noise/whining).

8. Verify the fluid level. Repeat the bleed procedure, if necessary.

CONTROL LINKS

REMOVAL & INSTALLATION

See Figure 160.

1. Before servicing the vehicle, refer to the Precautions Section.
2. Raise the vehicle and safely support the vehicle.
3. Remove the tire and wheel assembly.
4. Remove the control link bolt and nut.
5. Remove the control link from the vehicle.

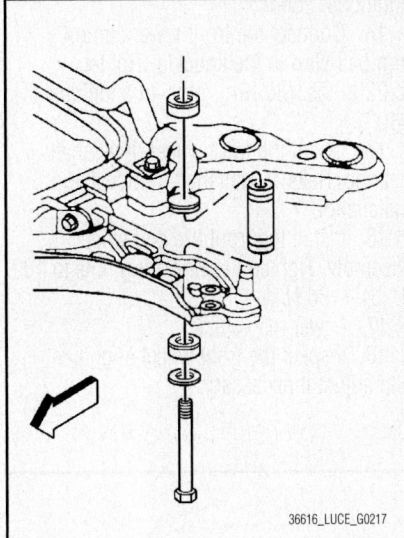

Fig. 160 Front control link (stabilizer shaft link) and related components

To install:

6. Install the control link into the vehicle.
7. Install the control link bolt and nut. Tighten the nut to 13 ft. lbs. (17 Nm).
8. Install the tire and wheel assembly. Tighten the lug nut to 100 ft. lbs. (136 Nm) using a crisscross torque pattern.
9. Lower the vehicle.

LOWER BALL JOINT

REMOVAL & INSTALLATION

The lower ball joint is serviced as part of the lower control arm. Refer to Lower Control Arm, removal & installation.

LOWER CONTROL ARM

REMOVAL & INSTALLATION

See Figure 161.

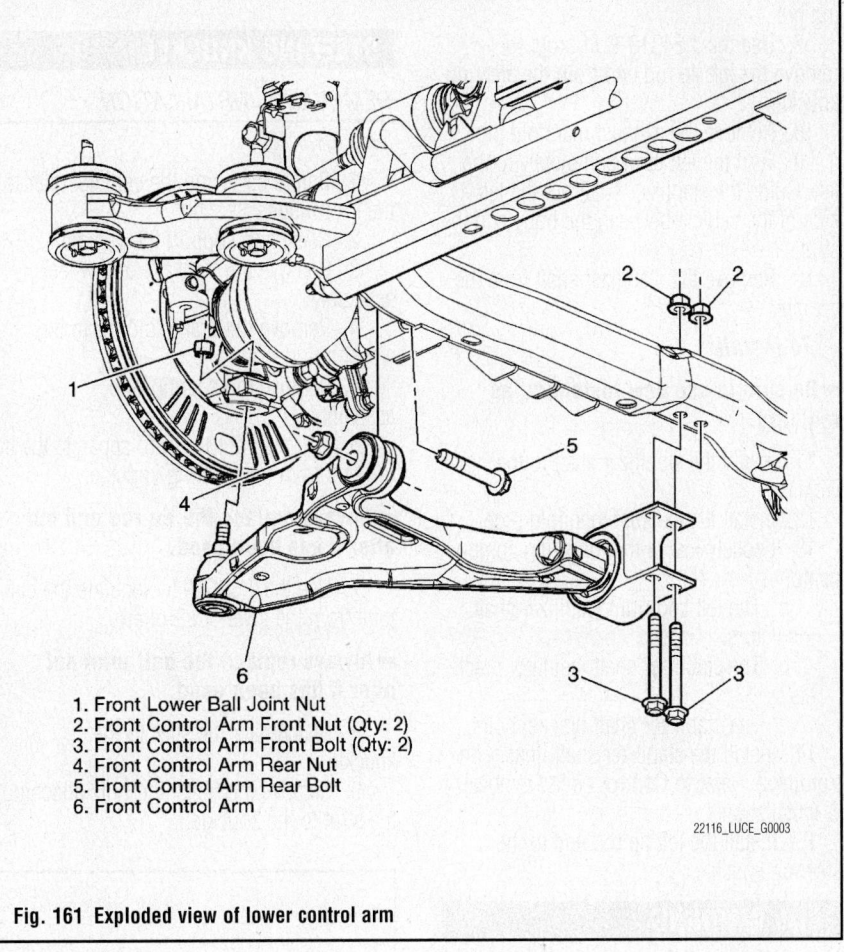

1. Front Lower Ball Joint Nut
2. Front Control Arm Front Nut (Qty: 2)
3. Front Control Arm Front Bolt (Qty: 2)
4. Front Control Arm Rear Nut
5. Front Control Arm Rear Bolt
6. Front Control Arm

22116_LUCE_G0003

Fig. 161 Exploded view of lower control arm

1. Before servicing the vehicle, refer to the Precautions Section.
2. Raise and support the vehicle.
3. Remove the front tire and wheel assembly.
4. Remove the front stabilizer shaft link (control link). Refer to Control Links, removal & installation.
5. Use the J 39549 to separate the ball joint from the control arm.

➡**Always replace the ball joint nut after it has been used.**

6. Remove the bolts from the control arm bracket.
7. Remove the bolt from the control arm.
8. Remove the control arm from the vehicle.

To install:

9. Installation is the reverse of the removal procedure.

➡**Do not tighten the control arm nut until the weight of the vehicle is supported by the control arm. The vehicle needs to be sitting at normal trim height.**

10. Tighten the front control arm rear nut to 116 ft. lbs. (157 Nm).
11. Tighten the front control arm front nuts to 111 ft. lbs. (150 Nm).
12. Tighten the lower ball joint nut in 2 steps:
    a. Step 1: tighten to 22 ft. lbs. (30 Nm).
    b. Step 2: tighten an additional 210°.
13. Tighten the wheel lug nuts to 100 ft. lbs. (136 Nm).

STABILIZER BAR

REMOVAL & INSTALLATION

1. Before servicing the vehicle, refer to the Precautions Section.
2. Raise and support the vehicle.
3. Remove the front tires and wheels.
4. Remove the stabilizer shaft links (control links). Refer to Control Links, removal & installation.

5. Remove the stabilizer shaft insulators.

6. Remove the left outer tie rod retaining nut.

7. Use the J 24319-B in order to remove the left tie rod end from the steering knuckle.

8. Remove the exhaust manifold pipe.

9. Turn the left strut completely to the left. Guide the stabilizer shaft out the left side of the vehicle between the body and the strut.

10. Remove the stabilizer shaft from the vehicle.

To install:

→Be sure to use new fasteners, as required.

11. Install the stabilizer shaft to the vehicle.

12. Install the exhaust manifold pipe.

13. Loosely install the following components:

  a. The left and right stabilizer shaft insulators.

  b. The stabilizer shaft insulator brackets.

  c. The stabilizer shaft bracket bolts.

14. Install the stabilizer shaft links (control links). Refer to Control Links, removal & installation.

15. Install the left tie rod end to the steering knuckle.

✳✳ WARNING

Use the correct fastener in the correct location. Replacement fasteners must be the correct part number for that application. Fasteners requiring replacement or fasteners requiring the use of thread locking compound or sealant are identified in the service procedure. Do not use paints, lubricants, or corrosion inhibitors on fasteners or fastener joint surfaces unless specified. These coatings affect fastener torque and joint clamping force and may damage the fastener. Use the correct tightening sequence and specifications when installing fasteners in order to avoid damage to parts and systems.

16. Tighten the stabilizer shaft insulator bracket bolts to 37 ft. lbs. (50 Nm).

17. Tighten the outer tie rod end to steering knuckle retaining nut in 2 steps:

  a. Step 1: tighten to 22 ft. lbs. (30 Nm).

  b. Step 2: tighten an additional 200°.

18. Install the front tires and wheels.

Tighten the wheel lug nuts to 100 ft. lbs. (136 Nm).

19. Lower the vehicle.

STEERING KNUCKLE

REMOVAL & INSTALLATION

See Figure 162.

1. Before servicing the vehicle, refer to the Precautions Section.

2. Raise and support the vehicle.

3. Remove the front tire and wheel assembly.

4. Remove the brake rotor from the wheel hub/bearing.

5. Remove the bearing/hub assembly.

6. Use the J 24319-B to separate the tie rod end from the steering knuckle.

→Always replace the tie rod end nut after it has been used.

7. Use the J 39549 to separate the ball joint from the lower control arm.

→Always replace the ball joint nut after it has been used.

8. Matchmark the strut to the knuckle.

9. Remove the bolts and nuts attaching the strut to the knuckle.

10. Remove the steering knuckle from the vehicle.

To install:

→Be sure to use new fasteners, as required.

11. Install the steering knuckle to the vehicle.

12. Install the through bolts and nuts attaching the strut to the knuckle. Align the matchmarks made during removal. Tighten the through bolts and nuts to 131 ft. lbs. (177 Nm).

13. Connect the outer tie rod to the steering knuckle. Tighten the outer tie rod end nuts to 22 ft. lbs. (30 Nm), plus an additional 200°.

14. Connect the front lower control arm ball stud to the knuckle. Tighten to 22 ft. lbs. (30 Nm), plus an additional 210°.

15. Install the front wheel drive shaft bearing. Refer to Halfshaft, removal and installation.

16. Install the front tire and wheel assembly. Tighten the wheel lug nuts to 100 ft. lbs. (136 Nm).

17. Lower the vehicle.

18. Inspect the front wheel alignment and adjust if necessary.

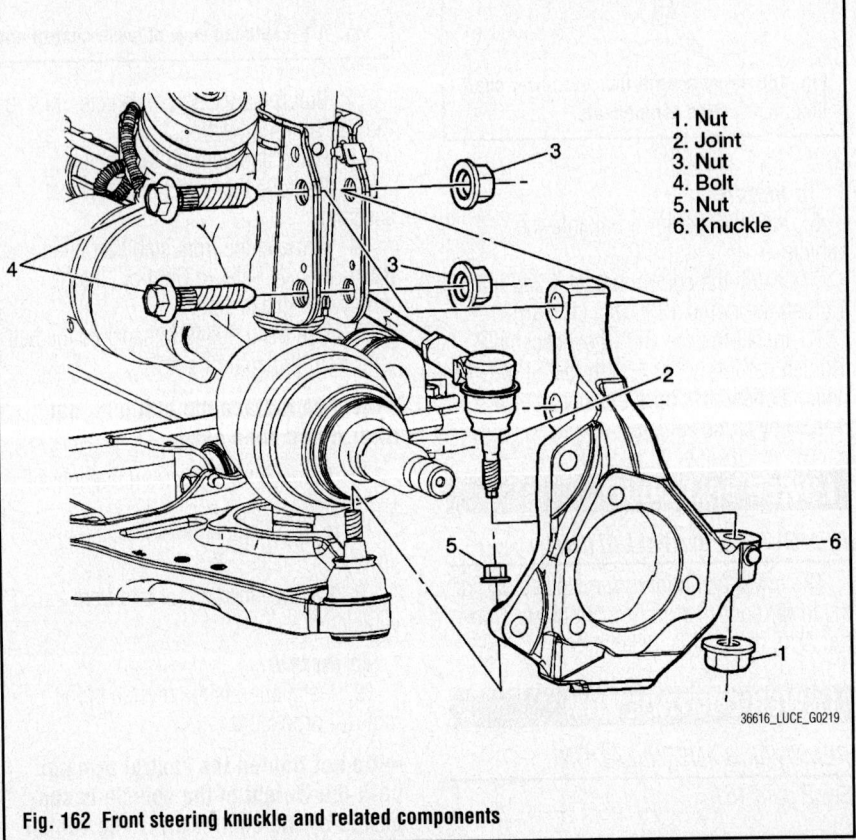

1. Nut
2. Joint
3. Nut
4. Bolt
5. Nut
6. Knuckle

36616_LUCE_G0219

Fig. 162 Front steering knuckle and related components

STRUT

REMOVAL & INSTALLATION

See Figure 163.

> ✳✳ **WARNING**
>
> **Care should be taken to avoid chipping or scratching the coating when handling the suspension coil spring. Damage to the coating can cause premature failure.**

1. Before servicing the vehicle, refer to the Precautions Section.
2. Remove the strut upper mounting nuts.

➡ **Lift the vehicle using ONLY a frame-contact vehicle lift. Do NOT lift the vehicle using a suspension-contact vehicle lift.**

3. Raise and support the vehicle.
4. Remove the tire and wheel.
5. Disconnect the ABS speed sensor electrical connector.
6. If applicable, remove the speed sensor bracket from the strut.

➡ **The knuckle must be retained after the strut-to-knuckle bolts have been removed. Failure to observe this may cause ball joint and/or wheel halfshaft damage.**

7. On the left side, remove the brake line bracket from the strut.
8. Remove the strut to knuckle retaining bolts.
9. Remove the strut from the vehicle.

To install:

➡ **Be sure to use new fasteners, as required.**

10. Install the strut.
11. Install the strut upper mounting nuts. Tighten the nuts to 35 ft. lbs. (47 Nm).
12. Install the strut lower bolts and nuts.
13. Tighten the strut lower nuts to 108 ft. lbs. (147 Nm).

14. Continue the installation in the reverse order of the removal procedure.
15. Install the tire and wheel.
16. Lower the vehicle.
17. Align the front wheels.

WHEEL HUB & BEARING

REMOVAL & INSTALLATION

See Figures 164 and 165.

1. Before servicing the vehicle, refer to the Precautions Section.
2. Raise and support the vehicle.
3. Remove the front tire and wheel assembly.

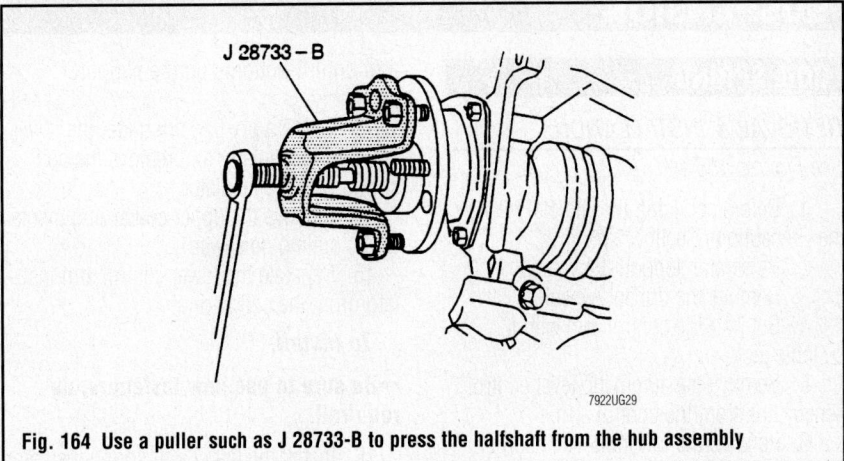

Fig. 164 Use a puller such as J 28733-B to press the halfshaft from the hub assembly

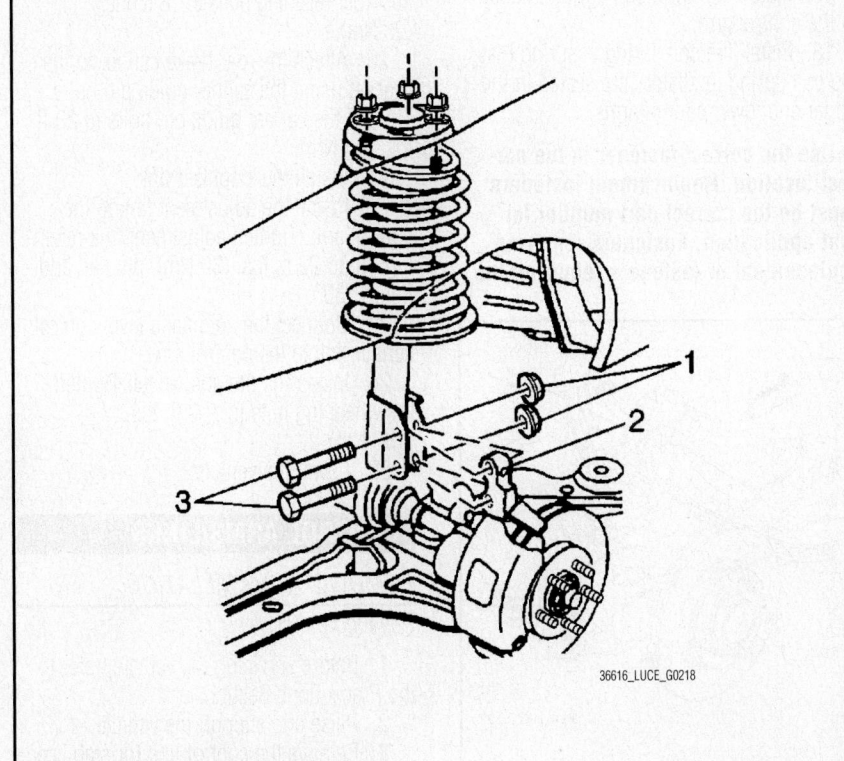

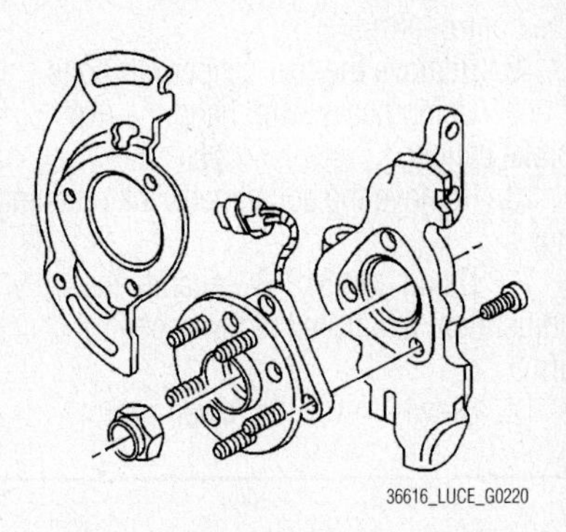

Fig. 165 Front hub and bearing assembly

➡ **Insert a drift punch through the caliper and into the rotor cooling fins to prevent the rotor from turning.**

4. Remove or disconnect the following:
   • The halfshaft nut and washer
   • The brake caliper
   • The brake rotor
   • The Anti-Lock Brake System (ABS) speed sensor
   • The 3 hub/bearing assembly bolts
   • The dust shield

Fig. 163 Front strut and related components

- The hub/bearing assembly from the halfshaft, using a puller
- The hub/bearing assembly from the steering knuckle

To install:

➡ **Be sure to use new fasteners, as required.**

5. Install the hub/bearing assembly over the halfshaft splines. Be sure the splines engage smoothly.

6. Apply a light coating of grease to the steering knuckle bore.

7. Slide the hub assembly onto the halfshaft as far as possible. If the hub will not bottom out on the halfshaft, install the hub mounting bolts and use the halfshaft nut to draw the hub onto the halfshaft.

8. Once the hub is flush with the steering knuckle, remove the mounting bolts and install the dust shield.

9. Install the mounting bolts. Torque the bolts to 70 ft. lbs. (95 Nm).

10. Place the transaxle in **N**.

11. Install or connect the following:
- The ABS front wheel speed sensor connector, and clip to the dust shield
- The brake rotor
- The caliper

12. Torque the halfshaft nut to 118 ft. lbs. (160 Nm).

13. Install the front wheels. Tighten the wheel lug nuts to 100 ft. lbs. (136 Nm).

14. Road test the vehicle.

ADJUSTMENT

No adjustment is possible.

The wheel bearings are not adjustable. If a wheel bearing is out of specification, it must be replaced. Using a dial indicator, check for looseness. If play exceeds 0.005 inch (0.127mm), the bearing wear is excessive and the hub/bearing should be replaced.

SUSPENSION

COIL SPRING

REMOVAL & INSTALLATION

See Figures 166 and 167.

1. Before servicing the vehicle, refer to the Precautions Section.

2. Raise and support the vehicle.

3. Remove the tire and wheel.

4. Support the control arm with a suitable jack.

5. Remove the automatic level control sensor link from the control arm.

6. Remove the lower shock absorber retaining bolts.

7. Disconnect the stabilizer link from the control arm.

8. Remove the rear caliper pin bolts.

9. Using heavy wire, hang the rear brake caliper.

10. Remove the adjustment link retaining nut.

11. Using J 24319-B, separate the adjustment link from the lower control arm.

12. Slowly lower the lower control

arm until it bottoms on the support assembly.

13. Using a pry bar, pry under the lower coil spring insulator and remove the coil spring with the insulator.

14. Remove the upper coil spring insulator by pulling downward.

15. Separate the lower control arm insulator from the coil spring.

To install:

➡ **Be sure to use new fasteners, as required.**

16. Install the upper coil spring insulator to the body.

17. Install the lower coil spring insulator in the control arm.

18. Install the coil spring ensuring that the coil spring insulators are seated in the upper and lower control arms.

➡**Use the correct fastener in the correct location. Replacement fasteners must be the correct part number for that application. Fasteners requiring replacement or fasteners requiring the**

REAR SUSPENSION

use of thread locking compound or sealant are identified in the service procedure. Do not use paints, lubricants, or corrosion inhibitors on fasteners or fastener joint surfaces unless specified. These coatings affect fastener torque and joint clamping force and may damage the fastener. Use the correct tightening sequence and specifications when installing fasteners in order to avoid damage to parts and systems.

19. Raise the lower control arm and install the shock absorber retaining bolts in the lower control arm. Tighten the lower shock absorber retaining bolts to 18 ft. lbs. (25 Nm).

20. Attach the rear brake caliper to the bracket using the caliper guide pin bolts. Tighten the caliper guide pin bolts to 25 ft. lbs. (34 Nm).

21. Install the stabilizer link.

22. Install the adjustment link to the control arm. Tighten adjustment link retaining nut to 22 ft. lbs. (30 Nm), plus an additional 180°.

23. Connect the automatic level control sensor link to the control arm.

24. Install the tire and wheel. Tighten the wheel lug nuts to 100 ft. lbs. (136 Nm).

25. Lower the vehicle.

CONTROL ARMS/LINKS

REMOVAL & INSTALLATION

See Figure 168.

1. Before servicing the vehicle, refer to the Precautions Section.

2. Raise and support the vehicle.

3. Remove the control link (or stabilizer shaft link) bolts.

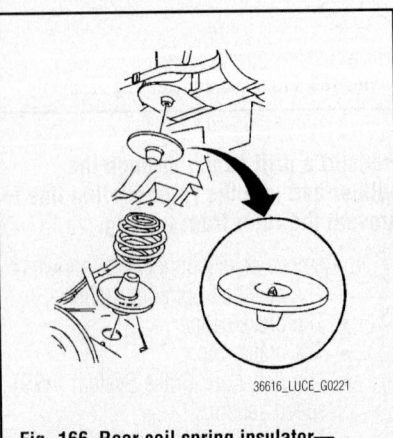

36616_LUCE_G0221

Fig. 166 Rear coil spring insulator—upper

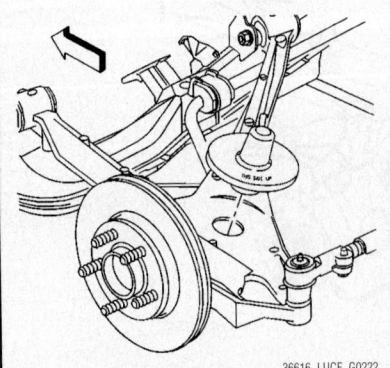

36616_LUCE_G0222

Fig. 167 Rear coil spring insulator—lower

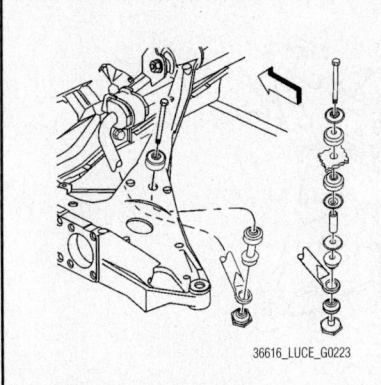

Fig. 168 Rear control link (stabilizer shaft link) and related components

4. Remove the control link insulators and spacer.

To install:

➡Be sure to use new fasteners, as required.

➡Use the correct fastener in the correct location. Replacement fasteners must be the correct part number for that application. Fasteners requiring replacement or fasteners requiring the use of thread locking compound or sealant are identified in the service procedure. Do not use paints, lubricants, or corrosion inhibitors on fasteners or fastener joint surfaces unless specified. These coatings affect fastener torque and joint clamping force and may damage the fastener. Use the correct tightening sequence and specifications when installing fasteners in order to avoid damage to parts and systems.

5. Loosely install the stabilizer link insulators, spacer, nut and bolt. Tighten the stabilizer shaft link nut to 11 ft. lbs. (15 Nm).
6. Lower the vehicle.

SHOCK ABSORBER

REMOVAL & INSTALLATION

See Figure 169.

1. Before servicing the vehicle, refer to the Precautions Section.
2. Raise and support the vehicle.
3. Remove the tire and wheel.
4. Support the control arm with a jack stand.
5. Disconnect the automatic level control air tube from the shock.
6. Remove the lower shock absorber retaining bolts.
7. Remove the trunk trim to gain access

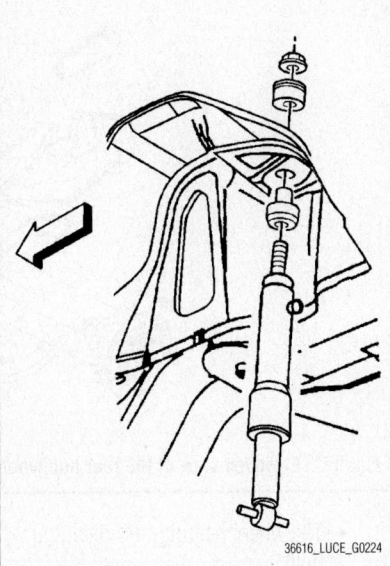

Fig. 169 Rear shock absorber and related components

to the shock absorber upper mounting nuts.

8. Remove the upper shock absorber cover.
9. Remove the upper shock absorber retaining nuts.
10. Remove the upper shock absorber reinforcement.
11. Remove the shock from the vehicle.

To install:

➡Be sure to use new fasteners, as required.

➡Use the correct fastener in the correct location. Replacement fasteners must be the correct part number for that application. Fasteners requiring replacement or fasteners requiring the use of thread locking compound or sealant are identified in the service procedure. Do not use paints, lubricants, or corrosion inhibitors on fasteners or fastener joint surfaces unless specified. These coatings affect fastener torque and joint clamping force and may damage the fastener. Use the correct tightening sequence and specifications when installing fasteners in order to avoid damage to parts and systems.

12. Install the shock, reinforcement, and the retaining nuts. Tighten the upper shock absorber retaining nuts to 18 ft. lbs. (25 Nm).
13. Install the upper shock absorber cover.

14. Install the trunk trim.
15. Install the lower shock absorber retaining bolts. Tighten the lower shock absorber retaining bolts to 18 ft. lbs. (25 Nm).
16. Connect the automatic level control air tube to the shock.
17. Install the tire and wheel.
18. Lower the vehicle.

STABILIZER BAR

REMOVAL & INSTALLATION

See Figure 170.

1. Before servicing the vehicle, refer to the Precautions Section.
2. Raise and support the vehicle.
3. Remove the stabilizer shaft links.
4. Remove the stabilizer shaft insulator bracket bolt.
5. Bend the open end of the stabilizer shaft insulator bracket clamp upward.
6. Remove the stabilizer shaft insulators.
7. Remove the stabilizer shaft.

To install:

➡Be sure to use new fasteners, as required.

8. Install the stabilizer shaft to the vehicle.
9. Install the stabilizer shaft insulators to the stabilizer shaft with the slits forward.
10. Bend the stabilizer shaft insulator brackets downward.

➡Use the correct fastener in the correct location. Replacement fasteners must be the correct part number for

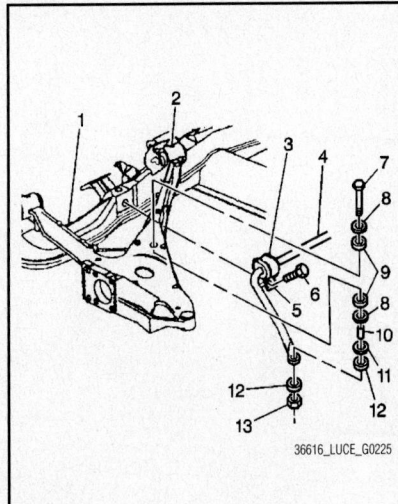

Fig. 170 Rear stabilizer shaft and related components

that application. Fasteners requiring replacement or fasteners requiring the use of thread locking compound or sealant are identified in the service procedure. Do not use paints, lubricants, or corrosion inhibitors on fasteners or fastener joint surfaces unless specified. These coatings affect fastener torque and joint clamping force and may damage the fastener. Use the correct tightening sequence and specifications when installing fasteners in order to avoid damage to parts and systems.

11. Install the stabilizer shaft bracket retaining bolt. Tighten the stabilizer shaft bracket retaining bolts to 24 ft. lbs. (33 Nm).
12. Install the stabilizer shaft links.
13. Lower the vehicle.

WHEEL HUB & BEARING

REMOVAL & INSTALLATION

See Figure 171.

1. Before servicing the vehicle, refer to the Precautions Section.
2. Raise and support the vehicle.
3. Remove or disconnect the following:
   - The tire and wheel
   - The brake rotor
   - The wheel bearing/hub electrical connector

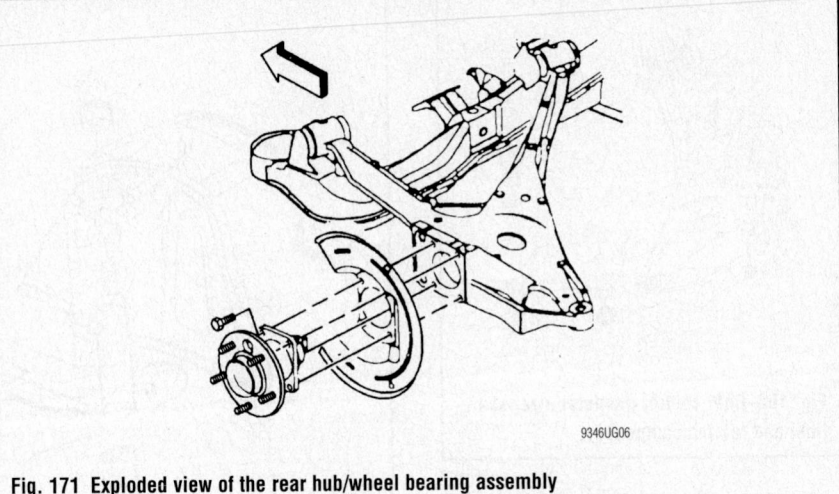

Fig. 171 Exploded view of the rear hub/wheel bearing assembly

- The wheel bearing/hub retaining bolts
- The wheel bearing/hub from lower control arm
- The brake shield from the lower control arm

To install:

4. Clean the control arm face and the bore before installing the hub and the bearing.
5. Install or connect the following:
   - The brake shield and the wheel bearing/hub to the control arm
   - The wheel bearing/hub retaining bolts. Tighten the wheel

bearing/hub bolts to 50 ft. lbs. (68 Nm).
- The wheel/hub electrical connector
- The brake rotor
- The tire and wheel. Tighten the wheel lug nuts to 100 ft. lbs. (136 Nm)
6. Lower the vehicle.

ADJUSTMENT

All models use sealed wheel bearings that are pre-adjusted. If the bearing needs replacing, replace the rear wheel hub/bearing assembly.

SPECIFICATIONS AND MAINTENANCE CHARTS

ENGINE AND VEHICLE IDENTIFICATION

		Engine					Model Year	
Code ①	Liters (cc)	Cu. In.	Cyl.	Fuel Sys.	Engine Type	Eng. Mfg.	Code ②	Year
B	2.4 (2189)	146	4	SFI	DOHC	General Motors	8	2008
N	3.5 (3500)	214	6	SFI	DOHC	General Motors	9	2009
7	3.6 (3600)	217	6	SFI	DOHC	General Motors		

SFI: Sequential Fuel Injection

MFI: Multi-point Fuel Injection

① 8th position of VIN

② 10th position of VIN

36616_MALI_C0001

GENERAL ENGINE SPECIFICATIONS

Year	Model	Engine Displacement Liters	Engine Series VIN	Net Horsepower @ rpm	Net Torque @ rpm (ft. lbs.)	Bore x Stroke (in.)	Compression Ratio	Oil Pressure @ rpm
2008	Malibu	2.4	B	169@6400	160@4500	3.47x3.86	10.0:1	50-80@1000
		3.5	N	224@5800	220@4000	3.90x2.99	9.8:1	30-45@1850
		3.6	7	252@6300	251@3200	3.70x3.37	10.2:1	20@2000
2009	Malibu	2.4	B	169@6400	160@4500	3.47x3.86	10.0:1	50-80@1000
		3.5	N	224@5800	220@4000	3.90x2.99	9.8:1	30-45@1850
		3.6	7	252@6300	251@3200	3.70x3.37	10.2:1	20@2000

36616_MALI_C0002

ENGINE TUNE-UP SPECIFICATIONS

Year	Engine Displacement Liters	Engine VIN	Spark Plug Gap (in.)	Ignition Timing (deg.)	Fuel Pump (psi)	Idle Speed (rpm)	Valve Clearance In.	Ex.
2008	2.4	B	0.037-0.043	①	50-60	②	HYD	HYD
	3.5	N	0.040	①	56-62	②	HYD	HYD
	3.6	7	0.043	①	56-62	②	HYD	HYD
2009	2.4	B	0.037-0.043	①	50-60	②	HYD	HYD
	3.5	N	0.040	①	56-62	②	HYD	HYD
	3.6	7	0.043	①	56-62	②	HYD	HYD

HYD: Hydraulic

① Engines equipped with Distributorless Ignition System (DIS). Ignition timing is not adjustable

② Refer to the Vehicle Emission Control Information label

36616_MALI_C0003

CAPACITIES

Year	Model	Engine Displacement Liters	Engine VIN	Engine Oil with Filter (qts.)	Transmission (qts.)	Fuel Tank (gal.)	Cooling System (qts.)
2008	Malibu	2.4	B	5.0	① ②	16.3	7.5
	Malibu	3.5	N	4.0	① ②	16.3	9.7
	Malibu	3.6	7	5.5	① ②	16.3	9.7
2009	Malibu	2.4	B	5.0	① ②	16.3	7.5
	Malibu	3.5	N	4.0	① ②	16.3	9.7
	Malibu	3.6	7	5.5	① ②	16.3	9.7

NOTE: All capacities are approximate. Add fluid gradually and ensure a proper fluid level is obtained.

① 4 speed: Bottom pan: 7 qts., Overhaul: 9.5 qts.

② 6 speed: Fluid change: 5.3-7.4 qts., Overhaul: 7.4-9.5 qts.

36616_MALI_C0005

FLUID SPECIFICATIONS

Year	Model	Engine Displacement Liters	Engine VIN	Engine Oil	Auto. Trans.	Drive Axle	Power Steering Fluid	Brake Master Cylinder	Engine Coolant
2008	Malibu	2.4	B	5W-30	DEXRON® VI	NA	GM PS Fluid	DOT 3	DEX-COOL®
		3.5	N	5W-30	DEXRON® VI	NA	GM PS Fluid	DOT 3	DEX-COOL®
		3.6	7	5W-30	DEXRON® VI	NA	GM PS Fluid	DOT 3	DEX-COOL®
2009	Malibu	2.4	B	5W-30	DEXRON® VI	NA	GM PS Fluid	DOT 3	DEX-COOL®
		3.5	N	5W-30	DEXRON® VI	NA	GM PS Fluid	DOT 3	DEX-COOL®
		3.6	7	5W-30	DEXRON® VI	NA	GM PS Fluid	DOT 3	DEX-COOL®

DOT: Department Of Transpotation

NA: Information not available

36616_MALI_C0004

VALVE SPECIFICATIONS

Year	Engine Displacement Liters	Engine VIN	Seat Angle (deg.)	Face Angle (deg.)	Spring Test Pressure (lbs. @ in.)	Spring Installed Height (in.)	Stem-to-Guide Clearance (in.)		Stem Diameter (in.)	
							Intake	Exhaust	Intake	Exhaust
2008	2.4	B	46	45	① ②	NA	0.0012-0.0022	0.0020-0.0026	0.2344-0.2355	0.2337 0.2343
	3.5	N	46	45	③ ④	2.080	0.0010-0.0027	0.0010-0.0027	NA	NA
	3.6	7	⑤	44.25	⑥ ⑦	1.6555-1.766	0.0010-0.0026	0.0014-0.0030	0.2344-0.2355	0.2341 0.2348
2009	2.4	B	46	45	① ②	NA	0.0012-0.0022	0.0020-0.0026	0.2344-0.2355	0.2337 0.2343
	3.5	N	46	45	③ ④	2.080	0.0010-0.0027	0.0010-0.0027	NA	NA
	3.6	7	⑤	44.25	⑥ ⑦	1.6555-1.766	0.0010-0.0026	0.0014-0.0030	0.2344-0.2355	0.2341 0.2348

NA: Not available

① Valve spring load closed: 252-575 N @ 22.5mm
② Valve spring load open: 245-271 N @32mm
③ Valve spring load closed: 321-359 N @ 43.2mm
④ Valve spring load open: 979-1067 N @32mm
⑤ Valve seat angle - seating surface: 45
  Valve seat angle - relief surface: 30
  Valve seat angle - undercut surface: 60
⑥ Valve spring load closed: 247-273 N @ 56-61 lb.
⑦ Valve spring load open: 598-662 N @ 134-149 lb.

CAMSHAFT AND BEARING SPECIFICATIONS CHART

All measurements are given in inches.

Year	Engine Displ. Liters	Engine VIN	Journal Dia.	Brg. Oil Clearance	Shaft End-play	Runout	Journal Bore	Lobe Height	
								Intake	Exhaust
2008	2.4	B	1.0604-1.0614	NA	0.0016-0.0057	0.001	NA	NA	NA
	3.5	N	2.0240-2.0250	2.0280-2.0290	—	0.001	NA	0.2727	0.2727
	3.6	7	① ②	—	0.0016-0.0035	③ ④	NA	1.6687-1.6805	1.6703-1.6821
2009	2.2	B	1.0604-1.0614	NA	0.0016-0.0057	0.001	NA	NA	NA
	3.5	N	2.0240-2.0250	2.0280-2.0290	—	0.001	NA	0.2727	0.2727
	3.6	7	① ②	—	0.0018-0.0085	③ ④	NA	1.6687-1.6805	1.6703-1.6821

NA: Not Available

① Front number 1: 1.3754-1.3765 inch
② Middle and rear numbers 2-4: 1.0605-1.0614 inch
③ Front and rear number 1 and 4: 0.001 inch
④ Middle 2 and 3: 0.002 inch

CRANKSHAFT AND CONNECTING ROD SPECIFICATIONS

All measurements are given in inches.

Year	Engine Displacement Liters	Engine VIN	Crankshaft				Connecting Rod		
			Main Brg. Journal Dia.	Main Brg. Oil Clearance	Shaft End-play	Thrust on No.	Journal Diameter	Oil Clearance	Side Clearance
2008	2.4	B	2.2045-2.2050	0.0012 0.0026	0.0012-0.0150	2	2.0519-2.0525	0.0011-0.0029	0.0028-0.0146
	3.5	N	2.840-2.841	①	0.0024-0.0083	3	2.3750-2.3760	0.0007-0.0170	0.008-0.009
	3.6	7	2.6768-2.6775	0.0004-0.0024	0.0039-0.0130	3	2.2044-2.2050	0.0004-0.0028	0.0374-0.0140
2009	2.4	B	2.2045-2.2050	0.0012 0.0026	0.0012-0.0150	2	2.0519-2.0525	0.0011-0.0029	0.0028-0.0146
	3.5	N	2.840-2.841	①	0.0024-0.0083	3	2.3750-2.3760	0.0007-0.0170	0.008-0.009
	3.6	7	2.6768-2.6775	0.0004-0.0024	0.0039-0.0130	3	2.2044-2.2050	0.0004-0.0028	0.0374-0.0140

NA: Not available

① Except # 3: 0.0008-0.0025 in.

  # 3: 0.0012-0.0030 in.

36616_MALI_C0008

PISTON AND RING SPECIFICATIONS

All measurements are given in inches.

Year	Engine Displacement Liters	Engine ID/VIN	Piston Clearance	Ring Gap			Ring Side Clearance	
				Top Compression	Bottom Compression	Oil Control	Top Compression	Bottom Compression
2008	2.4	B	0.0004-0.0016	0.006-0.012	0.0080 0.0180	0.0060 0.0020	0.0015-0.0031	0.0012-0.0030
	3.5	N	0.0011-0.0110	0.007-0.015	0.019-0.029	0.010 0.029	0.0010-0.0030	0.0020-0.0030
	3.6	7	0.0010-0.0021	0.0059-0.0118	0.0110-0.0189	0.0059-0.0236	0.0012-0.0026	0.0006-0.0024
2009	2.4	B	0.0004-0.0016	0.006-0.012	0.0080 0.0180	0.0060 0.0020	0.0015-0.0031	0.0012-0.0030
	3.5	N	0.0011-0.0110	0.007-0.015	0.019-0.029	0.010 0.029	0.0010-0.0030	0.0020-0.0030
	3.6	7	0.0010-0.0021	0.0059-0.0118	0.0110-0.0189	0.0059-0.0236	0.0012-0.0026	0.0006-0.0024

36616_MALI_C0009

TORQUE SPECIFICATIONS
All readings in ft. lbs.

Year	Engine Displacement Liters	Engine VIN	Cylinder Head Bolts	Main Bearing Bolts	Rod Bearing Bolts	Crankshaft Damper Bolts	Flywheel Bolts	Manifold		Spark Plug	Oil Pan Drain Plug
								Intake	Exhaust		
2008	2.4	B	①	②	③	④	⑤	⑥	⑦	15	18
	3.5	N	⑧	⑨	⑩	⑪	52	⑫	15	11	18
	3.6	7	⑬	⑭	⑮	⑯	⑰	⑱	15	13	18
2009	2.4	B	①	②	③	④	⑤	⑥	⑦	15	18
	3.5	N	⑧	⑨	⑩	⑪	52	⑫	15	11	18
	3.6	7	⑬	⑭	⑮	⑯	⑰	⑱	15	13	18

① Step 1: 22 ft. lbs.
   Step 2: Plus 155 degrees

② Step 1: 15 ft. lbs.
   Step 2: Plus 70 degrees

③ Step 1: 18 ft. lbs.
   Step 2: Plus 100 degrees

④ Step 1: 74 ft. lbs.
   Step 2: Plus 125 degrees

⑤ Step 1: 39 ft. lbs.
   Step 2: Plus 25 degrees

⑥ Intake manifold to head nut/bolt: 89 inch lbs.
   Intake manifold to head stud: 53 inch lbs.

⑦ Exhaust manifold to head nut: 124 inch lbs.
   Exhaust manifold to head stud: 89 inch lbs.

⑧ Step 1: 44 ft. lbs.
   Step 2: Plus 140 degrees

⑨ Step 1: 37 ft. lbs.
   Step 2: Plus 77 degrees

⑩ Step 1: 18 ft. lbs.
   Step 2: Plus 110 degrees

⑪ Step 1: 92 ft. lbs.
   Step 2: Plus 130 degrees

⑫ Lower manifold center ; Step 1; 62 in. lbs.
   Step 2: 115 in. lbs.
   Lower manifold corner: Step 1: 62 in. lbs.
   Step 2: 18 ft. lbs. lbs.
   Upper manifold: 18 ft. lbs.

⑬ M8 bolt Step 1: 11 ft. lbs.
   Step 2: 75 degrees
   M11 bolt Step 1: 22 ft. lbs.
   Step 2: 150 degrees

⑭ Inner Step 1: 15 ft. lbs.
   Step 2: 80 degrees
   Outer Step 1: 10 ft. lbs.
   Step 2: 110 degrees
   Side Step 1:22 ft. lbs
   Step 2: 60 degrees

⑮ Step 1: 22 ft. lbs.
   Step 2: back off to zero
   Step 3: 18 ft. lbs
   Step 4: 110 degrees

⑯ 74 ft. lbs. Plus 150 degrees

⑰ Flywheel specification: 22 ft. lbs. Plus 45 degree

⑱ Upper manifold: 17 ft. lbs.
   Tuning valve bolt: 89 inch lbs.

36616_MALI_C0010

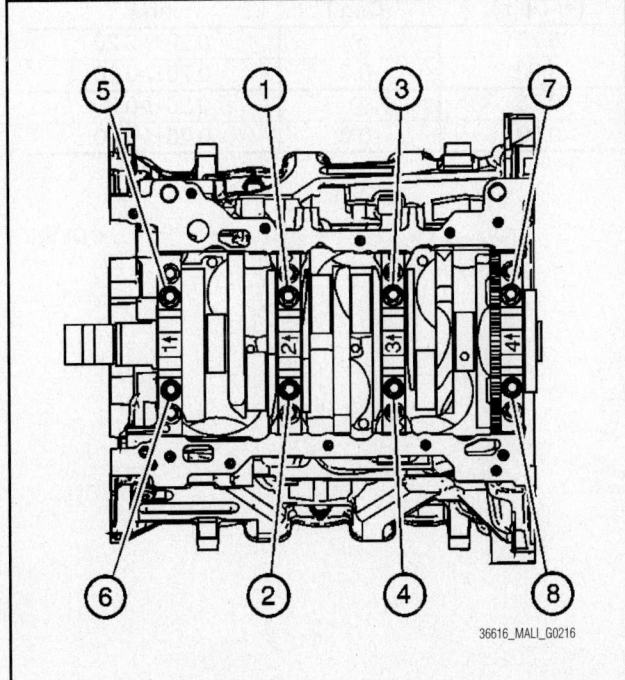

Fig. 1 Main bearing inboard bolt tightening sequence—3.6L engine

36616_MALI_G0216

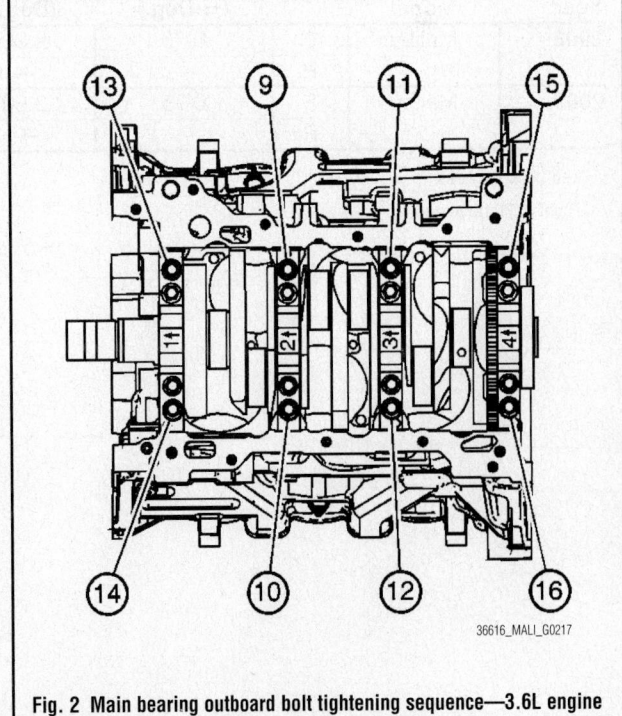

Fig. 2 Main bearing outboard bolt tightening sequence—3.6L engine

36616_MALI_G0217

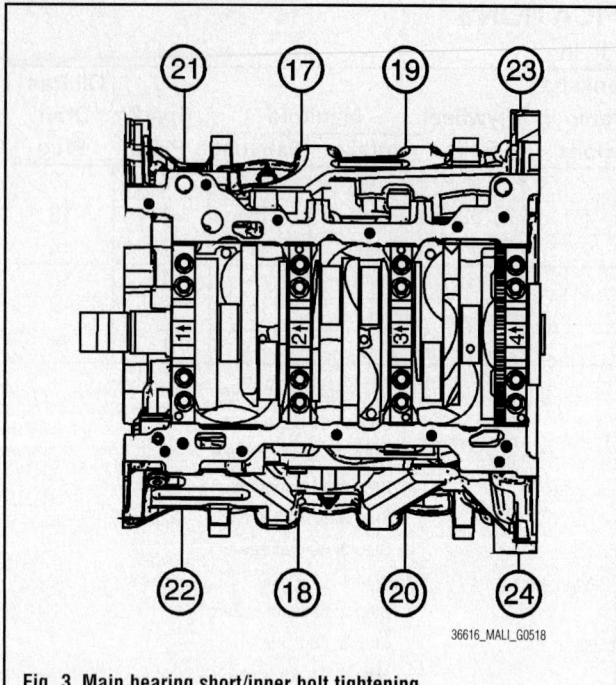

Fig. 3 Main bearing short/inner bolt tightening
sequence—3.6L engine

36616_MALI_G0518

WHEEL ALIGNMENT

Year	Model		Caster Range (+/-Deg.)	Caster Preferred Setting (Deg.)	Camber Range (+/-Deg.)	Camber Preferred Setting (Deg.)	Toe-in (in.)
2008	Malibu	F	0.75	2.90	0.75	①	0.20+/-0.20
		R	—	—	0.60	-0.8	0.20+/-0.20
2009	Malibu	F	0.75	2.90	0.75	①	0.20+/-0.20
		R	—	—	0.60	-0.8	0.20+/-0.20

① Left: 1.00 degrees
  Right: 0.70 degrees

36616_MALI_C0011

TIRE, WHEEL AND BALL JOINT SPECIFICATIONS

| Year | Model | OEM Tires | | Tire Pressures (psi) | | Wheel Size | Ball Joint Inspection | Lug Nut Torque (ft. lbs.) |
		Standard	Optional	Front	Rear			
2008	Malibu	①	①	①	①	①	①	100
2009	Malibu	①	①	①	①	①	①	100

OEM: Original Equipment Manufacturer

PSI: Pounds Per Square Inch

① For tire size and information, check the label located inside the glove compartment door.

36616_MALI_C0012

BRAKE SPECIFICATIONS

All measurements in inches unless noted

| Year | Model | | Brake Disc | | | Brake Drum Diameter | | | Minimum Lining Thickness | | Brake Caliper | |
			Original Thickness	Minimum Thickness	Maximum Runout	Original Inside Diameter	Max. Wear Limit	Maximum Machine Diameter	Front	Rear	Bracket Bolts (ft. lbs.)	Mounting Bolts (ft. lbs.)
2008	Malibu	F	1.023	0.898	0.002	—	—	—	NA	NA	96	26
		R	0.551	0.465	0.002	—	—	—	NA	NA	96	26
2009	Malibu	F	1.023	0.898	0.002	—	—	—	NA	NA	96	26
		R	0.551	0.465	0.002	—	—	—	NA	NA	96	26

36616_MALI_C0013

MAINTENANCE I AND II SERVICE SCHEDULES
2008-09 Chevrolet Malibu

When the CHANGE ENGINE OIL light appears, certain services and inspections are required.

Required services are described as Maintenance I and Maintenance II.

The first service on a vehicle should be Maintenance I, and the second service should be Maintenance II. Alternate between the 2 thereafter. However, in some cases, Maintenance II may be required more often.

Maintenance I: Use Maintenance I if the CHANGE ENGINE OIL light comes on within 10 months since vehicle was purchased or, if Maintenance II was performed.

Maintenance II: Use Maintenance II if the previous service performed was Maintenance I. Always use Maintenance II whenever the CHANGE ENGINE OIL light comes on 10 months or more since the last service, or, if the CHANGE ENGINE OIL light has not come on at all for one year.

Service	Maintenance I	Maintenance II
Change the engine oil and filter. Reset the oil life system.	✓	✓
Visually inspect the vehicle for leaks or damage. A fluid loss in the vehicle system could indicate a problem. Inspected, repair and add fluid to the system if necessary.	✓	✓
Inspect the engine air cleaner filter. If necessary, replace the filter.		✓
Rotate the tires. Inspect the tire inflation pressures and the tire wear.	✓	✓
Visually inspect the brake lines and hoses for proper hook-up, binding, leaks, cracks, chafing, etc. Inspect the disc brake pads for wear and the rotors for surface condition. Inspect the drum brake linings for wear or cracks. Inspect other brake parts, including drums, wheel cylinders, calipers, parking brake, etc. Inspect the parking brake adjustment.	✓	✓
Inspect the engine coolant and the windshield washer fluid levels. Add fluid as needed.	✓	✓
Inspect the suspension and steering components. Inspect the front and rear suspension and the steering system for damaged, loose or missing parts, or signs of wear. Inspect the power steering lines and the hoses for proper hook-up, binding, leaks, cracks.	--	✓
Visually inspect the coolant hoses and replace the hoses if they are cracked, swollen or deteriorated. Inspect all pipes, fittings and clamps; replace with GM parts as needed. To help ensure proper operation, a pressure test of the cooling system and pressure cap and cleaning the outside of the radiator and air conditioning condenser is recommended at least once a year.	--	✓
Inspect the front and rear suspension and the steering system for damaged, loose or missing parts, or signs of wear. Inspect power steering lines and hoses for proper hook-up, binding, leaks, cracks, chafing, etc.	--	✓
Inspect the throttle system for interference or binding and for damaged or missing parts. Replace the parts as needed. Replace any components that have high effort or excessive wear. Do not lubricate the accelerator or the cruise control cables.	--	✓
Replace the passenger compartment air filter.	--	✓

Reset the oil life system:
1. Display OIL LIFE RESET on the DIC.
2. Press and hold the ENTER button for at least one second. An ACKNOWLEDGED display message will appear for three seconds or until the next button is pressed. This will tell you the system has been reset.
3. Turn the key to OFF.
If the Change Oil Soon message comes back on when you start your vehicle, the engine oil life system has not reset, repeat the procedure.

36616_MALI_C0014

PRECAUTIONS

Before servicing any vehicle, please be sure to read all of the following precautions, which deal with personal safety, prevention of component damage, and important points to take into consideration when servicing a motor vehicle:

• Never open, service or drain the radiator or cooling system when the engine is hot; serious burns can occur from the steam and hot coolant.

• Observe all applicable safety precautions when working around fuel. Whenever servicing the fuel system, always work in a well-ventilated area. Do not allow fuel spray or vapors to come in contact with a spark, open flame, or excessive heat (a hot drop light, for example). Keep a dry chemical fire extinguisher near the work area. Always keep fuel in a container specifically designed for fuel storage; also, always properly seal fuel containers to avoid the possibility of fire or explosion. Refer to the additional fuel system precautions later in this section.

• Fuel injection systems often remain pressurized, even after the engine has been turned **OFF**. The fuel system pressure must be relieved before disconnecting any fuel lines. Failure to do so may result in fire and/or personal injury.

• Brake fluid often contains polyglycol ethers and polyglycols. Avoid contact with the eyes and wash your hands thoroughly after handling brake fluid. If you do get brake fluid in your eyes, flush your eyes with clean, running water for 15 minutes. If eye irritation persists, or if you have taken brake fluid internally, IMMEDIATELY seek medical assistance.

• The EPA warns that prolonged contact with used engine oil may cause a number of skin disorders, including cancer. You should make every effort to minimize your exposure to used engine oil. Protective gloves should be worn when changing oil. Wash your hands and any other exposed skin areas as soon as possible after exposure to used engine oil. Soap and water, or waterless hand cleaner should be used.

• All new vehicles are now equipped with an air bag system, often referred to as a Supplemental Restraint System (SRS) or Supplemental Inflatable Restraint (SIR) system. The system must be disabled before performing service on or around system components, steering column, instrument panel components, wiring and sensors. Failure to follow safety and disabling procedures could result in accidental air bag deployment, possible personal injury and unnecessary system repairs.

• Always wear safety goggles when working with, or around, the air bag system. When carrying a non-deployed air bag, be sure the bag and trim cover are pointed away from your body. When placing a non-deployed air bag on a work surface, always face the bag and trim cover upward, away from the surface. This will reduce the motion of the module if it is accidentally deployed. Refer to the additional air bag system precautions later in this section.

• Clean, high quality brake fluid from a sealed container is essential to the safe and proper operation of the brake system. You should always buy the correct type of brake fluid for your vehicle. If the brake fluid becomes contaminated, completely flush the system with new fluid. Never reuse any brake fluid. Any brake fluid that is removed from the system should be discarded. Also, do not allow any brake fluid to come in contact with a painted surface; it will damage the paint.

• Never operate the engine without the proper amount and type of engine oil; doing so WILL result in severe engine damage.

• Timing belt maintenance is extremely important. Many models utilize an interference-type, non-freewheeling engine. If the timing belt breaks, the valves in the cylinder head may strike the pistons, causing potentially serious (also time-consuming and expensive) engine damage. Refer to the maintenance interval charts for the recommended replacement interval for the timing belt, and to the timing belt section for belt replacement and inspection.

• Disconnecting the negative battery cable on some vehicles may interfere with the functions of the on-board computer system(s) and may require the computer to undergo a relearning process once the negative battery cable is reconnected.

• When servicing drum brakes, only disassemble and assemble one side at a time, leaving the remaining side intact for reference.

• Only an MVAC-trained, EPA-certified automotive technician should service the air conditioning system or its components.

BRAKES

GENERAL INFORMATION

PRECAUTIONS

• Certain components within the ABS system are not intended to be serviced or repaired individually.

• Do not use rubber hoses or other parts not specifically specified for and ABS system. When using repair kits, replace all parts included in the kit. Partial or incorrect repair may lead to functional problems and require the replacement of components.

• Lubricate rubber parts with clean, fresh brake fluid to ease assembly. Do not use shop air to clean parts; damage to rubber components may result.

• Use only DOT 3 brake fluid from an unopened container.

• If any hydraulic component or line is removed or replaced, it may be necessary to bleed the entire system.

• A clean repair area is essential. Always clean the reservoir and cap thoroughly before removing the cap. The slightest amount of dirt in the fluid may plug an orifice and impair the system function. Perform repairs after components have been thoroughly cleaned; use

ANTI-LOCK BRAKE SYSTEM (ABS)

only denatured alcohol to clean components. Do not allow ABS components to come into contact with any substance containing mineral oil; this includes used shop rags.

• The Anti-Lock control unit is a microprocessor similar to other computer units in the vehicle. Ensure that the ignition switch is **OFF** before removing or installing controller harnesses. Avoid static electricity discharge at or near the controller.

• If any arc welding is to be done on the vehicle, the control unit should be unplugged before welding operations begin.

BLEEDING PROCEDURE

BLEEDING PROCEDURE

1. Place a clean shop cloth beneath the brake master cylinder to catch brake fluid spills.

2. With the ignition OFF and the brakes cool, apply the brakes 3–5 times, or until the brake pedal effort increases significantly, in order to deplete the brake booster power reserve.

3. If you have performed a brake master cylinder bench bleeding on this vehicle, or if you disconnected the brake pipes from the master cylinder, or if you have disconnected the brake pipes from the proportioning valve assembly or the brake modulator assembly, you must perform the following steps to bleed air at the ports of the hydraulic component.

   a. Ensure that the brake master cylinder reservoir is full to the maximum-fill level.

If removal of the reservoir cap and diaphragm is necessary, clean the outside of the reservoir on and around the cap prior to removal.

   a. With the brake pipes installed securely to the master cylinder, proportioning valve assembly, or brake modulator assembly, loosen and separate one of the brake pipes from the port of the component.

For the proportioning valve assembly or the brake modulator assembly, perform these steps in the sequence of system flow; begin with the fluid feed pipes from the master cylinder.

   a. Allow a small amount of brake fluid to gravity bleed from the open port of the component.

   b. Connect the brake pipe to the component and tighten securely.

   c. Have an assistant slowly press the brake pedal fully and maintain steady pressure on the pedal.

   d. Loosen the same brake pipe to purge air from the open port of the component.

   e. Tighten the brake pipe, then have the assistant slowly release the brake pedal.

   f. Wait 15 seconds, then repeat the steps until all air is purged from the same port of the component.

   g. With the brake pipe installed securely to the master cylinder, proportioning valve assembly, or brake modulator assembly, after all air has been purged from the first port of the component that was bled, loosen and separate the next brake pipe from the component, until each of the ports on the component has been bled.

   l. After completing the final component port bleeding procedure, ensure that each of the brake pipe-to-component fittings are properly tightened.

4. Fill the brake master cylinder reservoir. Make sure that the brake master cylinder reservoir remains at least half-full during this bleeding procedure. Add fluid as needed to maintain the proper level.

Clean the outside of the reservoir on and around the reservoir cap prior to removing the cap and diaphragm.

5. Install a box-end wrench onto the right rear wheel hydraulic circuit bleeder valve.

6. Install a transparent hose over the end of the bleeder valve.

7. Submerge the open end of the transparent hose into a transparent container partially filled with brake fluid from a clean, sealed brake fluid container.

8. Have an assistant slowly press the brake pedal fully and maintain steady pressure on the pedal.

9. Loosen the bleeder valve to purge air from the wheel hydraulic circuit.

10. Tighten the bleeder valve, then have the assistant slowly release the brake pedal.

11. Wait 15 seconds, then repeat steps 8-10 until all air is purged from the same wheel hydraulic circuit.

12. With the right rear wheel hydraulic circuit bleeder valve tightened securely, after all air has been purged from the right rear hydraulic circuit, install a proper box-end wrench onto the left front wheel hydraulic circuit bleeder valve.

13. Install a transparent hose over the end of the bleeder valve and perform the same procedure used to bleed the right rear.

14. Bleed the left rear and front right in the same manner.

15. Fill the brake master cylinder reservoir to the maximum-fill level with brake fluid from a clean, sealed brake fluid container.

16. Slowly press and release the brake pedal. Observe the feel of the brake pedal.

17. If the brake pedal feels spongy, repeat the bleeding procedure again. If the brake pedal still feels spongy after repeating the bleeding procedure check for leaks in the system and pressure test the system to purge trapped air.

18. Turn the ignition key ON, with the engine OFF. Check to see if the brake system warning lamp remains illuminated.

➡**DO NOT allow the vehicle to be driven until it is diagnosed and repaired.**

BLEEDING THE ABS SYSTEM

✳✳ CAUTION

The Auto Bleed Procedure may be terminated at any time during the process by pressing the EXIT button. No further Scan Tool prompts pertaining to the Auto Bleed procedure will be given. After exiting the bleed procedure, relieve bleed pressure and disconnect bleed equipment per manufacturer's instructions. Failure to properly relieve pressure may result in spilled brake fluid causing damage to components and painted surfaces.

1. Raise the vehicle on a suitable support.
2. Remove all four tire and wheel assemblies.
3. Inspect the brake system for leaks and visual damage.
4. Repair or replace as needed.
5. Lower the vehicle.
6. Prepare the brake bleeding equipment and the vehicle for a pressure bleed of the base hydraulic brake system.
7. Inspect the battery state of charge.
8. Install a scan tool.
9. Turn **ON** the ignition, with the engine OFF.
10. With the scan tool, perform the following steps:

   a. Select Diagnostics

   b. Select the appropriate vehicle information

   c. Select Chassis

   d. Select Electronic Brake Control Module (EBCM)

   e. Select Special Functions

   f. Select Automated Bleed

BRAKES   **FRONT DISC BRAKES**

BRAKE CALIPER

REMOVAL & INSTALLATION

See Figure 4.

1. Empty the master cylinder reservoir until it is half full.
2. Raise and support the vehicle.
3. Remove the tire and wheel assembly.
4. Install and firmly hand tighten 2 wheel nuts to opposite wheel studs in order to retain the rotor to the hub.
5. Install a large C-clamp over the body of the brake caliper with the C-clamp ends against the rear of the caliper body and against the outer brake pad.
6. Tighten the C-clamp until the caliper piston is compressed into the caliper bore enough to allow the caliper to slide past the brake rotor.
7. Remove the C-clamp from the caliper.
8. Remove the brake hose-to-caliper bolt from the brake caliper.
9. Remove the brake hose from the brake caliper.
10. Remove and discard the 2 copper brake hose gaskets. These gaskets may be stuck to the brake caliper and/or the brake hose end.

11. Cap or plug the opening in the brake caliper and the brake hose to prevent fluid loss and contamination.
12. Remove the brake caliper guide pin bolts.
13. Remove the brake caliper from the caliper bracket.
14. Inspect the brake caliper guide pins for freedom of movement, and inspect the condition of the guide pin boots. Move the guide pins inboard and outboard within the bracket bores, without disengaging the slides from the boots, and observe the following:
   - Restricted caliper guide pin movement
   - Looseness in the brake caliper mounting bracket
   - Seized or binding caliper guide pins
   - Split or torn boots
15. If any of the conditions listed are found, the brake caliper guide pins and/or boots require replacement.

To install:

16. Install the brake caliper to the brake caliper bracket.
17. Install the brake caliper guide pin bolts and tighten to 26 ft. lbs. (35 Nm).
18. Remove the caps or plugs from the brake caliper opening and the brake hose.

➡**Do not reuse the copper brake hose gaskets.**

19. Install NEW copper brake hose gaskets to the brake hose-to-caliper bolt and to the brake hose.
20. Install the brake hose and the brake hose-to-brake caliper bolt to the brake caliper. Tighten to 37 ft. lbs. (50 Nm).
21. Bleed the hydraulic brake system.
22. Remove the wheel nuts retaining the brake rotor to the wheel hub.
23. Install the tire and wheel assembly.
24. Lower the vehicle.
25. With the engine OFF, gradually apply the brake pedal to approximately ⅔ of its travel distance.
26. Slowly release the brake pedal.
27. Wait 15 seconds, then repeat the last 2 steps until a firm brake pedal is obtained.
28. Fill the master cylinder reservoir to the proper level.

DISC BRAKE PADS

REMOVAL & INSTALLATION

See Figures 5 through 7.

1. Empty the master cylinder reservoir until it is half full.
2. Raise and support the vehicle.
3. Remove the tire and wheel assembly.
4. Install and firmly hand tighten 2 wheel nuts to opposite wheel studs in order to retain the rotor to the hub.

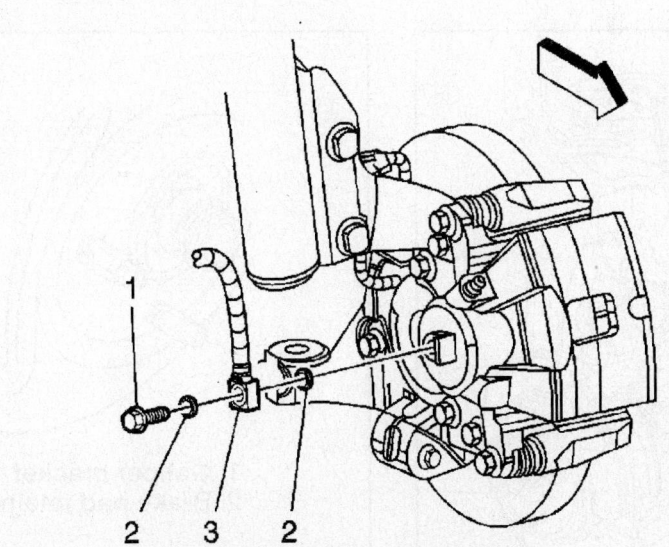

1. Brake hose-to-caliper bolt
2. Copper brake hose gaskets
3. Brake hose

36616_MALI_G0057

Fig. 4 Removing and installing brake hose and gaskets

5. Remove the brake caliper lower guide pin bolt.

➡ **Support the brake caliper with heavy mechanic wire, or equivalent, whenever it is separated from its mount and the hydraulic flexible brake hose is still connected. Failure to support the caliper in this manner will cause the flexible brake hose to bear the weight of the caliper, which may cause damage to the brake hose and in turn may cause a brake fluid leak.**

6. Without disconnecting the hydraulic brake flexible hose, pivot the caliper upward

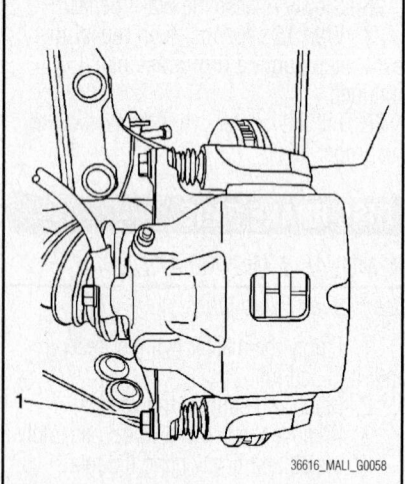

Fig. 5 Locating the brake caliper lower guide pin bolt (1)

and secure the caliper with heavy mechanics wire, or equivalent.

7. Remove the brake pads from the caliper mounting bracket.

8. Push the disc brake caliper piston into the caliper bore using an old inner disc brake pad and a disc brake piston installation tool.

9. Remove the brake pad retainers from the caliper bracket.

10. Thoroughly clean the brake pad hardware mating surfaces of the caliper bracket, of any debris and corrosion.

11. Inspect the brake caliper guide pins for freedom of movement, and inspect the condition of the guide pin boots. Move the guide pins inboard and outboard within the bracket bores, without disengaging the slides from the boots, and observe for the following:

- Restricted caliper guide pin movement
- Looseness in the brake caliper mounting bracket
- Seized or binding caliper guide pins
- Split or torn boots

a. If any of the conditions listed are found, the brake caliper guide pins and/or boots require replacement.

To install:

12. Make sure the brake pad hardware mating surfaces are clean.

13. Install the brake pad retainers to the brake caliper bracket.

➡ **The wear sensor equipped disc brake pad must be mounted inboard of the rotor with the leading edge of the sensor facing the brake rotor during forward wheel rotation, or at the top of the pad when installed in vehicle position.**

14. Install the brake pads to the caliper bracket.

15. Remove the support, and rotate the brake caliper into position over the disc brake pads and to the caliper mounting bracket.

16. Install the lower brake caliper guide pin bolt. Tighten to 26 ft. lbs. (35 Nm).

17. Remove the wheel nuts retaining the brake rotor to the hub.

18. Install the tire and wheel assembly. Lower the vehicle.

19. With the engine OFF, gradually apply the brake pedal to approximately ⅔ of its travel distance.

20. Slowly release the brake pedal.

21. Wait 15 seconds, then repeat the last 2 steps until a firm brake pedal is obtained

22. Fill the master cylinder reservoir to the proper level.

23. Burnish the brake pad and rotor.

❈❈ CAUTION

Road test a vehicle under safe conditions and while obeying all traffic laws. Do not attempt any maneuvers that could jeopardize vehicle control. Failure to adhere to these precau-

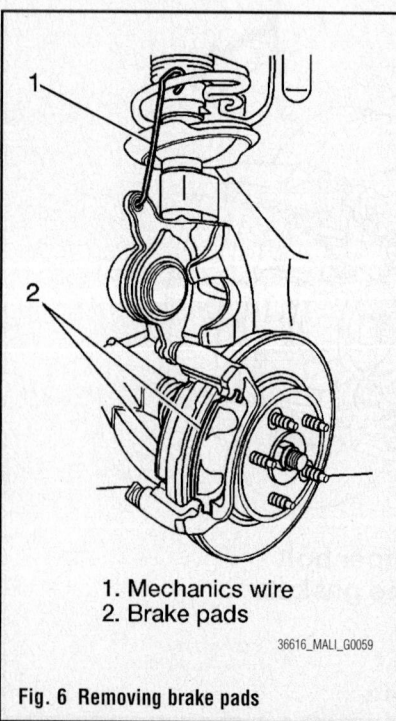

1. Mechanics wire
2. Brake pads

Fig. 6 Removing brake pads

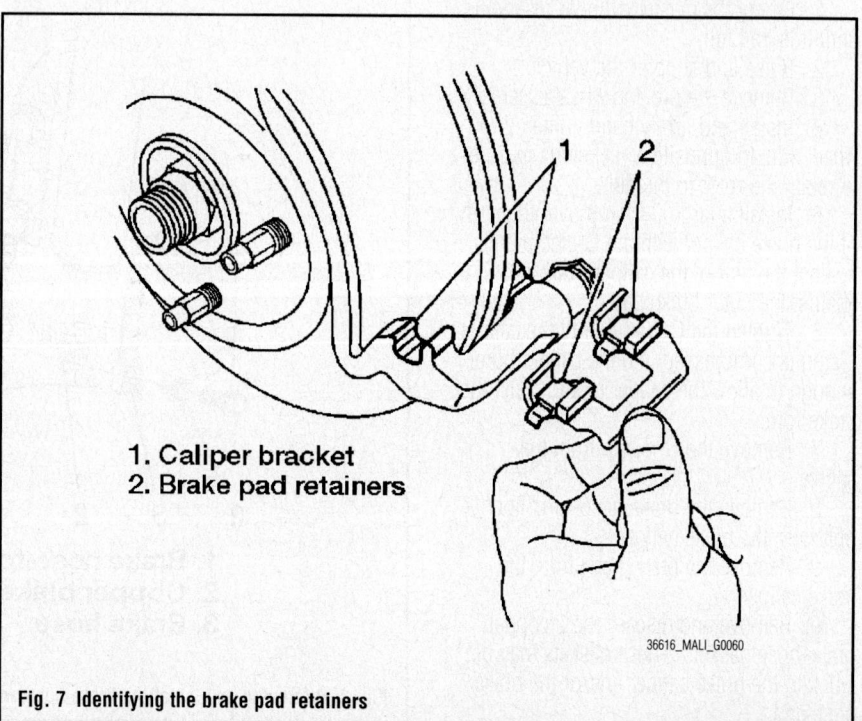

1. Caliper bracket
2. Brake pad retainers

Fig. 7 Identifying the brake pad retainers

tions could lead to serious personal injury and vehicle damage.

Burnishing the brake pads and brake rotors is necessary in order to ensure that the braking surfaces are properly prepared after service has been performed on the disc brake system.

This procedure should be performed whenever the disc brake rotors have been refinished or replaced, and/or whenever the disc brake pads have been replaced.

a. Select a smooth road with little or no traffic.

b. Accelerate the vehicle to 30 mph (48 km/h).

➡ Use care to avoid overheating the brakes while performing this step.

c. Using moderate to firm pressure, apply the brakes to bring the vehicle to a stop. Do not allow the brakes to lock.

d. Repeat the previous 2 steps until approximately 20 stops have been completed. Allow sufficient cooling periods between stops in order to properly burnish the brake pads and rotors.

BRAKES

✳✳ CAUTION

Dust and dirt accumulating on brake parts during normal use may contain asbestos fibers from production or aftermarket brake linings. Breathing excessive concentrations of asbestos fibers can cause serious bodily harm. Exercise care when servicing brake parts. Do not sand or grind brake lining unless equipment used is designed to contain the dust residue. Do not clean brake parts with compressed air or by dry brushing. Cleaning should be done by dampening the brake components with a fine mist of water, then wiping the brake components clean with a dampened cloth. Dispose of cloth and all residue containing asbestos fibers in an impermeable container with the appropriate label. Follow practices prescribed by the Occupational Safety and Health Administration (OSHA) and the Environmental Protection Agency (EPA) for the handling, processing, and disposing of dust or debris that may contain asbestos fibers.

BRAKE CALIPER

REMOVAL & INSTALLATION

See Figures 8 and 9.

1. Empty the master cylinder reservoir until it is half full.
2. Raise and suitably support the vehicle.
3. Remove the tire and wheel assembly.
4. Install a large C-clamp over the body of the brake caliper with the C-clamp ends against the rear of the caliper body and against the outer brake pad.

✳✳ CAUTION

When using a large C-clamp to compress a caliper piston into a caliper bore of a caliper equipped with an integral park brake mechanism, do not exceed more than 0.039 in. (1mm) of piston travel. Exceeding this amount of piston travel will cause damage to the internal adjusting mechanism and/or the integral park brake mechanism.

5. Tighten the C-clamp until the caliper piston is compressed into the caliper bore enough to allow the caliper to slide past the brake rotor. Do not exceed 0.039 in. (1mm) of caliper piston travel.
6. Remove the C-clamp from the caliper.
7. Remove the brake hose to caliper bolt from the brake caliper.
8. Remove the brake hose from the brake caliper.
9. Remove and discard the 2 copper brake hose gaskets. These gaskets may be stuck to the brake caliper and/or the brake hose end.
10. Cap or plug the opening in the brake caliper and the brake hose to prevent fluid loss and contamination.
11. Remove the 2 brake caliper pin bolts.
12. Remove the park brake cable from the caliper.

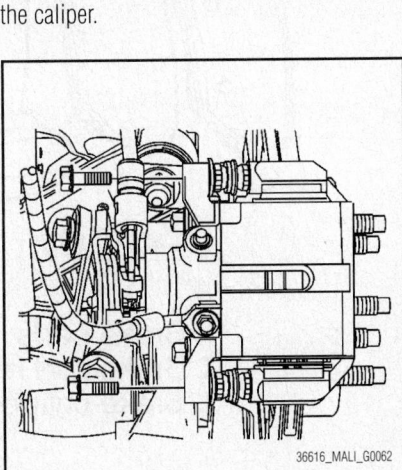

Fig. 8 Locating the 2 brake caliper pin bolts

REAR DISC BRAKES

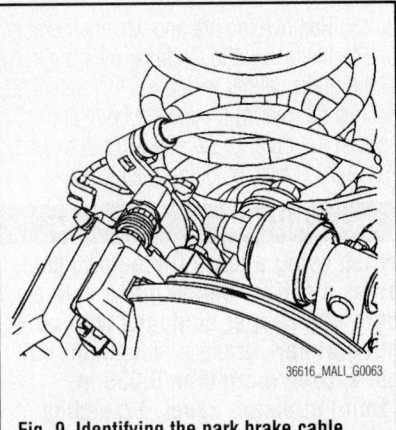

Fig. 9 Identifying the park brake cable

13. Remove the brake caliper from the brake caliper bracket.

To install:

14. Inspect the caliper slide boots for cuts, tears, or deterioration. If damaged, replace the slides and boots.
15. Install the brake caliper to the brake caliper bracket.
16. Install the 2 brake caliper pin bolts. Tighten the bolts to 26 ft. lbs. (35 Nm).
17. Install the park brake cable to the caliper.
18. Remove the caps or plugs from the brake caliper opening and the brake hose.

➡ DO NOT reuse the copper brake hose gaskets.

19. Install NEW copper brake hose gaskets to the brake hose-to-caliper bolt and to the brake hose.
20. Install the brake hose and the brake hose-to-caliper bolt to the brake caliper. Tighten the bolts to 37 ft. lbs. (50 Nm).
21. Bleed the hydraulic brake system.
22. With the engine OFF, gradually apply the brake pedal to approximately ⅔ of its travel distance.
23. Slowly release the brake pedal.
24. Wait 15 seconds, then repeat the last 2 steps until a firm brake pedal is obtained.
25. Fill the master cylinder reservoir to the proper level.

26. Install the tire and wheel assembly.

27. Lower the vehicle.

28. Apply and release the park brake lever 4 times.

DISC BRAKE PADS

REMOVAL & INSTALLATION

See Figures 10 and 11.

1. Empty the master cylinder reservoir until it is half full.

2. Raise and suitably support the vehicle.

3. Remove the tire and wheel assembly.

4. Install a large C-clamp over the body of the brake caliper with the C-clamp ends against the rear of the caliper body and against the outer brake pad. Do not exceed 0.039 in. (1mm) of caliper piston travel.

✳✳ CAUTION

When using a large C-clamp to compress a caliper piston into a caliper bore of a caliper equipped with an integral park brake mechanism, do not exceed more than 0.039 in. (1mm) of piston travel. Exceeding this amount of piston travel will cause damage to the internal adjusting mechanism and/or the integral park brake mechanism.

5. Tighten the C-clamp until the caliper piston is compressed into the caliper bore enough to allow the caliper to slide past the brake rotor.

6. Remove the C-clamp from the caliper.

7. Remove the lower brake caliper guide pin bolt.

➡**Support the brake caliper with heavy mechanic wire, or equivalent, when-**ever it is separated from its mount and the hydraulic flexible brake hose is still connected. Failure to support the caliper in this manner will cause the flexible brake hose to bear the weight of the caliper, which may cause damage to the brake hose and in turn may cause a brake fluid leak.

8. Pivot the brake caliper upward from the caliper bracket and support the caliper out of the way with heavy mechanic's wire; ensure that there is no tension on the hydraulic brake flexible hose. Do NOT disconnect the hydraulic brake flexible hose from the caliper.

9. Remove the brake pads from the brake caliper mounting bracket.

10. Remove and the brake pad retainers from the brake caliper mounting bracket.

To install:

➡**Do not attempt to clean away any corrosion. If damaged or corroded replace the necessary components.**

11. Inspect the brake caliper piston boot for deterioration, replace if damaged.

12. Use a piston installation tool in order to twist the brake caliper piston into the brake caliper bore.

13. Install the brake pad retainers to the brake caliper mounting bracket.

14. Install the brake pads to the brake caliper mounting bracket.

15. Pivot the brake caliper downward, over the brake pads and into the caliper bracket.

16. Install the brake caliper guide pin bolt to the brake caliper guide pin. Tighten the bolts to 26 ft. lbs. (35 Nm).

17. Install the tire and wheel assembly.

18. Lower the vehicle.

19. With the engine OFF, gradually apply the brake pedal to approximately ⅔ of its travel distance.

20. Slowly release the brake pedal.

21. Wait 15 seconds, then repeat the last 2 steps until a firm brake pedal is obtained

22. Fill the master cylinder reservoir to the proper level.

23. Apply and release the park brake lever 4 times.

24. Burnish the pads and rotors.

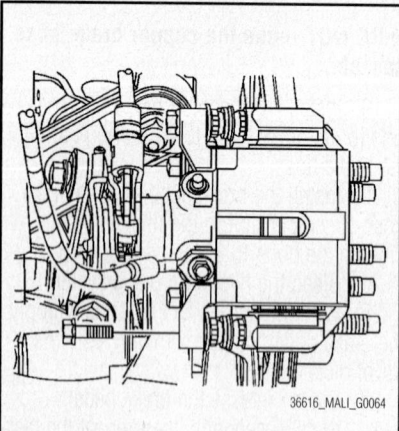

36616_MALI_G0064

Fig. 10 Locating the lower brake caliper guide pin bolt

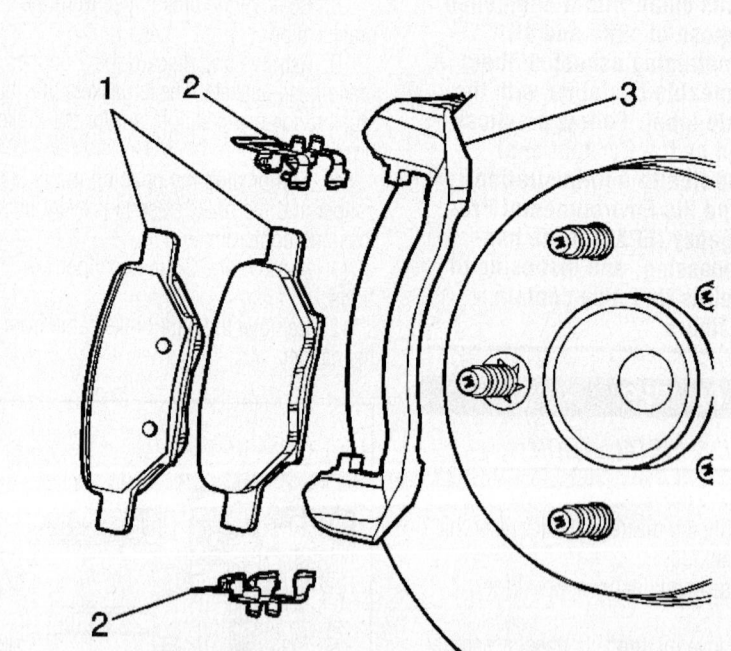

36616_MALI_G0065

1. Brake pads
2. Brake pad retainers
3. Brake caliper mounting bracket

Fig. 11 Removing and installing the rear brake pad

BRAKES

Park brake application is completely independent of the hydraulic brake system. The park brake system is a mechanical system which operates the rear disc brakes through the calipers. The system is activated by depressing the park brake pedal, which applies the rear disc brakes via cables. When the park brake is set and the ignition switch is on, the BRAKE warning lamp on the instrument panel will be on. The park brake is released by pushing the pedal down until a click is heard and then releasing. The pedal will click again and the BRAKE lamp in the instrument panel will go out when the park brake system is fully released.

PARKING BRAKE CABLES

ADJUSTMENT

➡**This vehicle utilizes a self-tensioning, or self-adjusting park brake cable system. The park brake system does not require adjustment under normal operating conditions. The tension on** the park brake cables can be disabled and enabled when necessary during service of the disc brake and/or the park brake system.

1. Apply and fully release the park brake several times. Verify that the park brake pedal releases completely.
2. Turn **ON** the ignition. Verify the red BRAKE warning lamp is not illuminated.
3. If the red BRAKE warning lamp is illuminated, check that the park brake pedal is in the fully released position and against the stop or that there is no slack in the cables.
4. If the red BRAKE warning lamp remained illuminated and there were no other visible causes.
5. Turn **OFF** the ignition.
6. Raise and support the vehicle.
7. With the park brake pedal fully released, check the park brake levers on the rear calipers. The levers should be against the stops on the caliper housings. If the levers are not against the stops, binding may exist.

PARKING BRAKE

8. Fully apply and release the park brake pedal 3–5 times in order for the cable tensioner to take up any slack in the park brake cables.
9. Fully apply the park brake pedal, a firm pedal should be obtained by depressing the pedal less than one full stroke.
10. Attempt to rotate the rear tire and wheel assemblies. There should be no rotation forward or rearward.
11. Fully release the park brake pedal.
12. Verify the park brake is released by rotating the rear tire and wheel assemblies. The rear tire and wheel assemblies should rotate freely and exhibit no brake drag.
13. Lower the vehicle.

PARKING BRAKE SHOES

REMOVAL & INSTALLATION

The rear disc brake pads serve as the parking brakes. Refer to the procedures under Rear Disc Brakes.

CHASSIS ELECTRICAL

GENERAL INFORMATION

✳✳ CAUTION

These vehicles are equipped with an air bag system. The system must be disarmed before performing service on, or around, system components, the steering column, instrument panel components, wiring and sensors. Failure to follow the safety precautions and the disarming procedure could result in accidental air bag deployment, possible injury and unnecessary system repairs.

SERVICE PRECAUTIONS

Disconnect and isolate the battery negative cable before beginning any airbag system component diagnosis, testing, removal, or installation procedures. Allow system capacitor to discharge for two minutes before beginning any component service. This will disable the airbag system. Failure to disable the airbag system may result in accidental airbag deployment, personal injury, or death.

Do not place an intact undeployed airbag face down on a solid surface. The airbag will propel into the air if accidentally

AIR BAG (SUPPLEMENTAL RESTRAINT SYSTEM)

deployed and may result in personal injury or death.

When carrying or handling an undeployed airbag, the trim side (face) of the airbag should be pointing towards the body to minimize possibility of injury if accidental deployment occurs. Failure to do this may result in personal injury or death.

Replace airbag system components with OEM replacement parts. Substitute parts may appear interchangeable, but internal differences may result in inferior occupant protection. Failure to do so may result in occupant personal injury or death.

Wear safety glasses, rubber gloves, and long sleeved clothing when cleaning powder residue from vehicle after an airbag deployment. Powder residue emitted from a deployed airbag can cause skin irritation. Flush affected area with cool water if irritation is experienced. If nasal or throat irritation is experienced, exit the vehicle for fresh air until the irritation ceases. If irritation continues, see a physician.

Do not use a replacement airbag that is not in the original packaging. This may result in improper deployment, personal injury, or death.

The factory installed fasteners, screws and bolts used to fasten airbag components have a special coating and are specifically designed for the airbag system. Do not use substitute fasteners. Use only original equipment fasteners listed in the parts catalog when fastener replacement is required.

During, and following, any child restraint anchor service, due to impact event or vehicle repair, carefully inspect all mounting hardware, tether straps, and anchors for proper installation, operation, or damage. If a child restraint anchor is found damaged in any way, the anchor must be replaced. Failure to do this may result in personal injury or death.

Deployed and non-deployed airbags may or may not have live pyrotechnic material within the airbag inflator.

Do not dispose of driver/passenger/curtain airbags or seat belt tensioners unless you are sure of complete deployment. Refer to the Hazardous Substance Control System for proper disposal.

Dispose of deployed airbags and tensioners consistent with state, provincial, local, and federal regulations.

After any airbag component testing or service, do not connect the battery negative cable. Personal injury or death may result if the system test is not performed first.

If the vehicle is equipped with the Occupant Classification System (OCS), do not connect the battery negative cable before performing the OCS Verification Test using the scan tool and the appropriate diagnostic information. Personal injury or death may result if the system test is not performed properly.

Never replace both the Occupant Restraint Controller (ORC) and the Occupant Classification Module (OCM) at the same time. If both require replacement, replace one, then perform the Airbag System test before replacing the other.

Both the ORC and the OCM store Occupant Classification System (OCS) calibration data, which they transfer to one another when one of them is replaced. If both are replaced at the same time, an irreversible fault will be set in both modules and the OCS may malfunction and cause personal injury or death.

If equipped with OCS, the Seat Weight Sensor is a sensitive, calibrated unit and must be handled carefully. Do not drop or handle roughly. If dropped or damaged, replace with another sensor. Failure to

do so may result in occupant injury or death.

If equipped with OCS, the front passenger seat must be handled carefully as well. When removing the seat, be careful when setting on floor not to drop. If dropped, the sensor may be inoperative, could result in occupant injury, or possibly death.

If equipped with OCS, when the passenger front seat is on the floor, no one should sit in the front passenger seat. This uneven force may damage the sensing ability of the seat weight sensors. If sat on and damaged, the sensor may be inoperative, could result in occupant injury, or possibly death.

DISARMING THE SYSTEM

1. Turn the steering wheel so that the vehicles wheels are pointing straight ahead.
2. Place the ignition in the **OFF** position.

➡ **The SDM may have more than one fused power input. To ensure there is no unwanted SIR deployment, personal**

injury, or unnecessary SIR system repairs, remove all fuses supplying power to the SDM. With all SDM fuses removed and the ignition switch in the ON position, the AIR BAG warning indicator illuminates. This is normal operation, and does not indicate a SIR system malfunction.

3. Locate and remove the fuse(s) supplying power to the SDM. Or you may disconnect the negative battery cable from the battery.
4. Wait 1 minute before working on the system.

ARMING THE SYSTEM

1. Place the ignition in the **OFF** position.
2. Install the fuse(s) or reconnect the negative battery cable supplying power to the SDM.
3. Turn the ignition switch to the **ON** position. The AIR BAG indicator will flash then turn OFF.

DRIVE TRAIN

AUTOMATIC TRANSAXLE ASSEMBLY

REMOVAL & INSTALLATION

4T45-E Transaxle

See Figures 12 and 13.

1. Remove the air cleaner outlet duct.
2. Disconnect the negative battery cable. Refer
3. Disconnect the transaxle wiring harness from the transaxle and the Park Neutral Position (PNP) switch.
4. Remove the shift cable bracket front bolt and shift cable from the lever.
5. Remove the transmission wiring harness from the retainer on the transmission.
6. Disconnect bank 2, Oxygen Sensor (O2S) sensor 1 electrical connector.
7. Remove the left exhaust manifold heat shield.
8. Remove the exhaust manifold heat shield.
9. Remove the front exhaust pipe nuts.
10. Remove the upper transmission to engine bolts and stud.
11. Install the engine support fixture.
12. Support the radiator and condenser from above using the condenser tabs on each side.
13. Raise the vehicle.
14. Remove the front wheels and tires.
15. Disconnect the bank 2, O2S sensor 2 electrical connector.

16. Remove the left catalytic converter to right catalytic converter nuts.
17. Remove the left catalytic converter.
18. Remove the steering gear intermediate shaft.

➡ **It is only necessary to remove the control arms from the frame if the frame is being replaced.**

19. Remove the frame as follows:
    a. Support the radiator and condenser from above.
    b. Raise the vehicle on a hoist.
20. Remove the front fender liner.
    a. Remove the engine splash shield.
    b. Remove the lower ball joints from the steering knuckles.
    c. Remove the tie rod ends from the steering knuckles.
    d. Remove both stabilizer links from the stabilizer bar.
    e. Remove the power steering gear mounting bolts and secure the gear out of the way using mechanic's wire, being sure not to overextend the intermediate shaft.
    f. Remove the engine mount fasteners from the frame.
    g. Remove the front transmission mount bolt from the frame.
    h. Remove the left transmission mount fasteners from the frame.
    i. Remove the rear transmission mount bracket fasteners from the frame.
    j. Remove the brake lines from the retainers on the frame.

    k. Remove the power steering outlet pipe/hose from the frame. .
    l. Remove the rear catalytic converter.
    m. Lower the vehicle until the frame contacts the engine support stand.
    n. Remove the reinforcement bolts.
    o. Remove the front frame bolts.
    p. Remove the rear frame bolts.
    q. Remove the frame reinforcements.
    r. Raise the vehicle off of the frame.
21. Disconnect the wheel drive shafts from the transaxle.
22. Remove the 3 bolts from the transmission brace near the right axle shaft.

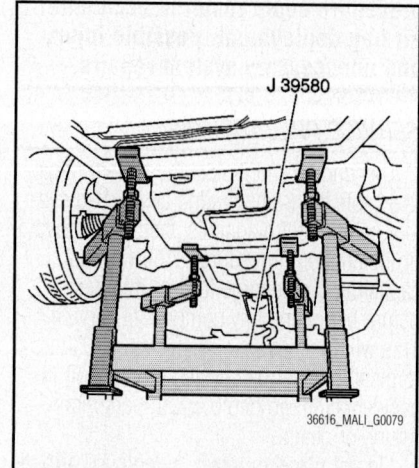

J 39580

36616_MALI_G0079

Fig. 12 Lower the vehicle until the frame contacts the engine support stand

23. Remove the oil pan to bellhousing bolts and bracket.

24. Remove the flywheel inspection cover.

25. Remove the starter.

26. Mark the relationship of the flywheel to the torque converter for reassembly.

27. Remove the torque converter to flywheel bolts.

28. Remove the transmission oil cooler lines by removing the nut holding the bracket to the transaxle case.

29. Disconnect the Vehicle Speed Sensor (VSS) wiring harness from the sensor.

30. Disconnect the rear Heated Oxygen Sensor (HO2S) harness from the rear transmission mount.

31. Remove the remaining (rear) bolt from the shift cable bracket.

32. Remove the front transmission mount bracket from the transmission.

33. Use a transmission jack in order to support the transmission.

34. Remove the remaining bellhousing bolts and separate the transmission from the engine.

35. Lower the transmission with the transmission jack far enough to remove the transmission.

To install:

36. Position the transaxle in the vehicle.

37. Install the lower transmission to engine bolts and tighten to 66 ft. lbs. (90 Nm).

38. Install the front transmission mount bracket to the transmission.

39. Install the wheel drive shafts to the transaxle.

40. Connect the wiring harness to the VSS.

41. Install the torque converter to flywheel bolts and tighten to 46 ft. lbs. (62 Nm).

42. Install the starter.

43. Install the flywheel inspection cover bolts and tighten to 89 inch lbs. (10 Nm).

44. Connect the transaxle oil cooler pipes to the transaxle. Tighten the pipes to 70 inch lbs. (8 Nm).

45. Install the oil pan to bellhousing bracket and bolts. Tighten the bolts to 53 ft. lbs. (72 Nm).

46. Install the 3 bolts to the transmission brace at the final drive area and tighten.

47. Remove the transmission jack.

48. Install the frame as follows:

  a. Lower the vehicle on to the frame.

  b. Install the frame reinforcements.

  c. Install the front frame bolts and hand tighten only.

  d. Install the reinforcement bolts and hand tighten only.

  e. Tighten the rear frame bolts. Tighten to 74 ft. lbs. (100 Nm) , plus an additional 90 degrees.

  f. Tighten the front frame bolts. Tighten to 74 ft. lbs. (100 Nm) , plus an additional 90 degrees.

  g. Install the reinforcement bolts. Tighten to 74 ft. lbs. (100 Nm).

  h. Raise the vehicle.

  i. Install the power steering outlet pipe/hose to the frame.

  j. Install the brake lines to the retainers on the frame.

  k. Install the rear transmission mount bracket fasteners. Tighten the transaxle mount to transmission bolts to 37 ft. lbs. (50 Nm) and the transaxle to mount bracket through bolt to 66 ft. lbs. (90 Nm).

  l. Install the left transmission mount fasteners to the frame. Tighten the transmission mount nuts to 37 ft. lb. (50 Nm).

  m. Install the front transmission mount bracket bolt. Tighten the transaxle mount to transmission bolts to 66 ft. lbs. (90 Nm) and the transaxle to mount bracket through bolt to 66 ft. lbs. (90 Nm).

  n. Install the engine mount fasteners to the frame. Tighten the nuts/bolts to 37 ft. lbs. (50 Nm).

  o. Install the power steering gear mounting fasteners.

  p. Install both stabilizer links to the stabilizer bar. Tighten to 48 ft. lbs. (65 Nm) plus an additional 180 degrees.

  q. Install the tie rod ends to the steering knuckles.

  r. Install the lower ball joints to the steering knuckles. Tighten the ball stud to steering knuckle pinch nut to 37 ft. lbs. (50 Nm). Reverse the nut 3¼ of a turn. Tighten to 37 ft. lbs. (50 Nm) plus an additional 60 degrees.

  s. Install the rear catalytic converter.

  t. Install the front fender liner.

  u. Install the engine splash shield.

  v. Lower the vehicle.

  w. Remove the temporary radiator and condenser support.

  x. Remove the engine support fixture.

49. Install the engine splash shields.

50. Install the front wheels and tires.

51. Lower the vehicle.

52. Remove the radiator and condenser support and the engine support fixture.

53. Install the upper transmission to engine bolts and stud and tighten to 66 ft. lbs. (90 Nm).

54. Install the shift cable bracket and shift cable to the lever.

55. Install the remaining components in the reverse order of removal.

56. Connect bank 2, O2 sensor 2 electrical connector.

57. Connect the negative battery cable.

58. Add automatic transmission fluid (ATF) and verify the proper fluid level of the transaxle.

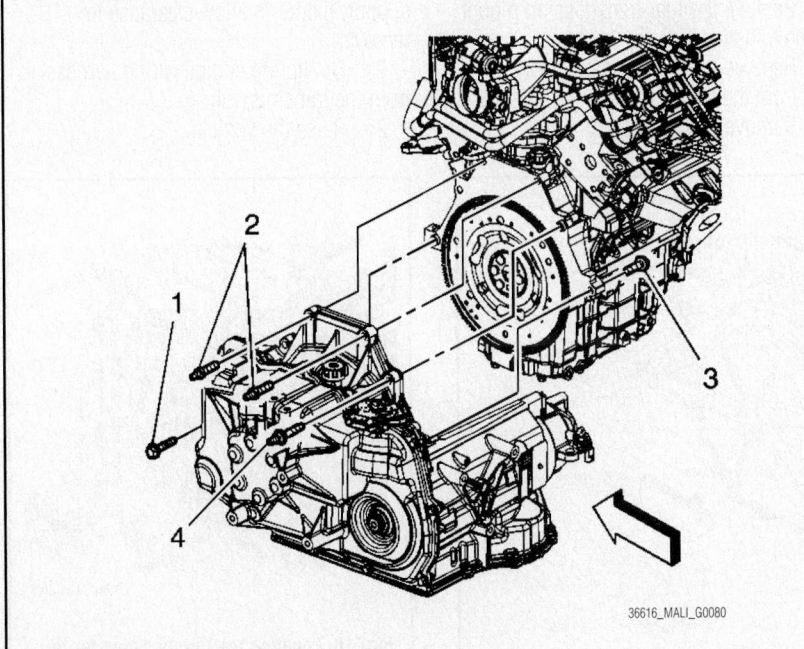

36616_MALI_G0080

Fig. 13 Removing the remaining bellhousing bolts (1, 3)

➡It is recommended that Transmission Adaptive Pressure (TAP) information be reset. Reset the TAP values using a scan tool will erase all learned values in all cells. As a result, the ECM, PCM, or TCM will need to relearn TAP values. Transmission performance may be affected as new TAP values are learned.

59. Reset the TAP values by selecting the following:
   - Scan tool
   - Special functions
   - Transmission output controls
   - Reset transmission adapts
60. Road test the vehicle.

6T40/6T45

See Figures 14 through 17.

1. Remove the battery tray.
2. Remove the transmission range select lever cable and bracket.
3. Drain the transmission fluid.
4. Disconnect the control valve body Transmission Control Module (TCM) electrical connector then unclip the connector from the transmission.
5. Disconnect the control valve body Transmission Control Module (TCM) electrical connector then unclip the connector from the transmission.
6. Remove the oil cooler inlet and outlet hoses from the retainer on the control valve body cover.
7. Remove the transmission fluid cooler inlet hose nut from the transmission.
8. Remove the transmission fluid cooler inlet hose from the transmission.
9. Remove the transmission fluid cooler outlet hose nut from the transmission.
10. Remove the transmission fluid cooler outlet hose from the transmission.

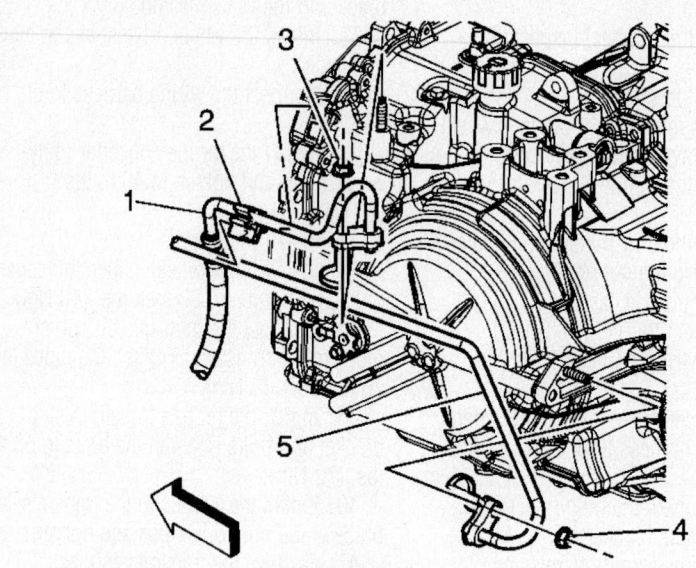

1. Oil cooler inlet
2. Retainer
3. Inlet hose nut
4. Outlet hose nut
5. Outlet hose

36616_MALI_G0082

Fig. 15 Disconnecting the transmission fluid cooler lines

11. Plug and/or cap the hose and transmission to prevent contamination.
12. Remove the upper transmission to engine bolts.
13. Remove the frame.
14. Disconnect the wheel drive shafts from the transmission.
15. Remove the intermediate drive shaft.
16. Remove the rear transmission mount from the transmission.
17. Remove the front transmission mount from the transmission.
18. Remove the starter.

19. Mark the relationship of the flywheel to the torque converter for reassembly.
20. Remove the torque converter to flywheel bolts.
21. Lower the vehicle.
22. Remove the 3 left transmission mount bolts from the transmission.
23. Lower the transmission side with the support fixture to allow clearance for removal.
24. Unclip the engine wiring harness from the transmission.
25. Raise the vehicle.

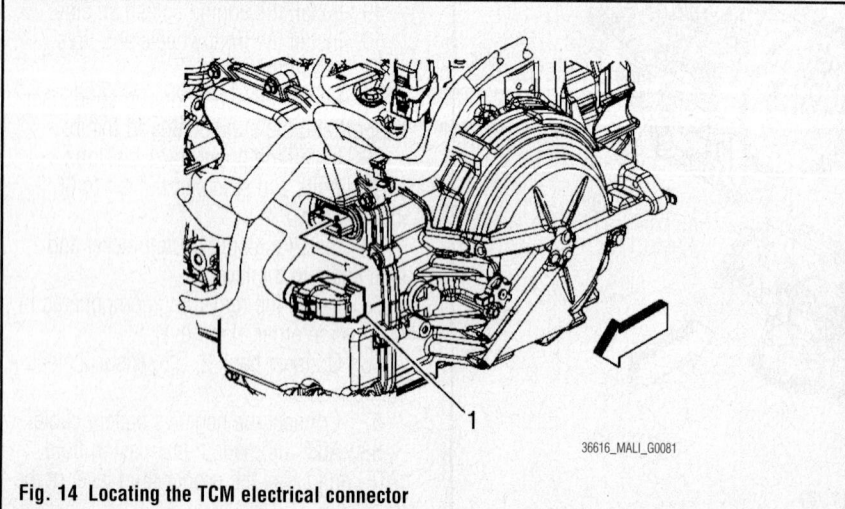

36616_MALI_G0081

Fig. 14 Locating the TCM electrical connector

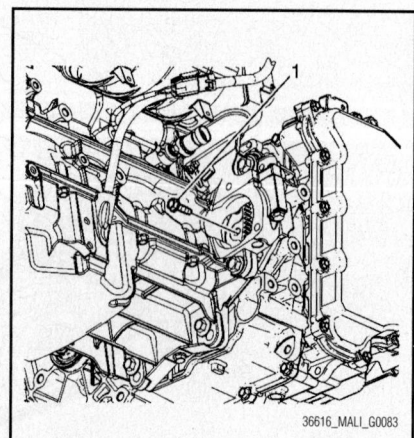

36616_MALI_G0083

Fig. 16 Locating the torque converter to flywheel bolts

26. Use a transmission jack in order to support the transmission.

27. Remove the remaining transmission fasteners.

➡**Insure the torque converter remains securely in place on the transmission input shaft while separating and removing the transmission.**

28. Separate the transmission from the engine.

29. Lower the transmission with the transmission jack far enough to remove the transmission.

To install:

30. Raise the transmission with the transmission jack and position the transmission to the engine.

31. Install the transmission bolts (1, 3, and 4) and tighten to 55 ft. lbs. (75 Nm).

32. Remove the transmission jack.

➡**If reusing the torque converter bolts, clean the threads and apply LOC-TITE®242, GM P/N 36616382 (Canadian P/N 10953489) or equivalent to the threads prior to installation.**

33. Install the torque converter to flywheel bolts and tighten to 46 ft. lbs. (62 Nm).

34. Install the starter.

35. Install the front transmission mount to the transmission.

36. Install the rear transmission mount to the transmission.

37. Install the intermediate drive shaft.

38. Install the wheel drive shafts to the transmission.

39. Install the frame.

40. Install the upper transmission to engine bolts and tighten to 55 ft. lbs. (75 Nm).

41. Install the transmission fluid cooler outlet hose to the transmission.

42. Install the transmission fluid cooler outlet hose retainer nut and tighten to 16 ft. lbs. (22 Nm).

43. Install the transmission fluid cooler inlet hose to the transmission.

44. Install the transmission fluid cooler inlet hose retainer nut.

45. Install the oil cooler inlet and outlet hoses to the retainer on the control valve body cover.

46. Connect the control valve body TCM electrical connector.

47. Install the transmission range select lever cable and bracket.

48. Install the battery tray.

49. Adjust the automatic transmission range selector lever cable.

50. Fill the transmission with fluid.

➡**It is recommended that Transmission Adaptive Pressure (TAP) information be reset. Reset the TAP values using a scan tool will erase all learned values in all cells. As a result, the ECM, PCM, or TCM will need to relearn TAP values. Transmission performance may be affected as new TAP values are learned.**

51. Reset the TAP values by selecting the following:
- Scan tool
- Special functions
- Transmission output controls
- Reset transmission adapts

52. Road test the vehicle.

6T70/6T75

See Figures 18 and 19.

1. Remove the battery tray.

2. Remove the transmission range select lever cable and bracket.

3. Drain the transmission fluid.

4. Remove the wire harness retainer from the control valve body cover stud.

5. Disconnect the control valve body Transmission Control Module (TCM) electrical connector.

6. Remove the transmission fluid cooler pipe retainer nut.

7. Remove the transmission fluid cooler inlet hose and seal from the transmission.

8. Plug and/or cap the hose and transmission to prevent contamination.

9. Remove the transmission fluid cooler pipe retainer nut.

10. Remove the transmission fluid cooler outlet hose and seal from the transmission.

11. Plug and/or cap the hose and transmission to prevent contamination.

12. Disconnect both pipes from the retainer.

13. Install the engine support fixture.

14. Remove the rear transmission mount from the transmission.

15. Remove the front transmission mount from the transmission.

16. Remove the left transmission mount from the transmission.

17. Remove the upper transmission to engine bolts.

18. Remove the frame as follows:
   a. Install the engine support fixture.
   b. Support the radiator and condenser from above.
   c. Raise the vehicle on a hoist.
   d. Remove the tire and wheel assemblies.
   e. Remove the front fender liner.
   f. Remove the engine splash shield.
   g. Remove the lower ball joints from the steering knuckles.
   h. Remove the tie rod ends from the steering knuckles.
   i. Remove both stabilizer links from the stabilizer bar.
   j. Remove the power steering gear mounting bolts and secure the gear out

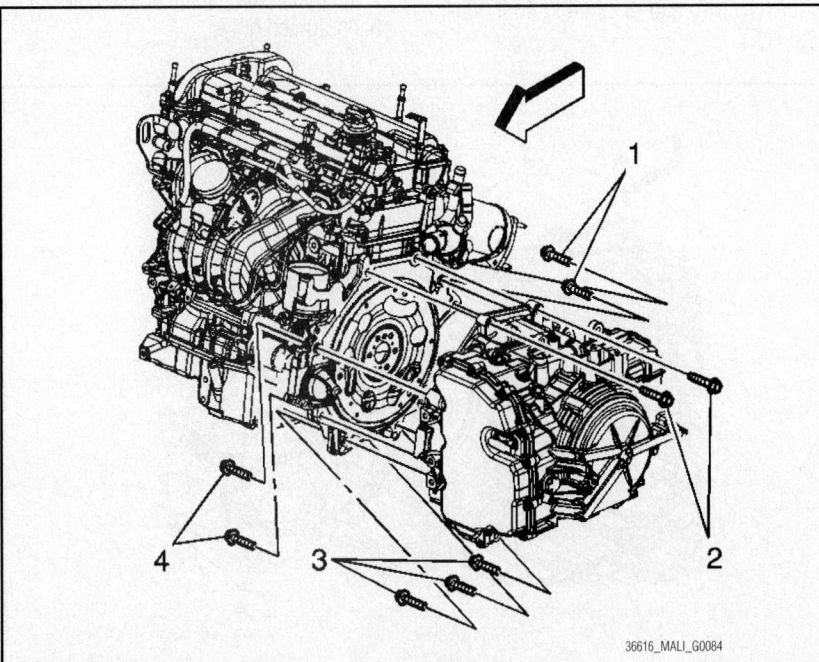

36616_MALI_G0084

Fig. 17 Removing the remaining transmission fasteners (1, 3, 4)

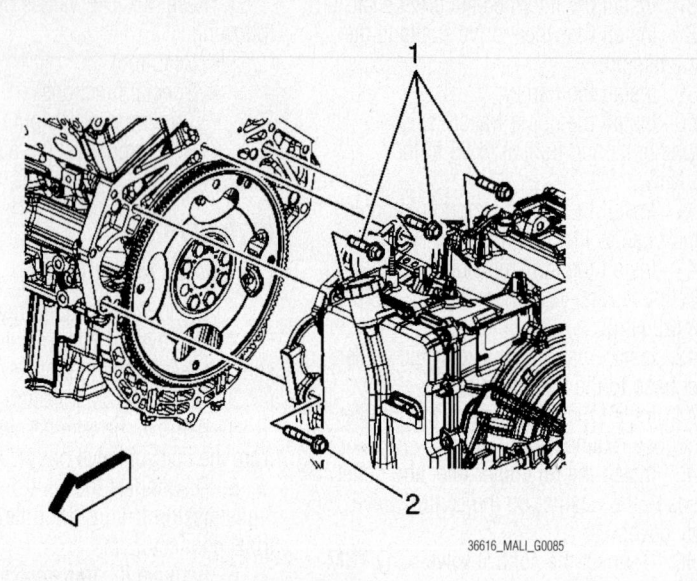

Fig. 18 Locating the upper transmission to engine bolts

of the way using mechanic's wire or equivalent, being sure not to overextend the intermediate shaft.

    k. Remove the engine mount fasteners from the frame.

    l. Remove the front transmission mount bolt from the frame.

    m. Remove the left transmission mount fasteners from the frame.

    n. Remove the rear transmission mount bracket fasteners from the frame.

    o. Remove the brake lines from the retainers on the frame.

    p. Remove the power steering outlet pipe/hose from the frame.

    q. Remove the rear catalytic converter.

    r. Lower the vehicle until the frame contacts the engine support fixture.

    s. Remove the reinforcement bolts.

    t. Remove the front frame bolts.

    u. Remove the rear frame bolts.

    v. Remove the frame reinforcements.

    w. Raise the vehicle off of the frame.

  19. Disconnect the wheel drive shafts from the transmission.

  20. Remove the intermediate drive shaft.

  21. Remove the starter.

  22. Mark the relationship of the flywheel to the torque converter for reassembly.

  23. Remove the torque converter to flywheel bolts.

  24. Use a transmission jack in order to support the transmission.

  25. Remove the flywheel inspection cover bolts.

  26. Remove the flywheel inspection cover.

  27. Remove the remaining transmission bolts.

➡**Ensure the torque converter remains securely in place on the transmission input shaft while separating and removing the transmission.**

  28. Separate the transmission from the engine.

  29. Lower the transmission with the transmission jack far enough to remove the transmission.

   To install:

  30. Raise the transmission with the transmission jack and position the transmission to the engine.

  31. Install the transmission bolts (2) to 55 ft. lbs. (75 Nm) and (3 and 4 to 43 ft. lbs. (58 Nm).

  32. Install the flywheel inspection cover and bolts. Tighten the bolts to 55 ft. lbs. (75 Nm).

  33. Remove the transmission jack.

➡**If reusing the torque converter bolts, clean the threads and apply LOCTITE®242, GM P/N 36616382 (Canadian P/N 10953489) or equivalent to the threads prior to installation.**

  34. Install the torque converter to flywheel bolts. Tighten the bolts to 46 ft. lbs. (62 Nm).

  35. Install the starter.

  36. Install the front transmission mount to the transmission. Tighten the nut to 66 ft. lbs. (90 Nm) and the bolts to 37 ft. lbs. (50 Nm).

  37. Install the rear transmission mount to the transmission. Tighten the transaxle mount to transmission bolts to 37 ft. lbs. (50 Nm) and the transaxle to mount bracket through bolt to 66 ft. lbs. (90 Nm).

  38. Install the left transmission mount to the transmission. Tighten the mount bolt to 66 ft. lbs. (90 Nm) and the nuts to 37 ft. lbs. (50 Nm).

  39. Install the transmission brace.

  40. Install the transmission brace bolts. Tighten the bolts to 37 ft. lbs. (50 Nm)

  41. Install the intermediate drive shaft.

  42. Install the wheel drive shafts to the transmission.

  43. Install the frame as follows:

    a. Lower the vehicle on to the frame.

    b. Install the frame reinforcements.

    c. Install the front frame bolts and hand tighten only.

    d. Install the reinforcement bolts and hand tighten only.

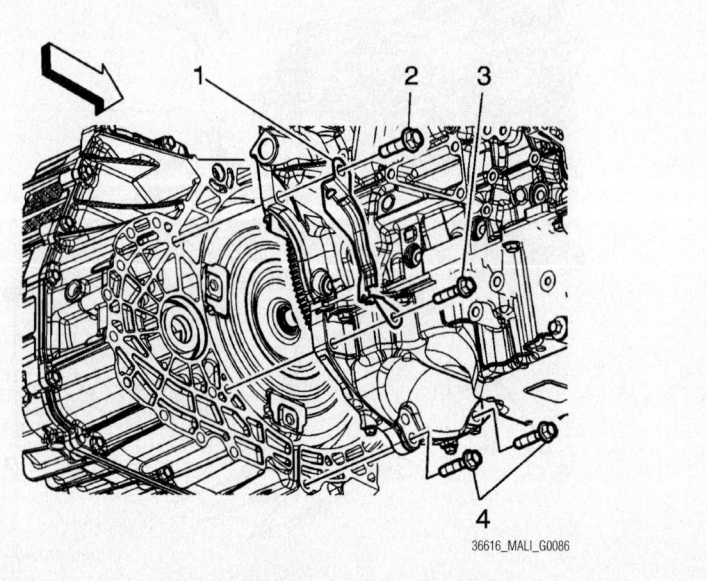

Fig. 19 Identifying the transmission and flywheel inspection cover bolts for installation

e. Tighten the rear frame bolts. Tighten to 74 ft. lbs. (100 Nm) , plus an additional 90 degrees.

f. Tighten the front frame bolts. Tighten to 74 ft. lbs. (100 Nm) , plus an additional 90 degrees.

g. Install the reinforcement bolts. Tighten to 74 ft. lbs. (100 Nm).

h. Raise the vehicle.

i. Install the power steering outlet pipe/hose to the frame.

j. Install the brake lines to the retainers on the frame.

k. Install the rear transmission mount bracket fasteners. Tighten the transaxle mount to transmission bolts to 37 ft. lbs. (50 Nm) and the transaxle to mount bracket through bolt to 66 ft. lbs. (90 Nm).

l. Install the left transmission mount fasteners to the frame. Tighten the transaxle mount to transmission bolts to 66 ft. lbs. (90 Nm) and the transaxle to mount bracket through bolt to 66 ft. lbs. (90 Nm).

m. Install the front transmission mount bracket bolt. Tighten the transaxle mount to transmission bolts to 66 ft. lbs. (90 Nm) and the transaxle to mount bracket through bolt to 66 ft. lbs. (90 Nm).

n. Install the engine mount fasteners to the frame. Tighten the nuts/bolts to 38 ft. lbs. (50 Nm).

o. Install the power steering gear mounting fasteners.

p. Install both stabilizer links to the stabilizer bar. Tighten to 48 ft. lbs. (65 Nm) plus an additional 180 degrees.

q. Install the tie rod ends to the steering knuckles.

r. Install the lower ball joints to the steering knuckles. Tighten the ball stud to steering knuckle pinch nut to 37 ft. lbs. (50 Nm). Reverse the nut ¾ of a turn. Tighten to 37 ft. lbs. (50 Nm) plus an additional 60 degrees.

s. Install the rear catalytic converter.

t. Install the front fender liner.

u. Install the engine splash shield.

v. Lower the vehicle.

w. Remove the temporary radiator and condenser support.

x. Remove the engine support fixture.

44. Install the upper transmission to engine bolt. Tighten the bolts to 43 ft. lbs. (58 Nm).

45. Remove the engine support fixture.

46. Install the transmission fluid cooler outlet and inlet hoses and seal to the transmission.

47. Install the transmission fluid cooler pipe retainer nut. Tighten to 16 ft. lbs. (22 Nm).

48. Install the remaining components in the reverse order of removal.

49. Fill the transmission with fluid.

➡It is recommended that Transmission Adaptive Pressure (TAP) information be reset. Reset the TAP values using a scan tool will erase all learned values in all cells. As a result, the ECM, PCM, or TCM will need to relearn TAP values. Transmission performance may be affected as new TAP values are learned.

50. Reset the TAP values by selecting the following:

- Scan tool
- Special functions
- Transmission output controls
- Reset transmission adapts

51. Road test the vehicle.

FRONT AXLE SHAFT, BEARING & SEAL

REMOVAL & INSTALLATION

See Figures 20 and 21.

1. Remove the drive shaft.
2. Remove the intermediate shaft bolts and the shaft.

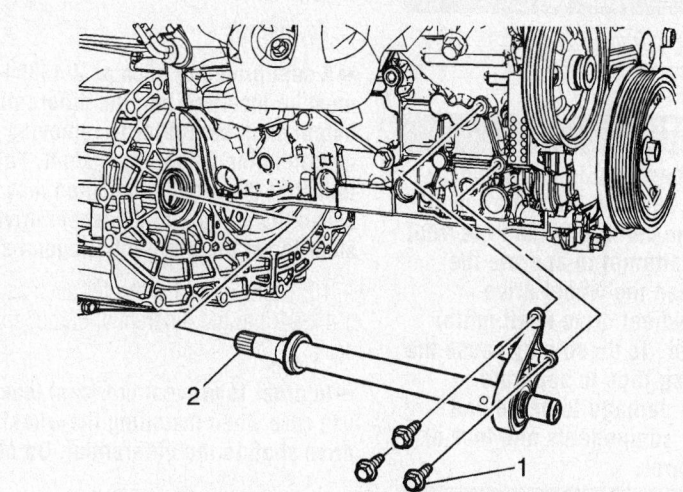

1. Front wheel drive intermediate shaft bracket bolt
2. Front wheel drive intermediate shaft

36616_MALI_G0087

Fig. 20 Removing the intermediate shaft—3.6L engine

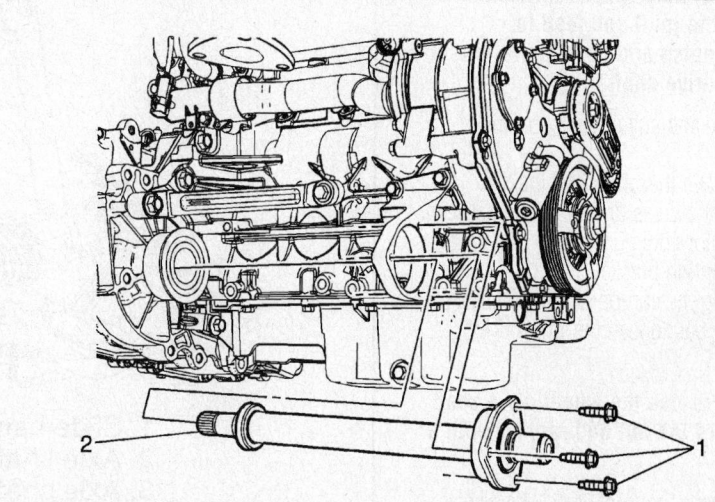

1. Front wheel drive intermediate shaft bracket bolt
2. Front wheel drive intermediate shaft

36616_MALI_G0088

Fig. 21 Removing the intermediate shaft—2.4L engine

➡Use care when removing the intermediate drive shaft from the transmission as not to damage the seal.

To install:

3. Installation is the reverse of removal. Tighten the intermediate shaft bolts to 44 ft. lbs. (60 Nm).

➡A seal protector such as J-44394 must be installed into the differential output shaft seal prior to removing and installing the intermediate shaft. Failure to install the tool as indicated may cause the splines of the intermediate shaft to cut the differential output seal.

FRONT HALFSHAFTS

REMOVAL & INSTALLATION

See Figure 22.

✳✳ CAUTION

To prevent personal injury and/or component damage, do not allow the weight of the vehicle to load the front wheels, or attempt to operate the vehicle, when the wheel drive shaft(s) or wheel drive shaft nut(s) are removed. To do so may cause the inner bearing race to separate, resulting in damage to brake and suspension components and loss of vehicle control.

➡Wheel drive shaft boots, seals and clamps should be protected from sharp objects any time service is performed on or near the wheel drive shaft(s). Damage to the boot(s), the seal(s) or the clamp(s) may cause lubricant to leak from the joint and lead to increased noise and possible failure of the wheel drive shaft.

1. Raise and suitably support the vehicle.
2. Remove the wheel and the tire.
3. Insert a brass drift or punch between the brake rotor cooling fins and the brake caliper mounting bracket.
4. Using the appropriate size socket and breaker bar, loosen the wheel drive shaft nut.

➡Do NOT re-use the wheel drive shaft nut. Discard the nut and replace with a NEW one.

5. Remove the front wheel drive shaft nut from the wheel drive shaft.
6. Using the hub spindle remover (J 42129), separate the brake rotor and wheel bearing/hub assembly.

7. Remove the outer tie rod assembly from the steering knuckle.
8. Remove the ball joint from the steering knuckle.

➡A seal protector such as J-44394 must be installed into the differential output shaft seal prior to removing and installing the wheel drive shaft. Failure to install the tool as indicated may cause the splines of the wheel drive shaft to cut the differential output seal.

9. Using the slide hammer (J 2619-01), the axle shaft remover extension (J 29794), and the axle shaft remover (J 33008-A), remove the wheel drive shaft from the vehicle.

To install:

➡A seal protector such as J-44394 must be installed into the differential output shaft seal prior to removing and installing the wheel drive shaft. Failure to install the tool as indicated may cause the splines of the wheel drive shaft to cut the differential output seal.

10. Install a seal protector such as J-44394 into the differential output shaft seal.

➡In order to prevent lubricant leaks, use care when installing the wheel drive shaft to the differential. Do not damage the oil seal. Replace the oil seal if it becomes nicked, distorted, or otherwise damaged.

11. Carefully install the wheel drive shaft into the differential until the splines are past the seal protector.
12. Carefully remove the seal protector from the differential output shaft seal.
13. Carefully continue installing the wheel drive shaft into the differential until the retaining ring is fully seated.
14. Verify the front wheel drive shaft retaining ring is properly seated by grasping the inner housing and pull the inner housing outward.
15. Install the front wheel drive shaft into the front wheel bearing/hub.
16. Install the ball joint to the steering knuckle.
17. Install the outer tie rod assembly to the steering knuckle.
18. Install the NEW wheel drive shaft nut on the wheel drive shaft.
19. Insert a drift or punch into the cooling fin of the brake rotor caliper and against the brake caliper mounting bracket.
20. Using a torque wrench and the appropriate size socket, tighten the wheel drive shaft nut to 159 ft. lbs. (215 Nm).
21. Install the wheel and the tire.
22. Lower the vehicle.
23. Inspect the transaxle fluid level.

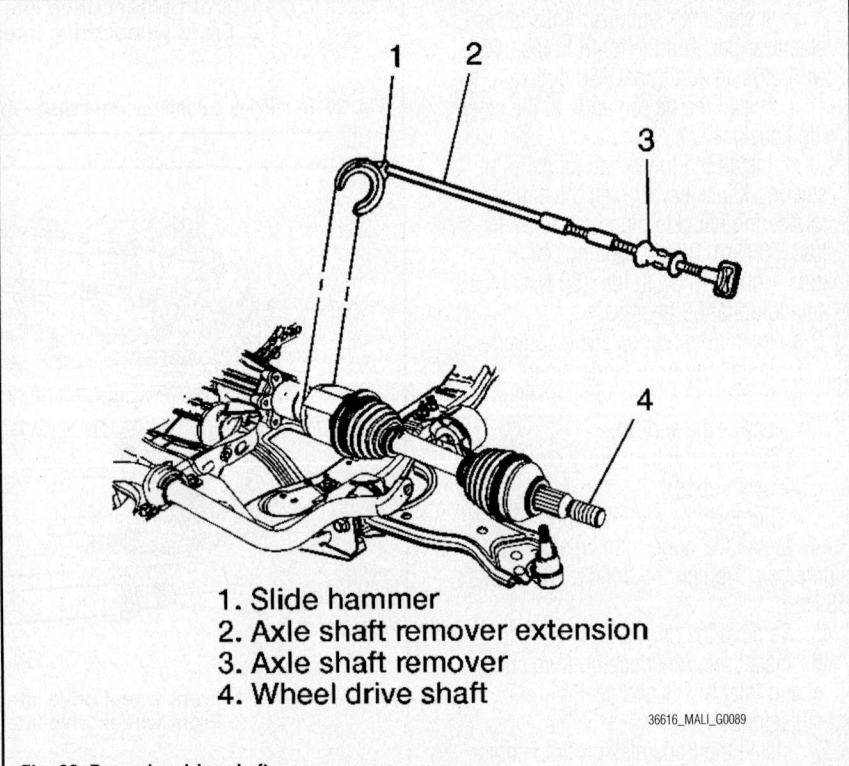

1. Slide hammer
2. Axle shaft remover extension
3. Axle shaft remover
4. Wheel drive shaft

36616_MALI_G0089

Fig. 22 Removing drive shaft

ENGINE COOLING

ENGINE FAN

REMOVAL & INSTALLATION

See Figures 23 and 24.

1. Drain and recycle the engine coolant.
2. Remove the air cleaner outlet air duct on the 2.4L engine.
3. Remove the air cleaner inlet air duct on the 3.5 and 3.6L engines
4. Remove the upper radiator air deflector.
5. Remove the transmission oil cooler pipes from the radiator.
6. Loop a rope around each of the upper 2 tabs of the condenser and tie a rope around the upper tie bar.
7. Remove the upper radiator support bracket bolts.
8. Remove the upper radiator support brackets.
9. Pry upward on the fan shroud tabs at the radiator clips to release the fan shroud from the radiator.
10. Remove the lower radiator air deflector.
11. Lower the vehicle.
12. Remove the radiator inlet hose from the radiator.
13. Remove the radiator outlet hose from the radiator.
14. Disconnect the cooling fan wire harness connectors.
15. Remove the A/C compressor and condenser hose assembly.
16. Raise the vehicle.
17. Remove the lower radiator support bracket bolts.
18. Remove the lower radiator support brackets.
19. Remove the transmission oil cooler pipe clip from the fan shroud.
20. Remove the fan assembly.

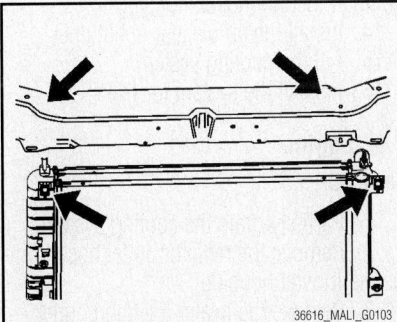

Fig. 23 Locating the tie bar and upper tabs on the condenser

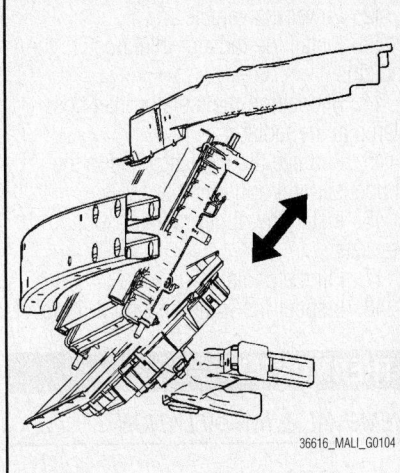

Fig. 24 Removing the cooling fan and shroud assembly

To install:

21. Install the fan shroud assembly.
22. Install the transmission oil cooler pipes to the radiator.
23. Install the transmission oil cooler pipe clip to the fan shroud.
24. Install the lower radiator support brackets.
25. Install the lower radiator support bracket bolts and tighten to 44 ft. lbs. (60 Nm).
26. Install the cooling fan wire harness connectors.
27. Install the radiator outlet hose to the radiator.
28. Install the lower radiator air deflector.
29. Lower the vehicle.
30. Snap fan shroud tabs into the radiator clips.
31. Remove the rope attached to the condenser and upper tie bar.
32. Install the upper radiator support brackets.
33. Install the upper radiator support bracket bolts and tighten to 89 inch lbs. (10 Nm).
34. Install the radiator inlet hose to the radiator.
35. Install the A/C compressor and condenser hose assembly.
36. Install the upper radiator air deflector.
37. Install the air duct.
38. Fill the cooling system.
39. Inspect the transmission fluid level.

RADIATOR

REMOVAL & INSTALLATION

See Figure 25.

1. Drain and recycle the engine coolant.
2. Loop a rope around each of the upper 2 tabs of the condenser and tie the rope around the upper tie bar.
3. Remove the upper radiator support brackets.
4. Reposition the radiator inlet hose clamp at the radiator.
5. Remove the radiator inlet hose from the radiator.
6. Remove the front air dam.
7. Remove the right engine splash shield retainers.
8. Remove the right engine splash shield.
9. Remove the left engine splash shield retainers.
10. Remove the left engine splash shield.
11. Reposition the radiator outlet hose clamp at the radiator.
12. Remove the radiator outlet hose from the radiator.
13. Remove the transmission oil cooler pipes from the transmission.
14. Remove the lower radiator support bracket bolts.
15. Remove the lower radiator support brackets.
16. Remove the radiator lower mounts.
17. Remove and discard the condenser mounting bolts from the radiator.
18. Push upward on the radiator and downward on the condenser to unsnap the condenser mounting tabs from the radiator clips.
19. Remove and discard the condenser mounting nuts from the radiator.

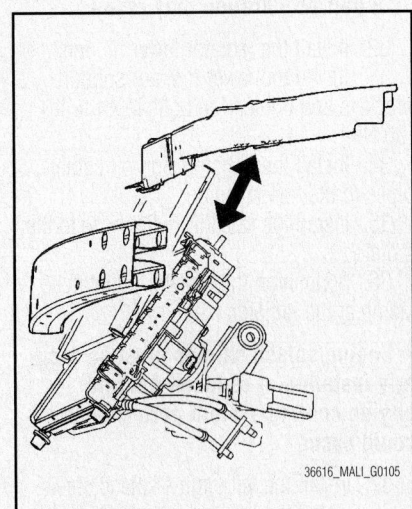

Fig. 25 Removing and installing the radiator

20. Remove the radiator air side seals.
21. Remove the radiator and cooling fan shroud assembly from the vehicle.
22. Pry upward on the fan shroud tabs at the radiator clips.
23. Remove the cooling fan and shroud assembly from the radiator.

To install:

24. Install the cooling fan and shroud assembly to the radiator.
25. Snap the fan shroud tabs into the radiator clips.
26. Install the radiator and cooling fan shroud assembly to the vehicle.
27. Install the radiator air side seals onto the condenser mounting tabs on the radiator.

➡The bolt retaining the condenser to the radiator end tank is a special length and should be the ONLY bolt used upon reinstallation. The use of a longer bolt will damage the radiator end tank.

➡Replace the condenser mounting bolts and nuts.

28. Install the condenser mounting nuts to the radiator.
29. Insert the condenser mounting tabs into the radiator clips.
30. Install the condenser to the radiator bolts and tighten to 53 inch lbs. (6 Nm).
31. Bend the radiator air side seals and insert the seals into the channel of the intake air splash shields.

➡The radiator air side seals must be in the proper position for proper air flow.

➡Replace the radiator lower mounts as a pair or vibration may result.

32. Install the radiator lower mounts.
33. Install the lower radiator support brackets and tighten the bolts to 44 ft. lbs. (60 Nm).
34. Install the transmission oil cooler pipes to the transmission.
35. Install the radiator outlet hose to the radiator.
36. Reposition the radiator outlet hose clamp at the radiator.

➡Engine splash shields must be properly installed or reduced A/C and engine cooling system performance could occur.

37. Install the left engine splash shield.
38. Install the left engine splash shield retainers.
39. Install the right engine splash shield.

40. Install the right engine splash shield retainers.
41. Install the front air dam.
42. Lower the vehicle.
43. Install the radiator inlet hose to the radiator.
44. Reposition the radiator inlet hose clamp at the radiator.
45. Remove the rope attached to the condenser and upper tie bar.
46. Install the upper radiator support brackets.
47. Fill the coolant.
48. Inspect the transmission fluid level.

THERMOSTAT

REMOVAL & INSTALLATION

2.4L Engine

See Figure 26.

1. Drain the cooling system.
2. Reposition the radiator outlet hose clamp at the thermostat cover.
3. Remove the radiator outlet hose from the thermostat cover.
4. Remove the thermostat cover bolts and cover.
5. Remove the thermostat.
6. Remove and discard the thermostat cover o-ring seal.

To install:

7. Install a NEW thermostat cover O-ring seal into the recess groove.
8. Install the thermostat, if necessary.
9. Install the thermostat cover bolts. Tighten the bolts to 89 inch lbs. (10 Nm).
10. Install the radiator outlet hose to the thermostat cover.
11. Position the radiator outlet hose clamp at the thermostat cover.
12. Fill the cooling system.

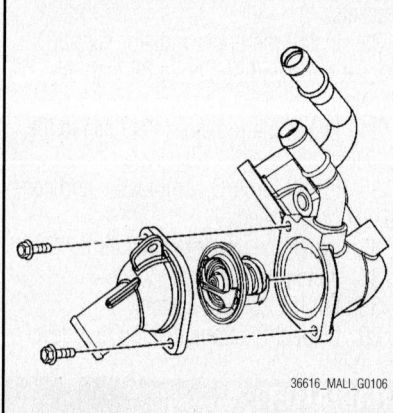

Fig. 26 Removing the thermostat—2.4L engine

3.5L Engine

See Figure 27.

1. Drain and recycle the engine coolant.
2. Remove the air cleaner outlet duct.
3. Reposition the radiator outlet hose clamp at the thermostat housing.
4. Remove the radiator outlet hose from the thermostat housing.
5. Remove the thermostat housing bolt/stud.
6. Remove the thermostat housing and gasket.
7. Remove the thermostat.
8. Clean the gasket surfaces.

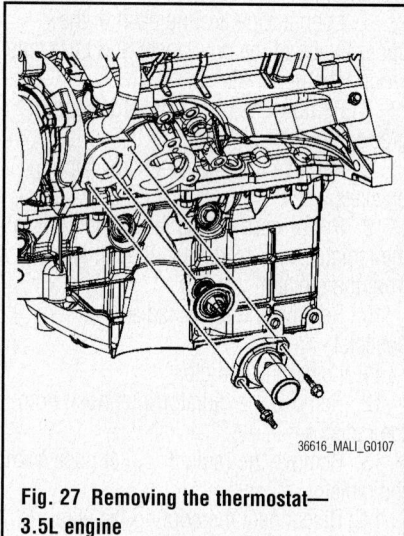

36616_MALI_G0107

Fig. 27 Removing the thermostat—3.5L engine

To install:

9. Install a NEW thermostat.
10. Position a NEW gasket and the thermostat housing to the engine block.
11. Install the thermostat housing bolt/stud. Tighten the bolt/stud to 89 inch lbs. (10 Nm).
12. Install the radiator outlet hose to the thermostat housing.
13. Position the radiator outlet hose clamp at the thermostat housing.
14. Install the air cleaner outlet duct.
15. Fill the cooling system.
16. Inspect the system for leaks

3.6L Engine

See Figure 28.

1. Partially drain the cooling system.
2. Remove the radiator outlet hose from the thermostat housing.
3. Remove the heater inlet and outlet hoses.
4. Remove the surge tank outlet hose.
5. Remove the thermostat housing bolts.
6. Remove the housing.

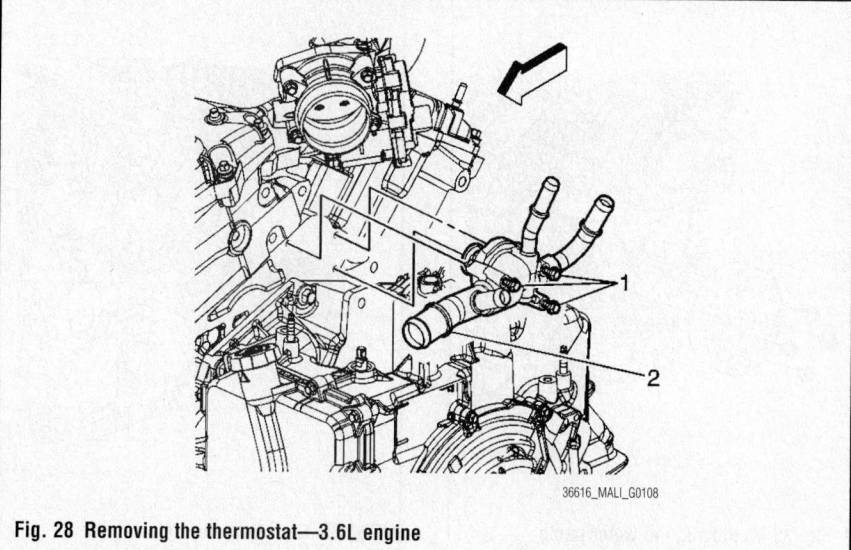

Fig. 28 Removing the thermostat—3.6L engine

7. Remove the thermostat and discard the thermostat gasket.

To install:

8. Install the thermostat with a NEW thermostat gasket.

9. Install the thermostat housing bolts. Tighten the bolts to 89 inch lbs. (10 Nm).

10. Install the surge tank outlet hose.

11. Install the heater inlet and outlet hoses.

12. Install the radiator outlet hose to the thermostat housing.

13. Fill the cooling system.

WATER PUMP

REMOVAL & INSTALLATION

2.4L Engine

See Figures 29 through 32.

1. Drain and recycle the engine coolant.
2. Remove the thermostat housing.
3. Remove the coolant heater.
4. Remove the water pump access plate from the front cover.

➡ The water pump holding tool supports the sprocket and chain during water pump service. The tool must be used or the balance shaft must be re-timed.

5. Install a water pump holding tool such as J 43651 into position.

6. Tighten the bolts on the water pump holding tool into the threads on the water pump sprocket. Install the access cover bolts that were removed earlier to secure the water pump holding tool to the front cover assembly.

7. Remove the 3 inner water pump sprocket to water pump blots.

➡ Be sure to remove both water pump bolts from the front of the engine block.

8. Remove the 2 water pump bolts.

9. Remove the rear 2 water pump bolts.

10. Remove the water pump.

11. Remove and discard the water pump O-ring seal.

To install:

12. Apply sealant GM P/N 12378521 (Canadian P/N 88901148) or equivalent to the water pump drain plug.

13. Install the water pump drain plug and tighten to 15 ft. lbs. (20 Nm).

➡ A guide pin can be created to aid in the water pump alignment. Use a M6 x 6mm stud. Thread the pin into the water pump sprocket.

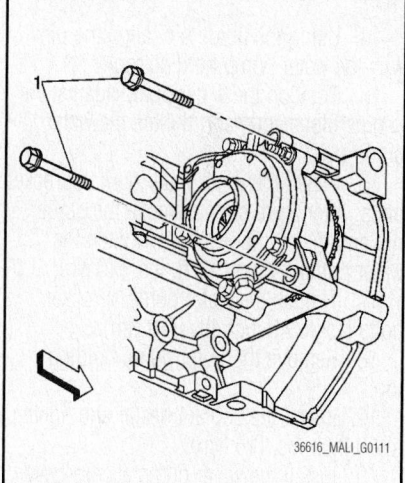

Fig. 31 Removing the 2 rear water pump bolts—2.4L engine

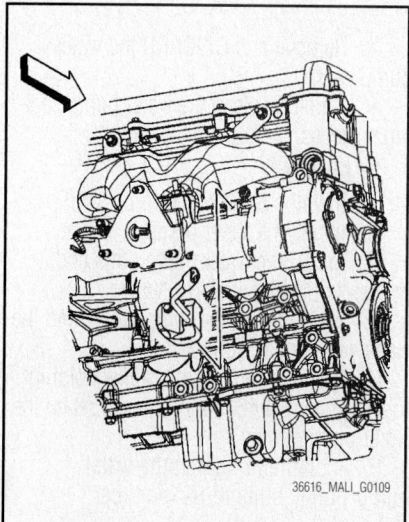

Fig. 29 Removing the coolant heater— 2.4L engine

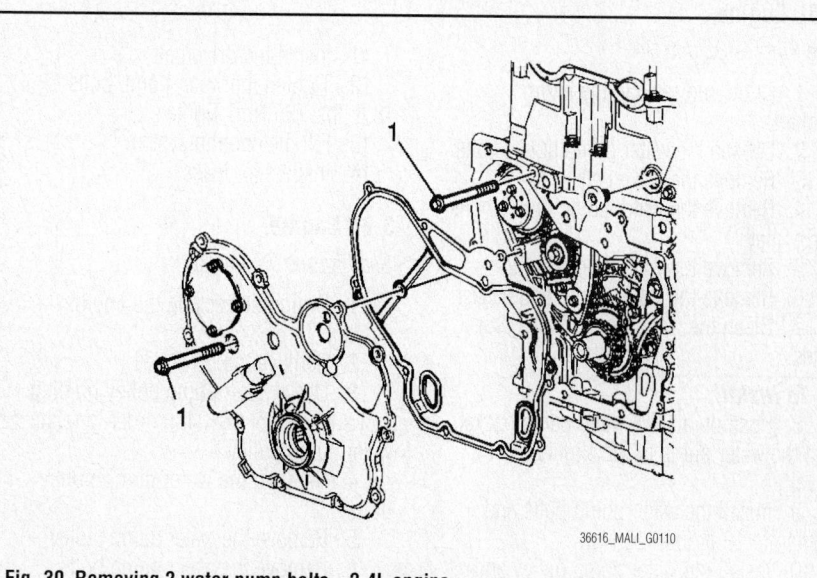

Fig. 30 Removing 2 water pump bolts—2.4L engine

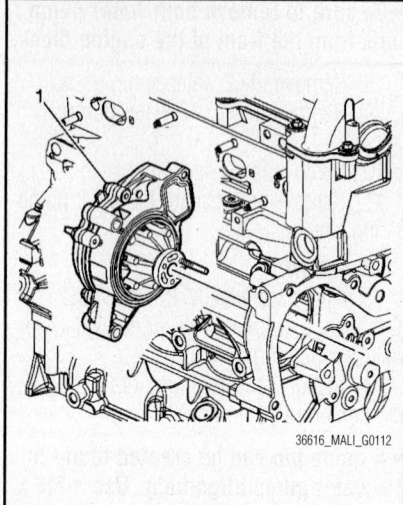

Fig. 32 Removing the water pump—2.4L engine

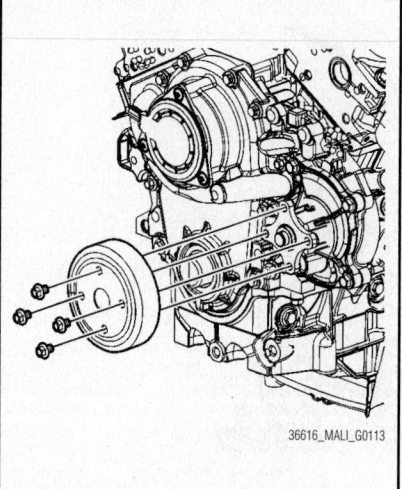

Fig. 33 Removing the water pump pulley—3.5L engine

Fig. 35 Removing the water pump pulley—3.6L engine

14. Using the guide pin, align the pin with the water pump holding tool.

15. Position the water pump against the engine block and hand tighten the water pump bolts.

16. Install the inner water pump sprocket bolts. After 2 are snug, remove the guide pin and install the 3rd bolt. Tighten the water pump bolts to 18 ft. lbs. (25 Nm).

17. Tighten the water pump sprocket bolts last to 89 inch lbs. (10 Nm).

18. Remove the water pump holding tool.

19. Install the coolant heater and tighten to 89 inch lbs. (10 Nm).

20. Install the water pump access plate and bolts and tighten to 89 inch lbs. (10 Nm).

21. Install the thermostat housing.

3.5L Engine

See Figures 33 and 34.

1. Drain and recycle the engine coolant.

2. Loosen the water pump pulley bolts.

3. Remove the drive belt.

4. Remove the water pump pulley bolts and pulley.

5. Remove the water pump bolts.

6. Remove the water pump and gasket.

7. Clean the water pump mating surfaces.

To install:

8. Position a NEW water pump gasket and the water pump to the engine front cover.

9. Install the water pump bolts and tighten to 18 ft. lbs. (25 Nm).

10. Install the water pump pulley and bolts.

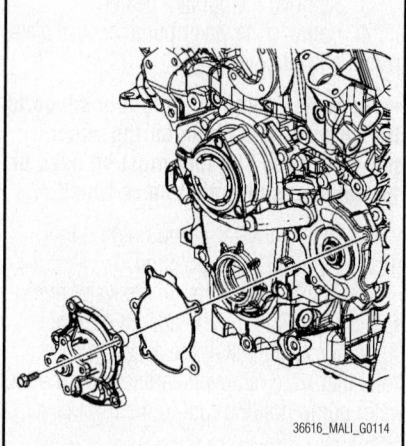

Fig. 34 Removing and installing the water pump—3.5L engine

11. Install the drive belt.

12. Tighten the water pump bolts to 18 ft. lbs. (25 Nm).Tighten

13. Fill the cooling system.

14. Inspect for leaks.

3.6L Engine

See Figures 35 and 36.

1. Drain and recycle the engine coolant.

2. Remove the drive belt.

3. Use a water pump pulley holding tool such as EN 46104 in order to retain the water pump pulley.

4. Remove the water pump pulley bolts.

5. Remove the water pump pulley.

6. Remove the water pump bolts.

7. Remove the water pump.

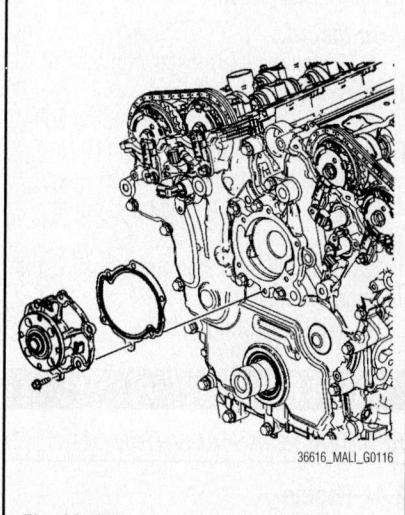

Fig. 36 Removing the water pump—3.6L engine

8. Remove and DISCARD the water pump seal.

9. Carefully clean the water pump sealing surfaces.

To install:

10. Install a NEW water pump seal.

11. Install the water pump.

12. Install the water pump bolts and tighten to 89 inch lbs. (10 Nm).

13. Install the water pump pulley and the water pump pulley bolts.

14. Use the water pump pulley holding tool such as EN 46104 in order to retain the water pump pulley.

15. Install and tighten the water pump pulley bolts to 89 inch lbs. (10 Nm).

16. Install the drive belt.

17. Fill the cooling system.

ENGINE ELECTRICAL

ALTERNATOR

REMOVAL & INSTALLATION

2.4L Engine

See Figures 37 and 38.

1. Disconnect negative battery cable.
2. Remove the drive belt.
3. Disconnect the generator electrical connector.
4. Reposition the rubber boot.
5. Remove the engine harness terminal lead to generator nut.
6. Remove the engine harness terminal from the generator stud.
7. Remove the generator fasteners.
8. Remove the generator.

To install:

9. Position the generator to the engine block.
10. Install the generator fasteners loosely.
11. Install the fastener (1) and tighten to 89 inch lbs. (10 Nm).
12. Install the fastener (3) and tighten to 16 ft. lbs. (22 Nm).
13. Tighten the fasteners (4) to 16 ft. lbs. (22 Nm).
14. Install the engine harness terminal to the generator stud.
15. Install the engine harness lead to generator nut and tighten to 15 ft. lbs. (20 Nm).
16. Position the rubber boot over the stud.

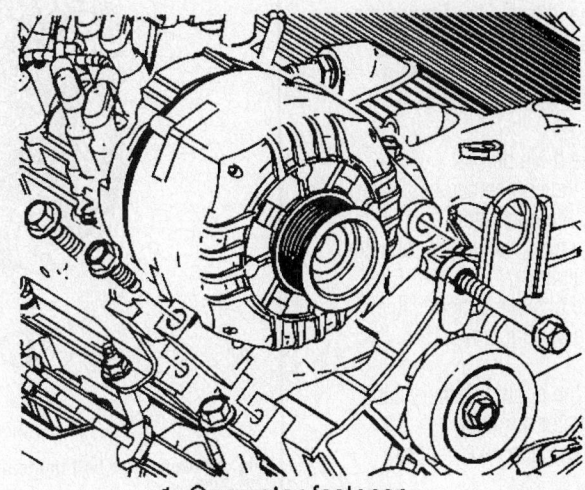

1. Generator fastener
2. Generator
3. Generator fastener
4. Generator fastener

36616_MALI_G0119

Fig. 38 Removing the generator—2.4L engine

17. Connect the generator electrical connector.
18. Install the drive belt.
19. Connect negative battery cable.

3.5L Engine

➡ **Service the generator as a complete unit.**

1. Disconnect the negative battery cable.
2. Remove the drive belt.
3. Remove the generator electrical connections.
4. Remove the generator mounting nuts and bolts.
5. Remove the generator.

To install:

6. Installation is the reverse of removal, tighten the bolts to 37 ft. lbs. (50 Nm) and the nuts to 22 ft. lbs. (30 Nm).

3.6L Engine

See Figure 39.

1. Disconnect the negative battery cable.
2. Remove the air cleaner outlet duct.
3. Reposition the positive battery cable boot at the generator terminal.
4. Remove the positive battery cable nut at the generator.
5. Remove the positive battery cable terminal from the generator.
6. Disconnect the engine harness electrical connector from the generator.
7. Remove the drive belt.
8. Remove the idler pulley.
9. Remove the alternator bolts.

➡ **When removing the alternator from the vehicle, it may be necessary to maneuver the alternator to remove it from the vehicle.**

10. Remove the alternator.

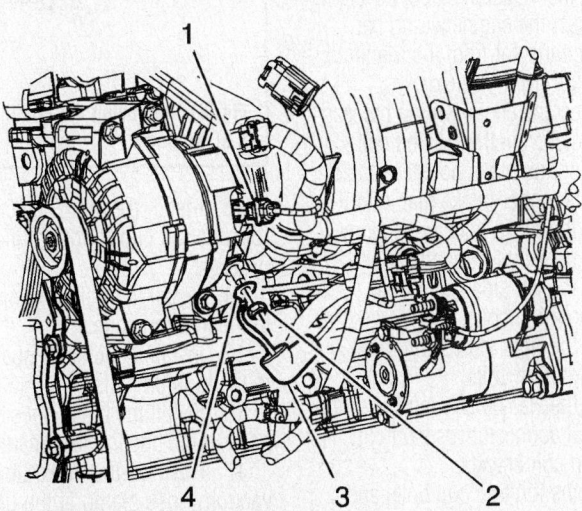

1. Generator electrical connector
2. Engine harness terminal lead to generator nut
3. Rubber boot
4. Engine harness terminal from generator stud

36616_MALI_G0118

Fig. 37 Disconnecting the generator—2.4L engine

To install:

11. Install the alternator.

12. Loosely install the alternator bolts.

13. Install the idler pulley. Tighten the bolts to 43 ft. lbs. (58 Nm).

14. Tighten the generator bolts in the sequence shown to 37 ft. lbs. (50 Nm).

15. Install the drive belt.

16. Connect the engine harness electrical connector to the generator.

17. Install the positive battery cable terminal to the generator.

18. Install the positive battery cable nut at the generator. Tighten to 15 ft. lbs. (20 Nm).

19. Position the positive battery cable boot at the generator terminal.

20. Connect the negative battery cable.

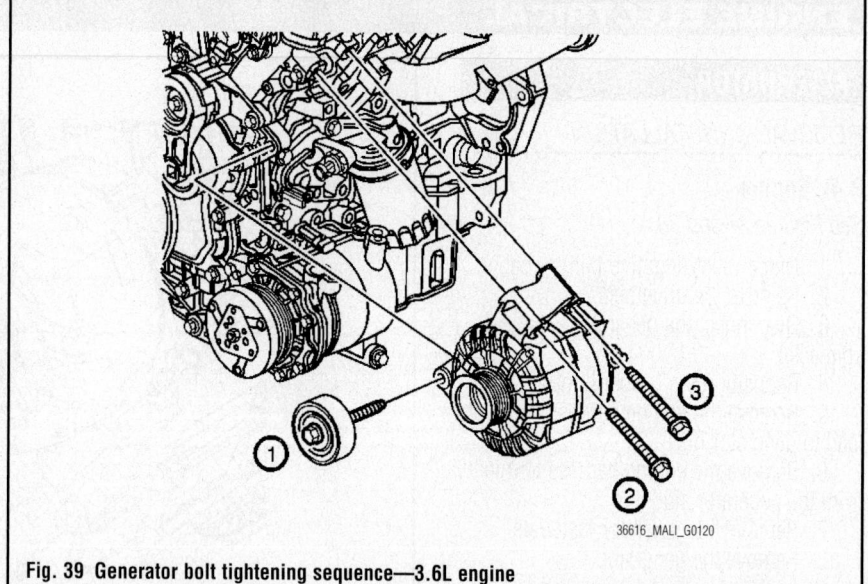

36616_MALI_G0120

Fig. 39 Generator bolt tightening sequence—3.6L engine

ENGINE ELECTRICAL

FIRING ORDER

The firing order for the 2.4L engine is 1-3-4-2.

The firing order for the 3.5L and 3.6L engine is 1-2-3-4-5-6.

IGNITION COIL PACK

REMOVAL & INSTALLATION

2.4L Engine

See Figure 40.

1. Remove the air cleaner outlet duct.

2. Disconnect the engine wiring harness electrical connectors from the ignition coil(s).

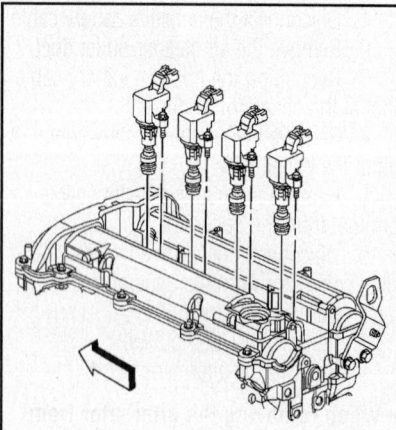

36616_MALI_G0121

Fig. 40 Removing the ignition coil pack— 2.4L engine

3. Remove the ignition coil bolt(s).

4. Remove the ignition coil(s).

To install:

5. Install the ignition coil(s).

6. Install the ignition coil bolts and tighten to 89 inch lbs. (10 Nm).

7. Connect the engine wiring harness electrical connectors to the ignition coils.

8. Install the air cleaner outlet duct.

3.5L Engine

See Figure 41.

1. Remove the intake manifold cover.

2. Disconnect the engine wiring harness electrical connector from the Manifold Absolute Pressure (MAP) sensor.

3. Disconnect the engine wiring harness electrical connector from the ignition coil.

4. Reposition the brake booster vacuum hose clamp at the upper intake manifold.

5. Remove the brake booster vacuum hose from the upper intake manifold.

6. Remove the left side spark plug wires from the ignition coils.

7. Remove the right side spark plug wires from the ignition coils.

8. Remove the Heated Oxygen Sensor (HO2S) electrical connector rosebud clip from the ignition coil bracket.

9. Remove the ignition coil bolts and nuts.

10. Remove the ignition coil.

To install:

11. Install the ignition coil.

12. Install the ignition coil bolts and nuts and tighten to 18 ft. lbs. (25 Nm).

IGNITION SYSTEM

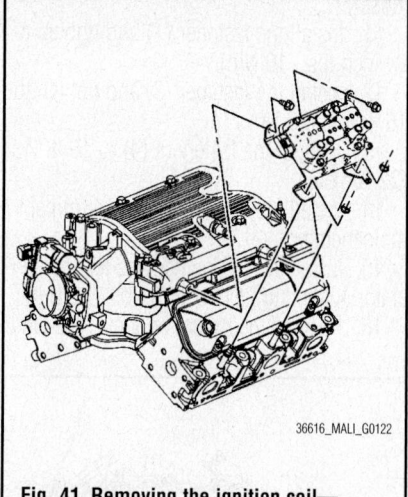

36616_MALI_G0122

Fig. 41 Removing the ignition coil— 3.5L engine

13. Install the HO2S electrical connector rosebud clip to the ignition coil bracket.

14. Install the right side spark plug wires to the ignition coils.

15. Install the left side spark plug wires to the ignition coils.

16. Install the brake booster vacuum hose to the upper intake manifold.

17. Position the brake booster vacuum hose clamp at the upper intake manifold.

18. Connect the engine wiring harness electrical connector to the ignition coil.

19. Connect the engine wiring harness electrical connector to the MAP sensor.

20. Install the intake manifold cover.

3.6L Engine

Bank 1

See Figure 42.

1. Remove the fuel injector sight shield.
2. Disconnect the engine wiring harness electrical connector(s) from the ignition coil(s).
3. If removing the number 5 cylinder ignition coil, remove the Evaporative Emission (EVAP) canister purge tube.
4. If removing the number one ignition coil, remove the canister purge solenoid.
5. Remove the ignition coil bolt(s).
6. Remove the ignition coil(s).

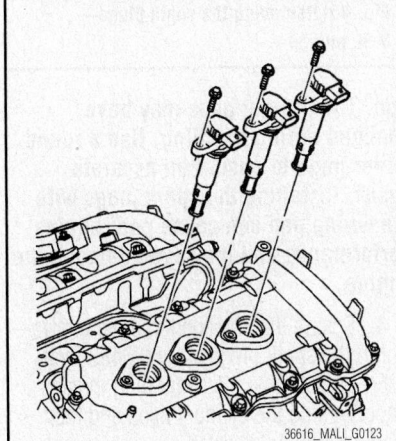

Fig. 42 Removing and installing the ignition coil pack (bank 1)—3.6L engine

To install:

7. Install the ignition coil(s).
8. Install the ignition coil bolt(s) and tighten to 89 inch lbs. (10 Nm).
9. If the number 5 cylinder ignition coil was removed, install the EVAP canister purge tube.
10. If the number one ignition coil was removed, install the canister purge solenoid.
11. Connect the engine wiring harness electrical connector(s) to the ignition coil(s).
12. Install the fuel injector sight shield.

Bank 2

See Figure 43.

1. Remove the fuel injector sight shield.
2. Disconnect the engine wiring harness electrical connector(s) from the ignition coil(s).
3. Remove the ignition coil bolt(s).
4. Remove the ignition coil(s).

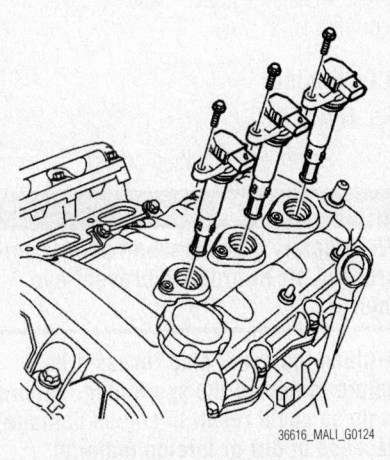

Fig. 43 Removing and installing the ignition coil pack (bank 2)—3.6L engine

To install:

To install, reverse the removal procedure. Tighten the ignition coil bolts to 89 inch lbs. (10 Nm).

SPARK PLUGS

REMOVAL & INSTALLATION

2.4L Engine

See Figure 44.

➡This engine has aluminum cylinder heads. Do not remove the spark plugs from a hot engine, allow it to cool first. Removing the spark plugs from a hot engine may cause spark plug thread damage or cylinder head damage.

1. Remove the air cleaner outlet duct..
2. Disconnect the engine wiring harness electrical connectors from the ignition coil.
3. Remove the ignition coil bolt(s).
4. Remove the ignition coil(s).

➡Make sure that any water and or debris is blown out of the spark plug holes prior to removing the spark plugs.

5. Remove the spark plugs using a ⅝ inch spark plug socket.

To install:

❊❊ CAUTION

Do not coat spark plug threads with anti-seize compound. If anti-seize compound is used and spark plugs are over-torqued, damage to the cylinder head threads may result.

6. Install the spark plugs and tighten to 15 ft. lbs. (20 Nm).

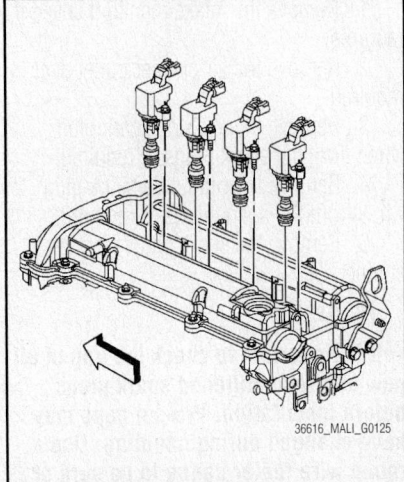

Fig. 44 Removing and installing the spark plugs—2.4L engine

7. The spark plug gap is 0.040 inch (1.0mm).
8. Install the ignition coils.

3.5L Engine

See Figure 45.

➡Allow the engine to cool before removing the spark plugs. Attempting to remove the spark plugs from a hot engine can cause the spark plugs to seize. This can damage the cylinder head threads.

➡Clean the spark plug recess area before removing the spark plug. Failure to do so can result in engine damage due to dirt or foreign material entering the cylinder head, or in contamination of the cylinder head threads. Contaminated threads may prevent proper seating of the new spark plug.

➡Use only the spark plugs specified for use in the vehicle. Do not install spark plugs that are either hotter or colder than those specified for the vehicle. Installing spark plugs of another type can severely damage the engine.

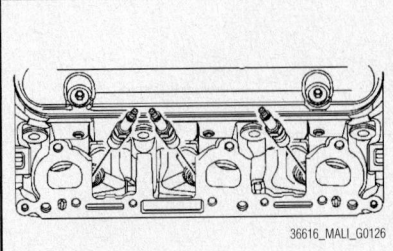

Fig. 45 Removing the spark plugs— 3.5L engine

1. Remove the intake manifold cover, if required.

2. Remove the air cleaner outlet duct, if required.

3. Remove the left side spark plug wires from the spark plugs, if required.

4. Remove the right side spark plug wires from the spark plugs, if required.

5. Remove the spark plugs from the engine.

To install:

➡ It is important to check the gap of all new and reconditioned spark plugs before installation. Pre-set gaps may have changed during handling. Use a round wire feeler gauge to be sure of an accurate check, particularly on used plugs. Installing plugs with the wrong gap can cause poor engine performance and may even damage the engine.

➡ Be sure plug threads smoothly into cylinder head and is fully seated. Use a thread chaser if necessary to clean threads in cylinder head. Cross-threading or failing to fully seat spark plug can cause overheating of plug, exhaust blow-by, or thread damage. Follow the recommended torque specifications carefully. Over or under-tightening can also cause severe damage to engine or spark plug.

6. Gap the NEW spark plugs to 0.040 inch (1mm).

7. Install the NEW spark plugs and tighten to 15 ft. lbs. (20 Nm).

8. Install the right side spark plug wires to the spark plugs, if required.

9. Install the left side spark plug wires to the spark plugs, if required.

10. Install the air cleaner outlet duct, if required.

11. Install the intake manifold cover, if required.

3.6L Engine

See Figure 46.

1. Remove the ignition coil(s).

✳✳ CAUTION

Wear safety glasses when using compressed air in order to prevent eye injury.

➡ Clean the spark plug recess area before removing the spark plug. Failure to do so could result in engine damage because of dirt or foreign material entering the cylinder head, or by the contamination of the cylinder head threads. The contaminated threads may prevent the proper seating of the new plug. Use a thread chaser to clean the threads of any contamination.

2. Use compressed air in order to remove debris from the spark plug cavity.

➡ Allow the engine to cool before removing the spark plugs. Attempting to remove the spark plugs from a hot engine may cause the plug threads to seize, causing damage to cylinder head threads.

3. Remove the spark plug(s).

To install:

➡ Use only the spark plugs specified for use in the vehicle. Do not install spark plugs that are either hotter or colder than those specified for the vehicle. Installing spark plugs of another type can severely damage the engine.

➡ Check the gap of all new and reconditioned spark plugs before installa-

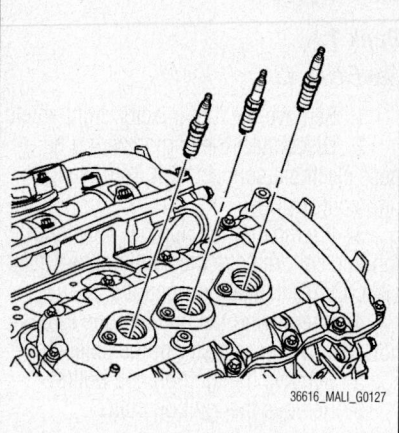

Fig. 46 Removing the spark plugs—3.6L engine

tion. The pre-set gaps may have changed during handling. Use a round feeler gage to ensure an accurate check. Installing the spark plugs with the wrong gap can cause poor engine performance and may even damage the engine.

4. Ensure that the spark plug is equivalent to the spark plug gap of 0.0433 inch.

5. Be sure that the spark plug threads smoothly into the cylinder head and the spark plug is fully seated.

➡ Be sure that the spark plug threads smoothly into the cylinder head and the spark plug is fully seated. Use a thread chaser, if necessary, to clean threads in the cylinder head. Cross-threading or failing to fully seat the spark plug can cause overheating of the plug, exhaust blow-by, or thread damage.

6. Install the spark plug. Tighten the spark plug to 15 ft. lbs. (20 Nm).

7. Install the ignition coil(s).

STARTER

REMOVAL & INSTALLATION

2.4L Engine

See Figure 47.

1. Disconnect the negative battery cable.
2. Raise and support the vehicle.
3. Disconnect the engine wiring harness electrical connector from the generator control module coolant pump.
4. Remove the generator control module coolant pump bolt.
5. Remove the generator control module coolant pump (with the hoses attached) from the oil pan.
6. Reposition and secure the generator control module coolant pump (with the hoses attached) out of the way.
7. Disconnect the engine wiring harness electrical connector from the starter.
8. Remove the positive battery cable to starter motor nut.
9. Remove the positive battery cable lead from the starter motor.
10. Remove the starter motor bolts and starter.

To install:

11. Install the starter motor and bolts. Tighten to 39 ft. lbs. (53 Nm).
12. Install the positive battery cable lead to the starter motor.
13. Install the positive battery cable to starter motor nut. Tighten the nut to 89 inch lbs. (10 Nm).
14. Connect the engine wiring harness electrical connector to the starter.

15. Unsecure the generator control module coolant pump.
16. Position the generator control module coolant pump (with the hoses attached) to the oil pan. Ensure the anti-rotation tab is inserted into the hole in the oil pan.
17. Install the generator control module coolant pump bolt. Tighten the bolt to 16 ft. lbs. (22 Nm).
18. Connect the engine wiring harness electrical connector to the generator control module coolant pump.
19. Lower the vehicle.
20. Connect the negative battery cable.

3.5L Engine

See Figure 48.

1. Disconnect the negative battery cable.
2. Raise the vehicle.
3. Remove the flywheel inspection cover bolts.
4. Remove the flywheel inspection cover.
5. Remove the electrical connections from the starter motor.
6. Remove the starter motor mounting bolts.
7. Remove the starter motor.

To install:

➡ **Before installing the starter motor to the engine, tighten the nut next to the cap on the solenoid BAT terminal. If this terminal is not tight in the solenoid cap, the cap may be damaged during installation of electrical connections and cause the starter motor to fail later.**

8. Install the starter motor to the engine. Tighten the bolts to 30 ft. lbs. (40 Nm).

9. Install the electrical connection to the battery terminal on the solenoid. Tighten to 13 ft. lbs. (17 Nm).
10. Install the electrical connections to the S terminal on the solenoid. Tighten the S terminal nut to 27 inch lbs. (3 Nm).
11. Install the flywheel inspection cover and bolts. Tighten the flywheel inspection cover bolts to 89 inch lbs. (10 Nm).
12. Lower the vehicle.
13. Connect the negative battery cable

3.6L Engine

See Figure 49.

1. Disconnect the negative battery cable.
2. Raise the vehicle.
3. Remove the starter solenoid BAT terminal nut.
4. Disconnect the engine harness electrical connector.
5. Unclip battery positive cable from starter bracket.
6. Disconnect the starter motor bolts and the starter.

To install:

7. Position the starter motor in the engine block. Tighten the bolts to 37 ft. lbs. (50 Nm).
8. Connect the engine harness electrical connector to the starter.
9. Install the starter solenoid BAT terminal nut. Tighten the nut to 115 inch lbs. (13 Nm).
10. Install the knock sensor Bank 2.
11. Install the front catalytic converter.
12. Lower the vehicle.
13. Connect the negative battery cable.

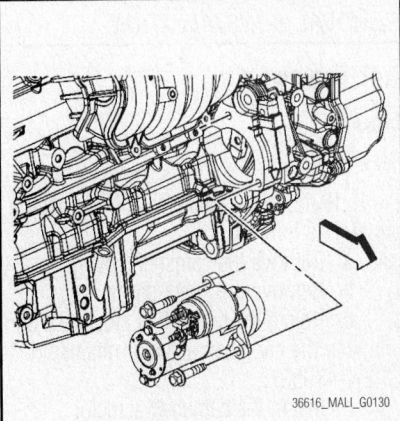

**Fig. 47 Removing the starter—
2.4L engine**

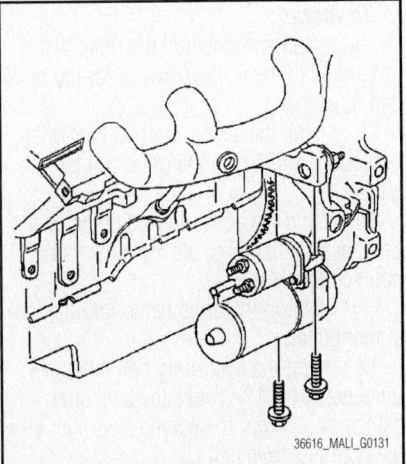

**Fig. 48 Removing the starter—
3.5L engine**

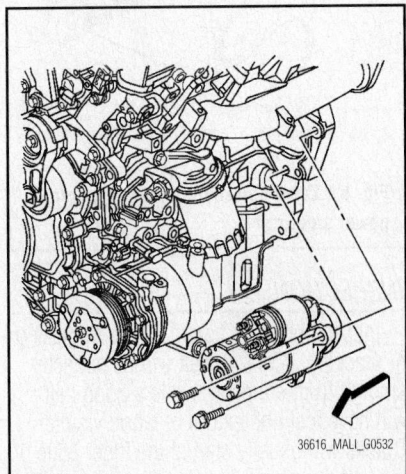

**Fig. 49 Removing the starter—
3.6L engine**

ENGINE MECHANICAL

ACCESSORY DRIVE BELTS

ACCESSORY BELT ROUTING

See Figures 50 through 52.

Refer to the accompanying illustrations for belt routing.

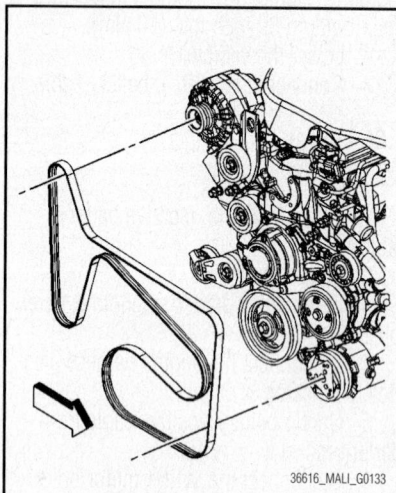

Fig. 50 Drive belt routing (with hydraulic power steering)—3.5L engine

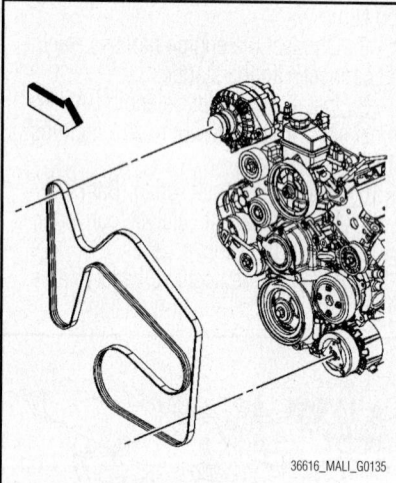

Fig. 51 Drive belt routing (with electronic power steering)

INSPECTION

Inspect the drive belt for signs of glazing or cracking. A glazed belt will be perfectly smooth from slippage, while a good belt will have a slight texture of fabric visible. Cracks will usually start at the inner edge of the belt and run outward. All worn or damaged drive belts should be replaced immediately.

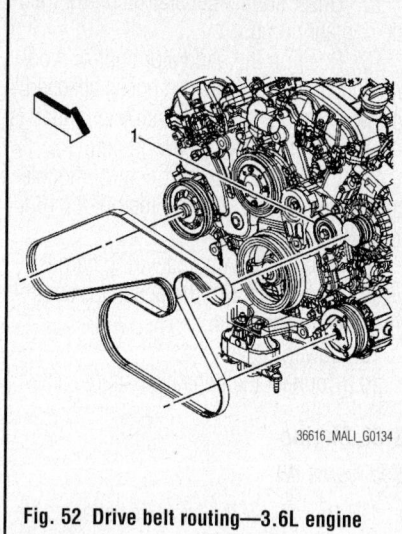

Fig. 52 Drive belt routing—3.6L engine

REMOVAL & INSTALLATION

2.4L Engine

1. Remove the engine splash shield.
2. Remove the air cleaner assembly.
3. Install the accessory belt tensioner unloader (J44811) to the drive belt tensioner.
4. Using the accessory belt tensioner unloader (J44811), rotate the tensioner counterclockwise in order to release the tensioner from the drive belt.
5. Remove the drive belt.
6. Slowly rotate the accessory belt tensioner unloader (J44811) and the tensioner clockwise in order to allow the tensioner to rest.
7. Remove the accessory belt tensioner unloader (J44811) from the drive belt tensioner.

To install:

8. Install and position the drive belt around all of the pulleys except for the drive belt tensioner.
9. Install the accessory belt tensioner unloader (J44811) to the drive belt tensioner.
10. Using the accessory belt tensioner unloader (J44811), rotate the tensioner counterclockwise.
11. Position the drive belt under the tensioner pulley.
12. Using the accessory belt tensioner unloader (J44811), rotate the tensioner clockwise in order to seat the tensioner pulley onto the drive belt.
13. Install the air cleaner assembly.
14. Install the engine splash shield.

3.5L Engine

See Figures 50 and 51.

1. Remove the air cleaner assembly.
2. Remove the engine mount snubber.
3. Install a breaker bar to the drive belt tensioner.
4. Rotate the drive belt tensioner clockwise to release the spring tension.
5. Remove the drive belt.

To install:

6. Install the drive belt tensioner.
7. Rotate the drive belt tensioner clockwise to release the spring tension.
8. Route and install the drive belt.
9. Slowly release the drive belt tensioner.
10. Install the engine mount snubber.
11. Install the air cleaner assembly.

3.6L Engine

See Figure 52.

1. Remove the air cleaner assembly.
2. Remove the engine mount snubber bracket.
3. Install a breaker bar to the drive belt tensioner.
4. Rotate the drive belt tensioner counterclockwise to release the spring tension.
5. Remove the drive belt.

To install:

➡**Ensure the drive belt is properly aligned and seated into the grooves of the accessory drive pulleys.**

6. Installation is the reverse of removal.

CAMSHAFT AND VALVE LIFTERS

REMOVAL & INSTALLATION

2.4L Engine

Intake

See Figures 53 and 54.

1. Remove the intake camshaft position actuator as follows:
   a. Remove the camshaft cover.
   b. Remove the spark plugs.
   c. Rotate the crankshaft clockwise and install the camshaft actuator retainer (EN-48953).
   d. Install the camshaft actuator retainer bolts and tighten to 89 inch lbs. (10 Nm).
   e. Loosen, but DO NOT remove the intake camshaft actuator bolt.

f. Remove the camshaft actuator locking tool (EN-48953).

➡**Ensure the timing chain and the camshaft position actuators are marked for proper assembly.**

g. Mark the intake and exhaust camshaft actuators and the respective locations on the timing chain.

h. Remove the upper timing chain guide bolts and guide.

i. Remove the timing chain tensioner.

➡**The intake camshaft actuator should not rotate during the removal or installation.**

➡**Ensure the tips of the timing chain tensioner tool are fully engaged into the timing chain. The retention tool rod can be used on the back side of the chain to ensure the teeth from the retention tool are engaged.**

j. Install the timing chain retention tool (EN-48749) to the intake side of the timing chain.

k. Install the timing chain retention tool (EN-48749) to the exhaust side of the timing chain.

l. Remove and discard the intake camshaft actuator bolt.

m. Rotate the exhaust camshaft clockwise slightly to take the tension off of the timing chain on the intake actuator.

n. Remove the intake camshaft actuator from the camshaft while also

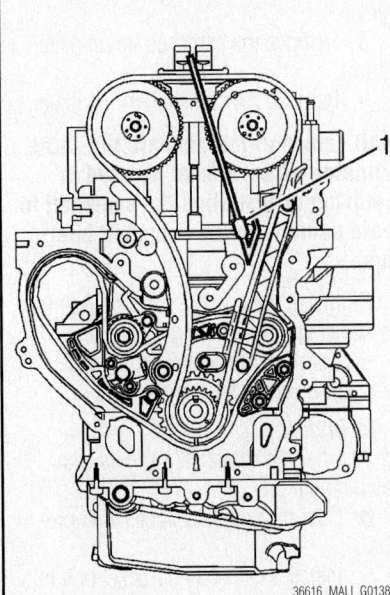

Fig. 53 Installing the timing chain retention tool to the intake side of the timing chain

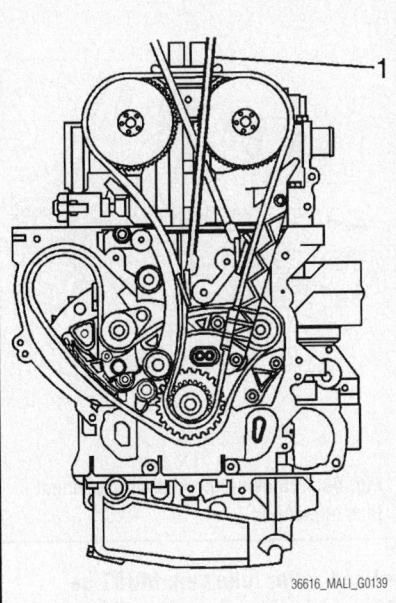

36616_MALI_G0139

Fig. 54 Installing the timing chain retention tool to the exhaust side of the timing chain

removing the actuator from the timing chain.

➡**Remove each bolt on each cap one turn at a time until there is no spring tension pushing on the camshaft.**

2. Mark the bearing caps to ensure they are installed in the original position.

3. Remove the bearing cap bolts.

4. Remove the bearing caps.

5. Remove the intake camshaft.

➡**Keep all of the roller followers and hydraulic adjusters in order so that they can be reinstalled in their respective locations.**

6. Remove the camshaft roller followers.

7. Remove the hydraulic element lash adjusters.

To install:

8. Install the hydraulic element lash adjusters into their bores in the cylinder head.

9. Lubricate the hydraulic lash adjusters with molylube.

10. Lubricate the valve tips with GM molylube.

➡**Used roller followers MUST be returned to their original position on the camshaft. If the camshaft is being replaced, the roller followers actuated by the camshaft must also be replaced.**

11. Position the camshaft roller followers on the tip of the valve stem and on the lash adjuster. Lubricate the roller followers with molylube.

12. Install the intake camshaft and lubricate with molylube.

13. Install the camshaft bearing caps. Hand tighten the cap bolts.

14. Tighten the bearing cap bolts in increments of 3 turns until they are seated to 89 inch lbs. (10 Nm).

15. Install the intake camshaft position actuator as follows:

➡**Ensure that the alignment mark made previously on the exhaust camshaft actuator is still aligned properly with the mark on the timing chain.**

a. Install the timing chain onto the intake camshaft actuator.

b. Align the intake camshaft actuator alignment mark made previously with the timing chain mark and install the actuator onto the camshaft rotating the exhaust camshaft clockwise, if required.

c. Install a NEW intake camshaft actuator bolt until snug.

d. Remove the timing chain retention tool from the intake side of the timing chain.

➡**Ensure that the alignment mark previously on the intake camshaft actuator is still aligned properly with the timing chain. If the mark made previously on the intake camshaft actuator is not aligned properly, refer to replacement procedure.**

a. Remove the timing chain retention tool from the exhaust side of the timing chain.

➡**Failure to reset the tensioner will allow the tensioner to over extend limiting the timing chain life.**

b. Reset and install the timing chain tensioner.

c. Install the camshaft actuator retainer (EN-48953) Camshaft Actuator Locking Tool.

d. Install the camshaft actuator retainer bolts and tighten to 89 inch lbs. (10 Nm).

e. Tighten the NEW camshaft actuator bolt to 22 ft. lbs. (30 Nm) plus an additional 100 degrees.

➡**You must have the Camshaft Actuator Locking Tool (EN-48953) installed to perform this procedure.**

f. To release the tensioner apply a counterclockwise rotational torque to the crankshaft balancer bolt of 33 ft. lbs. (45 Nm).

g. Remove the camshaft actuator retainer.

h. Install the upper timing chain guide and bolts and tighten to 89 inch lbs. (10 Nm).

i. Install the spark plugs.

j. Install the camshaft cover.

Exhaust

See Figures 55 and 56.

1. Remove the exhaust camshaft position actuator.

➡ **Remove each bolt on each cap one turn at a time until there is no spring tension pushing on the camshaft.**

2. Mark the bearing caps to ensure they are installed in the original position.

3. Remove the bearing cap bolts.

4. Remove the bearing caps.

5. Remove the exhaust camshaft.

➡ **Keep all of the roller followers and hydraulic adjusters in order so that they can be reinstalled in their respective locations.**

6. Remove the camshaft roller followers.

7. Remove the hydraulic element lash adjusters.

To install:

8. Install the hydraulic element lash adjusters into their bores in the cylinder head.

9. Lubricate the hydraulic lash adjusters.

10. Lubricate the valve tips.

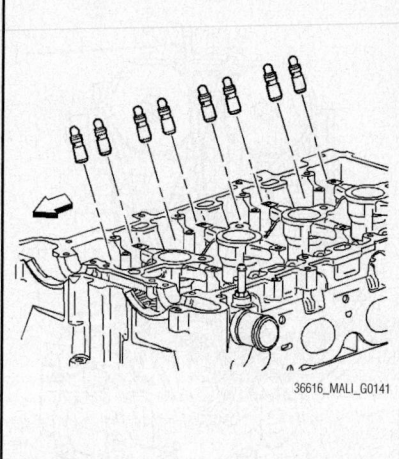

Fig. 56 Removing the hydraulic element lash adjusters

➡ **Used roller followers MUST be returned to the original position on the camshaft. If the camshaft is being replaced, the roller followers actuated by the camshaft must also be replaced.**

11. Position the roller followers on the tip of the valve stem and on the lash adjuster.

12. Install and lubricate the exhaust camshaft.

13. Install the camshaft bearing caps. Hand tighten the cap bolts.

14. Tighten the bearing cap bolts in increments of 3 turns until they are seated. Tighten the bolts to 89 inch lbs. (10 Nm).

15. Install the exhaust camshaft position actuator.

3.5L Engine

See Figures 57 through 59.

1. Remove the camshaft position sensor bolt.

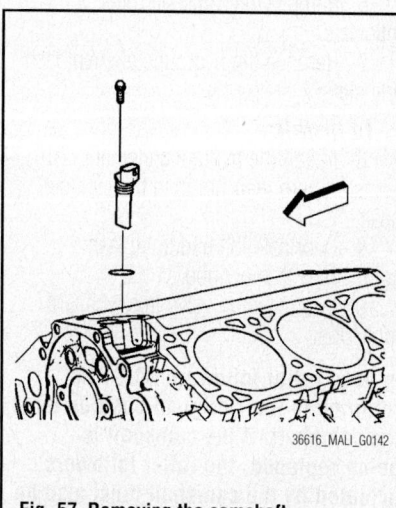

Fig. 57 Removing the camshaft position sensor

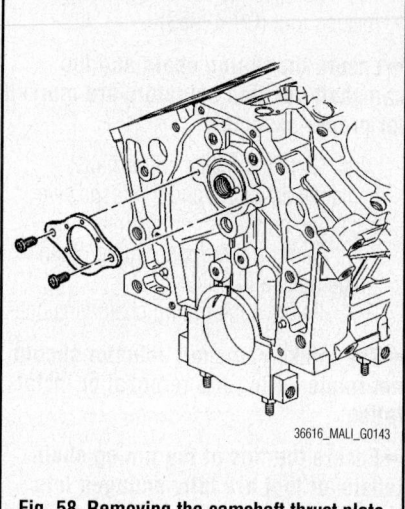

Fig. 58 Removing the camshaft thrust plate

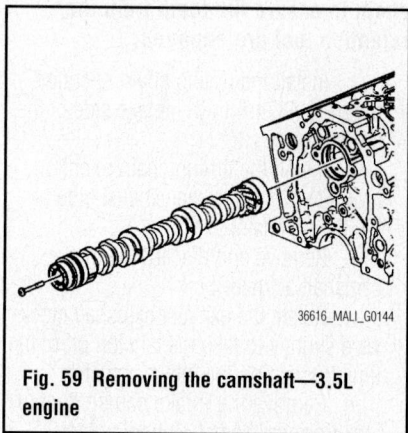

Fig. 59 Removing the camshaft—3.5L engine

2. Remove the camshaft position sensor.

3. Remove the camshaft thrust plate screws.

4. Remove the camshaft thrust plate.

➡ **All camshaft journals are the same diameter, so care must be used in removing or installing the camshaft to avoid damage to the camshaft bearings.**

5. Install a camshaft sprocket bolt into the camshaft. Tighten finger tight only.

6. Carefully rotate and remove the camshaft from the engine block.

To install:

7. Coat the camshaft journals with clean engine oil.

8. Coat the camshaft lobes with pre-lube.

9. Install a camshaft sprocket bolt into the camshaft. Tighten finger tight only.

10. Carefully rotate the camshaft while installing the camshaft into the camshaft bearings.

11. Install the camshaft thrust plate.

Fig. 55 Removing the camshaft roller followers

12. Install the camshaft thrust plate screws. Tighten to 89 inch lbs. (10 Nm).

13. Install the camshaft position sensor.

14. Install the camshaft position sensor bolt. Tighten to 89 inch lbs. (10 Nm).

3.6L Engine

Right Side

See Figures 60 through 64.

1. Remove the lower intake manifold.

2. Remove the camshaft cover.

3. Remove the camshaft sensors.

4. Remove the intake camshaft position actuator solenoid.

5. Remove the crankshaft balancer.

6. Rotate the crankshaft with a camshaft rotation socket such as EN 46111 until the camshafts are in a neutral (low tension) position. The camshaft flats will be parallel with the camshaft cover rail.

➡**Use an open-end wrench at the camshaft hex to prevent camshaft/engine rotation.**

➡**DO NOT remove the camshaft position actuator bolt at this time.**

7. Loosen the camshaft position actuator bolt.

8. Make sure that the tips of a timing chain tensioner tool such as EN 46108 are fully engaged into the timing chain.

9. Install a timing chain tensioner tool such as EN 46108 in order to retain the timing chain. Firmly tighten the tool nuts.

➡**Ensure that the camshaft timing chain and the camshaft position actuators are marked for proper assembly.**

10. Mark the timing chain and the respective locations on camshaft position actuators (15-18).

11. Remove the camshaft position actuator bolt.

12. Observe the markings on the bearing caps. Each bearing cap is marked in order to identify its location. The markings have the following meanings:
   - The raised feature must always be oriented toward the center of the cylinder head.
   - The I indicates the intake camshaft.
   - The E indicates the exhaust camshaft.
   - The number indicates the journal position from the front of the engine.

13. Remove the camshaft bearing cap bolts.

14. Remove the camshaft bearing caps.

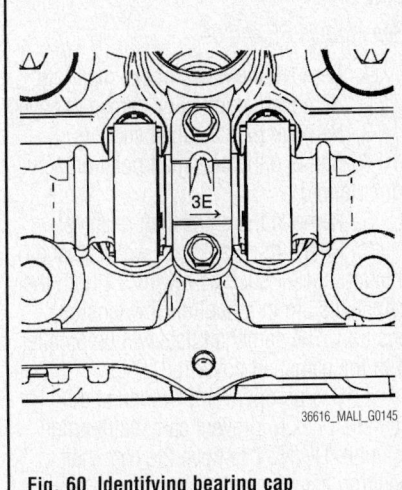

Fig. 60 Identifying bearing cap markings—3.6L engine

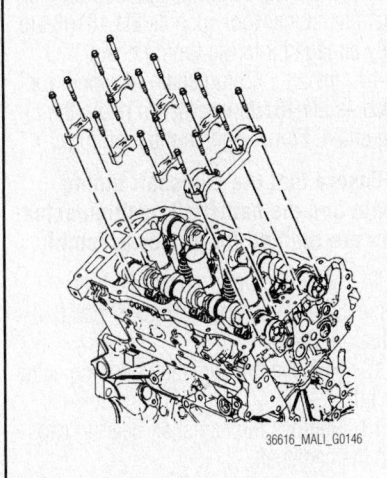

Fig. 61 Removing the bearing caps—3.6L engine

➡**Mark the camshafts upon removal to ensure installation is in the correct position.**

15. Remove the camshafts.

16. Replace the camshaft bearing caps and bolts.

To install:

➡**Make sure that the marks on the camshaft position actuators and the timing chain (15-18) are aligned.**

➡**DO NOT tighten the camshaft position actuator bolt at this time.**

17. Locate the camshafts to the cylinder head and assemble the camshaft actuators to the camshafts.

18. Install the camshafts and the camshaft bearing caps as follows:
   a. Ensure that the camshaft sealing rings are in place in the camshaft grooves.

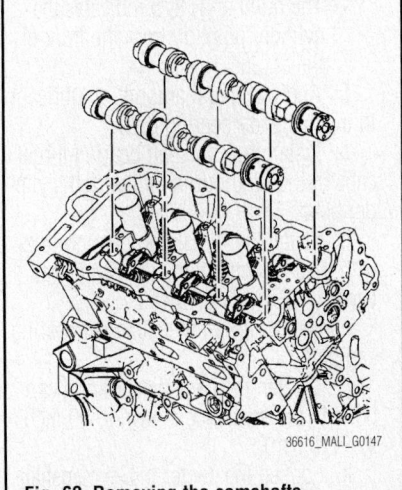

Fig. 62 Removing the camshafts—3.6L engine

Camshaft sealing rings must be in place below the surface of the camshaft journal in order to avoid being pinched between the cylinder head and the camshaft caps.

   b. Apply a liberal amount of lubricant to the camshaft journals and the right cylinder head camshaft carriers.

   c. Place the right intake and right exhaust camshafts in position in the right cylinder head.

   d. Position the camshaft lobes in a neutral position with the flats on the back of the camshafts up and parallel with the right cylinder head camshaft cover rail.

   e. Observe the markings on the right cylinder head camshaft bearing caps. Each bearing cap is marked in order to identify its location. The markings have the following meanings:
   - The raised feature must always be oriented toward the center of the cylinder head.
   - The I indicates the intake camshaft
   - The E indicates the exhaust camshaft

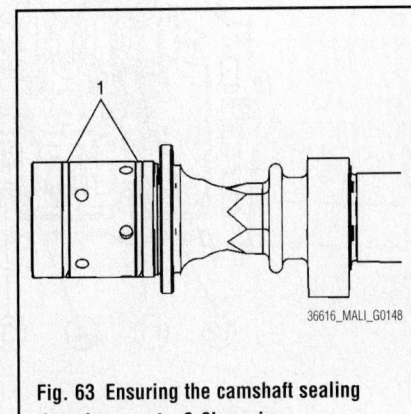

Fig. 63 Ensuring the camshaft sealing ring placement—3.6L engine

- The number 1, 3, 5 indicates the cylinder position from the front of the engine

f. Apply a liberal amount of lubricant to the camshaft bearing caps.

g. Install the camshaft bearing thrust caps in the first journal of the right cylinder head.

h. Install the remaining bearing caps with their orientation mark toward the center of the cylinder head.

i. Hand start all the camshaft bearing cap bolts.

j. Tighten the camshaft bearing cap bolts in the sequence shown to 89 inch lbs. (10 Nm).

k. Loosen the center intake camshaft bearing cap bolts (1, 2) and the center exhaust camshaft bearing cap bolts (3, 4).

l. Retighten the center camshaft bearing cap bolts (1, 2, 3, and 4) to 89 inch lbs. (10 Nm).

m. Remove the timing chain retention tool.

19. Install the crankshaft balancer.

➡**Use an open-end wrench at the camshaft hex to prevent camshaft/engine rotation.**

20. Install and tighten the camshaft position actuators.

21. Install the intake camshaft position actuator solenoid.

22. Install the camshaft sensors.

23. Install the camshaft cover.

24. Install the lower intake manifold.

Left Side

See Figures 65 and 66.

1. Remove the lower intake manifold.

2. Remove the left bank camshaft cover.

3. Remove the camshaft sensors.

4. Remove the camshaft position actuator solenoid.

5. Remove the crankshaft balancer.

6. Rotate the crankshaft with camshaft rotation socket such as EN 46111 until the camshafts are in a neutral (low tension) position. The camshaft flats will be parallel with the camshaft cover rail.

7. Use an open-end wrench at the camshaft hex to prevent camshaft/engine rotation. DO NOT remove the camshaft position actuator bolt at this time.

8. Loosen the camshaft position actuator bolt.

9. Make sure that the tips of a timing chain tensioner tool such as EN 46108 are fully engaged into the timing chain.

10. Install a timing chain tensioner tool such as EN 46108 in order to retain the timing chain. Firmly tighten the tool nuts.

➡**Ensure that the camshaft timing chain and the camshaft position actuators are marked for proper assembly.**

11. Mark the timing chain and the respective locations on camshaft position actuators (1-4).

12. Remove the camshaft position actuator bolt.

13. Remove the camshaft bearing caps and the camshaft.

14. Observe the markings on the bearing caps. Each bearing cap is marked in order to identify its location. The markings have the following meanings:

- The raised feature must always be oriented toward the center of the cylinder head.
- The I indicates the intake camshaft.
- The E indicates the exhaust camshaft.
- The number indicates the journal position from the front of the engine.

15. Remove the camshaft bearing cap bolts.

16. Remove the camshaft bearing caps.

➡**Mark the camshafts upon removal to ensure installation is in the correct position.**

17. Remove the camshafts.

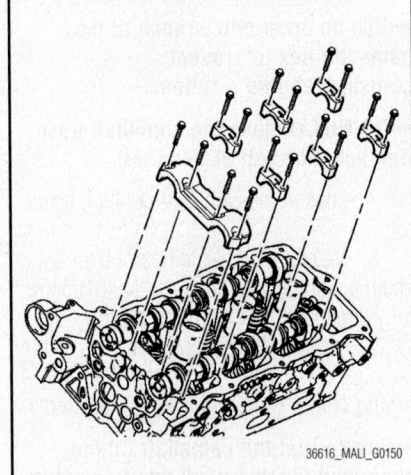

Fig. 65 Removing the camshaft bearing caps—3.6L engine

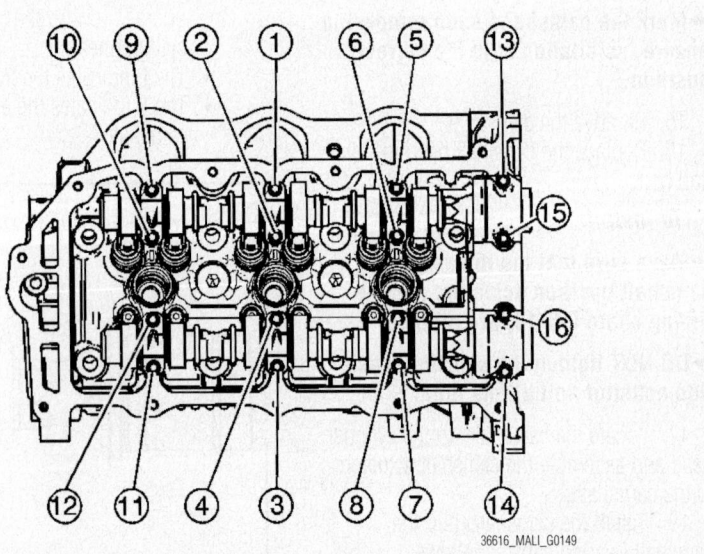

Fig. 64 Identifying the camshaft bearing cap bolt tightening sequence—3.6L engine

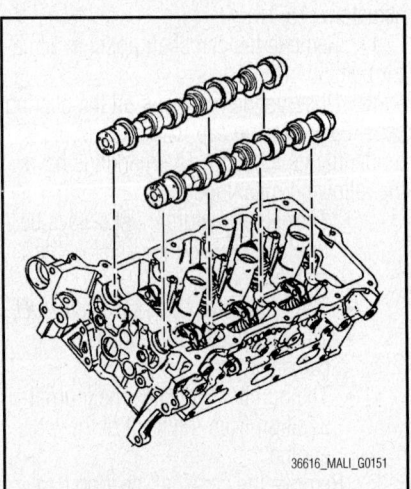

Fig. 66 Removing the camshafts—3.6L engine

To install:

18. Ensure that the marks on the camshaft position actuator and the timing chain (1-4) are aligned. DO NOT tighten the camshaft position actuator bolt at this time

19. Locate the camshafts to the cylinder head and assemble the camshaft actuators to the camshafts.

20. Install the camshafts and the camshaft bearing caps as follows:

a. Ensure that the crankshaft is in the stage one timing drive assembly position using a crankshaft rotation socket such as EN 46108.

b. Ensure that the camshaft sealing rings are in place in the camshaft grooves. Camshaft sealing rings must be in place below the surface of the camshaft journal in order to avoid being pinched between the cylinder head and the camshaft caps.

c. Apply a liberal amount of lubricant to the camshaft journals and the right cylinder head camshaft carriers.

d. Place the left intake and left exhaust camshafts in position in the left cylinder head.

e. Position the camshaft lobes in a neutral position with the flats on the back of the camshafts up and parallel with the right cylinder head camshaft cover rail.

f. Observe the markings on the left cylinder head camshaft bearing caps. Each bearing cap is marked in order to identify its location. The markings have the following meanings:

- The raised feature must always be oriented toward the center of the cylinder head.
- The I indicates the intake camshaft
- The E indicates the exhaust camshaft
- The number 2, 4, 6 indicates the cylinder position from the front of the engine

g. Apply a liberal amount of lubricant to the camshaft bearing caps.

h. Install the camshaft bearing thrust caps in the first journal of the left cylinder head.

i. Install the remaining bearing caps with their orientation mark toward the center of the cylinder head.

j. Hand start all the camshaft bearing cap bolts.

k. Tighten the camshaft bearing cap bolts in sequence to 89 inch lbs. (10 Nm).

l. Loosen the center intake camshaft bearing cap bolts (1, 2) and the center exhaust camshaft bearing cap bolts (3, 4). Retighten the center camshaft bearing cap bolts (1, 2, 3, and 4) to 89 inch lbs. (10 Nm).

m. Remove the timing chain retention tool.

n. Install the crankshaft balancer.

➡ **Use an open-end wrench at the camshaft hex to prevent camshaft/engine rotation.**

21. Install and tighten the camshaft position actuators.

22. Install the intake camshaft position actuator solenoid.

23. Install the camshaft sensors.

24. Install the camshaft cover.

25. Install the lower intake manifold.

CATALYTIC CONVERTER

REMOVAL & INSTALLATION

2.4L Engine

See Figure 67.

➡ **The oxygen sensor uses a permanently attached pigtail and connector. Do not remove the pigtail from the oxygen sensor. Damage to or removal of the pigtail connector could affect proper operation of the oxygen sensor.**

➡ **The use of excessive force may damage the threads in the exhaust manifold/pipe.**

➡ **The in-line connector and louvered end must be kept clear of grease, dirt or other contaminants. Avoid using cleaning solvents of any type. DO NOT drop or roughly handle the Heated Oxygen Sensor (HO2S).**

➡ **The HO2S may be difficult to remove when the engine temperature is less than 120°F (48°C).**

1. Raise and suitably support the vehicle.
2. Remove the Connector Position Assurance (CPA) retainer.
3. Disconnect the HO2S electrical connector from the engine wiring harness electrical connector.
4. Remove the HO2S, if necessary use an oxygen sensor wrench (J 39194-C).
5. Remove the catalytic converter to exhaust manifold nuts.
6. Remove the catalytic converter to muffler nuts.
7. Separate the exhaust pipe from the catalytic converter studs.
8. Position and support the exhaust pipe out of the way.
9. Remove the catalytic converter and gasket.

To install:

10. Install the catalytic converter along with a NEW gasket to the exhaust manifold.

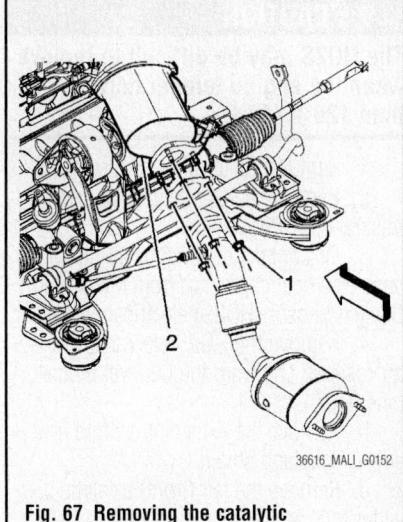

Fig. 67 Removing the catalytic converter—2.4L engine

36616_MALI_G0152

11. Position and join the exhaust pipe to the catalytic converter studs.

12. Install the catalytic converter to muffler nuts and tighten to 13 ft. lbs. (17 Nm).

13. Install the catalytic converter to exhaust manifold nuts and tighten to 37 ft. lbs. (50 Nm).

14. Install the HO2S and tighten to 31 ft. lbs. (42 Nm).

➡ **If necessary, coat the threads of the HO2S with anti-seize compound GM P/N 12377953 or equivalent.**

15. Connect the HO2S electrical connector to the engine wiring harness electrical connector.

16. Install the CPA retainer.

17. Lower the vehicle.

3.5L Engine

Left Side

See Figures 68 and 69.

➡ **The oxygen sensor uses a permanently attached pigtail and connector. Do not remove the pigtail from the oxygen sensor. Damage to or removal of the pigtail connector could affect proper operation of the oxygen sensor.**

➡ **The use of excessive force may damage the threads in the exhaust manifold/pipe.**

✳✳ CAUTION

The in-line connector and louvered end must be kept clear of grease, dirt or other contaminants. Avoid using cleaning solvents of any type. DO NOT drop or roughly handle the HO2S.

✳✳ CAUTION

The HO2S may be difficult to remove when the engine temperature is less than 120°F (48°C).

1. Remove the air cleaner assembly.
2. Remove the Connector Position Assurance (CPA) retainer.
3. Disconnect the engine wiring harness electrical connector from the Heated Oxygen Sensor (HO2S) electrical connector.
4. Remove the HO2S electrical connector rosebud clip from the oil level indicator tube tab.
5. Remove the exhaust manifold heat shield bolts and shield.
6. Remove the left (front) catalytic converter nuts at the exhaust manifold.
7. Remove the muffler assembly.
8. Remove the lower right HO2S electrical connector CPA retainer.
9. Disconnect the rear HO2S electrical connector from the engine wiring harness electrical connector.
10. Remove the lower left HO2S CPA retainer.
11. Disconnect the front engine wiring harness electrical connector from the HO2S electrical connector.
12. Remove the lower right and left HO2S using the heated oxygen sensor wrench (J 39194-B).
13. Remove the left (front) catalytic converter to right (rear) catalytic converter nuts.
14. Remove the right (rear) catalytic converter bolt and nuts at the exhaust manifold.
15. Remove and discard the gasket.
16. Remove the right (rear) catalytic converter.
17. Remove the left (front) catalytic converter.
18. Remove and discard the left (front) catalytic converter to manifold gasket.
19. Inspect the catalytic converter-to-exhaust manifold flange. The standard and

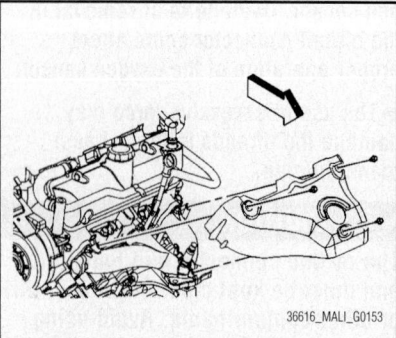

Fig. 68 Removing the exhaust manifold heat shield (left side)—3.5L engine

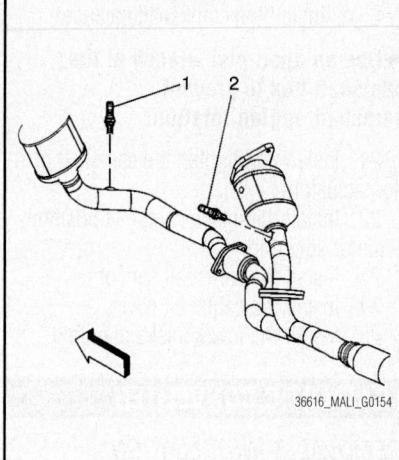

Fig. 69 Removing the lower right and left HO2S—3.5L engine

service limit for the converter to manifold flange warpage is 0.028 inch (0.7 mm).

To install:

20. Install a NEW gasket to the left (front) catalytic converter studs.
21. Install the left (front) catalytic converter.
22. Install a NEW gasket to the right (rear) catalytic converter studs.
23. Install the right (rear) catalytic converter.
24. Install the right (rear) catalytic converter bolt and nuts at the exhaust manifold and tighten to 33 ft. lbs. (45 Nm).
25. Install the left (front) catalytic converter to right (rear) catalytic converter nuts and tighten to 18 ft. lbs. (25 Nm).

✳✳ CAUTION

A special anti-seize compound is used on the HO2S threads. The compound consists of graphite suspended in fluid and glass beads. The graphite will burn away, but the glass beads will remain, making the sensor easier to remove. New or service sensors will already have the compound applied to the threads. If a sensor is removed from an engine and is to be reinstalled, the threads must have anti-seize compound applied before the reinstallation.

26. If reinstalling the old HO2S, coat the threads with anti-seize compound GM P/N 12377953 or equivalent.
27. Install the lower right and left HO2S and tighten to 31 ft. lbs. (42 Nm).
28. Connect the front engine wiring harness electrical connector to the HO2S electrical connector.

29. Install the lower left HO2S CPA retainer.
30. Connect the rear HO2S electrical connector to the engine wiring harness electrical connector.
31. Install the lower right HO2S electrical connector CPA retainer.
32. Remove the muffler assembly.
33. Install the left (front) catalytic converter nuts at the exhaust manifold and tighten to 33 ft. lbs. (45 Nm).
34. Remove the exhaust manifold heat shield bolts and shield and tighten to 89 inch lbs. (10 Nm).
35. Connect the engine wiring harness electrical connector to the HO2S electrical connector.
36. Install the CPA retainer.
37. Install the HO2S electrical connector rosebud clip to the oil level indicator tube tab.
38. Install the air cleaner assembly.

Right Side
See Figure 70.

➡**The oxygen sensor uses a permanently attached pigtail and connector. Do not remove the pigtail from the oxygen sensor. Damage to or removal of the pigtail connector could affect proper operation of the oxygen sensor.**

➡**The use of excessive force may damage the threads in the exhaust manifold/pipe.**

✳✳ CAUTION

The in-line connector and louvered end must be kept clear of grease, dirt or other contaminants. Avoid using cleaning solvents of any type. DO NOT drop or roughly handle the HO2S.

➡**The HO2S may be difficult to remove when the engine temperature is less than 120°F (48D°C).**

1. Remove the muffler assembly.
2. Remove the rear stabilizer shaft.
3. Remove the Connector Position Assurance (CPA) retainer.
4. Disconnect the lower right heated oxygen sensor (HO2S) electrical connector from the engine wiring harness electrical connector.
5. Remove the lower right HO2S using the heated oxygen sensor wrench.
6. Remove the left (front) catalytic converter to right (rear) catalytic converter nuts.
7. Remove the right (rear) catalytic converter bolt and nuts at the exhaust manifold.

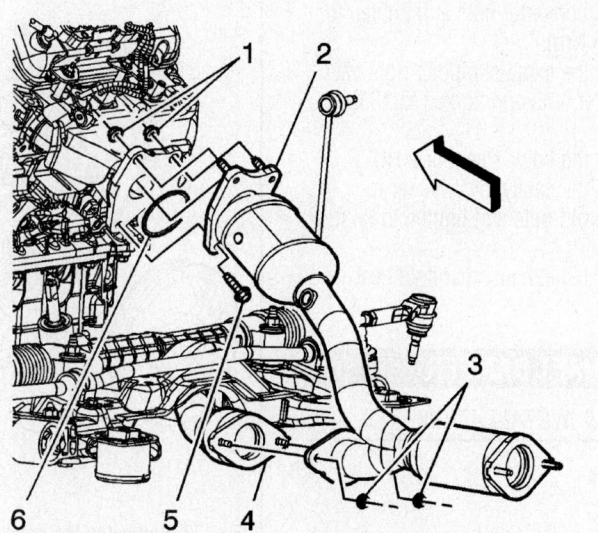

1. Right rear catalytic converter nuts
2. Right rear catalytic converter
3. Left front catalytic converter to right rear catalytic converter nuts
4. Left front catalytic converter
5. Right rear catalytic converter bolts

36616_MALI_G0155

Fig. 70 Removing the catalytic converters—3.5L engine

8. Remove the right catalytic converter.

9. Remove and discard the gasket.

10. Inspect the catalytic converter-to-exhaust manifold flange. The standard and service limit for the converter to manifold flange warpage is 0.028 inch (0.7 mm).

To install:

11. Install a NEW gasket to the catalytic converter.

12. Install the right (rear) catalytic converter.

13. Install the right (rear) catalytic converter bolt (5) and nuts (1) at the exhaust manifold and tighten to 33 ft. lbs. (45 Nm).

14. Install the left (front) catalytic converter to right (rear) catalytic converter nuts and tighten to 18 ft. lbs. (25 Nm).

✳✳ CAUTION

A special anti-seize compound is used on the HO2S threads. The compound consists of graphite suspended in fluid and glass beads. The graphite will burn away, but the glass beads will remain, making the sensor easier to remove. New or service sensors will already have the compound applied to the threads. If a sensor is removed from an engine and is to be reinstalled, the threads must have anti-seize compound applied before the reinstallation.

15. If reinstalling the old HO2S, coat the threads with anti-seize compound GM P/N 12377953 or equivalent.

16. Install the lower right HO2S using the heated oxygen sensor wrench. Tighten to 31 ft. lbs. (42 Nm).

17. Connect the lower right HO2S electrical connector to the engine wiring harness electrical connector.

18. Install the CPA retainer.

19. Install the rear stabilizer shaft.

20. Install the muffler assembly.

3.6L Engine

Left Side

See Figure 71.

1. Remove the exhaust manifold heat shield.

2. Remove the left catalytic converter to exhaust manifold nuts.

3. Raise and support the vehicle.

4. Disconnect the bank 2 sensor 2 heated oxygen sensor (HO2S) electrical connector from the engine wiring harness electrical connector.

5. Remove the left catalytic converter to right catalytic converter nuts.

6. Remove the left catalytic converter from the vehicle.

7. Discard the catalytic converter to exhaust manifold gasket.

8. Discard the left catalytic converter to right catalytic converter gasket.

To install:

9. Install a NEW catalytic converter seal onto the catalytic converter.

10. Install the catalytic converter to the vehicle.

11. Install a NEW left catalytic converter to right catalytic converter gasket.

12. Install the left catalytic converter to right catalytic converter nuts and tighten to 18 ft. lbs. (25 Nm).

13. Connect the bank 2 sensor 2 HO2S electrical connector to the engine wiring harness electrical connector.

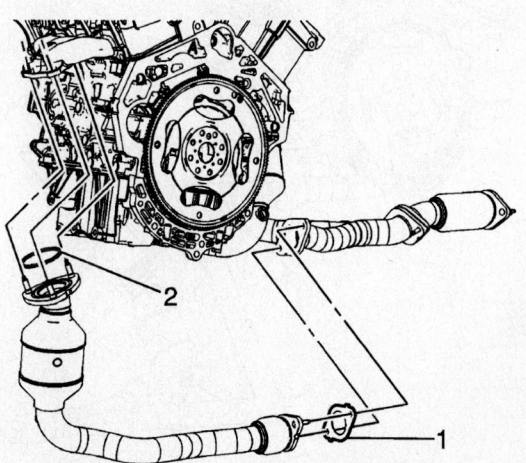

1. Left catalytic converter to right catalytic converter gasket
2. Catalytic converter to exhaust manifold gasket

36616_MALI_G0156

Fig. 71 Removing the left catalytic converter—3.6L engine

14. Install the left catalytic converter to exhaust manifold nuts and tighten to 33 ft. lbs. (45 Nm).

15. Install the exhaust manifold heat shield.

16. Lower the vehicle and inspect for exhaust leaks.

Right Side

See Figure 72.

1. Remove the exhaust manifold heat shield.

2. Remove the catalytic converter to exhaust manifold nuts.

3. Remove the bank 1 sensor 2 heated oxygen sensor (HO2S).

4. Remove the left catalytic converter to right catalytic converter nuts.

5. Remove the exhaust pipe to right catalytic converter nuts.

6. Remove the catalytic converter from the vehicle.

7. Remove and discard the catalytic converter to exhaust manifold gasket.

8. Remove and discard the left catalytic converter to right catalytic converter gasket.

To install:

9. Install a NEW catalytic converter to exhaust manifold gasket onto the catalytic converter.

10. Install the catalytic converter to the vehicle.

11. Install a NEW left catalytic converter to right catalytic converter gasket between the converters.

12. Install the left catalytic converter to right catalytic converter nuts and tighten to 18 ft. lbs. (25 Nm).

13. Install the exhaust pipe to right catalytic converter nuts and tighten to 18 ft. lbs. (25 Nm).

14. Install the bank 1 sensor 2 HO2S.

15. Install the catalytic converter to exhaust manifold nuts and tighten to 33 ft. lbs. (45 Nm).

16. Install the exhaust manifold heat shield.

CRANKSHAFT DAMPER

REMOVAL & INSTALLATION

2.4L Engine

See Figure 73.

1. Remove the drive belt.

2. Install a crankshaft holding tool and a breaker bar to the balancer in order to prevent the balancer from rotating when loosening the balancer bolt.

3. Remove and discard the crankshaft balancer bolt.

4. Remove the crankshaft balancer.

To install:

5. Position the crankshaft balancer.

6. Install a NEW crankshaft balancer bolt.

7. Install the holding tool and a breaker bar to the balancer in order to prevent the balancer from rotating while tightening the bolt.

8. Tighten the crankshaft balancer bolt

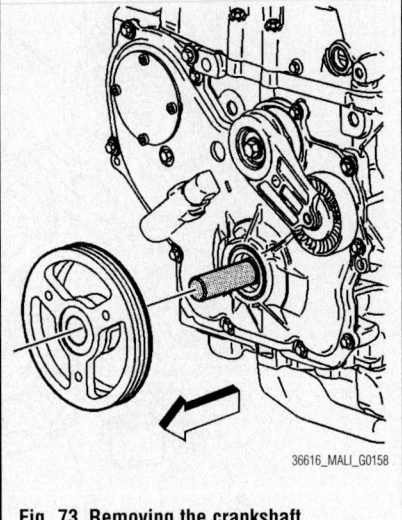

Fig. 73 Removing the crankshaft balancer—2.4L engine

to 74 ft. lbs. (100 Nm) plus an additional 125 degrees.

9. Install the engine splash shield.

10. Install the drive belt.

3.5L Engine

See Figure 74.

➡ The inertial weight section of the crankshaft balancer is assembled to the hub with a rubber type material. The correct installation procedures (with the proper tool) must be followed or movement of the inertial weight section of the hub will destroy the tuning of the crankshaft balancer.

1. Remove the drive belt.

2. Raise and support the vehicle.

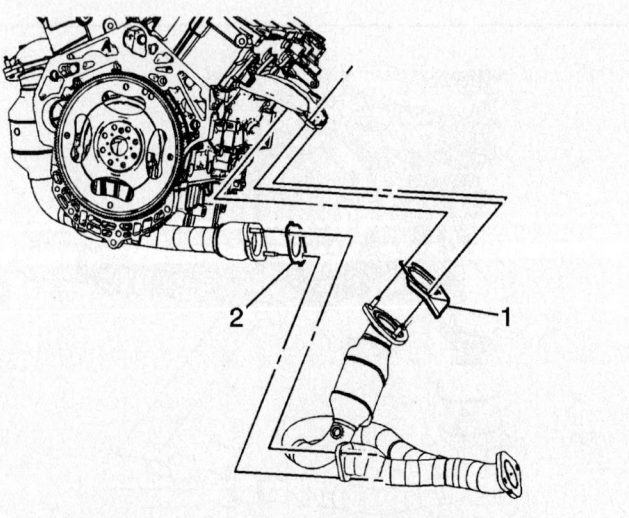

1. Catalytic converter to exhaust manifold gasket
2. Left catalytic converter to right catalytic converter gasket

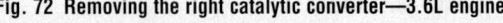

Fig. 72 Removing the right catalytic converter—3.6L engine

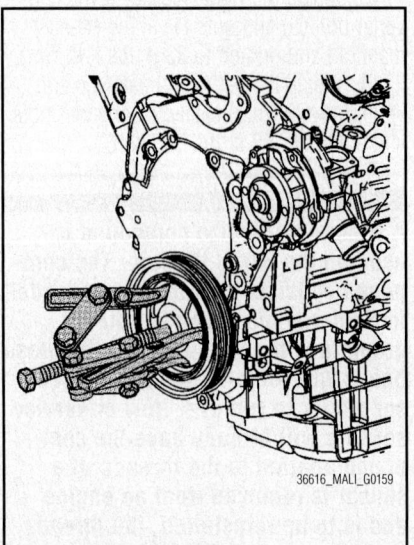

Fig. 74 Removing the crankshaft balancer—3.5L engine

3. Remove the right front tire and wheel.

4. Remove the right engine splash shield.

5. Install adjustable jack stands under the frame.

6. Loosen the left frame bolts and remove the right side frame bolts.

7. Using the jack stands, lower the right side of the frame to access the crankshaft balancer.

8. Remove the torque converter covers.

9. Install the a suitable holding tool to the flywheel to prevent flywheel rotation.

10. Remove the crankshaft balancer bolt and the washer.

11. Remove the crankshaft balancer.

To install:

➡**The inertial weight section of the crankshaft balancer is assembled to the hub with a rubber type material. The correct installation procedures (with the proper tool) must be followed or movement of the inertial weight section of the hub will destroy the tuning of the crankshaft balancer.**

12. Apply sealant to the keyway of the crankshaft balancer.

13. Place the crankshaft balancer into position over the key in the crankshaft.

➡**Do NOT use a power-assisted tool with the special tool in order to remove or install this component. You cannot properly control the alignment of this component using a power-assisted tool, and this can damage the component.**

14. Install a balancer and crankshaft sprocket installer onto the crankshaft.

15. Rotate the hex nut on the tool in order to install the crankshaft balancer onto the crankshaft.

16. Remove the tool from the crankshaft.

17. Install the crankshaft balancer washer and the bolt.

18. Install the used crankshaft balancer bolt, tighten to 92 ft. lbs. (125 Nm).

19. Remove the used crankshaft balancer bolt.

20. Install the NEW crankshaft balancer bolt, tighten to 92 ft. lbs. (125 Nm) plus an additional 130 degrees.

21. Remove the tool from the flywheel.

22. Install the torque converter covers.

23. Raise the frame to the original position.

24. Install and tighten the right and left side frame bolts to 74 ft. lbs. (100 Nm) plus an additional 90 degrees.

25. Install the right engine splash shield.

26. Install the right front tire and wheel.

27. Lower the vehicle.

28. Install the drive belt.

3.6L Engine

See Figure 75.

1. Remove the drive belt.

2. Install the engine support fixture.

3. Remove the engine mount strut bracket.

4. Remove the engine mount.

5. Remove the starter.

6. Install a flywheel holding tool through the starter mounting hole.

7. Using engine support fixture, lower engine approximately two inches.

8. Remove the crankshaft balancer bolt.

9. Install a crankshaft button tool such as J 38416-2 in the nose of the crankshaft.

10. Install crankshaft balancer remover tool such as J 41816 in order to remove the crankshaft balancer.

11. Tighten the center bolt of the crankshaft balancer remover tool in order to pull the crankshaft balancer off of the crankshaft.

12. Remove the crankshaft balancer remover tool from the crankshaft balancer.

To install:

➡**The crankshaft balancer remover tool must be installed onto the flywheel.**

13. Use the tool , nut, bearing and washer to install the crankshaft balancer.

➡**Do not lubricate the crankshaft front oil seal or crankshaft balancer sealing surfaces. The crankshaft balancer is installed into a dry seal.**

14. Apply lubricant to the inside of the crankshaft balancer hub bore.

15. Place the crankshaft balancer in position on the crankshaft.

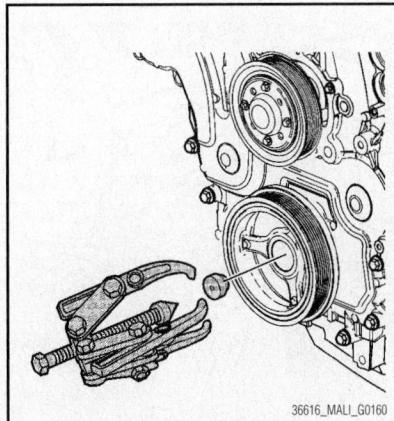

Fig. 75 Removing the crankshaft balancer—3.6L engine

16. Thread the tool in the crankshaft. Ensure you engage at least 10 threads of the tool before pressing the crankshaft balancer in place.

17. Push the crankshaft balancer into position by tightening the nut on the tool until the large washer bottoms out on the crankshaft end.

18. Remove the tool.

19. Install the crankshaft balancer bolt.

20. Tighten the crankshaft balancer bolt and tighten to 74 ft. lbs. (100 Nm) plus an additional 150 degrees.

21. Remove the flywheel holding tool.

22. Install the starter.

23. Using engine support fixture, raise the engine into position.

24. Install the engine mount.

25. Install the engine mount strut bracket.

26. Install the drive belt.

CRANKSHAFT FRONT SEAL

REMOVAL & INSTALLATION

2.4L Engine

See Figure 76.

1. Remove the crankshaft damper.

2. Use a flat-bladed tool to remove the seal from the front cover.

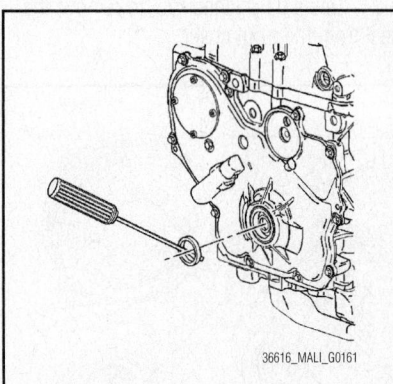

36616_MALI_G0161

Fig. 76 Removing the crankshaft front oil seal—2.4L engine

To install:

3. Use a suitable seal driver in order to install the crankshaft front oil seal to the engine front cover.

4. Install the crankshaft damper.

3.5L Engine

See Figure 77.

1. Remove the crankshaft damper.

2. Remove the crankshaft key from the keyway.

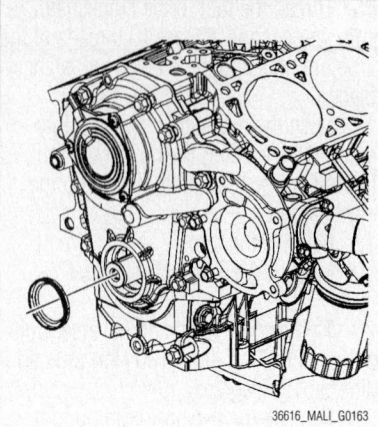

Fig. 77 Removing the crankshaft front oil seal—3.5L engine

3. Use a flat-bladed tool to remove the seal from the front cover.

To install:

4. Use a suitable seal driver in order to install the crankshaft front oil seal to the engine front cover.

5. Install the crankshaft key from the keyway.

6. Install the crankshaft damper.

3.6L Engine

See Figure 78.

1. Remove the crankshaft damper.

2. Use a flat-bladed tool to remove the seal from the front cover.

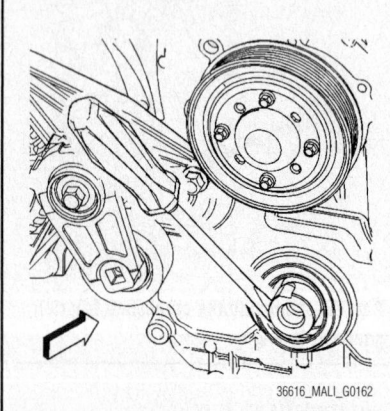

Fig. 78 Removing the crankshaft front oil seal—3.6L engine

To install:

➡ **Do not lubricate the crankshaft front oil seal or the crankshaft balancer sealing surfaces.**

3. Use a suitable seal driver in order to install the crankshaft front oil seal.

4. Install the crankshaft damper.

CYLINDER HEAD

REMOVAL & INSTALLATION

2.4L Engine

See Figures 79 through 83.

1. Drain and recycle the engine coolant.

2. Remove the exhaust manifold.

3. Remove the intake manifold.

4. Reposition the radiator surge tank air bleed hose clamp.

5. Remove the radiator surge tank air bleed hose from the cylinder head.

6. Reposition the radiator inlet hose clamp using the hose clamp pliers (J 38185).

7. Remove the radiator inlet hose from the cylinder head.

8. Disconnect all electrical connectors as necessary.

9. Remove the spark plugs.

10. Remove the camshaft cover.

➡ **If the intake camshaft actuator is moving independently of the camshaft, this means the camshaft is not locked to the actuator. Rotate the camshaft counter-clockwise while the holing tool is installed and this will lock the camshaft to the actuator.**

11. Rotate the crankshaft clockwise to install the Camshaft Actuator Retaining Tool (EN-48953).

12. Install the Camshaft Actuator Locking Tool (EN-48953).

13. Install the camshaft actuator retainer bolts and tighten to 89 inch lbs. (10 Nm).

14. Remove the upper timing chain guide bolts and guide.

15. Clean the timing chain and gears with solvent.

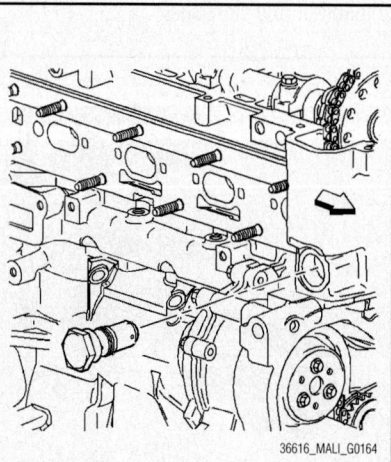

Fig. 79 Removing the timing chain tensioner—2.4L engine

➡ **Ensure the timing chain and the camshaft position actuators are marked for proper assembly.**

16. Mark the timing gear sprockets and the timing chain. It is recommended that the paint marks are located in the 12 o'clock position.

17. Loosen, but do not remove the intake and exhaust camshaft actuator bolts.

18. Remove the Camshaft Actuator Locking Tool (EN-48953).

➡ **Ensure the tips of the Timing Chain Retention Tool Kit (EN-48749) are fully engaged into the timing chain. The retention tool rod can be used on the back side of the chain to ensure the teeth from the retention tool are engaged.**

19. Install the Timing Chain Retention Tool (EN-48749) to the intake side of the timing chain.

20. Remove the timing chain tensioner.

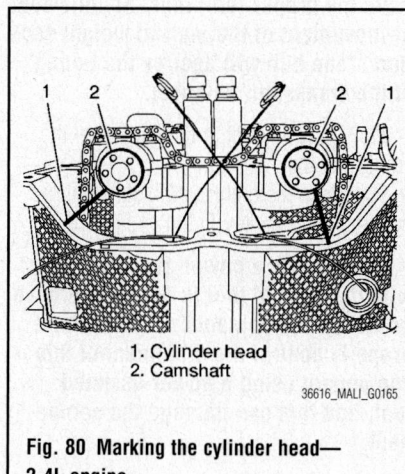

1. Cylinder head
2. Camshaft

Fig. 80 Marking the cylinder head—2.4L engine

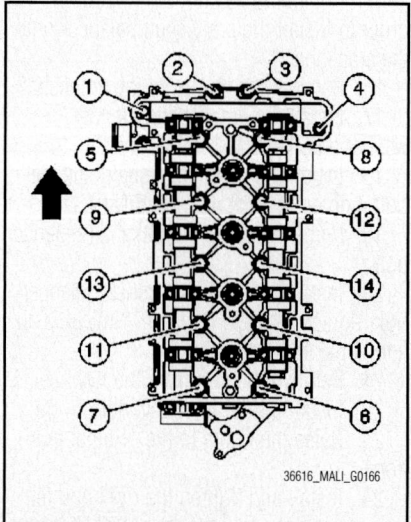

Fig. 81 Cylinder head bolt removal sequence—2.4L engine

➡The intake camshaft and actuator should not rotate during the removal or installation.

21. Install the Timing Chain Retention Tool (EN-48749) to the exhaust side of the timing chain.

22. Remove and discard the exhaust camshaft actuator bolt.

23. Remove the exhaust cam actuator from the exhaust camshaft while also removing the actuator from the chain.

24. Remove and discard the intake camshaft actuator bolt.

25. Remove the intake camshaft actuator from the camshaft while also removing the actuator from the timing chain.

26. Mark the cylinder head in relationship to the camshaft actuator notch is on the camshaft.

27. Remove the fixed timing chain guide access plug.

28. Remove the upper fixed timing chain guide bolt.

➡The threaded rod from the timing chain retention tool can be used to help feed the rubber band around the chain guides.

29. Install the rubber band around the top of the timing chain guides in order to pull the guides together.

30. Remove the cylinder head bolts in the sequence shown. Discard the bolts.

31. Remove the cylinder head.

32. Remove the cylinder head gasket.

33. Clean all of the gasket surfaces.

34. Use the following steps when cleaning the cylinder head and cylinder block surfaces:

   a. Use a razor blade gasket scraper to clean the cylinder head and cylinder block gasket surfaces. Do not scratch or gouge either surface.

➡DO NOT use any other method or technique to clean these gasket surfaces.

   b. Use a NEW razor blade on the cylinder head and a NEW blade on the cylinder block.

➡Be careful not to gouge or scratch the gasket surfaces. DO NOT gouge or scrape the combustion chamber surfaces. The feel of the gasket surface is important, not the appearance. There will be indentations from the gasket left in the cylinder head after all of the gasket material is removed. These small indentations will be filled in by the NEW gasket.

   c. Hold the razor blade as parallel to the gasket surface as possible.

35. Clean the old sealer/lube and any dirt from around the bolt holes.

➡DO NOT use a tap to clean the cylinder head bolt holes.

36. Clean the bolt holes with a nylon bristle brush.

37. When cleaning the cylinder head bolt holes use suitable commercial spray liquid solvent and compressed air from an extended-tip blow gun in order to reach the bottom of the holes.

38. If replacing the cylinder head, transfer all parts as necessary.

To install:

➡DO NOT use any sealing material.

39. Install the cylinder head gasket.

40. Install the cylinder head.

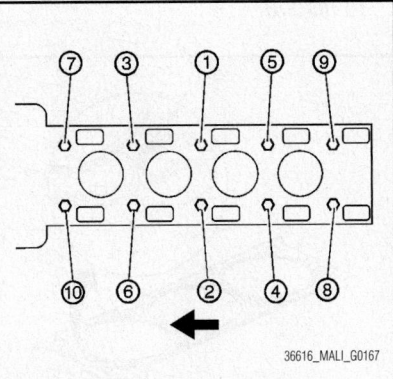

36616_MALI_G0167

Fig. 82 Cylinder head bolt tightening sequence—2.4L engine

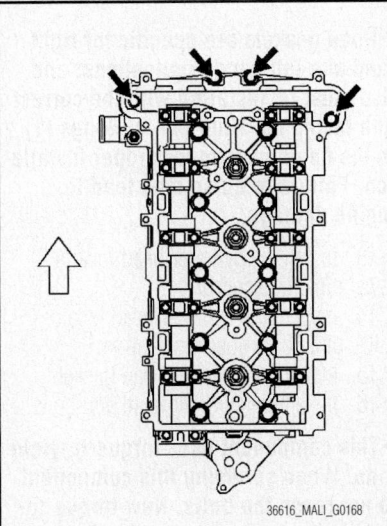

36616_MALI_G0168

Fig. 83 Location of the front cylinder head bolts—2.4L engine

41. Install NEW cylinder head bolts.

42. Install and tighten the cylinder head bolts in the sequence shown in 2 steps to 22 ft. lbs. (30 Nm) plus an additional 155 degrees.

43. Install the NEW front cylinder head bolts and tighten to 26 ft. lbs. (35 Nm).

44. Ensure the cylinder head and the camshaft are correctly aligned.

45. Remove the rubber band from around the top of the upper timing chain guides.

46. Install the fixed guide bolt into the cylinder head and tighten to 106 inch lbs. (12 Nm).

47. Apply sealant compound to the thread and install the timing chain guide bolt access hole plug.

48. Install the fixed timing chain guide access plug and tighten the plug to 59 ft. lbs. (90 Nm).

➡Ensure that the alignment mark made previously on the intake camshaft actuator is still aligned properly with the mark on the timing chain. If the mark made previously on the intake camshaft actuator is not aligned properly, refer to CAMSHAFT TIMING CHAIN, SPROCKET, AND TENSIONER.

49. Install the timing chain onto the intake camshaft actuator.

50. Align the intake camshaft actuator alignment mark made previously with the timing chain mark and install the actuator onto the camshaft.

51. Install a NEW intake camshaft actuator bolt until snug.

52. Remove the Timing Chain Retention Tool (EN-48749) from the intake side of the timing chain.

➡Ensure that the alignment mark made previously on the exhaust camshaft actuator is still aligned properly with the mark on the timing chain. The exhaust cam may have to be rotated clockwise to install the exhaust actuator.

53. Install the timing chain onto the exhaust camshaft actuator.

54. Align the exhaust camshaft actuator alignment mark made previously with the timing chain mark and install the actuator onto the camshaft.

55. Install a NEW exhaust camshaft actuator bolt until snug.

56. Remove the Timing Chain Retention Tool (EN-48749) from the exhaust side of the timing chain.

➡**Failure to reset the chain tensioner will put excess tension on the chain, limiting the chains life.**

57. Reset and install the timing chain tensioner.

58. Install the Camshaft Actuator Locking Tool (EN-48953) to the actuators.

59. Install the camshaft actuator locking tool bolts and tighten to 89 inch lbs. (10 Nm).

60. Tighten the ENW camshaft actuator bolt to 22 ft. lbs. (30 Nm), plus an additional 100 degrees using the Angle Meter (J 45059).

61. Release the tensioner by applying a counterclockwise rotational torque of 33 ft. lbs. (45 Nm) to the harmonic balancer bolt.

62. Remove the Camshaft Actuator Locking tool.

63. Install the upper timing chain guide bolts and guide. Tighten the bolts to 89 inch lbs. (10 Nm).

64. Install the camshaft cover.

65. Install the spark plugs.

66. Connect all necessary electrical connectors.

67. Install the radiator inlet hose to the cylinder head.

68. Position the radiator inlet hose clamp.

69. Install the radiator surge tank air bleed hose to the cylinder head.

70. Position the radiator surge tank air bleed hose clamp.

71. Install the exhaust manifold.

72. Install the intake manifold.

73. Fill the cooling system

3.5L Engine

Right Side

See Figures 84 through 86.

1. Drain the engine oil.
2. Lower the vehicle.
3. Remove the lower intake manifold.
4. Remove the valve rocker arms and push rods.
5. Remove the exhaust manifold.
6. Remove the right spark plugs.
7. Remove the alternator.

➡ **This component uses torque-to-yield bolts. When servicing this component do not reuse the bolts, New torque-to-yield bolts must be installed. Reusing used torque-to-yield bolts will not provide proper bolt torque and clamp load. Failure to install NEW torque-to-yield bolts may lead to engine damage.**

8. Remove and discard the cylinder head bolts.

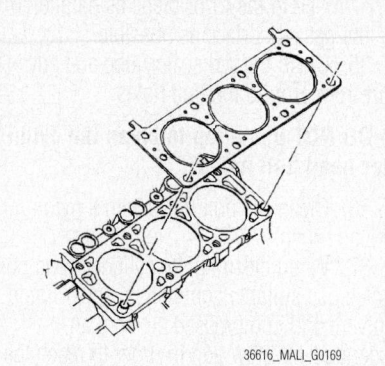

Fig. 84 Removing the cylinder head gasket (right side)—3.5L engine

9. Remove the cylinder head.

10. Remove and discard the cylinder head gasket.

11. Remove the cylinder locator dowel pins, if necessary.

12. Clean and inspect the cylinder head.

To install:

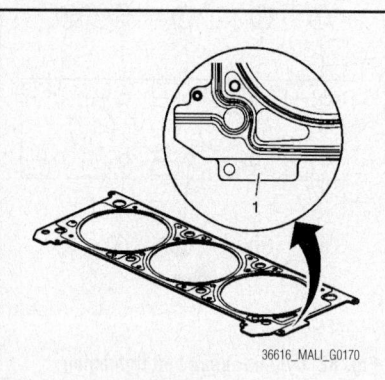

Fig. 85 Cylinder head gasket installation—3.5L engine

➡**Head gaskets are specific for right hand and left hand applications, and also must be installed with the correct side facing up. Note the markings (1) on the head gaskets for proper installation. Failure to do so may lead to engine damage.**

13. Install the cylinder head locator dowel pins, if necessary.

14. Inspect the cylinder head locator dowel pins for proper installation.

15. Install the cylinder head gasket.

16. Install the cylinder head and bolts.

➡**This component uses torque-to-yield bolts. When servicing this component do not reuse the bolts, New torque-to-yield bolts must be installed. Reusing used torque-to-yield bolts will not provide proper bolt torque and clamp load.**

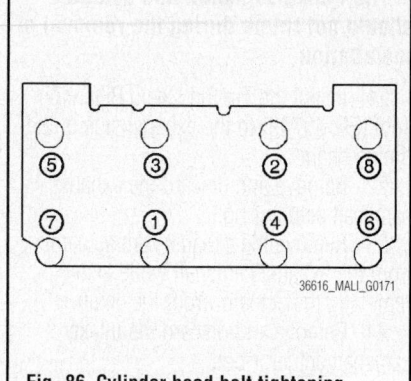

Fig. 86 Cylinder head bolt tightening sequence—3.5L engine

Failure to install NEW torque-to-yield bolts may lead to engine damage.

17. Install the NEW small hex cylinder head bolts (5 and 8).

18. Install the NEW large hex cylinder head bolts (1, 2, 3, 4, 6 and 7).

19. Tighten the NEW cylinder head bolts using the following 2 steps:

  a. Step 1: in sequence to 44 ft. lbs. (60 Nm).

  b. Step 2: in sequence an additional 140 degrees.

20. Install the alternator.

21. Install the right spark plugs.

22. Install the exhaust manifold.

23. Install the valve rocker arms and push rods.

24. Install the lower intake manifold.

25. Fill the engine with oil.

26. Inspect for leaks.

Left Side

See Figures 87 and 88.

1. Drain the engine oil.
2. Lower the vehicle.
3. Remove the lower intake manifold.
4. Remove the valve rocker arms and pushrods.
5. Remove the exhaust manifold.
6. Remove the oil level indicator tube.
7. Remove the left spark plugs.

➡**This component uses torque-to-yield bolts. When servicing this component do not reuse the bolts, New torque-to-yield bolts must be installed. Reusing used torque-to-yield bolts will not provide proper bolt torque and clamp load. Failure to install NEW torque-to-yield bolts may lead to engine damage.**

8. Remove and discard the cylinder head bolts.

9. Remove the cylinder head.

10. Remove and discard the cylinder head gasket.

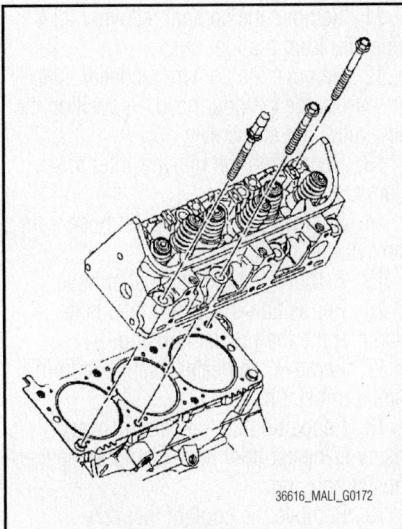

Fig. 87 Removing the cylinder head (left side)—3.5L engine

11. Remove the cylinder head locator dowel pins, if necessary.

12. Clean and inspect the cylinder head.

To install:

➡ **Head gaskets are specific for right hand and left hand applications, and also must be installed with the correct side facing up. Note the markings (1) on the head gaskets for proper installation. Failure to do so may lead to engine damage.**

13. Install the cylinder head locator dowel pins, if necessary.

14. Inspect the cylinder head locator dowel pins for proper installation.

15. Install the cylinder head gasket.

16. Install the cylinder head and bolts.

➡ **This component uses torque-to-yield bolts. When servicing this component do not reuse the bolts, New torque-to-yield bolts must be installed. Reusing used torque-to-yield bolts will not provide proper bolt torque and clamp load.**

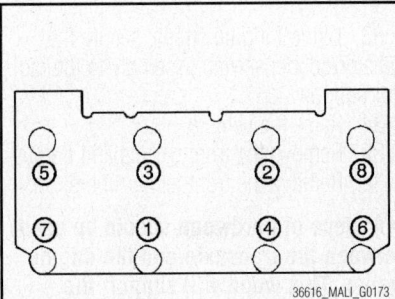

Fig. 88 Left side cylinder head bolt tightening sequence 3.5L engine

Failure to install NEW torque-to-yield bolts may lead to engine damage.

17. Install the NEW small hex cylinder head bolts (5 and 8).

18. Install the NEW large hex cylinder head bolts (1, 2, 3, 4, 6 and 7).

19. Tighten the NEW cylinder head bolts using the following 2 steps:

a. Step 1: in sequence to 44 ft. lbs. (60 Nm).

b. Step 2: in sequence an additional 140 degrees.

20. Install the left spark plugs.

21. Install the oil level indicator tube.

22. Install the exhaust manifold.

23. Install the valve rocker arms and pushrods.

24. Install the lower intake manifold. Fill the engine with oil.

25. Inspect for leaks

3.6L Engine

Right Side

See Figures 89 and 90.

1. Remove the hood.

2. Remove the right bank secondary timing chain.

3. With the aid of an assistant, remove the cylinder head with the exhaust manifold.

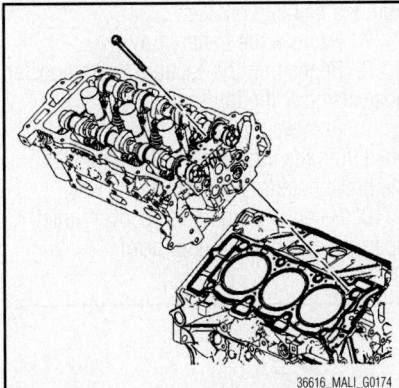

Fig. 89 Removing the cylinder head with the exhaust manifold (right side)—3.6L engine

4. Remove and discard the cylinder head gasket.

5. Clean and inspect the cylinder head and the engine block sealing surfaces.

To install:

6. Install a NEW cylinder head gasket.

7. With the aid of an assistant, carefully install the cylinder head with the exhaust manifold to the engine. Ensure the cylinder head locating pins are securely mounted in the cylinder block deck face.

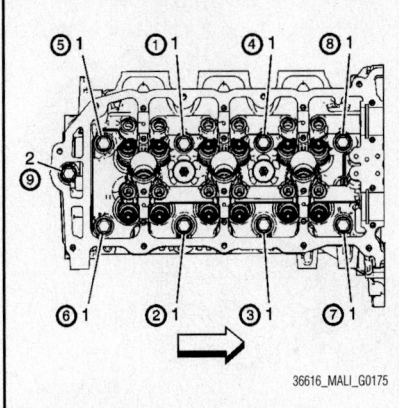

Fig. 90 Right side cylinder head bolt tightening sequence—3.6L engine

8. Install a NEW right cylinder head gasket using the deck face locating pins for retention.

9. Align the right cylinder head with the deck face locating pins.

10. Place the right cylinder head in position on the deck face.

➡ **DO NOT allow oil on the cylinder head bolt bosses or DO NOT reuse the old M11 cylinder head bolts.**

11. Tighten the NEW M11 cylinder head bolts using the following 2 steps:

a. Step 1: in sequence to 22 ft. lbs. (30 Nm).

b. Step 2: in sequence an additional 150 degrees.

12. Install and tighten the NEW M8 cylinder head bolt using the following 2 steps:

a. Step 1: first pass to 11 ft. lbs. (15 Nm).

b. Step 2: second pass an additional 75 degrees.

13. Install the right bank secondary timing chain.

14. Install the hood.

Left Side

See Figures 91 and 92.

1. Remove the left bank secondary timing chain.

2. Remove the oil level indicator.

3. Disconnect the coolant temperature sensor electrical connector.

4. Remove the wiring harness ground from the cylinder head.

5. Remove the catalytic converter.

6. Remove the cylinder head with the exhaust manifold.

7. Remove and discard the left cylinder head gasket.

8. Clean and inspect the cylinder head and the engine block sealing surfaces.

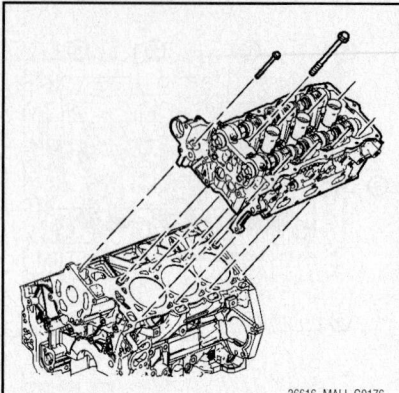

Fig. 91 Removing the cylinder head with the exhaust manifold (left side)—3.6L engine

To install:

9. Ensure the cylinder head locating pins are securely mounted in the cylinder block deck face.

10. Install a NEW left cylinder head gasket using the deck face locating pins for retention.

11. Align the left cylinder head with the deck face locating pins.

12. Place the left cylinder head in position on the deck face.

➡**DO NOT allow oil on the cylinder head bolt bosses.**

➡**DO Not reuse the oil cylinder head bolts.**

13. Install the NEW M11 cylinder head bolts (1) and tighten the first pass in sequence to 22 ft. lbs. (30 Nm). Tighten the bolts a second pass an additional 150° using an angle meter (J 45059).

14. Install 2 NEW front M8 left cylinder head bolts and tighten the first pass in

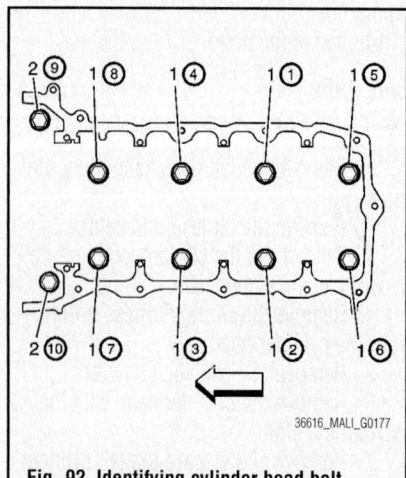

Fig. 92 Identifying cylinder head bolt tightening sequence (left side)—3.6L engine

sequence to 11 ft. lbs. (15 Nm). Tighten the bolts a second pass an additional 75° using an angle meter (J 45059).

15. Install the catalytic converter to the exhaust manifold.

16. Connect the wiring harness electrical connector located at the side of the cylinder head.

17. Install the wiring harness ground to the cylinder head.

18. Install the coolant temperature sensor electrical connector.

19. Install the oil level indicator.

20. Install the left bank secondary timing chain.

ENGINE ASSEMBLY

REMOVAL & INSTALLATION

2.4L Engine

See Figures 93 and 94.

1. Relieve the fuel system pressure.
2. Remove the air cleaner assembly.
3. Disconnect the fuel feed pipe quick connect fitting at the fuel rail.
4. Disconnect the Evaporative Emission (EVAP) line quick connect fitting from the EVAP purge solenoid.
5. Remove the fuel feed pipe clip from the fuel line bracket.
6. Remove the transaxle shift cable clip from the fuel line bracket.
7. Remove the battery tray.
8. Reposition the vacuum brake booster hose clamp at the intake manifold.
9. Remove the vacuum brake booster hose from the intake manifold. Reposition the brake booster hose out of the way.
10. Remove the coolant recovery inlet hose clamp at the cylinder head.

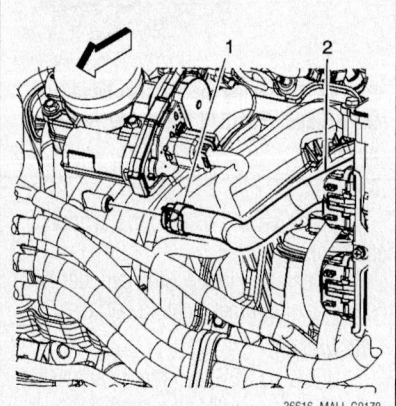

Fig. 93 Removing the vacuum brake booster hose from the intake manifold—2.4L engine

11. Remove the coolant recovery inlet pipe clip from the fuel rail.

12. Remove the coolant recovery inlet hose from the cylinder head. Reposition the hose/pipe out of the way.

13. Reposition the radiator inlet hose clamp.

14. Remove the radiator inlet hose from the cylinder head.

15. Remove the radiator outlet hose.

16. Reposition the heater inlet hose clamp at the thermostat housing.

17. Remove the heater inlet hose from the thermostat housing.

18. Reposition the coolant recovery reservoir/heater inlet hose clamp at the thermostat housing.

19. Remove the coolant recovery reservoir/heater inlet hose from the thermostat housing.

20. Raise and support the vehicle.

21. Drain the engine oil.

22. Unbolt the A/C compressor and reposition out of the way.

23. Remove the positive battery cable to starter motor nut.

24. Remove the positive battery cable lead from the starter motor.

25. Remove the positive battery cable from in between the starter and the engine. Reposition the positive battery cable out of the way.

26. Disconnect the generator electrical connector.

27. Reposition the engine harness boot.

28. Remove the generator nut.

29. Remove the engine harness lead from the generator.

30. Lower the vehicle.

31. Remove the transaxle shift cable from the range select lever.

32. Release the shift control cable retaining clip and remove the cable from the shift control cable bracket.

➡**The radiator/condenser/fan assembly will stay in the vehicle during engine removal.**

33. Using long tie straps, secure the radiator/condenser/fan assembly to the radiator support.

34. Raise the vehicle.

35. Remove the front wheels and tires.

36. Remove the front fender liners.

➡**A piece of hardwood should be used between the transaxle and the engine cradle. This wood will support the engine when the left side engine mounts bolts are removed.**

37. Install a piece of hardwood 1 x 2 x 4 between the transaxle and the frame.

➡A piece of hardwood should be used between the oil pan and the frame. This wood will support the engine when the right side engine mounts are removed.

38. Install a piece of hardwood 1 x 2 x 4 between the oil pan and the frame.

39. Drain the transaxle fluid.

40. Remove the transaxle oil cooler line to transaxle nut.

41. Remove the transaxle oil cooler lines from the transaxle.

42. Remove the catalytic converter.

➡Secure the steering wheel in the straight forward position before separating the intermediate shaft from the steering gear, or damage to the SIR coil will occur.

43. Remove the intermediate to steering gear pinch bolt and disconnect the intermediate shaft from the steering gear. Discard the pinch bolt.

44. Remove and discard both outer tie rod to steering knuckle nuts.

➡Hold the ball stud to prevent turning during removal of the nut.

45. Separate the tie rods from the steering knuckles.

46. Remove the stabilizer link to stabilizer shaft nuts and disconnect the stabilizer links from the stabilizer shaft.

47. Remove and discard both of the lower control arm ball stud cotter pins.

48. Loosen the ball stud nuts until the nuts are level with the top of the ball stud.

49. Separate the lower control arms from the steering knuckles.

50. Remove the ball stud nuts.

51. Remove the wheel drive shafts.

52. Lower the vehicle.

53. Remove the engine mount to bracket bolts.

54. Remove the transaxle mount to transaxle bolts.

55. Raise the vehicle.

➡During the powertrain removal support the vehicle body by placing a jack at the rear of the vehicle.

56. Position a engine support table under the powertrain assembly.

➡Blocks of wood can be used between the front of the cradle and the oil pan to table in order to level the powertrain during the removal.

57. With the table positioned, fully raise the table to contact with the powertrain assembly.

58. Remove the cradle to body bolts. Discard the bolts.

➡When lowering the engine/transaxle assembly, verify all brake lines, shifter cables and other components are free during removal.

59. Lower the engine table and raise the body on the hoist until the engine/transaxle and cradle are free from the vehicle.

60. Disconnect the engine wiring harness electrical connector from the throttle actuator.

61. Disconnect the engine wiring harness electrical connector from the fuel injector wiring harness electrical connector.

62. Remove the engine wiring harness clip from the oil level indicator tube bracket.

63. Disconnect the engine wiring harness electrical connectors from the ignition coils.

64. Disconnect the engine wiring harness electrical connectors from the camshaft actuators.

65. Disconnect the engine wiring harness electrical connector from the Crankshaft Position (CKP) sensor.

66. Disconnect the engine wiring harness electrical connector from the oil pressure sensor.

67. Disconnect the engine wiring harness electrical connector from the knock sensor.

68. Disconnect the engine wiring harness electrical connector from the intake Camshaft Position (CMP) sensor.

69. Disconnect the engine wiring harness electrical connector from the EVAP emission canister purge solenoid valve.

70. Disconnect the engine wiring harness electrical connector from the exhaust CMP sensor.

71. Disconnect the engine wiring harness electrical connector) from the Engine Coolant Temperature (ECT) sensor.

72. Disconnect the engine wiring harness electrical connector from the Heated Oxygen Sensor (HO2S) electrical connector.

73. Remove the engine wiring harness clip from the stud.

74. Remove the engine wiring harness ground bolt and reposition the ground terminal from the engine.

75. Gather all branches of the engine wiring harness and reposition the harness out of the way.

76. Remove the starter motor bolts and starter.

77. Remove the torque converter to flexplate bolts.

78. Install a suitable lifting devise to the engine.

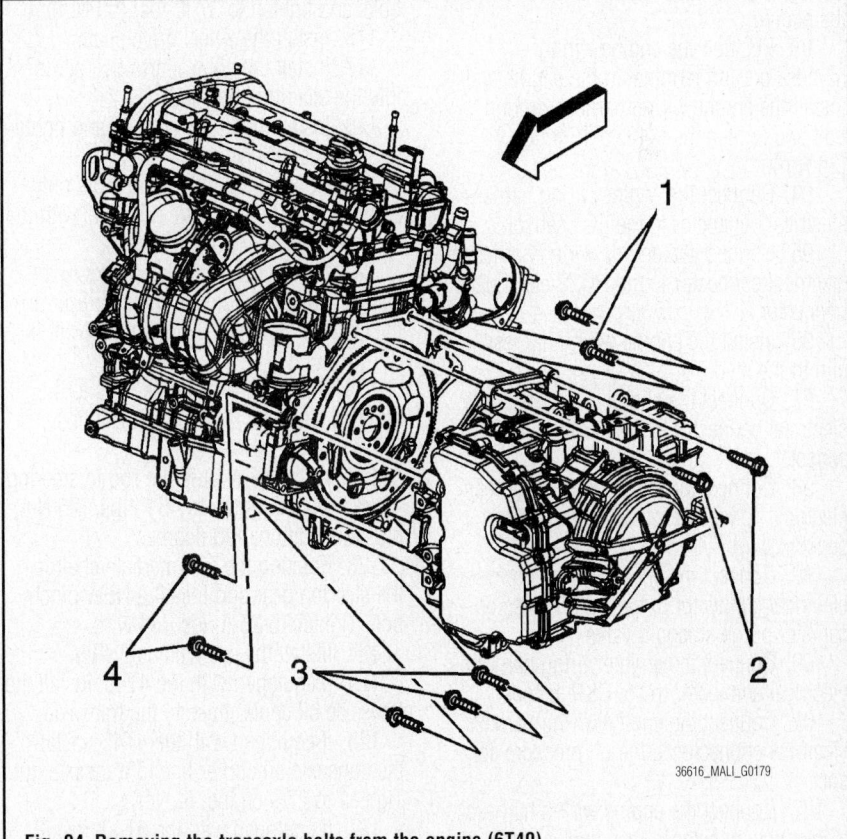

36616_MALI_G0179

Fig. 94 Removing the transaxle bolts from the engine (6T40)

79. If equipped with the 4T40, remove the transaxle bolts from the engine.

80. If equipped with the 6T40, remove the transaxle bolts (1, 2, 3, 4) from the engine.

81. If equipped with the 6T40, remove the intermediate drive shaft.

82. Separate the engine from the transaxle.

83. Install the engine to a suitable engine stand.

To install:

84. Install a suitable lifting devise to the engine.

85. Using the lifting devise, position and install the engine to the transaxle.

86. If equipped with the 4T40, install the transaxle bolts to the engine and tighten to 55 ft. lbs. (75 Nm).

87. If equipped with the 6T40, install the transaxle bolts to the engine and tighten to 55 ft. lbs. (75 Nm).

88. Install the transaxle bolts to the engine and tighten to 55 ft. lbs. (75 Nm).

89. Install the torque converter to flexplate bolts and tighten to 44 ft. lbs. (60 Nm).

90. Remove the engine lifting devise.

91. Install the starter motor and bolts. Tighten to 39 ft. lbs. (53 Nm).

92. Gather all branches of the engine wiring harness and position the harness to the engine.

93. Position the engine wiring harness ground terminal to the engine and install the engine wiring harness ground bolt and tighten the bolts to 15 ft. lbs. (20 Nm).

94. Connect the engine wiring harness electrical connector to the ECT sensor.

95. Connect the engine wiring harness electrical connector to the HO2S electrical connector.

96. Install the engine wiring harness clip to the stud.

97. Connect the engine wiring harness electrical connector to the exhaust CMP sensor.

98. Connect the engine wiring harness electrical connector to the intake CMP sensor.

99. Connect the engine wiring harness electrical connector to the EVAP emission canister purge solenoid valve.

100. Connect the engine wiring harness electrical connector to the CKP sensor.

101. Connect the engine wiring harness electrical connector to the oil pressure sensor.

102. Connect the engine wiring harness electrical connector to the knock sensor.

103. Connect the engine wiring harness electrical connectors to the ignition coils.

104. Connect the engine wiring harness electrical connectors to the camshaft actuators.

105. Connect the engine wiring harness electrical connector to the throttle actuator.

106. Connect the engine wiring harness electrical connector to the fuel injector wiring harness electrical connector .

107. Install the engine wiring harness clip to the oil level indicator tube bracket.

108. Position the powertrain and support table under the vehicle.

109. Raise the powertrain into position under the vehicle.

110. With the table positioned, if required, lower the vehicle over the powertrain.

111. Align the lower radiator pins with the cradle. Ensure all hoses and electrical harnesses are correctly routed and free from the loading path of the powertrain.

112. Install the NEW cradle to body bolts and tighten to 114 ft. lbs. (155 Nm).

113. Lower the vehicle.

114. Install the transaxle mount to transaxle bolts. Tighten to 41 ft. lbs. (55 Nm).

➡The engine mount to bracket bolts must be hand started. Do not pry the engine mount to align the holes.

115. Install the engine mount to bracket bolts and tighten to 37 ft. lbs. (50 Nm).

116. Install the wheel drive shafts.

117. Install the control arm ball studs into the steering knuckles.

118. Install the ball stud nuts and tighten to 30 ft. lbs. (40 Nm).

119. Continue to tighten the nuts only enough to align the castle nut slots with the ball stud, install NEW cotter pins.

120. Connect the stabilizer links to the stabilizer shaft and install the stabilizer link to stabilizer shaft nuts. Tighten to 48 ft. lbs. (65 Nm).

121. Connect the outer tie rods to the steering knuckles. Tighten to 30 ft. lbs. (40 Nm).

122. Install NEW outer tie rod to steering knuckle nuts. Tighten to 48 ft. lbs. (25 Nm) plus an additional 90 degrees.

123. Position the intermediate shaft to the steering gear and install a NEW pinch bolt. Tighten to 25 ft. lbs. (34 Nm).

124. Install the catalytic converter.

125. If equipped with the 4T45, install transaxle oil cooler lines to the transaxle.

126. If equipped with the 4T45, install the transaxle oil cooler line to transaxle nut. Tighten to 27 inch lbs. (4 Nm).

127. If equipped with the 6T40, install the fluid cooler at the transaxle.

128. Remove the wood from between the oil pan and the engine cradle.

129. Remove the wood from between the transaxle and the engine cradle.

130. Install the front fender liners.

131. Install the front wheels and tires.

132. Lower the vehicle.

133. Unsecure and position the radiator/condenser/fan assembly.

134. Install the shift control cable to the shift control cable bracket and engage the shift control cable retaining clip.

135. Install the transaxle shift cable to the range select lever.

136. Raise and support the vehicle.

137. Install the engine harness lead to the generator.

138. Install the generator nut and tighten to 15 ft. lbs. (20 Nm).

139. Seat the engine harness boot.

140. Connect the generator electrical connector.

141. Position and install the positive battery cable between the starter and the engine.

142. Install the positive battery cable lead to the starter motor.

143. Install the positive battery cable to starter motor nut. Tighten the nut to 80 inch lbs. (9 Nm).

144. Position the A/C compressor and install the bolts. Tighten to 37 ft. lbs. (50 Nm).

145. Connect the engine wiring harness electrical connector to the A/C compressor.

146. Lower the vehicle.

147. Install the coolant recovery reservoir/heater inlet hose to the thermostat housing.

148. Position the coolant recovery reservoir/heater inlet hose clamp at the thermostat housing.

149. Install the heater inlet hose to the thermostat housing.

150. Position the heater inlet hose clamp at the thermostat housing.

151. Reposition the radiator inlet hose clamp.

152. Remove the radiator inlet hose from the cylinder head.

153. Remove the radiator outlet hose.

154. Position and install the coolant recovery inlet hose to the cylinder head.

155. Install the coolant recovery inlet pipe clip to the fuel rail.

156. Install the coolant recovery inlet hose clamp at the cylinder head.

157. Position and install the vacuum brake booster hose to the intake manifold.

158. Position the vacuum brake booster hose clamp at the intake manifold.

159. Install the alternator starter.

160. Install the battery tray.

161. Install the transaxle shift cable clip to the fuel line bracket.

162. Install the fuel feed pipe clip (2) to the fuel line bracket.

163. Connect the EVAP line quick connect fitting to the EVAP purge solenoid.

164. Connect the fuel feed pipe quick connect fitting at the fuel rail.

165. Install the air cleaner assembly.

166. Fill the transaxle with fluid.

167. Refill the engine with oil.

168. Start the engine and allow the engine to run, inspect for leaks. Correct as necessary.

3.5L Engine

See Figures 95 through 100.

1. Disconnect the negative battery cable.

2. Remove the air cleaner assembly.

3. Remove the hood.

4. Remove the intake manifold cover.

5. Remove the engine mount snubber and drive belt.

6. Drain the cooling system.

7. Drain the engine oil.

8. Remove the starter motor.

9. Remove the oil pressure sensor heat shield nuts and shield.

10. Disconnect the engine wiring harness electrical connector from the oil pressure sensor.

11. Disconnect the engine wiring harness electrical connector from the knock sensor.

12. Remove the engine wiring harness ground bolt.

13. Separate the engine wiring harness ground terminal from the engine boss.

14. Remove the engine wiring harness clip from the Air Conditioning (A/C) compressor bracket.

15. Remove the engine wiring harness clip bolt.

16. Separate the engine wiring harness clip from the engine boss.

17. Disconnect the engine wiring harness electrical connector from the A/C compressor.

18. Remove the Connector Position Assurance (CPA) retainer.

19. Disconnect the lower front Heated Oxygen Sensor (HO2S) electrical connector from the engine wiring harness electrical connector.

20. Remove the engine wiring harness electrical connector clip from the thermostat housing stud.

21. Remove the lower rear CPA retainer.

22. Disconnect the lower rear HO2S electrical connector from the engine wiring harness electrical connector.

23. Remove the engine wiring harness electrical connector rosebud from the transaxle mount.

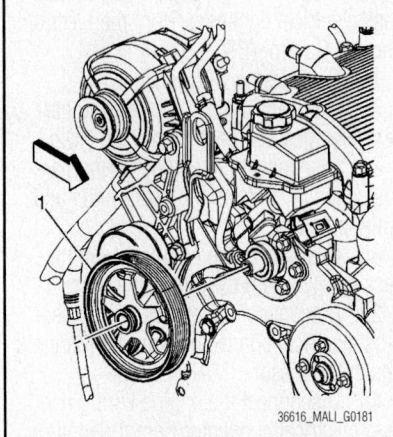

Fig. 96 Removing the power steering pump pulley—3.5L engine

24. Disconnect the engine wiring harness electrical connector from the knock sensor.

25. Disconnect the engine wiring harness electrical connector from the Crankshaft Position (CKP) sensor.

26. Remove the engine wiring harness clip from the engine stud.

27. Lower the vehicle.

28. Using the pulley remover (J 25034-C), remove the power steering pump pulley.

29. Remove the power steering pump bolts.

30. Remove the power steering line clip bolt from the generator stud.

31. Remover the power steering line clip from the stud.

32. Reposition and secure the power steering pump assembly out of the way.

33. Disconnect the engine wiring harness electrical connector from the Evaporative Emission (EVAP) canister purge solenoid.

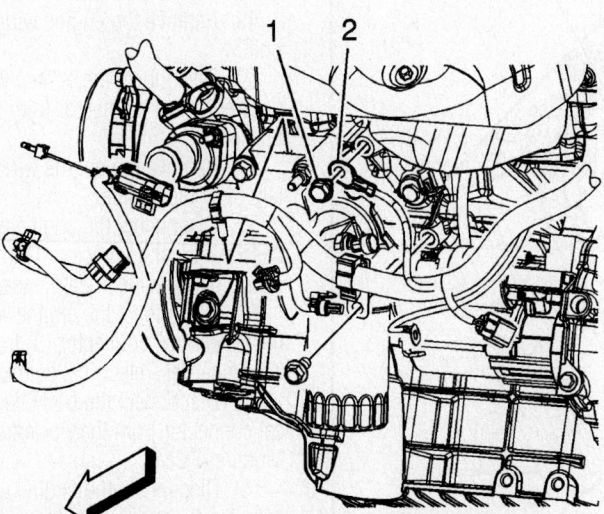

1. Engine wiring harness ground bolt
2. Engine wiring harness ground terminal from engine boss

Fig. 95 Separating the engine wiring harness ground terminal from the engine boss—3.5L engine

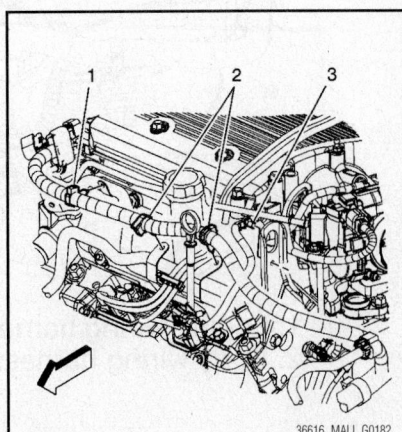

Fig. 97 Disconnecting the engine wiring harness clips—3.5L engine

34. Disconnect the engine wiring harness electrical connector from the Electronic Throttle Control (ETC).

35. Remove the CPA retainer.

36. Disconnect the engine wiring harness electrical connector from the HO2S.

37. Disconnect the engine wiring harness clips (1, 2) from the heater inlet and outlet pipe brackets.

38. Disconnect the engine wiring harness clip (3) from the engine lift bracket.

39. Disconnect the engine wiring harness electrical connector from the Manifold Absolute Pressure (MAP) sensor.

40. Disconnect the engine wiring harness electrical connector from the ignition control module.

41. Remove the CPA retainer.

42. Disconnect the engine wiring harness electrical connector from the rear upper HO2S.

43. Remove the engine wiring harness clips from the ignition control module bracket.

44. Reposition the engine wiring harness terminal boot.

45. Remove the engine wiring harness to generator stud nut.

46. Remove the engine wiring harness terminal from the generator.

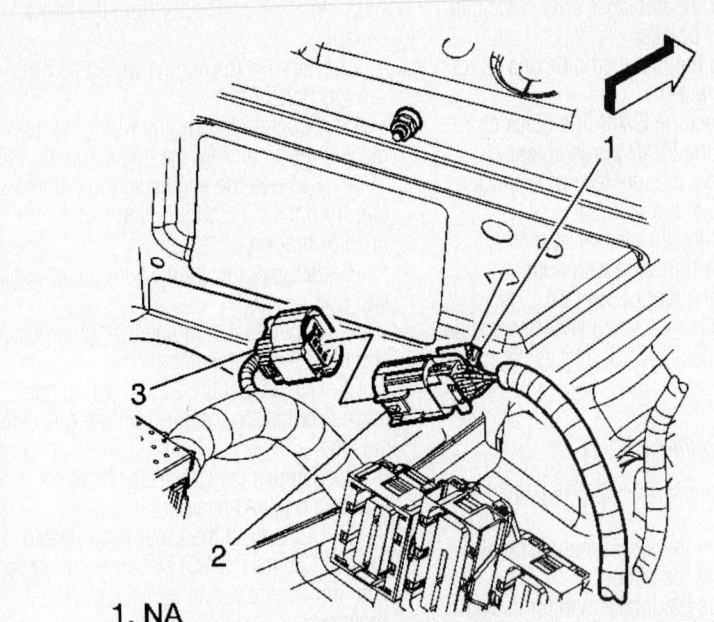

1. NA
2. Body wiring harness electrical connector
3. Engine wiring harness electrical connector

36616_MALI_G0184

Fig. 99 Disconnecting the engine wiring harness electrical connector from the body wiring harness electrical connector (2 of 2)—3.5L engine

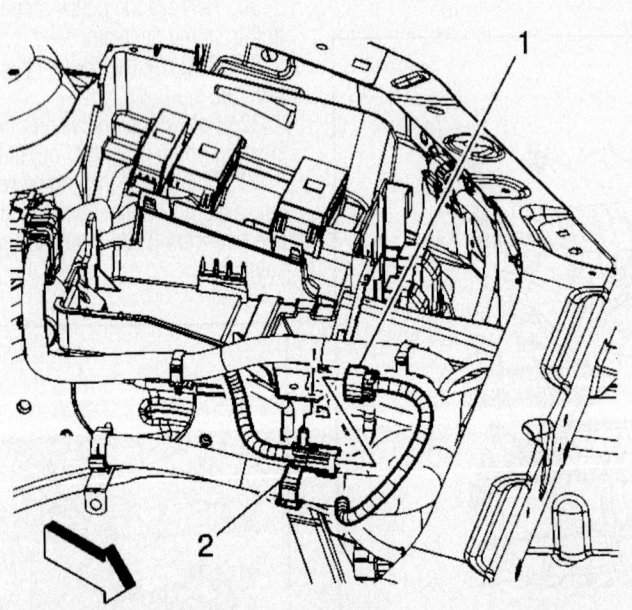

1. Engine wiring harness electrical connector
2. Body wiring harness electrical connector

36616_MALI_G0183

Fig. 98 Disconnecting the engine wiring harness electrical connector from the body wiring harness electrical connector (1 of 2)—3.5L engine

47. Disconnect the engine wiring harness electrical connector from the generator.

48. Disconnect the engine wiring harness electrical connector from the fuel injector inline electrical connector.

49. Remove the engine wiring harness bolt.

50. Disconnect the engine wiring harness electrical connector from the camshaft phaser.

51. Remove the engine wiring harness clip from the engine.

52. Disconnect the engine wiring harness electrical connector (1) from the body wiring harness electrical connector (2).

53. Disconnect the engine wiring harness electrical connector (3) from the body wiring harness electrical connector (2).

54. Disconnect the body harness electrical connector from the Powertrain Control Module (PCM).

55. Disconnect the engine wiring harness electrical connector from the PCM.

56. Disconnect the engine wiring harness electrical connector from the Transmission Control Module (TCM).

57. Disconnect the engine wiring harness electrical connector from the vehicle speed sensor.

58. Remove the engine wiring harness clip from the vehicle speed sensor bracket.

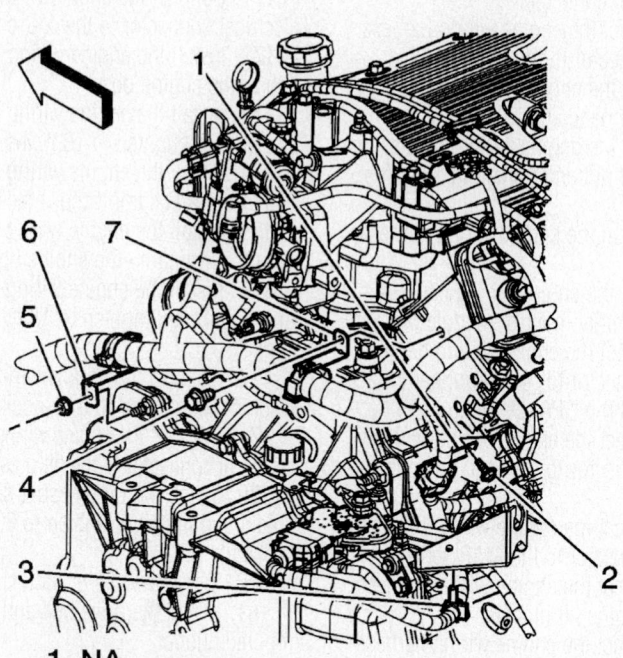

1. NA
2. NA
3. NA
4. Engine wiring harness clip bolt
5. Engine wiring harness clip nut
6. Engine wiring harness clip

36616_MALI_G0185

Fig. 100 Removing the engine wiring harness clip from the transaxle stud

59. Disconnect the engine wiring harness electrical connector from the neutral safety backup switch.

60. Disconnect the engine wiring harness electrical connector from the transaxle.

61. Remove the engine wiring harness clip bolt.

62. Remove the engine wiring harness clip nut.

63. Remove the engine wiring harness clip from the transaxle stud.

64. Remove the engine wiring harness ground nut.

65. Remove the engine wiring harness ground terminal and the battery cable ground terminal from the transaxle stud.

66. Gather all branches of the engine wiring harness and reposition the harness out of the way.

67. Remove the catalytic converter.

68. Remove the engine mount.

69. Remove the torque converter cover bolts and cover.

70. Remove the flexplate to torque converter bolts.

71. Unbolt and reposition the A/C compressor off to the side. DO NOT discharge the A/C system.

72. Remove the transaxle brace bolts and brace.

73. Reposition the radiator outlet hose clamp at the thermostat housing.

74. Remove the radiator outlet hose from the thermostat housing.

75. Lower the vehicle and support the transaxle.

76. Reposition the radiator surge tank hose clamp at the surge tank pipe.

77. Remove the radiator surge tank hose from the surge tank pipe.

78. Reposition the brake booster vacuum hose clamp at the intake manifold.

79. Remove the brake booster vacuum hose from the intake manifold.

80. Reposition the heater inlet and outlet hose clamps at the engine.

81. Remove the heater outlet and inlet hoses from the engine.

82. Disengage the fuel/EVAP line clip from the MAP sensor bracket.

83. Disconnect the fuel feed line quick connect fitting from the fuel rail.

84. Disconnect the EVAP purge line quick connect fitting from the canister purge solenoid.

85. Reposition the radiator inlet hose clamp at the engine.

86. Remove the radiator inlet hose from the engine.

87. Install a engine lifting device to the engine.

88. Remove the transaxle-to-engine bolts/studs.

89. Separate the engine from the transaxle and remove the engine from the vehicle.

90. Using the flywheel holder, secure the flexplate in order to prevent the flexplate from rotating.

91. Loosen the flexplate bolts.

92. Remove 5 of the 6 flexplate bolts leaving one bolt at the top of the crankshaft.

93. Grip the flexplate and remove the remaining bolt. Do not drop the flexplate when removing the final bolt.

94. Remove the flexplate.

95. Install the engine to the engine stand.

To install:

96. Install a engine lifting device to the engine.

97. Remove the engine from the engine stand.

98. Position the flexplate to the crankshaft.

99. Install the flywheel bolts finger tight.

100. Install the flywheel holder to the flexplate in order to prevent the flexplate from rotating.

101. Tighten the flexplate bolts to 52 ft. lbs. (70 Nm).

102. Remove the flywheel holder.

103. Install the engine to the vehicle and install the engine to the transaxle.

104. Install the transaxle-to-engine bolts/studs and tighten to 55 ft. lbs. (75 Nm).

105. Install the radiator inlet hose to the engine.

106. Position the radiator inlet hose clamp at the engine.

107. Connect the EVAP purge line quick connect fitting to the canister purge solenoid.

108. Connect the fuel feed line quick connect fitting to the fuel rail.

109. Engage the fuel/EVAP line clip to the MAP sensor bracket.

110. Install the heater outlet and inlet hoses to the engine.

111. Position the heater inlet and outlet hose clamps at the engine.

112. Install the brake booster vacuum hose to the intake manifold.

113. Position the brake booster vacuum hose clamp at the intake manifold.

114. Install the radiator surge tank hose to the surge tank pipe.

115. Position the radiator surge tank hose clamp at the surge tank pipe.

116. Remove the support from the transaxle and raise the vehicle.

117. Install the radiator outlet hose to the thermostat housing.

118. Position the radiator outlet hose clamp at the thermostat housing.

119. Install the transaxle brace and bolts and tighten the bolts to 37 ft. lbs. (50 Nm).

120. Install the flexplate to torque converter bolts and tighten to 46 ft. lbs. (62 Nm).

121. Install the torque converter cover and bolts and tighten to 89 inch lbs. (10 Nm).

122. Install the catalytic converter.

123. Install the engine mount.

124. Position the branches of the engine wiring harness over the engine.

125. Install the battery cable ground terminal and the engine wiring harness ground terminal to the transaxle stud.

126. Install the engine wiring harness ground nut and tighten to 18 ft. lbs. (25 Nm).

127. Install the engine wiring harness clip to the transaxle stud.

128. Install the engine wiring harness clip nut and tighten to 18 ft. lbs. (25 Nm).

129. Install the engine wiring harness clip bolt and tighten to 18 ft. lbs. (25 Nm).

130. Connect the engine wiring harness electrical connector to the transaxle.

131. Connect the engine wiring harness electrical connector to the neutral safety backup switch.

132. Install the engine wiring harness clip to the vehicle speed sensor bracket.

133. Connect the engine wiring harness electrical connector to the vehicle speed sensor.

134. Connect the engine wiring harness electrical connector to the TCM.

135. Connect the engine wiring harness electrical connector to the PCM.

136. Connect the body harness electrical connector to the PCM.

137. Connect the engine wiring harness electrical connector to the body wiring harness electrical connector.

138. Connect the engine wiring harness electrical connector to the body wiring harness electrical connector.

139. Install the engine wiring harness clip to the engine.

140. Connect the engine wiring harness electrical connector to the camshaft phaser.

141. Install the engine wiring harness bolt and tighten to 89 inch lbs. (10 Nm).

142. Connect the engine wiring harness electrical connector to the fuel injector inline electrical connector.

143. Connect the engine wiring harness electrical connector to the generator.

144. Install the engine wiring harness terminal to the generator.

145. Install the engine wiring harness to generator stud nut and tighten to 15 ft. lbs. (20 Nm).

146. Position the engine wiring harness terminal boot.

147. Install the engine wiring harness clips to the ignition control module bracket.

148. Connect the engine wiring harness electrical connector to the rear upper HO2S.

149. Install the CPA retainer.

150. Connect the engine wiring harness electrical connector to the ignition control module.

151. Connect the engine wiring harness electrical connector to the MAP sensor.

152. Connect the engine wiring harness clip to the engine lift bracket.

153. Connect the engine wiring harness clips to the heater inlet and outlet pipe brackets.

154. Connect the engine wiring harness electrical connector to the HO2S.

155. Install the CPA retainer.

156. Connect the engine wiring harness electrical connector to the ETC.

157. Connect the engine wiring harness electrical connector to the EVAP canister purge solenoid.

158. Unsecure and position the power steering pump.

159. Install the power steering line clip to the stud.

160. Install the power steering line clip nut to the generator stud and tighten the nut to 44 inch lbs. (5 Nm).

161. Install the power steering pump bolts and tighten to 18 ft. lbs. (25 Nm).

162. Install the power steering pump pulley using the special tool (J 25033-C).

163. Connect the engine wiring harness electrical connector to the CKP sensor.

164. Connect the engine wiring harness electrical connector to the knock sensor.

165. Install the engine wiring harness electrical connector rosebud to the transaxle mount.

166. Connect the lower rear HO2S electrical connector to the engine wiring harness electrical connector.

167. Install the lower rear CPA retainer.

168. Install the engine wiring harness electrical connector clip to the thermostat housing stud.

169. Connect the lower front HO2S electrical connector to the engine wiring harness electrical connector.

170. Install the CPA retainer.

171. Connect the engine wiring harness electrical connector to the A/C compressor.

172. Install the engine wiring harness clip to the engine boss.

173. Install the engine wiring harness clip bolt and tighten to 18 ft. lbs. (25 Nm).

174. Install the engine wiring harness clip to the A/C compressor bracket.

175. Install the engine wiring harness ground terminal to the engine boss.

176. Install the engine wiring harness ground bolt and tighten to 18 ft. lbs. (25 Nm).

177. Connect the engine wiring harness electrical connector to the knock sensor.

178. Connect the engine wiring harness electrical connector to the oil pressure sensor.

179. Install the oil pressure sensor heat shield and nuts and tighten to 89 inch lbs. (10 Nm).

180. Install the starter motor.

181. Install the drive belt and the engine mount snubber.

182. Install the intake manifold cover.

183. Install the air cleaner assembly.

184. Install the hood.

185. Fill the cooling system.

186. Connect the negative battery cable.

187. Prelube the engine.

188. Perform the CKP system variation learn procedure.

189. After an overhaul the engine should be tested. Use the following procedure after the engine is installed in the vehicle.

   a. Disable the ignition system.

   b. Crank the engine several times. Listen for any unusual noises or evidence that parts are binding.

   c. Enable the ignition system.

   d. Start the engine and listen for unusual noises.

   e. Check the vehicle oil pressure gage or light and confirm that the engine has acceptable oil pressure.

   f. Run the engine speed at about 1,000 RPM until the engine has reached normal operating temperature.

   g. Listen for sticking lifters or other unusual noises.

   h. Inspect for fuel, oil, and/or coolant leaks while the engine is running.

   i. Perform a final inspection for the proper oil and coolant levels.

190. Close the hood.

3.6L Engine

See Figures 101 and 102.

1. Disconnect the negative battery cable.
2. Remove the intake manifold cover.
3. Drain the cooling system.

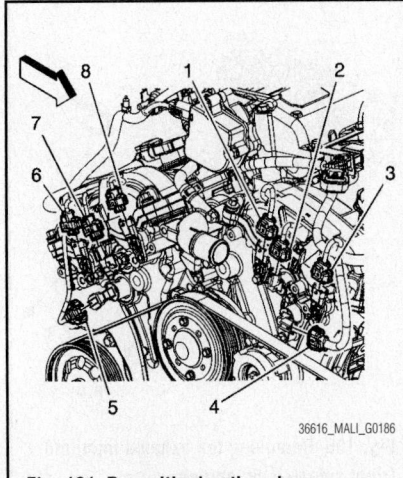

Fig. 101 Repositioning the wire loom/shield on each valve cover

Fig. 102 Removing the transaxle to oil pan brace bolts and brace—3.6L engine

4. Drain the engine oil.

5. Remove the air cleaner assembly.

6. Remove the hood.

7. Remove the engine mount strut.

8. Remove the drive belt.

9. Disconnect the front Knock Sensor (KS).

10. Disconnect the rear KS and the crank sensor.

11. Re-position the plastic wire loom/shield on each valve cover, then disconnect the Camshaft Position (CMP) sensor.

12. Disconnect the Manifold Absolute Pressure (MAP) sensor.

13. Disconnect the Evaporative Emission (EVAP) canister purge solenoid.

14. Disconnect the front and rear ignition coils.

15. Disconnect the A/C compressor.

16. Disconnect the coolant temperature sensor, Heated Oxygen Sensor (HO2S), Exhaust Gas Recirculation (EGR) valve, electronic throttle control and body wiring harness-to-engine harness.

17. Raise and support the vehicle.

18. Remove the catalytic converters.

19. Remove the engine wiring harness grounds from the transaxle.

20. Remove the engine mount lower bolts.

21. Remove the torque converter covers.

22. Remove the starter motor.

23. Remove the Air Conditioning (A/C) compressor. DO NOT discharge the A/C system. Support the compressor.

24. Remove the power steering pump and position aside.

25. Remove the torque converter bolts.

26. Remove the engine mount bracket.

27. Remove the transaxle to oil pan brace bolts and brace.

28. Remove the lower transaxle-to-engine bolt and the stud.

29. Remove the radiator outlet hose from the engine.

30. Lower the vehicle and support transaxle.

31. Remove the engine coolant thermostat housing from the engine.

32. Remove the vacuum hoses from the upper intake manifold.

33. Remove the brake booster vacuum hose from the upper intake manifold.

34. Remove the fuel lines from the fuel rail.

35. Remove the battery ground from the rear of engine.

36. Remove the radiator inlet hose from the engine.

37. Install the engine lifting device to the engine.

38. Remove the upper transaxle-to-engine bolts and the stud.

39. Remove the engine from the vehicle.

40. Remove the flywheel.

41. Install the engine to the engine stand.

To install:

42. Remove the engine from the engine stand.

43. Install the flywheel. Install the engine to the vehicle.

44. Install the upper transaxle-to-engine bolts and the stud. Tighten to 55 ft. lbs. (75 Nm).

45. Remove the engine lifting device.

46. Install the radiator inlet hose to the engine.

47. Install the battery ground to the rear of engine.

48. Install the fuel lines to the fuel rail.

49. Install the brake booster vacuum hose to the upper intake manifold.

50. Install the vacuum hoses to the upper intake manifold.

51. Install the engine coolant thermostat housing to the engine.

52. Raise the vehicle and remove the transaxle support.

53. Install the radiator outlet hose to the engine.

54. Install the lower transaxle-to-engine bolt and the stud. Tighten to 55 ft. lbs. (75 Nm).

55. Position the transaxle to oil pan brace and install the bolts. Tighten to 37 ft. lbs. (50 Nm).

56. Install the engine mount bracket.

57. Install the torque converter bolts.

58. Install the power steering pump.

59. Install the A/C compressor.

60. Install the starter motor.

61. Install the torque converter covers.

62. Install the engine mount lower bolts. Tighten to 38 ft. lbs. (50 Nm).

63. Install the engine wiring harness grounds to the transaxle.

64. Install the engine wiring harness ground nut to the transaxle stud. Tighten to 26 ft. lbs. (35 Nm).

65. Install the remaining components in the reverse order of removal.

66. Fill the crankcase with engine oil.

67. Fill cooling system.

68. Perform a CKP system variation learn procedure.

69. install the intake manifold cover.

70. Inspect for leaks.

EXHAUST MANIFOLD

REMOVAL & INSTALLATION

2.4L Engine

See Figures 103 and 104.

1. Remove the exhaust manifold heat shield.

2. Remove the Heated Oxygen Sensor (HO2S).

3. Remove and discard the exhaust manifold pipe.

4. Lower the vehicle.

5. Remove the upper exhaust manifold brace bolt.

6. Remove and discard the exhaust manifold nuts.

7. Remove the exhaust manifold/catalytic converter assembly.

8. Remove and discard the exhaust manifold gasket.

To install:

9. Install a NEW exhaust manifold gasket onto the manifold studs.

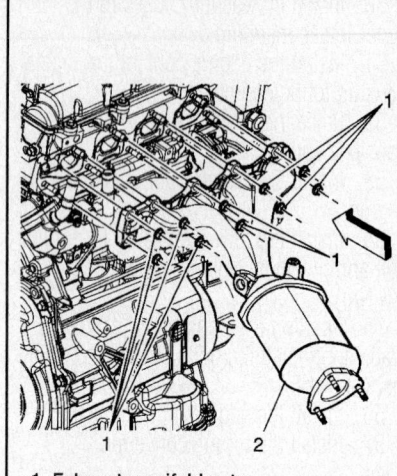

1. Exhaust manifold nuts
2. Exhaust manifold/catalytic converter assembly

36616_MALI_G0188

Fig. 103 Removing the exhaust manifold—2.4L engine

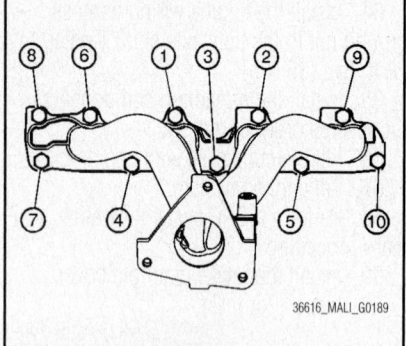

36616_MALI_G0189

Fig. 104 Exhaust manifold torque sequence—2.4L engine

10. Install the exhaust manifold/catalytic converter assembly.

11. Install the NEW exhaust manifold nuts finger tight.

12. Install the upper exhaust manifold brace bolt and tighten to 43 ft. lbs. (58 Nm).

13. Tighten the exhaust manifold nuts in sequence to 10 ft. lbs. (14 Nm).

14. Raise and suitably support the vehicle.

15. Install the exhaust manifold pipe.

16. Install the HO2S.

17. Install the exhaust manifold heat shield. Tighten the bolts to 89 inch lbs. (10 Nm).

3.5L Engine

Right Side

See Figures 105 and 106.

⁂ CAUTION

The oxygen sensor uses a permanently attached pigtail and connector. Do not remove the pigtail from the oxygen sensor. Damage to or removal of the pigtail connector could affect proper operation of the oxygen sensor.

⁂ CAUTION

The use of excessive force may damage the threads in the exhaust manifold/pipe.

➡The in-line connector and louvered end must be kept clear of grease, dirt or other contaminants. Avoid using cleaning solvents of any type. DO NOT drop or roughly handle the Heated Oxygen Sensor (HO2S).

➡The HO2S may be difficult to remove when the engine temperature is less than 120°F (48°C).

1. Remove the generator.
2. Remove the Connector Position Assurance (CPA) retainer.
3. Disconnect the engine wiring harness electrical connector from the HO2S electrical connector.
4. Remove the HO2S electrical connector rosebud clip from the ignition coil bracket.
5. Remove the HO2S using the heated oxygen sensor socket (J 39194-B).
6. Remove the exhaust manifold heat shield bolts and shield.
7. Remove the upper exhaust manifold bolts.
8. Remove the right catalytic converter.
9. Remove the lower exhaust manifold bolts.
10. Remove the exhaust manifold.
11. Remove and discard the exhaust manifold gasket.

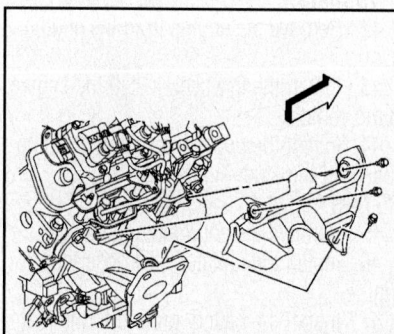

36616_MALI_G0190

Fig. 105 Removing the exhaust manifold heat shield (right side)—3.5L engine

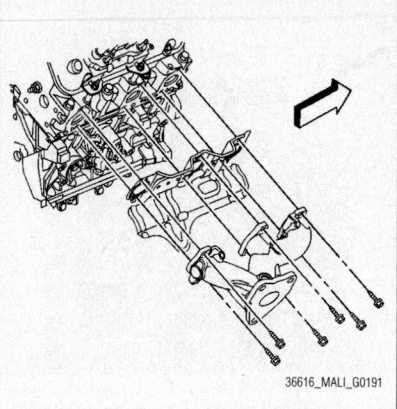

36616_MALI_G0191

Fig. 106 Removing the exhaust manifold (right side)—3.5L engine

To install:

12. Install a NEW exhaust manifold gasket onto the cylinder head studs.

13. Install the exhaust manifold.

14. Install the exhaust manifold bolts and tighten to 15 ft. lbs. (20 Nm).

15. Install the right catalytic converter.

16. Install the exhaust manifold heat shield and bolts. Tighten the bolts to 89 inch lbs. (10 Nm).

➡A special anti-seize compound is used on the HO2S threads. The compound consists of graphite suspended in fluid and glass beads. The graphite will burn away, but the glass beads will remain, making the sensor easier to remove. New or service sensors will already have the compound applied to the threads. If a sensor is removed from an engine and is to be reinstalled, the threads must have anti-seize compound applied before the reinstallation.

17. Coat the threads of the HO2S with anti-seize compound GM P/N 12377953 or equivalent, if necessary.

18. Install the HO2S using the heated oxygen sensor socket. Tighten the sensor to 31 ft. lbs. (42 Nm).

19. Connect the engine wiring harness electrical connector to the HO2S electrical connector.

20. Install the CPA retainer.

21. Install the HO2S electrical connector rosebud clip to the ignition coil bracket.

22. Install the generator.

Left Side

See Figure 107.

⁂ CAUTION

The oxygen sensor uses a permanently attached pigtail and connector. Do not remove the pigtail from the

oxygen sensor. Damage to or removal of the pigtail connector could affect proper operation of the oxygen sensor.

✷✷ CAUTION

The use of excessive force may damage the threads in the exhaust manifold/pipe.

➡The in-line connector and louvered end must be kept clear of grease, dirt or other contaminants. Avoid using cleaning solvents of any type. DO NOT drop or roughly handle the Heated Oxygen Sensor (HO2S).

➡The HO2S may be difficult to remove when the engine temperature is less than 120°F (48°C).

1. Remove the air intake duct.
2. Remove the Connector Position Assurance (CPA) retainer.
3. Disconnect the engine wiring harness electrical connector from the HO2S electrical connector.
4. Remove the HO2S electrical connector rosebud clip from the oil level indicator tube tab.
5. Using the heated oxygen sensor socket remove the HO2S.
6. Remove the exhaust manifold heat shield bolts and shield.
7. Remove the upper exhaust manifold bolts.
8. Raise and support the vehicle.
9. Remove the left catalytic converter.
10. Remove the lower exhaust manifold bolts.
11. Remove the exhaust manifold.
12. Remove and discard the exhaust manifold gasket.

To install:

13. Install a NEW exhaust manifold gasket onto the cylinder head studs.
14. Install the exhaust manifold.
15. Install the exhaust manifold bolts and tighten to 15 ft. lbs. (20 Nm).
16. Install the catalytic converter.
17. Lower the vehicle.
18. Install the exhaust manifold heat shield and bolts. Tighten the bolts to 89 inch lbs. (10 Nm).

➡A special anti-seize compound is used on the HO2S threads. The compound consists of graphite suspended in fluid and glass beads. The graphite will burn away, but the glass beads will remain, making the sensor easier to remove. New or service sensors will already have the compound applied to the threads. If a sensor is removed from an engine and is to be reinstalled, the threads must have anti-seize compound applied before the reinstallation.

19. Coat the threads of the HO2S with anti-seize compound GM P/N 12377953 or equivalent, if necessary.
20. Install the HO2S using the heated oxygen sensor socket. Tighten the sensor to 31 ft. lbs. (42 Nm).
21. Connect the engine wiring harness electrical connector to the HO2S electrical connector.
22. Install the HO2S electrical connector rosebud clip to the oil level indicator tube tab.
23. Install the CPA retainer.
24. Install the air intake duct.

3.6L Engine

Right Side

See Figure 108.

1. Remove the catalytic converter.
2. Remove the exhaust manifold lower bolts.
3. Lower the vehicle half way.
4. Remove the exhaust manifold upper bolts.
5. Remove the exhaust manifold.
6. Remove and discard the exhaust manifold gasket.

To install:

7. Install one upper exhaust manifold bolt to the exhaust manifold.
8. Place the NEW exhaust manifold gasket onto the bolt.
9. Position and install the exhaust manifold (with gasket) to the cylinder head.
10. Loosely install the remaining upper exhaust manifold bolts.
11. Raise and support the vehicle.
12. Loosely install the lower exhaust manifold bolts.
13. Tighten the exhaust manifold bolts to 15 ft. lbs. (20 Nm).
14. Install the catalytic converter.

Left Side

See Figure 109.

1. Remove the left exhaust manifold heat shield bolts.
2. Remove the left exhaust manifold heat shield.
3. Remove the oil level indicator.
4. Remove the catalytic converter to exhaust manifold nuts.
5. Remove the exhaust manifold bolts.
6. Remove the exhaust manifold and gasket. Discard the gasket.

To install:

7. Install one exhaust manifold bolt to the exhaust manifold.

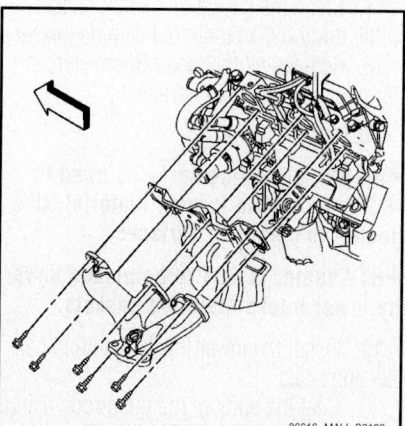

Fig. 107 Removing the exhaust manifold (left side)—3.5L engine

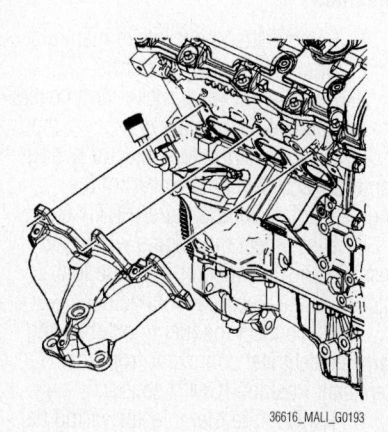

Fig. 108 Removing the exhaust manifold (right side)—3.6L engine

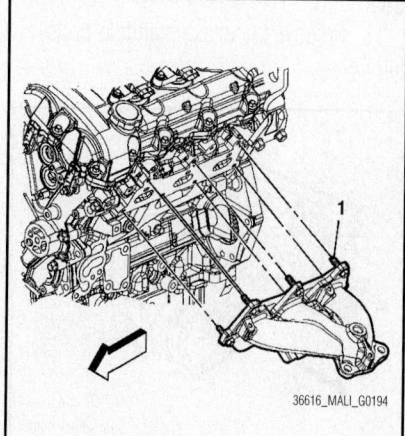

Fig. 109 Removing the exhaust manifold (left side)—3.6L engine

8. Install the NEW exhaust manifold gasket onto the cylinder head and bolt.

9. Install the exhaust manifold (with gasket) to the catalytic converter and the cylinder head.

10. Install the remaining exhaust manifold bolts and tighten to 15 ft. lbs. (20 Nm).

11. Install the catalytic converter to exhaust manifold nuts and tighten to 33 ft. lbs. (45 Nm).

12. Install the oil level indicator.

13. Install the exhaust manifold heat shield.

14. Inspect for exhaust leaks.

INTAKE MANIFOLD

REMOVAL & INSTALLATION

2.4L Engine

See Figure 110.

1. Remove the throttle body.
2. Remove the fuel rail.
3. Remove the Evaporative Emission (EVAP) canister purge solenoid valve tube.
4. Reposition the brake booster vacuum hose clamp at the intake manifold.
5. Remove the brake booster hose from the intake manifold.
6. Remove the oil level indicator tube bolt.
7. Disconnect the engine harness electrical connector from the fuel injector inline electrical connector.
8. Remove the fuel injector inline connector clip from the intake manifold.
9. Disconnect the engine harness electrical connector from the knock sensor harness.
10. Remove the knock sensor connector clip from the oil level indicator tube.
11. Remove the intake manifold bolts and nuts.

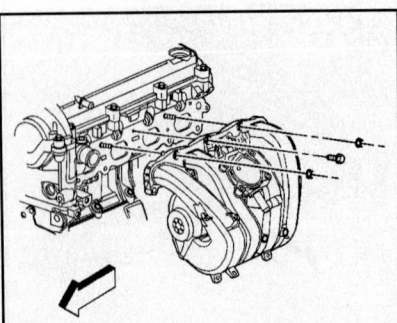

Fig. 110 Removing the intake manifold— 2.4L engine

12. Remove the intake manifold.

➡ **The intake manifold gasket is reusable. Only replace the gasket if damage has occurred.**

13. Remove the intake manifold gasket, if necessary.

To install:

14. Install the intake manifold gasket, if necessary.
15. Install the intake manifold.
16. Install the intake manifold bolts and nuts and tighten to 89 inch lbs. (10 Nm).
17. Connect the engine harness electrical connector to the knock sensor harness.
18. Install the knock sensor connector clip to the oil level indicator tube.
19. Connect the engine harness electrical connector to the fuel injector inline electrical connector.
20. Install the fuel injector inline connector clip to the intake manifold.
21. Install the oil level indicator tube bolt and tighten to 89 inch lbs. (10 Nm).
22. Install the brake booster hose to the intake manifold.
23. Position the brake booster vacuum hose clamp at the intake manifold.
24. Install the EVAP canister purge solenoid valve tube.
25. Install the fuel rail.
26. Install the throttle body.

3.5L Engine

Lower

See Figures 111 and 112.

➡ **This engine uses a sequential multi-port fuel injection system. Injector wiring harness connectors must be connected to their appropriate fuel injector or exhaust emissions and engine performance may be seriously affected.**

1. Remove the upper intake manifold.
2. Drain the cooling system.
3. Remove the valve rocker arm covers.
4. Remove the coolant crossover pipe.
5. Disconnect the fuel injector wiring harness electrical connector from the Engine Coolant Temperature (ECT) sensor.
6. Disconnect the engine wiring harness electrical connector from the fuel injector inline electrical connector.
7. Disconnect the fuel injector wiring harness electrical connector from the Camshaft Position (CMP) sensor.
8. Remove the fuel injector wiring harness connector bracket bolt from the intake manifold.
9. Remove the fuel rail bolts and rail.

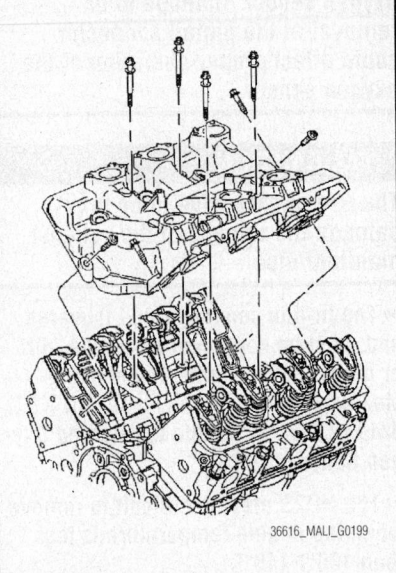

Fig. 111 Removing the lower intake manifold—3.5L engine

10. Remove the lower intake manifold bolts.
11. Remove the lower intake manifold.
12. Loosen the rocker arm bolts.

➡ **Place the valve train components in a rack in order to ensure that the components are installed in the same locations from which they were removed.**

13. Remove the rocker arms.
14. Remove the push rods. The intake push rods measure 5.81 inch (147.51mm). The exhaust push rods measure 6.1 inch (154.87 mm).
15. Remove the lower intake manifold gaskets and seals.
16. Clean the lower intake manifold gasket and seal surfaces on the cylinder heads and the engine block.
17. Clean the gasket and seal surfaces on the lower intake manifold with degreaser.
18. Remove all the loose Room Temperature Vulcanizing (RTV) sealer.

To install:

➡ **All gasket-mating surfaces need to be free of oil and foreign material. Use cleaner to clean the surfaces.**

➡ **RTV sealer is NOT to be placed under the lower intake manifold gaskets.**

19. Install the lower intake manifold gaskets and seals.
20. Coat the ends of the push rods using prelube GM P/N 36616501 (Canadian P/N 992704) or equivalent.
21. Install push rods in their original location. The intake pushrods are identified

with yellow stripes. The exhaust pushrods are identified with green stripes.

22. Coat the rocker arm friction surfaces using prelube GM P/N 36616501 (Canadian P/N 992704) or equivalent.

→**Shims (P/N 88894006) may be required under the valve rocker arm pedestals if reconditioning has been performed on the cylinder head or its components.**

23. Install the rocker arms in their original locations.

24. Install the rocker arm bolts. Tighten to 25 ft. lbs. (34 Nm).

25. With the NEW gaskets and seals in place, apply a small drop, 0.31-0.39 inch (8-10 mm) or RTV sealer to the 4 corners of the intake manifold to block joints.

26. Install the lower intake manifold.

※※ CAUTION

Maximum gasket performance is achieved when using new fasteners, which contain a thread-locking patch. If the fasteners are not replaced, a thread locking chemical must be applied to the fastener threads. Failure to replace the fasteners or apply a thread-locking chemical MAY reduce gasket sealing capability.

※※ CAUTION

Failure to tighten vertical bolts before the diagonal bolts may cause an oil leak.

27. Apply sealer to the lower intake manifold bolt threads.

28. Install the lower intake manifold bolts.

29. Tighten the lower intake manifold bolts in the sequence shown. Tighten the center lower intake manifold bolts (1, 2, 3, 4) in sequence to 15 ft. lbs. (20 Nm).

Tighten the visible corner lower intake manifold bolts (5, 8) to 18 ft. lbs. (25 Nm). Tighten the hidden corner lower intake manifold bolts (6, 7) to 18 ft. lbs. (25 Nm).

30. Inspect the fuel rail, fuel injectors for damage and replace as necessary.

31. Lubricate and install NEW injector lower O-rings seals onto the injectors. Lubricate the NEW O-rings seals with GM P/N 36616616 (Canadian P/N 993182).

32. Install the injector nozzles into the lower intake manifold injector bores.

33. Press on the injector rail using the palms of both hands until the injectors are fully seated.

34. Install the fuel injector rail bolts. Tighten the bolts to 89 inch lbs. (10 Nm).

35. Position the fuel injector wiring harness electrical connector bracket to the intake manifold and install the bolt. Tighten the bolts to 10 ft. lbs. (14 Nm).

36. Connect the fuel injector wiring harness electrical connector to the CMP sensor.

37. Connect the engine wiring harness electrical connector to the fuel injector inline electrical connector.

38. Connect the fuel injector wiring harness electrical connector to the ECT sensor.

39. Install the coolant crossover pipe.

40. Install the valve rocker arm covers.

41. Install the upper intake manifold.

42. Fill the coolant system.

Upper

See Figures 113 and 114.

1. Remove the intake manifold cover.

2. Disconnect the fuel feed pipe quick connect fitting from the fuel rail.

3. Disconnect the Evaporative Emission (EVAP) pipe quick connect fitting from the purge solenoid.

4. Remove the fuel line clip from the Manifold Absolute Pressure (MAP) sensor bracket.

5. Reposition the fuel/EVAP lines out of the way.

6. Drain the cooling system.

7. Remove the air cleaner outlet duct.

8. Remove the Positive Crankcase Ventilation (PCV) fresh air tube from the rocker cover.

9. Remove the PCV foul air tube quick connect fitting from the rocker cover.

10. Remove the PCV foul air tube from the intake manifold.

11. Reposition the brake booster vacuum hose clamp at the intake manifold.

12. Remove the brake booster vacuum hose from the intake manifold.

13. Reposition the radiator surge tank inlet hose clamp (1).

14. Remove the radiator surge tank inlet hose from the inlet pipe.

15. Remove the radiator surge tank inlet pipe bolts.

16. Remove the radiator surge tank inlet pipe.

17. Remove and discard the O-ring seal.

18. Disconnect the engine wiring harness electrical connector from the MAP sensor.

19. Disconnect the engine wiring harness electrical connector from the EVAP canister purge solenoid.

20. Disconnect the engine wiring harness electrical connector from the Electronic Throttle Control (ETC).

21. Disconnect the left side spark plug wires from the spark plugs.

22. Disconnect the left side spark plug wires from the ignition coil.

23. Disengage the spark plug wire retainer clips from the heater inlet and outlet pipe bracket and the MAP sensor bracket.

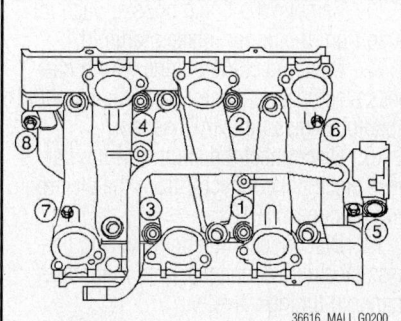

36616_MALI_G0200

Fig. 112 Identifying the lower intake manifold bolt tightening sequence—3.5L engine

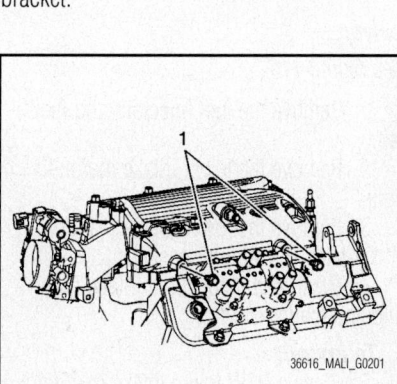

36616_MALI_G0201

Fig. 113 Removing the ignition coil bracket bolts

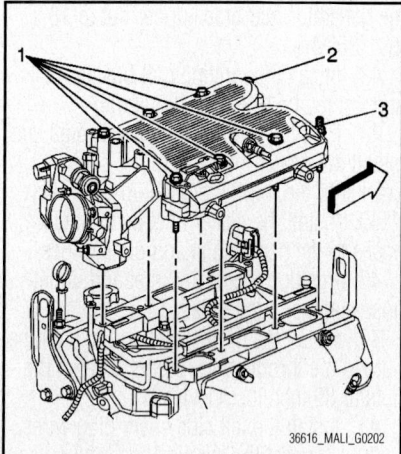

36616_MALI_G0202

Fig. 114 Removing the upper intake manifold from the lower intake manifold—3.5L engine

24. Remove the left side spark plug wires.

25. Remove the heater inlet and outlet pipe nuts from the throttle body studs.

26. Reposition the heater inlet and outlet hose clamps from the pipes.

27. Remove the heater inlet and outlet hoses from the heater inlet and outlet pipes.

28. Remove the heater inlet and outlet pipe bracket from the throttle body studs. Reposition the inlet and outlet pipe out of the way.

29. Remove the ignition coil bracket bolts.

30. Remove the generator rear brace upper nut.

31. Remove the generator through bolt.

32. Remove the generator rear brace.

33. Remove the upper intake manifold bolts (1, 2) and stud (3).

34. Separate and remove the upper intake manifold from the lower intake manifold.

35. Remove the upper to lower intake manifold gaskets.

To install:

36. Install the NEW upper to lower intake manifold gaskets.

37. Set the upper intake manifold onto the lower intake manifold.

38. Apply threadlock to the upper intake manifold bolts/stud threads.

39. Install the upper intake manifold bolts (1, 2) and stud (3). Tighten the bolts/studs to 18 ft. lbs. (25 Nm).

40. Place the generator rear brace onto the stud.

41. Install the generator through bolt until snug.

42. Install the generator rear brace upper nut until snug. Tighten the generator through bolt to 37 ft. lbs. (50 Nm). Tighten the generator rear brace upper nut to 18 ft. lbs. (25 Nm).

43. Install the ignition coil bracket bolts and tighten to 18 ft. lbs. (25 Nm).

44. Position the inlet and outlet pipe and install the heater inlet and outlet pipe bracket to the throttle body studs.

45. Install the heater inlet and outlet hoses to the heater inlet and outlet pipes.

46. Position the heater inlet and outlet hose clamps to the pipes.

47. Install the heater inlet and outlet pipe nuts to the throttle body studs. Tighten the nuts to 89 inch lbs. (10 Nm).

48. Install the left side spark plug wires.

49. Connect the left side spark plug wires to the spark plugs.

50. Connect the left side spark plug wires to the ignition coil.

51. Engage the spark plug wire retainer clips to the heater inlet and outlet pipe bracket and the MAP sensor bracket.

52. Connect the engine wiring harness electrical connector to the EVAP canister purge solenoid.

53. Connect the engine wiring harness electrical connector to the ETC.

54. Connect the engine wiring harness electrical connector to the MAP sensor.

55. Install a NEW O-ring seal to the inlet pipe.

56. Install the radiator surge tank inlet pipe.

57. Install the radiator surge tank inlet pipe bolts tighten the bolts to 89 inch lbs. (10 Nm).

58. Install the radiator surge tank inlet hose to the inlet pipe.

59. Position the radiator surge tank inlet hose clamp.

60. Install the brake booster vacuum hose to the intake manifold.

61. Position the brake booster vacuum hose clamp at the intake manifold.

62. Install the PCV foul air tube to the intake manifold.

63. Install the PCV foul air tube quick connect fitting to the rocker cover.

64. Install the PCV fresh air tube to the rocker cover.

65. Install the air cleaner outlet duct.

66. Fill the cooling system.

67. Position the fuel/EVAP lines.

68. Install the fuel line clip to the MAP sensor bracket.

69. Connect the fuel feed pipe quick connect fitting to the fuel rail.

70. Connect the EVAP pipe quick connect fitting to the purge solenoid.

71. Install the intake manifold cover.

72. Connect the negative battery cable.

3.6L Engine

Lower

See Figure 115.

1. Remove the fuel injectors and fuel rail.

2. Remove the lower intake manifold bolts.

3. Remove the lower intake manifold and gasket. Discard the gasket.

4. Clean and inspect the intake manifold and mating surfaces.

To install:

5. Place a NEW lower intake manifold gasket onto the cylinder heads.

6. Place the lower intake manifold onto the cylinder heads.

36616_MALI_G0203

Fig. 115 Removing the lower intake manifold—3.6L engine

7. Install the lower intake manifold bolts and tighten to 17 ft. lbs. (23 Nm).

8. Install the fuel injectors and fuel rail.

Upper

See Figure 116.

1. Remove the fuel injector sight shield.

2. Remove the air cleaner outlet duct.

3. Disconnect the fuel feed line quick connect fitting from the fuel rail.

4. Remove the fuel feed pipe line nut and remove the fuel feed line clip from the stud.

5. Reposition the fuel feed line out of the way.

6. Remove the coolant air bleed hose/pipe clip bolt from the upper intake manifold.

7. Reposition the coolant air bleed hose clamp at the water outlet.

8. Remove the coolant air bleed hose from the water outlet.

9. Remove the coolant air bleed hose/pipe clip from the upper intake manifold stud and reposition out of the way.

10. Reposition the brake booster vacuum hose clamp at the upper intake manifold.

11. Remove the brake booster vacuum hose from the upper intake manifold.

12. Disconnect the engine wiring harness electrical connector from the Manifold Absolute Pressure (MAP) sensor.

13. Disconnect the engine wiring harness electrical connector from the electronic throttle control (ETC).

14. Disconnect the engine wiring harness electrical connector from the intake manifold tuning valve.

15. Disconnect the engine wiring harness electrical connector from the Evaporative Emission (EVAP) canister purge solenoid.

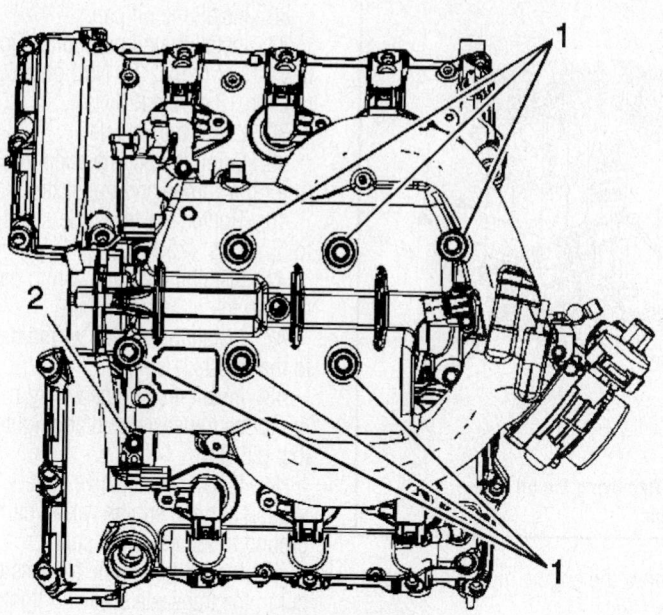

1. Upper intake bolts
2. Fuel rail wiring harness electrical connector bolt

36616_MALI_G0204

Fig. 116 Removing the upper intake bolts—3.6L engine

16. Disconnect the Positive Crankcase Ventilation (PCV) tube from the upper intake manifold and reposition aside.

17. Disconnect the EVAP canister purge solenoid tube quick connect fitting at the upper intake manifold and reposition aside.

18. Remove the fuel rail to bracket bolt.

19. Remove the fuel rail wiring harness electrical connector bolt and reposition the harness out of the way.

20. Remove the upper intake bolts.

21. Remove the upper intake manifold and gaskets. Discard gaskets.

22. Clean the gasket mating surfaces.

To install:

23. Place NEW upper intake manifold gaskets onto the lower intake manifold.

24. Place the upper intake manifold onto the lower intake manifold.

25. Install the upper intake bolts and tighten to 17 ft. lbs. (23 Nm).

26. Position the fuel rail wiring harness and install the fuel rail wiring harness electrical connector bolt Tighten to 89 inch lbs. (10 Nm).

27. Install the fuel rail to bracket bolt. Tighten to 89 inch lbs. (10 Nm).

28. Position and install the EVAP canister purge solenoid tube quick connect fitting to the upper intake manifold.

29. Position and install the PCV tube to the upper intake manifold.

30. Connect the engine wiring harness electrical connector to the EVAP canister purge solenoid.

31. Connect the engine wiring harness electrical connector to the intake manifold tuning valve.

32. Connect the engine wiring harness electrical connector to the ETC.

33. Connect the engine wiring harness electrical connector to the MAP sensor.

34. Install the brake booster vacuum hose to the upper intake manifold.

35. Position the brake booster vacuum hose clamp at the upper intake manifold.

36. Position and install the coolant air bleed hose/pipe clip to the upper intake manifold stud.

37. Install the coolant air bleed hose to the water outlet.

38. Position the coolant air bleed hose clamp at the water outlet.

39. Install the coolant air bleed hose/pipe clip bolt to the upper intake manifold. Tighten to 89 inch lbs. (10 Nm).

40. Position the fuel feed line and install the fuel feed line clip to the stud.

41. Install the fuel feed line nut. Tighten to 89 inch lbs. (10 Nm).

42. Connect the fuel feed line quick connect fitting to the fuel rail.

43. Install the air cleaner outlet duct.

44. Install the fuel injector sight shield.

OIL PAN

REMOVAL & INSTALLATION

2.4L Engine

See Figures 117 and 118.

1. Remove the drive belt.

2. Remove the oil level indicator tube.

➡The support fixture bar must be installed to provide enough access to remove and properly tighten the oil pan bolts.

3. Install the engine support fixture.

4. Remove engine mount.

5. Using the engine support fixture, raise the engine approximately 3 inches.

6. Raise and support the vehicle.

7. Loosen the upper Air Conditioning (A/C) compressor bolts.

8. Remove the lower A/C compressor bolt.

9. Place a suitable drain pan under the oil pan drain plug.

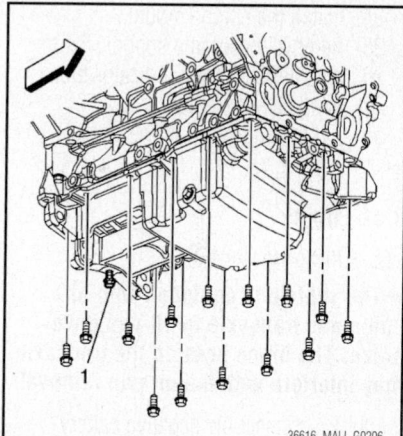

36616_MALI_G0206

Fig. 117 Removing the oil pan bolts—2.4L engine

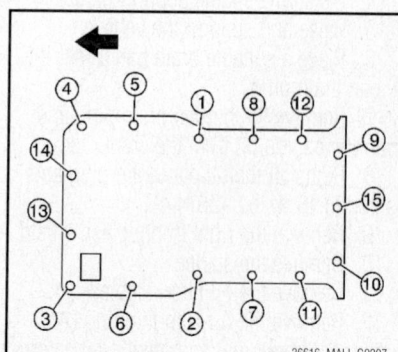

36616_MALI_G0207

Fig. 118 Identifying the oil pan bolt tightening sequence—2.4L engine

10. Remove the oil pan drain plug.

11. Drain the engine oil.

12. Reinstall the oil pan drain plug until snug.

13. Remove the 4 oil pan to transaxle bolts.

14. Remove the oil pan bolts.

15. Remove the oil pan

16. Remove any old oil pan sealant.

To install:

17. Ensure that the oil pan and the sealing surface on the lower crankcase are free of all oil and debris. Apply a 2 mm bead of sealant around the perimeter of the oil pan and the oil suction port opening. DO NOT over apply the sealant. More than a 2 mm bead is not required.

18. Install the oil pan.

19. Install the oil pan bolts and hand tighten.

20. Install the 4 oil pan to transaxle bolts. Tighten the bolts to 55 ft. lbs. (75 Nm).

21. Tighten the oil pan bolts in the sequence shown to 18 ft. lbs. (25 Nm).

22. Lower the vehicle.

23. Using the engine support fixture, lower the engine.

24. Install the engine mount.

25. Remove the engine support fixture.

26. Install the oil level indicator tube.

27. Install the drive belt.

28. Fill the engine oil to the proper level.

3.5L Engine

See Figure 119.

➡The vehicle is equipped with an automatic transaxle to oil pan lower brace. The brace boss on the transaxle may interfere with the oil pan removal.

1. Disconnect the negative battery cable.

2. Remove the drive belt.

3. Remove the air cleaner inlet duct.

4. Install the engine support fixture.

5. Raise and support the vehicle.

6. Place a suitable drain pan under the oil pan drain plug.

7. Remove the oil pan drain plug and drain the engine oil from the crankcase.

8. Reinstall the oil pan drain plug and tighten to 19 ft. lbs. (26 Nm).

9. Remove the right front splash shield.

10. Remove the starter.

11. Remove the oil filter adapter.

12. Remove the Air Conditioning (A/C) compressor bolts/nut and position the compressor aside.

13. Remove the catalytic converters.

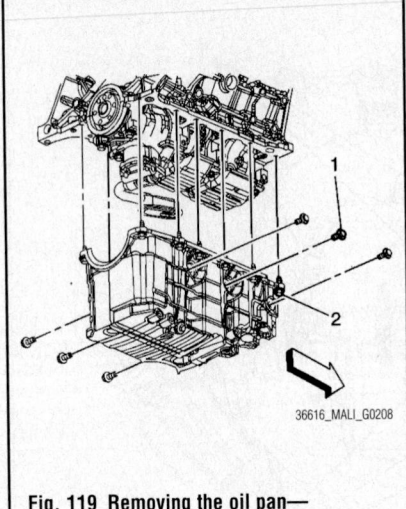

Fig. 119 Removing the oil pan—3.5L engine

36616_MALI_G0208

14. Remove the engine mount bracket bolts and bracket.

15. Remove the transaxle brace bolts and remove the brace.

16. Remove the transaxle to oil pan brace bolts and brace.

17. Remove the flexplate to torque converter bolts.

18. Lower the vehicle.

19. Remove the engine harness ground nut from the transaxle stud.

20. Remove the engine wiring harness ground and the negative battery cable ground from the transaxle stud.

21. Remove the engine wiring harness clip nut from the transaxle stud.

22. Remove the engine wiring harness clip from the transaxle stud.

23. Remove the engine wiring harness clips from the oil pan.

24. Loosen, DO NOT REMOVE the transaxle studs and bolts.

25. Using the engine support fixture, raise the engine and transaxle slightly.

26. Raise and support the vehicle.

27. Remove the oil pan bolts.

28. Separate the engine and transaxle approximately 1² inch (13 mm.

29. Ensure that when removing the oil pan, the pan clears the boss on the transaxle.

30. Remove the oil pan.

31. Remove and discard the oil pan gasket.

32. Clean the oil pan sealing surfaces.

To install:

33. Apply sealer to both sides of the front cover/block mating area.

34. Apply sealer to both sides of the crankcase rear main bearing cap. Press the sealer into the gap using a putty knife.

35. Install a NEW oil pan gasket.

36. Install the oil pan.

37. Install the oil pan bolts. Tighten bolts to 37 ft. lbs. (50 Nm) plus 50° and bolts to 18 ft. lbs. (25 Nm).

38. Lower the vehicle.

39. Using the engine support fixture, lower the engine and transaxle.

40. Tighten the transaxle studs and bolts to 55 ft. lbs. (75 Nm).

41. Install the engine wiring harness clips to the oil pan.

42. Install the engine wiring harness clip to the transaxle stud.

43. Install the engine wiring harness clip nut to the transaxle stud and tighten to 18 ft. lbs. (25 Nm).

44. Install the negative battery cable ground and the engine wiring harness ground to the transaxle stud.

45. Install the engine harness ground nut to the transaxle stud and tighten to 18 ft. lbs. (25 Nm).

46. Raise and support the vehicle.

47. Install the flexplate to torque converter bolts and tighten to 46 ft. lbs. (62 Nm).

48. Position the transaxle to oil pan brace, install the bolts and tighten to 37 ft. lbs. (50 Nm).

49. Position the transaxle brace to the transaxle and install the bolts until snug.

50. Install the engine wiring harness clip to the rear of the transaxle brace.

51. Position the engine mount bracket to the engine and install the bolts until snug.

52. Tighten the engine mount bracket upper bolt to 66 ft. lbs. (90 Nm).

53. Tighten the engine mount bracket lower bolts to 37 ft. lbs. (50 Nm).

54. Tighten the transaxle brace bolts to 53 ft. lbs. (72 Nm).

55. Install the catalytic converters.

56. Install the A/C compressor and bolts. Tighten the bolts to 37 ft. lbs. (50 Nm).

57. Install the oil filter adapter.

58. Install the starter.

59. Install the right front splash shield.

60. Tighten the oil pan drain plug to 19 ft. lbs. (26 Nm).

61. Lower the vehicle.

62. Remove the engine support fixture.

63. Install the air cleaner inlet duct.

64. Install the drive belt.

65. Fill the crankcase with oil.

66. Connect the negative battery cable.

67. Start the vehicle and inspect for leaks.

3.6L Engine

See Figures 120 and 121.

1. Raise and support the vehicle.
2. Drain the engine oil and remove the oil filter.
3. Remove the catalytic converter.
4. Remove the Air Conditioning (A/C) compressor.
5. Remove the transmission bellhousing bolts.
6. Remove the oil pan bolts.
7. Remove the oil pan.
8. Clean the oil pan and the engine block gasket surface.

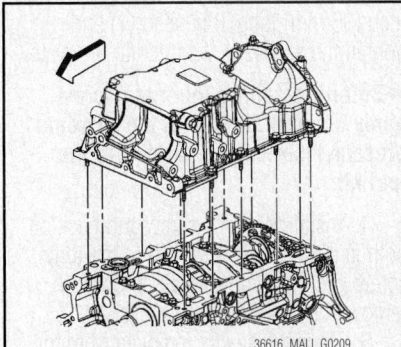

Fig. 120 Removing the oil pan—3.6L engine

To install:

9. Install the 0.315 inch (8mm) guides from the a guide pin set such as EN 46109 into the center oil pan rail bolt hole on each side of the engine block.
10. Place a 0.118 inch (3mm) bead of RTV sealant on the block pan rail and the crankshaft rear oil seal housing.
11. Position the oil pan onto the block.
12. Remove guide pin set guides from the engine block.
13. Loosely install the oil pan bolts.
14. Tighten the oil pan bolts in sequence shown as follows:

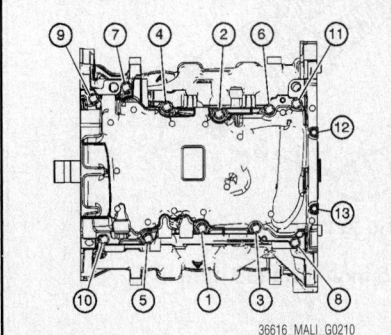

Fig. 121 Identifying the oil pan bolt tightening sequence—3.6L engine

a. 8 mm bolts 1 through 11 to 17 ft. lbs. (23 Nm).
b. 6 mm bolts 12 and 13 to 89 inch lbs. (10 Nm).
15. Install the Air Conditioning (A/C) compressor.
16. Install the catalytic converter.
17. Lower the vehicle.
18. Refill the engine oil.

OIL PUMP

REMOVAL & INSTALLATION

2.4L Engine

See Figure 122.

1. Remove the accessory drive belt tensioner.
2. Remove the drive belt tensioner bracket.
3. Remove the engine front cover bolts.
4. Remove the long water pump bolt.
5. Remove the engine front cover and gaskets.
6. Remove the crankshaft front cover oil seal with an appropriate tool.
7. Remove the oil pump.

To install:

8. Install the oil pump.
9. Install the engine front cover with a new gasket.

➡Use the correct fastener in the correct location. Replacement fasteners must be the correct part number for that application. Fasteners requiring replacement or fasteners requiring the use of thread locking compound or sealant are identified in the service procedure. Do not use paints, lubricants, or corrosion inhibitors on fasteners or fastener joint surfaces unless specified. These coatings affect fastener torque and joint clamping force and may damage the fastener. Use the correct tightening sequence and speci-

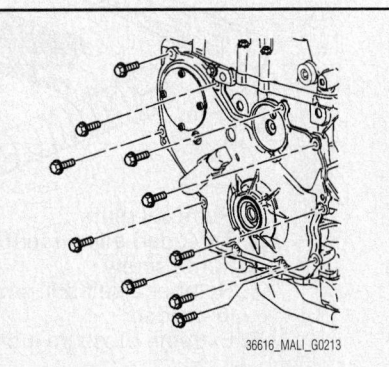

Fig. 122 Removing the engine front cover—2.4L engine

fications when installing fasteners in order to avoid damage to parts and systems.

10. Install the long water pump bolt and tighten to 18 ft. lbs. (25 Nm).
11. Install the engine front cover bolts and tighten to 18 ft. lbs. (25 Nm).
12. Install the drive belt tensioner bracket and tighten to 33 ft. lbs. (45 Nm).
13. Install the accessory drive belt tensioner and tighten to 33 ft. lbs. (45 Nm).

3.5L Engine

See Figure 123.

1. Remove the oil pan.
2. Remove the oil pump bolt.
3. Remove the oil pump and the oil pump drive shaft.

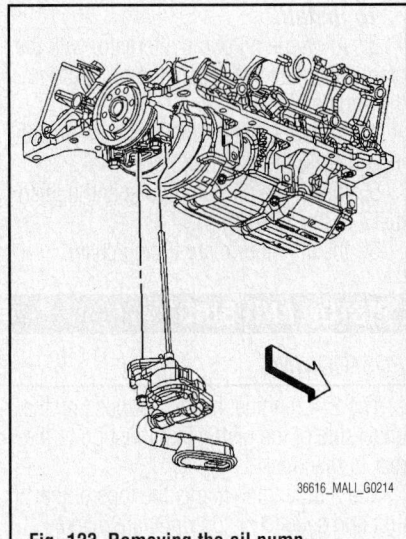

Fig. 123 Removing the oil pump—3.5L engine

To install:

➡Rotate the oil pump drive shaft as necessary in order to obtain the engagement with the oil pump drive unit.

4. Install the oil pump drive shaft and the oil pump.
5. Install the oil pump bolt attaching the oil pump to the rear crankshaft bearing cap and tighten to 30 ft. lbs. (41 Nm).
6. Install the oil pan

3.6L Engine

See Figure 124.

➡Do not remove the left bank idler sprocket.

1. Remove the primary timing chain.
2. Remove the oil pump bolts and the oil pump.

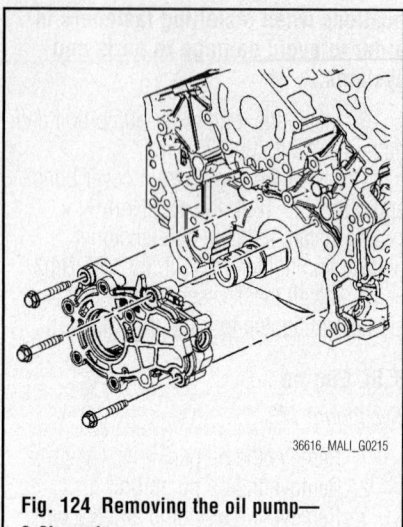

Fig. 124 Removing the oil pump—
3.6L engine

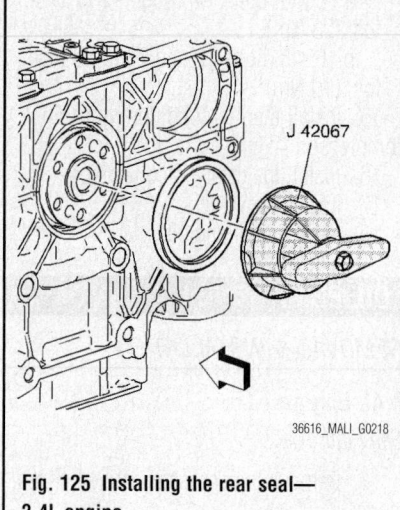

Fig. 125 Installing the rear seal—
2.4L engine

To install:

3. Align the oil pump alternator with the crankshaft flats and install the oil pump to the engine block.

4. Align the pump body with the mounting holes in the cylinder block.

5. Install the oil pump bolts and tighten to 17 ft. lbs. (23 Nm).

6. Install the primary timing chain.

PISTON AND RING

POSITIONING

The 2.4L engine, has a cast boss on the underside of the piston that must go to the rear of the block.

The 3.5L engine marks the tops of the first and second piston rings are marked with light green stripes to insure proper orientation on the piston. The top ring has a light green stripe 180 degrees from the gap, and the second ring has a light green stripe 90 degrees from the gap. These stripes must be facing up and in this orientation prior to installing the pistons. This is necessary for proper operation. Make sure the connecting rod reference mark is facing towards front of engine, and is in proper correlation with the front of engine piston reference mark.

The 3.6L engine has a dot showing proper piston orientation is located on the top of the piston must face the front of the engine.

REAR MAIN SEAL

REMOVAL & INSTALLATION

2.4L Engine

See Figure 125.

1. Remove the transmission and flywheel.

➥Do not damage the outside diameter of the crankshaft or chamber with any tool.

2. Pry out the crankshaft rear oil seal using a flat-bladed tool.

To install:

3. Using a seal installer such as J 42067 , install a NEW crankshaft real oil seal.

4. Install the flywheel and transmission.

3.5L Engine

See Figures 126 through 129.

1. Remove the transmission and flywheel.

➥The rear main seal removal tool has a unique design to allow the technician to easily remove the rear main seal without nicking the crankshaft sealing surface when removing the seal. Before proceeding with removal, review the illustration to become familiar with its components.

2. Install the removal plate and both threaded adjustment pins and jam nuts into the back of the crankshaft flange and secure the plate with adjustment pins and jam nuts.

3. Install the #2 self drill screws 1.5 inch (38 mm) long, 8 needed (1) and tighten the screws down flush to the plate.

➥Before installing the force screw, apply a small amount of the extreme pressure lubricant, provided in the tool kit.

4. Install the force screw and back off both jam nuts. Continue to turn the force screw into the removal plate in order to remove the seal from the crankshaft.

5. Once the seal is removed from the crankshaft, remove and save all 8 screws. Discard the old seal.

To install:

✳✳ CAUTION

Do not remove the protective sleeve from the seal. The sleeve assures the seal is installed correctly and pro-

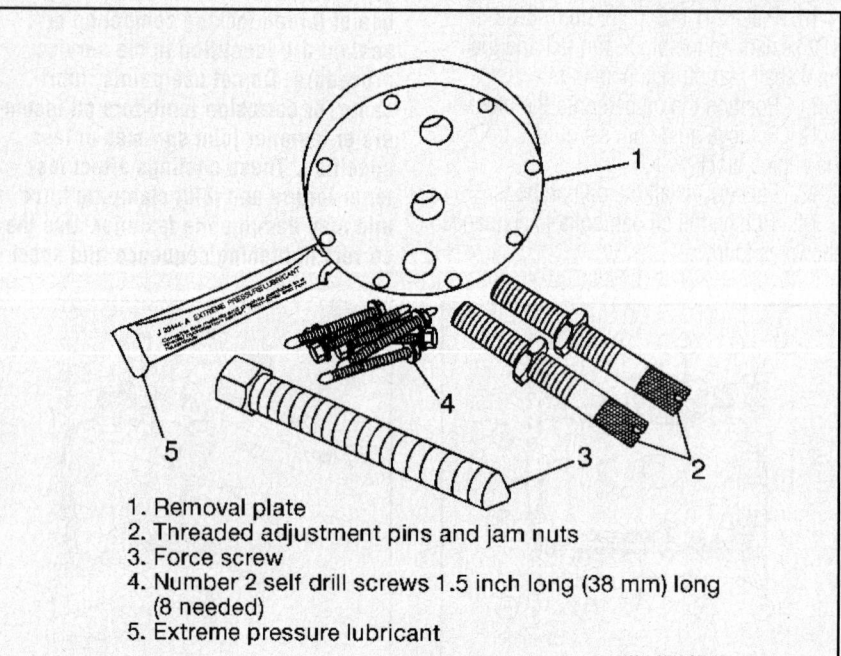

1. Removal plate
2. Threaded adjustment pins and jam nuts
3. Force screw
4. Number 2 self drill screws 1.5 inch long (38 mm) long (8 needed)
5. Extreme pressure lubricant

Fig. 126 Identifying rear main seal remover components

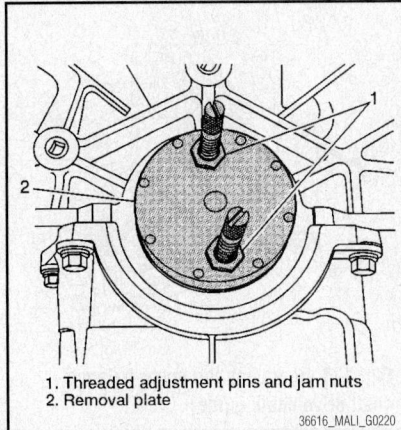

1. Threaded adjustment pins and jam nuts
2. Removal plate

36616_MALI_G0220

Fig. 127 Installing the removal plate and the threaded adjustment pins and jam nuts

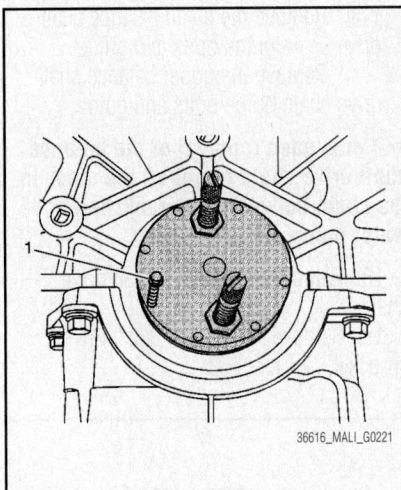

36616_MALI_G0221

Fig. 128 Installing the #2 self drill screws

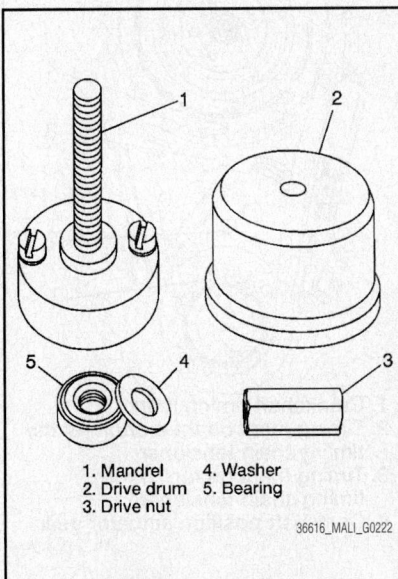

1. Mandrel   4. Washer
2. Drive drum 5. Bearing
3. Drive nut

36616_MALI_G0222

Fig. 129 Identifying the rear main seal installer components

tects the seal from damage. If removed, the EN-48108 installation tool will not work.

✳✳ CAUTION

Clean the crankshaft sealing surface with a clean, lint-free towel. Inspect lead-in edge of crankshaft for burrs/sharp edges that could damage the rear main oil seal. Remove burrs/sharp edges with crocus cloth before proceeding.

✳✳ CAUTION

Do not remove protective nylon sleeve prior to installation. The rear main oil seal installation tool is designed to install the rear main seal with the protective sleeve in place. Never apply or use any oil, lubricants or sealing compounds on the crankshaft rear main oil seal.

➡Before replacement of the new design crankshaft rear main oil seal, ensure the Positive Crankcase Ventilation (PCV) system is operating correctly.

A new design crankshaft rear main oil seal and installation tool, EN-48108 installer , has been released. This seal incorporates features that improve high mileage durability. Replace the crankshaft rear main oil seal with the new design rear main oil seal, GM P/N 12592195 (Canadian P/N 12592195).

The EN-48108 installer has a unique design to allow the technician to easily install the rear main seal squarely to the correct depth and direction. Before proceeding with installation, review the illustration to become familiar with the components.

6. Align the mandrel dowel pin to the dowel pin hole in the crankshaft.

7. Using a large flat-blade screwdriver, tighten the 2 mandrel screws to the crankshaft. Ensure the mandrel is snug to the crankshaft hub.

8. Install the rear main seal, with the protective nylon sleeve attached, onto the mandrel. The seal, if properly installed, will center on a step that protrudes from the center of the mandrel. As an error proof, the seal will fit only one way onto the mandrel.

➡Before installing the outer drive drum, bearing, washer, and drive nut onto the threaded shaft, apply a small amount of the extreme pressure lubricant, provided in the tool kit.

9. Install the outer drive drum onto the mandrel.

10. Install the bearing, washer, and drive nut onto the threaded shaft.

11. Using a wrench, turn the drive nut on the mandrel, which will push the seal into the engine block bore. Turn the wrench until the drive drum is snug and flush against the engine block.

12. Loosen and remove the drive nut, washer, bearing, and drive drum. Discard the protective nylon sleeve.

13. Verify that the seal has seated properly.

14. Use a flat-blade screwdriver in order to remove the 2 attachment screws from the mandrel and remove the mandrel from the crankshaft hub.

15. Install the engine flywheel.

16. Install the transmission.

17. Inspect for proper fluid levels.

18. Inspect for leaks.

3.6L Engine

See Figures 130 and 131.

1. Remove the oil pan. Remove the engine flywheel.

2. Remove the crankshaft rear oil seal housing bolts.

3. Use the pry points located at the edge of the crankshaft rear oil seal housing to separate the RTV sealant

4. Remove and discard the crankshaft rear oil seal housing.

To install:

5. Using a guide pin set such as EN 46109, install the 0.236 inch (6mm) guides from the tool into the 2 crankshaft rear oil seal housing corner bolt holes of the engine block.

6. Install crankshaft rear oil seal installation tool such as EN 47839 and handle onto the rear of the crankshaft flange.

7. Place a 0.118 in. (3mm) bead of RTV sealant to the NEW crankshaft rear oil seal housing.

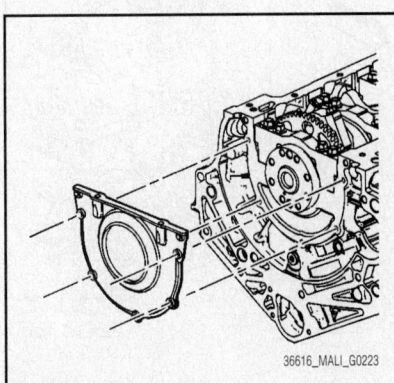

36616_MALI_G0223

Fig. 130 Removing the rear main seal—3.6L engine

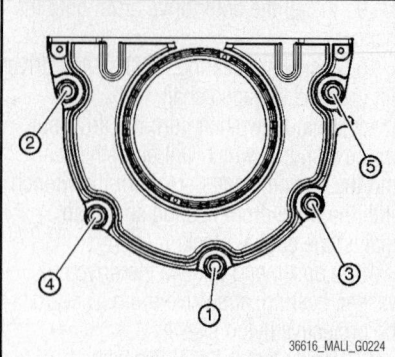

Fig. 131 Crankshaft rear oil seal housing bolt tightening sequence–3.6L engine

➡ **Do NOT allow any engine oil on the area where the crankshaft rear oil seal housing is to be installed.**

8. Install the crankshaft rear oil seal housing to the engine block

9. Remove the guides from the block.

10. Install the crankshaft rear oil seal housing bolts in sequence and tighten to 89 inch lbs. (10 Nm) in the sequence illustrated.

11. Remove the guide pin set.

12. Install the oil pan.

13. Install the engine flywheel.

TIMING CHAIN AND SPROCKETS

REMOVAL & INSTALLATION

2.4L Engine

See Figures 132 through 134.

1. Remove the No. 1 cylinder spark plug.

2. Rotate the crankshaft in the engine rotational direction clockwise, until the No.

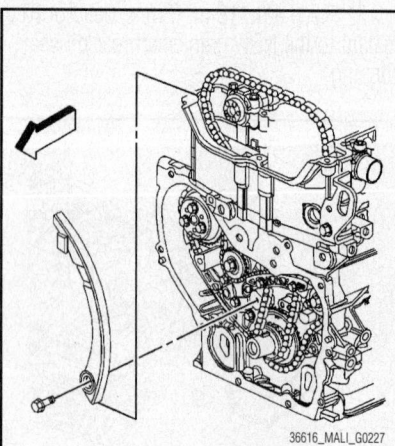

Fig. 132 Removing the upper timing chain guide

1 piston is at Top Dead Center (TDC) on the compression stroke.

3. Remove the camshaft cover.

4. Remove the engine front cover as follows:

   a. Remove the drive belt tensioner.

   b. Remove the crankshaft balancer.

   c. Install the engine support fixture.

   d. Remove the engine mount to bracket bolts.

   e. Remove the engine mount to side rail nuts.

   f. Remove the engine mount from the engine compartment.

   g. Remove the engine mount bracket to engine bolts.

   h. Remove the engine mount bracket.

   i. Remove the engine front cover to water pump bolt.

   j. Raise and suitably support the vehicle.

   k. Remove the engine front cover bolts.

   l. Remove the engine front cover.

   m. Remove and discard the engine front cover gasket.

5. Remove the upper timing chain guide bolts and guide.

➡ **The timing chain tensioner must be removed to unload chain tension before the timing chain is removed. If it is not, the timing chain will become cocked and it will be difficult to remove.**

6. Remove the timing chain tensioner.

7. Install a 24 mm wrench on the hex on the exhaust camshaft in order to hold the camshaft.

8. Remove and discard the exhaust camshaft actuator bolt.

9. Remove the exhaust camshaft actuator from the camshaft and timing chain.

10. Remove the timing chain tensioner guide bolt and guide.

11. Remove the fixed timing chain guide access plug.

12. Remove the fixed timing chain guide bolts and guide.

13. Install a 24 mm wrench on the hex on the intake camshaft in order to hold the camshaft.

14. Remove and discard the intake camshaft actuator bolt.

15. Remove the intake camshaft actuator, and the timing chain through the top of the cylinder head.

16. Remove the timing chain crankshaft sprocket.

17. If replacing the balance shaft timing chain and sprocket, perform the following:

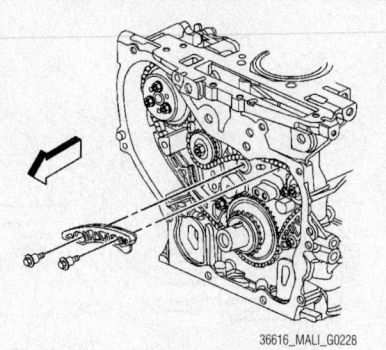

Fig. 133 Removing the upper balance shaft drive chain guide

   a. Remove the balance shaft drive chain tensioner bolts and tensioner.

   b. Remove the adjustable balance shaft chain guide bolt and guide.

   c. Remove the small balance shaft drive chain guide bolts and guide.

   d. Remove the upper balance shaft drive chain guide bolts and guide.

➡ **It may ease removal of the balance shaft drive chain to get all the slack in the chain between the crankshaft and water pump sprockets.**

18. Remove the balance shaft drive chain.

19. Remove the balance shaft drive sprocket.

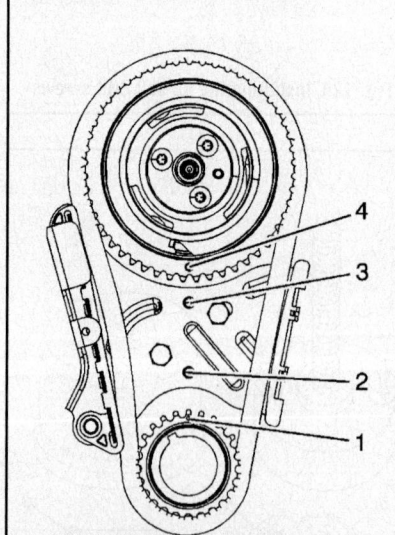

1. Crankshaft timing mark
2. Timing mark on the bottom of the timing chain tensioner
3. Timing mark on top of the timing chain tensioner
4. Camshaft position actuator gear

Fig. 134 Removing the balance shaft drive chain

To install:

20. If replacing the balance shaft timing chain, perform the following:

   a. Install the balance shaft drive sprocket.

➡**If the balance shafts are not properly timed to the engine, the engine may vibrate or make noise.**

   b. Install the balance shaft drive chain with the colored link lined up with the marks on the balance shaft sprockets and the balance shaft drive sprocket. There are 3 colored links on the chain. Two are chrome and 1 is copper.

   c. Use the following steps in order to line up the links with the sprockets:

   - Place the copper link so that it lines up with the timing mark on the intake side balance shaft sprocket.
   - Working clockwise around the chain, place the chrome link in line with the timing on the balance shaft drive sprocket. (approximately 6 o'clock position on the sprocket).
   - Place the chain on the water pump drive sprocket. The alignment is not critical
      Align the last chrome link with the timing mark on the exhaust side balance shaft drive sprocket.

   d. Install the upper balance shaft drive chain guide and bolts and tighten to 11 ft. lbs. (15 Nm).

   e. Install the small balance shaft drive chain guide and bolts and tighten to 11 ft. lbs. (15 Nm).

21. Install the adjustable balance shaft chain guide and bolt and tighten to 89 inch lbs. (10 Nm).

22. Reset the timing chain tensioner by performing the following:

   a. Rotate the tensioner plunger 90 degrees in its bore and compress the plunger

   b. Rotate the tensioner back to the original 12 o'clock position and insert a paper clip through the hole in the plunger body and into the hose in the tensioner plunger.

   c. Install the balance shaft drive chain tensioner and bolt and tighten to 89 inch lbs. (10 Nm).

   d. Remove the paper clip from the balance shaft drive chain tensioner.

23. Ensure the intake camshaft notch is in the 5 o'clock position and the exhaust camshaft notch is in the 7 o'clock position. The number 1 piston should be at Top Dead Center (TDC), crankshaft key at 12 o'clock.

24. Install the timing chain drive sprocket to the crankshaft with the timing mark in the 5 o'clock position and the front of the sprocket facing out.

➡**There are 3 colored links on the timing chain. Two links are of matching color, and 1 link is of a unique color. Use the following procedure to line up the links with the actuators. Orient the chain so that the colored links are visible. Always use new actuator bolts.**

25. Assemble the intake camshaft actuator into the timing chain with the timing mark lined up with the uniquely colored link.

26. Lower the timing chain through the opening in the cylinder head. Use care to ensure that the chain goes around both sides of the cylinder block bosses.

27. Install the intake camshaft actuator onto the intake camshaft while aligning the dowel pin into the camshaft slot.

28. Hand tighten the new intake camshaft actuator bolt.

29. Route the timing chain around the crankshaft sprocket and line up the first matching colored link with the timing mark on the crankshaft sprocket, in approximately the 5 o'clock position.

30. Rotate the crankshaft clockwise to remove all chain slack. Do not rotate the intake camshaft.

31. Install the adjustable timing chain guide down through the opening in the cylinder head and install the adjustable timing chain bolt and tighten to 89 inch lbs. (10 Nm).

➡**Always install NEW actuator bolts.**

32. Install the exhaust camshaft actuator into the timing chain with the timing mark lined up with the second matching colored link.

33. Install the exhaust camshaft actuator onto the exhaust camshaft, aligning the dowel pin into the camshaft slot.

34. Using a 23 mm open end wrench, rotate the exhaust camshaft approximately 45 degrees until the dowel pin in the camshaft actuator goes into the camshaft slot.

35. When the actuator seats on the cam, tighten the new exhaust camshaft actuator bolt hand tight.

36. Verify that all of the colored links and the appropriate timing marks are still aligned. If they are not aligned, repeat the portion of the procedure necessary to align the timing marks

37. Install the fixed timing chain guide and bolts and tighten to 106 inch lbs. (12 Nm).

38. Install the upper timing chain guide and bolts and tighten to 89 inch lbs. (10 Nm).

39. Reset the timing chain tensioner by performing the following:

   a. Remove the snap ring.

   b. Remove the piston assembly from the body of the timing chain tensioner.

   c. Install tensioner tool J 45027-2 into a vise.

   d. Install the notch end of the piston assembly into the tool.

   e. Using the J 45027-1 handle, turn the ratchet cylinder into the piston.

   f. Reinstall the piston assembly into the body of the tensioner.

   g. Install the snap ring.

40. Inspect the timing chain tensioner seal for damage. If damaged, replace the seal.

41. Inspect to ensure all dirt and debris is removed from the timing chain tensioner threaded hole in the cylinder head.

➡**Ensure the timing chain tensioner seal is centered throughout the torque procedure to eliminate the possibility of an oil leak.**

42. Install the timing chain tensioner assembly.

43. Tighten the timing chain tensioner to 55 ft. lbs. (75 Nm).

➡**The timing chain tensioner is released by compressing it 2 mm (0.079 in), which will release the locking mechanism in the ratchet.**

44. To release the timing chain tensioner, use a suitable tool with a rubber tip on the end. Feed the tool down through the cam drive chest to rest on the cam chain. Then give a sharp jolt diagonally downwards to release the tensioner.

45. Using a 23 mm wrench, engage the hex on the intake camshaft, and using a torque wrench, tighten the camshaft actuator bolt.

46. Tighten the intake camshaft position actuator bolt to 22 ft. lbs. (30 Nm), plus an additional 100 degrees.

47. Using a 23 mm wrench, engage the hex on the exhaust camshaft, and using a torque wrench, tighten the camshaft actuator bolt.

48. Tighten the exhaust camshaft position actuator bolt to 22 ft. lbs. (30 Nm), plus an additional 100 degrees.

49. Install the timing chain oiling nozzle and bolt and tighten to 89 inch lbs. (10 Nm).

50. Apply sealant compound to the thread of the timing chain guide bolt access hole plug.

51. Install the timing chain guide bolt access hole plug and tighten to 66 ft. lbs. lbs. (90 Nm).

52. Install the engine front cover as follows:

a. Install a NEW engine front cover gasket to the dowel pins.

b. Install the engine front cover.

c. Install the engine front cover bolts and tighten to 18 ft. lbs. (25 Nm).

d. Lower the vehicle.

e. Install the engine front cover to water pump bolt and tighten to 18 ft. lbs. (25 Nm).

f. Position the engine mount bracket to the engine.

g. Install the engine mount bracket bolts in the following locations:

- The long bolts in the forward and lower rear holes
- The short bolt in the upper rear hole

h. Tighten the engine mount bracket bolts to 74 ft. lbs. (100 Nm) in the following sequence.

- Upper left
- Lower left
- Right

i. Install the engine mount to the engine compartment.

j. Install the engine mount to side rail nuts and tighten to 74 ft. lbs. (100 Nm)

k. Install the engine mount to bracket bolts.

l. Tighten the engine mount to bracket bolts to 37 ft. lbs. (50 Nm) in the following sequence.

- Middle
- Rear
- Front

m. Remove the engine support fixture.

n. Install the crankshaft balancer.

o. Install the drive belt tensioner.

53. Install the camshaft cover.

54. Install the No. 1 cylinder spark plug.

3.5L Engine

See Figures 134 and 135.

1. Remove the engine front cover as follows:

a. Drain the cooling system.

b. Remove the drive belt tensioner.

c. Remove the oil pan.

d. Remove the crankshaft balancer.

e. Remove the crankshaft position actuator magnet.

f. Remove the thermostat housing.

g. Remove the water pump.

h. Remove the engine front cover bolts.

i. Remove the engine front cover.

j. Remove the engine front cover gasket.

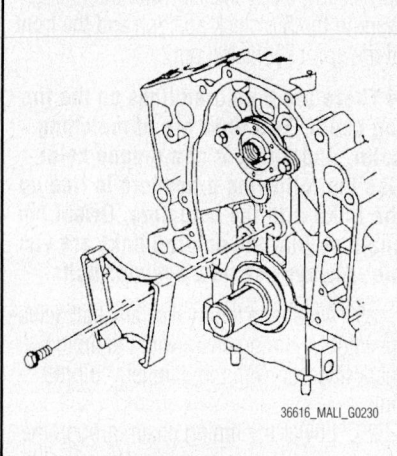

Fig. 135 Removing the timing chain dampener—3.5L engine

2. Align the crankshaft timing mark to the timing mark on the bottom of the timing chain tensioner. Refer to the illustration for mark locations.

3. Align the timing mark on the camshaft position actuator gear with the timing mark on top of the timing chain tensioner. Refer to the illustration for mark locations.

4. Remove the camshaft position actuator bolts.

5. Remove the timing chain, camshaft position actuator, and crankshaft sprockets.

6. Remove the timing chain tensioner bolts.

7. Remove the timing chain tensioner.

8. Remove the crankshaft sprocket.

9. Remove the timing chain dampener bolts.

10. Remove the timing chain dampener.

11. Remove and discard the camshaft position actuator filter from the end of the camshaft.

➡**Always install a NEW camshaft position actuator filter anytime the camshaft actuator is removed.**

To install:

12. Install a NEW the camshaft position actuator filter to the end of the camshaft.

13. Install the crankshaft sprocket.

14. Apply prelube to the crankshaft sprocket thrust surface.

15. Install the timing chain tensioner. Tighten the bolts to 15 ft. lbs. (21 Nm).

16. Use tensioner compressor EN-47719, fully collapse the tensioner, and place he tensioner retaining pin into the retaining hole.

17. Align the crankshaft timing mark to the timing mark on the bottom of the timing chain tensioner.

18. Hold the camshaft sprocket with the timing chain hanging down and install the timing chain to the crankshaft gear.

19. Align the timing mark on the camshaft position actuator gear with the timing mark on top of the timing chain tensioner.

20. Align the dowel in the camshaft position actuator with the dowel hole in the camshaft.

21. Install the camshaft position actuator bolts.

➡**Use only a Torx® Plus Bit when removing or installing the camshaft position actuator fasteners. The Torx® Plus design differs from typical Torx® fastener. Use of a standard Torx® bit on Torx® Plus fasteners may result in a rounded out fastener head or incorrect faster torque.**

➡**DO NOT use any type of threadlocking compound on the camshaft position actuator bolts. Usage of a threadlocking compound on the threads could lead to contamination of the camshaft position actuator, possibly resulting in potential damage to the actuator.**

22. Draw the camshaft actuator onto the camshaft using the bolts. Tighten op 12 ft. lbs. (16 Nm).

23. Remove the retaining pin from the timing chain tensioner in order to make the tensioner active.

24. Coat the crankshaft and camshaft sprockets with clean engine oil.

25. Install the engine front cover as follows:

a. Install the engine front cover gasket.

b. Install the engine front cover.

c. Apply sealant to the bolts in the locations pointed out in the illustration.

d. Install the engine front cover bolts. Tighten to 18 ft. lbs. (25 Nm).

e. Install the water pump.

f. Install the thermostat housing.

g. Install the crankshaft position actuator magnet.

h. Install the crankshaft balancer.

i. Install the oil pan. Install the drive belt tensioner.

j. Fill the cooling system.

3.6L Engine

See Figures 136 through 141.

1. Remove the spark plugs in order to ease crankshaft/engine rotation.

2. Remove the engine front cover as follows:

a. Remove the lower intake manifold.

b. Remove the camshaft covers.

c. Drain the engine coolant.

d. Remove the drive belt tensioner.

e. Remove the water pump.

f. Remove the power steering pump and position aside.

g. Remove the Camshaft Position sensors (CMP).

h. Remove the camshaft position actuator valves from the front cover.

i. Remove the camshaft position actuator solenoid valves from the front cover.

j. Remove the alternator.

k. Remove the crankshaft balancer. Clean the front cover of the components first before installing a support fixture.

l. Insert a block of hard wood between the frame and engine before using the support fixture. Lower the engine onto the block of wood.

m. Install the engine support fixture.

n. Remove the lift hook and strut mount bracket from the front cover.

➡**There are a total of 22 M8 bolts that must be removed and 3 optional M12 bolts that may need to be removed before the front cover will separate from the engine block.**

o. Remove the engine front cover bolts that hold the engine front cover deadener into position.

p. Remove the engine front cover deadener.

q. Remove the remaining front cover bolts.

➡**Do not use the jackscrew hole without first removing all engine front cover bolts. Failure to remove all engine front cover bolts before using the jackscrew hole could result in damage to components.**

➡**Do not pry between the engine front cover and the camshaft position sensors or the camshaft position actuators in order to separate the RTV. Use the pry points and a bolt in the jackscrew hole in order to remove the engine front cover. Damage to the camshaft position sensors or the camshaft position actuators are used to pry against in order to remove the engine front cover.**

r. Loosely install a 10 x 1.5 mm bolt in the "jackscrew" hole (1).

s. Using the pry points (2) located at the edge of the front cover and the "jackscrew", separate the room temperature vulcanizing RTV sealant.

t. Remove the engine front cover.

3. Using the crankshaft rotational socket EN 48589, rotate the crankshaft until

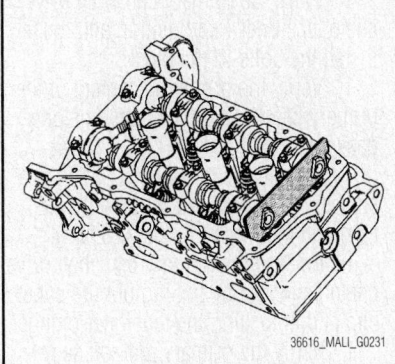

Fig. 136 Install a camshaft locking tool to the right camshafts–3.6L engine

the left cylinder head camshafts align with the a camshaft locking tool and the right cylinder head camshafts align with the a camshaft locking tool

a. Install a camshaft locking tool to the right camshafts.

b. Install a camshaft locking tool to the left camshafts.

4. Remove the right bank secondary camshaft drive chain tensioner.

5. Remove the right bank secondary camshaft drive chain shoe.

6. Remove the right bank secondary camshaft drive chain guide.

7. Remove the right secondary camshaft drive chain from the right camshaft position actuators and the right camshaft intermediate drive chain idler sprocket.

8. Remove the primary camshaft drive chain tensioner.

9. Remove the primary camshaft drive chain upper guide.

10. Remove the primary camshaft timing chain.

11. Remove the crankshaft sprocket from the nose of the crankshaft.

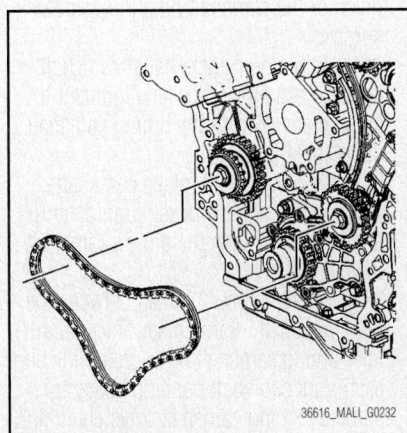

Fig. 137 Primary camshaft drive chain–3.6L engine

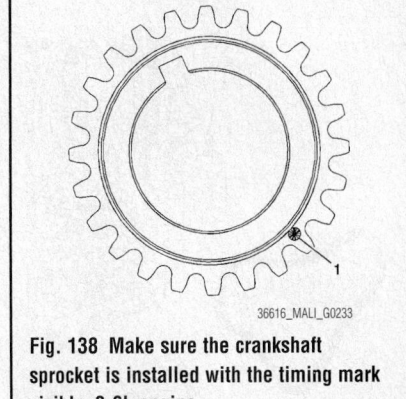

Fig. 138 Make sure the crankshaft sprocket is installed with the timing mark visible–3.6L engine

To install:

12. Ensure the crankshaft sprocket is installed with the timing mark visible.

13. Install the crankshaft sprocket on to the nose of the crankshaft.

14. Align the notch in the crankshaft sprocket with the pin in the crankshaft.

15. Slide the crankshaft sprocket on the crankshaft nose until the crankshaft sprocket contacts the step in the crankshaft.

16. Ensure the crankshaft is in the stage one timing position with the crankshaft sprocket timing mark aligned to the stage one timing mark on the oil pump cover.

17. Install the primary camshaft timing chain as follows:

a. Install the primary camshaft drive chain.

b. Wrap the primary camshaft drive chain around the large sprockets of each camshaft intermediate drive chain idler and the crankshaft sprocket.

c. The left camshaft intermediate drive chain idler timing mark will align with a timing camshaft drive chain link.

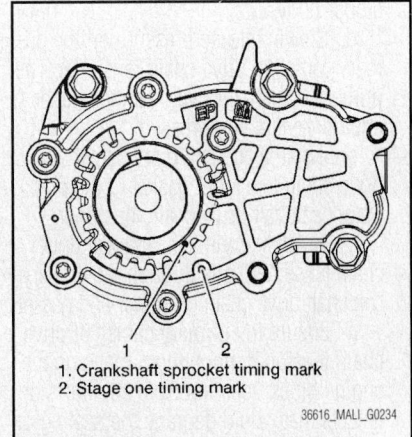

1. Crankshaft sprocket timing mark
2. Stage one timing mark

Fig. 139 Make sure the crankshaft is in the stage one timing –3.6L engine

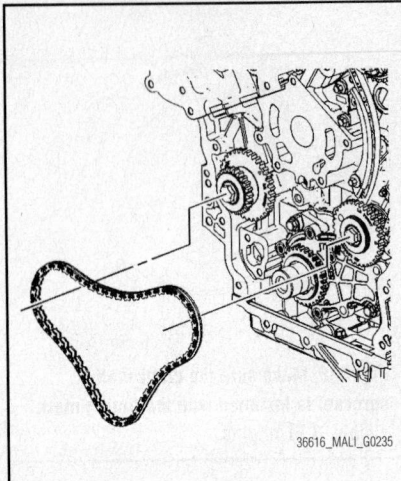

Fig. 140 Install the primary camshaft drive chain—3.6L engine

d. The right camshaft intermediate drive chain idler timing mark will align with a timing camshaft drive chain link.

e. The crankshaft sprocket timing mark will align with a timing camshaft drive chain link.

f. Ensure all the timing marks are properly aligned with the timing camshaft drive chain links.

18. Install the primary upper camshaft drive chain guide. Tighten the bolts to 17 ft. lbs. (23 Nm).

19. Install the primary camshaft drive chain tensioner as follows:

a. Using the tensioner tool J 45027 , reset the primary camshaft drive chain tensioner plunger.

b. Install the plunger into the primary camshaft drive chain tensioner body.

c. Compress the plunger into the body and lock the primary camshaft drive chain tensioner by inserting the paper clip into the access hole in the side of the primary camshaft drive chain tensioner body.

d. Slowly release pressure on the primary camshaft drive chain tensioner. The primary camshaft drive chain tensioner should remain compressed.

e. Install a NEW primary camshaft drive chain tensioner gasket to the primary camshaft drive chain tensioner.

f. Install the primary camshaft drive chain tensioner bolts through the primary camshaft drive chain tensioner and gasket.

g. Ensure the primary camshaft drive chain tensioner mounting surface on the engine block does not have any burrs or defects that would degrade the sealing of the NEW primary camshaft drive chain tensioner gasket.

h. Place the primary camshaft drive chain tensioner into position and loosely install the bolts to the block.

i. Verify the proper placement of the primary camshaft drive chain tensioner gasket tab.

j. Tighten the tensioner bolts in two stages. First tighten to 44 inch lbs. (5 Nm) and then to 17 ft. lbs. (23 Nm).

k. Release the primary camshaft drive chain tensioner by pulling out the paper clip and unlocking the tensioner plunger.

l. Verify the primary and left secondary camshaft drive chain timing mark alignments (1-12).

m. Remove the camshaft holding tool from the rear of the left camshafts.

n. Rotate the crankshaft and crankshaft sprocket from the stage 1 alignment position (1) to the stage 2 alignment position, 115 crankshaft degrees, in order to install the right secondary camshaft drive chain components.

o. Install the camshaft holding tool onto the rear of the left camshafts.

p. Install the camshaft holding tool onto the rear of the right camshafts

20. Install the right bank secondary camshaft drive chain as follows:

a. Ensure that the crankshaft is in the stage 2 timing drive assembly position.

b. Install the right secondary camshaft drive chain.

c. Place the secondary camshaft drive chain around the right camshaft intermediate drive chain idler outer sprocket, aligning the timing camshaft drive chain link with the alignment access hole (2) made in the right camshaft intermediate drive chain idler inner sprocket.

d. Wrap the secondary camshaft drive chain around both right actuator drive sprockets. Ensure there are 10 links between the timing camshaft drive chain links for the camshaft position actuator sprockets.

e. Align the right exhaust camshaft position actuator sprocket alignment triangle mark (1) with the timing camshaft drive chain link.

f. Align the right intake camshaft position actuator sprocket alignment triangle mark (2) with the timing camshaft drive chain link.

g. There will be 22 links between the right camshaft intermediate drive chain idler timing camshaft drive chain link and each right camshaft position actuator sprocket timing camshaft drive chain link.

21. Install the right bank secondary camshaft drive chain guide. Tighten the bolts to 17 ft. lbs. (23 Nm).

22. Install the right bank secondary camshaft drive chain shoe. Tighten the bolts to 17 ft. lbs. (23 Nm).

23. Install the right bank secondary camshaft drive chain tensioner as follows:

a. Using the tensioner tool J 45027 , reset the right secondary camshaft drive chain tensioner plunger.

b. Install the plunger into the right secondary camshaft drive chain tensioner body.

c. Compress the plunger into the body and lock the right secondary camshaft drive chain tensioner by inserting a paper clip into the access hole in the side of the right secondary camshaft drive chain tensioner body.

d. Slowly release pressure on the right secondary camshaft drive chain tensioner. The right secondary camshaft drive chain tensioner should remain compressed.

e. Install a NEW right secondary camshaft drive chain tensioner gasket to the right secondary camshaft drive chain tensioner.

f. Install the right secondary camshaft drive chain tensioner bolts through the right secondary camshaft drive chain tensioner and gasket.

g. Ensure the right secondary camshaft drive chain tensioner mounting surface on the right cylinder head does not have any burrs or defects that would degrade the sealing of the NEW right secondary camshaft drive chain tensioner gasket.

h. Place the right secondary camshaft drive chain tensioner into position and loosely install the bolts to the block.

i. Verify the proper placement of the right secondary camshaft drive chain tensioner gasket tab.

j. Tighten the tensioner bolts in two stages. First tighten to 44 inch lbs. (5 Nm) and then to 17 ft. lbs. (23 Nm).

k. Release the right camshaft drive

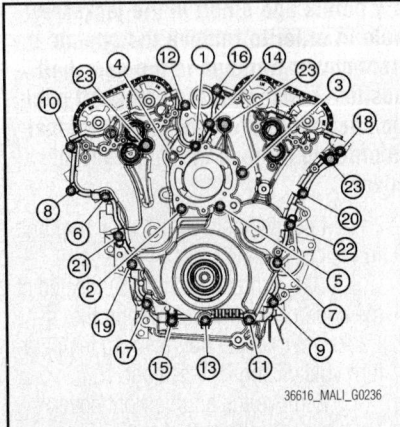

Fig. 141 Front cover fastener torque sequence—3.6L engine

chain tensioner by pulling out the paper clip and unlocking the tensioner plunger.

l. Ensure that all timing chain tensioners are completely released. A timing chain tensioner that is not properly released can lead to serious engine damage.

m. Verify all primary and secondary camshaft drive chain timing mark alignments (1-18).

24. Install the spark plugs.

25. Install the engine front cove as follows:

a. Install the 0.315 inch (8 mm) guide from a guide pin set such as EN 46109 into the cylinder block positions as shown.

b. Install the engine front cover to cylinder block seal.

c. Place a 0.118 inch (3 mm) bead of RTV sealant, on the engine front cover at points indicated by.

d. Place the engine front cover onto the guide pin set and slide into position.

e. Remove the guide pin set from the cylinder block.

f. Hand start all the front cover bolts.

g. Tighten the engine front cover bolts in the sequence show to 17 ft. lbs. (23 Nm).

h. Install the engine oil pan.

i. Install the engine coolant thermostat housing.

j. Reinstall the engine support fixture.

k. Remove the engine mount bracket.

l. Install the camshaft position actuator solenoid valves to the front cover.

m. Install the camshaft position actuator valves to the front cover.

n. Install the crankshaft balancer.

o. Install the power steering pump and position aside.

p. Install the water pump.

q. Install the drive belt tensioner.

r. Install the camshaft covers.

s. Install the lower intake manifold.

t. Refill the engine coolant.

VALVE LASH

ADJUSTMENT

All engines utilize hydraulic lash adjusters; no adjustment is necessary.

ENGINE PERFORMANCE & EMISSION CONTROLS

CAMSHAFT POSITION (CMP) SENSOR

LOCATION

On 2.4L engines, the Camshaft Position (CMP) sensor (exhaust), is located on the upper rear of the engine, near the camshaft cover. The 2.4L engines Camshaft Position (CMP) sensor (intake), is located on the upper front of the engine, near the camshaft cover.

On 3.5L engines, the Camshaft Position (CMP) sensor is located in the right side of the engine compartment, above the timing chain cover, below the power steering pump.

On 3.6L engines, Camshaft Position (CMP) sensors are located on the right side of the engine, near the front and rear.

REMOVAL & INSTALLATION

2.4L Engine

Intake

See Figure 142.

1. Remove the air cleaner outlet duct.
2. Disconnect the engine wiring harness electrical connector from the intake Camshaft Position (CMP) sensor.
3. Remove the CMP sensor bolt.
4. Remove the CMP sensor.

To install:

➡**Inspect the CMP sensor for damage, replace as necessary.**

5. Lubricate the CMP sensor O-ring seal with clean engine oil.
6. Install the CMP sensor.
7. Install the CMP sensor bolt and tighten to 89 inch lbs. (10 Nm).

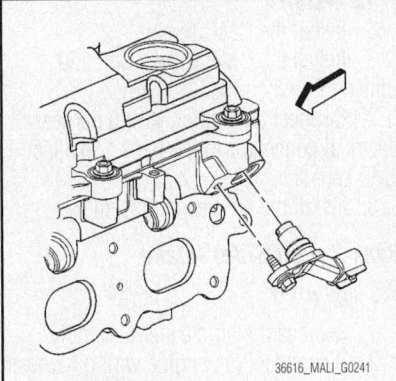

Fig. 142 Removing and installing the CMP sensor (intake)—2.4L engine

8. Connect the engine wiring harness electrical connector to the intake CMP sensor.
9. Install the air cleaner outlet duct.

Exhaust

See Figure 143.

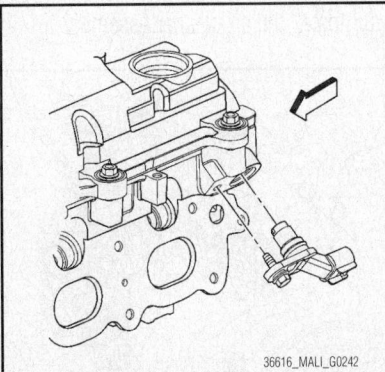

Fig. 143 Removing and installing the CMP sensor (exhaust)—2.4L engine (intake shown, exhaust CMP similar)

1. Remove the air cleaner outlet duct.
2. Disconnect the engine wiring harness electrical connector from the exhaust CMP sensor.
3. Remove the CMP sensor bolt.
4. Remove the CMP sensor.

To install:

➡**Inspect the CMP sensor for damage, replace as necessary.**

5. Lubricate the CMP sensor O-ring seal with clean engine oil.
6. Install the CMP sensor.
7. Install the CMP sensor bolt. Tighten the bolt to 89 inch lbs. (10 Nm).
8. Connect the engine wiring harness electrical connector to the exhaust CMP sensor.
9. Install the air cleaner outlet duct.

3.5L Engine

See Figure 144.

1. Remove the intake manifold cover.
2. Remove the power steering pump.

Fig. 144 Removing and installing the CMP sensor—3.5L engine

3. Disconnect the fuel injector wiring harness electrical connector from the CMP sensor.

4. Remove the CMP sensor bolt.

5. Remove the CMP sensor.

6. Inspect the sensor O-ring for wear, cracks, or leakage if the sensor is not being replaced.

To install:

7. Replace the O-ring seal if damaged, lubricate the NEW O-ring with clean engine oil.

8. Install the CMP sensor.

9. Install the CMP bolt and tighten to 89 inch lbs. (10 Nm).

10. Connect the fuel injector wiring harness electrical connector to the CMP sensor.

11. Install the power steering pump.

12. Install the intake manifold cover.

3.6L Engine

Bank 2 (Left Side) Exhaust

See Figure 145.

1. Remove the air cleaner assembly.

2. Disconnect the engine wiring harness electrical connector from the bank 2 exhaust Camshaft Position (CMP) sensor.

3. Remove the CMP sensor bolt.

4. Remove the CMP sensor.

Fig. 145 Removing and installing the CMP sensor (bank 2, exhaust)—3.6L engine

To install:

5. Install the CMP sensor.

6. Install the CMP sensor bolt and tighten to 89 inch lbs. (10 Nm).

7. Connect the engine wiring harness electrical connector to the bank 2 exhaust CMP sensor.

8. Install the air cleaner assembly.

Bank 1 (Right Side) Exhaust

See Figure 146.

1. Remove the air cleaner assembly.

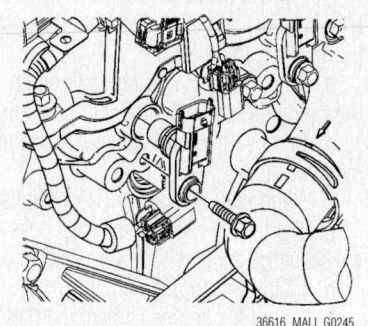

Fig. 146 Removing and installing the CMP sensor (bank 1, exhaust)—3.6L engine

2. Disconnect the engine wiring harness electrical connector from the bank 1 exhaust Camshaft Position (CMP) sensor.

3. Remove the CMP sensor bolt.

4. Remove the CMP sensor.

To install:

5. Install the CMP sensor.

6. Install the CMP sensor bolt and tighten to 89 inch lbs. (10 Nm).

7. Connect the engine wiring harness electrical connector to the bank 1 exhaust CMP sensor.

8. Install the air cleaner assembly.

Bank 2 (Left Side) Intake

See Figure 147.

1. Remove the air cleaner assembly.

2. Disconnect the engine wiring harness electrical connector from the bank 2 intake Camshaft position (CMP) sensor.

3. Remove the CMP sensor bolt.

4. Remove the CMP sensor.

To install:

5. Install the CMP sensor.

6. Install the CMP sensor bolt. Tighten the bolt to 89 inch lbs. (10 Nm).

7. Connect the engine wiring harness electrical connector to the bank 2 intake CMP sensor.

8. Install the air cleaner assembly.

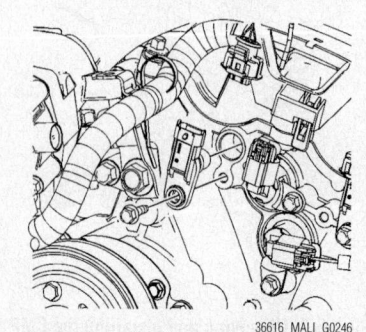

Fig. 147 Removing and installing the CMP sensor (bank 2, intake)—3.6L engine

Bank 1 (Right Side) Intake

See Figure 148.

1. Remove the air cleaner assembly.

2. Disconnect the engine wiring harness electrical connector from the bank 1 intake Camshaft position (CMP) sensor.

3. Remove the CMP sensor bolt.

4. Remove the CMP sensor.

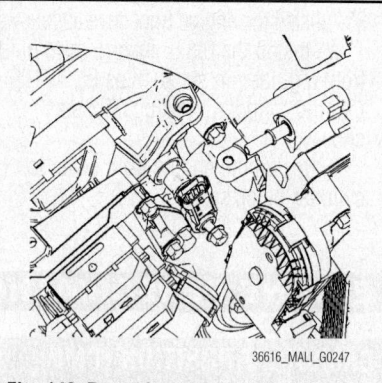

Fig. 148 Removing and installing the CMP sensor (bank 1, intake)—3.6L engine

To install:

5. Install the CMP sensor.

6. Install the CMP sensor bolt. Tighten the bolt to 89 inch lbs. (10 Nm).

7. Connect the engine wiring harness electrical connector to the bank 1 intake CMP sensor.

8. Install the air cleaner assembly.

CRANKSHAFT POSITION (CKP) SENSOR

LOCATION

The Crankshaft Position (CKP) sensor for the 2.4L engine is located in the front lower engine block, above the starter, next to the engine oil pressure switch.

The Crankshaft Position (CKP) sensor for the 3.5L engine is located at the rear center of the lower engine block above the transaxle.

The Crankshaft Position (CKP) sensor for the 3.6L engine is located at the rear of the engine, on the left side of the engine block.

REMOVAL & INSTALLATION

2.4L Engine

See Figure 149.

1. Remove the starter motor.

2. Disconnect the engine wiring harness electrical connector from the Crankshaft Position (CKP) sensor.

3. Remove the CKP sensor bolt and sensor.

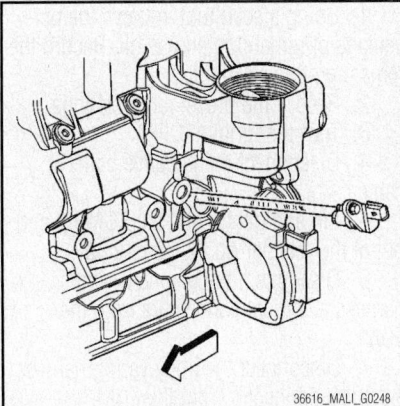

Fig. 149 Removing and installing the CKP sensor—2.4L engine

To install:

4. Lubricate the CKP sensor O-ring seal with clean engine oil.

5. Install the CKP sensor.

6. Install the CKP sensor bolt and tighten to 89 inch lbs. (10 Nm).

7. Connect the engine wiring harness electrical connector to the CKP sensor.

8. Install the starter.

9. Perform the CKP system variation learn procedure.

3.5L Engine

See Figure 150.

1. Raise and support the vehicle.

2. Disconnect the engine wiring harness electrical connector from the Crankshaft Position (CKP) sensor.

3. Remove the CKP sensor stud.

4. Remove the CKP sensor.

To install:

5. Lubricate the CKP sensor O-ring with clean engine oil .

6. Install the CKP sensor.

7. Install the CKP sensor stud.

8. Tighten the CKP sensor stud to 89 inch lbs. (10 Nm).

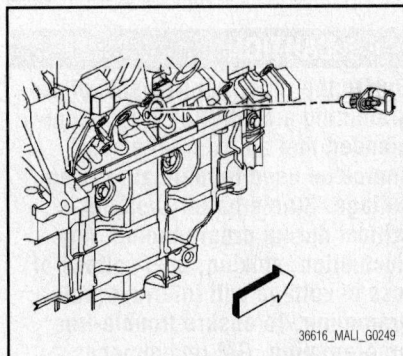

Fig. 150 Removing and installing the CKP sensor—3.5L engine

9. Connect the engine wiring harness electrical connector to the CKP sensor.

10. Lower the vehicle.

11. Perform the CKP system variation learn procedure.

3.6L Engine

See Figure 151.

1. Remove the exhaust manifold lower heat shield.

2. Disconnect the engine wiring harness electrical connector (2) from the Crankshaft Position (CKP) sensor.

3. Remove the crankshaft sensor bolt.

4. Remove the crankshaft sensor.

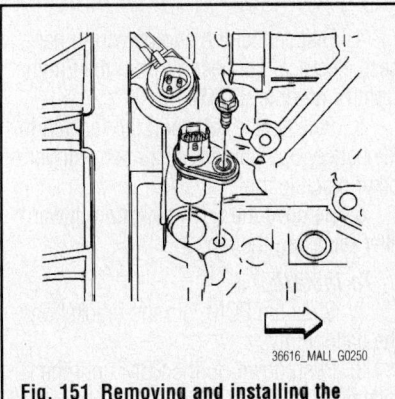

Fig. 151 Removing and installing the CKP sensor—3.6L engine

To install:

5. Install the crankshaft position sensor.

6. Install the crankshaft position sensor bolt and tighten to 89 inch lbs. (10 Nm).

7. Connect the engine wiring harness electrical connector to the CKP sensor.

8. Install the exhaust manifold lower heat shield.

9. Perform the Crankshaft Position System Variation Learn procedure.

PROGRAMMING

➡The Crankshaft Position (CKP) system variation learn procedure is also required when the following service procedures have been performed, regardless of whether DTC P0315 is set:

- An engine replacement
- A Engine Control Module (ECM) replacement
- A crankshaft balancer replacement
- A CKP sensor replacement
- Any engine repairs which disturb the crankshaft to CKP sensor relationship.

➡The ECM monitors certain component signals to determine if all the condi-

tions are met to continue with the CKP System Variation Learn Procedure. The scan tool only displays the condition that inhibits the procedure. The scan tool displays the signals of the following components:

a. CKP sensors activity—If there is a CKP sensor condition, refer to the applicable DTC that set.

b. Camshaft Position (CMP) signal activity—If there is a CMP signal condition, refer to the applicable DTC that set.

c. Engine Coolant Temperature (ECT)—If the engine coolant temperature is not warm enough, idle the engine until the engine coolant temperature reaches a correct temperature.

1. Install the scan tool.

2. Monitor the ECM for DTCs with the scan tool. If other DTCs are set, except DTC P0315, refer to the DTC list for the applicable DTC.

3. With the scan tool, select CKP System Variation Learn Procedure and perform the following:

a. Block the drive wheels.

b. Set the parking brake.

c. DO NOT apply the brake pedal.

d. Cycle the ignition from OFF to ON.

e. Apply and hold the brake pedal for the duration of the procedure.

f. Start and idle the engine.

g. Turn the Air Conditioning (A/C) OFF.

h. The vehicle must remain in Park or Neutral.

➡While the learn procedure is in progress, release the throttle immediately when the engine starts to decelerate. The engine control is returned to the operator and the engine responds to throttle position after the learn procedure is complete.

i. Accelerate to Wide Open Throttle (WOT) and release when the fuel cut-off occurs.

4. The scan tool displays Learn Status: Learned this Ignition. If the scan tool indicates that DTC P0315 ran and passed, the CKP variation learn procedure is complete. If the scan tool indicated DTC P0315 failed or did not run, or another DTC is present, refer to the DTC List and perform the appropriate diagnostic procedure.

5. Turn **OFF** the ignition for 30n seconds after the learn procedure is completed successfully in order to store the CKP system variation values in the ECM memory.

ELECTRONIC CONTROL MODULE (ECM)

LOCATION

The Engine Control Module (ECM) is located on the left side of the engine compartment, in front of the battery.

OPERATION

The Engine Control Module (ECM) is the control center of the engine controls system. The ECM controls the following components:

- Fuel injection system
- Ignition system
- Emission control systems
- On-board diagnostics
- A/C and fan systems
- Throttle Actuation Control (TAC) system

The ECM constantly monitors the information from various sensors and other inputs, and controls the systems that affect the vehicle performance and the emissions. The ECM also performs diagnostic tests on various parts of the system. The ECM can recognize operational problems and alert the driver via the MIL. When the ECM detects a malfunction, the ECM stores a DTC. The condition area is identified by the particular DTC that is set. This aids the technician in making repairs.

The engine control module (ECM) can supply 5 volts or 12 volts to the various sensors or switches. This is done through pull-up resistors to the regulated power supplies within the ECM. In some cases, even an ordinary shop voltmeter will not give an accurate reading because the resistance is too low. Therefore, a DMM with at least 10 megaohms input impedance is required in order to ensure accurate voltage readings.

The ECM controls the output circuits by controlling the ground or the power feed circuit through the transistors or a device called an output driver module.

REMOVAL & INSTALLATION

2.4L and 3.5L Engine

See Figure 152.

1. Using a scan tool, retrieve the percentage of remaining engine oil. Record the remaining engine oil life.
2. Disconnect the negative battery cable.
3. Slide the lever locks to the up position in order to release the engine wiring harness electrical connectors.

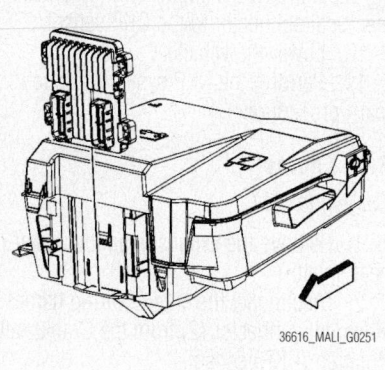

Fig. 152 Removing the ECM—2.4L and 3.5L engine

4. Disconnect the engine wiring harness electrical connectors from the Engine Control Module (ECM).
5. Release the retaining tab located in the battery tray using a small screwdriver or other suitable tool.
6. Remove the ECM by lifting upward after releasing the tab.

To install:
7. Slide the ECM into the bracket on the battery tray.
8. Push down on the ECM until the retaining tab snaps into place.
9. Connect the engine wiring harness electrical connectors to the ECM.
10. Slide the lever locks to the down position in order to engage the engine wiring harness electrical connectors.
11. Connect the negative battery cable.
12. If a NEW ECM was installed, program the ECM.

3.6L Engine

See Figure 153.

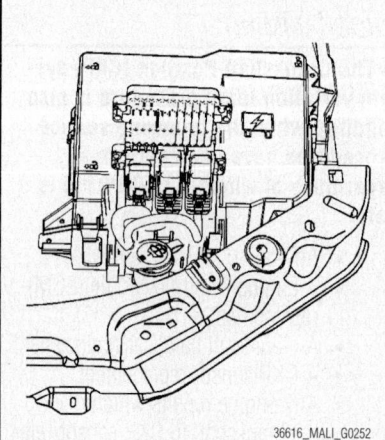

Fig. 153 Disconnecting the ECM—3.6L engine

1. Using a scan tool, retrieve the percentage of remaining engine oil. Record the remaining engine oil life.
2. Record the preset radio stations.
3. Turn the ignition OFF.
4. Disconnect the negative battery cable.
5. Lift and gently pull the ECM up and out of the retainer on the battery tray.
6. Disconnect the engine wiring harness electrical connectors from the ECM.
7. Disconnect the body wiring harness electrical connector from the ECM.

To install:
8. Connect the engine wiring harness electrical connectors to the ECM.
9. Connect the body wiring harness electrical connector to the ECM.
10. Position the ECM above the retainer in the battery tray and slide the ECM down into the retainer.
11. Connect the negative battery cable.
12. Reset the clock and preset radio stations.
13. If a NEW ECM was installed, the ECM must be programmed.

REPROGRAMMING

✲✲ CAUTION

DO NOT program a control module unless you are directed by a service procedure or you are directed by a General Motors Corporation service bulletin. Programming a control module at any other time will not permanently correct a customer's concern.

✲✲ CAUTION

It is essential that the Tech 2, MDI and the TIS terminal are all equipped with the latest software before performing service programming.

✲✲ CAUTION

Due to the time requirements of programming a controller, it is recommended that an external power source be used to maintain system voltage. Stable battery voltage is critical during programming. Any fluctuation, spiking, over voltage or loss of voltage will interrupt programming. To ensure trouble-free programming, GM recommends using one of the following external power sources:

- A Midtronics PSC charge
- A fully charged 12V jumper or booster pack disconnected from the AC voltage supply

✳✳ CAUTION

Some modules will require additional programming/setup events performed before or after programming.

✳✳ CAUTION

Some vehicles may require the use of a CANDi or MDI module for programming.

✳✳ CAUTION

Review the appropriate service information for these procedures.

✳✳ CAUTION

DTCs may set during programming. Clear DTCs after programming is complete.

✳✳ CAUTION

Clearing powertrain DTCs will set the Inspection/Maintenance (I/M) system status indicators to NO.

Ensure the following conditions are met before programming a control module:
1. Vehicle system voltage:
   a. There is not a charging system concern. All charging system concerns must be repaired before programming a control module.
   b. Battery voltage is greater than 12V but less than 16V. The battery must be fully charged before programming the control module.
   c. Turn OFF or disable any system that may put a load on the vehicles battery, such as the following:
   - Twilight sentinel
   - Interior lights
   - Daytime Running Lights (DRL) - Applying the parking brake, on most vehicles, disables the DRL system
   - Heating, ventilation, and air conditioning (HVAC) systems
   - Engine cooling fans, radio, etc.
   d. The ignition switch must be in the proper position. SPS prompts you to Turn **ON** the ignition, with the engine OFF. DO NOT change the position of the ignition switch during the programming procedure, unless instructed to do so.

e. Make certain all tool connections are secure, including the following components and circuits:
2. Tech 2
   - The RS-232 communication cable port
   - The connection at the Data Link Connector (DLC)
   - The voltage supply circuits
3. MDI
   - The USB, Ethernet or Wireless communication port
   - The connection at the Data Link Connector (DLC)
   a. DO NOT disturb the tool harnesses while programming. If an interruption occurs during the programming procedure, programming failure or control module damage may occur.
   b. DO NOT Turn **OFF** the ignition if the programming procedure is interrupted or unsuccessful. Ensure that all control module and DLC connections are secure and TIS terminal operating software is up to date. Attempt to reprogram the control module. If the control module cannot be programmed, replace the control module.
4. Engine Oil Life Remaining—When available, use a scan tool to reset the Engine Oil Life Remaining back to the original percentage recorded before the module was reprogrammed.

✳✳ CAUTION

After programming, perform the following to avoid future misdiagnosis.

5. Turn the ignition OFF for 30 seconds.
6. Turn the ignition ON with the engine OFF.
7. Use the scan tool in order to retrieve history DTCs from all modules.
8. Clear all history DTCs.

ENGINE COOLANT TEMPERATURE (ECT) SENSOR

LOCATION

The Engine Coolant Temperature (ECT) sensor for the 2.4L engine is located on the rear of the engine, below the Camshaft Position (CMP) exhaust sensor.

The Engine Coolant Temperature (ECT) sensor for the 3.5L engine is mounted in the front cylinder head, on the left side, below the throttle body.

The Engine Coolant Temperature (ECT) sensor for the 3.6L engine on the right front side of the cylinder head between exhaust ports 2 and 4.

REMOVAL & INSTALLATION

2.4L Engine

See Figure 154.

➡Use care when handling the coolant sensor. Damage to the coolant sensor will affect the operation of the fuel system.

1. Drain the cooling system.
2. Disconnect the engine wiring harness electrical connector from the Engine Coolant Temperature (ECT) sensor.
3. Remove the ECT sensor from the thermostat housing.

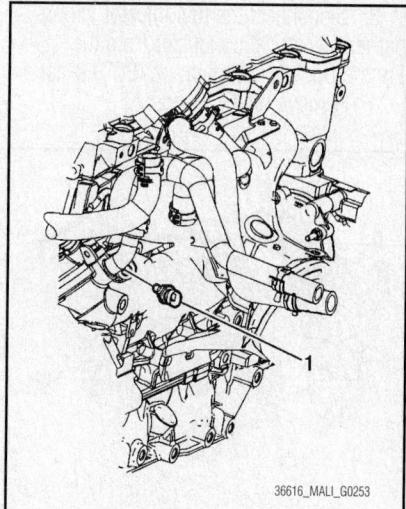

36616_MALI_G0253

Fig. 154 Removing and installing the ECT senor—2.4L engine

To install:

➡ **Replacement components must be the correct part number for the application. Components requiring the use of the thread locking compound, lubricants, corrosion inhibitors, or sealants are identified in the service procedure. Some replacement components may come with these coatings already applied. Do not use these coatings on components unless specified. These coatings can affect the final torque, which may affect the operation of the component. Use the correct torque specification when installing components in order to avoid damage.**

➡ **Use care when handling the coolant sensor. Damage to the coolant sensor will affect the operation of the fuel control system.**

4. If reinstalling the original sensor, or if installing a NEW sensor without a sealer, coat the threads with sealant.

5. Install the ECT sensor to the thermostat housing.

6. Connect the engine wiring harness electrical connector to the ECT sensor.

7. Fill the cooling system.

3.5L Engine

See Figure 155.

➡ **Use care when handling the coolant sensor. Damage to the coolant sensor will affect the operation of the fuel control system.**

1. Drain the cooling system.

2. Remove the intake manifold cover, if necessary.

3. Disconnect the fuel injector wiring harness electrical connector from the Engine Coolant Temperature (ECT) sensor.

4. Remove the ECT sensor.

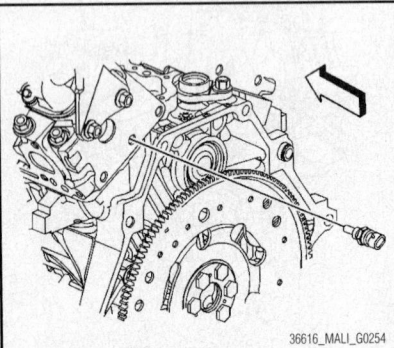

Fig. 155 Removing and installing the ECT sensor—3.5L engine

To install:

➡**Replacement components must be the correct part number for the application. Components requiring the use of the thread locking compound, lubricants, corrosion inhibitors, or sealants are identified in the service procedure. Some replacement components may come with these coatings already applied. Do not use these coatings on components unless specified. These coatings can affect the final torque, which may affect the operation of the component. Use the correct torque specification when installing components in order to avoid damage.**

5. Coat the threads of the ECT sensor with sealer GM P/N 13246004 (Canadian P/N 10953480) or equivalent.

6. Install the ECT sensor and tighten to 15 ft. lbs. (20 Nm).

7. Connect the fuel injector wiring harness electrical connector to the ECT sensor.

8. Install the intake manifold cover, if necessary.

9. Fill the cooling system.

3.6L Engine

See Figure 156.

1. Disconnect the engine wiring harness electrical connector from the Engine Coolant Temperature (ECT) sensor.

2. Remove the ECT sensor.

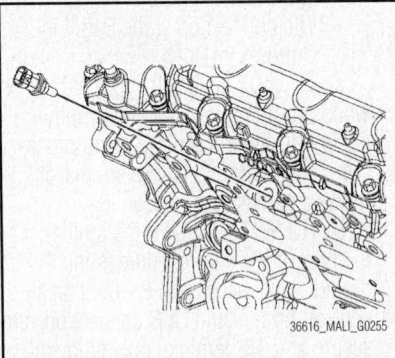

Fig. 156 Removing and installing the ECT sensor—3.6L engine

To install:

3. Install the ECT sensor and tighten to 16 ft. lbs. (22 Nm).

4. Connect the engine wiring harness electrical connector to the ECT sensor.

HEATED OXYGEN SENSOR (HO2S)

LOCATION

For the 3.5L and 3.6L engines, the Heated Oxygen Sensor (HO2S) is located in the center of the rear exhaust manifold (bank 1, sensor 1). In the rear of the engine compartment after the catalytic convertor (bank 1, sensor 2). In the front of the engine compartment, on the exhaust manifold (bank 2, sensor 1). In the lower front of the engine compartment, after the catalytic convertor (bank 2, sensor 2).

For the 2.4L engine, the HO2S 1 is located on the rear of the engine, between the exhaust manifold and the catalytic convertor. HO2S 2 is on the rear of the engine, just after the catalytic convertor and before the muffler.

REMOVAL & INSTALLATION

2.4L Engine

Sensor 1

See Figure 157.

➡The oxygen sensor uses a permanently attached pigtail and connector. Do not remove the pigtail from the oxygen sensor. Damage to or removal of the pigtail connector could affect proper operation of the oxygen sensor.

➡The use of excessive force may damage the threads in the exhaust manifold/pipe.

✳ CAUTION

The in-line connector and louvered end must be kept clear of grease, dirt or other contaminants. Avoid using cleaning solvents of any type. DO NOT drop or roughly handle the heated oxygen sensor (HO2S).

➡The HO2S may be difficult to remove when the engine temperature is less than 120°F (48°C).

1. Remove the Connector Position Assurance (CPA) retainer.

2. Disconnect the engine wiring harness electrical connector from the HO2S electrical connector.

3. Remove the HO2S connector clip from the thermostat housing tab.

4. Remove the HO2S.

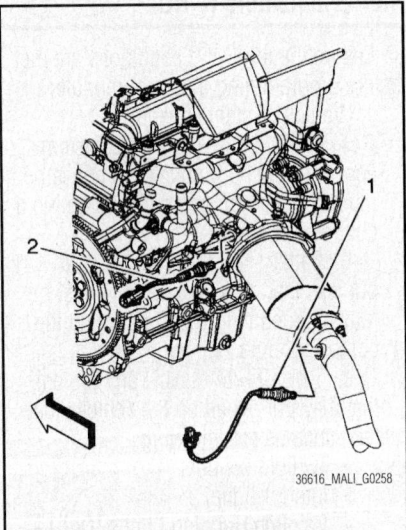

Fig. 157 Removing and installing the HO2S (sensor 1)—2.4L engine

To install:

➡A special anti-seize compound is used on the heated oxygen sensor threads. The compound consists of a liquid graphite and glass beads. The graphite will burn away, but the glass beads will remain, making the sensor easier to remove. New or service replacement sensors will have the compound applied to the threads. If a sensor is removed and is to be reinstalled, the threads must have an anti-seize compound applied prior to installation.

5. If necessary, coat the threads of the HO2S with anti-seize compound GM P/N 12377953 or equivalent.

6. Install the HO2S and tighten to 31 ft. lbs. (42 Nm).

7. Install the HO2S connector clip to the thermostat housing tab.

8. Connect the engine wiring harness electrical connector to the HO2S electrical connector.

9. Install the CPA retainer.

Sensor 2

See Figure 158.

➡The oxygen sensor uses a permanently attached pigtail and connector. Do not remove the pigtail from the oxygen sensor. Damage to or removal of the pigtail connector could affect proper operation of the oxygen sensor.

➡The use of excessive force may damage the threads in the exhaust manifold/pipe.

✳ CAUTION

The in-line connector and louvered end must be kept clear of grease, dirt or other contaminants. Avoid using cleaning solvents of any type. DO NOT drop or roughly handle the heated oxygen sensor (HO2S).

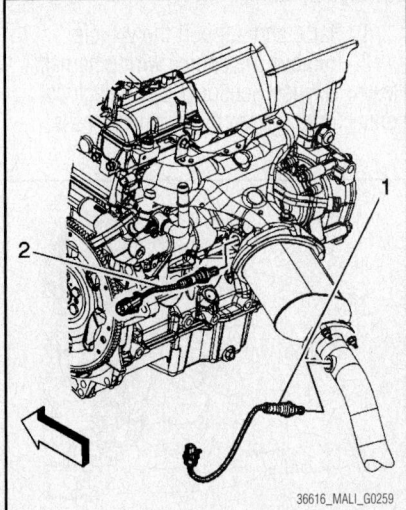

Fig. 158 Removing and installing the HO2S (sensor 2)—2.4L engine

➡The HO2S may be difficult to remove when the engine temperature is less than 120°F (48°C).

1. Raise and suitably support the vehicle.

2. Remove the Connector Position Assurance (CPA) retainer.

3. Disconnect the HO2S electrical connector (2) from the engine wiring harness electrical connector.

4. Remove the HO2S.

To install:

➡A special anti-seize compound is used on the heated oxygen sensor threads. The compound consists of a liquid graphite and glass beads. The graphite will burn away, but the glass beads will remain, making the sensor easier to remove. New or service replacement sensors will have the compound applied to the threads. If a sensor is removed and is to be reinstalled, the threads must have an anti-seize compound applied prior to installation.

5. If necessary, coat the threads of the HO2S with anti-seize compound GM P/N 12377953 or equivalent.

6. Install the HO2S and tighten to 31 ft. lbs. (42 Nm).

7. Connect the HO2S electrical connector to the engine wiring harness electrical connector.

8. Install the CPA retainer.

9. Lower the vehicle.

3.5L Engine

Bank 1 Sensor 1

See Figure 159.

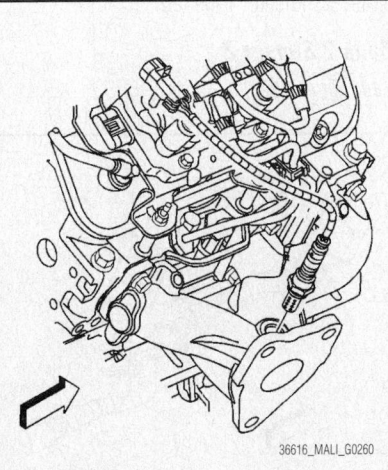

Fig. 159 Removing and installing the HO2S (bank 1 sensor 1)—3.5L engine

➡When replacing the HO2S perform the following resistance learned value to avoid possible HO2S failure:

- A code clear with a scan tool, regardless of whether or not a DTC is set
- HO2S heater resistance learn reset with a scan tool, where available

1. Remove the intake manifold cover.

2. Remove the Connector Position Assurance (CPA) retainer.

3. Disconnect the engine wiring harness electrical connector from the Heated Oxygen Sensor (HO2S) electrical connector.

4. Remove the HO2S electrical connector rosebud clip from the ignition coil bracket.

➡The HO2S may be difficult to remove when the engine temperature is less than 120°F (48°C).

5. Remove the HO2S using the Heated Oxygen Sensor Wrench (J39194-B).

To install:

➡A special anti-seize compound is used on the heated oxygen sensor threads. The compound consists of a liquid graphite and glass beads. The graphite will burn away, but the glass beads will remain, making the sensor easier to remove. New or service replacement sensors will have the compound applied to the threads. If a sensor is removed and is to be reinstalled, the threads must have an anti-seize compound applied prior to installation.

6. Coat the threads of the HO2S with anti-seize compound GM P/N 12377953 or equivalent.

7. Install the HO2S and tighten to 31 ft. lbs. (42 Nm).

8. Connect the HO2S electrical connector to the engine wiring harness electrical connector.

9. Install the CPA retainer.

10. Install the HO2S electrical connector rosebud clip to the ignition coil bracket.

11. Install the intake manifold cover.

Bank 1 Sensor 2

See Figure 160.

➡The HO2S may be difficult to remove when the engine temperature is less than 120°F (48°C).

1. Raise and suitably support the vehicle.

2. Remove the Connector Position Assurance (CPA) retainer.

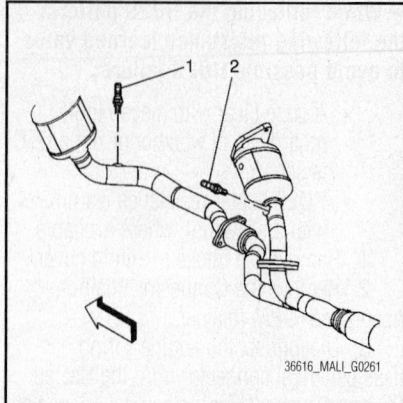

Fig. 160 Removing and installing HO2S (bank 1 sensor 2)—3.5L engine

3. Disconnect the HO2S electrical connector from the engine wiring harness electrical connector.

4. Remove the HO2S.

To install:

➡A special anti-seize compound is used on the heated oxygen sensor threads. The compound consists of a liquid graphite and glass beads. The graphite will burn away, but the glass beads will remain, making the sensor easier to remove. New or service replacement sensors will have the compound applied to the threads. If a sensor is removed and is to be reinstalled, the threads must have an anti-seize compound applied prior to installation.

5. Coat the threads of the HO2S with anti-seize compound GM P/N 12377953 or equivalent.

6. Install the HO2S and tighten to 31 ft. lbs. (42 Nm).

7. Connect the HO2S electrical connector to the engine wiring harness electrical connector.

8. Install the CPA retainer.

9. Lower the vehicle.

Bank 2 Sensor 1

See Figure 161.

1. Remove the Connector Position Assurance (CPA) retainer.

2. Disconnect the engine wiring harness electrical connector from the Heated Oxygen Sensor (HO2S) electrical connector.

3. Remove the HO2S rosebud clip from the oil level indicator tube tab.

➡The HO2S may be difficult to remove when the engine temperature is less than 120°F (48°C).

4. Remove the HO2S.

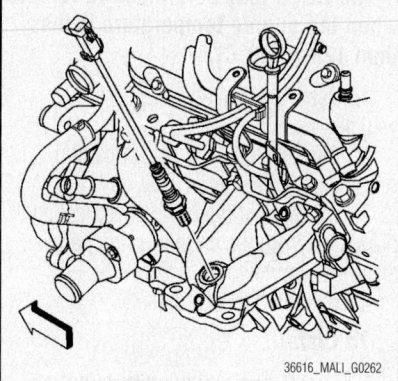

Fig. 161 Removing and installing the HO2S (bank 2 sensor 1)—3.5L engine

To install:

➡A special anti-seize compound is used on the heated oxygen sensor threads. The compound consists of a liquid graphite and glass beads. The graphite will burn away, but the glass beads will remain, making the sensor easier to remove. New or service replacement sensors will have the compound applied to the threads. If a sensor is removed and is to be reinstalled, the threads must have an anti-seize compound applied prior to installation.

5. Coat the threads of the HO2S with anti-seize compound GM P/N 12377953 or equivalent.

6. Install the HO2S and tighten to 31 ft. lbs. (42 Nm).

7. Connect the HO2S electrical connector to the engine wiring harness electrical connector.

8. Install the CPA retainer.

9. Install the HO2S rosebud clip to the oil level indicator tube tab.

Bank 2 Sensor 2

See Figure 162.

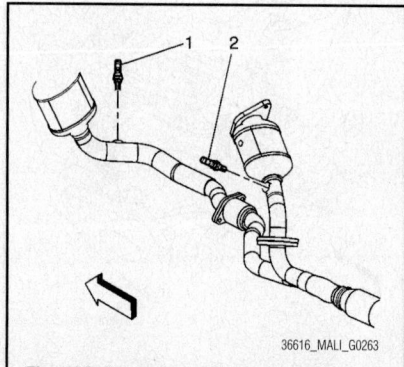

Fig. 162 Removing and installing the HO2S (bank 2 sensor 2)—3.5L engine

➡The HO2S may be difficult to remove when the engine temperature is less than 120°F (48°C).

1. Raise and suitably support the vehicle.

2. Remove the Connector Position Assurance (CPA) retainer.

3. Disconnect the HO2S electrical connector from the engine wiring harness electrical connector.

4. Remove the HO2S.

To install:

➡A special anti-seize compound is used on the heated oxygen sensor threads. The compound consists of a liquid graphite and glass beads. The graphite will burn away, but the glass beads will remain, making the sensor easier to remove. New or service replacement sensors will have the compound applied to the threads. If a sensor is removed and is to be reinstalled, the threads must have an anti-seize compound applied prior to installation.

5. Coat the threads of the HO2S with anti-seize compound GM P/N 12377953 or equivalent.

6. Install the HO2S and tighten to 31 ft. lbs. (42 Nm).

7. Connect the HO2S electrical connector to the engine wiring harness electrical connector.

8. Install the CPA retainer.

9. Lower the vehicle.

3.6L Engine

Bank 1 Sensor 1

See Figure 163.

1. Raise and support the vehicle.

2. Remove the engine wiring harness Heated Oxygen Sensor (HO2S) electrical connector clip from the engine harness.

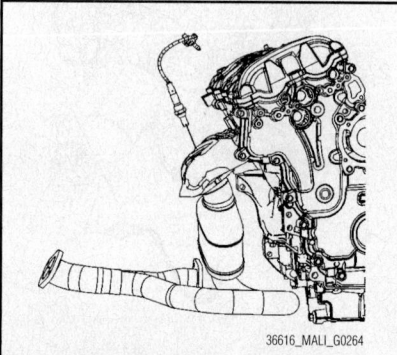

Fig. 163 Removing and installing the HO2S (bank 1, sensor 1)—3.6L engine

3. Remove the Connector Position Assurance (CPA) retainer from the HO2S electrical connection.

4. Disconnect the engine wiring harness electrical connector (2) from the HO2S electrical connector.

5. Raise and support the vehicle to an appropriate height to reach the HO2S.

6. Remove the HO2S from the exhaust manifold.

To install:

➡A special anti-seize compound is used on the heated oxygen sensor threads. The compound consists of a liquid graphite and glass beads. The graphite will burn away, but the glass beads will remain, making the sensor easier to remove. New or service replacement sensors will have the compound applied to the threads. If a sensor is removed and is to be reinstalled, the threads must have an anti-seize compound applied prior to installation.

7. If reinstalling the old sensor, coat the threads with anti-seize compound GM P/N 12377953, or equivalent.

8. Install the HO2S to the exhaust manifold and tighten to 31 ft. lbs. (42 Nm).

9. Lower the vehicle.

10. Connect the engine wiring harness electrical connector to the HO2S electrical connector.

11. Install the engine wiring harness HO2S electrical connector clip to the engine harness.

12. Install the CPA retainer to the HO2S electrical connection.

Bank 1 Sensor 2

See Figure 164.

1. Raise and support the vehicle.

2. Remove the Connector Position Assurance (CPA) retainer from the HO2S electrical connection.

3. Disconnect the heated oxygen sensor (HO2S) electrical connector from the engine wiring harness electrical connector.

4. Remove the bank 1 sensor 2 HO2S from the catalytic converter.

To install:

➡A special anti-seize compound is used on the heated oxygen sensor threads. The compound consists of a liquid graphite and glass beads. The graphite will burn away, but the glass beads will remain, making the sensor easier to remove. New or service replacement sensors will have the

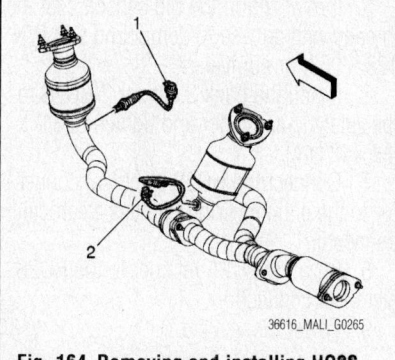

Fig. 164 Removing and installing HO2S (bank 1 sensor 2)–3.6L engine

compound applied to the threads. If a sensor is removed and is to be reinstalled, the threads must have an anti-seize compound applied prior to installation.

5. If reinstalling the old sensor, coat threads with anti-seize compound GM P/N 12377953, or equivalent.

6. Install the bank 1 sensor 2 HO2S to the catalytic converter and tighten to 31 ft. lbs. (42 Nm).

7. Connect the HO2S electrical connector to the engine wiring harness electrical connector.

8. Install the CPA retainer to the HO2S electrical connection.

9. Lower the vehicle.

Bank 2 Sensor 1

See Figure 165.

1. Remove the fuel injector sight shield by performing the following:

a. Remove the oil fill cap.

b. Grasp the cover by the upper left and the lower right corners and lift up, disengaging the cover grommets from the ball studs.

c. If necessary, lift upward on front of cover, then reach under center of cover

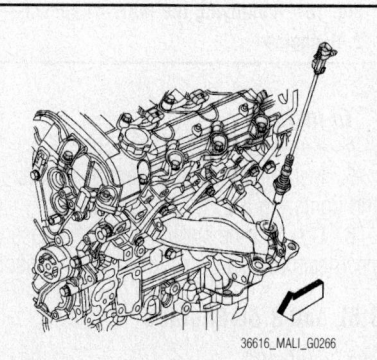

Fig. 165 Removing the HO2S (bank 2, sensor 1)—3.6L engine

disengaging the cover grommet for the ball stud.

2. Remove the air cleaner outlet duct by performing the following:

a. Disconnect the Positive Crankcase Ventilation (PCV) fresh air tube fitting from the air cleaner outlet duct.

b. Reposition the tube out of the way.

c. Loosen the air cleaner outlet duct clamps at the Mass Air Flow (MAF)/Intake Air Temperature (IAT) sensor and throttle body.

d. Remove the air cleaner outlet duct bolt.

e. Remove the air cleaner outlet duct.

3. Remove the Connector Position Assurance (CPA) retainer from the HO2S electrical connection.

4. Disconnect the engine wiring harness electrical connector from the Heated Oxygen Sensor (HO2S) electrical connector.

5. Remove the HO2S electrical connector clip from the engine wiring harness tab.

6. Remove the HO2S from the exhaust manifold.

To install:

➡A special anti-seize compound is used on the heated oxygen sensor threads. The compound consists of a liquid graphite and glass beads. The graphite will burn away, but the glass beads will remain, making the sensor easier to remove. New or service replacement sensors will have the compound applied to the threads. If a sensor is removed and is to be reinstalled, the threads must have an anti-seize compound applied prior to installation.

7. If reinstalling the old sensor, coat the threads with anti-seize compound GM P/N 12377953, or equivalent.

8. Install the HO2 to the exhaust manifold and tighten to 31 ft. lbs. (42 Nm).

9. Connect the engine wiring harness electrical connector to the HO2S electrical connector.

10. Install the HO2S electrical connector clip to the engine wiring harness tab.

11. Install the CPA retainer to the HO2S electrical connection.

12. Install the air cleaner outlet duct by performing the following:

a. Position and install the air cleaner outlet duct to the MAF/IAT sensor and the throttle body.

b. Install the air cleaner outlet duct bolt and tighten to 89 inch lbs. (10 Nm).

c. Tighten the air cleaner outlet duct clamps at the MAF/IAT sensor and throttle body to 35 inch lbs. (4 Nm).

d. Position the PCV tube.

e. Connect the PCV fresh air tube quick connect fitting to the air cleaner outlet duct.

13. Install the fuel injector sight shield by performing the following:

a. If necessary, place the cover into position over the ball stud. Press down near the center of the cover, engaging the cover to the ball stud.

b. Place the cover into position over the ball studs. Press down near the upper left and the lower right corners, engaging the cover to the ball studs.

c. Install the oil fill cap.

Bank 2 Sensor 2

See Figure 166.

1. Raise and support the vehicle.

2. Remove the Connector Position Assurance (CPA) retainer from the HO2S electrical connection.

3. Disconnect the Heated Oxygen Sensor (HO2S) electrical connector from the engine wiring harness electrical connector

4. Remove the bank 2 sensor 2 HO2S from the catalytic converter.

To install:

➡A special anti-seize compound is used on the heated oxygen sensor threads. The compound consists of a liquid graphite and glass beads. The graphite will burn away, but the glass beads will remain, making the sensor easier to remove. New or service replacement sensors will have the compound applied to the threads. If a sensor is removed and is to be reinstalled, the threads must have an anti-seize compound applied prior to installation.

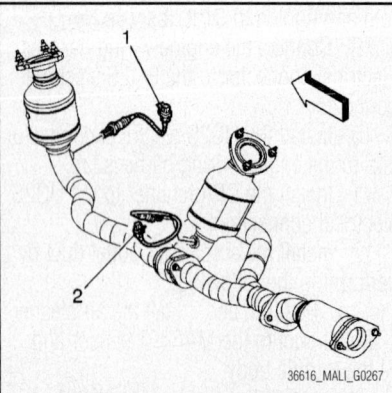

Fig. 166 Removing and installing HO2S (bank 2 sensor 2)–3.6L engine

5. If reinstalling the old sensor, coat the threads with anti-seize compound GM P/N 12377953, or equivalent.

6. Install the bank 2 sensor 2 HO2S to the catalytic converter and tighten to 31 ft. lbs. (42 Nm).

7. Connect the HO2S electrical connector to the engine wiring harness electrical connector.

8. Install the CPA retainer to the HO2S electrical connection.

9. Lower the vehicle.

INTAKE AIR TEMPERATURE (IAT) SENSOR

LOCATION

The Intake Air Temperature (IAT)/Mass Air Flow (MAF) sensor is located on the top right side of the engine, at the air cleaner.

REMOVAL & INSTALLATION

2.4L Engine

See Figure 167.

1. Disconnect the engine wiring harness electrical connector from the Mass Air Flow (MAF)/Intake Air Temperature (IAT) sensor.

2. Remove the MAF/IAT sensor screws.

3. Remove the MAF/IAT sensor.

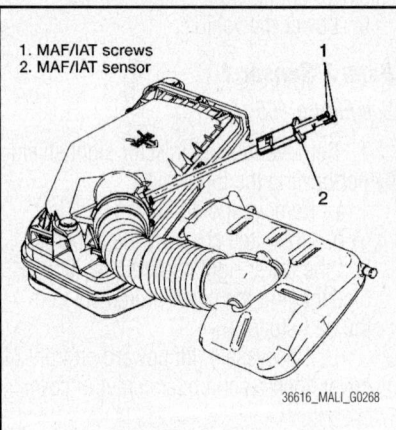

1. MAF/IAT screws
2. MAF/IAT sensor

Fig. 167 Identifying the MAF/IAT sensor— 2.4L engine

To install:

4. Install the MAF/IAT sensor.

5. Install the MAF/IAT sensor screws and tighten to 5 inch lbs. (0.6 Nm).

6. Connect the engine wiring harness electrical connector to the MAF/IAT sensor.

3.5L and 3.6L Engines

See Figure 168.

1. Remove the air cleaner outlet duct.

a. Remove the intake manifold cover.

b. Disconnect the Positive Crankcase Ventilation (PCV) fresh air tube quick connect fitting from the air cleaner outlet duct.

c. Reposition the tube out of the way.

d. Loosen the air cleaner outlet duct clamps at the Mass Air Flow (MAF)/Intake Air Temperature (IAT) sensor and throttle body.

e. Remove the air cleaner outlet duct bolt.

f. Remove the air cleaner outlet duct spacer and insulator, if required.

g. Remove the air cleaner outlet duct.

2. Disconnect the engine wiring harness electrical connector (1) from the mass airflow (MAF)/intake air temperature (IAT) sensor.

3. Remove the MAF/IAT sensor screws.

4. Remove the MAF/IAT sensor.

5. Remove and discard the MAF/IAT sensor seal.

To install:

6. Install a NEW MAF/IAT sensor seal.

7. Install the MAF/IAT sensor. Tighten the screws to 44 inch lbs. (5 Nm).

8. Connect the engine wiring harness electrical connector to the MAF/IAT sensor.

9. Install the air cleaner outlet duct.

a. Position and install the air cleaner outlet duct to the MAF/IAT sensor and the throttle body.

b. Position the air cleaner outlet duct insulator and spacer, if required.

c. Install the air cleaner outlet duct bolt and tighten to 89 inch lbs. (10 Nm).

d. Tighten the air cleaner outlet duct clamps at the MAF/IAT sensor and throttle body to 35 inch lbs. (4 Nm).

e. Position the PCV tube.

f. Connect the PCV fresh air tube quick connect fitting to the air cleaner outlet duct.

g. Install the intake manifold cover.

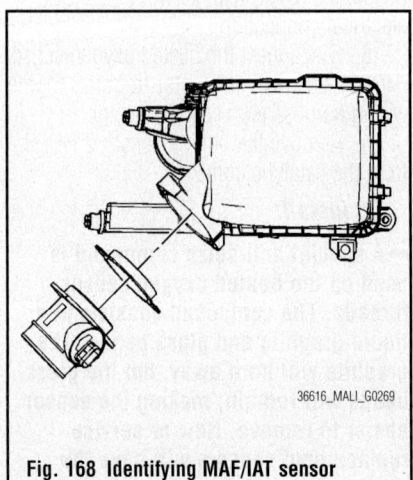

Fig. 168 Identifying MAF/IAT sensor

KNOCK SENSOR (KS)

LOCATION

For the 2.4L engine, the Knock Sensor (KS) is located at the lower left side of the engine, in front of the starter motor.

For the 3.5L and 3.6L engine, the Knock Sensor (KS) 1 is located at the front of the engine above the starter. The KS 2 is located at the rear of the engine, below the exhaust manifold, above the transaxle.

REMOVAL & INSTALLATION

2.4L Engine

See Figure 169.

1. Disconnect the negative battery cable.
2. Raise and support the vehicle.
3. Disconnect the engine wiring harness electrical connector from the Knock Sensor (KS) pigtail electrical connector.
4. Remove the knock sensor electrical connector pigtail clip from the oil level indicator tube bracket.
5. Remove the KS bolt.
6. Remove the KS.

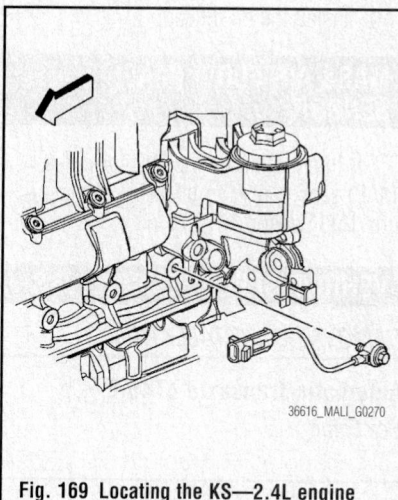

Fig. 169 Locating the KS—2.4L engine

To install:

➡**Rotate the pigtail 90 degrees from vertical before securing the fastener.**

7. Install the KS.
8. Install the KS bolt and tighten to 18 ft. lbs. (25 Nm).
9. Install the KS electrical connector pigtail clip to the oil level indicator tube bracket.
10. Connect the engine wiring harness electrical connector to the KS pigtail electrical connector.
11. Lower the vehicle.
12. Connect the negative battery cable.

3.5L Engine

See Figure 170.

Bank 1

1. Raise and support the vehicle.
2. Disconnect the engine wiring harness electrical connector from the knock senor.
3. Remove the knock sensor bolt and sensor.

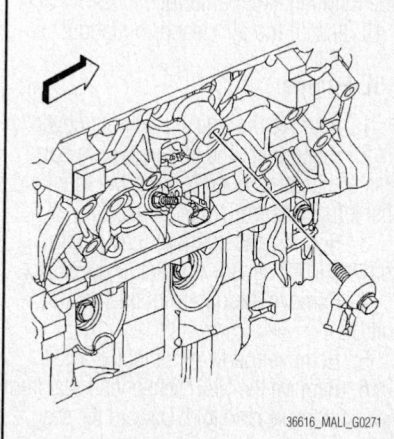

Fig. 170 Locating the KS bank 2—3.5L engine

To install:

4. Position the KS to the engine block and install the KS bolt. Tighten the bolt to 18 ft. lbs. (25 Nm).
5. Connect the engine wiring harness electrical connector to the KS.
6. Lower the vehicle.

Bank 2

1. Raise and support the vehicle.
2. Disconnect the engine wiring harness electrical connector from the Knock Sensor (KS).
3. Remove the KS bolt and sensor.

To install:

4. Position the KS to the engine block and install the KS bolt. Tighten the bolt to 18 ft. lbs. (25 Nm).
5. Connect the engine wiring harness electrical connector to the KS.
6. Lower the vehicle.

3.6L Engine

Bank 1

See Figure 171.

1. Remove the exhaust manifold lower heat shield.
2. Disconnect the engine wiring harness electrical connector from the bank 1 Knock Sensor (KS).

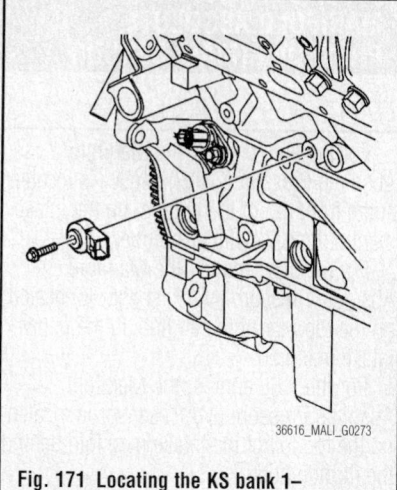

Fig. 171 Locating the KS bank 1–3.6L engine

3. Loosen the KS bolt and remove the KS.

To install:

4. Position the KS and tighten the bolt to 17 ft. lbs. (23 Nm).
5. Connect the engine wiring harness electrical connector to the bank 1 KS.
6. Install the exhaust manifold lower heat shield.

Bank 2

See Figure 172.

1. Raise and support the vehicle.
2. Disconnect the engine wiring harness electrical connector from the bank 2 Knock Sensor (KS).
3. Loosen the KS bolt and remove the KS.

To install:

4. Position the KS and tighten the bolt to 17 ft. lbs. (23 Nm).
5. Connect the engine wiring harness electrical connector to the bank 2 KS.
6. Lower the vehicle.

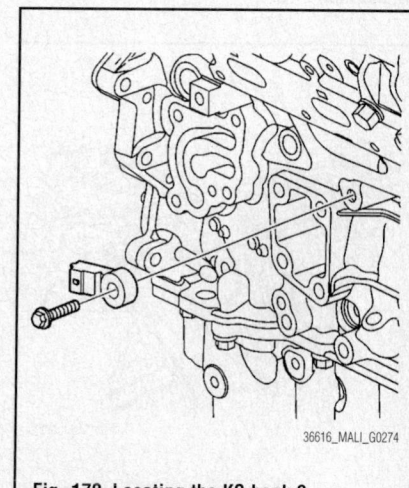

Fig. 172 Locating the KS bank 2–3.6L engine

MANIFOLD ABSOLUTE PRESSURE (MAP) SENSOR

LOCATION

For the 2.4L engine, the Manifold Absolute Pressure (MAP) sensor is located at the front top of the engine, on the intake manifold, near cylinder number 3.

For the 3.5L engine, the Manifold Absolute Pressure (MAP) sensor is located on the top rear of the engine, in the upper intake manifold.

For the 3.6L engine, the Manifold Absolute Pressure (MAP) sensor is located on the top left of the intake manifold behind the throttle body.

REMOVAL & INSTALLATION

2.4L Engine

See Figure 173.

1. Remove the air cleaner outlet duct.
2. Disconnect the Evaporative Emission (EVAP) canister purge tube from the intake manifold.
3. Reposition the EVAP canister purge tube out of the way.
4. Disconnect the fuel injector wiring harness electrical connector from the Manifold Absolute Pressure (MAP) sensor.
5. Remove the fuel injector wiring harness clips from the fuel rail tabs.
6. Disconnect the fuel injector wiring harness electrical connector from the number 3 fuel injector.
7. Squeeze tabs and slide the MAP sensor upward.

To install:

8. Lubricate the NEW MAP sensor seal with clean engine oil.
9. Install the MAP sensor into the intake manifold.

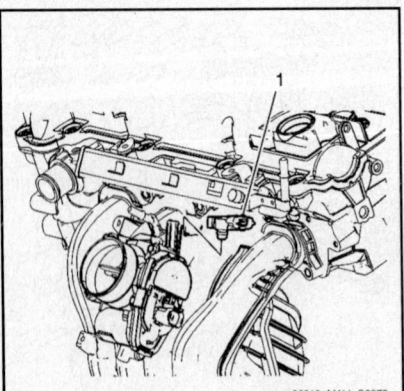

Fig. 173 Removing and installing the MAP sensor (1)—2.4L engine

10. Connect the fuel injector wiring harness electrical connector to the number 3 fuel injector.
11. Install the fuel injector wiring harness clips to the fuel rail tabs.
12. Connect the fuel injector wiring harness electrical connector to the MAP sensor.
13. Position the EVAP canister purge tube out of the way.
14. Connect the EVAP canister purge tube to the intake manifold.
15. Install the air cleaner outlet duct.

3.5L Engine

1. Remove the intake manifold cover.
2. Disconnect the engine wiring harness electrical connector from the Manifold Absolute Pressure (MAP) sensor.
3. Remove the spark plug wire clip from the MAP sensor bracket, if necessary.
4. Remove the upper intake manifold bolt.
5. Remove the MAP sensor bracket.
6. Remove the MAP sensor and seal from the upper intake manifold. Discard the seal.

To install:

7. Lubricate the NEW MAP sensor seal with clean engine oil.
8. Install the MAP sensor into the upper intake manifold.
9. Place the MAP sensor bracket into position.
10. Install the upper intake manifold bolt. Tighten the bolt to 18 ft. lbs. (25 Nm).
11. Install the spark plug wire clip to the MAP sensor bracket, if necessary.
12. Connect the engine wiring harness electrical connector to the MAP sensor.
13. Install the intake manifold cover.

3.6L Engine

See Figure 174.

1. Remove the fuel injector sight shield.
   a. Remove the oil fill cap.
   b. Grasp the cover by the upper left and the lower right corners and lift up, disengaging the cover grommets from the ball studs.
   c. If necessary, lift upward on the front of the cover, then reach under the center of the cover disengaging the cover grommet for the ball stud.
2. Disconnect the engine wiring harness electrical connector from the Manifold Absolute Pressure (MAP) sensor.
3. Remove the MAP sensor bolt and sensor.

To install:

4. Lubricate the MAP sensor O-ring seal with clean engine oil.

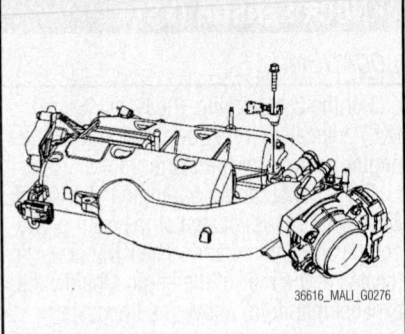

Fig. 174 Locating the MAP sensor—3.6L engine

5. Install the MAP sensor and bolt. Tighten the bolt to 89 inch lbs. (10 Nm).
6. Connect the engine wiring harness electrical connector to the MAP sensor.
7. Install the fuel injector sight shield.
   a. If necessary, place the cover into position over the ball stud. Press down near the center of the cover, engaging the cover to the ball stud.
8. Place the cover into position over the ball studs. Press down near the upper left and the lower right corners, engaging the cover to the ball studs.
9. Install the oil fill cap.

MASS AIR FLOW (MAF) SENSOR

For information on the Mass Air Flow (MAF) sensor, refer to Intake Air Temperature (IAT) Sensor.

VEHICLE SPEED SENSOR (VSS)

REMOVAL & INSTALLATION

Automatic Transaxle 4T45-E

See Figure 175.

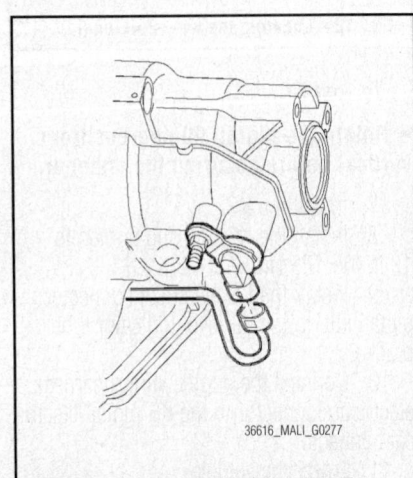

Fig. 175 Removing the VSS—4T45-E

✳✳ CAUTION

Ensure that the vehicle is properly supported and squarely positioned. To help avoid personal injury when a vehicle is on a hoist, provide additional support for the vehicle on the opposite end from which the components are being removed.

1. Position the vehicle on a hoist and raise the vehicle.

2. Disconnect the Vehicle Speed Sensor (VSS) electrical connector.
3. Remove the VSS electrical harness retainer from the VSS stud.
4. Remove the VSS stud.
5. Remove the output VSS from the transmission case.

✳✳ CAUTION

Inspect the O-ring for damage and replace if necessary.

6. Remove the O-ring from the VSS.

To install:
7. Install the O-ring onto the VSS.
8. Install the output VSS into the transmission case.
9. Install the VSS stud and tighten to 106 inch lbs. (12 Nm).
10. Install the VSS electrical harness retainer to the VSS stud.
11. Connect the VSS electrical connector.
12. Lower the vehicle.

FUEL   **GASOLINE FUEL INJECTION SYSTEM**

FUEL SYSTEM SERVICE PRECAUTIONS

Safety is the most important factor when performing not only fuel system maintenance but any type of maintenance. Failure to conduct maintenance and repairs in a safe manner may result in serious personal injury or death. Maintenance and testing of the vehicle's fuel system components can be accomplished safely and effectively by adhering to the following rules and guidelines.

• To avoid the possibility of fire and personal injury, always disconnect the negative battery cable unless the repair or test procedure requires that battery voltage be applied.

• Always relieve the fuel system pressure prior to disconnecting any fuel system component (injector, fuel rail, pressure regulator, etc.), fitting or fuel line connection. Exercise extreme caution whenever relieving fuel system pressure to avoid exposing skin, face and eyes to fuel spray. Please be advised that fuel under pressure may penetrate the skin or any part of the body that it contacts.

• Always place a shop towel or cloth around the fitting or connection prior to loosening to absorb any excess fuel due to spillage. Ensure that all fuel spillage (should it occur) is quickly removed from engine surfaces. Ensure that all fuel soaked cloths or towels are deposited into a suitable waste container.

• Always keep a dry chemical (Class B) fire extinguisher near the work area.

• Do not allow fuel spray or fuel vapors to come into contact with a spark or open flame.

• Always use a back-up wrench when loosening and tightening fuel line connection fittings. This will prevent unnecessary stress and torsion to fuel line piping.

• Always replace worn fuel fitting O-rings with new Do not substitute fuel hose or equivalent where fuel pipe is installed.

Before servicing the vehicle, make sure to also refer to the precautions in the beginning of this section as well.

RELIEVING FUEL SYSTEM PRESSURE

1. Loosen the fuel fill cap in order to relieve the fuel tank vapor pressure.
2. Remove the engine cover, if required.
3. Remove the fuel rail service port cap.
4. Wrap a shop towel around the fuel rail service port and using a small flat bladed tool, depress (open) the fuel rail test port valve.
5. Remove the shop towel from around the fuel rail service port, and place in an approved gasoline container.
6. Install the fuel rail service port cap.
7. Install the engine cover, if required.
8. Tighten the fuel fill cap.

FUEL PUMP

REMOVAL & INSTALLATION

1. Remove the fuel tank.
2. Disconnect the fuel tank fuel pump module wiring harness electrical connectors from the fuel pressure sensor and the pump.
3. Disconnect the fuel tank vent pipe quick connect fittings from the module.
4. Install a fuel pump lock ring wrench such as J 45722 to the fuel pump module lock ring.

➡**Avoid damaging the lock ring. Use only a fuel pump lock ring wrench such as J 45722 to prevent damage to the lock ring.**

➡**Do Not handle the fuel sender assembly by the fuel pipes. The amount of leverage generated by handling the fuel pipes could damage the joints.**

➡**Do NOT use impact tools. Significant force will be required to release the lock ring. The use of a hammer and screwdriver is not recommended. Secure the fuel tank in order to prevent fuel tank rotation.**

5. Using a fuel pump lock ring wrench such as J 45722 and a long breaker-bar, rotate the lock ring in a counterclockwise direction in order to unlock the lock ring.
6. Remove the fuel pump lock ring wrench such as J 45722 from the fuel pump module lock ring.
7. Lift the fuel pump module up slightly in order to disconnect the fuel tank vent pipe quick connect fitting from the pump cover.
8. Raise the fuel pump up from the fuel tank. Tilt the pump in order to allow the fuel level sensor arm and float to clear the pump opening.
9. Remove the fuel pump.
10. Remove and discard the fuel pump module seal.
11. Clean the fuel pump sealing surfaces.

To install:

✳✳ CAUTION

Drain the fuel from the fuel sender assembly into an approved container in order to reduce the risk of fire and personal injury. Never store the fuel in an open container.

➡**Some lock rings were manufactured with "DO NOT REUSE" stamped into them. These lock rings may be reused if they are not damaged or warped. Inspect the lock ring for damage due to improper removal or installation procedures. If damage is found, install a NEW fuel pump module. Inspect the lock ring for flatness as best as possible. If the lock ring is warped, replace the fuel pump module.**

12. Clean any contamination from the male pipe ends of the fuel pump.

13. Place a NEW fuel tank pump seal onto the fuel tank.

14. Insert the fuel pump into the fuel tank allowing the sensor arm and float to clear the module opening.

15. Lower the pump down into the fuel tank until the fuel tank vent pipe quick connect fitting can be connected.

16. Connect the fuel tank vent pipe quick connect fitting at the pump cover.

17. Press the fuel tank pump downward.

18. Install the pump lock ring wrench such as J 45722 to the fuel pump module lock ring.

➡**Ensure that the lock ring is installed with the correct side facing upward. A correctly installed lock ring will only turn in a clockwise direction.**

19. Using the pump lock ring wrench such as J 45722 and a long breaker-bar, rotate the lock ring in a clockwise direction in order the lock the lock ring.

20. Remove the pump lock ring wrench from the fuel pump module lock ring.

21. Connect the fuel tank vent pipe quick connect fittings to the pump.

22. Connect the fuel tank fuel pump module wiring harness electrical connectors to the fuel pressure sensor and the pump.

23. Install the fuel tank

FUEL RAIL AND INJECTORS

REMOVAL & INSTALLATION

2.4L Engine

See Figures 176 and 177.

1. Disconnect the negative battery cable.
2. Relieve the fuel system pressure.
3. Remove the air cleaner outlet duct.
4. Disconnect the fuel feed line quick connect fitting from the fuel rail
5. Disconnect the engine wiring harness electrical connector from the fuel injector wiring harness electrical connector.
6. Disconnect the fuel injector wiring harness electrical from the Manifold Absolute Pressure (MAP) sensor.
7. Remove the engine wiring harness clips from the fuel rail tabs.
8. Remove the fuel rail bolts.

➡**Use care when removing the fuel rail assembly in order to prevent damage to the fuel injector spray tips.**

9. Pull the fuel rail back and upward in order to release the fuel injectors from the cylinder head ports.

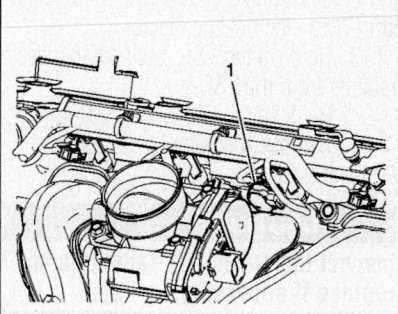

Fig. 176 Disconnecting the fuel injector wiring harness from the MAP sensor (1)— 2.4L engine

10. Remove the fuel rail.

➡**The fuel injector tip insulators may be located on the injector or may still be located in the cylinder head. Either way, ensure that all 4 injector tip insulators are removed and discarded.**

11. Remove and discard the fuel injector tip insulators.

12. Disconnect the fuel injector wiring harness electrical connectors from the fuel injectors.

13. Remove the fuel injector wiring harness clips from the fuel rail.

14. Remove the fuel injector wiring harness from the fuel rail.

➡**Use care in removing the fuel injectors in order to prevent damage to the fuel injector electrical connector pins**

or the fuel injector nozzles. Do not immerse the fuel injector in any type of cleaner. The fuel injector is an electrical component and may be damaged by this cleaning method.

➡**If the fuel injectors are found to be leaking, the engine oil may be contaminated with fuel.**

15. Remove the fuel injector retainer.
16. Remove the fuel injector from the fuel rail.
17. Remove the fuel injector upper O-ring.
18. Remove the fuel injector lower O-ring.

To install:

➡**The fuel injector assembly is stamped with a part number identification. Be sure to use the correct part number when ordering replacement fuel injectors.**

19. Lubricate the NEW fuel injector O-rings with clean engine oil.
20. Install the NEW fuel injector O-rings.
21. Install the fuel injector to the fuel rail.
22. Install the fuel injector retainer.
23. Install the fuel injector wiring harness clips to the fuel rail.
24. Connect the fuel injector wiring harness electrical connectors to the fuel injectors.
25. Lubricate the NEW fuel injector tip insulators with clean engine oil.

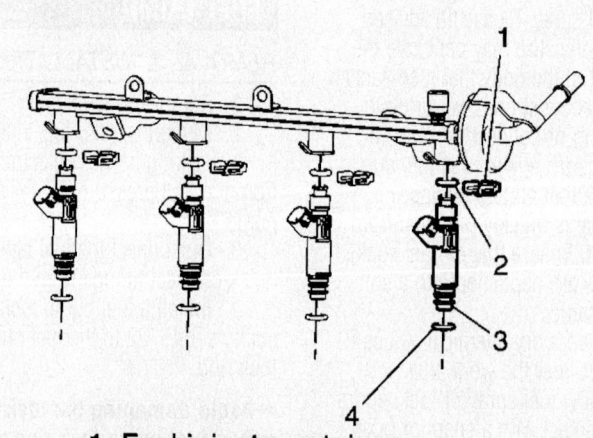

1. Fuel injector retainer
2. Fuel injector upper o-ring
3. Fuel injector
4. Fuel injector lower o-ring

Fig. 177 Removing the fuel injectors—2.4L engine

26. Install the NEW fuel injector tip insulators to the cylinder head.

27. With the fuel injectors positioned downward, lower the fuel injectors into the cylinder head ports.

28. Carefully push down on the fuel rail in order to insert the injectors into the cylinder head ports.

29. Install the fuel rail bolts. Tighten the bolts to 89 inch lbs. (10 Nm).

30. Install the engine wiring harness clips to the fuel rail tabs.

31. Connect the fuel injector wiring harness electrical to the MAP sensor.

32. Connect the engine wiring harness electrical connector to the fuel injector wiring harness electrical connector.

33. Connect the fuel feed line quick connect fitting to the fuel rail.

34. Install the air cleaner outlet duct.

35. Connect the negative battery cable.

36. Inspect for fuel leaks using the following procedure:

a. Turn **ON** the ignition, with the engine OFF for 2 seconds.

b. Turn **OFF** the ignition for 10 seconds

c. Turn **ON** the ignition

d. Inspect for fuel leaks.

3.5L Engine

See Figure 178.

> ✳✳ **CAUTION**

In order to reduce the risk of fire and personal injury that may result from a fuel leak, always install the fuel injector O-rings in the proper position. If the upper and lower O-rings are different colors (black and brown), be sure to install the black O-ring in the upper position and the brown O-ring in the lower position on the fuel injector. The O-rings are the same size but are made of different materials.

➡**Cap the fittings and plug the holes when servicing the fuel system in order to prevent dirt and other contaminants from entering the open pipes and passages.**

➡**An 8-digit identification number is stamped on the fuel rail. Refer to this number if servicing or part replacement is required.**

1. Disconnect the fuel feed pipe quick connect fitting from the fuel rail.

2. Remove the upper intake manifold.

3. Disconnect the fuel injector wiring harness electrical connector from the Engine Coolant Temperature (ECT) sensor.

4. Disconnect the fuel injector wiring harness electrical connector from the Camshaft Position (CMP) sensor.

5. Remove the fuel injector wiring harness electrical connector bracket bolt from the intake manifold.

6. Remove the fuel rail bolts.

7. Remove the fuel rail.

8. Remove the fuel injector O-ring seal from the spray tip end of each injector, if the fuel rail was removed for other purposes.

9. Disconnect the fuel injector wiring harness electrical connectors from the fuel injectors.

10. Remove the fuel injector wiring harness retainers from the fuel rail.

11. Remove the fuel injector wiring harness.

12. Remove the fuel injector retainers.

13. Remove the fuel injectors.

14. Remove the fuel injector upper and lower O-ring seals.

To install:

15. Lubricate the NEW injector O-ring seals with clean engine oil.

16. Install the NEW fuel injector upper and lower O-ring seals.

17. Install the fuel injectors.

18. Install the fuel injector retainers.

19. Position the fuel injector wiring harness.

20. Install the fuel injector wiring harness retainers to the fuel rail.

21. Connect the fuel injector wiring harness electrical connectors to the fuel injectors.

➡**Use care when servicing the fuel system components, especially the fuel injector electrical connectors, the fuel**

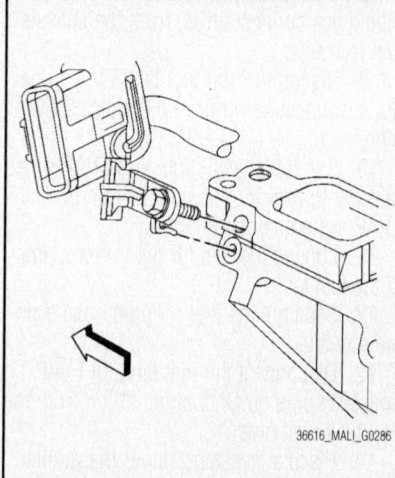

Fig. 178 Removing the fuel injector wiring harness electrical connector bracket bolt from the intake manifold—3.5L engine

injector tips, and the injector O-rings. Plug the inlet and the outlet ports of the fuel rail in order to prevent contamination. Do not use compressed air to clean the fuel rail assembly as this may damage the fuel rail components. Do not immerse the fuel rail assembly in a solvent bath in order to prevent damage to the fuel rail assembly.

22. Install NEW fuel injector O-ring seals onto the spray tip end of each injector, if the fuel rail was removed for other purposes.

23. Install the fuel rail.

24. Install the fuel rail bolts. Tighten the bolts to 89 inch lbs. (10 Nm).

25. Align the bracket pin to the hole in the lower intake manifold.

26. Install the fuel injector wiring harness electrical connector bracket bolt to the intake manifold. Tighten the bolt to 10 ft. lbs. (14 Nm).

27. Connect the fuel injector wiring harness electrical connector to the CMP sensor.

28. Connect the fuel injector wiring harness electrical connector to the ECT sensor.

29. Install the upper intake manifold.

30. Connect the fuel feed pipe quick connect fitting to the fuel rail.

31. Connect the negative battery cable. Refer

32. Tighten the fuel fill cap.

33. Inspect for fuel leaks using the following procedure:

a. Turn **ON** the ignition, with the engine OFF for 10 seconds.

b. Turn **OFF** the ignition for 10 seconds.

c. Turn **ON** the ignition for 10 seconds.

d. Inspect for fuel leaks.

3.6L Engine

See Figure 179.

1. Remove the fuel injector sight shield.

2. Disconnect the engine wiring harness electrical connector from the fuel injector wiring harness electrical connector.

3. Disconnect the fuel feed pipe quick connect fitting from the fuel rail.

4. Remove the upper intake manifold.

> ✳✳ **CAUTION**

Wear safety glasses while using the compressed air to avoid eye injury.

5. Use compressed air in order to remove any debris from the around the area where the fuel injectors enter the lower intake manifold.

6. Remove the fuel rail bolts.

➡ Remove the fuel rail assembly carefully in order to prevent damage to the injector electrical connector terminals and the injector spray tips. Support the fuel rail after the fuel rail is removed in order to avoid damaging the fuel rail components. Cap the fittings and plug the holes when servicing the fuel system in order to prevent dirt and other contaminants from entering open pipes and passages.

7. Remove the fuel rail with fuel injectors from the lower intake manifold.

8. Lift up the fuel injector electrical connector retainer.

9. Push in the fuel injector electrical connector tab in order to disconnect the connector from the injector.

10. Remove the fuel injector retainer clip.

11. Remove the fuel injector.

12. Remove and discard the fuel injector seals.

To install:

13. Install NEW fuel injector seals.

14. Install the fuel injector.

15. Install the fuel injector retainer clip.

16. Install the fuel injector electrical connector.

17. Push down on the fuel injector electrical connector retainer, securing the electrical connector.

18. Install the fuel rail with fuel injectors to the lower intake manifold. Tighten the bolts to 89 inch lbs. (10 Nm).

19. Install the upper intake manifold.

20. Connect the fuel feed pipe quick connect fitting to the fuel rail.

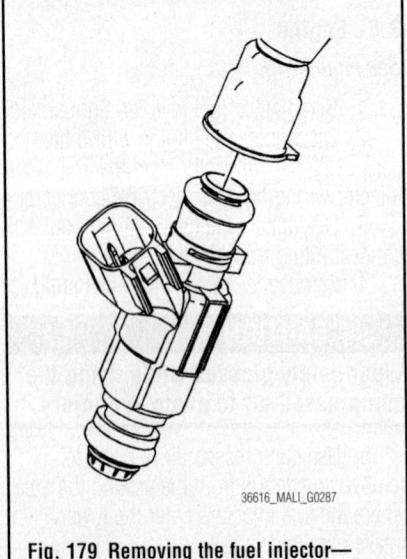

Fig. 179 Removing the fuel injector— 3.6L engine

21. Connect the engine wiring harness electrical connector to the fuel injector wiring harness electrical connector.

22. Inspect for fuel leaks using the following procedure:

a. Turn **ON** the ignition, with the engine **OFF** for 10 seconds.

b. Turn **OFF** the ignition for 10 seconds.

c. Turn **ON** the ignition for 10 seconds.

d. Inspect for fuel leaks.

23. Install the fuel injector sight shield.

FUEL TANK

REMOVAL & INSTALLATION

See Figure 180.

➡ Clean the fuel and Evaporative Emission (EVAP) connections and surrounding areas prior to disconnecting the lines in order the avoid possible system contamination.

1. Relieve the fuel system pressure.

2. Drain the fuel tank.

3. Raise and support the vehicle.

4. Disconnect the fuel tank fuel pump module wiring harness electrical connector from body wiring harness electrical connector.

5. Remove the body wiring harness electrical connector clip from the EVAP canister.

6. Disconnect the body wiring harness electrical connector from the rear Antilock Brake System (ABS) wiring harness electrical connector.

7. Remove the rear ABS wiring harness electrical connector clip from the EVAP canister.

8. Disconnect the fuel tank fuel feed pipe quick connect fitting from the chassis fuel feed pipe.

9. Disconnect the fuel tank EVAP pipe quick connect fitting from the chassis EVAP pipe.

10. Cap the chassis fuel and EVAP pipes in order to prevent possible fuel and/or EVAP system contamination.

11. Loosen the fuel fill pipe hose clamp at the fuel tank.

12. Separate the fuel fill pipe hose from the fuel tank.

13. Disconnect the fuel tank fill EVAP emission pipe quick connect fitting from the fuel tank vent pipe.

14. Place a jackstand under the muffler assembly.

15. With the aid of an assistant, separate the muffler insulators from the underbody hangers.

16. Slowly lower the muffler assembly

allowing it to rest on the jackstand. If this is not possible, remove the muffler assembly.

17. Have assistants support either side of the fuel tank.

18. Place a suitable adjustable jack under the fuel tank, and have the assistants rest the fuel tank on the adjustable jack.

19. Remove fuel tank strap bolts and straps.

20. If applicable, in order to clear the muffler assembly, slowly lower the right side of the fuel tank.

21. Once the tank is clear of the right frame rail, lower the fuel tank down and remove forward toward the right side of the vehicle.

To install:

22. Have assistants support either side of the fuel tank.

23. If applicable, begin to install the right side of the fuel tank over the muffler assembly.

24. If applicable, raise the right side of the fuel tank into position inboard of the right frame rail. Use care in feeding the fuel feed, EVAP line wiring harness over the muffler assembly.

25. If applicable and the muffler assembly was removed, have assistants raise the fuel tank into position.

26. Install fuel tank straps and bolts. Tighten the bolts to 15 ft. lbs. (20 Nm).

27. Raise the muffler assembly into position if applicable, otherwise install the muffler assembly.

28. With the aid of an assistant, install the muffler insulators to the underbody hangers.

29. Remove the jackstand from under the muffler assembly.

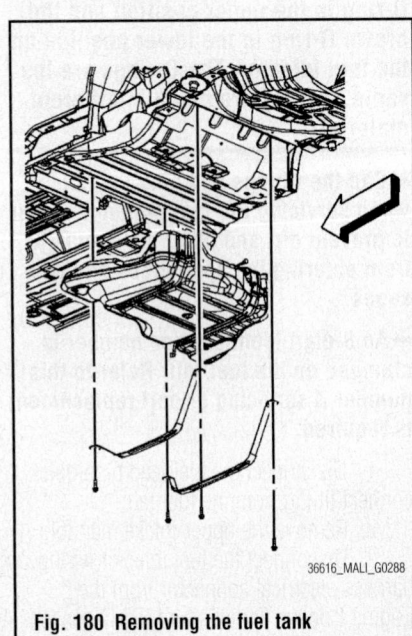

Fig. 180 Removing the fuel tank

30. Install the fuel fill pipe hose to the fuel tank.

31. Connect the fuel tank fill EVAP emission pipe quick connect fitting to the fuel tank vent pipe.

32. Tighten the fuel fill pipe hose clamp at the fuel tank to 35 inch lbs. (4 Nm).

33. Remove the caps from the fuel and EVAP pipes.

34. Connect the fuel tank EVAP pipe quick connect fitting to the chassis EVAP pipe.

35. Connect the fuel tank fuel feed pipe quick connect fitting to the chassis fuel feed pipe.

36. Install the rear ABS wiring harness electrical connector clip to the EVAP canister.

37. Connect the body wiring harness electrical connector to the rear ABS wiring harness electrical connector.

38. Install the body wiring harness electrical connector clip to the underbody.

39. Connect the fuel tank fuel pump module wiring harness electrical connector to the body wiring harness electrical connector.

40. Lower the vehicle.

41. Refill the fuel tank.

42. Tighten the fuel fill cap.

43. Inspect for fuel leaks using the following procedure:

 a. Turn **ON** the ignition, with the engine OFF for 10 seconds.

 b. Turn **OFF** the ignition for 10 seconds.

 c. Turn **ON** the ignition, with the engine OFF.

 d. Inspect for fuel leaks.

IDLE SPEED

ADJUSTMENT

Idle speed is maintained by the Powertrain Control Module (PCM). No adjustment is necessary or possible.

THROTTLE BODY

REMOVAL & INSTALLATION

2.4L Engine

See Figure 181.

➡Do not use solvent of any type when cleaning the gasket surfaces on the intake manifold and the throttle body assembly, as damage to the gasket surfaces and throttle body assembly may result. Use care in cleaning the gasket surfaces on the intake manifold and the throttle body assembly, as sharp tools may damage the gasket surfaces.

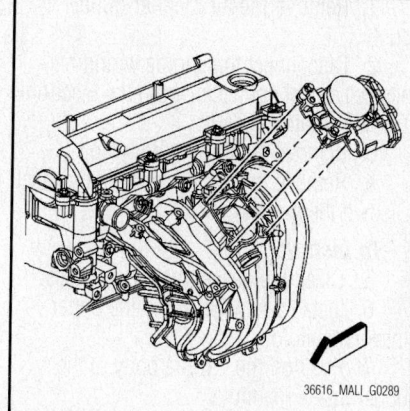

Fig. 181 Removing and installing the throttle body—2.4L engine

➡Do not use any solvent that contains Methyl Ethyl Ketone (MEK). This solvent may damage fuel system components.

➡DO NOT prop open the throttle blade with the ignition key in the ON position as it may set a Diagnostic Trouble Code (DTC).

1. Remove the air cleaner outlet duct.

2. Disconnect the engine wiring harness electrical connector from the Electronic Throttle Control (ETC).

3. Remove the throttle body bolts.

4. Remove the throttle body.

5. Inspect the throttle body gasket, and replace if necessary.

To install:

6. Install the throttle body. Tighten the bolts to 89 inch lbs. (10 Nm).

7. Connect the engine wiring harness electrical connector to the ETC.

8. Install the air cleaner outlet duct.

3.5L Engine

See Figure 182.

➡Do not use solvent of any type when cleaning the gasket surfaces on the intake manifold and the throttle body assembly, as damage to the gasket surfaces and throttle body assembly may result. Use care in cleaning the gasket surfaces on the intake manifold and the throttle body assembly, as sharp tools may damage the gasket surfaces.

1. Remove the intake manifold cover.

2. Remove the air cleaner outlet duct.

3. Disconnect the engine wiring harness electrical connector from the Electronic Throttle Control (ETC).

4. Remove the heater inlet and outlet pipe nuts.

5. Remove the heater inlet and outlet pipe bracket from the throttle body studs. Reposition the pipes aside.

6. Remove the throttle body bolts and nuts.

7. Remove the throttle body.

8. Remove and discard the throttle body gasket.

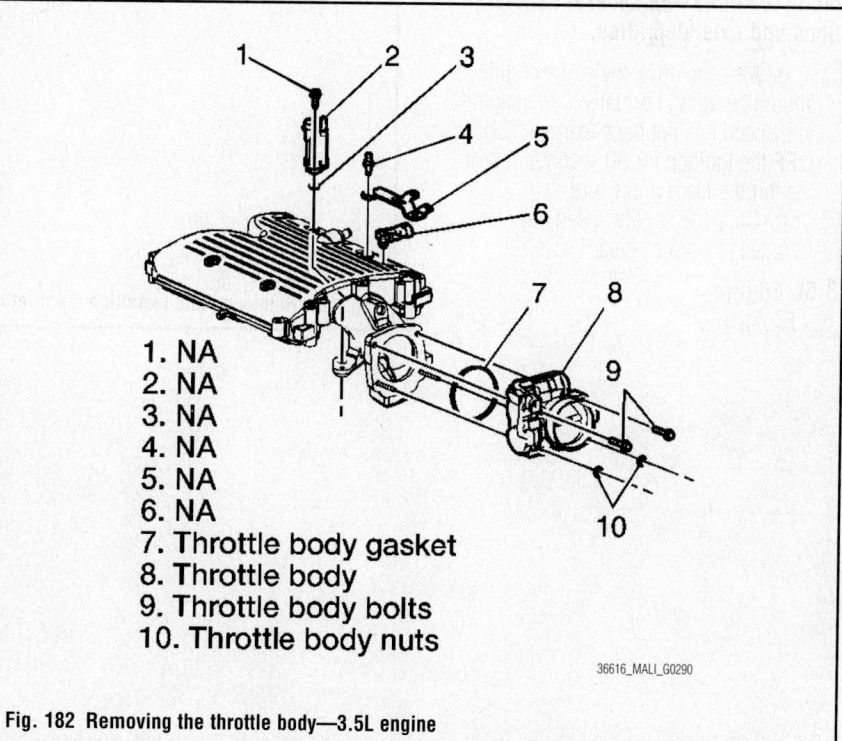

1. NA
2. NA
3. NA
4. NA
5. NA
6. NA
7. Throttle body gasket
8. Throttle body
9. Throttle body bolts
10. Throttle body nuts

Fig. 182 Removing the throttle body—3.5L engine

To install:

9. Clean the gasket mating surfaces.

10. Install a new gasket.

11. Install the throttle body. Tighten the bolts and nuts to 89 inch lbs. (10 Nm).

12. Reposition the heater inlet and outlet pipes and install the pipe bracket to the throttle body studs. Tighten the nuts to 89 inch lbs. (10 Nm).

13. Connect the engine wiring harness electrical connector to the ETC.

14. Install the air cleaner outlet duct.

15. Install the intake manifold cover.

16. Perform the Throttle Learn Procedure as follows:

a. Start and idle the engine in PARK for 3 minutes.

b. With a scan tool, monitor desired and actual RPM.

c. The ECM will start to learn the new idle cells and Desired RPM should start to decrease.

d. Turn the ignition OFF for 60 seconds.

e. Start and idle the engine in PARK for 3 minutes.

f. After the 3 minute run time the engine should be idling normal.

➡ During the drive cycle the check engine light may come on with idle speed DTCs. If idle speed codes are set, clear codes so the ECM can continue to learn. If the engine idle speed has not been learned the vehicle will need to be driven at speeds above 44 mph (70 km/h) with several decelerations and extended idles.

g. After the drive cycle, the engine should be idling normally. If the engine idle speed has not been learned, Turn **OFF** the ignition for 60 seconds repeat the throttle learn procedure.

h. Once the engine speed has returned to normal, clear DTCs.

3.6L Engine

See Figure 183.

1. Remove the air cleaner outlet duct.

2. Disconnect the engine wiring harness electrical connector from the Electronic Throttle Control (ETC).

3. Remove the throttle body bolts.

4. Remove the throttle body and gasket. Discard the gasket.

To install:

5. Clean the gasket mating surfaces.

6. Install a new gasket to the upper intake manifold.

7. Position the throttle body to the upper intake manifold.

8. Install the throttle body. Tighten the bolts to 89 inch lbs. (10 Nm).

9. Connect the engine wiring harness electrical connector to the ETC.

10. Install the air cleaner outlet duct.

11. Perform the Throttle Learn Procedure as follows:

a. Start and idle the engine in PARK for 3 minutes.

b. With a scan tool, monitor desired and actual RPM.

c. The ECM will start to learn the new idle cells and Desired RPM should start to decrease.

d. Turn the ignition OFF for 60 seconds.

e. Start and idle the engine in PARK for 3 minutes.

f. After the 3 minute run time the engine should be idling normal.

➡ During the drive cycle the check engine light may come on with idle speed DTCs. If idle speed codes are set, clear codes so the ECM can continue to learn. If the engine idle speed has not been learned the vehicle will need to be driven at speeds above 44 mph (70 km/h) with several decelerations and extended idles.

g. After the drive cycle, the engine should be idling normally. If the engine idle speed has not been learned, Turn **OFF** the ignition for 60 seconds repeat the throttle learn procedure.

h. Once the engine speed has returned to normal, clear DTCs.

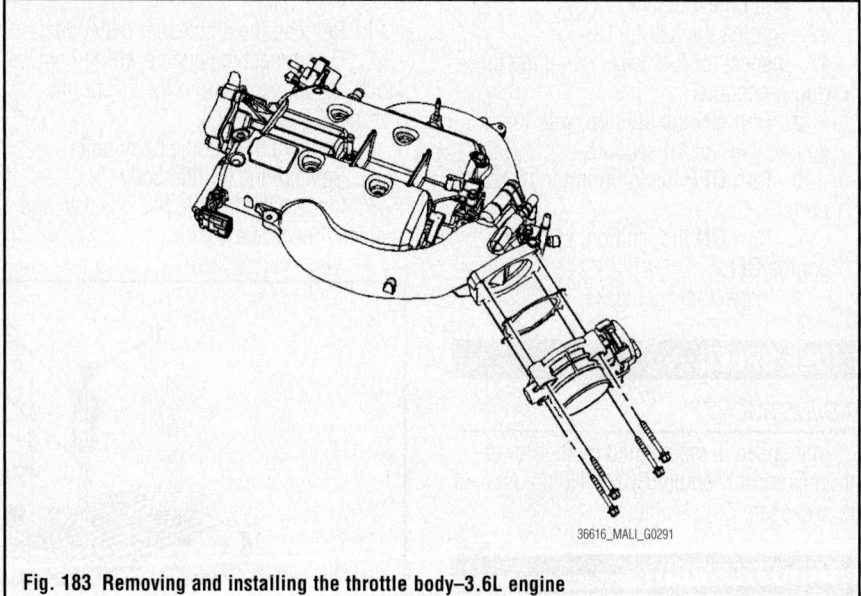

36616_MALI_G0291

Fig. 183 Removing and installing the throttle body–3.6L engine

HEATING & AIR CONDITIONING SYSTEM

BLOWER MOTOR

REMOVAL & INSTALLATION

See Figure 184.

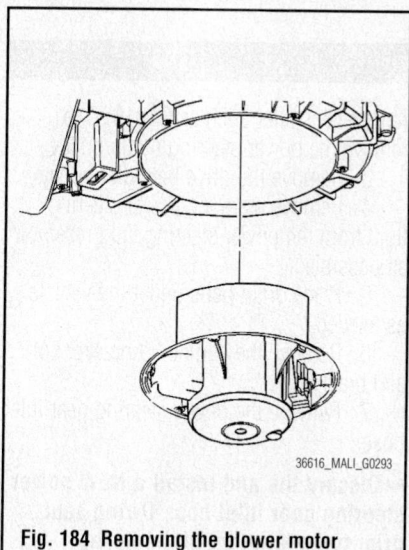

Fig. 184 Removing the blower motor

1. Remove the right closeout panel.
2. Remove the blower motor wire harness connector.

➡ **Cut through the case as straight as possible because the motor cup must be replaced. In order to prevent damage to the component, do not cut any deeper than necessary to remove the motor cup.**

3. Cut out the blower motor using a utility knife in the narrow groove of the lower case.
4. Remove the blower motor.
5. Remove the blower motor nuts.
6. Remove the blower motor from the blower motor cup.

To install:

7. Install the new blower motor to the blower motor cup.
8. Install the blower motor nuts. Tighten to 21 inch lbs. (2.4 Nm).
9. Install the motor blower seal to the blower motor service ring.
10. Install the blower motor.
11. Install the blower motor attachment ring.
12. Install the blower motor screws. Tighten the screws to 13 inch lbs. (1.5 Nm).
13. Install the blower motor wire harness connector.
14. Install the right closeout panel.

HEATER CORE

REMOVAL & INSTALLATION

See Figure 185.

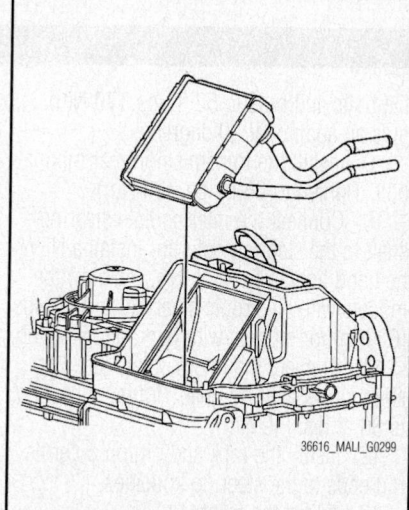

Fig. 185 Removing the heater core

1. Remove the HVAC module assembly.
2. Remove the center floor air outlet duct screws.
3. Remove the center floor air outlet duct.
4. Drill out the heater core cover heat stakes.
5. Remove the heater core cover screws.
6. Remove the heater core cover.
7. Remove the heater core.

To install:

8. Install the heater core cover.
9. Install the heater core cover screws and tighten to 13 inch lbs. (1.5 Nm).

10. Install the center floor air outlet duct.
11. Install the upper floor air outlet duct screws and tighten to 13 inch lbs. (1.5 Nm).
12. Install the HVAC module assembly.

HVAC MODULE

REMOVAL & INSTALLATION

See Figure 186.

1. Remove the Air Conditioner (A/C) lines from the thermal expansion valve.
2. Remove the heater hose from the heater core.
3. Remove the Instrument Panel (I/P) assembly.
4. Remove the recirculation actuator wire harness connector.
5. Remove the air temperature actuator wire harness connector.
6. Remove the mode actuator wire harness connector.
7. Remove the blower motor wire harness connector.
8. Remove the blower motor resistor wire harness connector.
9. Remove the left hand side window defogger outlet duct.
10. Remove the HVAC module assembly mounting bolts from the instrument panel reinforcement.
11. Remove the HVAC module assembly to dash panel bolts.
12. Remove the HVAC module assembly.

To install:

13. Install the HVAC module assembly.
14. Install the HVAC module assembly to

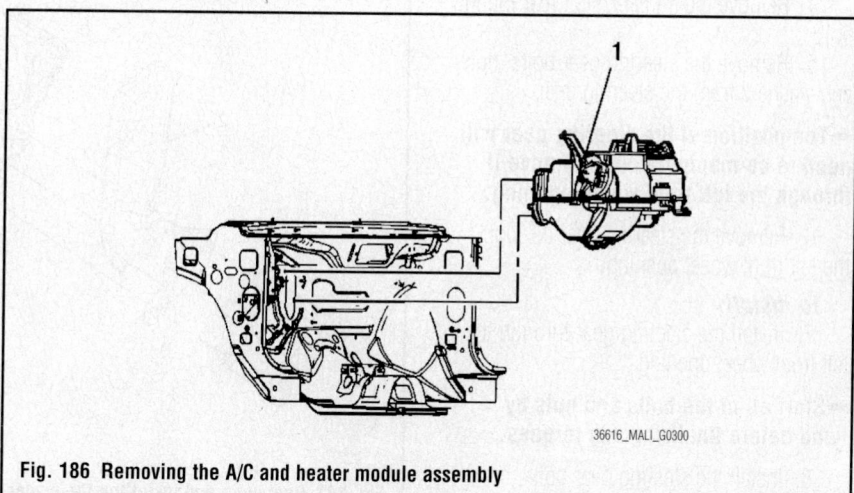

Fig. 186 Removing the A/C and heater module assembly

dash panel bolts and tighten to 88 inch lbs. (10 Nm).

15. Install the HVAC module assembly mounting bolts to the instrument panel reinforcement and tighten the bolts to 44 inch lbs. (5 Nm).

16. Install the left hand side window defogger outlet duct.

17. Install the blower motor resistor wire harness connector.

18. Install the blower motor wire harness connector.

19. Install the mode actuator wire harness connector.

20. Install the air temperature actuator wire harness connector.

21. Install the recirculation actuator wire harness connector.

22. Install the I/P assembly.

23. Install the heater hoses to the heater core.

24. Install the A/C lines to the thermal expansion valve.

STEERING

ELECTRONIC STEERING GEAR

REMOVAL & INSTALLATION

✳✳ CAUTION

With the wheels of the vehicle facing straight ahead, secure the steering wheel utilizing a steering column anti-rotation pin, steering column lock, or a strap to prevent rotation. Locking of the steering column will prevent damage and a possible malfunction of the SIR system. The steering wheel must be secured in position before disconnecting the steering column, intermediate shaft or steering gear. After disconnecting these components, do not move the front tires and wheels. Failure to follow these procedures may cause improper alignment of some components during installation and result in possible damage to the SIR coil.

1. Turn the front wheels to the straight forward position and secure the steering wheel from moving.

2. Disengage the rack and pinion outer tie rod ends from the steering knuckles.

3. Separate the intermediate steering shaft from the steering gear.

4. Remove the transmission rear mount bolt.

5. Remove the steering gear bolts, nuts, and washers from the steering gear.

➡**The position of the steering gear will need to be manipulated to remove it through the left front wheel opening.**

6. Remove the steering gear through the left front wheel opening.

To install:

7. Install the steering gear through the left front wheel opening.

➡**Start all of the bolts and nuts by hand before finalizing any torques.**

8. Install the steering gear bolts, nuts, and washers to the steering gear. Tighten

the bolts and nuts to 52 ft. lbs. (70 Nm) plus an additional 90 degrees.

9. Install the transmission rear mount bolt. Tighten to 66 ft. lbs. (90 Nm).

10. Connect the intermediate steering shaft to the steering column. Install a NEW bolt and tighten to 36 ft. lbs. (49 Nm) for models with electronic steering or 46 ft. lbs. (62 Nm) for models with hydraulic steering.

11. Connect the intermediate steering shaft to the steering gear. Tighten a new bolt to 36 ft. lbs. (49 Nm).

12. Install the rack and pinion outer tie rod ends to the steering knuckles.

13. Adjust the front toe.

POWER STEERING PUMP

REMOVAL & INSTALLATION

3.5L Engine

See Figure 187.

1. Remove the drive belt.

2. Use a power steering pulley remover/installer such as SA9162C to remove the power steering pump pulley.

3. Remove the drive belt idler pulley

4. Remove as much power steering fluid from the power steering fluid reservoir as possible.

5. Place drain pans under the vehicle as needed.

6. Remove the engine lift bracket bolt and bracket.

7. Remove the power steering gear inlet hose.

➡**Discard the and install a NEW power steering gear inlet hose O-ring seal prior to installation of the hose.**

8. Remove the power steering reservoir inlet hose.

9. Remove the power steering pump bolt and pump.

To install:

10. Installation is the reverse of removal:
   a. Tighten the pump bolts to 18 ft. lbs. (25 Nm).

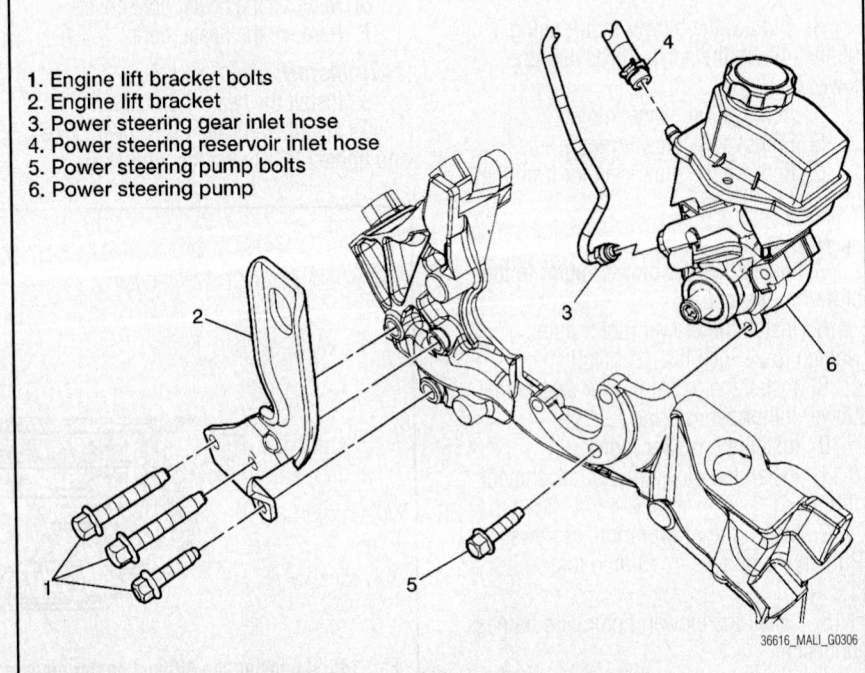

1. Engine lift bracket bolts
2. Engine lift bracket
3. Power steering gear inlet hose
4. Power steering reservoir inlet hose
5. Power steering pump bolts
6. Power steering pump

36616_MALI_G0306

Fig. 187 Removing and installing the power steering pump—3.5L engine

b. Install a new inlet hose O-ring seal and tighten the hose sitting to 20 ft. lbs. (27 Nm).

c. Tighten the engine lift bracket bolts to 37 ft. lbs. (50 Nm).

d. Use a power steering pulley remover/installer such as SA9162C to install the power steering pump pulley.

e. Fill and bleed the power steering system.

3.6L Engine

See Figure 188.

1. Remove the drive belt.
2. Remove the right front tire and wheel assembly.
3. Remove as much power steering fluid from the remote power steering fluid reservoir as possible.
4. Place drain pans under the vehicle as needed.
5. Disconnect the power steering fluid reservoir outlet hose clamp.
6. Disconnect the power steering fluid reservoir outlet hose.
7. Remove the power steering gear inlet hose.

➡Discard the and install a NEW power steering gear inlet hose O-ring seal prior to installation of the hose.

8. Remove the engine mount adapter bolt.
9. Remove the power steering pump bolt
10. Use a power steering pulley remover/installer such as SA9162C to remove the power steering pump pulley.
11. Remove the engine mount adapter bracket bolts and bracket.
12. Remove the power steering pump.

To install:

13. Installation is the reverse of removal:

a. Tighten the pump bolts to 37 ft. lbs. (50 Nm).

b. Use an installer tool such as CJ138 or OTC7771or 8 mm x 1.25 inch tool to install the power steering pump pulley.

c. Tighten the engine mount adapter bolts to 43 ft. lbs. (58 Nm).

d. Install a new inlet hose O-ring seal and tighten the hose sitting to 20 ft. lbs. (27 Nm).

e. Fill and bleed the power steering system.

BLEEDING

➡Use clean, new power steering fluid only. Hoses touching the frame, body or engine may cause system noise. Verify that the hoses do not touch any other part of the vehicle. Loose connections may not leak, but could allow air into the steering system. Verify that all hoses connections are tight.

➡Power steering fluid level must be maintained throughout bleed procedure.

1. Fill pump reservoir with fluid to minimum system level, FULL COLD level, or middle of hash mark on cap stick fluid level indicator.

➡With hydro-boost only, the oil level will appear falsely high if the hydro-boost accumulator is not fully charged. Do not apply the brake pedal with the engine OFF. This will discharge the hydro-boost accumulator.

2. If equipped with hydro-boost, fully charge the hydro-boost accumulator, start

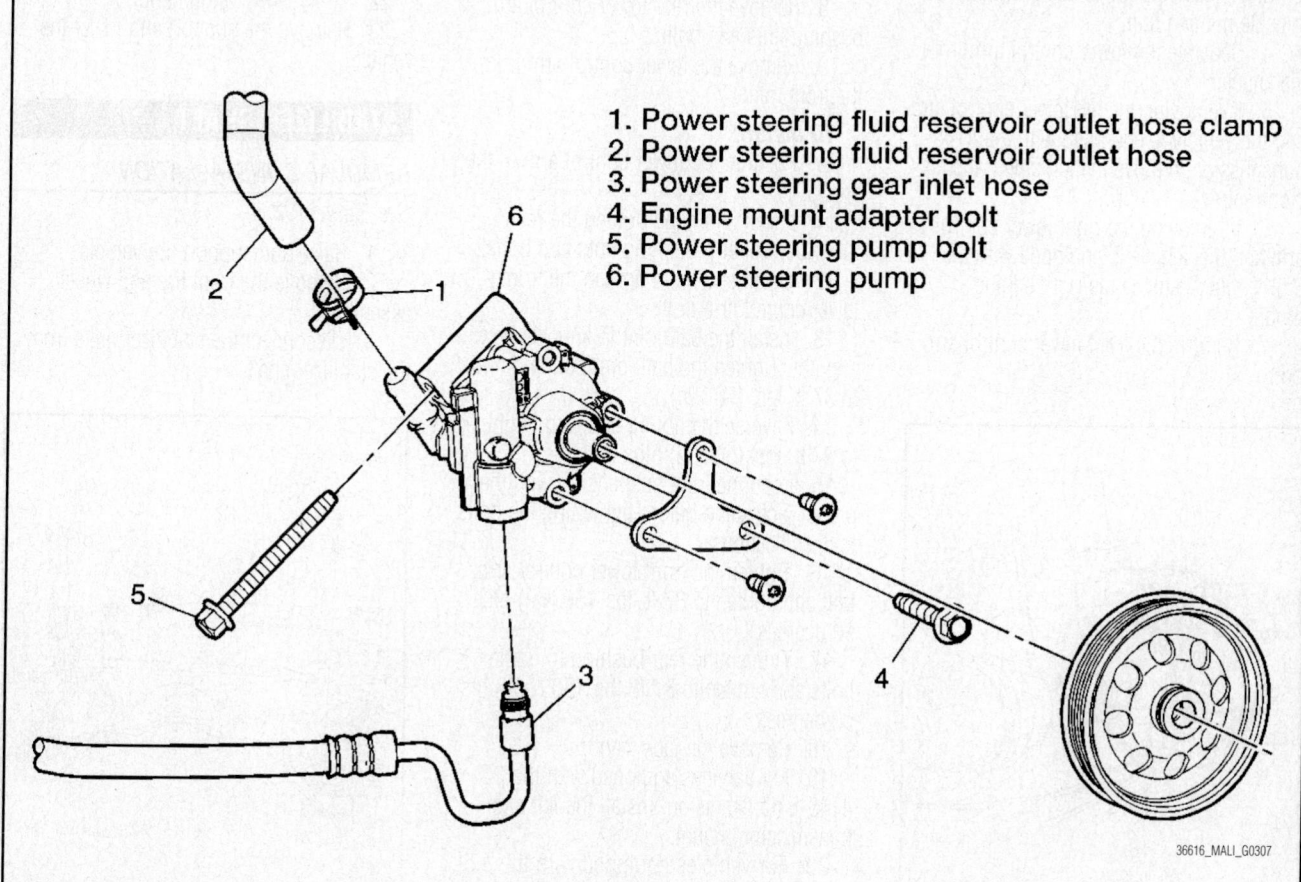

1. Power steering fluid reservoir outlet hose clamp
2. Power steering fluid reservoir outlet hose
3. Power steering gear inlet hose
4. Engine mount adapter bolt
5. Power steering pump bolt
6. Power steering pump

36616_MALI_G0307

Fig. 188 Exploded view of the power steering pump assembly–3.6L engine

the engine, firmly apply the brake pedal 10-15 times and turn the engine off.

3. Raise the vehicle until the front wheels are off the ground.

4. Key on engine OFF, turn the steering wheel from stop to stop 12 times.

5. Vehicles equipped with hydro-boost systems or longer length power steering hoses may require turns up to 15 to 20 stop to stops.

6. Verify power steering fluid level per operating specification.

7. Start the engine. Rotate steering wheel from left to right. Check for sign of cavitation or fluid aeration (pump noise/whining).

8. Verify the fluid level. Repeat the bleed procedure, if necessary.

SUSPENSION

FRONT SUSPENSION

LOWER BALL JOINT

REMOVAL & INSTALLATION

The ball joint is an integral part of the control arm, if defective replace the control arm.

LOWER CONTROL ARM

REMOVAL & INSTALLATION

See Figures 189 through 191.

1. Raise and support the vehicle.
2. Remove the tire and wheel.

✳✳ CAUTION

DO NOT re-use the lower ball joint bolt. Discard and use NEW only.

3. Remove the lower ball joint to knuckle nut and bolt.

4. Separate the lower control arm from the knuckle.

5. If removing the left lower control arm and the vehicle is equipped with the 4T45-E transmission, remove the left side transmission mount.

6. If removing the right lower control arm and the vehicle is equipped with the 3.5L engine, remove the right engine mount.

7. Remove the front lower control arm bolt.

Fig. 189 Removing the lower ball joint to knuckle and bolt

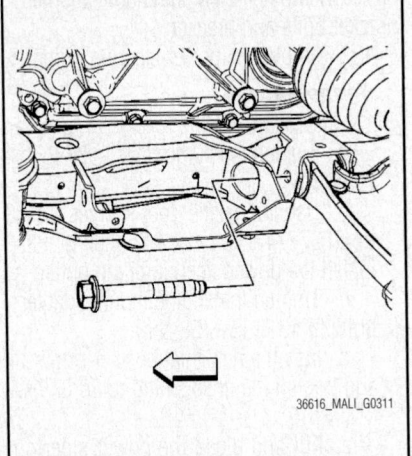

Fig. 190 Removing the front lower control arm bolt

8. Remove the rear lower control arm bushing nuts and bolts.

9. Remove the lower control arm from the front frame.

To install:

10. Position the lower control arm in the cradle.

11. Install and hand tighten the rear lower control arm bushing nuts and bolts.

12. Install and hand tighten the front lower control arm bolt.

13. Install the ball joint to knuckle bolt and nut. Tighten the ball joint bolt and nut to 37 ft. lbs. (50 Nm).

14. Reverse the nut ¾ of a turn. Tighten to 37 ft. lbs. (50 Nm) plus 30°.

15. Load the front suspension with the proper jack stand before tightening the bolts to specifications.

16. Tighten the front lower control arm bolt and tighten to 37 ft. lbs. (50 Nm) plus 90 degrees.

17. Tighten the rear bushing to frame bolts and tighten to 37 ft. lbs. (50 Nm) plus 90 degrees.

18. Remove the jack stand.

19. For vehicles equipped with the 4T45-E transmission, install the left side transmission mount.

20. For vehicles equipped with the 3.5L engine, install the right side engine mount.

21. Install the tire and wheel.

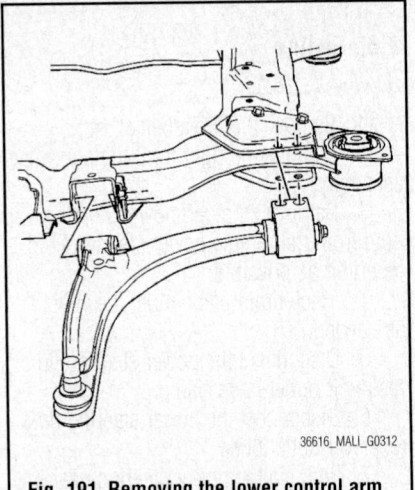

Fig. 191 Removing the lower control arm from the front frame

22. Verify wheel alignment.

23. Remove the support and lower the vehicle.

STABILIZER SHAFT

REMOVAL & INSTALLATION

See Figure 192.

1. Raise and support the vehicle.
2. Remove the front tire and wheel assemblies.
3. Disconnect the stabilizer links from the stabilizer shaft.

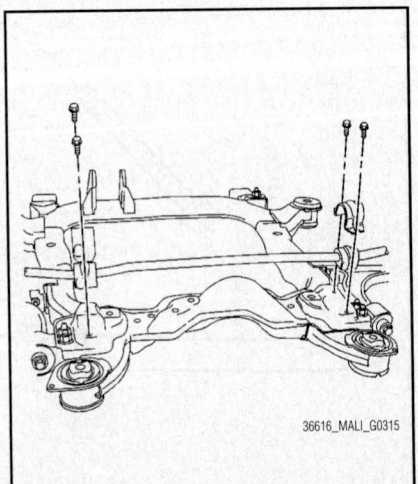

Fig. 192 Removing the stabilizer shaft

4. For vehicles equipped with the 3.6L LY7, remove the exhaust pipe.

5. Using a suitable jack stand, support the rear of the frame assembly.

6. Remove the frame to body bolts.

7. Lower the rear of the frame in order to gain clearance to the stabilizer shaft.

8. Remove the stabilizer shaft clamp bolts.

9. Remove the stabilizer shaft clamps and insulators.

10. Remove the stabilizer shaft from the frame.

To install:

➡**Install the insulators so that the slit in the insulator is facing the rear of the vehicle.**

11. Install the insulators on the stabilizer shaft.

12. Position the stabilizer shaft to the frame.

13. Install the stabilizer bar clamps.

14. Install the stabilizer shaft clamp bolts and tighten to 18 ft. lbs. (25 Nm).

15. Raise the rear of the cradle and install the cradle bolts.

16. Remove the jack stand.

17. Connect the stabilizer link to the stabilizer bar.

18. For vehicles equipped with the 3.6L LY7, install the exhaust pipe.

19. Install the front tire and wheel assemblies.

20. Remove the support and lower the vehicle.

STEERING KNUCKLE

REMOVAL & INSTALLATION

See Figure 193.

1. Raise and support the vehicle.

2. Remove the wheel bearing/hub.

3. Remove the outer tie rod to knuckle nut.

4. Remove the nuts and bolts from the strut to the knuckle.

5. Separate the lower ball joint from the knuckle.

6. Remove the steering knuckle from the vehicle.

To install:

7. Install the steering knuckle and verify the front end alignment.

8. Connect the lower ball joint to the knuckle.

9. Install the nuts and bolts to the strut and knuckle.

10. Connect the outer tie rod end to the knuckle.

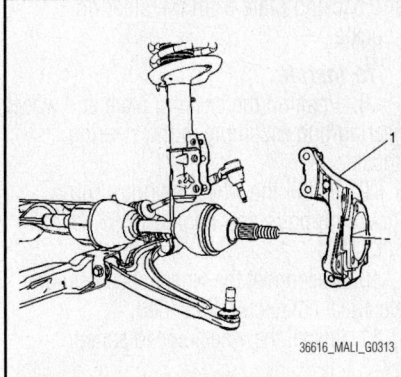

Fig. 193 Removing the steering knuckle

11. Install the wheel bearing/hub.

12. Lower the vehicle.

STRUT

REMOVAL & INSTALLATION

See Figure 194.

1. Raise and the vehicle.

2. Remove the tire and wheel assembly.

3. Support the lower control arm with a suitable jack stand.

4. Disconnect the wheel speed sensor electrical connector at the wheel speed sensor bracket, if equipped.

5. Remove the stabilizer shaft link from the front strut.

6. Remove the front strut nuts from the bolts.

7. Remove the wheel speed sensor bracket from the strut.

8. Remove the strut bolts from the front strut.

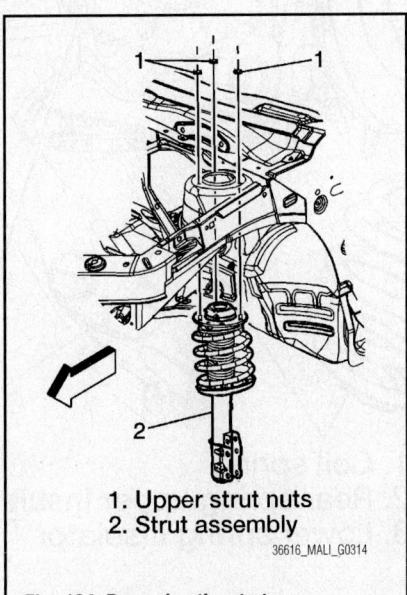

1. Upper strut nuts
2. Strut assembly

36616_MALI_G0314

Fig. 194 Removing the strut

9. Separate the front strut from the knuckle.

10. Remove the upper strut nuts from the strut.

11. Remove the front strut assembly from the vehicle.

To install:

12. Install the front strut assembly.

13. Install the upper strut nuts and tighten to 18 ft. lbs. (25 Nm).

14. Insert the front strut in the knuckle.

15. Install the strut bolts.

16. Install the wheel speed sensor bracket.

17. Install the front strut nuts on the bolts and tighten to 89 ft. lbs. (120 Nm).

18. Reconnect the wheel speed sensor electrical connector at the wheel speed sensor bracket, if equipped.

19. Install the stabilizer shaft link.

20. Remove the support from the lower control arm.

21. Install the front tire and wheel assembly.

22. Lower the vehicle.

23. Check the front end alignment specifications.

FRONT WHEEL HUB & BEARING

REMOVAL & INSTALLATION

See Figure 195.

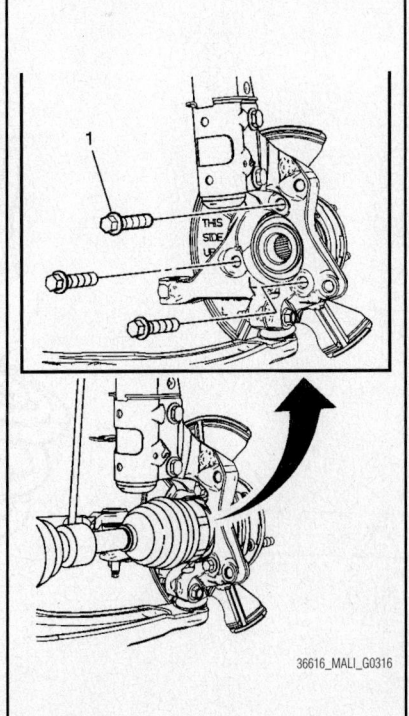

36616_MALI_G0316

Fig. 195 Locating the wheel bearing/hub mounting bolts

1. Raise and support the vehicle.
2. Remove the brake rotor.
3. Disconnect the wheel speed sensor electrical connector, if equipped.
4. Remove the wheel speed sensor electrical connector from the mounting bracket, if needed.
5. Loosen the wheel drive shaft from the wheel bearing/hub.
6. Remove the wheel bearing/hub mounting bolts.
7. Remove the wheel bearing/hub

and backing plate from the steering knuckle.

To install:

8. Position the backing plate and wheel bearing/hub assembly in the steering knuckle.
9. Install the wheel bearing/hub mounting bolts and tighten to 85 ft. lbs. (115 Nm).
10. Reconnect the wheel speed senor electrical connector, if needed.
11. Install the wheel speed sensor

electrical connector on the retaining bracket, if needed.
12. Install the brake rotor.
13. Install the wheel drive shaft retaining nut and washer.
14. Remove the support and lower the vehicle.

ADJUSTMENT

The wheel bearing are sealed at the factory and do not require any adjustment or maintenance.

SUSPENSION

REAR SUSPENSION

COIL SPRING

REMOVAL & INSTALLATION

See Figure 196.

1. Raise and support the vehicle.
2. Remove the rear tire and wheel assembly.
3. Using a suitable jack stand, support the lower control arm.
4. Remove the lower control arm to knuckle bolt and nut.

✳✳ CAUTION

To prevent personal injury and/or component damage, use the proper

tools to support the lower control arm when removing the coil spring. The coil spring is under extreme pressure and can become a projectile should the spring separate from the lower control arm before all of the tension is relieved.

5. Use the jackstand to swing the lower control arm downward with the coil spring attached.
6. Remove the coil spring from the lower control arm.
7. Inspect the coil spring upper and lower insulators for damage, replace as necessary.

To install:

➡Be sure that the coil spring upper and lower insulators are properly seated prior to installation of the coil spring.

8. Position the coil spring onto the lower control arm.
9. Use the jack stand to raise the lower control arm upward into position.
10. Install the lower control arm to knuckle bolt and nut. Tighten to 81 ft. lbs. (110 Nm).
11. Remove the jack stand from under the vehicle.
12. Install the rear tire and wheel assembly.

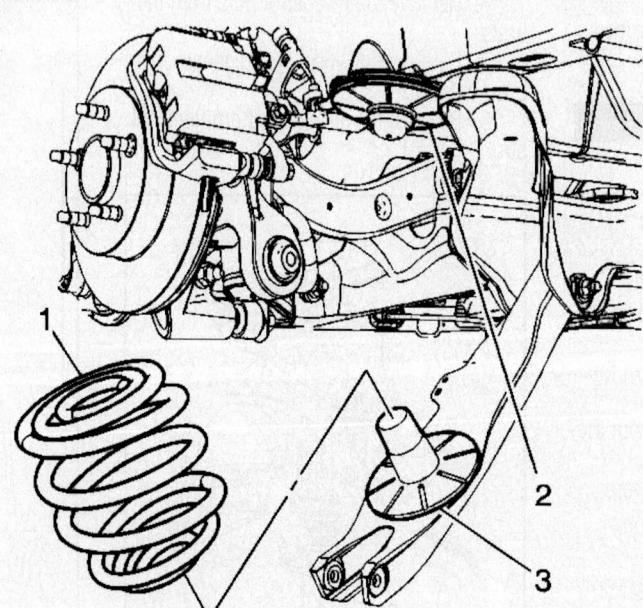

1. Coil spring
2. Rear spring upper insulator
3. Lower spring insulator

36616_MALI_G0317

Fig. 196 Rear spring mounting

13. Lower the vehicle.
14. Check the rear wheel alignment.

CONTROL ARMS/LINKS

REMOVAL & INSTALLATION

Lower

See Figure 197.

1. Raise and suitably support the vehicle.
2. Remove the rear tire and wheel assembly.
3. Remove the coil spring.
4. Remove the lower control arm bolts and nuts, then remove the arm.

To install:

5. Installation is the reverse of removal. Tighten the bolt/nut to 81 ft. lbs. (110 Nm).
6. Inspect the wheel alignment and adjust as needed.

Upper

See Figure 198.

1. Raise and support the vehicle.
2. Remove the rear tire and wheel assembly.
3. Disconnect the wheel speed sensor wiring harness retaining clips and relocate to the side.
4. Remove the rear muffler from the hangers and lower the muffler to gain access to the upper control arm nut and bolt.

➡️Note that the head of the bolt is facing the front of the vehicle and must be installed in the same position.

5. Remove the upper control arm assembly bolt and nut.
6. Remove the upper control arm to knuckle bolt and nut.
7. Remove the upper control arm from the vehicle through the wheelhouse opening.

To install:

8. Install the upper control arm to support assembly bolt. Tighten the upper control arm to support assembly bolt to 44 ft. lbs. (60 Nm). Tighten the upper control arm to knuckle bolt to 81 ft. lbs. (110 Nm) plus an additional 70 degrees.

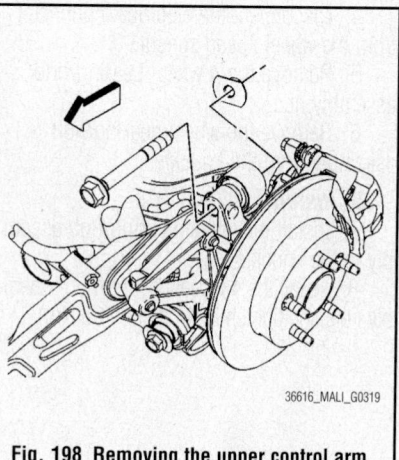

Fig. 198 Removing the upper control arm

9. Reposition the wheel speed sensor wiring harness retaining clips on the upper control arm.
10. Install the rear muffler.
11. Install the rear tire and wheel assembly.
12. Lower the vehicle.

Rear Axle Control Trailing Arm and Rear Suspension Control Arm Bracket

1. Raise and support the vehicle.
2. Remove the tire and wheel assembly.
3. Remove the park brake cable retaining bolt and the bracket from the trailing arm.
4. Using the appropriate tool, remove the park brake cable retaining clip from the trailing arm bracket.
5. Remove the trailing arm bracket mounting bolts.
6. Remove the bolts from the trailing arm to the knuckle.
7. Remove the trailing arm and the bracket from the frame and the knuckle.
8. Remove the bolt and nut from the trailing arm bracket to the trailing arm.

To install:

9. Install the bolt and nut from the trailing arm bracket to the trailing arm.
10. Tighten the trailing arm to bracket nut to 44 ft. lbs. (60 Nm). Using the angle meter rotate the nut an additional 60 degrees.

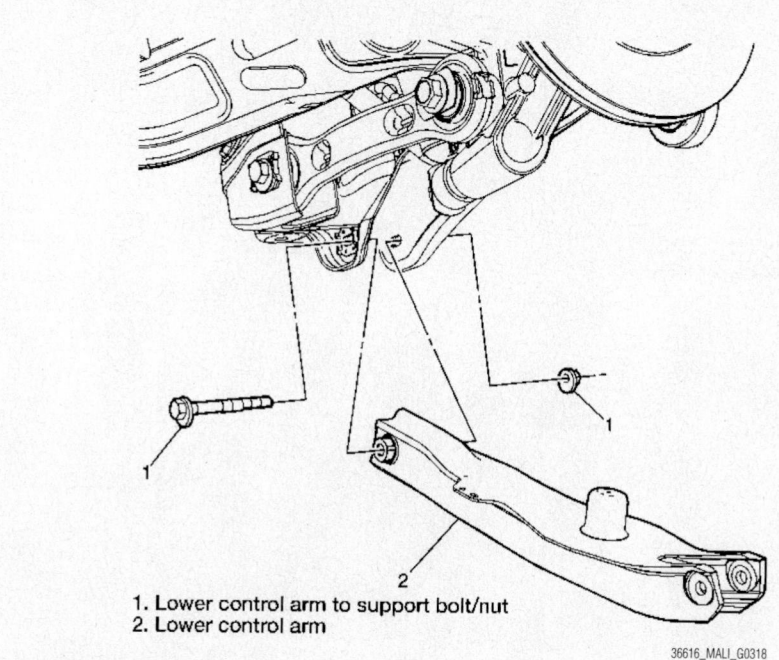

1. Lower control arm to support bolt/nut
2. Lower control arm

Fig. 197 Removing the lower control arm

11. Position the trailing arm and bracket assembly on the knuckle and the frame.

12. Install the bolts from the trailing arm to the knuckle and tighten to 133 ft. lbs. (180 Nm).

13. Install the mounting bolts for the trailing arm bracket. Tighten the mounting bolts to 44 ft. lbs. (60 Nm). Using the angle meter, rotate the bolt an additional 60 degrees.

14. Install the park brake cable retaining clip to the trailing arm bracket.

15. Install the park brake cable retaining bracket and the bolt to the trailing arm. Tighten the mounting bolt to 89 inch lbs. (10 Nm).

16. Install the tire and wheel assembly.

17. Lower the vehicle.

SHOCK ABSORBER

REMOVAL & INSTALLATION

1. Raise and support the vehicle.
2. Remove the tire and wheel.
3. Using a suitable jack stand, raise the rear knuckle to remove spring tension.
4. Remove the lower shock bolt, and the washer from the knuckle.
5. Remove the upper shock nuts.
6. Remove the shock from the vehicle.

To install:

7. Place the shock in the vehicle.
8. Install the shock absorber to body nuts. Tighten to 18 ft. lbs. (25 Nm).
9. Install the shock absorber to knuckle bolt. Tighten to 133 ft. lbs. (180 Nm).
10. Remove the jack stand from the rear knuckle.
11. Install the tire and wheel.
12. Lower the vehicle.

WHEEL HUB & BEARING

REMOVAL & INSTALLATION

See Figure 199.

1. Raise and support the vehicle.
2. Remove the tire and wheel assembly.
3. Remove the brake rotor.
4. Disconnect the electrical connector from the wheel speed sensor.
5. Remove the 4 wheel bearing/hub assembly nuts.
6. Remove the wheel bearing/hub assembly from the knuckle.

To install:

7. Install the wheel bearing/hub assembly to the knuckle.
8. Install the 4 wheel bearing/hub assembly nuts and tighten to 47 ft. lbs. (63 Nm).

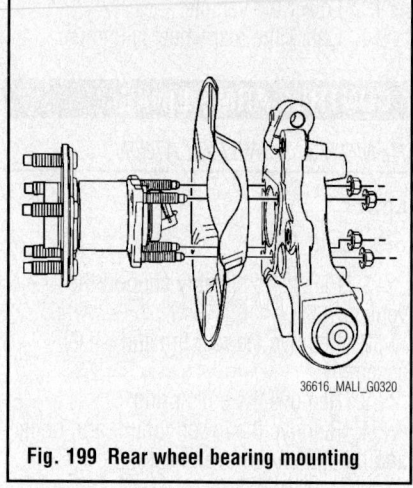

Fig. 199 Rear wheel bearing mounting

9. Install the stabilizer link bolt at the knuckle.
10. Connect the electrical connector to the wheel speed sensor.
11. Install the brake rotor.
12. Install the tire and wheel assembly.
13. Lower the vehicle.

ADJUSTMENT

The wheel bearing are sealed at the factory and do not require any adjustment or maintenance.

CHEVROLET

Malibu Hybrid

SPECIFICATIONS AND MAINTENANCE CHARTS

ENGINE AND VEHICLE IDENTIFICATION

Engine							Model Year	
Code ①	Liters (cc)	Cu. In.	Cyl.	Fuel Sys.	Engine Type	Eng. Mfg.	Code ②	Year
5	2.4 (2189)	146	4	SFI	DOHC	General Motors	8	2008
							9	2009

SFI: Sequential Fuel Injection

MFI: Multi-point Fuel Injection

① 8th position of VIN

② 10th position of VIN

36616_MALH_C0001

GENERAL ENGINE SPECIFICATIONS

Year	Model	Engine Displacement Liters	Engine Series VIN	Net Horsepower @ rpm	Net Torque @ rpm (ft. lbs.)	Bore x Stroke (in.)	Compression Ratio	Oil Pressure @ rpm
2008	Malibu	2.4	5	169@6400	160@4500	3.47x3.86	10.0:1	50-80@1000
2009	Malibu	2.4	5	169@6400	160@4500	3.47x3.86	10.0:1	50-80@1000

36616_MALH_C0002

ENGINE TUNE-UP SPECIFICATIONS

Year	Engine Displacement Liters	Engine VIN	Spark Plug Gap (in.)	Ignition Timing (deg.)	Fuel Pump (psi) ①	Idle Speed (rpm) ②	Valve Clearance In.	Ex.
2008	2.4	5	0.037-0.043	③	50-60	④	HYD	HYD
2009	2.4	5	0.037-0.043	③	50-60	④	HYD	HYD

HYD: Hydraulic

① Pressure measured at idle

② Idle speed measured with manual transmission in Neutral; automatic transmission in D (drive)

③ Engines equipped with Distributorless Ignition System (DIS). Ignition timing is not adjustable

④ Refer to the Vehicle Emission Control Information label

36616_MALH_C0003

CAPACITIES

Year	Model	Engine Displacement Liters	Engine VIN	Engine Oil with Filter (qts.)	Transmission (qts.)	Fuel Tank (gal.)	Cooling System (qts.)
2008	Malibu	2.4	5	5.0	①	16.3	8.1
2009	Malibu	2.4	5	5.0	①	16.3	8.1

NOTE: All capacities are approximate. Add fluid gradually and ensure a proper fluid level is obtained.

① 4 speed: Bottom pan: 7 qts., Overhaul: 9.5 qts.

   6 speed: Fluid change: 5.3-7.4 qts., Overhaul: 7.4-9.5 qts.

36616_MALH_C0005

FLUID SPECIFICATIONS

Year	Model	Engine Displacement Liters	Engine VIN	Engine Oil	Auto. Trans.	Drive Axle	Power Steering Fluid	Brake Master Cylinder	Engine Coolant
2008	Malibu	2.4	5	5W-30	DEXRON® VI	NA	GM PS Fluid	DOT 3	DEX-COOL®
2009	Malibu	2.4	5	5W-30	DEXRON® VI	NA	GM PS Fluid	DOT 3	DEX-COOL®

DOT: Department Of Transpotation

NA: Information not available

36616_MALH_C0004

VALVE SPECIFICATIONS

Year	Engine Displacement Liters	Engine VIN	Seat Angle (deg.)	Face Angle (deg.)	Spring Test Pressure (lbs. @ in.)	Spring Installed Height (in.)	Stem-to-Guide Clearance (in.) Intake	Stem-to-Guide Clearance (in.) Exhaust	Stem Diameter (in.) Intake	Stem Diameter (in.) Exhaust
2008	2.4	5	46	45	① ②	NA	0.0012-0.0022	0.0020-0.0026	0.2344-0.2355	0.2337-0.2343
2009	2.4	5	46	45	① ②	NA	0.0012-0.0022	0.0020-0.0026	0.2344-0.2355	0.2337-0.2343

NA: Not available

① Valve spring load closed: 252-575 N @ 22.5mm

② Valve spring load open: 245-271 N @32mm

③ Valve spring load closed: 321-359 N @ 43.2mm

④ Valve spring load open: 979-1067 N @32mm

⑤ Valve seat angle - seating surface: 45

   Valve seat angle - relief surface: 30

   Valve seat angle - undercut surface: 60

⑥ Valve spring load closed: 247-273 N @ 56-61 lb.

⑦ Valve spring load open: 598-662 N @ 134-149 lb.

36616_MALH_C0006

CAMSHAFT AND BEARING SPECIFICATIONS CHART

All measurements are given in inches.

Year	Engine Displ. Liters	Engine VIN	Journal Dia.	Brg. Oil Clearance	Shaft End-play	Runout	Journal Bore	Lobe Height Intake	Lobe Height Exhaust
2008	2.4	5	1.0604-1.0614	NA	0.0016-0.0057	0.001	NA	NA	NA
2009	2.4	5	1.0604-1.0614	NA	0.0016-0.0057	0.001	NA	NA	NA

NA: Not Available

36616_MALH_C0007

CRANKSHAFT AND CONNECTING ROD SPECIFICATIONS

All measurements are given in inches.

Year	Engine Displacement Liters	Engine VIN	Crankshaft Main Brg. Journal Dia.	Crankshaft Main Brg. Oil Clearance	Crankshaft Shaft End-play	Crankshaft Thrust on No.	Connecting Rod Journal Diameter	Connecting Rod Oil Clearance	Connecting Rod Side Clearance
2008	2.4	5	2.2045-2.2050	0.0012-0.0026	0.0012-0.0150	2	2.0519-2.0525	0.0011-0.0029	0.0028-0.0146
2009	2.4	5	2.2045-2.2050	0.0012-0.0026	0.0012-0.0150	2	2.0519-2.0525	0.0011-0.0029	0.0028-0.0146

36616_MALH_C0008

PISTON AND RING SPECIFICATIONS

All measurements are given in inches.

Year	Engine Displacement Liters	Engine ID/VIN	Piston Clearance	Ring Gap Top Compression	Ring Gap Bottom Compression	Ring Gap Oil Control	Ring Side Clearance Top Compression	Ring Side Clearance Bottom Compression
2008	2.4	5	0.0004-0.0016	0.006-0.012	0.0080-0.0180	0.0060-0.0020	0.0015-0.0031	0.0012-0.0030
2009	2.4	5	0.0004-0.0016	0.006-0.012	0.0080-0.0180	0.0060-0.0020	0.0015-0.0031	0.0012-0.0030

36616_MALH_C0009

TORQUE SPECIFICATIONS
All readings in ft. lbs.

Year	Engine Displacement Liters	Engine VIN	Cylinder Head Bolts	Main Bearing Bolts	Rod Bearing Bolts	Crankshaft Damper Bolts	Flywheel Bolts	Manifold		Spark Plug	Oil Pan Drain Plug
								Intake	Exhaust		
2008	2.4	5	①	②	③	④	⑤	⑥	⑦	15	18
2009	2.4	5	①	②	③	④	⑤	⑥	⑦	15	18

① Step 1: 22 ft. lbs.
Step 2: Plus 155 degrees

② Step 1: 15 ft. lbs.
Step 2: Plus 70 degrees

③ Step 1: 18 ft. lbs.
Step 2: Plus 100 degrees

④ Step 1: 74 ft. lbs.
Step 2: Plus 125 degrees

⑤ Step 1: 39 ft. lbs.
Step 2: Plus 25 degrees

⑥ Intake manifold to head nut and bolt: 89 inch lbs.
Intake manifold to head stud: 53 inch lbs.

⑦ Exhaust manifold to head nut: 124 inch lbs.
Exhaust manifold to head stud: 89 inch lbs.

36616_MALH_C0010

WHEEL ALIGNMENT

Year	Model		Caster		Camber		Toe-in (in.)
			Range (+/-Deg.)	Preferred Setting (Deg.)	Range (+/-Deg.)	Preferred Setting (Deg.)	
2008	Malibu	F	0.75	2.90	0.75	①	0.20+/-0.20
		R	—	—	0.60	-0.8	0.20+/-0.20
2009	Malibu	F	0.75	2.90	0.75	①	0.20+/-0.20
		R	—	—	0.60	-0.8	0.20+/-0.20

① Left: 1.00 degrees
Right: 0.70 degrees

36616_MALH_C0011

TIRE, WHEEL AND BALL JOINT SPECIFICATIONS

Year	Model	OEM Tires		Tire Pressures (psi)		Wheel Size	Ball Joint Inspection	Lug Nut Torque (ft. lbs.)
		Standard	Optional	Front	Rear			
2008	Malibu	①	①	①	①	①	①	100
2009	Malibu	①	①	①	①	①	①	100

OEM: Original Equipment Manufacturer

PSI: Pounds Per Square Inch

① For tire size and information, check the label located inside the glove compartment door.

36616_MALH_C0012

BRAKE SPECIFICATIONS

All measurements in inches unless noted

Year	Model		Brake Disc			Brake Drum Diameter			Minimum Lining Thickness		Brake Caliper	
			Original Thickness	Minimum Thickness	Maximum Runout	Original Inside Diameter	Max. Wear Limit	Maximum Machine Diameter	Front	Rear	Bracket Bolts (ft. lbs.)	Mounting Bolts (ft. lbs.)
2008	Malibu	F	1.023	0.898	0.002	—	—	—	NA	NA	96	26
		R	0.551	0.465	0.002	—	—	—	NA	NA	96	26
2009	Malibu	F	1.023	0.898	0.002	—	—	—	NA	NA	96	26
		R	0.551	0.465	0.002	—	—	—	NA	NA	96	26

36616_MALH_C0013

MAINTENANCE I AND II SERVICE SCHEDULES
Chevrolet Malibu Hybrid

When the CHANGE ENGINE OIL light appears, certain services and inspections are required.
Required services are described as Maintenance I and Maintenance II.
The first service on a vehicle should be Maintenance I, and the second service should be Maintenance II.
Alternate between the 2 thereafter. However, in some cases, Maintenance II may be required more often.

Maintenance I: Use Maintenance I if the CHANGE ENGINE OIL light comes on within 10 months since vehicle was purchased or, if Maintenance II was performed.

Maintenance II: Use Maintenance II if the previous service performed was Maintenance I. Always use Maintenance II whenever the CHANGE ENGINE OIL light comes on 10 months or more since the last service, or, if the CHANGE ENGINE OIL light has not come on at all for one year.

Service	Maintenance	Maintenance II
Change the engine oil and filter. Reset the oil life system.	✓	✓
Visually inspect the vehicle for leaks or damage. A fluid loss in the vehicle system could indicate a problem. Inspected, repair and add fluid to the system if necessary.	✓	✓
Inspect the engine air cleaner filter. If necessary, replace the filter.		✓
Rotate the tires. Inspect the tire inflation pressures and the tire wear.	✓	✓
Visually inspect the brake lines and hoses for proper hook-up, binding, leaks, cracks, chafing, etc. Inspect the disc brake pads for wear and the rotors for surface condition. Inspect the drum brake linings for wear or cracks. Inspect other brake parts, including drums, wheel cylinders, calipers, parking brake, etc. Inspect the parking brake adjustment.	✓	✓
Inspect the engine coolant and the windshield washer fluid levels. Add fluid as needed.	✓	✓
Inspect the suspension and steering components. Inspect the front and rear suspension and the steering system for damaged, loose or missing parts, or signs of wear. Inspect the power steering lines and the hoses for proper hook-up, binding, leaks, cracks.	--	✓
Visually inspect the coolant hoses and replace the hoses if they are cracked, swollen or deteriorated. Inspect all pipes, fittings and clamps; replace with GM parts as needed. To help ensure proper operation, a pressure test of the cooling system and pressure cap and cleaning the outside of the radiator and air conditioning condenser is recommended at least once a year.	--	✓
Inspect the front and rear suspension and the steering system for damaged, loose or missing parts, or signs of wear. Inspect power steering lines and hoses for proper hook-up, binding, leaks, cracks, chafing, etc.	--	✓
Inspect the throttle system for interference or binding and for damaged or missing parts. Replace the parts as needed. Replace any components that have high effort or excessive wear. Do not lubricate the accelerator or the cruise control cables.	--	✓
Replace the passenger compartment air filter.	--	✓

Reset the oil life system:

1. Display OIL LIFE RESET on the DIC.
2. Press and hold the ENTER button for at least one second. An ACKNOWLEDGED display message will appear for three seconds or until the next button is pressed. This will tell you the system has been reset.
3. Turn the key to OFF.
If the Change Oil Soon message comes back on when you start your vehicle, the engine oil life system has not reset, repeat the procedure.

36616_MALH_C0014

ADDITIONAL MAINTENANCE SERVICES
Chevrolet Malibu Hybrid

TO BE SERVICED	TYPE OF SERVICE	VEHICLE MILEAGE INTERVAL (x1000)					
		25	50	75	100	125	150
Air cleaner filter	R		✓		✓		✓
Accessory drive belt	I						✓
Auto. Trans. Fluid ①	R		✓		✓		✓
Cooling system hoses and clamps	S/I						✓
Engine coolant ②	R						✓
Fuel system	I	✓	✓	✓	✓	✓	✓
Exhaust system & heat shields	S/I	✓	✓	✓	✓	✓	✓
Spark plugs	R				✓		

R: Replace   S/I: Inspect and service, if necessary

① Replace if any of the following conditions are met:

Heavy city traffic where the outside temperature regularly reaches 32°C (90°F) or higher

Hilly or mountainous terrain

Frequent trailer towing

Taxi, police or delivery service

Otherwise, change every 100,000 miles

② Drain, flush, and refill cooling system. This service should be performed by the dealer/retailer.

Clean radiator, condenser, pressure cap, and filler neck. Pressure test the cooling system and pressure cap.

36616_MALH_C0015

PRECAUTIONS

Before servicing any vehicle, please be sure to read all of the following precautions, which deal with personal safety, prevention of component damage, and important points to take into consideration when servicing a motor vehicle:

• Never open, service or drain the radiator or cooling system when the engine is hot; serious burns can occur from the steam and hot coolant.

• Observe all applicable safety precautions when working around fuel. Whenever servicing the fuel system, always work in a well-ventilated area. Do not allow fuel spray or vapors to come in contact with a spark, open flame, or excessive heat (a hot drop light, for example). Keep a dry chemical fire extinguisher near the work area. Always keep fuel in a container specifically designed for fuel storage; also, always properly seal fuel containers to avoid the possibility of fire or explosion. Refer to the additional fuel system precautions later in this section.

• Fuel injection systems often remain pressurized, even after the engine has been turned **OFF**. The fuel system pressure must be relieved before disconnecting any fuel lines. Failure to do so may result in fire and/or personal injury.

• Brake fluid often contains polyglycol ethers and polyglycols. Avoid contact with the eyes and wash your hands thoroughly after handling brake fluid. If you do get brake fluid in your eyes, flush your eyes with clean, running water for 15 minutes. If eye irritation persists, or if you have taken brake fluid internally, IMMEDIATELY seek medical assistance.

• The EPA warns that prolonged contact with used engine oil may cause a number of skin disorders, including cancer. You should make every effort to minimize your exposure to used engine oil. Protective gloves should be worn when changing oil. Wash your hands and any other exposed skin areas as soon as possible after exposure to used engine oil. Soap and water, or waterless hand cleaner should be used.

• All new vehicles are now equipped with an air bag system, often referred to as a Supplemental Restraint System (SRS) or Supplemental Inflatable Restraint (SIR) system. The system must be disabled before performing service on or around system components, steering column, instrument panel components, wiring and sensors. Failure to follow safety and disabling procedures could result in accidental air bag deployment, possible personal injury and unnecessary system repairs.

• Always wear safety goggles when working with, or around, the air bag system. When carrying a non-deployed air bag, be sure the bag and trim cover are pointed away from your body. When placing a non-deployed air bag on a work surface, always face the bag and trim cover upward, away from the surface. This will reduce the motion of the module if it is accidentally deployed. Refer to the additional air bag system precautions later in this section.

• Clean, high quality brake fluid from a sealed container is essential to the safe and proper operation of the brake system. You should always buy the correct type of brake fluid for your vehicle. If the brake fluid becomes contaminated, completely flush the system with new fluid. Never reuse any brake fluid. Any brake fluid that is removed from the system should be discarded. Also, do not allow any brake fluid to come in contact with a painted surface; it will damage the paint.

• Never operate the engine without the proper amount and type of engine oil; doing so WILL result in severe engine damage.

• Timing belt maintenance is extremely important. Many models utilize an interference-type, non-freewheeling engine. If the timing belt breaks, the valves in the cylinder head may strike the pistons, causing potentially serious (also time-consuming and expensive) engine damage. Refer to the maintenance interval charts for the recommended replacement interval for the timing belt, and to the timing belt section for belt replacement and inspection.

• Disconnecting the negative battery cable on some vehicles may interfere with the functions of the on-board computer system(s) and may require the computer to undergo a relearning process once the negative battery cable is reconnected.

• When servicing drum brakes, only disassemble and assemble one side at a time, leaving the remaining side intact for reference.

• Only an MVAC-trained, EPA-certified automotive technician should service the air conditioning system or its components.

BRAKES

ANTI-LOCK BRAKE SYSTEM (ABS)

GENERAL INFORMATION

PRECAUTIONS

• Certain components within the ABS system are not intended to be serviced or repaired individually.

• Do not use rubber hoses or other parts not specifically specified for and ABS system. When using repair kits, replace all parts included in the kit. Partial or incorrect repair may lead to functional problems and require the replacement of components.

• Lubricate rubber parts with clean, fresh brake fluid to ease assembly. Do not use shop air to clean parts; damage to rubber components may result.

• Use only DOT 3 brake fluid from an unopened container.

• If any hydraulic component or line is removed or replaced, it may be necessary to bleed the entire system.

• A clean repair area is essential. Always clean the reservoir and cap thoroughly before removing the cap. The slightest amount of dirt in the fluid may plug an orifice and impair the system function. Perform repairs after components have been thoroughly cleaned; use only denatured alcohol to clean components. Do not allow ABS components to come into contact with any substance containing mineral oil; this includes used shop rags.

• The Anti-Lock control unit is a microprocessor similar to other computer units in the vehicle. Ensure that the ignition switch is **OFF** before removing or installing controller harnesses. Avoid static electricity discharge at or near the controller.

• If any arc welding is to be done on the vehicle, the control unit should be unplugged before welding operations begin.

BRAKES

BLEEDING PROCEDURE

1. Place a clean shop cloth beneath the brake master cylinder to catch brake fluid spills.

2. With the ignition OFF and the brakes cool, apply the brakes 3–5 times, or until the brake pedal effort increases significantly, in order to deplete the brake booster power reserve.

3. If you have performed a brake master cylinder bench bleeding on this vehicle, or if you disconnected the brake pipes from the master cylinder, or if you have disconnected the brake pipes from the proportioning valve assembly or the brake modulator assembly, you must perform the following steps to bleed air at the ports of the hydraulic component.

   a. Ensure that the brake master cylinder reservoir is full to the maximum-fill level.

   If removal of the reservoir cap and diaphragm is necessary, clean the outside of the reservoir on and around the cap prior to removal.

   b. With the brake pipes installed securely to the master cylinder, proportioning valve assembly, or brake modulator assembly, loosen and separate one of the brake pipes from the port of the component.

   For the proportioning valve assembly or the brake modulator assembly, perform these steps in the sequence of system flow; begin with the fluid feed pipes from the master cylinder.

   c. Allow a small amount of brake fluid to gravity bleed from the open port of the component.

   d. Connect the brake pipe to the component and tighten securely.

   e. Have an assistant slowly press the brake pedal fully and maintain steady pressure on the pedal.

   f. Loosen the same brake pipe to purge air from the open port of the component.

   g. Tighten the brake pipe, then have the assistant slowly release the brake pedal.

   h. Wait 15 seconds, then repeat the steps until all air is purged from the same port of the component.

   i. With the brake pipe installed securely to the master cylinder, proportioning valve assembly, or brake modulator assembly, after all air has been purged from the first port of the component that was bled, loosen and separate

the next brake pipe from the component, until each of the ports on the component has been bled.

   j. After completing the final component port bleeding procedure, ensure that each of the brake pipe-to-component fittings are properly tightened.

4. Fill the brake master cylinder reservoir. Make sure that the brake master cylinder reservoir remains at least half-full during this bleeding procedure. Add fluid as needed to maintain the proper level.

   Clean the outside of the reservoir on and around the reservoir cap prior to removing the cap and diaphragm.

5. Install a box-end wrench onto the right rear wheel hydraulic circuit bleeder valve.

6. Install a transparent hose over the end of the bleeder valve.

7. Submerge the open end of the transparent hose into a transparent container partially filled with brake fluid from a clean, sealed brake fluid container.

8. Have an assistant slowly press the brake pedal fully and maintain steady pressure on the pedal.

9. Loosen the bleeder valve to purge air from the wheel hydraulic circuit.

10. Tighten the bleeder valve, then have the assistant slowly release the brake pedal.

11. Wait 15 seconds, then repeat steps 8-10 until all air is purged from the same wheel hydraulic circuit.

12. With the right rear wheel hydraulic circuit bleeder valve tightened securely, after all air has been purged from the right rear hydraulic circuit, install a proper box-end wrench onto the left front wheel hydraulic circuit bleeder valve.

13. Install a transparent hose over the end of the bleeder valve and perform the same procedure used to bleed the right rear.

14. Bleed the left rear and front right in the same manner.

15. Fill the brake master cylinder reservoir to the maximum-fill level with brake fluid from a clean, sealed brake fluid container.

16. Slowly press and release the brake pedal. Observe the feel of the brake pedal.

17. If the brake pedal feels spongy, repeat the bleeding procedure again. If the brake pedal still feels spongy after repeating the bleeding procedure check for leaks in the system and pressure test the system to purge trapped air.

18. Turn the ignition key ON, with the engine OFF. Check to see if the brake system warning lamp remains illuminated.

➡**DO NOT allow the vehicle to be driven until it is diagnosed and repaired.**

ANTI-LOCK BRAKE SYSTEM AUTOMATED BLEED PROCEDURE

Perform a manual or pressure bleeding procedure. If the desired brake pedal height results are not achieved, perform the automated bleed procedure below. The procedure cycles the system valves and runs the pump in order to purge the air from the secondary circuits normally closed off during normal base brake operation and bleeding. The automated bleed procedure is recommended when air ingestion is suspected in the secondary circuits, or when the BPMV has been replaced.

❋❋ CAUTION

The Auto Bleed Procedure may be terminated at any time during the process by pressing the EXIT button. No further Scan Tool prompts pertaining to the Auto Bleed procedure will be given. After exiting the bleed procedure, relieve bleed pressure and disconnect bleed equipment per manufacturer's instructions. Failure to properly relieve pressure may result in spilled brake fluid causing damage to components and painted surfaces.

1. Raise the vehicle on a suitable support.

2. Remove all four tire and wheel assemblies.

3. Inspect the brake system for leaks and visual damage.

4. Repair or replace as needed.

5. Lower the vehicle.

6. Prepare the brake bleeding equipment and the vehicle for a pressure bleed of the base hydraulic brake system.

7. Inspect the battery state of charge.

8. Install a scan tool.

9. Turn ON the ignition, with the engine OFF.

10. With the scan tool, perform the following steps:

   a. Select Diagnostics

   b. Select the appropriate vehicle information

   c. Select Chassis

   d. Select Electronic Brake Control Module (EBCM)

   e. Select Special Functions

   f. Select Automated Bleed

✳✳ CAUTION

Dust and dirt accumulating on brake parts during normal use may contain asbestos fibers from production or aftermarket brake linings. Breathing excessive concentrations of asbestos fibers can cause serious bodily harm. Exercise care when servicing brake parts. Do not sand or grind brake lining unless equipment used is designed to contain the dust residue. Do not clean brake parts with compressed air or by dry brushing. Cleaning should be done by dampening the brake components with a fine mist of water, then wiping the brake components clean with a dampened cloth. Dispose of cloth and all residue containing asbestos fibers in an impermeable container with the appropriate label. Follow practices prescribed by the Occupational Safety and Health Administration (OSHA) and the Environmental Protection Agency (EPA) for the handling, processing, and disposing of dust or debris that may contain asbestos fibers.

BRAKE CALIPER

REMOVAL & INSTALLATION

See Figure 1.

1. Empty the master cylinder reservoir until it is half full.
2. Raise and support the vehicle.
3. Remove the tire and wheel assembly.
4. Install and firmly hand tighten 2 wheel nuts to opposite wheel studs in order to retain the rotor to the hub.
5. Install a large C-clamp over the body of the brake caliper with the C-clamp ends against the rear of the caliper body and against the outer brake pad.
6. Tighten the C-clamp until the caliper piston is compressed into the caliper bore enough to allow the caliper to slide past the brake rotor.
7. Remove the C-clamp from the caliper.
8. Remove the brake hose-to-caliper bolt from the brake caliper.
9. Remove the brake hose from the brake caliper.
10. Remove and discard the 2 copper brake hose gaskets. These gaskets may be stuck to the brake caliper and/or the brake hose end.

11. Cap or plug the opening in the brake caliper and the brake hose to prevent fluid loss and contamination.
12. Remove the brake caliper guide pin bolts.
13. Remove the brake caliper from the caliper bracket.
14. Inspect the brake caliper guide pins for freedom of movement, and inspect the condition of the guide pin boots. Move the guide pins inboard and outboard within the bracket bores, without disengaging the slides from the boots, and observe the following:

- Restricted caliper guide pin movement
- Looseness in the brake caliper mounting bracket
- Seized or binding caliper guide pins
- Split or torn boots

15. If any of the conditions listed are found, the brake caliper guide pins and/or boots require replacement.

To install:

16. Install the brake caliper to the brake caliper bracket.
17. Install the brake caliper guide pin bolts and tighten to 26 ft. lbs. (35 Nm).
18. Remove the caps or plugs from the brake caliper opening and the brake hose.

➡ **Do not reuse the copper brake hose gaskets.**

19. Install NEW copper brake hose gaskets to the brake hose-to-caliper bolt and to the brake hose.
20. Install the brake hose and the brake hose-to-brake caliper bolt to the brake caliper. Tighten to 37 ft. lbs. (50 Nm).
21. Bleed the hydraulic brake system.
22. Remove the wheel nuts retaining the brake rotor to the wheel hub.
23. Install the tire and wheel assembly.
24. Lower the vehicle.
25. With the engine OFF, gradually apply the brake pedal to approximately ⅔ of its travel distance.
26. Slowly release the brake pedal.
27. Wait 15 seconds, then repeat the last 2 steps until a firm brake pedal is obtained.
28. Fill the master cylinder reservoir to the proper level.

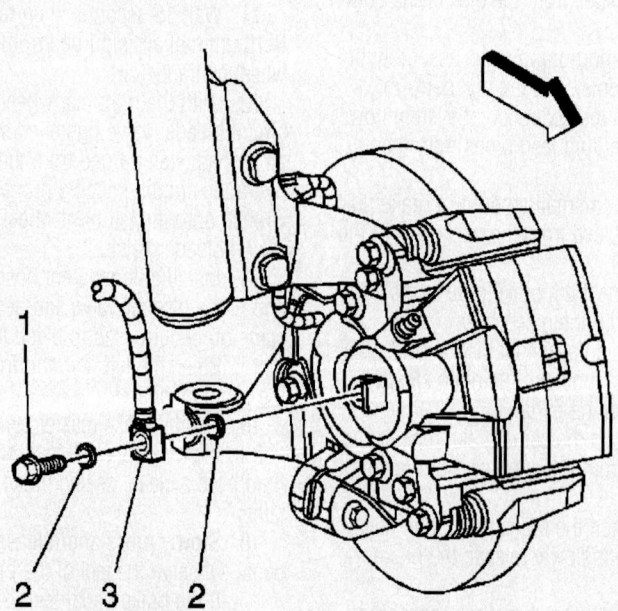

1. **Brake hose-to-caliper bolt**
2. **Copper brake hose gaskets**
3. **Brake hose**

36616_MALI_G0057

Fig. 1 Removing and installing brake hose and gaskets

DISC BRAKE PADS

REMOVAL & INSTALLATION

See Figures 2 through 4.

1. Empty the master cylinder reservoir until it is half full.
2. Raise and support the vehicle.
3. Remove the tire and wheel assembly.
4. Install and firmly hand tighten 2 wheel nuts to opposite wheel studs in order to retain the rotor to the hub.
5. Remove the brake caliper lower guide pin bolt.

➡ **Support the brake caliper with heavy mechanic wire, or equivalent, whenever it is separated from its mount and the hydraulic flexible brake hose is still connected. Failure to support the caliper in this manner will cause the flexible brake hose to bear the weight of the caliper, which may cause damage to the brake hose and in turn may cause a brake fluid leak.**

6. Without disconnecting the hydraulic brake flexible hose, pivot the caliper upward and secure the caliper with heavy mechanics wire, or equivalent.
7. Remove the brake pads from the caliper mounting bracket.
8. Push the disc brake caliper piston into the caliper bore using an old inner disc brake pad and a disc brake piston installation tool.
9. Remove the brake pad retainers from the caliper bracket.
10. Thoroughly clean the brake pad hardware mating surfaces of the caliper bracket, of any debris and corrosion.

11. Inspect the brake caliper guide pins for freedom of movement, and inspect the condition of the guide pin boots. Move the guide pins inboard and outboard within the bracket bores, without disengaging the slides from the boots, and observe for the following:
  - Restricted caliper guide pin movement
  - Looseness in the brake caliper mounting bracket
  - Seized or binding caliper guide pins
  - Split or torn boots
  a. If any of the conditions listed are found, the brake caliper guide pins and/or boots require replacement.

To install:

12. Make sure the brake pad hardware mating surfaces are clean.
13. Install the brake pad retainers to the brake caliper bracket.

➡ **The wear sensor equipped disc brake pad must be mounted inboard of the rotor with the leading edge of the sensor facing the brake rotor during forward wheel rotation, or at the top of the pad when installed in vehicle position.**

14. Install the brake pads to the caliper bracket.
15. Remove the support, and rotate the brake caliper into position over the disc brake pads and to the caliper mounting bracket.
16. Install the lower brake caliper guide pin bolt. Tighten to 26 ft. lbs. (35 Nm).
17. Remove the wheel nuts retaining the brake rotor to the hub.
18. Install the tire and wheel assembly. Lower the vehicle.

19. With the engine OFF, gradually apply the brake pedal to approximately 2/3 of its travel distance.
20. Slowly release the brake pedal.
21. Wait 15 seconds, then repeat the last 2 steps until a firm brake pedal is obtained
22. Fill the master cylinder reservoir to the proper level.
23. Burnish the brake pad and rotor.

✱✱ CAUTION

Road test a vehicle under safe conditions and while obeying all traffic laws. Do not attempt any maneuvers that could jeopardize vehicle control. Failure to adhere to these precautions could lead to serious personal injury and vehicle damage.

Burnishing the brake pads and brake rotors is necessary in order to ensure that the braking surfaces are properly prepared after service has been performed on the disc brake system.

This procedure should be performed whenever the disc brake rotors have been refinished or replaced, and/or whenever the disc brake pads have been replaced.
  a. Select a smooth road with little or no traffic.
  b. Accelerate the vehicle to 30 mph (48 km/h).

➡ **Use care to avoid overheating the brakes while performing this step.**

  c. Using moderate to firm pressure, apply the brakes to bring the vehicle to a stop. Do not allow the brakes to lock.
  d. Repeat the previous 2 steps until approximately 20 stops have been completed. Allow sufficient cooling periods between stops in order to properly burnish the brake pads and rotors.

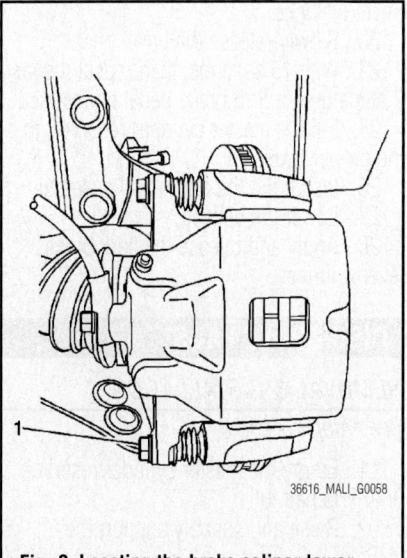

1

36616_MALI_G0058

Fig. 2 Locating the brake caliper lower guide pin bolt

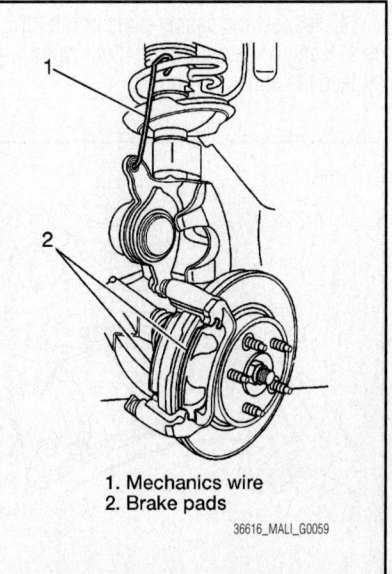

1. Mechanics wire
2. Brake pads

36616_MALI_G0059

Fig. 3 Removing brake pads

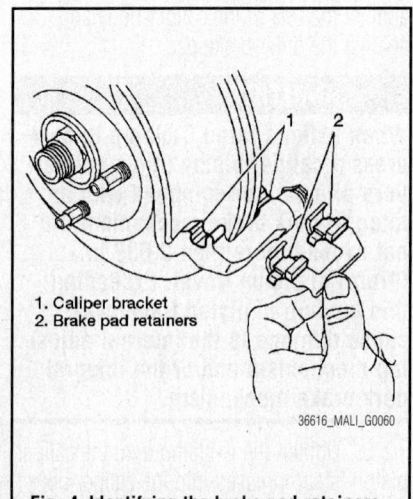

1. Caliper bracket
2. Brake pad retainers

36616_MALI_G0060

Fig. 4 Identifying the brake pad retainers

BRAKES

REAR DISC BRAKES

✳✳ CAUTION

Dust and dirt accumulating on brake parts during normal use may contain asbestos fibers from production or aftermarket brake linings. Breathing excessive concentrations of asbestos fibers can cause serious bodily harm. Exercise care when servicing brake parts. Do not sand or grind brake lining unless equipment used is designed to contain the dust residue. Do not clean brake parts with compressed air or by dry brushing. Cleaning should be done by dampening the brake components with a fine mist of water, then wiping the brake components clean with a dampened cloth. Dispose of cloth and all residue containing asbestos fibers in an impermeable container with the appropriate label. Follow practices prescribed by the Occupational Safety and Health Administration (OSHA) and the Environmental Protection Agency (EPA) for the handling, processing, and disposing of dust or debris that may contain asbestos fibers.

BRAKE CALIPER

REMOVAL & INSTALLATION

See Figures 5 and 6.

1. Empty the master cylinder reservoir until it is half full.
2. Raise and suitably support the vehicle.
3. Remove the tire and wheel assembly.
4. Install a large C-clamp over the body of the brake caliper with the C-clamp ends against the rear of the caliper body and against the outer brake pad.

✳✳ CAUTION

When using a large C-clamp to compress a caliper piston into a caliper bore of a caliper equipped with an integral park brake mechanism, do not exceed more than 0.039 in. (1mm) of piston travel. Exceeding this amount of piston travel will cause damage to the internal adjusting mechanism and/or the integral park brake mechanism.

5. Tighten the C-clamp until the caliper piston is compressed into the caliper bore enough to allow the caliper to slide past the

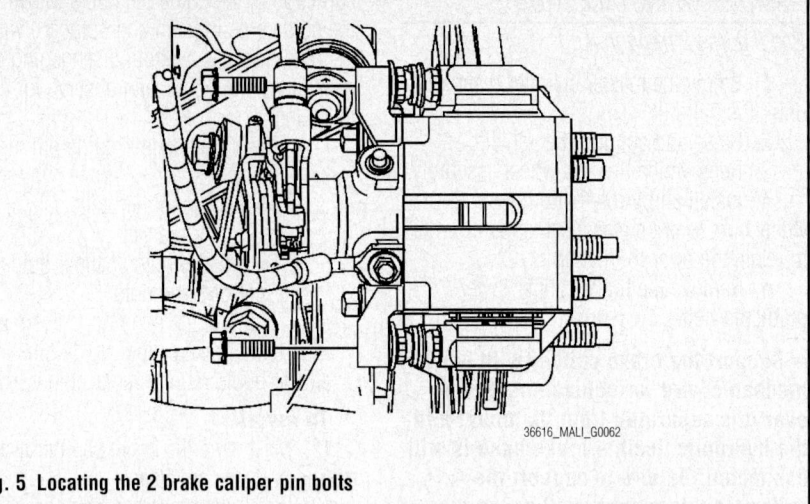

Fig. 5 Locating the 2 brake caliper pin bolts

brake rotor. Do not exceed 0.039 in. (1mm) of caliper piston travel.

6. Remove the C-clamp from the caliper.
7. Remove the brake hose to caliper bolt from the brake caliper.
8. Remove the brake hose from the brake caliper.
9. Remove and discard the 2 copper brake hose gaskets. These gaskets may be stuck to the brake caliper and/or the brake hose end.
10. Cap or plug the opening in the brake caliper and the brake hose to prevent fluid loss and contamination.
11. Remove the 2 brake caliper pin bolts.
12. Remove the park brake cable from the caliper.
13. Remove the brake caliper from the brake caliper bracket.

To install:

14. Inspect the caliper slide boots for cuts, tears, or deterioration. If damaged, replace the slides and boots.

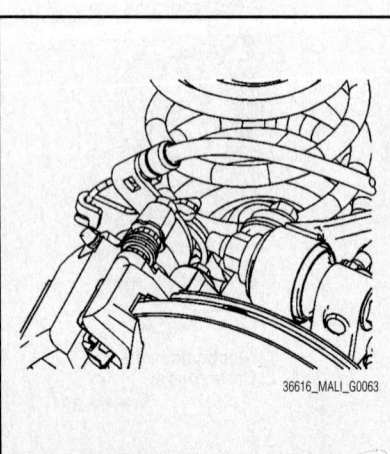

Fig. 6 Identifying the park brake cable

15. Install the brake caliper to the brake caliper bracket.
16. Install the 2 brake caliper pin bolts. Tighten the bolts to 26 ft. lbs. (35 Nm).
17. Install the park brake cable to the caliper.
18. Remove the caps or plugs from the brake caliper opening and the brake hose.

➡ DO NOT reuse the copper brake hose gaskets.

19. Install NEW copper brake hose gaskets to the brake hose-to-caliper bolt and to the brake hose.
20. Install the brake hose and the brake hose-to-caliper bolt to the brake caliper. Tighten the bolts to 37 ft. lbs. (50 Nm).
21. Bleed the hydraulic brake system.
22. With the engine OFF, gradually apply the brake pedal to approximately 2/3 of its travel distance.
23. Slowly release the brake pedal.
24. Wait 15 seconds, then repeat the last 2 steps until a firm brake pedal is obtained.
25. Fill the master cylinder reservoir to the proper level.
26. Install the tire and wheel assembly.
27. Lower the vehicle.
28. Apply and release the park brake lever 4 times.

DISC BRAKE PADS

REMOVAL & INSTALLATION

See Figures 7 and 8.

1. Empty the master cylinder reservoir until it is half full.
2. Raise and suitably support the vehicle.
3. Remove the tire and wheel assembly.

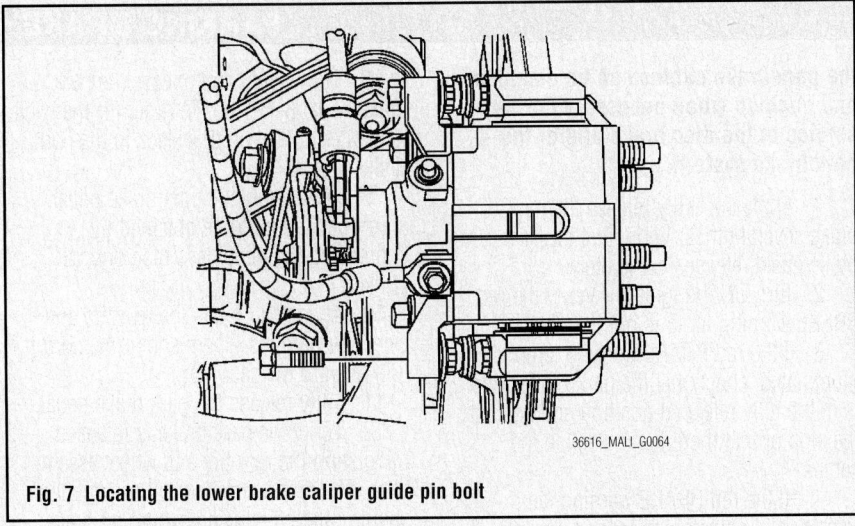

Fig. 7 Locating the lower brake caliper guide pin bolt

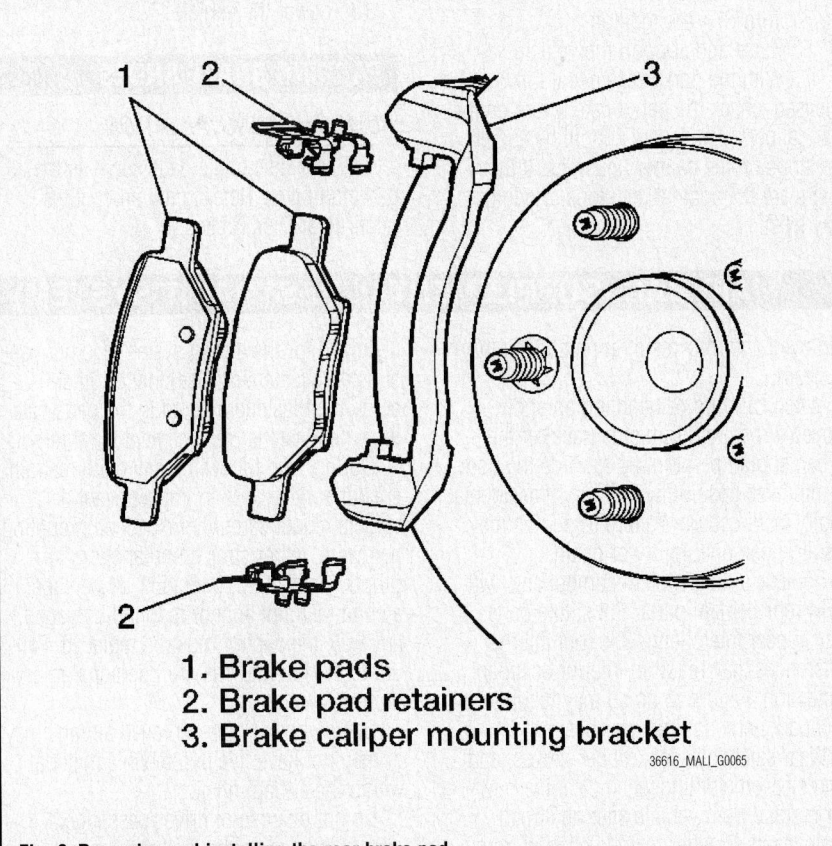

1. Brake pads
2. Brake pad retainers
3. Brake caliper mounting bracket

Fig. 8 Removing and installing the rear brake pad

4. Install a large C-clamp over the body of the brake caliper with the C-clamp ends against the rear of the caliper body and against the outer brake pad. Do not exceed 0.039 in. (1mm) of caliper piston travel.

☆☆ CAUTION

When using a large C-clamp to compress a caliper piston into a caliper bore of a caliper equipped with an integral park brake mechanism, do
not exceed more than 0.039 in. (1mm) of piston travel. Exceeding this amount of piston travel will cause damage to the internal adjusting mechanism and/or the integral park brake mechanism.

5. Tighten the C-clamp until the caliper piston is compressed into the caliper bore enough to allow the caliper to slide past the brake rotor.

6. Remove the C-clamp from the caliper.

7. Remove the lower brake caliper guide pin bolt.

➡Support the brake caliper with heavy mechanic wire, or equivalent, whenever it is separated from its mount and the hydraulic flexible brake hose is still connected. Failure to support the caliper in this manner will cause the flexible brake hose to bear the weight of the caliper, which may cause damage to the brake hose and in turn may cause a brake fluid leak.

8. Pivot the brake caliper upward from the caliper bracket and support the caliper out of the way with heavy mechanic's wire; ensure that there is no tension on the hydraulic brake flexible hose. Do NOT disconnect the hydraulic brake flexible hose from the caliper.

9. Remove the brake pads from the brake caliper mounting bracket.

10. Remove and the brake pad retainers from the brake caliper mounting bracket.

To install:

➡Do not attempt to clean away any corrosion. If damaged or corroded replace the necessary components.

11. Inspect the brake caliper piston boot for deterioration, replace if damaged.

12. Use a piston installation tool in order to twist the brake caliper piston into the brake caliper bore.

13. Install the brake pad retainers to the brake caliper mounting bracket.

14. Install the brake pads to the brake caliper mounting bracket.

15. Pivot the brake caliper downward, over the brake pads and into the caliper bracket.

16. Install the brake caliper guide pin bolt to the brake caliper guide pin. Tighten the bolts to 26 ft. lbs. (35 Nm).

17. Install the tire and wheel assembly.

18. Lower the vehicle.

19. With the engine OFF, gradually apply the brake pedal to approximately ⅔ of its travel distance.

20. Slowly release the brake pedal.

21. Wait 15 seconds, then repeat the last 2 steps until a firm brake pedal is obtained

22. Fill the master cylinder reservoir to the proper level.

23. Apply and release the park brake lever 4 times.

24. Burnish the pads and rotors.

BRAKES

PARKING BRAKE

Park brake application is completely independent of the hydraulic brake system. The park brake system is a mechanical system which operates the rear disc brakes through the calipers. The system is activated by depressing the park brake pedal, which applies the rear disc brakes via cables. When the park brake is set and the ignition switch is on, the BRAKE warning lamp on the instrument panel will be on. The park brake is released by pushing the pedal down until a click is heard and then releasing. The pedal will click again and the BRAKE lamp in the instrument panel will go out when the park brake system is fully released.

PARKING BRAKE CABLES

ADJUSTMENT

➡**This vehicle utilizes a self-tensioning, or self-adjusting park brake cable system. The park brake system does not require adjustment under normal operating conditions. The tension on**

the park brake cables can be disabled and enabled when necessary during service of the disc brake and/or the park brake system.

1. Apply and fully release the park brake several times. Verify that the park brake pedal releases completely.
2. Turn ON the ignition. Verify the red BRAKE warning lamp is not illuminated.
3. If the red BRAKE warning lamp is illuminated, check that the park brake pedal is in the fully released position and against the stop or that there is no slack in the cables.
4. If the red BRAKE warning lamp remained illuminated and there were no other visible causes.
5. Turn OFF the ignition.
6. Raise and support the vehicle.
7. With the park brake pedal fully released, check the park brake levers on the rear calipers. The levers should be against the stops on the caliper housings. If the levers are not against the stops, binding may exist.

8. Fully apply and release the park brake pedal 3–5 times in order for the cable tensioner to take up any slack in the park brake cables.
9. Fully apply the park brake pedal, a firm pedal should be obtained by depressing the pedal less than one full stroke.
10. Attempt to rotate the rear tire and wheel assemblies. There should be no rotation forward or rearward.
11. Fully release the park brake pedal.
12. Verify the park brake is released by rotating the rear tire and wheel assemblies. The rear tire and wheel assemblies should rotate freely and exhibit no brake drag.
13. Lower the vehicle.

PARKING BRAKE SHOES

REMOVAL & INSTALLATION

The rear disc brake pads serve as the parking brakes. Refer to the procedures under Rear Disc Brakes.

CHASSIS ELECTRICAL

AIR BAG (SUPPLEMENTAL RESTRAINT SYSTEM)

GENERAL INFORMATION

❊ CAUTION

Some vehicles are equipped with an air bag system. The system must be disarmed before performing service on, or around, system components, the steering column, instrument panel components, wiring and sensors. Failure to follow the safety precautions and the disarming procedure could result in accidental air bag deployment, possible injury and unnecessary system repairs.

SERVICE PRECAUTIONS

Disconnect and isolate the battery negative cable before beginning any airbag system component diagnosis, testing, removal, or installation procedures. Allow system capacitor to discharge for two minutes before beginning any component service. This will disable the airbag system. Failure to disable the airbag system may result in accidental airbag deployment, personal injury, or death.

Do not place an intact undeployed airbag face down on a solid surface. The airbag will propel into the air if accidentally

deployed and may result in personal injury or death.

When carrying or handling an undeployed airbag, the trim side (face) of the airbag should be pointing towards the body to minimize possibility of injury if accidental deployment occurs. Failure to do this may result in personal injury or death.

Replace airbag system components with OEM replacement parts. Substitute parts may appear interchangeable, but internal differences may result in inferior occupant protection. Failure to do so may result in occupant personal injury or death.

Wear safety glasses, rubber gloves, and long sleeved clothing when cleaning powder residue from vehicle after an airbag deployment. Powder residue emitted from a deployed airbag can cause skin irritation. Flush affected area with cool water if irritation is experienced. If nasal or throat irritation is experienced, exit the vehicle for fresh air until the irritation ceases. If irritation continues, see a physician.

Do not use a replacement airbag that is not in the original packaging. This may result in improper deployment, personal injury, or death.

The factory installed fasteners, screws and bolts used to fasten airbag components have a special coating and are specifically

designed for the airbag system. Do not use substitute fasteners. Use only original equipment fasteners listed in the parts catalog when fastener replacement is required.

During, and following, any child restraint anchor service, due to impact event or vehicle repair, carefully inspect all mounting hardware, tether straps, and anchors for proper installation, operation, or damage. If a child restraint anchor is found damaged in any way, the anchor must be replaced. Failure to do this may result in personal injury or death.

Deployed and non-deployed airbags may or may not have live pyrotechnic material within the airbag inflator.

Do not dispose of driver/passenger/curtain airbags or seat belt tensioners unless you are sure of complete deployment. Refer to the Hazardous Substance Control System for proper disposal.

Dispose of deployed airbags and tensioners consistent with state, provincial, local, and federal regulations.

After any airbag component testing or service, do not connect the battery negative cable. Personal injury or death may result if the system test is not performed first.

If the vehicle is equipped with the Occupant Classification System (OCS), do not connect the battery negative cable before performing the OCS Verification Test using the scan tool and the appropriate diagnostic information. Personal injury or death may result if the system test is not performed properly.

Never replace both the Occupant Restraint Controller (ORC) and the Occupant Classification Module (OCM) at the same time. If both require replacement, replace one, then perform the Airbag System test before replacing the other.

Both the ORC and the OCM store Occupant Classification System (OCS) calibration data, which they transfer to one another when one of them is replaced. If both are replaced at the same time, an irreversible fault will be set in both modules and the OCS may malfunction and cause personal injury or death.

If equipped with OCS, the Seat Weight Sensor is a sensitive, calibrated unit and must be handled carefully. Do not drop or handle roughly. If dropped or damaged, replace with another sensor. Failure to

do so may result in occupant injury or death.

If equipped with OCS, the front passenger seat must be handled carefully as well. When removing the seat, be careful when setting on floor not to drop. If dropped, the sensor may be inoperative, could result in occupant injury, or possibly death.

If equipped with OCS, when the passenger front seat is on the floor, no one should sit in the front passenger seat. This uneven force may damage the sensing ability of the seat weight sensors. If sat on and damaged, the sensor may be inoperative, could result in occupant injury, or possibly death.

DISARMING THE SYSTEM

1. Turn the steering wheel so that the vehicles wheels are pointing straight ahead.
2. Place the ignition in the OFF position.

➡**The SDM may have more than one fused power input. To ensure there is no unwanted SIR deployment, personal**

injury, or unnecessary SIR system repairs, remove all fuses supplying power to the SDM. With all SDM fuses removed and the ignition switch in the ON position, the AIR BAG warning indicator illuminates. This is normal operation, and does not indicate a SIR system malfunction.

3. Locate and remove the fuse(s) supplying power to the SDM. Or you may disconnect the negative battery cable from the battery.
4. Wait 1 minute before working on the system.

ARMING THE SYSTEM

1. Place the ignition in the OFF position.
2. Install the fuse(s) or reconnect the negative battery cable supplying power to the SDM.
3. Turn the ignition switch to the ON position. The AIR BAG indicator will flash then turn OFF.

DRIVE TRAIN

AUTOMATIC TRANSAXLE ASSEMBLY

REMOVAL & INSTALLATION

4T45-E Transaxle

See Figures 9 and 10.

1. Remove the air cleaner outlet duct.
2. Disconnect the negative battery cable. Refer
3. Disconnect the transaxle wiring harness from the transaxle and the Park Neutral Position (PNP) switch.
4. Remove the shift cable bracket front bolt and shift cable from the lever.
5. Remove the transmission wiring harness from the retainer on the transmission.
6. Disconnect bank 2, Oxygen Sensor (O2S) sensor 1 electrical connector.
7. Remove the left exhaust manifold heat shield.
8. Remove the exhaust manifold heat shield.
9. Remove the front exhaust pipe nuts.
10. Remove the upper transmission to engine bolts and stud.
11. Install the engine support fixture.
12. Support the radiator and condenser from above using the condenser tabs on each side.
13. Raise the vehicle.
14. Remove the front wheels and tires.
15. Disconnect the bank 2, O2S sensor 2 electrical connector.

16. Remove the left catalytic converter to right catalytic converter nuts.
17. Remove the left catalytic converter.
18. Remove the steering gear intermediate shaft.

➡**It is only necessary to remove the control arms from the frame if the frame is being replaced.**

19. Remove the frame as follows:

a. Support the radiator and condenser from above.
b. Raise the vehicle on a hoist.
20. Remove the front fender liner.
a. Remove the engine splash shield.
b. Remove the lower ball joints from the steering knuckles.
c. Remove the tie rod ends from the steering knuckles.
d. Remove both stabilizer links from the stabilizer bar.

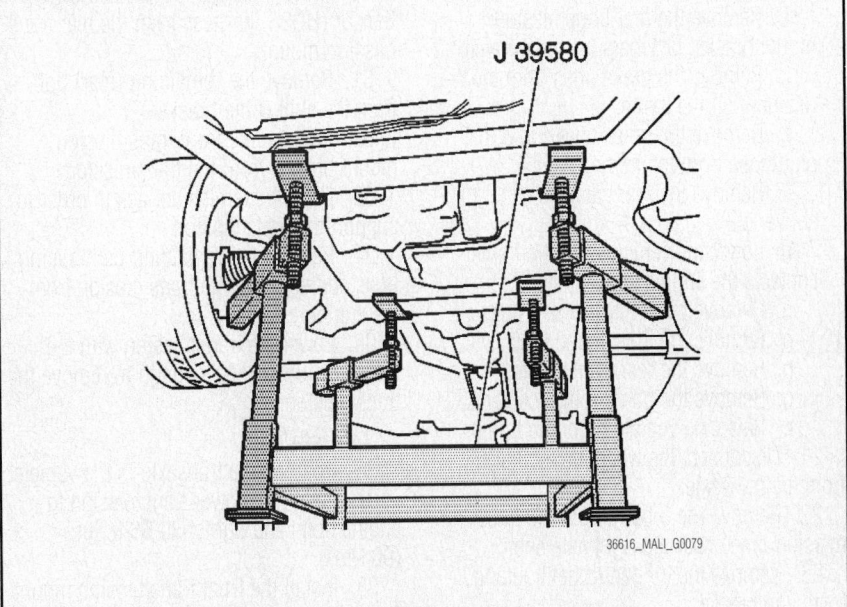

J 39580

36616_MALI_G0079

Fig. 9 Lower the vehicle until the frame contacts the engine support stand

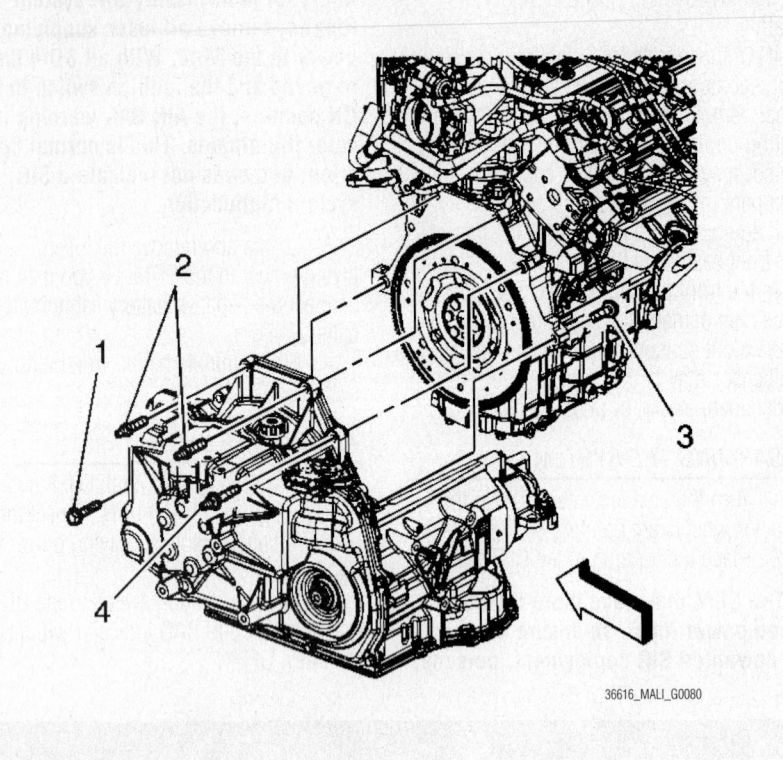

Fig. 10 Removing the remaining bellhousing bolts (1, 3)

36616_MALI_G0080

e. Remove the power steering gear mounting bolts and secure the gear out of the way using mechanic's wire, being sure not to overextend the intermediate shaft.

f. Remove the engine mount fasteners from the frame.

g. Remove the front transmission mount bolt from the frame.

h. Remove the left transmission mount fasteners from the frame.

i. Remove the rear transmission mount bracket fasteners from the frame.

j. Remove the brake lines from the retainers on the frame.

k. Remove the power steering outlet pipe/hose from the frame. .

l. Remove the rear catalytic converter.

m. Lower the vehicle until the frame contacts the engine support stand.

n. Remove the reinforcement bolts.

o. Remove the front frame bolts.

p. Remove the rear frame bolts.

q. Remove the frame reinforcements.

r. Raise the vehicle off of the frame.

21. Disconnect the wheel drive shafts from the transaxle.

22. Remove the 3 bolts from the transmission brace near the right axle shaft.

23. Remove the oil pan to bellhousing bolts and bracket.

24. Remove the flywheel inspection cover.

25. Remove the starter.

26. Mark the relationship of the flywheel to the torque converter for reassembly.

27. Remove the torque converter to flywheel bolts.

28. Remove the transmission oil cooler lines by removing the nut holding the bracket to the transaxle case.

29. Disconnect the Vehicle Speed Sensor (VSS) wiring harness from the sensor.

30. Disconnect the rear Heated Oxygen Sensor (HO2S) harness from the rear transmission mount.

31. Remove the remaining (rear) bolt from the shift cable bracket.

32. Remove the front transmission mount bracket from the transmission.

33. Use a transmission jack in order to support the transmission.

34. Remove the remaining bellhousing bolts and separate the transmission from the engine.

35. Lower the transmission with the transmission jack far enough to remove the transmission.

To install:

36. Position the transaxle in the vehicle.

37. Install the lower transmission to engine bolts and tighten to 66 ft. lbs. (90 Nm).

38. Install the front transmission mount bracket to the transmission.

39. Install the wheel drive shafts to the transaxle.

40. Connect the wiring harness to the VSS.

41. Install the torque converter to flywheel bolts and tighten to 46 ft. lbs. (62 Nm).

42. Install the starter.

43. Install the flywheel inspection cover bolts and tighten to 89 inch lbs. (10 Nm).

44. Connect the transaxle oil cooler pipes to the transaxle. Tighten the pipes to 70 inch lbs. (8 Nm).

45. Install the oil pan to bellhousing bracket and bolts. Tighten the bolts to 53 ft. lbs. (72 Nm).

46. Install the 3 bolts to the transmission brace at the final drive area and tighten.

47. Remove the transmission jack.

48. Install the frame as follows:

a. Lower the vehicle on to the frame.

b. Install the frame reinforcements.

c. Install the front frame bolts and hand tighten only.

d. Install the reinforcement bolts and hand tighten only.

e. Tighten the rear frame bolts. Tighten to 74 ft. lbs. (100 Nm) , plus an additional 90 degrees.

f. Tighten the front frame bolts. Tighten to 74 ft. lbs. (100 Nm) , plus an additional 90 degrees.

g. Install the reinforcement bolts. Tighten to 74 ft. lbs. (100 Nm).

h. Raise the vehicle.

i. Install the power steering outlet pipe/hose to the frame.

j. Install the brake lines to the retainers on the frame.

k. Install the rear transmission mount bracket fasteners. Tighten the transaxle mount to transmission bolts to 37 ft. lbs. (50 Nm) and the transaxle to mount bracket through bolt to 66 ft. lbs. (90 Nm).

l. Install the left transmission mount fasteners to the frame. Tighten the transmission mount nuts to 37 ft. lb. (50 Nm).

m. Install the front transmission mount bracket bolt. Tighten the transaxle mount to transmission bolts to 66 ft. lbs. (90 Nm) and the transaxle to mount bracket through bolt to 66 ft. lbs. (90 Nm).

n. Install the engine mount fasteners to the frame. Tighten the nuts/bolts to 37 ft. lbs. (50 Nm).

o. Install the power steering gear mounting fasteners.

p. Install both stabilizer links to the stabilizer bar. Tighten to 48 ft. lbs. (65 Nm) plus an additional 180 degrees.

q. Install the tie rod ends to the steering knuckles.

r. Install the lower ball joints to the steering knuckles. Tighten the ball stud to steering knuckle pinch nut to 37 ft. lbs. (50 Nm). Reverse the nut ¾ of a turn. Tighten to 37 ft. lbs. (50 Nm) plus an additional 60 degrees.

s. Install the rear catalytic converter.

t. Install the front fender liner.

u. Install the engine splash shield.

v. Lower the vehicle.

w. Remove the temporary radiator and condenser support.

x. Remove the engine support fixture.

49. Install the engine splash shields.

50. Install the front wheels and tires.

51. Lower the vehicle.

52. Remove the radiator and condenser support and the engine support fixture.

53. Install the upper transmission to engine bolts and stud and tighten to 66 ft. lbs. (90 Nm).

54. Install the shift cable bracket and shift cable to the lever.

55. Install the remaining components in the reverse order of removal.

56. Connect bank 2, O2 sensor 2 electrical connector.

57. Connect the negative battery cable.

58. Add automatic transmission fluid (ATF) and verify the proper fluid level of the transaxle.

➡️ **It is recommended that Transmission Adaptive Pressure (TAP) information be reset. Reset the TAP values using a scan tool will erase all learned values in all cells. As a result, the ECM, PCM, or TCM will need to relearn TAP values. Transmission performance may be affected as new TAP values are learned.**

59. Reset the TAP values by selecting the following:
- Scan tool
- Special functions
- Transmission output controls
- Reset transmission adapts

60. Road test the vehicle.

6T40/6T45

See Figures 11 through 14.

1. Remove the battery tray.

2. Remove the transmission range select lever cable and bracket.

3. Drain the transmission fluid.

4. Disconnect the control valve body Transmission Control Module (TCM) electrical connector then unclip the connector from the transmission.

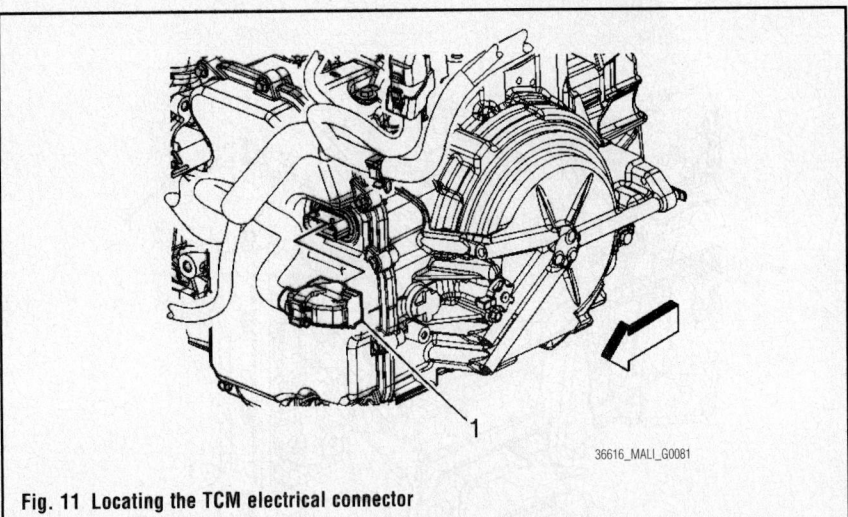

Fig. 11 Locating the TCM electrical connector

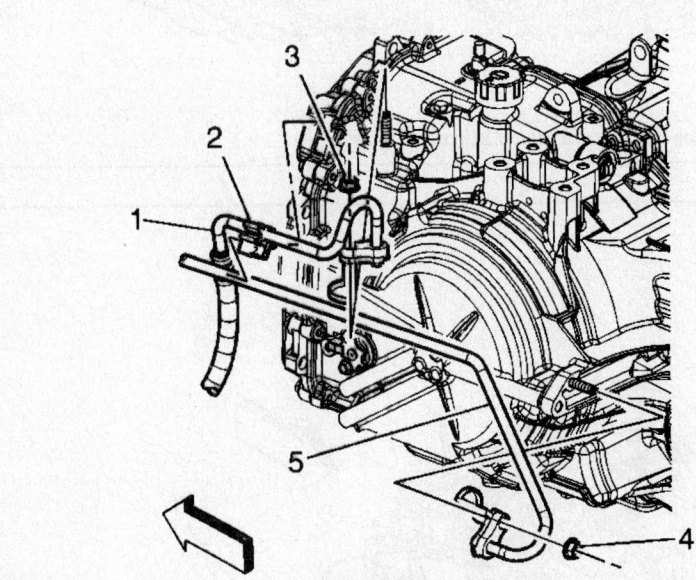

1. Oil cooler inlet
2. Retainer
3. Inlet hose nut
4. Outlet hose nut
5. Outlet hose

Fig. 12 Disconnecting the transmission fluid cooler lines

5. Disconnect the control valve body Transmission Control Module (TCM) electrical connector then unclip the connector from the transmission.

6. Remove the oil cooler inlet and outlet hoses from the retainer on the control valve body cover.

7. Remove the transmission fluid cooler inlet hose nut from the transmission.

8. Remove the transmission fluid cooler inlet hose from the transmission.

9. Remove the transmission fluid cooler outlet hose nut from the transmission.

10. Remove the transmission fluid cooler outlet hose from the transmission.

11. Plug and/or cap the hose and transmission to prevent contamination.

12. Remove the upper transmission to engine bolts.

13. Remove the frame.

14. Disconnect the wheel drive shafts from the transmission.

15. Remove the intermediate drive shaft.

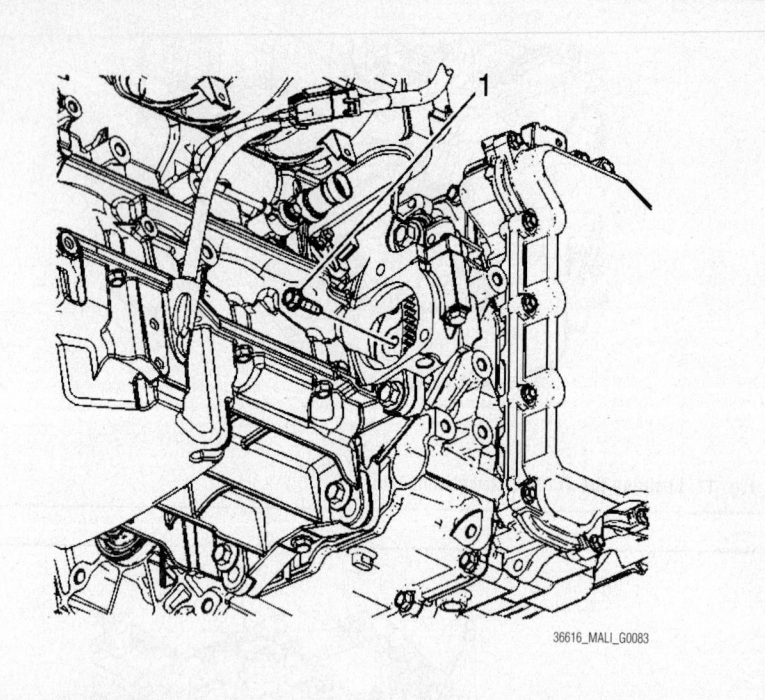

Fig. 13 Locating the torque converter to flywheel bolts

36616_MALI_G0083

36616_MALI_G0084

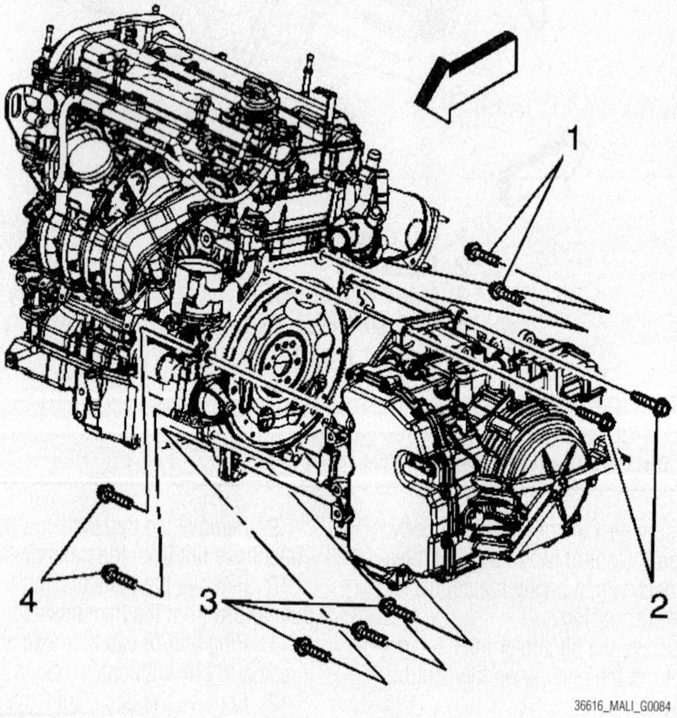

Fig. 14 Removing the remaining transmission fasteners (1, 3, 4)

16. Remove the rear transmission mount from the transmission.

17. Remove the front transmission mount from the transmission.

18. Remove the starter.

19. Mark the relationship of the flywheel to the torque converter for reassembly.

20. Remove the torque converter to flywheel bolts.

21. Lower the vehicle.

22. Remove the 3 left transmission mount bolts from the transmission.

23. Lower the transmission side with the support fixture to allow clearance for removal.

24. Unclip the engine wiring harness from the transmission.

25. Raise the vehicle.

26. Use a transmission jack in order to support the transmission.

27. Remove the remaining transmission fasteners.

➡ **Insure the torque converter remains securely in place on the transmission input shaft while separating and removing the transmission.**

28. Separate the transmission from the engine.

29. Lower the transmission with the transmission jack far enough to remove the transmission.

To install:

30. Raise the transmission with the transmission jack and position the transmission to the engine.

31. Install the transmission bolts (1, 3, 4) and tighten to 55 ft. lbs. (75 Nm).

32. Remove the transmission jack.

➡ **If reusing the torque converter bolts, clean the threads and apply LOCTITE®242, GM P/N 36616382 (Canadian P/N 10953489) or equivalent to the threads prior to installation.**

33. Install the torque converter to flywheel bolts and tighten to 46 ft. lbs. (62 Nm).

34. Install the starter.

35. Install the front transmission mount to the transmission.

36. Install the rear transmission mount to the transmission.

37. Install the intermediate drive shaft.

38. Install the wheel drive shafts to the transmission.

39. Install the frame.

40. Install the upper transmission to engine bolts and tighten to 55 ft. lbs. (75 Nm).

41. Install the transmission fluid cooler outlet hose to the transmission.

42. Install the transmission fluid cooler

outlet hose retainer nut and tighten to 16 ft. lbs. (22 Nm).

43. Install the transmission fluid cooler inlet hose to the transmission.

44. Install the transmission fluid cooler inlet hose retainer nut.

45. Install the oil cooler inlet and outlet hoses to the retainer on the control valve body cover.

46. Connect the control valve body TCM electrical connector.

47. Install the transmission range select lever cable and bracket.

48. Install the battery tray.

49. Adjust the automatic transmission range selector lever cable.

50. Fill the transmission with fluid.

➡**It is recommended that Transmission Adaptive Pressure (TAP) information be reset. Reset the TAP values using a scan tool will erase all learned values in all cells. As a result, the ECM, PCM, or TCM will need to relearn TAP values. Transmission performance may be affected as new TAP values are learned.**

51. Reset the TAP values by selecting the following:
  • Scan tool
  • Special functions
  • Transmission output controls
  • Reset transmission adapts
52. Road test the vehicle.

6T70/6T75

See Figures 15 and 16.

1. Remove the battery tray.

2. Remove the transmission range select lever cable and bracket.

3. Drain the transmission fluid.

4. Remove the wire harness retainer from the control valve body cover stud.

5. Disconnect the control valve body Transmission Control Module (TCM) electrical connector.

6. Remove the transmission fluid cooler pipe retainer nut.

7. Remove the transmission fluid cooler inlet hose and seal from the transmission.

8. Plug and/or cap the hose and transmission to prevent contamination.

9. Remove the transmission fluid cooler pipe retainer nut.

10. Remove the transmission fluid cooler outlet hose and seal from the transmission.

11. Plug and/or cap the hose and transmission to prevent contamination.

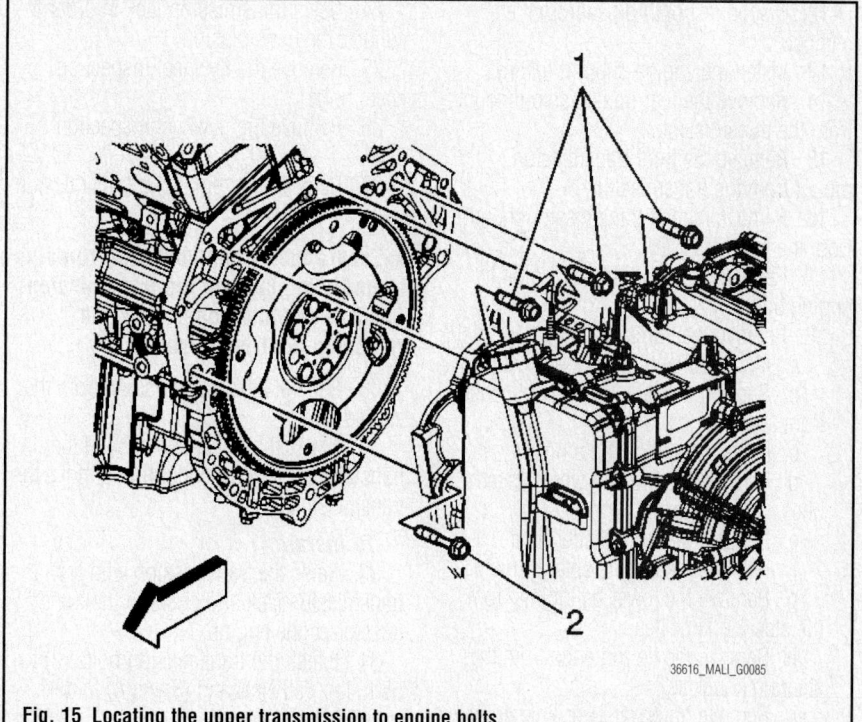

36616_MALI_G0085

Fig. 15 Locating the upper transmission to engine bolts

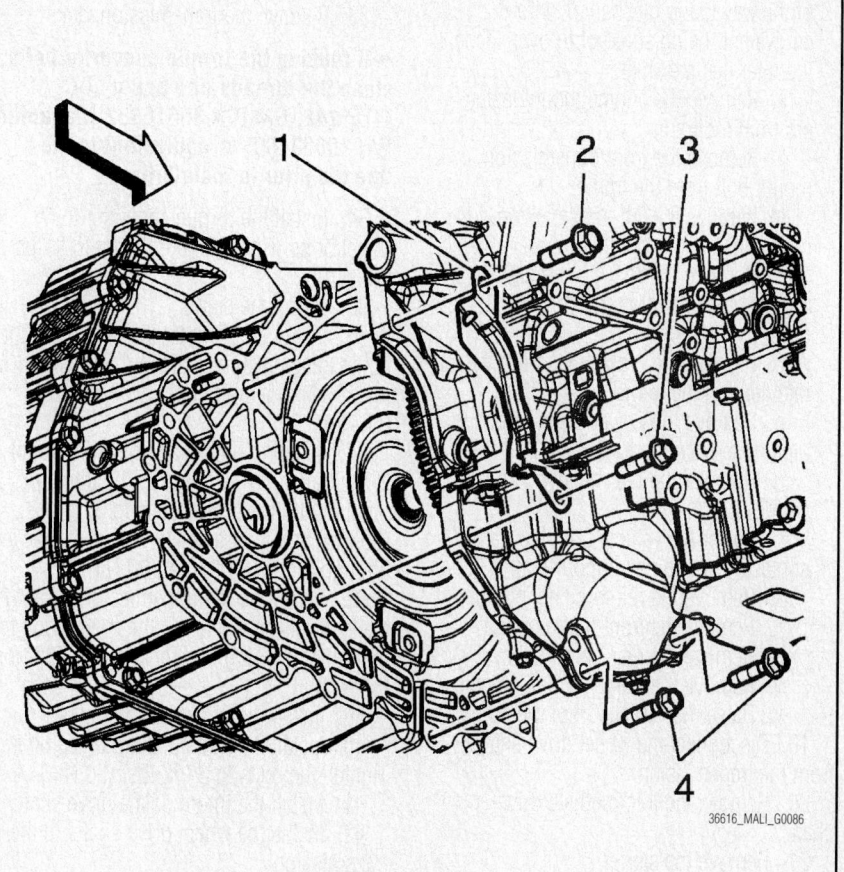

36616_MALI_G0086

Fig. 16 Identifying the transmission and flywheel inspection cover bolts for installation

12. Disconnect both pipes from the retainer.

13. Install the engine support fixture.

14. Remove the rear transmission mount from the transmission.

15. Remove the front transmission mount from the transmission.

16. Remove the left transmission mount from the transmission.

17. Remove the upper transmission to engine bolts.

18. Remove the frame as follows:

    a. Install the engine support fixture.

    b. Support the radiator and condenser from above.

    c. Raise the vehicle on a hoist.

    d. Remove the tire and wheel assemblies.

    e. Remove the front fender liner.

    f. Remove the engine splash shield.

    g. Remove the lower ball joints from the steering knuckles.

    h. Remove the tie rod ends from the steering knuckles.

    i. Remove both stabilizer links from the stabilizer bar.

    j. Remove the power steering gear mounting bolts and secure the gear out of the way using mechanic's wire or equivalent, being sure not to overextend the intermediate shaft.

    k. Remove the engine mount fasteners from the frame.

    l. Remove the front transmission mount bolt from the frame.

    m. Remove the left transmission mount fasteners from the frame.

    n. Remove the rear transmission mount bracket fasteners from the frame.

    o. Remove the brake lines from the retainers on the frame.

    p. Remove the power steering outlet pipe/hose from the frame.

    q. Remove the rear catalytic converter.

    r. Lower the vehicle until the frame contacts the engine support fixture.

    s. Remove the reinforcement bolts.

    t. Remove the front frame bolts.

    u. Remove the rear frame bolts.

    v. Remove the frame reinforcements.

    w. Raise the vehicle off of the frame.

19. Disconnect the wheel drive shafts from the transmission.

20. Remove the intermediate drive shaft.

21. Remove the starter.

22. Mark the relationship of the flywheel to the torque converter for reassembly.

23. Remove the torque converter to flywheel bolts.

24. Use a transmission jack in order to support the transmission.

25. Remove the flywheel inspection cover bolts.

26. Remove the flywheel inspection cover.

27. Remove the remaining transmission bolts.

➡ **Ensure the torque converter remains securely in place on the transmission input shaft while separating and removing the transmission.**

28. Separate the transmission from the engine.

29. Lower the transmission with the transmission jack far enough to remove the transmission.

To install:

30. Raise the transmission with the transmission jack and position the transmission to the engine.

31. Install the transmission bolts (2) to 55 ft. lbs. (75 Nm) and (3 and 4) to 43 ft. lbs. (58 Nm).

32. Install the flywheel inspection cover and bolts. Tighten the bolts to 55 ft. lbs. (75 Nm).

33. Remove the transmission jack.

➡ **If reusing the torque converter bolts, clean the threads and apply LOC-TITE®242, GM P/N 36616382 (Canadian P/N 10953489) or equivalent to the threads prior to installation.**

34. Install the torque converter to flywheel bolts. Tighten the bolts to 46 ft. lbs. (62 Nm).

35. Install the starter.

36. Install the front transmission mount to the transmission. Tighten the nut to 66 ft. lbs. (90 Nm) and the bolts to 37 ft. lbs. (50 Nm).

37. Install the rear transmission mount to the transmission. Tighten the transaxle mount to transmission bolts to 37 ft. lbs. (50 Nm) and the transaxle to mount bracket through bolt to 66 ft. lbs. (90 Nm).

38. Install the left transmission mount to the transmission. Tighten the mount bolt to 66 ft. lbs. (90 Nm) and the nuts to 37 ft. lbs. (50 Nm).

39. Install the transmission brace.

40. Install the transmission brace bolts. Tighten the bolts to 37 ft. lbs. (50 Nm)

41. Install the intermediate drive shaft.

42. Install the wheel drive shafts to the transmission.

43. Install the frame as follows:

    a. Lower the vehicle on to the frame.

    b. Install the frame reinforcements.

    c. Install the front frame bolts and hand tighten only.

    d. Install the reinforcement bolts and hand tighten only.

    e. Tighten the rear frame bolts. Tighten to 74 ft. lbs. (100 Nm), plus an additional 90 degrees.

    f. Tighten the front frame bolts. Tighten to 74 ft. lbs. (100 Nm), plus an additional 90 degrees.

    g. Install the reinforcement bolts. Tighten to 74 ft. lbs. (100 Nm).

    h. Raise the vehicle.

    i. Install the power steering outlet pipe/hose to the frame.

    j. Install the brake lines to the retainers on the frame.

    k. Install the rear transmission mount bracket fasteners. Tighten the transaxle mount to transmission bolts to 37 ft. lbs. (50 Nm) and the transaxle to mount bracket through bolt to 66 ft. lbs. (90 Nm).

    l. Install the left transmission mount fasteners to the frame. Tighten the transaxle mount to transmission bolts to 66 ft. lbs. (90 Nm) and the transaxle to mount bracket through bolt to 66 ft. lbs. (90 Nm).

    m. Install the front transmission mount bracket bolt. Tighten the transaxle mount to transmission bolts to 66 ft. lbs. (90 Nm) and the transaxle to mount bracket through bolt to 66 ft. lbs. (90 Nm).

    n. Install the engine mount fasteners to the frame. Tighten the nuts/bolts to 38 ft. lbs. (50 Nm).

    o. Install the power steering gear mounting fasteners.

    p. Install both stabilizer links to the stabilizer bar. Tighten to 48 ft. lbs. (65 Nm) plus an additional 180 degrees.

    q. Install the tie rod ends to the steering knuckles.

    r. Install the lower ball joints to the steering knuckles. Tighten the ball stud to steering knuckle pinch nut to 37 ft. lbs. (50 Nm). Reverse the nut ¾ of a turn. Tighten to 37 ft. lbs. (50 Nm) plus an additional 60 degrees.

    s. Install the rear catalytic converter.

    t. Install the front fender liner.

    u. Install the engine splash shield.

    v. Lower the vehicle.

    w. Remove the temporary radiator and condenser support.

    x. Remove the engine support fixture.

44. Install the upper transmission to engine bolt. Tighten the bolts to 43 ft. lbs. (58 Nm).

45. Remove the engine support fixture.

46. Install the transmission fluid cooler outlet and inlet hoses and seal to the transmission.

47. Install the transmission fluid cooler pipe retainer nut. Tighten to 16 ft. lbs. (22 Nm).

48. Install the remaining components in the reverse order of removal.

49. Fill the transmission with fluid.

➡**It is recommended that Transmission Adaptive Pressure (TAP) information be reset. Reset the TAP values using a scan tool will erase all learned values in all cells. As a result, the ECM, PCM, or TCM will need to relearn TAP values. Transmission performance may be affected as new TAP values are learned.**

50. Reset the TAP values by selecting the following:
- Scan tool
- Special functions
- Transmission output controls
- Reset transmission adapts
51. Road test the vehicle.

FRONT AXLE SHAFT, BEARING & SEAL

REMOVAL & INSTALLATION

See Figure 17.

1. Remove the drive shaft.
2. Remove the intermediate shaft bolts and the shaft.

➡**Use care when removing the intermediate drive shaft from the transmission as not to damage the seal.**

To install:

3. Installation is the reverse of removal. Tighten the intermediate shaft bolts to 44 ft. lbs. (60 Nm).

➡**A seal protector such as J-44394 must be installed into the differential output shaft seal prior to removing and installing the intermediate shaft. Failure to install the tool as indicated may cause the splines of the intermediate shaft to cut the differential output seal.**

FRONT HALFSHAFTS (WHEEL DRIVE SHAFT)

REMOVAL & INSTALLATION

See Figure 18.

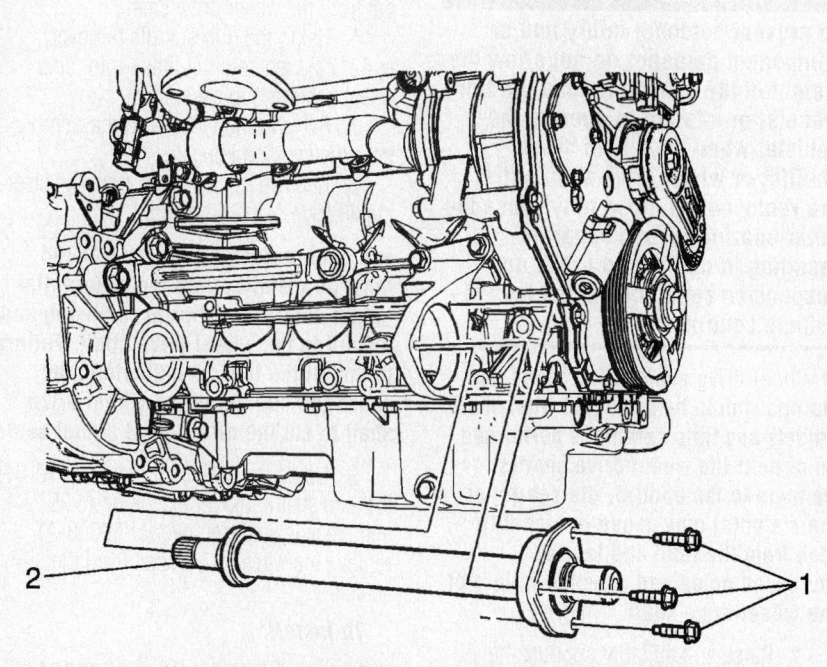

1. Front wheel drive intermediate shaft bracket bolt
2. Front wheel drive intermediate shaft

36616_MALI_G0088

Fig. 17 Removing the intermediate shaft

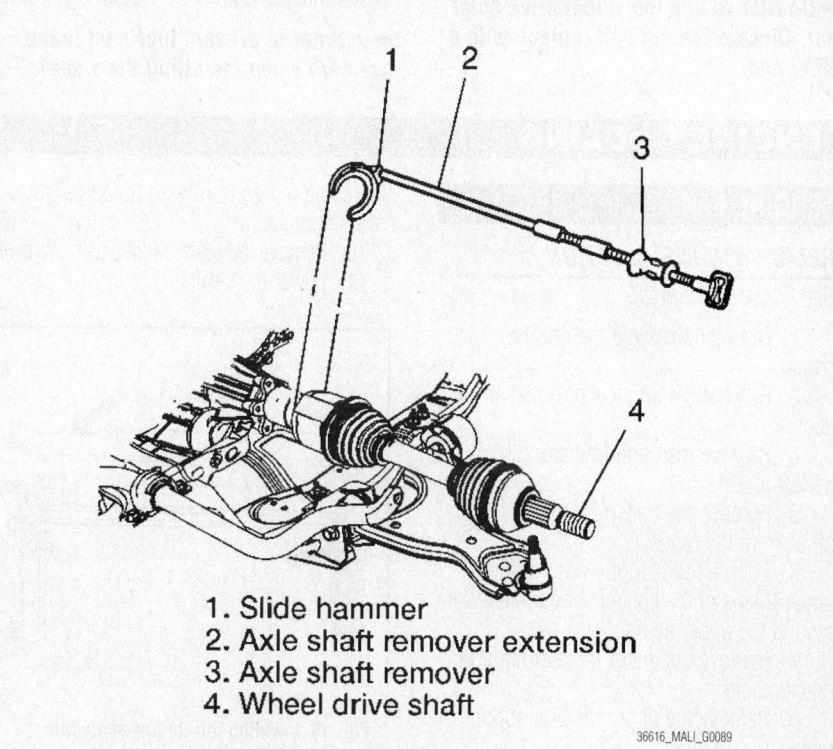

1. Slide hammer
2. Axle shaft remover extension
3. Axle shaft remover
4. Wheel drive shaft

36616_MALI_G0089

Fig. 18 Removing drive shaft

❊❊ CAUTION

To prevent personal injury and/or component damage, do not allow the weight of the vehicle to load the front wheels, or attempt to operate the vehicle, when the wheel drive shaft(s) or wheel drive shaft nut(s) are removed. To do so may cause the inner bearing race to separate, resulting in damage to brake and suspension components and loss of vehicle control.

→Wheel drive shaft boots, seals and clamps should be protected from sharp objects any time service is performed on or near the wheel drive shaft(s). Damage to the boot(s), the seal(s) or the clamp(s) may cause lubricant to leak from the joint and lead to increased noise and possible failure of the wheel drive shaft.

1. Raise and suitably support the vehicle.
2. Remove the wheel and the tire.
3. Insert a brass drift or punch between the brake rotor cooling fins and the brake caliper mounting bracket.
4. Using the appropriate size socket and breaker bar, loosen the wheel drive shaft nut.

→Do NOT re-use the wheel drive shaft nut. Discard the nut and replace with a NEW one.

5. Remove the front wheel drive shaft nut from the wheel drive shaft.
6. Using the hub spindle remover (J 42129), separate the brake rotor and wheel bearing/hub assembly.
7. Remove the outer tie rod assembly from the steering knuckle.
8. Remove the ball joint from the steering knuckle.

→A seal protector such as J-44394 must be installed into the differential output shaft seal prior to removing and installing the wheel drive shaft. Failure to install the tool as indicated may cause the splines of the wheel drive shaft to cut the differential output seal.

9. Using the slide hammer (J 2619-01), the axle shaft remover extension (J 29794), and the axle shaft remover (J 33008-A), remove the wheel drive shaft from the vehicle.

To install:

→A seal protector such as J-44394 must be installed into the differential output shaft seal prior to removing and installing the wheel drive shaft. Failure to install the tool as indicated may cause the splines of the wheel drive shaft to cut the differential output seal.

10. Install a seal protector such as J-44394 into the differential output shaft seal.

→In order to prevent lubricant leaks, use care when installing the wheel

drive shaft to the differential. Do not damage the oil seal. Replace the oil seal if it becomes nicked, distorted, or otherwise damaged.

11. Carefully install the wheel drive shaft into the differential until the splines are past the seal protector.
12. Carefully remove the seal protector from the differential output shaft seal.
13. Carefully continue installing the wheel drive shaft into the differential until the retaining ring is fully seated.
14. Verify the front wheel drive shaft retaining ring is properly seated by grasping the inner housing and pull the inner housing outward.
15. Install the front wheel drive shaft into the front wheel bearing/hub.
16. Install the ball joint to the steering knuckle.
17. Install the outer tie rod assembly to the steering knuckle.
18. Install the NEW wheel drive shaft nut on the wheel drive shaft.
19. Insert a drift or punch into the cooling fin of the brake rotor caliper and against the brake caliper mounting bracket.
20. Using a torque wrench and the appropriate size socket, tighten the wheel drive shaft nut to 159 ft. lbs. (215 Nm).
21. Install the wheel and the tire.
22. Lower the vehicle.
23. Inspect the transaxle fluid level.

ENGINE COOLING

ENGINE FAN

REMOVAL & INSTALLATION

See Figures 19 and 20.

1. Drain and recycle the engine coolant.
2. Remove the air cleaner outlet air duct.
4. Remove the upper radiator air deflector.
5. Remove the transmission oil cooler pipes from the radiator.
6. Loop a rope around each of the upper 2 tabs of the condenser and tie a rope around the upper tie bar.
7. Remove the upper radiator support bracket bolts.
8. Remove the upper radiator support brackets.
9. Pry upward on the fan shroud tabs at

the radiator clips to release the fan shroud from the radiator.
10. Remove the lower radiator air deflector.
11. Lower the vehicle.

12. Remove the radiator inlet hose from the radiator.
13. Remove the radiator outlet hose from the radiator.

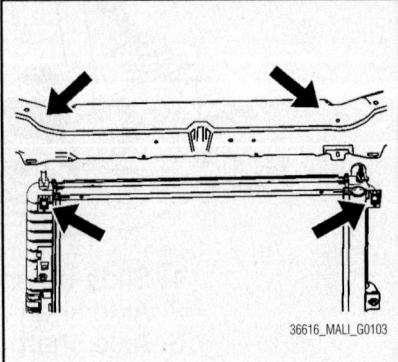

36616_MALI_G0103

Fig. 19 Locating the tie bar and upper tabs on the condenser

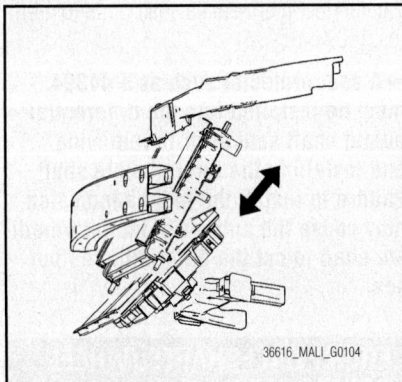

36616_MALI_G0104

Fig. 20 Removing the cooling fan and shroud assembly

14. Disconnect the cooling fan wire harness connectors.

15. Remove the A/C compressor and condenser hose assembly.

16. Raise the vehicle.

17. Remove the lower radiator support bracket bolts.

18. Remove the lower radiator support brackets.

19. Remove the transmission oil cooler pipe clip from the fan shroud.

20. Remove the fan assembly.

To install:

21. Install the fan shroud assembly.

22. Install the transmission oil cooler pipes to the radiator.

23. Install the transmission oil cooler pipe clip to the fan shroud.

24. Install the lower radiator support brackets.

25. Install the lower radiator support bracket bolts and tighten to 44 ft. lbs. (60 Nm).

26. Install the cooling fan wire harness connectors.

27. Install the radiator outlet hose to the radiator.

28. Install the lower radiator air deflector.

29. Lower the vehicle.

30. Snap fan shroud tabs into the radiator clips.

31. Remove the rope attached to the condenser and upper tie bar.

32. Install the upper radiator support brackets.

33. Install the upper radiator support bracket bolts and tighten to 89 inch lbs. (10 Nm).

34. Install the radiator inlet hose to the radiator.

35. Install the A/C compressor and condenser hose assembly.

36. Install the upper radiator air deflector.

37. Install the air duct.

38. Fill the cooling system.

39. Inspect the transmission fluid level.

RADIATOR

REMOVAL & INSTALLATION

See Figure 21.

1. Drain and recycle the engine coolant.

2. Loop a rope around each of the upper 2 tabs of the condenser and tie the rope around the upper tie bar.

3. Remove the upper radiator support brackets.

4. Reposition the radiator inlet hose clamp at the radiator.

5. Remove the radiator inlet hose from the radiator.

6. Remove the front air dam.

7. Remove the right engine splash shield retainers.

8. Remove the right engine splash shield.

9. Remove the left engine splash shield retainers.

10. Remove the left engine splash shield.

11. Reposition the radiator outlet hose clamp at the radiator.

12. Remove the radiator outlet hose from the radiator.

13. Remove the transmission oil cooler pipes from the transmission.

14. Remove the lower radiator support bracket bolts.

15. Remove the lower radiator support brackets.

16. Remove the radiator lower mounts.

17. Remove and discard the condenser mounting bolts from the radiator.

18. Push upward on the radiator and downward on the condenser to unsnap the condenser mounting tabs from the radiator clips.

19. Remove and discard the condenser mounting nuts from the radiator.

20. Remove the radiator air side seals.

21. Remove the radiator and cooling fan shroud assembly from the vehicle.

22. Pry upward on the fan shroud tabs at the radiator clips.

23. Remove the cooling fan and shroud assembly from the radiator.

To install:

24. Install the cooling fan and shroud assembly to the radiator.

25. Snap the fan shroud tabs into the radiator clips.

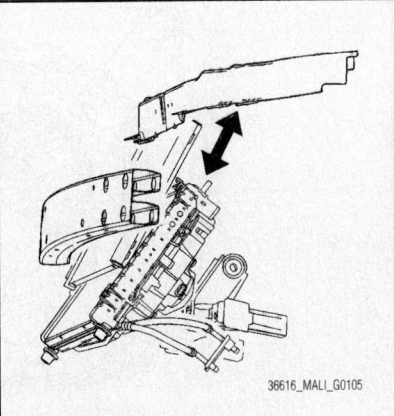

36616_MALI_G0105

Fig. 21 Removing and installing the radiator

26. Install the radiator and cooling fan shroud assembly to the vehicle.

27. Install the radiator air side seals onto the condenser mounting tabs on the radiator.

➡ **The bolt retaining the condenser to the radiator end tank is a special length and should be the ONLY bolt used upon reinstallation. The use of a longer bolt will damage the radiator end tank.**

➡ **Replace the condenser mounting bolts and nuts.**

28. Install the condenser mounting nuts to the radiator.

29. Insert the condenser mounting tabs into the radiator clips.

30. Install the condenser to the radiator bolts and tighten to 53 inch lbs. (6 Nm).

31. Bend the radiator air side seals and insert the seals into the channel of the intake air splash shields.

➡ **The radiator air side seals must be in the proper position for proper air flow.**

➡ **Replace the radiator lower mounts as a pair or vibration may result.**

32. Install the radiator lower mounts.

33. Install the lower radiator support brackets and tighten the bolts to 44 ft. lbs. (60 Nm).

34. Install the transmission oil cooler pipes to the transmission.

35. Install the radiator outlet hose to the radiator.

36. Reposition the radiator outlet hose clamp at the radiator.

➡ **Engine splash shields must be properly installed or reduced A/C and engine cooling system performance could occur.**

37. Install the left engine splash shield.

38. Install the left engine splash shield retainers.

39. Install the right engine splash shield.

40. Install the right engine splash shield retainers.

41. Install the front air dam.

42. Lower the vehicle.

43. Install the radiator inlet hose to the radiator.

44. Reposition the radiator inlet hose clamp at the radiator.

45. Remove the rope attached to the condenser and upper tie bar.

46. Install the upper radiator support brackets.

47. Fill the coolant.

48. Inspect the transmission fluid level.

THERMOSTAT

REMOVAL & INSTALLATION

See Figure 22.

1. Drain the cooling system.
2. Reposition the radiator outlet hose clamp at the thermostat cover.
3. Remove the radiator outlet hose from the thermostat cover.
4. Remove the thermostat cover bolts and cover.
5. Remove the thermostat.
6. Remove and discard the thermostat cover o-ring seal.

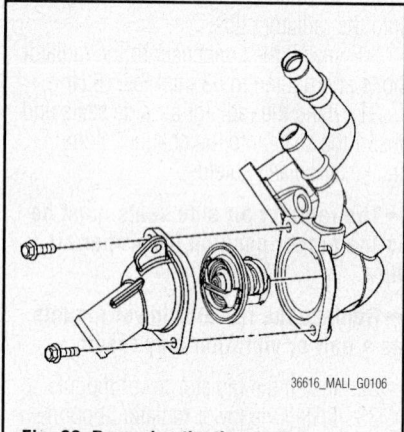

Fig. 22 Removing the thermostat

To install:

7. Install a NEW thermostat cover O-ring seal into the recess groove.
8. Install the thermostat, if necessary.
9. Install the thermostat cover bolts. Tighten the bolts to 89 inch lbs. (10 Nm).
10. Install the radiator outlet hose to the thermostat cover.
11. Position the radiator outlet hose clamp at the thermostat cover.
12. Fill the cooling system.

WATER PUMP

REMOVAL & INSTALLATION

See Figures 23 and 24.

1. Remove the thermostat housing.
2. Remove the water pump access plate from the front cover.

➡**A drain plug has been provided at the bottom of the water pump assembly for additional coolant drainage from the engine block and water pump.**

3. Drain the coolant from the water pump using the plug at the bottom of the pump.

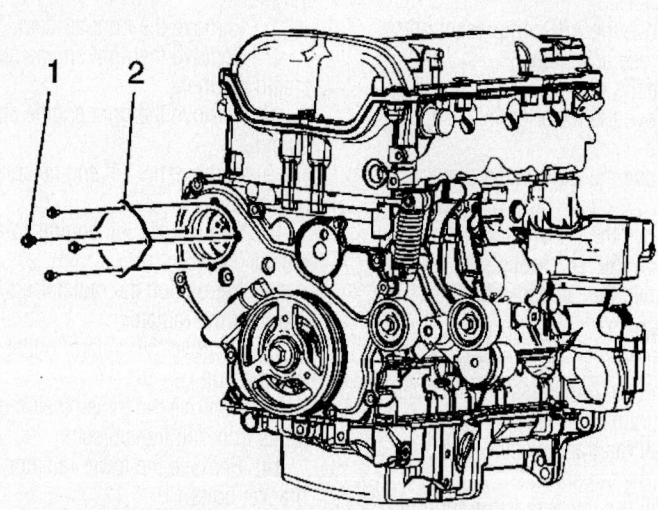

1. Water pump access plate screws
2. Water pump access plate

Fig. 23 Removing the water pump access plate

➡**The water pump holding tool supports the sprocket and chain during the water pump service. The tool must be used or the balance shaft must be re-timed.**

4. Install the water pump holding tool into position.
5. Tighten the bolts on the water pump holding tool into the threads on the water pump sprocket.
6. Install the access cover bolts that were removed earlier to secure the water pump holding tool to the front cover assembly.

7. Remove the 3 inner water pump sprocket to water pump blots.

➡**Be sure to remove both water pump bolts from the front of the engine block.**

8. Remove the 2 water pump bolts.
9. Remove the water pump.
10. Remove and discard the water pump O-ring seal.

To install:

➡**Prior to installing the water pump, read the entire procedure. This will**

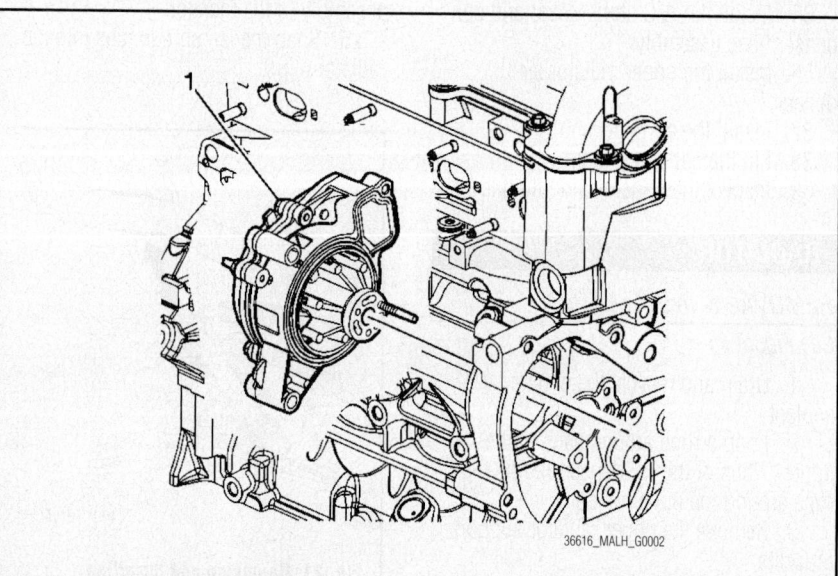

Fig. 24 Removing the water pump (1)

help avoid balance shaft chain re-timing and ensure proper sealing.

11. Install a NEW water pump O-ring seal.

12. A guide pin can be created to aid in water pump alignment. Use a M6 m x 6 mm stud. Thread the pin into the water pump sprocket.

13. Using the guide pin, align the pin with the water pump holding tool.

14. Position the water pump against the engine block and hand tighten the water pump bolts.

15. Install the inner water pump sprocket bolts. After 2 are snug, remove the guide pin and install the 3rd bolt. Tighten the water pump bolts to 18 ft. lbs. (25 Nm).

16. Tighten the water pump sprocket bolts last to 89 inch lbs. (10 Nm).

17. Remove the water pump holding tool.

18. Install the water pump access plate and bolts. Tighten the bolts to 89 inch lbs. (10 Nm).

19. Install the engine splash shield.

20. Install the thermostat housing.

ENGINE ELECTRICAL

FIRING ORDERS

The firing order for the 2.4L engine is 1-3-4-2.

IGNITION COIL

REMOVAL & INSTALLATION
See Figure 25.

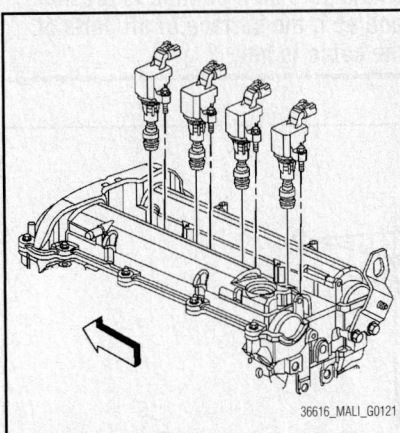

Fig. 25 Removing the ignition coil pack

1. Remove the air cleaner outlet duct.

2. Disconnect the engine wiring harness electrical connectors from the ignition coil(s).

3. Remove the ignition coil bolt(s).

4. Remove the ignition coil(s).

To install:

5. Install the ignition coil(s).

6. Install the ignition coil bolts and tighten to 89 inch lbs. (10 Nm).

7. Connect the engine wiring harness electrical connectors to the ignition coils.

8. Install the air cleaner outlet duct.

IGNITION TIMING

ADJUSTMENT

The ignition timing is controlled by the Powertrain Control Module (PCM). No adjustment is necessary or possible.

SPARK PLUGS

REMOVAL & INSTALLATION
See Figure 26.

➡This engine has aluminum cylinder heads. Do not remove the spark plugs from a hot engine, allow it to cool first. Removing the spark plugs from a hot engine may cause spark plug thread damage or cylinder head damage.

1. Remove the air cleaner outlet duct..

2. Disconnect the engine wiring harness electrical connectors from the ignition coil.

3. Remove the ignition coil bolt(s).

4. Remove the ignition coil(s).

➡Make sure that any water and or debris is blown out of the spark plug holes prior to removing the spark plugs.

IGNITION SYSTEM

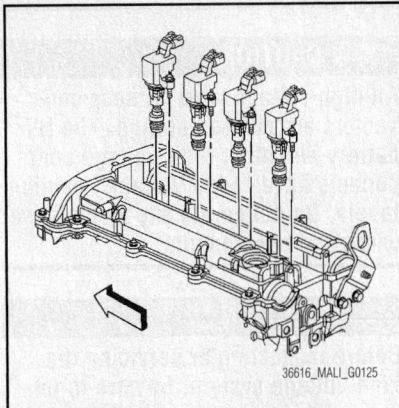

Fig. 26 Removing and installing the spark plugs

5. Remove the spark plugs using a ⅝ inch spark plug socket.

To install:

✳✳ CAUTION

Do not coat spark plug threads with anti-seize compound. If anti-seize compound is used and spark plugs are over-torqued, damage to the cylinder head threads may result.

6. Install the spark plugs and tighten to 15 ft. lbs. (20 Nm).

7. The spark plug gap is 0.040 inch (1.0 mm).

8. Install the ignition coils.

✳✳ CAUTION

The hybrid system operates at voltages up to 650 volts. Be sure to follow the instructions in this manual to handle the system correctly. Failure to do so may result in serious injury or electrocution. Engineer must undergo special training to be able to perform high-voltage system inspection and servicing.

✳✳ CAUTION

All high-voltage wire harness connectors are colored orange. The HV battery and other high-voltage components have "High Voltage" caution labels. Do not carelessly touch these wires and components.

✳✳ CAUTION

Before inspecting or servicing the high-voltage system, be sure to follow safety measures, such as wearing insulated gloves and removing the service plug to prevent electrocution. Carry the removed service plug in your pocket to prevent other technicians from reinstalling it while you are servicing the vehicle.

✳✳ CAUTION

After removing the service plug, wait 5 minutes before touching any of the high-voltage connectors and terminals.

175 AMP MEGA FUSE

REMOVAL & INSTALLATION
See Figure 27.

1. Disconnect the hybrid battery.
2. Remove the 2 Connector Position Assurance (CPA) retainers.

✳✳ WARNING

To help avoid personal injury, additional precautions must be taken prior to working on the generator control module or the generator starter. After removing the 36V battery cables from the generator battery, remove both engine wiring harness connectors from the generator control module. Wait at least 5 minutes and then remove the generator control module

cover. Verify voltage levels at all 36V, 12V, and 3-phase connections, are less than 3 volts using a DMM before proceeding.

3. Disconnect the 2 engine wiring harness electrical connectors from the generator control module.
4. WAIT at least 5 minutes in order to allow the voltage stored in the generator control module to discharge.
5. Remove the generator control module bracket reinforcement bolt and nuts.
6. Remove the generator control module bracket reinforcement
7. Loosen the generator control module cover integral bolts and remove the cover.
8. The generator control module will have to be checked for voltage potential using a voltmeter. First, verify that the voltmeter works.
   a. Set the voltmeter to DC voltage.
   b. Measure the vehicle's 12V battery voltage.
   c. The meter should read greater than +12V DC.
9. Now, check the generator control module for voltage potential, in order to ensure that the module has been disabled.
   a. Measure from the 36V positive terminal to a known good chassis ground. The voltage should be less than 3V.
   b. Measure from the 12V positive terminal to a known good chassis ground. The voltage should be less than 3V.
   c. Measure from the ground terminal to know good chassis ground, checking for continuity.

✳✳ WARNING

To help avoid personal injury, always treat the 3-phase cable and connectors as if voltage is present and as if the surface of all parts of the cable is hot.

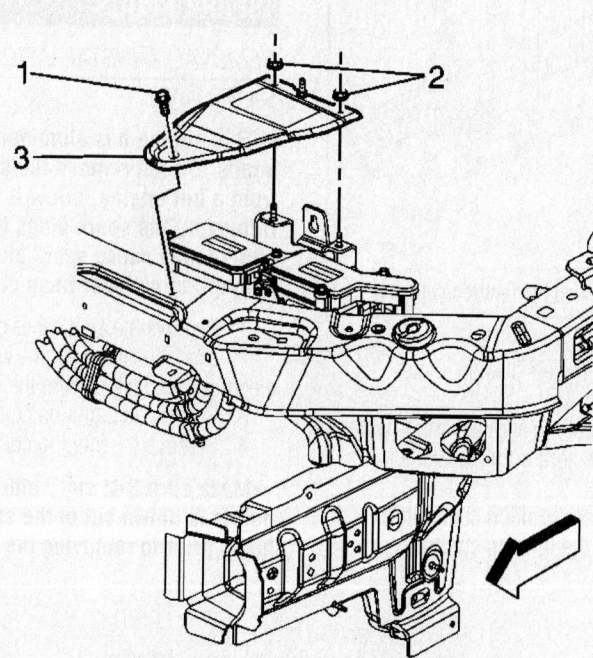

1. Generator control module bracket reinforcement bolt
2. Generator control module bracket reinforcement nuts
3. Generator control module bracket reinforcement

36616_MALH_G0022

Fig. 27 Removing the battery positive cable fuse from the generator control module

10. Verify that the generator control module 3-phase cables are disabled.

   a. Measure from each phase 1, 2, and 3 connection to a known good chassis ground. The voltage should be less than 3V.

   b. After verifying that there is no voltage present, the battery positive fuse can now be removed from the generator control module.

11. Remove the battery positive cable extension cable nut from the generator control module.

12. Carefully lift the extension cable off of the lug and position aside.

13. Remove the battery positive cable fuse nut.

14. Remove the battery positive cable fuse from the generator control module.

To install:

15. Install the battery positive cable fuse to the generator control module.

16. Loosely install the battery positive cable fuse nut.

17. Carefully install the extension cable to the lug.

18. Install the battery positive cable extension cable nut to the generator control module.

19. Tighten the fuse and the battery positive cable extension cable nuts. Tighten the nuts to 89 inch lbs. (10 Nm).

20. Place the generator control module cover on top of the generator control module and tighten the bolts. Tighten the bolts to 89 inch lbs. (10 Nm).

21. Install the generator control module bracket reinforcement.

22. Install the generator control module bracket reinforcement bolt and nuts. Tighten the bolt/nuts to 89 inch lbs. (10 Nm).

23. Connect the 2 engine wiring harness electrical connectors to the generator control module.

24. Install the 2 CPA retainers.

25. Connect the hybrid battery.

36V BATTERY INTERNAL CABLE

REMOVAL & INSTALLATION

See Figures 28 and 29.

1. Disconnect the generator battery.

2. Remove the 2 generator battery vent fan cover bolts.

3. Remove the 12 generator battery cover bolts.

4. Remove the generator battery cover.

➡**Removing the interconnect cables will disable the 36 volts within the generator battery control module.**

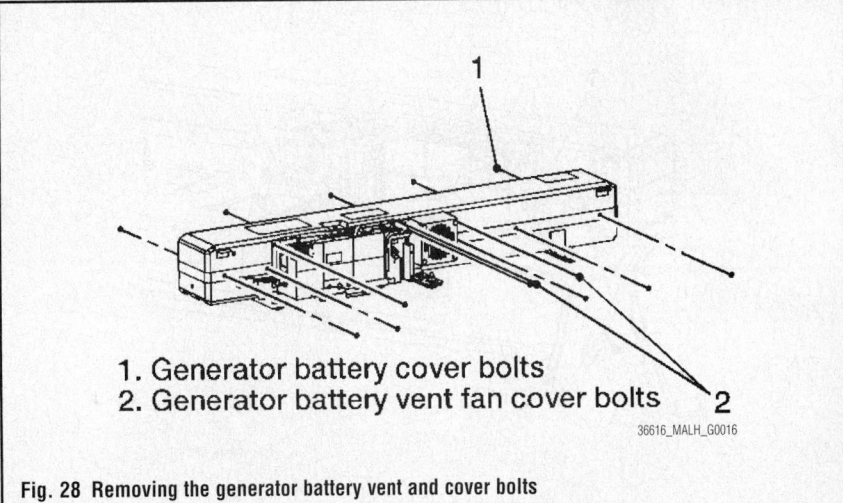

1. Generator battery cover bolts
2. Generator battery vent fan cover bolts

36616_MALH_G0016

Fig. 28 Removing the generator battery vent and cover bolts

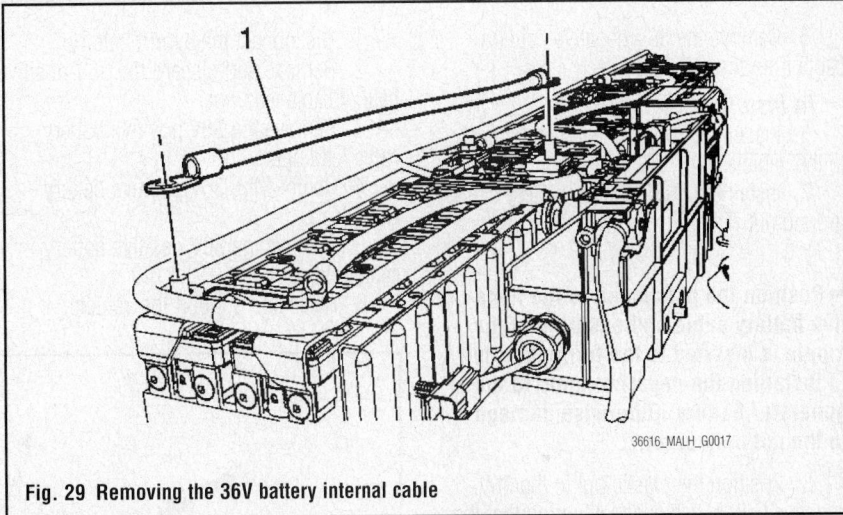

36616_MALH_G0017

Fig. 29 Removing the 36V battery internal cable

5. Remove the generator battery terminal rubber cups.

6. Remove the generator battery cable nuts.

7. Remove the 36-Volt battery internal cable from the battery.

To install:

8. Install the 36-Volt battery internal cable to the battery.

9. Install the generator battery cable nuts and tighten to 71 inch lbs. (8 Nm).

10. Install the generator battery terminal rubber cups.

11. Install the generator battery cover.

12. Install the 12 generator battery cover bolts and tighten to 71 inch lbs. (8 Nm).

13. Install the 2 generator battery vent fan cover bolts and tighten to 71 inch lbs. (8 Nm).

14. Connect the generator battery.

36V BATTERY NEGATIVE CABLE

REMOVAL & INSTALLATION

See Figure 30.

❄❄ WARNING

To help avoid personal injury, be careful when working in the vicinity of the generator battery disconnect control module. Internal components will still be live, 36V potential, even when the cover has been opened or removed.

1. Disconnect the hybrid battery.

2. Remove the plastic nut from the generator battery disconnect control module negative stud.

3. Remove the 36V negative battery cable lead from the generator battery disconnect control module negative stud.

4. Remove the 36V negative battery cable ground nut.

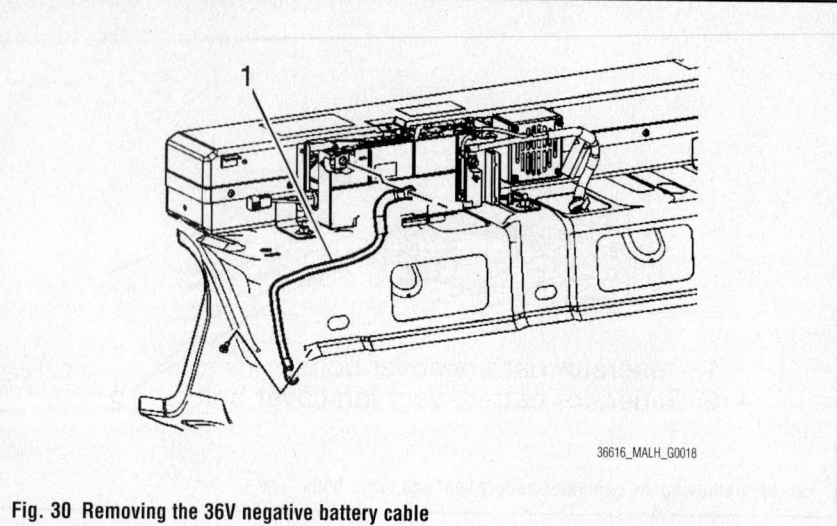

Fig. 30 Removing the 36V negative battery cable

5. Remove the 36V negative battery cable from the vehicle.

To install:

6. Install the 36V negative battery cable to the vehicle.

7. Install the 36V negative battery cable ground nut. Tighten the nut to 80 inch lbs. (9 Nm).

➡**Position the plastic nut to the negative battery cable and ensure that the nipple is inserted to the terminal prior to installing the negative cable to the generator battery, Otherwise damage to the nut may occur.**

8. Position the plastic nut to the 36V negative battery cable lead ensuring that the nipple on the plastic nut is inserted through the hole in the terminal.

9. Install the 36V negative battery cable lead and nut to the generator battery disconnect module negative stud. Tighten the nut to 95 inch lbs. (10.7 Nm).

10. Connect the hybrid battery.

36V BATTERY POSITIVE CABLE (ENGINE COMPARTMENT TO MODULE)

REMOVAL & INSTALLATION

See Figure 31.

✳✳ WARNING

To help avoid personal injury, be careful when working in the vicinity of the generator battery disconnect control module. Internal components will still be live, 36V potential, even when the cover has been opened or removed.

1. Disconnect the hybrid battery.
2. Remove and discard the 36V positive battery cable lead nut.
3. Remove the 36V positive battery cable lead nut.
4. Remove the 36V positive battery cable leads.
5. Remove the 36V positive battery cable retainer bolt.
6. Raise and support the vehicle.

7. Remove the 36V positive battery cable clip nut.
8. Remove the 36V positive battery cable casting nuts.
9. Carefully lower the 36V positive battery cable casting until the cable connector and 36V positive battery cable pigtail connector is accessible.
10. Disconnect the 36V positive battery cable pigtail connector from the 36V positive battery cable casting by rotating the connector ring on the pigtail counterclockwise.
11. Lower the vehicle.
12. Remove the 36V positive battery cable pigtail connector.

To install:

13. Install the 36Vpositive battery cable pigtail connector.
14. Raise and suitably support the vehicle.
15. Align the 36V positive battery cable pigtail connection keyway with the paint dot on the 36V positive battery cable casting. Once aligned, rotate the pigtail lock ring securing the connection.
16. Carefully feed the 36V positive battery cable pigtail into the rear compartment panel until the 36V positive battery cable casting is seated onto the studs.

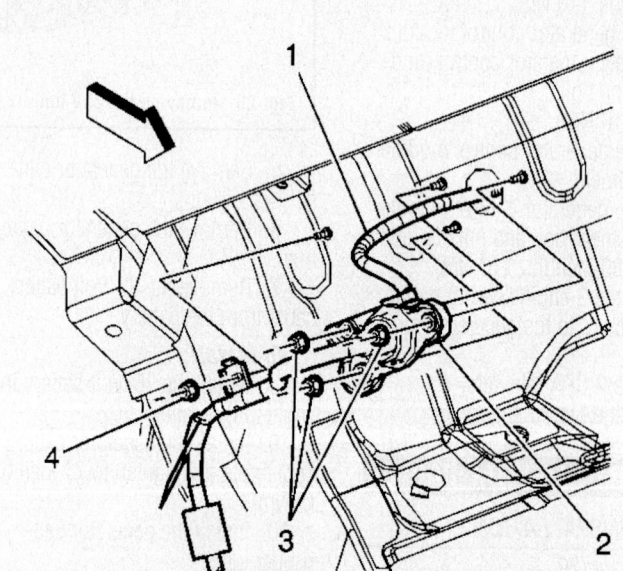

1. 36-volt positive battery cable pigtail connector
2. 36-volt positive battery cable casting
3. 36-volt positive battery cable casting nuts
4. 36-volt positive battery cable clip nut

Fig. 31 Locating the 36V positive battery cable clip nut, casting nuts, casting and pigtail connector

17. Install the 36V positive battery cable casting nuts. Tighten the nuts to 80 inch lbs. (9 Nm).

18. Install the 36V positive battery cable clip nut. Tighten the nuts to 80 inch lbs. (9 Nm).

19. Lower the vehicle.

20. Position the 36V positive battery cable retainer to the fan cover.

21. Install the 36V positive battery cable retainer bolt. Tighten the bolt to 71 inch lbs. (8 Nm).

22. Install the 36V positive battery cable leads.

23. Install the 36V positive battery cable lead nut. Tighten the nut to 18 inch lbs. (9 Nm).

24. Install a NEW 36V positive battery cable lead nut. Start the nut finger tight, and then torque to the specification given. Tighten the nut to 11 ft. lbs. (15 Nm).

25. Connect the hybrid battery.

36V BATTERY POSITIVE CABLE (ENGINE TO PASSENGER COMPARTMENT)

REMOVAL & INSTALLATION

See Figures 32 and 33.

1. Disconnect the hybrid battery.
2. Remove the fuel tank.
3. Remove the (12V) battery tray.
4. Remove the left rear frame bolts.
5. Remove the left rear frame reinforcement.
6. Lower the vehicle.
7. Disconnect the 2 Connector Position Assurance (CPA) retainers.

✳✳ WARNING

To help avoid personal injury, additional precautions must be taken prior to working on the generator control module or the generator starter. After removing the 36V battery cables from the generator battery, remove both engine wiring harness connectors from the generator control module. Wait at least 5 minutes and then remove the generator control module cover. Verify voltage levels at all 36V, 12V, and 3-phase connections, are less than 3 volts using a DMM before proceeding.

8. Disconnect the 2 engine wiring harness electrical connectors (2) from the generator control module.

9. WAIT at least 5 minutes in order to

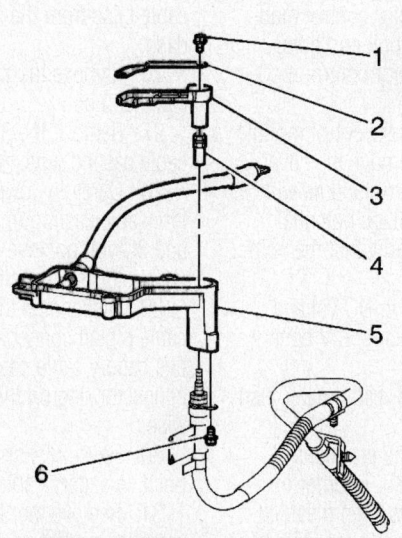

1. 36-volt terminal block to cable bolt
2. 36-volt contact
3. 36-volt retainer
4. 36-volt cable insulator
5. 36-volt cable terminal block
6. 36-volt cable to terminal block bolt

36616_MALH_G0020

Fig. 32 Removing the 36V cable terminal block from the cable

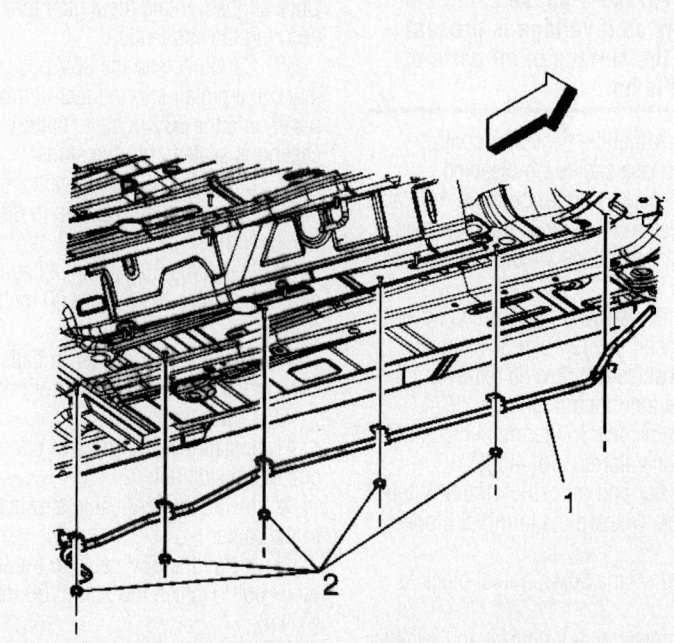

1. 36-volt positive battery cable
2. 36-volt positive battery cable to underbody nuts

36616_MALH_G0021

Fig. 33 Locating 36V positive battery cable to underbody nuts

allow the voltage stored in the generator control module to discharge.

10. Remove the generator control module bracket reinforcement bolt and nuts.

11. Remove the generator control module bracket reinforcement.

12. Loosen the generator control module cover integral bolts and remove the cover.

13. The generator control module will have to be checked for voltage potential using a voltmeter. First, verify that the voltmeter works:

    a. Set the voltmeter to DC voltage.

    b. Measure the vehicle's 12V battery voltage.

    c. The meter should read greater than +12V DC.

14. Now, check the generator control module for voltage potential, in order to ensure that the module has been disabled.

    a. Measure from the 36V positive terminal to a known good chassis ground. The voltage should be less than 3V.

    b. Measure the 12V positive terminal to a known good chassis ground. The voltage should be less than 3 volts.

    c. Measure the ground terminal to a known good chassis ground, checking for continuity.

❊❊ WARNING

To help avoid personal injury, always treat the 3-phase cable and connectors as if voltage is present and as if the surface of all parts of the cable is hot.

15. Verify that the generator control module 3-phase cables are disabled.

    a. Measure from each phase 1, 2, and 3 connection to a known good chassis ground. The voltage should be less than 3V.

    b. After verifying that there is no voltage present, the 12V and 36V positive battery cables can now be removed from the generator control module.

16. Remove the 36V terminal block nuts from the generator control module.

17. Lift up, and reposition the 36V terminal block. Discard the terminal block seal.

18. Remove the 36V terminal block to cable bolt.

19. Remove the 36V contact and retainer.

20. Remove the 36V cable insulator.

21. Remove the 36V cable to terminal block bolt.

22. Remove the 36V cable terminal block from the cable.

23. Remove the 36V positive battery cable clip from the side rail.

24. Raise and support the vehicle.

25. Remove the 36V positive battery cable clips from the side rail and the front of dash.

26. Remove the 36V positive battery cable clip nut.

27. Remove the 36V positive battery cable casting nuts.

28. Carefully lower the 36V positive battery cable casting until the cable connector and 36-volt positive battery cable pigtail connector is accessible.

29. Disconnect the 36V positive battery cable pigtail connector from the 36V positive battery cable casting by rotating the connector ring on the pigtail counterclockwise.

30. Have an assistant support the 36V positive battery cable.

31. Remove the 36V positive battery cable to underbody nuts.

32. Remove the 36V positive battery cable from the vehicle.

To install:

33. With the aid of an assistant, position the 36V positive battery cable to the vehicle.

34. Install the 36V positive battery cable to underbody nuts. Tighten the nuts to 80 inch lbs. (9 Nm).

35. Align the 36V positive battery cable pigtail connection keyway to the paint dot on the 36V positive battery cable casting. Once aligned, rotate the pigtail lock ring securing the connection.

36. Carefully feed the 36V positive battery cable pigtail into the rear compartment panel until the 36V positive battery cable casting is seated onto the studs.

37. Install the 36V positive battery cable casting nuts. Tighten the nuts to 80 inch lbs. (9 Nm).

38. Install the 36V positive battery cable clip nut. Tighten the nuts to 80 inch lbs. (9 Nm).

39. Install the 36V positive battery cable clips to the side rail and the front of dash.

40. Lower the vehicle.

41. Install the 36V positive battery cable clip to the side rail.

42. Install the 36V cable terminal block to the cable.

43. Install the 36V cable to the terminal block bolt. Tighten the bolt to 80 inch lbs. (9 Nm).

44. Install the 36V cable insulator.

45. Install the 36V retainer and contact.

46. Install the 36V terminal block to cable bolt. Tighten the bolt to 80 inch lbs. (9 Nm).

47. Place a NEW terminal block seal onto the generator control module.

48. Position the 36V terminal block to the generator control module.

49. Install the 36V terminal block nuts to the generator control module. Tighten the nuts to 89 inch lbs. (10 Nm).

50. Place the generator control module cover on top of the generator control module and tighten the bolts.

51. Tighten the nuts to 89 inch lbs. (10 Nm).

52. Install the generator control module bracket reinforcement.

53. Install the generator control module bracket reinforcement bolt and nuts. Tighten the nuts to 89 inch lbs. (10 Nm).

54. Connect the 2 engine wiring harness electrical connectors to the generator control module.

55. Connect the 2 CPA retainers.

56. Raise and suitably support the vehicle.

57. Install the left rear frame reinforcement.

58. Install the left rear frame bolts. Tighten the bolts to 74 ft. lbs. (100 Nm) plus an additional 90 degrees using the Angle Meter (J 45059).

59. Install the (12V) battery tray.

60. Install the fuel tank.

61. Connect the hybrid battery.

BATTERY POSITIVE CABLE EXTENSION CABLE

REMOVAL & INSTALLATION

See Figures 34 through 36.

1. Disconnect the hybrid battery.

2. Remove the 2 Connector Position Assurance (CPA) retainers.

❊❊ WARNING

To help avoid personal injury, additional precautions must be taken prior to working on the generator control module or the generator starter. After removing the 36V battery cables from the generator battery, remove both engine wiring harness connectors from the generator control module.

3. Wait at least 5 minutes and then remove the generator control module cover. Verify voltage levels at all 36V, 12V, and 3-phase connections, are less than 3 volts using a DMM before proceeding.

4. Disconnect the 2 engine wiring harness electrical connectors from the generator control module.

5. WAIT at least 5 minutes in order to allow the voltage stored in the generator control module to discharge.

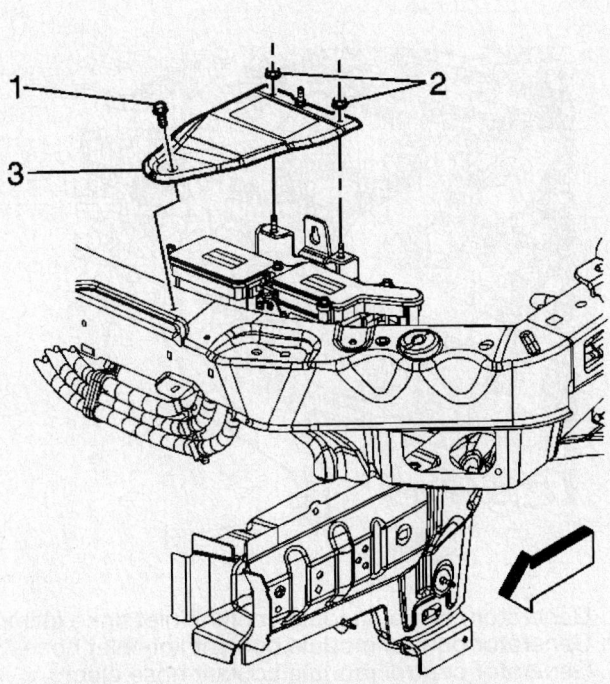

1. Generator control module bracket reinforcement bolt
2. Generator control module bracket reinforcement nuts
3. Generator control module bracket reinforcement

36616_MALH_G0022

Fig. 34 Removing the generator control bracket reinforcement

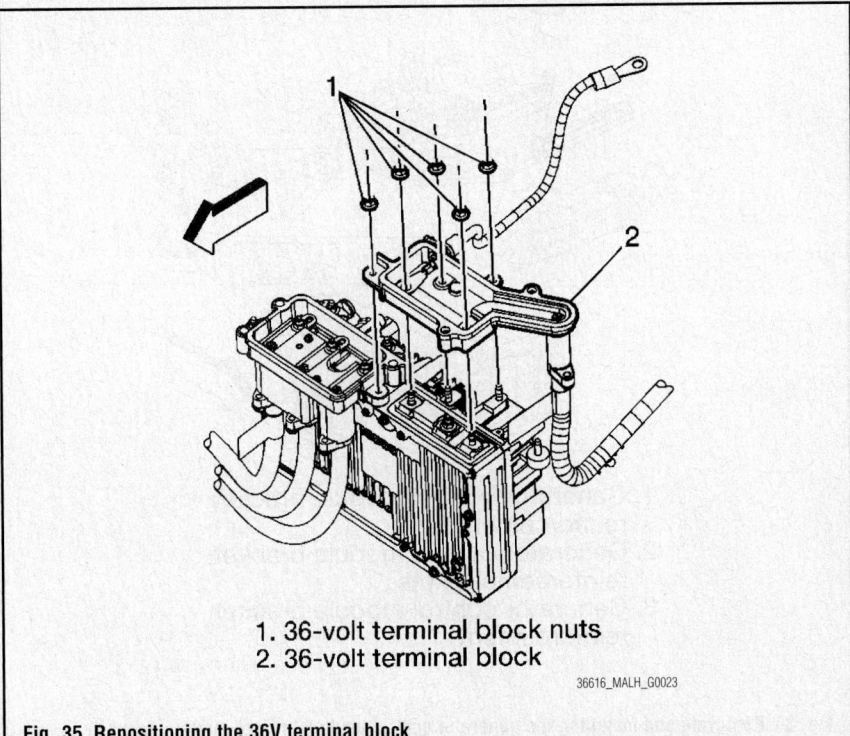

1. 36-volt terminal block nuts
2. 36-volt terminal block

36616_MALH_G0023

Fig. 35 Repositioning the 36V terminal block

6. Remove the generator control module bracket reinforcement bolt and nuts.

7. Remove the generator control module bracket reinforcement.

8. Loosen the generator control module cover integral bolts and remove the cover.

9. The generator control module will have to be checked for voltage potential using a voltmeter. First, verify that the voltmeter works:

   a. Set the voltmeter to DC voltage.

   b. Measure the vehicle's 12V battery voltage.

   c. The meter should read greater than +12 volts DC.

10. Now, check the generator control module for voltage potential, in order to ensure that the module has been disabled.

   a. Measure from the 36V positive terminal to a known good chassis ground. The voltage should be less than 3 volts.

   b. Measure from the 12V positive terminal to a known good chassis ground. The voltage should be less than 3 volts.

   c. Measure from the ground terminal to known good chassis ground, checking for continuity.

✷✷ WARNING

To help avoid personal injury, always treat the 3-phase cable and connectors as if voltage is present and as if the surface of all parts of the cable is hot.

11. Verify that the generator control module 3-phase cables are disabled.

   a. Measure from each phase 1, 2, and 3 connection to a known good chassis ground. The voltage should be less than 3 volts.

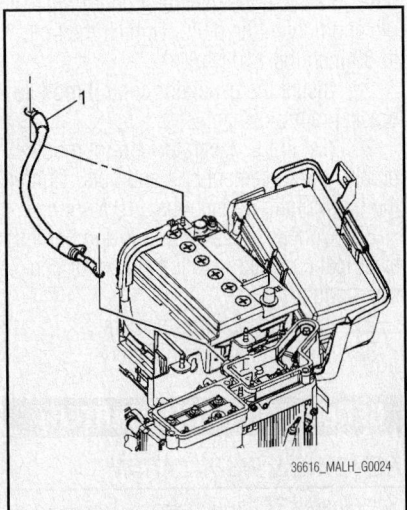

36616_MALH_G0024

Fig. 36 Removing the battery positive cable extension cable

b. After verifying that there is no voltage present, the battery positive fuse can now be removed from the generator control module.

12. Remove the 36V terminal block nuts from the generator control module.

13. Lift up, and reposition the 36V terminal block. Discard the terminal block seal.

14. Remove the battery positive cable extension cable bolt.

15. Disengage the two side retaining tabs on the positive battery cable, and open the cover.

16. Remove the battery positive cable extension cable nut.

17. Remove the battery positive cable extension cable lead from the positive battery cable.

18. Remove the battery positive cable extension cable from the vehicle.

To install:

19. Install the battery positive cable extension cable to the vehicle.

20. Install the battery positive cable extension cable lead to the positive battery cable.

21. Install the battery positive cable extension cable nut. Tighten the nut to 89 inch lbs. (10 Nm).

22. Close the positive battery cable cover.

23. Install the battery positive cable extension cable bolt. Tighten the bolt to 89 inch lbs. (10 Nm).

24. Place a NEW terminal block seal onto the generator control module.

25. Position the 36V terminal block to the generator control module.

26. Install the 36V terminal block nuts to the generator control module. Tighten the nuts to 89 inch lbs. (10 Nm).

27. Place the generator control module cover on top of the generator control module and tighten the bolts. Tighten the bolts to 89 inch lbs. (10 Nm).

28. Install the generator control module bracket reinforcement.

29. Install the generator control module bracket reinforcement bolt and nuts. Tighten the bolt/nuts to 89 inch lbs. (10 Nm).

30. Connect the 2 engine wiring harness electrical connectors to the generator control module.

31. Install the 2 CPA retainers.

32. Connect the hybrid battery.

GENERATOR (WITH STARTER)

REMOVAL & INSTALLATION

See Figures 37 through 45.

1. Disconnect the hybrid battery.
2. Remove the drive belt tensioner.

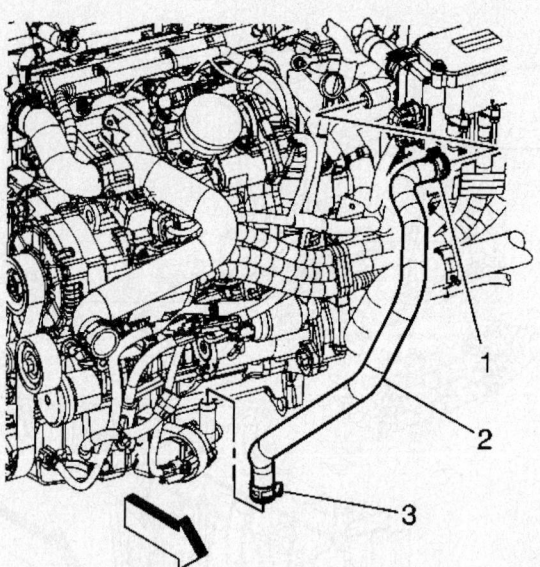

1. Generator control module coolant inlet hose clamp
2. Generator control module coolant line inlet hose
3. Generator control module coolant hose clamp

36616_MALH_G0025

Fig. 37 Removing the generator control module coolant inlet hose

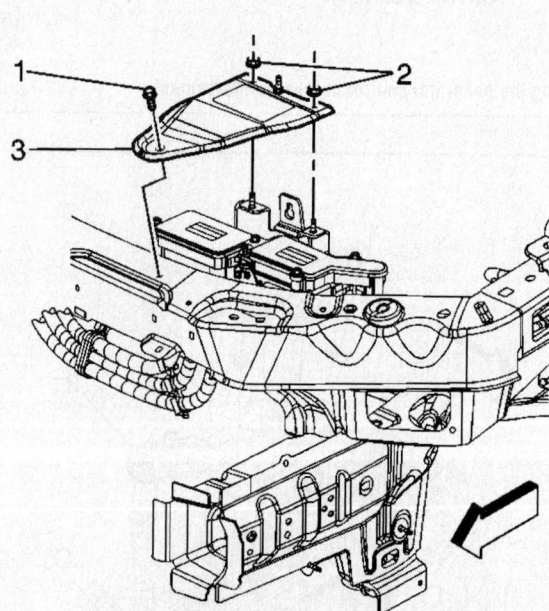

1. Generator control module bracket reinforcement bolt
2. Generator control module bracket reinforcement nuts
3. Generator control module bracket reinforcement

36616_MALH_G0026

Fig. 38 Removing and installing the generator control module bracket reinforcement

3. Remove the radiator inlet hose.

4. Reposition the power brake booster vacuum hose clamp at the intake manifold.

5. Remove the power brake booster vacuum hose from the intake manifold.

6. Remove the power brake booster vacuum hose from the clamp on the generator control module coolant outlet hose.

7. Reposition the power brake booster vacuum hose out of the way.

✳ WARNING

To help avoid personal injury, additional precautions must be taken prior to working on the generator control module or the generator starter. After removing the 36V battery cables from the generator battery, remove both engine wiring harness connectors from the generator control module. Wait at least 5 minutes and then remove the generator control module cover. Verify voltage levels at all 36V, 12V, and 3-phase connections, are less than 3 volts using a DMM before proceeding.

8. Remove the 2 Connector Position Assurance (CPA) retainers.

9. Disconnect the 2 engine wiring harness electrical connectors from the generator control module.

10. WAIT at least 5 minutes in order to allow the voltage stored in the generator control module to discharge.

11. Reposition the generator control module coolant inlet hose clamp at the generator control module using the Hose Clamp Pliers (J 38185) or equivalent.

12. Remove the generator control module coolant inlet hose from the generator control module.

13. Remove the generator control module bracket reinforcement bolt and nuts.

14. Remove the generator control module bracket reinforcement.

15. Loosen the generator control module cover integral bolts and remove the cover.

16. The generator control module will have to be checked for voltage potential using a voltmeter. First verify that the voltmeter works. Set the voltmeter to DC voltage. Measure the vehicle 12V battery voltage. The meter should read greater than +12V DC.

17. Now, check the generator control module for voltage potential, in order to ensure that the module has been disabled.

a. Measure from the 36V positive terminal to a known good chassis ground. The voltage should be less than 3 volts.

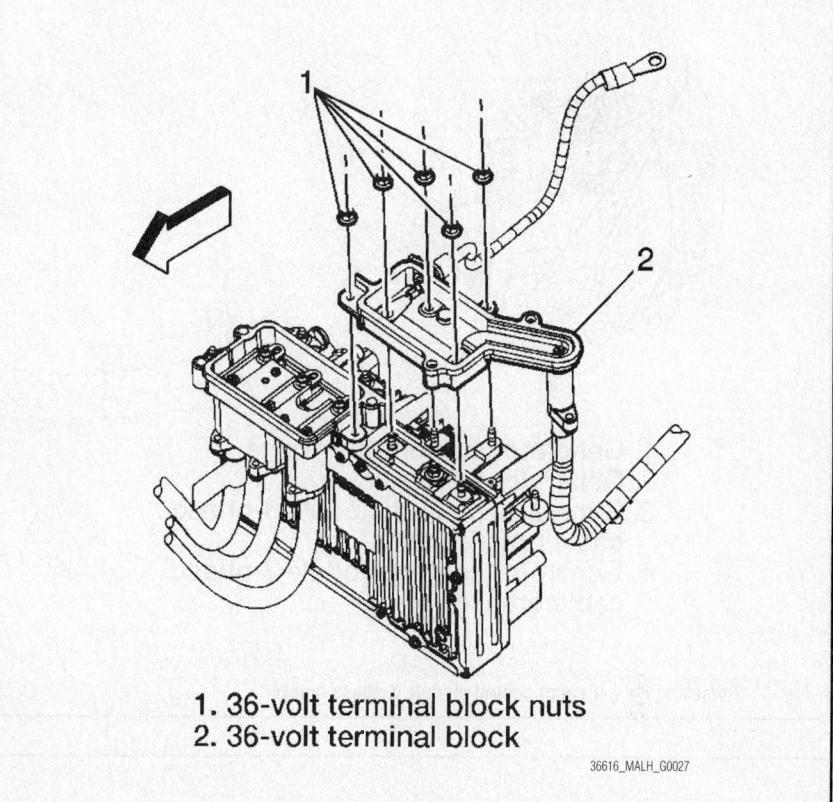

1. 36-volt terminal block nuts
2. 36-volt terminal block

36616_MALH_G0027

Fig. 39 Repositioning the generator control module 3-phase cable terminal block

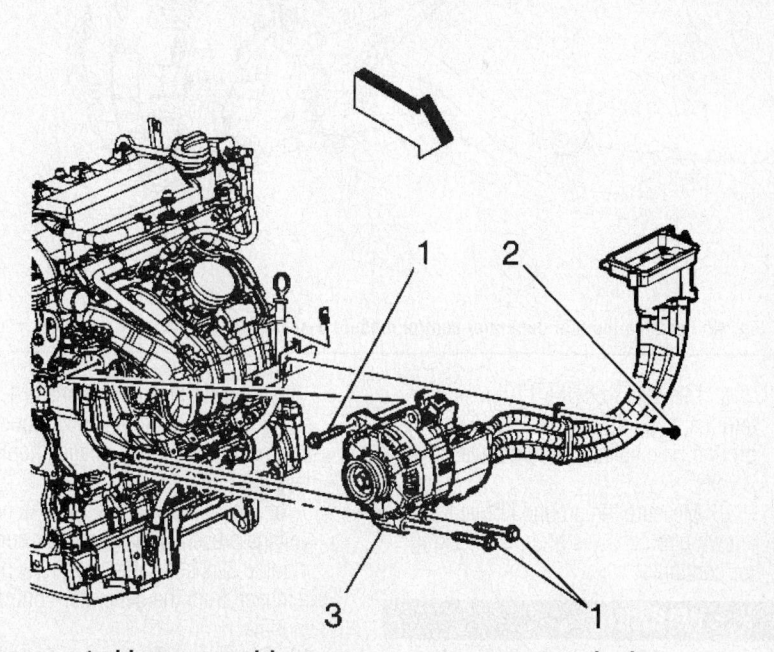

1. Upper and lower generator starter bolt
2. Starter 3-phase cable clip bolt
3. Generator starter

36616_MALH_G0028

Fig. 40 Removing and installing the generator

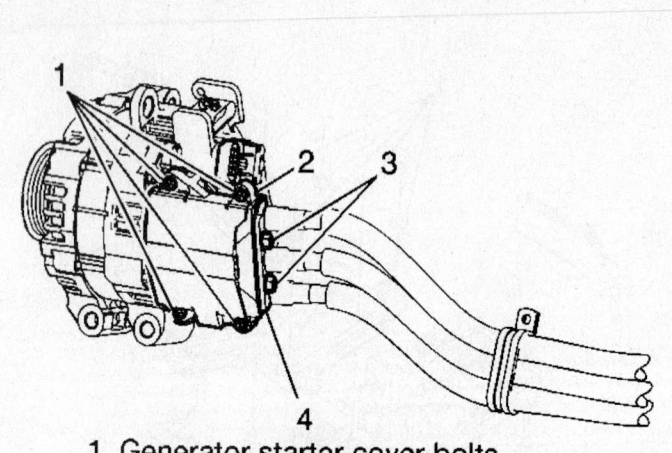

1. Generator starter cover bolts
2. Generator starter cover
3. Generator control module 3-phase cable bracket bolts
4. Generator control module 3-phase cable bracket

36616_MALH_G0029

Fig. 41 Removing the generator control module 3-phase bracket

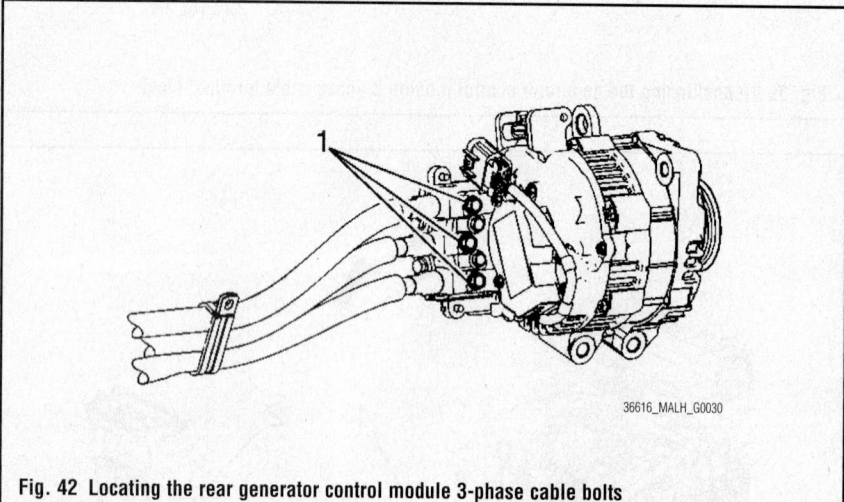

36616_MALH_G0030

Fig. 42 Locating the rear generator control module 3-phase cable bolts

b. Measure from the 12V positive terminal to a known good chassis ground. The voltage should be less than 3 volts.

c. Measure the ground terminal to a known good chassis ground, checking for continuity.

✳✳ WARNING

To help avoid personal injury, always treat the 3-phase cable and connectors as if voltage is present and as if the surface of all parts of the cable is hot.

18. Verify that the generator control module 3-phase cables are disabled.

a. Measure front each phase 1, 2, and 3 connection to a known good chassis ground. The voltage should be less than 3V.

b. After verifying that there is not voltage presents, the generator control module 3-phase cables can now be removed from the generator control module.

19. Disconnect the engine wiring harness electrical connectors from the generator starter.

20. Reposition the wiring harness out of the way.

21. Remove the 36V terminal block nuts from the generator control module.

22. Lift up, and reposition the 36-volt terminal block, secure the block out of the way. Discard the terminal block seal.

23. Remove the Air Conditioning (A/C) condenser/evaporator tube clip from the front end upper tie bar reinforcement.

24. Reposition the A/C condenser/evaporator tube out of the way.

25. Remove the starter 3-phase cable clip bolt from the oil level indicator tube bracket.

26. Remove the upper generator starter bolt.

27. Raise and suitably support the vehicle.

28. Remove the 2 lower generator starter bolts.

29. Lower the vehicle.

30. Remove the generator starter (with the generator control module 3-phase cables attached) from the vehicle and place on a clean work surface.

31. Remove the generator starter cover bolts and cover.

32. Remove the generator control module 3-phase cable bracket bolts and bracket.

33. From inside the generator starter, remove the generator control module 3-phase cable to generator starter nuts.

34. Remove the rear generator control module 3-phase cable bolts.

35. Remove the generator control module 3-phase cable assembly from the generator starter.

To install:

36. Install the generator control module 3-phase cable assembly to the NEW generator starter.

37. Inside the generator starter, install the generator control module 3-phase cable to the studs and install the generator starter nuts. Tighten the nuts to 71 inch lbs. (8 Nm).

38. Install the generator control module 3-phase cable bracket and bolts. Tighten the bolts to 71 inch lbs. (8 Nm).

39. Install the generator starter cover and bolts. Tighten the bolts to 44 inch lbs. (5 Nm).

40. Install the rear generator control module 3-phase cable bolts. Tighten to 71 inch lbs. (8 Nm).

41. Position the generator starter (with the generator control module 3-phase cables attached) to the vehicle and install the upper bolt until snug.

42. Raise and suitably support the vehicle.

43. Install the 2 lower generator starter bolts until snug.

44. Install the generator starter 3-phase cable clip bolt to the oil level indicator tube

bracket. Tighten the bolt to 89 inch lbs. (10 Nm).

45. Tighten the generator starter bolts in the sequence shown. Tighten the bolts to 43 ft. lbs. (58 Nm).

46. Position the A/C condenser/evaporator tube to the front end upper tie bar reinforcement.

47. Install the A/C condenser/evaporator tube clip to the front end upper tie bar reinforcement.

48. Place a NEW terminal block seal onto the generator control module.

49. Install the generator control module 3-phase cable terminal block onto the generator control module.

50. Install the generator control module 3-phase cable terminal block nuts until snug.

51. Tighten the generator control module 3-phase cable terminal block nuts in the sequence shown. Tighten the nuts to 71 inch lbs. (8 Nm).

52. Place a NEW terminal block seal onto the generator control module.

53. Unsecure, and position the 36-volt terminal block to the generator control module.

54. Install the 36-volt terminal block nuts to the generator control module. Tighten the nuts to 89 inch lbs. (10 Nm).

55. Position the engine wiring harness.

56. Connect the engine wiring harness electrical connectors to the starter generator.

57. Place the generator control module cover on top of the generator control module and tighten the bolts. Tighten the bolts to 89 inch lbs. (10 Nm).

58. Install the generator control module bracket reinforcement.

59. Install the generator control module bracket reinforcement bolt and nuts. Tighten the bolt/nuts to 89 inch lbs. (10 Nm).

60. Install the generator control module coolant inlet hose to the generator control module.

61. Position the generator control module coolant inlet hose clamp at the generator control module using the Hose Clamp Pliers (J 38185) or equivalent.

62. Connect the 2 engine wiring harness electrical connectors to the generator control module.

63. Install the 2 CPA retainers.

64. Position and install the power brake booster vacuum hose to the intake manifold.

65. Position the power brake booster vacuum hose clamp at the intake manifold.

66. Install the power brake booster vacuum hose to the clamp to the generator control module coolant outlet hose.

67. Install the radiator inlet hose.

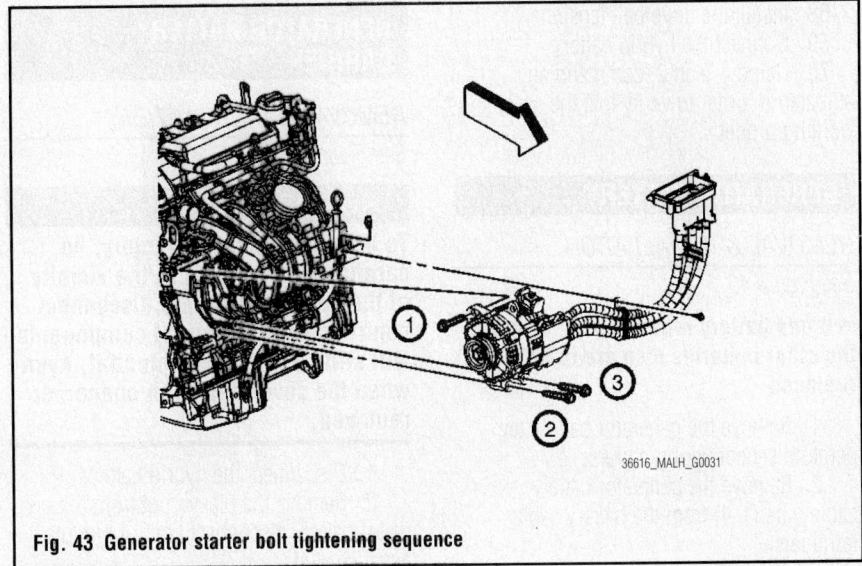
Fig. 43 Generator starter bolt tightening sequence

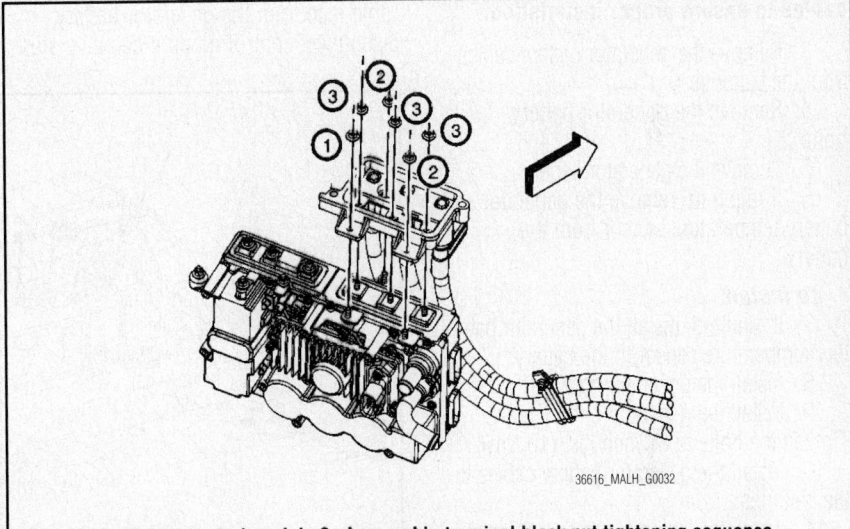
Fig. 44 Generator control module 3-phase cable terminal block nut tightening sequence

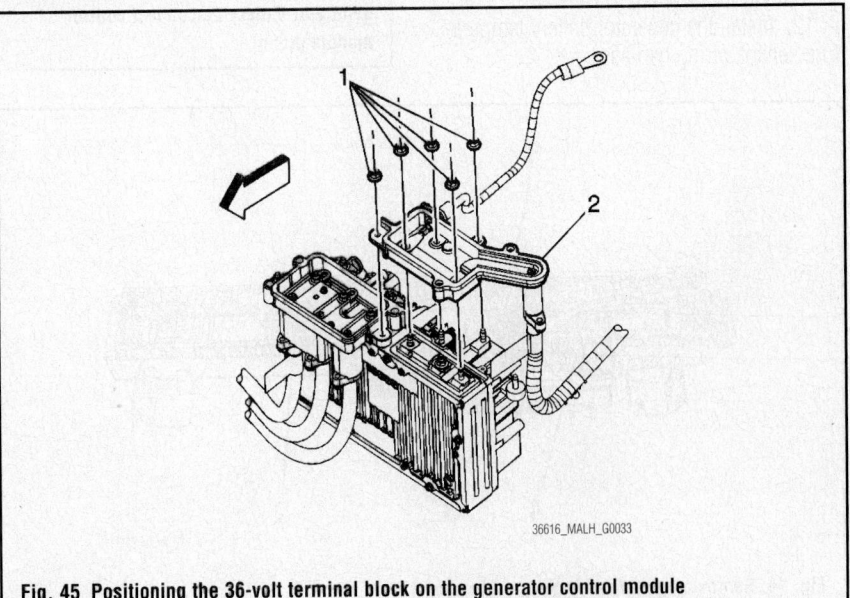
Fig. 45 Positioning the 36-volt terminal block on the generator control module

68. Install the drive belt tensioner.
69. Connect the hybrid battery.
70. Using a Tech 2, command an autostart in order to verify that the system is working properly.

GENERATOR BATTERY

REMOVAL & INSTALLATION

See Figure 46.

➡**If one battery requires replacement, the other batteries also are to be replaced.**

1. Remove the generator battery temperature sensor wiring harness.
2. Remove the generator battery cable nuts (1-4) from the battery cable terminals.

➡**Note original routing of battery cables to ensure proper installation.**

3. Remove the generator battery cables from the batteries.
4. Remove the generator battery bolts.
5. Remove the generator battery.
6. If required, remove the generator battery temperature sensor from the battery.

To install:
7. If required, install the generator battery temperature sensor to the battery.
8. Install the generator battery
9. Install the generator battery bolts. Tighten the bolts to 89 inch lbs. (10 Nm).
10. Install the generator battery cables to the batteries.
11. Install the generator battery cable nuts to the battery cable terminals. Tighten the nuts to 71 inch lbs. (8 Nm).
12. Install the generator battery temperature sensor wiring harness.

GENERATOR BATTERY CARRIER

REMOVAL & INSTALLATION

See Figure 47.

✳✳ WARNING

To help avoid personal injury, be careful when working in the vicinity of the generator battery disconnect control module. Internal components will still be live, 36V potential, even when the cover has been opened or removed.

1. Disconnect the hybrid battery.
2. Remove the plastic nut from the generator battery disconnect control module negative stud.
3. Remove the 36V negative battery cable lead from the generator battery disconnect control module negative stud.

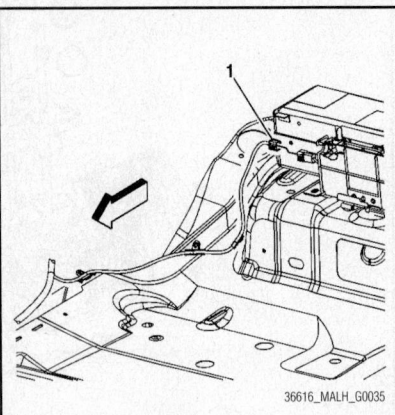

Fig. 47 Disconnecting the body wiring harness electrical connector from the generator battery disconnect control module pigtail

4. Remove the generator battery fuse from the generator battery disconnect module negative stud.
5. Remove the 36V positive battery cable retainer bolt.
6. Remove and discard the 36V positive battery cable lead nut.
7. Remove the 36V positive battery cable lead nut.
8. Remove the 36V positive battery cable leads.
9. Secure the cables out of the way, ensuring that the cables CANNOT be reinstalled without your knowledge.
10. Disconnect the body wiring harness electrical connector from the generator battery disconnect control module pigtail.
11. Remove the generator battery carrier nuts.
12. With the aid of an assistant, lift the generator battery carrier up off of the studs, and rotate and position the carrier towards the rear of the vehicle.
13. With the aid of an assistant, remove the generator battery carrier out though the truck opening.

To install:
14. With the aid of an assistant, install the generator battery carrier in though the truck opening and rotate and position the carrier towards the front of the vehicle.
15. With the aid of an assistant, lift the generator battery carrier up onto the studs.
16. Install the generator battery carrier nuts. Tighten the nuts to 18 ft. lbs. (25 Nm).
17. Connect the body wiring harness electrical connector to the generator battery disconnect control module pigtail.
18. Install the 36V positive battery cable leads.
19. Install the 36V positive battery cable lead nut. Tighten the nut to 18 inch lbs. (9 Nm).
20. Install a NEW 36V positive battery cable lead nut. Start the nut finger tight, and then torque to the specification given. Tighten the nut to 11 ft. lbs. (15 Nm).
21. Position the 36V positive battery cable retainer to the fan cover.
22. Install the 36V positive battery cable retainer bolt. Tighten the bolt to 71 inch lbs. (8 Nm).
23. Install the generator battery fuse to the generator battery disconnect module negative stud.

➡**Position the plastic nut to the negative battery cable and ensure that the nipple is inserted to the terminal prior to installing the negative cable to the generator battery, Otherwise damage to the nut may occur.**

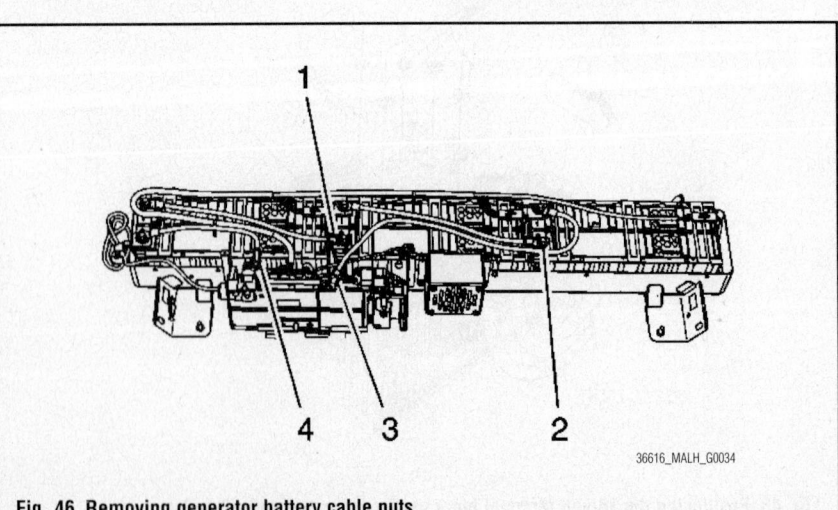

Fig. 46 Removing generator battery cable nuts

24. Position the plastic nut to the 36V negative battery cable lead ensuring that the nipple on the plastic nut is inserted through the hole in the terminal.

25. Install the 36V negative battery cable lead and nut to the generator battery disconnect module negative stud. Tighten the nut to 95 inch lbs. (10.7 Nm).

26. Connect the hybrid battery.

GENERATOR BATTERY TEMPERATURE SENSOR

REMOVAL & INSTALLATION

See Figure 48.

1. Remove the generator battery.
2. Remove the generator battery temperature sensor from the battery.

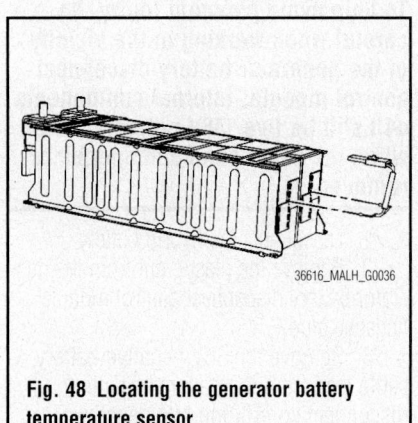

Fig. 48 Locating the generator battery temperature sensor

To install:

3. Install the generator battery temperature sensor to the battery.
4. Install the generator battery.

GENERATOR BATTERY TEMPERATURE SENSOR WIRING HARNESS

REMOVAL & INSTALLATION

See Figures 49 through 52.

1. Disconnect the generator battery.
2. Remove the 2 generator battery vent fan cover bolts.
3. Remove the 12 generator battery cover bolts.
4. Remove the generator battery cover.

➡**Removing the interconnect cables will disable the 36 volts within the generator battery control module.**

5. Remove the generator battery terminal covers.

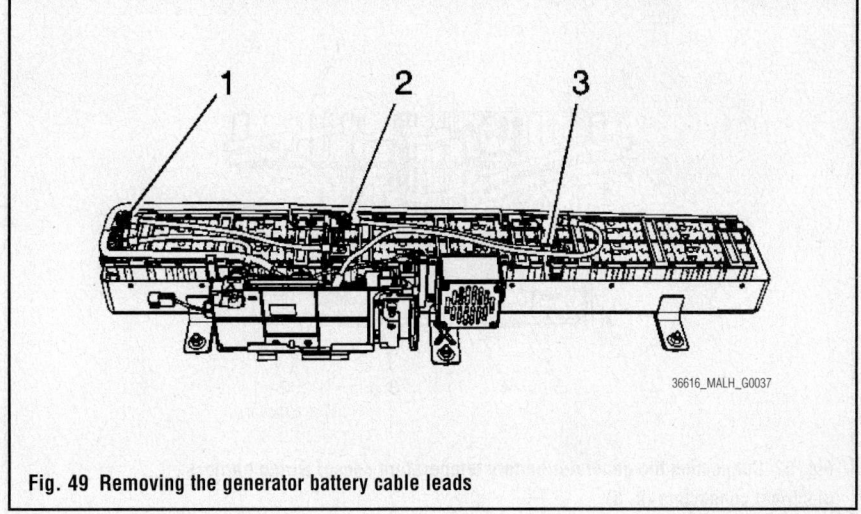

Fig. 49 Removing the generator battery cable leads

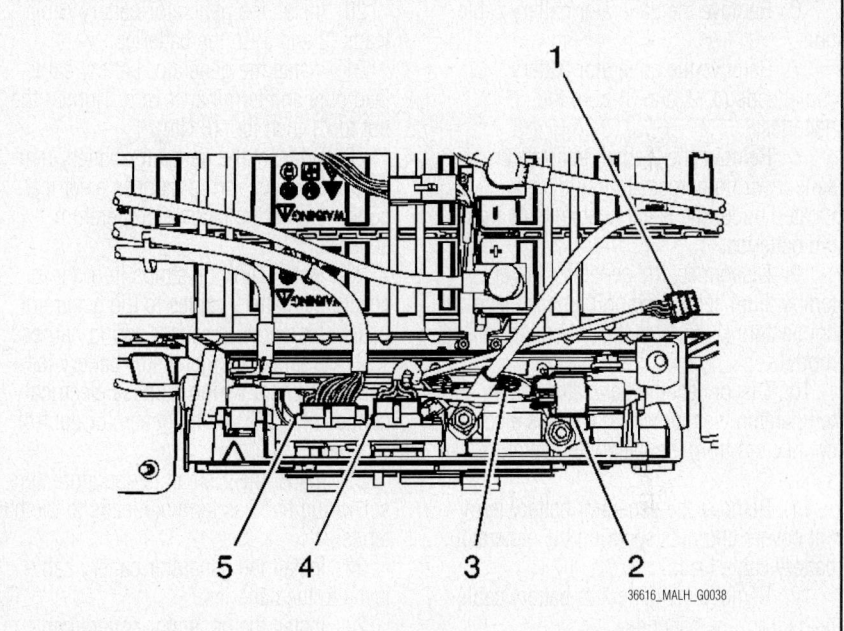

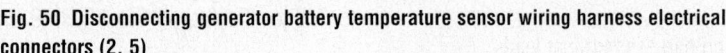

Fig. 50 Disconnecting generator battery temperature sensor wiring harness electrical connectors (2, 5)

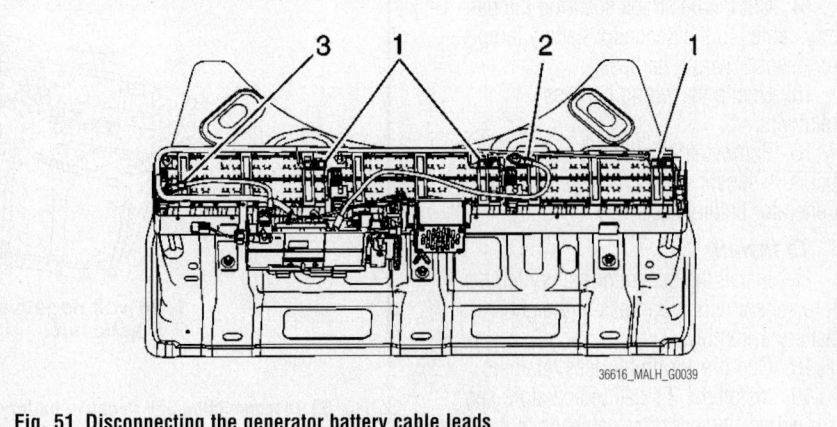

Fig. 51 Disconnecting the generator battery cable leads

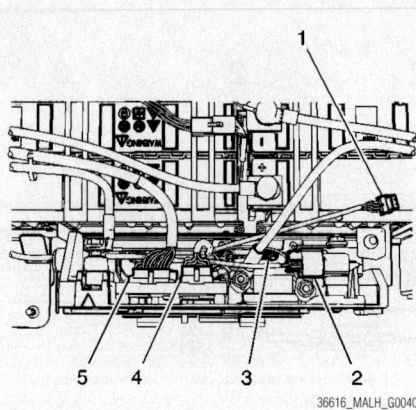

Fig. 52 Connecting the generator battery temperature sensor wiring harness electrical connectors (2, 5)

6. Remove the generator battery cable nuts.

7. Remove the generator battery cable leads (1, 2, and 3) from the batteries.

8. Remove the 2 small temperature sensor wiring harness terminal leads located under the battery cable leads from the batteries.

9. Disconnect the generator battery temperature sensor wiring harness electrical connectors (2, 5) from the generator control module.

10. Disconnect the generator battery temperature sensor wiring harness electrical connectors from the battery temperature sensors.

11. Remove the generator battery terminal covers and nuts securing the generator battery cable leads.

12. Remove the generator battery cable leads from the batteries.

13. Remove the 2 small temperature sensor wiring harness terminal leads located under the battery cable leads from the batteries.

14. Cut the tie straps securing the battery cables to the generator battery temperature sensor wiring harness.

15. Unclip the wiring harness retainers.

16. Remove the generator battery temperature sensor wiring harness from the generator battery assembly.

To install:

17. Install the generator battery temperature sensor wiring harness to the generator battery assembly.

18. Clip the wiring harness retainers.

19. Install the 2 small temperature sensor wiring harness terminal leads to the batteries.

20. Install the generator battery cable leads (2 and 3) to the batteries.

21. Install the generator battery cable lead nuts and terminal covers. Tighten the nut to 71 inch lbs. (8 Nm).

22. Connect the generator battery temperature sensor wiring harness electrical connectors to the battery temperature sensors.

23. Install NEW tie straps in order to secure the battery cables to the generator battery temperature sensor wiring harness.

24. Connect the generator battery temperature sensor wiring harness electrical connectors (2, 5) to the generator control module.

25. Install the 2 small temperature sensor wiring harness terminal leads to the batteries.

26. Install the generator battery cable leads to the batteries.

27. Install the generator battery cable nuts. Tighten the nut to 71 inch lbs. (8 Nm).

28. Install the generator battery terminal covers.

29. Install the generator battery cover

30. Install the 12 generator battery cover bolts. Tighten the bolts to 71 inch lbs. (8 Nm).

31. Install the 2 generator battery vent fan cover bolts. Tighten the bolts to 71 inch lbs. (8 Nm).

32. Connect the generator battery.

GENERATOR BATTERY DISCONNECT CONTROL MODULE

REMOVAL & INSTALLATION
See Figures 53 through 57.

✳✳ WARNING

To help avoid personal injury, be careful when working in the vicinity of the generator battery disconnect control module. Internal components will still be live, 36V potential, even when the cover has been opened or removed.

1. Disconnect the hybrid battery.

2. Remove the plastic nut from the generator battery disconnect control module negative stud.

3. Remove the 36V negative battery cable lead from the generator battery disconnect control module negative stud.

4. Remove the generator battery fuse from the generator battery disconnect module negative stud.

5. Remove and discard the 36V positive battery cable lead nut.

6. Remove the 36V positive battery cable lead nut.

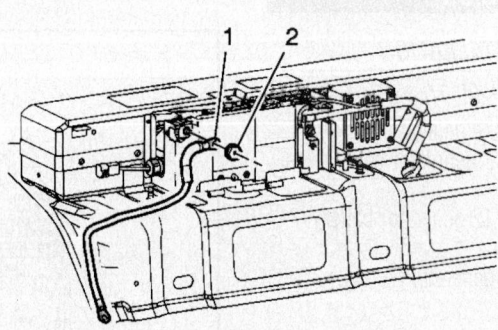

1. 36-volt negative battery cable lead
2. Plastic nut

Fig. 53 Disconnecting 36V negative battery cable lead from the generator battery disconnect control module negative stud

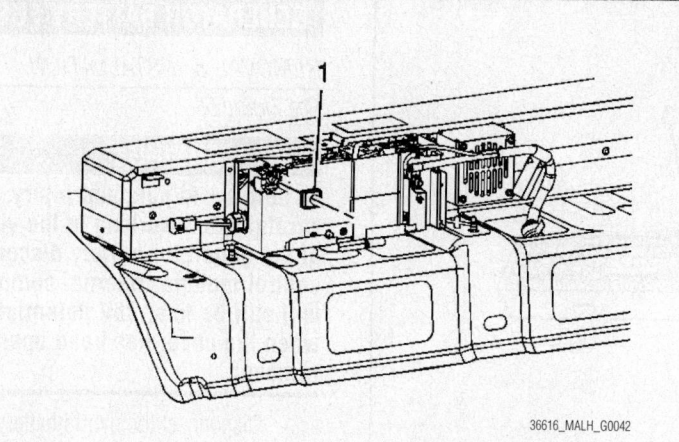

Fig. 54 Removing the generator battery fuse from the generator batter disconnect module negative stud

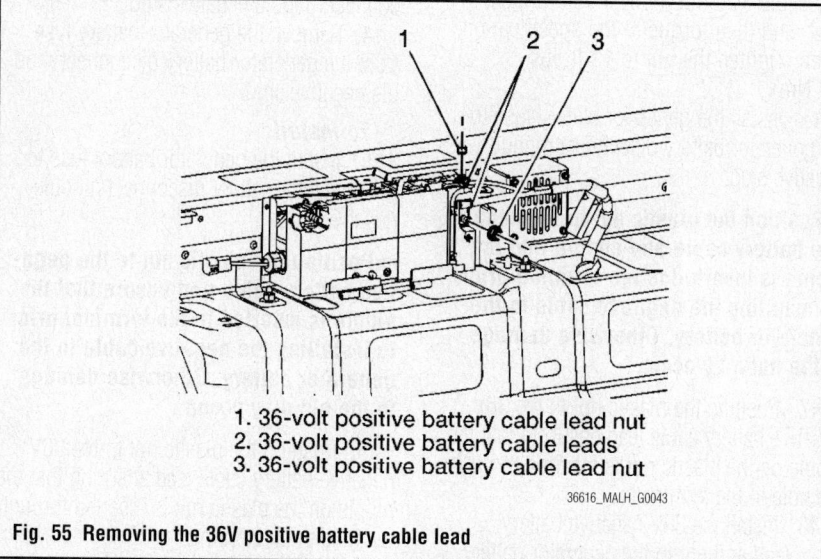

1. 36-volt positive battery cable lead nut
2. 36-volt positive battery cable leads
3. 36-volt positive battery cable lead nut

36616_MALH_G0043

Fig. 55 Removing the 36V positive battery cable lead

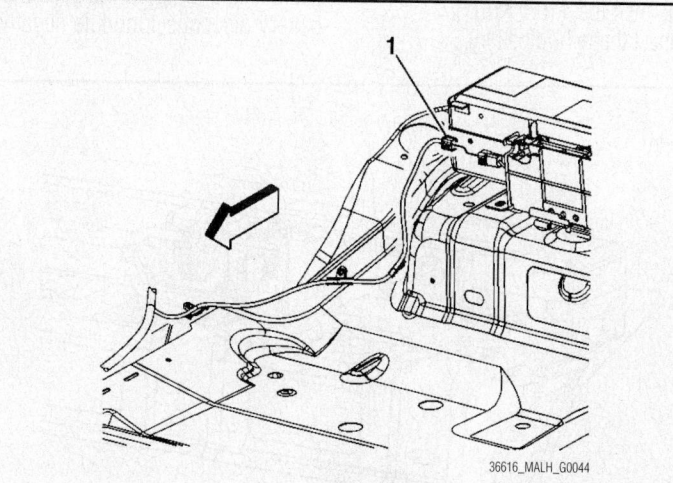

36616_MALH_G0044

Fig. 56 Disconnecting the body wiring harness electrical connector from the generator battery disconnect control module pigtail

7. Remove the 36V positive battery cable leads.

8. Secure the cables out of the way, ensuring that the cables CANNOT be reinstalled without your knowledge.

9. Disconnect the body wiring harness electrical connector from the generator battery disconnect control module pigtail.

10. Remove the 2 generator battery vent fan cover bolts.

11. Remove the 12 generator battery cover bolts.

12. Remove the generator battery cover.

➡**Removing the interconnect cables will disable the 36 volts within the generator battery control module.**

13. Remove the generator battery terminal covers.

14. Remove the generator battery cable nuts.

15. Remove the generator battery cable leads from the batteries.

16. Remove the 2 small temperature sensor wiring harness terminal leads located under the battery cable leads from the batteries.

17. Remove the generator battery control module nuts, and the battery cables from the studs.

18. Disconnect the wiring harness electrical connector from the vent fan electrical connector.

19. Disconnect the generator battery temperature sensor wiring harness electrical connectors from the generator control module.

20. Reposition the battery cables and the generator battery temperature sensor wiring harness out of the way.

21. Remove the generator battery disconnect control module pigtail clip from the side of the battery carrier.

22. Unclip the fan harness retainer from the battery.

23. Remove the 4 generator battery disconnect control module bolts.

24. Remove the generator battery disconnect control module.

To install:

25. Install the generator battery disconnect control module.

26. Install the 4 generator battery disconnect control module bolts. Tighten the bolts to 71 inch lb (8 Nm).

27. Clip the fan harness retainer to the battery.

28. Install the generator battery disconnect control module pigtail clip to the side of the battery carrier.

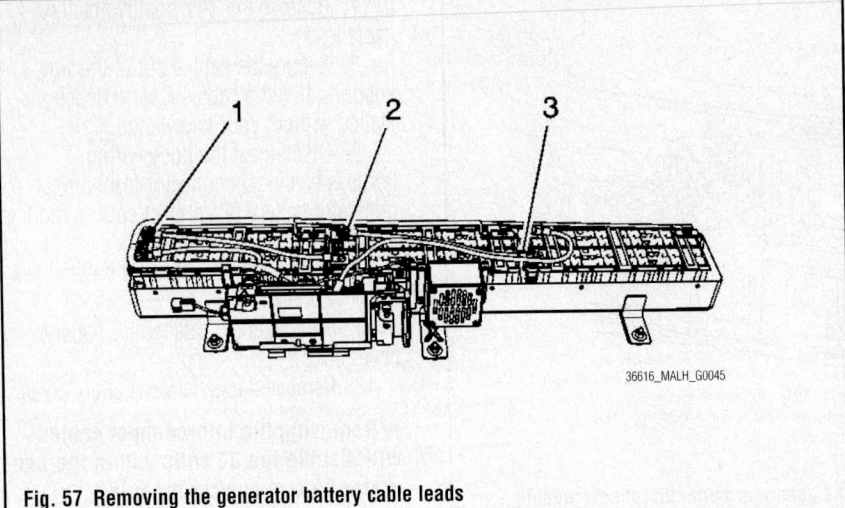

Fig. 57 Removing the generator battery cable leads

29. Position the generator battery temperature sensor wiring harness and the battery cables to the generator control module.

30. Connect the generator battery temperature sensor wiring harness electrical connectors to the generator control module.

31. Connect the wiring harness electrical connector to the vent fan electrical connector.

32. Ensure that the generator battery temperature sensor wiring harness terminals and installed on the generator battery control module studs.

33. Install the battery cable, and the generator battery control module nut to the stud. Tighten the nut to 71 inch lbs. (8 Nm).

34. Install the battery cable, and the generator battery control module nut to the stud. Tighten the nut to 71 inch lbs. (8 Nm).

35. Install the 2 small temperature sensor wiring harness terminal leads to the batteries.

36. Install the generator battery cable leads to the batteries.

37. Install the generator battery cable nuts. Tighten the nut to 71 inch lbs. (8 Nm).

38. Install the generator battery terminal covers.

39. Install the generator battery cover

40. Install the 12 generator battery cover bolts. Tighten the bolts to 71 inch lbs. (8 Nm).

41. Install the 2 generator battery vent fan cover bolts. Tighten the bolts to 71 inch lbs. (8 Nm).

42. Connect the body wiring harness electrical connector to the generator battery disconnect control module pigtail.

43. Install the 36V positive battery cable leads.

44. Install the 36V positive battery cable lead nut. Tighten the nut to 18 inch lbs. (9 Nm).

45. Install a NEW 36-volt positive battery cable lead nut. Start the nut finger tight, and then torque to the specification given. Tighten the nut to 11 ft. lbs. (15 Nm).

46. Install the generator battery fuse to the generator battery disconnect module negative stud.

➡Position the plastic nut to the negative battery cable and ensure that the nipple is inserted to the terminal prior to installing the negative cable to the generator battery, Otherwise damage to the nut may occur.

47. Position the plastic nut to the 36V negative battery cable lead ensuring that the nipple on the plastic nut is inserted through the hole in the terminal.

48. Install the 36V negative battery cable lead and nut to the generator battery disconnect module negative stud. Tighten the nut to 95 inch lbs. (10.7 Nm).

49. Connect the hybrid battery.

GENERATOR BATTERY FUSE

REMOVAL & INSTALLATION
See Figure 58.

✽✽ WARNING

To help avoid personal injury, be careful when working in the vicinity of the generator battery disconnect control module. Internal components will still be live, 36V potential, even when the cover has been opened or removed.

1. Disconnect the hybrid battery.
2. Remove the plastic nut from the generator battery disconnect control module negative stud.
3. Remove the 36V negative battery cable lead from the generator battery disconnect module negative stud.
4. Remove the generator battery fuse from the generator battery disconnect module negative stud.

To install:
5. Install the generator battery fuse to the generator battery disconnect module negative stud.

➡Position the plastic nut to the negative battery cable and ensure that the nipple is inserted to the terminal prior to installing the negative cable to the generator battery, Otherwise damage to the nut may occur.

6. Position the plastic nut to the 36V negative battery cable lead ensuring that the nipple on the plastic nut is inserted through the hole in the terminal.

7. Install the 36V negative battery cable lead and nut to the generator battery disconnect module negative

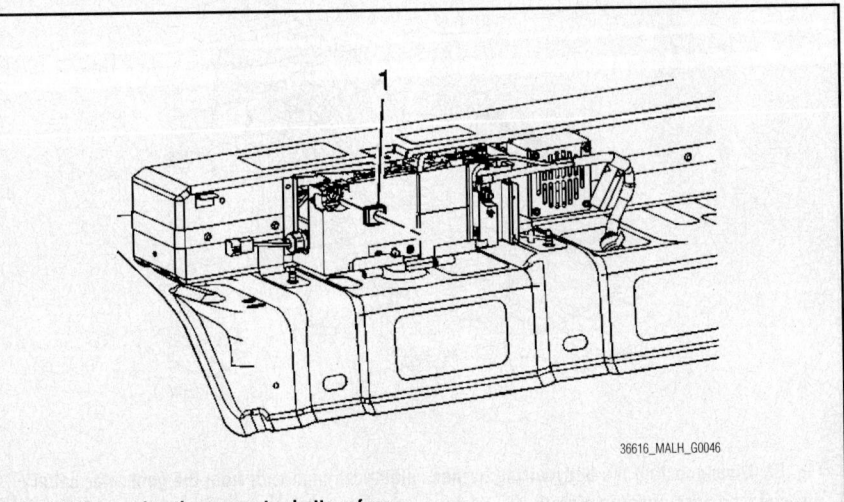

Fig. 58 Removing the generator battery fuse

stud. Tighten the nut to 95 inch lbs.
(10.7 Nm).

8. Connect the hybrid battery.

GENERATOR BATTERY VENT FAN

REMOVAL & INSTALLATION

See Figure 59.

1. Remove the hybrid battery service disconnect/connect cover.
2. Remove the fan screws.
3. Remove the generator battery vent fan. Disconnect the electrical connector.

To install:

4. Install the generator battery vent fan.
5. Install the vent fan screws to 80 inch lbs. (9 Nm).
6. Install the hybrid battery service disconnect/connect cover.

GENERATOR CONTROL MODULE

REMOVAL & INSTALLATION

See Figures 60 through 62.

1. Disconnect the hybrid battery.
2. Drain the cooling system.
3. Remove the battery tray.
4. Reposition the power brake booster vacuum hose clamp at the intake manifold.
5. Reposition the power brake booster vacuum hose clamp at the intake manifold.
6. Remove the power brake booster vacuum hose from the intake manifold.
7. Remove the power brake booster vacuum hose from the clamp on the generator control module coolant outlet hose.
8. Reposition the power brake booster vacuum hose out of the way.

✸✸ WARNING

To help avoid personal injury, additional precautions must be taken prior to working on the generator control module or the generator starter. After removing the 36V battery cables from the generator battery, remove both engine wiring harness connectors from the generator control module. Wait at least 5 minutes and then remove the generator control module cover. Verify voltage levels at all 36V, 12V, and 3-phase connections, are less than 3 volts using a DMM before proceeding.

9. Remove the 2 Connector Position Assurance (CPA) retainers.

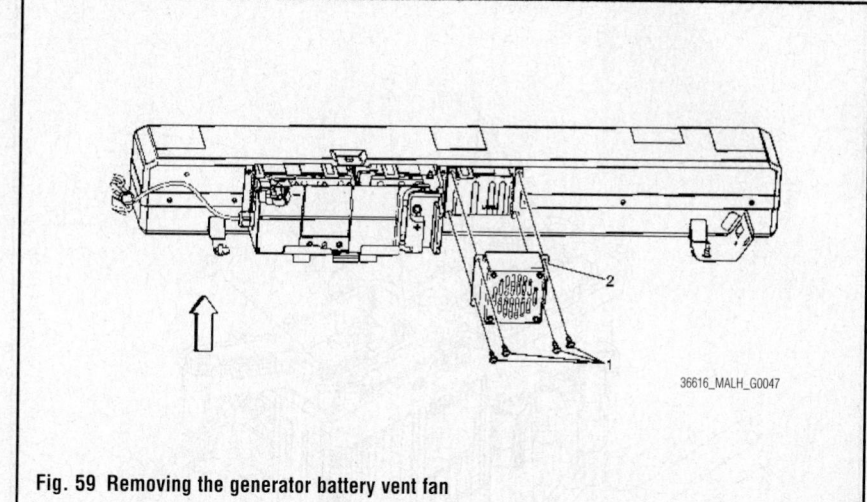

Fig. 59 Removing the generator battery vent fan

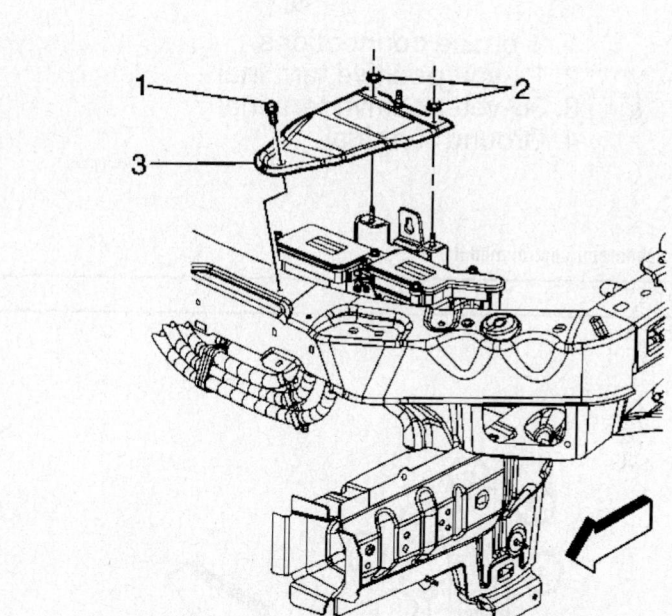

1. Generator control module bracket reinforcement bolt
2. Generator control module bracket reinforcement nuts
3. Generator control module bracket reinforcement

36616_MALH_G0048

Fig. 60 Removing the generator control module bracket reinforcement

10. Disconnect the 2 engine wiring harness electrical connectors from the generator control module.
11. WAIT at least 5 minutes in order to allow the voltage stored in the generator control module to discharge.
12. Remove the generator control module bracket reinforcement bolt and nuts.
13. Remove the generator control module bracket reinforcement.

14. Reposition the generator control module coolant inlet hose clamp at the generator control module using the Hose Clamp Pliers (J 38185) or equivalent.
15. Remove the generator control module coolant inlet hose from the generator control module.
16. Loosen the generator control module cover integral bolts and remove the cover.
17. The generator control module will have to be checked for voltage potential

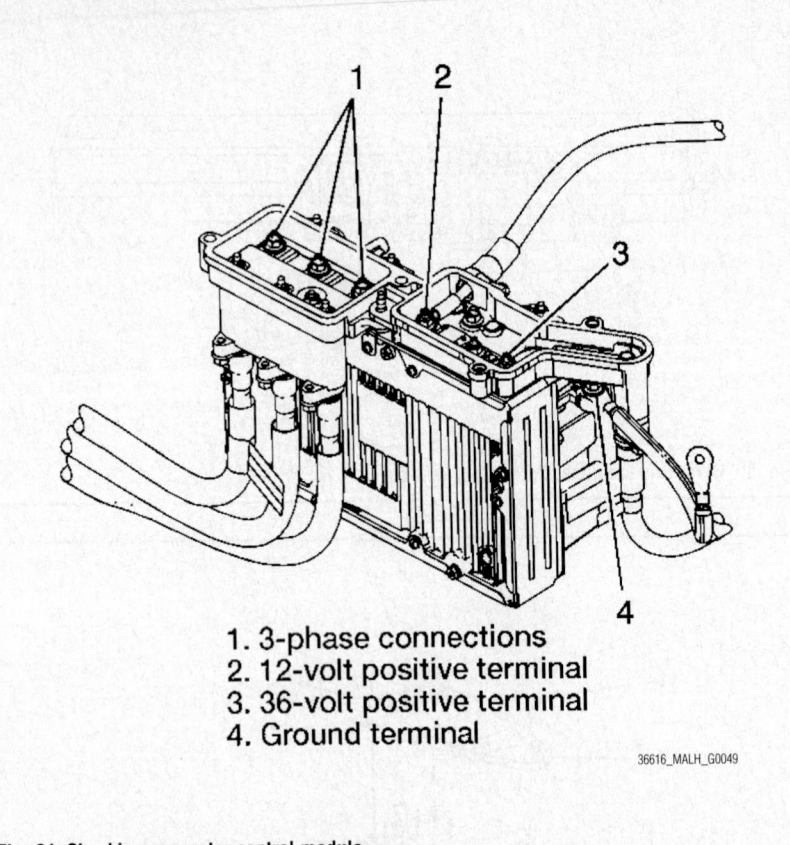

1. 3-phase connections
2. 12-volt positive terminal
3. 36-volt positive terminal
4. Ground terminal

36616_MALH_G0049

Fig. 61 Checking generator control module

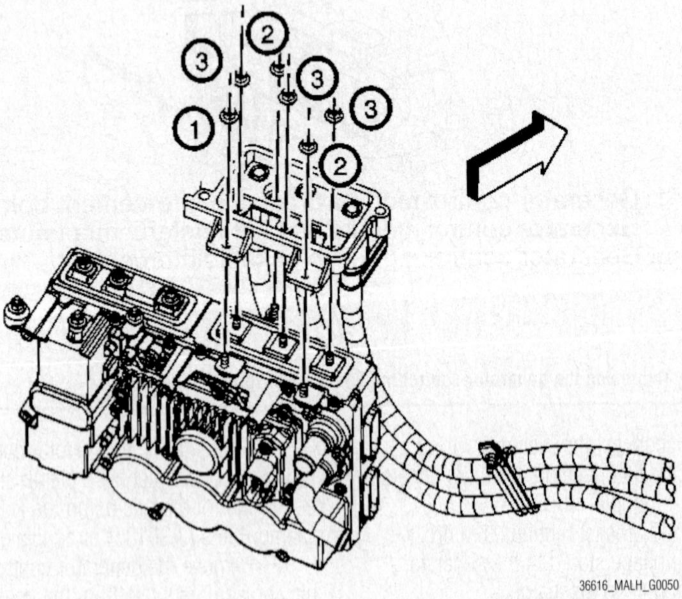

Fig. 62 Identifying generator control module 3-phase cable terminal block nut tightening sequence

36616_MALH_G0050

using a voltmeter. First verify that the voltmeter works:

    a. Set the voltmeter to DC voltage.

    b. Measure the vehicle 12V battery voltage.

    c. The meter should read greater than +12V DC.

18. Check the generator control module for voltage potential, in order to ensure that the module has been disabled.

    a. Measure from the 36V positive terminal to a known good chassis ground. The voltage should be less than 3V.

    b. Measure from the 12V positive terminal to a known good chassis ground. The voltage should be less than 3V.

    c. Measure from the ground terminal to a known good chassis ground, checking for continuity.

✳ WARNING

To help avoid personal injury, always treat the 3-phase cable and connectors as if voltage is present and as if the surface of all parts of the cable is hot.

19. Verify that the generator control module 3-phase cables are disabled.

    a. Measure from each phase 1, 2, and 3 connection to a known good ground. The voltage should be less than 3V.

    b. After verifying that there is no voltage present, the generator control module 3-phase cables can now be removed from the generator control module.

20. Remove the 36V terminal block nuts from the generator control module.

21. Lift up, and reposition the 36V terminal block, secure the block out of the way. Discard the terminal block seal.

22. Remove the generator control module 3-phase cable terminal block nuts from the generator control module.

23. Lift up, and reposition the generator control module 3-phase cable terminal block, secure the block out of the way. Discard the terminal block seal.

24. Disconnect the engine wiring harness electrical connector from the transaxle auxiliary pump module.

25. Remove the generator control module ground strap nut and strap from the module stud.

26. Remove the engine wiring harness clips from the battery tray bracket studs.

27. Remove the generator control module nuts.

28. Remove the generator control module (with bracket) from the vehicle.

29. Place the generator control module assembly on a clean work surface.

30. Remove the generator control module bracket to module bolts. Separate the generator control module from the bracket.

31. If replacing the generator control module. Remove the transaxle auxiliary pump control module.

To install:

32. If the generator control module was replaced. install the transaxle auxiliary pump control module.

33. Position the generator control module to the bracket, and install the generator control module bracket to module bolts. Tighten the bolts to 89 inch lbs. (10 Nm).

34. Install the generator control module (with bracket) to the vehicle.

35. Install the generator control module bracket nuts. Tighten the nuts to 89 inch lbs. (10 Nm).

36. Connect the engine wiring harness electrical connector to the transaxle auxiliary pump.

37. Place a NEW terminal block seal onto the generator control module.

38. Install the generator control module 3-phase cable terminal block onto the generator control module.

39. Install the generator control module 3-phase cable terminal block nuts until snug.

40. Tighten the generator control module 3-phase cable terminal block nuts in the sequence shown.

41. Tighten the nuts to 71 inch lbs. (8 Nm).

42. Place a NEW terminal block seal onto the generator control module.

43. Unsecure, and position the 36V terminal block to the generator control module.

44. Install the 36V terminal block nuts to the generator control module. Tighten the nuts to 89 inch lbs. (10 Nm).

45. Place the generator control module cover on top of the generator control module and tighten bolts.

46. Tighten the bolts to 89 inch lbs. (10 Nm).

47. Install the generator control module coolant outlet hose to the generator control module.

48. Position the generator control module coolant outlet hose clamp at the generator control module using the Hose Clamp Pliers (J 38185) or equivalent.

49. Install the generator control module coolant inlet hose to the generator control module.

50. Position the generator control module coolant inlet hose clamp at the generator

control module using the Hose Clamp Pliers (J 38185) or equivalent.

51. Install the generator control module bracket reinforcement.

52. Install the generator control module bracket reinforcement bolt and nuts. Tighten the bolt/nuts to 89 inch lbs. (10 Nm).

53. Connect the 2 engine wiring harness electrical connectors to the generator control module.

54. Install the 2 CPA retainers.

55. Position and install the power brake booster vacuum hose to the intake manifold.

56. Position the power brake booster vacuum hose clamp at the intake manifold.

57. Install the power brake booster vacuum hose to the clamp to the generator control module coolant outlet hose.

58. Install the battery tray.

59. Fill the cooling system.

60. Connect the hybrid battery.

61. If the generator control module was replaced, program the NEW module.

62. Using a Tech 2, command an autostart in order to verify that the system is working properly.

GENERATOR CONTROL MODULE COOLANT PUMP

REMOVAL & INSTALLATION

See Figure 63.

1. Drain the cooling system.
2. Raise and support the vehicle.
3. Remove the generator control module coolant pump bolt.
4. Remove the generator control module coolant pump.

　a. Using Hose Clamp Pliers (J 38185) reposition the generator coolant pump hose clamps.

　b. Remove the hoses from the generator control module coolant pump.

　c. Disconnect the electrical connection.

To install:

To install, reverse the removal procedures. Fill and check the cooling system.

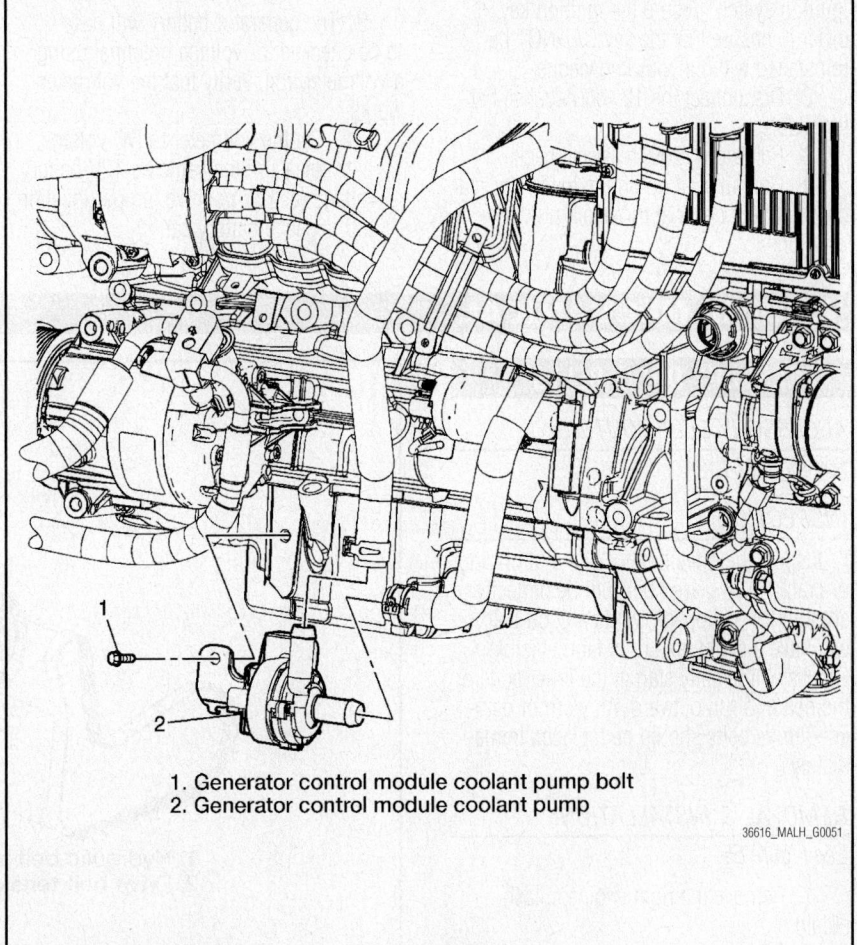

1. Generator control module coolant pump bolt
2. Generator control module coolant pump

36616_MALH_G0051

Fig. 63 Locating the generator control module coolant pump

HYBRID BATTERY

DISCONNECT PROCEDURE

✳✳ WARNING

To help avoid personal injury, always ensure the ignition switch is in the OFF position and the ignition key has been removed prior to working on any 36V components. After the key has been removed, disconnect the negative 12V battery cable and then open the generator battery disconnect control module cover. After waiting for at least 5 minutes, measure the voltage potential using a DMM between the following:

- 36V positive and negative battery cables
- 36V positive battery cable and vehicle ground
- 36V negative battery cable and vehicle ground

All measured voltage levels must be below 3V.

1. Remove the ignition key from the ignition switch. Secure the ignition key in order to ensure that the key CANNOT be reinstalled without your knowledge.

2. Disconnect the 12 volt negative battery cable.

3. Fold down both rear seat backs.

4. Carefully lift up on the load floor rear compartment cover at the retaining clip locations.

5. Tilt the load floor rear compartment cover towards the rear of the vehicle slightly, disengaging the tabs and remove the load floor rear compartment cover.

✳✳ WARNING

To help avoid personal injury, be careful when working in the vicinity of the generator battery disconnect control module. Internal components will still be live, 36V potential, even when the cover has been opened or removed.

6. Remove the generator battery disconnect control module cover bolt.

7. Open and slide the generator battery disconnect control module cover to the right, removing the cover.

8. WAIT at least 5 minutes in order to allow the generator control module capacitors to discharge.

➡**Never assume the battery pack is disabled when the generator battery disconnect control module cover is opened.**

9. The generator battery will have to be checked for voltage potential using a voltmeter first, verify that the voltmeter works:

  a. Set the voltmeter to DC voltage.

  b. Measure the vehicle's 12V battery voltage (at 12V positive jumper location and negative battery cable).

  c. The meter should read greater than +12V DC.

10. Now, check the generator battery for voltage potential in order to ensure that the generator battery has been disabled.

  a. Measure from the positive stud to the negative stud. The voltage should be less than 3V.

  b. Measure from the positive stud to the vehicle chassis ground. The voltage should be less than 3V.

  c. Measure from the negative stud to the vehicle chassis ground. The voltage should be less than 3V.

  d. After verifying that there is no voltage present, the vehicle is now safe to work on.

CONNECT PROCEDURE

1. Install and close the generator battery disconnect control module cover.

2. Install the generator battery cover bolt. Tighten the bolt to 89 inch lbs. (10 Nm).

3. Tilt the load floor rear compartment cover towards the rear of the vehicle slightly in order to insert the tabs into the battery tray rear support.

4. Set the load floor rear compartment cover down ensuring that the retaining clips align to the proper locations, carefully push down securing the cover.

5. Return both rear seat backs to their proper positions.

6. Connect the 12V negative battery cable.

ENGINE MECHANICAL

ACCESSORY DRIVE BELTS

ACCESSORY BELT ROUTING

See Figure 64.

INSPECTION

Inspect the drive belt for signs of glazing or cracking. A glazed belt will be perfectly smooth from slippage, while a good belt will have a slight texture of fabric visible. Cracks will usually start at the inner edge of the belt and run outward. All worn or damaged drive belts should be replaced immediately.

REMOVAL & INSTALLATION

See Figure 65.

1. Remove the right engine splash shield.

2. Remove the air cleaner assembly.

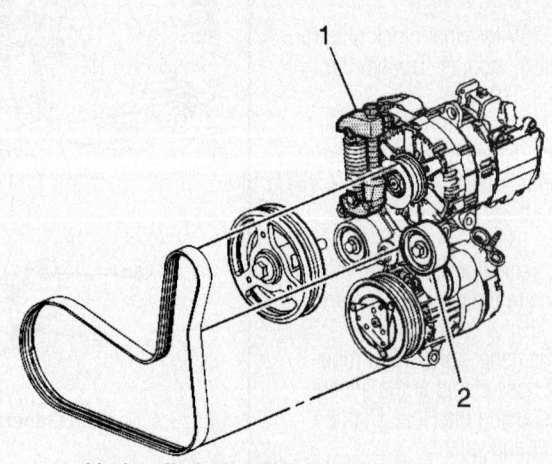

1. Hydraulic belt tensioner compressor
2. Drive belt tensioner spring

36616_MALH_G0004

Fig. 64 Drive belt routing

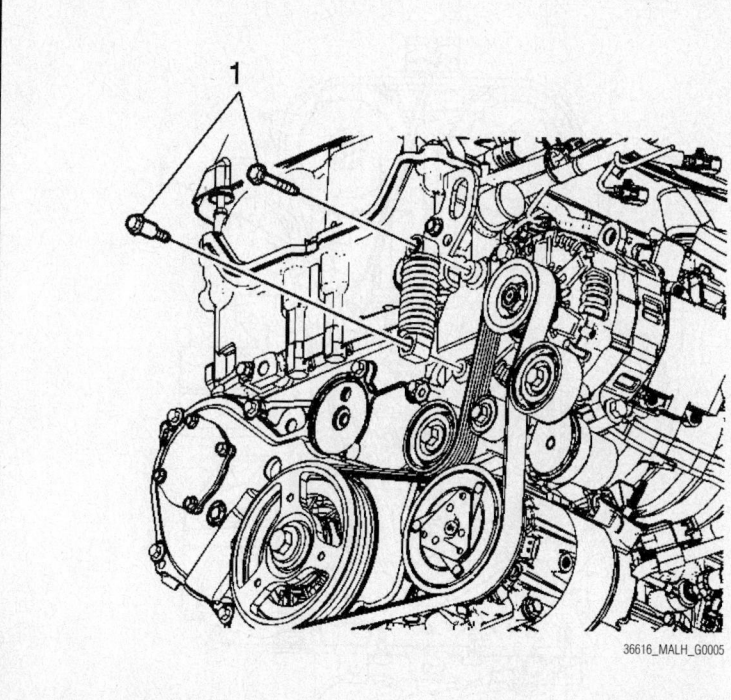

Fig. 65 Removing the drive belt

3. Install the hydraulic belt tensioner compressor to the drive belt tensioner spring.

4. Compress the drive belt tensioner spring fully using the hydraulic belt tensioner compressor.

5. Remove the tensioner spring bolts from the tensioner.

6. Remove the tensioner spring from the tensioner.

7. Remove the drive belt from under the middle idler pulley.

8. Remove the drive belt from the vehicle.

To install:

9. Install and position the drive belt around all of the pulleys except for the middle idler pulley.

10. Install the tensioner spring on the tensioner.

11. Install the tensioner spring bolts and tighten to 16 ft. lbs. (22 Nm).

12. Install the drive belt under the middle idler pulley.

13. Loosen the forcing bolt on the hydraulic belt tensioner compressor and remove from the drive belt tensioner spring.

14. Install and position the drive belt around all of the pulleys except for the middle idler pulley.

15. Ensure that the drive belt tensioner idler is fully seated against the drive belt.

16. Install the air cleaner assembly.

17. Install the right engine splash shield.

BALANCE SHAFT

REMOVAL & INSTALLATION

See Figures 66 and 67.

1. Remove the balance shaft bearing carrier bolts.

➡️It is possible to install the intake side balance shaft into the exhaust side and vice versa. Please use care not to install the balance shafts into the wrong bores. Engine vibration will result.

➡️Do not remove the bolt holding the sprocket.

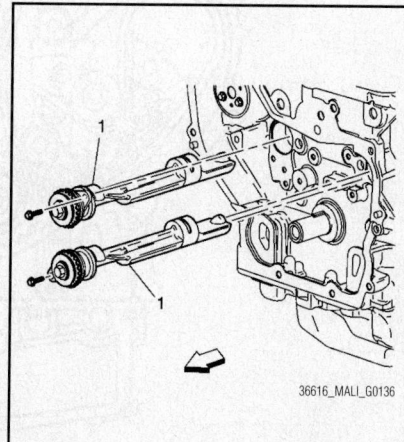

Fig. 66 Removing the balance shaft bearing carrier bolts

2. Remove the balance shaft assemblies.

➡️Proper centering of the tool is required on the balance shaft bushing. If the tool is not properly centered then damage to the bearing bore and block will occur.

3. Install the balance shaft bearing remover/installer (J 43650) into the balance shaft hole. Insert the tool with the foot parallel to the shaft.

4. When the tool is inserted in the block turn the tool so that the foot becomes perpendicular to the shaft.

5. Center the foot of the tool on the balance shaft bushing.

6. Once the tool is centered on the balance shaft bushing, then insert the centering guide into the front balance shaft bore and tighten the nut with an appropriate wrench.

➡️When the tool is properly installed, before removing the busing, the end of the tool should be 4.6 inches (116 mm) from the block face. If the tool is less than 4.5 inches (116 mm), recheck the tool alignment.

7. Tighten the nut on the tool until the tension releases. When the tension releases, remove the balance shaft bushing.

To install:

8. Install the balance shaft bushing using the balance shaft bearing remover/installer tool.

9. Seat the balance shaft bushing into the bore using the tool and wrench.

10. When the tool is fully seated in the engine block, remove it with a wrench.

➡️If the balance shafts are not properly timed to the engine, the engine may vibrate or make noise.

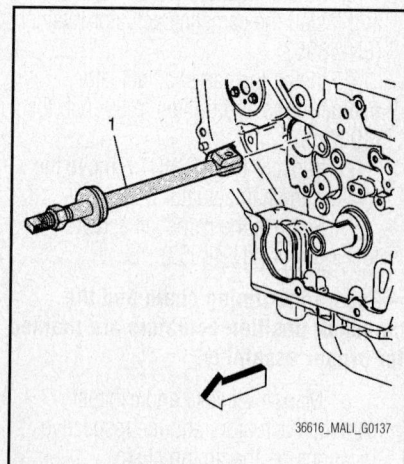

Fig. 67 Installing the balance shaft bearing remover/installer tool

➡ **Install the balance shaft assemblies to the engine using the following steps.**

11. Place the number one piston at Top Dead Center (TDC).

12. Lubricate the balance shaft lobes with engine oil.

13. Install the balance shafts into their bores.

➡ **Use the correct fastener in the correct location. Replacement fasteners must be the correct part number for that application. Fasteners requiring replacement or fasteners requiring the use of thread locking compound or sealant are identified in the service procedure. Do not use paints, lubricants, or corrosion inhibitors on fasteners or fastener joint surfaces unless specified. These coatings affect fastener torque and joint clamping force and may damage the fastener. Use the correct tightening sequence and specifications when installing fasteners in order to avoid damage to parts and systems.**

14. Install the balance shaft retaining bolts. Tighten the bolts to 89 inch lbs. (10 Nm).

CAMSHAFT AND VALVE LIFTERS

REMOVAL & INSTALLATION

Intake

See Figures 68 and 69.

1. Remove the intake camshaft position actuator as follows:

    a. Remove the camshaft cover.

    b. Remove the spark plugs.

    c. Rotate the crankshaft clockwise and install the camshaft actuator retainer (EN-48953).

    d. Install the camshaft actuator retainer bolts and tighten to 89 inch lbs. (10 Nm).

    e. Loosen, but DO NOT remove the intake camshaft actuator bolt.

    f. Remove the camshaft actuator locking tool (EN-48953).

➡ **Ensure the timing chain and the camshaft position actuators are marked for proper assembly.**

    g. Mark the intake and exhaust camshaft actuators and the respective locations on the timing chain.

    h. Remove the upper timing chain guide bolts and guide.

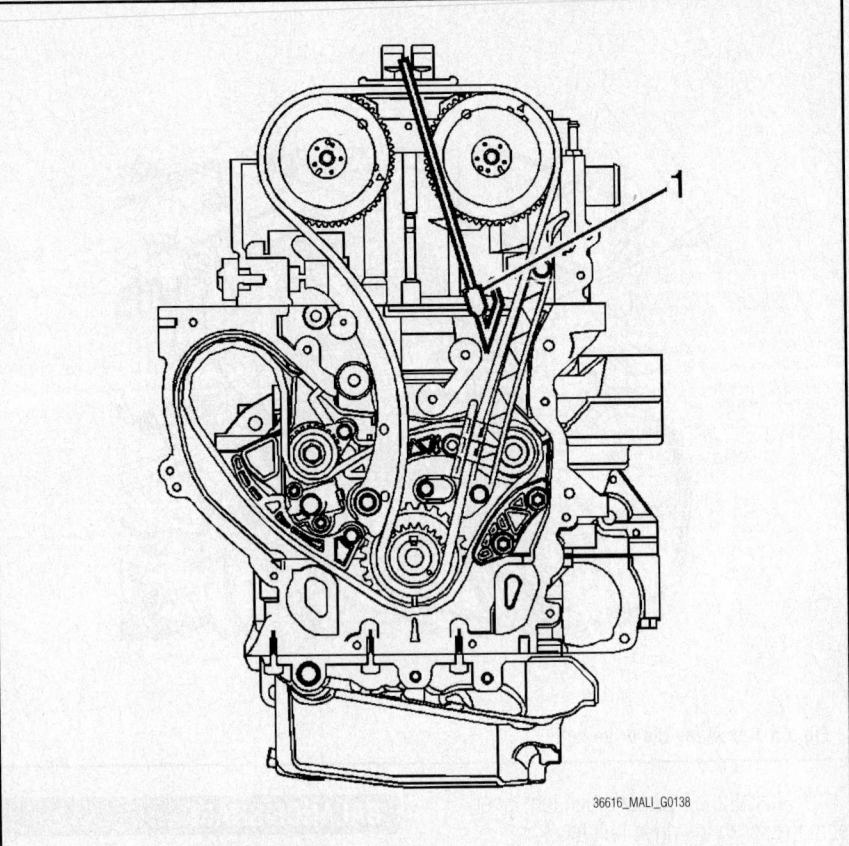

36616_MALI_G0138

Fig. 68 Installing the timing chain retention tool to the intake side of the timing chain

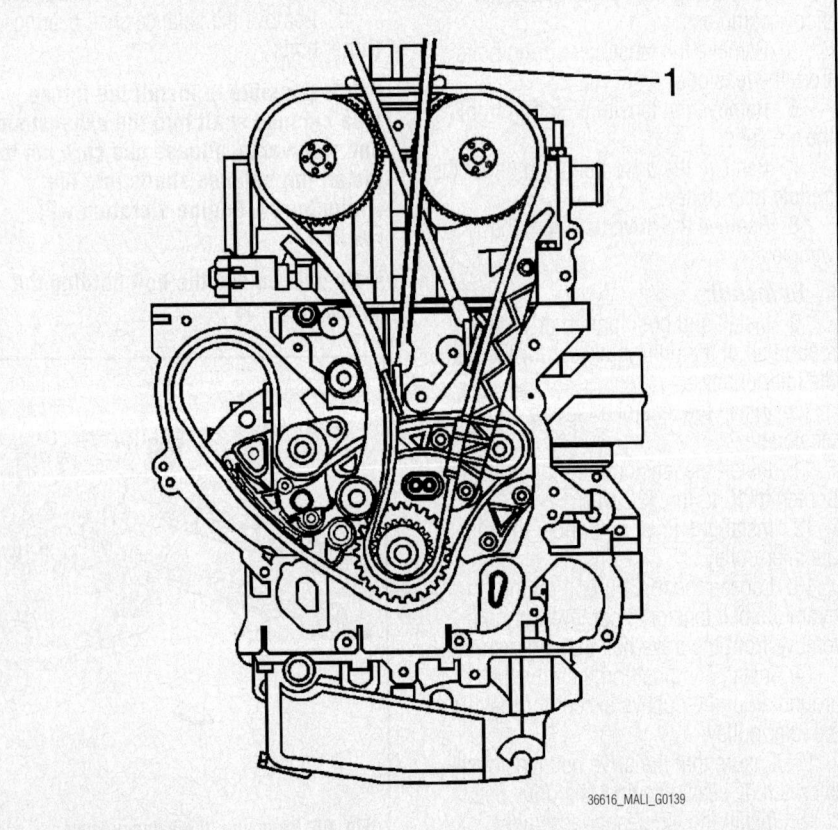

36616_MALI_G0139

Fig. 69 Installing the timing chain retention tool to the exhaust side of the timing chain

i. Remove the timing chain tensioner.

➡ The intake camshaft actuator should not rotate during the removal or installation.

➡ Ensure the tips of the timing chain tensioner tool are fully engaged into the timing chain. The retention tool rod can be used on the back side of the chain to ensure the teeth from the retention tool are engaged.

j. Install the timing chain retention tool (EN-48749) to the intake side of the timing chain.

k. Install the timing chain retention tool (EN-48749) to the exhaust side of the timing chain.

l. Remove and discard the intake camshaft actuator bolt.

m. Rotate the exhaust camshaft clockwise slightly to take the tension off of the timing chain on the intake actuator.

n. Remove the intake camshaft actuator from the camshaft while also removing the actuator from the timing chain.

➡ Remove each bolt on each cap one turn at a time until there is no spring tension pushing on the camshaft.

2. Mark the bearing caps to ensure they are installed in the original position.
3. Remove the bearing cap bolts.
4. Remove the bearing caps.
5. Remove the intake camshaft.

➡ Keep all of the roller followers and hydraulic adjusters in order so that they can be reinstalled in their respective locations.

6. Remove the camshaft roller followers.
7. Remove the hydraulic element lash adjusters.

To install:

8. Install the hydraulic element lash adjusters into their bores in the cylinder head.
9. Lubricate the hydraulic lash adjusters with molylube.
10. Lubricate the valve tips with GM molylube.

➡ Used roller followers MUST be returned to their original position on the camshaft. If the camshaft is being replaced, the roller followers actuated by the camshaft must also be replaced.

11. Position the camshaft roller followers on the tip of the valve stem and on the lash adjuster. Lubricate the roller followers with molylube.

12. Install the intake camshaft and lubricate with molylube.
13. Install the camshaft bearing caps. Hand tighten the cap bolts.
14. Tighten the bearing cap bolts in increments of 3 turns until they are seated to 89 inch lbs. (10 Nm).
15. Install the intake camshaft position actuator as follows:

➡ Ensure that the alignment mark made previously on the exhaust camshaft actuator is still aligned properly with the mark on the timing chain.

a. Install the timing chain onto the intake camshaft actuator.

b. Align the intake camshaft actuator alignment mark made previously with the timing chain mark and install the actuator onto the camshaft rotating the exhaust camshaft clockwise, if required.

c. Install a NEW intake camshaft actuator bolt until snug.

d. Remove the timing chain retention tool from the intake side of the timing chain.

➡ Ensure that the alignment mark previously on the intake camshaft actuator is still aligned properly with the timing chain. If the mark made previously on the intake camshaft actuator is not aligned properly, refer to replacement procedure.

e. Remove the timing chain retention tool from the exhaust side of the timing chain.

➡ Failure to reset the tensioner will allow the tensioner to over extend limiting the timing chain life.

f. Reset and install the timing chain tensioner.

g. Install the camshaft actuator retainer (EN-48953) Camshaft Actuator Locking Tool.

h. Install the camshaft actuator retainer bolts and tighten to 89 inch lbs. (10 Nm).

i. Tighten the NEW camshaft actuator bolt to 22 ft. lbs. (30 Nm) plus an additional 100 degrees.

➡ You must have the Camshaft Actuator Locking Tool (EN-48953) installed to perform this procedure.

j. To release the tensioner apply a counterclockwise rotational torque to the crankshaft balancer bolt of 33 ft. lbs. (45 Nm).

k. Remove the camshaft actuator retainer.

l. Install the upper timing chain guide and bolts and tighten to 89 inch lbs. (10 Nm).

m. Install the spark plugs.
n. Install the camshaft cover.

Exhaust

See Figures 70 and 71.

1. Remove the exhaust camshaft position actuator.

➡ Remove each bolt on each cap one turn at a time until there is no spring tension pushing on the camshaft.

2. Mark the bearing caps to ensure they are installed in the original position.
3. Remove the bearing cap bolts.
4. Remove the bearing caps.
5. Remove the exhaust camshaft.

➡ Keep all of the roller followers and hydraulic adjusters in order so that they can be reinstalled in their respective locations.

36616_MALI_G0140

Fig. 70 Removing the camshaft roller followers

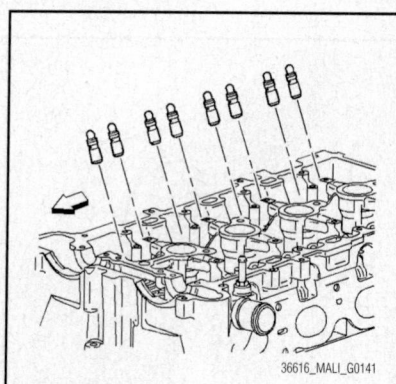

36616_MALI_G0141

Fig. 71 Removing the hydraulic element lash adjusters

6. Remove the camshaft roller followers.

7. Remove the hydraulic element lash adjusters.

To install:

8. Install the hydraulic element lash adjusters into their bores in the cylinder head.

9. Lubricate the hydraulic lash adjusters.

10. Lubricate the valve tips.

➡**Used roller followers MUST be returned to the original position on the camshaft. If the camshaft is being replaced, the roller followers actuated by the camshaft must also be replaced.**

11. Position the roller followers on the tip of the valve stem and on the lash adjuster.

12. Install and lubricate the exhaust camshaft.

13. Install the camshaft bearing caps. Hand tighten the cap bolts.

14. Tighten the bearing cap bolts in increments of 3 turns until they are seated. Tighten the bolts to 89 inch lbs. (10 Nm).

15. Install the exhaust camshaft position actuator.

CATALYTIC CONVERTER

REMOVAL & INSTALLATION

See Figure 72.

✳✳ WARNING

In order to avoid being burned, do not service the exhaust system while it is still hot. Service the system when it is cool.

1. Remove the heated oxygen sensor.

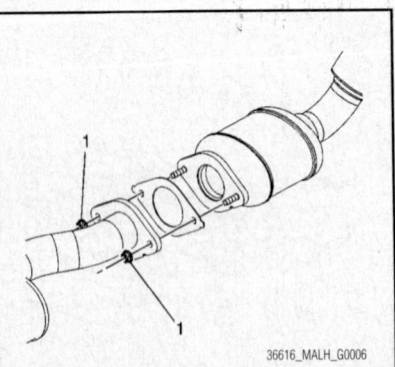

Fig. 72 Removing the catalytic converter and gasket

2. Remove the catalytic converter to exhaust manifold nuts.

3. Remove the catalytic converter to muffler nuts.

4. Separate the exhaust pipe from the catalytic converter studs.

5. Position and support the exhaust pipe out of the way.

6. Remove the catalytic converter and gasket.

To install:

7. Install the catalytic converter along with a NEW gasket to the exhaust manifold.

8. Position and join the exhaust pipe to the catalytic converter studs.

9. Install the catalytic converter to muffler nuts and tighten to 13 ft. lbs. (17 Nm).

10. Install the catalytic converter to exhaust manifold nuts and tighten to 37 ft. lbs. (50 Nm).

11. Install the heated oxygen sensor.

CRANKSHAFT DAMPER

REMOVAL & INSTALLATION

See Figure 73.

1. Remove the drive belt.

2. Install the harmonic balancer holder, and a breaker bar to the balancer in order to prevent the balancer from rotating when loosening the balancer bolt.

3. Remove the harmonic balancer holder and breaker bar.

4. Remove and discard the crankshaft balancer bolt.

5. Remove the crankshaft balancer.

To install:

6. Position the crankshaft balancer.

7. Install a NEW crankshaft balancer bolt.

8. Install the harmonic balancer holder and a breaker bar to the balancer in order to prevent the balancer from rotating while tightening the bolt.

9. Tighten the crankshaft balancer bolt to 74 ft. lbs. (100 Nm) plus an additional 125° using the angle meter.

10. Install the drive belt.

CRANKSHAFT FRONT SEAL

REMOVAL & INSTALLATION

See Figure 74.

1. Remove the crankshaft damper.

2. Use a flat-bladed tool to remove the seal from the front cover.

To install:

3. Use a suitable seal driver in order to install the crankshaft front oil seal to the engine front cover.

4. Install the crankshaft damper.

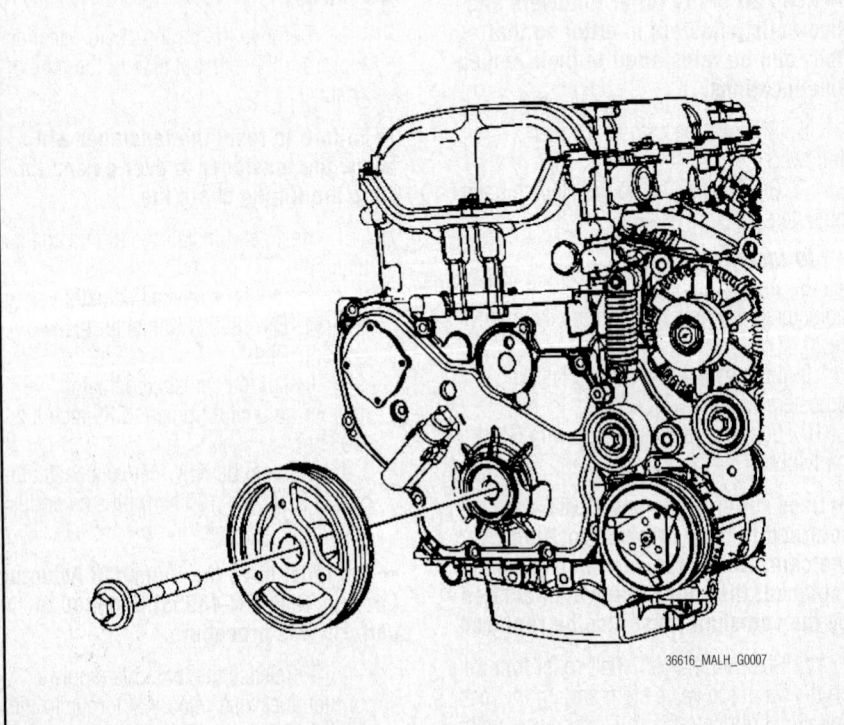

Fig. 73 Removing the crankshaft balancer

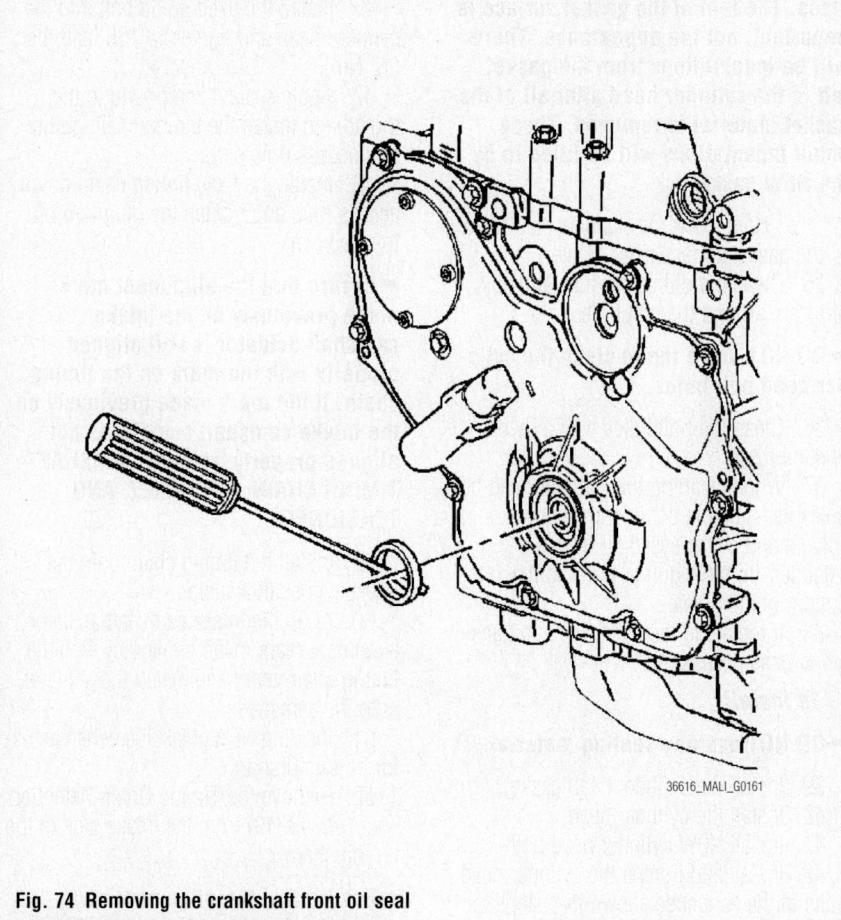

Fig. 74 Removing the crankshaft front oil seal

CYLINDER HEAD

REMOVAL & INSTALLATION

See Figures 75 through 79.

1. Drain and recycle the engine coolant.
2. Remove the exhaust manifold.
3. Remove the intake manifold.
4. Reposition the radiator surge tank air bleed hose clamp.
5. Remove the radiator surge tank air bleed hose from the cylinder head.
6. Reposition the radiator inlet hose clamp using the hose clamp pliers (J 38185).
7. Remove the radiator inlet hose from the cylinder head.
8. Disconnect all electrical connectors as necessary.
9. Remove the spark plugs.
10. Remove the camshaft cover.

➡️**If the intake camshaft actuator is moving independently of the camshaft, this means the camshaft is not locked to the actuator. Rotate the camshaft counter-clockwise while the holing tool is installed and this will lock the camshaft to the actuator.**

11. Rotate the crankshaft clockwise to install the Camshaft Actuator Retaining Tool (EN-48953).
12. Install the Camshaft Actuator Locking Tool (EN-48953).
13. Install the camshaft actuator retainer bolts and tighten to 89 inch lbs. (10 Nm).

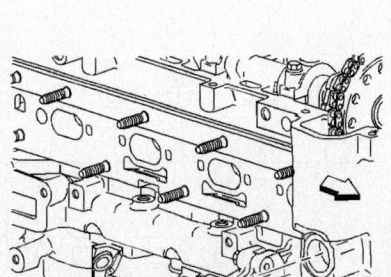

Fig. 75 Removing the timing chain tensioner

14. Remove the upper timing chain guide bolts and guide.
15. Clean the timing chain and gears with solvent.

➡️**Ensure the timing chain and the camshaft position actuators are marked for proper assembly.**

16. Mark the timing gear sprockets and the timing chain. It is recommended that the paint marks are located in the 12 o'clock position.
17. Loosen, but do not remove the intake and exhaust camshaft actuator bolts.
18. Remove the Camshaft Actuator Locking Tool (EN-48953).

➡️**Ensure the tips of the Timing Chain Retention Tool Kit (EN-48749) are fully engaged into the timing chain. The retention tool rod can be used on the back side of the chain to ensure the teeth from the retention tool are engaged.**

19. Install the Timing Chain Retention Tool (EN-48749) to the intake side of the timing chain.
20. Remove the timing chain tensioner.

➡️**The intake camshaft and actuator should not rotate during the removal or installation.**

21. Install the Timing Chain Retention Tool (EN-48749) to the exhaust side of the timing chain.
22. Remove and discard the exhaust camshaft actuator bolt.
23. Remove the exhaust cam actuator from the exhaust camshaft while also removing the actuator from the chain.
24. Remove and discard the intake camshaft actuator bolt.

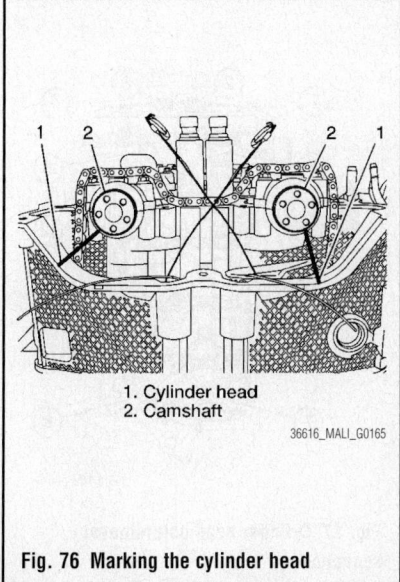

1. Cylinder head
2. Camshaft

Fig. 76 Marking the cylinder head

25. Remove the intake camshaft actuator from the camshaft while also removing the actuator from the timing chain.

26. Mark the cylinder head in relationship to the camshaft actuator notch is on the camshaft.

27. Remove the fixed timing chain guide access plug.

28. Remove the upper fixed timing chain guide bolt.

➡The threaded rod from the timing chain retention tool can be used to help feed the rubber band around the chain guides.

29. Install the rubber band around the top of the timing chain guides in order to pull the guides together.

30. Remove the cylinder head bolts in the sequence shown. Discard the bolts.

31. Remove the cylinder head.

32. Remove the cylinder head gasket.

33. Clean all of the gasket surfaces.

34. Use the following steps when cleaning the cylinder head and cylinder block surfaces:

a. Use a razor blade gasket scraper to clean the cylinder head and cylinder block gasket surfaces. Do not scratch or gouge either surface.

➡DO NOT use any other method or technique to clean these gasket surfaces.

b. Use a NEW razor blade on the cylinder head and a NEW blade on the cylinder block.

➡Be careful not to gouge or scratch the gasket surfaces. DO NOT gouge or scrape the combustion chamber surfaces. The feel of the gasket surface is important, not the appearance. There will be indentations from the gasket left in the cylinder head after all of the gasket material is removed. These small indentations will be filled in by the NEW gasket.

c. Hold the razor blade as parallel to the gasket surface as possible.

35. Clean the old sealer/lube and any dirt from around the bolt holes.

➡DO NOT use a tap to clean the cylinder head bolt holes.

36. Clean the bolt holes with a nylon bristle brush.

37. When cleaning the cylinder head bolt holes use suitable commercial spray liquid solvent and compressed air from an extended-tip blow gun in order to reach the bottom of the holes.

38. If replacing the cylinder head transfer all parts as necessary.

To install:

➡DO NOT use any sealing material.

39. Install the cylinder head gasket.

40. Install the cylinder head.

41. Install NEW cylinder head bolts.

42. Install and tighten the cylinder head bolts in the sequence shown in 2 steps to 22 ft. lbs. (30 Nm) plus an additional 155 degrees.

43. Install the NEW front cylinder head bolts and tighten to 26 ft. lbs. (35 Nm).

44. Ensure the cylinder head and the camshaft are correctly aligned.

45. Remove the rubber band from around the top of the upper timing chain guides.

46. Install the fixed guide bolt into the cylinder head and tighten to 106 inch lbs. (12 Nm).

47. Apply sealant compound to the thread and install the timing chain guide bolt access hole plug.

48. Install the fixed timing chain guide access plug and tighten the plug to 59 ft. lbs. (90 Nm).

➡Ensure that the alignment mark made previously on the intake camshaft actuator is still aligned properly with the mark on the timing chain. If the mark made previously on the intake camshaft actuator is not aligned properly, refer to CAMSHAFT TIMING CHAIN, SPROCKET, AND TENSIONER.

49. Install the timing chain onto the intake camshaft actuator.

50. Align the intake camshaft actuator alignment mark made previously with the timing chain mark and install the actuator onto the camshaft.

51. Install a NEW intake camshaft actuator bolt until snug.

52. Remove the Timing Chain Retention Tool (EN-48749) from the intake side of the timing chain.

➡Ensure that the alignment mark made previously on the exhaust camshaft actuator is still aligned properly with the mark on the timing chain. The exhaust cam may have to be rotated clockwise to install the exhaust actuator.

53. Install the timing chain onto the exhaust camshaft actuator.

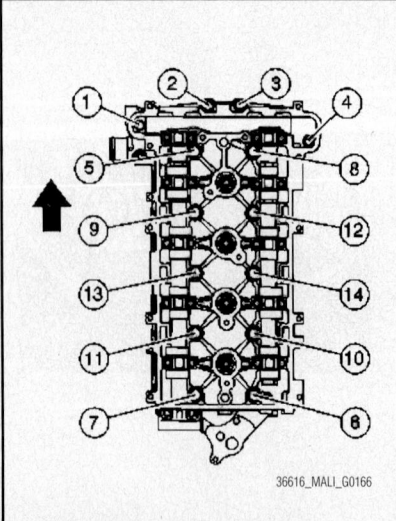

Fig. 77 Cylinder head bolt removal sequence

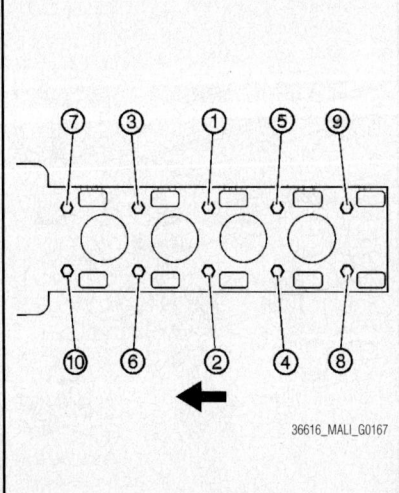

Fig. 78 Cylinder head bolt tightening sequence

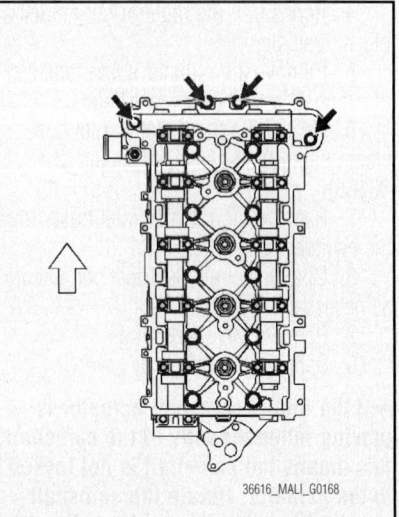

Fig. 79 Location of the front cylinder head bolts

54. Align the exhaust camshaft actuator alignment mark made previously with the timing chain mark and install the actuator onto the camshaft.

55. Install a NEW exhaust camshaft actuator bolt until snug.

56. Remove the Timing Chain Retention Tool (EN-48749) from the exhaust side of the timing chain.

➡**Failure to reset the chain tensioner will put excess tension on the chain, limiting the chains life.**

57. Reset and install the timing chain tensioner.

58. Install the Camshaft Actuator Locking Tool (EN-48953) to the actuators.

59. Install the camshaft actuator locking tool bolts and tighten to 89 inch lbs. (10 Nm).

60. Tighten the ENW camshaft actuator bolt to 22 ft. lbs. (30 Nm), plus an additional 100 degrees using the Angle Meter (J 45059).

61. Release the tensioner by applying a counterclockwise rotational torque of 33 ft. lbs. (45 Nm) to the harmonic balancer bolt.

62. Remove the Camshaft Actuator Locking tool.

63. Install the upper timing chain guide bolts and guide. Tighten the bolts to 89 inch lbs. (10 Nm).

64. Install the camshaft cover.

65. Install the spark plugs.

66. Connect all necessary electrical connectors.

67. Install the radiator inlet hose to the cylinder head.

68. Position the radiator inlet hose clamp.

69. Install the radiator surge tank air bleed hose to the cylinder head.

70. Position the radiator surge tank air bleed hose clamp.

71. Install the exhaust manifold.

72. Install the intake manifold.

73. Fill the cooling system

ENGINE ASSEMBLY

REMOVAL & INSTALLATION

See Figures 80 and 81.

1. Relieve the fuel system pressure.
2. Remove the air cleaner assembly.
3. Disconnect the fuel feed pipe quick connect fitting at the fuel rail.
4. Disconnect the Evaporative Emission (EVAP) line quick connect fitting from the EVAP purge solenoid.
5. Remove the fuel feed pipe clip from the fuel line bracket.

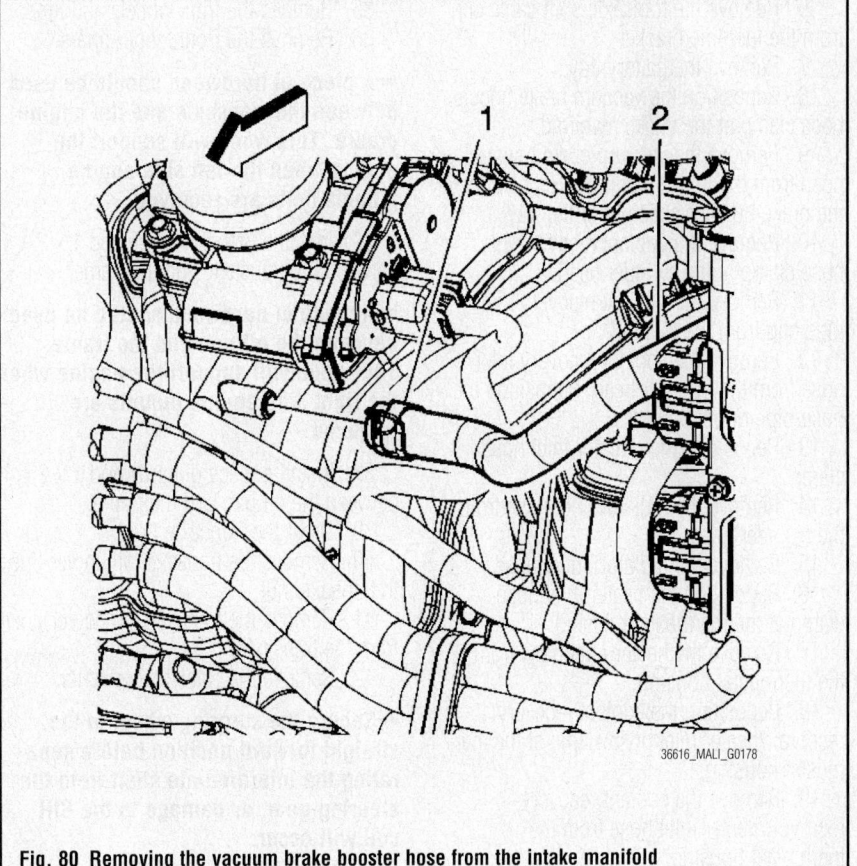

Fig. 80 Removing the vacuum brake booster hose from the intake manifold

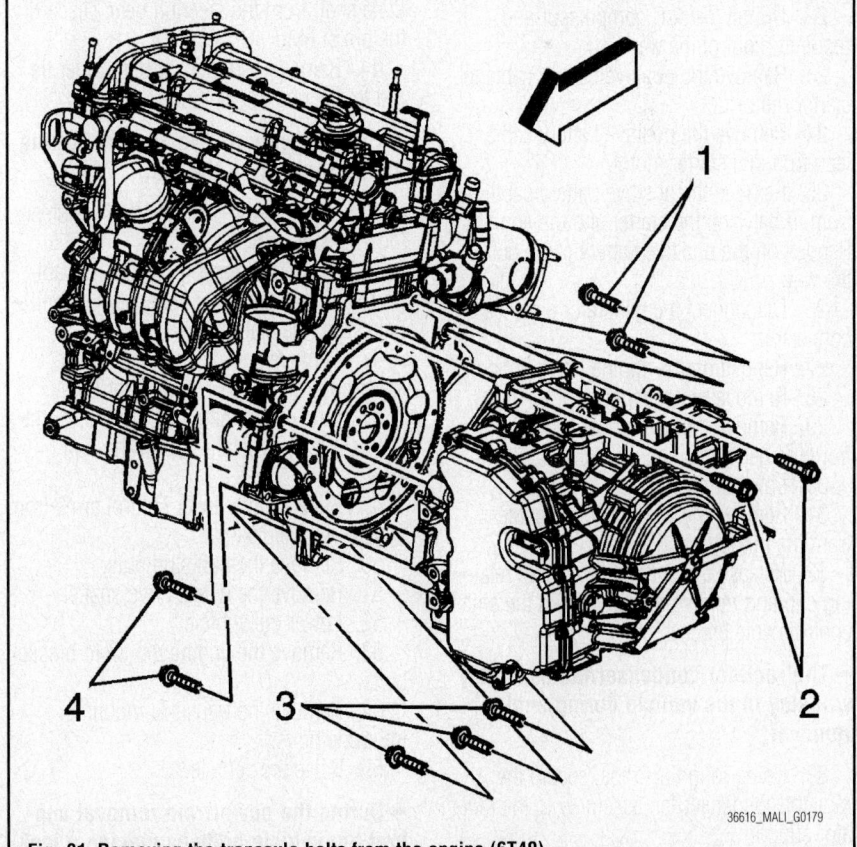

Fig. 81 Removing the transaxle bolts from the engine (6T40)

6. Remove the transaxle shift cable clip from the fuel line bracket.

7. Remove the battery tray.

8. Reposition the vacuum brake booster hose clamp at the intake manifold.

9. Remove the vacuum brake booster hose from the intake manifold. Reposition the brake booster hose out of the way.

10. Remove the coolant recovery inlet hose clamp at the cylinder head.

11. Remove the coolant recovery inlet pipe clip from the fuel rail.

12. Remove the coolant recovery inlet hose from the cylinder head. Reposition the hose/pipe out of the way.

13. Reposition the radiator inlet hose clamp.

14. Remove the radiator inlet hose from the cylinder head.

15. Remove the radiator outlet hose.

16. Reposition the heater inlet hose clamp at the thermostat housing.

17. Remove the heater inlet hose from the thermostat housing.

18. Reposition the coolant recovery reservoir/heater inlet hose clamp at the thermostat housing.

19. Remove the coolant recovery reservoir/heater inlet hose from the thermostat housing.

20. Raise and support the vehicle.

21. Drain the engine oil.

22. Unbolt the A/C compressor and reposition out of the way.

23. Remove the positive battery cable to starter motor nut.

24. Remove the positive battery cable lead from the starter motor.

25. Remove the positive battery cable from in between the starter and the engine. Reposition the positive battery cable out of the way.

26. Disconnect the generator electrical connector.

27. Reposition the engine harness boot.

28. Remove the generator nut.

29. Remove the engine harness lead from the generator.

30. Lower the vehicle.

31. Remove the transaxle shift cable from the range select lever.

32. Release the shift control cable retaining clip and remove the cable from the shift control cable bracket.

➡ **The radiator/condenser/fan assembly will stay in the vehicle during engine removal.**

33. Using long tie straps, secure the radiator/condenser/fan assembly to the radiator support.

34. Raise the vehicle.

35. Remove the front wheels and tires.

36. Remove the front fender liners.

➡ **A piece of hardwood should be used between the transaxle and the engine cradle. This wood will support the engine when the left side engine mounts bolts are removed.**

37. Install a piece of hardwood 1 x 2 x 4 between the transaxle and the frame.

➡ **A piece of hardwood should be used between the oil pan and the frame. This wood will support the engine when the right side engine mounts are removed.**

38. Install a piece of hardwood 1 x 2 x 4 between the oil pan and the frame.

39. Drain the transaxle fluid.

40. Remove the transaxle oil cooler line to transaxle nut.

41. Remove the transaxle oil cooler lines from the transaxle.

42. Remove the catalytic converter.

➡ **Secure the steering wheel in the straight forward position before separating the intermediate shaft from the steering gear, or damage to the SIR coil will occur.**

43. Remove the intermediate to steering gear pinch bolt and disconnect the intermediate shaft from the steering gear. Discard the pinch bolt.

44. Remove and discard both outer tie rod to steering knuckle nuts.

➡ **Hold the ball stud to prevent turning during removal of the nut.**

45. Separate the tie rods from the steering knuckles.

46. Remove the stabilizer link to stabilizer shaft nuts and disconnect the stabilizer links from the stabilizer shaft.

47. Remove and discard both of the lower control arm ball stud cotter pins.

48. Loosen the ball stud nuts until the nuts are level with the top of the ball stud.

49. Separate the lower control arms from the steering knuckles.

50. Remove the ball stud nuts.

51. Remove the wheel drive shafts.

52. Lower the vehicle.

53. Remove the engine mount to bracket bolts.

54. Remove the transaxle mount to transaxle bolts.

55. Raise the vehicle.

➡ **During the powertrain removal support the vehicle body by placing a jack at the rear of the vehicle.**

56. Position a engine support table under the powertrain assembly.

➡ **Blocks of wood can be used between the front of the cradle and the oil pan to table in order to level the powertrain during the removal.**

57. With the table positioned, fully raise the table to contact with the powertrain assembly.

58. Remove the cradle to body bolts. Discard the bolts.

➡ **When lowering the engine/transaxle assembly, verify all brake lines, shifter cables and other components are free during removal.**

59. Lower the engine table and raise the body on the hoist until the engine/transaxle and cradle are free from the vehicle.

60. Disconnect the engine wiring harness electrical connector from the throttle actuator.

61. Disconnect the engine wiring harness electrical connector from the fuel injector wiring harness electrical connector.

62. Remove the engine wiring harness clip from the oil level indicator tube bracket.

63. Disconnect the engine wiring harness electrical connectors from the ignition coils.

64. Disconnect the engine wiring harness electrical connectors from the camshaft actuators.

65. Disconnect the engine wiring harness electrical connector from the Crankshaft Position (CKP) sensor.

66. Disconnect the engine wiring harness electrical connector from the oil pressure sensor.

67. Disconnect the engine wiring harness electrical connector from the knock sensor.

68. Disconnect the engine wiring harness electrical connector from the intake Camshaft Position (CMP) sensor.

69. Disconnect the engine wiring harness electrical connector from the EVAP emission canister purge solenoid valve.

70. Disconnect the engine wiring harness electrical connector from the exhaust CMP sensor.

71. Disconnect the engine wiring harness electrical connector) from the Engine Coolant Temperature (ECT) sensor.

72. Disconnect the engine wiring harness electrical connector from the Heated Oxygen Sensor (HO2S) electrical connector.

73. Remove the engine wiring harness clip from the stud.

74. Remove the engine wiring harness ground bolt and reposition the ground terminal from the engine.

75. Gather all branches of the engine wiring harness and reposition the harness out of the way.

76. Remove the starter motor bolts and starter.

77. Remove the torque converter to flex-plate bolts.

78. Install a suitable lifting devise to the engine.

79. If equipped with the 4T40, remove the transaxle bolts from the engine.

80. If equipped with the 6T40, remove the transaxle bolts (1, 2, 3, 4) from the engine.

81. If equipped with the 6T40, remove the intermediate drive shaft.

82. Separate the engine from the transaxle.

83. Install the engine to a suitable engine stand.

To install:

84. Install a suitable lifting devise to the engine.

85. Using the lifting devise, position and install the engine to the transaxle.

86. If equipped with the 4T40, install the transaxle bolts to the engine and tighten to 55 ft. lbs. (75 Nm).

87. If equipped with the 6T40, install the transaxle bolts to the engine and tighten to 55 ft. lbs. (75 Nm).

88. Install the transaxle bolts to the engine and tighten to 55 ft. lbs. (75 Nm).

89. Install the torque converter to flex-plate bolts and tighten to 44 ft. lbs. (60 Nm).

90. Remove the engine lifting devise.

91. Install the starter motor and bolts. Tighten to 39 ft. lbs. (53 Nm).

92. Gather all branches of the engine wiring harness and position the harness to the engine.

93. Position the engine wiring harness ground terminal to the engine and install the engine wiring harness ground bolt and tighten the bolts to 15 ft. lbs. (20 Nm).

94. Connect the engine wiring harness electrical connector to the ECT sensor.

95. Connect the engine wiring harness electrical connector to the HO2S electrical connector.

96. Install the engine wiring harness clip to the stud.

97. Connect the engine wiring harness electrical connector to the exhaust CMP sensor.

98. Connect the engine wiring harness electrical connector to the intake CMP sensor.

99. Connect the engine wiring harness electrical connector to the EVAP emission canister purge solenoid valve.

100. Connect the engine wiring harness electrical connector to the CKP sensor.

101. Connect the engine wiring harness electrical connector to the oil pressure sensor.

102. Connect the engine wiring harness electrical connector to the knock sensor.

103. Connect the engine wiring harness electrical connectors to the ignition coils.

104. Connect the engine wiring harness electrical connectors to the camshaft actuators.

105. Connect the engine wiring harness electrical connector to the throttle actuator.

106. Connect the engine wiring harness electrical connector to the fuel injector wiring harness electrical connector.

107. Install the engine wiring harness clip to the oil level indicator tube bracket.

108. Position the powertrain and support table under the vehicle.

109. Raise the powertrain into position under the vehicle.

110. With the table positioned, if required, lower the vehicle over the powertrain.

111. Align the lower radiator pins with the cradle. Ensure all hoses and electrical harnesses are correctly routed and free from the loading path of the powertrain.

112. Install the NEW cradle to body bolts and tighten to 114 ft. lbs. (155 Nm).

113. Lower the vehicle.

114. Install the transaxle mount to transaxle bolts. Tighten to 41 ft. lbs. (55 Nm).

➡The engine mount to bracket bolts must be hand started. Do not pry the engine mount to align the holes.

115. Install the engine mount to bracket bolts and tighten to 37 ft. lbs. (50 Nm).

116. Install the wheel drive shafts.

117. Install the control arm ball studs into the steering knuckles.

118. Install the ball stud nuts and tighten to 30 ft. lbs. (40 Nm).

119. Continue to tighten the nuts only enough to align the castle nut slots with the ball stud install NEW cotter pins.

120. Connect the stabilizer links to the stabilizer shaft and install the stabilizer link to stabilizer shaft nuts. Tighten to 48 ft. lbs. (65 Nm).

121. Connect the outer tie rods to the steering knuckles. Tighten to 30 ft. lbs. (40 Nm).

122. Install NEW outer tie rod to steering knuckle nuts. Tighten to 48 ft. lbs. (25 Nm) plus an additional 90 degrees.

123. Position the intermediate shaft to the steering gear and install a NEW pinch bolt. Tighten to 25 ft. lbs. (34 Nm).

124. Install the catalytic converter.

125. If equipped with the 4T45, install the transaxle oil cooler lines to the transaxle.

126. If equipped with the 4T45, install the transaxle oil cooler line to transaxle nut. Tighten to 27 inch lbs. (4 Nm).

127. If equipped with the 6T40, install the fluid cooler at the transaxle.

128. Remove the wood from between the oil pan and the engine cradle.

129. Remove the wood from between the transaxle and the engine cradle.

130. Install the front fender liners.

131. Install the front wheels and tires.

132. Lower the vehicle.

133. Unsecure and position the radiator/condenser/fan assembly.

134. Install the shift control cable to the shift control cable bracket and engage the shift control cable retaining clip.

135. Install the transaxle shift cable to the range select lever.

136. Raise and support the vehicle.

137. Install the engine harness lead to the generator.

138. Install the generator nut and tighten to 15 ft. lbs. (20 Nm).

139. Seat the engine harness boot.

140. Connect the generator electrical connector.

141. Position and install the positive battery cable between the starter and the engine.

142. Install the positive battery cable lead to the starter motor.

143. Install the positive battery cable to starter motor nut. Tighten the nut to 80 inch lbs. (9 Nm).

144. Position the A/C compressor and install the bolts. Tighten to 37 ft. lbs. (50 Nm).

145. Connect the engine wiring harness electrical connector to the A/C compressor.

146. Lower the vehicle.

147. Install the coolant recovery reservoir/heater inlet hose to the thermostat housing.

148. Position the coolant recovery reservoir/heater inlet hose clamp at the thermostat housing.

149. Install the heater inlet hose to the thermostat housing.

150. Position the heater inlet hose clamp at the thermostat housing.

151. Reposition the radiator inlet hose clamp.

152. Remove the radiator inlet hose from the cylinder head.

153. Remove the radiator outlet hose.

154. Position and install the coolant recovery inlet hose to the cylinder head.

155. Install the coolant recovery inlet pipe clip to the fuel rail.

156. Install the coolant recovery inlet hose clamp at the cylinder head.

157. Position and install the vacuum brake booster hose to the intake manifold.

158. Position the vacuum brake booster hose clamp at the intake manifold.

159. Install the alternator starter.

160. Install the battery tray.

161. Install the transaxle shift cable clip to the fuel line bracket.

162. Install the fuel feed pipe clip (2) to the fuel line bracket.

163. Connect the EVAP line quick connect fitting to the EVAP purge solenoid.

164. Connect the fuel feed pipe quick connect fitting at the fuel rail.

165. Install the air cleaner assembly.

166. Fill the transaxle with fluid.

167. Refill the engine with oil.

168. Start the engine and allow the engine to run, inspect for leaks. Correct as necessary.

EXHAUST MANIFOLD

REMOVAL & INSTALLATION

See Figures 82 and 83.

1. Remove the exhaust manifold heat shield.

2. Remove the Heated Oxygen Sensor (HO2S).

3. Remove and discard the exhaust manifold pipe.

4. Lower the vehicle.

5. Remove the upper exhaust manifold brace bolt.

6. Remove and discard the exhaust manifold nuts.

7. Remove the exhaust manifold/catalytic converter assembly.

8. Remove and discard the exhaust manifold gasket.

To install:

9. Install a NEW exhaust manifold gasket onto the manifold studs.

10. Install the exhaust manifold/catalytic converter assembly.

11. Install the NEW exhaust manifold nuts finger tight.

12. Install the upper exhaust manifold brace bolt and tighten to 43 ft. lbs. (58 Nm).

13. Tighten the exhaust manifold nuts in sequence to 10 ft. lbs. (14 Nm).

14. Raise and suitably support the vehicle.

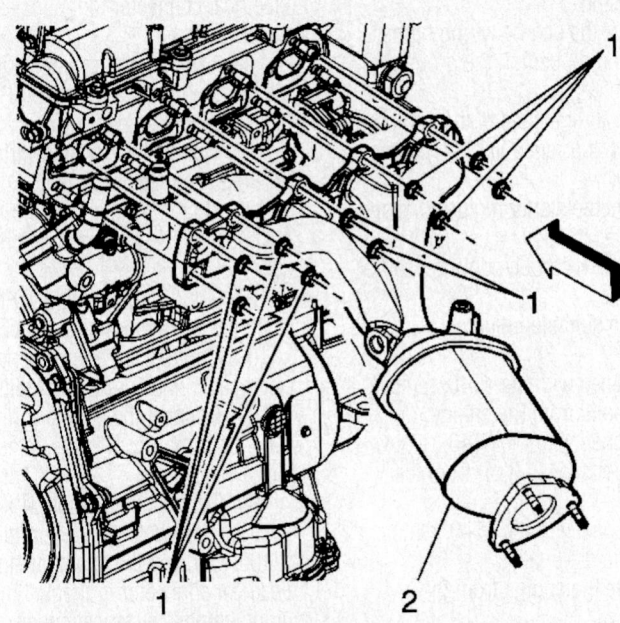

1. Exhaust manifold nuts
2. Exhaust manifold/catalytic converter assembly

36616_MALI_G0188

Fig. 82 Removing the exhaust manifold

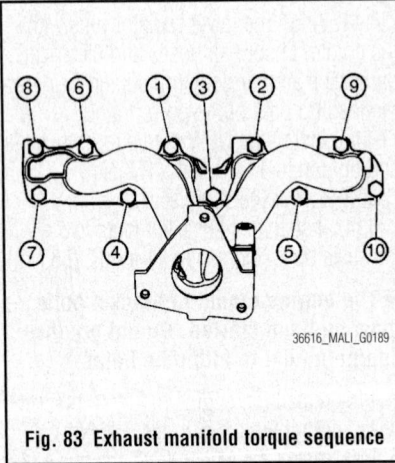

36616_MALI_G0189

Fig. 83 Exhaust manifold torque sequence

15. Install the exhaust manifold pipe.

16. Install the HO2S.

17. Install the exhaust manifold heat shield. Tighten the bolts to 89 inch lbs. (10 Nm).

FLYWHEEL

REMOVAL & INSTALLATION

See Figure 84.

1. Remove the transaxle.

2. Have an assistant install crankshaft balancer holding tool, and a breaker bar to the crankshaft balancer in order to prevent the flywheel from rotating when loosening the flywheel bolts.

➡ It may be necessary to remove the chamfer (bevel) from the edge of an 18 mm socket in order to get full engagement on the thin-headed flywheel bolts.

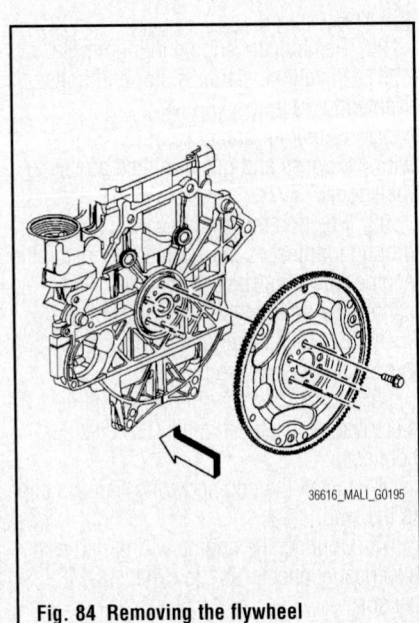

36616_MALI_G0195

Fig. 84 Removing the flywheel

3. Loosen, remove and discard the flywheel bolts.

➡**Do not orientate the flywheel to the crankshaft. It is balanced separately from the engine.**

4. Remove the flywheel.

5. Clean the thread adhesive from the flywheel bolt holes. Use a nylon bristle brush to clean the holes in the crankshaft.

To install:

6. Position the flywheel to the crankshaft.

7. Install the NEW flywheel bolts until snug.

8. Have an assistant install a crankshaft balancer holding tool, and a breaker bar to the crankshaft balancer in order to prevent the flywheel from rotating when tightening the flywheel bolts.

9. Tighten the flywheel bolts to 39 ft. lbs. (53 Nm) plus an additional 25 degrees.

10. Install the transaxle.

INTAKE MANIFOLD

REMOVAL & INSTALLATION

See Figures 85 and 86.

1. Remove the air cleaner outlet duct.
2. Remove the radiator inlet hose.
3. Disconnect the engine wiring harness electrical connector from the Throttle Actuator Control (TAC).
4. Disconnect the engine wiring harness electrical connector from the generator starter.
5. Disconnect the engine wiring harness electrical connector from the generator starter.
6. Remove the fuel injector wiring

harness electrical connector retainer from the generator starter.

7. Disconnect the fuel injector wiring harness electrical connector from the engine wiring harness electrical connector.

8. Remove the engine wiring harness clips from the intake manifold.

9. Reposition the vacuum brake booster hose clamp at the intake manifold.

10. Remove the vacuum brake booster hose from the intake manifold.

11. Remove the throttle body.

12. Disconnect the engine wiring harness electrical connector from the Manifold Absolute Pressure (MAP) sensor.

13. Disconnect the Evaporative Emission (EVAP) canister purge tube from the intake manifold and the EVAP solenoid.

14. Remove the oil level indicator tube.

15. Remove the fuel rail.

16. Remove the 3-phase voltage cable bracket bolt at the oil level indicator tube.

17. Remove the generator starter bolts.

18. Reposition and secure the generator starter out of the way.

19. Remove the intake manifold lower bolts.

20. Remove the intake manifold upper bolt and nuts.

21. Remove the intake manifold.

➡**The intake manifold gasket is reusable; only replace the gasket if damage has occurred.**

22. Remove and inspect the intake manifold gasket.

To install:

23. Install a NEW intake manifold gasket if necessary, otherwise install the old gasket.

24. Install the intake manifold.

25. Install the intake manifold upper bolt and nuts.

26. Install the intake manifold lower bolts and tighten to 89 inch lbs. (10 Nm).

27. Position the starter/generator to the bracket.

28. Install the starter/generator bolts until snug.

29. Tighten the starter generator bolts starting with the front followed by the bottom. Tighten to 43 ft. lbs. (58 Nm).

30. Install the 3-phase voltage cable bracket to the tie bar.

31. Install the 3-phase voltage cable bracket bolt at the oil level indicator tube and tighten to 89 inch lbs. (10 Nm).

32. Install the fuel rail.

33. Install the oil level indicator tube.

34. Connect the EVAP canister purge tube to the intake manifold and the EVAP solenoid.

35. Connect the engine wiring harness electrical connector to the MAP sensor.

36. Install the throttle body.

37. Install the vacuum brake booster hose to the intake manifold.

38. Position the vacuum brake booster hose clamp at the intake manifold.

39. Install the engine wiring harness clips to the intake manifold.

40. Connect the fuel injector wiring harness electrical connector to the engine wiring harness electrical connector.

41. Install the fuel injector wiring harness electrical connector retainer to the generator starter.

42. Connect the engine wiring harness electrical connector to the generator starter.

43. Connect the engine wiring harness electrical connector to the generator starter.

44. Connect the engine wiring harness electrical connector to the TAC.

45. Install the radiator inlet hose.

46. Install the air cleaner outlet duct.

OIL PAN

REMOVAL & INSTALLATION

See Figures 87 and 88.

1. Remove the drive belt.
2. Remove the oil level indicator tube.

➡**The support fixture bar must be installed to provide enough access to remove and properly tighten the oil pan bolts.**

3. Install the engine support fixture.
4. Remove engine mount.
5. Using the engine support fixture, raise the engine approximately 3 inches.
6. Raise and support the vehicle.
7. Loosen the upper Air Conditioning (A/C) compressor bolts.

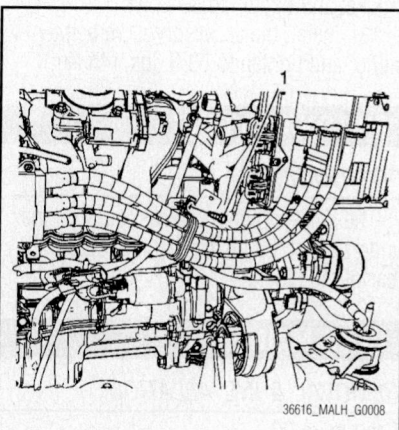

36616_MALH_G0008

Fig. 85 Removing the 3-phase voltage cable bracket bolt

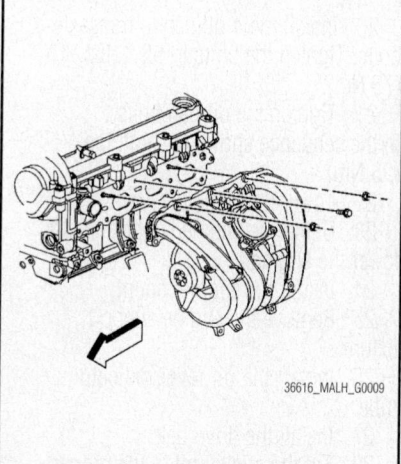

36616_MALH_G0009

Fig. 86 Removing the intake manifold

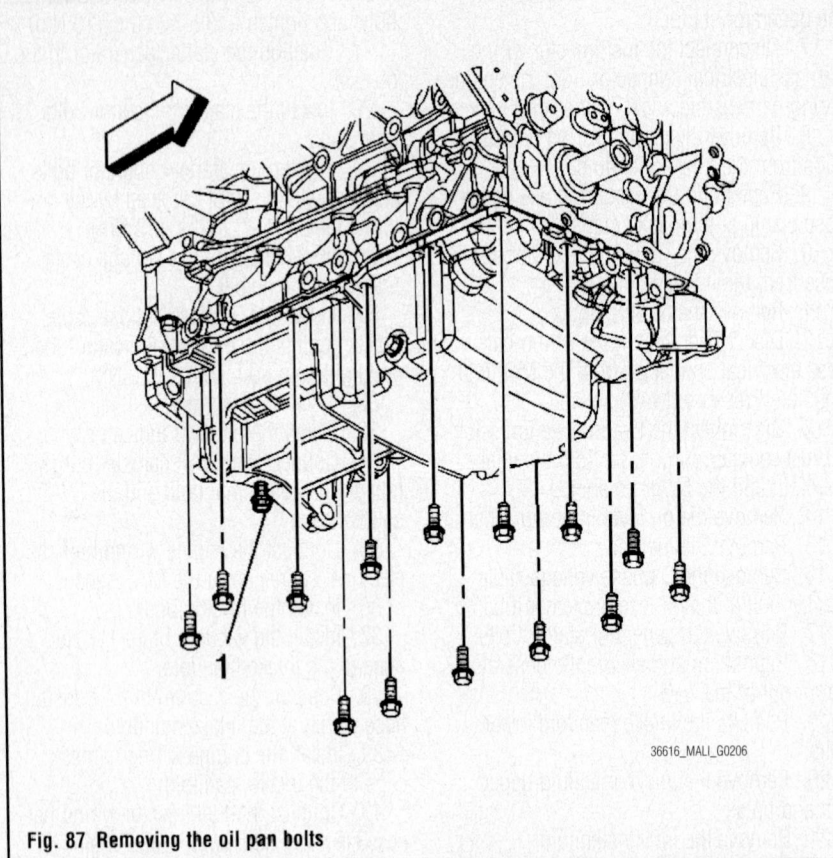

Fig. 87 Removing the oil pan bolts

8. Remove the lower A/C compressor bolt.

9. Place a suitable drain pan under the oil pan drain plug.

10. Remove the oil pan drain plug.

11. Drain the engine oil.

12. Reinstall the oil pan drain plug until snug.

13. Remove the 4 oil pan to transaxle bolts.

14. Remove the oil pan bolts.

15. Remove the oil pan

16. Remove any old oil pan sealant.

To install:

17. Ensure that the oil pan and the sealing surface on the lower crankcase are free of all oil and debris. Apply a 2 mm bead of sealant around the perimeter of the oil pan and the oil suction port opening. DO NOT over apply the sealant. More than a 2 mm bead is not required.

18. Install the oil pan.

19. Install the oil pan bolts and hand tighten.

20. Install the 4 oil pan to transaxle bolts. Tighten the bolts to 55 ft. lbs. (75 Nm).

21. Tighten the oil pan bolts in the sequence shown to 18 ft. lbs. (25 Nm).

22. Lower the vehicle.

23. Using the engine support fixture, lower the engine.

24. Install the engine mount.

25. Remove the engine support fixture.

26. Install the oil level indicator tube.

27. Install the drive belt.

28. Fill the engine oil to the proper level.

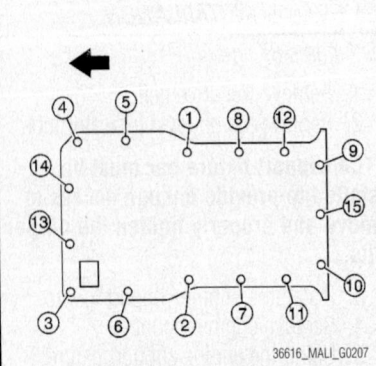

Fig. 88 Identifying the oil pan bolt tightening sequence

OIL PUMP

REMOVAL & INSTALLATION

See Figure 89.

1. Remove the accessory drive belt tensioner.

2. Remove the drive belt tensioner bracket.

3. Remove the engine front cover bolts.

4. Remove the long water pump bolt.

5. Remove the engine front cover and gaskets.

6. Remove the crankshaft front cover oil seal with an appropriate tool.

7. Remove the oil pump.

To install:

8. Install the oil pump.

9. Install the engine front cover with a new gasket.

➡Use the correct fastener in the correct location. Replacement fasteners must be the correct part number for that application. Fasteners requiring replacement or fasteners requiring the use of thread locking compound or sealant are identified in the service procedure. Do not use paints, lubricants, or corrosion inhibitors on fasteners or fastener joint surfaces unless specified. These coatings affect fastener torque and joint clamping force and may damage the fastener. Use the correct tightening sequence and specifications when installing fasteners in order to avoid damage to parts and systems.

10. Install the long water pump bolt and tighten to 18 ft. lbs. (25 Nm).

11. Install the engine front cover bolts and tighten to 18 ft. lbs. (25 Nm).

12. Install the drive belt tensioner bracket and tighten to 33 ft. lbs. (45 Nm).

13. Install the accessory drive belt tensioner and tighten to 33 ft. lbs. (45 Nm).

PISTON AND RING

POSITIONING

The 2.4L engine has a cast boss on the underside of the piston that must go to the rear of the block.

REAR MAIN SEAL

REMOVAL & INSTALLATION

See Figure 90.

1. Remove the transmission and flywheel.

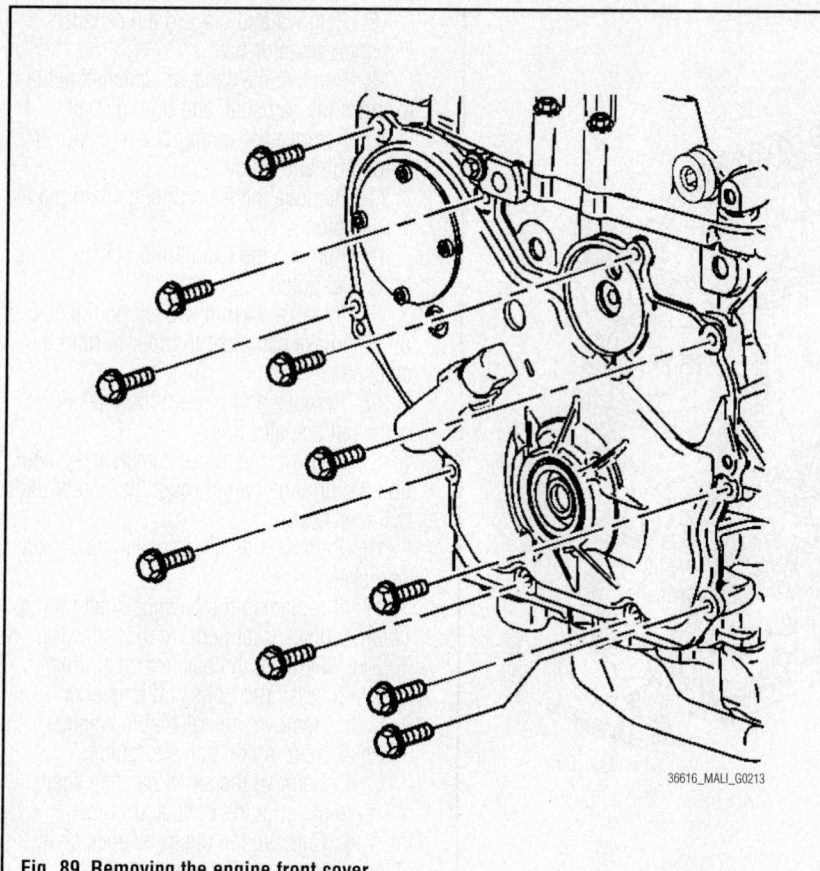

Fig. 89 Removing the engine front cover

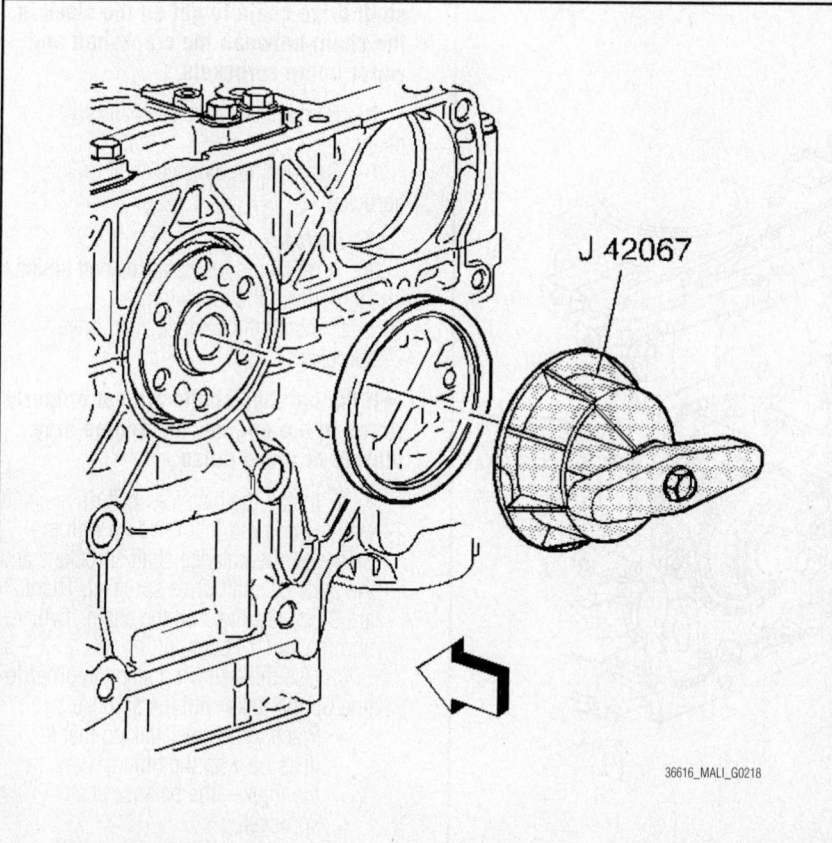

Fig. 90 Installing the rear seal

➡Do not damage the outside diameter of the crankshaft or chamber with any tool.

2. Pry out the crankshaft rear oil seal using a flat-bladed tool.

To install:

3. Using a seal installer such as J 42067, install a NEW crankshaft real oil seal.

4. Install the flywheel and transmission.

TIMING CHAIN AND SPROCKETS

REMOVAL & INSTALLATION

See Figures 91 through 93.

1. Remove the No. 1 cylinder spark plug.

2. Rotate the crankshaft in the engine rotational direction clockwise, until the No. 1 piston is at Top Dead Center (TDC) on the compression stroke.

3. Remove the camshaft cover.

4. Remove the engine front cover as follows:

  a. Remove the drive belt tensioner.

  b. Remove the crankshaft balancer.

  c. Install the engine support fixture.

  d. Remove the engine mount to bracket bolts.

  e. Remove the engine mount to side rail nuts.

  f. Remove the engine mount from the engine compartment.

  g. Remove the engine mount bracket to engine bolts.

  h. Remove the engine mount bracket.

  i. Remove the engine front cover to water pump bolt.

  j. Raise and suitably support the vehicle.

  k. Remove the engine front cover bolts.

  l. Remove the engine front cover.

  m. Remove and discard the engine front cover gasket.

5. Remove the upper timing chain guide bolts and guide.

➡The timing chain tensioner must be removed to unload chain tension before the timing chain is removed. If it is not, the timing chain will become cocked and it will be difficult to remove.

6. Remove the timing chain tensioner.

7. Install a 24 mm wrench on the hex on the exhaust camshaft in order to hold the camshaft.

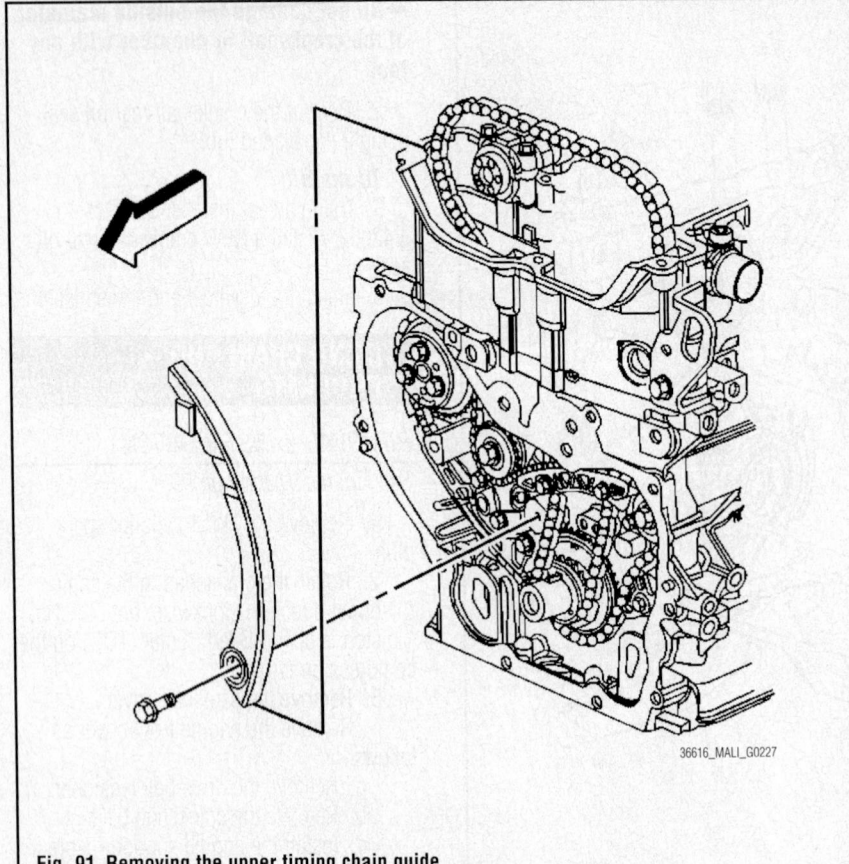

Fig. 91 Removing the upper timing chain guide

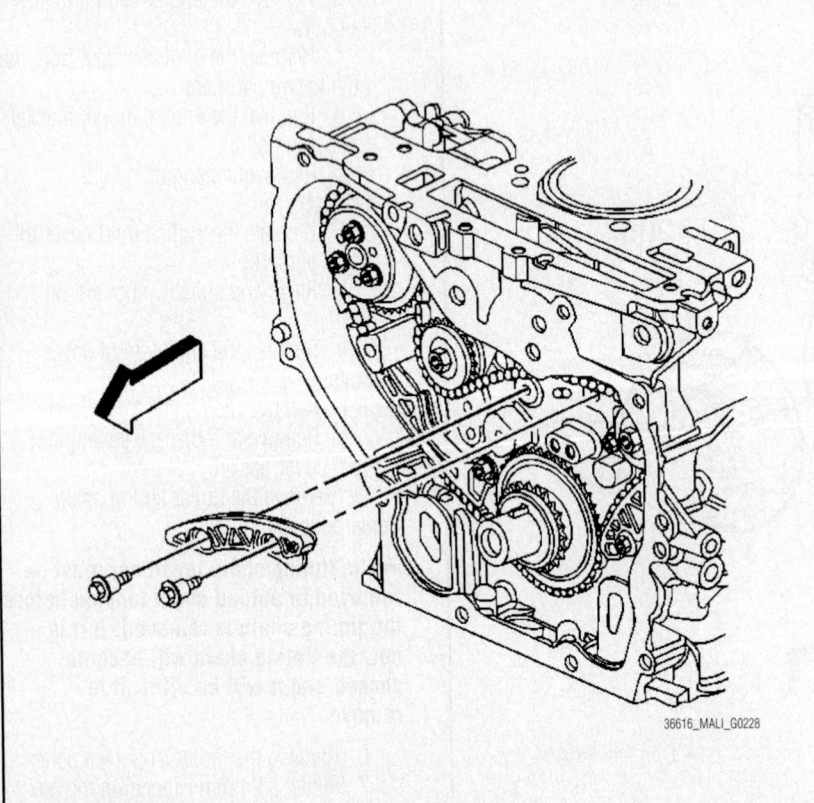

Fig. 92 Removing the upper balance shaft drive chain guide

8. Remove and discard the exhaust camshaft actuator bolt.

9. Remove the exhaust camshaft actuator from the camshaft and timing chain.

10. Remove the timing chain tensioner guide bolt and guide.

11. Remove the fixed timing chain guide access plug.

12. Remove the fixed timing chain guide bolts and guide.

13. Install a 24 mm wrench on the hex on the intake camshaft in order to hold the camshaft.

14. Remove and discard the intake camshaft actuator bolt.

15. Remove the intake camshaft actuator, and the timing chain through the top of the cylinder head.

16. Remove the timing chain crankshaft sprocket.

17. If replacing the balance shaft timing chain and sprocket perform the following:

a. Remove the balance shaft drive chain tensioner bolts and tensioner.

b. Remove the adjustable balance shaft chain guide bolt and guide.

c. Remove the small balance shaft drive chain guide bolts and guide.

d. Remove the upper balance shaft drive chain guide bolts and guide.

➡ It may ease removal of the balance shaft drive chain to get all the slack in the chain between the crankshaft and water pump sprockets.

18. Remove the balance shaft drive chain.

19. Remove the balance shaft drive sprocket.

To install:

20. If replacing the balance shaft timing chain, perform the following:

a. Install the balance shaft drive sprocket.

➡ If the balance shafts are not properly timed to the engine, the engine may vibrate or make noise.

b. Install the balance shaft drive chain with the colored link lined up with the marks on the balance shaft sprockets and the balance shaft drive sprocket. There are 3 colored links on the chain. Two are chrome and 1 is copper.

c. Use the following steps in order to line up the links with the sprockets:

• Place the copper link so that it lines up with the timing mark on the intake side balance shaft sprocket.

• Working clockwise around the

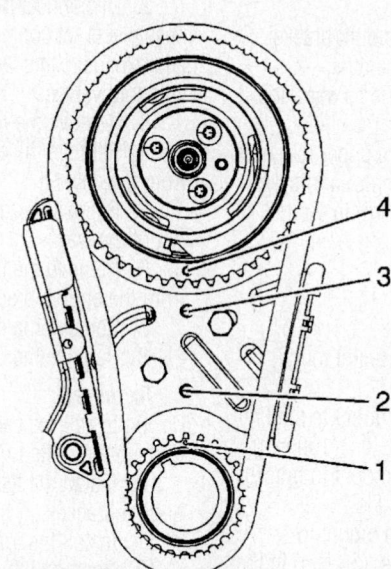

1. Crankshaft timing mark
2. Timing mark on the bottom of the timing chain tensioner
3. Timing mark on top of the timing chain tensioner
4. Camshaft position actuator gear

36616_MALI_G0229

Fig. 93 Removing the balance shaft drive chain

chain, place the chrome link in line with the timing on the balance shaft drive sprocket. (approximately 6 o'clock position on the sprocket).
• Place the chain on the water pump drive sprocket. The alignment is not critical
   Align the last chrome link with the timing mark on the exhaust side balance shaft drive sprocket.
   d. Install the upper balance shaft drive chain guide and bolts and tighten to 11 ft. lbs. (15 Nm).
   e. Install the small balance shaft drive chain guide and bolts and tighten to 11 ft. lbs. (15 Nm).
21. Install the adjustable balance shaft chain guide and bolt and tighten to 89 inch lbs. (10 Nm).
22. Reset the timing chain tensioner by performing the following:
   a. Rotate the tensioner plunger 90 degrees in its bore and compress the plunger
   b. Rotate the tensioner back to the original 12 o'clock position and insert a paper clip through the hole in the plunger body and into the hose in the tensioner plunger.
   c. Install the balance shaft drive chain

tensioner and bolt and tighten to 89 inch lbs. (10 Nm).
   d. Remove the paper clip from the balance shaft drive chain tensioner.
23. Ensure the intake camshaft notch is in the 5 o'clock position and the exhaust camshaft notch is in the 7 o'clock position. The number 1 piston should be at Top Dead Center (TDC), crankshaft key at 12 o'clock.
24. Install the timing chain drive sprocket to the crankshaft with the timing mark in the 5 o'clock position and the front of the sprocket facing out.

➡There are 3 colored links on the timing chain. Two links are of matching color, and 1 link is of a unique color. Use the following procedure to line up the links with the actuators. Orient the chain so that the colored links are visible. Always use new actuator bolts.

25. Assemble the intake camshaft actuator into the timing chain with the timing mark lined up with the uniquely colored link.
26. Lower the timing chain through the opening in the cylinder head. Use care to ensure that the chain goes around both sides of the cylinder block bosses.
27. Install the intake camshaft actuator

onto the intake camshaft while aligning the dowel pin into the camshaft slot.
28. Hand tighten the new intake camshaft actuator bolt.
29. Route the timing chain around the crankshaft sprocket and line up the first matching colored link with the timing mark on the crankshaft sprocket, in approximately the 5 o'clock position.
30. Rotate the crankshaft clockwise to remove all chain slack. Do not rotate the intake camshaft.
31. Install the adjustable timing chain guide down through the opening in the cylinder head and install the adjustable timing chain bolt and tighten to 89 inch lbs. (10 Nm).

➡Always install NEW actuator bolts.

32. Install the exhaust camshaft actuator into the timing chain with the timing mark lined up with the second matching colored link.
33. Install the exhaust camshaft actuator onto the exhaust camshaft, aligning the dowel pin into the camshaft slot.
34. Using a 23 mm open end wrench, rotate the exhaust camshaft approximately 45 degrees until the dowel pin in the camshaft actuator goes into the camshaft slot.
35. When the actuator seats on the cam, tighten the new exhaust camshaft actuator bolt hand tight.
36. Verify that all of the colored links and the appropriate timing marks are still aligned. If they are not aligned, repeat the portion of the procedure necessary to align the timing marks
37. Install the fixed timing chain guide and bolts and tighten to 106 inch lbs. (12 Nm).
38. Install the upper timing chain guide and bolts and tighten to 89 inch lbs. (10 Nm).
39. Reset the timing chain tensioner by performing the following:
   a. Remove the snap ring.
   b. Remove the piston assembly from the body of the timing chain tensioner.
   c. Install tensioner tool J 45027-2 into a vise.
   d. Install the notch end of the piston assembly into the tool.
   e. Using the J 45027-1 handle, turn the ratchet cylinder into the piston.
   f. Reinstall the piston assembly into the body of the tensioner.
   g. Install the snap ring.
40. Inspect the timing chain tensioner seal for damage. If damaged, replace the seal.

41. Inspect to ensure all dirt and debris is removed from the timing chain tensioner threaded hole in the cylinder head.

➡ **Ensure the timing chain tensioner seal is centered throughout the torque procedure to eliminate the possibility of an oil leak.**

42. Install the timing chain tensioner assembly.

43. Tighten the timing chain tensioner to 55 ft. lbs. (75 Nm).

➡ **The timing chain tensioner is released by compressing it 2 mm (0.079 in), which will release the locking mechanism in the ratchet.**

44. To release the timing chain tensioner; use a suitable tool with a rubber tip on the end. Feed the tool down through the cam drive chest to rest on the cam chain. Then give a sharp jolt diagonally downwards to release the tensioner.

45. Using a 23 mm wrench, engage the hex on the intake camshaft, and using a torque wrench, tighten the camshaft actuator bolt.

46. Tighten the intake camshaft position actuator bolt to 22 ft. lbs. (30 Nm), plus an additional 100 degrees.

47. Using a 23 mm wrench, engage the hex on the exhaust camshaft, and using a torque wrench, tighten the camshaft actuator bolt.

48. Tighten the exhaust camshaft position actuator bolt to 22 ft. lbs. (30 Nm), plus an additional 100 degrees.

49. Install the timing chain oiling nozzle and bolt and tighten to 89 inch lbs. (10 Nm).

50. Apply sealant compound to the thread of the timing chain guide bolt access hole plug.

51. Install the timing chain guide bolt access hole plug and tighten to 66 ft. lbs. lbs. (90 Nm).

52. Install the engine front cover as follows:

a. Install a NEW engine front cover gasket to the dowel pins.

b. Install the engine front cover.

c. Install the engine front cover bolts and tighten to 18 ft. lbs. (25 Nm).

d. Lower the vehicle.

e. Install the engine front cover to water pump bolt and tighten to 18 ft. lbs. (25 Nm).

f. Position the engine mount bracket to the engine.

g. Install the engine mount bracket bolts in the following locations:
- The long bolts in the forward and lower rear holes
- The short bolt in the upper rear hole

h. Tighten the engine mount bracket bolts to 74 ft. lbs. (100 Nm) in the following sequence.
- Upper left
- Lower left
- Right

i. Install the engine mount to the engine compartment.

j. Install the engine mount to side rail nuts and tighten to 74 ft. lbs. (100 Nm).

k. Install the engine mount to bracket bolts.

l. Tighten the engine mount to bracket bolts to 37 ft. lbs. (50 Nm) in the following sequence.
- Middle
- Rear
- Front

m. Remove the engine support fixture.

n. Install the crankshaft balancer.

o. Install the drive belt tensioner.

53. Install the camshaft cover.

54. Install the No. 1 cylinder spark plug.

VALVE COVERS

REMOVAL & INSTALLATION
See Figure 94.

1. Remove the air cleaner outlet duct.
2. Disconnect the engine wiring harness electrical connectors from the intake and exhaust camshaft position actuator solenoid valves.
3. Remove the ignition coils.
4. Remove the engine harness clips from the cover.
5. Reposition the engine wiring harness out of the way.
6. Remove the fuel feed line retainers from the engine brackets.
7. Remove the camshaft cover bolts.
8. Remove the camshaft cover.

To install:
9. Install the camshaft cover and bolts. Tighten the bolts to 89 inch lbs. (10 Nm).
10. Install the feed line retainers to the engine brackets.
11. Install the ignition coils.
12. Position the engine wiring harness and install the clips to the cover.
13. Connect the engine wiring harness electrical connectors to the intake and exhaust camshaft position actuator solenoid valves.
14. Install the battery box cover.
15. Install the air cleaner outlet duct.

VALVE LASH

ADJUSTMENT

All engines utilize hydraulic lash adjusters; no adjustment is necessary.

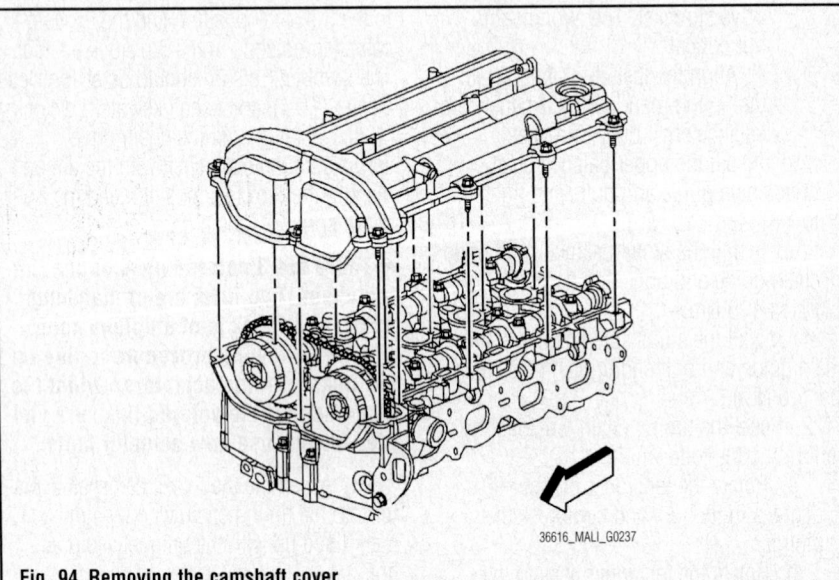

Fig. 94 Removing the camshaft cover

36616_MALI_G0237

ENGINE PERFORMANCE & EMISSION CONTROLS

ACCELERATOR PEDAL POSITION (APP) SENSOR

LOCATION

The Accelerator Pedal Position (APP) sensor is located at the top of the accelerator pedal.

REMOVAL & INSTALLATION

See Figure 95.

1. Disconnect the Accelerator Pedal Position (APP) sensor electrical connector.
2. Remove the APP sensor bolts.
3. Remove the APP sensor.

To install:

4. Install the APP sensor.
5. Install the APP bolts. Tighten the bolts to 89 inch lbs. (10 Nm).
6. Connect the APP sensor electrical connector.
7. Confirm that the APP sensor connector locking clip is fully secured.

CAMSHAFT POSITION (CMP) SENSOR

LOCATION

The 2.4L engines Camshaft Position (CMP) sensor (exhaust), is located on the upper rear of the engine, near the camshaft cover. The 2.4L engines Camshaft Position (CMP) sensor (intake), is located on the upper front of the engine, near the camshaft cover.

REMOVAL & INSTALLATION

Intake

See Figure 96.

1. Remove the air cleaner outlet duct.
2. Disconnect the engine wiring harness electrical connector from the intake Camshaft Position (CMP) sensor.
3. Remove the CMP sensor bolt.
4. Remove the CMP sensor.

To install:

➡**Inspect the CMP sensor for damage, replace as necessary.**

5. Lubricate the CMP sensor O-ring seal with clean engine oil.
6. Install the CMP sensor.
7. Install the CMP sensor bolt and tighten to 89 inch lbs. (10 Nm).
8. Connect the engine wiring harness electrical connector to the intake CMP sensor.
9. Install the air cleaner outlet duct.

Exhaust

See Figure 97.

1. Remove the air cleaner outlet duct.

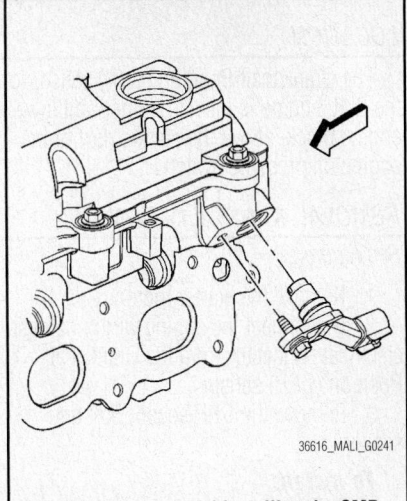

Fig. 96 Removing and installing the CMP sensor (intake)

2. Disconnect the engine wiring harness electrical connector from the exhaust CMP sensor.
3. Remove the CMP sensor bolt.
4. Remove the CMP sensor.

To install:

➡**Inspect the CMP sensor for damage, replace as necessary.**

5. Lubricate the CMP sensor O-ring seal with clean engine oil.
6. Install the CMP sensor.
7. Install the CMP sensor bolt. Tighten the bolt to 89 inch lbs. (10 Nm).
8. Connect the engine wiring harness electrical connector to the exhaust CMP sensor.
9. Install the air cleaner outlet duct.

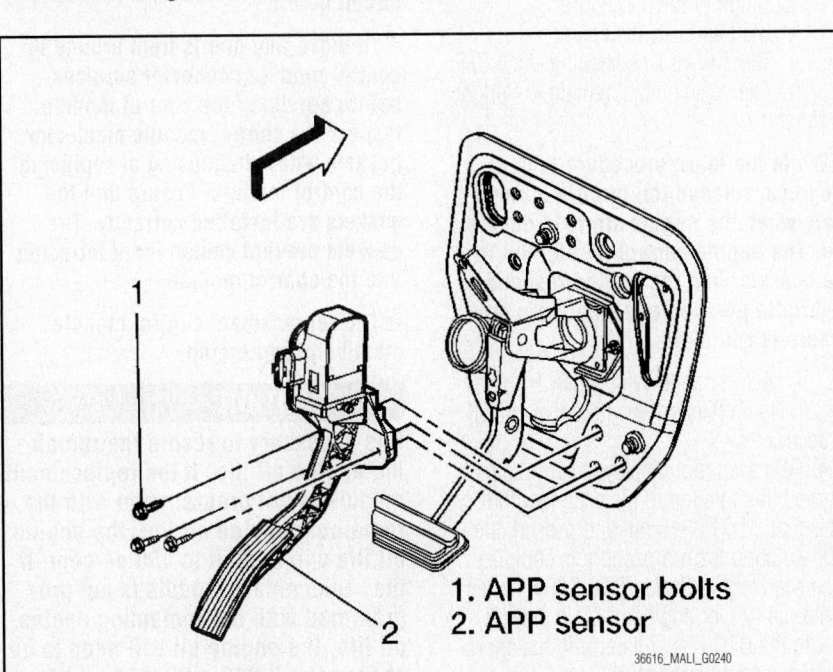

1. APP sensor bolts
2. APP sensor

Fig. 95 Removing and installing the APP sensor

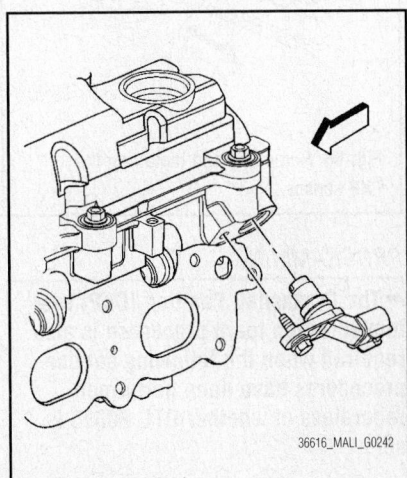

Fig. 97 Removing and installing the CMP sensor (exhaust) (intake shown, exhaust CMP similar)

CRANKSHAFT POSITION (CKP) SENSOR

LOCATION

The Crankshaft Position (CKP) sensor for the 2.4L engine is located in the front lower engine block, above the starter, next to the engine oil pressure switch.

REMOVAL & INSTALLATION

See Figure 98.

1. Remove the starter motor.
2. Disconnect the engine wiring harness electrical connector from the Crankshaft Position (CKP) sensor.
3. Remove the CKP sensor bolt and sensor.

To install:

4. Lubricate the CKP sensor O-ring seal with clean engine oil.
5. Install the CKP sensor.
6. Install the CKP sensor bolt and tighten to 89 inch lbs. (10 Nm).
7. Connect the engine wiring harness electrical connector to the CKP sensor.
8. Install the starter.
9. Perform the CKP system variation learn procedure.

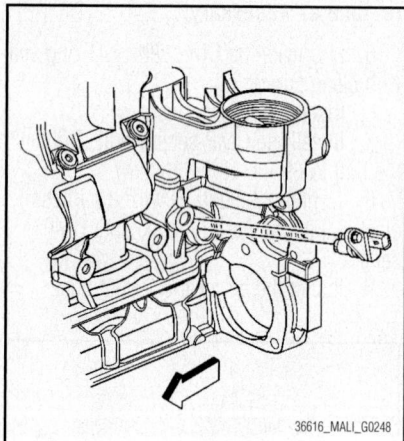

36616_MALI_G0248

Fig. 98 Removing and installing the CKP sensor

PROGRAMMING

➡The Crankshaft Position (CKP) system variation learn procedure is also required when the following service procedures have been performed, regardless of whether DTC P0315 is set:

- An engine replacement
- A Engine Control Module (ECM) replacement
- A crankshaft balancer replacement

- A CKP sensor replacement
- Any engine repairs which disturb the crankshaft to CKP sensor relationship.

➡The ECM monitors certain component signals to determine if all the conditions are met to continue with the CKP System Variation Learn Procedure. The scan tool only displays the condition that inhibits the procedure. The scan tool displays the signals of the following components:

   a. CKP sensors activity—If there is a CKP sensor condition, refer to the applicable DTC that set.
   b. Camshaft Position (CMP) signal activity—If there is a CMP signal condition, refer to the applicable DTC that set.
   c. Engine Coolant Temperature (ECT)—If the engine coolant temperature is not warm enough, idle the engine until the engine coolant temperature reaches a correct temperature.
1. Install the scan tool.
2. Monitor the ECM for DTCs with the scan tool. If other DTCs are set, except DTC P0315, refer to the DTC list for the applicable DTC.
3. With the scan tool, select CKP System Variation Learn Procedure and perform the following:
   a. Block the drive wheels.
   b. Set the parking brake.
   c. DO NOT apply the brake pedal.
   d. Cycle the ignition from OFF to ON.
   e. Apply and hold the brake pedal for the duration of the procedure.
   f. Start and idle the engine.
   g. Turn the Air Conditioning (A/C) OFF.
   h. The vehicle must remain in Park or Neutral.

➡While the learn procedure is in progress, release the throttle immediately when the engine starts to decelerate. The engine control is returned to the operator and the engine responds to throttle position after the learn procedure is complete.

   i. Accelerate to Wide Open Throttle (WOT) and release when the fuel cut-off occurs.
4. The scan tool displays Learn Status: Learned this Ignition. If the scan tool indicates that DTC P0315 ran and passed, the CKP variation learn procedure is complete. If the scan tool indicated DTC P0315 failed or did not run, or another DTC is present, refer to the DTC List and perform the appropriate diagnostic procedure.
5. Turn OFF the ignition for 30n seconds after the learn procedure is completed suc-

cessfully in order to store the CKP system variation values in the ECM memory.

ENGINE CONTROL MODULE (ECM)

LOCATION

The Engine Control Module (ECM) is located on the left side of the engine compartment, in front of the battery.

REMOVAL & INSTALLATION

See Figures 99 and 100.

➡Turn the ignition OFF when installing or removing the control module connectors and disconnecting or reconnecting the power to the control module (battery cable, Powertrain Control Module (PCM)/Engine Control Module (ECM)/Transaxle Control Module (TCM) pigtail, control module fuse, jumper cables, etc.) in order to prevent internal control module damage.

➡Control module damage may result when the metal case contacts battery voltage. DO NOT contact the control module metal case with battery voltage when servicing a control module, using battery booster cables, or when charging the vehicle battery.

➡In order to prevent any possible electrostatic discharge damage to the control module, do not touch the connector pins or the soldered components on the circuit board.

➡Remove any debris from around the control module connector surfaces before servicing the control module. Inspect the control module connector gaskets when diagnosing or replacing the control module. Ensure that the gaskets are installed correctly. The gaskets prevent contaminant intrusion into the control module

➡The replacement control module must be programmed.

✳✳ CAUTION

It is necessary to record the remaining engine oil life. If the replacement module is not programmed with the remaining engine oil life, the engine oil life will default to 100 percent. If the replacement module is not programmed with the remaining engine oil life, the engine oil will need to be changed at 3,000 mi (5 000 km) from the last engine oil change.

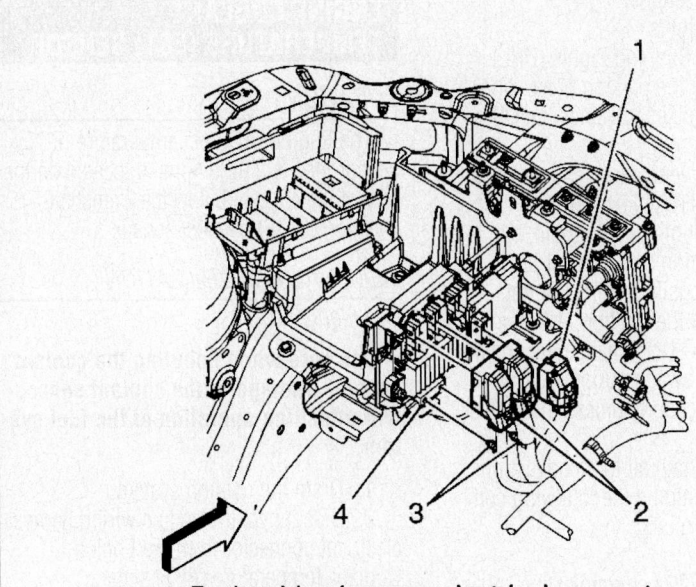

1. Body wiring harness electrical connector
2. Engine wiring harness
   electrical connector
3. Engine wiring harness clips
4. ECM bracket

36616_MALH_G0010

Fig. 99 Disconnecting the body wiring harness electrical connector from the Engine Control Module (ECM)

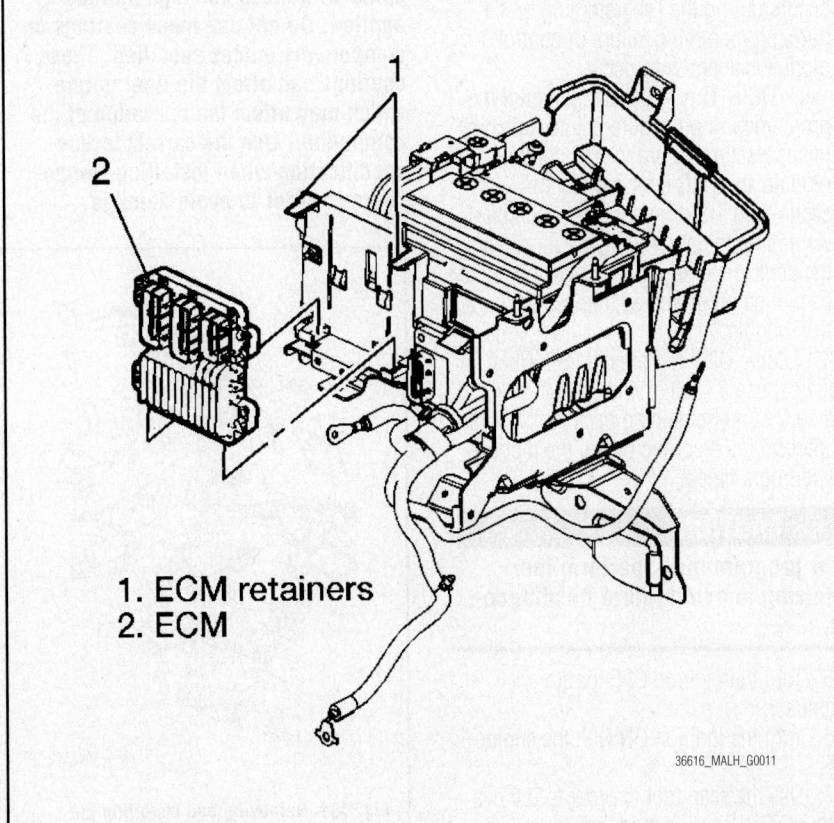

1. ECM retainers
2. ECM

36616_MALH_G0011

Fig. 100 Removing the ECM

1. Using a scan tool, retrieve the percentage of remaining engine oil. Record the remaining engine oil life.
2. Disconnect the negative battery cable.
3. Disconnect the body wiring harness electrical connector from the Engine Control Module (ECM).
4. Disconnect the engine wiring harness electrical connectors from the ECM.
5. Remove the engine wiring harness clips from the ECM bracket.

➡ Control module damage may result when the metal case contacts battery voltage. DO NOT contact the control module metal case with battery voltage when servicing a control module, using battery booster cables or when charging the vehicles battery.

6. Gently lift the ECM retainers up, disengaging the retainers from the ECM.
7. Tilt the ECM towards the engine and remove the ECM from the bracket.

To install:

8. Set the ECM into the bottom of the bracket and push the ECM towards the battery until the ECM snaps into place and is secured by the retainers
9. Connect the engine wiring harness electrical connectors to the ECM.
10. Install the engine wiring harness clips to the ECM bracket.
11. Connect the body wiring harness electrical connector to the ECM.
12. Connect the negative battery cable.
13. Program the ECM.

RESET

Engine Control Module Reprogramming

✳✳ CAUTION

DO NOT program a control module unless you are directed by a service procedure or you are directed by a General Motors Corporation service bulletin. Programming a control module at any other time will not permanently correct a customer's concern.

✳✳ CAUTION

It is essential that the Tech 2, MDI and the TIS terminal are all equipped with the latest software before performing service programming.

❊❊ **CAUTION**

Due to the time requirements of programming a controller, it is recommended that an external power source be used to maintain system voltage. Stable battery voltage is critical during programming. Any fluctuation, spiking, over voltage or loss of voltage will interrupt programming. To ensure trouble-free programming, GM recommends using one of the following external power sources:

- A Midtronics PSC charge
- A fully charged 12V jumper or booster pack disconnected from the AC voltage supply

❊❊ **CAUTION**

Some modules will require additional programming/setup events performed before or after programming.

❊❊ **CAUTION**

Some vehicles may require the use of a CANDi or MDI module for programming.

❊❊ **CAUTION**

Review the appropriate service information for these procedures.

❊❊ **CAUTION**

DTCs may set during programming. Clear DTCs after programming is complete.

❊❊ **CAUTION**

Clearing powertrain DTCs will set the Inspection/Maintenance (I/M) system status indicators to NO.

Ensure the following conditions are met before programming a control module:
1. Vehicle system voltage:
 a. There is not a charging system concern. All charging system concerns must be repaired before programming a control module.
 b. Battery voltage is greater than 12V but less than 16V. The battery must be fully charged before programming the control module.
 c. Turn OFF or disable any system that may put a load on the vehicles battery, such as the following:

- Twilight sentinel
- Interior lights
- Daytime Running Lights (DRL) - Applying the parking brake, on most vehicles, disables the DRL system
- Heating, ventilation, and air conditioning (HVAC) systems
- Engine cooling fans, radio, etc.

 d. The ignition switch must be in the proper position. SPS prompts you to turn ON the ignition, with the engine OFF. DO NOT change the position of the ignition switch during the programming procedure, unless instructed to do so.
 e. Make certain all tool connections are secure, including the following components and circuits:
2. Tech 2

- The RS-232 communication cable port
- The connection at the Data Link Connector (DLC)
- The voltage supply circuits

3. MDI

- The USB, Ethernet or Wireless communication port
- The connection at the Data Link Connector (DLC)

 a. DO NOT disturb the tool harnesses while programming. If an interruption occurs during the programming procedure, programming failure or control module damage may occur.
 b. DO NOT turn off the ignition if the programming procedure is interrupted or unsuccessful. Ensure that all control module and DLC connections are secure and TIS terminal operating software is up to date. Attempt to reprogram the control module. If the control module cannot be programmed, replace the control module.
4. Engine Oil Life Remaining—When available, use a scan tool to reset the Engine Oil Life Remaining back to the original percentage recorded before the module was reprogrammed.

❊❊ **CAUTION**

After programming, perform the following to avoid future misdiagnosis.

5. Turn the ignition OFF for 30 seconds.
6. Turn the ignition ON with the engine OFF.
7. Use the scan tool in order to retrieve history DTCs from all modules.
8. Clear all history DTCs.

ENGINE COOLANT TEMPERATURE (ECT) SENSOR

LOCATION

The Engine Coolant Temperature (ECT) sensor for the 2.4L engine is located on the rear of the engine, below the Camshaft Position (CMP) exhaust sensor.

REMOVAL & INSTALLATION

See Figure 101.

➡Use care when handling the coolant sensor. Damage to the coolant sensor will affect the operation of the fuel system.

1. Drain the cooling system.
2. Disconnect the engine wiring harness electrical connector from the Engine Coolant Temperature (ECT) sensor.
3. Remove the ECT sensor from the thermostat housing.

To install:

➡Replacement components must be the correct part number for the application. Components requiring the use of the thread locking compound, lubricants, corrosion inhibitors, or sealants are identified in the service procedure. Some replacement components may come with these coatings already applied. Do not use these coatings on components unless specified. These coatings can affect the final torque, which may affect the operation of the component. Use the correct torque specification when installing components in order to avoid damage.

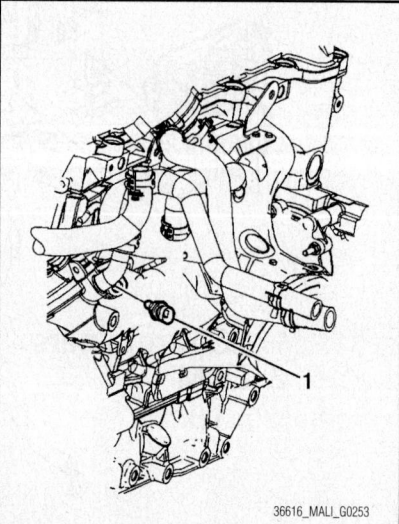

36616_MALI_G0253

Fig. 101 Removing and installing the ECT senor

➡**Use care when handling the coolant sensor. Damage to the coolant sensor will affect the operation of the fuel control system.**

4. If reinstalling the original sensor, or if installing a NEW sensor without a sealer, coat the threads with sealant.

5. Install the ECT sensor to the thermostat housing.

6. Connect the engine wiring harness electrical connector to the ECT sensor.

7. Fill the cooling system.

EVAPORATIVE EMISSIONS (EVAP) CANISTER

LOCATION

The Evaporative Emissions (EVAP) canister is located on the right rear of the vehicle, under the vehicle at the right top of the fuel tank.

REMOVAL & INSTALLATION

See Figure 102.

1. Drain the fuel tank.

2. Place a jackstand under the muffler assembly.

3. With the aid of an assistant, separate the muffler insulators from the underbody hangers.

4. Slowly lower the muffler assembly allowing it to rest on the jackstand.

5. Disconnect the fuel tank fill evaporative emission pipe quick connect fitting from the fuel tank fill evaporative emission pipe.

6. Support the fuel tank with a suitable adjustable jackstand.

7. Loosen, DO NOT REMOVE the left side fuel tank strap bolts.

8. Loosen, DO NOT REMOVE the right side front fuel tank strap bolt.

9. Remove the right side rear fuel tank strap bolt.

10. Using the adjustable jack, lower the right side of the fuel tank enough to access the evaporative canister vent solenoid valve.

11. Disconnect the evaporative canister line quick connect fitting (2) from the evaporative canister vent solenoid valve.

12. Remove the evaporative emission canister bolt and evaporative emission canister.

To install:

13. Install the evaporative emission canister bolt and evaporative emission canister.

14. Connect the evaporative canister line quick connect fitting to the evaporative canister vent solenoid valve.

15. Using the adjustable jack, raise the right side of the fuel tank.

16. Install the right side rear fuel tank strap bolt.

17. Tighten the left side fuel tank strap bolts to 15 ft. lbs. (20 Nm).

18. Tighten the right side front fuel tank strap bolt to 15 ft. lbs. (20 Nm).

19. Remove the support from the fuel tank.

20. Install the fuel fill pipe hose to the fuel tank.

21. Connect the fuel tank fill evaporative emission pipe quick connect fitting to the fuel tank fill evaporative emission pipe.

22. Tighten the fuel fill pipe hose clamp at the fuel tank to 35 inch lbs. (4 Nm).

23. Raise the muffler assembly into position.

24. With the aid of an assistant, install the muffler insulators to the underbody hangers.

25. Remove the jackstand from under the muffler assembly.

26. Lower the vehicle.

HEATED OXYGEN (HO2S) SENSOR

LOCATION

For the 2.4L engine, the HO2S 1 is located on the rear of the engine, between the exhaust manifold and the catalytic convertor. HO2S 2 is on the rear of the engine, just after the catalytic convertor and before the muffler.

REMOVAL & INSTALLATION

Sensor 1

See Figure 103.

➡**The oxygen sensor uses a permanently attached pigtail and connector. Do not remove the pigtail from the oxygen sensor. Damage to or removal of the pigtail connector could affect proper operation of the oxygen sensor.**

➡**The use of excessive force may damage the threads in the exhaust manifold/pipe.**

✳✳ CAUTION

The in-line connector and louvered end must be kept clear of grease, dirt or other contaminants. Avoid using cleaning solvents of any type. DO NOT drop or roughly handle the heated oxygen sensor (HO2S).

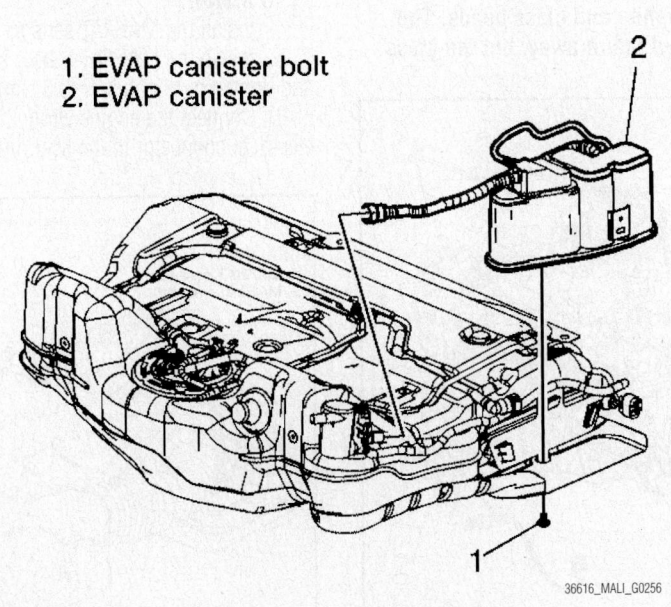

1. EVAP canister bolt
2. EVAP canister

36616_MALI_G0256

Fig. 102 Removing and installing the EVAP canister

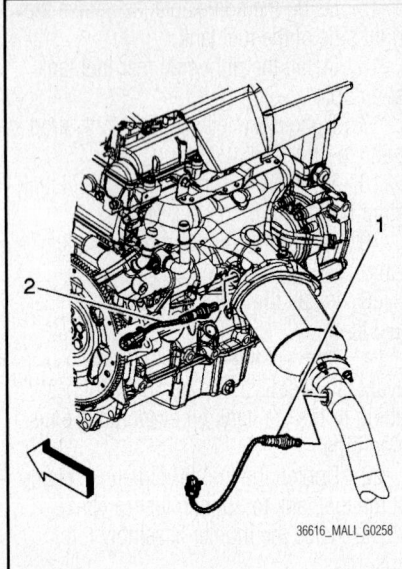

Fig. 103 Removing and installing the HO2S (sensor 1)

➡The HO2S may be difficult to remove when the engine temperature is less than 120°F (48°C).

1. Remove the Connector Position Assurance (CPA) retainer.
2. Disconnect the engine wiring harness electrical connector from the HO2S electrical connector.
3. Remove the HO2S connector clip from the thermostat housing tab.
4. Remove the HO2S.

To install:

➡A special anti-seize compound is used on the heated oxygen sensor threads. The compound consists of a liquid graphite and glass beads. The graphite will burn away, but the glass beads will remain, making the sensor easier to remove. New or service replacement sensors will have the compound applied to the threads. If a sensor is removed and is to be reinstalled, the threads must have an anti-seize compound applied prior to installation.

5. If necessary, coat the threads of the HO2S with anti-seize compound GM P/N 12377953 or equivalent.
6. Install the HO2S and tighten to 31 ft. lbs. (42 Nm).
7. Install the HO2S connector clip to the thermostat housing tab.
8. Connect the engine wiring harness electrical connector to the HO2S electrical connector.
9. Install the CPA retainer.

Sensor 2

See Figure 104.

➡The oxygen sensor uses a permanently attached pigtail and connector. Do not remove the pigtail from the oxygen sensor. Damage to or removal of the pigtail connector could affect proper operation of the oxygen sensor.

➡The use of excessive force may damage the threads in the exhaust manifold/pipe.

✴✴ CAUTION

The in-line connector and louvered end must be kept clear of grease, dirt or other contaminants. Avoid using cleaning solvents of any type. DO NOT drop or roughly handle the heated oxygen sensor (HO2S).

➡The HO2S may be difficult to remove when the engine temperature is less than 120°F (48°C).

1. Raise and suitably support the vehicle.
2. Remove the Connector Position Assurance (CPA) retainer.
3. Disconnect the HO2S electrical connector (2) from the engine wiring harness electrical connector.
4. Remove the HO2S.

To install:

➡A special anti-seize compound is used on the heated oxygen sensor threads. The compound consists of a liquid graphite and glass beads. The graphite will burn away, but the glass

beads will remain, making the sensor easier to remove. New or service replacement sensors will have the compound applied to the threads. If a sensor is removed and is to be reinstalled, the threads must have an anti-seize compound applied prior to installation.

5. If necessary, coat the threads of the HO2S with anti-seize compound GM P/N 12377953 or equivalent.
6. Install the HO2S and tighten to 31 ft. lbs. (42 Nm).
7. Connect the HO2S electrical connector to the engine wiring harness electrical connector.
8. Install the CPA retainer.
9. Lower the vehicle.

INTAKE AIR TEMPERATURE (IAT) SENSOR

LOCATION

The Intake Air Temperature (IAT)/Mass Air Flow (MAF) sensor is located on the top right side of the engine, at the air cleaner.

REMOVAL & INSTALLATION

See Figure 105.

1. Disconnect the engine wiring harness electrical connector from the Mass Air Flow (MAF)/Intake Air Temperature (IAT) sensor.
2. Remove the MAF/IAT sensor screws.
3. Remove the MAF/IAT sensor.

To install:

4. Install the MAF/IAT sensor.
5. Install the MAF/IAT sensor screws and tighten to 5 inch lbs. (0.6 Nm).
6. Connect the engine wiring harness electrical connector to the MAF/IAT sensor.

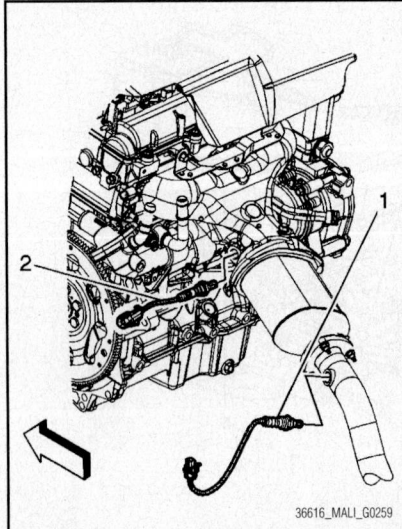

Fig. 104 Removing and installing the HO2S (sensor 2)

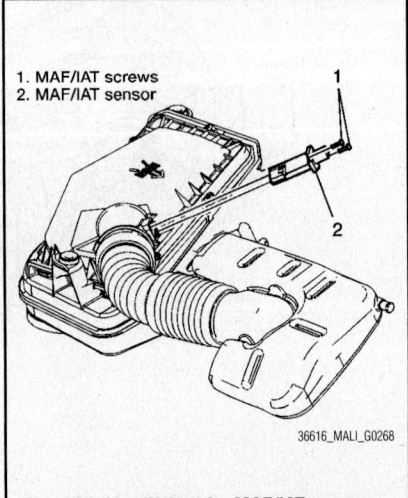

1. MAF/IAT screws
2. MAF/IAT sensor

Fig. 105 Identifying the MAF/IAT sensor

KNOCK SENSOR (KS)

LOCATION

For the 2.4L engine, the Knock Sensor (KS) is located at the lower left side of the engine, in front of the starter motor.

REMOVAL & INSTALLATION

See Figure 106.

1. Disconnect the negative battery cable.
2. Raise and support the vehicle.
3. Disconnect the engine wiring harness electrical connector from the Knock Sensor (KS) pigtail electrical connector.
4. Remove the knock sensor electrical connector pigtail clip from the oil level indicator tube bracket.
5. Remove the KS bolt.
6. Remove the KS.

To install:

➡**Rotate the pigtail 90 degrees from vertical before securing the fastener.**

7. Install the KS.
8. Install the KS bolt and tighten to 18 ft. lbs. (25 Nm).
9. Install the KS electrical connector pigtail clip to the oil level indicator tube bracket.
10. Connect the engine wiring harness electrical connector to the KS pigtail electrical connector.
11. Lower the vehicle.
12. Connect the negative battery cable.

MASS AIR FLOW (MAF) SENSOR

For information on the Mass Air Flow (MAF) sensor, refer to INTAKE AIR TEMPERATURE (IAT) SENSOR.

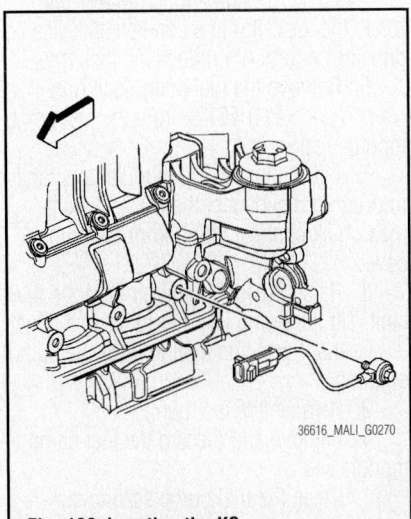

36616_MALI_G0270

Fig. 106 Locating the KS

MANIFOLD ABSOLUTE PRESSURE (MAP) SENSOR

LOCATION

For the 2.4L engine, the Manifold Absolute Pressure (MAP) sensor is located at the front top of the engine, on the intake manifold, near cylinder number 3.

REMOVAL & INSTALLATION

See Figure 107.

1. Remove the air cleaner outlet duct.
2. Disconnect the Evaporative Emission (EVAP) canister purge tube from the intake manifold.
3. Reposition the EVAP canister purge tube out of the way.
4. Disconnect the fuel injector wiring harness electrical connector from the Manifold Absolute Pressure (MAP) sensor.
5. Remove the fuel injector wiring harness clips from the fuel rail tabs.
6. Disconnect the fuel injector wiring harness electrical connector from the number 3 fuel injector.
7. Squeeze tabs and slide the MAP sensor upward.

To install:

8. Lubricate the NEW MAP sensor seal with clean engine oil.
9. Install the MAP sensor into the intake manifold.
10. Connect the fuel injector wiring

harness electrical connector to the number 3 fuel injector.
11. Install the fuel injector wiring harness clips to the fuel rail tabs.
12. Connect the fuel injector wiring harness electrical connector to the MAP sensor.
13. Position the EVAP canister purge tube out of the way.
14. Connect the EVAP canister purge tube to the intake manifold.
15. Install the air cleaner outlet duct.

POSITIVE CRANKCASE VENTILATION (PCV) VALVE

LOCATION

The Positive Crankcase Ventilation (PCV) valve is on the valve rocker arm cover.

REMOVAL & INSTALLATION

➡**Do not attempt to remove the valve from the valve rocker arm cover, as damage may occur to the rocker arm valve cover. The Positive Crankcase Ventilation (PCV) valve is a fixed orifice system.**

VEHICLE SPEED SENSOR (VSS)

REMOVAL & INSTALLATION

Automatic Transaxle 4T45-E

See Figure 108.

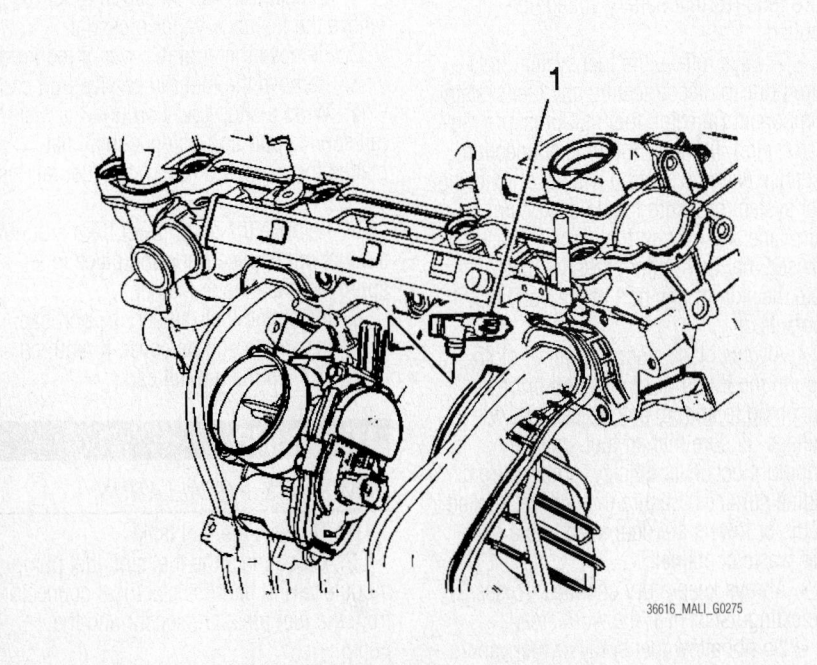

36616_MALI_G0275

Fig. 107 Removing and installing the MAP sensor

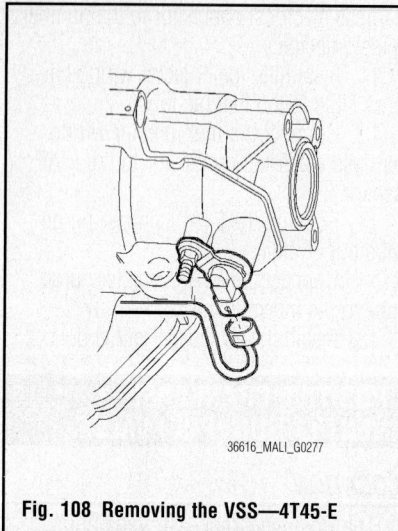

Fig. 108 Removing the VSS—4T45-E

✳✳ CAUTION

Ensure that the vehicle is properly supported and squarely positioned. To help avoid personal injury when a vehicle is on a hoist, provide additional support for the vehicle on the opposite end from which the components are being removed.

1. Position the vehicle on a hoist and raise the vehicle.
2. Disconnect the Vehicle Speed Sensor (VSS) electrical connector.
3. Remove the VSS electrical harness retainer from the VSS stud.
4. Remove the VSS stud.
5. Remove the output VSS from the transmission case.

✳✳ CAUTION

Inspect the O-ring for damage and replace if necessary.

6. Remove the O-ring from the VSS.

To install:

7. Install the O-ring onto the VSS.
8. Install the output VSS into the transmission case.
9. Install the VSS stud and tighten to 106 inch lbs. (12 Nm).
10. Install the VSS electrical harness retainer to the VSS stud.
11. Connect the VSS electrical connector.
12. Lower the vehicle.

FUEL   GASOLINE FUEL INJECTION SYSTEM

FUEL SYSTEM SERVICE PRECAUTIONS

Safety is the most important factor when performing not only fuel system maintenance but any type of maintenance. Failure to conduct maintenance and repairs in a safe manner may result in serious personal injury or death. Maintenance and testing of the vehicle's fuel system components can be accomplished safely and effectively by adhering to the following rules and guidelines.

• To avoid the possibility of fire and personal injury, always disconnect the negative battery cable unless the repair or test procedure requires that battery voltage be applied.
• Always relieve the fuel system pressure prior to disconnecting any fuel system component (injector, fuel rail, pressure regulator, etc.), fitting or fuel line connection. Exercise extreme caution whenever relieving fuel system pressure to avoid exposing skin, face and eyes to fuel spray. Please be advised that fuel under pressure may penetrate the skin or any part of the body that it contacts.
• Always place a shop towel or cloth around the fitting or connection prior to loosening to absorb any excess fuel due to spillage. Ensure that all fuel spillage (should it occur) is quickly removed from engine surfaces. Ensure that all fuel soaked cloths or towels are deposited into a suitable waste container.
• Always keep a dry chemical (Class B) fire extinguisher near the work area.
• Do not allow fuel spray or fuel vapors to come into contact with a spark or open flame.

• Always use a back-up wrench when loosening and tightening fuel line connection fittings. This will prevent unnecessary stress and torsion to fuel line piping.
• Always replace worn fuel fitting O-rings with new. Do not substitute fuel hose or equivalent where fuel pipe is installed.

Before servicing the vehicle, make sure to also refer to the precautions in the beginning of this section as well.

RELIEVING FUEL SYSTEM PRESSURE

1. Loosen the fuel fill cap in order to relieve the fuel tank vapor pressure.
2. Remove the engine cover, if required.
3. Remove the fuel rail service port cap.
4. Wrap a shop towel around the fuel rail service port and using a small flat bladed tool, depress (open) the fuel rail test port valve.
5. Remove the shop towel from around the fuel rail service port, and place in an approved gasoline container.
6. Install the fuel rail service port cap.
7. Install the engine cover, if required.
8. Tighten the fuel fill cap.

FUEL PUMP

REMOVAL & INSTALLATION

1. Remove the fuel tank.
2. Disconnect the fuel tank fuel pump module wiring harness electrical connectors from the fuel pressure sensor and the pump.
3. Disconnect the fuel tank vent pipe quick connect fittings from the module.

4. Install a fuel pump lock ring wrench such as J 45722 to the fuel pump module lock ring.

➡**Avoid damaging the lock ring. Use only a fuel pump lock ring wrench such as J 45722 to prevent damage to the lock ring.**

➡**Do Not handle the fuel sender assembly by the fuel pipes. The amount of leverage generated by handling the fuel pipes could damage the joints.**

➡**Do NOT use impact tools. Significant force will be required to release the lock ring. The use of a hammer and screwdriver is not recommended. Secure the fuel tank in order to prevent fuel tank rotation.**

5. Using a fuel pump lock ring wrench such as J 45722 and a long breaker-bar, rotate the lock ring in a counterclockwise direction in order to unlock the lock ring.
6. Remove the fuel pump lock ring wrench such as J 45722 from the fuel pump module lock ring.
7. Lift the fuel pump module up slightly in order to disconnect the fuel tank vent pipe quick connect fitting from the pump cover.
8. Raise the fuel pump up from the fuel tank. Tilt the pump in order to allow the fuel level sensor arm and float to clear the pump opening.
9. Remove the fuel pump.
10. Remove and discard the fuel pump module seal.
11. Clean the fuel pump sealing surfaces.

To install:

Drain the fuel from the fuel sender assembly into an approved container in order to reduce the risk of fire and personal injury. Never store the fuel in an open container.

➡**Some lock rings were manufactured with "DO NOT REUSE" stamped into them. These lock rings may be reused if they are not damaged or warped. Inspect the lock ring for damage due to improper removal or installation procedures. If damage is found, install a NEW fuel pump module. Inspect the lock ring for flatness as best as possible. If the lock ring is warped, replace the fuel pump module.**

12. Clean any contamination from the male pipe ends of the fuel pump.

13. Place a NEW fuel tank pump seal onto the fuel tank.

14. Insert the fuel pump into the fuel tank allowing the sensor arm and float to clear the module opening.

15. Lower the pump down into the fuel tank until the fuel tank vent pipe quick connect fitting can be connected.

16. Connect the fuel tank vent pipe quick connect fitting at the pump cover.

17. Press the fuel tank pump downward.

18. Install the pump lock ring wrench such as J 45722 to the fuel pump module lock ring.

➡**Ensure that the lock ring is installed with the correct side facing upward. A correctly installed lock ring will only turn in a clockwise direction.**

19. Using the pump lock ring wrench such as J 45722 and a long breaker-bar, rotate the lock ring in a clockwise direction in order the lock the lock ring.

20. Remove the pump lock ring wrench from the fuel pump module lock ring.

21. Connect the fuel tank vent pipe quick connect fittings to the pump.

22. Connect the fuel tank fuel pump module wiring harness electrical connectors to the fuel pressure sensor and the pump.

23. Install the fuel tank

FUEL RAIL & INJECTORS

REMOVAL & INSTALLATION

See Figures 109 and 110.

1. Disconnect the negative battery cable.

2. Relieve the fuel system pressure.

3. Remove the air cleaner outlet duct.

4. Disconnect the fuel feed line quick connect fitting from the fuel rail

5. Disconnect the engine wiring harness electrical connector from the fuel injector wiring harness electrical connector.

6. Disconnect the fuel injector wiring harness electrical from the Manifold Absolute Pressure (MAP) sensor.

7. Remove the engine wiring harness clips from the fuel rail tabs.

8. Remove the fuel rail bolts.

➡**Use care when removing the fuel rail assembly in order to prevent damage to the fuel injector spray tips.**

9. Pull the fuel rail back and upward in order to release the fuel injectors from the cylinder head ports.

10. Remove the fuel rail.

➡**The fuel injector tip insulators may be located on the injector or may still be located in the cylinder head. Either way, ensure that all 4 injector tip insulators are removed and discarded.**

11. Remove and discard the fuel injector tip insulators.

12. Disconnect the fuel injector wiring harness electrical connectors from the fuel injectors.

13. Remove the fuel injector wiring harness clips from the fuel rail.

14. Remove the fuel injector wiring harness from the fuel rail.

➡**Use care in removing the fuel injectors in order to prevent damage to the fuel injector electrical connector pins or the fuel injector nozzles. Do not immerse the fuel injector in any type of cleaner. The fuel injector is an electrical component and may be damaged by this cleaning method.**

➡**If the fuel injectors are found to be leaking, the engine oil may be contaminated with fuel.**

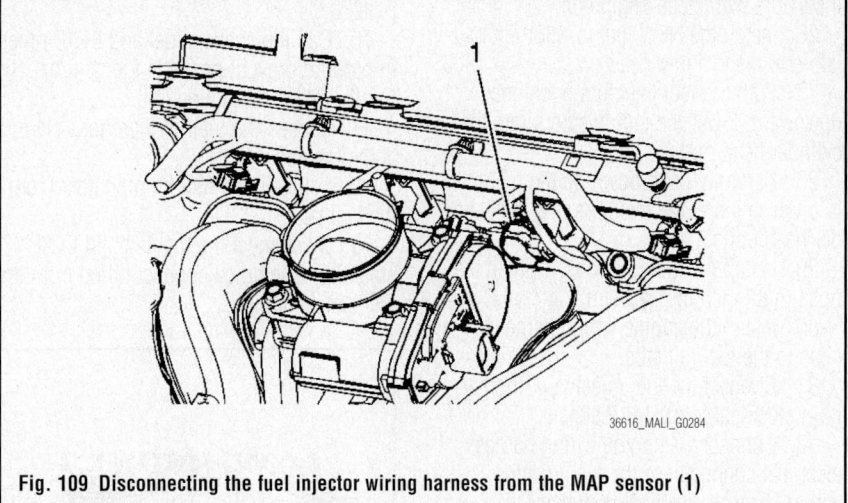

36616_MALI_G0284

Fig. 109 Disconnecting the fuel injector wiring harness from the MAP sensor (1)

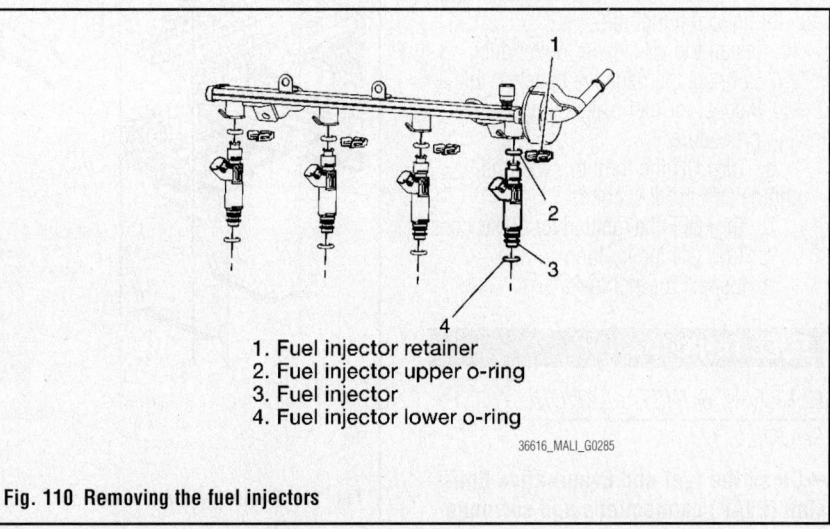

1. Fuel injector retainer
2. Fuel injector upper o-ring
3. Fuel injector
4. Fuel injector lower o-ring

36616_MALI_G0285

Fig. 110 Removing the fuel injectors

15. Remove the fuel injector retainer.

16. Remove the fuel injector from the fuel rail.

17. Remove the fuel injector upper O-ring.

18. Remove the fuel injector lower O-ring.

To install:

➡The fuel injector assembly is stamped with a part number identification. Be sure to use the correct part number when ordering replacement fuel injectors.

19. Lubricate the NEW fuel injector O-rings with clean engine oil.

20. Install the NEW fuel injector O-rings.

21. Install the fuel injector to the fuel rail.

22. Install the fuel injector retainer.

23. Install the fuel injector wiring harness clips to the fuel rail.

24. Connect the fuel injector wiring harness electrical connectors to the fuel injectors.

25. Lubricate the NEW fuel injector tip insulators with clean engine oil.

26. Install the NEW fuel injector tip insulators to the cylinder head.

27. With the fuel injectors positioned downward, lower the fuel injectors into the cylinder head ports.

28. Carefully push down on the fuel rail in order to insert the injectors into the cylinder head ports.

29. Install the fuel rail bolts. Tighten the bolts to 89 inch lbs. (10 Nm).

30. Install the engine wiring harness clips to the fuel rail tabs.

31. Connect the fuel injector wiring harness electrical to the MAP sensor.

32. Connect the engine wiring harness electrical connector to the fuel injector wiring harness electrical connector.

33. Connect the fuel feed line quick connect fitting to the fuel rail.

34. Install the air cleaner outlet duct.

35. Connect the negative battery cable.

36. Inspect for fuel leaks using the following procedure:

   a. Turn ON the ignition, with the engine OFF for 2 seconds.

   b. Turn OFF the ignition for 10 seconds

   c. Turn ON the ignition

   d. Inspect for fuel leaks.

FUEL TANK

REMOVAL & INSTALLATION

See Figure 111.

➡Clean the fuel and Evaporative Emission (EVAP) connections and surrounding areas prior to disconnecting the lines in order the avoid possible system contamination.

1. Relieve the fuel system pressure.

2. Drain the fuel tank.

3. Raise and support the vehicle.

4. Disconnect the fuel tank fuel pump module wiring harness electrical connector from body wiring harness electrical connector.

5. Remove the body wiring harness electrical connector clip from the EVAP canister.

6. Disconnect the body wiring harness electrical connector from the rear Antilock Brake System (ABS) wiring harness electrical connector.

7. Remove the rear ABS wiring harness electrical connector clip from the EVAP canister.

8. Disconnect the fuel tank fuel feed pipe quick connect fitting from the chassis fuel feed pipe.

9. Disconnect the fuel tank EVAP pipe quick connect fitting from the chassis EVAP pipe.

10. Cap the chassis fuel and EVAP pipes in order to prevent possible fuel and/or EVAP system contamination.

11. Loosen the fuel fill pipe hose clamp at the fuel tank.

12. Separate the fuel fill pipe hose from the fuel tank.

13. Disconnect the fuel tank fill EVAP emission pipe quick connect fitting from the fuel tank vent pipe.

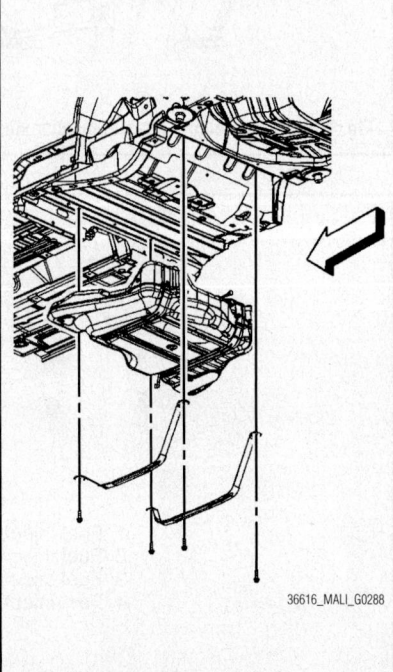

36616_MALI_G0288

Fig. 111 Removing the fuel tank

14. Place a jackstand under the muffler assembly.

15. With the aid of an assistant, separate the muffler insulators from the underbody hangers.

16. Slowly lower the muffler assembly allowing it to rest on the jackstand. If this is not possible, remove the muffler assembly.

17. Have assistants support either side of the fuel tank.

18. Place a suitable adjustable jack under the fuel tank, and have the assistants rest the fuel tank on the adjustable jack.

19. Remove fuel tank strap bolts and straps.

20. If applicable, in order to clear the muffler assembly, slowly lower the right side of the fuel tank.

21. Once the tank is clear of the right frame rail, lower the fuel tank down and remove forward toward the right side of the vehicle.

To install:

22. Have assistants support either side of the fuel tank.

23. If applicable, begin to install the right side of the fuel tank over the muffler assembly.

24. If applicable, raise the right side of the fuel tank into position inboard of the right frame rail. Use care in feeding the fuel feed, EVAP line wiring harness over the muffler assembly.

25. If applicable and the muffler assembly was removed, have assistants raise the fuel tank into position.

26. Install fuel tank straps and bolts. Tighten the bolts to 15 ft. lbs. (20 Nm).

27. Raise the muffler assembly into position if applicable, otherwise install the muffler assembly.

28. With the aid of an assistant, install the muffler insulators to the underbody hangers.

29. Remove the jackstand from under the muffler assembly.

30. Install the fuel fill pipe hose to the fuel tank.

31. Connect the fuel tank fill EVAP emission pipe quick connect fitting to the fuel tank vent pipe.

32. Tighten the fuel fill pipe hose clamp at the fuel tank to 35 inch lbs. (4 Nm).

33. Remove the caps from the fuel and EVAP pipes.

34. Connect the fuel tank EVAP pipe quick connect fitting to the chassis EVAP pipe.

35. Connect the fuel tank fuel feed pipe quick connect fitting to the chassis fuel feed pipe.

36. Install the rear ABS wiring harness electrical connector clip to the EVAP canister.

37. Connect the body wiring harness electrical connector to the rear ABS wiring harness electrical connector.

38. Install the body wiring harness electrical connector clip to the underbody.

39. Connect the fuel tank fuel pump module wiring harness electrical connector to the body wiring harness electrical connector.

40. Lower the vehicle.

41. Refill the fuel tank.

42. Tighten the fuel fill cap.

43. Inspect for fuel leaks using the following procedure:

a. Turn ON the ignition, with the engine OFF for 10 seconds.

b. Turn OFF the ignition for 10 seconds.

c. Turn ON the ignition, with the engine OFF.

d. Inspect for fuel leaks.

IDLE SPEED

ADJUSTMENT

Idle speed is maintained by the Powertrain Control Module (PCM). No adjustment is necessary or possible.

THROTTLE BODY

REMOVAL & INSTALLATION

See Figure 112.

➡ **Do not use solvent of any type when cleaning the gasket surfaces on the intake manifold and the throttle body assembly, as damage to the gasket surfaces and throttle body assembly may result. Use care in cleaning the gasket surfaces on the intake manifold**

and the throttle body assembly, as sharp tools may damage the gasket surfaces.

➡ **Do not use any solvent that contains Methyl Ethyl Ketone (MEK). This solvent may damage fuel system components.**

➡ **DO NOT prop open the throttle blade with the ignition key in the ON position as it may set a Diagnostic Trouble Code (DTC).**

1. Remove the air cleaner outlet duct.

2. Disconnect the engine wiring harness electrical connector from the Electronic Throttle Control (ETC).

3. Remove the throttle body bolts.

4. Remove the throttle body.

5. Inspect the throttle body gasket, and replace if necessary.

To install:

6. Install the throttle body. Tighten the bolts to 89 inch lbs. (10 Nm).

7. Connect the engine wiring harness electrical connector to the ETC.

8. Install the air cleaner outlet duct.

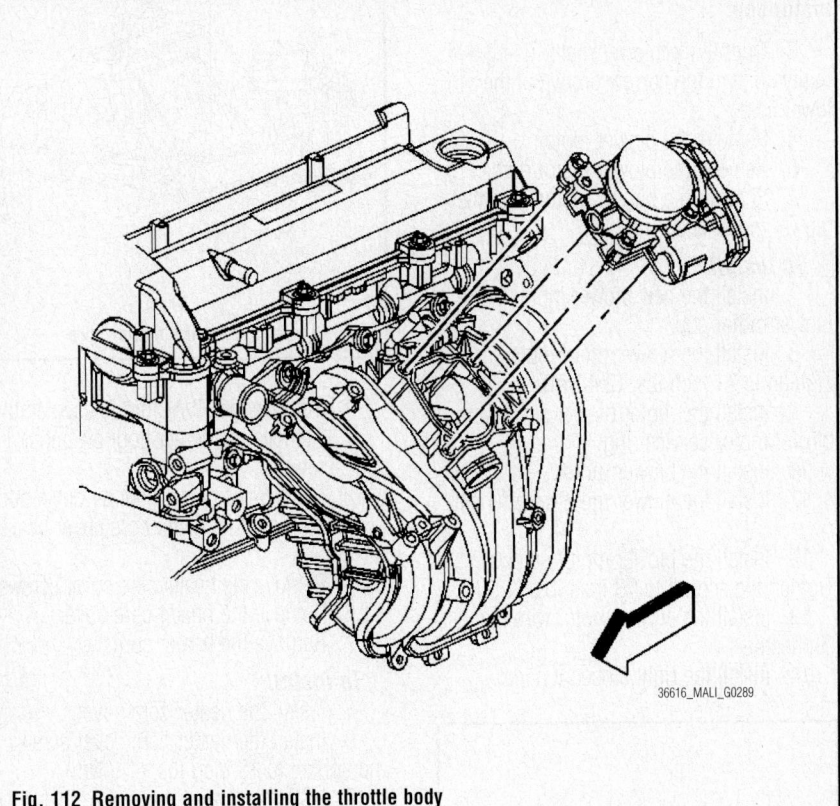

36616_MALI_G0289

Fig. 112 Removing and installing the throttle body

HEATING & AIR CONDITIONING SYSTEM

BLOWER MOTOR

REMOVAL & INSTALLATION

See Figure 113.

1. Remove the right closeout panel.
2. Remove the blower motor wire harness connector.

➡ **Cut through the case as straight as possible because the motor cup must be replaced. In order to prevent damage to the component, do not cut any deeper than necessary to remove the motor cup.**

3. Cut out the blower motor using a utility knife in the narrow groove of the lower case.
4. Remove the blower motor.
5. Remove the blower motor nuts.
6. Remove the blower motor from the blower motor cup.

To install:

7. Install the new blower motor to the blower motor cup.
8. Install the blower motor nuts. Tighten to 21 inch lbs. (2.4 Nm).
9. Install the motor blower seal to the blower motor service ring.
10. Install the blower motor.
11. Install the blower motor attachment ring.
12. Install the blower motor screws. Tighten the screws to 13 inch lbs. (1.5 Nm).
13. Install the blower motor wire harness connector.
14. Install the right closeout panel.

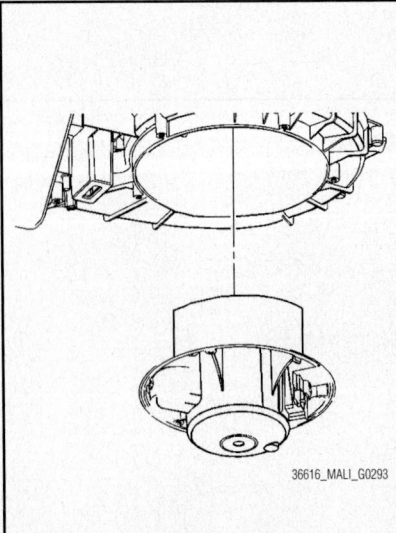

Fig. 113 Removing the blower motor

HEATER CORE

REMOVAL & INSTALLATION

See Figure 114.

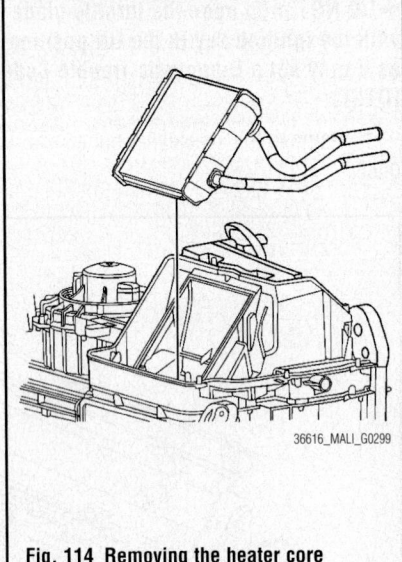

36616_MALI_G0299

Fig. 114 Removing the heater core

1. Remove the HVAC module assembly.
2. Remove the center floor air outlet duct screws.
3. Remove the center floor air outlet duct.
4. Drill out the heater core cover heat stakes.
5. Remove the heater core cover screws.
6. Remove the heater core cover.
7. Remove the heater core.

To install:

8. Install the heater core cover.
9. Install the heater core cover screws and tighten to 13 inch lbs. (1.5 Nm).
10. Install the center floor air outlet duct.
11. Install the upper floor air outlet duct screws and tighten to 13 inch lbs. (1.5 Nm).
12. Install the HVAC module assembly.

HVAC MODULE

REMOVAL & INSTALLATION

See Figure 115.

1. Remove the Air Conditioner (A/C) lines from the thermal expansion valve.
2. Remove the heater hose from the heater core.
3. Remove the Instrument Panel (I/P) assembly.
4. Remove the recirculation actuator wire harness connector.

5. Remove the air temperature actuator wire harness connector.
6. Remove the mode actuator wire harness connector.
7. Remove the blower motor wire harness connector.
8. Remove the blower motor resistor wire harness connector.
9. Remove the left hand side window defogger outlet duct.
10. Remove the HVAC module assembly mounting bolts from the instrument panel reinforcement.
11. Remove the HVAC module assembly to dash panel bolts.
12. Remove the HVAC module assembly.

To install:

13. Install the HVAC module assembly.
14. Install the HVAC module assembly to dash panel bolts and tighten to 88 inch lbs. (10 Nm).
15. Install the HVAC module assembly mounting bolts to the instrument panel reinforcement and tighten the bolts to 44 inch lbs. (5 Nm).
16. Install the left hand side window defogger outlet duct.
17. Install the blower motor resistor wire harness connector.
18. Install the blower motor wire harness connector.
19. Install the mode actuator wire harness connector.
20. Install the air temperature actuator wire harness connector.
21. Install the recirculation actuator wire harness connector.
22. Install the I/P assembly.
23. Install the heater hoses to the heater core.
24. Install the A/C lines to the thermal expansion valve.

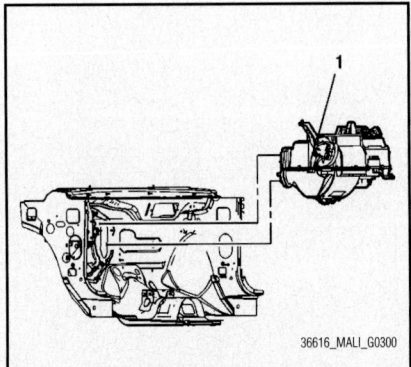

36616_MALI_G0300

Fig. 115 Removing the A/C and heater module assembly

STEERING

ELECTRONIC STEERING GEAR

REMOVAL & INSTALLATION

✳✳ CAUTION

With the wheels of the vehicle facing straight ahead, secure the steering wheel utilizing a steering column anti-rotation pin, steering column lock, or a strap to prevent rotation. Locking of the steering column will prevent damage and a possible malfunction of the SIR system. The steering wheel must be secured in position before disconnecting the steering column, intermediate shaft or steering gear. After disconnecting these components, do not move the front tires and wheels. Failure to follow these procedures may cause improper alignment of some components during installation and result in possible damage to the SIR coil.

1. Turn the front wheels to the straight forward position and secure the steering wheel from moving.
2. Disengage the rack and pinion outer tie rod ends from the steering knuckles.
3. Separate the intermediate steering shaft from the steering gear.
4. Remove the transmission rear mount bolt.
5. Remove the steering gear bolts, nuts, and washers from the steering gear.

➡**The position of the steering gear will need to be manipulated to remove it** through the left front wheel opening.

6. Remove the steering gear through the left front wheel opening.

To install:

7. Install the steering gear through the left front wheel opening.

➡**Start all of the bolts and nuts by hand before finalizing any torques.**

8. Install the steering gear bolts, nuts, and washers to the steering gear. Tighten the bolts and nuts to 52 ft. lbs. (70 Nm) plus an additional 90 degrees.
9. Install the transmission rear mount bolt. Tighten to 66 ft. lbs. (90 Nm).
10. Connect the intermediate steering shaft to the steering column. Install a NEW bolt and tighten to 36 ft. lbs. (49 Nm) for models with electronic steering or 46 ft. lbs. (62 Nm) for models with hydraulic steering.
11. Connect the intermediate steering shaft to the steering gear. Tighten a new bolt to 36 ft. lbs. (49 Nm).
12. Install the rack and pinion outer tie rod ends to the steering knuckles.
13. Adjust the front toe.

POWER STEERING PUMP

BLEEDING

➡**Use clean, new power steering fluid only. Hoses touching the frame, body or engine may cause system noise. Verify that the hoses do not touch any other part of the vehicle. Loose con-**nections may not leak, but could allow air into the steering system. Verify that all hoses connections are tight.

➡**Power steering fluid level must be maintained throughout bleed procedure.**

1. Fill pump reservoir with fluid to minimum system level, FULL COLD level, or middle of hash mark on cap stick fluid level indicator.

➡**With hydro-boost only, the oil level will appear falsely high if the hydro-boost accumulator is not fully charged. Do not apply the brake pedal with the engine OFF. This will discharge the hydro-boost accumulator.**

2. If equipped with hydro-boost, fully charge the hydro-boost accumulator, start the engine, firmly apply the brake pedal 10-15 times and turn the engine off.
3. Raise the vehicle until the front wheels are off the ground.
4. Key on engine OFF, turn the steering wheel from stop to stop 12 times.
5. Vehicles equipped with hydro-boost systems or longer length power steering hoses may require turns up to 15 to 20 stop to stops.
6. Verify power steering fluid level per operating specification.
7. Start the engine. Rotate steering wheel from left to right. Check for sign of cavitation or fluid aeration (pump noise/whining).
8. Verify the fluid level. Repeat the bleed procedure, if necessary.

SUSPENSION

FRONT SUSPENSION

LOWER BALL JOINT

REMOVAL & INSTALLATION

The ball joint is an integral part of the control arm, if defective replace the control arm.

LOWER CONTROL ARM

REMOVAL & INSTALLATION

See Figures 116 through 118.

1. Raise and support the vehicle.
2. Remove the tire and wheel.

✳✳ CAUTION

DO NOT re-use the lower ball joint bolt. Discard and use NEW only.

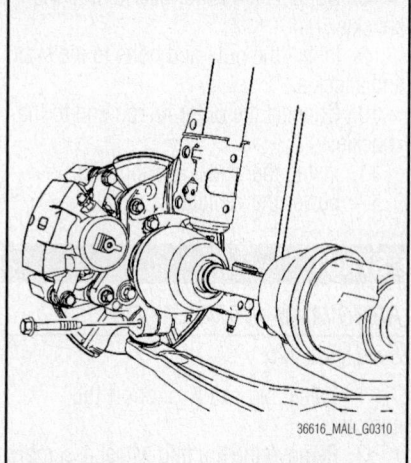

36616_MALI_G0310

Fig. 116 Removing the lower ball joint to knuckle and bolt

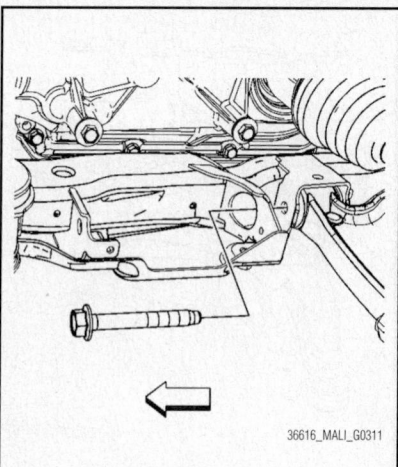

36616_MALI_G0311

Fig. 117 Removing the front lower control arm bolt

3. Remove the lower ball joint to knuckle nut and bolt.

4. Separate the lower control arm from the knuckle.

5. If removing the left lower control arm and the vehicle is equipped with the 4T45-E transmission, remove the left side transmission mount.

7. Remove the front lower control arm bolt.

8. Remove the rear lower control arm bushing nuts and bolts.

9. Remove the lower control arm from the front frame.

To install:

10. Position the lower control arm in the cradle.

11. Install and hand tighten the rear lower control arm bushing nuts and bolts.

12. Install and hand tighten the front lower control arm bolt.

13. Install the ball joint to knuckle bolt and nut. Tighten the ball joint bolt and nut to 37 ft. lbs. (50 Nm).

14. Reverse the nut ¾ of a turn. Tighten to 37 ft. lbs. (50 Nm) plus 30°.

15. Load the front suspension with the proper jack stand before tightening the bolts to specifications.

16. Tighten the front lower control arm bolt and tighten to 37 ft. lbs. (50 Nm) plus 90 degrees.

17. Tighten the rear bushing to frame bolts and tighten to 37 ft. lbs. (50 Nm) plus 90 degrees.

18. Remove the jack stand.

19. For vehicles equipped with the 4T45-E transmission, install the left side transmission mount.

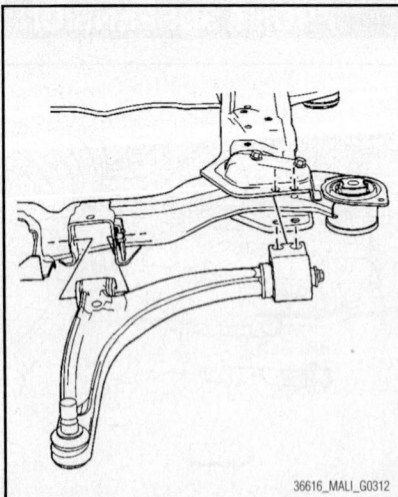

Fig. 118 Removing the lower control arm from the front frame

21. Install the tire and wheel.

22. Verify wheel alignment.

23. Remove the support and lower the vehicle.

STEERING KNUCKLE

REMOVAL & INSTALLATION

See Figure 119.

1. Raise and support the vehicle.

2. Remove the wheel bearing/hub.

3. Remove the outer tie rod to knuckle nut.

4. Remove the nuts and bolts from the strut to the knuckle.

5. Separate the lower ball joint from the knuckle.

6. Remove the steering knuckle from the vehicle.

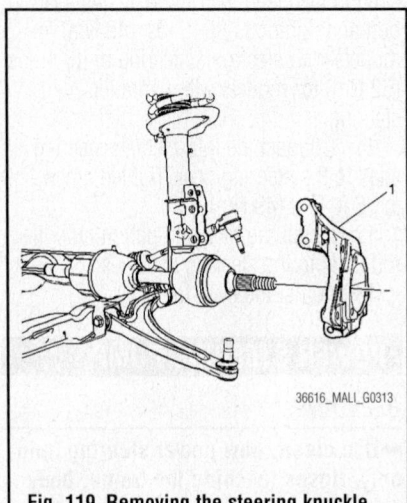

Fig. 119 Removing the steering knuckle

To install:

7. Install the steering knuckle and verify the front end alignment.

8. Connect the lower ball joint to the knuckle.

9. Install the nuts and bolts to the strut and knuckle.

10. Connect the outer tie rod end to the knuckle.

11. Install the wheel bearing/hub.

12. Lower the vehicle.

STRUT

REMOVAL & INSTALLATION

See Figure 120.

1. Raise and safely support the vehicle.

2. Remove the tire and wheel assembly.

3. Support the lower control arm with a suitable jack stand.

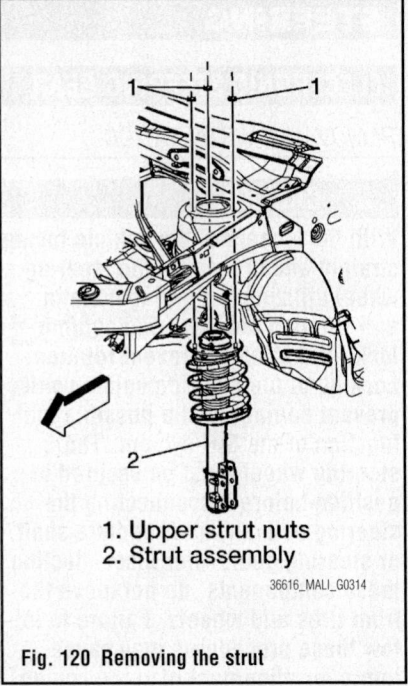

1. Upper strut nuts
2. Strut assembly

Fig. 120 Removing the strut

4. Disconnect the wheel speed sensor electrical connector at the wheel speed sensor bracket, if equipped.

5. Remove the stabilizer shaft link from the front strut.

6. Remove the front strut nuts from the bolts.

7. Remove the wheel speed sensor bracket from the strut.

8. Remove the strut bolts from the front strut.

9. Separate the front strut from the knuckle.

10. Remove the upper strut nuts from the strut.

11. Remove the front strut assembly from the vehicle.

To install:

12. Install the front strut assembly.

13. Install the upper strut nuts and tighten to 18 ft. lbs. (25 Nm).

14. Insert the front strut in the knuckle.

15. Install the strut bolts.

16. Install the wheel speed sensor bracket.

17. Install the front strut nuts on the bolts and tighten to 89 ft. lbs. (120 Nm).

18. Reconnect the wheel speed sensor electrical connector at the wheel speed sensor bracket, if equipped.

19. Install the stabilizer shaft link.

20. Remove the support from the lower control arm.

21. Install the front tire and wheel assembly.

22. Lower the vehicle.
23. Check the front end alignment specifications.

STABILIZER SHAFT

REMOVAL & INSTALLATION

See Figure 121.

1. Raise and support the vehicle.
2. Remove the front tire and wheel assemblies.
3. Disconnect the stabilizer links from the stabilizer shaft.
5. Using a suitable jack stand, support the rear of the frame assembly.
6. Remove the frame to body bolts.
7. Lower the rear of the frame in order to gain clearance to the stabilizer shaft.
8. Remove the stabilizer shaft clamp bolts.
9. Remove the stabilizer shaft clamps and insulators.
10. Remove the stabilizer shaft from the frame.

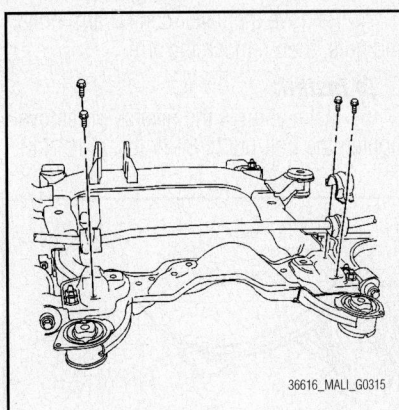

36616_MALI_G0315

Fig. 121 Removing the stabilizer shaft

To install:

→Install the insulators so that the slit in the insulator is facing the rear of the vehicle.

11. Install the insulators on the stabilizer shaft.
12. Position the stabilizer shaft to the frame.
13. Install the stabilizer bar clamps.
14. Install the stabilizer shaft clamp bolts and tighten to 18 ft. lbs. (25 Nm).
15. Raise the rear of the cradle and install the cradle bolts.
16. Remove the jack stand.
17. Connect the stabilizer link to the stabilizer bar.
19. Install the front tire and wheel assemblies.
20. Remove the support and lower the vehicle.

WHEEL HUB & BEARING

REMOVAL & INSTALLATION

See Figure 122.

1. Raise and support the vehicle.
2. Remove the brake rotor.
3. Disconnect the wheel speed sensor electrical connector, if equipped.
4. Remove the wheel speed sensor electrical connector from the mounting bracket, if needed.
5. Loosen the wheel drive shaft from the wheel bearing/hub.
6. Remove the wheel bearing/hub mounting bolts.
7. Remove the wheel bearing/hub and backing plate from the steering knuckle.

To install:

8. Position the backing plate and wheel bearing/hub assembly in the steering knuckle.
9. Install the wheel bearing/hub

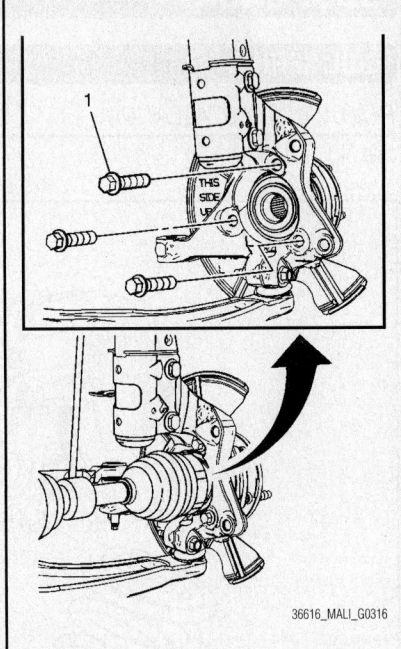

36616_MALI_G0316

Fig. 122 Locating the wheel bearing/hub mounting bolts

mounting bolts and tighten to 85 ft. lbs. (115 Nm).
10. Reconnect the wheel speed senor electrical connector, if needed.
11. Install the wheel speed sensor electrical connector on the retaining bracket, if needed.
12. Install the brake rotor.
13. Install the wheel drive shaft retaining nut and washer.
14. Remove the support and lower the vehicle.

ADJUSTMENT

The wheel bearing are sealed at the factory and do not require any adjustment or maintenance.

COIL SPRING

REMOVAL & INSTALLATION

See Figure 123.

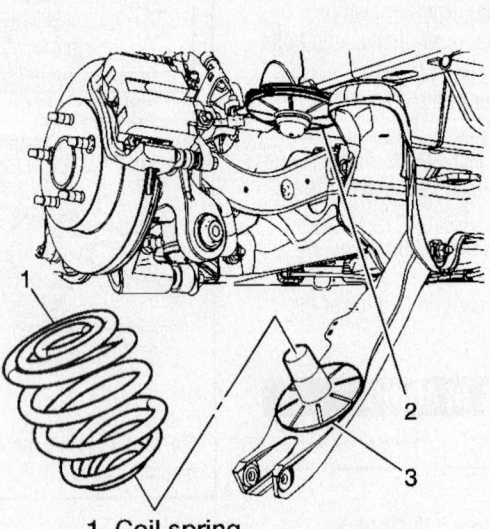

1. Coil spring
2. Rear spring upper insulator
3. Lower spring insulator

36616_MALI_G0317

Fig. 123 Rear spring mounting

1. Raise and support the vehicle.
2. Remove the rear tire and wheel assembly.
3. Using a suitable jack stand, support the lower control arm.
4. Remove the lower control arm to knuckle bolt and nut.

※※ CAUTION

To prevent personal injury and/or component damage, use the proper tools to support the lower control arm when removing the coil spring. The coil spring is under extreme pressure and can become a projectile should the spring separate from the lower control arm before all of the tension is relieved.

5. Use the jackstand to swing the lower control arm downward with the coil spring attached.
6. Remove the coil spring from the lower control arm.
7. Inspect the coil spring upper and lower insulators for damage, replace as necessary.

To install:

➡ Be sure that the coil spring upper and lower insulators are properly seated prior to installation of the coil spring.

8. Position the coil spring onto the lower control arm.
9. Use the jack stand to raise the lower control arm upward into position.
10. Install the lower control arm to knuckle bolt and nut. Tighten to 81 ft. lbs. (110 Nm).
11. Remove the jack stand from under the vehicle.
12. Install the rear tire and wheel assembly.
13. Lower the vehicle.
14. Check the rear wheel alignment.

CONTROL ARMS/LINKS

REMOVAL & INSTALLATION

Lower

See Figure 124.

1. Raise and suitably support the vehicle.
2. Remove the rear tire and wheel assembly.
3. Remove the coil spring.
4. Remove the lower control arm bolts and nuts, then remove the arm.

To install:

5. Installation is the reverse of removal. Tighten the bolt/nut to 81 ft. lbs. (110 Nm).

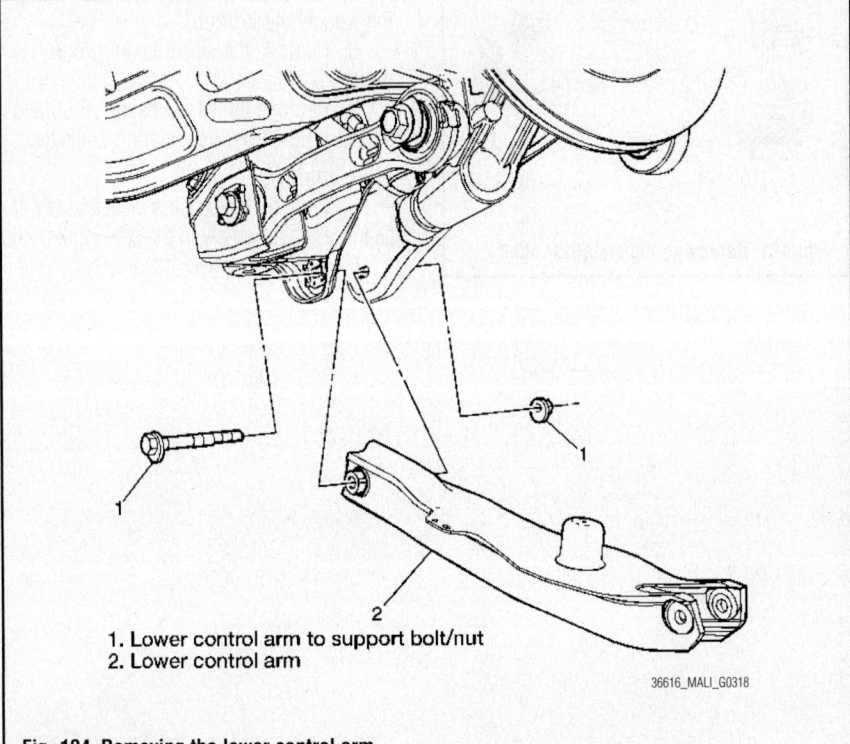

1. Lower control arm to support bolt/nut
2. Lower control arm

36616_MALI_G0318

Fig. 124 Removing the lower control arm

6. Inspect the wheel alignment and adjust as needed.

Upper

See Figure 125.

1. Raise and support the vehicle.
2. Remove the rear tire and wheel assembly.
3. Disconnect the wheel speed sensor wiring harness retaining clips and relocate to the side.
4. Remove the rear muffler from the hangers and lower the muffler to gain access to the upper control arm nut and bolt.

➡**Note that the head of the bolt is facing the front of the vehicle and must be installed in the same position.**

5. Remove the upper control arm assembly bolt and nut.
6. Remove the upper control arm to knuckle bolt and nut.
7. Remove the upper control arm from the vehicle through the wheelhouse opening.

To install:

8. Install the upper control arm to support assembly bolt. Tighten the upper control arm to support assembly bolt to 44 ft. lbs. (60 Nm). Tighten the upper control arm to knuckle bolt to 81 ft. lbs. (110 Nm) plus an additional 70 degrees.
9. Reposition the wheel speed sensor wiring harness retaining clips on the upper control arm.
10. Install the rear muffler.
11. Install the rear tire and wheel assembly.
12. Lower the vehicle.

Rear Axle Control Trailing Arm and Rear Suspension Control Arm Bracket

1. Raise and support the vehicle.
2. Remove the tire and wheel assembly.
3. Remove the park brake cable retaining bolt and the bracket from the trailing arm.
4. Using the appropriate tool, remove the park brake cable retaining clip from the trailing arm bracket.
5. Remove the trailing arm bracket mounting bolts.
6. Remove the bolts from the trailing arm to the knuckle.
7. Remove the trailing arm and the bracket from the frame and the knuckle.

8. Remove the bolt and nut from the trailing arm bracket to the trailing arm.

To install:

9. Install the bolt and nut from the trailing arm bracket to the trailing arm.
10. Tighten the trailing arm to bracket nut to 44 ft. lbs. (60 Nm). Using the angle meter rotate the nut an additional 60 degrees.
11. Position the trailing arm and bracket assembly on the knuckle and the frame.
12. Install the bolts from the trailing arm to the knuckle and tighten to 133 ft. lbs. (180 Nm).
13. Install the mounting bolts for the trailing arm bracket. Tighten the mounting bolts to 44 ft. lbs. (60 Nm). Using the angle meter, rotate the bolt an additional 60 degrees.
14. Install the park brake cable retaining clip to the trailing arm bracket.
15. Install the park brake cable retaining bracket and the bolt to the trailing arm. Tighten the mounting bolt to 89 inch lbs. (10 Nm).
16. Install the tire and wheel assembly.
17. Lower the vehicle.

SHOCK ABSORBER

REMOVAL & INSTALLATION

1. Raise and support the vehicle.
2. Remove the tire and wheel.
3. Using a suitable jack stand, raise the rear knuckle to remove spring tension.
4. Remove the lower shock bolt, and the washer from the knuckle.
5. Remove the upper shock nuts.
6. Remove the shock from the vehicle.

To install:

7. Place the shock in the vehicle.
8. Install the shock absorber to body nuts. Tighten to 18 ft. lbs. (25 Nm).
9. Install the shock absorber to knuckle bolt. Tighten to 133 ft. lbs. (180 Nm).
10. Remove the jack stand from the rear knuckle.
11. Install the tire and wheel.
12. Lower the vehicle.

WHEEL HUB & BEARING

REMOVAL & INSTALLATION

See Figure 126.

1. Raise and support the vehicle.
2. Remove the tire and wheel assembly.
3. Remove the brake rotor.
4. Disconnect the electrical connector from the wheel speed sensor.

36616_MALI_G0319

Fig. 125 Removing the upper control arm

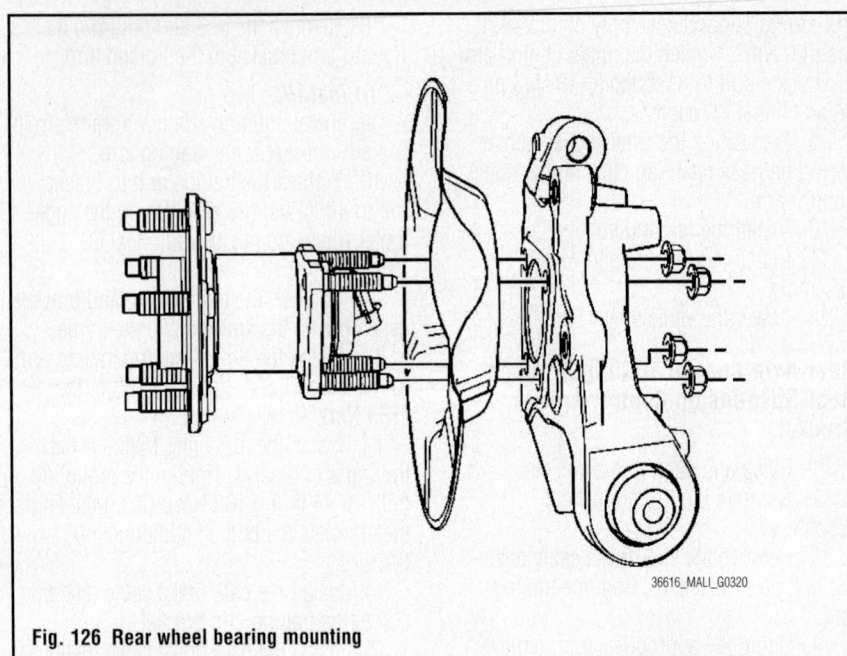

36616_MALI_G0320

Fig. 126 Rear wheel bearing mounting

5. Remove the 4 wheel bearing/hub assembly nuts.

6. Remove the wheel bearing/hub assembly from the knuckle.

To install:

7. Install the wheel bearing/hub assembly to the knuckle.

8. Install the 4 wheel bearing/hub assembly nuts and tighten to 47 ft. lbs. (63 Nm).

9. Install the stabilizer link bolt at the knuckle.

10. Connect the electrical connector to the wheel speed sensor.

11. Install the brake rotor.

12. Install the tire and wheel assembly.

13. Lower the vehicle.

ADJUSTMENT

The wheel bearing are sealed at the factory and do not require any adjustment or maintenance.

GENERAL MOTORS

Diagnostic Trouble Codes

DIAGNOSTIC TROUBLE CODES

OBD II VEHICLE APPLICATIONS

GENERAL MOTORS

Envoy
2008–2009
- 4.2L .... VIN S
- 5.3L .... VIN M

Equinox
2008–2009
- 3.4L .... VIN F
- 3.6L .... VIN 7

Express
2008–2009
- 4.3L .... VIN X
- 5.3L .... VIN 4
- 4.8L .... VIN C
- 6.0L .... VIN K
- 6.6L .... VIN 6

G6
2008–2009
- 2.4L .... VIN B
- 3.5L .... VIN N
- 3.5L .... VIN K
- 3.6L .... VIN 7
- 3.9L .... VIN 1

G8
2008–2009
- 3.6L .... VIN 7
- 6.0L .... VIN Y
- 6.2L .... VIN W

HHR
2008–2009
- 2.0L .... VIN X
- 2.2L .... VIN D

- 2.2L .... VIN B
- 2.4L .... VIN V
- 2.4L .... VIN P

Impala
2008–2009
- 3.5L .... VIN K
- 3.5L .... VIN N
- 3.9L .... VIN 3
- 3.9L .... VIN M
- 5.3L .... VIN C

Lucerne
2008–2009
- 3.8L .... VIN 2
- 3.9L .... VIN M
- 3.9L .... VIN 1
- 4.6L .... VIN 9
- 4.6L .... VIN Y
- 3.6L .... VIN 7

Malibu
2008–2009
- 2.2L .... VIN F
- 2.4L .... VIN 5
- 2.4L .... VIN B
- 3.5L .... VIN N
- 3.6L .... VIN 7

Torrent
2008–2009
- 3.4L .... VIN F
- 3.6L .... VIN 7

Savana
2008–2009
- 4.3L .... VIN X
- 5.3L .... VIN 4

Trailblazer
2008–2009

- 4.2L .... VIN S
- 5.3L .... VIN M
- 6.0L .... VIN H

GM REFERENCE INFORMATION

OBD II TROUBLE CODE LIST

To use this information, first read and record All codes in memory along with Freeze Frame data. *If a ECM Reset function is done prior to recording this data,* All *codes and freeze frame data are lost!*

Look up the appropriate trouble code in the list on the following pages. The left hand column includes the code number, the number of trips to set the code (e.g., **1T or 2T**), the year, model description and type of OBD II Monitor that failed (e.g., **CCM or O2S**). This data can be used to determine how to drive a vehicle after a repair in order to validate the repair has been completed.

The **(N/MIL)** designator in the left hand column indicates the trouble code does not turn on the Malfunction Indicator Lamp or MIL. The **(STS Lamp)** indicator in the left column indicates a code that turns on the Service Transmission Soon lamp. This code may or may not turn "on" the MIL.

OBD II Trouble Code List (P0xxx Codes)

DTC	Trouble Code Title, Conditions & Possible Causes
DTC: P0008 **1T CCM, MIL: Yes** **Years:** 2008, 2009 **Models:** Envoy, Equinox, G6, G8, Impala, Lucerne, Malibu, Savana, Trailblazer, Torrent **Engines:** 4.2L VIN S, 4.8L VIN C, 3.5L VIN N, 3.5L VIN K, 3.9L VIN 3, 3.9L VIN M, 3.6L VIN 2, 3.9L VIN 1 5.3L VIN M, 5.3L VIN C 5.3L VIN 4 **Transmissions:** All	**Engine Position System Performance (Bank 1)** The ECM detects that both camshafts on either bank of the engine are mis-aligned with the crankshaft, greater than 6 degrees, for greater than 4 seconds or a cumulative of 30 seconds. **Possible Causes:** • Timing chains and tensioners for excessive wear or misalignment • Crankshaft reluctor wheel for being mis-positioned
DTC: P0009 **1T CCM, MIL: Yes** **Years:** 2008, 2009 **Models:** Envoy, Equinox, G6, G8, Impala, Lucerne, Malibu, Savana, Trailblazer, Torrent **Engines:** 4.2L VIN S, 4.8L VIN C, 3.5L VIN N, 3.5L VIN K, 3.9L VIN 3, 3.9L VIN M, 3.6L VIN 2, 3.9L VIN 1 **Transmissions:** All	**Engine Position System Performance (Bank 2)** The ECM detects that both camshafts on either bank of the engine are mis-aligned with the crankshaft, greater than 6 degrees, for greater than 4 seconds or a cumulative of 30 seconds. **Possible Causes:** • Timing chains and tensioners for excessive wear or misalignment • Crankshaft reluctor wheel for being mis-positioned
DTC: P000A **1T CCM, MIL: Yes** **Years:** 2008, 2009 **Models:** G6, HHR, Malibu **Engines:** 2.0L VIN X, 2.2L VIN D, 2.2L VIN B, 2.2L VIN F, 2.4L VIN B, 2.4L VIN V, 2.4L VIN P, 2.4L VIN 5 **Transmissions:** All	**Intake Camshaft Position (CMP) System Slow Response** The engine speed is between 736-6,016 RPM and engine oil temperature is between +14 and +266°F (−10 and +130°C). The actual camshaft position does not match the commanded position. **Possible Causes:** • Engine oil low or in need of changing • CMP Actuator Solenoid ignition voltage for an open/high resistance • CMP Actuator Solenoid ignition voltage for an open/high resistance • CMP Actuator Solenoid control circuit for an open/high resistance • Engine timing components • CMP Actuator Solenoid malfunction
DTC: P000A **1T CCM, MIL: Yes** **Years:** 2008, 2009 **Models:** Envoy, Equinox, G6, G8, Impala, Lucerne, Malibu, Savana, Trailblazer, Torrent **Engines:** 4.2L VIN S, 4.8L VIN C, 3.5L VIN N, 3.5L VIN K, 3.9L VIN 3, 3.9L VIN M, 3.6L VIN 2, 3.9L VIN 1 **Transmissions:** All	**Intake Camshaft Position (CMP) System Slow Response (Bank 1)** The ECM detects the difference between the desired camshaft position angle and the actual camshaft position angle is greater than 6-11 degrees. Or the ECM detects a slow response, a deviation greater than 1.5 degrees in time greater than 2.5 seconds, for the actual camshaft position angle to match the desired position angle during the test. Either condition exists for greater than 1 second or a cumulative of 10 seconds **Possible Causes:** • Control circuit for an open or high resistance • Torn,restricted, mis-positioned, or missing screens at the CMP actuator solenoid • Oil leaks between the oil sealing lands of the CMP actuator solenoid • Lands of the CMP actuator solenoid for nicks • Crankshaft reluctor wheel for being mis-positioned • Oil seepage at the CMP actuator solenoind connector
DTC: P000B **1T CCM, MIL: Yes** **Years:** 2008, 2009 **Models:** Equinox, G6, G8, Torrent **Engines:** All **Transmissions:** All	**Exhaust Camshaft Position (CMP) System Slow Response** The engine speed is between 736-6,016 RPM and engine oil temperature is between +14 and +266°F (−10 and +130°C). The actual camshaft position does not match the commanded position. **Possible Causes:** • Engine oil low or in need of changing • CMP Actuator Solenoid ignition voltage for an open/high resistance • CMP Actuator Solenoid ignition voltage for an open/high resistance • CMP Actuator Solenoid control circuit for an open/high resistance • Engine timing components • CMP Actuator Solenoid malfunction

DTC	Trouble Code Title, Conditions & Possible Causes
DTC: P000C **1T CCM, MIL: Yes** **Years:** 2008, 2009 **Models:** Envoy, Equinox, G6, G8, Impala, Lucerne, Malibu, Savana, Trailblazer, Torrent **Engines:** 4.2L VIN S, 4.8L VIN C, 3.5L VIN N, 3.5L VIN K, 3.9L VIN 3, 3.9L VIN M, 3.6L VIN 2, 3.9L VIN 1 **Transmissions:** All	**Intake Camshaft Position (CMP) System Slow Response (Bank 2)** The ECM detects the difference between the desired camshaft position angle and the actual camshaft position angle is greater than 6-11 degrees. Or the ECM detects a slow response, a deviation greater than 1.5 degrees in time greater than 2.5 seconds, for the actual camshaft position angle to match the desired position angle during the test. Either condition exists for greater than 1 second or a cumulative of 10 seconds **Possible Causes:** • Control circuit for an open or high resistance • Torn,restricted, mis-positioned, or missing screens at the CMP actuator solenoid • Oil leaks between the oil sealing lands of the CMP actuator solenoid • Lands of the CMP actuator solenoid for nicks • Crankshaft reluctor wheel for being mis-positioned • Oil seepage at the CMP actuator solenoind connector
DTC: P000D **1T CCM, MIL: Yes** **Years:** 2008, 2009 **Models:** Envoy, Equinox, G6, G8, Impala, Lucerne, Malibu, Savana, Trailblazer, Torrent **Engines:** 4.2L VIN S, 4.8L VIN C, 3.5L VIN N, 3.5L VIN K, 3.9L VIN 3, 3.9L VIN M, 3.6L VIN 2, 3.9L VIN 1 **Transmissions:** All	**Exhaust Camshaft Position (CMP) System Slow Response (Bank 2)** The ECM detects the difference between the desired camshaft position angle and the actual camshaft position angle is greater than 6-11 degrees. Or the ECM detects a slow response, a deviation greater than 1.5 degrees in time greater than 2.5 seconds, for the actual camshaft position angle to match the desired position angle during the test. Either condition exists for greater than 1 second or a cumulative of 10 seconds **Possible Causes:** • Control circuit for an open or high resistance • Torn,restricted, mis-positioned, or missing screens at the CMP actuator solenoid • Oil leaks between the oil sealing lands of the CMP actuator solenoid • Lands of the CMP actuator solenoid for nicks • Crankshaft reluctor wheel for being mis-positioned • Oil seepage at the CMP actuator solenoind connector
DTC: P0010 **2T CCM, MIL: Yes** **Models:** Express, G8, Lucerne, Trailblazer **Engines:** 4.6L VIN Y, 4.6L VIN 9, 6.0L VIN H, 6.0L VIN Y, 6.0L VIN K, 6.2L VIN W, 6.6L VIN 6 **Transmissions:** All	**Camshaft Position (CMP) Actuator Solenoid Control Circuit** The ignition switch is in the Crank or Run position. The system voltage is between 9-18 volts. The CMP actuator is command ON. DTC P0010 runs continuously when the above conditions are met. The ECM detects that the state of the high side driver and the state of the CMP solenoid control circuit does not match. The ECM will detect an open, high resistance, short to ground, or a short to voltage on the CMP solenoid control circuit, or an open on the low reference circuit, if the condition is present for more than 6 seconds. **Possible Causes:** • Solenoid control circuit for a short to voltage • Solenoid control circuit for an open/high resistance or a short to ground • Low reference circuit for an open/high resistance • Faulty CMP actuator solenoid • ECM has failed
DTC: P0010 **1T CCM, MIL: Yes** **Years:** 2008, 2009 **Models:** Envoy, Equinox, G6, G8, Impala, Lucerne, Malibu, Savana, Trailblazer, Torrent **Engines:** 4.2L VIN S, 4.8L VIN C, 3.5L VIN N, 3.5L VIN K, 3.9L VIN 3, 3.9L VIN M, 3.6L VIN 2, 3.9L VIN 1 **Transmissions:** All	**Intake Camshaft Position (CMP) Actuator Solenoid Control Circuit (Bank 1)** The ECM detects an open in the CMP actuator solenoid circuits for greater than 1 seconds or a cumulative of 10 seconds, when the solenoid is commanded OFF. **Possible Causes:** • Ignition circuit for a short to ground or an open/high resistance • Control circuit for a short to voltage or an open/high resistance • Control circuit for a short to ground • CMP actuator solenoid • Faulty ECM
DTC: P0010 **1T CCM, MIL: Yes** **Years:** 2008, 2009 **Models:** G6, HHR, Malibu **Engines:** 2.0L VIN X, 2.2L VIN D, 2.2L VIN B, 2.2L VIN F, 2.4L VIN B, 2.4L VIN V, 2.4L VIN P, 2.4L VIN 5 **Transmissions:** All	**Intake Camshaft Position (CMP) System Performance** The engine speed is between 736-6,016 RPM and engine oil temperature is between +14 and +266°F (−10 and +130°C). The actual camshaft position does not match the commanded position. **Possible Causes:** • Engine oil low or in need of changing • CMP Actuator Solenoid ignition voltage for an open/high resistance • CMP Actuator Solenoid ignition voltage for an open/high resistance • CMP Actuator Solenoid control circuit for an open/high resistance • Engine timing components • CMP Actuator Solenoid malfunction • ECM has failed

DTC	Trouble Code Title, Conditions & Possible Causes
DTC: P0011 **1T CCM, MIL: Yes** **Years:** 2008, 2009 **Models:** Envoy, Equinox, G6, G8, Impala, Lucerne, Malibu, Savana, Trailblazer, Torrent **Engines:** 4.2L VIN S, 4.8L VIN C, 3.5L VIN N, 3.5L VIN K, 3.9L VIN 3, 3.9L VIN M, 3.6L VIN 2, 3.9L VIN 1 **Transmissions:** All	**Intake Camshaft Position (CMP) System Performance (Bank 1)** The ECM detects the difference between the desired camshaft position angle and the actual camshaft position angle is greater than 6-11 degrees. Or the ECM detects a slow response, a deviation greater than 1.5 degrees in time greater than 2.5 seconds, for the actual camshaft position angle to match the desired position angle during the test. Either condition exists for greater than 1 second or a cumulative of 10 seconds **Possible Causes:** • Control circuit for an open or high resistance • Torn, restricted, mis-positioned, or missing screens at the CMP actuator solenoid • Oil leaks between the oil sealing lands of the CMP actuator solenoid • Lands of the CMP actuator solenoid for nicks • Crankshaft reluctor wheel for being mis-positioned • Oil seepage at the CMP actuator solenoind connector
DTC: P0011 **1T CCM, MIL: Yes** **Years:** 2008, 2009 **Models:** G6, HHR, Malibu **Engines:** 2.0L VIN X, 2.2L VIN D, 2.2L VIN B, 2.2L VIN F, 2.4L VIN B, 2.4L VIN V, 2.4L VIN P, 2.4L VIN 5 **Transmissions:** All	**Intake Camshaft Position (CMP) System Performance** The ECM detects the difference between the desired camshaft position angle and the actual camshaft position angle is greater than 6-11 degrees. Or the ECM detects a slow response, a deviation greater than 1.5 degrees in time greater than 2.5 seconds, for the actual camshaft position angle to match the desired position angle during the test. Either condition exists for greater than 1 second or a cumulative of 10 seconds **Possible Causes:** • Control circuit for an open or high resistance • Torn, restricted, mis-positioned, or missing screens at the CMP actuator solenoid • Oil leaks between the oil sealing lands of the CMP actuator solenoid • Lands of the CMP actuator solenoid for nicks • Crankshaft reluctor wheel for being mis-positioned • Oil seepage at the CMP actuator solenoind connector
DTC: P0013 **1T CCM, MIL: Yes** **Years:** 2008, 2009 **Models:** G6, HHR, Malibu **Engines:** 2.0L VIN X, 2.2L VIN D, 2.2L VIN B, 2.2L VIN F, 2.4L VIN B, 2.4L VIN V, 2.4L VIN P, 2.4L VIN 5 **Transmissions:** All	**Exhaust Camshaft Position (CMP) Actuator Solenoid Control Circuit** The ignition is ON. The ignition voltage is between 10-16 volts. The ECM detects an open in the CMP actuator solenoid circuits for greater than 1 second or a cumulative of 5 seconds when the solenoid is commanded OFF **Possible Causes:** • Engine oil low or in need of changing • CMP Actuator Solenoid ignition voltage for an open/high resistance • CMP Actuator Solenoid ignition voltage for an open/high resistance • CMP Actuator Solenoid control circuit for an open/high resistance • Engine timing components • CMP Actuator Solenoid malfunction • ECM has failed
DTC: P0013 **1T CCM, MIL: Yes** **Years:** 2008, 2009 **Models:** Envoy, Express, G6, Impala, Lucerne, Savana, Trailblazer **Engines:** 4.2L VIN S, 4.8L VIN C, 3.5L VIN N, 3.5L VIN K, 3.9L VIN 3, 3.9L VIN M, 3.8L VIN K, 3.9L VIN 1 **Transmissions:** All	**Exhaust Camshaft Position (CMP) Actuator Solenoid Control Circuit** The engine is running. The ECM has commanded the Camshaft Position Actuator Solenoid Valve ON. The system voltage is between 11-18 volts. The ECM detects that the commanded state of the driver and the actual state of the control circuit do not match for greater than 7.5 seconds. **Possible Causes:** • Engine oil low or in need of changing • CMP Actuator Solenoid ignition voltage for an open/high resistance • CMP Actuator Solenoid ignition voltage for an open/high resistance • CMP Actuator Solenoid control circuit for an open/high resistance • Engine timing components • CMP Actuator Solenoid malfunction • ECM has failed
DTC: P0013 **1T CCM, MIL: Yes** **Years:** 2008, 2009 **Models:** Envoy, Equinox, G6, G8, Impala, Lucerne, Malibu, Savana, Trailblazer, Torrent **Engines:** 4.2L VIN S, 4.8L VIN C, 3.5L VIN N, 3.5L VIN K, 3.9L VIN 3, 3.9L VIN M, 3.6L VIN 2, 3.9L VIN 1 **Transmissions:** All	**Exhaust Camshaft Position (CMP) System Performance** DTC P0017, P0335, P0336, P0365, P0366 are not set.. The engine is running. The system voltage is between 9-18 volts. The ECM has enabled the CMP actuator and commanded greater than 0 degrees. DTC P0014 runs continuously when the above conditions are met. The difference between the desired CMP and the actual CMP angle is greater than 3.75 degrees for 14.5 s. **Possible Causes:** • Ignition circuit for a short to ground or an open/high resistance • Control circuit for a short to voltage or an open/high resistance • Control circuit for a short to ground • CMP actuator solenoid • Faulty ECM

DTC	Trouble Code Title, Conditions & Possible Causes
DTC: P0014 **1T CCM, MIL: Yes** **Years:** 2008, 2009 **Models:** G6, HHR, Malibu **Engines:** 2.0L VIN X, 2.2L VIN D, 2.2L VIN B, 2.2L VIN F, 2.4L VIN B, 2.4L VIN V, 2.4L VIN P, 2.4L VIN 5 **Transmissions:** All	**Exhaust Camshaft Position (CMP) Actuator Solenoid Control Circuit (Bank 1)** The ECM detects an open in the CMP actuator solenoid circuits for greater than 1 seconds or a cumulative of 10 seconds, when the solenoid is commanded OFF. **Possible Causes:** • Engine oil low or in need of changing • CMP Actuator Solenoid ignition voltage for an open/high resistance • CMP Actuator Solenoid ignition voltage for an open/high resistance • CMP Actuator Solenoid control circuit for an open/high resistance • Engine timing components • CMP Actuator Solenoid malfunction • ECM has failed
DTC: P0014 **1T CCM, MIL: Yes** **Years:** 2008, 2009 **Models:** Envoy, Express, G6, Impala, Lucerne, Savana, Trailblazer **Engines:** 4.2L VIN S, 4.8L VIN C, 3.5L VIN N, 3.5L VIN K, 3.9L VIN 3, 3.9L VIN M, 3.8L VIN K, 3.9L VIN 1 **Transmissions:** All	**Exhaust Camshaft Position (CMP) System Performance** The engine speed is between 736-6,016 RPM and engine oil temperature is between +14 and +266°F (−10 and +130°C). The actual camshaft position does not match the commanded position. **Possible Causes:** • Engine oil low or in need of changing • CMP Actuator Solenoid ignition voltage for an open/high resistance • CMP Actuator Solenoid ignition voltage for an open/high resistance • CMP Actuator Solenoid control circuit for an open/high resistance • Engine timing components • CMP Actuator Solenoid malfunction • ECM has failed
DTC: P0014 **1T CCM, MIL: Yes** **Years:** 2008, 2009 **Models:** Envoy, Equinox, G6, G8, Impala, Lucerne, Malibu, Savana, Trailblazer, Torrent **Engines:** 4.2L VIN S, 4.8L VIN C, 3.5L VIN N, 3.5L VIN K, 3.9L VIN 3, 3.9L VIN M, 3.6L VIN 2, 3.9L VIN 1 **Transmissions:** All	**Exhaust Camshaft Position (CMP) System Performance (Bank 1)** The ECM detects the difference between the desired camshaft position angle and the actual camshaft position angle is greater than 6-11 degrees. Or the ECM detects a slow response, a deviation greater than 1.5 degrees in time greater than 2.5 seconds, for the actual camshaft position angle to match the desired position angle during the test. Either condition exists for greater than 1 second or a cumulative of 10 seconds **Possible Causes:** • Control circuit for an open or high resistance • Torn, restricted, mis-positioned, or missing screens at the CMP actuator solenoid • Oil leaks between the oil sealing lands of the CMP actuator solenoid • Lands of the CMP actuator solenoid for nicks • Crankshaft reluctor wheel for being mis-positioned • Oil seepage at the CMP actuator solenoind connector
DTC: P0016 **1T CCM, MIL: Yes** **Years:** 2008, 2009 **Models:** Envoy, Equinox, G6, G8, Impala, Lucerne, Malibu, Savana, Trailblazer, Torrent **Engines:** 4.2L VIN S, 4.8L VIN C, 3.5L VIN N, 3.5L VIN K, 3.9L VIN 3, 3.9L VIN M, 3.6L VIN 2, 3.9L VIN 1 **Transmissions:** All	**Crankshaft Position (CKP) - Intake Camshaft Position (CMP) Correlation Bank 1** The ECM detects the learned camshaft angle is greater than 10 degrees advanced or 10 degrees retarded in relationship to the crankshaft. **Possible Causes:** • Timing chain tensioner condition • Incorrectly installed timing chain • Excessive play in the timing chain • Cam actuator that is stuck in the full advance or retard position • Crankshaft reluctor wheel that has moved in relationship to top dead • Center (TDC) on the crankshaft
DTC: P0016 **1T CCM, MIL: Yes** **Years:** 2008, 2009 **Models:** Envoy, Equinox, Savana, Torrent **Engines:** 3.4L VIN F, 4.3L VIN X, 5.3L VIN M **Transmissions:** All	**Crankshaft Position (CKP) - Intake Camshaft Position (CMP) Correlation** DTC P0335, P0336, P0340, P0341, P0641, or P0651 is not set. The engine is running. The engine speed is less than 2,000 RPM. DTC P0016 runs continuously when the above conditions are met. The ECM detects that the CMP sensor pulses occur more than 11 crank degrees before, or 11 crank degrees after, nominal position for 24 out of 30 engine cycles. **Possible Causes:** • Timing chain tensioner condition • Incorrectly installed timing chain • Excessive play in the timing chain • Cam actuator that is stuck in the full advance or retard position • Crankshaft reluctor wheel that has moved in relationship to top dead • Center (TDC) on the crankshaft

DTC	Trouble Code Title, Conditions & Possible Causes
DTC: P0016 **1T CCM, MIL: Yes** **Years:** 2008, 2009 **Models:** Express, G8, Lucerne, Trailblazer **Engines:** 4.6L VIN Y, 4.6L VIN 9, 6.0L VIN H, 6.0L VIN Y, 6.0L VIN K, 6.2L VIN W, 6.6L VIN 6 **Transmissions:** All	**Crankshaft Position (CKP) - Camshaft Position (CMP) Correlation** DTC P0335, P0336, P0340, P0341, P0641, or P0651 is not set. The engine is running. The engine speed is less than 2,000 RPM. DTC P0016 runs continuously when the above conditions are met. The ECM detects that the CMP sensor pulses occur more than 11 crank degrees before, or 11 crank degrees after, nominal position for 24 out of 30 engine cycles. **Possible Causes:** • Timing chain tensioner condition • Incorrectly installed timing chain • Excessive play in the timing chain • Cam actuator that is stuck in the full advance or retard position • Crankshaft reluctor wheel that has moved in relationship to top dead • Center (TDC) on the crankshaft
DTC: P0016 **1T CCM, MIL: Yes** **Years:** 2008, 2009 **Models:** G6, HHR, Malibu **Engines:** 2.0L VIN X, 2.2L VIN D, 2.2L VIN B, 2.2L VIN F, 2.4L VIN B, 2.4L VIN V, 2.4L VIN P, 2.4L VIN 5 **Transmissions:** All	**Crankshaft Position (CKP) - Intake Camshaft Position (CMP) Correlation** The engine is running. The engine oil temperature is more than −10°C (+14°F). The ECM detects an incorrect CMP sensor signal for 2 seconds. **Possible Causes:** • Timing chain tensioner condition • Incorrectly installed timing chain • Excessive play in the timing chain • Cam actuator that is stuck in the full advance or retard position • Crankshaft reluctor wheel that has moved in relationship to top dead • Center (TDC) on the crankshaft
DTC: P0017 **1T CCM, MIL: Yes** **Years:** 2008, 2009 **Models:** G6, HHR, Malibu **Engines:** 2.0L VIN X, 2.2L VIN D, 2.2L VIN B, 2.2L VIN F, 2.4L VIN B, 2.4L VIN V, 2.4L VIN P, 2.4L VIN 5 **Transmissions:** All	**Crankshaft Position (CKP) - Exhaust Camshaft Position (CMP) Correlation** The engine is running. The engine oil temperature is more than −10°C (+14°F). The ECM detects an incorrect CMP sensor signal for 2 seconds. **Possible Causes:** • Timing chain tensioner condition • Incorrectly installed timing chain • Excessive play in the timing chain • Cam actuator that is stuck in the full advance or retard position • Crankshaft reluctor wheel that has moved in relationship to top dead • Center (TDC) on the crankshaft
DTC: P0017 **1T CCM, MIL: Yes** **Years:** 2008, 2009 **Models:** Envoy, Equinox, G6, G8, Impala, Lucerne, Malibu, Savana, Trailblazer, Torrent **Engines:** 4.2L VIN S, 4.8L VIN C, 3.5L VIN N, 3.5L VIN K, 3.9L VIN 3, 3.9L VIN M, 3.6L VIN 2, 3.9L VIN 1 **Transmissions:** All	**Crankshaft Position (CKP) - Exhaust Camshaft Position (CMP) Correlation (Bank1)** The ECM detects the learned camshaft angle is greater than 10 degrees advanced or 10 degrees retarded in relationship to the crankshaft. **Possible Causes:** • Timing chain tensioner condition • Incorrectly installed timing chain • Excessive play in the timing chain • Cam actuator that is stuck in the full advance or retard position • Crankshaft reluctor wheel that has moved in relationship to top dead • Center (TDC) on the crankshaft
DTC: P0017 **1T CCM, MIL: Yes** **Years:** 2008, 2009 **Models:** Envoy, Express, G6, Impala, Lucerne, Savana, Trailblazer **Engines:** 4.2L VIN S, 4.8L VIN C, 3.5L VIN N, 3.5L VIN K, 3.9L VIN 3, 3.9L VIN M, 3.8L VIN K, 3.9L VIN 1 **Transmissions:** All	**Crankshaft Position (CKP) - Exhaust Camshaft Position (CMP) Correlation** DTCs P0335, P0336, P0365, P0366, P0641, and P0651 are not set. The engine is cranking or running. The engine speed is less than 1,200 RPM and the CMP actuator is commanded to the home or parked position. This DTC runs continuously when the above conditions are met. The ECM detects that the CMP sensor pulses occur less than 9 or more than 12 crankshaft degrees outside of the normal position for 24 out of 30 engine cycles. **Possible Causes:** • Timing chain tensioner condition • Incorrectly installed timing chain • Excessive play in the timing chain • Cam actuator that is stuck in the full advance or retard position • Crankshaft reluctor wheel that has moved in relationship to top dead • Center (TDC) on the crankshaft

DTC	Trouble Code Title, Conditions & Possible Causes
DTC: P0018 **1T CCM, MIL: Yes** **Years:** 2008, 2009 **Models:** Envoy, Equinox, G6, G8, Impala, Lucerne, Malibu, Savana, Trailblazer, Torrent **Engines:** 4.2L VIN S, 4.8L VIN C, 3.5L VIN N, 3.5L VIN K, 3.9L VIN 3, 3.9L VIN M, 3.6L VIN 2, 3.9L VIN 1 **Transmissions:** All	**Crankshaft Position (CKP) - Intake Camshaft Position (CMP) Correlation (Bank 2)** The ECM detects the learned camshaft angle is greater than 10 degrees advanced or 10 degrees retarded in relationship to the crankshaft. **Possible Causes:** • Timing chain tensioner condition • Incorrectly installed timing chain • Excessive play in the timing chain • Cam actuator that is stuck in the full advance or retard position • Crankshaft reluctor wheel that has moved in relationship to top dead • Center (TDC) on the crankshaft
DTC: P0019 **1T CCM, MIL: Yes** **Years:** 2008, 2009 **Models:** Envoy, Equinox, G6, G8, Impala, Lucerne, Malibu, Savana, Trailblazer, Torrent **Engines:** 4.2L VIN S, 4.8L VIN C, 3.5L VIN N, 3.5L VIN K, 3.9L VIN 3, 3.9L VIN M, 3.6L VIN 2, 3.9L VIN 1 **Transmissions:** All	**Crankshaft Position (CKP) - Exhaust Camshaft Position (CMP) Correlation (Bank 2)** The ECM detects the learned camshaft angle is greater than 10 degrees advanced or 10 degrees retarded in relationship to the crankshaft. **Possible Causes:** • Timing chain tensioner condition • Incorrectly installed timing chain • Excessive play in the timing chain • Cam actuator that is stuck in the full advance or retard position • Crankshaft reluctor wheel that has moved in relationship to top dead Center (TDC) on the crankshaft
DTC: P0020 **1T CCM, MIL: Yes** **Years:** 2008, 2009 **Models:** Envoy, Equinox, G6, G8, Impala, Lucerne, Malibu, Savana, Trailblazer, Torrent **Engines:** 4.2L VIN S, 4.8L VIN C, 3.5L VIN N, 3.5L VIN K, 3.9L VIN 3, 3.9L VIN M, 3.6L VIN 2, 3.9L VIN 1 **Transmissions:** All	**Intake Camshaft Position (CMP) Actuator Solenoid Control Circuit (Bank 2)** The ECM detects an open in the CMP actuator solenoid circuits for greater than 1 seconds or a cumulative of 10 seconds, when the solenoid is commanded OFF. **Possible Causes:** • Ignition circuit for a short to ground or an open/high resistance • Control circuit for a short to voltage or an open/high resistance • Control circuit for a short to ground • CMP actuator solenoid • Faulty ECM
DTC: P0021 **1T CCM, MIL: Yes** **Years:** 2008, 2009 **Models:** Envoy, Equinox, G6, G8, Impala, Lucerne, Malibu, Savana, Trailblazer, Torrent **Engines:** 4.2L VIN S, 4.8L VIN C, 3.5L VIN N, 3.5L VIN K, 3.9L VIN 3, 3.9L VIN M, 3.6L VIN 2, 3.9L VIN 1 **Transmissions:** All	**Intake Camshaft Position (CMP) System Performance (Bank 2)** The ECM detects the difference between the desired camshaft position angle and the actual camshaft position angle is greater than 6-11 degrees. Or the ECM detects a slow response, a deviation greater than 1.5 degrees in time greater than 2.5 seconds, for the actual camshaft position angle to match the desired position angle during the test. Either condition exists for greater than 1 second or a cumulative of 10 seconds **Possible Causes:** • Control circuit for an open or high resistance • Torn,restricted, mis-positioned, or missing screens at the CMP actuator solenoid • Oil leaks between the oil sealing lands of the CMP actuator solenoid • Lands of the CMP actuator solenoid for nicks • Crankshaft reluctor wheel for being mis-positioned • Oil seepage at the CMP actuator solenoind connector
DTC: P0023 **1T CCM, MIL: Yes** **Years:** 2008, 2009 **Models:** Envoy, Equinox, G6, G8, Impala, Lucerne, Malibu, Savana, Trailblazer, Torrent **Engines:** 4.2L VIN S, 4.8L VIN C, 3.5L VIN N, 3.5L VIN K, 3.9L VIN 3, 3.9L VIN M, 3.6L VIN 2, 3.9L VIN 1 **Transmissions:** All	**Exhaust Camshaft Position (CMP) Actuator Solenoid Control Circuit (Bank 2)** The ECM detects an open in the CMP actuator solenoid circuits for greater than 1 seconds or a cumulative of 10 seconds, when the solenoid is commanded OFF. **Possible Causes:** • Ignition circuit for a short to ground or an open/high resistance • Control circuit for a short to voltage or an open/high resistance • Control circuit for a short to ground • CMP actuator solenoid • Faulty ECM

DTC	Trouble Code Title, Conditions & Possible Causes
DTC: P0024 **1T CCM, MIL: Yes** **Years:** 2008, 2009 **Models:** Envoy, Equinox, G6, G8, Impala, Lucerne, Malibu, Savana, Trailblazer, Torrent **Engines:** 4.2L VIN S, 4.8L VIN C, 3.5L VIN N, 3.5L VIN K, 3.9L VIN 3, 3.9L VIN M, 3.6L VIN 2, 3.9L VIN 1 **Transmissions:** All	**Intake Camshaft Position (CMP) System Performance (Bank 2)** The ECM detects the difference between the desired camshaft position angle and the actual camshaft position angle is greater than 6-11 degrees. Or the ECM detects a slow response, a deviation greater than 1.5 degrees in time greater than 2.5 seconds, for the actual camshaft position angle to match the desired position angle during the test. Either condition exists for greater than 1 second or a cumulative of 10 seconds **Possible Causes:** • Control circuit for an open or high resistance • Torn,restricted, mis-positioned, or missing screens at the CMP actuator solenoid • Oil leaks between the oil sealing lands of the CMP actuator solenoid • Lands of the CMP actuator solenoid for nicks • Crankshaft reluctor wheel for being mis-positioned • Oil seepage at the CMP actuator solenoind connector
DTC: P0030 **1T CCM, MIL: Yes** **Years:** 2008, 2009 **Models:** Express, G8, Lucerne, Trailblazer **Engines:** 4.6L VIN Y, 4.6L VIN 9, 6.0L VIN H, 6.0L VIN Y, 6.0L VIN K, 6.2L VIN W, 6.6L VIN 6 **Transmissions:** All	**HO2S Heater Control Circuit (Bank 1 Sensor 1)** Engine started, system voltage from 9-18v, and the ECM detected the heater low control circuit current was more than the capacity of the ECM internal driver for over 20 seconds. **Possible Causes:** • HO2S low control circuit is shorted to system power (B+) • HO2S low control circuit driver is shorted inside the ECM • HO2S is damaged or it has failed • ECM has failed
DTC: P0030 **1T CCM, MIL: Yes** **Years:** 2008, 2009 **Models:** Envoy, Equinox, G6, G8, Impala, Lucerne, Malibu, Savana, Trailblazer, Torrent **Engines:** 4.2L VIN S, 4.8L VIN C, 3.5L VIN N, 3.5L VIN K, 3.9L VIN 3, 3.9L VIN M, 3.6L VIN 2, 3.9L VIN 1 **Transmissions:** All	**HO2S Heater Control Circuit (Bank 1 Sensor 1)** The ECM detects an open in the heater circuits of the HO2S when the heater is commanded OFF. The condition exists for greater than 4 seconds or a cumulative of 30 seconds. **Possible Causes:** • HO2S ignition circuit for a short to ground or an open/high resistance • HO2S low control circuit driver is shorted to ground • HO2S is damaged or it has failed • ECM has failed
DTC: P0030 **1T CCM, MIL: Yes** **Years:** 2008, 2009 **Models:** G6, HHR, Malibu **Engines:** 2.0L VIN X, 2.2L VIN D, 2.2L VIN B, 2.2L VIN F, 2.4L VIN B, 2.4L VIN V, 2.4L VIN P, 2.4L VIN 5 **Transmissions:** All	**HO2S Heater Control Circuit Sensor 1** Engine started, system voltage from 9-18v, and the ECM detected the heater low control circuit current was more than the capacity of the ECM internal driver for over 20 seconds. **Possible Causes:** • HO2S ignition circuit for a short to ground or an open/high resistance • HO2S low control circuit driver is shorted to ground • HO2S is damaged or it has failed • ECM has failed
DTC: P0030 **1T CCM, MIL: Yes** **Years:** 2008, 2009 **Models:** Envoy, Equinox, Savana, Torrent **Engines:** 3.4L VIN F, 4.3L VIN X, 5.3L VIN M **Transmissions:** All	**HO2S Heater Control Circuit Sensor 1** The ignition 1 signal is between 11-18 volts. The engine speed is more than 400 RPM. DTC P0030, P0036, P0053, P0054 runs continuously when the above conditions are met for 1 second. The ECM detects that the affected HO2S heater low control circuit is not within a specified range. DTCs P0030 or P0036 set within 3 seconds when the above condition is met. **Possible Causes:** • HO2S ignition circuit for a short to ground or an open/high resistance • HO2S low control circuit driver is shorted to ground • HO2S is damaged or it has failed • ECM has failed
DTC: P0030 **1T CCM, MIL: Yes** **Years:** 2008, 2009 **Models:** Envoy, Express, G6, Impala, Lucerne, Savana, Trailblazer **Engines:** 4.2L VIN S, 4.8L VIN C, 3.5L VIN N, 3.5L VIN K, 3.9L VIN 3, 3.9L VIN M, 3.8L VIN K, 3.9L VIN 1 **Transmissions:** All	**HO2S Heater Control Circuit Sensor 1** The engine speed is more than 400 RPM. The Ignition 1 Signal parameter is between 11-18V. The engine speed is more than 400 RPM. DTC P0030 and P0036 runs continuously when the above conditions are met for 1 second. The ECM detects that the actual state of the affected HO2S heater low control circuit does not match the expected state. DTCs P0030 and P0036 set within 10 seconds when the above condition is met. **Possible Causes:** • HO2S ignition circuit for a short to ground or an open/high resistance • HO2S low control circuit driver is shorted to ground • HO2S is damaged or it has failed • ECM has failed

DTC	Trouble Code Title, Conditions & Possible Causes
DTC: P0031 **1T CCM, MIL: Yes** **Years:** 2008, 2009 **Models:** G6, HHR, Malibu **Engines:** 2.0L VIN X, 2.2L VIN D, 2.2L VIN B, 2.2L VIN F, 2.4L VIN B, 2.4L VIN V, 2.4L VIN P, 2.4L VIN 5 **Transmissions:** All	**HO2S Heater Control Circuit Low Voltage Sensor 1** The ECM detects a short to ground in the heater circuits of the HO2S when the heater is commanded OFF. The condition exists for greater than 4 seconds or a cumulative of 30 seconds. **Possible Causes:** • HO2S ignition circuit for a short to ground or an open/high resistance • HO2S low control circuit driver is shorted to ground • HO2S is damaged or it has failed • ECM has failed
DTC: P0031 **1T CCM, MIL: Yes** **Years:** 2008, 2009 **Models:** Envoy, Equinox, G6, G8, Impala, Lucerne, Malibu, Savana, Trailblazer, Torrent **Engines:** 4.2L VIN S, 4.8L VIN C, 3.5L VIN N, 3.5L VIN K, 3.9L VIN 3, 3.9L VIN M, 3.6L VIN 2, 3.9L VIN 1 **Transmissions:** All	**HO2S Heater Control Circuit Low Voltage (Bank 1 Sensor 1)** The ECM detects a short to ground in the heater circuits of the HO2S when the heater is commanded OFF. The condition exists for greater than 4 seconds or a cumulative of 30 seconds. **Possible Causes:** • HO2S ignition circuit for a short to ground or an open/high resistance • HO2S low control circuit driver is shorted to ground • HO2S is damaged or it has failed • ECM has failed
DTC: P0032 **1T CCM, MIL: Yes** **Years:** 2008, 2009 **Models:** G6, HHR, Malibu **Engines:** 2.0L VIN X, 2.2L VIN D, 2.2L VIN B, 2.2L VIN F, 2.4L VIN B, 2.4L VIN V, 2.4L VIN P, 2.4L VIN 5 **Transmissions:** All	**HO2S Heater Control Circuit High Voltage Sensor 1** The ECM detects a short to voltage in the heater circuits of the HO2S when the heater is commanded ON. The condition exists for greater than 4 seconds or a cumulative of 30 seconds. **Possible Causes:** • HO2S ignition circuit for a short to ground or an open/high resistance • HO2S low control circuit driver is shorted to ground • HO2S is damaged or it has failed • ECM has failed
DTC: P0032 **1T CCM, MIL: Yes** **Years:** 2008, 2009 **Models:** Envoy, Equinox, G6, G8, Impala, Lucerne, Malibu, Savana, Trailblazer, Torrent **Engines:** 4.2L VIN S, 4.8L VIN C, 3.5L VIN N, 3.5L VIN K, 3.9L VIN 3, 3.9L VIN M, 3.6L VIN 2, 3.9L VIN 1 **Transmissions:** All	**HO2S Heater Control Circuit High Voltage (Bank 1 Sensor 1)** The ECM detects a short to voltage in the heater circuits of the HO2S when the heater is commanded ON. The condition exists for greater than 4 seconds or a cumulative of 30 seconds. **Possible Causes:** • HO2S ignition circuit for a short to ground or an open/high resistance • HO2S low control circuit driver is shorted to ground • HO2S is damaged or it has failed • ECM has failed
DTC: P0033 **1T CCM, MIL: Yes** **Years:** 2008, 2009 **Models:** Express, G8, Lucerne, Trailblazer **Engines:** 4.6L VIN Y, 4.6L VIN 9, 6.0L VIN H, 6.0L VIN Y, 6.0L VIN K, 6.2L VIN W, 6.6L VIN 6 **Transmissions:** All	**Supercharger Bypass Valve Solenoid Control Circuit** The ignition is ON. The engine is running. The ignition 1 voltage is between 11-18V. This DTC runs continuously within the enabling conditions. The ECM detects an improper voltage level on the boost control solenoid control circuit for greater than 20 seconds. **Possible Causes:** • ignition circuit for a short to ground or an open/high resistance • SCB solenoid control circuit terminal 2 for a short to ground • SCB solenoid control circuit terminal 2 for a short to voltage or an open/high resistance • SCB solenoid has failed • ECM has failed
DTC: P0036 **1T CCM, MIL: Yes** **Years:** 2008, 2009 **Models:** G6, HHR, Malibu **Engines:** 2.0L VIN X, 2.2L VIN D, 2.2L VIN B, 2.2L VIN F, 2.4L VIN B, 2.4L VIN V, 2.4L VIN P, 2.4L VIN 5 **Transmissions:** All	**HO2S Heater Control Circuit Sensor 2** The ECM detects an open in the heater circuits of the HO2S when the heater is commanded OFF. The condition exists for greater than 4 seconds or a cumulative of 30 seconds. **Possible Causes:** • HO2S ignition circuit for a short to ground or an open/high resistance • HO2S low control circuit driver is shorted to ground • HO2S is damaged or it has failed • ECM has failed

DTC	Trouble Code Title, Conditions & Possible Causes
DTC: P0036 **1T CCM, MIL: Yes** **Years:** 2008, 2009 **Models:** Envoy, Express, G6, Impala, Lucerne, Savana, Trailblazer **Engines:** 4.2L VIN S, 4.8L VIN C, 3.5L VIN N, 3.5L VIN K, 3.9L VIN 3, 3.9L VIN M, 3.8L VIN K, 3.9L VIN 1 **Transmissions:** All	**HO2S Heater Control Circuit Sensor 2** The engine speed is more than 400 RPM. The Ignition 1 Signal parameter is between 11-18V. The engine speed is more than 400 RPM. DTC P0030 and P0036 runs continuously when the above conditions are met for 1 second. The ECM detects that the actual state of the affected HO2S heater low control circuit does not match the expected state. DTCs P0030 and P0036 set within 10 seconds when the above condition is met. **Possible Causes:** • HO2S ignition circuit for a short to ground or an open/high resistance • HO2S low control circuit driver is shorted to ground • HO2S is damaged or it has failed • ECM has failed
DTC: P0036 **1T CCM, MIL: Yes** **Years:** 2008, 2009 **Models:** Express, G8, Lucerne, Trailblazer **Engines:** 4.6L VIN Y, 4.6L VIN 9, 6.0L VIN H, 6.0L VIN Y, 6.0L VIN K, 6.2L VIN W, 6.6L VIN 6 **Transmissions:** All	**Heater Control Circuit (Bank 1 Sensor 2)** The ignition 1 voltage is between 11-18 volts. The engine speed is greater than 400 RPM. The DTCs run continuously when the above conditions are met for 1 second. The ECM detects that the commanded state of the driver and the actual state of the control circuit do not match for greater than 5 seconds. **Possible Causes:** • HO2S ignition circuit for a short to ground or an open/high resistance • HO2S low control circuit driver is shorted to ground • HO2S is damaged or it has failed • ECM has failed
DTC: P0036 **1T CCM, MIL: Yes** **Years:** 2008, 2009 **Models:** Envoy, Equinox, Savana, Torrent **Engines:** 3.4L VIN F, 4.3L VIN X, 5.3L VIN M **Transmissions:** All	**HO2S Heater Control Circuit Sensor 2** The ignition 1 signal is between 11-18 volts. The engine speed is more than 400 RPM. DTC P0036 runs continuously when the above conditions are met for 1 second. The ECM detects that the affected HO2S heater low control circuit is not within a specified range. DTCs P0036 set within 3 seconds when the above condition is met. **Possible Causes:** • HO2S ignition circuit for a short to ground or an open/high resistance • HO2S low control circuit driver is shorted to ground • HO2S is damaged or it has failed • ECM has failed
DTC: P0036 **1T CCM, MIL: Yes** **Years:** 2008, 2009 **Models:** Envoy, Equinox, G6, G8, Impala, Lucerne, Malibu, Savana, Trailblazer, Torrent **Engines:** 4.2L VIN S, 4.8L VIN C, 3.5L VIN N, 3.5L VIN K, 3.9L VIN 3, 3.9L VIN M, 3.6L VIN 2, 3.9L VIN 1 **Transmissions:** All	**Heater Control Circuit (Bank 1 Sensor 2)** The ECM detects an open in the heater circuits of the HO2S when the heater is commanded OFF. The condition exists for greater than 4 seconds or a cumulative of 30 seconds. **Possible Causes:** • HO2S ignition circuit for a short to ground or an open/high resistance • HO2S low control circuit driver is shorted to ground • HO2S is damaged or it has failed • ECM has failed
DTC: P0036 **1T CCM, MIL: Yes** **Years:** 2008, 2009 **Models:** G6, HHR, Malibu **Engines:** 2.0L VIN X, 2.2L VIN D, 2.2L VIN B, 2.2L VIN F, 2.4L VIN B, 2.4L VIN V, 2.4L VIN P, 2.4L VIN 5 **Transmissions:** All	**HO2S Heater Control Circuit Sensor 2** The ignition 1 signal is between 11-18 volts. The engine speed is more than 400 RPM. DTC P0036 runs continuously when the above conditions are met for 1 second. The ECM detects that the affected HO2S heater low control circuit is not within a specified range. DTCs P0036 set within 3 seconds when the above condition is met. **Possible Causes:** • HO2S ignition circuit for a short to ground or an open/high resistance • HO2S low control circuit driver is shorted to ground • HO2S is damaged or it has failed • ECM has failed
DTC: P0037 **1T CCM, MIL: Yes** **Years:** 2008, 2009 **Models:** G6, HHR, Malibu **Engines:** 2.0L VIN X, 2.2L VIN D, 2.2L VIN B, 2.2L VIN F, 2.4L VIN B, 2.4L VIN V, 2.4L VIN P, 2.4L VIN 5 **Transmissions:** All	**HO2S Heater Control Circuit Low Voltage Sensor 2** The ECM detects a short to ground in the heater circuits of the HO2S when the heater is commanded OFF. The condition exists for greater than 4 seconds or a cumulative of 30 seconds. **Possible Causes:** • HO2S low control circuit is shorted to system power (B+) • HO2S low control circuit driver is shorted inside the ECM • HO2S is damaged or it has failed • ECM has failed

DTC	Trouble Code Title, Conditions & Possible Causes
DTC: P0037 **1T CCM, MIL: Yes** **Years:** 2008, 2009 **Models:** Envoy, Equinox, G6, G8, Impala, Lucerne, Malibu, Savana, Trailblazer, Torrent **Engines:** 4.2L VIN S, 4.8L VIN C, 3.5L VIN N, 3.5L VIN K, 3.9L VIN 3, 3.9L VIN M, 3.6L VIN 2, 3.9L VIN 1 **Transmissions:** All	**HO2S Heater Control Circuit Low Voltage (Bank 1 Sensor 2)** The ECM detects a short to ground in the heater circuits of the HO2S when the heater is commanded OFF. The condition exists for greater than 4 seconds or a cumulative of 30 seconds. **Possible Causes:** • HO2S low control circuit is shorted to system power (B+) • HO2S low control circuit driver is shorted inside the ECM • HO2S is damaged or it has failed • ECM has failed
DTC: P0038 **1T CCM, MIL: Yes** **Years:** 2008, 2009 **Models:** G6, HHR, Malibu **Engines:** 2.0L VIN X, 2.2L VIN D, 2.2L VIN B, 2.2L VIN F, 2.4L VIN B, 2.4L VIN V, 2.4L VIN P, 2.4L VIN 5 **Transmissions:** All	**HO2S Heater Control Circuit High Voltage Sensor 2** The ECM detects a short to voltage in the heater circuits of the HO2S when the heater is commanded ON. The condition exists for greater than 4 seconds or a cumulative of 30 seconds. **Possible Causes:** • HO2S ignition circuit for a short to ground or an open/high resistance • HO2S low control circuit driver is shorted to ground • HO2S is damaged or it has failed • ECM has failed
DTC: P0038 **1T CCM, MIL: Yes** **Years:** 2008, 2009 **Models:** Envoy, Equinox, G6, G8, Impala, Lucerne, Malibu, Savana, Trailblazer, Torrent **Engines:** 4.2L VIN S, 4.8L VIN C, 3.5L VIN N, 3.5L VIN K, 3.9L VIN 3, 3.9L VIN M, 3.6L VIN 2, 3.9L VIN 1 **Transmissions:** All	**HO2S Heater Control Circuit High Voltage (Bank 1 Sensor 2)** The ECM detects a short to voltage in the heater circuits of the HO2S when the heater is commanded ON. The condition exists for greater than 4 seconds or a cumulative of 30 seconds. **Possible Causes:** • HO2S ignition circuit for a short to ground or an open/high resistance • HO2S low control circuit driver is shorted to ground • HO2S is damaged or it has failed • ECM has failed
DTC: P0050 **1T CCM, MIL: Yes** **Years:** 2008, 2009 **Models:** Envoy, Equinox, G6, G8, Impala, Lucerne, Malibu, Savana, Trailblazer, Torrent **Engines:** 4.2L VIN S, 4.8L VIN C, 3.5L VIN N, 3.5L VIN K, 3.9L VIN 3, 3.9L VIN M, 3.6L VIN 2, 3.9L VIN 1 **Transmissions:** All	**HO2S Heater Control Circuit (Bank 2 Sensor 1)** The ECM detects an open in the heater circuits of the HO2S when the heater is commanded OFF. The condition exists for greater than 4 seconds or a cumulative of 30 seconds. **Possible Causes:** • HO2S ignition circuit for a short to ground or an open/high resistance • HO2S low control circuit driver is shorted to ground • HO2S is damaged or it has failed • ECM has failed
DTC: P0051 **1T CCM, MIL: Yes** **Years:** 2008, 2009 **Models:** Envoy, Equinox, G6, G8, Impala, Lucerne, Malibu, Savana, Trailblazer, Torrent **Engines:** 4.2L VIN S, 4.8L VIN C, 3.5L VIN N, 3.5L VIN K, 3.9L VIN 3, 3.9L VIN M, 3.6L VIN 2, 3.9L VIN 1 **Transmissions:** All	**HO2S Heater Control Circuit Low Voltage (Bank 2 Sensor 1)** The ECM detects a short to ground in the heater circuits of the HO2S when the heater is commanded OFF. The condition exists for greater than 4 seconds or a cumulative of 30 seconds. **Possible Causes:** • HO2S ignition circuit for a short to ground or an open/high resistance • HO2S low control circuit driver is shorted to ground • HO2S is damaged or it has failed • ECM has failed
DTC: P0052 **1T CCM, MIL: Yes** **Years:** 2008, 2009 **Models:** Envoy, Equinox, G6, G8, Impala, Lucerne, Malibu, Savana, Trailblazer, Torrent **Engines:** 4.2L VIN S, 4.8L VIN C, 3.5L VIN N, 3.5L VIN K, 3.9L VIN 3, 3.9L VIN M, 3.6L VIN 2, 3.9L VIN 1 **Transmissions:** All	**HO2S Heater Control Circuit High Voltage (Bank 2 Sensor 1)** The ECM detects a short to voltage in the heater circuits of the HO2S when the heater is commanded ON. The condition exists for greater than 4 seconds or a cumulative of 30 seconds. **Possible Causes:** • HO2S ignition circuit for a short to ground or an open/high resistance • HO2S low control circuit driver is shorted to ground • HO2S is damaged or it has failed • ECM has failed

DTC	Trouble Code Title, Conditions & Possible Causes
DTC: P0053 **1T CCM, MIL: Yes** **Years:** 2008, 2009 **Models:** Envoy, Equinox, Savana, Torrent **Engines:** 3.4L VIN F, 4.3L VIN X, 5.3L VIN M **Transmissions:** All	**HO2S Heater Resistance Circuit Sensor 1** DTCs P0112, P0113, P0117 and P0118 are not set. The engine is started. The ignition voltage is less than 18 volts. The ignition is OFF for more than 10 hours. The Engine Coolant Temperature (ECT) sensor is between -22 to $+113°F$ (-30 to $+45°C$) at engine start-up. The ECT sensor minus the Intake Air Temperature (IAT) sensor is less than 14°F (8°C) at engine start-up. DTCs P0053 and P0054 run once per drive cycle when the above conditions are met. The ECM detects that the affected HO2S heater low control circuit is not within a specified resistance range at engine start-up. DTC P0053 sets within 3 seconds when the above condition is met. **Possible Causes:** • HO2S ignition circuit for a short to ground or an open/high resistance • HO2S low control circuit driver is shorted to ground • HO2S is damaged or it has failed • ECM has failed
DTC: P0053 **1T CCM, MIL: Yes** **Years:** 2008, 2009 **Models:** G6, HHR, Malibu **Engines:** 2.0L VIN X, 2.2L VIN D, 2.2L VIN B, 2.2L VIN F, 2.4L VIN B, 2.4L VIN V, 2.4L VIN P, 2.4L VIN 5 **Transmissions:** All	**HO2S Heater Resistance Circuit Sensor 1** The engine is started.The ignition voltage is less than 18 volts. The ignition is OFF for more than 10 hours. The Engine Coolant Temperature (ECT) sensor is between -22 to $+113°F$ (-30 to $+45°C$) at engine start-up. The ECT sensor minus the Intake Air Temperature (IAT) sensor is less than 14°F (8°C) at engine start-up. DTCs P0053 and P0054 run once per drive cycle when the above conditions are met. The ECM detects that the affected HO2S heater low control circuit is not within a specified resistance range at engine start-up. DTC P0053 sets within 3 seconds when the above condition is met. **Possible Causes:** • HO2S ignition circuit for a short to ground or an open/high resistance • HO2S low control circuit driver is shorted to ground • HO2S is damaged or it has failed • ECM has failed
DTC: P0053 **1T CCM, MIL: Yes** **Models:** Envoy, Equinox, G6, G8, Impala, Lucerne, Malibu, Savana, Trailblazer, Torrent **Engines:** 4.2L VIN S, 4.8L VIN C, 3.5L VIN N, 3.5L VIN K, 3.9L VIN 3, 3.9L VIN M, 3.6L VIN 2, 3.9L VIN 1 **Transmissions:** All	**HO2S Heater Resistance (Bank 1 Sensor 1)** The engine run time is greater than 3 seconds. The ignition voltage is less than 18 volts. The ignition is OFF for greater than 8 hours. The Engine Coolant Temperature (ECT) is between -30 to $+45°C$ (-22 to $+113°F$) at engine start-up. The DTCs run once per drive cycle when the above conditions are met. The ECM detects the HO2S heater is not within a specified resistance range at engine start-up for greater than 1 second. **Possible Causes:** • HO2S ignition circuit for a short to ground or an open/high resistance • HO2S control circuit for a short to voltage, or an open/high resistance • HO2S control circuit for a short to ground • HO2S is damaged or it has failed • ECM has failed
DTC: P0053 **1T CCM, MIL: Yes** **Years:** 2008, 2009 **Models:** Express, G8, Lucerne, Trailblazer **Engines:** 4.6L VIN Y, 4.6L VIN 9, 6.0L VIN H, 6.0L VIN Y, 6.0L VIN K, 6.2L VIN W, 6.6L VIN 6 **Transmissions:** All	**HO2S Heater Resistance (Bank 1 Sensor 1)** DTCs P0112, P0113, P0117, P0118, or P2610 are not set. The engine run time is greater than 3 seconds. The ignition voltage is less than 18 volts. The ignition is OFF for greater than 8 hours. The Engine Coolant Temperature (ECT) is between -30 to $+45°C$ (-22 to $+113°F$) at engine start-up. The ECT and the Intake Air Temperature (IAT) are within 8°C (14°F) at engine start-up. The DTCs run once per drive cycle when the above conditions are met. The ECM detects the HO2S heater is not within a specified resistance range at engine start-up for greater than 1 second. **Possible Causes:** • HO2S ignition circuit for a short to ground or an open/high resistance • HO2S control circuit for a short to voltage, or an open/high resistance • HO2S control circuit for a short to ground • HO2S is damaged or it has failed • ECM has failed
DTC: P0054 **1T CCM, MIL: Yes** **Years:** 2008, 2009 **Models:** Express, G8, Lucerne, Trailblazer **Engines:** 4.6L VIN Y, 4.6L VIN 9, 6.0L VIN H, 6.0L VIN Y, 6.0L VIN K, 6.2L VIN W, 6.6L VIN 6 **Transmissions:** All	**HO2S Heater Resistance (Bank 1 Sensor 2)** DTCs P0112, P0113, P0117, P0118, or P2610 are not set. The engine run time is greater than 3 seconds. The ignition voltage is less than 18 volts. The ignition is OFF for greater than 8 hours. The Engine Coolant Temperature (ECT) is between -30 to $+45°C$ (-22 to $+113°F$) at engine start-up. The ECT and the Intake Air Temperature (IAT) are within 8°C (14°F) at engine start-up. The DTCs run once per drive cycle when the above conditions are met. The ECM detects the HO2S heater is not within a specified resistance range at engine start-up for greater than 1 second. **Possible Causes:** • HO2S ignition circuit for a short to ground or an open/high resistance • HO2S control circuit for a short to voltage, or an open/high resistance • HO2S control circuit for a short to ground • HO2S is damaged or it has failed • ECM has failed

DTC	Trouble Code Title, Conditions & Possible Causes
DTC: P0056 **1T CCM, MIL: Yes** **Years:** 2008, 2009 **Models:** Express, G8, Lucerne, Trailblazer **Engines:** 4.6L VIN Y, 4.6L VIN 9, 6.0L VIN H, 6.0L VIN Y, 6.0L VIN K, 6.2L VIN W, 6.6L VIN 6 **Transmissions:** All	**HO2S Heater Control Circuit (Bank 2 Sensor 2)** Engine started, system voltage from 9-18v, and the ECM detected the heater low control circuit current was more than the capacity of the ECM internal driver for over 20 seconds. **Possible Causes:** • HO2S ignition circuit for a short to ground or an open/high resistance • HO2S control circuit for a short to voltage, or an open/high resistance • HO2S control circuit for a short to ground • HO2S is damaged or it has failed • ECM has failed
DTC: P0059 **1T CCM, MIL: Yes** **Years:** 2008, 2009 **Models:** Express, G8, Lucerne, Trailblazer **Engines:** 4.6L VIN Y, 4.6L VIN 9, 6.0L VIN H, 6.0L VIN Y, 6.0L VIN K, 6.2L VIN W, 6.6L VIN 6 **Transmissions:** All	**HO2S Heater Resistance (Bank 2 Sensor 1)** DTCs P0112, P0113, P0117, P0118, or P2610 are not set. The engine run time is greater than 3 seconds. The ignition voltage is less than 18 volts. The ignition is OFF for greater than 8 hours. The Engine Coolant Temperature (ECT) is between −30 to +45°C (−22 to +113°F) at engine start-up. The ECT and the Intake Air Temperature (IAT) are within 8°C (14°F) at engine start-up. The DTCs run once per drive cycle when the above conditions are met. The ECM detects the HO2S heater is not within a specified resistance range at engine start-up for greater than 1 second. **Possible Causes:** • HO2S ignition circuit for a short to ground or an open/high resistance • HO2S control circuit for a short to voltage, or an open/high resistance • HO2S control circuit for a short to ground • HO2S is damaged or it has failed • ECM has failed
DTC: P0060 **1T CCM, MIL: Yes** **Years:** 2008, 2009 **Models:** Express, G8, Lucerne, Trailblazer **Engines:** 4.6L VIN Y, 4.6L VIN 9, 6.0L VIN H, 6.0L VIN Y, 6.0L VIN K, 6.2L VIN W, 6.6L VIN 6 **Transmissions:** All	**HO2S Heater Resistance (Bank 2 Sensor 2)** DTCs P0112, P0113, P0117, P0118, or P2610 are not set. The engine run time is greater than 3 seconds. The ignition voltage is less than 18 volts. The ignition is OFF for greater than 8 hours. The Engine Coolant Temperature (ECT) is between −30 to +45°C (−22 to +113°F) at engine start-up. The ECT and the Intake Air Temperature (IAT) are within 8°C (14°F) at engine start-up. The DTCs run once per drive cycle when the above conditions are met. The ECM detects the HO2S heater is not within a specified resistance range at engine start-up for greater than 1 second. **Possible Causes:** • HO2S ignition circuit for a short to ground or an open/high resistance • HO2S control circuit for a short to voltage, or an open/high resistance • HO2S control circuit for a short to ground • HO2S is damaged or it has failed • ECM has failed
DTC: P0060 **1T CCM, MIL: Yes** **Models:** Envoy, Equinox, G6, G8, Impala, Lucerne, Malibu, Savana, Trailblazer, Torrent **Engines:** 4.2L VIN S, 4.8L VIN C, 3.5L VIN N, 3.5L VIN K, 3.9L VIN 3, 3.9L VIN M, 3.6L VIN 2, 3.9L VIN 1 **Transmissions:** All	**HO2S Heater Resistance (Bank 2 Sensor 2)** DTCs P0117, P0118, or P2610 are not set. The engine run time is greater than 5 seconds. The ignition voltage is less than 18 volts. The ignition is OFF for greater than 8 hours. The Engine Coolant Temperature (ECT) is between −30 to +45°C (−22 to +113°F) at engine start-up. The ECT and the Intake Air Temperature (IAT) are within 8°C (14°F) at engine start-up. The DTCs run once per drive cycle when the above conditions are met. The ECM detects the HO2S heater is not within a specified resistance range at engine start-up for greater than 1 second. **Possible Causes:** • HO2S ignition circuit for a short to ground or an open/high resistance • HO2S control circuit for a short to voltage, or an open/high resistance • HO2S control circuit for a short to ground • HO2S is damaged or it has failed • ECM has failed
DTC: P0068 **1T CCM, MIL: Yes** **Years:** 2008, 2009 **Models:** Express, G8, Lucerne, Trailblazer **Engines:** 4.6L VIN Y, 4.6L VIN 9, 6.0L VIN H, 6.0L VIN Y, 6.0L VIN K, 6.2L VIN W, 6.6L VIN 6 **Transmissions:** All	**Throttle Body Airflow Performance** DTCs P0641, P0651, P1516, P2101, P2119, P2176 are not set. The engine is running. DTC P0068 run continuously when the above conditions are met. The ECM detects that the throttle position and the indicated engine load do not correspond with the expected load and throttle position for less than 1 second. **Possible Causes:** • Throttle body for dirt, debris, and coking • Vacuum hoses for splits, kinks, and proper connections • Loose or damaged throttle blade • Broken throttle shaft • Any throttle body damage • Throttle body assembly has failed

DTC	Trouble Code Title, Conditions & Possible Causes
DTC: P0068 **1T CCM, MIL: Yes** **Models:** Envoy, Equinox, G6, G8, Impala, Lucerne, Malibu, Savana, Trailblazer, Torrent **Engines:** 4.2L VIN S, 4.8L VIN C, 3.5L VIN N, 3.5L VIN K, 3.9L VIN 3, 3.9L VIN M, 3.6L VIN 2, 3.9L VIN 1 **Transmissions:** All	**Throttle Body Airflow Performance** The ECM detects that the throttle position and the indicated engine load do not correspond with the expected load and throttle position for less than 1 second. DTC P0068 run continuously when the above conditions are met **Possible Causes:** • Throttle body for dirt, debris, and coking • Vacuum hoses for splits, kinks, and proper connections • Loose or damaged throttle blade • Broken throttle shaft • Any throttle body damage • Throttle body assembly has failed
DTC: P0068 **1T CCM, MIL: Yes** **Years:** 2008, 2009 **Models:** G6, HHR, Malibu **Engines:** 2.0L VIN X, 2.2L VIN D, 2.2L VIN B, 2.2L VIN F, 2.4L VIN B, 2.4L VIN V, 2.4L VIN P, 2.4L VIN 5 **Transmissions:** All	**Throttle Body Airflow Performance** The engine is running. The ECM detects that the throttle position and the indicated engine load do not correspond with the expected load and throttle position for less than 1 second. **Possible Causes:** • Throttle body for dirt, debris, and coking • Vacuum hoses for splits, kinks, and proper connections • Loose or damaged throttle blade • Broken throttle shaft • Any throttle body damage • Throttle body assembly has failed
DTC: P006D **1T CCM, MIL: Yes** **Years:** 2008, 2009 **Models:** Express, G8, Lucerne, Trailblazer **Engines:** 4.6L VIN Y, 4.6L VIN 9, 6.0L VIN H, 6.0L VIN Y, 6.0L VIN K, 6.2L VIN W, 6.6L VIN 6 **Transmissions:** All	**Supercharger Inlet Pressure (SCIP) - Barometric Pressure (BARO) Correlation** DTCs P0068, P0101, P0102, P0103, P0107, P0108, P0112, P0113, P0116, P0117, P0118, P0120, P0121, P0128, P012B, P012C, P012D, P0220, P0502, P1516, P2101, P2227, P2228, P2229 are not set. The ignition is ON. OR the engine is running. DTC P006D runs continuously when the above conditions are met. The ECM detects that during ignition ON, with the engine OFF, the calculated difference between BARO and SCIAP, whether that value is negative or positive, is greater than 12 kPa for greater than 30 seconds. Or The ECM has detected that a wide open throttle update event has occurred within the previous 2 kilometers (1.2 miles) and the difference between BARO, and a calculated BARO using the SCIAP sensor, is greater than 12 kPa for greater than 30 seconds.OrThe ECM has not detected a wide open throttle update event within the previous 2 kilometers (1.2 miles) and the difference between BARO, and a calculated BARO using the SCIAP sensor, is greater than 60 kPa for greater than 30 seconds **Possible Causes:** • SCIAP and BARO sensor, loose or improper installation • SCIAP and BARO sensor, low reference circuit for an open/high resistance • SCIAP and BARO sensor, 5V reference circuit for a short to ground or an open/high resistance. • SCIAP and BARO sensor, 5V reference circuit for a short to voltage • SCIAP and BARO sensor, signal circuit for a short to voltage • SCIAP and BARO sensor, signal circuit for an open/high resistance
DTC: P0096 **1T CCM, MIL: Yes** **Years:** 2008, 2009 **Models:** Express, G8, Lucerne, Trailblazer **Engines:** 4.6L VIN Y, 4.6L VIN 9, 6.0L VIN H, 6.0L VIN Y, 6.0L VIN K, 6.2L VIN W, 6.6L VIN 6 **Transmissions:** All	**Intake Air Temperature (IAT) Sensor 2 Performance** DTCs P0097, P0098, P0112, P0113, P0116, P0117, P0118, P0128, P0500, P0502, P0603 are not set. DTC P0116 has run and passed. The engine has been OFF for greater than 8 hours. The IAT sensor is greater than 10°C (50°F). DTC P0096 runs once per key cycle within the enabling conditions. DTC P0116 must run and pass. At start-up, after an 8 hour engine soak time, the IAT sensor 2 temperature is greater than 20°C (36°F) higher or lower than the IAT sensor. **Possible Causes:** • MAF/IAT low reference circuit for an open/high resistance • MAF/IAT low reference circuit for an open/high resistance • MAF/IAT signal circuit for an open/high resistance • MAF/IAT sensor has failed • ECM has failed
DTC: P0096 **1T CCM, MIL: Yes** **Years:** 2008, 2009 **Models:** G6, HHR, Malibu **Engines:** 2.0L VIN X, 2.2L VIN D, 2.2L VIN B, 2.2L VIN F, 2.4L VIN B, 2.4L VIN V, 2.4L VIN P, 2.4L VIN 5 **Transmissions:** All	**Intake Air Temperature (IAT) Sensor 2 Performance** DTCs P0116, P0117, P0118, P0128, P0500, P0502, P0603 are not set.. The engine has been OFF for greater than 8 hours. The IAT sensor is greater than 10°C (50°F). DTC P0096 runs once per key cycle within the enabling conditions. DTC P0116 must run and pass. At start-up, after an 8 hour engine soak time, the IAT sensor 2 temperature is greater than 20°C (36°F) higher or lower than the IAT sensor. **Possible Causes:** • MAF/IAT low reference circuit for an open/high resistance • MAF/IAT low reference circuit for an open/high resistance • MAF/IAT signal circuit for an open/high resistance • MAF/IAT sensor has failed • ECM has failed

DTC	Trouble Code Title, Conditions & Possible Causes
DTC: P0096 **1T CCM, MIL: Yes** **Models:** Envoy, Equinox, G6, G8, Impala, Lucerne, Malibu, Savana, Trailblazer, Torrent **Engines:** 4.2L VIN S, 4.8L VIN C, 3.5L VIN N, 3.5L VIN K, 3.9L VIN 3, 3.9L VIN M, 3.6L VIN 2, 3.9L VIN 1 **Transmissions:** All	**Intake Air Temperature (IAT) Sensor 2 Performance** DTCs P0117, P0118, P0128, P0500, P0502, P0603 are not set. DTC P0116 has run and passed. The engine has been OFF for greater than 8 hours. The IAT sensor is greater than 12°C (52°F). DTC P0096 runs once per key cycle within the enabling conditions. DTC P0116 must run and pass. At start-up, after an 8 hour engine soak time, the IAT sensor 2 temperature is greater than 20°C (36°F) higher or lower than the IAT sensor. **Possible Causes:** • MAF/IAT low reference circuit for an open/high resistance • MAF/IAT low reference circuit for an open/high resistance • MAF/IAT signal circuit for an open/high resistance • MAF/IAT sensor has failed • ECM has failed
DTC: P0097 **1T CCM, MIL: Yes** **Years:** 2008, 2009 **Models:** Express, G8, Lucerne, Trailblazer **Engines:** 4.6L VIN Y, 4.6L VIN 9, 6.0L VIN H, 6.0L VIN Y, 6.0L VIN K, 6.2L VIN W, 6.6L VIN 6 **Transmissions:** All	**Intake Air Temperature (IAT) Sensor 2 Circuit Low Voltage** The engine run has been in operation for greater than 10 seconds. The engine coolant temperature (ECT) is greater than −40°C (−40°F). The vehicle speed is greater than 1 km/h (1 mph). The MAF is less than 512 g/s. DTC P0097 and P0098 run continuously within the enabling conditionsThe IAT sensor 2 is greater than 148°C (298°F) for greater than 5 seconds. This is equal to or less than 0.24V on the IAT sensor 2 signal circuit as measured by the ECM for P0097. **Possible Causes:** • IAT signal circuit for a short to ground • IAT signal circuit terminal A for a short to voltage or an open/high resistance • IAT sensor 2 has failed • ECM has failed
DTC: P0097 **1T CCM, MIL: Yes** **Years:** 2008, 2009 **Models:** Express, G8, Lucerne, Trailblazer **Engines:** 4.6L VIN Y, 4.6L VIN 9, 6.0L VIN H, 6.0L VIN Y, 6.0L VIN K, 6.2L VIN W, 6.6L VIN 6 **Transmissions:** All	**Intake Air Temperature (IAT) Sensor 2 Circuit High Voltage** The engine run has been in operation for greater than 10 seconds. The engine coolant temperature (ECT) is greater than -40°C (−40°F). The vehicle speed is greater than 1 km/h (1 mph). The MAF is less than 512 g/s. DTC P0097 and P0098 run continuously within the enabling conditionsThe IAT sensor 2 is colder than −39°C (−38°F) for greater than 5 seconds. This is equal to or greater than 4.86V on the IAT signal circuit as measured by the ECM for P0098. **Possible Causes:** • IAT signal circuit for a short to ground • IAT signal circuit terminal A for a short to voltage or an open/high resistance • IAT sensor 2 has failed • ECM has failed
DTC: P0098 **1T CCM, MIL: Yes** **Years:** 2008, 2009 **Models:** Express, G8, Lucerne, Trailblazer **Engines:** 4.6L VIN Y, 4.6L VIN 9, 6.0L VIN H, 6.0L VIN Y, 6.0L VIN K, 6.2L VIN W, 6.6L VIN 6 **Transmissions:** All	**Mass Air Flow (MAF) Sensor Performance** DTCs P0102, P0103, P0107, P0108, P0112, P0113, P0116, P0117, P0118, P0128, P0335, P0336 are not set. The engine speed is between 450-6,800 RPM. The IAT Sensor parameter is between −7 to +125°C (+19 to +257°F). The ECT Sensor parameter is between 70-125°C (158-257°F). This DTC runs continuously when the above conditions are met. The Engine Control Module (ECM) detects that the actual measured airflow from the MAF, MAP, and TP sensors is not within range of the calculated airflow that is derived from the system of models for more than 0.5 second. **Possible Causes:** • MAF/IAT sensor for loose or improper installation • An air flow restriction • Any vacuum leak • Water intrusion • In cold climates, inspect for any snow or ice buildup • MAF sensor element for contamination • MAF/IAT sensorground circuit for an open/high resistance • MAF/IAT sensorignition circuit for a short to ground or an open/high resistance. • MAF/IAT sensorsignal circuit for a short to ground or an open/high resistance • MAF/IAT sensorsignal circuit for a short to voltage

DTC	Trouble Code Title, Conditions & Possible Causes
DTC: P0097 **1T CCM, MIL: Yes** **Years:** 2008, 2009 **Models:** Express, G8, Lucerne, Trailblazer **Engines:** 4.6L VIN Y, 4.6L VIN 9, 6.0L VIN H, 6.0L VIN Y, 6.0L VIN K, 6.2L VIN W, 6.6L VIN 6 **Transmissions:** All	**Intake Air Flow System Performance** DTCs P0102, P0103, P0107, P0108, P0112, P0113, P0116, P0117, P0118, P0128, P0335, P0336 are not set. The engine speed is between 450-6,800 RPM. The IAT Sensor parameter is between −7 to +125°C (+19 to +257°F). The ECT Sensor parameter is between 70-125°C (158-257°F). This DTC runs continuously when the above conditions are met. The Engine Control Module (ECM) detects that the actual measured airflow from the MAF, MAP, and TP sensors is not within range of the calculated airflow that is derived from the system of models for more than 0.5 second. **Possible Causes:** • MAF/IAT sensor for loose or improper installation • An air flow restriction • Any vacuum leak • Water intrusion • In cold climates, inspect for any snow or ice buildup • MAF sensor element for contamination • MAF/IAT sensorground circuit for an open/high resistance • MAF/IAT sensorignition circuit for a short to ground or an open/high resistance. • MAF/IAT sensorsignal circuit for a short to ground or an open/high resistance • MAF/IAT sensorsignal circuit for a short to voltage
DTC: P0097 **1T CCM, MIL: Yes** **Models:** Envoy, Equinox, G6, G8, Impala, Lucerne, Malibu, Savana, Trailblazer, Torrent **Engines:** 4.2L VIN S, 4.8L VIN C, 3.5L VIN N, 3.5L VIN K, 3.9L VIN 3, 3.9L VIN M, 3.6L VIN 2, 3.9L VIN 1 **Transmissions:** All	**Intake Air Flow System Performance** The engine speed is between 450-6,800 RPM. The IAT Sensor parameter is between −7 to +125°C (+19 to +257°F). The ECT Sensor parameter is between 70-125°C (158-257°F). This DTC runs continuously when the above conditions are met. The Engine Control Module (ECM) detects that the actual measured airflow from the MAF, MAP, and TP sensors is not within range of the calculated airflow that is derived from the system of models for more than 0.5 second. **Possible Causes:** • MAF/IAT sensor for loose or improper installation • An air flow restriction • Any vacuum leak • Water intrusion • In cold climates, inspect for any snow or ice buildup • MAF sensor element for contamination • MAF/IAT sensorground circuit for an open/high resistance • MAF/IAT sensorignition circuit for a short to ground or an open/high resistance. • MAF/IAT sensorsignal circuit for a short to ground or an open/high resistance • MAF/IAT sensorsignal circuit for a short to voltage
DTC: P009A **1T CCM, MIL: Yes** **Years:** 2008, 2009 **Models:** G6, HHR, Malibu **Engines:** 2.0L VIN X, 2.2L VIN D, 2.2L VIN B, 2.2L VIN F, 2.4L VIN B, 2.4L VIN V, 2.4L VIN P, 2.4L VIN 5 **Transmissions:** All	**Intake Air Temperature (IAT)-Ambient Air Temperature (AAT) Correlation** The engine is running. The ignition voltage is greater than 10 volts. The MAF Sensor parameter is between 70-500 kg/h. The ECT Sensor parameter is between 69-120°C (156-248°F). The Engine Speed parameter is between 928-6496 RPM. The vehicle speed is between 35-160 km/h (22-100 mph). The above conditions have been met for greater than 15 seconds. This DTC runs continuously within the enabling conditions. The ECM detects that the AAT sensor signal is not within a calibrated range of the modeled AAT for greater than 2 seconds. **Possible Causes:** • AAT sensor reference circuit high resistance • AAT sensor cinal circuit high resistance • AAT sensor has failed • ECM has failed
DTC: P0102 **1T CCM, MIL: Yes** **Years:** 2008, 2009 **Models:** Express, G8, Lucerne, Trailblazer **Engines:** 4.6L VIN Y, 4.6L VIN 9, 6.0L VIN H, 6.0L VIN Y, 6.0L VIN K, 6.2L VIN W, 6.6L VIN 6 **Transmissions:** All	**Mass Air Flow (MAF) Sensor Circuit Low Frequency** The engine is running for greater than 1 second. The engine speed is greater than 300 RPM. The ignition 1 signal is greater than 8 volts. The above conditions are met for greater than 1 second. These DTCs run continuously when the above conditions are met. The ECM detects that the MAF Sensor parameter is less than 1,867 Hz for greater than 5 seconds. **Possible Causes:** • Restricted or collapsed air intake duct • Misaligned air intake duct • Dirty or deteriorating air filter element • Objects blocking the air inlet screen of the MAF/IAT sensor • Water intrusion in the induction system • Contamination or debris on the sensing elements of the MAF sensor • Any vacuum leak • MAF/IAT sensor ground circuit for an open/high resistance • MAF/IAT sensor ignition circuit terminal C for a short to ground or an open/high resistance • MAF/IAT sensor signal circuit for a short to ground or an open/high resistance. • MAF/IAT sensor signal circuit for a short to voltage • MAF/IAT sensor has failed • ECM has failed

DTC	Trouble Code Title, Conditions & Possible Causes
DTC: P0103 **1T CCM, MIL: Yes** **Years:** 2008, 2009 **Models:** Express, G8, Lucerne, Trailblazer **Engines:** 4.6L VIN Y, 4.6L VIN 9, 6.0L VIN H, 6.0L VIN Y, 6.0L VIN K, 6.2L VIN W, 6.6L VIN 6 **Transmissions:** All	**Mass Air Flow (MAF) Sensor Circuit High Frequency** The engine is running for greater than 1 second. The engine speed is greater than 300 RPM. The ignition 1 signal is greater than 8 volts. The above conditions are met for greater than 1 second. These DTCs run continuously when the above conditions are met. The ECM detects that the MAF Sensor parameter is greater than 14,500 Hz for greater than 5 seconds. **Possible Causes:** • Restricted or collapsed air intake duct • Misaligned air intake duct • Dirty or deteriorating air filter element • Objects blocking the air inlet screen of the MAF/IAT sensor • Water intrusion in the induction system • Contamination or debris on the sensing elements of the MAF sensor • Any vacuum leak • MAF/IAT sensor ground circuit for an open/high resistance • MAF/IAT sensor ignition circuit terminal C for a short to ground or an open/high resistance • MAF/IAT sensor signal circuit for a short to ground or an open/high resistance. • MAF/IAT sensor signal circuit for a short to voltage • MAF/IAT sensor has failed • ECM has failed
DTC: P0106 **1T CCM, MIL: Yes** **Years:** 2008, 2009 **Models:** Express, G8, Lucerne, Trailblazer **Engines:** 4.6L VIN Y, 4.6L VIN 9, 6.0L VIN H, 6.0L VIN Y, 6.0L VIN K, 6.2L VIN W, 6.6L VIN 6 **Transmissions:** All	**Manifold Absolute Pressure (MAP) Sensor Performance** DTCs P0102, P0103, P0107, P0108, P0112, P0113, P0116, P0117, P0118, P0128, P0335, P0336 are not set. The engine is running. The IAT Sensor is between −7 and +125°C (+19 and +257°F). The ECT Sensor is between 70-125°C (158-257°F). This DTC runs continuously when the above conditions are met. The engine control module (ECM) detects that the MAP sensor pressure is not within range of the calculated pressure that is derived from the system of models for more than 0.5 second. **Possible Causes:** • MAP sensor low reference circuit for an open/high resistance • MAP sensor 5-volt reference circuit for a short to ground or an open/high resistance • MAP sensor 5-volt reference circuit for a short to voltage • MAP sensor signal circuit for a short to voltage • MAP sensor signal circuit for a short to ground or an open/high resistance • MAP sensor has failed • ECM has failed
DTC: P0107 **1T CCM, MIL: Yes** **Years:** 2008, 2009 **Models:** Express, G8, Lucerne, Trailblazer **Engines:** 4.6L VIN Y, 4.6L VIN 9, 6.0L VIN H, 6.0L VIN Y, 6.0L VIN K, 6.2L VIN W, 6.6L VIN 6 **Transmissions:** All	**Manifold Absolute Pressure (MAP) Sensor Circuit Low Voltage** DTCs P0641, P0651, P1516, P2101, P2125, P2135, P2138, P2176 are not set. The engine speed is greater than 400 RPM. The throttle angle is greater than 0 percent when the engine speed is less than 800 RPM. Or the throttle angle is greater than 13 percent when the engine speed is greater than 800 RPM. This DTC runs continuously when the above conditions are met. The ECM detects that the MAP sensor voltage is less than 0.1 volt for more than 4 seconds. **Possible Causes:** • Intake manifold vacuum leaks • A loose or improperly installed MAP sensor • A restriction in the vacuum source of the MAP sensor • MAP sensor low reference circuit for an open/high resistance • MAP sensor 5-volt reference circuit for a short to ground or an open/high resistance • MAP sensor 5-volt reference circuit for a short to voltage • MAP sensor signal circuit for a short to voltage • MAP sensor signal circuit for a short to ground or an open/high resistance • MAP sensor has failed • ECM has failed

DTC	Trouble Code Title, Conditions & Possible Causes
DTC: P0108 **1T CCM, MIL: Yes** **Years:** 2008, 2009 **Models:** Express, G8, Lucerne, Trailblazer **Engines:** 4.6L VIN Y, 4.6L VIN 9, 6.0L VIN H, 6.0L VIN Y, 6.0L VIN K, 6.2L VIN W, 6.6L VIN 6 **Transmissions:** All	**Manifold Absolute Pressure (MAP) Sensor Circuit High Voltage** DTCs P1516, P2101, P2125, P2135, P2138, P2176 are not set. The engine has been running for a period of time that is determined by the start-up engine coolant temperature (ECT). The time ranges from 8 seconds at less than −30°C (−22°F) to 3 seconds at greater than 30°C (86°F). The throttle angle is less than 1 percent when the engine speed is less than 1,200 RPM. Or the throttle angle is less than 20 percent when the engine speed is greater than 1,200 RPM. This DTC runs continuously when the above conditions are met. **Possible Causes:** • Intake manifold vacuum leaks • A loose or improperly installed MAP sensor • A restriction in the vacuum source of the MAP sensor • MAP sensor low reference circuit for an open/high resistance • MAP sensor 5-volt reference circuit for a short to ground or an open/high resistance • MAP sensor 5-volt reference circuit for a short to voltage • MAP sensor signal circuit for a short to voltage • MAP sensor signal circuit for a short to ground or an open/high resistance • MAP sensor has failed • ECM has failed
DTC: P0111 **1T CCM, MIL: Yes** **Years:** 2008, 2009 **Models:** Express, G8, Lucerne, Trailblazer **Engines:** 4.6L VIN Y, 4.6L VIN 9, 6.0L VIN H, 6.0L VIN Y, 6.0L VIN K, 6.2L VIN W, 6.6L VIN 6 **Transmissions:** All	**Intake Air Temperature (IAT) Sensor Performance** DTCs P0112, P0113, P0117, P0118, P0128, P0502, P0503, P0601, P1621, P1627, P1680, P1681, P2610 are not set. The vehicle has had a minimum ignition OFF time of 8 hours. The ignition is ON. The start-up IAT is greater than 10°C (50°F). The Fuel Level Sensor parameter is greater than 2.5 percent. This DTC runs once per ignition cycle when the enabling conditions are met. The ECM detects a temperature difference at power-up that indicates that the IAT sensor is 20°C (68°F) greater than the IAT sensor 2. Or. The ECM detects a temperature difference at power-up that indicates that the IAT sensor is 16°C (29°F) greater than the IAT sensor 2, and the time spent cranking the engine is greater than 30 seconds, when the fuel level is greater than 2.5 percent. **Possible Causes:** • MAF/IAT sensor low reference circuit for an open or high resistance. • MAF/IAT sensor low reference circuit for high resistance • MAF/IAT sensor signal circuit open or high resistance on the signal circuit • MAF/IAT sensor has failed • ECM has failed
DTC: P0112 **1T CCM, MIL: Yes** **Years:** 2008, 2009 **Models:** Express, G8, Lucerne, Trailblazer **Engines:** 4.6L VIN Y, 4.6L VIN 9, 6.0L VIN H, 6.0L VIN Y, 6.0L VIN K, 6.2L VIN W, 6.6L VIN 6 **Transmissions:** All	**Intake Air Temperature (IAT) Sensor Circuit Low Voltage** DTCs P0116, P0117, P0118, P0128, P0502, P0503 are not set. The engine is running for greater than 10 seconds. The Engine Coolant Temperature (ECT) is less than 150°C (302°F). This DTC runs continuously when the above conditions are met. The ECM detects that the IAT is greater than 150°C (302°F) for greater than 5 seconds. **Possible Causes:** • MAF/IAT sensor low reference circuit for an open or high resistance. • MAF/IAT sensor low reference circuit for high resistance • MAF/IAT sensor signal circuit open or high resistance on the signal circuit • MAF/IAT sensor has failed • ECM has failed
DTC: P0113 **1T CCM, MIL: Yes** **Years:** 2008, 2009 **Models:** Express, G8, Lucerne, Trailblazer **Engines:** 4.6L VIN Y, 4.6L VIN 9, 6.0L VIN H, 6.0L VIN Y, 6.0L VIN K, 6.2L VIN W, 6.6L VIN 6 **Transmissions:** All	**Intake Air Temperature (IAT) Sensor Circuit High Voltage** DTCs P0101, P0102, P0103, P0116, P0117, P0118, P0128, P0502, P0503 are not set. The engine is running for greater than 10 seconds. The ECT is greater than −40°C (−40°F). The MAF Sensor parameter is greater than 512 g/s. This DTC runs continuously when the above conditions are met. The ECM detects that the IAT is less than −39°C (−38°F) for greater than 5 seconds. **Possible Causes:** • MAF/IAT sensor low reference circuit for an open or high resistance. • MAF/IAT sensor low reference circuit for high resistance • MAF/IAT sensor signal circuit open or high resistance on the signal circuit • MAF/IAT sensor has failed • ECM has failed

DTC	Trouble Code Title, Conditions & Possible Causes
DTC: P0116 **1T CCM, MIL: Yes** **Years:** 2008, 2009 **Models:** Express, G8, Lucerne, Trailblazer **Engines:** 4.6L VIN Y, 4.6L VIN 9, 6.0L VIN H, 6.0L VIN Y, 6.0L VIN K, 6.2L VIN W, 6.6L VIN 6 **Transmissions:** All	**Engine Coolant Temperature (ECT) Sensor Performance** DTCs P0112, P0113, P0117, P0118, P0502, P0503, P0601, P0603, P062F, P2610 are not set. The vehicle has had a minimum ignition OFF time of 10 hours. The ignition is ON. The start-up IAT is greater than −7°C (+19°F) The Fuel Level Sensor parameter is greater than 5 percent. This DTC runs once per ignition cycle when the above conditions are met. The ECM detects a temperature difference at power-up that indicates that the ECT sensor is 30°C (54°F) greater than the IAT sensor.Or. The ECM detects a temperature difference at power-up that indicates that the ECT sensor is 10°C (18°F) greater than the IAT sensor, and the time spent cranking the engine is greater than 10 seconds, when the fuel level is greater than 5 percent.Or. With the power-up IAT greater than −7°C (+19°F), the ECM detects a temperature difference at power-up that indicates that the ECT sensor is 20°C (36°F) greater than the IAT sensor. Then the vehicle must be driven for greater than 6 minutes and 40 seconds at greater than 40 km/h (25 mph). If the IAT sensor then decreases greater than 4°C (7°F), an engine block heater was detected and the test is aborted. If the IAT sensor does not decrease, an engine block heater was not detected and DTC P0116 will set. **Possible Causes:** • ECT sensor low reference circuit for an open/high resistance. • ECT sensor signal circuit for a short to ground • ECT sensor signal circuit for a short to voltage or an open/high resistance • ECT sensor has failed • ECM has failed
DTC: P0117 **1T CCM, MIL: Yes** **Years:** 2008, 2009 **Models:** Express, G8, Lucerne, Trailblazer **Engines:** 4.6L VIN Y, 4.6L VIN 9, 6.0L VIN H, 6.0L VIN Y, 6.0L VIN K, 6.2L VIN W, 6.6L VIN 6 **Transmissions:** All	**Engine Coolant Temperature (ECT) Sensor Circuit Low Voltage** The engine is running for greater than 10 seconds.Or. The ignition is ON when the intake air temperature (IAT) is less than 50°C (122°F). This DTC runs continuously when the above conditions are met. The ECM detects that the ECT is more than 149°C (300°F) for greater than 5 seconds. **Possible Causes:** • ECT sensor low reference circuit for an open/high resistance. • ECT sensor signal circuit for a short to ground • ECT sensor signal circuit for a short to voltage or an open/high resistance • ECT sensor has failed • ECM has failed
DTC: P0118 **1T CCM, MIL: Yes** **Years:** 2008, 2009 **Models:** Express, G8, Lucerne, Trailblazer **Engines:** 4.6L VIN Y, 4.6L VIN 9, 6.0L VIN H, 6.0L VIN Y, 6.0L VIN K, 6.2L VIN W, 6.6L VIN 6 **Transmissions:** All	**Engine Coolant Temperature (ECT) Sensor Circuit High Voltage** The engine is running for greater than 10 seconds. Or. The ignition is ON when the IAT is greater than 0°C (32°F). This DTC runs continuously when the above conditions are met. The ECM detects that the ECT is less than −39°C (−38°F) for greater than 5 seconds. **Possible Causes:** • ECT sensor low reference circuit for an open/high resistance. • ECT sensor signal circuit for a short to ground • ECT sensor signal circuit for a short to voltage or an open/high resistance • ECT sensor has failed • ECM has failed
DTC: P0118 **1T CCM, MIL: Yes** **Models:** Envoy, Equinox, G6, G8, Impala, Lucerne, Malibu, Savana, Trailblazer, Torrent **Engines:** 4.2L VIN S, 4.8L VIN C, 3.5L VIN N, 3.5L VIN K, 3.9L VIN 3, 3.9L VIN M, 3.6L VIN 2, 3.9L VIN 1 **Transmissions:** All	**Engine Coolant Temperature (ECT) Sensor Circuit High Voltage** The engine is running for greater than 10 seconds. Or. The ignition is ON when the IAT is greater than 0°C (30°F). DTC P0118 runs continuously when the above conditions are met. The ECM detects that the ECT is less than −39°C (−40°F) for greater than 5 seconds. **Possible Causes:** • ECT sensor low reference circuit for an open/high resistance. • ECT sensor signal circuit for a short to ground • ECT sensor signal circuit for a short to voltage or an open/high resistance • ECT sensor has failed • ECM has failed
DTC: P0120 **1T CCM, MIL: Yes** **Years:** 2008, 2009 **Models:** Express, G8, Lucerne, Trailblazer **Engines:** 4.6L VIN Y, 4.6L VIN 9, 6.0L VIN H, 6.0L VIN Y, 6.0L VIN K, 6.2L VIN W, 6.6L VIN 6 **Transmissions:** All	**Throttle Position (TP) Sensor 1 Circuit** DTCs P0601, P0602, P0603, P0604, P0606, P0607, P0641, P0651 are not set. The system voltage is more than 5.23 volts. The ignition is in the Unlock/Accessory or Run position. DTC P0120, P0122, P0123, P0220, P0222, P0223 run continuously when the above conditions are met. TP sensor 1 voltage is less than 0.325 volt or more than 4.75 volts for more than 1 second. **Possible Causes:** • TP sensor low reference circuit for an open/high resistance • TP sensor 5-volt reference circuit for a short to ground or an open/high resistance • TP sensor 5-volt reference circuit for a short to voltage • TP sensor signal circuit terminal F for a short to ground • TP sensor 1 signal circuit for a short to ground or an open/high resistance • TP sensor 2 signal circuit for a short to voltage • TP sensor 2 signal circuit for an open/high resistance. • Throttle body has failed • ECM has failed

DTC	Trouble Code Title, Conditions & Possible Causes
DTC: P0121 **1T CCM, MIL: Yes** **Years:** 2008, 2009 **Models:** Express, G8, Lucerne, Trailblazer **Engines:** 4.6L VIN Y, 4.6L VIN 9, 6.0L VIN H, 6.0L VIN Y, 6.0L VIN K, 6.2L VIN W, 6.6L VIN 6 **Transmissions:** All	**Throttle Position (TP) Sensor 1 Performance** DTCs P0102, P0103, P0107, P0108, P0112, P0113, P0116, P0117, P0118, P0128, P0315, P0335, P0336 are not set. The engine speed is more than 450 RPM. DTC P0121 run continuously when the above conditions are met. The predicted air flow and the predicted MAP combined are outside a calibrated range for more than 3 seconds. **Possible Causes:** • Loose or damaged throttle blade • Broken throttle shaft • Any throttle body damage • Throttle body assembly has failed
DTC: P0121 **1T CCM, MIL: Yes** **Models:** Envoy, Equinox, G6, G8, Impala, Lucerne, Malibu, Savana, Trailblazer, Torrent **Engines:** 4.2L VIN S, 4.8L VIN C, 3.5L VIN N, 3.5L VIN K, 3.9L VIN 3, 3.9L VIN M, 3.6L VIN 2, 3.9L VIN 1 **Transmissions:** All	**Throttle Position (TP) Sensor 1 Performance** The engine speed is more than 450 RPM. DTC P0121 run continuously when the above conditions are met. The predicted air flow and the predicted MAP combined are outside a calibrated range for more than 3 seconds. **Possible Causes:** • Loose or damaged throttle blade • Broken throttle shaft • Any throttle body damage • Throttle body assembly has failed
DTC: P0122 **1T CCM, MIL: Yes** **Years:** 2008, 2009 **Models:** Express, G8, Lucerne, Trailblazer **Engines:** 4.6L VIN Y, 4.6L VIN 9, 6.0L VIN H, 6.0L VIN Y, 6.0L VIN K, 6.2L VIN W, 6.6L VIN 6 **Transmissions:** All	**Throttle Position (TP) Sensor 1 Circuit Low Voltage** DTCs P0601, P0602, P0603, P0604, P0606, P0607, P0641, P0651 are not set. The system voltage is more than 5.23 volts. The ignition is in the Unlock/Accessory or Run position. DTC P0120, P0122, P0123, P0220, P0222, P0223 run continuously when the above conditions are met. The ECM detects that the TP sensor 1 voltage is less than 0.325 volt for more than 1 second. **Possible Causes:** • TP sensor low reference circuit for an open/high resistance • TP sensor 5-volt reference circuit for a short to ground or an open/high resistance • TP sensor 5-volt reference circuit for a short to voltage • TP sensor signal circuit terminal F for a short to ground • TP sensor 1 signal circuit for a short to ground or an open/high resistance • TP sensor 2 signal circuit for a short to voltage • TP sensor 2 signal circuit for an open/high resistance. • Throttle body has failed • ECM has failed
DTC: P0123 **1T CCM, MIL: Yes** **Years:** 2008, 2009 **Models:** Express, G8, Lucerne, Trailblazer **Engines:** 4.6L VIN Y, 4.6L VIN 9, 6.0L VIN H, 6.0L VIN Y, 6.0L VIN K, 6.2L VIN W, 6.6L VIN 6 **Transmissions:** All	**Throttle Position (TP) Sensor 1 Circuit High Voltage** DTCs P0601, P0602, P0603, P0604, P0606, P0607, P0641, P0651 are not set. The system voltage is more than 5.23 volts. The ignition is in the Unlock/Accessory or Run position. DTC P0120, P0122, P0123, P0220, P0222, P0223 run continuously when the above conditions are met. The ECM detects that the TP sensor 1 voltage is more than 4.75 volts for more than 1 second. **Possible Causes:** • TP sensor low reference circuit for an open/high resistance • TP sensor 5-volt reference circuit for a short to ground or an open/high resistance • TP sensor 5-volt reference circuit for a short to voltage • TP sensor signal circuit terminal F for a short to ground • TP sensor 1 signal circuit for a short to ground or an open/high resistance • TP sensor 2 signal circuit for a short to voltage • TP sensor 2 signal circuit for an open/high resistance. • Throttle body has failed • ECM has failed
DTC: P0128 **1T CCM, MIL: Yes** **Years:** 2008, 2009 **Models:** Express, G8, Lucerne, Trailblazer **Engines:** 4.6L VIN Y, 4.6L VIN 9, 6.0L VIN H, 6.0L VIN Y, 6.0L VIN K, 6.2L VIN W, 6.6L VIN 6 **Transmissions:** All	**Engine Coolant Temperature (ECT) Below Thermostat Regulating Temperature** DTCs P0101, P0102, P0103, P0106, P0107, P0108, P0112, P0113, P0116, P0117, P0118, P0171, P0172, P0174, P0175, P0502, P0503 are not set. The start-up IAT is more than −7°C (+19°F). The start-up ECT is less than 70°C (158°F), when the IAT is above 10°C (50°F). The start-up ECT is less than 50°C (122°F), when the IAT is below 10°C (50°F). The engine run time is between 90 seconds and 22 minutes. The vehicle has traveled more than 2.4 kilometers (1.5 miles) at greater than 8 km/h (5 mph). The accumulated airflow is between 20-75 g/s, with the minimum average airflow greater than 10 g/s. The fuel ethanol percentage is less than 85 percent. This DTC runs once per ignition cycle within the enabling conditions. The ECM detects that the minimum ECT of 75°C (167°F) has not been met, when the IAT is greater than 10°C (50°F). **Note: A critical analysis of the operation of the thermostat is necessary to properly diagnose these DTCs.** **Possible Causes:** • Open thermostat • ECT sensor low reference circuit for an open/high resistance • ECT sensor signal circuit for a short to voltage or an open/high resistance • ECT sensor signal circuit for a short to ground • ECT sensor has failed • ECM has failed

DTC	Trouble Code Title, Conditions & Possible Causes
DTC: P012B **1T CCM, MIL: Yes** **Years:** 2008, 2009 **Models:** Express, G8, Lucerne, Trailblazer **Engines:** 4.6L VIN Y, 4.6L VIN 9, 6.0L VIN H, 6.0L VIN Y, 6.0L VIN K, 6.2L VIN W, 6.6L VIN 6 **Transmissions:** All	**Supercharger Inlet Pressure Sensor Performance** DTCs P0096, P0097, P0098, P0102, P0103, P0111, P0112, P0113, P0117, P0118, P0120, P0121, P0128, P012C, P012D, P0220, P0401, P0405, P0506, P0507, P1404, P2135 are not set. The engine is running. The engine coolant temperature (ECT) is between −7 to +129°C (+19 to +264°F). The IAT is between −7 to +125°C (+19 to +257°F). The change in the TP is less than 5 percent. The above enabling criteria must be stable for more than 5 seconds. This DTC runs continuously when the above conditions are met. The engine control module (ECM) detects that the actual measured airflow from the MAF, MAP, SC Inlet Pressure and TP sensors is not within a range of the calculated airflow that is derived from the system of models by greater than a calibrated threshold, for greater than 10 seconds. **Possible Causes:** • Restricted or collapsed air intake duct • Misaligned or damaged air intake duct • Any vacuum leak downstream of the MAF/IAT sensor • An intake manifold leak • SCIAP sensorlow reference circuit for an open/high resistance • SCIAP sensorsignal circuit terminal 3 for a short to voltage • SCIAP sensorsignal circuit for a short to ground, open/high resistance • SCIAP sensor has failed • ECM has failed
DTC: P012B **1T CCM, MIL: Yes** **Years:** 2008, 2009 **Models:** Express, G8, Lucerne, Trailblazer **Engines:** 4.6L VIN Y, 4.6L VIN 9, 6.0L VIN H, 6.0L VIN Y, 6.0L VIN K, 6.2L VIN W, 6.6L VIN 6 **Transmissions:** All	**Supercharger Inlet Pressure (SCIP) Sensor Circuit Low Voltage** DTCs P0120, P0121, P0122, P0123, P0220, P0221, P0222, P0223, P0641, or P0651 are not set. The throttle angle is greater than 0 percent when the engine speed is less than 800 RPM. Or. The throttle angle is greater than 12 percent when the engine speed is greater than 800 RPM. This DTC runs continuously when the above enabling conditions are met. The ECM detects that the SCIAP sensor voltage is less than 0.10V for greater than 5 seconds. **Possible Causes:** • SCIAP sensor low reference circuit for an open/high resistance • SCIAP sensor 5V reference circuit for a short to ground or an open/high resistance • SCIAP sensor signal circuit terminal 3 for a short to voltage • SCIAP sensor signal circuit for a short to ground, open/high resistance • SCIAP sensor has failed • ECM has failed
DTC: P012B **1T CCM, MIL: Yes** **Years:** 2008, 2009 **Models:** Express, G8, Lucerne, Trailblazer **Engines:** 4.6L VIN Y, 4.6L VIN 9, 6.0L VIN H, 6.0L VIN Y, 6.0L VIN K, 6.2L VIN W, 6.6L VIN 6 **Transmissions:** All	**Supercharger Inlet Pressure (SCIP) Sensor Circuit High Voltage** DTCs P0120, P0121, P0122, P0123, P0220, P0221, P0222, P0223, P0641, or P0651 are not set. The engine has been running for a period of time that is determined by the start-up Engine Coolant Temperature (ECT). The time ranges from 4 minutes at less than −30°C (−22°F) to 2 seconds at greater than 30°C (86°F). The throttle angle is less than one percent when the engine speed is less than 1,200 RPM.Or. The throttle angle is less than 20 percent when the engine speed is greater than 1,200 RPM. This DTC runs continuously when the above enabling conditions are met. The ECM detects that the SCIAP sensor voltage is more than 4.50V for greater than 5 seconds. **Possible Causes:** • SCIAP sensor low reference circuit for an open/high resistance • SCIAP sensor 5V reference circuit for a short to ground or an open/high resistance • SCIAP sensor signal circuit terminal 3 for a short to voltage • SCIAP sensor signal circuit for a short to ground, open/high resistance • SCIAP sensor has failed • ECM has failed
DTC: P0131 **1T CCM, MIL: Yes** **Years:** 2008, 2009 **Models:** Express, G8, Lucerne, Trailblazer **Engines:** 4.6L VIN Y, 4.6L VIN 9, 6.0L VIN H, 6.0L VIN Y, 6.0L VIN K, 6.2L VIN W, 6.6L VIN 6 **Transmissions:** All	**HO2S Circuit Low Voltage (Bank 1 Sensor 1)** DTCs P0068, P0101, P0102, P0103, P0106, P0107, P0108, P0112, P0113, P0116, P0117, P0118, P0120, P0121, P0122, P0123, P0128, P0201, P0202, P0203, P0204, P0205, P0206, P0207, P0208, P0220, P0222, P0223, P0442, P0443, P0446, P0449, P0455, P0496, P1516, P2101, P2119, P2135, P2176 are not set. The engine is operating in Closed Loop. The Ignition 1 voltage is between 10-18 volts. The fuel level is greater than 10 percent. The throttle position (TP) is between 3-70 percent. The DTCs run continuously when the above conditions are met for 2 seconds. The ECM detects that the HO2S voltage is less than 50 mV. The DTCs set within 100 seconds when the above condition is met. **Possible Causes:** • HO2S low reference circuit for an open/high resistance • HO2S signal circuit for a short to ground • HO2S signal circuit for a short to voltage • HO2S signal circuit for an open/high resistance • HO2S has failed • ECM has failed

DTC	Trouble Code Title, Conditions & Possible Causes
DTC: P0131 **1T CCM, MIL: Yes** **Models:** Envoy, Equinox, G6, G8, Impala, Lucerne, Malibu, Savana, Trailblazer, Torrent **Engines:** 4.2L VIN S, 4.8L VIN C, 3.5L VIN N, 3.5L VIN K, 3.9L VIN 3, 3.9L VIN M, 3.6L VIN 2, 3.9L VIN 1 **Transmissions:** All	**HO2S Circuit Low Voltage (Bank 1 Sensor 1)** The engine is operating in Closed Loop. The Ignition 1 voltage is between 10-18 volts. The fuel level is greater than 10 percent. The TP is between 3-70 percent. The DTCs run continuously when the above conditions are met for 2 seconds. The ECM detects that the HO2S voltage is less than 50 mV. The DTCs set within 100 seconds when the above condition is met. **Possible Causes:** • HO2S low reference circuit for an open/high resistance • HO2S signal circuit for a short to ground • HO2S signal circuit for a short to voltage • HO2S signal circuit for an open/high resistance • HO2S has failed • ECM has failed
DTC: P0132 **1T CCM, MIL: Yes** **Years:** 2008, 2009 **Models:** Express, G8, Lucerne, Trailblazer **Engines:** 4.6L VIN Y, 4.6L VIN 9, 6.0L VIN H, 6.0L VIN Y, 6.0L VIN K, 6.2L VIN W, 6.6L VIN 6 **Transmissions:** All	**HO2S Circuit High Voltage (Bank 1 Sensor 1)** DTCs P0068, P0101, P0102, P0103, P0106, P0107, P0108, P0112, P0113, P0116, P0117, P0118, P0120, P0121, P0122, P0123, P0128, P0201, P0202, P0203, P0204, P0205, P0206, P0207, P0208, P0220, P0222, P0223, P0442, P0443, P0446, P0449, P0455, P0496, P1516, P2101, P2119, P2135, P2176 are not set. The engine is operating in Closed Loop. The Ignition 1 voltage is between 10-18 volts. The fuel level is greater than 10 percent. The throttle position (TP) is between 0-70 percent. The DTCs run continuously when the above conditions are met for 2 seconds. The ECM detects that the HO2S voltage is greater than 1,050 mV. The DTCs set within 15 seconds when the above condition is met. **Possible Causes:** • HO2S low reference circuit for an open/high resistance • HO2S signal circuit for a short to ground • HO2S signal circuit for a short to voltage • HO2S signal circuit for an open/high resistance • HO2S has failed • ECM has failed
DTC: P0132 **1T CCM, MIL: Yes** **Models:** Envoy, Equinox, G6, G8, Impala, Lucerne, Malibu, Savana, Trailblazer, Torrent **Engines:** 4.2L VIN S, 4.8L VIN C, 3.5L VIN N, 3.5L VIN K, 3.9L VIN 3, 3.9L VIN M, 3.6L VIN 2, 3.9L VIN 1 **Transmissions:** All	**HO2S Circuit High Voltage (Bank 1 Sensor 1)** The engine is operating in Closed Loop. The Ignition 1 voltage is between 10-18 volts. The fuel level is greater than 10 percent. The throttle position (TP) is between 0-70 percent. The DTCs run continuously when the above conditions are met for 2 seconds. The ECM detects that the HO2S voltage is greater than 1,050 mV. The DTCs set within 15 seconds when the above condition is met. **Possible Causes:** • HO2S low reference circuit for an open/high resistance • HO2S signal circuit for a short to ground • HO2S signal circuit for a short to voltage • HO2S signal circuit for an open/high resistance • HO2S has failed • ECM has failed
DTC: P0135 **1T CCM, MIL: Yes** **Years:** 2008, 2009 **Models:** Express, G8, Lucerne, Trailblazer **Engines:** 4.6L VIN Y, 4.6L VIN 9, 6.0L VIN H, 6.0L VIN Y, 6.0L VIN K, 6.2L VIN W, 6.6L VIN 6 **Transmissions:** All	**HO2S Heater Performance (Bank 1 Sensor 1)** DTCs P0116, P0117, P0118, P0125, or P0128 are not set. The ignition 1 voltage is between 10-18 volts. The HO2S is at operating temperature. The HO2S is commanded ON. The DTCs run once per drive cycle when the above conditions are met for 120 seconds. The ECM detects that the HO2S 1 heater current is greater than 3.1 amps, or less than 0.3 amps for greater than 8 seconds. **Possible Causes:** • HO2S ignition circuit for a short to ground or an open/high resistance • HO2S control circuit for a short to voltage, or an open/high resistance • HO2S control circuit for a short to ground • HO2S is damaged or it has failed • ECM has failed
DTC: P0135 **1T CCM, MIL: Yes** **Models:** Envoy, Equinox, G6, G8, Impala, Lucerne, Malibu, Savana, Trailblazer, Torrent **Engines:** 4.2L VIN S, 4.8L VIN C, 3.5L VIN N, 3.5L VIN K, 3.9L VIN 3, 3.9L VIN M, 3.6L VIN 2, 3.9L VIN 1 **Transmissions:** All	**HO2S Heater Performance (Bank 1 Sensor 1)** DTCs P0116, P0117, P0118, P0125, or P0128 are not set. The ignition 1 voltage is between 10-18 volts. The HO2S is at operating temperature. The HO2S is commanded ON. The DTCs run once per drive cycle when the above conditions are met for 120 seconds. The ECM detects that the HO2S 1 heater current is greater than 3.1 amps, or less than 0.3 amps for greater than 8 seconds. **Possible Causes:** • HO2S ignition circuit for a short to ground or an open/high resistance • HO2S control circuit for a short to voltage, or an open/high resistance • HO2S control circuit for a short to ground • HO2S is damaged or it has failed • ECM has failed

DTC	Trouble Code Title, Conditions & Possible Causes
DTC: P0137 **1T CCM, MIL: Yes** **Years:** 2008, 2009 **Models:** Express, G8, Lucerne, Trailblazer **Engines:** 4.6L VIN Y, 4.6L VIN 9, 6.0L VIN H, 6.0L VIN Y, 6.0L VIN K, 6.2L VIN W, 6.6L VIN 6 **Transmissions:** All	**HO2S Circuit Low Voltage (Bank 1 Sensor 2)** DTCs P0068, P0101, P0102, P0103, P0106, P0107, P0108, P0112, P0113, P0116, P0117, P0118, P0120, P0121, P0122, P0123, P0128, P0201, P0202, P0203, P0204, P0205, P0206, P0207, P0208, P0220, P0222, P0223, P0442, P0443, P0446, P0449, P0455, P0496, P1516, P2101, P2119, P2135, P2176 are not set. The engine is operating in Closed Loop. The Ignition 1 voltage is between 10-18 volts. The fuel level is greater than 10 percent. The throttle position (TP) is between 3-70 percent. The DTCs run continuously when the above conditions are met for 2 seconds. The ECM detects that the HO2S voltage is less than 50 mV. The DTCs set within 100 seconds when the above condition is met. **Possible Causes:** • HO2S low reference circuit for an open/high resistance • HO2S signal circuit for a short to ground • HO2S signal circuit for a short to voltage • HO2S signal circuit for an open/high resistance • HO2S has failed • ECM has failed
DTC: P0138 **1T CCM, MIL: Yes** **Years:** 2008, 2009 **Models:** Express, G8, Lucerne, Trailblazer **Engines:** 4.6L VIN Y, 4.6L VIN 9, 6.0L VIN H, 6.0L VIN Y, 6.0L VIN K, 6.2L VIN W, 6.6L VIN 6 **Transmissions:** All	**HO2S Circuit High Voltage (Bank 1 Sensor 2)** DTCs P0068, P0101, P0102, P0103, P0106, P0107, P0108, P0112, P0113, P0116, P0117, P0118, P0120, P0121, P0122, P0123, P0128, P0201, P0202, P0203, P0204, P0205, P0206, P0207, P0208, P0220, P0222, P0223, P0442, P0443, P0446, P0449, P0455, P0496, P1516, P2101, P2119, P2135, P2176 are not set. The engine is operating in Closed Loop. The Ignition 1 voltage is between 10-18 volts. The fuel level is greater than 10 percent. The throttle position (TP) is between 0-70 percent. The DTCs run continuously when the above conditions are met for 2 seconds. The ECM detects that the HO2S voltage is greater than 1,050 mV. The DTCs set within 15 seconds when the above condition is met. **Possible Causes:** • HO2S low reference circuit for an open/high resistance • HO2S signal circuit for a short to ground • HO2S signal circuit for a short to voltage • HO2S signal circuit for an open/high resistance • HO2S has failed • ECM has failed
DTC: P0138 **1T CCM, MIL: Yes** **Models:** Envoy, Equinox, G6, G8, Impala, Lucerne, Malibu, Savana, Trailblazer, Torrent **Engines:** 4.2L VIN S, 4.8L VIN C, 3.5L VIN N, 3.5L VIN K, 3.9L VIN 3, 3.9L VIN M, 3.6L VIN 2, 3.9L VIN 1 **Transmissions:** All	**HO2S Circuit High Voltage (Bank 1 Sensor 2)** DTCs P0206, P0207, P0208, P0220, P0222, P0223, P0442, P0443, P0446, P0449, P0455, P0496, P1516, P2101, P2119, P2135, P2176 are not set. The engine is operating in Closed Loop. The Ignition 1 voltage is between 10-18 volts. The fuel level is greater than 10 percent. The Throttle Position (TP) is between 0-70 percent. The DTCs run continuously when the above conditions are met for 2 seconds. The ECM detects that the HO2S voltage is greater than 1,050 mV. The DTCs set within 15 seconds when the above condition is met. **Possible Causes:** • HO2S low reference circuit for an open/high resistance • HO2S signal circuit for a short to ground • HO2S signal circuit for a short to voltage • HO2S signal circuit for an open/high resistance • HO2S has failed • ECM has failed
DTC: P0140 **1T CCM, MIL: Yes** **Years:** 2008, 2009 **Models:** Express, G8, Lucerne, Trailblazer **Engines:** 4.6L VIN Y, 4.6L VIN 9, 6.0L VIN H, 6.0L VIN Y, 6.0L VIN K, 6.2L VIN W, 6.6L VIN 6 **Transmissions:** All	**HO2S Circuit Insufficient Activity (Bank 1 Sensor 2)** DTCs P0068, P0101, P0102, P0103, P0106, P0107, P0108, P0112, P0113, P0116, P0117, P0118, P0120, P0121, P0122, P0123, P0128, P0201, P0202, P0203, P0204, P0205, P0206, P0207, P0208, P0220, P0222, P0223, P0442, P0443, P0446, P0449, P0455, P0496, P1516, P2101, P2119, P2135, P2176 are not set. The Ignition 1 Signal parameter is between 10-18 volts. The Engine Run Time parameter is more than 300 seconds. The Loop Status parameter is closed. DTC P0140 runs once per drive cycle when the above conditions are met. The ECM detects that the HO2S 1 parameter is between 410-490 mV. The TP Indicated Angle parameter changes more than 5 percent 6 times. DTC P0140 sets within 100 seconds when the above conditions are met. **Possible Causes:** • HO2S low reference circuit for an open/high resistance • HO2S signal circuit for a short to ground • HO2S signal circuit for a short to voltage • HO2S signal circuit for an open/high resistance • HO2S has failed • ECM has failed

DTC	Trouble Code Title, Conditions & Possible Causes
DTC: P0140 **1T CCM, MIL: Yes** **Models:** Envoy, Equinox, G6, G8, Impala, Lucerne, Malibu, Savana, Trailblazer, Torrent **Engines:** 4.2L VIN S, 4.8L VIN C, 3.5L VIN N, 3.5L VIN K, 3.9L VIN 3, 3.9L VIN M, 3.6L VIN 2, 3.9L VIN 1 **Transmissions:** All	**HO2S Circuit Insufficient Activity (Bank 1 Sensor 2)** The Ignition 1 Signal parameter is between 10-18 volts. The Engine Run Time parameter is more than 300 seconds. The Loop Status parameter is closed. The ECM detects that the HO2S 1 parameter is between 410-490 mV. The TP Indicated Angle parameter changes more than 5 percent 6 times. DTC P0140 sets within 100 seconds when the above conditions are met. **Possible Causes:** • HO2S low reference circuit for an open/high resistance • HO2S signal circuit for a short to ground • HO2S signal circuit for a short to voltage • HO2S signal circuit for an open/high resistance • HO2S has failed • ECM has failed
DTC: P0141 **1T CCM, MIL: Yes** **Years:** 2008, 2009 **Models:** Express, G8, Lucerne, Trailblazer **Engines:** 4.6L VIN Y, 4.6L VIN 9, 6.0L VIN H, 6.0L VIN Y, 6.0L VIN K, 6.2L VIN W, 6.6L VIN 6 **Transmissions:** All	**HO2S Heater Performance (Bank 1 Sensor 2)** DTCs P0116, P0117, P0118, P0125, or P0128 are not set. The ignition 1 voltage is between 10-18 volts. The HO2S is at operating temperature. The HO2S is commanded ON. The DTCs run once per drive cycle when the above conditions are met for 120 seconds. The ECM detects that the HO2S 2 heater current is greater than 2.9 amps, or less than 0.3 amps for greater than 8 seconds. **Possible Causes:** • HO2S ignition circuit for a short to ground or an open/high resistance • HO2S control circuit for a short to voltage, or an open/high resistance • HO2S control circuit for a short to ground • HO2S is damaged or it has failed • ECM has failed
DTC: P0141 **1T CCM, MIL: Yes** **Models:** Envoy, Equinox, G6, G8, Impala, Lucerne, Malibu, Savana, Trailblazer, Torrent **Engines:** 4.2L VIN S, 4.8L VIN C, 3.5L VIN N, 3.5L VIN K, 3.9L VIN 3, 3.9L VIN M, 3.6L VIN 2, 3.9L VIN 1 **Transmissions:** All	**HO2S Heater Performance (Bank 1 Sensor 2)** DTCs P0125, or P0128 are not set. The ignition 1 voltage is between 10-18 volts. The HO2S is at operating temperature. The HO2S is commanded ON. The ECM detects that the HO2S 2 heater current is greater than 2.9 amps, or less than 0.3 amps for greater than 7 seconds. **Possible Causes:** • HO2S ignition circuit for a short to ground or an open/high resistance • HO2S control circuit for a short to voltage, or an open/high resistance • HO2S control circuit for a short to ground • HO2S is damaged or it has failed • ECM has failed
DTC: P0151 **1T CCM, MIL: Yes** **Years:** 2008, 2009 **Models:** Express, G8, Lucerne, Trailblazer **Engines:** 4.6L VIN Y, 4.6L VIN 9, 6.0L VIN H, 6.0L VIN Y, 6.0L VIN K, 6.2L VIN W, 6.6L VIN 6 **Transmissions:** All	**HO2S Circuit Low Voltage Bank (2 Sensor 1)** DTCs P0068, P0101, P0102, P0103, P0106, P0107, P0108, P0112, P0113, P0116, P0117, P0118, P0120, P0121, P0122, P0123, P0128, P0201, P0202, P0203, P0204, P0205, P0206, P0207, P0208, P0220, P0222, P0223, P0442, P0443, P0446, P0449, P0455, P0496, P1516, P2101, P2119, P2135, P2176 are not set. The engine is operating in Closed Loop. The Ignition 1 voltage is between 10-18 volts. The fuel level is greater than 10 percent. The throttle position (TP) is between 3-70 percent. The DTCs run continuously when the above conditions are met for 2 seconds. The ECM detects that the HO2S voltage is less than 50 mV. The DTCs set within 100 seconds when the above condition is met. **Possible Causes:** • HO2S low reference circuit for an open/high resistance • HO2S signal circuit for a short to ground • HO2S signal circuit for a short to voltage • HO2S signal circuit for an open/high resistance • HO2S has failed • ECM has failed
DTC: P0151 **1T CCM, MIL: Yes** **Models:** Envoy, Equinox, G6, G8, Impala, Lucerne, Malibu, Savana, Trailblazer, Torrent **Engines:** 4.2L VIN S, 4.8L VIN C, 3.5L VIN N, 3.5L VIN K, 3.9L VIN 3, 3.9L VIN M, 3.6L VIN 2, 3.9L VIN 1 **Transmissions:** All	**HO2S Circuit Low Voltage Bank (2 Sensor 1)** DTCs P0206, P0207, P0208, P0220, P0222, P0223, P0442, P0443, P0446, P0449, P0455, P0496, P1516, P2101, P2119, P2135, P2176 are not set. The engine is operating in Closed Loop. The Ignition 1 voltage is between 10-18 volts. The fuel level is greater than 10 percent. The throttle position (TP) is between 3-70 percent. The DTCs run continuously when the above conditions are met for 2 seconds. The ECM detects that the HO2S voltage is less than 50 mV. The DTCs set within 100 seconds when the above condition is met. **Possible Causes:** • HO2S low reference circuit for an open/high resistance • HO2S signal circuit for a short to ground • HO2S signal circuit for a short to voltage • HO2S signal circuit for an open/high resistance • HO2S has failed • ECM has failed

DTC	Trouble Code Title, Conditions & Possible Causes
DTC: P0152 **1T CCM, MIL: Yes** **Years:** 2008, 2009 **Models:** Express, G8, Lucerne, Trailblazer **Engines:** 4.6L VIN Y, 4.6L VIN 9, 6.0L VIN H, 6.0L VIN Y, 6.0L VIN K, 6.2L VIN W, 6.6L VIN 6 **Transmissions:** All	**HO2S Circuit High Voltage (Bank 2 Sensor 1)** DTCs P0068, P0101, P0102, P0103, P0106, P0107, P0108, P0112, P0113, P0116, P0117, P0118, P0120, P0121, P0122, P0123, P0128, P0201, P0202, P0203, P0204, P0205, P0206, P0207, P0208, P0220, P0222, P0223, P0442, P0443, P0446, P0449, P0455, P0496, P1516, P2101, P2119, P2135, P2176 are not set. The engine is operating in Closed Loop. The Ignition 1 voltage is between 10-18 volts. The fuel level is greater than 10 percent. The throttle position (TP) is between 0-70 percent. The DTCs run continuously when the above conditions are met for 2 seconds. The ECM detects that the HO2S voltage is greater than 1,050 mV. The DTCs set within 15 seconds when the above condition is met. **Possible Causes:** • HO2S low reference circuit for an open/high resistance • HO2S signal circuit for a short to ground • HO2S signal circuit for a short to voltage • HO2S signal circuit for an open/high resistance • HO2S has failed • ECM has failed
DTC: P0152 **1T CCM, MIL: Yes** **Models:** Envoy, Equinox, G6, G8, Impala, Lucerne, Malibu, Savana, Trailblazer, Torrent **Engines:** 4.2L VIN S, 4.8L VIN C, 3.5L VIN N, 3.5L VIN K, 3.9L VIN 3, 3.9L VIN M, 3.6L VIN 2, 3.9L VIN 1 **Transmissions:** All	**HO2S Circuit High Voltage (Bank 2 Sensor 1)** DTCs P0068, P0101, P0102, P0103, P0106, P0107, P0108, P0112, P0113, P0116, P0117, P0118, P0120, P0121, P0122, P0123, P0128, P0201, P0202, P0203, P0204, P0205, P0206, P0207, P0208, P0220, P0222, P0223, P0442, P0443, P0446, P0449, P0455, P0496, P1516, P2101, P2119, P2135, P2176 are not set. The engine is operating in Closed Loop. The Ignition 1 voltage is between 10-18 volts. The fuel level is greater than 10 percent. The throttle position (TP) is between 0-70 percent. The DTCs run continuously when the above conditions are met for 2 seconds. The ECM detects that the HO2S voltage is greater than 1,050 mV. The DTCs set within 15 seconds when the above condition is met. **Possible Causes:** • HO2S low reference circuit for an open/high resistance • HO2S signal circuit for a short to ground • HO2S signal circuit for a short to voltage • HO2S signal circuit for an open/high resistance • HO2S has failed • ECM has failed
DTC: P0154 **1T CCM, MIL: Yes** **Years:** 2008, 2009 **Models:** Envoy, Equinox, G6, G8, Impala, Lucerne, Malibu, Savana, Trailblazer, Torrent **Engines:** 4.2L VIN S, 4.8L VIN C, 3.5L VIN N, 3.5L VIN K, 3.9L VIN 3, 3.9L VIN M, 3.6L VIN 2, 3.9L VIN 1 **Transmissions:** All	**HO2S 21 (Bank 2 Sensor 1) Insufficient Activity** DTC P0201, P0202, P0203, P0204, P0205, P0206, P0261, P0262, P0264, P0265, P0267, P0268, P0270, P0271, P0273, P0274, P0276, P0277, P2146, P2149, P2152, P2155, P216A, or P216D is not set. The ignition voltage is greater than 10 volts. The engine speed is greater than 240 RPM. The HO2S 1 heater duty cycle is greater than 90 percent for more than 5 seconds. The HO2S 1 signal voltage is between 400-520 mV, or 400-550 mV when the calculated exhaust temperature is warmer than 800°C (1,472°F). O. the calculated internal resistance of the HO2S 1 is greater than 40,000 ohms when the calculated exhaust temperature is warmer than 600°C (1,112°F). **Possible Causes:** • HO2S damaged or has failed • Low or high fuel system pressure • Engine vacuum leaks • HO2S signal or ground circuit has a high resistance condition • HO2S signal circuit is open or shorted to system power (B+) • HO2S has failed (i.e., it is silicon, water or fuel contaminated) • ECM has failed
DTC: P0154 **1T CCM, MIL: Yes** **Models:** Envoy, Equinox, G6, G8, Impala, Lucerne, Malibu, Savana, Trailblazer, Torrent **Engines:** 4.2L VIN S, 4.8L VIN C, 3.5L VIN N, 3.5L VIN K, 3.9L VIN 3, 3.9L VIN M, 3.6L VIN 2, 3.9L VIN 1 **Transmissions:** All	**Insufficient Activity (Bank 2 Sensor 1)** The ignition voltage is greater than 10 volts. The engine speed is greater than 240 RPM. The HO2S 1 heater duty cycle is greater than 90 percent for more than 5 seconds. The HO2S 1 signal voltage is between 400-520 mV, or 400-550 mV when the calculated exhaust temperature is warmer than 800°C (1,472°F). O. the calculated internal resistance of the HO2S 1 is greater than 40,000 ohms when the calculated exhaust temperature is warmer than 600°C (1,112°F). **Possible Causes:** • HO2S damaged or has failed • Low or high fuel system pressure • Engine vacuum leaks • HO2S signal or ground circuit has a high resistance condition • HO2S signal circuit is open or shorted to system power (B+) • HO2S has failed (i.e., it is silicon, water or fuel contaminated) • ECM has failed

DTC	Trouble Code Title, Conditions & Possible Causes
DTC: P0155 **1T CCM, MIL: Yes** **Years:** 2008, 2009 **Models:** Express, G8, Lucerne, Trailblazer **Engines:** 4.6L VIN Y, 4.6L VIN 9, 6.0L VIN H, 6.0L VIN Y, 6.0L VIN K, 6.2L VIN W, 6.6L VIN 6 **Transmissions:** All	**HO2S Heater Performance (Bank 2 Sensor 1)** DTCs P0116, P0117, P0118, P0125, or P0128 are not set. The ignition 1 voltage is between 10-18 volts. The HO2S is at operating temperature. The HO2S is commanded ON. The DTCs run once per drive cycle when the above conditions are met for 120 seconds. The ECM detects that the HO2S 1 heater current is greater than 3.1 amps, or less than 0.3 amps for greater than 8 seconds. **Possible Causes:** • HO2S ignition circuit for a short to ground or an open/high resistance • HO2S control circuit for a short to voltage, or an open/high resistance • HO2S control circuit for a short to ground • HO2S is damaged or it has failed • ECM has failed
DTC: P0155 **1T CCM, MIL: Yes** **Years:** 2008, 2009 **Models:** Envoy, Equinox, G6, G8, Impala, Lucerne, Malibu, Savana, Trailblazer, Torrent **Engines:** 4.2L VIN S, 4.8L VIN C, 3.5L VIN N, 3.5L VIN K, 3.9L VIN 3, 3.9L VIN M, 3.6L VIN 2, 3.9L VIN 1 **Transmissions:** All	**HO2S Heater Performance (Bank 2 Sensor 1)** The ECM detects that the internal resistance of the HO2S 1 heater is not within the expected range for greater than 12 seconds. The internal HO2S 1 resistance is less than 10,000 ohms. **Possible Causes:** • HO2S heater control circuit is open or it is shorted to ground • HO2S control circuit open or high resistance condition • HO2S signal circuit is open or shorted to system power (B+) • HO2S has failed (i.e., it is silicon, water or fuel contaminated) • ECM has failed
DTC: P0155 **2T O2S HTR, MIL: Yes** **Years:** 2008, 2009 **Models:** Express, G8, Lucerne, Trailblazer **Engines:** 4.6L VIN Y, 4.6L VIN 9, 6.0L VIN H, 6.0L VIN Y, 6.0L VIN K, 6.2L VIN W, 6.6L VIN 6 **Transmissions:** All	**HO2S-21 (Bank 2 Sensor 1) Heater Circuit Malfunction** DTC P0101-P0103, P0106-P0108, P0112, P0113, P0116-P0118, P0120, P0121-P0123, P0169, P0178, P0179, P0200, P0220, P0300, P0442, P0446, P0452, P0453, P0455, P0496, P1125, P1258, P1514, P1515, P1516, P1518, P2108 and P2135 not set, engine speed from 500-3000 RPM for 120 seconds, system voltage at 10-18v, ECT sensor over 122°F, MAF sensor at 3-40 g/sec, Fuel Alcohol content below 90%, and the ECM detected the HO2S heater current was below 0.25 amps or over 3.125 amps (more than 1.375 amps on 4.8L V8). **Possible Causes:** • HO2S heater low control circuit is open or shorted to ground • HO2S heater circuit is open or it is shorted to ground • HO2S heater power circuit is open (test O2A fuse in fuse block) • HO2S heater element is damaged or has failed • ECM has failed
DTC: P0157 **1T CCM, MIL: Yes** **Years:** 2008, 2009 **Models:** Express, G8, Lucerne, Trailblazer **Engines:** 4.6L VIN Y, 4.6L VIN 9, 6.0L VIN H, 6.0L VIN Y, 6.0L VIN K, 6.2L VIN W, 6.6L VIN 6 **Transmissions:** All	**HO2S Circuit Low Voltage (Bank 2 Sensor 2)** DTCs P0068, P0101, P0102, P0103, P0106, P0107, P0108, P0112, P0113, P0116, P0117, P0118, P0120, P0121, P0122, P0123, P0128, P0201, P0202, P0203, P0204, P0205, P0206, P0207, P0208, P0220, P0222, P0223, P0442, P0443, P0446, P0449, P0455, P0496, P1516, P2101, P2119, P2135, P2176 are not set. The engine is operating in Closed Loop. The Ignition 1 voltage is between 10-18 volts. The fuel level is greater than 10 percent. The throttle position (TP) is between 3-70 percent. The DTCs run continuously when the above conditions are met for 2 seconds. The ECM detects that the HO2S voltage is less than 50 mV. The DTCs set within 100 seconds when the above condition is met. **Possible Causes:** • HO2S low reference circuit for an open/high resistance • HO2S signal circuit for a short to ground • HO2S signal circuit for a short to voltage • HO2S signal circuit for an open/high resistance • HO2S has failed • ECM has failed
DTC: P0157 **2T CCM, MIL: Yes** **Years:** 2008, 2009 **Models:** G6, HHR, Malibu **Engines:** 2.0L VIN X, 2.2L VIN D, 2.2L VIN B, 2.2L VIN F, 2.4L VIN B, 2.4L VIN V, 2.4L VIN P, 2.4L VIN 5 **Transmissions:** All	**HO2S-22 (Bank 2 Sensor 2) Circuit Low Input** DTC P0101-P0103, P0106-P0108, P0112, P0113, P0116-P0118, P0120, P0121-P0123, P0169, P0178, P0179, P0200, P0220, P0300, P0442, P0446, P0452-P0496, P1125, P1258, P1514, P1515, P1516, P1518, P2108 and P2135 not set, engine started, engine running in closed loop, system voltage from 10-18v, Fuel Alcohol content less than 90%, fuel level over 10%, TP angle from 3-70% over the idle value, Lean Test enabled, the ECM detected the HO2S signal was below 80 mv for 200 seconds or with engine runtime over 30 seconds, and during the P/E test, the ECM detected the HO2S signal was below 490 mv for 10 seconds. **Possible Causes:** • Air leaks in the exhaust system, intake manifold, vacuum lines • Engine misfire condition present (look for P0300 series codes) • Fuel system too lean (possible low fuel pressure, water in fuel) • HO2S signal circuit is shorted to the sensor or chassis ground • HO2S is damaged (i.e., cracked) or air reference hole clogged • ECM has failed

DTC	Trouble Code Title, Conditions & Possible Causes
DTC: P0157 **1T CCM, MIL: Yes** **Years:** 2008, 2009 **Models:** Envoy, Equinox, G6, G8, Impala, Lucerne, Malibu, Savana, Trailblazer, Torrent **Engines:** 4.2L VIN S, 4.8L VIN C, 3.5L VIN N, 3.5L VIN K, 3.9L VIN 3, 3.9L VIN M, 3.6L VIN 2, 3.9L VIN 1 **Transmissions:** All	**HO2S Circuit Low Voltage (Bank 2 Sensor 2)** DTC P0036, P0037, P0038, P0056, P0057, P0058, P0116, P0117, P0118, P0119, or P0128 is not set, engine startedThe engine coolant temperature is colder than 40°C (104°F) at start-up and the engine coolant temperature was warmer than 60°C (140°F) when the ignition was turned OFF last ignition cycle. The calculated exhaust temperature at the HO2S 2 is warmer than 700°C (1,292°F) and the HO2S 2 is warmed up for greater than 90 seconds. The ECM detects the HO2S 2 signal voltage is less than 60 mV for greater than 1 seconds of for a cumulative of 10 seconds. **Possible Causes:** • Air leaks in the exhaust system, intake manifold, vacuum lines • low reference circuit for an open/high resistance or for a short to voltage • Fuel pressure that is too low or too high • HO2S signal circuit is shorted to the sensor or chassis ground • HO2S is damaged (i.e., cracked) or air reference hole clogged • Lean, rich, or leaking fuel injectors • ECM has failed
DTC: P0158 **1T CCM, MIL: Yes** **Years:** 2008, 2009 **Models:** Express, G8, Lucerne, Trailblazer **Engines:** 4.6L VIN Y, 4.6L VIN 9, 6.0L VIN H, 6.0L VIN Y, 6.0L VIN K, 6.2L VIN W, 6.6L VIN 6 **Transmissions:** All	**HO2S Circuit High Voltage (Bank 2 Sensor 2)** DTCs P0068, P0101, P0102, P0103, P0106, P0107, P0108, P0112, P0113, P0116, P0117, P0118, P0120, P0121, P0122, P0123, P0128, P0201, P0202, P0203, P0204, P0205, P0206, P0207, P0208, P0220, P0222, P0223, P0442, P0443, P0446, P0449, P0455, P0496, P1516, P2101, P2119, P2135, P2176 are not set. The engine is operating in Closed Loop. The Ignition 1 voltage is between 10-18 volts. The fuel level is greater than 10 percent. The throttle position (TP) is between 0-70 percent. The DTCs run continuously when the above conditions are met for 2 seconds. The ECM detects that the HO2S voltage is greater than 1,050 mV. The DTCs set within 15 seconds when the above condition is met. **Possible Causes:** • HO2S low reference circuit for an open/high resistance • HO2S signal circuit for a short to ground • HO2S signal circuit for a short to voltage • HO2S signal circuit for an open/high resistance • HO2S has failed • ECM has failed
DTC: P0158 **1T CCM, MIL: Yes** **Years:** 2008, 2009 **Models:** Envoy, Equinox, G6, G8, Impala, Lucerne, Malibu, Savana, Trailblazer, Torrent **Engines:** 4.2L VIN S, 4.8L VIN C, 3.5L VIN N, 3.5L VIN K, 3.9L VIN 3, 3.9L VIN M, 3.6L VIN 2, 3.9L VIN 1 **Transmissions:** All	**HO2S Circuit High Voltage (Bank 2 Sensor 2)** DTC P0036, P0037, P0038, P0056, P0057, P0058, P0116, P0117, P0118, P0119, or P0128 is not set, engine startedThe engine coolant temperature is colder than 40°C (104°F) at start-up and the engine coolant temperature was warmer than 60°C (140°F) when the ignition was turned OFF last ignition cycle. The calculated exhaust temperature at the HO2S 2 is warmer than 700°C (1,292°F) and the HO2S 2 is warmed up for greater than 90 seconds. The ECM detects the HO2S 2 signal voltage is less than 60 mV for greater than 1 seconds of for a cumulative of 10 seconds. **Possible Causes:** • Fuel system is too rich (fuel pressure too high, fuel pressure regulator leaking, or one or more fuel injectors sticking/leaking) • HO2S element is silicon, water or fuel contaminated • HO2S signal circuit is shorted to system power (B+) • HO2S signal tracking (water intrusion) in the connector causing a short between the HO2S signal and heater power circuits • ECM has failed
DTC: P0158 **2T CCM, MIL: Yes** **Years:** 2008, 2009 **Models:** G6, HHR, Malibu **Engines:** 2.0L VIN X, 2.2L VIN D, 2.2L VIN B, 2.2L VIN F, 2.4L VIN B, 2.4L VIN V, 2.4L VIN P, 2.4L VIN 5 **Transmissions:** All	**HO2S-22 (Bank 2 Sensor 2) Circuit High Input** DTC P0101, P0102, P0103, P0106, P0107, P0108, P0112, P0113, P0116, P0117, P0118, P0120, P0121, P0122, P0123, P0169, P0178, P0179, P0200, P0220, P0300, P0442, P0446, P0452, P0453, P0455, P0496, P1125, P1258, P1514, P1515, P1516, P1518, P2108 and P2135 not set, engine started, engine running in closed loop, system voltage from 10-18v, Fuel Alcohol content less than 90%, fuel level over 10%, TP angle from 3-70% more than the idle value, then during the Rich Test, the ECM detected the HO2S signal was more than 950 mv for 200 seconds or with engine runtime over 30 seconds, and during the Decel Fuel Cutoff test, the ECM detected the HO2S signal was less than 250 mv for 5 seconds. **Possible Causes:** • Fuel system rich (high fuel pressure, fuel pressure regulator leaking, or injector sticking) • HO2S element is silicon, water or fuel contaminated • HO2S signal tracking (water intrusion) in the connector causing a short between the HO2S signal and heater power circuits • ECM has failed

DTC	Trouble Code Title, Conditions & Possible Causes
DTC: P0160 **1T CCM, MIL: Yes** **Years:** 2008, 2009 **Models:** Envoy, Equinox, G6, G8, Impala, Lucerne, Malibu, Savana, Trailblazer, Torrent **Engines:** 4.2L VIN S, 4.8L VIN C, 3.5L VIN N, 3.5L VIN K, 3.9L VIN 3, 3.9L VIN M, 3.6L VIN 2, 3.9L VIN 1 **Transmissions:** All	**HO2S Circuit Insufficient Activity (Bank 2 Sensor 2)** DTC P0036, P0037, P0038, P0056, P0057, P0058, P0116, P0117, P0118, P0119, or P0128 is not set, engine startedThe engine coolant temperature is colder than 40°C (104°F) at start-up and the engine coolant temperature was warmer than 60°C (140°F) when the ignition was turned OFF last ignition cycle. The calculated exhaust temperature at the HO2S 2 is warmer than 700°C (1,292°F) and the HO2S 2 is warmed up for greater than 90 seconds. The ECM detects the HO2S 2 signal voltage is less than 60 mV for greater than 1 seconds of for a cumulative of 10 seconds. **Possible Causes:** • Fuel system is too rich (fuel pressure too high, fuel pressure regulator leaking, or one or more fuel injectors sticking/leaking) • HO2S element is silicon, water or fuel contaminated • HO2S signal circuit is shorted to system power (B+) • HO2S signal tracking (water intrusion) in the connector causing a short between the HO2S signal and heater power circuits • ECM has failed
DTC: P0160 **2T O2S, MIL: Yes** **Years:** 2008, 2009 **Models:** G6, HHR, Malibu **Engines:** 2.0L VIN X, 2.2L VIN D, 2.2L VIN B, 2.2L VIN F, 2.4L VIN B, 2.4L VIN V, 2.4L VIN P, 2.4L VIN 5 **Transmissions:** All	**HO2S-22 (Bank 2 Sensor 2) Insufficient Activity** DTC P0101, P0102, P0103, P0106, P0107, P0108, P0112, P0113, P0116, P0117, P0118, P0120, P0121, P0122, P0123, P0169, P0178, P0179, P0200, P0220, P0300, P0442, P0446, P0452, P0453, P0455, P0496, P1125, P1258, P1514, P1515, P1516, P1518, P2108 and P2135 not set, engine runtime over 300 seconds, system voltage from 10-18v, Fuel Alcohol content less than 90%, then after the TP indicated angle changed more than 5% within one seconds six times on models with a TAC system, the ECM detected the HO2S signal remained between 410-490 mv for 150 seconds. **Possible Causes:** • HO2S heater is damaged or it has failed • HO2S signal or ground circuit has a high resistance condition • HO2S has failed (i.e., it is silicon, water or fuel contaminated) • ECM has failed
DTC: P0161 **1T CCM, MIL: Yes** **Years:** 2008, 2009 **Models:** Express, G8, Lucerne, Trailblazer **Engines:** 4.6L VIN Y, 4.6L VIN 9, 6.0L VIN H, 6.0L VIN Y, 6.0L VIN K, 6.2L VIN W, 6.6L VIN 6 **Transmissions:** All	**HO2S Heater Performance (Bank 2 Sensor 2)** DTCs P0116, P0117, P0118, P0125, or P0128 are not set. The ignition 1 voltage is between 10-18 volts. The HO2S is at operating temperature. The HO2S is commanded ON. The DTCs run once per drive cycle when the above conditions are met for 120 seconds. The ECM detects that the HO2S 2 heater current is greater than 2.9 amps, or less than 0.3 amps for greater than 8 seconds. **Possible Causes:** • HO2S ignition circuit for a short to ground or an open/high resistance • HO2S control circuit for a short to voltage, or an open/high resistance • HO2S control circuit for a short to ground • HO2S is damaged or it has failed • ECM has failed
DTC: P0161 **1T CCM, MIL: Yes** **Years:** 2008, 2009 **Models:** Envoy, Equinox, G6, G8, Impala, Lucerne, Malibu, Savana, Trailblazer, Torrent **Engines:** 4.2L VIN S, 4.8L VIN C, 3.5L VIN N, 3.5L VIN K, 3.9L VIN 3, 3.9L VIN M, 3.6L VIN 2, 3.9L VIN 1 **Transmissions:** All	**HO2S Heater Performance (Bank 2 Sensor 2)** The ECM detects that the internal resistance of the HO2S 1 heater is not within the expected range for greater than 12 seconds. The internal HO2S 1 resistance is less than 10,000 ohms. **Possible Causes:** • HO2S heater control circuit is open or it is shorted to ground • HO2S control circuit open or high resistance condition • HO2S signal circuit is open or shorted to system power (B+) • HO2S has failed (i.e., it is silicon, water or fuel contaminated) • ECM has failed
DTC: P0161 **2T O2S HTR, MIL: Yes** **Years:** 2008, 2009 **Models:** G6, HHR, Malibu **Engines:** 2.0L VIN X, 2.2L VIN D, 2.2L VIN B, 2.2L VIN F, 2.4L VIN B, 2.4L VIN V, 2.4L VIN P, 2.4L VIN 5 **Transmissions:** All	**HO2S-22 (Bank 2 Sensor 2) Heater Circuit Malfunction** DTC P0101, P0102, P0103, P0106, P0107, P0108, P0112, P0113, P0116, P0117, P0118, P0120, P0121, P0122, P0123, P0169, P0178, P0179, P0200, P0220, P0300, P0442, P0446, P0452, P0453, P0455, P0496, P1125, P1258, P1514, P1515, P1516, P1518, P2108 and P2135 not set, engine runtime 2 minutes, engine speed from 500-3000 RPM, system voltage from 10-18v, ECT sensor more than 122°F, MAF sensor from 3-40 g/sec, Fuel Alcohol content less than 90%, and the ECM detected the HO2S heater current was less than 0.25 amps, or over 3.125 amps (over 1.375 amps on 4.8L). **Possible Causes:** • HO2S heater low control circuit is open or shorted to ground • HO2S heater circuit is open or it is shorted to ground • HO2S heater power circuit is open (test O2A fuse in fuse block) • HO2S heater element is damaged or has failed • ECM has failed

DTC	Trouble Code Title, Conditions & Possible Causes
DTC: P0167D **1T CCM, MIL: Yes** **Years:** 2008, 2009 **Models:** Envoy, Equinox, G6, G8, Impala, Lucerne, Malibu, Savana, Trailblazer, Torrent **Engines:** 4.2L VIN S, 4.8L VIN C, 3.5L VIN N, 3.5L VIN K, 3.9L VIN 3, 3.9L VIN M, 3.6L VIN 2, 3.9L VIN 1 **Transmissions:** All	**Control Module Ignition Coil Internal Circuit** The ECM detects a condition with the integrated circuits of the fuel injector driver module for greater than 4 seconds, or a cumulative of 30 seconds. **Possible Causes:** • The ECM must be replaced to correct this problem. A new ECM must be programmed with the correct software/calibration.
DTC: P0171 **1T CCM, MIL: Yes** **Years:** 2008, 2009 **Models:** Express, G8, Lucerne, Trailblazer **Engines:** 4.6L VIN Y, 4.6L VIN 9, 6.0L VIN H, 6.0L VIN Y, 6.0L VIN K, 6.2L VIN W, 6.6L VIN 6 **Transmissions:** All	**Fuel Trim System Lean (Bank 1)** DTCs P0050, P0056, P0059, P0060, P0068, P0101, P0102, P0103, P0107, P0108, P0112, P0113, P0120, P0122, P0123, P0128, P0151, P0152, P0153, P0154, P0155, P0157, P0158, P0160, P0201-P0208, P0220, P0222, P0223, P0300, P0301-P0308, P0442, P0443, P0446, P0449, P0451, P0452, P0453, P0454, P0455, P0496, P0506, P0507, P1153, P1516, P2101, P2119, P2120, P2125, P2135, P2138, P2A03, P2A04 are not set. The engine is in Closed Loop status. The Fuel Trim Learn is enabled. The Engine Coolant Temperature (ECT) is between −40 and +150°C (−40 and +302°F). The Intake Air Temperature (IAT) is between −40 and +150°C (−40 and +302°F). The Manifold absolute Pressure (MAP) is between 5-255 kPa (0.7-36.9 psi). The vehicle speed is less than 134 km/h (83 mph). The engine speed is between 400-6,000 RPM. The Mass Air Flow (MAF) is between 0.5-510 g/s. The Barometric Pressure (BARO) is more than 70 kPa (10.1 psi). The fuel level is more than 10 percent. This diagnostic runs continuously when the above conditions have been met. **Possible Causes:** • Malfunctioning MAF • Low fuel pressure • Fuel contamination • Malfunctioning fuel injectors • Leaking exhaust components from the HO2S forward • Vacuum leaks at the intake manifold, the throttle body, and the injector O-rings • Air induction system and the air intake ducts for leaks or for a missing air filter element • Cracked or damaged EVAP canister • Crankcase ventilation system for leaks • HO2S signal circuit open, shorted to ground, or shorted to the low reference circuit • HO2S sensor 1 low signal circuit for an open circuit or high resistance • HO2S has failed • ECM has failed
DTC: P0171 **1T CCM, MIL: Yes** **Years:** 2008, 2009 **Models:** Envoy, Equinox, Savana, Torrent **Engines:** 3.4L VIN F, 4.3L VIN X, 5.3L VIN M **Transmissions:** All	**Fuel Trim System Lean** DTCs P0030, P0036, P0068, P0101, P0102, P0103, P0106, P0107, P0108, P0117, P0118, P0120, P0121, P0128, P0130, P0131, P0132, P0133, P0134, P0135, P0137, P0138, P0140, P0141, P0201-P0208, P0220, P0300, P0301-P0308, P0442, P0443, P0446, P0449, P0452, P0453, P0455, P0496, P1106, P1107, P1114, P1115, P1133, P1153, P1516, P2101, P2119, P2120, P2125, P2135, P2138, P2176 are not set. The engine is in Closed Loop status. The Engine Coolant Temperature (ECT) is between −40 and +150°C (−40 and +302°F). The Intake Air Temperature (IAT) is between −20 and +150°C (−4 and +302°F). The Manifold Absolute Pressure (MAP) is between 10-255 kPa (1.45-37 psi). The vehicle speed is less than 134 km/h (83 mph). The engine speed is between 375-7,000 RPM. The Mass Air Flow (MAF) is between 1-510 g/s. The Barometric Pressure (BARO) is more than 70 kPa (10.2 psi). The fuel level is more than 10 percent. This diagnostic runs continuously when the above conditions have been met. The average long term FT weighted average value is more or less than a calibrated value. The above condition is present for approximately 3 minutes after the conditions for running the DTC have been met. **Possible Causes:** • Low fuel pressure • Fuel contamination • Malfunctioning fuel injectors • Missing, loose, or leaking exhaust components from the HO2S forward • Vacuum leaks at the intake manifold, the throttle body, and the injector O-rings • Air induction system and the air intake ducts for leaks or for a missing air filter element • Cracked EVAP canister • Crankcase ventilation system for leaks • The HO2S signal circuit open, shorted to ground, or shorted to the low reference circuit • HO2S for improper installation and for electrical wires or connectors that may have contacted the exhaust system • Malfunctioning engine components • HO2S sensor has failed • MAP sensor • MAF sensor

DTC	Trouble Code Title, Conditions & Possible Causes
DTC: P0171 **2T FUEL, MIL: Yes** **Years:** 2008, 2009 . **Models:** G6, HHR, Malibu **Engines:** 2.0L VIN X, 2.2L VIN D, 2.2L VIN B, 2.2L VIN F, 2.4L VIN B, 2.4L VIN V, 2.4L VIN P, 2.4L VIN 5 **Transmissions:** All	**Fuel Trim System Lean (Bank 1)** DTC P0101-P0103, P0108, P0135, P0137, P0141, P0200, P0300, P0410, P0420, P0430, P0440, P0442, P0443, P0446, P0449, P0506, P0507 and P1441 not set, engine started, ECT sensor from 167-239°F, IAT sensor from 4-194°F, engine speed from 400-3000 RPM, BARO sensor over 74 kPa, MAF sensor from 5-90 gm/s, TP angle less than 90%, VSS less than 85 MPH, and the ECM detected the Long Term fuel trim value was more than 23% for 6 seconds (i.e., indicating that a lean A/F mixture was present). **Possible Causes:** • Air leaks in intake manifold, exhaust pipes or exhaust manifold • Fuel control sensor is out of calibration (ECT, IAT or MAF) • Low fuel pressure (fuel filter clogged, pressure regulator failure) • One or more injectors restricted or pressure regulator has failed • HO2S element is contaminated, deteriorated or has failed • Vacuum hose is disconnected, broken, leaking or loose
DTC: P0172 **1T CCM, MIL: Yes** **Years:** 2008, 2009 **Models:** Express, G8, Lucerne, Trailblazer **Engines:** 4.6L VIN Y, 4.6L VIN 9, 6.0L VIN H, 6.0L VIN Y, 6.0L VIN K, 6.2L VIN W, 6.6L VIN 6 **Transmissions:** All	**Fuel Trim System Rich (Bank 1)** DTCs P0050, P0056, P0059, P0060, P0068, P0101, P0102, P0103, P0107, P0108, P0112, P0113, P0120, P0122, P0123, P0128, P0151, P0152, P0153, P0154, P0155, P0157, P0158, P0160, P0201-P0208, P0220, P0222, P0223, P0300, P0301-P0308, P0442, P0443, P0446, P0449, P0451, P0452, P0453, P0454, P0455, P0496, P0506, P0507, P1153, P1516, P2101, P2119, P2120, P2125, P2135, P2138, P2A03, P2A04 are not set. The engine is in Closed Loop status. The Fuel Trim Learn is enabled. The Engine Coolant Temperature (ECT) is between −40 and +150°C (−40 and +302°F). The Intake Air Temperature (IAT) is between −40 and +150°C (−40 and +302°F). The Manifold absolute Pressure (MAP) is between 5-255 kPa (0.7-36.9 psi). The vehicle speed is less than 134 km/h (83 mph). The engine speed is between 400-6,000 RPM. The Mass Air Flow (MAF) is between 0.5-510 g/s. The Barometric Pressure (BARO) is more than 70 kPa (10.1 psi). The fuel level is more than 10 percent. This diagnostic runs continuously when the above conditions have been met. **Possible Causes:** • Malfunctioning MAF • Excessive fuel pressure • Fuel contamination • Malfunctioning fuel injectors • Vacuum hoses for splits, kinks, and improper connections • Air duct for being collapsed or restricted element • Objects blocking the throttle body • Excessive fuel in the crankcase • Evaporative emissions control system for improper operation • HO2S signal circuit open, shorted to ground, or shorted to the low reference circuit • HO2S sensor 1 low signal circuit for an open circuit or high resistance • HO2S has failed • ECM has failed
DTC: P0172 **1T CCM, MIL: Yes** **Years:** 2008, 2009 **Models:** Envoy, Equinox, Savana, Torrent **Engines:** 3.4L VIN F, 4.3L VIN X, 5.3L VIN M **Transmissions:** All	**Fuel Trim System Rich** DTCs P0030, P0036, P0068, P0101, P0102, P0103, P0106, P0107, P0108, P0117, P0118, P0120, P0121, P0128, P0130, P0131, P0132, P0133, P0134, P0135, P0137, P0138, P0140, P0141, P0201-P0208, P0220, P0300, P0301-P0308, P0442, P0443, P0446, P0449, P0452, P0453, P0455, P0496, P1106, P1107, P1114, P1115, P1133, P1153, P1516, P2101, P2119, P2120, P2125, P2135, P2138, P2176 are not set. The engine is in Closed Loop status. The Engine Coolant Temperature (ECT) is between −40 and +150°C (−40 and +302°F). The Intake Air Temperature (IAT) is between −20 and +150°C (−4 and +302°F). The Manifold Absolute Pressure (MAP) is between 10-255 kPa (1.45-37 psi). The vehicle speed is less than 134 km/h (83 mph). The engine speed is between 375-7,000 RPM. The Mass Air Flow (MAF) is between 1-510 g/s. The Barometric Pressure (BARO) is more than 70 kPa (10.2 psi). The fuel level is more than 10 percent. This diagnostic runs continuously when the above conditions have been met. The average long term FT weighted average value is more or less than a calibrated value. The above condition is present for approximately 3 minutes after the conditions for running the DTC have been met. **Possible Causes:** • Vacuum hoses for splits, kinks, and improper connections • Air intake duct for being collapsed or restricted • Air filter for being dirty or restricted • Objects blocking the throttle body • Excessive fuel in the crankcase due to leaking fuel injectors • evaporative emissions control system for improper operation • Excessive fuel pressure– • Malfunctioning fuel injectors • Fuel contamination • The HO2S for improper installation and for electrical wires or connectors that may have contacted the exhaust system • HO2S signal circuit shorted to voltage • HO2S sensor has failed • MAP sensor • MAF sensor

DTC	Trouble Code Title, Conditions & Possible Causes
DTC: P0172 **1T CCM, MIL: Yes** **Years:** 2008, 2009 **Models:** G6, HHR, Malibu **Engines:** 2.0L VIN X, 2.2L VIN D, 2.2L VIN B, 2.2L VIN F, 2.4L VIN B, 2.4L VIN V, 2.4L VIN P, 2.4L VIN 5 **Transmissions:** All	**Fuel Trim System Rich** DTCs P0030, P0031, P0032, P0068, P0071, P0072, P0073, P0074, P009A, P0101, P0102, P0103, P0111, P0112, P0113, P0114, P0116, P0117, P0118, P0119, P0122, P0123, P0130, P0131, P0132, P0133, P0134, P0135, P0201, P0202, P0203, P0204, P0222, P0223, P0261, P0262, P0264, P0265, P0267, P0268, P0270, P0271, P0301, P0302, P0303, P0304, P0335, P0336, P0340, P0341, P0365, P0366, P0443, P0458, P0459, P0496, P1101, P2227, P2228, P2229, P2297, P2A00 are not set. The engine is in CL status. The engine coolant temperature (ECT) is warmer than 65.3°C (149.5°F). The intake air temperature (IAT) is warmer than −9.8°C (+14.4°F). The engine speed is greater than 608 RPM. The mass air flow (MAF) is within a calibrated range. The barometric pressure (BARO) is more than 70 kPa. The long term FT weighted average value is more or less than a calibrated value. The above condition is present for approximately 3 minutes after the conditions for running the DTC have been met. **Possible Causes** • Base engine "mechanical" fault affecting one or more cylinders • EVAP system component has failed or canister fuel saturated • Fuel control sensor is out of calibration (i.e., ECT, IAT or MAP) • Fuel system supplying too much fuel at idle speed or at cruise • Fuel injector(s) is leaking or stuck partially open (one or more) • HO2S is contaminated, deteriorated or it has failed
DTC: P0172 **2T FUEL, MIL: Yes** **Years:** 2008, 2009 **Models:** G6, HHR, Malibu **Engines:** 2.0L VIN X, 2.2L VIN D, 2.2L VIN B, 2.2L VIN F, 2.4L VIN B, 2.4L VIN V, 2.4L VIN P, 2.4L VIN 5 **Transmissions:** All	**Fuel Trim System Rich (Bank 1)** DTC P0101-P0103, P0108, P0135, P0137, P0141, P0200, P0300, P0410, P0420, P0430, P0440, P0442, P0443, P0446, P0449, P0506, P0507 and P1441 not set, engine started, ECT sensor from 167-239°F, IAT sensor from 4-194°F, engine speed from 400-3000 RPM, BARO sensor over 74 kPa, MAF sensor from 5-90 gm/s, TP angle less than 90%, VSS less than 85 MPH, and the ECM detected the Long Term fuel trim value was less than −13% for 6 seconds (i.e., indicating that a rich A/F mixture was present). **Possible Causes:** • Base engine "mechanical" fault affecting one or more cylinders • Excess fuel vapors in crankcase (the oil needs to be changed) • EVAP system component has failed or canister fuel saturated • Fuel control sensor is out of calibration (i.e., ECT, IAT or MAF) • Fuel delivery system supplying too much fuel during cruise or idle periods (e.g., faulty fuel pump, or faulty pressure regulator) • Fuel injector(s) is leaking or stuck partially open (one or more) • HO2S is contaminated, deteriorated or it has failed
DTC: P0174 **1T CCM, MIL: Yes** **Years:** 2008, 2009 **Models:** Express, G8, Lucerne, Trailblazer **Engines:** 4.6L VIN Y, 4.6L VIN 9, 6.0L VIN H, 6.0L VIN Y, 6.0L VIN K, 6.2L VIN W, 6.6L VIN 6 **Transmissions:** All	**Fuel Trim System Lean (Bank 2)** DTCs P0050, P0056, P0059, P0060, P0068, P0101, P0102, P0103, P0107, P0108, P0112, P0113, P0120, P0122, P0123, P0128, P0151, P0152, P0153, P0154, P0155, P0157, P0158, P0160, P0201-P0208, P0220, P0222, P0223, P0300, P0301-P0308, P0442, P0443, P0446, P0449, P0451, P0452, P0453, P0454, P0455, P0496, P0506, P0507, P1153, P1516, P2101, P2119, P2120, P2125, P2135, P2138, P2A03, P2A04 are not set. The engine is in Closed Loop status. The Fuel Trim Learn is enabled. The Engine Coolant Temperature (ECT) is between −40 and +150°C (−40 and +302°F). The Intake Air Temperature (IAT) is between −40 and +150°C (−40 and +302°F). The Manifold absolute Pressure (MAP) is between 5-255 kPa (0.7-36.9 psi). The vehicle speed is less than 134 km/h (83 mph). The engine speed is between 400-6,000 RPM. The Mass Air Flow (MAF) is between 0.5-510 g/s. The Barometric Pressure (BARO) is more than 70 kPa (10.1 psi). The fuel level is more than 10 percent. This diagnostic runs continuously when the above conditions have been met. **Possible Causes:** • Malfunctioning MAF • Low fuel pressure • Fuel contamination • Malfunctioning fuel injectors • Leaking exhaust components from the HO2S forward • Vacuum leaks at the intake manifold, the throttle body, and the injector O-rings • Air induction system and the air intake ducts for leaks or for a missing air filter element • Cracked or damaged EVAP canister • Crankcase ventilation system for leaks • HO2S signal circuit open, shorted to ground, or shorted to the low reference circuit • HO2S sensor 1 low signal circuit for an open circuit or high resistance • HO2S has failed • ECM has failed

DTC	Trouble Code Title, Conditions & Possible Causes
DTC: P0174 **2T FUEL, MIL: Yes** **Years:** 2008, 2009 **Models:** Express, G8, Lucerne, Trailblazer **Engines:** 4.6L VIN Y, 4.6L VIN 9, 6.0L VIN H, 6.0L VIN Y, 6.0L VIN K, 6.2L VIN W, 6.6L VIN 6 **Transmissions:** All	**Fuel Trim System Lean (Bank 2)** DTC P0101-P0103, P0108, P0135, P0137, P0141, P0200, P0300, P0410, P0420, P0430, P0440, P0442, P0443, P0446, P0449, P0506, P0507 and P1441 not set, engine started, ECT sensor from 167-239°F, IAT sensor from 4-194°F, engine speed from 400-3000 RPM, BARO sensor over 74 kPa, MAF sensor from 5-90 gm/s, TP angle less than 90%, VSS less than 85 MPH, and the ECM detected the Long Term fuel trim value was more than 23% for 6 seconds (i.e., indicating that a lean A/F mixture was present). **Possible Causes:** • Air leaks in intake manifold, exhaust pipes or exhaust manifold • Fuel control sensor is out of calibration (ECT, IAT or MAF) • Low fuel pressure (fuel filter clogged, pressure regulator failure) • One or more injectors restricted or pressure regulator has failed • HO2S element is contaminated, deteriorated or has failed • Vacuum hose is disconnected, broken, leaking or loose
DTC: P0175 **1T CCM, MIL: Yes** **Years:** 2008, 2009 **Models:** Express, G8, Lucerne, Trailblazer **Engines:** 4.6L VIN Y, 4.6L VIN 9, 6.0L VIN H, 6.0L VIN Y, 6.0L VIN K, 6.2L VIN W, 6.6L VIN 6 **Transmissions:** All	**Fuel Trim System Rich (Bank 2)** DTCs P0050, P0056, P0059, P0060, P0068, P0101, P0102, P0103, P0107, P0108, P0112, P0113, P0120, P0122, P0123, P0128, P0151, P0152, P0153, P0154, P0155, P0157, P0158, P0160, P0201-P0208, P0220, P0222, P0223, P0300, P0301-P0308, P0442, P0443, P0446, P0449, P0451, P0452, P0453, P0454, P0455, P0496, P0506, P0507, P1153, P1516, P2101, P2119, P2120, P2125, P2135, P2138, P2A03, P2A04 are not set. The engine is in Closed Loop status. The Fuel Trim Learn is enabled. The Engine Coolant Temperature (ECT) is between −40 and +150°C (−40 and +302°F). The Intake Air Temperature (IAT) is between −40 and +150°C (−40 and +302°F). The Manifold absolute Pressure (MAP) is between 5-255 kPa (0.7-36.9 psi). The vehicle speed is less than 134 km/h (83 mph). The engine speed is between 400-6,000 RPM. The Mass Air Flow (MAF) is between 0.5-510 g/s. The Barometric Pressure (BARO) is more than 70 kPa (10.1 psi). The fuel level is more than 10 percent. This diagnostic runs continuously when the above conditions have been met. **Possible Causes:** • Malfunctioning MAF • Excessive fuel pressure • Fuel contamination • Malfunctioning fuel injectors • Vacuum hoses for splits, kinks, and improper connections • Air duct for being collapsed or restricted element • Objects blocking the throttle body • Excessive fuel in the crankcase • Evaporative emissions control system for improper operation • HO2S signal circuit open, shorted to ground, or shorted to the low reference circuit • HO2S sensor 1 low signal circuit for an open circuit or high resistance • HO2S has failed • ECM has failed
DTC: P0175 **2T FUEL, MIL: Yes** **Years:** 2008, 2009 **Models:** Express, G8, Lucerne, Trailblazer **Engines:** 4.6L VIN Y, 4.6L VIN 9, 6.0L VIN H, 6.0L VIN Y, 6.0L VIN K, 6.2L VIN W, 6.6L VIN 6 **Transmissions:** All	**Fuel Trim System Rich (Bank 2)** DTC P0101-P0103, P0108, P0135, P0137, P0141, P0200, P0300, P0410, P0420, P0430, P0440, P0442, P0443, P0446, P0449, P0506, P0507 and P1441 not set, engine speed from 400-3000 RPM, ECT sensor from 167-239°F, IAT sensor from 4-194°F, BARO sensor over 74 kPa, MAF sensor from 5-90 gm/s, TP angle under 90%, VSS below 85 MPH, and the ECM detected the LT fuel trim was less than −13% for 6 seconds (i.e., a possible rich A/F mixture). **Possible Causes:** • Air leaks in intake manifold, exhaust pipes or exhaust manifold • Fuel control sensor is out of calibration (ECT, IAT or MAF) • Low fuel pressure (fuel filter clogged, pressure regulator failure) • One or more injectors restricted or pressure regulator has failed • HO2S element is contaminated, deteriorated or has failed • Vacuum hose is disconnected, broken, leaking or loose
DTC: P0191 **1T CCM, MIL: Yes** **Years:** 2008, 2009 **Models:** Express, G8, Lucerne, Trailblazer **Engines:** 4.6L VIN Y, 4.6L VIN 9, 6.0L VIN H, 6.0L VIN Y, 6.0L VIN K, 6.2L VIN W, 6.6L VIN 6 **Transmissions:** All	**Fuel Rail Pressure (FRP) Sensor Performance** The engine is running. DTC P0192, P0193, or P1255 are not active. DTC P0641 has not failed this ignition cycle. Fuel pump control is enabled and the fuel pump control state is normal. The engine has been running for at least 5 seconds. The FPCM does not detect a change in the fuel rail pressure of at least 30 kPa (4.4 psi). **Note: Verify that the fuel tank is not empty. Only perform this diagnostic if there is at least 2 gallons of fuel in the fuel tank. Clear the DTC, and start and run the engine. Verify that the DTC P0191 resets before proceeding with the circuit system testing. If the DTC does not reset, refer to diagnostic aids.** **Possible Causes:** • FRP sensor low reference circuit for an open/high resistance • FRP sensor 5-V reference circuit for a short to ground or an open/high resistance • FRP sensor 5-V reference circuit for a short to voltage • FRP sensor signal circuit for a short to ground or an open/high resistance • Fuel pump flow control module has failed • Fuel pressure sensor has failed

DTC	Trouble Code Title, Conditions & Possible Causes
DTC: P0191 **1T CCM, MIL: Yes** **Years:** 2008, 2009 **Models:** Envoy, Equinox, G6, G8, Impala, Lucerne, Malibu, Savana, Trailblazer, Torrent **Engines:** 4.2L VIN S, 4.8L VIN C, 3.5L VIN N, 3.5L VIN K, 3.9L VIN 3, 3.9L VIN M, 3.6L VIN 2, 3.9L VIN 1 **Transmissions:** All	**Fuel Rail Pressure (FRP) Sensor Performance** DTC P0087, P2187, or P2188 is set, and the fuel pressure at ignition ON is less than 120 kPa (17.4 psi) for greater than 4 seconds or for a cumulative of 30 seconds. Or DTC P0088, P2177, or P2187 is set, and the fuel pressure at ignition ON is greater than 1500 kPa (218 psi) for greater than 4 seconds or for a cumulative of 30 seconds. Or the fuel pressure at ignition ON is greater than 1500 kPa (218 psi) and a fuel pressure increase of greater than 385 kPa (56 psi) occurs during the fuel pump prime. The condition exists for greater than 4 seconds or for a cumulative of 30 seconds. **Possible Causes:** • (A condition with the fuel tank module or the fuel pump control module (FECM) will set this DTC) • low reference circuit for an open/high resistance • 5-volt reference circuit for a short to ground or an open/high resistance • 5-volt reference circuit for a short to voltage • signal circuit terminal 12 for a short to ground • FRP sensor is damaged or it has failed • ECM has failed
DTC: P0192 **1T CCM, MIL: Yes** **Years:** 2008, 2009 **Models:** Express, G8, Lucerne, Trailblazer **Engines:** 4.6L VIN Y, 4.6L VIN 9, 6.0L VIN H, 6.0L VIN Y, 6.0L VIN K, 6.2L VIN W, 6.6L VIN 6 **Transmissions:** All	**Fuel Rail Pressure (FRP) Sensor Circuit Low Voltage** The ignition is on. The FPCM detects that the Fuel Rail Pressure (FRP) sensor signal circuit is above 4.9 V or below 0.1 V. **Note: Using the Failure Records data may help locate an intermittent condition. If you cannot duplicate the DTC, the information in the Failure Records can help determine how many miles since the DTC set. The Fail Counter and Pass Counter can help determine how many ignition cycles that the diagnostic test reported a pass and/or a fail.** **Possible Causes:** • FRP sensor low reference circuit for an open/high resistance • FRP sensor 5-V reference circuit for a short to ground or an open/high resistance • FRP sensor 5-V reference circuit for a short to voltage • FRP sensor signal circuit for a short to ground or an open/high resistance • Fuel pump flow control module has failed • Fuel pressure sensor has failed
DTC: P0192 **1T CCM, MIL: Yes** **Years:** 2008, 2009 **Models:** Envoy, Equinox, G6, G8, Impala, Lucerne, Malibu, Savana, Trailblazer, Torrent **Engines:** 4.2L VIN S, 4.8L VIN C, 3.5L VIN N, 3.5L VIN K, 3.9L VIN 3, 3.9L VIN M, 3.6L VIN 2, 3.9L VIN 1 **Transmissions:** All	**Fuel Rail Pressure (FRP) Sensor Circuit Low Voltage** Key on or engine running; and the ECM detected the FRP sensor was less than 0.45v for 5 seconds. The fuel rail pressure (FRP) sensor is a pressure sensor. The fuel injector control module (FICM) supplies 5v on the FRP sensor reference voltage circuit. The FICM also supplies a ground circuit and a signal circuit to the FRP sensor. When the fuel rail pressure is normal, the FRP signal voltage rises to near 2.5v. If the fuel rail pressure increases, the FRP signal voltage increases. The FICM monitors the FRP sensor and communicates the data to the ECM by a dedicated pulse width modulated (PWM) circuit. **Possible Causes:** • FRP sensor 5-volt power circuit is open or shorted to ground • FRP Sensor signal circuit is shorted to ground • FRP Sensor is damaged or has failed • ECM has failed
DTC: P0193 **1T CCM, MIL: Yes** **Years:** 2008, 2009 **Models:** Express, G8, Lucerne, Trailblazer **Engines:** 4.6L VIN Y, 4.6L VIN 9, 6.0L VIN H, 6.0L VIN Y, 6.0L VIN K, 6.2L VIN W, 6.6L VIN 6 **Transmissions:** All	**Fuel Rail Pressure (FRP) Sensor Circuit High Voltage** The ignition is on. The FPCM detects that the Fuel Rail Pressure (FRP) sensor signal circuit is above 4.9 V or below 0.1 V. **Note: Using the Failure Records data may help locate an intermittent condition. If you cannot duplicate the DTC, the information in the Failure Records can help determine how many miles since the DTC set. The Fail Counter and Pass Counter can help determine how many ignition cycles that the diagnostic test reported a pass and/or a fail.** **Possible Causes:** • FRP sensor low reference circuit for an open/high resistance • FRP sensor 5-V reference circuit for a short to ground or an open/high resistance • FRP sensor 5-V reference circuit for a short to voltage • FRP sensor signal circuit for a short to ground or an open/high resistance • Fuel pump flow control module has failed • Fuel pressure sensor has failed
DTC: P0193 **1T CCM, MIL: Yes** **Years:** 2008, 2009 **Models:** Envoy, Equinox, G6, G8, Impala, Lucerne, Malibu, Savana, Trailblazer, Torrent **Engines:** 4.2L VIN S, 4.8L VIN C, 3.5L VIN N, 3.5L VIN K, 3.9L VIN 3, 3.9L VIN M, 3.6L VIN 2, 3.9L VIN 1 **Transmissions:** All	**Fuel Rail Pressure Sensor Circuit High Voltage** Key on or engine running; and the ECM detected the Fuel Rail Pressure (FRP) sensor was more than 4.7 volts for 5 seconds. **Possible Causes:** • FRP sensor signal circuit is open between sensor and the ECM • FRP Sensor ground circuit is open between sensor and ECM • FRP sensor signal circuit is shorted to VREF or system power • FRP Sensor is damaged or has failed • ECM has failed

DTC	Trouble Code Title, Conditions & Possible Causes
DTC: P0200 **2T CCM, MIL: Yes** **Years:** 2008, 2009 **Models:** Express, G8, Lucerne, Trailblazer **Engines:** 4.6L VIN Y, 4.6L VIN 9, 6.0L VIN H, 6.0L VIN Y, 6.0L VIN K, 6.2L VIN W, 6.6L VIN 6 **Transmissions:** All	**Fuel Injector Circuit Malfunction** Engine started; engine speed over 400 RPM, system voltage 6-18v, and the ECM detected an unexpected voltage on one or more of the Fuel Injector driver circuits for 5 seconds. Drive the vehicle at off-idle speeds and monitor the misfire current counters. Observe if more than one cylinder is misfiring. This may not be apparent until after a repair is completed. If an injector fuse is open on one cylinder bank, the Scan Tool may only display 2 or 3 cylinders as misfiring. **Possible Causes:** • Fuel injector control circuit is open between injector and ECM • Fuel injector control circuit is grounded between injector and ECM • Fuel injector power circuit is open (test INJ A, B in fuse block) • Fuel injector is damaged or has failed • ECM is damaged
DTC: P0201 **1T CCM, MIL: Yes** **Years:** 2008, 2009 **Models:** Envoy, Equinox, Savana, Torrent **Engines:** 3.4L VIN F, 4.3L VIN X, 5.3L VIN M **Transmissions:** All	**Injector 1 Control Circuit** The engine is running. The ignition voltage is more than 11 volts. DTC P0201-P0208 runs continuously when the above conditions are met. The control module detects an incorrect voltage on the fuel injector control circuit. The above condition is met for 1 second. **Note: Performing the Fuel Injector Diagnosis may help isolate an intermittent condition.** **Possible Causes:** • Fuel Injector ignition 1 voltage circuit for a short to ground or an open/high resistance • Fuel Injector ignition 1 voltage circuit fuse is open • Fuel Injector control circuit for a short to ground • Fuel Injector control circuit for a short to voltage or an open/high resistance • Fuel injector has failed • ECM has failed
DTC: P0201 **2T CCM, MIL: Yes** **Years:** 2008, 2009 **Models:** All **Engines:** All **Transmissions:** All	**Fuel Injector 1 Control Circuit Malfunction** Engine started; engine speed over 400 RPM, system voltage over 11.0v and the ECM detected an unexpected voltage condition on the Fuel Injector driver circuit for Cylinder 1 for 6 seconds. **Note: Drive the vehicle at cruise speed. Record the misfire current counters for review to detect if more than one cylinder is misfiring.** **Possible Causes:** • Injector 1 power circuit (B+) is open (check the power fuse) • Injector 1 control circuit is open between injector and ECM • Injector 1 control circuit is grounded between injector and ECM • Injector 1 is damaged or it has failed • ECM is damaged
DTC: P0202 **2T CCM, MIL: Yes** **Years:** 2008, 2009 **2T CCM, MIL: Yes** **Years:** 2008, 2009 **Models:** All **Engines:** All **Transmissions:** All	**Fuel Injector 2 Control Circuit Malfunction** Engine started; engine speed over 400 RPM, system voltage over 11.0v and the ECM detected an unexpected voltage condition on the Fuel Injector driver circuit for Cylinder 2 for 6 seconds. **Note: Drive the vehicle at cruise speed. Record the misfire current counters for review to detect if more than one cylinder is misfiring.** **Possible Causes:** • Injector 2 power circuit (B+) is open (check the power fuse) • Injector 2 control circuit is open between injector and ECM • Injector 2 control circuit is grounded between injector and ECM • Injector 2 is damaged or it has failed • ECM is damaged
DTC: P0203 **2T CCM, MIL: Yes** **Years:** 2008, 2009 **2T CCM, MIL: Yes** **Years:** 2008, 2009 **Models:** All **Engines:** All **Transmissions:** All	**Fuel Injector 3 Control Circuit Malfunction** Engine started; engine speed over 400 RPM, system voltage over 11.0v and the ECM detected an unexpected voltage condition on the Fuel Injector driver circuit for Cylinder 3 for 6 seconds. **Note: Drive the vehicle at cruise speed. Record the misfire current counters for review to detect if more than one cylinder is misfiring.** **Possible Causes:** • Injector 3 power circuit (B+) is open (check the power fuse) • Injector 3 control circuit is open between injector and ECM • Injector 3 control circuit is grounded between injector and ECM • Injector 3 is damaged or it has failed • ECM is damaged

DTC	Trouble Code Title, Conditions & Possible Causes
DTC: P0204 **2T CCM, MIL: Yes** **Years:** 2008, 2009 **2T CCM, MIL: Yes** **Years:** 2008, 2009 **Models:** All **Engines:** All **Transmissions:** All	**Fuel Injector 4 Control Circuit Malfunction** Engine started; engine speed over 400 RPM, system voltage over 11.0v and the ECM detected an unexpected voltage condition on the Fuel Injector driver circuit for Cylinder 4 for 6 seconds. **Note: Drive the vehicle at cruise speed. Record the misfire current counters for review to detect if more than one cylinder is misfiring.** **Possible Causes:** • Injector 4 power circuit (B+) is open (check the power fuse) • Injector 4 control circuit is open between injector and ECM • Injector 4 control circuit is grounded between injector and ECM • Injector 4 is damaged or it has failed • ECM is damaged
DTC: P0205 **2T CCM, MIL: Yes** **Years:** 2008, 2009 **2T CCM, MIL: Yes** **Years:** 2008, 2009 **Models:** All **Engines:** All **Transmissions:** All	**Fuel Injector 5 Control Circuit Malfunction** Engine started; engine speed over 400 RPM, system voltage over 11.0v and the ECM detected an unexpected voltage condition on the Fuel Injector driver circuit for Cylinder 5 for 6 seconds. **Note: Drive the vehicle at cruise speed. Record the misfire current counters for review to detect if more than one cylinder is misfiring.** **Possible Causes:** • Injector 5 power circuit (B+) is open (check the power fuse) • Injector 5 control circuit is open between injector and ECM • Injector 5 control circuit is grounded between injector and ECM • Injector 5 is damaged or it has failed • ECM is damaged
DTC: P0206 **2T CCM, MIL: Yes** **Years:** 2008, 2009 **2T CCM, MIL: Yes** **Years:** 2008, 2009 **Models:** All **Engines:** All **Transmissions:** All	**Fuel Injector 6 Control Circuit Malfunction** Engine started; engine speed over 400 RPM, system voltage over 11.0v and the ECM detected an unexpected voltage condition on the Fuel Injector driver circuit for Cylinder 6 for 6 seconds. **Note: Drive the vehicle at cruise speed. Record the misfire current counters for review to detect if more than one cylinder is misfiring.** **Possible Causes:** • Injector 6 power circuit (B+) is open (check the power fuse) • Injector 6 control circuit is open between injector and ECM • Injector 6 control circuit is grounded between injector and ECM • Injector 6 is damaged or it has failed • ECM is damaged
DTC: P0207 **2T CCM, MIL: Yes** **Years:** 2008, 2009 **2T CCM, MIL: Yes** **Years:** 2008, 2009 **Models:** All **Engines:** All **Transmissions:** All	**Fuel Injector 7 Control Circuit Malfunction** Engine started; engine speed over 400 RPM, system voltage over 11.0v and the ECM detected an unexpected voltage condition on the Fuel Injector driver circuit for Cylinder 7 for 6 seconds. **Note: Drive the vehicle at cruise speed. Record the misfire current counters for review to detect if more than one cylinder is misfiring.** **Possible Causes:** • Injector 7 power circuit (B+) is open (check the power fuse) • Injector 7 control circuit is open between injector and ECM • Injector 7 control circuit is grounded between injector and ECM • Injector 7 is damaged or it has failed • ECM is damaged
DTC: P0208 **2T CCM, MIL: Yes** **Years:** 2008, 2009 **2T CCM, MIL: Yes** **Years:** 2008, 2009 **Models:** All **Engines:** All **Transmissions:** All	**Fuel Injector 8 Control Circuit Malfunction** Engine started; engine speed over 400 RPM, system voltage over 11.0v and the ECM detected an unexpected voltage condition on the Fuel Injector driver circuit for Cylinder 8 for 6 seconds. **Note: Drive the vehicle at cruise speed. Record the misfire current counters for review to detect if more than one cylinder is misfiring.** **Possible Causes:** • Injector 8 power circuit (B+) is open (check the power fuse) • Injector 8 control circuit is open between injector and ECM • Injector 8 control circuit is grounded between injector and ECM • Injector 8 is damaged or it has failed • ECM is damaged

DTC	Trouble Code Title, Conditions & Possible Causes
DTC: P0220 **1T CCM, MIL: Yes** **Years:** 2008, 2009 **Models:** Express, G8, Lucerne, Trailblazer **Engines:** 4.6L VIN Y, 4.6L VIN 9, 6.0L VIN H, 6.0L VIN Y, 6.0L VIN K, 6.2L VIN W, 6.6L VIN 6 **Transmissions:** All	**Throttle Position (TP) Sensor 2 Circuit** DTCs P0601, P0602, P0603, P0604, P0606, P0607, P0641, P0651 are not set. The system voltage is more than 5.23 volts. The ignition is in the Unlock/Accessory or Run position. DTC P0120, P0122, P0123, P0220, P0222, P0223 run continuously when the above conditions are met. The TP sensor 2 voltage is less than 0.25 volt or more than 4.59 volts for more than 1 second. **Possible Causes:** • TP sensor low reference circuit for an open/high resistance • TP sensor 5-volt reference circuit for a short to ground or an open/high resistance • TP sensor 5-volt reference circuit for a short to voltage • TP sensor signal circuit terminal F for a short to ground • TP sensor 1 signal circuit for a short to ground or an open/high resistance • TP sensor 2 signal circuit for a short to voltage • TP sensor 2 signal circuit for an open/high resistance. • Throttle body has failed • ECM has failed
DTC: P0220 **1T CCM, MIL: Yes** **Years:** 2008, 2009 **Models:** Envoy, Equinox, Savana, Torrent **Engines:** 3.4L VIN F, 4.3L VIN X, 5.3L VIN M **Transmissions:** All	**Throttle Position Sensor 2 Circuit Malfunction** DTP P1518 and P2108 not set, engine cranking or running; system voltage over 5.23v, and the ECM detected the TP Sensor 2 signal was less than 0.28v or more than 4.60v for one second. The ECM provides the TP sensor with a 5v, low reference and signal circuit. The signal is low at closed throttle and higher as the throttle opens. **Possible Causes:** • TP Sensor 2 signal circuit is open or shorted to ground • TP Sensor 2 VREF (5v) circuit is open, or TP Sensor 2 ground circuit is open • TP Sensor 2 is damaged or has failed • ECM is damaged • TSB 03-04-06-034 contains a repair procedure for this code
DTC: P0221 **1T CCM, MIL: Yes** **Years:** 2008, 2009 **Models:** Envoy, Equinox, G6, G8, Impala, Lucerne, Malibu, Savana, Trailblazer, Torrent **Engines:** 4.2L VIN S, 4.8L VIN C, 3.5L VIN N, 3.5L VIN K, 3.9L VIN 3, 3.9L VIN M, 3.6L VIN 2, 3.9L VIN 1 **Transmissions:** All	**Throttle Position (TP) Sensor 2 Circuit Low Voltage** DTC P0601, P0602, P0603, P0604, P0606, P0607, P0641, P0651 are not set. The system voltage is more than 5.23 volts. The ignition is in the Unlock/Accessory or Run position. DTC P0120, P0122, P0123, P0220, P0222, P0223 run continuously when the above conditions are met. The ECM detects that the TP sensor 2 voltage is less than 0.25 volt for greater than 1 s. **Possible Causes:** • TP sensor low reference circuit for an open/high resistance • TP sensor 5-volt reference circuit for a short to ground or an open/high resistance • TP sensor 5-volt reference circuit for a short to voltage • TP sensor signal circuit for a short to voltage • TP sensor signal circuit for a short to ground or an open/high resistance • TP sensor has failed (replace throttle body) • ECM has failed
DTC: P0222 **1T CCM, MIL: Yes** **Years:** 2008, 2009 **Models:** Express, G8, Lucerne, Trailblazer **Engines:** 4.6L VIN Y, 4.6L VIN 9, 6.0L VIN H, 6.0L VIN Y, 6.0L VIN K, 6.2L VIN W, 6.6L VIN 6 **Transmissions:** All	**Throttle Position (TP) Sensor2 Circuit Low Voltage** DTCs P0601, P0602, P0603, P0604, P0606, P0607, P0641, P0651 are not set. The system voltage is more than 5.23 volts. The ignition is in the Unlock/Accessory or Run position. DTC P0120, P0122, P0123, P0220, P0222, P0223 run continuously when the above conditions are met. The ECM detects that the TP sensor 2 voltage is less than 0.25 volt for more than 1 second. **Possible Causes:** • TP sensor low reference circuit for an open/high resistance • TP sensor 5-volt reference circuit for a short to ground or an open/high resistance • TP sensor 5-volt reference circuit for a short to voltage • TP sensor signal circuit terminal F for a short to ground • TP sensor 1 signal circuit for a short to ground or an open/high resistance • TP sensor 2 signal circuit for a short to voltage • TP sensor 2 signal circuit for an open/high resistance. • Throttle body has failed • ECM has failed
DTC: P0222 **1T CCM, MIL: Yes** **Years:** 2008, 2009 **Models:** Envoy, Equinox, Savana, Torrent **Engines:** 3.4L VIN F, 4.3L VIN X, 5.3L VIN M **Transmissions:** All	**Throttle Position (TP) Sensor 2 Circuit Low Voltage** The ignition is ON, with the engine OFF, or the engine is operating. The ignition voltage is greater than 7 volts. DTC P0122 runs continuously once the above conditions met. The ECM detects the TP sensor 1 signal voltage is less than 0.18 volt. **Possible Causes:** • TP Sensor 2 signal circuit is open or shorted to ground • TP Sensor 2 VREF (5v) circuit is open, or TP Sensor 2 ground circuit is open • TP Sensor 2 is damaged or has failed (replace the throttle body assembly) • ECM is damaged

DTC	Trouble Code Title, Conditions & Possible Causes
DTC: P0222 **1T CCM, MIL: Yes** **Years:** 2008, 2009 **Models:** Envoy, Equinox, G6, G8, Impala, Lucerne, Malibu, Savana, Trailblazer, Torrent **Engines:** 4.2L VIN S, 4.8L VIN C, 3.5L VIN N, 3.5L VIN K, 3.9L VIN 3, 3.9L VIN M, 3.6L VIN 2, 3.9L VIN 1 **Transmissions:** All	**Throttle Position (TP) Sensor 2 Circuit Low Voltage** The ignition is in the Unlock/Accessory or Run position. DTC P0642 or P0643 is not set. DTC P0222 runs continuously when the above conditions are met. The ECM detects that the TP sensor 2 voltage is less than 0.19 volt for more than 0.4 second. **Possible Causes:** • TP Sensor 2 signal circuit is open or shorted to ground • TP Sensor 2 VREF (5v) circuit is open, or TP Sensor 2 ground circuit is open • TP Sensor 2 is damaged or has failed (replace the throttle body assembly) • ECM is damaged
DTC: P0222 **1T CCM, MIL: Yes** **Years:** 2008, 2009 **Models:** G6, HHR, Malibu **Engines:** 2.0L VIN X, 2.2L VIN D, 2.2L VIN B, 2.2L VIN F, 2.4L VIN B, 2.4L VIN V, 2.4L VIN P, 2.4L VIN 5 **Transmissions:** All	**Throttle Position (TP) Sensor 2 Circuit High Voltage** DTC P0601, P0602, P0603, P0604, P0606, P0607, P0641, P0651 are not set. The system voltage is more than 5.23 volts. The ignition is in the Unlock/Accessory or Run position. DTC P0120, P0122, P0123, P0220, P0222, P0223 run continuously when the above conditions are met. The ECM detects that the TP sensor 2 voltage is greater than 4.59 volts for greater than 1 s. **Possible Causes:** • TP sensor low reference circuit for an open/high resistance • TP sensor 5-volt reference circuit for a short to ground or an open/high resistance • TP sensor 5-volt reference circuit for a short to voltage • TP sensor signal circuit for a short to voltage • TP sensor signal circuit for a short to ground or an open/high resistance • TP sensor has failed (replace throttle body) • ECM has failed
DTC: P0223 **1T CCM, MIL: Yes** **Years:** 2008, 2009 **Models:** Express, G8, Lucerne, Trailblazer **Engines:** 4.6L VIN Y, 4.6L VIN 9, 6.0L VIN H, 6.0L VIN Y, 6.0L VIN K, 6.2L VIN W, 6.6L VIN 6 **Transmissions:** All	**Throttle Position (TP) Sensor 2 Circuit High Voltage** DTCs P0601, P0602, P0603, P0604, P0606, P0607, P0641, P0651 are not set. The system voltage is more than 5.23 volts. The ignition is in the Unlock/Accessory or Run position. DTC P0120, P0122, P0123, P0220, P0222, P0223 run continuously when the above conditions are met. The ECM detects that the TP sensor 2 voltage is more than 4.59 volts for more than 1 second. **Possible Causes:**
DTC: P0223 **1T CCM, MIL: Yes** **Years:** 2008, 2009 **Models:** Envoy, Equinox, Savana, Torrent **Engines:** 3.4L VIN F, 4.3L VIN X, 5.3L VIN M **Transmissions:** All	**Throttle Position (TP) Sensor 2 Circuit High Voltage** The ignition voltage is greater than 7 volts. The TP sensor 2 voltage is between 0.16-4.9 volts. The TP sensor 1 disagrees greater than 9 percent from TP sensor 2, or TP sensor 1 disagrees greater than 9 percent from the predicted value for greater than 1 second or a cumulative of 10 seconds. **Possible Causes:** • TP Sensor 2 signal circuit is open or shorted to ground • TP Sensor 2 VREF (5v) circuit is open, or TP Sensor 2 ground circuit is open • TP Sensor 2 is damaged or has failed (replace the throttle body assembly) • ECM is damaged
DTC: P0223 **1T CCM, MIL: Yes** **Years:** 2008, 2009 **Models:** Envoy, Equinox, G6, G8, Impala, Lucerne, Malibu, Savana, Trailblazer, Torrent **Engines:** 4.2L VIN S, 4.8L VIN C, 3.5L VIN N, 3.5L VIN K, 3.9L VIN 3, 3.9L VIN M, 3.6L VIN 2, 3.9L VIN 1 **Transmissions:** All	**Throttle Position (TP) Sensor 2 Circuit High Voltage** The ignition is in the Unlock/Accessory or Run position. DTC P0642 or P0643 is not set. DTC P0222 runs continuously when the above conditions are met. The ECM detects that the TP sensor 2 voltage is more than 4.82 volts for more than 0.4 second. **Possible Causes:** • TP Sensor 2 signal circuit is open or shorted to ground • TP Sensor 2 VREF (5v) circuit is open, or TP Sensor 2 ground circuit is open • TP Sensor 2 is damaged or has failed (replace the throttle body assembly) • ECM is damaged
DTC: P0223 **1T CCM, MIL: Yes** **Years:** 2008, 2009 **Models:** G6, HHR, Malibu **Engines:** 2.0L VIN X, 2.2L VIN D, 2.2L VIN B, 2.2L VIN F, 2.4L VIN B, 2.4L VIN V, 2.4L VIN P, 2.4L VIN 5 **Transmissions:** All	**Fuel Pump Relay Control Circuit** The ignition voltage is between 9-18 volts. DTC P0230 runs continuously when the above conditions are met. The control module detects that the commanded state of the driver and the actual state of the control circuit do not match. The above condition is met for a minimum of 2.5 seconds. **Possible Causes:** • Fuel pump relay shorted to ground • Fuel pump relay shorted to Voltage • Fuel pump relay open condition • Fuel pump relay has failed • ECM has failed

DTC	Trouble Code Title, Conditions & Possible Causes
DTC: P0230 **1T CCM, MIL: Yes** **Years:** 2008, 2009 **Models:** Express, G8, Lucerne, Trailblazer **Engines:** 4.6L VIN Y, 4.6L VIN 9, 6.0L VIN H, 6.0L VIN Y, 6.0L VIN K, 6.2L VIN W, 6.6L VIN 6 **Transmissions:** All	**Fuel Pump Relay Control Circuit** The ignition voltage is between 9-18 volts. DTC P0230 runs continuously when the above condition is met. The control module detects that the commanded state of the driver and the actual state of the control circuit do not match. The above condition is met for a minimum of 2.5 seconds. **Possible Causes:** • Fuel pump relay control circuit for a short to ground • Fuel pump relay control circuit for an open/high resistance • Fuel pump relay control circuit for an short to voltage • Fuel pump control module (FPCM) has failed • ECM has failed
DTC: P0230 **1T CCM, MIL: Yes** **Years:** 2008, 2009 **Models:** Envoy, Equinox, Savana, Torrent **Engines:** 3.4L VIN F, 4.3L VIN X, 5.3L VIN M **Transmissions:** All	**Fuel Pump Relay Control Circuit Malfunction** Engine started; engine speed more than 400 RPM, system voltage from 6-18v, and the ECM detected the Actual state and the Commanded state of the Fuel Pump control circuit did not match for 2.5 seconds. **Possible Causes:** • Fuel pump relay control circuit is open or shorted to ground • Fuel pump relay power circuit is open (ECM Fuse B fuse block) • Fuel pump relay is damaged or it has failed • ECM is damaged
DTC: P0230 **2T CCM, MIL: Yes** **Years:** 2008, 2009 **Models:** Express, G8, Lucerne, Trailblazer **Engines:** 4.6L VIN Y, 4.6L VIN 9, 6.0L VIN H, 6.0L VIN Y, 6.0L VIN K, 6.2L VIN W, 6.6L VIN 6 **Transmissions:** All	**Fuel Pump Control Circuit Malfunction** Engine started; engine speed over 400 RPM, system voltage over 10.0v and the ECM detected that the Actual and Commanded state of the Fuel Pump driver control circuit did not match for 2.5 seconds. **Possible Causes:** • Fuel pump relay power circuit is open (test B+ from fuse box) • Fuel pump control circuit is open or shorted to ground • Fuel pump control circuit is shorted to system power • ECM has failed • TSB 00-06-04-023 contains a repair procedure for this code
DTC: P0231 **1T CCM, MIL: Yes** **Years:** 2008, 2009 **Models:** Express, G8, Lucerne, Trailblazer **Engines:** 4.6L VIN Y, 4.6L VIN 9, 6.0L VIN H, 6.0L VIN Y, 6.0L VIN K, 6.2L VIN W, 6.6L VIN 6 **Transmissions:** All	**Fuel Pump Control Circuit Low Voltage** The ignition voltage is between 9-18 volts. The FPCM detects a fault on the fuel pump voltage circuit that is above or below a predetermined voltage threshold. **Possible Causes:** • FPCM control circuit for a short to voltage • FPCM control circuit for a short to ground or an open/high resistance • FPCM control circuit terminal A for a short to voltage or an open/high resistance • Fuel pump tank module has failed • FPCM has failed
DTC: P0231 **1T CCM, MIL: Yes** **Years:** 2008, 2009 **Models:** Envoy, Equinox, G6, G8, Impala, Lucerne, Malibu, Savana, Trailblazer, Torrent **Engines:** 4.2L VIN S, 4.8L VIN C, 3.5L VIN N, 3.5L VIN K, 3.9L VIN 3, 3.9L VIN M, 3.6L VIN 2, 3.9L VIN 1 **Transmissions:** All	**Fuel Pump Control Circuit High Voltage** The control enable voltage signal supplied for the ECM to FECM is inactive for 4 seconds after engine has been shut off. The FECM detects a fault on the fuel pump voltage circuit that is above or below a predetermined voltage threshold. **Possible Causes:** • ECM fuel pump output control circuit for a short to voltage. • ECM fuel pump output control circuit for a short to ground or an open/high resistance • FECM control circuit terminal 2 for a short to voltage or an open/high resistance • Faulty FECM • Faulty fuel tank fuel pump module
DTC: P0232 **1T CCM, MIL: Yes** **Years:** 2008, 2009 **Models:** Express, G8, Lucerne, Trailblazer **Engines:** 4.6L VIN Y, 4.6L VIN 9, 6.0L VIN H, 6.0L VIN Y, 6.0L VIN K, 6.2L VIN W, 6.6L VIN 6 **Transmissions:** All	**Fuel Pump Control Circuit High Voltage** The control enable voltage signal supplied for the ECM to FPCM is inactive for 4 seconds after engine has been shut off. The FPCM detects a fault on the fuel pump voltage circuit that is above or below a predetermined voltage threshold. **Possible Causes:** • FPCM control circuit for a short to voltage • FPCM control circuit for a short to ground or an open/high resistance • FPCM control circuit terminal A for a short to voltage or an open/high resistance • Fuel pump tank module has failed • FPCM has failed

DTC	Trouble Code Title, Conditions & Possible Causes
DTC: P0232 **1T CCM, MIL: Yes** **Years:** 2008, 2009 **Models:** Envoy, Equinox, G6, G8, Impala, Lucerne, Malibu, Savana, Trailblazer, Torrent **Engines:** 4.2L VIN S, 4.8L VIN C, 3.5L VIN N, 3.5L VIN K, 3.9L VIN 3, 3.9L VIN M, 3.6L VIN 2, 3.9L VIN 1 **Transmissions:** All	**Fuel Pump Control Circuit** The ignition voltage is between 9-18 volts. The FECM detects a fault on the fuel pump voltage circuit that is above or below a predetermined voltage threshold. **Possible Causes:** • ECM fuel pump output control circuit for a short to voltage. • ECM fuel pump output control circuit for a short to ground or an open/high resistance • FECM control circuit terminal 2 for a short to voltage or an open/high resistance • Faulty FECM • Faulty fuel tank fuel pump module
DTC: P023A **1T CCM, MIL: Yes** **Years:** 2008, 2009 **Models:** Express, G8, Lucerne, Trailblazer **Engines:** 4.6L VIN Y, 4.6L VIN 9, 6.0L VIN H, 6.0L VIN Y, 6.0L VIN K, 6.2L VIN W, 6.6L VIN 6 **Transmissions:** All	**Charge Air Cooler (CAC) Coolant Pump Relay Control Circuit** The Intake Air Temperature (IAT) sensor 2 is greater than 0°C (32°F). The battery voltage is between 9-18V. The engine run time is greater than 10 seconds. The Charge Air Cooler (CAC) pump relay has been commanded ON. The IAT is greater than −25°C (−13°F). This DTC runs continuously when the above conditions are met. The ECM detects an improper voltage on the supercharger (SC) intercooler pump relay circuit for greater than 30 seconds. **Possible Causes:** • CAC relay control circuit for a short to voltage. • CAC relay control B+ coil supply circuit for a short to ground or an open/high resistance • CAC relay control B+ switch supply circuit for an open/high resistance • CAC pump voltage supply circuit for a short to ground • CAC pump ground circuit for an open/high resistance • CAC pump voltage supply circuit for an open/high resistance • CAC pump control circuit for a short to ground • CAC coolant pump relay has failed • CAC coolant pump has failed • ECM has failed
DTC: P023F **1T CCM, MIL: Yes** **Models:** Express, G8, Lucerne, Trailblazer **Engines:** 4.6L VIN Y, 4.6L VIN 9, 6.0L VIN H, 6.0L VIN Y, 6.0L VIN K, 6.2L VIN W, 6.6L VIN 6 **Transmissions:** All	**Fuel Pump Control Circuit** The ignition voltage is between 9-18 volts. The FPCM detects a fault on the fuel pump voltage circuit that is above or below a predetermined voltage threshold. **Possible Causes**: • FPCM control circuit for a short to voltage • FPCM control circuit for a short to ground or an open/high resistance • FPCM control circuit terminal A for a short to voltage or an open/high resistance • Fuel pump tank module has failed • FPCM has failed
DTC: P023F **1T CCM, MIL: Yes** **Years:** 2008, 2009 **Models:** Envoy, Equinox, G6, G8, Impala, Lucerne, Malibu, Savana, Trailblazer, Torrent **Engines:** 4.2L VIN S, 4.8L VIN C, 3.5L VIN N, 3.5L VIN K, 3.9L VIN 3, 3.9L VIN M, 3.6L VIN 2, 3.9L VIN 1 **Transmissions:** All	**Supercharger Boost Solenoid Control Circuit Malfunction** Key on or engine running; and the ECM detected an unexpected voltage on the Boost Control Solenoid control circuit for 30 seconds. The ECM uses an output driver module (ODM) to enable several current-driven devices that are needed to control various engine and transaxle functions. Each ODM can control several output device functions. **Possible Causes:** • Boost solenoid circuit is open between the solenoid and ECM • Boost solenoid circuit is shorted to ground • Boost solenoid power circuit is open to system power • Boost solenoid is damaged or has failed • ECM has failed
DTC: P025A **1T CCM, MIL: Yes** **Years:** 2008, 2009 **Models:** Express, G8, Lucerne, Trailblazer **Engines:** 4.6L VIN Y, 4.6L VIN 9, 6.0L VIN H, 6.0L VIN Y, 6.0L VIN K, 6.2L VIN W, 6.6L VIN 6 **Transmissions:** All	**Fuel Pump Control Module Enable Circuit** The ignition is ON. The serial data message from the ECM to the FPCM does not agree with the state of the control enable circuit voltage supplied from the ECM to the FPCM for more than 2 seconds. **Possible Causes:** • FPCM has failed • ECM has failed

DTC	Trouble Code Title, Conditions & Possible Causes
DTC: P0261 **1T CCM, MIL: Yes** **Years:** 2008, 2009 **Models:** Envoy, Equinox, G6, G8, Impala, Lucerne, Malibu, Savana, Trailblazer, Torrent, G6, HHR, Malibu **Engines:** 4.2L VIN S, 4.8L VIN C, 3.5L VIN N, 3.5L VIN K, 3.9L VIN 3, 3.9L VIN M, 3.8L VIN 2, 3.9L VIN 1, 2.0L VIN X, 2.2L VIN D, 2.2L VIN B, 2.2L VIN F, 2.4L VIN B, 2.4L VIN V, 2.4L VIN P, 2.4L VIN 5 **Transmissions:** All	**Injector 1 Control Circuit High Voltage** The engine speed is greater than 80 RPM. The ignition voltage is between 8-18 volts. The injector has been commanded ON and OFF at least once. The DTCs run continuously once the above conditions are met. The ECM detects the injector low voltage control circuit is shorted to ground for greater than 4 seconds or for a cumulative of 30 seconds. **Possible Causes:** • High voltage control circuit shorted to voltage • High voltage control circuit short to ground or an open/high resistance • Low voltage control circuit shorted to voltage • Low voltage control circuit short to ground or an open/high resistance • Faulty fuel injector • ECM has failed.
DTC: P0262 **1T CCM, MIL: Yes** **Years:** 2008, 2009 **Models:** Envoy, Equinox, G6, G8, Impala, Lucerne, Malibu, Savana, Trailblazer, Torrent, G6, HHR, Malibu **Engines:** 4.2L VIN S, 4.8L VIN C, 3.5L VIN N, 3.5L VIN K, 3.9L VIN 3, 3.9L VIN M, 3.8L VIN 2, 3.9L VIN 1, 2.0L VIN X, 2.2L VIN D, 2.2L VIN B, 2.2L VIN F, 2.4L VIN B, 2.4L VIN V, 2.4L VIN P, 2.4L VIN 5 **Transmissions:** All	**Injector 2 Control Circuit Low Voltage** The engine speed is greater than 80 RPM. The ignition voltage is between 8-18 volts. The injector has been commanded ON and OFF at least once. The DTCs run continuously once the above conditions are met. The ECM detects the injector low voltage control circuit is shorted to ground for greater than 4 seconds or for a cumulative of 30 seconds. **Possible Causes:** • High voltage control circuit shorted to voltage • High voltage control circuit short to ground or an open/high resistance • Low voltage control circuit shorted to voltage • Low voltage control circuit short to ground or an open/high resistance • Faulty fuel injector • ECM has failed.
DTC: P0264 **1T CCM, MIL: Yes** **Years:** 2008, 2009 **Models:** Envoy, Equinox, G6, G8, Impala, Lucerne, Malibu, Savana, Trailblazer, Torrent, G6, HHR, Malibu **Engines:** 4.2L VIN S, 4.8L VIN C, 3.5L VIN N, 3.5L VIN K, 3.9L VIN 3, 3.9L VIN M, 3.8L VIN 2, 3.9L VIN 1, 2.0L VIN X, 2.2L VIN D, 2.2L VIN B, 2.2L VIN F, 2.4L VIN B, 2.4L VIN V, 2.4L VIN P, 2.4L VIN 5 **Transmissions:** All	**Injector 2 Control Circuit High Voltage** The engine speed is greater than 80 RPM. The ignition voltage is between 8-18 volts. The injector has been commanded ON and OFF at least once. The DTCs run continuously once the above conditions are met. The ECM detects the injector low voltage control circuit is shorted to ground for greater than 4 seconds or for a cumulative of 30 seconds. **Possible Causes:** • High voltage control circuit shorted to voltage • High voltage control circuit short to ground or an open/high resistance • Low voltage control circuit shorted to voltage • Low voltage control circuit short to ground or an open/high resistance • Faulty fuel injector • ECM has failed.
DTC: P0265 **1T CCM, MIL: Yes** **Years:** 2008, 2009 **Models:** Envoy, Equinox, G6, G8, Impala, Lucerne, Malibu, Savana, Trailblazer, Torrent, G6, HHR, Malibu **Engines:** 4.2L VIN S, 4.8L VIN C, 3.5L VIN N, 3.5L VIN K, 3.9L VIN 3, 3.9L VIN M, 3.6L VIN 2, 3.9L VIN 1, 2.0L VIN X, 2.2L VIN D, 2.2L VIN B, 2.2L VIN F, 2.4L VIN B, 2.4L VIN V, 2.4L VIN P, 2.4L VIN 5 **Transmissions:** All	**Injector 3 Control Circuit Low Voltage** The engine speed is greater than 80 RPM. The ignition voltage is between 8-18 volts. The injector has been commanded ON and OFF at least once. The DTCs run continuously once the above conditions are met. The ECM detects the injector low voltage control circuit is shorted to ground for greater than 4 seconds or for a cumulative of 30 seconds. **Possible Causes:** • High voltage control circuit shorted to voltage • High voltage control circuit short to ground or an open/high resistance • Low voltage control circuit shorted to voltage • Low voltage control circuit short to ground or an open/high resistance • Faulty fuel injector • ECM has failed.

DTC	Trouble Code Title, Conditions & Possible Causes
DTC: P0267 **1T CCM, MIL: Yes** **Years:** 2008, 2009 **Models:** Envoy, Equinox, G6, G8, Impala, Lucerne, Malibu, Savana, Trailblazer, Torrent, G6, HHR, Malibu **Engines:** 4.2L VIN S, 4.8L VIN C, 3.5L VIN N, 3.5L VIN K, 3.9L VIN 3, 3.9L VIN M, 3.8L VIN 2, 3.9L VIN 1, 2.0L VIN X, 2.2L VIN D, 2.2L VIN B, 2.2L VIN F, 2.4L VIN B, 2.4L VIN V, 2.4L VIN P, 2.4L VIN 5 **Transmissions:** All	**Injector 3 Control Circuit High Voltage** The engine speed is greater than 80 RPM. The ignition voltage is between 8-18 volts. The injector has been commanded ON and OFF at least once. The DTCs run continuously once the above conditions are met. The ECM detects the injector low voltage control circuit is shorted to ground for greater than 4 seconds or for a cumulative of 30 seconds. **Possible Causes:** • High voltage control circuit shorted to voltage • High voltage control circuit short to ground or an open/high resistance • Low voltage control circuit shorted to voltage • Low voltage control circuit short to ground or an open/high resistance • Faulty fuel injector • ECM has failed.
DTC: P0268 **1T CCM, MIL: Yes** **Years:** 2008, 2009 **Models:** Envoy, Equinox, G6, G8, Impala, Lucerne, Malibu, Savana, Trailblazer, Torrent, G6, HHR, Malibu **Engines:** 4.2L VIN S, 4.8L VIN C, 3.5L VIN N, 3.5L VIN K, 3.9L VIN 3, 3.9L VIN M, 3.8L VIN 2, 3.9L VIN 1, 2.0L VIN X, 2.2L VIN D, 2.2L VIN B, 2.2L VIN F, 2.4L VIN B, 2.4L VIN V, 2.4L VIN P, 2.4L VIN 5 **Transmissions:** All	**Injector 4 Control Circuit Low Voltage** The engine speed is greater than 80 RPM. The ignition voltage is between 8-18 volts. The injector has been commanded ON and OFF at least once. The DTCs run continuously once the above conditions are met. The ECM detects the injector low voltage control circuit is shorted to ground for greater than 4 seconds or for a cumulative of 30 seconds. **Possible Causes:** • High voltage control circuit shorted to voltage • High voltage control circuit short to ground or an open/high resistance • Low voltage control circuit shorted to voltage • Low voltage control circuit short to ground or an open/high resistance • Faulty fuel injector • ECM has failed.
DTC: P0270 **1T CCM, MIL: Yes** **Years:** 2008, 2009 **Models:** Envoy, Equinox, G6, G8, Impala, Lucerne, Malibu, Savana, Trailblazer, Torrent, G6, HHR, Malibu **Engines:** 4.2L VIN S, 4.8L VIN C, 3.5L VIN N, 3.5L VIN K, 3.9L VIN 3, 3.9L VIN M, 3.8L VIN 2, 3.9L VIN 1, 2.0L VIN X, 2.2L VIN D, 2.2L VIN B, 2.2L VIN F, 2.4L VIN B, 2.4L VIN V, 2.4L VIN P, 2.4L VIN 5 **Transmissions:** All	**Injector 4 Control Circuit High Voltage** The engine speed is greater than 80 RPM. The ignition voltage is between 8-18 volts. The injector has been commanded ON and OFF at least once. The DTCs run continuously once the above conditions are met. The ECM detects the injector low voltage control circuit is shorted to ground for greater than 4 seconds or for a cumulative of 30 seconds. **Possible Causes:** • High voltage control circuit shorted to voltage • High voltage control circuit short to ground or an open/high resistance • Low voltage control circuit shorted to voltage • Low voltage control circuit short to ground or an open/high resistance • Faulty fuel injector • ECM has failed.
DTC: P0271 **1T CCM, MIL: Yes** **Years:** 2008, 2009 **Models:** Envoy, Equinox, G6, G8, Impala, Lucerne, Malibu, Savana, Trailblazer, Torrent, G6, HHR, Malibu **Engines:** 4.2L VIN S, 4.8L VIN C, 3.5L VIN N, 3.5L VIN K, 3.9L VIN 3, 3.9L VIN M, 3.8L VIN 2, 3.9L VIN 1, 2.0L VIN X, 2.2L VIN D, 2.2L VIN B, 2.2L VIN F, 2.4L VIN B, 2.4L VIN V, 2.4L VIN P, 2.4L VIN 5 **Transmissions:** All	**Injector 5 Control Circuit Low Voltage** The engine speed is greater than 80 RPM. The ignition voltage is between 8-18 volts. The injector has been commanded ON and OFF at least once. The DTCs run continuously once the above conditions are met. The ECM detects the injector low voltage control circuit is shorted to ground for greater than 4 seconds or for a cumulative of 30 seconds. **Possible Causes:** • High voltage control circuit shorted to voltage • High voltage control circuit short to ground or an open/high resistance • Low voltage control circuit shorted to voltage • Low voltage control circuit short to ground or an open/high resistance • Faulty fuel injector • ECM has failed.

DTC	Trouble Code Title, Conditions & Possible Causes
DTC: P0273 **1T CCM, MIL: Yes** **Years:** 2008, 2009 **Models:** Envoy, Equinox, G6, G8, Impala, Lucerne, Malibu, Savana, Trailblazer, Torrent **Engines:** 4.2L VIN S, 4.8L VIN C, 3.5L VIN N, 3.5L VIN K, 3.9L VIN 3, 3.9L VIN M, 3.6L VIN 2, 3.9L VIN 1 **Transmissions:** All	**Injector 5 Control Circuit High Voltage** The engine speed is greater than 80 RPM. The ignition voltage is between 8-18 volts. The injector has been commanded ON and OFF at least once. The DTCs run continuously once the above conditions are met. The ECM detects the injector low voltage control circuit is shorted to ground for greater than 4 seconds or for a cumulative of 30 seconds. **Possible Causes:** • High voltage control circuit shorted to voltage • High voltage control circuit short to ground or an open/high resistance • Low voltage control circuit shorted to voltage • Low voltage control circuit short to ground or an open/high resistance • Faulty fuel injector • ECM has failed.
DTC: P0274 **1T CCM, MIL: Yes** **Years:** 2008, 2009 **Models:** Envoy, Equinox, G6, G8, Impala, Lucerne, Malibu, Savana, Trailblazer, Torrent **Engines:** 4.2L VIN S, 4.8L VIN C, 3.5L VIN N, 3.5L VIN K, 3.9L VIN 3, 3.9L VIN M, 3.6L VIN 2, 3.9L VIN 1 **Transmissions:** All	**Injector 6 Control Circuit Low Voltage** The engine speed is greater than 80 RPM. The ignition voltage is between 8-18 volts. The injector has been commanded ON and OFF at least once. The DTCs run continuously once the above conditions are met. The ECM detects the injector low voltage control circuit is shorted to ground for greater than 4 seconds or for a cumulative of 30 seconds. **Possible Causes:** • High voltage control circuit shorted to voltage • High voltage control circuit short to ground or an open/high resistance • Low voltage control circuit shorted to voltage • Low voltage control circuit short to ground or an open/high resistance • Faulty fuel injector • ECM has failed.
DTC: P0276 **1T CCM, MIL: Yes** **Years:** 2008, 2009 **Models:** Envoy, Equinox, G6, G8, Impala, Lucerne, Malibu, Savana, Trailblazer, Torrent **Engines:** 4.2L VIN S, 4.8L VIN C, 3.5L VIN N, 3.5L VIN K, 3.9L VIN 3, 3.9L VIN M, 3.6L VIN 2, 3.9L VIN 1 **Transmissions:** All	**Injector 6 Control Circuit High Voltage** The engine speed is greater than 80 RPM. The ignition voltage is between 8-18 volts. The injector has been commanded ON and OFF at least once. The DTCs run continuously once the above conditions are met. The ECM detects the injector low voltage control circuit is shorted to ground for greater than 4 seconds or for a cumulative of 30 seconds. **Possible Causes:** • High voltage control circuit shorted to voltage • High voltage control circuit short to ground or an open/high resistance • Low voltage control circuit shorted to voltage • Low voltage control circuit short to ground or an open/high resistance • Faulty fuel injector • ECM has failed.
DTC: P0277 **1T CCM, MIL: Yes** **Years:** 2008, 2009 **Models:** Envoy, Equinox, G6, G8, Impala, Lucerne, Malibu, Savana, Trailblazer, Torrent **Engines:** 4.2L VIN S, 4.8L VIN C, 3.5L VIN N, 3.5L VIN K, 3.9L VIN 3, 3.9L VIN M, 3.6L VIN 2, 3.9L VIN 1 **Transmissions:** All	**Injector 1 Leak** The engine speed is between 1,520-6,000 RPM The engine load is less than 100 percent. The misfire monitor is enabled. DTC P029D runs continuously once the conditions above have been met for approximately 20 seconds. The ECM detects a specific cylinder misfire rate of greater than 100 counts in less than 17 engine revolutions, and P0087 is set. The condition exists for greater than 4 seconds or for a cumulative of 30 seconds. **Possible Causes:** • Test or replace the appropriate fuel injector
DTC: P029D **1T CCM, MIL: Yes** **Years:** 2008, 2009 **Models:** Envoy, Equinox, G6, G8, Impala, Lucerne, Malibu, Savana, Trailblazer, Torrent **Engines:** 4.2L VIN S, 4.8L VIN C, 3.5L VIN N, 3.5L VIN K, 3.9L VIN 3, 3.9L VIN M, 3.6L VIN 2, 3.9L VIN 1 **Transmissions:** All	**Injector 2 Leak** The engine speed is between 1,520-6,000 RPM The engine load is less than 100 percent. The misfire monitor is enabled. DTC P02A5 runs continuously once the conditions above have been met for approximately 20 seconds. The ECM detects a specific cylinder misfire rate of greater than 100 counts in less than 17 engine revolutions, and P0087 is set. The condition exists for greater than 4 seconds or for a cumulative of 30 seconds. **Possible Causes:** • Test or replace the appropriate fuel injector

DTC	Trouble Code Title, Conditions & Possible Causes
DTC: P02A5 **1T CCM, MIL: Yes** **Years:** 2008, 2009 **Models:** Envoy, Equinox, G6, G8, Impala, Lucerne, Malibu, Savana, Trailblazer, Torrent **Engines:** 4.2L VIN S, 4.8L VIN C, 3.5L VIN N, 3.5L VIN K, 3.9L VIN 3, 3.9L VIN M, 3.6L VIN 2, 3.9L VIN 1 **Transmissions:** All	**Injector 3 Leak** The engine speed is between 1,520-6,000 RPM The engine load is less than 100 percent. The misfire monitor is enabled. DTC P02A9 runs continuously once the conditions above have been met for approximately 20 seconds. The ECM detects a specific cylinder misfire rate of greater than 100 counts in less than 17 engine revolutions, and P0087 is set. The condition exists for greater than 4 seconds or for a cumulative of 30 seconds. **Possible Causes:** • Test or replace the appropriate fuel injector
DTC: P02A9 **1T CCM, MIL: Yes** **Years:** 2008, 2009 **Models:** Envoy, Equinox, G6, G8, Impala, Lucerne, Malibu, Savana, Trailblazer, Torrent **Engines:** 4.2L VIN S, 4.8L VIN C, 3.5L VIN N, 3.5L VIN K, 3.9L VIN 3, 3.9L VIN M, 3.6L VIN 2, 3.9L VIN 1 **Transmissions:** All	**Injector 4 Leak** The engine speed is between 1,520-6,000 RPM The engine load is less than 100 percent. The misfire monitor is enabled. DTC P02AD runs continuously once the conditions above have been met for approximately 20 seconds. The ECM detects a specific cylinder misfire rate of greater than 100 counts in less than 17 engine revolutions, and P0087 is set. The condition exists for greater than 4 seconds or for a cumulative of 30 seconds. **Possible Causes:** • Test or replace the appropriate fuel injector
DTC: P02AD **1T CCM, MIL: Yes** **Years:** 2008, 2009 **Models:** Envoy, Equinox, G6, G8, Impala, Lucerne, Malibu, Savana, Trailblazer, Torrent **Engines:** 4.2L VIN S, 4.8L VIN C, 3.5L VIN N, 3.5L VIN K, 3.9L VIN 3, 3.9L VIN M, 3.6L VIN 2, 3.9L VIN 1 **Transmissions:** All	**Injector 6 Leak** The engine speed is between 1,520-6,000 RPM The engine load is less than 100 percent. The misfire monitor is enabled. DTC P02B1 runs continuously once the conditions above have been met for approximately 20 seconds. The ECM detects a specific cylinder misfire rate of greater than 100 counts in less than 17 engine revolutions, and P0087 is set. The condition exists for greater than 4 seconds or for a cumulative of 30 seconds. **Possible Causes:** • Test or replace the appropriate fuel injector
DTC: P02B1 **1T CCM, MIL: Yes** **Years:** 2008, 2009 **Models:** Envoy, Equinox, G6, G8, Impala, Lucerne, Malibu, Savana, Trailblazer, Torrent **Engines:** 4.2L VIN S, 4.8L VIN C, 3.5L VIN N, 3.5L VIN K, 3.9L VIN 3, 3.9L VIN M, 3.6L VIN 2, 3.9L VIN 1 **Transmissions:** All	**Multiple Engine Misfire Detected** The ECM detects a crankshaft rotation speed variation indicating a single cylinder misfire rate sufficient to cause emissions levels to exceed mandated standards. The ECM disables the fuel injector of the misfiring cylinder when a misfire is present. **Possible Causes:** • Base engine mechanical fault that affects one or more cylinders • Fuel metering fault (high fuel pressure or fuel contaminated) • EVAP system problem or the EVAP canister is fuel saturated • EGR valve is stuck open or the PCV system has a vacuum leak • Ignition system fault (a coil) that affects more than one cylinder • MAF sensor contamination (it can cause a very lean condition)
DTC: P0300 **2T CCM, MIL: Yes** **Years:** 2008, 2009 **Models:** All **Engines:** All **Transmissions:** All	**Multiple Engine Misfire Detected** DTC P0101-P0103, P0116-P0118, P0121-P0123, P0125, P0335, P0336, P0341-P0343, P0500-P0503 and P1258 not set, engine speed from 450-3000 RPM, system voltage over 10.0v, ECT sensor from 19-230°F, fuel level over 10%, TP angle steady (1%), ABS and Traction Control inactive, ABS signal not indicating rough road thresholds, transmission not shifting, A/C clutch stable, AIR Test and DFCO "off", and the PCM detected a crankshaft speed variation in two or more cylinders characteristic of a misfire condition. **Note: If the misfire is severe, the MIL will flash on/off on the 1st trip!** **Possible Causes:** • Base engine mechanical fault that affects one or more cylinders • Fuel metering fault that affects more than one cylinder • Fuel pressure too low or too high, fuel supply contaminated • EVAP system problem or the EVAP canister is fuel saturated • EGR valve is stuck open or the PCV system has a vacuum leak • IC control circuit is shorted to ground (an intermittent fault) • Ignition system fault (a coil) that affects more than one cylinder • MAF sensor contamination (it can cause a very lean condition)

DTC	Trouble Code Title, Conditions & Possible Causes
DTC: P0301 **2T CCM, MIL: Yes** **Years:** 2008, 2009 **Models:** All **Engines:** All **Transmissions:** All	**Cylinder 1 Misfire Detected** The ECM detects a crankshaft rotation speed variation indicating a single cylinder misfire rate sufficient to cause emissions levels to exceed mandated standards. The ECM disables the fuel injector of the misfiring cylinder when a misfire is present. **Note: A misfire DTC could be caused by an excessive vibration from sources other than the engine. If the misfire is severe, the MIL will flash on/off on the 1st trip!** **Possible Causes:** • Air leak in the intake manifold, or in the EGR or PCV system • Base engine mechanical fault that affects only Cylinder 1 • Fuel delivery component fault that affects only Cylinder 1 (i.e., a contaminated, dirty or sticking fuel injector) • Ignition system problem (coil, plug) that affects only Cylinder 1
DTC: P0302 **2T CCM, MIL: Yes** **Years:** 2008, 2009 **Models:** All **Engines:** All **Transmissions:** All	**Cylinder 2 Misfire Detected** The ECM detects a crankshaft rotation speed variation indicating a single cylinder misfire rate sufficient to cause emissions levels to exceed mandated standards. The ECM disables the fuel injector of the misfiring cylinder when a misfire is present. **Note: A misfire DTC could be caused by an excessive vibration from sources other than the engine. If the misfire is severe, the MIL will flash on/off on the 1st trip!** **Possible Causes:** • Air leak in the intake manifold, or in the EGR or PCV system • Base engine mechanical fault that affects only Cylinder 2 • Fuel delivery component fault that affects only Cylinder 2 (i.e., a contaminated, dirty or sticking fuel injector) • Ignition system problem (coil, plug) that affects only Cylinder 2
DTC: P0303 **2T CCM, MIL: Yes** **Years:** 2008, 2009 **Models:** All **Engines:** All **Transmissions:** All	**Cylinder 3 Misfire Detected** The ECM detects a crankshaft rotation speed variation indicating a single cylinder misfire rate sufficient to cause emissions levels to exceed mandated standards. The ECM disables the fuel injector of the misfiring cylinder when a misfire is present. **Note: A misfire DTC could be caused by an excessive vibration from sources other than the engine. If the misfire is severe, the MIL will flash on/off on the 1st trip!** **Possible Causes:** • Air leak in the intake manifold, or in the EGR or PCV system • Base engine mechanical fault that affects only Cylinder 3 • Fuel delivery component fault that affects only Cylinder 3 (i.e., a contaminated, dirty or sticking fuel injector) • Ignition system problem (coil, plug) that affects only Cylinder 3
DTC: P0304 **2T CCM, MIL: Yes** **Years:** 2008, 2009 **Models:** All **Engines:** All **Transmissions:** All	**Cylinder 4 Misfire Detected** The ECM detects a crankshaft rotation speed variation indicating a single cylinder misfire rate sufficient to cause emissions levels to exceed mandated standards. The ECM disables the fuel injector of the misfiring cylinder when a misfire is present. **Note: A misfire DTC could be caused by an excessive vibration from sources other than the engine. If the misfire is severe, the MIL will flash on/off on the 1st trip!** **Possible Causes:** • Air leak in the intake manifold, or in the EGR or PCV system • Base engine mechanical fault that affects only Cylinder 4 • Fuel delivery component fault that affects only Cylinder 4 (i.e., a contaminated, dirty or sticking fuel injector) • Ignition system problem (coil, plug) that affects only Cylinder 4
DTC: P0305 **2T CCM, MIL: Yes** **Years:** 2008, 2009 **Models:** All **Engines:** 6 & 8 Cylinder **Transmissions:** All	**Cylinder 5 Misfire Detected** The ECM detects a crankshaft rotation speed variation indicating a single cylinder misfire rate sufficient to cause emissions levels to exceed mandated standards. The ECM disables the fuel injector of the misfiring cylinder when a misfire is present. **Note: A misfire DTC could be caused by an excessive vibration from sources other than the engine. If the misfire is severe, the MIL will flash on/off on the 1st trip!** **Possible Causes:** • Air leak in the intake manifold, or in the EGR or PCV system • Base engine mechanical fault that affects only Cylinder 5 • Fuel delivery component fault that affects only Cylinder 5 (i.e., a contaminated, dirty or sticking fuel injector) • Ignition system problem (coil, plug) that affects only Cylinder 5
DTC: P0306 **2T CCM, MIL: Yes** **Years:** 2008, 2009 **Models:** All **Engines:** 6 & 8 Cylinder **Transmissions:** All	**Cylinder 6 Misfire Detected** The ECM detects a crankshaft rotation speed variation indicating a single cylinder misfire rate sufficient to cause emissions levels to exceed mandated standards. The ECM disables the fuel injector of the misfiring cylinder when a misfire is present. **Note: A misfire DTC could be caused by an excessive vibration from sources other than the engine. If the misfire is severe, the MIL will flash on/off on the 1st trip!** **Possible Causes:** • Air leak in the intake manifold, or in the EGR or PCV system • Base engine mechanical fault that affects only Cylinder 6 • Fuel delivery component fault that affects only Cylinder 6 (i.e., a contaminated, dirty or sticking fuel injector) • Ignition system problem (coil, plug) that affects only Cylinder 6

DTC	Trouble Code Title, Conditions & Possible Causes
DTC: P0307 **2T CCM, MIL: Yes** **Years:** 2008, 2009 **Models:** All **Engines:** 8 Cylinder **Transmissions:** All	**Cylinder 7 Misfire Detected** The ECM detects a crankshaft rotation speed variation indicating a single cylinder misfire rate sufficient to cause emissions levels to exceed mandated standards. The ECM disables the fuel injector of the misfiring cylinder when a misfire is present. **Note: A misfire DTC could be caused by an excessive vibration from sources other than the engine. If the misfire is severe, the MIL will flash on/off on the 1st trip!** **Possible Causes:** • Air leak in the intake manifold, or in the EGR or PCV system • Base engine mechanical fault that affects only Cylinder 7 • Fuel delivery component fault that affects only Cylinder 7 (i.e., a contaminated, dirty or sticking fuel injector) • Ignition system problem (coil, plug) that affects only Cylinder 7
DTC: P0308 **2T CCM, MIL: Yes** **Years:** 2008, 2009 **Models:** All **Engines:** 8 Cylinder **Transmissions:** All	**Cylinder 8 Misfire Detected** The ECM detects a crankshaft rotation speed variation indicating a single cylinder misfire rate sufficient to cause emissions levels to exceed mandated standards. The ECM disables the fuel injector of the misfiring cylinder when a misfire is present. **Note: A misfire DTC could be caused by an excessive vibration from sources other than the engine. If the misfire is severe, the MIL will flash on/off on the 1st trip!** **Possible Causes:** • Air leak in the intake manifold, or in the EGR or PCV system • Base engine mechanical fault that affects only Cylinder 8 • Fuel delivery component fault that affects only Cylinder 8 (i.e., a contaminated, dirty or sticking fuel injector) • Ignition system problem (coil, plug) that affects only Cylinder 8
DTC: P0313 **2T CCM, MIL: Yes** **Years:** 2008, 2009 **Models:** All **Engines:** All 8 cylinders **Transmissions:** All	**Misfire Detected With Low Fuel Level** DTCs P0016, P0101, P0102, P0103, P0121, P0122, P0123, P0221, P0222, P0223, P0335, P0336 or P1101 are not set. The engine speed is between 600-6,528 RPM. The ECM is not in fuel cut-off mode. DTCs P0313 runs continuously when the above conditions are met. **Possible Causes:** • Damaged reluctor wheel • Damaged accessory drive component or belt • Certain rough road conditions • Variable thickness brake rotors • Tire or wheel that is out of round or out of balance • Engine vacuum leaks • Fuel pressure that is too low or too high • Contaminated fuel • Restricted exhaust system
DTC: P0313 **1T CCM, MIL: Yes** **Years:** 2008, 2009 **Models:** G6, HHR, Malibu **Engines:** 2.0L VIN X, 2.2L VIN D, 2.2L VIN B, 2.2L VIN F, 2.4L VIN B, 2.4L VIN V, 2.4L VIN P, 2.4L VIN 5 **Transmissions:** All	**Crankshaft Position (CKP) System Variation Not Learned** The diagnostic runs continuously. The ECM detects that the CKP system variation values are not stored in memory. **Possible Causes:** • Any worn crankshaft main bearings • Damaged or misaligned reluctor wheel • Excessive crankshaft runout • A damaged crankshaft • Interference in the signal circuit of the CKP sensor • Ignition switch is left in the ON position, until the battery is discharged • ECM power disconnect, with the ignition ON, that may have erased the • CKP system variation values • Debris between the CKP sensor and the reluctor wheel • CKP System lost Variation Learn Procedure • ECM has failed
DTC: P0315 **1T CCM, MIL: Yes** **Years:** 2008, 2009 **Models:** Express, G8, Lucerne, Trailblazer **Engines:** 4.6L VIN Y, 4.6L VIN 9, 6.0L VIN H, 6.0L VIN Y, 6.0L VIN K, 6.2L VIN W, 6.6L VIN 6 **Transmissions:** All	**Crankshaft Position (CKP) System Variation Not Learned** The diagnostic runs continuously. The ECM detects that the CKP system variation values are not stored in memory. **Possible Causes:** • Worn crankshaft main bearings • Damaged or misaligned reluctor wheel • Excessive crankshaft runout • Damaged crankshaft • Interference in the signal circuit of the CKP sensor • The ignition switch is left in the ON position, until the battery is discharged • An ECM power disconnect, with the ignition ON, that may have erased the CKP system variation values and set DTC P0315 • Any debris between the CKP sensor and the reluctor wheel • ECM has failed

DTC	Trouble Code Title, Conditions & Possible Causes
DTC: P0315 **1T CCM, MIL: Yes** **Years:** 2008, 2009 **Models:** Envoy, Equinox, Savana, Torrent **Engines:** 3.4L VIN F, 4.3L VIN X, 5.3L VIN M **Transmissions:** All	**Crankshaft Position Sensor Variation Not Learned** DTC P0335, P0336, P0341, P0342 and P0343 not set, engine started, ECT sensor more than 149°F, and the ECM determined the CKP sensor variation values were not stored in memory. The CKP System variation "learning" feature is used to calculate reference period errors caused by slight tolerance variations in the crankshaft and the CKP sensor. The calculated error Allows the ECM to accurately compensate for reference period variations. The ECM stores CKP variation values after a learn procedure is done. **Possible Causes:** • CKP sensor signal circuit has an interference condition (EMI) • Crankshaft main bearings worn or reluctor wheel is damaged • Crankshaft run-out is excessive or the crankshaft is damaged • ECT sensor not within the conditions for running the code test • Ignition switch is on, but the battery has insufficient voltage • ECM power disconnected with key on (erases learned values) • Debris that passes between the CKP sensor and reluctor wheel
DTC: P0324 **1T CCM, MIL: Yes** **Years:** 2008, 2009 **Models:** Express, G8, Lucerne, Trailblazer **Engines:** 4.6L VIN Y, 4.6L VIN 9, 6.0L VIN H, 6.0L VIN Y, 6.0L VIN K, 6.2L VIN W, 6.6L VIN 6 **Transmissions:** All	**Knock Sensor (KS) Module Performance** DTC P0325, P0326, P0327, P0328, P0330, P0332, or P0333 is not set. The engine speed is greater than 300 RPM. The engine air flow is greater than 50 mg/cylinder. DTC P0324 runs continuously when the above conditions are met. The ECM has detected an internal circuitry fault. **Possible Causes:** • KS sensor signal circuit for a short to ground or an open/high resistance • KS sensor signal circuit for a short to voltage • KS sensor low reference circuit for a short to ground or an open/high resistance • KS sensor • KS sensor has failed • ECM has failed
DTC: P0324 **1T CCM, MIL: Yes** **Years:** 2008, 2009 **Models:** Envoy, Equinox, Savana, Torrent **Engines:** 3.4L VIN F, 4.3L VIN X, 5.3L VIN M **Transmissions:** All	**Knock Sensor (KS) Module Performance** The ECM is controlling spark. The engine coolant temperature is warmer than 60°C (140°F). DTC P0324 runs continuously once the above conditions are met. The ECM detects an incorrect response to the self tests performed on the internal KS circuitry. The condition exists for greater than 1 seconds or for a cumulative of 10 seconds. **Note: If you can hear an engine knock, repair the engine mechanical condition before proceeding with this diagnostic.** **Possible Causes:** • Knock sensor signal circuit is open, shorted to ground or power • Knock sensor ground circuit is open (i.e., not mounted properly) • Knock sensor is damaged or has failed • ECM has failed.
DTC: P0324 **1T CCM, MIL: Yes** **Years:** 2008, 2009 **Models:** Equinox, G6, G8, Torrent **Engines:** 4.2L VIN S, 4.8L VIN C, 3.5L VIN N, 3.5L VIN K, 3.9L VIN 3, 3.9L VIN M, 3.6L VIN 2, 3.9L VIN 1 4.6L VIN Y, 6.2L VIN P, 7.0L VIN E **Transmissions:** All	**Knock Sensor (KS) Circuit (Bank 1)** DTC P0324, P0326, P0327, P0328, P0330, P0332, or P0333 is not set. The engine speed is greater than 400 RPM. The Engine Coolant Temperature (ECT) is greater than −40°C (−40°F). The engine run time is greater than 2 minutes. DTCs P0325 and P0330 run continuously when the above conditions are met. **Possible Causes:** • KS circuits A and B for a short to ground or an open/high resistance • KS circuits A and B for a short to voltage • KS sensor has failed • ECM has failed
DTC: P0325 **1T CCM, MIL: Yes** **Years:** 2008, 2009 **Models:** Express, G8, Lucerne, Trailblazer **Engines:** 4.6L VIN Y, 4.6L VIN 9, 6.0L VIN H, 6.0L VIN Y, 6.0L VIN K, 6.2L VIN W, 6.6L VIN 6 **Transmissions:** All	**Knock Sensor (KS) Circuit (Bank 1)** DTC P0324, P0325, P0326, P0327, P0328, P0330, P0332, or P0333 is not set. The engine speed is greater than 400 RPM. The Engine Coolant Temperature (ECT) is greater than −40°C (−40°F). The engine run time is greater than 2 minutes. DTCs P0325 and P0330 run continuously when the above conditions are met. The KS signal circuits are open or shorted together for 5 seconds. **Possible Causes:** • KS sensor signal circuit for a short to ground or an open/high resistance • KS sensor signal circuit for a short to voltage • KS sensor low reference circuit for a short to ground or an open/high resistance • KS sensor • KS sensor has failed • ECM has failed

DTC	Trouble Code Title, Conditions & Possible Causes
DTC: P0325 **1T CCM, MIL: Yes** **Years:** 2008, 2009 **Models:** Envoy, Equinox, Savana, Torrent **Engines:** 3.4L VIN F, 4.3L VIN X, 5.3L VIN M **Transmissions:** All	**Knock Sensor (KS) Circuit** DTCs P0335, P0336, P0340, P0341, P0365, P0366, P0601, P0602, or P0604 are not set. The engine speed is greater than 2,500 RPM. The mass air flow (MAF) is greater than 20 g/s. The engine is NOT in decel fuel cut-off. The KS signal voltage is above or below a calibrated range for 20 engine revolutions. **Note: If the KS lead is damaged in any way, replace the KS.** **Possible Causes:** • Knock sensor signal circuit is open, shorted to ground or power • Knock sensor ground circuit is open (i.e., not mounted properly) • Knock sensor is damaged or has failed • ECM has failed.
DTC: P0325 **1T CCM, MIL: Yes** **Years:** 2008, 2009 **Models:** G6, HHR, Malibu **Engines:** 2.0L VIN X, 2.2L VIN D, 2.2L VIN B, 2.2L VIN F, 2.4L VIN B, 2.4L VIN V, 2.4L VIN P, 2.4L VIN 5 **Transmissions:** All	**Knock Sensor Circuit Malfunction** DTC P0122 and P0123 not set, engine started, vehicle driven at an engine speed of 1600-6400 RPM for 20 seconds, ECT sensor over 131°F, MAP sensor more than 60 kPa, and the ECM detected the KS sensor signal variation was out of normal range for 15 seconds. **Possible Causes:** • Knock sensor signal circuit is open, shorted to ground or power • Knock sensor ground circuit is open (not mounted properly) • Knock sensor is damaged or has failed • On modules with an integrated sensor, clear the codes and retest for codes. If the same code resets, the ECM has failed.
DTC: P0325 **1T CCM, MIL: Yes** **Years:** 2008, 2009 **Models:** Equinox, G6, G8, Torrent **Engines:** 4.2L VIN S, 4.8L VIN C, 3.5L VIN N, 3.5L VIN K, 3.9L VIN 3, 3.9L VIN M, 3.6L VIN 2, 3.9L VIN 1 4.6L VIN Y, 6.2L VIN P, 7.0L VIN E **Transmissions:** All	**Knock Sensor Circuit Malfunction** DTC P0327 not set, engine started, engine runtime from 10 seconds to 2 minutes, system voltage over 10.0v and the ECM detected an unexpected voltage condition for a period of 5-25 seconds on the diagnostic circuit used during diagnosis of the Knock sensor. **Possible Causes:** • Knock sensor signal circuit is open, shorted to ground or power • Knock sensor ground circuit is open (i.e., not mounted properly) • Knock sensor is damaged or has failed • On modules with an integrated sensor, clear the codes and retest for codes. If the same code resets, the ECM has failed.
DTC: P0325 **2T CCM, MIL: Yes** **Years:** 2008, 2009 **Models:** G6, HHR, Malibu **Engines:** 2.0L VIN X, 2.2L VIN D, 2.2L VIN B, 2.2L VIN F, 2.4L VIN B, 2.4L VIN V, 2.4L VIN P, 2.4L VIN 5 **Transmissions:** All	**Knock Sensor Circuit Malfunction** DTC P0101, P0102, P0103, P0116, P0117, P0118, P0121, P0122, P0123, P0125, P0336, P0341, P0502, P0503, P1114, P1115, P1121, P1122 and P1336 are not set, engine speed from 1000-5000 RPM for 30 seconds, TP sensor over 15%, engine load over 45%, ECT sensor over 140°F, spark retard less than 15 degrees, and the ECM detected an unexpected voltage condition on the Knock Sensor circuit used by the ECM to test the sensor. **Possible Causes:** • Knock sensor signal circuit is open, shorted to ground or power • Knock sensor ground circuit is open (i.e., not mounted properly) • Knock sensor is damaged or has failed • On modules with an integrated sensor, clear the codes and retest for codes. If the same code resets, the ECM has failed.
DTC: P0326 **1T CCM, MIL: Yes** **Years:** 2008, 2009 **Models:** Express, G8, Lucerne, Trailblazer **Engines:** 4.6L VIN Y, 4.6L VIN 9, 6.0L VIN H, 6.0L VIN Y, 6.0L VIN K, 6.2L VIN W, 6.6L VIN 6 **Transmissions:** All	**Knock Sensor (KS) Performance** DTC P0068, P0120, P0121, P0122, P0123, P0220, P0222, P0223, P0606, P1516, P2101, P2135, or P2176 is not set. The engine speed is greater than 400 RPM. The Manifold Air Pressure (MAP) is greater than 10 kPa. DTC P0326 runs continuously when the above conditions are met. The KS signal indicates an engine knock is present. The ECM has commanded the spark retard to a value which is more than the calibrated valve, for a specific engine load and speed. The above conditions exist for more than 5 seconds. **Possible Causes:** • KS sensor signal circuit for a short to ground or an open/high resistance • KS sensor signal circuit for a short to voltage • KS sensor low reference circuit for a short to ground or an open/high resistance • KS sensor • KS sensor has failed • ECM has failed
DTC: P0326 **1T CCM, MIL: Yes** **Years:** 2008, 2009 **Models:** Envoy, Equinox, Savana, Torrent **Engines:** 3.4L VIN F, 4.3L VIN X, 5.3L VIN M **Transmissions:** All	**Knock Sensor (KS) System Performance (Bank 1)** The Engine Coolant Temperature (ECT) sensor is warmer than 60°C (140°F). The engine speed is greater than 2,200 RPM. DTC P0326 runs continuously once the above conditions are met for approximately 20 seconds. The ECM detects a short to ground or a voltage on the KS signal circuits in 25 of 250 test samples. The condition exists for greater than 1 second or for a cumulative of 10 seconds. **Possible Causes:** • Knock sensor signal circuit is open, shorted to ground or power • Knock sensor ground circuit is open (check for proper torque) • Knock sensor is damaged or has failed • ECM has failed

DTC	Trouble Code Title, Conditions & Possible Causes
DTC: P0326 **1T CCM, MIL: Yes** **Years:** 2008, 2009 **Models:** Equinox, G6, G8, Torrent **Engines:** 4.2L VIN S, 4.8L VIN C, 3.5L VIN N, 3.5L VIN K, 3.9L VIN 3, 3.9L VIN M, 3.6L VIN 2, 3.9L VIN 1, 4.6L VIN Y, 6.2L VIN P, 7.0L VIN E **Transmissions:** All	**Knock Sensor (KS) System Performance** DTCs P0335, P0336, P0340, P0341, P0365, P0366, P0601, P0602, or P0604 are not set. The engine speed is greater than 2,500 RPM. The mass air flow (MAF) is greater than 20 g/s. The engine is NOT in decel fuel cut-off. The KS signal is not present for 20 engine revolutions. **Possible Causes:** • Knock sensor signal circuit is open, shorted to ground or power • Knock sensor ground circuit is open (check for proper torque) • Knock sensor is damaged or has failed • ECM has failed
DTC: P0326 **1T CCM, MIL: Yes** **Years:** 2008, 2009 **Models:** G6, HHR, Malibu **Engines:** 2.0L VIN X, 2.2L VIN D, 2.2L VIN B, 2.2L VIN F, 2.4L VIN B, 2.4L VIN V, 2.4L VIN P, 2.4L VIN 5 **Transmissions:** All	**Knock Sensor (KS) Circuit Low Voltage (Bank 1)** The KS signal circuits are shorted to voltage or ground. The ignition timing is retarded to reduce the potential of engine damaging spark knock. **Possible Causes:** • KS circuits A and B for a short to ground or an open/high resistance • KS circuits A and B for a short to voltage • KS sensor has failed • ECM has failed
DTC: P0327 **1T CCM, MIL: Yes** **Years:** 2008, 2009 **Models:** Express, G8, Lucerne, Trailblazer **Engines:** 4.6L VIN Y, 4.6L VIN 9, 6.0L VIN H, 6.0L VIN Y, 6.0L VIN K, 6.2L VIN W, 6.6L VIN 6 **Transmissions:** All	**Knock Sensor (KS) Circuit Low Voltage (Bank 1)** DTC P0112, P0113, P0116, P0117, P0118, or P0128 is not set. The Engine Coolant Temperature (ECT) is greater than −40°C (−40°F). The engine oil temperature is less than 256°C (492.8°F). The engine run time is greater than 2 minutes. DTCs P0327, P0328, P0332, and P0333 run continuously when the above conditions are met. The KS signal circuits are shorted to voltage or ground. **Possible Causes:** • KS sensor signal circuit for a short to ground or an open/high resistance • KS sensor signal circuit for a short to voltage • KS sensor low reference circuit for a short to ground or an open/high resistance • KS sensor • KS sensor has failed • ECM has failed
DTC: P0327 **1T CCM, MIL: Yes** **Years:** 2008, 2009 **Models:** Envoy, Equinox, Savana, Torrent **Engines:** 3.4L VIN F, 4.3L VIN X, 5.3L VIN M **Transmissions:** All	**Knock Sensor (KS) System Performance (Bank 1)** The Engine Coolant Temperature (ECT) sensor is warmer than 60°C (140°F). The increase in engine speed is less than a range of 500-2300 RPM per second. The engine speed is greater than 2,200 RPM. DTC P0326 runs continuously once the above conditions are met for approximately 20 seconds. The ECM detects a short to ground or a voltage on the KS signal circuits in 25 of 250 test samples. The condition exists for greater than 1 second or for a cumulative of 10 seconds. **Possible Causes:** • Knock sensor signal circuit is open, shorted to ground or power • Knock sensor ground circuit is open (check for proper torque) • Knock sensor is damaged or has failed • ECM has failed
DTC: P0327 **1T CCM, MIL: Yes** **Years:** 2008, 2009 **Models:** Envoy, Equinox, G6, G8, Impala, Lucerne, Malibu, Savana, Trailblazer, Torrent **Engines:** 4.2L VIN S, 4.8L VIN C, 3.5L VIN N, 3.5L VIN K, 3.9L VIN 3, 3.9L VIN M, 3.6L VIN 2, 3.9L VIN 1 **Transmissions:** All	**Knock Sensor Circuit Low Input (Bank 1)** DTC P0117, P0118, P0121, P0122, P0123, P0125, P1114, P1115, P1121, P1122 and P1258 not set, engine speed from 475-975 for 10 seconds, ECT sensor over 140°F, system voltage over 10.0v, minimum noise level learned, then with the engine speed from 1500-3000 RPM for 10 seconds, the MAP sensor less than 49 kPa, TP angle over 0%, and the ECM detected the Knock sensor was within an assigned average range for 9 seconds. **Possible Causes:** • Knock sensor signal circuit is open, shorted to ground or power • Knock sensor ground circuit is open (check for proper torque) • Knock sensor is damaged or has failed • ECM has failed
DTC: P0328 **1T CCM, MIL: Yes** **Years:** 2008, 2009 **Models:** Express, G8, Lucerne, Trailblazer **Engines:** 4.6L VIN Y, 4.6L VIN 9, 6.0L VIN H, 6.0L VIN Y, 6.0L VIN K, 6.2L VIN W, 6.6L VIN 6 **Transmissions:** All	**Knock Sensor (KS) Circuit High Voltage (Bank 1)** DTC P0112, P0113, P0116, P0117, P0118, or P0128 is not set. The Engine Coolant Temperature (ECT) is greater than −40°C (-40°F). The engine oil temperature is less than 256°C (492.8°F). The engine run time is greater than 2 minutes. DTCs P0327, P0328, P0332, and P0333 run continuously when the above conditions are met. The KS signal circuits are shorted to voltage or ground. **Possible Causes:** • KS sensor signal circuit for a short to ground or an open/high resistance • KS sensor signal circuit for a short to voltage • KS sensor low reference circuit for a short to ground or an open/high resistance • KS sensor • KS sensor has failed • ECM has failed

DTC	Trouble Code Title, Conditions & Possible Causes
DTC: P0328 **1T CCM, MIL: Yes** **Years:** 2008, 2009 **Models:** Envoy, Equinox, Savana, Torrent **Engines:** 3.4L VIN F, 4.3L VIN X, 5.3L VIN M **Transmissions:** All	**Knock Sensor (KS) System Performance (Bank 1)** The Engine Coolant Temperature (ECT) sensor is warmer than 60°C (140°F). The increase in engine speed is less than a range of 500-2300 RPM per second.The engine speed is greater than 2,200 RPM. DTC P0326 runs continuously once the above conditions are met for approximately 20 seconds. The ECM detects a short to ground or a voltage on the KS signal circuits in 25 of 250 test samples. The condition exists for greater than 1 second or for a cumulative of 10 seconds. **Possible Causes:** • Knock sensor signal circuit is open, shorted to ground or power • Knock sensor ground circuit is open (check for proper torque) • Knock sensor is damaged or has failed • ECM has failed
DTC: P0328 **1T CCM, MIL: Yes** **Years:** 2008, 2009 **Models:** Envoy, Equinox, G6, G8, Impala, Lucerne, Malibu, Savana, Trailblazer, Torrent **Engines:** 4.2L VIN S, 4.8L VIN C, 3.5L VIN N, 3.5L VIN K, 3.9L VIN 3, 3.9L VIN M, 3.6L VIN 2, 3.9L VIN 1 **Transmissions:** All	**Knock Sensor Circuit Low Input (Bank 1)** DTC P0117, P0118 and P0125 not set, engine runtime 10 seconds, minimum noise level learned with the engine speed from 475-975 RPM, then with the engine speed from 1500-3000, ECT sensor more than 140°F, MAP sensor under 49 kPa, TP angle over 0%, system voltage over 10.0v, the ECM detected the Knock Sensor signal was within a calculated voltage range or no signal existed for 9 seconds. **Possible Causes:** • Knock sensor signal circuit is open, shorted to ground or power • Knock sensor ground circuit is open (check for proper torque) • Knock sensor is damaged or it has failed • ECM has failed
DTC: P0330 **1T CCM, MIL: Yes** **Years:** 2008, 2009 **Models:** Express, G8, Lucerne, Trailblazer **Engines:** 4.6L VIN Y, 4.6L VIN 9, 6.0L VIN H, 6.0L VIN Y, 6.0L VIN K, 6.2L VIN W, 6.6L VIN 6 **Transmissions:** All	**Knock Sensor (KS) Circuit (Bank 2)** DTC P0324, P0325, P0326, P0327, P0328, P0330, P0332, or P0333 is not set. The engine speed is greater than 400 RPM. The Engine Coolant Temperature (ECT) is greater than −40°C (−40°F). The engine run time is greater than 2 minutes. DTCs P0325 and P0330 run continuously when the above conditions are met. The KS signal circuits are open or shorted together for 5 seconds. **Possible Causes:** • KS sensor signal circuit for a short to ground or an open/high resistance • KS sensor signal circuit for a short to voltage • KS sensor low reference circuit for a short to ground or an open/high resistance • KS sensor • KS sensor has failed • ECM has failed
DTC: P0330 **1T CCM, MIL: Yes** **Years:** 2008, 2009 **Models:** Envoy, Equinox, Savana, Torrent **Engines:** 3.4L VIN F, 4.3L VIN X, 5.3L VIN M **Transmissions:** All	**Knock Sensor (KS) System Performance (Bank 1)** The engine coolant temperature (ECT) sensor is warmer than 60°C (140°F). The engine speed is greater than 2,200 RPM. DTC P0326 runs continuously once the above conditions are met for approximately 20 seconds. The ECM detects a short to ground or a voltage on the KS signal circuits in 25 of 250 test samples. The condition exists for greater than 1 second or for a cumulative of 10 seconds. **Possible Causes:** • Knock sensor signal circuit is open, shorted to ground or power • Knock sensor ground circuit is open (check for proper torque) • Knock sensor is damaged or has failed • ECM has failed
DTC: P0331 **1T CCM, MIL: Yes** **Years:** 2008, 2009 **Models:** Express, G8, Lucerne, Trailblazer **Engines:** 4.6L VIN Y, 4.6L VIN 9, 6.0L VIN H, 6.0L VIN Y, 6.0L VIN K, 6.2L VIN W, 6.6L VIN 6 **Transmissions:** All	**Knock Sensor (KS) System Performance (Bank 2)** Before the ECM can report DTC P0326 or P0331 failed, DTCs P0324, P0335, P0336, and P0338 must run and pass. DTC P0341, P0342, P0343, P0346, P0347, P0348, P0366, P0367, P0368, P0391, P0392, or P0393 is not set. The Engine Coolant Temperature (ECT) sensor is warmer than 60°C (140°F). The engine speed is greater than 2,200 RPM. DTCs P0331 runs continuously once the above conditions are met for approximately 20 seconds. The ECM detects a short to ground or a voltage on the KS signal circuits in 25 of 250 test samples. The condition exists for greater than 1 second or for a cumulative of 10 seconds. **Possible Causes:** • KS sensor signal circuit for a short to ground or an open/high resistance • KS sensor signal circuit for a short to voltage • KS sensor low reference circuit for a short to ground or an open/high resistance • KS sensor • KS sensor has failed • ECM has failed

DTC	Trouble Code Title, Conditions & Possible Causes
DTC: P0331 **1T CCM, MIL: Yes** **Years:** 2008, 2009 **Models:** Envoy, Equinox, G6, G8, Impala, Lucerne, Malibu, Savana, Trailblazer, Torrent **Engines:** 4.2L VIN S, 4.8L VIN C, 3.5L VIN N, 3.5L VIN K, 3.9L VIN 3, 3.9L VIN M, 3.6L VIN 2, 3.9L VIN 1 **Transmissions:** All	**Knock Sensor (KS) Circuit Low Voltage (Bank 2)** The KS signal circuits are shorted to voltage or ground. The ignition timing is retarded to reduce the potential of engine damaging spark knock. **Possible Causes** • KS circuits A and B for a short to ground or an open/high resistance • KS circuits A and B for a short to voltage • KS sensor has failed • ECM has failed
DTC: P0332 **1T CCM, MIL: Yes** **Years:** 2008, 2009 **Models:** Express, G8, Lucerne, Trailblazer **Engines:** 4.6L VIN Y, 4.6L VIN 9, 6.0L VIN H, 6.0L VIN Y, 6.0L VIN K, 6.2L VIN W, 6.6L VIN 6 **Transmissions:** All	**Knock Sensor (KS) Circuit Low Voltage (Bank 2)** DTC P0112, P0113, P0116, P0117, P0118, or P0128 is not set. The Engine Coolant Temperature (ECT) is greater than −40°C (−40°F). The engine oil temperature is less than 256°C (492.8°F). The engine run time is greater than 2 minutes. DTCs P0327, P0328, P0332, and P0333 run continuously when the above conditions are met. The KS signal circuits are shorted to voltage or ground. **Possible Causes:** • KS sensor signal circuit for a short to ground or an open/high resistance • KS sensor signal circuit for a short to voltage • KS sensor low reference circuit for a short to ground or an open/high resistance • KS sensor • KS sensor has failed • ECM has failed
DTC: P0332 **1T CCM, MIL: Yes** **Years:** 2008, 2009 **Models:** Envoy, Equinox, Savana, Torrent **Engines:** 3.4L VIN F, 4.3L VIN X, 5.3L VIN M **Transmissions:** All	**Knock Sensor (KS) System Performance (Bank 1)** The Engine Coolant Temperature (ECT) sensor is warmer than 60°C (140°F). The increase in engine speed is less than a range of 500-2300 RPM per second. The engine speed is greater than 2,200 RPM. DTC P0326 runs continuously once the above conditions are met for approximately 20 seconds. The ECM detects a short to ground or a voltage on the KS signal circuits in 25 of 250 test samples. The condition exists for greater than 1 second or for a cumulative of 10 seconds. **Possible Causes:** • Knock sensor signal circuit is open, shorted to ground or power • Knock sensor ground circuit is open (check for proper torque) • Knock sensor is damaged or has failed • ECM has failed
DTC: P0332 **1T CCM, MIL: Yes** **Years:** 2008, 2009 **Models:** Envoy, Equinox, G6, G8, Impala, Lucerne, Malibu, Savana, Trailblazer, Torrent **Engines:** 4.2L VIN S, 4.8L VIN C, 3.5L VIN N, 3.5L VIN K, 3.9L VIN 3, 3.9L VIN M, 3.6L VIN 2, 3.9L VIN 1 **Transmissions:** All	**Knock Sensor Circuit Malfunction (Bank 2)** DTC P0101-P0103, P0116-P0118, P0121-P0123, P0125, P0128, P0336, P0341, P0502, P0503, P1114, P1115, P1121 and P1336 not set, engine started, engine speed at 1000-4000 RPM for 30 seconds, system voltage over 10.0v, ECT sensor over 140°F, TP angle from 3-15%, engine load 20-45%, spark retard less than 15 degrees, and the ECM detected an invalid voltage on the Knock sensor circuit. **Possible Causes:** • Knock sensor signal circuit is open, shorted to ground or power • Knock sensor ground circuit is open (i.e., not mounted properly) • Knock sensor is damaged or has failed • On modules with an integrated sensor, clear the codes and retest for codes. If the same code resets, the ECM has failed.
DTC: P0332 **2T CCM, MIL: Yes** **Years:** 2008, 2009 **Engines:** 4.6L VIN Y, 4.6L VIN 9, 6.0L VIN H, 6.0L VIN Y, 6.0L VIN K, 6.2L VIN W, 6.6L VIN 6 **Transmissions:** All	**Knock Sensor Circuit Malfunction (Bank 2)** DTC P0117, P0118, P0121-P0123, P0125, P1114, P1115, P1120 and P1122 not set, engine started, engine speed from 475-975 for 10 seconds, system voltage from 10-18v, ECT sensor more than 140°F, minimum noise level learned, then with the engine speed from 1500-3000 RPM, MAP sensor less than 49 kPa, TP angle more than 0% for 10 seconds, the ECM detected the KS signal was less than or more than the expected amount for 9 seconds. **Possible Causes:** • Knock sensor signal circuit is open, shorted to ground or power • Knock sensor ground circuit is open (check for proper torque) • Knock sensor is damaged or has failed • ECM has failed • TSB 02-06-04-023A contains a repair procedure for this code

DTC	Trouble Code Title, Conditions & Possible Causes
DTC: P0333 **1T CCM, MIL: Yes** **Years:** 2008, 2009 **Models:** Express, G8, Lucerne, Trailblazer **Engines:** 4.6L VIN Y, 4.6L VIN 9, 6.0L VIN H, 6.0L VIN Y, 6.0L VIN K, 6.2L VIN W, 6.6L VIN 6 **Transmissions:** All	**Knock Sensor (KS) Circuit High Voltage (Bank 2)** DTC P0112, P0113, P0116, P0117, P0118, or P0128 is not set. The Engine Coolant Temperature (ECT) is greater than −40°C (−40°F). The engine oil temperature is less than 256°C (492.8°F). The engine run time is greater than 2 minutes. DTCs P0327, P0328, P0332, and P0333 run continuously when the above conditions are met. The KS signal circuits are shorted to voltage or ground. **Possible Causes:** • KS sensor signal circuit for a short to ground or an open/high resistance • KS sensor signal circuit for a short to voltage • KS sensor low reference circuit for a short to ground or an open/high resistance • KS sensor • KS sensor has failed • ECM has failed
DTC: P0333 **1T CCM, MIL: Yes** **Years:** 2008, 2009 **Models:** Envoy, Equinox, Savana, Torrent **Engines:** 3.4L VIN F, 4.3L VIN X, 5.3L VIN M **Transmissions:** All	**Knock Sensor (KS) System Performance (Bank 1)** The Engine Coolant Temperature (ECT) sensor is warmer than 60°C (140°F). The increase in engine speed is less than a range of 500-2300 RPM per second. The engine speed is greater than 2,200 RPM. DTC P0326 runs continuously once the above conditions are met for approximately 20 seconds. The ECM detects a short to ground or a voltage on the KS signal circuits in 25 of 250 test samples. The condition exists for greater than 1 second or for a cumulative of 10 seconds. **Possible Causes:** • Knock sensor signal circuit is open, shorted to ground or power • Knock sensor ground circuit is open (check for proper torque) • Knock sensor is damaged or has failed • ECM has failed
DTC: P0333 **1T CCM, MIL: Yes** **Years:** 2008, 2009 **Models:** Envoy, Equinox, G6, G8, Impala, Lucerne, Malibu, Savana, Trailblazer, Torrent **Engines:** 4.2L VIN S, 4.8L VIN C, 3.5L VIN N, 3.5L VIN K, 3.9L VIN 3, 3.9L VIN M, 3.6L VIN 2, 3.9L VIN 1 **Transmissions:** All	**Crankshaft Position (CKP) Sensor Circuit** DTC P0340, P0341, P0641, or P0651 is not set. The engine is cranking or running. DTC P0335 runs continuously when the above conditions are met. DTC P0335 runs continuously when the above conditions are met. Or the ECM detects that the engine is running, but has not received a CKP sensor pulse for 2 of 10 engine cycles. **Possible Causes:** • CKP sensor low reference circuit for an open/high resistance • CKP sensor 5-volt reference circuit for an open/high resistance or short to ground • CKP sensor 5-volt reference circuit for a short to voltage • CKP sensor signal circuit for an open/high resistance or short to ground • CKP sensor signal circuit for a short to voltage • CKP sensor has failed • ECM has failed
DTC: P0335 **1T CCM, MIL: Yes** **Years:** 2008, 2009 **Models:** Express, G8, Lucerne, Trailblazer **Engines:** 4.6L VIN Y, 4.6L VIN 9, 6.0L VIN H, 6.0L VIN Y, 6.0L VIN K, 6.2L VIN W, 6.6L VIN 6 **Transmissions:** All	**Crankshaft Position (CKP) Sensor Circuit** DTC P0340, P0341, P0641, or P0651 is not set. The engine is cranking or running. DTC P0335 runs continuously when the above conditions are met. The ECM detects that the starter is commanded on and the engine has been cranking for more than 4 seconds without a CKP sensor pulse. The ECM detects that the engine is running, but has not received a CKP sensor pulse for 2 of 10 engine cycles. **Possible Causes:** • CKP sensor low reference circuit for an open/high resistance • CKP sensor 5-volt reference circuit for an open/high resistance or short to ground • CKP sensor 5-volt reference circuit for a short to voltage. • CKP sensor signal circuit for an open/high resistance or short to ground • CKP sensor signal circuit for a short to voltage • CKP sensor has failed • ECM has failed
DTC: P0335 **1T CCM, MIL: Yes** **Years:** 2008, 2009 **Models:** Envoy, Equinox, Savana, Torrent **Engines:** 3.4L VIN F, 4.3L VIN X, 5.3L VIN M **Transmissions:** All	**Crankshaft Position (CKP) Sensor Circuit** The engine is cranking or operating. The ECM has detected greater than 12 camshaft revolutions. The ECM does not detect a signal from the CKP sensor. Or the ECM detects a CKP signal without a reference pulse for greater than 6 revolutions. **Possible Causes:** • Physical damage to the CKP sensor or the reluctor wheel • 5 volt reference circuit for a short to ground or for an open/high resistance. • 5.volt reference circuit for a short to voltage • Short to voltage in the signal circuit • Short to ground or an open/high resistance in the signal circuit • CKP has failed • ECM has failed

DTC	Trouble Code Title, Conditions & Possible Causes
DTC: P0335 **1T CCM, MIL: Yes** **Years:** 2008, 2009 **Models:** Envoy, Equinox, G6, G8, Impala, Lucerne, Malibu, Savana, Trailblazer, Torrent **Engines:** 4.2L VIN S, 4.8L VIN C, 3.5L VIN N, 3.5L VIN K, 3.9L VIN 3, 3.9L VIN M, 3.6L VIN 2, 3.9L VIN 1 **Transmissions:** All	**CKP Sensor Circuit Malfunction** DTC P0101, P0102, P0103, P0341, P0342 and P0343 not set; engine cranking, CMP signal varying, MAF sensor more than 3 g/sec, and the ECM did not detect any signals from the CKP sensor for less than 8 seconds during the CCM test period. **Possible Causes:** • CKP sensor signal circuit is open or shorted to ground • CKP sensor ground (low reference) circuit is open • CKP sensor power circuit is open between sensor and the ECM • Crankshaft reluctor wheel is damaged or improper installation • ECM has failed
DTC: P0335 **1T CCM, MIL: Yes** **Years:** 2008, 2009 **Models:** Express, G8, Lucerne, Trailblazer **Engines:** All **Transmissions:** All	**Crankshaft Position Sensor Circuit Malfunction** DTC P0101, P0102, P0103, P0341, P0342 and P0343 not set, engine cranking, CMP sensor signals transitioning, MAF sensor more than 3 g/sec, and the ECM did not detect any signals from the CKP sensor (Hall Effect) for up 4-8 seconds during the CCM test. **Possible Causes:** • CKP sensor signal circuit is open or shorted to ground • CKP sensor VREF circuit is open between the sensor and ECM • CKP sensor ground (Low Reference) circuit is open • CKP sensor is damaged or it failed (check crankshaft reluctor) • ECM has failed
DTC: P0335 **1T CCM, MIL: Yes** **Years:** 2008, 2009 **Models:** G6, HHR, Malibu **Engines:** 2.0L VIN X, 2.2L VIN D, 2.2L VIN B, 2.2L VIN F, 2.4L VIN B, 2.4L VIN V, 2.4L VIN P, 2.4L VIN 5 **Transmissions:** All	**Crankshaft Position Sensor Circuit Malfunction** DTC P0562 not set, engine started; system voltage less than 18v, and the ECM did not detect any CKP sensor signals. **Possible Causes:** • CKP sensor signal (+) circuit or (−) circuit is open or shorted to ground • CKP sensor is damaged or has failed • ECM has failed
DTC: P0336 **1T CCM, MIL: Yes** **Years:** 2008, 2009 **Models:** Express, G8, Lucerne, Trailblazer **Engines:** 4.6L VIN Y, 4.6L VIN 9, 6.0L VIN H, 6.0L VIN Y, 6.0L VIN K, 6.2L VIN W, 6.6L VIN 6 **Transmissions:** All	**Crankshaft Position (CKP) Sensor Performance** DTC P0340, P0341, P0641, or P0651 is not set. The engine is cranking or running. DTC P0336 runs continuously when the above conditions are met. The ECM detects that the engine is running, but receives less than 53 or more than 63 CKP sensor pulses, during each engine revolution, for 8 of 10 engine revolutions. The ECM detects that the engine is running, but more than 25 crankshaft resyncs have occurred within 20 seconds. The ECM detects that the engine has been running, but the crankshaft does not sync for 0.4 second. **Possible Causes:** • Crankshaft reluctor wheel for damage • Timing chain, tensioner, and sprockets for wear or damage • CKP sensor for correct installation • Harness connector to the CKP sensor • CKP sensor has failed
DTC: P0336 **1T CCM, MIL: Yes** **Years:** 2008, 2009 **Models:** Envoy, Equinox, Savana, Torrent **Engines:** 3.4L VIN F, 4.3L VIN X, 5.3L VIN M **Transmissions:** All	**Crankshaft Position (CKP) Sensor Performance** The engine is cranking or operating. The ECM has detected greater than 12 camshaft revolutions The ECM re-syncs the engine position greater than 2,600 times during an ignition cycle. The ECM detects 28 or more interruptions in the engine speed signal during an ignition cycle. **Possible Causes:** • Physical damage to the CKP sensor or the reluctor wheel • 5 volt reference circuit for a short to ground or for an open/high resistance. • 5.volt reference circuit for a short to voltage • Short to voltage in the signal circuit • Short to ground or an open/high resistance in the signal circuit • CKP has failed • ECM has failed
DTC: P0336 **1T CCM, MIL: Yes** **Years:** 2008, 2009 **Models:** Envoy, Equinox, G6, G8, Impala, Lucerne, Malibu, Savana, Trailblazer, Torrent **Engines:** 4.2L VIN S, 4.8L VIN C, 3.5L VIN N, 3.5L VIN K, 3.9L VIN 3, 3.9L VIN M, 3.6L VIN 2, 3.9L VIN 1 **Transmissions:** All	**Crankshaft Reference 24X Circuit Malfunction** Engine started; 3X signals detected for 3 seconds, and the ECM detected an invalid ratio of 24X to 3X CKP REF pulses. The circuit uses 2 different types of crankshaft position (CKP) sensors. The CKP Sensor 'A' connects directly to the ECM through the 12v VREF, Medium Resolution engine speed signal and the low reference circuits. The CKP Sensor 'B' connects directly to the ignition control (IC) module via the CKP 'B' signal and low reference circuits. **Possible Causes:** • CKP sensor signal circuit is open or shorted to ground • CKP sensor ground (Low Reference) circuit is open • CKP sensor is damaged or it failed (check crankshaft reluctor) • ECM has failed

DTC	Trouble Code Title, Conditions & Possible Causes
DTC: P0333 **1T CCM, MIL: Yes** **Years:** 2008, 2009 **Models:** Express, G8, Lucerne, Trailblazer **Engines:** 4.6L VIN Y, 4.6L VIN 9, 6.0L VIN H, 6.0L VIN Y, 6.0L VIN K, 6.2L VIN W, 6.6L VIN 6 **Transmissions:** All	**Knock Sensor (KS) Circuit High Voltage (Bank 2)** DTC P0112, P0113, P0116, P0117, P0118, or P0128 is not set. The Engine Coolant Temperature (ECT) is greater than −40°C (−40°F). The engine oil temperature is less than 256°C (492.8°F). The engine run time is greater than 2 minutes. DTCs P0327, P0328, P0332, and P0333 run continuously when the above conditions are met. The KS signal circuits are shorted to voltage or ground. **Possible Causes:** • KS sensor signal circuit for a short to ground or an open/high resistance • KS sensor signal circuit for a short to voltage • KS sensor low reference circuit for a short to ground or an open/high resistance • KS sensor • KS sensor has failed • ECM has failed
DTC: P0333 **1T CCM, MIL: Yes** **Years:** 2008, 2009 **Models:** Envoy, Equinox, Savana, Torrent **Engines:** 3.4L VIN F, 4.3L VIN X, 5.3L VIN M **Transmissions:** All	**Knock Sensor (KS) System Performance (Bank 1)** The Engine Coolant Temperature (ECT) sensor is warmer than 60°C (140°F). The increase in engine speed is less than a range of 500-2300 RPM per second.The engine speed is greater than 2,200 RPM. DTC P0326 runs continuously once the above conditions are met for approximately 20 seconds. The ECM detects a short to ground or a voltage on the KS signal circuits in 25 of 250 test samples. The condition exists for greater than 1 second or for a cumulative of 10 seconds. **Possible Causes:** • Knock sensor signal circuit is open, shorted to ground or power • Knock sensor ground circuit is open (check for proper torque) • Knock sensor is damaged or has failed • ECM has failed
DTC: P0333 **1T CCM, MIL: Yes** **Years:** 2008, 2009 **Models:** Envoy, Equinox, G6, G8, Impala, Lucerne, Malibu, Savana, Trailblazer, Torrent **Engines:** 4.2L VIN S, 4.8L VIN C, 3.5L VIN N, 3.5L VIN K, 3.9L VIN 3, 3.9L VIN M, 3.6L VIN 2, 3.9L VIN 1 **Transmissions:** All	**Crankshaft Position (CKP) Sensor Circuit** DTC P0340, P0341, P0641, or P0651 is not set. The engine is cranking or running. DTC P0335 runs continuously when the above conditions are met. DTC P0335 runs continuously when the above conditions are met. Or the ECM detects that the engine is running, but has not received a CKP sensor pulse for 2 of 10 engine cycles. **Possible Causes:** • CKP sensor low reference circuit for an open/high resistance • CKP sensor 5-volt reference circuit for an open/high resistance or short to ground • CKP sensor 5-volt reference circuit for a short to voltage • CKP sensor signal circuit for an open/high resistance or short to ground • CKP sensor signal circuit for a short to voltage • CKP sensor has failed • ECM has failed
DTC: P0335 **1T CCM, MIL: Yes** **Years:** 2008, 2009 **Models:** Express, G8, Lucerne, Trailblazer **Engines:** 4.6L VIN Y, 4.6L VIN 9, 6.0L VIN H, 6.0L VIN Y, 6.0L VIN K, 6.2L VIN W, 6.6L VIN 6 **Transmissions:** All	**Crankshaft Position (CKP) Sensor Circuit** DTC P0340, P0341, P0641, or P0651 is not set. The engine is cranking or running. DTC P0335 runs continuously when the above conditions are met. The ECM detects that the starter is commanded on and the engine has been cranking for more than 4 seconds without a CKP sensor pulse. The ECM detects that the engine is running, but has not received a CKP sensor pulse for 2 of 10 engine cycles. **Possible Causes:** • CKP sensor low reference circuit for an open/high resistance • CKP sensor 5-volt reference circuit for an open/high resistance or short to ground • CKP sensor 5-volt reference circuit for a short to voltage. • CKP sensor signal circuit for an open/high resistance or short to ground • CKP sensor signal circuit for a short to voltage • CKP sensor has failed • ECM has failed
DTC: P0335 **1T CCM, MIL: Yes** **Years:** 2008, 2009 **Models:** Envoy, Equinox, Savana, Torrent **Engines:** 3.4L VIN F, 4.3L VIN X, 5.3L VIN M **Transmissions:** All	**Crankshaft Position (CKP) Sensor Circuit** The engine is cranking or operating. The ECM has detected greater than 12 camshaft revolutions. The ECM does not detect a signal from the CKP sensor. Or the ECM detects a CKP signal without a reference pulse for greater than 6 revolutions. **Possible Causes:** • Physical damage to the CKP sensor or the reluctor wheel • 5 volt reference circuit for a short to ground or for an open/high resistance. • 5.volt reference circuit for a short to voltage • Short to voltage in the signal circuit • Short to ground or an open/high resistance in the signal circuit • CKP has failed • ECM has failed

DTC	Trouble Code Title, Conditions & Possible Causes
DTC: P0335 **1T CCM, MIL: Yes** **Years:** 2008, 2009 **Models:** Envoy, Equinox, G6, G8, Impala, Lucerne, Malibu, Savana, Trailblazer, Torrent **Engines:** 4.2L VIN S, 4.8L VIN C, 3.5L VIN N, 3.5L VIN K, 3.9L VIN 3, 3.9L VIN M, 3.6L VIN 2, 3.9L VIN 1 **Transmissions:** All	**CKP Sensor Circuit Malfunction** DTC P0101, P0102, P0103, P0341, P0342 and P0343 not set; engine cranking, CMP signal varying, MAF sensor more than 3 g/sec, and the ECM did not detect any signals from the CKP sensor for less than 8 seconds during the CCM test period. **Possible Causes:** • CKP sensor signal circuit is open or shorted to ground • CKP sensor ground (low reference) circuit is open • CKP sensor power circuit is open between sensor and the ECM • Crankshaft reluctor wheel is damaged or improper installation • ECM has failed
DTC: P0335 **1T CCM, MIL: Yes** **Years:** 2008, 2009 **Models:** Express, G8, Lucerne, Trailblazer **Engines:** All **Transmissions:** All	**Crankshaft Position Sensor Circuit Malfunction** DTC P0101, P0102, P0103, P0341, P0342 and P0343 not set, engine cranking, CMP sensor signals transitioning, MAF sensor more than 3 g/sec, and the ECM did not detect any signals from the CKP sensor (Hall Effect) for up 4-8 seconds during the CCM test. **Possible Causes:** • CKP sensor signal circuit is open or shorted to ground • CKP sensor VREF circuit is open between the sensor and ECM • CKP sensor ground (Low Reference) circuit is open • CKP sensor is damaged or it failed (check crankshaft reluctor) • ECM has failed
DTC: P0335 **1T CCM, MIL: Yes** **Years:** 2008, 2009 **Models:** G6, HHR, Malibu **Engines:** 2.0L VIN X, 2.2L VIN D, 2.2L VIN B, 2.2L VIN F, 2.4L VIN B, 2.4L VIN V, 2.4L VIN P, 2.4L VIN 5 **Transmissions:** All	**Crankshaft Position Sensor Circuit Malfunction** DTC P0562 not set, engine started; system voltage less than 18v, and the ECM did not detect any CKP sensor signals. **Possible Causes:** • CKP sensor signal (+) circuit or (−) circuit is open or shorted to ground • CKP sensor is damaged or has failed • ECM has failed
DTC: P0336 **1T CCM, MIL: Yes** **Years:** 2008, 2009 **Models:** Express, G8, Lucerne, Trailblazer **Engines:** 4.6L VIN Y, 4.6L VIN 9, 6.0L VIN H, 6.0L VIN Y, 6.0L VIN K, 6.2L VIN W, 6.6L VIN 6 **Transmissions:** All	**Crankshaft Position (CKP) Sensor Performance** DTC P0340, P0341, P0641, or P0651 is not set. The engine is cranking or running. DTC P0336 runs continuously when the above conditions are met. The ECM detects that the engine is running, but receives less than 53 or more than 63 CKP sensor pulses, during each engine revolution, for 8 of 10 engine revolutions. The ECM detects that the engine is running, but more than 25 crankshaft resyncs have occurred within 20 seconds. The ECM detects that the engine has been running, but the crankshaft does not sync for 0.4 second. **Possible Causes:** • Crankshaft reluctor wheel for damage • Timing chain, tensioner, and sprockets for wear or damage • CKP sensor for correct installation • Harness connector to the CKP sensor • CKP sensor has failed
DTC: P0336 **1T CCM, MIL: Yes** **Years:** 2008, 2009 **Models:** Envoy, Equinox, Savana, Torrent **Engines:** 3.4L VIN F, 4.3L VIN X, 5.3L VIN M **Transmissions:** All	**Crankshaft Position (CKP) Sensor Performance** The engine is cranking or operating. The ECM has detected greater than 12 camshaft revolutions The ECM re-syncs the engine position greater than 2,600 times during an ignition cycle. The ECM detects 28 or more interruptions in the engine speed signal during an ignition cycle. **Possible Causes:** • Physical damage to the CKP sensor or the reluctor wheel • 5 volt reference circuit for a short to ground or for an open/high resistance. • 5.volt reference circuit for a short to voltage • Short to voltage in the signal circuit • Short to ground or an open/high resistance in the signal circuit • CKP has failed • ECM has failed
DTC: P0336 **1T CCM, MIL: Yes** **Years:** 2008, 2009 **Models:** Envoy, Equinox, G6, G8, Impala, Lucerne, Malibu, Savana, Trailblazer, Torrent **Engines:** 4.2L VIN S, 4.8L VIN C, 3.5L VIN N, 3.5L VIN K, 3.9L VIN 3, 3.9L VIN M, 3.6L VIN 2, 3.9L VIN 1 **Transmissions:** All	**Crankshaft Reference 24X Circuit Malfunction** Engine started; 3X signals detected for 3 seconds, and the ECM detected an invalid ratio of 24X to 3X CKP REF pulses. The circuit uses 2 different types of crankshaft position (CKP) sensors. The CKP Sensor 'A' connects directly to the ECM through the 12v VREF, Medium Resolution engine speed signal and the low reference circuits. The CKP Sensor 'B' connects directly to the ignition control (IC) module via the CKP 'B' signal and low reference circuits. **Possible Causes:** • CKP sensor signal circuit is open or shorted to ground • CKP sensor ground (Low Reference) circuit is open • CKP sensor is damaged or it failed (check crankshaft reluctor) • ECM has failed

DTC	Trouble Code Title, Conditions & Possible Causes
DTC: P0336 **1T CCM, MIL: Yes** **Years:** 2008, 2009 **Models:** G6, HHR, Malibu **Engines:** 2.0L VIN X, 2.2L VIN D, 2.2L VIN B, 2.2L VIN F, 2.4L VIN B, 2.4L VIN V, 2.4L VIN P, 2.4L VIN 5 **Transmissions:** All	**Crankshaft Reference 18X Circuit Malfunction** Engine started; 3X REF signals detected, and the ECM did not detect any 18X pulses, or the ratio of 18X REF pulses to 3X REF pulses did not equal 6:1, or ratio of 3X REF pulses to CMP pulses equaled 6:1, conditions met for 290 of 300 samples. The Crankshaft Position Sensor (CKP) circuit uses two types of CKP sensors. CKP Sensor 'B' is connected directly to the ignition control module (ICM), while CKP sensor 'A' connects directly to the ECM. **Possible Causes:** • CKP sensor signal circuit is open or shorted to ground • CKP sensor VREF circuit is open, or the ground (Low Reference) circuit is open • CKP sensor is damaged or it failed (check the crankshaft reluctor) • CKP sensor wiring routed close to spark plug wires (EMI/RFI) • ECM has failed
DTC: P0336 **2T CCM, MIL: Yes** **Years:** 2008, 2009 **Models:** Express, G8, Lucerne, Trailblazer **Engines:** 4.6L VIN Y, 4.6L VIN 9, 6.0L VIN H, 6.0L VIN Y, 6.0L VIN K, 6.2L VIN W, 6.6L VIN 6 **Transmissions:** All	**Crankshaft Position Sensor Range/Performance** Engine cranking or running; and the ECM detected the CKP sensor signal was out-of-range for 2 seconds during the CCM test. **Possible Causes:** • CKP sensor signal circuit has a high resistance condition • CKP sensor ground (Low Reference) circuit has high resistance • CKP sensor is damaged or it failed (check crankshaft reluctor) • ECM has failed • Vehicle have been driven while very low on fuel
DTC: P0338 **1T CCM, MIL: Yes** **Years:** 2008, 2009 **Models:** Envoy, Equinox, G6, G8, Impala, Lucerne, Malibu, Savana, Trailblazer, Torrent **Engines:** 4.2L VIN S, 4.8L VIN C, 3.5L VIN N, 3.5L VIN K, 3.9L VIN 3, 3.9L VIN M, 3.6L VIN 2, 3.9L VIN 1 **Transmissions:** All	**Camshaft Position (CMP) Sensor Circuit** DTC P0335, P0336, P0641, or P0651 is not set. The engine is cranking or running. DTC P0340 runs continuously when the above conditions are met. The ECM detects that the starter is commanded on and the engine has been cranking for more than 4 seconds without a CMP sensor pulse. The ECM detects that the engine has started, but did not receive a CMP sensor pulse during the first engine revolution. The ECM detects that the engine is running, but does not receive a CMP sensor pulse for 800 of 1000 engine cycles. **Possible Causes:** • CMP sensor 5-volt reference circuit for an open/high resistance or short to ground • CMP sensor 5-volt reference circuit for a short to voltage • CMP sensor signal circuit for an open/high resistance or short to ground • CMP sensor signal circuit for a short to voltage • CKP sensor has failed • ECM has failed
DTC: P0340 **1T CCM, MIL: Yes** **Years:** 2008, 2009 **Models:** Express, G8, Lucerne, Trailblazer **Engines:** 4.6L VIN Y, 4.6L VIN 9, 6.0L VIN H, 6.0L VIN Y, 6.0L VIN K, 6.2L VIN W, 6.6L VIN 6 **Transmissions:** All	**Camshaft Position (CMP) Sensor Circuit** DTC P0335, P0336, P0641, or P0651 is not set. The engine is cranking or running. DTC P0340 runs continuously when the above conditions are met. The ECM detects that the starter is commanded on and the engine has been cranking for more than 4 seconds without a CMP sensor pulse. The ECM detects that the engine has started, but did not receive a CMP sensor pulse during the first engine revolution. The ECM detects that the engine is running, but does not receive a CMP sensor pulse for 800 of 1000 engine cycles. **Possible Causes:** • Close routing of aftermarket electrical equipment. • Close to solenoids, motors, and relays. • CMP sensor low reference circuit for an open/high resistance • CMP sensor 5-volt reference circuit for an open/high resistance or short to ground • CMP sensor 5-volt reference circuit for a short to voltage • CMP sensor signal circuit for an open/high resistance or short to ground • CMP sensor signal circuit for a short to voltage • CMP sensor has failed • ECM has failed
DTC: P0340 **1T CCM, MIL: Yes** **Years:** 2008, 2009 **Models:** Envoy, Equinox, Savana, Torrent **Engines:** 3.4L VIN F, 4.3L VIN X, 5.3L VIN M **Transmissions:** All	**Intake Camshaft Position (CMP) Sensor Circuit** The engine is running. DTCs P0340 and P0365 run continuously when the above condition is met. The ECM does not receive 2 camshaft pulses within 3 seconds. **Possible Causes:** • CMP sensor signal circuit is open, shorted to ground or shorted to VREF between the sensor and the ECM • CMP sensor VREF circuit is open between sensor and ECM • CMP sensor ground circuit or "shielded" ground circuit is open • CMP sensor is cracked or damaged (check the reluctor wheel) • ECM has failed

DTC	Trouble Code Title, Conditions & Possible Causes
DTC: P0340 **1T CCM, MIL: Yes** **Years:** 2008, 2009 **Models:** G6, HHR, Malibu **Engines:** 2.0L VIN X, 2.2L VIN D, 2.2L VIN B, 2.2L VIN F, 2.4L VIN B, 2.4L VIN V, 2.4L VIN P, 2.4L VIN 5 **Transmissions:** All	**CMP Sensor Circuit Malfunction** Engine started; and the ECM detected the CMP sensor (Hall Effect) Active Counter did not increment (i.e., no change detected in the CMP sensor activity for 30 crankshaft revolutions). **Possible Causes:** • CMP sensor signal circuit is open, shorted to ground or shorted to VREF between the sensor and the ECM • CMP sensor VREF circuit is open between sensor and ECM • CMP sensor ground circuit or "shielded" ground circuit is open • CMP sensor is cracked or damaged (check the reluctor wheel) • ECM has failed
DTC: P0341 **1T CCM, MIL: Yes** **Years:** 2008, 2009 **Models:** Express, G8, Lucerne, Trailblazer **Engines:** 4.6L VIN Y, 4.6L VIN 9, 6.0L VIN H, 6.0L VIN Y, 6.0L VIN K, 6.2L VIN W, 6.6L VIN 6 **Transmissions:** All	**Camshaft Position (CMP) Sensor Performance** DTC P0335, P0336, P0641, or P0651 is not set. The engine is cranking or running. DTC P0341 runs continuously when the above conditions are met. The ECM detects that the engine was started, but has received less than 2 or more than 8 CMP sensor pulses during the first engine resolution. The ECM detects that the engine has started and is running, but receives less than 398 or more than 402 CMP pulses per 100 engine cycles in 800 of 1000 engine cycles. **Possible Causes:** • Engine oil for debris • CMP sensor is loose, • Camshaft reluctor wheel for damage • timing chain, timing chain tensioner, and sprockets for wear or damage • Harness connector to the CMP sensor • CMP sensor has failed
DTC: P0341 **1T CCM, MIL: Yes** **Years:** 2008, 2009 **Models:** Envoy, Equinox, Savana, Torrent **Engines:** 3.4L VIN F, 4.3L VIN X, 5.3L VIN M **Transmissions:** All	**Intake Camshaft Position (CMP) Sensor Performance (Bank 1)** The ECM detects greater than 10 crankshaft revolutions. The engine speed is less than 2,520 RPM The DTCs run continuously once the above condition is met. The ECM detects a signal from the CMP sensor, but the number of pulses are less than or greater than what is expected for one crankshaft revolution. Or the CMP sensor does NOT correlate to the crankshaft position. Either condition must exist for greater than 1 second, or cumulative of 10 seconds. **Note: The control module or the sensor may be damaged if the circuit is shorted to B+ voltage.** **Possible Causes:** • Low reference circuit for an open/high resistance or for a short to voltage • 5 volt reference circuit for an open/high resistance • Short to voltage in the signal circuit • Short to ground or an open/high resistance in the signal circuit. • CMP has failed • ECM has failed
DTC: P0341 **1T CCM, MIL: Yes** **Years:** 2008, 2009 **Models:** Envoy, Equinox, G6, G8, Impala, Lucerne, Malibu, Savana, Trailblazer, Torrent **Engines:** 4.2L VIN S, 4.8L VIN C, 3.5L VIN N, 3.5L VIN K, 3.9L VIN 3, 3.9L VIN M, 3.6L VIN 2, 3.9L VIN 1 **Transmissions:** All	**Intake Camshaft Position (CMP) Sensor Performance** The engine is cranking or running. DTCs P0335, P0336, and P0365 are not set. DTC P0341 runs continuously when the above conditions are met. The ECM detects the incorrect number of CMP sensor pulses in 2 revolutions of the crankshaft, which is usually within 1 second. **Note: Inspect the CMP sensor for correct installation. Remove the CMP sensor from the engine and inspect the sensor and the O-ring for damage.** **Possible Causes:** • Camshaft reluctor wheel for damage • Timing chain, tensioner, and sprockets for wear or damage. • CMP has failed • ECM has failed
DTC: P0341 **1T CCM, MIL: Yes** **Years:** 2008, 2009 **Models:** G6, HHR, Malibu **Engines:** 2.0L VIN X, 2.2L VIN D, 2.2L VIN B, 2.2L VIN F, 2.4L VIN B, 2.4L VIN V, 2.4L VIN P, 2.4L VIN 5 **Transmissions:** All	**CMP Sensor Signal Range/Performance** Engine started; and the ECM detected more than 15 CMP sensor resynchronizations during a 4 minute 16 second period. **Possible Causes:** • CMP sensor signal circuit is open, shorted to ground or VREF • CMP sensor signal wire is routed to close to the Generator, spark plug wires or any other possible cause of EMI/RFI under the hood (check for high power receivers causing interference) • CMP sensor "shield" ground circuit is open (intermittent fault) • CMP sensor is cracked or damaged (check the reluctor wheel) • ECM has failed

DTC	Trouble Code Title, Conditions & Possible Causes
DTC: P0341 **2T CCM, MIL: Yes** **Years:** 2008, 2009 **Models:** Express, G8, Lucerne, Trailblazer **Engines:** 4.6L VIN Y, 4.6L VIN 9, 6.0L VIN H, 6.0L VIN Y, 6.0L VIN K, 6.2L VIN W, 6.6L VIN 6 **Transmissions:** All	**CMP Sensor Signal Range/Performance** Engine started; at less than 4000 RPM, and the ECM detected incorrect correlation between the CKP and CMP signals. **Possible Causes:** • CMP sensor signal circuit is open, shorted to ground or VREF • CMP sensor signal wire is routed to close to the Generator, spark plug wires or any other possible cause of EMI/RFI • CMP sensor is cracked, damaged or has failed • ECM has failed • TSB 02-06-04-008 contains a repair procedure for this code
DTC: P0342 **1T CCM, MIL: Yes** **Years:** 2008, 2009 **Models:** Envoy, Equinox, G6, G8, Impala, Lucerne, Malibu, Savana, Trailblazer, Torrent **Engines:** 4.2L VIN S, 4.8L VIN C, 3.5L VIN N, 3.5L VIN K, 3.9L VIN 3, 3.9L VIN M, 3.6L VIN 2, 3.9L VIN 1 **Transmissions:** All	**CMP Sensor Circuit Low Input** Engine started; at less than 4000 RPM, and the ECM detected the CMP sensor signal was in a low state (when the signal should have been in a high state) for 1.5 seconds in the test. **Possible Causes:** • Camshaft reluctor wheel is damaged or foreign material present • CMP sensor signal circuit is open, shorted to ground or VREF • CMP sensor is contacting the reluctor wheel or is damaged • ECM has failed
DTC: P0342 **1T CCM, MIL: Yes** **Years:** 2008, 2009 **Models:** G6, HHR, Malibu **Engines:** 2.0L VIN X, 2.2L VIN D, 2.2L VIN B, 2.2L VIN F, 2.4L VIN B, 2.4L VIN V, 2.4L VIN P, 2.4L VIN 5 **Transmissions:** All	**CMP Sensor Signal Range/Performance** Engine started; and the ECM detected more than 15 CMP sensor resynchronizations during a 4 minute 16 second period. **Possible Causes:** • CMP sensor signal circuit is open, shorted to ground or VREF • CMP sensor signal wire is routed to close to the Generator, spark plug wires or any other possible cause of EMI/RFI under the hood (check for high power receivers causing interference) • CMP sensor "shield" ground circuit is open (intermittent fault) • CMP sensor is cracked or damaged (check the reluctor wheel) • ECM has failed
DTC: P0342 **2T CCM, MIL: Yes** **Years:** 2008, 2009 **Models:** Express, G8, Lucerne, Trailblazer **Engines:** 4.6L VIN Y, 4.6L VIN 9, 6.0L VIN H, 6.0L VIN Y, 6.0L VIN K, 6.2L VIN W, 6.6L VIN 6 **Transmissions:** All	**CMP Sensor Circuit Low Input** Engine started; at less than 4000 RPM, and the ECM detected the CMP sensor signal was in a low state (when the signal should have been in a high state) for 1.5 seconds in the test. **Possible Causes:** • Camshaft reluctor wheel is damaged or foreign material present • CMP sensor signal circuit is open, shorted to ground or VREF • CMP sensor is contacting the reluctor wheel or is damaged • ECM has failed
DTC: P0343 **1T CCM, MIL: Yes** **Years:** 2008, 2009 **Models:** Envoy, Equinox, G6, G8, Impala, Lucerne, Malibu, Savana, Trailblazer, Torrent **Engines:** 4.2L VIN S, 4.8L VIN C, 3.5L VIN N, 3.5L VIN K, 3.9L VIN 3, 3.9L VIN M, 3.6L VIN 2, 3.9L VIN 1 **Transmissions:** All	**CMP Sensor Circuit High Input** Engine started; engine speed less than 4000 RPM and the ECM detected the CMP sensor signal was stuck high (when the signal should have been in a low state) for 1.5 seconds in the CCM test. **Possible Causes:** • CMP sensor connector is damaged, loose or shorted • CMP sensor low reference circuit is open or shorted to VREF • Camshaft reluctor wheel is damaged or foreign material present • CMP sensor is contacting the reluctor wheel or is damaged • ECM has failed
DTC: P0346 **1T CCM, MIL: Yes** **Years:** 2008, 2009 **Models:** Envoy, Equinox, G6, G8, Impala, Lucerne, Malibu, Savana, Trailblazer, Torrent **Engines:** 4.2L VIN S, 4.8L VIN C, 3.5L VIN N, 3.5L VIN K, 3.9L VIN 3, 3.9L VIN M, 3.6L VIN 2, 3.9L VIN 1 **Transmissions:** All	**Intake Camshaft Position (CMP) Sensor Circuit Low Voltage (Bank 2)** The CMP sensor signal voltage is always high and the ECM detects no pulses from the CMP sensor for greater than 1 second or cumulative of 10 seconds. **Note: The control module or the sensor may be damaged if the circuit is shorted to B+ voltage.** **Possible Causes:** • Low reference circuit for an open/high resistance or for a short to voltage • 5 volt reference circuit for an open/high resistance • Short to voltage in the signal circuit • Short to ground or an open/high resistance in the signal circuit. • CMP has failed • ECM has failed

DTC	Trouble Code Title, Conditions & Possible Causes
DTC: P0347 **1T CCM, MIL: Yes** **Years:** 2008, 2009 **Models:** Envoy, Equinox, G6, G8, Impala, Lucerne, Malibu, Savana, Trailblazer, Torrent **Engines:** 4.2L VIN S, 4.8L VIN C, 3.5L VIN N, 3.5L VIN K, 3.9L VIN 3, 3.9L VIN M, 3.6L VIN 2, 3.9L VIN 1 **Transmissions:** All	**Intake Camshaft Position (CMP) Sensor Circuit High Voltage (Bank 2)** The CMP sensor signal voltage is always high and the ECM detects no pulses from the CMP sensor for greater than 1 second or cumulative of 10 seconds. **Note: The control module or the sensor may be damaged if the circuit is shorted to B+ voltage.** **Possible Causes:** • Low reference circuit for an open/high resistance or for a short to voltage • 5 volt reference circuit for an open/high resistance • Short to voltage in the signal circuit • Short to ground or an open/high resistance in the signal circuit. • CMP has failed • ECM has failed
DTC: P0348 **1T CCM, MIL: Yes** **Years:** 2008, 2009 **Models:** Envoy, Equinox, G6, G8, Impala, Lucerne, Malibu, Savana, Trailblazer, Torrent **Engines:** 4.2L VIN S, 4.8L VIN C, 3.5L VIN N, 3.5L VIN K, 3.9L VIN 3, 3.9L VIN M, 3.6L VIN 2, 3.9L VIN 1 **Transmissions:** All	**Ignition Coil 1 Control Circuit** The ignition is ON. DTC P0351-P0358 runs continuously when the above condition is met. The ECM detects an open, short to ground, short to voltage on the IC circuit. **Note: An IC circuit fault condition will result in an engine misfire, and under certain driving conditions could possibly overheat the 3-way catalytic converter.** **Possible Causes:** • Ignition coil • ECM has failed
DTC: P0351 **1T CCM, MIL: Yes** **Years:** 2008, 2009 **Models:** Envoy, Equinox, Savana, Torrent **Engines:** 3.4L VIN F, 4.3L VIN X, 5.3L VIN M **Transmissions:** All	**Ignition Coil 1 Control Circuit Malfunction** Engine started; and the ECM detected an unexpected voltage condition on the Coil Near Plug Ignition Control (IC) 1 circuit for less than one second during the CCM test period. **Possible Causes:** • IC circuit is open, shorted to ground or shorted to power (B+) • IC ground (Low REF) circuit or Module ground circuit is open • IC power circuit is open (check the INJ fuse in U/H fuse block) • Ignition Coil 1 is damaged or it has failed • ECM has failed
DTC: P0351 **1T CCM, MIL: Yes** **Years:** 2008, 2009 **Models:** Envoy, Equinox, G6, G8, Impala, Lucerne, Malibu, Savana, Trailblazer, Torrent **Engines:** 4.2L VIN S, 4.8L VIN C, 3.5L VIN N, 3.5L VIN K, 3.9L VIN 3, 3.9L VIN M, 3.6L VIN 2, 3.9L VIN 1 **Transmissions:** All	**Ignition Coil 1 Control Circuit** The ignition is ON. DTC P0351-P0358 runs continuously when the above condition is met. The ECM detects an open, short to ground, short to voltage on the IC circuit. **Note: An IC circuit fault condition will result in an engine misfire, and under certain driving conditions could possibly overheat the 3-way catalytic converter.** **Possible Causes:** • Ignition coil • ECM has failed
DTC: P0351 **1T CCM, MIL: Yes** **Models:** G6, HHR, Malibu **Engines:** 2.0L VIN X, 2.2L VIN D, 2.2L VIN B, 2.2L VIN F, 2.4L VIN B, 2.4L VIN V, 2.4L VIN P, 2.4L VIN 5 **Transmissions:** All	**Ignition Coil 1 Control Circuit Malfunction** Engine started; and the ECM detected an unexpected voltage condition on the Coil Near Plug Ignition Control (IC) 1 circuit for less than one second during the CCM test period. **Possible Causes:** • IC circuit is open, shorted to ground or shorted to power (B+) • IC ground (Low REF) circuit or Module ground circuit is open • IC power circuit is open (check the INJ fuse in U/H fuse block) • Ignition Coil 1 is damaged or it has failed • ECM has failed
DTC: P0351 **2T CCM, MIL: Yes** **Years:** 2008, 2009 **Models:** Express, G8, Lucerne, Trailblazer **Engines:** 4.6L VIN Y, 4.6L VIN 9, 6.0L VIN H, 6.0L VIN Y, 6.0L VIN K, 6.2L VIN W, 6.6L VIN 6 **Transmissions:** All	**Ignition Coil 1 Control Circuit Malfunction** Engine started; and the ECM detected an unexpected low or high voltage condition on Coil On Plug (COP) Ignition Control circuit for less than one second during the CCM test. **Note: Watch the Scan Tool Misfire Counters to identify the fault.** **Possible Causes:** • IC circuit is open, shorted to ground or shorted to power • Ignition coil (COP) is damaged or has failed • ECM has failed

DTC	Trouble Code Title, Conditions & Possible Causes
DTC: P0352 **1T CCM, MIL: Yes** **Years:** 2008, 2009 **Models:** Envoy, Equinox, Savana, Torrent **Engines:** 3.4L VIN F, 4.3L VIN X, 5.3L VIN M **Transmissions:** All	**Ignition Coil 2 Control Circuit Malfunction** Engine started; and the ECM detected an unexpected voltage condition on the Coil Near Plug Ignition Control (IC) 2 circuit for less than one second during the CCM test period. **Possible Causes:** • IC circuit is open, shorted to ground or shorted to power (B+) • IC ground (Low REF) circuit or Module ground circuit is open • IC power circuit is open (check the INJ fuse in U/H fuse block) • Ignition Coil 2 is damaged or it has failed • ECM has failed
DTC: P0352 **2T CCM, MIL: Yes** **Years:** 2008, 2009 **Models:** All **Engines:** All **Transmissions:** All	**Ignition Coil 2 Control Circuit Malfunction** Engine started; and the ECM detected an unexpected low or high voltage condition on Coil On Plug (COP) Ignition Control circuit for less than one second during the CCM test. **Note: Watch the Scan Tool Misfire Counters to identify the fault.** **Possible Causes:** • IC circuit is open, shorted to ground or shorted to power • Ignition coil (COP) is damaged or has failed • ECM has failed
DTC: P0353 **1T CCM, MIL: Yes** **Years:** 2008, 2009 **Models:** Envoy, Equinox, Savana, Torrent **Engines:** 3.4L VIN F, 4.3L VIN X, 5.3L VIN M **Transmissions:** All	**Ignition Coil 3 Control Circuit Malfunction** Engine started; and the ECM detected an unexpected voltage condition on the Coil Near Plug Ignition Control (IC) 3 circuit for less than one second during the CCM test period. **Possible Causes:** • IC circuit is open, shorted to ground or shorted to power (B+) • IC ground (Low REF) circuit or Module ground circuit is open • IC power circuit is open (check the INJ fuse in U/H fuse block) • Ignition Coil 3 is damaged or it has failed • ECM has failed
DTC: P0353 **2T CCM, MIL: Yes** **Years:** 2008, 2009 **Models:** All **Engines:** All **Transmissions:** All	**Ignition Coil 3 Control Circuit Malfunction** Engine started; and the ECM detected an unexpected low or high voltage condition on Coil On Plug (COP) Ignition Control circuit for less than one second during the CCM test. **Note: Watch the Scan Tool Misfire Counters to identify the fault.** **Possible Causes:** • IC circuit is open, shorted to ground or shorted to power between the coil and the ECM • Ignition coil (COP) is damaged or has failed • ECM has failed
DTC: P0354 **1T CCM, MIL: Yes** **Years:** 2008, 2009 **Models:** Envoy, Equinox, Savana, Torrent **Engines:** 3.4L VIN F, 4.3L VIN X, 5.3L VIN M **Transmissions:** All	**Ignition Coil 4 Control Circuit Malfunction** Engine started; and the ECM detected an unexpected voltage condition on the Coil Near Plug Ignition Control (IC) 4 circuit for less than one second during the CCM test period. **Possible Causes:** • IC circuit is open, shorted to ground or shorted to power (B+) • IC ground (Low REF) circuit or Module ground circuit is open • IC power circuit is open (check the INJ fuse in U/H fuse block) • Ignition Coil 4 is damaged or it has failed • ECM has failed
DTC: P0354 **2T CCM, MIL: Yes** **Years:** 2008, 2009 **Models:** All **Engines:** All **Transmissions:** All	**Ignition Coil 4 Control Circuit Malfunction** Engine started; and the ECM detected an unexpected low or high voltage condition on Coil On Plug (COP) Ignition Control circuit for less than one second during the CCM test. **Note: Watch the Scan Tool Misfire Counters to identify the fault.** **Possible Causes:** • IC circuit is open, shorted to ground or shorted to power between the coil and the ECM • Ignition coil (COP) is damaged or has failed, or the ECM has failed
DTC: P0355 **1T CCM, MIL: Yes** **Years:** 2008, 2009 **Models:** Envoy, Equinox, Savana, Torrent **Engines:** 3.4L VIN F, 4.3L VIN X, 5.3L VIN M **Transmissions:** All	**Ignition Coil 5 Control Circuit Malfunction** Engine started; and the ECM detected an unexpected voltage condition on the Coil Near Plug Ignition Control (IC) 5 circuit for less than one second during the CCM test period. **Possible Causes:** • IC circuit is open, shorted to ground or shorted to power (B+) • IC ground (Low REF) circuit or Module ground circuit is open • IC power circuit is open (check the INJ fuse in U/H fuse block) • Ignition Coil 5 is damaged or it has failed • ECM has failed

DTC	Trouble Code Title, Conditions & Possible Causes
DTC: P0355 **2T CCM, MIL:** Yes **Years:** 2008, 2009 **Models:** All **Engines:** 6 & 8 Cylinder **Transmissions:** All	**Ignition Coil 5 Control Circuit Malfunction** Engine started; and the ECM detected an unexpected low or high voltage condition on Coil On Plug (COP) Ignition Control circuit for less than one second during the CCM test. **Note: Watch the Scan Tool Misfire Counters to identify the fault.** **Possible Causes:** • IC circuit is open, shorted to ground or shorted to power between the coil and the ECM • Ignition coil (COP) is damaged or has failed • ECM has failed
DTC: P0356 **1T CCM, MIL:** Yes **Years:** 2008, 2009 **Models:** Envoy, Equinox, Savana, Torrent **Engines:** 3.4L VIN F, 4.3L VIN X, 5.3L VIN M **Transmissions:** All	**Ignition Coil 6 Control Circuit Malfunction** Engine started; and the ECM detected an unexpected voltage condition on the Coil Near Plug Ignition Control (IC) 6 circuit for less than one second during the CCM test period. **Possible Causes:** • IC circuit is open, shorted to ground or shorted to power (B+) • IC ground (Low REF) circuit or Module ground circuit is open • IC power circuit is open (check the INJ fuse in U/H fuse block) • Ignition Coil 6 is damaged or it has failed • ECM has failed
DTC: P0356 **2T CCM, MIL:** Yes **Years:** 2008, 2009 **Models:** All **Engines:** 6 & 8 Cylinder **Transmissions:** All	**Ignition Coil 6 Control Circuit Malfunction** Engine started; and the ECM detected an unexpected low or high voltage condition on Coil On Plug (COP) Ignition Control circuit for less than one second during the CCM test. **Note: Watch the Scan Tool Misfire Counters to identify the fault.** **Possible Causes:** • IC circuit is open, shorted to ground or shorted to power between the coil and the ECM • Ignition coil (COP) is damaged or has failed • ECM has failed
DTC: P0357 **2T CCM, MIL:** Yes **Years:** 2008, 2009 **Models:** All **Engines:** 8 Cylinder **Transmissions:** All	**Ignition Coil 7 Control Circuit** The ignition is ON. DTC P0351-P0358 runs continuously when the above condition is met. The ECM detects an open, short to ground, short to voltage on the IC circuit. **Note: An IC circuit fault condition will result in an engine misfire, and under certain driving conditions could possibly overheat the 3-way catalytic converter.** **Possible Causes:** • Ignition coil • ECM has failed
DTC: P0358 **1T CCM, MIL:** Yes **Years:** 2008, 2009 **Models:** Envoy, Equinox, Savana, Torrent **Engines:** 3.4L VIN F, 4.3L VIN X, 5.3L VIN M **Transmissions:** All	**Ignition Coil 8 Control Circuit Malfunction** Engine started; and the ECM detected an unexpected voltage condition on the Coil Near Plug Ignition Control (IC) 8 circuit for less than one second during the CCM test period. **Possible Causes:** • IC circuit is open, shorted to ground or shorted to power (B+) • IC ground (Low REF) circuit or Module ground circuit is open • IC power circuit is open (check the INJ fuse in U/H fuse block) • Ignition Coil 8 is damaged or it has failed • ECM has failed
DTC: P0358 **2T CCM, MIL:** Yes **Years:** All **Engines:** 8 Cylinder **Transmissions:** All	**Ignition Coil 8 Control Circuit Malfunction** Engine started; and the ECM detected an unexpected low or high voltage condition on Coil On Plug (COP) Ignition Control circuit for less than one second during the CCM test. **Note: Watch the Scan Tool Misfire Counters to identify the fault.** **Possible Causes:** • IC circuit is open, shorted to ground or shorted to power between the coil and the ECM • Ignition coil (COP) is damaged or has failed • ECM has failed

DTC	Trouble Code Title, Conditions & Possible Causes
DTC: P0365 **1T CCM, MIL: Yes** **Years:** 2008, 2009 **Models:** G6, HHR, Malibu **Engines:** 2.0L VIN X, 2.2L VIN D, 2.2L VIN B, 2.2L VIN F, 2.4L VIN B, 2.4L VIN V, 2.4L VIN P, 2.4L VIN 5 **Transmissions:** All	**Exhaust Camshaft Position (CMP) Sensor Performance** The engine is cranking or running. The medium resolution is less than or equal to 10 counts. DTC P0366 runs continuously when the above conditions are met. The ECM detects the incorrect number of CMP sensor pulses in 2 revolutions of the crankshaft, which is usually within 1 second. **Note: Inspect the CMP sensor for correct installation. Remove the CMP sensor from the engine and inspect the sensor and the O-ring for damage.** **Possible Causes:** • Camshaft reluctor wheel for damage • Engine oil for debris • Timing chain, tensioner, and sprockets for wear or damage. • CMP has failed • ECM has failed
DTC: P0366 **1T CCM, MIL: Yes** **Years:** 2008, 2009 **Models:** G6, HHR, Malibu **Engines:** 2.0L VIN X, 2.2L VIN D, 2.2L VIN B, 2.2L VIN F, 2.4L VIN B, 2.4L VIN V, 2.4L VIN P, 2.4L VIN 5 **Transmissions:** All	**Exhaust Camshaft Position (CMP) Sensor Performance (Bank 1)** The ECM detects greater than 10 crankshaft revolutions. The engine speed is less than 2,520 RPM. The DTCs run continuously once the above condition is met. The ECM detects a signal from the CMP sensor, but the number of pulses are less than or greater than what is expected for one crankshaft revolution. Or the CMP sensor does NOT correlate to the crankshaft position. Either condition must exist for greater than 1 second, or cumulative of 10 seconds. **Possible Causes:** • Low reference circuit for an open/high resistance or for a short to voltage • 5 volt reference circuit for an open/high resistance • Short to voltage in the signal circuit • Short to ground or an open/high resistance in the signal circuit. • CMP has failed • ECM has failed
DTC: P0366 **1T CCM, MIL: Yes** **Years:** 2008, 2009 **Models:** Envoy, Equinox, G6, G8, Impala, Lucerne, Malibu, Savana, Trailblazer, Torrent **Engines:** 4.2L VIN S, 4.8L VIN C, 3.5L VIN N, 3.5L VIN K, 3.9L VIN 3, 3.9L VIN M, 3.6L VIN 2, 3.9L VIN 1 **Transmissions:** All	**Exhaust Camshaft Position (CMP) Sensor Circuit Low Voltage (Bank 1)** The ECM detects greater than 10 crankshaft revolutions. The engine speed is less than 2,520 RPM. The DTCs run continuously once the above condition is met. The CMP sensor signal voltage is always high and the ECM detects no pulses from the CMP sensor for greater than 1 second or cumulative of 10 seconds. **Possible Causes:** • Low reference circuit for an open/high resistance or for a short to voltage • 5 volt reference circuit for an open/high resistance • Short to voltage in the signal circuit • Short to ground or an open/high resistance in the signal circuit. • CMP has failed • ECM has failed
DTC: P0367 **1T CCM, MIL: Yes** **Years:** 2008, 2009 **Models:** Envoy, Equinox, G6, G8, Impala, Lucerne, Malibu, Savana, Trailblazer, Torrent **Engines:** 4.2L VIN S, 4.8L VIN C, 3.5L VIN N, 3.5L VIN K, 3.9L VIN 3, 3.9L VIN M, 3.6L VIN 2, 3.9L VIN 1 **Transmissions:** All	**Exhaust Camshaft Position (CMP) Sensor Circuit High Voltage (Bank 1)** The ECM detects greater than 10 crankshaft revolutions. The engine speed is less than 2,520 RPM. The DTCs run continuously once the above condition is met. The CMP sensor signal voltage is always high and the ECM detects no pulses from the CMP sensor for greater than 1 second or cumulative of 10 seconds. **Possible Causes:** • Low reference circuit for an open/high resistance or for a short to voltage • 5 volt reference circuit for an open/high resistance • Short to voltage in the signal circuit • Short to ground or an open/high resistance in the signal circuit. • CMP has failed • ECM has failed
DTC: P0368 **1T CCM, MIL: Yes** **Years:** 2008, 2009 **Models:** Envoy, Equinox, G6, G8, Impala, Lucerne, Malibu, Savana, Trailblazer, Torrent **Engines:** 4.2L VIN S, 4.8L VIN C, 3.5L VIN N, 3.5L VIN K, 3.9L VIN 3, 3.9L VIN M, 3.6L VIN 2, 3.9L VIN 1 **Transmissions:** All	**Exhaust Camshaft Position (CMP) Sensor Performance (Bank 2)** The ECM detects greater than 10 crankshaft revolutions. The engine speed is less than 2,520 RPM. The DTCs run continuously once the above condition is met. The ECM detects a signal from the CMP sensor, but the number of pulses are less than or greater than what is expected for one crankshaft revolution. Or the CMP sensor does NOT correlate to the crankshaft position. Either condition must exist for greater than 1 second, or cumulative of 10 seconds. **Possible Causes:** • Low reference circuit for an open/high resistance or for a short to voltage • 5 volt reference circuit for an open/high resistance • Short to voltage in the signal circuit • Short to ground or an open/high resistance in the signal circuit. • CMP has failed • ECM has failed

DTC	Trouble Code Title, Conditions & Possible Causes
DTC: P0391 **1T CCM, MIL: Yes** **Years:** 2008, 2009 **Models:** Envoy, Equinox, G6, G8, Impala, Lucerne, Malibu, Savana, Trailblazer, Torrent **Engines:** 4.2L VIN S, 4.8L VIN C, 3.5L VIN N, 3.5L VIN K, 3.9L VIN 3, 3.9L VIN M, 3.6L VIN 2, 3.9L VIN 1 **Transmissions:** All	**Exhaust Camshaft Position (CMP) Sensor Circuit Low Voltage (Bank 2)** The ECM detects greater than 10 crankshaft revolutions. The engine speed is less than 2,520 RPM. The DTCs run continuously once the above condition is met. The CMP sensor signal voltage is always high and the ECM detects no pulses from the CMP sensor for greater than 1 second or cumulative of 10 seconds. **Possible Causes:** • Low reference circuit for an open/high resistance or for a short to voltage • 5 volt reference circuit for an open/high resistance • Short to voltage in the signal circuit • Short to ground or an open/high resistance in the signal circuit. • CMP has failed • ECM has failed
DTC: P0392 **1T CCM, MIL: Yes** **Years:** 2008, 2009 **Models:** Envoy, Equinox, G6, G8, Impala, Lucerne, Malibu, Savana, Trailblazer, Torrent **Engines:** 4.2L VIN S, 4.8L VIN C, 3.5L VIN N, 3.5L VIN K, 3.9L VIN 3, 3.9L VIN M, 3.6L VIN 2, 3.9L VIN 1 **Transmissions:** All	**Exhaust Camshaft Position (CMP) Sensor Circuit High Voltage (Bank 2)** The ECM detects greater than 10 crankshaft revolutions. The engine speed is less than 2,520 RPM. The DTCs run continuously once the above condition is met. The CMP sensor signal voltage is always high and the ECM detects no pulses from the CMP sensor for greater than 1 second or cumulative of 10 seconds. **Possible Causes:** • Low reference circuit for an open/high resistance or for a short to voltage • 5 volt reference circuit for an open/high resistance • Short to voltage in the signal circuit • Short to ground or an open/high resistance in the signal circuit. • CMP has failed • ECM has failed
DTC: P0393 **1T CCM, MIL: Yes** **Years:** 2008, 2009 **Models:** Envoy, Equinox, G6, G8, Impala, Lucerne, Malibu, Savana, Trailblazer, Torrent **Engines:** 4.2L VIN S, 4.8L VIN C, 3.5L VIN N, 3.5L VIN K, 3.9L VIN 3, 3.9L VIN M, 3.6L VIN 2, 3.9L VIN 1 **Transmissions:** All	**Insufficient EGR Flow Detected** DTC P0101, P0102, P0103, P0107, P0108, P0112, P0113, P0116, P0117, P0118, P0121, P0122, P0123, P0403, P0404, P0405, P0502, P0503, P0506, P0507, P0641, P0651, P1374, P1404 not set, engine started, ECT sensor more than 167°F, IAT sensor from 32-212°F, system voltage 11-18v, BARO sensor more than 74 kPa, IAC steady (5 counts), A/C Clutch and TR signals stable, then vehicle driven to over 50 MPH at an engine speed of 1050-1300 RPM, MAP sensor from 15-70 kPa, followed by a deceleration period with the TP angle less than 1.3%, and the ECM detected the amount of MAP sensor change monitored with the valve open and then closed during deceleration indicated insufficient EGR flow. The EGR flow test is enabled by the ECM during deceleration. A change from 0 to a value over +0 in the Desired EGR and Actual EGR Position PID will appear on a Scan Tool. The ECM Allows one EGR flow test in each key cycle. To verify a repair, the ECM will Allow up to 12 EGR flow test counts during the first key cycle after codes are cleared. From 9-12 EGR flow tests are enough to detect adequate EGR flow. **Possible Causes:** • Base engine problem (e.g., a severely restricted exhaust) • EGR vacuum hoses damaged, loose or routed incorrectly • EGR passages or intake passages clogged or restricted • EGR solenoid valve is clogged (carbon), damaged or has failed • TSB 87-65-22 contains a repair procedure for this code
DTC: P0403 **1T CCM, MIL: Yes** **Years:** 2008, 2009 **Models:** Equinox, Torrent **Engines:** 3.4L VIN F **Transmissions:** All	**Exhaust Gas Recirculation (EGR) Solenoid Control Circuit** The Ignition 1 Signal parameter is between 9-18 volts. The engine is cranking or running. The DTC P0401 intrusive test is not active. These DTCs run continuously once the above conditions are met. **Possible Causes:** • EGR valve low control circuit for an open/high resistance • EGR valve high control circuit for a short to voltage • EGR valve low reference circuit and ground • EGR valve low reference circuit for an open/high resistance • EGR valve 5-volt reference circuit for a short to ground • EGR valve 5-volt reference circuit for a short to voltage • EGR valve signal circuit for a short to voltage • EGR valve signal circuit for a short to ground or an open/high resistance • EGR sensor has failed • ECM has failed

DTC	Trouble Code Title, Conditions & Possible Causes
DTC: P0404 **1T CCM, MIL: Yes** **Years:** 2008, 2009 **Models:** Equinox, Torrent **Engines:** 3.4L VIN F **Transmissions:** All	**Exhaust Gas Recirculation (EGR) Open Position Performance** The Ignition 1 Signal parameter is between 9-18 volts. The engine is cranking or running. The DTC P0401 intrusive test is not active. These DTCs run continuously once the above conditions are met. The EGR valve is commanded open. DTC P0641 and P0651 are not set. **Possible Causes:** • EGR valve low control circuit for an open/high resistance • EGR valve high control circuit for a short to voltage • EGR valve low reference circuit and ground • EGR valve low reference circuit for an open/high resistance • EGR valve 5-volt reference circuit for a short to ground • EGR valve 5-volt reference circuit for a short to voltage • EGR valve signal circuit for a short to voltage • EGR valve signal circuit for a short to ground or an open/high resistance • EGR sensor has failed • ECM has failed
DTC: P0405 **1T CCM, MIL: Yes** **Years:** 2008, 2009 **Models:** Equinox, Torrent **Engines:** 3.4L VIN F **Transmissions:** All	**Exhaust Gas Recirculation (EGR) Position Sensor Circuit Low Voltage** The Ignition 1 Signal parameter is between 9-18 volts. The engine is cranking or running. The DTC P0401 intrusive test is not active. These DTCs run continuously once the above conditions are met. DTC P0641 and P0651 are not set. **Possible Causes:** • EGR valve low control circuit for an open/high resistance • EGR valve high control circuit for a short to voltage • EGR valve low reference circuit and ground • EGR valve low reference circuit for an open/high resistance • EGR valve 5-volt reference circuit for a short to ground • EGR valve 5-volt reference circuit for a short to voltage • EGR valve signal circuit for a short to voltage • EGR valve signal circuit for a short to ground or an open/high resistance • EGR sensor has failed • ECM has failed
DTC: P0406 **1T CCM, MIL: Yes** **Years:** 2008, 2009 **Models:** Equinox, Torrent **Engines:** 3.4L VIN F **Transmissions:** All	**Exhaust Gas Recirculation (EGR) Position Sensor Circuit High Voltage** The Ignition 1 Signal parameter is between 9-18 volts. The engine is cranking or running. The DTC P0401 intrusive test is not active. These DTCs run continuously once the above conditions are met. DTC P0641 and P0651 are not set. The EGR valve is not being commanded with a scan tool. **Possible Causes:** • EGR valve low control circuit for an open/high resistance • EGR valve high control circuit for a short to voltage • EGR valve low reference circuit and ground • EGR valve low reference circuit for an open/high resistance • EGR valve 5-volt reference circuit for a short to ground • EGR valve 5-volt reference circuit for a short to voltage • EGR valve signal circuit for a short to voltage • EGR valve signal circuit for a short to ground or an open/high resistance • EGR sensor has failed • ECM has failed
DTC: P0411 **1T CCM, MIL: Yes** **Years:** 2008, 2009 **Models:** All **Engines:** All **Transmissions:** All	**Secondary Air Injection (AIR) System Incorrect Air Flow Detected** DTCs P0068, P0101, P0102, P0103, P0106, P0107, P0108, P0112, P0113, P0116, P0117, P0118, P0128, P0201-P0208, P0300, P0301-P0308, P0351-P0358, P0412, P0418, P0420, P0606, P0641, P0651, P2430, P2431, P2432, P2433, P2440, 2444 are not set. The system voltage is between 11-18V. The start-up intake air temperature (IAT) is greater than 5°C (41°F). The start-up engine coolant temperature (ECT) is between 5-80°C (41-176°F). The AIR system is commanded ON. The conditions are stable for greater than 5 seconds. DTC P0411 runs once per trip start-up when the above conditions are met and AIR pump operation is requested. The ECM determines that the difference between the predicted system pressure and the actual system pressure is greater than 6 kPa.Or. The ECM determines that the difference between the predicted system pressure and the actual system pressure is less than -5 kPa. DTC P0411 sets during phase 1 and within 22 seconds when the above conditions are met. **Possible Causes:** • AIR pump relay has failed • AIR pump has failed • AIR solenoid relay has failed • AIR solenoid valve has failed • Test or inspect the AIR solenoid valve outlet pipe and exhaust manifold for a restriction • Air injection check valve

DTC	Trouble Code Title, Conditions & Possible Causes
DTC: P0412 **1T CCM, MIL: Yes** **Years:** 2008, 2009 **Models:** All **Engines:** All **Transmissions:** All	**Secondary Air Injection (AIR) Solenoid Control Circuit** The system voltage is between 9-18V. The ignition is ON. These DTCs run on a 250 ms loop. DTCs P0412 and P0418 run continuously when the above conditions are met. The ECM determines that the actual and expected states of the AIR solenoid and AIR pump relay control circuits do not match. DTCs P0412 or P0418 set when the above condition exists for greater than 4 seconds. **Possible Causes:** • AIR pump relay has failed • AIR pump has failed • AIR solenoid relay has failed • AIR solenoid valve has failed • Test or inspect the AIR solenoid valve outlet pipe and exhaust manifold for a restriction • Air injection check valve
DTC: P0418 **1T CCM, MIL: Yes** **Years:** 2008, 2009 **Models:** All **Engines:** All **Transmissions:** All	**Secondary Air Injection (AIR) Pump Control Circuit** The system voltage is between 9-18V. The ignition is ON. These DTCs run on a 250 ms loop. DTCs P0412 and P0418 run continuously when the above conditions are met. The ECM determines that the actual and expected states of the AIR solenoid and AIR pump relay control circuits do not match. DTCs P0412 or P0418 set when the above condition exists for greater than 4 seconds. **Possible Causes:** • AIR pump relay has failed • AIR pump has failed • AIR solenoid relay has failed • AIR solenoid valve has failed • Test or inspect the AIR solenoid valve outlet pipe and exhaust manifold for a restriction • Air injection check valve
DTC: P0420 **1T CCM, MIL: Yes** **Years:** 2008, 2009 **Models:** Express, G8, Lucerne, Trailblazer **Engines:** 4.6L VIN Y, 4.6L VIN 9, 6.0L VIN H, 6.0L VIN Y, 6.0L VIN K, 6.2L VIN W, 6.6L VIN 6 **Transmissions:** All	**Catalyst System Low Efficiency (Bank 1)** DTCs P0030, P0031, P0036, P0037, P0038, P0068, P0106, P0107, P0108, P0112, P0113, P0117, P0118, P0120, P0121, P0122, P0123, P0125, P0128, P0130, P0131, P0132, P0133, P0134, P0135, P0136, P0137, P0138, P0140, P0141, P0171, P0172, P0201, P0202, P0203, P0204, P0205, P0206, P0207, P0208, P0220, P0300, P0315, P0326, P0327, P0336, P0340, P0341, P0442, P0446, P0452, P0453, P0455, P0496, P0500 (manual transmission only), P0502, P0506, P0507, P0601, P0602, P0606, P0641, P0722, P0723, P1133, P1134, P1516, P1621, P2135, P2138, P2176 are not set. The engine has been running for greater than 2 minutes. The vehicle has been driven at greater than 1,000 RPM with the mass air flow (MAF) greater than 18 g/s for greater than 30 seconds. The vehicle is in Closed Loop. The vehicle has Fuel Trim Learn enabled. The Engine Coolant Temperature (ECT) parameter is between 45-128°C (113-262°F). The Barometric Pressure (BARO) parameter is greater than 70 kPa. The Catalytic Converter Calculated Temperature parameter is greater than or equal to 420°C (788°F). The Intake Air Temperature (IAT) parameter is between −20 and +85°C (−4 and +185°F). The battery voltage is more than 11 volts. The ECM has determined the catalyst efficiency has degraded below a calibrated threshold. This diagnostic may conclude in one test attempt. However, this diagnostic may require as many as 18 test attempts, which would require at least 3 drive cycles. Each test attempt may conclude within approximately 1 minute. **Possible Causes:** • Engine misfire • High engine oil or high coolant consumption • Retarded spark timing • A weak or poor spark • A lean fuel mixture • A rich fuel mixture • A damaged oxygen sensor or wiring harness • Catalytic converter

DTC	Trouble Code Title, Conditions & Possible Causes
DTC: P0420 **1T CCM, MIL: Yes** **Years:** 2008, 2009 **Models:** Envoy, Equinox, Savana, Torrent **Engines:** 3.4L VIN F, 4.3L VIN X, 5.3L VIN M **Transmissions:** All	**Catalyst System Bank 1 Low Efficiency** DTC P0030, P0101-P0103, P0107, P0108, P0112, P0113, P0116-P0118, P0121-P0123, P0128, P0130-P0138, P0140, P0141, P0171, P0172, P0201-P0206, P0300, P0336, P0341, P0404, P0405, P0410, P0440, P0442, P0443, P0502, P0503, P0506, P0507, P1133, P1134, P1351, P1352, P1361, P1362 and P1441 not set, engine runtime over 10 minutes, system voltage over 10.0v, BARO sensor more than 75 kPa, ECT sensor from 169-255°F, IAT sensor from −4°F to 212°F, engine running in closed loop, and the ECM detected the catalyst oxygen storage capacity had degraded. Test Instructions: To activate the test, return to idle and place vehicle in Drive (depress the clutch pedal for manual transmission vehicles). Then within 60 seconds, the A/F ratio will go below 14.1 for up to 8 seconds (and may go to above 15.3 for up to 10 seconds). Use a Scan Tool to monitor DTC P0420 to determine if the current trip passes or fails. The catalytic catalyst promotes a chemical reaction that oxidizes the amount of HC and CO in the exhaust gas to convert them into water vapor and CO_2. It also reduces NOx by converting it to nitrogen. The converter has the ability to store excess oxygen and then release it. **Possible Causes:** • Air leaks at the exhaust manifold or in the exhaust pipes • Base engine problems (i.e., high engine oil or coolant usage) • Catalytic converter is damaged, contaminated or has failed • Continuous engine misfire conditions, or weak or low coil output • Front HO2S or rear HO2S is contaminated with fuel or moisture • Rear HO2S is loose in the mounting hole (check it for a leak) • Front HO2S older (aged) than the rear HO2S (HO2S-12 is lazy)
DTC: P0420 **1T CCM, MIL: Yes** **Years:** 2008, 2009 **Models:** Envoy, Equinox, G6, G8, Impala, Lucerne, Malibu, Savana, Trailblazer, Torrent **Engines:** 4.2L VIN S, 4.8L VIN C, 3.5L VIN N, 3.5L VIN K, 3.9L VIN 3, 3.9L VIN M, 3.6L VIN 2, 3.9L VIN 1 **Transmissions:** All	**Catalyst System Low Efficiency (Bank 1)** DTC P0101-P0103, P0106-P0108, P0112, P0113, P0117, P0118, P0120, P0121-123, P0125, P0128, P0131-P0138, P0140, P0141, P0171-P0172, P0177-P0179, P0200, P0220, P0300, P0325, P0327, P0332, P0335, P0336, P0341-P0343, P0351-P0358, P0442-P0446, P0452-P0453, P0455, P0496, P0502-P0503, P1125, P1133, P1153, P1258, P1514- P1518, P2108 or P2135 not set, engine started, ECT sensor from 158-248°F, BARO sensor over 74 kPa, IAT sensor at 5-185°F, vehicle driven in closed loop at cruise speed for 40-45 seconds, and the ECM detected that the Oxygen storage capability of the Catalyst was degraded. **Possible Causes:** • Air leaks at the exhaust manifold or in the exhaust pipes • Base engine problems (i.e., high engine oil or coolant usage) • Catalytic converter is damaged, contaminated or has failed • Continuous engine misfire conditions, or weak or low coil output • Front HO2S or rear HO2S is contaminated with fuel or moisture • Rear HO2S is loose in the mounting hole (check it for a leak) • TSB 81-65-37 contains a repair procedure for this code
DTC: P0420 **1T CCM, MIL: Yes** **Years:** 2008, 2009 **Models:** G6, HHR, Malibu **Engines:** 2.0L VIN X, 2.2L VIN D, 2.2L VIN B, 2.2L VIN F, 2.4L VIN B, 2.4L VIN V, 2.4L VIN P, 2.4L VIN 5 **Transmissions:** All	**Catalyst System Low Efficiency (Bank 1)** DTC P0101-P0103, P0106-P0108, P0112-P0118, P0128, P0131-P0137, P0140, P0141, P0151-P0158, P0160, P0161, P0171-P0175, P0200, P0300, P0335, P0336, P0341-P0343, P0351-P0358, P0410, P0440, P0502-P0503, P0506-P0507, P0606, P1120, P1133, P1134, P1153, P1154, P1220, P1336, P1415, P1416 and P1441 not set, engine speed over 850 RPM for 230 seconds since last idle, VSS under 85 MPH, BARO sensor over 75 kPa, ECT sensor over 167°F, IAT sensor at 19-167°F, MAF sensor at 14-40 g/sec, MAP sensor from 25-80 kPa, and the ECM detected the Catalyst was degraded. **Possible Causes:** • Air leaks at the exhaust manifold or in the exhaust pipes • Base engine problems (i.e., high engine oil or coolant usage) • Catalytic converter is damaged, contaminated or has failed • Continuous engine misfire conditions, or weak or low coil output • Front HO2S or rear HO2S is contaminated with fuel or moisture • Rear HO2S is loose in the mounting hole (check it for a leak) • Front HO2S older (aged) than the rear HO2S (HO2S-12 is lazy)
DTC: P042E **1T CCM, MIL: Yes** **Years:** 2008, 2009 **Models:** Equinox, Torrent **Engines:** 3.4L VIN F **Transmissions:** All	**Exhaust Gas Recirculation (EGR) Closed Position Performance** The Ignition 1 Signal parameter is between 9-18 volts. The engine is cranking or running. The DTC P0401 intrusive test is not active. These DTCs run continuously once the above conditions are met. DTC P0641 and P0651 are not set. **Possible Causes:** • EGR valve low control circuit for an open/high resistance • EGR valve high control circuit for a short to voltage • EGR valve low reference circuit and ground • EGR valve low reference circuit for an open/high resistance • EGR valve 5-volt reference circuit for a short to ground • EGR valve 5-volt reference circuit for a short to voltage • EGR valve signal circuit for a short to voltage • EGR valve signal circuit for a short to ground or an open/high resistance • EGR sensor has failed • ECM has failed

DTC	Trouble Code Title, Conditions & Possible Causes
DTC: P0430 **1T CCM, MIL: Yes** **Years:** 2008, 2009 **Models:** Envoy, Equinox, G6, G8, Impala, Lucerne, Malibu, Savana, Trailblazer, Torrent **Engines:** 4.2L VIN S, 4.8L VIN C, 3.5L VIN N, 3.5L VIN K, 3.9L VIN 3, 3.9L VIN M, 3.6L VIN 2, 3.9L VIN 1 **Transmissions:** All	**Catalyst System Low Efficiency (Bank 2)** DTC P0101-P0103, P0106-P0108, P0112-P0118, P0125, P0131, P0132-P0138, P0140, P0141, P0151-P0158, P0160, P0161, P0171-P0175, P0200, P0300, P0325, P0327, P0335, 336, P0341, P0343, P0351-P0358, P0443-P0449, P0502, P0503, P0506, P0507, P1120, P1125, P1133, P1134, P1153, P1154, P1220, P1221, P1275, P1276, P1280-P1286, P1441, P1514-P1518 not set, engine runtime over 6 minutes, ECT sensor over 167°F, BARO sensor over 72 kPa, IAT sensor over 16°F, MAF sensor from 15-50 g/sec, Catalyst Temperature over 840°F, engine running at idle speed for 2 minutes with Actual idle speed within 100-125 RPM of the Desired idle speed, vehicle driven to 22-85 MPH, less than a 10% change in engine load, fuel trim stable, and the ECM detected the Catalyst was degraded. **Possible Causes:** • Air leaks at the exhaust manifold or in the exhaust pipes • Base engine problems (i.e., high engine oil or coolant usage) • Catalytic converter is damaged, contaminated or has failed • Continuous engine misfire conditions, or weak or low coil output • Front HO2S or rear HO2S is contaminated with fuel or moisture • Rear HO2S is loose in the mounting hole (check it for a leak)
DTC: P0430 **2T CAT, MIL: Yes** **Years:** 2008, 2009 **Models:** G6, HHR, Malibu **Engines:** 2.0L VIN X, 2.2L VIN D, 2.2L VIN B, 2.2L VIN F, 2.4L VIN B, 2.4L VIN V, 2.4L VIN P, 2.4L VIN 5 **Transmissions:** All	**Catalyst System Low Efficiency (Bank 2)** DTC P0101-P0103, P0107, P0108, P0112-P0118, P0121-P0123, P0125, P0171-P0175, P0200, P0230, P0300, P0325-P0327, P0332-P0336, P0341-P0343, P0351-P0358, P0401-P0405, P0410, P0412, P0418, P0440-P0449, P0500, P0704, P0801-0803, P1258, P1336, P1404, P1415, P1416, P1441, no HO2S codes set, engine started, engine speed over 1000 RPM for a period of 37-44 seconds, BARO sensor more than 75 kPa, ECT sensor from 167-248°F, IAT sensor from 64-176°F, MAF sensor from 12-32 g/sec, and the ECM detected the Bank 2 Catalyst was degraded below a calibrated level. **Possible Causes:** • Air leaks at the exhaust manifold or in the exhaust pipes • Base engine problems (i.e., high engine oil or coolant usage) • Catalytic converter is damaged, contaminated or has failed • Continuous engine misfire conditions, or weak or low coil output • Front HO2S or rear HO2S is contaminated with fuel or moisture • Rear HO2S is loose in the mounting hole (check it for a leak) • Front HO2S older (aged) than the rear HO2S (HO2S-12 is lazy)
DTC: P0442 **1T CCM, MIL: Yes** **Years:** 2008, 2009 **Models:** Express, G8, Lucerne, Trailblazer **Engines:** 4.6L VIN Y, 4.6L VIN 9, 6.0L VIN H, 6.0L VIN Y, 6.0L VIN K, 6.2L VIN W, 6.6L VIN 6 **Transmissions:** All	**Evaporative Emission (EVAP) System Small Leak Detected** DTCs P0106, P0107, P0108, P0112, P0113, P0116, P0117, P0118, P0120, P0121, P0122, P0123, P0222, P0223, P0443, P0446, P0449, P0451, P0452, P0453, P0454, P0455, P0461, P0462, P0463, P0464, P0496, P0502, P0503, P0608, P0641, P0651, P1516, P2101, P2119, P2120, P2122, P2123, P2125, P2127, P2128, P2135, P2138 are not set. The ignition 1 voltage is between 10-16 volts. The Barometric Pressure (BARO) is greater than 74 kPa. No fuel filling during the EONV test period. The fuel level is between 15-85 percent. The start-up Engine Coolant Temperature (ECT) and the start-up Intake Air Temperature (IAT) are between 0-40°C (32-104°F). The Barometric Pressure (BARO) is more than 74 kPa. The engine run time before engine shut-off was greater than 10 minutes. The drive distance before engine shut-off was more than 5 kilometers (3.1 miles). The ignition is OFF. The ambient air temperature at the end of the drive cycle is between 0-32°C (32-93°F). DTC P0442 runs once per drive cycle during the hot soak period after the ignition is turned OFF and may require up to 45 minutes to complete. The controller will not make more than 2 test attempts per day. The time since the last completed EONV test must be at least 17 hours. The ECM detects a leak in the EVAP system that is greater than a calibrated amount. **Note:** Inject smoke in less than 2-minute cycles for optimum tester performance. **Possible Causes:** • Small leak in the EVAP system
DTC: P0442 **1T CCM, MIL: Yes** **Years:** 2008, 2009 **Models:** Envoy, Equinox, Savana, Torrent **Engines:** 3.4L VIN F, 4.3L VIN X, 5.3L VIN M **Transmissions:** All	**EVAP System Small Leak (0.040") Detected** DTC P0107, P0108, P0112, P0113, P0116, P0117, P0118, P0125, P0440, P0443, P0455, P0449, P0452, P0453, P1111, P1112, P1114, P1115, P1120, P1220 and P1221 not set, ECT and IAT sensors from 39-86°F and within 16°F at startup, engine started, vehicle driven at less than 75 MPH, system voltage over 10.0v, BARO sensor over 75 kPa, fuel level from 15-85%, DTC P0125 not active, and the ECM detected the EVAP system was able to achieve proper vacuum, but that a vacuum decay condition was detected. **Possible Causes:** • Charcoal canister is loaded with fuel or moisture • Fuel filler cap is loose, cross-threaded, damaged or wrong part • Fuel tank, fuel filler neck or fuel sending unit 'O' ring is leaking • Fuel tank pressure sensor is damaged, disconnected or it failed • Fuel tank vapor line(s) is clogged, damaged or disconnected • Purge valve vapor line is clogged, damaged, or disconnected • Purge solenoid or Vent solenoid has a small leaking (sticking) • ECM has failed

DTC	Trouble Code Title, Conditions & Possible Causes
DTC: P0442 **1T CCM, MIL: Yes** **Years:** 2008, 2009 **Models:** G6, HHR, Malibu **Engines:** 2.0L VIN X, 2.2L VIN D, 2.2L VIN B, 2.2L VIN F, 2.4L VIN B, 2.4L VIN V, 2.4L VIN P, 2.4L VIN 5 **Transmissions:** All	**Evaporative Emission (EVAP) System Small Leak Detected** The control module detects approximately 6 vacuum/pressure changes significantly less than a calibrated amount. The condition exists during the engine OFF test, then a 5 second delay for the MIL after engine start up **Note: Introduce smoke at 15 second intervals while testing the system.** **Possible Causes:** • Damaged EVAP purge solenoid • Damaged EVAP vent valve or EVAP canister • Incorrectly routed, kinked, or damaged EVAP pipes and hoses
DTC: P0442 **1T CCM, MIL: Yes** **Years:** 2008, 2009 **Models:** Envoy, Equinox, G6, G8, Impala, Lucerne, Malibu, Savana, Trailblazer, Torrent **Engines:** 4.2L VIN S, 4.8L VIN C, 3.5L VIN N, 3.5L VIN K, 3.9L VIN 3, 3.9L VIN M, 3.6L VIN 2, 3.9L VIN 1 **Transmissions:** All	**Evaporative Emission (EVAP) System Small Leak Detected** The control module detects approximately 6 vacuum/pressure changes significantly less than a calibrated amount. The condition exists during the engine OFF test, then a 5 second delay for the MIL after engine start up **Note: Introduce smoke at 15 second intervals while testing the system.** **Possible Causes:** • Damaged EVAP purge solenoid • Damaged EVAP vent valve or EVAP canister • Incorrectly routed, kinked, or damaged EVAP pipes and hoses
DTC: P0442 **1T CCM, MIL: Yes** **Years:** 2008, 2009 **Models:** Envoy, Equinox, G6, G8, Impala, Lucerne, Malibu, Savana, Trailblazer, Torrent **Engines:** 4.2L VIN S, 4.8L VIN C, 3.5L VIN N, 3.5L VIN K, 3.9L VIN 3, 3.9L VIN M, 3.6L VIN 2, 3.9L VIN 1 **Transmissions:** All	**Evaporative Emission (EVAP) Purge Solenoid Control Circuit** The ignition is ON. The system voltage is between 9-18 volts. DTCs P0443 and P0449 run continuously when the above conditions are met. The ECM detects that the commanded state of the driver and the actual state of the control circuit do not match for a minimum of 5 seconds. **Possible Causes:** • EVAP canister purge or vent solenoid valve voltage supply circuit for a short to ground or an open/high resistance • EVAP canister purge or vent solenoid valve control circuit for a short to ground • EVAP canister purge or vent solenoid valve control circuit for a short to voltage or an open/high resistance • EVAP canister purge or vent solenoid valve • ECM has failed
DTC: P0443 **1T CCM, MIL: Yes** **Years:** 2008, 2009 **Models:** Express, G8, Lucerne, Trailblazer **Engines:** 4.6L VIN Y, 4.6L VIN 9, 6.0L VIN H, 6.0L VIN Y, 6.0L VIN K, 6.2L VIN W, 6.6L VIN 6 **Transmissions:** All	**Evaporative Emission (EVAP) Purge Solenoid Control Circuit** The ignition is ON. The system voltage is between 9-18 volts. DTCs P0443 and P0449 run continuously when the above conditions are met. The ECM detects that the commanded state of the driver and the actual state of the control circuit do not match for a minimum of 5 seconds. **Possible Causes:** • EVAP canister purge or vent solenoid valve voltage supply circuit for a short to ground or an open/high resistance • EVAP canister purge or vent solenoid valve control circuit for a short to ground • EVAP canister purge or vent solenoid control circuit for a short to voltage or an open/high resistance • EVAP canister purge or vent solenoid valve has failed • ECM has failed
DTC: P0443 **1T CCM, MIL: Yes** **Years:** 2008, 2009 **Models:** Envoy, Equinox, Savana, Torrent **Engines:** 3.4L VIN F, 4.3L VIN X, 5.3L VIN M **Transmissions:** All	**EVAP Purge Solenoid Control Circuit Malfunction** Engine started; system voltage from 6-18v, and the ECM detected the Actual and Commanded state of the EVAP Purge solenoid driver control circuit did not match for over 5 seconds during the CCM test. **Possible Causes:** • Purge solenoid control circuit is open or shorted to ground • Purge solenoid control circuit is shorted to system power (B+) • Purge solenoid power circuit is open (test the ENG1 fuse) • Purge solenoid is damaged or has failed • ECM has failed
DTC: P0443 **1T CCM, MIL: Yes** **Years:** 2008, 2009 **Models:** G6, HHR, Malibu **Engines:** 2.0L VIN X, 2.2L VIN D, 2.2L VIN B, 2.2L VIN F, 2.4L VIN B, 2.4L VIN V, 2.4L VIN P, 2.4L VIN 5 **Transmissions:** All	**EVAP Purge Solenoid Control Circuit Malfunction** Engine started; system voltage over 10.0v and the ECM detected the Actual state and the Commanded state of the Purge Solenoid driver control circuit did not match for 30 seconds. An ignition voltage is supplied directly to the EVAP canister purge solenoid valve. The EVAP canister purge solenoid is driven by a pulse width modulated (PWM) signal. The Scan Tool displays the amount of signal on-time as a percentage. The ECM monitors the status of the solenoid driver. The ECM controls the EVAP canister purge valve on-time by grounding the control circuit via an internal switch called a driver. If the ECM detects an incorrect voltage for the commanded state of the driver, it will set this trouble code (P0443). **Possible Causes:** • Purge solenoid control circuit is open or shorted to ground • Purge solenoid control circuit is shorted to system power (B+) • Purge solenoid power circuit is open (test the IGN1 fuse) • Purge solenoid is damaged or has failed • ECM has failed

DTC	Trouble Code Title, Conditions & Possible Causes
DTC: P0443 **1T CCM, MIL: Yes** **Years:** 2008, 2009 **Models:** Envoy, Equinox, G6, G8, Impala, Lucerne, Malibu, Savana, Trailblazer, Torrent **Engines:** 4.2L VIN S, 4.8L VIN C, 3.5L VIN N, 3.5L VIN K, 3.9L VIN 3, 3.9L VIN M, 3.6L VIN 2, 3.9L VIN 1 **Transmissions:** All	**EVAP Purge Solenoid Control Circuit Malfunction** Engine started; system voltage at 6-18v, and the ECM detected the Actual and Commanded state of the EVAP Purge solenoid driver control circuit did not match for over 5 seconds during the CCM test period. **Possible Causes:** • Purge solenoid control circuit is open or shorted to ground • Purge solenoid control circuit is shorted to system power (B+) • Purge solenoid power circuit is open (test the ENG1 fuse) • Purge solenoid is damaged or has failed • ECM has failed
DTC: P0446 **1T CCM, MIL: Yes** **Years:** 2008, 2009 **Models:** Express, G8, Lucerne, Trailblazer **Engines:** 4.6L VIN Y, 4.6L VIN 9, 6.0L VIN H, 6.0L VIN Y, 6.0L VIN K, 6.2L VIN W, 6.6L VIN 6 **Transmissions:** All	**Evaporative Emissions (EVAP) Vent System Performance** Before the engine control module (ECM) can report DTC P0446 failed, DTCs P0442 and P0496 must run and pass. DTCs P0107, P0108, P0112, P0113, P0116, P0117, P0118, P0125, P0128, P0443, P0449, P0451, P0453, P0454, P1106, P1107, P1111, P1112, P1114, P1115, P1125, P1516, P2101, P2108, P2119, P2120, P2125, P2138 are not set. The ignition voltage is between 10-18 volts. The Barometric Pressure (BARO) is more than 74 kPa. The fuel level is between 15-85 percent. The start-up Engine Coolant Temperature (ECT) is less than 30°C (86°F). The start-up Intake Air Temperature (IAT) is less than 30°C (86°F). The start-up ECT and IAT are within 9°C (16°F) of each other. DTC P0446 runs once per trip when the above conditions have been met. The Fuel Tank Pressure (FTP) sensor is more than 8 inches H2O vacuum for 2 seconds during the 13 minute test.Or. The FTP is less than −2.5 inches H2O or more than +5 inches H2O for 3 seconds after a cold start ignition ON. The fuel tank vacuum is greater than a calibrated amount for a calibrated period of time. **Possible Causes:** • FTP sensor low reference circuit for an open/high resistance • FTP sensor has failed
DTC: P0446 **1T CCM, MIL: Yes** **Years:** 2008, 2009 **Models:** Envoy, Equinox, Savana, Torrent **Engines:** 3.4L VIN F, 4.3L VIN X, 5.3L VIN M **Transmissions:** All	**EVAP Vent System Performance** DTC P0106, P0107, P0108, P0112, P0113, P0116-P0118, P0125, P0440-P0453, P1111-P1115, P1120, P1220 and P1221 not set, engine started, ECT and IAT sensors from 39-86°F and within 16°F at startup, BARO over 75 kPa, fuel level from 15-85%, vehicle driven to a speed of less than 75 MPH, and the ECM detected the fuel tank pressure sensor indicated less than −10 inches H2O for 20 seconds. **Possible Causes:** • EVAP vent fresh air hose is clogged, kinked or restricted • EVAP Vent solenoid is contaminated, damaged or has failed • EVAP Canister plugged or severely restricted • Fuel Cap or EVAP Service Port leaking • Fuel vapor lines or purge lines damaged or leaking • FTP sensor is out-of-calibration, damaged or "skewed" • ECM has failed • TSB 02-06-04-037 contains a repair procedure for this code
DTC: P0446 **1T CCM, MIL: Yes** **Years:** 2008, 2009 **Models:** G6, HHR, Malibu **Engines:** 2.0L VIN X, 2.2L VIN D, 2.2L VIN B, 2.2L VIN F, 2.4L VIN B, 2.4L VIN V, 2.4L VIN P, 2.4L VIN 5 **Transmissions:** All	**Evaporative Emissions (EVAP) Vent System Performance** The Fuel Tank Pressure (FTP) is less than −7.5 mm Hg (−4.0 in. H2O). The condition is present for greater than 5 seconds during the test. **Note: An intermittent condition could be caused by a damaged EVAP vent housing, a temporary blockage at the EVAP canister vent solenoid valve inlet, or a pinched vent hose. A blockage in the vent system may also cause a poor fuel fill condition** **Possible Causes:** • EVAP vent fresh air hose is clogged, kinked or restricted • EVAP Vent solenoid is contaminated, damaged or has failed • FTP sensor is out-of-calibration, damaged or "skewed" • ECM has failed
DTC: P0446 **1T CCM, MIL: Yes** **Years:** 2008, 2009 **Models:** Envoy, Equinox, G6, G8, Impala, Lucerne, Malibu, Savana, Trailblazer, Torrent **Engines:** 4.2L VIN S, 4.8L VIN C, 3.5L VIN N, 3.5L VIN K, 3.9L VIN 3, 3.9L VIN M, 3.6L VIN 2, 3.9L VIN 1 **Transmissions:** All	**Evaporative Emission (EVAP) Vent Solenoid Control Circuit** The ignition is ON. The system voltage is between 9-18 volts. DTCs P0443 and P0449 run continuously when the above conditions are met. The ECM detects that the commanded state of the driver and the actual state of the control circuit do not match for a minimum of 5 seconds. **Possible Causes:** • EVAP canister purge or vent solenoid valve voltage supply circuit for a short to ground or an open/high resistance • EVAP canister purge or vent solenoid valve control circuit for a short to ground • EVAP canister purge or vent solenoid valve control circuit for a short to voltage or an open/high resistance • EVAP canister purge or vent solenoid valve • ECM has failed

DTC	Trouble Code Title, Conditions & Possible Causes
DTC: P0449 **1T CCM, MIL: Yes** **Years:** 2008, 2009 **Models:** Express, G8, Lucerne, Trailblazer **Engines:** 4.6L VIN Y, 4.6L 9, 6.0L VIN H, 6.0L VIN Y, 6.0L VIN K, 6.2L VIN W, 6.6L VIN 6 **Transmissions:** All	**Evaporative Emission (EVAP) Vent Solenoid Control Circuit** The ignition is ON. The system voltage is between 9-18 volts. DTCs P0443 and P0449 run continuously when the above conditions are met. The ECM detects that the commanded state of the driver and the actual state of the control circuit do not match for a minimum of 5 seconds. **Possible Causes:** • EVAP canister purge or vent solenoid valve voltage supply circuit for a short to ground or an open/high resistance • EVAP canister purge or vent solenoid valve control circuit for a short to ground • EVAP canister purge or vent solenoid control circuit for a short to voltage or an open/high resistance • EVAP canister purge or vent solenoid valve has failed • ECM has failed
DTC: P0449 **1T CCM, MIL: Yes** **Years:** 2008, 2009 **Models:** Envoy, Equinox, Savana, Torrent **Engines:** 3.4L VIN F, 4.3L VIN X, 5.3L VIN M **Transmissions:** All	**EVAP Vent Solenoid Control Circuit Malfunction** Engine started; system voltage from 6-18v, and the ECM detected the Actual and Commanded state of the Vent Solenoid driver control circuit did not match for over 5 seconds. **Possible Causes:** • Vent solenoid control circuit is open or shorted to ground • Vent solenoid control circuit is shorted to system power (B+) • Vent solenoid power circuit is open (test the ENG1 fuse) • Vent solenoid is damaged or has failed • ECM has failed
DTC: P0449 **1T CCM, MIL: Yes** **Years:** 2008, 2009 **Models:** G6, HHR, Malibu **Engines:** 2.0L VIN X, 2.2L VIN D, 2.2L VIN B, 2.2L VIN F, 2.4L VIN B, 2.4L VIN V, 2.4L VIN P, 2.4L VIN 5 **Transmissions:** All	**EVAP Vent Solenoid Control Circuit Malfunction** Engine started; system voltage from 6-18v, and the ECM detected the Actual and Commanded state of the Vent Solenoid driver control circuit did not match for over 5 seconds during the CCM test period. **Possible Causes:** • Vent solenoid control circuit is open or shorted to ground • Vent solenoid control circuit is shorted to system power (B+) • Vent solenoid power circuit is open (test the ENG1 fuse) • Vent solenoid is damaged or has failed • ECM has failed
DTC: P0449 **1T CCM, MIL: Yes** **Years:** 2008, 2009 **Models:** Envoy, Equinox, G6, G8, Impala, Lucerne, Malibu, Savana, Trailblazer, Torrent **Engines:** 4.2L VIN S, 4.8L VIN C, 3.5L VIN N, 3.5L VIN K, 3.9L VIN 3, 3.9L VIN M, 3.6L VIN 2, 3.9L VIN 1 **Transmissions:** All	**Fuel Tank Pressure (FTP) Sensor Circuit** The ECM detects that the FTP sensor signal oscillates greater than 6.09mm/Hg (3.26 in. H2O) for 4 seconds, or for a cumulative of 30 seconds. **Possible Causes:** • EVAP purge solenoid valve • FTP sensor • EVAP canister vent solenoid valve and vent pipe for a blockage or restriction
DTC: P0450 **1T CCM, MIL: Yes** **Years:** 2008, 2009 **Models:** Envoy, Equinox, G6, G8, Impala, Lucerne, Malibu, Savana, Trailblazer, Torrent **Engines:** 4.2L VIN S, 4.8L VIN C, 3.5L VIN N, 3.5L VIN K, 3.9L VIN 3, 3.9L VIN M, 3.6L VIN 2, 3.9L VIN 1 **Transmissions:** All	**Fuel Tank Pressure (FTP) Sensor Performance** DTC P0451 runs only when the engine-off natural vacuum small leak test, P0442, executes. The number of times this test runs can range from 0-2 per engine-off period. The length of the test can be up to 10 minutes. This DTC will set if the controller is unable to re-zero the FTP sensor voltage within a calibrated range during the engine-off small leak test, P0442. **Possible Causes:** • FTP sensor low reference circuit for an open/high resistance • FTP sensor 5-volt reference circuit for a short to ground or an open/high resistance. • FTP sensor 5-volt reference circuit for a short to voltage • FTP sensor signal circuit for short to ground or an open/high resistance • FTP sensor has failed • ECM has failed

DTC	Trouble Code Title, Conditions & Possible Causes
DTC: P0451 **1T CCM, MIL: Yes** **Years:** 2008, 2009 **Models:** Express, G8, Lucerne, Trailblazer **Engines:** 4.6L VIN Y, 4.6L VIN 9, 6.0L VIN H, 6.0L VIN Y, 6.0L VIN K, 6.2L VIN W, 6.6L VIN 6 **Transmissions:** All	**Fuel Tank Pressure (FTP) Sensor Performance** DTC P0451 runs only when the engine-off natural vacuum small leak test, P0442, executes. The number of times this test runs can range from 0-2 per engine-off period. The length of the test can be up to 10 minutes. This DTC will set if the controller is unable to re-zero the FTP sensor voltage within a calibrated range during the engine-off small leak test, P0442. **Possible Causes:** • FTP sensor 5-volt reference circuit for a short to ground or an open/high resistance • FTP sensor low reference circuit for an open/high resistance • FTP sensor 5-volt reference circuit for a short to ground or an open/high resistance • FTP sensor 5-volt reference circuit for a short to voltage • FTP sensor signal circuit terminal B for a short to voltage • FTP sensor signal circuit for a short to ground or an open/high resistance • FTP sensor has failed • ECM has failed
DTC: P0451 **1T CCM, MIL: Yes** **Years:** 2008, 2009 **Models:** Envoy, Equinox, Savana, Torrent **Engines:** 3.4L VIN F, 4.3L VIN X, 5.3L VIN M **Transmissions:** All	**Fuel Tank Pressure (FTP) Sensor Performance** DTCs P0452, P0453, P0642, P0643 are not set. The engine has been running for more than 10 seconds. The FTP signal is between 0.2-4.9 volts. The vehicle speed reached once during drive cycle of 20 kph (14.2 mph). The EVAP system has reached full purge and no purge once during drive cycle. The EVAP system is purging. DTC P0451 runs continuously when the above conditions have been met. The maximum minus the minimum FTP signal voltage is less than 0.039 volt for 5 seconds. **Possible Causes:** • EVAP purge solenoid valve • FTP sensor • EVAP canister vent solenoid valve and vent pipe for a blockage or restriction
DTC: P0451 **1T CCM, MIL: Yes** **Years:** 2008, 2009 **Models:** G6, HHR, Malibu **Engines:** 2.0L VIN X, 2.2L VIN D, 2.2L VIN B, 2.2L VIN F, 2.4L VIN B, 2.4L VIN V, 2.4L VIN P, 2.4L VIN 5 **Transmissions:** All	**Fuel Tank Pressure (FTP) Sensor Performance** The ECM detects that the FTP is less than −26.2 mm/Hg (−14.1 in. H2O) or greater than 11.0 mm/Hg (5.9 in. H2O) for 4 seconds or for a cumulative of 30 seconds. Or the ECM detects a change in the zero point of FTP sensor signal greater than +/−5.16 mm/Hg (2.76 in. H2O) from the zero point at start up for 4 seconds, or a cumulative of 30 seconds. **Possible Causes:** • EVAP purge solenoid valve • FTP sensor • EVAP canister vent solenoid valve and vent pipe for a blockage or restriction
DTC: P0451 **1T CCM, MIL: Yes** **Years:** 2008, 2009 **Models:** Envoy, Equinox, G6, G8, Impala, Lucerne, Malibu, Savana, Trailblazer, Torrent **Engines:** 4.2L VIN S, 4.8L VIN C, 3.5L VIN N, 3.5L VIN K, 3.9L VIN 3, 3.9L VIN M, 3.6L VIN 2, 3.9L VIN 1 **Transmissions:** All	**Fuel Tank Pressure (FTP) Sensor Circuit High Voltage** Key on or engine running; and the ECM detected the Fuel Tank Pressure (FTP) sensor signal was over 4.90v for 5 seconds during the CCM test period. The FTP sensor measures the difference between the air pressure and vacuum in the EVAP system. The ECM supplies a 5v VREF and a low reference circuit to the FTP sensor. The FTP sensor signal varies depending on EVAP system pressure or vacuum. **Possible Causes:** • FTP sensor signal circuit is shorted to VREF or system power • FTP sensor ground circuit is open between sensor and ECM • FTP sensor is damaged or has failed • ECM has failed
DTC: P0451 **1T CCM, MIL: Yes** **Years:** 2008, 2009 **Models:** Envoy, Equinox, G6, G8, Impala, Lucerne, Malibu, Savana, Trailblazer, Torrent **Engines:** 4.2L VIN S, 4.8L VIN C, 3.5L VIN N, 3.5L VIN K, 3.9L VIN 3, 3.9L VIN M, 3.6L VIN 2, 3.9L VIN 1 **Transmissions:** All	**Fuel Tank Pressure (FTP) Sensor Circuit Low Voltage** DTC P0452 and P0453 run continuously when the ignition is ON. The FTP sensor voltage is less than 0.1 volt for more than 5 seconds. **Possible Causes:** • FTP sensor low reference circuit for an open/high resistance • FTP sensor 5-volt reference circuit for a short to ground or an open/high resistance. • FTP sensor 5-volt reference circuit for a short to voltage • FTP sensor signal circuit for short to ground or an open/high resistance • FTP sensor has failed • ECM has failed
DTC: P0452 **1T CCM, MIL: Yes** **Years:** 2008, 2009 **Models:** Express, G8, Lucerne, Trailblazer **Engines:** 4.6L VIN Y, 4.6L VIN 9, 6.0L VIN H, 6.0L VIN Y, 6.0L VIN K, 6.2L VIN W, 6.6L VIN 6 **Transmissions:** All	**Fuel Tank Pressure (FTP) Sensor Circuit Low Voltage** DTC P0452 runs continuously when the ignition is ON. The FTP sensor voltage is less than 0.1 volt. **Possible Causes:** • FTP sensor 5-volt reference circuit for a short to ground or an open/high resistance • FTP sensor low reference circuit for an open/high resistance • FTP sensor 5-volt reference circuit for a short to ground or an open/high resistance • FTP sensor 5-volt reference circuit for a short to voltage • FTP sensor signal circuit terminal B for a short to voltage • FTP sensor signal circuit for a short to ground or an open/high resistance • FTP sensor has failed • ECM has failed

DTC	Trouble Code Title, Conditions & Possible Causes
DTC: P0452 **1T CCM, MIL: Yes** **Years:** 2008, 2009 **Models:** Envoy, Equinox, Savana, Torrent **Engines:** 3.4L VIN F, 4.3L VIN X, 5.3L VIN M **Transmissions:** All	**Fuel Tank Pressure Sensor Circuit Low Input** Key on or engine running; and the ECM detected the Fuel Tank Pressure (FTP) sensor circuit was less than 0.10v for 5 seconds during the CCM test period. **Possible Causes:** • FTP sensor connector is damaged or shorted • FTP sensor signal circuit is open or shorted to ground • FTP sensor VREF circuit is open or shorted to ground • FTP sensor is damaged or has failed • ECM has failed
DTC: P0452 **1T CCM, MIL: Yes** **Years:** 2008, 2009 **Models:** Envoy, Equinox, G6, G8, Impala, Lucerne, Malibu, Savana, Trailblazer, Torrent **Engines:** 4.2L VIN S, 4.8L VIN C, 3.5L VIN N, 3.5L VIN K, 3.9L VIN 3, 3.9L VIN M, 3.6L VIN 2, 3.9L VIN 1 **Transmissions:** All	**Fuel Tank Pressure (FTP) Sensor Circuit High Voltage** DTC P0452 and P0453 run continuously when the ignition is ON. The FTP sensor voltage is more than 4.9 volts for more than 5 seconds. **Possible Causes:** • FTP sensor low reference circuit for an open/high resistance • FTP sensor 5-volt reference circuit for a short to ground or an open/high resistance. • FTP sensor 5-volt reference circuit for a short to voltage • FTP sensor signal circuit for short to ground or an open/high resistance • FTP sensor has failed • ECM has failed
DTC: P0453 **1T CCM, MIL: Yes** **Years:** 2008, 2009 **Models:** Express, G8, Lucerne, Trailblazer **Engines:** 4.6L VIN Y, 4.6L VIN 9, 6.0L VIN H, 6.0L VIN Y, 6.0L VIN K, 6.2L VIN W, 6.6L VIN 6 **Transmissions:** All	**Fuel Tank Pressure (FTP) Sensor Circuit High Voltage** DTC P0453 runs continuously when the ignition is ON. The FTP sensor voltage is more than 4.9 volts. **Possible Causes:** • FTP sensor 5-volt reference circuit for a short to ground or an open/high resistance • FTP sensor low reference circuit for an open/high resistance • FTP sensor 5-volt reference circuit for a short to ground or an open/high resistance • FTP sensor 5-volt reference circuit for a short to voltage • FTP sensor signal circuit terminal B for a short to voltage • FTP sensor signal circuit for a short to ground or an open/high resistance • FTP sensor has failed • ECM has failed
DTC: P0453 **1T CCM, MIL: Yes** **Years:** 2008, 2009 **Models:** Envoy, Equinox, Savana, Torrent **Engines:** 3.4L VIN F, 4.3L VIN X, 5.3L VIN M **Transmissions:** All	**Fuel Tank Pressure Sensor Circuit High Input** Key on or engine running; and the ECM detected the Fuel Tank Pressure (FTP) sensor circuit was more than 4.85v for 4 seconds during the CCM test period. **Possible Causes:** • FTP sensor connector is damaged, loose or open • FTP sensor signal circuit is shorted to VREF (5v) • FTP sensor ground circuit is open between sensor and ECM • FTP sensor is damaged or has failed • ECM has failed
DTC: P0454 **1T CCM, MIL: Yes** **Years:** 2008, 2009 **Models:** Express, G8, Lucerne, Trailblazer **Engines:** 4.6L VIN Y, 4.6L VIN 9, 6.0L VIN H, 6.0L VIN Y, 6.0L VIN K, 6.2L VIN W, 6.6L VIN 6 **Transmissions:** All	**Fuel Tank Pressure (FTP) Sensor Intermittent** DTC P0454 runs only when the engine-off natural vacuum small leak test, P0442, executes. This test can run once per engine-off period. The length of the test can be up to 10 minutes. A refueling event is not detected. **Possible Causes:** • FTP sensor 5-volt reference circuit for a short to ground or an open/high resistance • FTP sensor low reference circuit for an open/high resistance • FTP sensor 5-volt reference circuit for a short to ground or an open/high resistance • FTP sensor 5-volt reference circuit for a short to voltage • FTP sensor signal circuit terminal B for a short to voltage • FTP sensor signal circuit for a short to ground or an open/high resistance • FTP sensor has failed • ECM has failed

DTC	Trouble Code Title, Conditions & Possible Causes
DTC: P0454 **1T CCM, MIL: Yes** **Years:** 2008, 2009 **Models:** Envoy, Equinox, Savana, Torrent **Engines:** 3.4L VIN F, 4.3L VIN X, 5.3L VIN M **Transmissions:** All	**Fuel Tank Pressure (FTP) Sensor Intermittent** DTCs P000A, P000B, P0010, P0013, P0016, P0017, P0030, P0031, P0032, P0068, P0072, P0073, P0074, P009A, P0101, P0102, P0103, P0111, P0112, P0113, P0114, P0116, P0117, P0118, P0119, P0121, P0122, P0123, P0130, P0131, P0132, P0133, P0134, P0135, P0171, P0172, P0201, P0202, P0203, P0204, P0221, P0222, P0223, P0261, P0262, P0264, P0265, P0267, P0268, P0270, P0271, P0300, P0301, P0302, P0303, P0304, P0335, P0336, P0340, P0341, P0365, P0366, P0442, P0443, P0446, P0449, P0451, P0452, P0453, P0454, P0455, P0456, P0458, P0459, P0496, P0498, P0499, P0500, P0501, P0506, P0507, P0562, P0563, P0601, P0602, P0603, P0604, P0605, P0606, P0607, P061A, P061B, P061C, P0642, P0643, P1101, P2088, P2089, P2090, P2091, P2100, P2101, P2119, P2176, P2227, P2228, P2229, P2297, P2301, P2304, P2307, P2310, and P2A00 are not set. The ignition is ON. The Barometric Pressure (BARO) is more than 75 kPa. The Engine Coolant Temperature (ECT) is less than 110°C (230°F). The engine has been running between 1-10 minutes. The engine is idling. The vehicle speed is 0 kph (0 mph). The fuel level is between 6-40 liters (2-10 gallons). The fuel tank pressure is between −3 and +1 kPa (−2 and +4 H2O). The intake air temperature (IAT) is between −8.25 and +70°C (+17 and +158°F). The battery voltage is more than 10 volts. The engine is operating in Closed Loop fuel control. DTC P0454 runs once per drive cycle when the above conditions have been met. The maximum minus the minimum fuel tank pressure is more than 0.1 kPa (0.4 in H2O) for 5 seconds. **Possible Causes:** • FTP sensor • FTP sensor 5-volt reference circuit shorted to ground or an open/high resistance • FTP sensor signal circuit terminal 1 for a short to voltage • FTP sensor signal circuit for short to ground or an open/high resistance • FTP sensor has failed • ECM has failed
DTC: P0454 **1T CCM, MIL: Yes** **Years:** 2008, 2009 **Models:** G6, HHR, Malibu **Engines:** 2.0L VIN X, 2.2L VIN D, 2.2L VIN B, 2.2L VIN F, 2.4L VIN B, 2.4L VIN V, 2.4L VIN P, 2.4L VIN 5 **Transmissions:** All	**Evaporative Emission (EVAP) System Large Leak Detected** Before the ECM can report DTC P0455 failed, DTC P0496 must run and pass. DTCs P0106, P0107, P0108, P0116, P0117, P0118, P0120, P0121, P0122, P0123, P0220, P0222, P0223, P0442, P0443, P0449, P0451, P0452, P0453, P0454, P0464, P0496, P0608, P0609, P0641, P0651, P1516, P2101, P2119, P2120, P2122, P2123, P2125, P2127, P2128, P2135, P2138 are not set. The ignition voltage is between 11-18 volts. The Barometric Pressure (BARO) is more than 74 kPa. The fuel level is between 15-85 percent. The Engine Coolant temperature (ECT) is less than 35°C (95°F). The Intake Air Temperature (IAT) is between 4-30°C (39-86°F). DTC P0455 runs once per cold start when the above conditions are met. The EVAP system is not able to achieve or maintain a calibrated level of vacuum within a set amount of time. **Possible Causes:** • Inspect for a damaged fuel filler neck seal surface. • Blockage or restriction in the EVAP purge solenoid valve, purge pipe, EVAP canister, or vapor pipe, • Inspect for a loose, missing, damaged, or incorrect fuel fill cap • FTP sensor has failed
DTC: P0455 **1T CCM, MIL: Yes** **Years:** 2008, 2009 **Models:** Express, G8, Lucerne, Trailblazer **Engines:** 4.6L VIN Y, 4.6L VIN 9, 6.0L VIN H, 6.0L VIN Y, 6.0L VIN K, 6.2L VIN W, 6.6L VIN 6 **Transmissions:** All	**Evaporative Emission (EVAP) System Large Leak Detected** Before the ECM can report DTC P0455 failed, DTC P0496 must run and pass. DTCs P0106, P0107, P0108, P0116, P0117, P0118, P0120, P0121, P0122, P0123, P0220, P0222, P0223, P0442, P0443, P0449, P0451, P0452, P0453, P0454, P0464, P0496, P0608, P0609, P0641, P0651, P1516, P2101, P2119, P2120, P2122, P2123, P2125, P2127, P2128, P2135, P2138 are not set. The ignition voltage is between 11-18 volts. The Barometric Pressure (BARO) is more than 74 kPa. The fuel level is between 15-85 percent. The Engine Coolant Temperature (ECT) is less than 35°C (95°F). The Intake Air Temperature (IAT) is between 4-30°C (39-86°F). DTC P0455 runs once per cold start when the above conditions are met. The EVAP system is not able to achieve or maintain a calibrated level of vacuum within a set amount of time. **Possible Causes:** • Fuel cap damaged or missing • Large leak in the EVAP sytem • FTP sensor has failed

DTC	Trouble Code Title, Conditions & Possible Causes
DTC: P0455 **1T CCM, MIL: Yes** **Years:** 2008, 2009 **Models:** Envoy, Equinox, Savana, Torrent **Engines:** 3.4L VIN F, 4.3L VIN X, 5.3L VIN M **Transmissions:** All	**EVAP System Large Leak (0.080") Detected** DTC P0106-P0108, P0112, P0113, P0116-P0118, P0120-P0123, P0125, P0131-P0138, P0140, P0141, P0147, P0151-P0158, P0160, P0161, P0167, P0220, P0442-P0443, P0449, P0452-P0453, P0455, P0502, P0503, P1111, P1112, P1114, P1115, P1120 not set, engine started, ECT and IAT sensors from 39-167°F and within 16°F at startup, system voltage from 10-18v, BARO sensor more than 75 kPa, Fuel Level from 15-85%, and the ECM detected it was unable to achieve or maintain vacuum during the EVAP system. The ECM monitors the FTP sensor signal to determine the EVAP system vacuum level. Once conditions are correct, the ECM commands the Purge valve open and the EVAP vent valve closed to Allow engine vacuum to enter the system. After a calibrated time or vacuum level, the ECM commands the Purge valve closed to seal the system, and monitors the FTP sensor to determine the EVAP system vacuum level. If the system is unable to achieve the correct vacuum level, or the vacuum level decreases too rapidly, the ECM will set this code. **Possible Causes:** • Fuel filler cap is very loose, missing or the wrong part • Fuel tank, fuel filler neck or fuel sending unit 'O' ring is leaking • Fuel tank pressure sensor is damaged, disconnected or it failed • Fuel tank vapor line(s) is clogged, damaged or disconnected • Purge valve vapor line is clogged, damaged, or disconnected • Purge solenoid is not opening (it may be damaged or sticking) • Vent solenoid is not closing (it may be damaged or sticking) • ECM has failed
DTC: P0455 **1T CCM, MIL: Yes** **Years:** 2008, 2009 **Models:** Envoy, Equinox, G6, G8, Impala, Lucerne, Malibu, Savana, Trailblazer, Torrent **Engines:** 4.2L VIN S, 4.8L VIN C, 3.5L VIN N, 3.5L VIN K, 3.9L VIN 3, 3.9L VIN M, 3.6L VIN 2, 3.9L VIN 1 **Transmissions:** All	**Evaporative Emission (EVAP) System Large Leak Detected** DTCs P000A, P000B, P0010, P0013, P0016, P0017, P0030, P0031, P0032, P0068, P0072, P0073, P0074, P009A, P0101, P0102, P0103, P0111, P0112, P0113, P0114, P0116, P0117, P0118, P0119, P0121, P0122, P0123, P0130, P0131, P0132, P0133, P0134, P0135, P0171, P0172, P0201, P0202, P0203, P0204, P0221, P0222, P0223, P0261, P0262, P0264, P0265, P0267, P0268, P0270, P0271, P0300, P0301, P0302, P0303, P0304, P0335, P0336, P0340, P0341, P0365, P0366, P0436, P0442, P0443, P0446, P0449, P0451, P0452, P0453, P0454, P0456, P0458, P0459, P0496, P0498, P0499, P0500, P0506, P0507, P0562, P0563, P0601, P0602, P0604, P0605, P0606, P0607, P061A, P061B, P061C, P0642, P0643, P1101, P2088, P2089, P2090, P2091, P2100, P2101, P2119, P2176, P2227, P2228, P2229, P2297, P2301, P2304, P2307, P2310, P2610, and P2A00 are not set. The Ignition is ON. The Barometric Pressure (BARO) is more than 75 kPa. The Engine Coolant Temperature (ECT) is less than 110°C (230°F). The engine has been running between 1-10 minutes. The engine is idling. The fuel level is between 6-40 liters (2-10 gallons). The Fuel Tank Pressure (FTP) is between −3 and +1 kPa (−12 and +4 in H2O). The vehicle speed is 0 kph (0 mph). The Intake Air Temperature (IAT) is between −8 and +70°C (+17 and +158°F). The battery voltage is more than 10 volts. The engine is operating in Closed Loop fuel control. DTC P0455 runs once per drive cycle when the above conditions are met. The EVAP system is not able to achieve or maintain vacuum before purge has reached a calibrated volume. **Possible Causes:** • Fuel filler cap is very loose, missing or the wrong part • Fuel tank, fuel filler neck or fuel sending unit 'O' ring is leaking • Fuel tank pressure sensor is damaged, disconnected or it failed • Fuel tank vapor line(s) is clogged, damaged or disconnected • Purge valve vapor line is clogged, damaged, or disconnected • Purge solenoid is not opening (it may be damaged or sticking) • Vent solenoid is not closing (it may be damaged or sticking) • ECM has failed
DTC: P0455 **1T CCM, MIL: Yes** **Years:** 2008, 2009 **Models:** G6, HHR, Malibu **Engines:** 2.0L VIN X, 2.2L VIN D, 2.2L VIN B, 2.2L VIN F, 2.4L VIN B, 2.4L VIN V, 2.4L VIN P, 2.4L VIN 5 **Transmissions:** All	**Evaporative Emissions (EVAP) System Very Small Leak Detected** DTCs P000A, P000B, P0010, P0013, P0016, P0017, P0030, P0031, P0032, P0068, P0072, P0073, P0074, P009A, P0101, P0102, P0103, P0111, P0112, P0113, P0114, P0116, P0117, P0118, P0119, P0121, P0122, P0123, P0130, P0131, P0132, P0133, P0134, P0135, P0171, P0172, P0201, P0202, P0203, P0204, P0221, P0222, P0223, P0261, P0262, P0264, P0265, P0267, P0268, P0270, P0271, P0300, P0301, P0302, P0303, P0304, P0335, P0336, P0340, P0341, P0365, P0366, P0442, P0443, P0446, P0449, P0451, P0452, P0453, P0454, P0455, P0456, P0458, P0459, P0496, P0498, P0499, P0501, P0506, P0507, P0562, P0563, P0601, P0603, P0604, P0605, P0606, P0607, P061A, P061B, P061C, P0642, P0643, P1101, P2088, P2089, P2090, P2091, P2100, P2101, P2119, P2176, P2227, P2228, P2297, P2301, P2304, P2307, P2310, P2610, and P2A00 are not set. The ignition is ON. The barometric pressure (BARO) is more than 75 kPa. The engine coolant temperature (ECT) is less than 110°C (230°F). The engine has been running between 1-10 minutes. The engine is idling. The fuel level is between 6-40 liters (2-10 gallons). The fuel tank pressure (FTP) is between -3 and +1 kPa (−12 and +4 in H2O). The vehicle speed is 0 kph (0 mph). The intake air temperature (IAT) is between −8 and +70°C (+17 and +158°F). The battery voltage is more than 10 volts. DTC P0456 runs once per drive cycle when the above conditions have been met. DTC P0456 sets when a leak between 0.85-0.39 mm (0.033-0.015 in) is detected. **Possible Causes:** • Damaged EVAP purge solenoid • Damaged EVAP vent valve or EVAP canister • Incorrectly routed, kinked, or damaged EVAP pipes and hoses

DTC	Trouble Code Title, Conditions & Possible Causes
DTC: P0456 **1T CCM, MIL: Yes** **Years:** 2008, 2009 **Models:** G6, HHR, Malibu **Engines:** 2.0L VIN X, 2.2L VIN D, 2.2L VIN B, 2.2L VIN F, 2.4L VIN B, 2.4L VIN V, 2.4L VIN P, 2.4L VIN 5 **Transmissions:** All	**Evaporative Emission (EVAP) Purge Solenoid Control Circuit Low Voltage** The engine speed is greater than 80 RPM. The ignition voltage is between 10-18 volts. The ECM has commanded the EVAP canister purge valve ON and OFF at least once during the ignition cycle. The DTCs run continuously once the above conditions are met. The ECM detects the EVAP canister purge solenoid control circuit is shorted to ground. The condition exists for 4 seconds or a cumulative of 30 seconds. **Possible Causes:** • EVAP purge solenoid control circuit for a shorted to ground. • EVAP purge solenoid shorted to voltage or an open/high resistance • Faulty EVAP purge solenoid. • ECM has failed
DTC: P0458 **1T CCM, MIL: Yes** **Years:** 2008, 2009 **Models:** Envoy, Equinox, G6, G8, Impala, Lucerne, Malibu, Savana, Trailblazer, Torrent **Engines:** 4.2L VIN S, 4.8L VIN C, 3.5L VIN N, 3.5L VIN K, 3.9L VIN 3, 3.9L VIN M, 3.6L VIN 2, 3.9L VIN 1 **Transmissions:** All	**Evaporative Emission (EVAP) Purge Solenoid Control Circuit Low Voltage** DTCs P0606, P0628, or P0629 are not set. The ignition is ON. The engine is running. The battery voltage is more than 10 volts. The EVAP canister purge solenoid valve is commanded between 8-91 percent. DTC P0458 runs continuously when the above conditions are met. This DTC sets when a short to ground is detected on the EVAP canister purge solenoid valve control circuit for 3 seconds. **Possible Causes:** • EVAP purge solenoid control circuit for a shorted to ground. • EVAP purge solenoid shorted to voltage or an open/high resistance • Faulty EVAP purge solenoid. • ECM has failed
DTC: P0458 **1T CCM, MIL: Yes** **Years:** 2008, 2009 **Models:** G6, HHR, Malibu **Engines:** 2.0L VIN X, 2.2L VIN D, 2.2L VIN B, 2.2L VIN F, 2.4L VIN B, 2.4L VIN V, 2.4L VIN P, 2.4L VIN 5 **Transmissions:** All	**Evaporative Emission (EVAP) Purge Solenoid Control Circuit High Voltage** The engine speed is greater than 80 RPM. The ignition voltage is between 10-18 volts. The ECM has commanded the EVAP canister purge valve ON and OFF at least once during the ignition cycle. The DTCs run continuously once the above conditions are met. The ECM detects the EVAP canister purge solenoid control circuit is shorted to voltage. The condition exists for 4 seconds or a cumulative of 30 seconds. **Possible Causes:** • EVAP purge solenoid control circuit for a shorted to ground. • EVAP purge solenoid shorted to voltage or an open/high resistance • Faulty EVAP purge solenoid. • ECM has failed
DTC: P0459 **1T CCM, MIL: Yes** **Years:** 2008, 2009 **Models:** Envoy, Equinox, G6, G8, Impala, Lucerne, Malibu, Savana, Trailblazer, Torrent **Engines:** 4.2L VIN S, 4.8L VIN C, 3.5L VIN N, 3.5L VIN K, 3.9L VIN 3, 3.9L VIN M, 3.6L VIN 2, 3.9L VIN 1 **Transmissions:** All	**Evaporative Emission (EVAP) Purge Solenoid Control Circuit High Voltage** DTCs P0606, P0628, or P0629 are not set. The ignition is ON. The engine is running. The battery voltage is more than 10 volts. The EVAP canister purge solenoid valve is commanded between 8-91 percent. DTC P0458 runs continuously when the above conditions are met. This DTC sets when an open circuit is detected on the EVAP canister vent solenoid valve control circuit for 3 seconds. **Possible Causes:** • EVAP purge solenoid control circuit for a shorted to ground. • EVAP purge solenoid shorted to voltage or an open/high resistance • Faulty EVAP purge solenoid. • ECM has failed
DTC: P0459 **1T CCM, MIL: Yes** **Years:** 2008, 2009 **Models:** G6, HHR, Malibu **Engines:** 2.0L VIN X, 2.2L VIN D, 2.2L VIN B, 2.2L VIN F, 2.4L VIN B, 2.4L VIN V, 2.4L VIN P, 2.4L VIN 5 **Transmissions:** All	**Fuel Level Sensor High Input** Engine started; system voltage over 10.0v and the ECM detected the Fuel Level sensor signal indicated more than 2.90v for 6 minutes under these conditions during the CCM test. **Possible Causes:** • Fuel level sensor signal circuit is shorted to system power • Fuel level sensor ground circuit is open • Fuel level sender is damaged, binding or not aligned properly • ECM has failed
DTC: P0463 **1T CCM, MIL: No** **Years:** 2008, 2009 **Models:** Express, G8, Lucerne, Trailblazer **Engines:** 4.6L VIN Y, 4.6L VIN 9, 6.0L VIN H, 6.0L VIN Y, 6.0L VIN K, 6.2L VIN W, 6.6L VIN 6 **Transmissions:** All	**Cooling Fan Relay 1 Control Circuit Malfunction** Key on or engine running; system voltage from 9-18v, and the ECM detected the Actual state and Commanded state of the Fan Relay 1 control circuit (Low Speed Fan) did not match for 30 seconds. **Possible Causes:** • Fan control relay control circuit is open or shorted to ground • Fan control relay control circuit is shorted to system power • Fan control relay power circuit is open (check Cool Fan 1 fuse) • Fan control relay is damaged or has failed • ECM has failed

DTC	Trouble Code Title, Conditions & Possible Causes
DTC: P0496 **1T CCM, MIL: Yes** **Years:** 2008, 2009 **Models:** Express, G8, Lucerne, Trailblazer **Engines:** 4.6L VIN Y, 4.6L VIN 9, 6.0L VIN H, 6.0L VIN Y, 6.0L VIN K, 6.2L VIN W, 6.6L VIN 6 **Transmissions:** All	**Evaporative Emission System Flow During Non-Purge** DTCs P0106, P0107, P0108, P0116, P0117, P0118, P0120, P0121, P0122, P0123, P0220, P0222, P0223, P0442, P0443, P0446, P0449, P0451, P0452, P0453, P0454, P0464, P0608, P0609, P0641, P0651, P1516, P2101, P2119, P2120, P2122, P2123, P2125, P2127, P2128, P2135, P2138 are not set. The ignition voltage is between 11-18 volts. The Barometric Pressure (BARO) is more than 74 kPa. The fuel level is between 15-85 percent. The engine coolant temperature (ECT) is less than 35°C (95°F). The Intake Air Temperature (IAT) is between 4-30°C (39-86°F). DTC P0496 runs once per cold start when the above conditions are met. The ECM detects more than 10 inch H2O vacuum for 5 seconds during a non-purge condition. **Possible Causes:** • EVAP canister purge solenoid valve
DTC: P0496 **1T CCM, MIL: Yes** **Years:** 2008, 2009 **Models:** Envoy, Equinox, Savana, Torrent **Engines:** 3.4L VIN F, 4.3L VIN X, 5.3L VIN M **Transmissions:** All	**EVAP Canister Purge System High Purge Flow** DTC P0106-P0108, P0112, P0113, P0116-P0118, P0120-P0123, P0125, P0131-P0138, P0140, P0141, P0147, P0151-P0158, P0160, P0161, P0167, P0220, P0442-P0443, P0449, P0452-P0453, P0455, P0502, P0503, P1111, P1112, P1114, P1115, P1120 not set, engine started, ECT and IAT sensors from 39-86°F and within 16°F at startup, system voltage from 10-18v, BARO sensor more than 75 kPa, fuel level at 15-85%, and the ECM detected a continuous open purge flow condition in the system (FTP less than −11 H2O). This diagnostic test is designed to test for undesired intake manifold vacuum flow to the EVAP system. During this test, the ECM seals the EVAP system by commanding the EVAP Purge valve closed and the EVAP canister vent valve closed. The ECM monitors the FTP sensor signal in order to determine if a vacuum is being drawn on the EVAP system. If vacuum in the EVAP system is more than a predetermined value within a certain time, this code is set. **Possible Causes:** • EVAP charcoal canister is damaged or restricted • EVAP purge pipe is damaged or restricted • FTP sensor is damaged or it has failed • Purge solenoid is damaged (it may be sticking) • Purge solenoid valve has failed
DTC: P0496 **1T CCM, MIL: Yes** **Years:** 2008, 2009 **Models:** Equinox, G6, G8, Torrent **Engines:** 2.0L VIN X, 2.2L VIN D, 2.2L VIN B, 2.2L VIN F, 2.4L VIN B, 2.4L VIN V, 2.4L VIN P, 2.4L VIN 5, 4.2L VIN S, 4.8L VIN C, 3.5L VIN N, 3.5L VIN K, 3.9L VIN 3, 3.9L VIN M, 3.6L VIN 2, 3.9L VIN 1 **Transmissions:** All	**Evaporative Emission (EVAP) System No Flow During Purge** The ECM detects the EVAP system is not able to achieve or maintain vacuum during the diagnostic test. The condition exists for greater than 4 seconds or for a cumulative of 30 seconds. **Possible Causes:** • Fuel filler cap is very loose, missing or the wrong part • Fuel tank, fuel filler neck or fuel sending unit 'O' ring is leaking • Fuel tank pressure sensor is damaged, disconnected or it failed • Fuel tank vapor line(s) is clogged, damaged or disconnected • Purge valve vapor line is clogged, damaged, or disconnected • Purge solenoid is not opening (it may be damaged or sticking) • Vent solenoid is not closing (it may be damaged or sticking) • ECM has failed
DTC: P0497 **1T CCM, MIL: Yes** **Years:** 2008, 2009 **Models:** Envoy, Equinox, G6, G8, Impala, Lucerne, Malibu, Savana, Trailblazer, Torrent **Engines:** 4.2L VIN S, 4.8L VIN C, 3.5L VIN N, 3.5L VIN K, 3.9L VIN 3, 3.9L VIN M, 3.6L VIN 2, 3.9L VIN 1 **Transmissions:** All	**Evaporative Emission (EVAP) Vent Solenoid Valve Control Circuit Low Voltage** The ECM detects the voltage on the EVAP canister vent valve control circuit is less than 2.6 volts when the driver is commanded OFF. The condition is present for greater than 4 seconds or for a cumulative of 30 seconds. **Possible Causes:** • Vent solenoid control circuit is open or shorted to ground • Vent solenoid control circuit is shorted to system power (B+) • Vent solenoid power circuit is open • Vent solenoid is damaged or has failed • ECM has failed
DTC: P0498 **1T CCM, MIL: Yes** **Years:** 2008, 2009 **Models:** Equinox, G6, G8, Torrent **Engines:** 2.0L VIN X, 2.2L VIN D, 2.2L VIN B, 2.2L VIN F, 2.4L VIN B, 2.4L VIN V, 2.4L VIN P, 2.4L VIN 5, 4.2L VIN S, 4.8L VIN C, 3.5L VIN N, 3.5L VIN K, 3.9L VIN 3, 3.9L VIN M, 3.6L VIN 2, 3.9L VIN 1 **Transmissions:** All	**Evaporative Emission (EVAP) Vent Solenoid Valve Control Circuit High Voltage** The ECM detects the voltage on the EVAP canister vent valve control circuit is greater than 4.6 volts when the driver is commanded ON. The condition is present for greater than 4 seconds or for a cumulative of 30 seconds. **Possible Causes:** • Vent solenoid control circuit is open or shorted to ground • Vent solenoid control circuit is shorted to system power (B+) • Vent solenoid power circuit is open • Vent solenoid is damaged or has failed • ECM has failed

DTC	Trouble Code Title, Conditions & Possible Causes
DTC: P0499 **1T CCM, MIL: Yes** **Years:** 2008, 2009 **Models:** Equinox, G6, G8, Torrent **Engines:** 2.0L VIN X, 2.2L VIN D, 2.2L VIN B, 2.2L VIN F, 2.4L VIN B, 2.4L VIN V, 2.4L VIN P, 2.4L VIN 5, 4.2L VIN S, 4.8L VIN C, 3.5L VIN N, 3.5L VIN K, 3.9L VIN 3, 3.9L VIN M, 3.6L VIN 2, 3.9L VIN 1 **Transmissions:** All	**Vehicle Speed Sensor Circuit Malfunction** DTC P0106, P0107, P0108, P0335, P0336, P1120, P1125, P1128, P1220, P1221, P1514, P1515, P1516, P1517 and P1518 not set, engine started, vehicle driven at a speed over 1000 RPM, ECT sensor more than 95°F, MAP sensor from 40-100 kPa (Turbo Boost Pressure from 40-100 kPa on Diesel) TP angle from 5-95%, and the ECM did not detect any VSS signals for from 50-100 seconds. **Possible Causes:** • Output shaft rotor is chipped or damaged • Output shaft rotor is not aligned properly with the VSS unit • VSS tip contains debris or metal shavings (an intermittent fault) • VSS positive (+) signal circuit is open or shorted to ground • VSS negative (-) signal circuit is open or shorted to ground • VSS is damaged or has failed
DTC: P0500 **2T CCM, MIL: Yes** **Years:** 2008, 2009 **Models:** Express, G8, Lucerne, Trailblazer **Engines:** 4.6L VIN Y, 4.6L VIN 9, 6.0L VIN H, 6.0L VIN Y, 6.0L VIN K, 6.2L VIN W, 6.6L VIN 6 **Transmissions:** All	**VSS Circuit Low Input** DTC P0106, P0107, P0108, P1106, P1107, P0121, P0122, P0123, P1121 and P1122 not set, engine started, Input Shaft Speed signal over 1500 RPM, MAP sensor from 12-15 kPa, transaxle not in P/N, TP angle over 12%, engine torque more than 25-150 lb ft., and the ECM detected the OSS signal was less than 150 RPM for 3 seconds. **Possible Causes:** • Output shaft rotor is chipped or damaged • OSS tip contains debris or metal shavings (an intermittent fault) • OSS positive (+) signal circuit is open or shorted to ground • OSS negative (−) signal circuit is open or shorted to ground • OSS is damaged or has failed
DTC: P0502 **2T CCM, MIL: Yes** **Years:** 2008, 2009 **Models:** Express, G8, Lucerne, Trailblazer **Engines:** 4.6L VIN Y, 4.6L VIN 9, 6.0L VIN H, 6.0L VIN Y, 6.0L VIN K, 6.2L VIN W, 6.6L VIN 6 **Transmissions:** All	**VSS Circuit Malfunction** DTC P0502 and P1810 not set, engine running, at least 6 seconds have passed since the last gear change, Decel Fuel Cutoff inactive, Transmission output shaft speed did not increase over 250 RPM for 2 seconds, and the ECM detected the OSS signal dropped more than 1500 RPM in 2 seconds during the CCM test. **Possible Causes:** • OSS assembly connector is damaged, loose or shorted • Output shaft rotor is chipped or damaged (intermittent fault) • OSS tip contains debris or metal shavings (an intermittent fault) • OSS (+) signal circuit is open or shorted to ground (intermittent) • OSS (-) signal circuit is open or shorted to ground (intermittent) • OSS is damaged or has failed (an intermittent fault)
DTC: P0503 **2T CCM, MIL: Yes** **Years:** 2008, 2009 **Models:** Express, G8, Lucerne, Trailblazer **Engines:** 4.6L VIN Y, 4.6L VIN 9, 6.0L VIN H, 6.0L VIN Y, 6.0L VIN K, 6.2L VIN W, 6.6L VIN 6 **Transmissions:** All	**Idle Speed Low** DTCs P0068, P0101, P0102, P0103, P0106, P0107, P0108, P0112, P0113, P0117, P0118, P0120, P0122, P0123, P0171, P0172, P0201, P0202, P0203, P0204, P0205, P0206, P0207, P0208, P0220, P0221, P0222, P0223, P0230, P0300, P0336, P0442, P0446, P0449, P0452, P0453, P0455, P0462, P0463, P0496, P1516, P2101, P2135, P2176 are not set. The engine is operating for at least 60 seconds. The Engine Coolant Temperature (ECT) is more than −60°C (−140°F). The Intake Air Temperature (IAT) is more than −10°C (−14°F). The Barometric Pressure (BARO) is more than 65 kPa. The system voltage is between 9-18 volts. The vehicle speed is less than 1.6 km/h (1 mph). DTC P0506 and P0507 run continuously when the above conditions are met.. The actual idle speed is approximately 150 RPM lower than the desired idle speed. The above condition is present for 15 seconds. **Possible Causes:** • Incorrect torque converter clutch (TCC) operation • Accessories that require additional torque to operate • Excessive deposits in the throttle bod • Restricted exhaust • Mechanical conditions that limit engine speed
DTC: P0506 **1T CCM, MIL: Yes** **Years:** 2008, 2009 **Models:** Express, G8, Lucerne, Trailblazer **Engines:** 4.6L VIN Y, 4.6L VIN 9, 6.0L VIN H, 6.0L VIN Y, 6.0L VIN K, 6.2L VIN W, 6.6L VIN 6 **Transmissions:** All	**Idle Speed Low** DTCs P0068, P0101, P0102, P0103, P0106, P0107, P0108, P0112, P0113, P0117, P0118, P0120, P0122, P0123, P0171, P0172, P0201, P0202, P0203, P0204, P0205, P0206, P0207, P0208, P0220, P0221, P0222, P0223, P0230, P0300, P0336, P0442, P0446, P0449, P0452, P0453, P0455, P0462, P0463, P0496, P1516, P2101, P2135, P2176 are not set. The engine has been running for greater than 60 seconds. The engine is idling for greater than 10 seconds. The AC mode state has not changed. The power steering load state has not changed. The transmission gear selector state has not changed. The engine coolant temperature (ECT) is greater than −60°C (−76°F). The system voltage is between 11-18 volts. The vehicle speed is less than 4.8 km/h (2 mph). The actual idle speed is approximately 100 RPM lower than the desired idle speed. The above condition is present for 15 seconds. **Possible Causes:** • Incorrect Torque Converter Clutch (TCC) operation • Dirty throttle body • Accessories that require additional torque to operate • Excessive deposits in the throttle body • Restricted exhaust

DTC	Trouble Code Title, Conditions & Possible Causes
DTC: P0506 **1T CCM, MIL: Yes** **Years:** 2008, 2009 **Models:** Envoy, Equinox, Savana, Torrent **Engines:** 3.4L VIN F, 4.3L VIN X, 5.3L VIN M **Transmissions:** All	**Idle Speed Too Low** DTC P0105, P0107, P0108, P0112, P0113, P0117, P0118, P0122, P0123, P0125, P0128, P0130-P0134, P0171, P0172, P0201-P0204, P0300, P0301-P0304, P0336, P0440, P0442, P0446, P0452, P0453, P0502, P0503, P1133 and P1441 not set, engine started, engine runtime over 20 seconds, system voltage over 10.0v, ECT sensor more than 104°F, BARO sensor more than 72 kPa, and the ECM detected the Actual idle speed was 60 RPM less than Desired idle speed for 13 seconds with the IAC position over 145 counts. **Possible Causes:** • Air inlet duct is collapsed, loose or air filter element is clogged • Base engine problem (i.e., compression or misfire condition) • Idle air inlet passage or throttle bore is dirty or full of deposits • IAC solenoid control circuit has a high resistance condition • IAC valve is damaged or has failed • MAF sensor is dirty, out-of-calibration or it is "skewed" • Throttle plate, throttle shaft or linkage is damaged or sticking • ECM has failed
DTC: P0506 **2T CCM, MIL: Yes** **Years:** 2008, 2009 **Models:** Express, G8, Lucerne, Trailblazer **Engines:** 4.6L VIN Y, 4.6L VIN 9, 6.0L VIN H, 6.0L VIN Y, 6.0L VIN K, 6.2L VIN W, 6.6L VIN 6 **Transmissions:** All	**Idle Speed Too Low** DTC P0107, P0108, P0112, P0113, P0117, P0118, P0125, P0171, P0172, P0200, P0300, P0336, P0440, P0442, P0446, P0452, P0453, P0502, P0503, P1120, P1220, P1221, P1514, P1515, P1516, P1635 and P1639 not set, engine runtime over 2 seconds, ECT sensor more than −40°F, IAT sensor more than −40°F, BARO sensor more than 65 kPa, system voltage from 6-18v, VSS less than 3 MPH, and the ECM detected the Actual idle speed was more than 105 RPM less than the Desired idle speed for 15 seconds. **Possible Causes:** • Air inlet duct is collapsed, loose or air filter element is clogged • Base engine problem (i.e., compression or misfire condition) • IAC valve is damaged or has failed • Idle air inlet passage or throttle bore is dirty or full of deposits • MAF sensor is dirty, out-of-calibration or it is "skewed" • Throttle plate, throttle shaft or linkage is damaged or sticking • ECM has failed
DTC: P0507 **1T CCM, MIL: Yes** **Years:** 2008, 2009 **Models:** Express, G8, Lucerne, Trailblazer **Engines:** 4.6L VIN Y, 4.6L VIN 9, 6.0L VIN H, 6.0L VIN Y, 6.0L VIN K, 6.2L VIN W, 6.6L VIN 6 **Transmissions:** All	**Idle Speed High** DTCs P0068, P0101, P0102, P0103, P0106, P0107, P0108, P0112, P0113, P0117, P0118, P0120, P0122, P0123, P0171, P0172, P0201, P0202, P0203, P0204, P0205, P0206, P0207, P0208, P0220, P0221, P0222, P0223, P0230, P0300, P0336, P0442, P0446, P0449, P0452, P0453, P0455, P0462, P0463, P0496, P1516, P2101, P2135, P2176 are not set. The engine has been running for greater than 60 seconds. The engine is idling for greater than 10 seconds. The AC mode state has not changed. The power steering load state has not changed. The transmission gear selector state has not changed. The Engine Coolant Temperature (ECT) is greater than −60°C (−76°F). The system voltage is between 11-18 volts. The vehicle speed is less than 4.8 km/h (2 mph). The actual idle speed is approximately 200 RPM greater than the desired idle speed. The above condition is present for 15 seconds. **Possible Causes:** • Vacuum leaks • A faulty Positive Crankcase Ventilation (PCV) valve • Dirty throttle body
DTC: P0507 **1T CCM, MIL: Yes** **Years:** 2008, 2009 **Models:** Envoy, Equinox, Savana, Torrent **Engines:** 3.4L VIN F, 4.3L VIN X, 5.3L VIN M **Transmissions:** All	**Idle Speed Too High** DTC P0105, P0107, P0108, P0112, P0113, P0117, P0118, P0122, P0123, P0125, P0128, P0130-P0134, P0171, P0172, P0201-P0204, P0300, P0301-P0304, P0336, P0440, P0442, P0446, P0452, P0453, P0502, P0503, P1133 and P1441 not set, engine started, engine runtime over 20 seconds, system voltage over 10.0v, ECT sensor more than 104°F, BARO sensor more than 72 kPa, and the ECM detected the Actual idle speed was 60 RPM more than Desired idle speed for 13 seconds with the IAC position under 2 counts. **Possible Causes:** • Engine vacuum leaks, ECM valve is leaking or the wrong valve • Idle air inlet passage or throttle bore is dirty or full of deposits • IAC valve is damaged or has failed • MAF sensor is dirty, "skewed" or installed improperly • Throttle plate, throttle shaft or linkage is damaged or sticking • TP sensor is out-of-range or "skewed" high • ECM has failed

DTC	Trouble Code Title, Conditions & Possible Causes
DTC: P0507 **1T CCM, MIL: Yes** **Years:** 2008, 2009 **Models:** Equinox, G6, G8, Torrent **Engines:** 2.0L VIN X, 2.2L VIN D, 2.2L VIN B, 2.2L VIN F, 2.4L VIN B, 2.4L VIN V, 2.4L VIN P, 2.4L VIN 5, 4.2L VIN S, 4.8L VIN C, 3.5L VIN N, 3.5L VIN K, 3.9L VIN 3, 3.9L VIN M, 3.6L VIN 2, 3.9L VIN 1 **Transmissions:** All	**Idle Speed Too High** The actual engine speed is greater than the desired idle speed by at least 200 RPM for greater than 4 seconds or for a cumulative of 30 seconds. The ECM detects 3 fuel cut-offs due to an engine over speed condition while the vehicle speed is zero. **Possible Causes:** • Air inlet duct is collapsed, loose or air filter element is clogged • A parasitic load on the engine • Base engine problem (i.e., compression or misfire condition) • MAF sensor is dirty, out-of-calibration or it is "skewed" • Throttle plate, throttle shaft or linkage is damaged or sticking • ECM has failed
DTC: P0508 **1T CCM, MIL: Yes** **Years:** 2008, 2009 **Models:** Equinox, G6, G8, Torrent **Engines:** 2.0L VIN X, 2.2L VIN D, 2.2L VIN B, 2.2L VIN F, 2.4L VIN B, 2.4L VIN V, 2.4L VIN P, 2.4L VIN 5, 4.2L VIN S, 4.8L VIN C, 3.5L VIN N, 3.5L VIN K, 3.9L VIN 3, 3.9L VIN M, 3.6L VIN 2, 3.9L VIN 1 **Transmissions:** All	**Cold Start Idle Air Control System Performance** DTCs P000A, P0010, P0016, P0068, P0071, P0072, P0073, P0101, P0102, P0103, P0116, P0117, P0118, P0119, P0121, P0123, P0171, P0172, P0201, P0202, P0203, P0204, P0222, P0261, P0262, P0264, P0265, P0267, P0268, P0270, P0271, P0335, P0336, P0340, P0341, P0365, P0366, P0443, P0459, P0496, P0501, P061A, P1101, P2088, P2089, P2100, P2101, P2122, P2123, P2127, P2128, P2138, P2227, P2228, P2229, P2301, P2304, P2307, P2310 are not set. The battery voltage is more than 10 volts. The engine speed is at idle. The vehicle speed equals 0 kph (0 mph). The Engine Coolant Temperature (ECT) is more than −9.75°C (+14.45°F). The Mass Air Flow (MAF) is within the calibrated range. The Pulse Width Modulated (PWM) signal for the canister purge solenoid is less than 90 percent. DTC P050A runs continuously when the above conditions are met. The actual idle speed is 175 RPM lower than the desired idle speed or 175 RPM greater than the desired idle speed during a cold start. The above condition is present for 3 seconds. **Possible Causes:** • Faulty Positive Crankcase Ventilation (PCV) system • Vacuum leaks • Mechanical conditions that limit engine speed • Restricted exhaust • Excessive deposits in the throttle body • Accessories that require additional torque to operate
DTC: P050A **2T CCM, MIL: Yes** **Years:** 2008, 2009 **Models:** G6, HHR, Malibu **Engines:** 2.0L VIN X, 2.2L VIN D, 2.2L VIN B, 2.2L VIN F, 2.4L VIN B, 2.4L VIN V, 2.4L VIN P, 2.4L VIN 5 **Transmissions:** All	**Cold Start Idle Air Control (IAC) System Performance** The actual engine speed is greater than the desired idle speed by at least 200 RPM for greater than 4 seconds or for a cumulative of 30 seconds. The ECM detects 3 fuel cut-offs due to an engine over speed condition while the vehicle speed is zero. **Possible Causes:** • Air inlet duct is collapsed, loose or air filter element is clogged • A parasitic load on the engine • Base engine problem (i.e., compression or misfire condition) • MAF sensor is dirty, out-of-calibration or it is "skewed" • Throttle plate, throttle shaft or linkage is damaged or sticking • ECM has failed
DTC: P050A **1T CCM, MIL: Yes** **Years:** 2008, 2009 **Models:** Envoy, Equinox, G6, G8, Impala, Lucerne, Malibu, Savana, Trailblazer, Torrent **Engines:** 4.2L VIN S, 4.8L VIN C, 3.5L VIN N, 3.5L VIN K, 3.9L VIN 3, 3.9L VIN M, 3.6L VIN 2, 3.9L VIN 1 **Transmissions:** All	**Engine Oil Pressure Sensor Circuit Low Input** DTC P1635 not set, engine started, and the ECM detected the Engine Oil Pressure (EOP) signal was less than 0.48v for 9 seconds. The sensor range is 0.5v (0 psi) to 4.5v (128 psi). **Possible Causes:** • Engine oil level it too low • EOP sensor signal circuit is open or shorted to ground • EOP sensor VREF circuit is open • EOP sensor is damaged or has failed • Instrument Cluster or ECM has failed
DTC: P0601 **1T CCM, MIL: Yes** **Years:** 2008, 2009 **Models:** Envoy, Equinox, Savana, Torrent **Engines:** 3.4L VIN F, 4.3L VIN X, 5.3L VIN M **Transmissions:** All	**Control Module ROM Malfunction** Key in crank or the run position, and the ECM detected more than 3 incorrect checksums during its initial self-test. The ECM uses an EEPROM to store software and calibration data. The ECM uses a checksum to verify the integrity of the information. At the time of programming, the ECM calculates a checksum and stores the value in the EEPROM. The ECM retrieves this data, performs a checksum test to compare the key "on" value to the value stored in EEPROM. If these two values do not match at key "on", it sets DTC P0601. **Possible Causes:** • The ECM must be replaced to correct this problem. A new ECM must be programmed with the correct software/calibration. • TSB 67-65-23 contains a repair procedure for this code

DTC	Trouble Code Title, Conditions & Possible Causes
DTC: P0601 **1T ECM, MIL: Yes** **Years:** 2008, 2009 **Models:** All **Engines:** All **Transmissions:** All	**Control Module Torque Performance** The ignition switch is in the Run or Crank position. DTC P061A runs continuously when the above condition is met. The ECM detects an internal failure or incomplete programming for more than 10 seconds. **Possible Causes:** • Voltage and ground inputs to the ECM • High resistance, short or open condition to the ECM • ECM is not properly programmed • ECM has failed
DTC: P0601A **2T CCM, MIL: Yes** **Years:** 2008, 2009 **Models:** G6, HHR, Malibu **Engines:** 2.0L VIN X, 2.2L VIN D, 2.2L VIN B, 2.2L VIN F, 2.4L VIN B, 2.4L VIN V, 2.4L VIN P, 2.4L VIN 5 **Transmissions:** All	**Control Module Torque Calculation Performance** The engine is running or cranking. DTC P061B runs continuously when the above condition is met. **Possible Causes:** • Voltage and ground inputs to the ECM • High resistance, short or open condition to the ECM • ECM is not properly programmed • ECM has failed
DTC: P0601B **2T CCM, MIL: Yes** **Years:** 2008, 2009 **Models:** G6, HHR, Malibu **Engines:** 2.0L VIN X, 2.2L VIN D, 2.2L VIN B, 2.2L VIN F, 2.4L VIN B, 2.4L VIN V, 2.4L VIN P, 2.4L VIN 5 **Transmissions:** All	**Control Module Engine Speed Performance** The engine is running and the engine speed is more than 1,760 RPM. DTC P061C runs continuously when the above condition is met. **Possible Causes:** • Voltage and ground inputs to the ECM • High resistance, short or open condition to the ECM • ECM is not properly programmed • ECM has failed
DTC: P0601C **2T CCM, MIL: Yes** **Years:** 2008, 2009 **Models:** G6, HHR, Malibu **Engines:** 2.0L VIN X, 2.2L VIN D, 2.2L VIN B, 2.2L VIN F, 2.4L VIN B, 2.4L VIN V, 2.4L VIN P, 2.4L VIN 5 **Transmissions:** All	**Control Module Not Programmed** The ignition switch is in Run or Crank. DTC P0602 runs once per ignition cycle. The ECM detects an internal failure or incomplete programming for more than 10 seconds. **Note: Attempt to program the ECM before replacing the ECM.** **Possible Causes:** • Check the voltage and ground inputs to the ECM for a, short, open or high resistance • ECM has failed
DTC: P0602 **1T CCM, MIL: Yes** **Years:** 2008, 2009 **Models:** Envoy, Equinox, Savana, Torrent **Engines:** 3.4L VIN F, 4.3L VIN X, 5.3L VIN M **Transmissions:** All	**Control Module Not Programmed** Key on, and the ECM detected it did not have the correct program to operate or that the EEPROM had been programmed incorrectly. **Possible Causes:** • Reprogram the ECM with the correct software and calibration. If this step does not correct the problem, the ECM must be replaced and programmed with the correct software/calibration.
DTC: P0602 **1T ECM, MIL: Yes** **Years:** 2008, 2009 **Models:** All **Engines:** All **Transmissions:** All	**Control Module Long Term Memory Reset** The ignition switch is in Run or Crank. DTC P0603 runs once per ignition cycle. The ECM detects an internal failure or incomplete programming for more than 10 seconds. **Possible Causes:** • Check the voltage and ground inputs to the ECM for a, short, open or high resistance • ECM has failed
DTC: P0603 **1T CCM, MIL: Yes** **Years:** 2008, 2009 **Models:** Envoy, Equinox, Savana, Torrent **Engines:** 3.4L VIN F, 4.3L VIN X, 5.3L VIN M **Transmissions:** All	**Control Module Long Term Memory Reset** DTC P0604 not set, and then with the key on, the ECM detected the calculated checksum that did not match the previous checksum. **Possible Causes:** • An interruption to the ECM main power and/or ground circuits • Check the ECM power and ground circuits and make repairs as necessary. Clear the codes and recheck. If it resets, the ECM must be replaced and programmed with the correct software.

DTC	Trouble Code Title, Conditions & Possible Causes
DTC: P0603 **1T ECM, MIL: Yes** **Years:** 2008, 2009 **Models:** All **Engines:** All **Transmissions:** All	**Control Module Random Access Memory (RAM)** The ignition switch is in Run or Crank. DTC P0604 runs continuously when the above condition is met. The ECM detects an internal failure or incomplete programming for more than 10 seconds. **Note: Attempt to program the ECM before replacing the ECM.** **Possible Causes:** • Check the voltage and ground inputs to the ECM for a, short, open or high resistance • ECM has failed
DTC: P0604 **1T CCM, MIL: Yes** **Years:** 2008, 2009 **Models:** Envoy, Equinox, Savana, Torrent **Engines:** 3.4L VIN F, 4.3L VIN X, 5.3L VIN M **Transmissions:** All	**Control Module Random Access Memory (RAM) Failure** Key on for 5 seconds, and the ECM detected the internal data test of its RAM failed. The ECM copies the program information stored in the RAM. This Allows the ECM to work with, and make any updates to this data. The ECM checks for problems in All areas of the RAM. **Possible Causes:** • The ECM must be replaced to correct this problem. A new ECM must be programmed with the correct software/calibration.
DTC: P0604 **1T ECM, MIL: Yes** **Years:** 2008, 2009 **Models:** All **Engines:** All **Transmissions:** All	**Control Module Programming Read Only Memory (ROM)** Key on, and the ECM detected the data checksum did not match the expected value, or that it was unable to read its flash memory data. **Possible Causes:** • The ECM must be replaced to correct this problem. A new ECM must be programmed with the correct software/calibration.
DTC: P0605 **1T ECM, MIL: Yes** **Years:** 2008, 2009 **Models:** Express, G8, Lucerne, Trailblazer **Engines:** 4.6L VIN Y, 4.6L VIN 9, 6.0L VIN H, 6.0L VIN Y, 6.0L VIN K, 6.2L VIN W, 6.6L VIN 6 **Transmissions:** All	**Control Module Programming Read Only Memory** Key on, and the ECM detected the data checksum did not match the expected value, or that it was unable to read its flash memory data. **Possible Causes:** • The ECM must be replaced to correct this problem. A new ECM must be programmed with the correct software/calibration.
DTC: P0605 **1T ECM, MIL: Yes** **Years:** 2008, 2009 **Models:** Envoy, Equinox, Savana, Torrent **Engines:** 3.4L VIN F, 4.3L VIN X, 5.3L VIN M **Transmissions:** All	**Control Module Internal Performance** The ignition switch is in the Unlock/Accessory, Run, or Crank positions. The system voltage is more than 5.23 volts. DTC P0606 runs continuously when the above conditions are met. The ECM detects an internal failure or incomplete programming for more than 10 seconds. **Possible Causes:** • Check the voltage and ground inputs to the ECM for a, short, open or high resistance • ECM has failed
DTC: P0606 **1T CCM, MIL: Yes** **Years:** 2008, 2009 **Models:** Envoy, Equinox, Savana, Torrent **Engines:** 3.4L VIN F, 4.3L VIN X, 5.3L VIN M **Transmissions:** All	**Control Module Internal Performance** DTC P0601 and P0604 not set, key on, and the ECM determined that an internal performance problem existed within its controller. **Possible Causes:** • The ECM must be replaced to correct this problem. A new ECM must be programmed with the correct software/calibration.
DTC: P0606 **1T ECM, MIL: Yes** **Years:** 2008, 2009 **Models:** All **Engines:** All **Transmissions:** All	**Control Module Performance** The ignition switch is in Unlock, Accessory, Run or Crank. The system voltage is more than 5.23 volts. DTCs P0601, P0602, P0603, P0604, P0606, P062F, P0641, P0651, P2610 are not set. DTC P0607 runs continuously when the above conditions are met. The ECM detects an internal failure or incomplete programming for more than 10 seconds. **Note: Attempt to program the ECM before replacing the ECM.** **Possible Causes:** • Check the voltage and ground inputs to the ECM for a, short, open or high resistance • ECM has failed

DTC	Trouble Code Title, Conditions & Possible Causes
DTC: P0607 **1T CCM, MIL: Yes** **Years:** 2008, 2009 **Models:** Envoy, Equinox, Savana, Torrent **Engines:** 3.4L VIN F, 4.3L VIN X, 5.3L VIN M **Transmissions:** All	**Control Module Performance** Key on or engine running; then after the initial ECM power up sequence, the ECM detected an internal performance problem. **Possible Causes:** • The ECM must be replaced to correct this problem. A new ECM must be programmed with the correct software/calibration.
DTC: P0607 **1T ECM, MIL: Yes** **Years:** 2008, 2009 **Models:** All **Engines:** All **Transmissions:** All	**Vehicle Speed Output Circuit Malfunction** Engine started, engine speed over 600 RPM, and the ECM detected the Actual and Commanded state of the VSS output circuit did not match for 5 seconds. The ECM creates the VSS output signal by causing the circuit to pulse to ground, and monitoring the operation. **Possible Causes:** • VSS output signal circuit is open, shorted to ground or to power • VSS output signal problem related to the Instrument Cluster or the Electronic Suspension Control Module (internal problem) • ECM has failed
DTC: P060D **1T ECM, MIL: Yes** **Years:** 2008, 2009 **Models:** All **Engines:** All **Transmissions:** All	**Control Module Vehicle Options Incorrect** The ignition is ON. The ECM detects that programming for vehicle options is incorrect. **Possible Causes:** • ECM is not properly programmed • ECM has failed
DTC: P0610 **2T CCM, MIL: Yes** **Years:** 2008, 2009 **Models:** G6, HHR, Malibu **Engines:** 2.0L VIN X, 2.2L VIN D, 2.2L VIN B, 2.2L VIN F, 2.4L VIN B, 2.4L VIN V, 2.4L VIN P, 2.4L VIN 5 **Transmissions:** All	**Generator Signal Range/Performance** Engine started, the Voltage Telltale lamp is on, or less than 1000 RPM for the low duty cycle test, or more than 1000 RPM for high duty cycle test, and the ECM detected the 'L' terminal voltage was low with the Generator commanded "on", or the 'F' terminal PWM was less than 5% with the engine speed below 2500 RPM for 30 seconds. **Note: Refer to the Freeze Frame Records for additional information.** **Possible Causes:** • Generator 'L' terminal circuit is open, shorted to ground or B+ • Generator 'F' terminal circuit is open, shorted to ground or B+ • ECM has failed
DTC: P0627 **1T CCM, MIL: Yes** **Years:** 2008, 2009 **Models:** Envoy, Equinox, G6, G8, Impala, Lucerne, Malibu, Savana, Trailblazer, Torrent **Engines:** 4.2L VIN S, 4.8L VIN C, 3.5L VIN N, 3.5L VIN K, 3.9L VIN 3, 3.9L VIN M, 3.6L VIN 2, 3.9L VIN 1 **Transmissions:** All	**Fuel Pump Enable Circuit Low Voltage** The ECM detects the fuel pump enable circuit voltage is less than 2.21 volts when the enable circuit is commanded OFF. The condition exists for greater than 4 seconds, or a cumulative of 30 seconds. **Possible Causes:** • Short to voltage on the enable circuit • Fuel Pump Control Module (FECM) • ECM has failed
DTC: P0628 **1T CCM, MIL: Yes** **Years:** 2008, 2009 **Models:** Envoy, Equinox, G6, G8, Impala, Lucerne, Malibu, Savana, Trailblazer, Torrent **Engines:** 4.2L VIN S, 4.8L VIN C, 3.5L VIN N, 3.5L VIN K, 3.9L VIN 3, 3.9L VIN M, 3.6L VIN 2, 3.9L VIN 1 **Transmissions:** All	**Fuel Pump Relay Control Circuit Low Voltage** The ignition is ON and the engine is running. The fuel pump is running. The ignition voltage is more than 9 volts. These DTCs run continuously when the above conditions are met. The ECM detects the fuel pump relay control circuit is shorted to ground. **Possible Causes:** • Fuel pump relay has failed • ECM has failed
DTC: P0628 **2T CCM, MIL: Yes** **Years:** 2008, 2009 **Models:** G6, HHR, Malibu **Engines:** 2.0L VIN X, 2.2L VIN D, 2.2L VIN B, 2.2L VIN F, 2.4L VIN B, 2.4L VIN V, 2.4L VIN P, 2.4L VIN 5 **Transmissions:** All	**Fuel Pump Enable Circuit High Voltage** The ECM detects the fuel pump enable circuit voltage is greater than 2.74 volts when the enable circuit is commanded OFF. The condition exists for greater than 4 seconds, or a cumulative of 30 seconds. **Possible Causes:** • Short to voltage on the enable circuit • Fuel Pump Control Module (FECM) • ECM has failed

DTC	Trouble Code Title, Conditions & Possible Causes
DTC: P0629 **1T CCM, MIL: Yes** **Years:** 2008, 2009 **Models:** Envoy, Equinox, G6, G8, Impala, Lucerne, Malibu, Savana, Trailblazer, Torrent **Engines:** 4.2L VIN S, 4.8L VIN C, 3.5L VIN N, 3.5L VIN K, 3.9L VIN 3, 3.9L VIN M, 3.6L VIN 2, 3.9L VIN 1 **Transmissions:** All	**Fuel Pump Enable Circuit High Voltage** The ignition is ON and the engine is running. The fuel pump is running. The ignition voltage is more than 9 volts. These DTCs run continuously when the above conditions are met. The ECM detects the fuel pump relay control circuit is open or shorted to voltage. **Possible Causes:** • Short to voltage on the enable circuit • Fuel pump relay • ECM has failed
DTC: P0629 **2T CCM, MIL: Yes** **Years:** 2008, 2009 **Models:** G6, HHR, Malibu **Engines:** 2.0L VIN X, 2.2L VIN D, 2.2L VIN B, 2.2L VIN F, 2.4L VIN B, 2.4L VIN V, 2.4L VIN P, 2.4L VIN 5 **Transmissions:** All	**Control Module Fuel Injector Control Performance** The engine speed is greater than 80 RPM. The ignition voltage is between 8-18 volts. DTC P062B runs continuously when the above condition is met for greater than 500 The ECM detects a condition with the integrated circuits of the fuel injector driver module for greater than 4 seconds, or a cumulative of 30 seconds. **Note: Verify that the battery cables are clean and tight and the battery is fully charged.** **Possible Causes:** • Module not properly programmed • ECM has failed
DTC: P062B **1T CCM, MIL: Yes** **Years:** 2008, 2009 **Models:** Envoy, Equinox, G6, G8, Impala, Lucerne, Malibu, Savana, Trailblazer, Torrent **Engines:** 4.2L VIN S, 4.8L VIN C, 3.5L VIN N, 3.5L VIN K, 3.9L VIN 3, 3.9L VIN M, 3.6L VIN 2, 3.9L VIN 1 **Transmissions:** All	**Control Module Long Term Memory Performance** The ignition is ON. DTC P062F runs once per ignition cycle. The ECM detects an internal failure or incomplete programming for more than 10 seconds. **Note: Attempt to program the ECM before replacing the ECM.** **Possible Causes:** • Check the voltage and ground inputs to the ECM for a, short, open or high resistance • ECM has failed
DTC: P062F **1T ECM, MIL: Yes** **Years:** 2008, 2009 **Models:** All **Engines:** All **Transmissions:** All	**Throttle Actuator Control (TAC) Command Performance** The ECM detects that the commanded duty cycle for the range test high is greater than 80 percent. Or the ECM detects that the commanded duty cycle for the range test low is greater than 80 percent. Either condition exists for greater than 1 second, or a cumulative of 10 seconds. **Note: Use a scan tool to help diagnose the condition.** **Possible Causes:** • Throttle blade that is not in the rest position • Throttle valve that is binding open or closed • Throttle valve that opens or closes without spring pressure • Throttle body has failed • ECM has failed
DTC: P0638 **1T CCM, MIL: Yes** **Years:** 2008, 2009 **Models:** Envoy, Equinox, G6, G8, Impala, Lucerne, Malibu, Savana, Trailblazer, Torrent **Engines:** 4.2L VIN S, 4.8L VIN C, 3.5L VIN N, 3.5L VIN K, 3.9L VIN 3, 3.9L VIN M, 3.6L VIN 2, 3.9L VIN 1 **Transmissions:** All	**5-Volt Reference 1 Circuit** The ignition is in Unlock, Accessory, Run, or Crank. The ignition voltage is more than 5.23 volts. DTCs P0641 and P0651 run continuously when the above conditions are met. The ECM detects a voltage out of tolerance condition on the 5-volt reference 1 or 2 circuit for more than 0.5 second. The 5-volt reference 1 circuit provides 5 volts to the following sensors, Fuel tank pressure (FTP) sensor, Accelerator Pedal Position (APP) sensor 2, Engine Oil Pressure (EOP) sensor and Camshaft Position (CMP) sensor. **Possible Causes:** • 5v VREF circuit is shorted to chassis or sensor ground • 5v VREF circuit to FTP. APP, EOP, and CMP sensors circuit is shorted to (B+) • ECM has failed
DTC: P0641 **1T CCM, MIL: Yes** **Years:** 2008, 2009 **Models:** Envoy, Equinox, Savana, Torrent **Engines:** 3.4L VIN F, 4.3L VIN X, 5.3L VIN M **Transmissions:** All	**5-Volt Reference Circuit (FECM)** The ignition is on. The Fuel Pump Control Module (FECM) detects that the fuel pressure 5-volt reference is above or below a predetermined voltage threshold. **Possible Causes:** • Fuel line pressure sensor, 5v VREF circuit shorted to ground or an open/high resistance • Fuel line pressure sensor, 5v VREF circuit for a shorted to voltage • Fuel line pressure sensor, low reference circuit for an open/high resistance • FECM has failed • ECM has failed

DTC	Trouble Code Title, Conditions & Possible Causes
DTC: P0641 **1T CCM, MIL: Yes** **Years:** 2008, 2009 **Models:** Equinox, G6, G8, Torrent **Engines:** All **Transmissions:** All	**5-Volt Reference 1 Circuit Low Voltage** Key on or engine running; and the ECM detected the 5v Reference circuit was out of tolerance for 10 seconds. The 5v VREF 1 circuit from the ECM is used to provide power to the The Fuel Tank Pressure (FTP) sensor. The air conditioning (A/C) refrigerant pressure sensorThe Accelerator Pedal Position (APP) sensor 1. The exhaust Camshaft Position (CMP) sensor. The intake CMP sensor. The Throttle Position (TP) sensor 2. The Intake Manifold Tuning Valve (IMTV) sensorThe ECM detects a voltage out of range condition on the 5-volt reference 1 or 2 buss for more than 0.5 second. **Possible Causes:** • 5v VREF circuit is shorted to chassis or sensor ground • 5v VREF circuit to FTP. CMP IMTV or TP sensor circuit is shorted to (B+) • Component failure • ECM has failed
DTC: P0642 **2T CCM, MIL: Yes** **Years:** 2008, 2009 **Models:** All **Engines:** All **Transmissions:** All	**5-Volt Reference 1 Circuit High Voltage** Key on or engine running; and the ECM detected the 5v Reference circuit was out of tolerance for 10 seconds. The 5v VREF 1 circuit from the ECM is used to provide power to the The Fuel Tank Pressure (FTP) sensor. The air conditioning (A/C) refrigerant pressure sensorThe Accelerator Pedal Position (APP) sensor 1. The exhaust Camshaft Position (CMP) sensor. The intake CMP sensor. The Throttle Position (TP) sensor 2. The Intake Manifold Tuning Valve (IMTV) sensorThe ECM detects a voltage out of range condition on the 5-volt reference 1 or 2 buss for more than 0.5 second. **Possible Causes:** • 5v VREF circuit is shorted to chassis or sensor ground • 5v VREF circuit to FTP. CMP IMTV or TP sensor circuit is shorted to (B+) • Component failure • ECM has failed
DTC: P0643 **2T CCM, MIL: Yes** **Years:** 2008, 2009 **Models:** All **Engines:** All **Transmissions:** All	**Air Conditioning Clutch Relay Control Circuit Malfunction** Engine started, engine speed over 400 RPM, system voltage over 10.0v, and the ECM detected the Actual and Commanded state of the A/C Relay Control circuit did not match for 5 seconds. **Possible Causes:** • A/C relay control circuit is open, shorted to ground or to power • A/C relay power circuit is open (test the A/C CRUISE mini fuse) • A/C relay is damaged or has failed • ECM has failed
DTC: P064A **1T CCM, MIL: Yes** **Years:** 2008, 2009 **Models:** Envoy, Equinox, G6, G8, Impala, Lucerne, Malibu, Savana, Trailblazer, Torrent **Engines:** 4.2L VIN S, 4.8L VIN C, 3.5L VIN N, 3.5L VIN K, 3.9L VIN 3, 3.9L VIN M, 3.6L VIN 2, 3.9L VIN 1 **Transmissions:** All	**Malfunction Indicator Lamp (MIL) Control Circuit** The ignition is in the Run or Crank position. The ignition voltage is between 9-18 volts. DTC P0650 runs continuously when the ignition is ON. The control module detects that the commanded state of the MIL driver and the actual state of the control circuit do not match for more than 5 seconds. **Possible Causes:** • IPC ignition circuit fuse is open, • IPC control circuit for a short to ground • IPC control circuit for a short to voltage or high resistance • IPC has failed • ECM has failed
DTC: P0650 **1T CCM, MIL: Yes** **Years:** 2008, 2009 **Models:** Envoy, Equinox, Savana, Torrent **Engines:** 3.4L VIN F, 4.3L VIN X, 5.3L VIN M **Transmissions:** All	**Malfunction Indicator Lamp (MIL) Control Circuit** The ECM detects an open, a short to ground, or a short to voltage on the circuit that controls the MIL. The condition exists for at least 4 seconds. **Possible Causes:** • MIL control circuit is open or shorted to ground • MIL control circuit is shorted to system power • MIL control power circuit is open in the Instrument Cluster • MIL (the lamp) is damaged or has failed • Instrument Control Panel (IPC) has failed • ECM has failed
DTC: P0650 **2T CCM, MIL: Yes** **Years:** 2008, 2009 **Models:** All **Engines:** All **Transmissions:** All	**5-Volt Reference 2 Circuit** The ignition is in Unlock, Accessory, Run, or Crank. The ignition voltage is more than 5.23 volts. DTCs P0641 and P0651 run continuously when the above conditions are met. The ECM detects a voltage out of tolerance condition on the 5-volt reference 1 or 2 circuit for more than 0.5 second. The 5-volt reference 2 circuit provides 5 volts to the following sensors, APP sensor 1, Throttle Position (TP) sensor 1 and 2, Crankshaft Position (CKP) and brake booster vacuum sensor. **Possible Causes:** • 5v VREF circuit is shorted to chassis or sensor ground • 5v VREF circuit to APP. CKP, and CMP brake booster vacuum sensor circuit is shorted to (B+) • ECM has failed

DTC	Trouble Code Title, Conditions & Possible Causes
DTC: P0651 **1T CCM, MIL: Yes** **Years:** 2008, 2009 **Models:** Envoy, Equinox, Savana, Torrent **Engines:** 3.4L VIN F, 4.3L VIN X, 5.3L VIN M **Transmissions:** All	**5-Volt Reference 2 Circuit Malfunction** Key on or engine running; and the ECM detected the 5v Reference circuit was out of tolerance for 10 seconds. The 5v VREF 2 circuit is used to provide power to the Fuel Tank Pressure (FTP) sensor on this vehicle application. **Possible Causes:** • 5v VREF circuit is shorted to chassis or sensor ground • 5v VREF circuit to MAP or TP sensor circuit is shorted to (B+) • ECM has failed
DTC: P0651 **1T CCM, MIL: No** **Years:** 2008, 2009 **Engines:** 4.6L VIN Y, 4.6L VIN 9, 6.0L VIN H, 6.0L VIN Y, 6.0L VIN K, 6.2L VIN W, 6.6L VIN 6 **Transmissions:** All	**5-Volt Reference 2 Circuit Malfunction** The 5-volt reference circuit voltage is greater or less than a predetermined threshold. The condition exists, then a 5 second delay for MIL ONThe 5-volt reference 2 circuit provides 5 volts to the following sensors. All four camshaft position (CMP) sensors and the Accelerator pedal position (APP) sensor 1 **Possible Causes:** • 5v VREF circuit is shorted to chassis or sensor ground • 5v VREF circuit to CMP or APP sensor circuit is shorted to (B+) • Component failure • ECM has failed
DTC: P0651 **1T CCM, MIL: Yes** **Years:** 2008, 2009 **Models:** Equinox, G6, G8, Torrent **Engines:** 4.2L VIN S, 4.8L VIN C, 3.5L VIN N, 3.5L VIN K, 3.9L VIN 3, 3.9L VIN M, 3.6L VIN 2, 3.9L VIN 1 **Transmissions:** All	**5-Volt Reference 2 Circuit Low Voltage** The 5-volt reference circuit voltage is greater or less than a predetermined threshold. The condition exists, then a 5 second delay for MIL ONThe 5-volt reference 2 circuit provides 5 volts to the following sensors. All four camshaft position (CMP) sensors and the Accelerator pedal position (APP) sensor 1 **Possible Causes:** • 5v VREF circuit is shorted to chassis or sensor ground • 5v VREF circuit to CMP or APP sensor circuit is shorted to (B+) • Component failure • ECM has failed
DTC: P0652 **1T CCM, MIL: Yes** **Years:** 2008, 2009 **Models:** Envoy, Equinox, G6, G8, Impala, Lucerne, Malibu, Savana, Trailblazer, Torrent **Engines:** 4.2L VIN S, 4.8L VIN C, 3.5L VIN N, 3.5L VIN K, 3.9L VIN 3, 3.9L VIN M, 3.6L VIN 2, 3.9L VIN 1 **Transmissions:** All	**5-Volt Reference 2 Circuit Low Voltage** The 5-volt reference circuit voltage is greater or less than a predetermined threshold. The condition exists, then a 5 second delay for MIL ONThe 5-volt reference 2 circuit provides 5 volts to the following sensors. The APP sensor 2. The Throttle Position (TP) sensor 1. The Crankshaft Position (CKP) sensor **Possible Causes:** • 5v VREF circuit is shorted to chassis or sensor ground • 5v VREF circuit to TP, CKP or APP sensor circuit is shorted to (B+) • ECM has failed
DTC: P0652 **2T CCM, MIL: Yes** **Years:** 2008, 2009 **Models:** G6, HHR, Malibu **Engines:** 2.0L VIN X, 2.2L VIN D, 2.2L VIN B, 2.2L VIN F, 2.4L VIN B, 2.4L VIN V, 2.4L VIN P, 2.4L VIN 5 **Transmissions:** All	**5-Volt Reference 2 Circuit High Voltage** The 5-volt reference circuit voltage is greater or less than a predetermined threshold. The condition exists, then a 5 second delay for MIL ON. The 5-volt reference 2 circuit provides 5 volts to the following sensors. The APP sensor 2. The Throttle Position (TP) sensor 1. The Crankshaft Position (CKP) sensor **Possible Causes:** • 5v VREF circuit is shorted to chassis or sensor ground • 5v VREF circuit to APP TP or CKP sensor circuit is shorted to (B+) • Component failure • ECM has failed
DTC: P0653 **1T CCM, MIL: Yes** **Years:** 2008, 2009 **Models:** Envoy, Equinox, G6, G8, Impala, Lucerne, Malibu, Savana, Trailblazer, Torrent **Engines:** 4.2L VIN S, 4.8L VIN C, 3.5L VIN N, 3.5L VIN K, 3.9L VIN 3, 3.9L VIN M, 3.6L VIN 2, 3.9L VIN 1 **Transmissions:** All	**5-Volt Reference 2 Circuit High Voltage** DTCs P0601, P0602, P0603, P0604, P0605, P0606, P0607, and P2610 are not set. The ignition is in Unlock, Accessory, Run, or Crank. The ignition voltage is more than 5.23 volts. DTCs P0653 runs continuously when the above conditions are met.The APP sensor 2. The Throttle Position (TP) sensor 1. The Crankshaft Position (CKP) sensor. **Possible Causes:** • 5v VREF circuit is shorted to chassis or sensor ground • 5v VREF circuit to APP TP or CKP sensor circuit is shorted to (B+) • Component failure • ECM has failed

DTC	Trouble Code Title, Conditions & Possible Causes
DTC: P0653 **2T CCM, MIL: Yes** **Years:** 2008, 2009 **Models:** G6, HHR, Malibu **Engines:** 2.0L VIN X, 2.2L VIN D, 2.2L VIN B, 2.2L VIN F, 2.4L VIN B, 2.4L VIN V, 2.4L VIN P, 2.4L VIN 5 **Transmissions:** All	**Intake Manifold Tuning (IMT) Valve Performance.** DTC P0111, P0112, P0113, P0114, P0116, P0117, P0118, P0119, P0642, P0643, P0652, P0653, P0652, P0653, P0661, P0662, P2227, P2228, or P2229 is not set. The engine is running for greater than 3 seconds. The engine speed is between 608-6,208 RPM. The Intake Air Temperature (IAT) is warmer than −10°C (14°F). This DTC runs continuously within the enabling conditions. The commanded ON or OFF position of the IMT valve is stable for greater than 0.5 second, and the ECM detects less than 1 volt on the IMT valve position sensor signal circuit, when the IMT valve is commanded OFF. Or The commanded ON or OFF position of the IMT valve is stable for greater than 0.5 second, and the ECM detects greater than 4 volts on the IMT valve position sensor signal circuit, when the IMT valve is commanded ON. **Possible Causes:** • IMT low reference circuit for an open/high resistance • IMT 5-volt reference circuit for a short to ground or an open/high resistance • IMT 5-volt reference circuit for a short to voltage • IMT signal circuit for an open/high resistance • IMT signal circuit for a short to ground or an open/high resistance • IMT signal circuit for a short to voltage • IMT has failed • ECM has failed
DTC: P065E **2T CCM, MIL: Yes** **Years:** 2008, 2009 **Models:** G6, HHR, Malibu **Engines:** 2.0L VIN X, 2.2L VIN D, 2.2L VIN B, 2.2L VIN F, 2.4L VIN B, 2.4L VIN V, 2.4L VIN P, 2.4L VIN 5 **Transmissions:** All	**Intake Manifold Tuning (IMT) Valve Solenoid Control Circuit Low Voltage.** DTC P0606 is not set. The ignition is ON, or the engine is running. The battery voltage is greater than 9 volts. This DTC runs continuously within the enabling conditions. The ECM detects a short to ground or an open on the IMT valve actuator solenoid control circuit for greater than 2 seconds. **Possible Causes:** • IMT ignition circuit for a short to ground or an open/high resistance. • IMT control circuit for a short to ground • IMT control circuit for a short to voltage or an open/high resistance • IMT component failure • ECM has failed
DTC: P0661 **2T CCM, MIL: Yes** **Years:** 2008, 2009 **Models:** G6, HHR, Malibu **Engines:** 2.0L VIN X, 2.2L VIN D, 2.2L VIN B, 2.2L VIN F, 2.4L VIN B, 2.4L VIN V, 2.4L VIN P, 2.4L VIN 5 **Transmissions:** All	**Intake Manifold Tuning (IMT) Valve Solenoid Control Circuit High Voltage.** DTC P0606 is not set. The ignition is ON, or the engine is running. The battery voltage is greater than 9 volts. This DTC runs continuously within the enabling conditions. The ECM detects a short to voltage on the IMT valve actuator solenoid control circuit for greater than 2 seconds. **Possible Causes:** • IMT ignition circuit for a short to ground or an open/high resistance. • IMT control circuit for a short to ground • IMT control circuit for a short to voltage or an open/high resistance • IMT component failure • ECM has failed
DTC: P0662 **2T CCM, MIL: Yes** **Years:** 2008, 2009 **Models:** G6, HHR, Malibu **Engines:** 2.0L VIN X, 2.2L VIN D, 2.2L VIN B, 2.2L VIN F, 2.4L VIN B, 2.4L VIN V, 2.4L VIN P, 2.4L VIN 5 **Transmissions:** All	**Engine Controls Ignition Relay Control Circuit** The ignition is ON. The battery voltage is between 9-16 volts. The commanded state of the ODM and the actual state of the control circuit do not match. The condition is present for more than 5 seconds. **Possible Causes:** • Powertrain relay shorted to ground on the control circuit • Powertrain relay shorted to voltage or an open/high resistance • Powertrain relay has failed • ECM has failed
DTC: P0685 **1T CCM, MIL: Yes** **Years:** 2008, 2009 **Models:** Envoy, Equinox, Savana, Torrent **Engines:** 3.4L VIN F, 4.3L VIN X, 5.3L VIN M **Transmissions:** All	**Engine Controls Ignition Relay Control Circuit** The ignition voltage is between 10-18 volts. The engine speed is greater than 80 RPM. The powertrain relay has been commanded ON and OFF. The commanded state of the ODM and the actual state of the control circuit do not match. **Possible Causes:** • Powertrain relay shorted to ground on the control circuit • Powertrain relay shorted to voltage or an open/high resistance • Powertrain relay has failed • ECM has failed
DTC: P0685 **1T CCM, MIL: Yes** **Years:** 2008, 2009 **Models:** Equinox, G6, G8, Torrent **Engines:** All **Transmissions:** All	**Engine Controls Ignition Relay Control Circuit Low Voltage** The ignition voltage is between 10-18 volts. The engine speed is greater than 80 RPM. The powertrain relay has been commanded ON and OFF. The commanded state of the ODM and the actual state of the control circuit do not match. **Possible Causes:** • Powertrain relay shorted to ground on the control circuit • Powertrain relay shorted to voltage or an open/high resistance • Powertrain relay has failed • ECM has failed

DTC	Trouble Code Title, Conditions & Possible Causes
DTC: P0686 **1T CCM, MIL: Yes** **Years:** 2008, 2009 **Models:** Equinox, G6, G8, Torrent **Engines:** 2.0L VIN X, 2.2L VIN D, 2.2L VIN B, 2.2L VIN F, 2.4L VIN B, 2.4L VIN V, 2.4L VIN P, 2.4L VIN 5, 4.2L VIN S, 4.8L VIN C, 3.5L VIN N, 3.5L VIN K, 3.9L VIN 3, 3.9L VIN M, 3.6L VIN 2, 3.9L VIN 1 **Transmissions:** All	**Engine Controls Ignition Relay Control Circuit High Voltage** The ignition voltage is between 10-18 volts. The engine speed is greater than 80 RPM. The powertrain relay has been commanded ON and OFF. The commanded state of the ODM and the actual state of the control circuit do not match. **Note: The ignition voltage circuit is between the powertrain relay and the ECM. The ignition voltage is a feedback circuit** **Possible Causes:** • Powertrain relay shorted to ground on the control circuit • Powertrain relay shorted to voltage or an open/high resistance • Powertrain relay has failed • ECM has failed
DTC: P0687 **1T CCM, MIL: Yes** **Years:** 2008, 2009 **Models:** Equinox, G6, G8, Torrent **Engines:** 2.0L VIN X, 2.2L VIN D, 2.2L VIN B, 2.2L VIN F, 2.4L VIN B, 2.4L VIN V, 2.4L VIN P, 2.4L VIN 5, 4.2L VIN S, 4.8L VIN C, 3.5L VIN N, 3.5L VIN K, 3.9L VIN 3, 3.9L VIN M, 3.6L VIN 2, 3.9L VIN 1 **Transmissions:** All	**Engine Controls Relay Feedback Circuit Low Voltage** The ignition is ON. The powertrain relay is commanded ON. DTC P0685 is not set. The ECM detects less than 5 volts on the ignition 1 voltage circuit to the ECM. The condition is present for more than 5 seconds. **Possible Causes:** • Powertrain relay shorted to ground on the control circuit • Powertrain relay shorted to voltage or an open/high resistance • Powertrain relay has failed • ECM has failed
DTC: P0689 **1T CCM, MIL: Yes** **Years:** 2008, 2009 **Models:** Equinox, G6, G8, Torrent, HHR, Malibu **Engines:** 2.0L VIN X, 2.2L VIN D, 2.2L VIN B, 2.2L VIN F, 2.4L VIN B, 2.4L VIN V, 2.4L VIN P, 2.4L VIN 5, 4.2L VIN S, 4.8L VIN C, 3.5L VIN N, 3.5L VIN K, 3.9L VIN 3, 3.9L VIN M, 3.6L VIN 2, 3.9L VIN 1 **Transmissions:** All	**Engine Controls Ignition Relay De-energized Too Late** The ignition is ON. The relay has been commanded ON. These DTCs run continuously when the above conditions have been met. The commanded state of the ODM and the actual state of the control circuit do not match. The ECM detects that the feedback voltage is not within a predicted range when the relay is commanded ON and OFF. Either condition is present for more than 2 seconds. **Possible Causes:** • Powertrain relay shorted to ground on the control circuit • Powertrain relay shorted to voltage or an open/high resistance • Powertrain relay has failed • ECM has failed
DTC: P068B **2T CCM, MIL: Yes** **Years:** 2008, 2009 **Models:** G6, HHR, Malibu **Engines:** 2.0L VIN X, 2.2L VIN D, 2.2L VIN B, 2.2L VIN F, 2.4L VIN B, 2.4L VIN V, 2.4L VIN P, 2.4L VIN 5 **Transmissions:** All	**Engine Controls Relay Feedback Circuit High Voltage** This DTC will run with the ignition ON or OFF. This DTC will run when the powertrain relay is commanded ON or OFF. DTC P0685 is not set. The ECM detects more than 16 volts on the ignition 1 voltage circuit to the ECM when the relay is commanded ON. The ECM detects more than 2 volts on the ignition 1 voltage circuit to the ECM when the relay is commanded OFF. The condition is present for more than 2 seconds. **Possible Causes:** • Powertrain relay shorted to ground on the control circuit • Powertrain relay shorted to voltage or an open/high resistance • Powertrain relay has failed • ECM has failed
DTC: P0690 **1T CCM, MIL: Yes** **Years:** 2008, 2009 **Engines:** 4.6L VIN Y, 4.6L VIN 9, 6.0L VIN H, 6.0L VIN Y, 6.0L VIN K, 6.2L VIN W, 6.6L VIN 6 **Transmissions:** All	**Engine Controls Ignition Relay Feedback Circuit High Voltage** The ignition voltage is between 10-18 volts. The ignition is ON. The DTCs runs continuously once the above condition is met. The ECM detects that powertrain relay feedback voltage is less than 6 volts for greater than 500 mS. **Possible Causes:** • Powertrain relay shorted to ground on the control circuit • Powertrain relay shorted to voltage or an open/high resistance • Powertrain relay has failed • ECM has failed
DTC: P0690 **1T CCM, MIL: Yes** **Years:** 2008, 2009 **Models:** Equinox, G6, G8, Torrent **Engines:** 4.2L VIN S, 4.8L VIN C, 3.5L VIN N, 3.5L VIN K, 3.9L VIN 3, 3.9L VIN M, 3.6L VIN 2, 3.9L VIN 1 **Transmissions:** All	**5-Volt Reference 3 Circuit** The 5-volt reference circuit voltage is greater or less than a predetermined threshold. The condition exists, then a 5 second delay for MIL ONThe 5-volt reference 2 circuit provides 5 volts to the following sensors. The Throttle position sensor (TPS) 1 and 2, Crankshaft position (CKP) sensorand the Accelerator pedal position (APP) sensor 2. **Possible Causes:** • 5v VREF circuit is shorted to chassis or sensor ground • 5v VREF circuit to TPS, CKP or APP sensor circuit is shorted to (B+) • ECM has failed

DTC	Trouble Code Title, Conditions & Possible Causes
DTC: P0697 **1T CCM, MIL: Yes** **Years:** 2008, 2009 **Models:** Envoy, Equinox, G6, G8, Impala, Lucerne, Malibu, Savana, Trailblazer, Torrent **Engines:** 4.2L VIN S, 4.8L VIN C, 3.5L VIN N, 3.5L VIN K, 3.9L VIN 3, 3.9L VIN M, 3.6L VIN 2, 3.9L VIN 1 **Transmissions:** All	**5-Volt Reference 3 Circuit Low Voltage** The 5-volt reference circuit voltage is greater or less than a predetermined threshold. The condition exists,then a 5 second delay for MIL ONThe 5-volt reference 2 circuit provides 5 volts to the following sensors. The Throttle position sensor (TPS) 1 and 2, Crankshaft position (CKP) sensorand the Accelerator pedal position (APP) sensor 2. **Possible Causes:** • 5v VREF circuit is shorted to chassis or sensor ground • 5v VREF circuit to TPS, CKP or APP sensor circuit is shorted to (B+) • ECM has failed
DTC: P0698 **1T CCM, MIL: Yes** **Years:** 2008, 2009 **Models:** Envoy, Equinox, G6, G8, Impala, Lucerne, Malibu, Savana, Trailblazer, Torrent **Engines:** 4.2L VIN S, 4.8L VIN C, 3.5L VIN N, 3.5L VIN K, 3.9L VIN 3, 3.9L VIN M, 3.6L VIN 2, 3.9L VIN 1 **Transmissions:** All	**5-Volt Reference 3 Circuit High Voltage** The 5-volt reference circuit voltage is greater or less than a predetermined threshold. The condition exists,then a 5 second delay for MIL ONThe 5-volt reference 2 circuit provides 5 volts to the following sensors. The Throttle position sensor (TPS) 1 and 2, Crankshaft position (CKP) sensorand the Accelerator pedal position (APP) sensor 2. **Possible Causes:** • 5v VREF circuit is shorted to chassis or sensor ground • 5v VREF circuit to TPS, CKP or APP sensor circuit is shorted to (B+) • ECM has failed
DTC: P0699 **1T CCM, MIL: Yes** **Years:** 2008, 2009 **Models:** Envoy, Equinox, G6, G8, Impala, Lucerne, Malibu, Savana, Trailblazer, Torrent **Engines:** 4.2L VIN S, 4.8L VIN C, 3.5L VIN N, 3.5L VIN K, 3.9L VIN 3, 3.9L VIN M, 3.6L VIN 2, 3.9L VIN 1 **Transmissions:** All	**Fuel Pump Control Module Requested MIL Illumination** The ignition is ON, or the engine is running. The fuel pump control module requests the ECM to illuminate the MIL. **Possible Causes:** • Emissions failure in fuel pump control system
DTC: P069E **1T CCM, MIL: Yes** **Years:** 2008, 2009 **Models:** Express, G8, Lucerne, Trailblazer **Engines:** 4.6L VIN Y, 4.6L VIN 9, 6.0L VIN H, 6.0L VIN Y, 6.0L VIN K, 6.2L VIN W, 6.6L VIN 6 **Transmissions:** All	**Fuel Pump Control Module Requested MIL Illumination** The ignition is ON, or the engine is running. The fuel pump control module requests the ECM to illuminate the MIL. **Possible Causes:** • Fuel line pressure sensor, 5v VREF circuit shorted to ground or an open/high resistance • Fuel line pressure sensor, 5v VREF circuit for a shorted to voltage • Fuel line pressure sensor, low reference circuit for an open/high resistance • FECM has failed
DTC: P069E **1T CCM, MIL: Yes** **Years:** 2008, 2009 **Models:** Equinox, G6, G8, Torrent **Engines:** 4.2L VIN S, 4.8L VIN C, 3.5L VIN N, 3.5L VIN K, 3.9L VIN 3, 3.9L VIN M, 3.6L VIN 2, 3.9L VIN 1 **Transmissions:** All	**5-Volt Reference Performance** The ignition is on. The Fuel Pump Control Module (FECM) detects that the fuel pressure 5-volt reference is above or below a predetermined voltage threshold **Possible Causes:** • Fuel line pressure sensor, 5v VREF circuit shorted to ground or an open/high resistance • Fuel line pressure sensor, 5v VREF circuit for a shorted to voltage • Fuel line pressure sensor, low reference circuit for an open/high resistance • FECM has failed
DTC: P06A6 **2T CCM, MIL: Yes** **Years:** 2008, 2009 **Models:** All **Engines:** All **Transmissions:** All	**Transmission Control Module (TCM) Requested MIL Illumination** The ignition is ON. The TCM is requesting MIL illumination. **Note: DTC P0700 can not be cleared from the ECM until the related TCM codes have been cleared.** **Possible Causes:** • MIL control circuit is shorted to ground • Check the TCM for any trouble codes in memory that are responsible for the request to turn on the MIL • TCM has failed

DTC	Trouble Code Title, Conditions & Possible Causes
DTC: P0700 **1T CCM, MIL: Yes** **Years:** 2008, 2009 **Models:** All **Engines:** All **Transmissions:** All	**Clutch Switch Circuit Malfunction (M49/MM6)** DTC P0500, P0502 and P0503 not set, engine started, engine load and vehicle acceleration indicate vehicle is in gear and moving, and the ECM detected a VSS signal indicating the vehicle went from 0 to over 24 MPH and then back to 0 MPH within 2 seconds without the ECM detecting a change in the Clutch Anticipate switch circuit. **Note: This fault must occur 7 times before ECM will set this code.** **Possible Causes:** • Clutch switch circuit is open, shorted to ground or to power • Clutch switch power circuit is open (test the ENG IGN fuse) • Clutch switch is out of adjustment, damaged or has failed • ECM has failed
DTC: P0706 **1T CCM, MIL: No** **Years:** 2008, 2009 **Models:** Express, Lucerne, Trailblazer **Engines:** 4.6L VIN Y, 4.6L VIN 9, 6.0L VIN H, 6.0L VIN Y, 6.0L VIN K, 6.2L VIN W, 6.6L VIN 6 **Transmissions:** All	**Transaxle Range Switch (PRNDL) Performance** Engine started, system voltage over 10.0v, and the ECM detected the Transaxle Range switch signal indicated a range other than P/N during startup. **Note: This test must fail 2 out of 4 consecutive tests in order to set this trouble code.** **Possible Causes:** • TR switch circuit is or shorted to ground • TR switch circuit is shorted to another PRNDL circuit • TR switch is damaged or out of adjustment • ECM has failed
DTC: P0711 **1T CCM, MIL: No** **Years:** 2008, 2009 **Models:** Express, G8, Lucerne, Trailblazer **Engines:** 4.6L VIN Y, 4.6L VIN 9, 6.0L VIN H, 6.0L VIN Y, 6.0L VIN K, 6.2L VIN W, 6.6L VIN 6 **Transmissions:** All	**TFT Sensor Circuit Low Input** DTC P0560 not set, engine started, engine running and the ECM detected the TFT sensor was more than 298°F for 10 seconds. **Possible Causes:** • TFT sensor signal circuit is shorted to sensor or chassis ground • TFT sensor is damaged or has failed (it may be shorted) • ECM has failed
DTC: P0712 **1T CCM, MIL: No** **Years:** 2008, 2009 **Models:** Express, G8, Lucerne, Trailblazer **Engines:** 4.6L VIN Y, 4.6L VIN 9, 6.0L VIN H, 6.0L VIN Y, 6.0L VIN K, 6.2L VIN W, 6.6L VIN 6 **Transmissions:** All	**TFT Sensor Circuit High Input** DTC P0117, P0118 and P0560 not set, engine started, and the ECM detected the TFT sensor was less than −33°F (a voltage of 4.92v or higher) for 10 seconds during the CCM test. **Possible Causes:** • TFT sensor signal circuit is open between the sensor and ECM • TFT sensor signal circuit is shorted to VREF or system power • TFT sensor is damaged or has failed (it may be open) • ECM has failed • TSB 02-07-30-15 contains a repair procedure for this code
DTC: P0713 **1T CCM, MIL: No** **Years:** 2008, 2009 **Models:** Express, G8, Lucerne, Trailblazer **Engines:** 4.6L VIN Y, 4.6L VIN 9, 6.0L VIN H, 6.0L VIN Y, 6.0L VIN K, 6.2L VIN W, 6.6L VIN 6 **Transmissions:** All	**A/T Input Speed Sensor Circuit Malfunction** DTC P0121, P0122, P0123, P0502, P0503, P0717, P0751, P0752, P0753, P0756, P0757 and P0758 not set, DTC P0717 test passed this key cycle, engine started, engine speed over 500 RPM for 5 seconds, Fuel Cutoff inactive, TP angle more than 14%, VSS over 5 MPH, and the ECM detected the Input Shaft Sensor speed changed by more than 1300 RPM within 800 ms during the CCM test. **Possible Causes:** • ISS positive (+) circuit is open, shorted to ground or to power • ISS negative (−) circuit is open, shorted to ground or to power • ISS is damaged or has failed • ECM has failed • TSB 02-07-30-022A contains a repair procedure for this code
DTC: P0716 **2T CCM, MIL: Yes** **Years:** 2008, 2009 **Models:** Express, G8, Lucerne, Trailblazer **Engines:** 4.6L VIN Y, 4.6L VIN 9, 6.0L VIN H, 6.0L VIN Y, 6.0L VIN K, 6.2L VIN W, 6.6L VIN 6 **Transmissions:** All	**A/T Input Speed Sensor Circuit Malfunction** DTC P0502, P0503, P0717, P0751, P0752, P1820, P1822, P1823, P1825, P1842 and P1843 not set, engine started, engine runtime over 5 seconds, Fuel Cutoff inactive, gearshift not in P/N, VSS over 10 MPH, and the ECM detected the ISS indicated less than 51 RPM for 6 seconds during the CCM test. **Possible Causes:** • ISS positive (+) or negative (−) circuit is open, shorted to ground or to power • ISS is damaged or has failed • ECM has failed • TSB 77-71-72 contains a repair procedure for this code

DTC	Trouble Code Title, Conditions & Possible Causes
DTC: P0717 **2T CCM, MIL: Yes** **Years:** 2008, 2009 **Models:** Express, G8, Lucerne, Trailblazer **Engines:** 4.6L VIN Y, 4.6L VIN 9, 6.0L VIN H, 6.0L VIN Y, 6.0L VIN K, 6.2L VIN W, 6.6L VIN 6 **Transmissions:** All	**A/T Input Speed Sensor Circuit Low Input** DTC P0502, P0503 and P1810 not set, engine started, TFP manual valve position switch not indicating Park or Neutral, system voltage over 10.0v, vehicle driven to a speed of over 5 MPH, Fuel Cutoff inactive, and the ECM detected the Input Shaft Speed sensor signal was less than 50 RPM for over 5 seconds during the CCM test. **Possible Causes:** • ISS positive (+) circuit is open, shorted to ground or to power • ISS negative (−) circuit is open, shorted to ground or to power • ISS is damaged or has failed • ECM has failed • TSB 02-07-30-022A contains a repair procedure for this code
DTC: P0719 **1T CCM, MIL: No** **Years:** 2008, 2009 **Models:** All **Engines:** All **Transmissions:** All	**TCC Brake Switch Circuit Low Input** DTC P0502, P0503 and P0719 not set, Key on or engine running; Brake switch status is open and DTC P0719 has not passed, and the ECM detected the Brake switch or circuit indicated open (0v) for 15 minutes without changing for 2 seconds, and the following events occurred (7) times: vehicle speed less than 5 MPH, then the vehicle speed from 5-20 MPH for 4 seconds; and then the vehicle speed was more than 20 MPH for 6 seconds during the test. **Possible Causes:** • TCC brake switch circuit is open or shorted to ground • TCC brake switch power circuit is open (test ABS or ERL fuse) • TCC brake switch is out of adjustment or damaged • ECM has failed
DTC: P0724 **1T CCM, MIL: No** **Years:** 2008, 2009 **Models:** Express, G8, Lucerne, Trailblazer **Engines:** 4.6L VIN Y, 4.6L VIN 9, 6.0L VIN H, 6.0L VIN Y, 6.0L VIN K, 6.2L VIN W, 6.6L VIN 6 **Transmissions:** All	**Incorrect Gear Ratio** DTC P0121, P0122, P0123, P0502, P0503, P0716, P0717 and P1810 not set, engine started, vehicle driven to over 7 MPH, Fuel Cutoff inactive, Transmission not in Park or Neutral, time since last gear select lever change over 6 seconds, TP angle over 14%, TFT sensor more than 68°F, engine torque from 50-300 ft lbs, and the ECM detected one of these conditions occurred for 7 seconds: - The gear ratio was more than 2.97:1 or it was 1.62:1 to 2.33:1 - The gear ratio was 1.05:1 to 1.52:1 or it was 0.75:1 to 0.95:1 **Possible Causes:** • ATF level is too low, or the fluid is burnt or contaminated • ISS or OSS signal circuit has an intermittent fault condition • Inspect for debris in the transmission pan or internal damaged • Possible vehicle overloading, exceeding the trailer towing limit, or towing in overdrive events occurred (discuss with customer) • TSB 02-07-30-022A contains a repair procedure for this code
DTC: P0730 **1T CCM, MIL: No** **Years:** 2008, 2009 **Models:** Express, G8, Lucerne, Trailblazer **Engines:** 4.6L VIN Y, 4.6L VIN 9, 6.0L VIN H, 6.0L VIN Y, 6.0L VIN K, 6.2L VIN W, 6.6L VIN 6 **Transmissions:** All	**TCC Solenoid Circuit Malfunction** Engine started, system voltage over 10.0v, Fuel Cutoff inactive, and the ECM detected the TCC feedback voltage was high with the TCC Solenoid commanded "on", or it was "low" with the TCC Solenoid commanded "off" for 5 seconds. **Possible Causes:** • TCC solenoid control circuit is open, shorted to ground or to B+ • TCC solenoid power circuit is open (test the TRANS fuse) • TCC solenoid is damaged or has failed • ECM has failed • TSB 01-07-30-002C contains a repair procedure for this code
DTC: P0740 **2T CCM, MIL: Yes** **Years:** 2008, 2009 **Models:** Express, G8, Lucerne, Trailblazer **Engines:** 4.6L VIN Y, 4.6L VIN 9, 6.0L VIN H, 6.0L VIN Y, 6.0L VIN K, 6.2L VIN W, 6.6L VIN 6 **Transmissions:** All	**TCC System Stuck Off - Mechanical** DTC P0121-P0123, P0502, P0503, P0716, P0717, P0742, P1820, P1860 and P1887 not set, engine started, Fuel Cutoff inactive, Transmission gear range was D2, D3 or D4, time since last gear select lever change more than 6 seconds, TFT sensor from 68-266°F, TP angle from 4-35%, TCC PWM solenoid commanded "on" for over 500 ms, TCC commanded to maximum apply pressure, and the ECM detected the TCC slip speed was more than 180 RPM twice during a 7 second period during this key cycle. **Possible Causes:** • ATF level is too low, or the fluid is burnt or contaminated • Inspect transmission lines to radiator for bends or restrictions • Oil pressure screen is clogged or debris in the oil pan • TCC control valve is stuck "off" due to sediment or binding • TCC regulator valve is stuck "off" due to sediment or binding • TCC solenoid valve O-ring or turbine shaft seals leaking or cut • TSB 00-07-30-007A contains a repair procedure for this code

DTC	Trouble Code Title, Conditions & Possible Causes
DTC: P0741 **2T CCM, MIL: Yes** **Years:** 2008, 2009 **Engines:** All **Transmissions:** All	**TCC System Mechanically Stuck Off** DTC P0502, P0503, P0740, P0742, P0753, P1120, P1220 and P1810 not set, engine runtime over 5 seconds, not in Fuel Cutoff mode, TFT sensor from 68-302°F, TP angle from 20-99%, speed ratio from 0.89-1.02, gear range is D2, D3 or D4 with no gear change for over 6 seconds, then with the TCC commanded "on" at over 75% for 5 seconds, the ECM detected the TCC slip speed was over 130 RPM for 20 seconds (fault detected 3 times). The TCC solenoid valve is a N.O. exhaust valve used with the TCC PWM solenoid to control fluid acting on the converter clutch apply valve. When the TCC solenoid is grounded, the valve stops converter signal oil from exhausting. This causes converter signal oil pressure to increase and move the converter clutch apply valve against spring force to the apply position. In this position, release fluid is open to an exhaust port and converter feed fluid fills the apply circuit. The converter feed fluid applies the TCC. **Possible Causes:** • Converter clutch apply valve stuck in "off" (release) position • Misaligned or damaged valve body gasket • Restricted apply valve passage • TCC PWM valve exhaust orifice in damaged or it has failed • TCC solenoid valve mechanically stuck in "off" position
DTC: P0742 **2T CCM, MIL: Yes** **Models:** Express, G8, Lucerne, Trailblazer **Engines:** 4.6L VIN Y, 4.6L VIN 9, 6.0L VIN H, 6.0L VIN Y, 6.0L VIN K, 6.2L VIN W, 6.6L VIN 6 **Transmissions:** All	**TCC System Mechanically Stuck Off** DTC P0120, P0220, P0502, P0503, P0740, P0742, P0753, P0758, P1810 and P1860 not set, engine runtime over 6 seconds, not in Fuel Cutoff mode, TP angle from 17-45%, engine torque at 50-400 lb ft., engine vacuum 0-105 kPa (0-15 psi), speed ratio at 0.64-1.35, TFT sensor from 68-266°F, gear range is D4 with no gear change for over 6 seconds, engine speed from 1,000-3,000 RPM, vehicle speed from 15-50 MPH, then with the TCC commanded "off", the ECM detected the TCC slip speed was −20 to +20 RPM for 5 seconds (fault occurs twice during one trip). The TCC solenoid valve is a normally open (N.O.) exhaust valve that is used with the TCC PWM solenoid to control the fluid that acts on the converter clutch apply valve. The TCC solenoid valve attaches to the transmission case assembly extending into the pump cover. When the TCC solenoid is grounded, the valve stops converter signal oil from exhausting. This causes converter signal oil pressure to increase and move the converter clutch apply valve against spring force to the apply position. In this position, release fluid is open to an exhaust port and converter feed fluid fills the apply circuit. The converter feed fluid applies the TCC. **Possible Causes:** • Apply valve passage is restricted • Converter clutch apply valve stuck in "off" (release) position • Misaligned or damaged valve body gasket • TCC PWM valve exhaust orifice in damaged or it has failed • TCC solenoid valve is mechanically stuck in the "off" position
DTC: P0751 **2T CCM, MIL: Yes** **Years:** 2008, 2009 **Models:** Express, G8, Lucerne, Trailblazer **Engines:** 4.6L VIN Y, 4.6L VIN 9, 6.0L VIN H, 6.0L VIN Y, 6.0L VIN K, 6.2L VIN W, 6.6L VIN 6 **Transmissions:** All	**A/T 1-2 Shift Solenoid - No 1st or 4th Gear** DTC P0122, P0123, P0502, P0503, P0740, P0742, P0753, P0758, P0785, P1810 and P1860 not set, engine started, vehicle driven to over 5 MPH, Fuel Cutoff inactive, TP angle more than 9%, TFT sensor from 68-266°F, gear range is D4, D3, D2 or D1, engine torque was 50-400 lb ft., transmission output speed was more than 150 RPM, then with 1st Gear "on" for 2 seconds, the ECM detected the engine speed was more than 2.44 times the TCC slip speed with an estimated gear ratio of 1.2-1.85 for 2 seconds; or with 4th Gear "on" for 1 second, the ECM detected the engine speed was 2.44 times the TCC slip speed with an estimated gear ratio of 0.95-1.15 for 6 seconds during the CCM test. **Possible Causes:** • ATF is burnt or contaminated, or the level is incorrect • Transmission has an internal damage to the torque converter • Shift solenoid valve seals are damaged or leaking • Transmission is damaged or it has failed
DTC: P0752 **1T CCM, MIL: Yes** **Years:** 2008, 2009 **Models:** Express, G8, Lucerne, Trailblazer **Engines:** 4.6L VIN Y, 4.6L VIN 9, 6.0L VIN H, 6.0L VIN Y, 6.0L VIN K, 6.2L VIN W, 6.6L VIN 6 **Transmissions:** All	**A/T 1-2 Shift Solenoid - No 2nd Or 3rd Gear** DTC P0122, P0123, P0502, P0503, P0740, P0742, P0753, P0758, P0785, P1810 and P1860 not set, vehicle driven to over 5 MPH, Fuel Cutoff inactive, TP angle more than 10%, gear range is D4, TFT sensor from 68-266°F, engine torque from 50-400 lb ft., transmission output speed more than 150 RPM, Transfer Case low ratio in 4WD Low at 0.9-1.2 or in 4WD High at 2.6-2.85; engine torque from 25-650 lb ft., then with 2nd Gear commanded "on" for 1 second, the ECM detected the estimated gear ratio was 3.0-3.3 for 2 seconds; or with 3rd Gear commanded "on" for 1 second, the gear ratio was 0.65-0.95 for 3 seconds. **Possible Causes:** • ATF is burnt or contaminated, or the level is incorrect • Transmission has an internal damage to the torque converter • Shift solenoid valve seals are damaged or leaking • Transmission has failed

DTC	Trouble Code Title, Conditions & Possible Causes
DTC: P0752 **2T CCM, MIL: Yes** **Years:** 2008, 2009 **Models:** Equinox, G6, G8, Torrent **Engines:** 4.2L VIN S, 4.8L VIN C, 3.5L VIN N, 3.5L VIN K, 3.9L VIN 3, 3.9L VIN M, 3.6L VIN 2, 3.9L VIN 1 **Transmissions:** All	**A/T 1-2 Shift Solenoid - No 2nd or 3rd Gear** DTC P0101-P0103, P0107, P0108, P0122, P0123, P0502, P0503, P0740, P1810 and P1860 not set, engine speed at 1000-3000 RPM, VSS at 20-75 MPH, Fuel Cutoff "off", TP angle from 13-99%, TFT sensor at 68-266°F, engine torque at 50-400 lb ft., vacuum at 0-15 kPa, gear range is D4 with no gear change for 6 seconds, transmission speed ratio at 0.95-1.7, not in 1st Gear, TCC off and the ECM detected the TCC slip speed was −20 to +58 for 3.8 seconds. **Possible Causes:** • ATF is burnt or contaminated, or the level is incorrect • Transmission has an internal damage to the torque converter • Shift solenoid valve seals are damaged or leaking • Transmission has failed
DTC: P0753 **2T CCM, MIL: Yes** **Years:** 2008, 2009 **Models:** Express, G8, Lucerne, Trailblazer **Engines:** 4.6L VIN Y, 4.6L VIN 9, 6.0L VIN H, 6.0L VIN Y, 6.0L VIN K, 6.2L VIN W, 6.6L VIN 6 **Transmissions:** All	**A/T 1-2 Shift Solenoid Circuit Malfunction** Engine started, Fuel Cutoff inactive, system voltage over 10.0v, and the ECM detected an unexpected voltage condition on the 1-2 Shift Solenoid control circuit during the CCM continuous test. **Possible Causes:** • 1-2 shift solenoid control circuit is open or shorted to ground • 1-2 shift solenoid control circuit is shorted to system power • 1-2 shift solenoid is damaged or has failed • ECM has failed • TSB 01-07-30-002C contains a repair procedure for this code
DTC: P0753 **2T CCM, MIL: Yes** **Years:** 2008, 2009 **Models:** Express, G8, Lucerne, Trailblazer **Engines:** 4.6L VIN Y, 4.6L VIN 9, 6.0L VIN H, 6.0L VIN Y, 6.0L VIN K, 6.2L VIN W, 6.6L VIN 6 **Transmissions:** All	**A/T 1-2 Shift Solenoid Circuit Malfunction** Engine started, Fuel Cutoff inactive, system voltage over 10.0v, and the ECM detected an unexpected voltage condition on the 1-2 Shift Solenoid control circuit during the CCM test. **Possible Causes:** • 1-2 shift solenoid control circuit is open or shorted to ground • 1-2 shift solenoid control circuit is shorted to system power • 1-2 shift solenoid is damaged or has failed • ECM has failed
DTC: P0756 **1T CCM, MIL: Yes** **Years:** 2008, 2009 **Models:** Express, G8, Lucerne, Trailblazer **Engines:** 4.6L VIN Y, 4.6L VIN 9, 6.0L VIN H, 6.0L VIN Y, 6.0L VIN K, 6.2L VIN W, 6.6L VIN 6 **Transmissions:** All	**2-3 Shift Solenoid - No 2nd Or 3rd Gear** DTC P0122, P0123, P0502, P0503, P0740, P0742, P0753, P0758, P0785, P1810 and P1860 not set, engine started, system voltage over 10.0v, vehicle speed over 5 MPH, TP angle over 10%, gear range is D4, TFT sensor from 68-266°F, engine torque from 50-400 lb ft., transmission output shaft speed more than 150 RPM, Fuel Cutoff inactive, then with 1st Gear commanded "on", the ECM detected the gear ratio indicated 4th Gear for 2.5 seconds; or with 2nd Gear commanded "on" for 1 second, the ECM detected the estimate gear ratio was 0.9-1.2 for 2 seconds during the CCM test **Possible Causes:** • ATF is burnt or contaminated • Transmission has plugged or restricted fluid circuits • Shift solenoid valve seals are leaking or damaged • Transmission has failed • TSB 01-07-30-036A contains a repair procedure for this code
DTC: P0756 **2T CCM, MIL: Yes** **Years:** 2008, 2009 **Models:** Equinox, G6, G8, Torrent **Engines:** 4.2L VIN S, 4.8L VIN C, 3.5L VIN N, 3.5L VIN K, 3.9L VIN 3, 3.9L VIN M, 3.6L VIN 2, 3.9L VIN 1 **Transmissions:** All	**A/T 2-3 Shift Solenoid - No 2nd or 3rd Gear** DTC P0101-P0103, P0107, P0108, P0122, P0123, P0502, P0503, P0740, P0742, P0753, P0758, P0785, P1810, P1860 and P1870 not set, engine started, vehicle driven to a speed of over 5 MPH, system voltage over 10.0v, Fuel Cutoff inactive, TP angle more than 9%, TFT sensor from 68-266°F, gear range is D4, no gear change for 6 seconds, engine torque from 50-400 lb ft., engine vacuum from 0-15 kPa, A/T output speed over 150 RPM, gear range is D4, D3, D2 or D1, then with 1st Gear commanded "on", engine speed more than the TCC slip speed and the Output speed over 300 RPM, the ECM detected the gear ratio was 0.0-0.895 for 1 second; or with 2nd Gear commanded "on", engine speed 5.26 times more than the TCC slip speed, the ECM detected the gear ratio was 0.9-1.2 for 2 seconds. **Possible Causes:** • ATF is burnt or contaminated • Transmission has plugged or restricted fluid circuits • Shift solenoid valve seals are leaking or damaged • Transmission has failed

DTC	Trouble Code Title, Conditions & Possible Causes
DTC: P0757 **1T CCM, MIL: No** **Years:** 2008, 2009 **Models:** Express, G8, Lucerne, Trailblazer **Engines:** 4.6L VIN Y, 4.6L VIN 9, 6.0L VIN H, 6.0L VIN Y, 6.0L VIN K, 6.2L VIN W, 6.6L VIN 6 **Transmissions:** All	**A/T 2-3 Shift Solenoid Circuit Malfunction** DTC P0560 not set, engine started, engine speed over 500 RPM for 5 seconds, 2-3 Shift Solenoid commanded "on" and then "off", and the ECM detected an unexpected voltage condition on the 2-3 Shift Solenoid Control circuit for 5 seconds during the CCM test. **Possible Causes:** • 2-3 shift solenoid control circuit is open or shorted to ground • 2-3 shift solenoid control circuit is shorted to system power • 2-3 shift solenoid power circuit is open (test TRANS SOL fuse) • 2-3 shift solenoid is damaged or has failed • ECM has failed • TSB 02-07-30-022A contains a repair procedure for this code
DTC: P0758 **1T CCM, MIL: Yes** **Years:** 2008, 2009 **Models:** Equinox, G6, G8, Torrent **Engines:** 4.2L VIN S, 4.8L VIN C, 3.5L VIN N, 3.5L VIN K, 3.9L VIN 3, 3.9L VIN M, 3.6L VIN 2, 3.9L VIN 1 **Transmissions:** All	**A/T 2-3 Shift Solenoid Circuit Malfunction** Engine speed over 450 RPM for 7 seconds, system voltage over 10.0v, and the ECM detected an unexpected voltage on the 2-3 Shift Solenoid control circuit for 4-5 seconds. **Possible Causes:** • 2-3 shift solenoid control circuit is open, shorted to ground or shorted to system power • 2-3 shift solenoid power circuit is open (test the TRANS fuse) • 2-3 shift solenoid has failed, or the ECM has failed
DTC: P0785 **1T CCM, MIL: Yes** **Years:** 2008, 2009 **Models:** Express, G8, Lucerne, Trailblazer **Engines:** 4.6L VIN Y, 4.6L VIN 9, 6.0L VIN H, 6.0L VIN Y, 6.0L VIN K, 6.2L VIN W, 6.6L VIN 6 **Transmissions:** All	**A/T 3-2 Shift Solenoid Circuit Malfunction** Engine started, engine speed over 450 RPM for 5 seconds, system voltage over 10.0v, and the ECM detected an unexpected voltage condition on the 3-2 Shift Solenoid control circuit for 4-5 seconds. **Possible Causes:** • 3-2 shift solenoid control circuit is open, shorted to ground or shorted to system power • 3-2 shift solenoid power circuit is open (check the TRANS fuse) • 3-2 shift solenoid is damaged or has failed • ECM has failed • TSB 01-07-30-002C contains a repair procedure for this code
DTC: P0785 **1T CCM, MIL: Yes** **Years:** 2008, 2009 **Models:** Equinox, G6, G8, Torrent **Engines:** 4.2L VIN S, 4.8L VIN C, 3.5L VIN N, 3.5L VIN K, 3.9L VIN 3, 3.9L VIN M, 3.6L VIN 2, 3.9L VIN 1 **Transmissions:** All	**A/T 2-3 Shift Solenoid Circuit Malfunction** P0560 not set, engine started, engine speed over 500 RPM for 5 seconds, and the ECM detected an unexpected voltage on the 2-3 Shift Solenoid Control circuit for 5 seconds. **Possible Causes:** • 2-3 shift solenoid control circuit is open or shorted to ground • 2-3 shift solenoid control circuit is shorted to system power • 2-3 shift solenoid power circuit is open (check ENG CTRL fuse) • 2-3 shift solenoid is damaged or has failed • ECM has failed

OBD II Trouble Code List (P1xxx Codes)

DTC	Trouble Code Title, Conditions & Possible Causes
DTC: P1111 **1T CCM, MIL: No** **Years:** 2008, 2009 **Models:** Express, Savana **Engines:** 4.3L VIN X **Transmissions:** All	**IAT Sensor Circuit Intermittent High Input** DTC P0101, P0102, P0103, P0116, P0117, P0118, P0125, P0128, P0502, P0503, P1114 and P1115 not set, engine started, engine runtime over 120 seconds, ECT sensor more than 140°F, VSS less than 7 MPH, MAF input less than 15 g/sec, and the ECM detected an intermittent high voltage condition (over 4.90v) on the IAT sensor signal circuit for 1 second during the CCM test. **Possible Causes:** • IAT sensor signal circuit is open (intermittent fault) • IAT sensor ground circuit is open (intermittent fault) • IAT sensor is damaged (an intermittent "open" condition) • ECM has failed
DTC: P1111 **1T CCM, MIL: No** **Years:** 2008, 2009 **Models:** Equinox, G6, G8, Torrent **Engines:** 4.2L VIN S, 4.8L VIN C, 3.5L VIN N, 3.5L VIN K, 3.9L VIN 3, 3.9L VIN M, 3.6L VIN 2, 3.9L VIN 1	**IAT Sensor Circuit Intermittent High Input** DTC P0101, P0102, P0103 and P0113 not set, engine runtime over 120 seconds, ECT sensor more than 140°F, VSS less than 7 MPH, MAF input less than 15 g/sec, and the ECM detected an intermittent high voltage condition (Scan Tool reads below −36°F) on the IAT sensor signal circuit during the CCM test period. **Possible Causes:** • IAT sensor signal circuit is open (intermittent fault) • IAT sensor ground circuit is open (intermittent fault) • IAT sensor is damaged (an intermittent "open" condition) • ECM has failed

DTC	Trouble Code Title, Conditions & Possible Causes
DTC: P1112 **1T CCM, MIL: No** **Years:** 2008, 2009 **Models:** Equinox, G6, G8, Torrent **Engines:** 4.2L VIN S, 4.8L VIN C, 3.5L VIN N, 3.5L VIN K, 3.9L VIN 3, 3.9L VIN M, 3.6L VIN 2, 3.9L VIN 1 **Transmissions:** All	**IAT Sensor Circuit Intermittent Low Input** DTC P0112, P0500, P0502 and P0503 not set, engine runtime over 45 seconds, ECT sensor less than 257°F, VSS more than 25 MPH, and the ECM detected an intermittent low voltage condition (Scan Tool reads over 262°F) on the IAT sensor signal circuit. **Possible Causes:** • IAT sensor signal circuit is open (intermittent fault) • IAT sensor ground circuit is open (intermittent fault) • IAT sensor is damaged (an intermittent "open" condition) • ECM has failed
DTC: P1114 **1T CCM, MIL: No** **Years:** 2008, 2009 **Models:** Equinox, G6, G8, Torrent **Engines:** 4.2L VIN S, 4.8L VIN C, 3.5L VIN N, 3.5L VIN K, 3.9L VIN 3, 3.9L VIN M, 3.6L VIN 2, 3.9L VIN 1 **Transmissions:** All	**ECT Sensor Circuit Intermittent Low Input** Engine started, engine runtime over 10 seconds, and the ECM detected an intermittent low voltage condition (Scan Tool reads over 280°F) on the ECT sensor signal circuit during the CCM test period. **Possible Causes:** • ECT sensor signal circuit shorted to ground (intermittent fault) • ECT sensor has failed (possible intermittent shorted condition) • ECM has failed
DTC: P1133 **1T CCM, MIL: Yes** **Years:** 2008, 2009 **Models:** Express, G8, Lucerne, Trailblazer **Engines:** 4.6L VIN Y, 4.6L VIN 9, 6.0L VIN H, 6.0L VIN Y, 6.0L VIN K, 6.2L VIN W, 6.6L VIN 6 **Transmissions:** All	**HO2S Insufficient Switching (Bank 1 Sensor 1)** DTCs P0068, P0101, P0102, P0103, P0106, P0107, P0108, P0112, P0113, P0116, P0117, P0118, P0120, P0121, P0122, P0123, P0128, P0201, P0202, P0203, P0204, P0205, P0206, P0207, P0208, P0220, P0222, P0223, P0442, P0443, P0446, P0449, P0455, P0496, P1516, P2101, P2119, P2135, P2176 are not set. The ECT Sensor parameter is more than 60°C (140°F). The Engine Speed parameter is between 1,100-2,500 RPM. The Ignition 1 Signal parameter is between 10-18 volts. The Engine Run Time parameter is more than 202 seconds. The Loop Status parameter is Closed. The TP Indicated Angle parameter is more than 5 percent. The Fuel Level Sensor parameter is more than 10 percent. The BARO parameter is more than 70 kPa. The MAF Sensor parameter is between 20-40 g/s. DTC P1133 runs once per drive cycle when the above conditions are met for 1 second. The control module detects that the HO2S 1 rich-to-lean counts, or the lean-to-rich counts are less than a calibrated value. DTC P1133 sets within 60 seconds when the above condition is met. **Possible Causes:** • HO2S low reference circuit for an open/high resistance • HO2S signal circuit for a short to ground • HO2S signal circuit for a short to voltage • HO2S signal circuit for an open/high resistance • HO2S has failed • ECM has failed
DTC: P1133 **2T O2S, MIL: Yes** **Years:** 2008, 2009 **Models:** Equinox, G6, G8, Torrent **Engines:** 4.2L VIN S, 4.8L VIN C, 3.5L VIN N, 3.5L VIN K, 3.9L VIN 3, 3.9L VIN M, 3.6L VIN 2, 3.9L VIN 1 **Transmissions:** All	**HO2S-11 (Bank 1 Sensor 1) Insufficient Switching** DTC P0101, P0102, P0103, P0106, P0107, P0108, P0112, P0113, P0116, P0117, P0118, P0120, P0131, P0132, P0134, P0135, P0151, P0152, P0154, P0155, P0169, P0178, P0179, P0200, P0220, P0300, P0442, P0446, P0452, P0453, P0455, P0496, P1125, P1258, P1514, P1515, P1516, P1518, P2108 and P2135 not set, engine runtime over 160 seconds, engine speed at 1200-3000 RPM in closed loop, system voltage from 10-18v, ECT sensor more than 149°F, fuel level over 10%, Purge command over 1%, MAF sensor from 23-50 g/sec, TP indicated angle more than 5% above the idle value on models with TAC, Fuel Alcohol content less than 90%, and the ECM detected the number of rich-to-lean or lean-to-rich HO2S signal transitions were less than a calibrated value. **Possible Causes:** • Air leaks present in the exhaust manifold or the exhaust pipes • Fuel pressure is too high (i.e., causing a rich air fuel mixture) • HO2S may be contaminated (due to improper fuel or silicone) • HO2S signal high or low reference circuit has high resistance • HO2S heater element has failed, or the heater circuit is open • ECM has failed
DTC: P1134 **2T O2S, MIL: Yes** **Years:** 2008, 2009 **Models:** Equinox, G6, G8, Torrent **Engines:** 4.2L VIN S, 4.8L VIN C, 3.5L VIN N, 3.5L VIN K, 3.9L VIN 3, 3.9L VIN M, 3.6L VIN 2, 3.9L VIN 1 **Transmissions:** All	**HO2S-11 (Bank 1 Sensor 1) Transition Time Ratio** DTC P0101-P0103, P0106-P0108, P0112-P0118, P0121-P0123, P0131-P0135, P0151-P0155, P0200, P0300, P0401-P0405, P0440-P0446, P0452, P0453, P1120, P1125, P1220, P1221, P1258, P1404, P1441 and P01514, and P1518 not set, engine speed from 1200-3000 RPM for over 3 minutes in closed loop, system voltage over 10.0v, ECT sensor over 149°F, fuel level over 10%, Purge command over 1%, MAF sensor from 23-50 g/sec, TP angle at 5% over idle value on models with TAC, Intrusive and Scan Tool tests "off" for 100 seconds, and the ECM detected the HO2S time ratio value was not within the calibrated range. **Possible Causes:** • Air leaks present in the exhaust manifold or the exhaust pipes • HO2S may be contaminated (due to improper fuel or silicone) • HO2S signal low reference circuit has high resistance • HO2S heater element has failed, or the heater circuit is open • ECM has failed

DTC	Trouble Code Title, Conditions & Possible Causes
DTC: P1153 **2T O2S, MIL: Yes** **Years:** 2008, 2009 **Models:** Equinox, G6, G8, Torrent **Engines:** 4.2L VIN S, 4.8L VIN C, 3.5L VIN N, 3.5L VIN K, 3.9L VIN 3, 3.9L VIN M, 3.6L VIN 2, 3.9L VIN 1 **Transmissions:** All	**HO2S-21 (Bank 2 Sensor 1) Insufficient Switching** DTC P0101, P0102, P0103, P0106, P0107, P0108, P0112, P0113, P0116, P0117, P0118, P0120, P0131, P0132, P0134, P0135, P0151, P0152, P0154-P0155, P0169, P0178-P0179, P0200, P0220, P0300, P0442, P0446, P0452-P0453, P0455-P0496, P1125, P1258, P1404, P1514, P1515, P1516, P1518, P2108 and P2135 not set, engine runtime over 160 seconds, engine speed at 1200-3000 RPM in closed loop, system voltage from 10-18v, ECT sensor more than 149°F, Fuel Level over 10%, Purge command over 1%, MAF sensor from 23-50 g/sec, TP indicated angle more than 5% above the idle value on models with TAC, Fuel Alcohol content less than 90%, and the ECM detected the number of rich-to-lean or lean-to-rich HO2S signal transitions were less than a calibrated value. **Possible Causes:** • Air leaks present in the exhaust manifold or the exhaust pipes • Fuel pressure is too high (i.e., causing a rich air fuel mixture) • HO2S may be contaminated (due to improper fuel or silicone) • HO2S signal high or low reference circuit has high resistance • HO2S heater element has failed, or the heater circuit is open • ECM has failed
DTC: P1153 **2T O2S, MIL: Yes** **Years:** 2008, 2009 **Models:** Equinox, G6, G8, Torrent **Engines:** 4.2L VIN S, 4.8L VIN C, 3.5L VIN N, 3.5L VIN K, 3.9L VIN 3, 3.9L VIN M, 3.6L VIN 2, 3.9L VIN 1 **Transmissions:** All	**HO2S-21 (Bank 2 Sensor 1) Insufficient Switching** DTC P0101-P0103, P0106-P0108, P0112-P0118, P0131-P0135, P0151-P0155, P0200, P0300, P0410, P0440-P0446, P0452, P0453, P1120, P1125, P1220, P1221, P1258, P1415, P1416, P1441, P1514-P1518 not set, engine started, engine speed from 1000-2300 RPM for 160 seconds in closed loop, system voltage over 10.0v, fuel level over 10%, ECT sensor more than 122°F, Purge command over 0%, MAF sensor from 18-50 g/sec, TP indicated angle 5% over the idle value for 60 seconds, and the ECM less than 10 lean-to-rich or rich-lean switch counts on the HO2S signal circuit during the test. **Possible Causes:** • Air leaks present in the exhaust manifold or the exhaust pipes • Fuel pressure is too high (i.e., causing a rich air fuel mixture) • HO2S may be contaminated (due to improper fuel or silicone) • HO2S signal high or low reference circuit has high resistance • HO2S heater element has failed, or the heater circuit is open • ECM has failed
DTC: P1154 **2T O2S, MIL: Yes** **Years:** 2008, 2009 **Models:** Express, G8, Lucerne, Trailblazer **Engines:** 4.6L VIN Y, 4.6L VIN 9, 6.0L VIN H, 6.0L VIN Y, 6.0L VIN K, 6.2L VIN W, 6.6L VIN 6 **Transmissions:** All	**HO2S-21 (Bank 2 Sensor 1) Transition Time Ratio** DTC P0101-P0103, P0106-P0108, P0112-P0118, P0121-P0123, P0131-P0135, P0151-P0155, P0200, P0300, P0401-P0405, P0440-P0446, P0452, P0453, P1120, P1125, P1220, P1221, P1258, P1404, P1441and P01514, and P1518 not set, engine speed from 1200-3000 RPM for over 3 minutes in closed loop, system voltage over 10.0v, ECT sensor over 149°F, fuel level over 10%, Purge command over 1%, MAF sensor from 23-50 g/sec, TP angle at 5% over idle value on models with TAC, Intrusive and Scan Tool tests "off" for 100 seconds, and the ECM detected the HO2S time ratio value was not within the calibrated range. **Possible Causes:** • Air leaks present in the exhaust manifold or the exhaust pipes • HO2S may be contaminated (due to improper fuel or silicone) • HO2S signal low reference circuit has high resistance • HO2S heater element has failed, or the heater circuit is open • ECM has failed
DTC: P1154 **2T O2S, MIL: Yes** **Years:** 2008, 2009 **Models:** Equinox, G6, G8, Torrent **Engines:** 4.2L VIN S, 4.8L VIN C, 3.5L VIN N, 3.5L VIN K, 3.9L VIN 3, 3.9L VIN M, 3.6L VIN 2, 3.9L VIN 1 **Transmissions:** All	**HO2S-21 (Bank 2 Sensor 1) Transition Time Ratio** DTC P0101-P0103, P0106-P0108, P0112-P0118, P0131-P0135, P0151-P0155, P0200, P0300, P0410, P0440-P0446, P0452, P0453, P1120, P1125, P1220, P1221, P1258, P1415, P1416, P1441, P1514-P1518 not set, engine speed from 1000-2300 RPM for 160 seconds in closed loop, system voltage over 10.0v, fuel level over 10%, ECT sensor over 122°F, Purge over 0%, MAF sensor from 18-50 g/sec, TP angle over 5% over the idle value for 1 minute (TAC models), and the ECM detected the HO2S transition time ratio was out of range. **Possible Causes:** • Air leaks present in the exhaust manifold or the exhaust pipes • HO2S may be contaminated (due to improper fuel or silicone) • HO2S signal low reference circuit has high resistance • HO2S heater element has failed, or the heater circuit is open • ECM has failed

DTC	Trouble Code Title, Conditions & Possible Causes
DTC: P1174 **1T CCM, MIL: Yes** **Years:** 2008, 2009 **Models:** Express, G8, Lucerne, Trailblazer **Engines:** 4.6L VIN Y, 4.6L VIN 9, 6.0L VIN H, 6.0L VIN Y, 6.0L VIN K, 6.2L VIN W, 6.6L VIN 6 **Transmissions:** All	**Fuel Trim Cylinder Balance (Bank 1)** DTCs P0030, P0036, P0050, P0053, P0059, P0101, P0102, P0103, P0106, P0107, P0108, P0117, P0118, P0128, P0131, P0132, P0133, P0134, P0135, P0151, P0152, P0153, P0154, P0155, P0201-P0206, P0300, P0301-P0306, P0411, P0412, P0418, P0442, P0443, P0446, P0449, P0452, P0453, P0454, P0455, P0496, P1133, P1153, P1516, P2101, P2119, P2120, P2125, P2135, P2138, P2176, P2431, P2432, P2433, P2440, P2A00, P2A03 are not set. The device control is not active. The intrusive diagnostics are not active. The engine overspeed protection is not active. The Power Take-Off (PTO) is not active. The traction control is not active. The fuel control is in air-fuel Closed Loop. The system voltage is more than 10 volts, or less than 18 volts. The engine run time is greater than 100 seconds. The Engine Coolant Temperature (ECT) is greater than −20°C (−4°F). The engine speed is greater than 425 RPM, but less than 6,000 RPM. The mass air flow is greater than 25 g/s, but less than 510 g/s Multiple samples of the pre-catalyst HO2S accumulated voltage are consistently greater than the desired value. **Possible Causes:** • Vacuum hoses for splits, kinks, and improper connections. • Crankcase ventilation system for improper operation • Air induction system for modified, damaged, leaking, or restricted components. • Restricted, damaged, leaking, or modified exhaust system from the catalytic converter forward • Fuel injectors for improper operation • Ignition system for improper operation
DTC: P1175 **1T CCM, MIL: Yes** **Years:** 2008, 2009 **Models:** Express, G8, Lucerne, Trailblazer **Engines:** 4.6L VIN Y, 4.6L VIN 9, 6.0L VIN H, 6.0L VIN Y, 6.0L VIN K, 6.2L VIN W, 6.6L VIN 6 **Transmissions:** All	**Fuel Trim Cylinder Balance (Bank 2)** DTCs P0030, P0036, P0050, P0053, P0059, P0101, P0102, P0103, P0106, P0107, P0108, P0117, P0118, P0128, P0131, P0132, P0133, P0134, P0135, P0151, P0152, P0153, P0154, P0155, P0201-P0206, P0300, P0301-P0306, P0411, P0412, P0418, P0442, P0443, P0446, P0449, P0452, P0453, P0454, P0455, P0496, P1133, P1153, P1516, P2101, P2119, P2120, P2125, P2135, P2138, P2176, P2431, P2432, P2433, P2440, P2A00, P2A03 are not set. The device control is not active. The intrusive diagnostics are not active. The engine overspeed protection is not active. The Power Take-Off (PTO) is not active. The traction control is not active. The fuel control is in air-fuel Closed Loop. The system voltage is more than 10 volts, or less than 18 volts. The engine run time is greater than 100 seconds. The Engine Coolant Temperature (ECT) is greater than −20°C (−4°F). The engine speed is greater than 425 RPM, but less than 6,000 RPM. The mass air flow is greater than 25 g/s, but less than 510 g/s Multiple samples of the pre-catalyst HO2S accumulated voltage are consistently greater than the desired value. **Possible Causes:** • Vacuum hoses for splits, kinks, and improper connections. • Crankcase ventilation system for improper operation • Air induction system for modified, damaged, leaking, or restricted components. • Restricted, damaged, leaking, or modified exhaust system from the catalytic converter forward • Fuel injectors for improper operation • Ignition system for improper operation
DTC: P1220 **1T CCM, MIL: Yes** **Years:** 2008, 2009 **Models:** Express, G8, Lucerne, Trailblazer **Engines:** 4.6L VIN Y, 4.6L VIN 9, 6.0L VIN H, 6.0L VIN Y, 6.0L VIN K, 6.2L VIN W, 6.6L VIN 6 **Transmissions:** All	**TP Sensor 2 Circuit Malfunction** DTC P1517 and P1518 not set, key in crank or run position, system voltage over 5.23v, and the ECM detected the TP2 signal was less than 0.13v or more than 4.87v for 1 second during the CCM test. **Possible Causes:** • TP2 sensor signal circuit is open, shorted to ground or to power • TP2 sensor VREF circuit is open, shorted to ground or shorted to system power (B+) • TP2 sensor ground circuit has a high resistance condition • TP2 sensor is damaged or has failed
DTC: P1220 **1T CCM, MIL: Yes** **Models:** Equinox, G6, G8, Torrent **Engines:** 4.2L VIN S, 4.8L VIN C, 3.5L VIN N, 3.5L VIN K, 3.9L VIN 3, 3.9L VIN M, 3.6L VIN 2, 3.9L VIN 1 **Transmissions:** All	**TP Sensor 2 Circuit Malfunction** DTC P0606, P1517 and P1518 not set, key in crank or run mode, system voltage over 5.23v, Electronic Throttle Control serial data operating, and the ECM detected the TP Sensor 2 signal was less than 0.13v or more than 4.87v during the CCM test. **Possible Causes:** • TP2 sensor signal circuit is open, shorted to ground or to power • TP2 sensor VREF circuit is open or shorted to ground • TP2 sensor VREF circuit is shorted to system power (B+) • TP2 sensor ground circuit has a high resistance condition • TP2 sensor is damaged or has failed

DTC	Trouble Code Title, Conditions & Possible Causes
DTC: P1221 **1T CCM, MIL: Yes** **Years:** 2008, 2009 **Models:** Express, G8, Lucerne, Trailblazer **Engines:** 4.6L VIN Y, 4.6L VIN 9, 6.0L VIN H, 6.0L VIN Y, 6.0L VIN K, 6.2L VIN W, 6.6L VIN 6 **Transmissions:** All	**TP Sensor 2 Signal Correlation** DTC P1517 and P1518 not set, key in crank or run position TP Sensor 1 (TP1) and TP Sensor 2 (TP2) more than 15% for 140 ms, and the ECM detected the TP2 signal disagreed with the TP1 signal by more than 7.5% for 1 second. The TP sensor has two separate signal, ground, and 5 volt reference circuits that are used to connect the TP sensor to the TAC module. These sensors have opposite functionality. The TP1 voltage increases from below 1.0v at 0% throttle to above 3.5v at 100% throttle opening. The TP2 voltage decreases from around 3.8v at 0 percent throttle to below 1.0v at 100% throttle opening. The TP1 signal circuit is pulled up to 5.0v and the TP2 signal circuit is pulled to ground in the TAC module. **Possible Causes:** • TP2 sensor connector is contaminated, dirty or contains water • TP2 sensor signal, ground or VREF circuit has high resistance • TP2 sensor VREF circuit has a high resistance condition • TP2 sensor ground circuit has a high resistance condition • TP2 sensor is damaged or has failed • TAC controller or the throttle body is damaged or has failed • TSB 02-06-04-005 contains a repair procedure for this code
DTC: P1221 **1T CCM, MIL: Yes** **Years:** 2008, 2009 **Models:** Equinox, G6, G8, Torrent **Engines:** 4.2L VIN S, 4.8L VIN C, 3.5L VIN N, 3.5L VIN K, 3.9L VIN 3, 3.9L VIN M, 3.6L VIN 2, 3.9L VIN 1 **Transmissions:** All	**TP Sensor 1-2 Signal Correlation** DTC P0606, P1517 and P1518 not set, key in crank or run mode, ETC serial data normal, and the ECM detected the TP1 disagreed with the TP2 input by over 7.5% for 1 second. **Possible Causes:** • TP1, 2 sensor signal circuit has a high resistance condition • TP1, 2 sensor VREF circuit has a high resistance condition • TP1, 2 sensor ground circuit has a high resistance condition • TP1, 2 sensor is damaged or has failed • TAC controller or the throttle body is damaged or has failed • TSB 02-06-04-005 contains a repair procedure for this code
DTC: P1255 **1T CCM, MIL: Yes** **Years:** 2008, 2009 **Models:** Equinox, G6, G8, Torrent **Engines:** All **Transmissions:** All	**Fuel Pump Control Module Driver Overtemperature** The engine is running. The FECM detects an overtemperature fault. **Note: Verify that DTC P0231, P0232 or P023F are not set as current or history before performing this diagnostic. If any of those codes are, diagnose first.** **Possible Causes:** • Dirty build up on FECM housing • FECM has failed
DTC: P1275 **1T CCM, MIL: No** **Models:** Equinox, G6, G8, Torrent **Engines:** 4.2L VIN S, 4.8L VIN C, 3.5L VIN N, 3.5L VIN K, 3.9L VIN 3, 3.9L VIN M, 3.6L VIN 2, 3.9L VIN 1 **Transmissions:** All	**Accelerator Pedal Position Sensor 1 Circuit Malfunction** DTC P0601, P0602, P0606, P1517 and P1518 not set, key in crank or run position, system voltage over 5.23v, and the ECM detected the APP1 sensor signal voltage ranged between 0.25v and 4.22v for less than 1 second during the test. **Possible Causes:** • APP1 sensor connector is contaminated, oily or contains water • APP1 sensor signal, ground or VREF circuit high resistance • APP1 sensor VREF circuit is open, shorted to ground or to B+ • APP1 sensor signal or ground circuit has high resistance • APP1 sensor is damaged or has failed • TAC module is damaged or has failed
DTC: P1276 **1T CCM, MIL: No** **Years:** 2008, 2009 **Models:** Express, G8, Lucerne, Trailblazer **Engines:** 4.6L VIN Y, 4.6L VIN 9, 6.0L VIN H, 6.0L VIN Y, 6.0L VIN K, 6.2L VIN W, 6.6L VIN 6 **Transmissions:** All	**Accelerator Pedal Position Sensor 1 Range/Performance** DTC P0606, P1517 and P1518 not set, key in crank or run position, system voltage over 5.23v, and the ECM detected the APP Sensor 1 and the APP Sensor 2 signals disagreed by more than 10%, or the APP Sensor 1 and APP Sensor 3 signals disagreed by over 13%. **Note: Refer to the information in the Failure Records as needed.** **Possible Causes:** • APP1 sensor connector is contaminated, oily or contains water • APP1 sensor signal circuit is open or shorted to ground • APP1 sensor signal circuit is shorted to VREF or system power • APP1 sensor ground circuit is open or has high resistance • APP1 sensor VREF circuit is open or shorted to ground • APP1 sensor is damaged or has failed

DTC	Trouble Code Title, Conditions & Possible Causes
DTC: P1280 **1T CCM, MIL: No** **Years:** 2008, 2009 **Models:** Express, G8, Lucerne, Trailblazer **Engines:** 4.6L VIN Y, 4.6L VIN 9, 6.0L VIN H, 6.0L VIN Y, 6.0L VIN K, 6.2L VIN W, 6.6L VIN 6 **Transmissions:** All	**Accelerator Pedal Position Sensor 2 Circuit Malfunction** DTC P0601, P0602, P0606, P1517 and P1518 not set, key in crank or run position, system voltage over 5.23v, and the ECM detected the TP2 signal was less than 0.83v, or it was more than 4.81v for 1 second during the test. **Possible Causes:** • APP2 sensor connector is contaminated, oily or contains water • APP2 sensor signal, ground or VREF circuit high resistance • APP2 sensor VREF circuit is open, shorted to ground or to B+ • APP2 sensor signal or ground circuit has high resistance • APP2 sensor is damaged or has failed • TAC module is damaged or has failed
DTC: P1336 **2T CCM, MIL: Yes** **Years:** 2008, 2009 **Models:** All **Engines:** All **Transmissions:** All	**CKP Sensor System Variation Not Learned** DTC P0336, P0341and P1374 not set, engine started, ECT sensor more than 158°F, and the ECM did not detect any CKP variation values. The Crankshaft Position system variation-learning feature is used to calculate reference period errors caused by slight tolerance variations in the crankshaft, and the CKP sensor(s). The calculated error Allows the ECM to accurately compensate for reference period variations to enhance the Misfire Detection capability of the system. **Possible Causes:** • Set the parking brake and block the drive wheels for safety. • Verify the hood is closed. • Read the trouble codes. If a code is set, refer to that code. • Start the engine. Allow engine temperature to reach at least 158°F (70°C). Then key off. • Select Crankshaft Position Variation Learn procedure on Scan Tool & start the vehicle. • Apply the brake pedal firmly and verify the selector is in Park. • Increase accelerator pedal position until fuel cutoff is reached at the test RPM (e.g., 5150). Quickly release the accelerator pedal after fuel cutoff is reached. The CKP system variation compensating values are learned when the engine speed (RPM) decreases back to idle speed and the procedure terminates. • Read the trouble codes and recheck for DTC P1336. • If DTC P1336 runs and passes, the CKP system variation "learn" procedure is complete. If not, look for other codes. If no codes are set, repeat the test procedure.
DTC: P1362 **2T CCM, MIL: Yes** **Years:** 2008, 2009 **Models:** All **Engines:** All **Transmissions:** All	**ICM Control Circuit High Input** Engine started; and the ECM detected an intermittent high voltage condition on the IC timing signal circuit for 300 3X reference periods (100 crankshaft revolutions). The ICM has independent power and ground circuits that connect it to the ECM. Both the CMP sensor and CKP sensor signals are input directly to the ICM. The ICM sends 3X signals to the ECM, and controls the timing advance during engine cranking. The timing advance changes to ECM control after the ECM receives the second 3X signal. At this point, the ECM applies a 5v signal to the to the ignition control (IC) timing signal circuit. **Possible Causes:** • IC timing signal is shorted to system power • IC timing control circuit and IC timing signal circuits are shorted • IC module is damaged or it has failed • ECM has failed
DTC: P1380 **2T CCM, MIL: Yes** **Years:** 2008, 2009 **Models:** All **Engines:** All **Transmissions:** All	**Misfire Detected, Rough Road Data Not Available** DTC P0101, P0102, P0103, P0120, P0335, P0336 and P0742 not set, engine started, vehicle driven to over 10 MPH at an engine load over 60%, engine speed less than 3200 RPM, Misfire code (P0300) set with MIL requested "on", and the ECM detected a malfunction occurred that prevented it from receiving rough road detection data from the EBCM. The ECM detects engine misfire events by monitoring variations in the crankshaft rotation speed. Wheel speed changes caused by rough road conditions can cause changes in crankshaft speed. The ABS (system) monitors the wheel speed sensors to determine when the vehicle is operating on a rough road. **Possible Causes:** • Use the Freeze Frame/Failure Records data to help find the cause on an intermittent fault. If the code cannot be duplicated, the data in the Freeze Frame/Failure Records can determine how many miles since the code set. The Fail Counter and Pass Counter can also help determine how many ignition cycles the diagnostic reported a pass or a fail. Operate the vehicle within the Freeze Frame conditions (i.e., load, engine and vehicle speed, temperature etc.). This will isolate when the code set. • Service the ABS before diagnosing a misfire because an actual engine misfire may or may not exist. Also, an actual engine misfire may have occurred during an ABS malfunction. • Determine if the vehicle was driven on a rough road, and the ABS could not detect this due to a malfunction. The ECM may interpret variations in crankshaft speed caused by the rough road as a misfire without an actual engine misfire present. • Refer to Diagnostic System Check for Antilock Brake System • Refer to Diagnostic System Check for the Engine Controls

DTC	Trouble Code Title, Conditions & Possible Causes
DTC: P1381 **2T CCM, MIL: Yes** **Years:** 2008, 2009 **Models:** All **Engines:** All **Transmissions:** All	**Misfire Detected - No Communication with Brake Control Module** The vehicle speed is greater than 8 km/h (5 mph). The engine speed is less than 7,000 RPM. The engine load is less than 60 percent. Engine misfire is detected and DTC P0300 sets with the MIL illuminated. DTCs P1381 run continuously when the above conditions are met. An ABS malfunction exists for more than 10 seconds, preventing the ECM from receiving rough road detection data. Engine misfire is detected and DTC P0300 set. **Possible Causes:** • If any ABS DTCs are set, diagnose those first • ABS module
DTC: P1400 **2T CCM, MIL: Yes** **Years:** 2008, 2009 **Models:** All **Engines:** All **Transmissions:** All	**Cold Start Emission Reduction Control System** The engine is running, and a cold start has been detected. Vehicle speed is less than 2 km/h (1 mph). The engine is at idle with no input from the accelerator pedal. DTCs P0068, P0101, P0102, P0103, P0106, P0107, P0108, P0112, P0113, P0116, P0117, P0118, P0120, P0121, P0122, P0123, P0220, P0222, P0223, P0201, P0202, P0203, P0204, P0205, P0206, P0300, P0335, P0336, P0351, P0352, P0353, P0501, P0502, P0506, P0507, P0601, P0602, P0603, P0604, P0606, P0607, P060D, P062F, P0641, P0651, P1101, P1516, P1682, P2101, P2119, P2120, P2122, P2123, P2125, P2127, P2128, P2135, P2138, P2176, P2610 are not set. This DTC runs for 15 seconds within the first 2 minutes of start-up. This diagnostic runs once per trip when a cold start has been determined. The actual exhaust energy model does not match the expected exhaust energy model. **Possible Causes:** • Air intake system for Damage, restriction, or modification • Dirty or deteriorating air filter element • Crankcase ventilation system for correct operation • Vacuum leak and other un-metered air downstream of the Mass Air Flow (MAF) sensor • Intake manifold leak • Damaged, restricted, modified or enhanced exhaust system • Exhaust leaks
DTC: P1404 **2T EGR, MIL: Yes** **Years:** 2008, 2009 **Models:** Equinox, Torrent **Engines:** 3.4L VIN F **Transmissions:** All	**EGR Valve Closed Position Performance** Engine started; system voltage from 11-18v, EGR valve enabled at least (6) times, and the ECM detected the EGR position sensor was 0.29v more than the EGR learned minimum position when the desired EGR position was commanded to 0% for over 2 seconds, or the EGR position sensor command is over 30% and steady for 2 seconds after a test failure and before the next test. **Possible Causes:** • EGR sensor signal circuit is shorted to VREF (5v) • EGR sensor ground circuit is open or has high resistance • EGR sensor is damaged or has failed (sensor/solenoid unit) • EGR valve pintle or valve seat contains carbon deposits • ECM has failed • TSB 01-06-04-043 contains a repair procedure for this code
DTC: P1415 **2T AIR, MIL: Yes** **Years:** 2008, 2009 **Models:** All **Transmissions:** All	**Secondary Air Injection System (Bank 1) Malfunction** DTC P0137, 0138 P0140-P0147, P0151-P0158, P0160, P0161, P0171, P0172, P0174, P0175, P0300, P0500, P1106, P1107, P1111-P1115, P1121, P1122, P1133, P1134, P1153, P1154, P1351 and P1361 not set, engine started, vehicle driven to an engine speed over 900 RPM at an engine load less than 33.25%, airflow less than 22 g/sec, A/F ratio at 13.125:1, ECT sensor from 158-230°F, system voltage over 10.0v, and the ECM detected the Bank 1 HO2S signal was less than 222 mv for 1 second with the AIR pump on while in closed loop. A secondary air injection (AIR) pump is used to reduce the tailpipe emissions during startup. The ECM supplies a ground to the AIR pump relay control circuit, and this action energizes the AIR pump. The ECM monitors the front HO2S signal in order to diagnose the AIR system. During the AIR test, the ECM activates the AIR pump during closed loop operation. Once the AIR pump is "on", the ECM monitors the HO2S signal and the Short Term fuel trim values of both banks of the engine. If the AIR system is operating properly, the HO2S signal should go low, and the Short Term fuel trim value should go high. If the ECM detects the HO2S signals for both banks did not respond as expected during the tests, it will set DTC P0410. If only one sensor responds, the ECM sets either a DTC P1415 or P1416 to indicate the bank where the AIR system failed. **Possible Causes:** • Air hoses disconnected, loose, kinked or failed (a burnt hose) • AIR pump is damaged or has failed (inspect air pump for water) • AIR system check valves and/or pipes are damaged or leaking • ECM has failed

DTC	Trouble Code Title, Conditions & Possible Causes
DTC: P1416 **2T AIR, MIL: Yes** **Years:** 2008, 2009 **Models:** All **Transmissions:** All	**Secondary Air Injection System (Bank 2) Malfunction** DTC P0137, 0138 P0140-P0147, P0151-P0158, P0160, P0161, P0171, P0172, P0174, P0175, P0300, P0500, P1106, P1107, P1111-P1115, P1121, P1122, P1133, P1134, P1153, P1154, P1351 and P1361 not set, engine started, vehicle driven to an engine speed over 900 RPM at an engine load less than 33.25%, airflow less than 22 g/sec, A/F ratio at 13.125:1, ECT sensor from 158-230°F, system voltage over 10.0v, and the ECM detected the Bank 2 HO2S signal was less than 222 mv for 1 second with the AIR pump on while in closed loop. The ECM supplies a ground to the AIR pump relay control circuit, and this action energizes the AIR pump. The ECM monitors the front HO2S signal in order to diagnose the AIR system. During the AIR test, the ECM activates the AIR pump during closed loop operation. Once the AIR pump is "on", the ECM monitors the HO2S signal and the Short Term fuel trim values of both banks of the engine. If the AIR system is operating properly, the HO2S signal should go low, and the Short Term fuel trim value should go high. If the ECM detects the HO2S signals for both banks did not respond as expected during the tests, it will set DTC P0410. If only one sensor responds, the ECM sets either a DTC P1415 or P1416 to indicate the bank where the AIR system failed. **Possible Causes:** • Air hoses disconnected, loose, kinked or failed (a burnt hose) • AIR pump is damaged or has failed (inspect air pump for water) • AIR system check valves and/or pipes are damaged or leaking • ECM has failed
DTC: P1514 **1T CCM, MIL: Yes** **Years:** 2008, 2009 **Models:** Express, G8, Lucerne, Trailblazer **Engines:** 4.6L VIN Y, 4.6L VIN 9, 6.0L VIN H, 6.0L VIN Y, 6.0L VIN K, 6.2L VIN W, 6.6L VIN 6 **Transmissions:** All	**Throttle Body Performance** DTC P0601, P0602, P0606, P1515, P1516, P1517 and P1518 not set, P1120, P1220 and P1221 not active at the time this code set, or P1120 and P1220 not set at the same time, engine speed over 500 RPM, and the ECM detected the difference between Actual (MAF) airflow and Speed Density Calculated airflow was more than expected for 1 second. The Reduced Engine Power message displays on the Driver Information Center if this code sets. **Possible Causes:** • Inspect the throttle blade for damage and/or proper installation • Inspect the TAC module connectors for signs of water intrusion. When water intrusion occurs, multiple codes can set with no circuit or component faults apparent during diagnostic testing. • Physically and visually inspect the throttle body assembly, and throttle position sensor for damage and/or a loose mounting. Move the throttle blade from closed to wide open position without applying too much force. The throttle blade should move smoothly through the full range and should return to a slightly open position on its own. • If the TAC module detects a fault in the system, it may set more than one related code because of the many redundant tests that run continuously on this system. Locating and repairing one individual condition may fix more than one code.
DTC: P1515 **1T CCM, MIL: Yes** **Years:** 2008, 2009 **Models:** Express, G8, Lucerne, Trailblazer **Engines:** 4.6L VIN Y, 4.6L VIN 9, 6.0L VIN H, 6.0L VIN Y, 6.0L VIN K, 6.2L VIN W, 6.6L VIN 6 **Transmissions:** All	**Control Module Throttle Actuator Position Performance** DTC P0601, P0602, P0606, P1515, P1516, P1517 and P1518 not set, P1120, P1220 and P1221 not active at the time this code set, or P1120 and P1220 not set at the same time, key in crank or run mode, ETC or TAC system not in Battery Saver Mode, and the ECM detected the Actual and Commanded throttle positions were out-of-range for under 1 second. **Possible Causes:** • Throttle actuator motor CKT 1 is open, shorted to ground or B+ • Throttle actuator motor CKT 2 is open, shorted to ground or B+ • Throttle actuator motor is damaged or has failed • Throttle actuator motor control module has failed • TSB 00-06-04-035 contains a repair procedure for this code
DTC: P1516 **1T CCM, MIL: Yes** **Years:** 2008, 2009 **Models:** Envoy, Equinox, Savana, Torrent **Engines:** 3.4L VIN F, 4.3L VIN X, 5.3L VIN M **Transmissions:** All	**Throttle Actuator Control (TAC) Module Throttle Actuator Position Performance** The ignition is ON. The ignition voltage is more than 8 volts. The system is not in the Battery Save mode. The engine is running. DTC P0068 is not set. DTC P1516 and P2101 run continuously when the above conditions are met. The indicated throttle position does not match the predicted throttle position for more than 0.5 second. **Note: Disconnecting the throttle body harness connector causes additional DTCs to set.** **Possible Causes:** • TAC motor control circuit for a short to voltage • TAC motor control circuit for a short to voltage • TAC motor control circuit for a short to ground • TAC motor control circuit for a short to ground • Throttle body has failed • ECM has failed

DTC	Trouble Code Title, Conditions & Possible Causes
DTC: P1516 **2T CCM, MIL: Yes** **Years:** 2008, 2009 **Models:**, Equinox, G6, G8, Torrent **Engines:** All **Transmissions:** All	**TAC Module Throttle Actuator Position Performance** DTC P1518 not set, key in crank or run mode, ETC or TAC system not in Battery Saver Mode, then the ETC/TAC module detected the predicted and actual throttle positions were not within a calibrated range of each other or the ECM and ETC/TAC could not determine the throttle position or that both TP sensors signals were invalid. **Possible Causes:** • TAC motor CKT 1 or CKT 2 is open, shorted to ground or B+ • Throttle actuator motor CKT 1 is shorted to CKT 2 • Throttle actuator motor control module has failed • TSB 03-04-06-032 contains a repair procedure for this code
DTC: P1517 **1T CCM, MIL: Yes** **Years:** 2008, 2009 **Models:** Express, G8, Lucerne, Trailblazer **Engines:** 4.6L VIN Y, 4.6L VIN 9, 6.0L VIN H, 6.0L VIN Y, 6.0L VIN K, 6.2L VIN W, 6.6L VIN 6 **Transmissions:** All	**Throttle Actuator Control Module Performance** DTC P1518 not set, key in the crank or run mode, system voltage over 5.23v, and the ETC or TAC module detected that an internal data test failed (did not pass) for a time period of less than 1 second. **Possible Causes:** • Test the charging system output (low voltage can set this code) • Inspect the TAC module connectors for signs of water intrusion. If water intrusion occurs, multiple codes may set without any circuit or component conditions found during diagnostic testing. • When the TAC module detects a fault condition, several TAC related codes set because there are redundant tests running. • TAC module has failed
DTC: P1517 **1T CCM, MIL: Yes** **Models:** Equinox, G6, G8, Torrent **Engines:** 4.2L VIN S, 4.8L VIN C, 3.5L VIN N, 3.5L VIN K, 3.9L VIN 3, 3.9L VIN M, 3.6L VIN 2, 3.9L VIN 1 **Transmissions:** All	**Throttle Actuator Control Module Performance** DTC P1518 not set, key in crank or run mode, system voltage over 5.23v, and the ETC or TAC module detected that an internal data test failed (did not pass) for less than 1 second. **Possible Causes:** • Test the charging system output (low voltage can set this code) • Inspect the TAC module connectors for signs of water intrusion. If water intrusion occurs, multiple codes may set without any circuit or component conditions present. • When the TAC module detects a fault condition, several TAC related codes set because there are redundant tests running. • TAC module has failed
DTC: P1518 **1T CCM, MIL: Yes** **Years:** 2008, 2009 **Models:** Equinox, G6, G8, Torrent **Engines:** 4.2L VIN S, 4.8L VIN C, 3.5L VIN N, 3.5L VIN K, 3.9L VIN 3, 3.9L VIN M, 3.6L VIN 2, 3.9L VIN 1 **Transmissions:** All	**Throttle Actuator Control Module Serial Data Malfunction** Key in the crank or run mode, system voltage over 5.23v, and the ETC or TAC module detected invalid or missing serial data present for a specified amount of time, condition met for less than 1 second. **Possible Causes:** • DTC P1518 sets if the battery voltage is low. If the customer's concern is slow cranking or no crank due to low battery voltage, ignore the DTC P1518. Clear codes and retest. • DTC P1518 also sets when there is a short to B+ on the TAC module ground circuit. Inspect the Brake & Cruise fuses first. • TSB 03-04-06-032 contains a repair procedure for this code
DTC: P1551 **1T CCM, MIL: Yes** **Years:** 2008, 2009 **Models:** Envoy, Equinox, G6, G8, Impala, Lucerne, Malibu, Savana, Trailblazer, Torrent **Engines:** 4.2L VIN S, 4.8L VIN C, 3.5L VIN N, 3.5L VIN K, 3.9L VIN 3, 3.9L VIN M, 3.6L VIN 2, 3.9L VIN 1 **Transmissions:** All	**Throttle Valve Rest Position Not Reached During Learn** The ECM detects the TP sensor angle is less than 10 percent or greater than 40 percent when the throttle actuator control motor is deactivated. The condition exists, and then a 5 second delay for MIL ON. **Possible Causes:** • Faulty throttle body, (binding, sticking or no spring pressure) • Throttle body has failed
DTC: P1585 **1T CCM, MIL: No** **Years:** 2008, 2009 **Models:** All **Engines:** All **Transmissions:** All	**Cruise Control Inhibit Output Circuit Malfunction** Engine started; system voltage over 10.0v and the ECM detected an unexpected voltage condition on the Cruise Control Inhibit driver circuit for at least 30 seconds. **Possible Causes:** • Cruise control inhibit circuit is shorted to system voltage • Cruise control inhibit circuit is open or shorted to ground • Cruise control module power circuit is open (test CR CNT fuse) • Cruise control module is damaged or has failed • ECM has failed

DTC	Trouble Code Title, Conditions & Possible Causes
DTC: P1631 **1T CCM, MIL: No** **Years:** 2008, 2009 **Models:** Express, G8, Lucerne, Trailblazer **Engines:** 4.6L VIN Y, 4.6L VIN 9, 6.0L VIN H, 6.0L VIN Y, 6.0L VIN K, 6.2L VIN W, 6.6L VIN 6 **Transmissions:** All	**Theft Deterrent - Start Enable Signal Not Correct** DTC P1626 not active, engine cranking with the ECM not in "password learn mode", VTD (Pass Lock) system enabled, and the ECM did not receive a valid password before the fuel disable decision point was reached. When the Passlock portion of the VTD system has sensed the proper operation of the ignition switch and lock, or determined that the switch and lock have not been tampered with, the VTD (Passlock) module transmits a password to the ECM. Fuel delivery is enabled if this password matches the password stored in the ECM memory. If a component in the Theft Deterrent system has been replaced, the two modules need to relearn the password of the new components. If the relearn procedure has not been performed, DTC P1631 will set. If a VTD failure occurs during an ignition cycle on which the ECM has enabled fuel, then the ECM will enter Fail Safe mode (VTD System Failure with Fuel Enabled). The ECM remains in Fail Enable Mode for the current and future ignition cycles, until the fault is corrected, a valid password is received, or until the battery is disconnected. If the codes are cleared, the vehicle will lose its Fail Enable status and will not start until the fault is corrected or the ten minute timer expires. At this point, the ECM receives the correct fuel delivery password. **Possible Causes:** • Refer to Diagnostic System Check for Theft Deterrent Module • Perform the Powertrain Onboard Diagnostic System Check • TSB 77-65-31 contains a repair procedure for this code
DTC: P1637 **1T CCM, MIL: No** **Years:** 2008, 2009 **Models:** Express, G8, Lucerne, Trailblazer **Engines:** 4.6L VIN Y, 4.6L VIN 9, 6.0L VIN H, 6.0L VIN Y, 6.0L VIN K, 6.2L VIN W, 6.6L VIN 6 **Transmissions:** All	**Generator 'L' Terminal Circuit Malfunction** Engine started; and the ECM detected an incorrect voltage on the Generator 'L' terminal during the CCM test. The ECM supplies the ignition voltage to the generator lamp feed. This voltage is pulled low by the generator once the circuit is supplied voltage. Once the generator begins to turn, the ECM detects ignition voltage. If there are no Charging system faults, the lamp terminal circuit will be low (0 volts) with the ignition switch "on" and then change to the system voltage after engine startup. If the Charging system detects this circuit is shorted to ground) the IPC will display a fault message. **Possible Causes:** • A Scan Tool should display Inactive for the 'L' Terminal and 10-40% for the 'F' Terminal with the ignition "on". With the engine running, the display should indicate the 'L' Terminal is Active and the 'F' Terminal is higher than 5% on the tool display. • Generator 'L terminal circuit shorted to ground or to power (B+) • Generator 'F' terminal circuit is open or shorted to ground • Generator is damaged or has failed or the ECM has failed
DTC: P1638 **1T CCM, MIL: No** **Years:** 2008, 2009 **Models:** Express, G8, Lucerne, Trailblazer **Engines:** 4.6L VIN Y, 4.6L VIN 9, 6.0L VIN H, 6.0L VIN Y, 6.0L VIN K, 6.2L VIN W, 6.6L VIN 6 **Transmissions:** All	**Generator 'F' Terminal Circuit Malfunction** No CKP, CMP or Generator codes set, key on and the ECM detected the PWM signal was from 10-40% for over 6 seconds; or with the engine speed under 3000 RPM, the ECM detected the PWM signal was less than 5% for 6 seconds. The ECM uses the generator field duty cycle signal circuit to monitor the duty cycle of the generator. The generator field duty cycle signal circuit connects to the high side of the field winding in the generator. A pulse width modulated (PWM) high side driver in the voltage regulator turns the field winding on/off. When the key is in run position and the engine is off, the ECM should detect a duty cycle near 0%. However, when the engine is running, the duty cycle should be from 5-100%. The ECM monitors the PWM signal using a key on test and a run test. During the tests, if the ECM detects an out of range PWM signal, DTC P1638 will set. When the DTC sets, the ECM will send a class 2 serial data message to the IPC to illuminate the charge indicator. **Possible Causes:** • Generator connector is damaged or has high resistance • Generator field duty cycle signal circuit is open or shorted • Generator is damaged or has failed • ECM has failed
DTC: P1639 **1T CCM, MIL: Yes** **Years:** 2008, 2009 **Models:** Express, G8, Lucerne, Trailblazer **Engines:** 4.6L VIN Y, 4.6L VIN 9, 6.0L VIN H, 6.0L VIN Y, 6.0L VIN K, 6.2L VIN W, 6.6L VIN 6 **Transmissions:** All	**5-Volt Reference 2 Circuit Malfunction** Key on or engine running; and the ECM detected the 5v Reference No. 2 circuit was out of tolerance for 2 seconds during the CCM test. This circuit is connected to the Fuel Tank Pressure (FTP) and TP sensor. **Possible Causes:** • 5v VREF circuit is shorted to sensor ground or chassis ground • 5v VREF circuit, FTP or TP sensor circuit is shorted to (B+) • 5v VREF circuit shorted to FTP or TP sensor signal circuit • FTP sensor or TP sensor is damaged or ECM has failed
DTC: P1682 **2T CCM, MIL: Yes** **Years:** 2008, 2009 **Models:**, Equinox, G6, G8, Torrent **Engines:** All **Transmissions:** All	**Ignition 1 Switch Circuit 2** The ignition is ON. System voltage is more than 7 volts. The powertrain relay is commanded ON. DTC P1682 runs continuously when the above conditions are met. The ECM detects that the voltage level difference is greater than 3 volts between the 2 ignition 1 voltage circuits for less than 1 second. **Possible Causes:** • Powertrain relay controlled output circuit for a short to voltage • Powertrain relay coil voltage supply circuit for a short to ground or an open/high resistance. • Powertrain relay switch voltage supply circuit for an open/high resistance. • Ignition 1 relay controlled output circuit for a short to ground or open/high resistance • Powertrain relay • ECM has failed

DTC	Trouble Code Title, Conditions & Possible Causes
DTC: P1810 **2T CCM, MIL: Yes** **Years:** 2008, 2009 **Models:** Envoy, Equinox, G6, G8, Impala, Lucerne, Malibu, Savana, Trailblazer, Torrent **Engines:** 4.2L VIN S, 4.8L VIN C, 3.5L VIN N, 3.5L VIN K, 3.9L VIN 3, 3.9L VIN M, 3.6L VIN 2, 3.9L VIN 1 **Transmissions:** All	**TFP Valve Position Switch Assembly** DTC P0502 and P0503 not set, system voltage over 10.0v, engine running for 5 seconds, Fuel Cutoff inactive, engine torque from 40-400 ft-lbs, engine vacuum from 0-105 kPa, then during Condition 1 the ECM detected an illegal TFP manual valve position switch state for 60 seconds; or during Condition 2 with the engine speed less than 80 RPM for 0.1 second, then the engine speed from 80-550 RPM for 100 ms, then the engine speed was greater than 550 RPM; then the vehicle speed was less than 2 MPH, and the ECM detected the gear range was D2, D4 or Reverse during startup for 5 seconds; or during Condition 3 with the TP angle from 10-50%, fourth gear commanded "on", TCC engaged, speed ratio from 0.6-0.75, and the ECM detected the gear range indicated Park or Neutral with the vehicle is operating in D4 for 10 seconds. The TFP manual valve position switch assembly cannot distinguish between P/N because the monitored valve body pressures are identical in both cases. **Possible Causes:** • TFP valve position switch signal circuit is open, grounded or shorted to another signal • TFP valve position switch is damaged or has failed • This code can set during fluid refilling. After refilling the fluid, cycle the key "off", then idle the engine for 20 seconds. Turn the key "off" and Allow the ECM to power down. • This code can set due to low pump pressure or due to a stuck pressure regulator. • This code can set due to a rolled forward clutch piston seal. It may Allow the ECM to see a 2.08:1 ratio (reverse) when the manual valve position is actually indicated in D4. • ECM has failed
DTC: P1860 **1T CCM, MIL: Yes** **Years:** 2008, 2009 **Models:** Envoy, Equinox, G6, G8, Impala, Lucerne, Malibu, Savana, Trailblazer, Torrent **Engines:** All **Transmissions:** All	**TCM PWM Solenoid Circuit Malfunction** Engine started, engine runtime over 5 seconds, system voltage over 10.0v, Fuel Cutoff inactive, 1st gear commanded "on", and the ECM detected a high voltage with the TCC solenoid commanded to 90%, or a low voltage with the TCC commanded to 0%. The TCC PWM solenoid controls fluid acting on the converter clutch valve that controls the application and release of the torque converter clutch. The solenoid attaches to the control valve body in the transmission. **Possible Causes:** • TCC solenoid control circuit is open or shorted to ground • TCC solenoid control circuit is shorted to system power (B+) • TCC solenoid power circuit is open (test TRANS or IGN fuse) • TCC solenoid is damaged or has failed • ECM has failed
DTC: P1870 **1T CCM, MIL: Yes** **Years:** 2008, 2009 **Models:** Envoy, Equinox, G6, G8, Impala, Lucerne, Malibu, Savana, Trailblazer, Torrent **Engines:** All **Transmissions:** All	**Transmission Component Slipping** DTC P0122, P0123, P0502, P0503, P0711-P0713, P0740, P0753, P0758, P1810 and P1860 not set, vehicle driven at a speed of 30-70 MPH at an engine speed of 1500-3000 RPM, Fuel Cutoff inactive, TP angle from 9-35%, engine vacuum 0-150 kPa, speed ratio is 0.69-0.88, Transmission not 1st gear, gear range is D4, TFT sensor from 68°F-266°F, shift solenoid diagnostic counter at zero, then with the TCC solenoid commanded "on" at a 95% duty cycle for 5 seconds, the ECM detected the TCC slip speed was 130-180 RPM for 7 seconds. The fault must be detected three times with the TCC commanded "off" each time between cycles. **Possible Causes:** • 1-2 shift solenoid valve has sediment, damage or leaking seals • 2-3 shift solenoid valve has sediment, damage or leaking seals • 3-2 shift solenoid valve has sediment, damage or leaking seals • Valve body regulator apply valve stuck or regulator is scored • Torque converter front stator shaft bushing is worn, the stator roller clutch is not holding or it has external damage/leaks • Converter clutch valve is stuck or it is installed backwards • Converter clutch valve retaining ring is not positioned properly • Converter clutch outer valve spring is cocked • Pump to case gasket is not positioned properly • Orifice cup plugs are restricted or damaged • Over-tightened, or unevenly tightened pump body to cover bolts • TSB 02-07-30-001 contains a repair procedure for this code
DTC: P1875 **2T CCM, MIL: Yes** **Years:** 2008, 2009 **Models:** Envoy, Equinox, Express, Savana, HHR, Trailblazer, Torrent **Engines:** All **Transmissions:** All	**4WD Low Switch Circuit Fault** DTC P0122, P0123, P0502, P0503, P0740, P0742, P0751, P0752, P0756, P0758, P1810, P1860 and P1870 not set, engine started, vehicle driven to a speed over 7 MPH for 5 seconds, gear range is D4, Fuel Cutoff not active, TP angle from 17-50%, engine torque from 50-400 lb ft, engine vacuum from 0-105 kPa, shift solenoid performance counters at zero, TFT sensor from 68-266°F, then during Condition 1 with the 4WD Low switch in 4WD low, transfer case not in 4WD low, TCC slip speed from -3000 to -50 RPM, the ECM detected the speed ratio was 0.8-1.2; or during Condition 2 with the 4WD Low switch not in 4WD low, transfer case in 4WD low, TCC commanded "on", TCC slip speed was 100 to 3000 RPM, the ECM detected the speed ratio was 2.5-2.9 for 10 seconds. **Possible Causes:** • 4WD low switch signal circuit is open, shorted to ground or B+ • 4WD low switch is damaged or has failed • ECM has failed

DTC	Trouble Code Title, Conditions & Possible Causes
DTC: P1887 **2T CCM, MIL: Yes** **Years:** 2008, 2009 **Models:** , Impala, **Engines:** 3.4L VIN X, 3.4L VIN E, 3.5L VIN N, 3.8L VIN 1, 3.8L VIN K **Transmissions:** A/T	**TCC Release Switch Circuit Malfunction** DTC P0716, P0717, P0741, P0742 and P1810 not set, engine started, Fuel Cutoff inactive, engine driven to a speed of 30-70 MPH, engine torque from 30-300 lb ft, Transmission gear is D4 with the TCC commanded "on", TCC pressure from 15-120 psi, TCC slip speed from -20 to +60 RPM, and the ECM detected the pressure switch was open for 6 seconds. The fault must occur twice in 1 trip to set this code. The TCC release switch is normally closed (N.C.) switch that signals the ECM that the TCC is released. This is accomplished by torque converter release fluid pressure acting on the switch contacts that open the circuit. When the circuit voltage is high, the ECM detects the TCC is no longer engaged. If the ECM determines the TCC release switch is open (indicating the TCC is not applied) and the TCC slip speed indicates the TCC is applied, then DTC P1887 sets . **Possible Causes:** • TCC release switch signal circuit is open • Turbine shaft O-ring seal leaks, oil seal rings missing/damaged. • TCC control valve damaged or No. 1 check ball is damaged • Spacer plate release exhaust blocked or case cover or spacer plate gaskets damaged • TSB 02-07-30-022A contains a repair procedure for this code

OBD II Trouble Code List (P2xxx Codes)

DTC	Trouble Code Title, Conditions & Possible Causes
DTC: P2088 **2T CCM, MIL: Yes** **Years:** 2008, 2009 **Models:** G6, HHR, Malibu **Engines:** 2.0L VIN X, 2.2L VIN D, 2.2L VIN B, 2.2L VIN F, 2.4L VIN B, 2.4L VIN V, 2.4L VIN P, 2.4L VIN 5 **Transmissions:** All	**Intake Camshaft Position (CMP) Actuator Solenoid Control Circuit Low Voltage** DTC P0606 is not set. The ignition is ON. The ignition voltage is between 10-16 volts. The ECM detects a short to ground in the CMP actuator solenoid circuits for greater than 1 second or a cumulative of 5 seconds when the solenoid is commanded OFF. **Possible Causes:** • Ignition circuit for a short to ground or an open/high resistance • Control circuit for a short to voltage or an open/high resistance • Control circuit for a short to ground • CMP actuator solenoid • Faulty ECM
DTC: P2088 **1T CCM, MIL: Yes** **Years:** 2008, 2009 **Models:** Envoy, Equinox, G6, G8, Impala, Lucerne, Malibu, Savana, Trailblazer, Torrent **Engines:** 4.2L VIN S, 4.8L VIN C, 3.5L VIN N, 3.5L VIN K, 3.9L VIN 3, 3.9L VIN M, 3.6L VIN 2, 3.9L VIN 1 **Transmissions:** All	**Intake Camshaft Position (CMP) Actuator Solenoid Control Circuit Low Voltage (Bank 1)** The ECM detects a short to ground in the CMP actuator solenoid circuits for greater than 1 seconds or a cumulative of 10 seconds, when the solenoid is commanded OFF. **Possible Causes:** • Ignition circuit for a short to ground or an open/high resistance • Control circuit for a short to voltage or an open/high resistance • Control circuit for a short to ground • CMP actuator solenoid • Faulty ECM
DTC: P2089 **2T CCM, MIL: Yes** **Years:** 2008, 2009 **Models:** G6, HHR, Malibu **Engines:** 2.0L VIN X, 2.2L VIN D, 2.2L VIN B, 2.2L VIN F, 2.4L VIN B, 2.4L VIN V, 2.4L VIN P, 2.4L VIN 5 **Transmissions:** All	**Intake Camshaft Position (CMP) Actuator Solenoid Control Circuit High Voltage** DTC P0606 is not set. The ignition is ON. The ignition voltage is between 10-16 volts The ECM detects a short to voltage in the CMP actuator solenoid circuits for greater than 1 seconds or a cumulative of 10 seconds, when the solenoid is commanded OFF. **Possible Causes:** • Ignition circuit for a short to ground or an open/high resistance • Control circuit for a short to voltage or an open/high resistance • Control circuit for a short to ground • CMP actuator solenoid • Faulty ECM
DTC: P2089 **1T CCM, MIL: Yes** **Years:** 2008, 2009 **Models:** Envoy, Equinox, G6, G8, Impala, Lucerne, Malibu, Savana, Trailblazer, Torrent **Engines:** 4.2L VIN S, 4.8L VIN C, 3.5L VIN N, 3.5L VIN K, 3.9L VIN 3, 3.9L VIN M, 3.6L VIN 2, 3.9L VIN 1 **Transmissions:** All	**Intake Camshaft Position (CMP) Actuator Solenoid Control Circuit High Voltage (Bank 1)** The ECM detects a short to voltage in the CMP actuator solenoid circuits for greater than 1 seconds or a cumulative of 10 seconds, when the solenoid is commanded OFF. **Possible Causes:** • Ignition circuit for a short to ground or an open/high resistance • Control circuit for a short to voltage or an open/high resistance • Control circuit for a short to ground • CMP actuator solenoid • Faulty ECM

DTC	Trouble Code Title, Conditions & Possible Causes
DTC: P2090 **1T CCM, MIL: Yes** **Years:** 2008, 2009 **Models:** Envoy, Equinox, G6, G8, Impala, Lucerne, Malibu, Savana, Trailblazer, Torrent **Engines:** 4.2L VIN S, 4.8L VIN C, 3.5L VIN N, 3.5L VIN K, 3.9L VIN 3, 3.9L VIN M, 3.6L VIN 2, 3.9L VIN 1 **Transmissions:** All	**Exhaust Camshaft Position (CMP) Actuator Solenoid Control Circuit Low Voltage (Bank 1)** The ECM detects a short to ground in the CMP actuator solenoid circuits for greater than 1 seconds or a cumulative of 10 seconds, when the solenoid is commanded OFF. **Possible Causes:** • Ignition circuit for a short to ground or an open/high resistance • Control circuit for a short to voltage or an open/high resistance • Control circuit for a short to ground • CMP actuator solenoid • Faulty ECM
DTC: P2091 **2T CCM, MIL: Yes** **Years:** 2008, 2009 **Models:** G6, HHR, Malibu **Engines:** 2.0L VIN X, 2.2L VIN D, 2.2L VIN B, 2.2L VIN F, 2.4L VIN B, 2.4L VIN V, 2.4L VIN P, 2.4L VIN 5 **Transmissions:** All	**Exhaust Camshaft Position (CMP) Actuator Solenoid Control Circuit High Voltage (Bank 1)** DTC P0606 is not set. The ignition is ON. The ignition voltage is between 10-16 volts. The ECM detects a short to voltage in the CMP actuator solenoid circuits for greater than 1 second or a cumulative of 5 seconds when the solenoid is commanded ON. **Possible Causes:** • Ignition circuit for a short to ground or an open/high resistance • Control circuit for a short to voltage or an open/high resistance • Control circuit for a short to ground • CMP actuator solenoid • Faulty ECM
DTC: P2091 **1T CCM, MIL: Yes** **Years:** 2008, 2009 **Models:** Envoy, Equinox, G6, G8, Impala, Lucerne, Malibu, Savana, Trailblazer, Torrent **Engines:** 4.2L VIN S, 4.8L VIN C, 3.5L VIN N, 3.5L VIN K, 3.9L VIN 3, 3.9L VIN M, 3.6L VIN 2, 3.9L VIN 1 **Transmissions:** All	**Exhaust Camshaft Position (CMP) Actuator Solenoid Control Circuit High Voltage (Bank 1)** The ECM detects a short to voltage in the CMP actuator solenoid circuits for greater than 1 seconds or a cumulative of 10 seconds, when the solenoid is commanded OFF. **Possible Causes:** • Ignition circuit for a short to ground or an open/high resistance • Control circuit for a short to voltage or an open/high resistance • Control circuit for a short to ground • CMP actuator solenoid • Faulty ECM
DTC: P2092 **1T CCM, MIL: Yes** **Years:** 2008, 2009 **Models:** Envoy, Equinox, G6, G8, Impala, Lucerne, Malibu, Savana, Trailblazer, Torrent **Engines:** 4.2L VIN S, 4.8L VIN C, 3.5L VIN N, 3.5L VIN K, 3.9L VIN 3, 3.9L VIN M, 3.6L VIN 2, 3.9L VIN 1 **Transmissions:** All	**Intake Camshaft Position (CMP) Actuator Solenoid Control Circuit Low Voltage Bank (Bank 2)** The ECM detects a short to ground in the CMP actuator solenoid circuits for greater than 1 seconds or a cumulative of 10 seconds, when the solenoid is commanded OFF. **Possible Causes:** • Ignition circuit for a short to ground or an open/high resistance • Control circuit for a short to voltage or an open/high resistance • Control circuit for a short to ground • CMP actuator solenoid • Faulty ECM
DTC: P2093 **1T CCM, MIL: Yes** **Years:** 2008, 2009 **Models:** Envoy, Equinox, G6, G8, Impala, Lucerne, Malibu, Savana, Trailblazer, Torrent **Engines:** 4.2L VIN S, 4.8L VIN C, 3.5L VIN N, 3.5L VIN K, 3.9L VIN 3, 3.9L VIN M, 3.6L VIN 2, 3.9L VIN 1 **Transmissions:** All	**Intake Camshaft Position (CMP) Actuator Solenoid Control Circuit High Voltage (Bank 2)** The ECM detects a short to ground in the CMP actuator solenoid circuits for greater than 1 seconds or a cumulative of 10 seconds, when the solenoid is commanded OFF. **Possible Causes:** • Ignition circuit for a short to ground or an open/high resistance • Control circuit for a short to voltage or an open/high resistance • Control circuit for a short to ground • CMP actuator solenoid • Faulty ECM
DTC: P2094 **1T CCM, MIL: Yes** **Years:** 2008, 2009 **Models:** Envoy, Equinox, G6, G8, Impala, Lucerne, Malibu, Savana, Trailblazer, Torrent **Engines:** 4.2L VIN S, 4.8L VIN C, 3.5L VIN N, 3.5L VIN K, 3.9L VIN 3, 3.9L VIN M, 3.6L VIN 2, 3.9L VIN 1 **Transmissions:** All	**Exhaust Camshaft Position (CMP) Actuator Solenoid Control Circuit Low Voltage (Bank 2)** The ECM detects a short to ground in the CMP actuator solenoid circuits for greater than 1 seconds or a cumulative of 10 seconds, when the solenoid is commanded OFF. **Possible Causes:** • Ignition circuit for a short to ground or an open/high resistance • Control circuit for a short to voltage or an open/high resistance • Control circuit for a short to ground • CMP actuator solenoid • Faulty ECM

DTC	Trouble Code Title, Conditions & Possible Causes
DTC: P2095 **1T CCM, MIL: Yes** **Years:** 2008, 2009 **Models:** Envoy, Equinox, G6, G8, Impala, Lucerne, Malibu, Savana, Trailblazer, Torrent **Engines:** 4.2L VIN S, 4.8L VIN C, 3.5L VIN N, 3.5L VIN K, 3.9L VIN 3, 3.9L VIN M, 3.6L VIN 2, 3.9L VIN 1 **Transmissions:** All	**Exhaust Camshaft Position (CMP) Actuator Solenoid Control Circuit High Voltage (Bank 2)** The ECM detects a short to ground in the CMP actuator solenoid circuits for greater than 1 seconds or a cumulative of 10 seconds, when the solenoid is commanded OFF. **Possible Causes:** • Ignition circuit for a short to ground or an open/high resistance • Control circuit for a short to voltage or an open/high resistance • Control circuit for a short to ground • CMP actuator solenoid • Faulty ECM
DTC: P2096 **1T CCM, MIL: Yes** **Years:** 2008, 2009 **Models:** Envoy, Equinox, G6, G8, Impala, Lucerne, Malibu, Savana, Trailblazer, Torrent **Engines:** 4.2L VIN S, 4.8L VIN C, 3.5L VIN N, 3.5L VIN K, 3.9L VIN 3, 3.9L VIN M, 3.6L VIN 2, 3.9L VIN 1 **Transmissions:** All	**Post Catalyst Fuel Trim System Low Limit (Bank 1)** The lean correction limit for a condition causing a rich air/fuel ratio has been exceeded for greater than 4 seconds or for a cumulative of 30 seconds. **Possible Causes:** • Malfunctioning fuel injectors • High fuel system pressure • Fuel that is contaminated • Fuel saturation of the evaporative emissions (EVAP) canister • Stuck open or leaking EVAP purge valve • Restricted exhaust • Incorrect PCV system operation
DTC: P2096 **2T CCM, MIL: Yes** **Years:** 2008, 2009 **Models:** G6, HHR, Malibu **Engines:** 2.0L VIN X, 2.2L VIN D, 2.2L VIN B, 2.2L VIN F, 2.4L VIN B, 2.4L VIN V, 2.4L VIN P, 2.4L VIN 5 **Transmissions:** All	**Post Catalyst Fuel Trim System Low Limit** DTCs P000A, P000B, P0010, P0011, P0013, P0014, P0016, P0017, P0030, P0031, P0032, P0036, P0037, P0038, P0068, P0101, P0102, P0103, P0116, P0117, P0118, P0119, P0121, P0122, P0123, P0130, P0131, P0132, P0133, P0137, P0138, P0139, P0140, P0141, P0171, P0172, P0201, P0202, P0203, P0204, P0221, P0222, P0223, P0261, P0262, P0264, P0265, P0267, P0268, P0270, P0271, P0300, P0301, P0302, P0303, P0304, P0313, P0335, P0336, P0340, P0341, P0365, P0366, P0420, P0443, P0458, P0459, P1101, P2088, P2089, P2090, P2091, P2100, P2101, P2176, P2270, P2271, P2297, P2300, P2301, P2303, P2304, P2306, P2307, P2309, P2310, P2A00, P2A01 are not set. The ignition is ON. The EVAP system is not purging. The post catalyst fuel trim is enabled. These DTCs run continuously when the above conditions have been met. The long term FT has reached its limit while the HO2S voltage is still trying to move the adjustment further in the same direction. **Possible Causes:** • Malfunctioning fuel injectors • Low fuel system pressure • Fuel that is contaminated • Missing, loose, or leaking exhaust components from the HO2S forward • Vacuum leaks • Ethanol concentration greater than 15 percent • Incorrect PCV system operation
DTC: P2096 **1T CCM, MIL: Yes** **Years:** 2008, 2009 **Models:** Envoy, Equinox, G6, G8, Impala, Lucerne, Malibu, Savana, Trailblazer, Torrent **Engines:** 4.2L VIN S, 4.8L VIN C, 3.5L VIN N, 3.5L VIN K, 3.9L VIN 3, 3.9L VIN M, 3.6L VIN 2, 3.9L VIN 1 **Transmissions:** All	**Post Catalyst Fuel Trim System Low Limit (Bank 1)** The lean correction limit for a condition causing a rich air/fuel ratio has been exceeded for greater than 4 seconds or for a cumulative of 30 seconds. **Possible Causes:** • Rich fuel injectors • High fuel system pressure • Fuel that is contaminated • Fuel saturation of the evaporative emissions (EVAP) canister • Stuck open or leaking EVAP purge valve • Restricted exhaust • Incorrect PCV system operation
DTC: P2097 **1T CCM, MIL: Yes** **Years:** 2008, 2009 **Models:** Envoy, Equinox, G6, G8, Impala, Lucerne, Malibu, Savana, Trailblazer, Torrent **Engines:** 4.2L VIN S, 4.8L VIN C, 3.5L VIN N, 3.5L VIN K, 3.9L VIN 3, 3.9L VIN M, 3.6L VIN 2, 3.9L VIN 1 **Transmissions:** All	**Post Catalyst Fuel Trim System High Limit (Bank 1)** The rich correction limit for a condition causing a lean air/fuel ratio has been exceeded for greater than 4 seconds or for a cumulative of 30 seconds. **Possible Causes:** • Malfunctioning fuel injectors • High fuel system pressure • Fuel that is contaminated • Fuel saturation of the evaporative emissions (EVAP) canister • Stuck open or leaking EVAP purge valve • Restricted exhaust • Incorrect PCV system operation

DTC	Trouble Code Title, Conditions & Possible Causes
DTC: P2098 **1T CCM, MIL: Yes** **Years:** 2008, 2009 **Models:** Envoy, Equinox, G6, G8, Impala, Lucerne, Malibu, Savana, Trailblazer, Torrent **Engines:** 4.2L VIN S, 4.8L VIN C, 3.5L VIN N, 3.5L VIN K, 3.9L VIN 3, 3.9L VIN M, 3.6L VIN 2, 3.9L VIN 1 **Transmissions:** All	**Post Catalyst Fuel Trim System Low Limit (Bank 2)** The lean correction limit for a condition causing a rich air/fuel ratio has been exceeded for greater than 4 seconds or for a cumulative of 30 seconds. **Possible Causes:** • Malfunctioning fuel injectors • Low fuel system pressure • Fuel that is contaminated • Missing, loose, or leaking exhaust components from the HO2S forward • Vacuum leaks • Ethanol concentration greater than 15 percent • Incorrect PCV system operation
DTC: P2098 **1T CCM, MIL: Yes** **Years:** 2008, 2009 **Models:** Envoy, Equinox, G6, G8, Impala, Lucerne, Malibu, Savana, Trailblazer, Torrent **Engines:** 4.2L VIN S, 4.8L VIN C, 3.5L VIN N, 3.5L VIN K, 3.9L VIN 3, 3.9L VIN M, 3.6L VIN 2, 3.9L VIN 1 **Transmissions:** All	**Post Catalyst Fuel Trim System Low Limit (Bank 2)** The lean correction limit for a condition causing a rich air/fuel ratio has been exceeded for greater than 4 seconds or for a cumulative of 30 seconds. **Possible Causes:** • Rich fuel injectors • High fuel system pressure • Fuel that is contaminated • Fuel saturation of the evaporative emissions (EVAP) canister • Stuck open or leaking EVAP purge valve • Restricted exhaust • Incorrect PCV system operation
DTC: P2099 **1T CCM, MIL: Yes** **Years:** 2008, 2009 **Models:** Envoy, Equinox, G6, G8, Impala, Lucerne, Malibu, Savana, Trailblazer, Torrent **Engines:** 4.2L VIN S, 4.8L VIN C, 3.5L VIN N, 3.5L VIN K, 3.9L VIN 3, 3.9L VIN M, 3.6L VIN 2, 3.9L VIN 1 **Transmissions:** All	**Post Catalyst Fuel Trim System High Limit (Bank 2)** The rich correction limit for a condition causing a lean air/fuel ratio has been exceeded for greater than 4 seconds or for a cumulative of 30 seconds. **Possible Causes:** • Exhaust system leaks • Engine vacuum leaks • Low fuel system pressure • Fuel that is contaminated • Malfunctioning fuel injectors
DTC: P2100 **1T CCM, MIL: Yes** **Years:** 2008, 2009 **Models:** Equinox, G6, G8, Torrent, G6, HHR, Malibu **Engines:** 2.0L VIN X, 2.2L VIN D, 2.2L VIN B, 2.2L VIN F, 2.4L VIN B, 2.4L VIN V, 2.4L VIN P, 2.4L VIN 5, 4.2L VIN S, 4.8L VIN C, 3.5L VIN N, 3.5L VIN K, 3.9L VIN 3, 3.9L VIN M, 3.6L VIN 2, 3.9L VIN 1 **Transmissions:** All	**Throttle Actuator Control (TAC) Motor Control Circuit** The ECM is active. The ECM detects the output circuit for the TAC motor is open, shorted to ground, or shorted to a voltage. The condition exists, then a 5 second delay for MIL ON. **Possible Causes:** • Throttle blade that is not in the rest position • Throttle valve that is binding open or closed • Throttle valve that opens or closes without spring pressure • Throttle body malfuntion • ECM has failed
DTC: P2100 **1T CCM, MIL: Yes** **Years:** 2008, 2009 **Models:** Envoy, Equinox, G6, G8, Impala, Lucerne, Malibu, Savana, Trailblazer, Torrent **Engines:** 4.2L VIN S, 4.8L VIN C, 3.5L VIN N, 3.5L VIN K, 3.9L VIN 3, 3.9L VIN M, 3.6L VIN 2, 3.9L VIN 1 **Transmissions:** All	**Throttle Actuator Control (TAC) Motor Control Circuit** The ECM is active. The ECM detects the output circuit for the TAC motor is open, shorted to ground, or shorted to a voltage. The condition exists, then a 5 second delay for MIL ON. **Possible Causes:** • Throttle blade that is not in the rest position • Throttle valve that is binding open or closed • Throttle valve that opens or closes without spring pressure • Throttle body malfuntion • ECM has failed

DTC	Trouble Code Title, Conditions & Possible Causes
DTC: P2101 **1T CCM, MIL: Yes** **Years:** 2008, 2009 **Models:** Equinox, G6, G8, Torrent, G6, HHR, Malibu **Engines:** 2.0L VIN X, 2.2L VIN D, 2.2L VIN B, 2.2L VIN F, 2.4L VIN B, 2.4L VIN V, 2.4L VIN P, 2.4L 5, 4.2L VIN S, 4.8L VIN C, 3.5L VIN N, 3.5L VIN K, 3.9L VIN 3, 3.9L VIN M, 3.6L VIN 2, 3.9L VIN 1 **Transmissions:** All	**Control Module Throttle Actuator Position Performance** The ECM detects a 4-50 percent difference between the commanded and the actual throttle plate position, dependant upon the rate of commanded throttle movement. The condition exists, then a 5 second delay for MIL ON. **Possible Causes:** • Throttle blade that is not in the rest position • Throttle valve that is binding open or closed • Throttle valve that opens or closes without spring pressure • Throttle body malfunction • ECM has failed
DTC: P2101 **1T CCM, MIL: Yes** **Years:** 2008, 2009 **Models:** Equinox, G6, G8, Torrent, G6, HHR, Malibu **Engines:** 2.0L VIN X, 2.2L VIN D, 2.2L VIN B, 2.2L VIN F, 2.4L VIN B, 2.4L VIN V, 2.4L VIN P, 2.4L 5, 4.2L VIN S, 4.8L VIN C, 3.5L VIN N, 3.5L VIN K, 3.9L VIN 3, 3.9L VIN M, 3.6L VIN 2, 3.9L VIN 1 **Transmissions:** All	**Throttle Closed Position Performance** The ECM determines that the throttle valve did not return to the rest position within 1 second. The condition exists, and then a 5 second delay for MIL ON. **Possible Causes:** • Throttle blade that is not in the rest position • Throttle valve that is binding open or closed • Throttle valve that opens or closes without spring pressure • Throttle body malfuntion • ECM has failed
DTC: P2101 **1T CCM, MIL: Yes** **Years:** 2008, 2009 **Models:** Envoy, Equinox, G6, G8, Impala, Lucerne, Malibu, Savana, Trailblazer, Torrent **Engines:** 4.2L VIN S, 4.8L VIN C, 3.5L VIN N, 3.5L VIN K, 3.9L VIN 3, 3.9L VIN M, 3.6L VIN 2, 3.9L VIN 1 **Transmissions:** All	**Control Module Throttle Actuator Position Performance** The ECM detects a 4-50 percent difference between the commanded and the actual throttle plate position, dependant upon the rate of commanded throttle movement. The condition exists, then a 5 second delay for MIL ON. **Possible Causes:** • Throttle blade that is not in the rest position • Throttle valve that is binding open or closed • Throttle valve that opens or closes without spring pressure • Throttle body malfuntion • ECM has failed
DTC: P2101 **1T CCM, MIL: Yes** **Years:** 2008, 2009 **Models:** Envoy, Equinox, Savana, Torrent **Engines:** 3.4L VIN F, 4.3L VIN X, 5.3L VIN M **Transmissions:** All	**Throttle Actuator Position Performance** The ignition is ON. The ignition voltage is more than 8 volts. The system is not in the Battery Save mode. The engine is running. DTC P0068 is not set. DTC P1516 and P2101 run continuously when the above conditions are met. The indicated throttle position does not match the predicted throttle position for more than 0.3 second. **Possible Causes:** • TAC motor control circuit for a short to voltage • TAC motor control circuit for a short to voltage • TAC motor control circuit for a short to ground • TAC motor control circuit for a short to ground • Throttle body has failed • ECM has failed
DTC: P2105 **1T CCM, MIL: Yes** **Years:** 2008, 2009 **Models:** Envoy, Equinox, G6, G8, Impala, Lucerne, Malibu, Savana, Trailblazer, Torrent **Engines:** 4.2L VIN S, 4.8L VIN C, 3.5L VIN N, 3.5L VIN K, 3.9L VIN 3, 3.9L VIN M, 3.6L VIN 2, 3.9L VIN 1 **Transmissions:** All	**Throttle Actuator Control (TAC) System - Forced Engine Shutdown** The ECM detects an incorrect voltage level at the ignition voltage supply circuits. Or the ECM detects an internal communication error. The condition exists, and then a 5 second delay for MIL ON. **This DTC will only set if the fuse is open and the circuits are not grounded. The ignition voltage circuits must be tested thoroughly for an intermittent short to ground.** **Possible Causes:** • Open ignition suppl fuse • Ignition voltage supply open or high resistance • ECM has failed

DTC	Trouble Code Title, Conditions & Possible Causes
DTC: P2105 **1T CCM, MIL: Yes** **Years:** 2008, 2009 **Models:** Envoy, Equinox, G6, G8, Impala, Lucerne, Malibu, Savana, Trailblazer, Torrent **Engines:** 4.2L VIN S, 4.8L VIN C, 3.5L VIN N, 3.5L VIN K, 3.9L VIN 3, 3.9L VIN M, 3.6L VIN 2, 3.9L VIN 1 **Transmissions:** All	**Throttle Actuator Control (TAC) System - Forced Engine Shutdown** The ECM detects an incorrect voltage level at the ignition voltage supply circuits. Or the ECM detects an internal communication error. The condition exists, and then a 5 second delay for MIL ON. **This DTC will only set if the fuse is open and the circuits are not grounded. The ignition voltage circuits must be tested thoroughly for an intermittent short to ground.** **Possible Causes:** • Open ignition suppl fuse • Ignition voltage supply open or high resistance • ECM has failed
DTC: P2108 **2T CCM, MIL: Yes** **Years:** 2008, 2009 **Models:** G6, HHR, Malibu **Engines:** 2.0L VIN X, 2.2L VIN D, 2.2L VIN B, 2.2L VIN F, 2.4L VIN B, 2.4L VIN V, 2.4L VIN P, 2.4L VIN 5 **Transmissions:** All	**Throttle Actuator Control (TAC) Module Performance** The ignition is ON. DTCs P0121, P0122, P0123, P0221, P0222, P0223, P2176 are not set. DTC P2176 run continuously when the above conditions are met. The indicated throttle position does not match the predicted throttle position for more than 0.3 second. **Possible Causes:** • Throttle blade that is not in the rest position • Throttle valve that is binding open or closed • Throttle valve that opens or closes without spring pressure • Throttle body malfunction • ECM has failed
DTC: P2108 **1T CCM, MIL: Yes** **Years:** 2008, 2009 **Models:** Express, G8, Lucerne, Trailblazer **Engines:** 4.6L VIN Y, 4.6L VIN 9, 6.0L VIN H, 6.0L VIN Y, 6.0L VIN K, 6.2L VIN W, 6.6L VIN 6 **Transmissions:** All	**Throttle Actuator Control Module Internal Data Test Failed** DTC P1518 not set, engine cranking or running, system voltage over 6.0v, and the TAC determined that its internal data test did not pass, condition met for 1 second. The TAC module contains data that is essential for proper TAC system operation. The TAC module continuously tests the integrity of this data. When the TAC module is unable to write or read data to and from random access memory, or the TAC module was unable to correctly read data from the flash memory or internal TAC processor fault is detected, it sets P2108. **Possible Causes:** • TAC module is damaged or it has failed
DTC: P2119 **2T CCM, MIL: Yes** **Years:** 2008, 2009 **Models:** G6, HHR, Malibu **Engines:** 2.0L VIN X, 2.2L VIN D, 2.2L VIN B, 2.2L VIN F, 2.4L VIN B, 2.4L VIN V, 2.4L VIN P, 2.4L VIN 5 **Transmissions:** All	**Throttle Closed Position Performance** The ignition is ON. DTCs P2101, P2119 and P2176 run continuously when the above conditions are met. The ECM determines that the throttle blade did not return to the rest position within 720 milliseconds. **Possible Causes:** • Throttle blade that is not in the rest position • Throttle valve that is binding open or closed • Throttle valve that opens or closes without spring pressure • Throttle body malfunction • ECM has failed
DTC: P2119 **1T CCM, MIL: Yes** **Years:** 2008, 2009 **Models:** Envoy, Equinox, G6, G8, Impala, Lucerne, Malibu, Savana, Trailblazer, Torrent **Engines:** 4.2L VIN S, 4.8L VIN C, 3.5L VIN N, 3.5L VIN K, 3.9L VIN 3, 3.9L VIN M, 3.6L VIN 2, 3.9L VIN 1 **Transmissions:** All	**Throttle Closed Position Performance** The ECM determines that the throttle valve did not return to the rest position within 1 second. The condition exists, and then a 5 second delay for MIL ON. **Possible Causes:** • Throttle blade that is not in the rest position • Throttle valve that is binding open or closed • Throttle valve that opens or closes without spring pressure • Throttle body malfunction • ECM has failed
DTC: P2119 **1T CCM, MIL: Yes** **Years:** 2008, 2009 **Models:** Envoy, Equinox, Savana, Torrent **Engines:** 3.4L VIN F, 4.3L VIN X, 5.3L VIN M **Transmissions:** All	**Throttle Closed Position Performance** The ignition is ON. The ignition voltage is more than 8 volts. The system is in the Battery Save mode. DTC P2119 runs continuously when the above conditions are met. The ECM determines that the throttle blade did not return to the rest position within 720 milliseconds. **Possible Causes:** • TAC motor control circuit for a short to voltage • TAC motor control circuit for a short to voltage • TAC motor control circuit for a short to ground • TAC motor control circuit for a short to ground • Throttle body has failed • ECM has failed

DTC	Trouble Code Title, Conditions & Possible Causes
DTC: P2120 **2T CCM, MIL: Yes** **Years:** 2008, 2009 **Models:** All **Engines:** All **Transmissions:** All	**Accelerator Pedal Position Sensor 1 Signal Performance** DTC P0601, P0602, P0606, P1518 and P2108 not set; engine cranking or running, system voltage more than 5.23v, and the ECM detected the APP Sensor 1 signal circuit voltage was less than 0.24v or more than 4.49v, or that the APP VREF (5v) circuit was less than 4.54v or more than 5.21v. The ECM provides the APP sensor with a 5v reference circuit and a low reference circuit. The APP sensor provides the control module a signal voltage proportional to pedal movement. The APP sensor 1 signal voltage is low at rest and increases as the pedal is depressed. When the control module detects that the APP sensor 1 signal or APP sensor 5-volt reference voltage is outside the predetermined range, it sets DTC P2120. **Possible Causes:** • APP sensor connector is damaged, open or shorted • APP1 sensor signal circuit is open or shorted to ground • APP1 sensor signal circuit is shorted to APP sensor 2 circuit • APP1 sensor signal circuit is open or shorted to VREF (5v) • APP sensor is damaged or it has failed • TAC module is damaged or it has failed
DTC: P2122 **2T CCM, MIL: Yes** **Years:** 2008, 2009 **Models:** All **Engines:** All **Transmissions:** All	**Accelerator Pedal Position (APP) Sensor 1 Circuit Low Voltage** The ignition is ON or the engine is operating. The ignition voltage is greater than 7 volts. The DTCs run continuously once the above conditions are met for greater than 200 ms. The APP sensor 1 voltage is less than 0.74 volt, then a 5 second delay for MIL ON. **Possible Causes:** • Low reference circuit of the APP sensor for a short to voltage, or an open/high resistance. • 5-volt reference circuit for a short to ground or open/high resistance. • Faulty APP Sensor • ECM has failed
DTC: P2123 **2T CCM, MIL: Yes** **Years:** 2008, 2009 **Models:** All **Engines:** All **Transmissions:** All	**Accelerator Pedal Position (APP) Sensor 1 Circuit High Voltage** The ignition is ON or the engine is operating. The ignition voltage is greater than 7 volts. The DTCs run continuously once the above conditions are met for greater than 200 ms. The APP sensor 1 voltage is greater than 4.82 volts, then a 5 second delay for MIL ON. **Possible Causes:** • Low reference circuit of the APP sensor for a short to voltage, or an open/high resistance. • 5-volt reference circuit for a short to ground or open/high resistance. • Faulty APP Sensor • ECM has failed
DTC: P2125 **2T CCM, MIL: Yes** **Years:** 2008, 2009 **Models:** All **Engines:** All **Transmissions:** All	**Accelerator Pedal Position (APP) Sensor 2 Circuit Low Voltage** The ignition is ON or the engine is operating. The ignition voltage is greater than 7 volts. The DTCs run continuously once the above conditions are met for greater than 200 ms. The APP sensor 2 voltage is less than 0.63 volt, then a 5 second delay for MIL ON. **Possible Causes:** • Low reference circuit of the APP sensor for a short to voltage, or an open/high resistance. • 5-volt reference circuit for a short to ground or open/high resistance. • Faulty APP Sensor • ECM has failed
DTC: P2127 **2T CCM, MIL: Yes** **Years:** 2008, 2009 **Models:** All **Engines:** All **Transmissions:** All	**Accelerator Pedal Position (APP) Sensor 2 Circuit Low Voltage** The ignition is ON or the engine is operating. The ignition voltage is greater than 7 volts. The DTCs run continuously once the above conditions are met for greater than 200 ms. The APP sensor 2 voltage is less than 0.63 volt, then a 5 second delay for MIL ON. **Possible Causes:** • Low reference circuit of the APP sensor for a short to voltage, or an open/high resistance. • 5-volt reference circuit for a short to ground or open/high resistance. • Faulty APP Sensor • ECM has failed
DTC: P2128 **2T CCM, MIL: Yes** **Years:** 2008, 2009 **Models:** All **Engines:** All **Transmissions:** All	**Accelerator Pedal Position (APP) Sensor 2 Circuit High Voltage** The ignition is ON or the engine is operating. The ignition voltage is greater than 7 volts. The DTCs run continuously once the above conditions are met for greater than 200 ms. The APP sensor 2 voltage is greater than 4.82 volts, then a 5 second delay for MIL ON. **Possible Causes:** • Low reference circuit of the APP sensor for a short to voltage, or an open/high resistance. • 5-volt reference circuit for a short to ground or open/high resistance. • Faulty APP Sensor • ECM has failed

DTC	Trouble Code Title, Conditions & Possible Causes
DTC: P2129 **1T CCM, MIL: Yes** **Years:** 2008, 2009 **Models:** Equinox, G6, G8, Torrent G6, HHR, Malibu **Engines:** 2.0L VIN X, 2.2L VIN D, 2.2L VIN B, 2.2L VIN F, 2.4L VIN B, 2.4L VIN V, 2.4L VIN P, 2.4L VIN 5, 4.2L VIN S, 4.8L VIN C, 3.5L VIN N, 3.5L VIN K, 3.9L VIN 3, 3.9L VIN M, 3.6L VIN 2, 3.9L VIN 1 **Transmissions:** All	**Barometric Pressure (BARO) Sensor Circuit High Voltage** The ignition is ON, or the engine is running. The ignition voltage is greater than 9 volts. The ECM detects that the BARO sensor voltage is greater than 4.87 volts for 1 second or for a cumulative of 10 seconds. **Possible Causes:** • Moisture in the vent inlet • Debris in the vent inlet
DTC: P2135 **1T CCM, MIL: Yes** **Years:** 2008, 2009 **Models:** Express, G8, Lucerne, Trailblazer **Engines:** 4.6L VIN Y, 4.6L VIN 9, 6.0L VIN H, 6.0L VIN Y, 6.0L VIN K, 6.2L VIN W, 6.6L VIN 6 **Transmissions:** All	**Throttle Position (TP) Sensor 1-2 Correlation** The system voltage is more than 5.23 volts. The ignition is in the Unlock/Accessory or Run position. DTC P0120, P0220, P0641, P0651 are not set. DTC P2135 runs continuously when the above conditions are met. The difference between the TP sensor 1 and TP sensor 2 exceeds a predetermined value for more than 2 seconds. **Possible Causes:** • TP sensor low reference circuit for an open/high resistance • TP sensor 5-volt reference circuit for a short to ground or an open/high resistance • TP sensor 5-volt reference circuit for a short to voltage • TP sensor signal circuit terminal F for a short to ground • TP sensor 1 signal circuit for a short to ground or an open/high resistance • TP sensor 2 signal circuit for a short to voltage • TP sensor 2 signal circuit for an open/high resistance. • Throttle body has failed • ECM has failed
DTC: P2135 **1T CCM, MIL: Yes** **Years:** 2008, 2009 **Models:** Equinox, G6, G8, Torrent, G6, HHR, Malibu **Engines:** 2.0L VIN X, 2.2L VIN D, 2.2L VIN B, 2.2L VIN F, 2.4L VIN B, 2.4L VIN V, 2.4L VIN P, 2.4L VIN 5, 4.2L VIN S, 4.8L VIN C, 3.5L VIN N, 3.5L VIN K, 3.9L VIN 3, 3.9L VIN M, 3.6L VIN 2, 3.9L VIN 1 **Transmissions:** All	**Throttle Position Sensor 1-2 Correlation Error** DTC P1518 and P2108 not set, key in crank or run mode, system voltage more than 5.23v, and the ECM detected the TP Sensor 2 signal disagreed with the TP Sensor 1 signal by more than 7.5% for one second. The TP sensors are used to determine the throttle plate angle for various engine management systems. The TP sensor signals are both low at closed throttle and increase as the throttle opens. When the ECM detects that TP sensor 1 and TP sensor 2 signals disagree or signal voltages are too far apart, this code is set. **Possible Causes:** • TP1 sensor signal circuit shorted to TP sensor signal 2 circuit • TP1 sensor signal circuit is shorted to the low reference circuit • TP2 sensor signal circuit is shorted to the low reference circuit • Throttle body assembly is damaged or it has failed
DTC: P2138 **1T CCM, MIL: Yes** **Years:** 2008, 2009 **Models:** Equinox, G6, G8, Torrent, G6, HHR, Malibu **Engines:** 2.0L VIN X, 2.2L VIN D, 2.2L VIN B, 2.2L VIN F, 2.4L VIN B, 2.4L VIN V, 2.4L VIN P, 2.4L VIN 5, 4.2L VIN S, 4.8L VIN C, 3.5L VIN N, 3.5L VIN K, 3.9L VIN 3, 3.9L VIN M, 3.6L VIN 2, 3.9L VIN 1 **Transmissions:** All	**Accelerator Pedal Position (APP) Sensor 1-2 Correlation** The ignition is ON or the engine is operating. The ignition voltage is greater than 7 volts. The DTCs run continuously once the above conditions are met for greater than 200 ms. The ECM detects that the voltage difference between APP sensor 1 and the calculated idle range is greater than 0.25 volts, with a released pedal. The ECM detects that the voltage difference between APP sensor 2 and the calculated idle range is greater than 0.31 volts, with a released pedal. The ECM detects that the voltage difference between APP sensor 1 and 2 is greater than 0.31 volts with a partially pressed pedal. The ECM detects that the voltage difference between APP sensor 1 and 2 is greater than 1.70 volts with a fully pressed pedal. Any of the above conditions exist, then a 5 second delay for MIL ON. **Possible Causes:** • Low reference circuit of the APP sensor for a short to voltage, or an open/high resistance. • 5-volt reference circuit for a short to ground or open/high resistance. • Faulty APP Sensor • ECM has failed
DTC: P2146 **1T CCM, MIL: Yes** **Years:** 2008, 2009 **Models:** Envoy, Equinox, G6, G8, Impala, Lucerne, Malibu, Savana, Trailblazer, Torrent **Engines:** 4.2L VIN S, 4.8L VIN C, 3.5L VIN N, 3.5L VIN K, 3.9L VIN 3, 3.9L VIN M, 3.6L VIN 2, 3.9L VIN 1 **Transmissions:** All	**Injector Positive Voltage Control Circuit (Group 1)** The ECM detects the injector high voltage control circuit is shorted to ground or shorted to a voltage for greater than 4 seconds or for a cumulative of 30 seconds. **Possible Causes:** • High voltage control circuit shorted to voltage • High voltage control circuit short to ground or an open/high resistance • Low voltage control circuit shorted to voltage • Low voltage control circuit short to ground or an open/high resistance • Faulty fuel injector • ECM has failed.

DTC	Trouble Code Title, Conditions & Possible Causes
DTC: P2146 **1T CCM, MIL: Yes** **Years:** 2008, 2009 **Models:** Express, G8, Lucerne, Trailblazer **Engines:** 4.6L VIN Y, 4.6L VIN 9, 6.0L VIN H, 6.0L VIN Y, 6.0L VIN K, 6.2L VIN W, 6.6L VIN 6 **Transmissions:** All	**Injector Positive Voltage Control Circuit (Group 1)** The ECM detects the injector high voltage control circuit is shorted to ground or shorted to a voltage for greater than 4 seconds or for a cumulative of 30 seconds. **Possible Causes:** • High voltage control circuit shorted to voltage • High voltage control circuit short to ground or an open/high resistance • Low voltage control circuit shorted to voltage • Low voltage control circuit short to ground or an open/high resistance • Faulty fuel injector • ECM has failed.
DTC: P2149 **1T CCM, MIL: Yes** **Years:** 2008, 2009 **Models:** Envoy, Equinox, G6, G8, Impala, Lucerne, Malibu, Savana, Trailblazer, Torrent **Engines:** 4.2L VIN S, 4.8L VIN C, 3.5L VIN N, 3.5L VIN K, 3.9L VIN 3, 3.9L VIN M, 3.6L VIN 2, 3.9L VIN 1 **Transmissions:** All	**Injector Positive Voltage Control Circuit (Group 2)** The ECM detects the injector high voltage control circuit is shorted to ground or shorted to a voltage for greater than 4 seconds or for a cumulative of 30 seconds. **Possible Causes:** • High voltage control circuit shorted to voltage • High voltage control circuit short to ground or an open/high resistance • Low voltage control circuit shorted to voltage • Low voltage control circuit short to ground or an open/high resistance • Faulty fuel injector • ECM has failed.
DTC: P2149 **1T CCM, MIL: Yes** **Years:** 2008, 2009 **Models:** Express, G8, Lucerne, Trailblazer **Engines:** 4.6L VIN Y, 4.6L VIN 9, 6.0L VIN H, 6.0L VIN Y, 6.0L VIN K, 6.2L VIN W, 6.6L VIN 6 **Transmissions:** All	**Injector Positive Voltage Control Circuit (Group 2)** The ECM detects the injector high voltage control circuit is shorted to ground or shorted to a voltage for greater than 4 seconds or for a cumulative of 30 seconds. **Possible Causes:** • High voltage control circuit shorted to voltage • High voltage control circuit short to ground or an open/high resistance • Low voltage control circuit shorted to voltage • Low voltage control circuit short to ground or an open/high resistance • Faulty fuel injector • ECM has failed.
DTC: P2152 **1T CCM, MIL: Yes** **Years:** 2008, 2009 **Models:** Envoy, Equinox, G6, G8, Impala, Lucerne, Malibu, Savana, Trailblazer, Torrent **Engines:** 4.2L VIN S, 4.8L VIN C, 3.5L VIN N, 3.5L VIN K, 3.9L VIN 3, 3.9L VIN M, 3.6L VIN 2, 3.9L VIN 1 **Transmissions:** All	**Injector Positive Voltage Control Circuit (Group 3)** The ECM detects the injector high voltage control circuit is shorted to ground or shorted to a voltage for greater than 4 seconds or for a cumulative of 30 seconds. **Possible Causes:** • High voltage control circuit shorted to voltage • High voltage control circuit short to ground or an open/high resistance • Low voltage control circuit shorted to voltage • Low voltage control circuit short to ground or an open/high resistance • Faulty fuel injector • ECM has failed.
DTC: P2152 **1T CCM, MIL: Yes** **Years:** 2008, 2009 **Models:** Express, G8, Lucerne, Trailblazer **Engines:** 4.6L VIN Y, 4.6L VIN 9, 6.0L VIN H, 6.0L VIN Y, 6.0L VIN K, 6.2L VIN W, 6.6L VIN 6 **Transmissions:** All	**Injector Positive Voltage Control Circuit (Group 3)** The ECM detects the injector high voltage control circuit is shorted to ground or shorted to a voltage for greater than 4 seconds or for a cumulative of 30 seconds. **Possible Causes:** • High voltage control circuit shorted to voltage • High voltage control circuit short to ground or an open/high resistance • Low voltage control circuit shorted to voltage • Low voltage control circuit short to ground or an open/high resistance • Faulty fuel injector • ECM has failed.
DTC: P2155 **1T CCM, MIL: Yes** **Years:** 2008, 2009 **Models:** Envoy, Equinox, G6, G8, Impala, Lucerne, Malibu, Savana, Trailblazer, Torrent **Engines:** 4.2L VIN S, 4.8L VIN C, 3.5L VIN N, 3.5L VIN K, 3.9L VIN 3, 3.9L VIN M, 3.6L VIN 2, 3.9L VIN 1 **Transmissions:** All	**Injector Positive Voltage Control Circuit (Group 4)** The ECM detects the injector high voltage control circuit is shorted to ground or shorted to a voltage for greater than 4 seconds or for a cumulative of 30 seconds. **Possible Causes:** • High voltage control circuit shorted to voltage • High voltage control circuit short to ground or an open/high resistance • Low voltage control circuit shorted to voltage • Low voltage control circuit short to ground or an open/high resistance • Faulty fuel injector • ECM has failed.

DTC	Trouble Code Title, Conditions & Possible Causes
DTC: P2155 **1T CCM, MIL: Yes** **Years:** 2008, 2009 **Models:** Express, G8, Lucerne, Trailblazer **Engines:** 4.6L VIN Y, 4.6L VIN 9, 6.0L VIN H, 6.0L VIN Y, 6.0L VIN K, 6.2L VIN W, 6.6L VIN 6 **Transmissions:** All	**Injector Positive Voltage Control Circuit (Group 4)** The ECM detects the injector high voltage control circuit is shorted to ground or shorted to a voltage for greater than 4 seconds or for a cumulative of 30 seconds. **Possible Causes:** • High voltage control circuit shorted to voltage • High voltage control circuit short to ground or an open/high resistance • Low voltage control circuit shorted to voltage • Low voltage control circuit short to ground or an open/high resistance • Faulty fuel injector • ECM has failed.
DTC: P216A **1T CCM, MIL: Yes** **Years:** 2008, 2009 **Models:** Envoy, Equinox, G6, G8, Impala, Lucerne, Malibu, Savana, Trailblazer, Torrent **Engines:** 4.2L VIN S, 4.8L VIN C, 3.5L VIN N, 3.5L VIN K, 3.9L VIN 3, 3.9L VIN M, 3.6L VIN 2, 3.9L VIN 1 **Transmissions:** All	**Injector Positive Voltage Control Circuit (Group 5)** The ECM detects the injector high voltage control circuit is shorted to ground or shorted to a voltage for greater than 4 seconds or for a cumulative of 30 seconds. **Possible Causes:** • High voltage control circuit shorted to voltage • High voltage control circuit short to ground or an open/high resistance • Low voltage control circuit shorted to voltage • Low voltage control circuit short to ground or an open/high resistance • Faulty fuel injector • ECM has failed.
DTC: P216A **1T CCM, MIL: Yes** **Years:** 2008, 2009 **Models:** Express, G8, Lucerne, Trailblazer **Engines:** 4.6L VIN Y, 4.6L VIN 9, 6.0L VIN H, 6.0L VIN Y, 6.0L VIN K, 6.2L VIN W, 6.6L VIN 6 **Transmissions:** All	**Injector Positive Voltage Control Circuit (Group 5)** The ECM detects the injector high voltage control circuit is shorted to ground or shorted to a voltage for greater than 4 seconds or for a cumulative of 30 seconds. **Possible Causes:** • High voltage control circuit shorted to voltage • High voltage control circuit short to ground or an open/high resistance • Low voltage control circuit shorted to voltage • Low voltage control circuit short to ground or an open/high resistance • Faulty fuel injector • ECM has failed.
DTC: P216D **1T CCM, MIL: Yes** **Years:** 2008, 2009 **Models:** Envoy, Equinox, G6, G8, Impala, Lucerne, Malibu, Savana, Trailblazer, Torrent **Engines:** 4.2L VIN S, 4.8L VIN C, 3.5L VIN N, 3.5L VIN K, 3.9L VIN 3, 3.9L VIN M, 3.6L VIN 2, 3.9L VIN 1 **Transmissions:** All	**Injector Positive Voltage Control Circuit (Group 6)** The ECM detects the injector high voltage control circuit is shorted to ground or shorted to a voltage for greater than 4 seconds or for a cumulative of 30 seconds. **Possible Causes:** • High voltage control circuit shorted to voltage • High voltage control circuit short to ground or an open/high resistance • Low voltage control circuit shorted to voltage • Low voltage control circuit short to ground or an open/high resistance • Faulty fuel injector • ECM has failed.
DTC: P216D **1T CCM, MIL: Yes** **Years:** 2008, 2009 **Models:** Express, G8, Lucerne, Trailblazer **Engines:** 4.6L VIN Y, 4.6L VIN 9, 6.0L VIN H, 6.0L VIN Y, 6.0L VIN K, 6.2L VIN W, 6.6L VIN 6 **Transmissions:** All	**Injector Positive Voltage Control Circuit (Group 6)** The ECM detects the injector high voltage control circuit is shorted to ground or shorted to a voltage for greater than 4 seconds or for a cumulative of 30 seconds. **Possible Causes:** • High voltage control circuit shorted to voltage • High voltage control circuit short to ground or an open/high resistance • Low voltage control circuit shorted to voltage • Low voltage control circuit short to ground or an open/high resistance • Faulty fuel injector • ECM has failed.

DTC	Trouble Code Title, Conditions & Possible Causes
DTC: P2176 **1T CCM, MIL: Yes** **Years:** 2008, 2009 **Models:** Equinox, G6, G8, Torrent, G6, HHR, Malibu **Engines:** 2.0L VIN X, 2.2L VIN D, 2.2L VIN B, 2.2L VIN F, 2.4L VIN B, 2.4L VIN V, 2.4L VIN P, 2.4L VIN 5, 4.2L VIN S, 4.8L VIN C, 3.5L VIN N, 3.5L VIN K, 3.9L VIN 3, 3.9L VIN M, 3.6L VIN 2, 3.9L VIN 1 **Transmissions:** All	**Minimum Throttle Position Not Learned** The ECM detects that the TP sensor 1 voltage is not between 4.12-4.55 volts after the throttle learn procedure, with the throttle at rest. The ECM detects that the TP sensor 2 voltage is not between 0.34-0.99 volts after the throttle learn procedure, with the throttle at rest. The minimum throttle position is not learned after an ECM replacement. If either condition exists, then a 5 second delay for MIL ON. **Possible Causes:** • Perform the throttle learn procedure • Throttle body has failed.
DTC: P2176 **1T CCM, MIL: Yes** **Years:** 2008, 2009 **Models:** Envoy, Equinox, G6, G8, Impala, Lucerne, Malibu, Savana, Trailblazer, Torrent **Engines:** 4.2L VIN S, 4.8L VIN C, 3.5L VIN N, 3.5L VIN K, 3.9L VIN 3, 3.9L VIN M, 3.6L VIN 2, 3.9L VIN 1 **Transmissions:** All	**Minimum Throttle Position Not Learned** The ECM detects that the TP sensor 1 voltage is not between 4.12-4.55 volts after the throttle learn procedure, with the throttle at rest. The ECM detects that the TP sensor 2 voltage is not between 0.34-0.99 volts after the throttle learn procedure, with the throttle at rest. The minimum throttle position is not learned after an ECM replacement. If either condition exists, then a 5 second delay for MIL ON. **Possible Causes:** • Perform the throttle learn procedure • Throttle body has failed.
DTC: P2176 **1T CCM, MIL: Yes** **Years:** 2008, 2009 **Models:** Envoy, Equinox, Savana, Torrent **Engines:** 3.4L VIN F, 4.3L VIN X, 5.3L VIN M **Transmissions:** All	**Minimum Throttle Position Not Learned** The ignition is ON. The ignition voltage is more than 8 volts. The system is not in the Battery Save mode. The engine is running. DTCs P0068, P0120, P0122, P0123, P0220, P0222, P0223 are not set. DTC P2176 runs continuously when the above conditions are met. The difference between the predicted and the actual throttle position is more than a calibrated amount for more than 1.5 seconds. **Possible Causes:** • TAC motor control circuit for a short to voltage • TAC motor control circuit for a short to voltage • TAC motor control circuit for a short to ground • TAC motor control circuit for a short to ground • Throttle body has failed • ECM has failed
DTC: P2177 **1T CCM, MIL: Yes** **Years:** 2008, 2009 **Models:** Envoy, Equinox, G6, G8, Impala, Lucerne, Malibu, Savana, Trailblazer, Torrent **Engines:** 4.2L VIN S, 4.8L VIN C, 3.5L VIN N, 3.5L VIN K, 3.9L VIN 3, 3.9L VIN M, 3.6L VIN 2, 3.9L VIN 1 **Transmissions:** All	**Fuel Trim System Lean at Cruise or Accel (Bank1)** The Long Term Fuel Trim Cruise/Accel is greater than 32 percent for 4 seconds or for a cumulative time of 30 seconds. **Possible Causes:** • Leaking crankcase ventilation system • Fuel system is operating lean • Vacuum leaks that only affect one bank of the engine • Lean injectors • Fuel contamination • Engine mechanical conditions • High engine oil level condition • engine control module grounds for being clean, tight, and in the correct locations • Mass Air Flow (MAF) sensor signal that is skewed • Air intake system after the MAF sensor for vacuum leaks • Missing, restricted, or leaking exhaust components • Heated oxygen sensor (HO2S)
DTC: P2178 **1T CCM, MIL: Yes** **Years:** 2008, 2009 **Models:** Envoy, Equinox, G6, G8, Impala, Lucerne, Malibu, Savana, Trailblazer, Torrent **Engines:** 4.2L VIN S, 4.8L VIN C, 3.5L VIN N, 3.5L VIN K, 3.9L VIN 3, 3.9L VIN M, 3.6L VIN 2, 3.9L VIN 1 **Transmissions:** All	**Fuel Trim System Rich at Cruise or Accel (Bank 1)** The Long Term Fuel Trim Cruise/Accel is less than −22 percent for 4 seconds or for a cumulative of 30 seconds. **Possible Causes:** • Mass Air Flow (MAF) sensor signal that is skewed • Collapsed air intake duct • Restricted air filter element • Excessive fuel in the crankcase • Fuel contamination • Engine control module grounds for being clean, tight, and in the correct locations • Rich injectors • Engine mechanical conditions • Restricted exhaust system

DTC	Trouble Code Title, Conditions & Possible Causes
DTC: P2179 **1T CCM, MIL: Yes** **Years:** 2008, 2009 **Models:** Envoy, Equinox, G6, G8, Impala, Lucerne, Malibu, Savana, Trailblazer, Torrent **Engines:** 4.2L VIN S, 4.8L VIN C, 3.5L VIN N, 3.5L VIN K, 3.9L VIN 3, 3.9L VIN M, 3.6L VIN 2, 3.9L VIN 1 **Transmissions:** All	**Fuel Trim System Lean at Cruise or Accel (Bank 2)** The Long Term Fuel Trim Cruise/Accel is greater than 32 percent for 4 seconds or for a cumulative time of 30 seconds. **Possible Causes:** • Leaking crankcase ventilation system • Fuel system is operating lean • Vacuum leaks that only affect one bank of the engine • Lean injectors • Fuel contamination • Engine mechanical conditions • High engine oil level condition • engine control module grounds for being clean, tight, and in the correct locations • Mass Air Flow (MAF) sensor signal that is skewed • Air intake system after the MAF sensor for vacuum leaks • Missing, restricted, or leaking exhaust components • Heated oxygen sensor (HO2S)
DTC: P2180 **1T CCM, MIL: Yes** **Years:** 2008, 2009 **Models:** Envoy, Equinox, G6, G8, Impala, Lucerne, Malibu, Savana, Trailblazer, Torrent **Engines:** 4.2L VIN S, 4.8L VIN C, 3.5L VIN N, 3.5L VIN K, 3.9L VIN 3, 3.9L VIN M, 3.6L VIN 2, 3.9L VIN 1 **Transmissions:** All	**Fuel Trim System Rich at Cruise or Accel Bank 2** The Long Term Fuel Trim Cruise/Accel is less than −22 percent for 4 seconds or for a cumulative of 30 seconds. **Possible Causes:** • Mass Air Flow (MAF) sensor signal that is skewed • Collapsed air intake duct • Restricted air filter element • Excessive fuel in the crankcase • Fuel contamination • Engine control module grounds for being clean, tight, and in the correct locations • Rich injectors • Engine mechanical conditions • Restricted exhaust system
DTC: P2187 **1T CCM, MIL: Yes** **Years:** 2008, 2009 **Models:** Envoy, Equinox, G6, G8, Impala, Lucerne, Malibu, Savana, Trailblazer, Torrent **Engines:** 4.2L VIN S, 4.8L VIN C, 3.5L VIN N, 3.5L VIN K, 3.9L VIN 3, 3.9L VIN M, 3.6L VIN 2, 3.9L VIN 1 **Transmissions:** All	**Fuel Trim System Lean at Idle (Bank 1)** The Long Term Fuel Trim Idle/Decel is greater than 6 percent for 4 seconds or for a cumulative of 30 seconds. **Possible Causes:** • Leaking crankcase ventilation system • Fuel system is operating lean • Vacuum leaks that only affect one bank of the engine • Lean injectors • Fuel contamination • Engine mechanical conditions • High engine oil level condition • engine control module grounds for being clean, tight, and in the correct locations • Mass Air Flow (MAF) sensor signal that is skewed • Air intake system after the MAF sensor for vacuum leaks • Missing, restricted, or leaking exhaust components • Heated oxygen sensor (HO2S)
DTC: P2188 **1T CCM, MIL: Yes** **Years:** 2008, 2009 **Models:** Envoy, Equinox, G6, G8, Impala, Lucerne, Malibu, Savana, Trailblazer, Torrent **Engines:** 4.2L VIN S, 4.8L VIN C, 3.5L VIN N, 3.5L VIN K, 3.9L VIN 3, 3.9L VIN M, 3.6L VIN 2, 3.9L VIN 1 **Transmissions:** All	**Fuel Trim System Rich at Idle Bank 1** The Long Term Fuel Trim Idle/Decel is less than −6 percent for 4 seconds or for a cumulative of 30 seconds. **Possible Causes:** • Mass Air Flow (MAF) sensor signal that is skewed • Collapsed air intake duct • Restricted air filter element • Excessive fuel in the crankcase • Fuel contamination • Engine control module grounds for being clean, tight, and in the correct locations • Rich injectors • Engine mechanical conditions • Restricted exhaust system

DTC	Trouble Code Title, Conditions & Possible Causes
DTC: P2189 **1T CCM, MIL: Yes** **Years:** 2008, 2009 **Models:** Envoy, Equinox, G6, G8, Impala, Lucerne, Malibu, Savana, Trailblazer, Torrent **Engines:** 3.6L VIN 7 **Transmissions:** All	**Fuel Trim System Lean at Idle (Bank 2)** **Possible Causes:** • Leaking crankcase ventilation system • Fuel system is operating lean • Vacuum leaks that only affect one bank of the engine • Lean injectors • Fuel contamination • Engine mechanical conditions • High engine oil level condition • Engine control module grounds for being clean, tight, and in the correct locations • Mass Air Flow (MAF) sensor signal that is skewed • Air intake system after the MAF sensor for vacuum leaks • Missing, restricted, or leaking exhaust components • Heated oxygen sensor (HO2S)
DTC: P2190 **1T CCM, MIL: Yes** **Years:** 2008, 2009 **Models:** Envoy, Equinox, G6, G8, Impala, Lucerne, Malibu, Savana, Trailblazer, Torrent **Engines:** 3.6L VIN 7 **Transmissions:** All	**Fuel Trim System Rich at Idle Bank 2** The Long Term Fuel Trim Idle/Decel is less than −6 percent for 4 seconds or for a cumulative of 30 seconds. **Possible Causes:** • Mass Air Flow (MAF) sensor signal that is skewed • Collapsed air intake duct • Restricted air filter element • Excessive fuel in the crankcase • Fuel contamination • Engine control module grounds for being clean, tight, and in the correct locations • Rich injectors • Engine mechanical conditions • Restricted exhaust system
DTC: P2227 **2T CCM, MIL: Yes** **Years:** 2008, 2009 **Models:**, Equinox, G6, G8, Torrent **Engines:** All **Transmissions:** All	**Barometric Pressure (BARO) Sensor Performance** DTCs P0068, P0101, P0102, P0103, P0107, P0108, P0112, P0113, P0116, P0117, P0118, P0120, P0128, P0220, P0502, P0503, P2135, P2228, P2229 are not set. The engine run time is greater than 10 seconds. The ECM detects that 80 out of 100 consecutive BARO sensor samples vary greater than 10 kPa between each sample, for 10 seconds. **Possible Causes:** • Vacuum leaks • BARO sensor low reference circuit for an open/high resistance • BARO sensor 5V reference circuit for an open/high resistance or a short to ground • BARO sensor 5V reference circuit for a short to voltage • BARO sensor signal circuit terminal 3 for a short to voltage • BARO sensor signal circuit for an open/high resistance or a short to ground • BARO sensor has failed
DTC: P2228 **2T CCM, MIL: Yes** **Years:** 2008, 2009 **Models:**, Equinox, G6, G8, Torrent **Engines:** All **Transmissions:** All	**Barometric Pressure (BARO) Sensor Circuit Low Voltage** DTCs P0120, P0121, P0122, P0123, P0220, P0222 or P0223 are not set. The ignition is ON. This DTC runs continuously when the above conditions are met. The BARO is less than 50 kPa for less than 1 minute. **Possible Causes:** • Vacuum leaks • BARO sensor low reference circuit for an open/high resistance • BARO sensor 5V reference circuit for an open/high resistance or a short to ground • BARO sensor 5V reference circuit for a short to voltage • BARO sensor signal circuit terminal 3 for a short to voltage • BARO sensor signal circuit for an open/high resistance or a short to ground • BARO sensor has failed
DTC: P2229 **2T CCM, MIL: Yes** **Years:** 2008, 2009 **Models:**, Equinox, G6, G8, Torrent **Engines:** All **Transmissions:** All	**Barometric Pressure (BARO) Sensor Circuit High Voltage** DTCs P0120, P0121, P0122, P0123, P0220, P0222, or P0223 are not set. The engine is running. The engine run time is greater than 4 minutes. The startup coolant temperature is between −30°C and +30°C (−22°F and +86°F). The throttle position is less than 1 percent. The engine speed is greater than 1,200 RPM. This DTC runs continuously when the above conditions are met. **Possible Causes:** • Vacuum leaks • BARO sensor low reference circuit for an open/high resistance • BARO sensor 5V reference circuit for an open/high resistance or a short to ground • BARO sensor 5V reference circuit for a short to voltage • BARO sensor signal circuit terminal 3 for a short to voltage • BARO sensor signal circuit for an open/high resistance or a short to ground • BARO sensor has failed

DTC	Trouble Code Title, Conditions & Possible Causes
DTC: P2232 **1T CCM, MIL: Yes** **Years:** 2008, 2009 **Models:** Envoy, Equinox, G6, G8, Impala, Lucerne, Malibu, Savana, Trailblazer, Torrent **Engines:** 4.2L VIN S, 4.8L VIN C, 3.5L VIN N, 3.5L VIN K, 3.9L VIN 3, 3.9L VIN M, 3.6L VIN 2, 3.9L VIN 1 **Transmissions:** All	**HO2S Signal Circuit Shorted to Heater Circuit (Bank 1 Sensor 2)** The ECM detects that the HO2S signal voltage increases greater than 2 volts within 40 ms, in 4 out of 6 HO2S heater switch OFF samples. The condition exists for greater than 1 second, or for a cumulative of 10 seconds. **Possible Causes:** • Signal circuit terminal B for a short to the heater control circuit terminal E • ECM has failed • Faulty HO2S
DTC: P2235 **1T CCM, MIL: Yes** **Years:** 2008, 2009 **Models:** Envoy, Equinox, G6, G8, Impala, Lucerne, Malibu, Savana, Trailblazer, Torrent **Engines:** 4.2L VIN S, 4.8L VIN C, 3.5L VIN N, 3.5L VIN K, 3.9L VIN 3, 3.9L VIN M, 3.6L VIN 2, 3.9L VIN 1 **Transmissions:** All	**HO2S Signal Circuit Shorted to Heater Circuit (Bank 2 Sensor 2)** The ECM detects that the HO2S signal voltage increases greater than 2 volts within 40 ms, in 4 out of 6 HO2S heater switch OFF samples. The condition exists for greater than 1 second, or for a cumulative of 10 seconds. **Possible Causes:** • Signal circuit terminal B for a short to the heater control circuit terminal E • ECM has failed • Faulty HO2S
DTC: P2270 **1T CCM, MIL: Yes** **Years:** 2008, 2009 **Models:** Express, G8, Lucerne, Trailblazer **Engines:** 4.6L VIN Y, 4.6L VIN 9, 6.0L VIN H, 6.0L VIN Y, 6.0L VIN K, 6.2L VIN W, 6.6L VIN 6 **Transmissions:** All	**HO2S Signal Stuck Lean (Bank 1 Sensor 2)** DTCs P0036, P0037, P0038, P0137, P0138, P0140, P0141, P0443, P0458, P0459, P2232 are not set. The Ignition 1 Signal parameter is between 10-18 volts. The Engine Run Time parameter is more than 5 minutes. The Engine Speed parameter is between 1,100-2,500 RPM. The MAF Sensor parameter is between 3-20 g/s. The Vehicle Speed parameter is between 50-120 km/h (31-75 mph). The Fuel Level Sensor parameter is more than 10 percent. The Loop Status parameter is closed. The Catalytic Converter Temperature parameter is between 550-900°C (1,022-1,652°F). DTC P2270 runs once per drive cycle when the above conditions are met. The ECM detects that the HO2S 2 voltage oscillations are slower than a calibrated value. DTC P2270 sets within 4 seconds when the above condition is met continuously, or within 50 seconds when the above condition is met cumulatively. **Possible Causes:** • HO2S low signal circuit for an open/high resistance • HO2S high signal circuit for a short to voltage • HO2S high signal circuit for a short to ground • HO2S high signal circuit for an open/high resistance • HO2S has failed • ECM has failed
DTC: P2270 **1T CCM, MIL: Yes** **Years:** 2008, 2009 **Models:** Envoy, Equinox, G6, G8, Impala, Lucerne, Malibu, Savana, Trailblazer, Torrent **Engines:** 4.2L VIN S, 4.8L VIN C, 3.5L VIN N, 3.5L VIN K, 3.9L VIN 3, 3.9L VIN M, 3.6L VIN 2, 3.9L VIN 1 **Transmissions:** All	**HO2S Signal Stuck Lean (Bank 1 Sensor 2)** The ECM detects that the HO2S 2 voltage is less than 629 mV for greater than 100 seconds, then an intrusive test is performed. The ECM will enrich the fuel mixture 2 percent per second up to 20 percent then hold the enrichment for 10 seconds. If the ECM detects that the HO2S 2 voltage is less than 629 mV during the intrusive test, for greater than 4 second or for a cumulative of 30 seconds, the DTC sets. **Possible Causes:** • Water intrusion in the HO2S harness connector • Signal circuit terminal B for a short to ground • Low fuel system pressure • Lean fuel injectors • Fuel that is contaminated • Vacuum hoses for splits, kinks, and proper connection • Air intake system after the Mass Air Flow (MAF) sensor for vacuum leaks • Exhaust system leaks • Contaminated HO2S – Silicon • Engine mechanical condition • Faulty HO2S • ECM has failed

DTC	Trouble Code Title, Conditions & Possible Causes
DTC: P2270 **2T CCM, MIL: Yes** **Years:** 2008, 2009 **Models:** G6, HHR, Malibu **Engines:** 2.0L VIN X, 2.2L VIN D, 2.2L VIN B, 2.2L VIN F, 2.4L VIN B, 2.4L VIN V, 2.4L VIN P, 2.4L VIN 5 **Transmissions:** All	**HO2S Signal Stuck Lean Sensor 2** DTCs P0036, P0037, P0038, P0137, P0138, P0140, P0141, P0443, P0458, P0459, and P2232 are not set. The engine is running. The ignition voltage is more than 10.5 V. The HO2S 2 has been in Closed Loop for more than 10 s. The DFCO is inactive. The engine air flow has been between 5.56-33.33 g/s for more than 3 s, and is currently more than 9.72 g/s. DTC P2270 runs continuously when the above conditions are met for 10 min. The ECM detects that the HO2S 2 voltage oscillations are slower than a calibrated value. DTC P2270 sets within 4 s when the above condition is met continuously, or within 50 s when the above condition is met cumulatively. **Possible Causes:** • HO2S signal circuit open/high resistance • HO2S signal circuit short to voltage • HO2S signal circuit open/high resistance • HO2S is damaged • ECM has failed
DTC: P2271 **1T CCM, MIL: Yes** **Years:** 2008, 2009 **Models:** Express, G8, Lucerne, Trailblazer **Engines:** 4.6L VIN Y, 4.6L VIN 9, 6.0L VIN H, 6.0L VIN Y, 6.0L VIN K, 6.2L VIN W, 6.6L VIN 6 **Transmissions:** All	**HO2S Signal Stuck Rich (Bank 1 Sensor 2)** DTCs P0036, P0037, P0038, P0137, P0138, P0140, P0141, P0443, P0458, P0459, P2232 are not set. The Ignition 1 Signal parameter is between 10-18 volts. The Engine Speed parameter is between 500-5,000 RPM. The MAF Sensor parameter is between 3-50 g/s. The Vehicle Speed parameter is between 24-132 km/h (15-82 mph). The Fuel Level Sensor parameter is more than 10 percent. The Loop Status parameter is closed. DTC P2270 runs once per drive cycle when the above conditions are met for 1 second. **Possible Causes:** • HO2S low signal circuit for an open/high resistance • HO2S high signal circuit for a short to voltage • HO2S high signal circuit for a short to ground • HO2S high signal circuit for an open/high resistance • HO2S has failed • ECM has failed
DTC: P2271 **2T CCM, MIL: Yes** **Years:** 2008, 2009 **Models:** G6, HHR, Malibu **Engines:** 2.0L VIN X, 2.2L VIN D, 2.2L VIN B, 2.2L VIN F, 2.4L VIN B, 2.4L VIN V, 2.4L VIN P, 2.4L VIN 5 **Transmissions:** All	**HO2S Signal Stuck Rich Sensor 2** DTCs P000A, P000B, P0010, P0011, P0013, P0014, P0016, P0017, P0030, P0031, P0032, P0036, P0037, P0038, P0068, P0101, P0102, P0103, P0116, P0117, P0118, P0119, P0121, P0122, P0123, P0130, P0131, P0132, P0133, P0137, P0138, P0139, P0141, P0171, P0172, P0221, P0222, P0223, P0300, P0301, P0302, P0303, P0304, P0313, P0335, P0336, P0340, P0341, P0365, P0366, P0443, P0458, P0459, P0496, P1101, P2088, P2089, P2090, P2091, P2176, P2270, P2271, P2297, P2A00, P2A01 are not set. The engine has been running for more than 5 min. The engine coolant temperature is hotter than 167°F (75°C). DTC P2271 runs continuously when the above conditions are met for 10 min. The ECM detects that the HO2S 2 voltage oscillations are faster than a calibrated value. DTC P2271 sets within 4 s when the above condition is met continuously, or within 50 s when the above condition is met cumulatively. **Possible Causes:** • HO2S signal circuit open/high resistance • HO2S signal circuit short to voltage • HO2S signal circuit open/high resistance • HO2S is damaged • ECM has failed
DTC: P2271 **1T CCM, MIL: Yes** **Years:** 2008, 2009 **Models:** Envoy, Equinox, G6, G8, Impala, Lucerne, Malibu, Savana, Trailblazer, Torrent **Engines:** 4.2L VIN S, 4.8L VIN C, 3.5L VIN N, 3.5L VIN K, 3.9L VIN 3, 3.9L VIN M, 3.6L VIN 2, 3.9L VIN 1 **Transmissions:** All	**HO2S Signal Stuck Rich (Bank 1 Sensor 2)** The ECM detects that the HO2S 2 voltage is greater than 629 mV for greater than 100 seconds, then an intrusive test is performed. The ECM will lean the fuel mixture −2 percent per second up to −15 percent then hold the enleanment for 10 seconds. If the ECM detects that the HO2S voltage is greater than 629 mV during the intrusive test, for greater than 4 seconds or for a cumulative of 30 seconds, the DTC sets. **Possible Causes:** • Collapsed air intake duct • Restricted air filter element • Excessive fuel in the crankcase • Fuel contamination • Rich injectors • Engine mechanical conditions • Restricted exhaust system • Faulty HO2S • ECM has failed

DTC	Trouble Code Title, Conditions & Possible Causes
DTC: P2272 **1T CCM, MIL: Yes** **Years:** 2008, 2009 **Models:** Envoy, Equinox, G6, G8, Impala, Lucerne, Malibu, Savana, Trailblazer, Torrent **Engines:** 4.2L VIN S, 4.8L VIN C, 3.5L VIN N, 3.5L VIN K, 3.9L VIN 3, 3.9L VIN M, 3.6L VIN 2, 3.9L VIN 1 **Transmissions:** All	**HO2S Signal Stuck Lean (Bank 2 Sensor 2)** The ECM detects that the HO2S 2 voltage is less than 629 mV for greater than 100 seconds, then an intrusive test is performed. The ECM will enrich the fuel mixture 2 percent per second up to 20 percent then hold the enrichment for 10 seconds. If the ECM detects that the HO2S 2 voltage is less than 629 mV during the intrusive test, for greater than 4 second or for a cumulative of 30 seconds, the DTC sets. **Possible Causes:** • Water intrusion in the HO2S harness connector • Signal circuit terminal B for a short to ground • Low fuel system pressure • Lean fuel injectors • Fuel that is contaminated • Vacuum hoses for splits, kinks, and proper connection • Air intake system after the Mass Air Flow (MAF) sensor for vacuum leaks • Exhaust system leaks • Contaminated HO2S – Silicon • Engine mechanical condition • Faulty HO2S • ECM has failed
DTC: P2273 **1T CCM, MIL: Yes** **Years:** 2008, 2009 **Models:** Envoy, Equinox, G6, G8, Impala, Lucerne, Malibu, Savana, Trailblazer, Torrent **Engines:** 4.2L VIN S, 4.8L VIN C, 3.5L VIN N, 3.5L VIN K, 3.9L VIN 3, 3.9L VIN M, 3.6L VIN 2, 3.9L VIN 1 **Transmissions:** All	**HO2S Signal Stuck Rich (Bank 1 Sensor 2)** The ECM detects that the HO2S 2 voltage is greater than 629 mV for greater than 100 seconds, then an intrusive test is performed. The ECM will lean the fuel mixture −2 percent per second up to −15 percent then hold the enleanment for 10 seconds. If the ECM detects that the HO2S voltage is greater than 629 mV during the intrusive test, for greater than 4 seconds or for a cumulative of 30 seconds, the DTC sets. **Possible Causes:** • Collapsed air intake duct • Restricted air filter element • Excessive fuel in the crankcase • Fuel contamination • Rich injectors • Engine mechanical conditions • Restricted exhaust system • Faulty HO2S • ECM has failed
DTC: P2300 **1T CCM, MIL: Yes** **Years:** 2008, 2009 **Models:** Envoy, Equinox, G6, G8, Impala, Lucerne, Malibu, Savana, Trailblazer, Torrent **Engines:** 4.2L VIN S, 4.8L VIN C, 3.5L VIN N, 3.5L VIN K, 3.9L VIN 3, 3.9L VIN M, 3.6L VIN 2, 3.9L VIN 1 **Transmissions:** All	**Ignition Coil 1 Control Circuit Low Voltage** The engine is running. The ignition 1 voltage signal is greater than 10 volts. The ECM detects the ignition control circuit is shorted to ground for greater than 4 seconds or a cumulative of 30 seconds. **Possible Causes:** • Ignition Coil circuit for a short to ground or an open/high resistance • Inition Coil circuit for a short to voltage • Ignition coil has failed • ECM has failed
DTC: P2301 **1T CCM, MIL: Yes** **Years:** 2008, 2009 **Models:** All **Engines:** All **Transmissions:** All	**Ignition Coil 1 Control Circuit High Voltage** The engine is running. The ignition 1 voltage signal is greater than 10 volts. The ECM detects the ignition control circuit is shorted to ground for greater than 4 seconds or a cumulative of 30 seconds. **Possible Causes:** • Ignition Coil circuit for a short to ground or an open/high resistance • Inition Coil circuit for a short to voltage • Ignition coil has failed • ECM has failed
DTC: P2303 **1T CCM, MIL: Yes** **Years:** 2008, 2009 **Models:** All **Engines:** All **Transmissions:** All	**Ignition Coil 2 Control Circuit Low Voltage** The engine is running. The ignition 1 voltage signal is greater than 10 volts. The ECM detects the ignition control circuit is shorted to ground for greater than 4 seconds or a cumulative of 30 seconds. **Possible Causes:** • Ignition Coil circuit for a short to ground or an open/high resistance • Inition Coil circuit for a short to voltage • Ignition coil has failed • ECM has failed

DTC	Trouble Code Title, Conditions & Possible Causes
DTC: P2304 **1T CCM, MIL: Yes** **Years:** 2008, 2009 **Models:** All **Engines:** All **Transmissions:** All	**Ignition Coil 2 Control Circuit High Voltage** The engine is running. The ignition 1 voltage signal is greater than 10 volts. The ECM detects the ignition control circuit is shorted to ground for greater than 4 seconds or a cumulative of 30 seconds. **Possible Causes:** • Ignition Coil circuit for a short to ground or an open/high resistance • Inition Coil circuit for a short to voltage • Ignition coil has failed • ECM has failed
DTC: P2306 **1T CCM, MIL: Yes** **Years:** 2008, 2009 **Models:** All **Engines:** All **Transmissions:** All	**Ignition Coil 3 Control Circuit Low Voltage** The engine is running. The ignition 1 voltage signal is greater than 10 volts. The ECM detects the ignition control circuit is shorted to ground for greater than 4 seconds or a cumulative of 30 seconds. **Possible Causes:** • Ignition Coil circuit for a short to ground or an open/high resistance • Inition Coil circuit for a short to voltage • Ignition coil has failed • ECM has failed
DTC: P2307 **1T CCM, MIL: Yes** **Years:** 2008, 2009 **Models:** All **Engines:** All **Transmissions:** All	**Ignition Coil 3 Control Circuit High Voltage** The engine is running. The ignition 1 voltage signal is greater than 10 volts. The ECM detects the ignition control circuit is shorted to ground for greater than 4 seconds or a cumulative of 30 seconds. **Possible Causes:** • Ignition Coil circuit for a short to ground or an open/high resistance • Inition Coil circuit for a short to voltage • Ignition coil has failed • ECM has failed
DTC: P2309 **1T CCM, MIL: Yes** **Years:** 2008, 2009 **Models:** All **Engines:** All **Transmissions:** All	**Ignition Coil 4 Control Circuit Low Voltage** The engine is running. The ignition 1 voltage signal is greater than 10 volts. The ECM detects the ignition control circuit is shorted to ground for greater than 4 seconds or a cumulative of 30 seconds. **Possible Causes:** • Ignition Coil circuit for a short to ground or an open/high resistance • Inition Coil circuit for a short to voltage • Ignition coil has failed • ECM has failed
DTC: P2310 **1T CCM, MIL: Yes** **Years:** 2008, 2009 **Models:** All **Engines:** All **Transmissions:** All	**Ignition Coil 4 Control Circuit High Voltage** The engine is running. The ignition 1 voltage signal is greater than 10 volts. The ECM detects the ignition control circuit is shorted to ground for greater than 4 seconds or a cumulative of 30 seconds. **Possible Causes:** • Ignition Coil circuit for a short to ground or an open/high resistance • Inition Coil circuit for a short to voltage • Ignition coil has failed • ECM has failed
DTC: P2312 **1T CCM, MIL: Yes** **Years:** 2008, 2009 **Models:** All **Engines:** All **Transmissions:** All	**Ignition Coil 5 Control Circuit Low Voltage** The engine is running. The ignition 1 voltage signal is greater than 10 volts. The ECM detects the ignition control circuit is shorted to ground for greater than 4 seconds or a cumulative of 30 seconds. **Possible Causes:** • Ignition Coil circuit for a short to ground or an open/high resistance • Inition Coil circuit for a short to voltage • Ignition coil has failed • ECM has failed
DTC: P2313 **1T CCM, MIL: Yes** **Years:** 2008, 2009 **Models:** All **Engines:** All **Transmissions:** All	**Ignition Coil 5 Control Circuit High Voltage** The engine is running. The ignition 1 voltage signal is greater than 10 volts. The ECM detects the ignition control circuit is shorted to ground for greater than 4 seconds or a cumulative of 30 seconds. **Possible Causes:** • Ignition Coil circuit for a short to ground or an open/high resistance • Inition Coil circuit for a short to voltage • Ignition coil has failed • ECM has failed

DTC	Trouble Code Title, Conditions & Possible Causes
DTC: P2315 **1T CCM, MIL: Yes** **Years:** 2008, 2009 **Models:** All **Engines:** All **Transmissions:** All	**Ignition Coil 6 Control Circuit Low Voltage** The engine is running. The ignition 1 voltage signal is greater than 10 volts. The ECM detects the ignition control circuit is shorted to ground for greater than 4 seconds or a cumulative of 30 seconds. **Possible Causes:** • Ignition Coil circuit for a short to ground or an open/high resistance • Inition Coil circuit for a short to voltage • Ignition coil has failed • ECM has failed
DTC: P2316 **1T CCM, MIL: Yes** **Years:** 2008, 2009 **Models:** All **Engines:** All **Transmissions:** All	**Ignition Coil 6 Control Circuit High Voltage** The engine is running. The ignition 1 voltage signal is greater than 10 volts. The ECM detects the ignition control circuit is shorted to ground for greater than 4 seconds or a cumulative of 30 seconds. **Possible Causes:** • Ignition Coil circuit for a short to ground or an open/high resistance • Inition Coil circuit for a short to voltage • Ignition coil has failed • ECM has failed
DTC: P2544 **1T CCM, MIL: Yes** **Years:** 2008, 2009 **Models:** Equinox, G6, G8, Torrent **Engines:** 2.0L VIN X, 2.2L VIN D, 2.2L VIN B, 2.2L VIN F, 2.4L VIN B, 2.4L VIN V, 2.4L VIN P, 2.4L VIN 5, 4.2L VIN S, 4.8L VIN C, 3.5L VIN N, 3.5L VIN K, 3.9L VIN 3, 3.9L VIN M, 3.6L VIN 2, 3.9L VIN 1 **Transmissions:** All	**Transmission Torque Request Circuit** The engine run time is greater than 5 seconds. No other CAN errors are present. The ECM notifies the TCM that a torque reduction request has failed for 2 seconds. **Possible Causes:** • If DTC P0604 is set, replace the ECM. • If DTC P0604 is not set, replace the TCM.
DTC: P2544 **2T CCM, MIL: Yes** **Years:** 2008, 2009 **Models:** G6, HHR, Malibu **Engines:** 2.0L VIN X, 2.2L VIN D, 2.2L VIN B, 2.2L VIN F, 2.4L VIN B, 2.4L VIN V, 2.4L VIN P, 2.4L VIN 5 **Transmissions:** All	**Transmission Torque Request Circuit** The engine run time is greater than 5 seconds. No other CAN errors are present. The ECM notifies the TCM that a torque reduction request has failed for 2 seconds. **Possible Causes:** • If DTC P0604 is set, replace the ECM. • If DTC P0604 is not set, replace the TCM.
DTC: P2610 **2T CCM, MIL: Yes** **Years:** 2008, 2009 **Models:** All **Engines:** All **Transmissions:** All	**Control Module Ignition OFF Timer Performance** The ECM is powered down. DTC P2610 runs once per ignition cycle. Or the ECM is powered up with the ignition switch in the Run or Crank position. The engine OFF timer value is less than or greater than an internal reference counter during an 2-second interval. DTC P2610 runs continuously when the above conditions are met. The ECM detects an internal failure or incomplete programming for more than 10 seconds. **Possible Causes:** • Voltage and ground inputs to the ECM • If DTC P0602 is set, attempt to program the ECM before replacing the ECM. If DTC P0602 resets, replace the ECM.
DTC: P2635 **1T CCM, MIL: Yes** **Years:** 2008, 2009 **Models:** Express, G8, Lucerne, Trailblazer **Engines:** 4.6L VIN Y, 4.6L VIN 9, 6.0L VIN H, 6.0L VIN Y, 6.0L VIN K, 6.2L VIN W, 6.6L VIN 6 **Transmissions:** All	**Fuel Pump Flow Performance** DTC P0191, P0192, P0193, P1255 or P06A6 are not active. DTC P0641 has not failed this ignition cycle. Fuel pump control is enabled and the fuel pump control state is normal. The system voltage is greater than 11 V. The engine has been running for more than 30 seconds. This DTC sets when the FPCM detects a predetermined fuel pressure performance degradation between the desired fuel rail pressure and the current estimated fuel rail pressure. **Possible Causes:** • FPCM relaycircuit for a short to voltage • FPCM relaycircuit for a short to ground or an open/high resistance • FPCM relay

DTC	Trouble Code Title, Conditions & Possible Causes
DTC: P2A00 **1T CCM, MIL: Yes** **Years:** 2008, 2009 **Models:** Express, G8, Lucerne, Trailblazer **Engines:** 4.6L VIN Y, 4.6L VIN 9, 6.0L VIN H, 6.0L VIN Y, 6.0L VIN K, 6.2L VIN W, 6.6L VIN 6 **Transmissions:** All	**HO2S Performance (Bank 1 Sensor 1)** DTCs P0068, P0101, P0102, P0103, P0106, P0107, P0108, P0112, P0113, P0116, P0117, P0118, P0120, P0121, P0122, P0123, P0125, P0128, P0201, P0202, P0203, P0204, P0205, P0206, P0207, P0208, P0220, P0222, P0223, P0442, P0443, P0446, P0449, P0455, P0496, P1516, P2101, P2119, P2135, P2176 are not set. The Engine Run Time parameter is more than 100 seconds. The Engine speed parameter is between 500-5,000 RPM. The Ignition 1 Signal parameter is between 10-18 volts. The Mass Airflow (MAF) Sensor parameter is between 3-30 g/s. The ECT Sensor parameter is more than 70°C (158°F). DTC P2A00 runs continuously when the above conditions are met for 5 seconds. The control module detects that the Loop Status parameter is open. DTC P2A00 sets within 5 seconds when the above condition is met. **Possible Causes:** • HO2S low reference circuit for an open/high resistance • HO2S signal circuit for a short to ground • HO2S signal circuit for a short to voltage • HO2S signal circuit for an open/high resistance • HO2S has failed • ECM has failed
DTC: P2A00 **2T CCM, MIL: Yes** **Years:** 2008, 2009 **Models:** G6, HHR, Malibu **Engines:** 2.0L VIN X, 2.2L VIN D, 2.2L VIN B, 2.2L VIN F, 2.4L VIN B, 2.4L VIN V, 2.4L VIN P, 2.4L VIN 5 **Transmissions:** All	**HO2S Performance Sensor 1** DTCs P0030, P0031, P0032, P0130, P0131, P0132, P0133, P0134, P2297 are not set. The ignition is ON. The ECM detects that the HO2S 1 is not ready after 30 s. DTC P2A00 sets immediately after the above condition is met. **Possible Causes:** • HO2S signal circuit open/high resistance • HO2S signal circuit short to voltage • HO2S signal circuit open/high resistance • HO2S is damaged • ECM has failed
DTC: P2A01 **1T CCM, MIL: Yes** **Years:** 2008, 2009 **Models:** Express, G8, Lucerne, Trailblazer **Engines:** 4.6L VIN Y, 4.6L VIN 9, 6.0L VIN H, 6.0L VIN Y, 6.0L VIN K, 6.2L VIN W, 6.6L VIN 6 **Transmissions:** All	**HO2S Performance (Bank 1 Sensor 2)** DTCs P0030, P0036, P0053, P0054, P0068, P0101, P0102, P0103, P0106, P0107, P0108, P0112, P0113, P0116, P0117, P0118, P0120, P0121, P0122, P0123, P0128, P0131, P0132, P0133, P0134, P0135, P0137, P0138, P0140, P0141, P0171, P0172, P0174, P0175, P0201, P0202, P0203, P0204, P0205, P0206, P0207, P0208, P0220, P0222, P0223, P0300, P0301, P0302, P0303, P0304, P0305, P0306, P0307, P0308, P0442, P0443, P0446, P0449, P0455, P0496, P1133, P1516, P2101, P2119, P2135, P2176, P2A00 are not set. The engine is running. The Engine Run Time parameter is less than 260 seconds. DTC P2A01 Passive Test runs the passive test once per drive cycle when the above conditions are met for 2 seconds. The control module detects that the HO2S 2 did not transition below 299 mV and above 751 mV during the passive test. One of the following tests fail once per trip/runs until pass or fail reporting: DTC P2A01 sets within 2 minutes when the above conditions are met. **Possible Causes:** • HO2S low reference circuit for an open/high resistance • HO2S signal circuit for a short to ground • HO2S signal circuit for a short to voltage • HO2S signal circuit for an open/high resistance • HO2S has failed • ECM has failed
DTC: P2A01 **2T CCM, MIL: Yes** **Years:** 2008, 2009 **Models:** G6, HHR, Malibu **Engines:** 2.0L VIN X, 2.2L VIN D, 2.2L VIN B, 2.2L VIN F, 2.4L VIN B, 2.4L VIN V, 2.4L VIN P, 2.4L VIN 5 **Transmissions:** All	**HO2S Performance Sensor 2** DTCs P0036, P0037, P0038, P0068, P0101, P0102, P0103, P0136, P0137, P0138, P0139, P0140, P0141, P0171, P0172, P0201, P0202, P0203, P0204, P0261, P0262, P0264, P0265, P0267, P0268, P0270, P0271, P0300, P0301, P0302, P0303, P0304, P0313, P0443, P0458, P0459, P0496, P1101, P2270, P2271 are not set. The ignition is ON. Decel fuel cut-off is active. The mass airflow is more than 10 grams per second. DTC P2A01 runs continuously when the above conditions are met. The ECM detects that the HO2S 2 voltage is more than 0.151 V. DTC P2A01 sets when the above condition is met. **Possible Causes:** • Collapsed air intake duct • Restricted air filter element • Excessive fuel in the crankcase • Fuel contamination • Rich injectors • Engine mechanical conditions • Restricted exhaust system • Faulty HO2S • ECM has failed

OBD II Trouble Code List (P3xxx Codes)

DTC	Trouble Code Title, Conditions & Possible Causes
DTC: P3400 **1T CCM, MIL: Yes** **Years:** 2008, 2009 **Models:** Envoy, Equinox, Savana, Torrent **Engines:** 3.4L VIN F, 4.3L VIN X, 5.3L VIN M **Transmissions:** All	**Cylinder Deactivation System Performance** DTCs P0102, P0103, P0107, P0108, P0112, P0113, P0117, P0119, P0335, and P0336 are not set. The engine speed is between 450-6,400 RPM. The IAT Sensor parameter is between −7 and +125°C (+19 and +257°F). The ECT Sensor parameter is between 70- 125°C (158-257°F). Time in V8 mode is more than 2 seconds. Time in V4 mode is more than 2 seconds. This DTC runs continuously within the enabling conditions. The ECM detects that the actual measured values from the MAF sensor, MAP sensor, and TP sensor, is not within the range of the calculated values for V4 mode. The above condition is met for more than 100 milliseconds. **Possible Causes:** • Low oil pressure • Oil contamination • Ignition 1 voltage circuit powertrain relay • Valve Lifter Oil Manifold (VLOM) • Powertrain relay • ECM has failed
DTC: P3401 **1T CCM, MIL: Yes** **Years:** 2008, 2009 **Models:** Envoy, Equinox, Savana, Torrent **Engines:** 3.4L VIN F, 4.3L VIN X, 5.3L VIN M **Transmissions:** All	**Cylinder 1 Deactivation Solenoid Control Circuit** The engine speed is greater than 400 RPM. The ignition voltage is between 9-18 volts. DTC P3401, P3425, P3441, and P3449 runs continuously when the above conditions are met. The ECM detects that the commanded state of the low side driver and the actual voltage level of the control circuit do not match. The condition is present for 20 out of 25 sample counts. **Possible Causes:** • Low oil pressure • Oil contamination • Ignition 1 voltage circuit powertrain relay • Valve Lifter Oil Manifold (VLOM) • Powertrain relay • ECM has failed
DTC: P3425 **1T CCM, MIL: Yes** **Years:** 2008, 2009 **Models:** Envoy, Equinox, Savana, Torrent **Engines:** 3.4L VIN F, 4.3L VIN X, 5.3L VIN M **Transmissions:** All	**Cylinder 4 Deactivation Solenoid Control Circuit** The engine speed is greater than 400 RPM. The ignition voltage is between 9-18 volts. DTC P3401, P3425, P3441, and P3449 runs continuously when the above conditions are met. The ECM detects that the commanded state of the low side driver and the actual voltage level of the control circuit do not match. The condition is present for 20 out of 25 sample counts. **Possible Causes:|** • Low oil pressure • Oil contamination • Ignition 1 voltage circuit powertrain relay • Valve Lifter Oil Manifold (VLOM) • Powertrain relay • ECM has failed
DTC: P3441 **1T CCM, MIL: Yes** **Years:** 2008, 2009 **Models:** Envoy, Equinox, Savana, Torrent **Engines:** 3.4L VIN F, 4.3L VIN X, 5.3L VIN M **Transmissions:** All	**Cylinder 6 Deactivation Solenoid Control Circuit** The engine speed is greater than 400 RPM. The ignition voltage is between 9-18 volts. DTC P3401, P3425, P3441, and P3449 runs continuously when the above conditions are met. The ECM detects that the commanded state of the low side driver and the actual voltage level of the control circuit do not match. The condition is present for 20 out of 25 sample counts. **Possible Causes:** • Low oil pressure • Oil contamination • Ignition 1 voltage circuit powertrain relay • Valve Lifter Oil Manifold (VLOM) • Powertrain relay • ECM has failed
DTC: P3449 **1T CCM, MIL: Yes** **Years:** 2008, 2009 **Models:** Envoy, Equinox, Savana, Torrent **Engines:** 3.4L VIN F, 4.3L VIN X, 5.3L VIN M **Transmissions:** All	**Cylinder 7 Deactivation Solenoid Control Circuit** The engine speed is greater than 400 RPM. The ignition voltage is between 9-18 volts. DTC P3401, P3425, P3441, and P3449 runs continuously when the above conditions are met. The ECM detects that the commanded state of the low side driver and the actual voltage level of the control circuit do not match. The condition is present for 20 out of 25 sample counts. **Possible Causes:** • Low oil pressure • Oil contamination • Ignition 1 voltage circuit powertrain relay • Valve Lifter Oil Manifold (VLOM) • Powertrain relay • ECM has failed

OBD II Trouble Code List (U1xxx Codes)

DTC	Trouble Code Title, Conditions & Possible Causes
DTC: U0020 **1T CCM, MIL: Yes** **Years:** 2008, 2009 **Models:** All **Engines:** All **Transmissions:** All	**Low Speed CAN Communication Bus Performance** Voltage at the modules is in the normal operating voltage range. The vehicle power mode requires serial data communication to occur. The DTC U2100 does not have a current status. A supervised periodic message that includes the transmitter module availability has not been received. **Possible Causes:** • Control modules the vehicle is equipped with • Control modules B+, ignition, ground, communication enable and serial data circuit terminals • Control module locations on the low and high speed GMLAN serial data circuits
DTC: U0073 **1T CCM, MIL: Yes** **Years:** 2008, 2009 **Models:** All **Engines:** All **Transmissions:** All	**Control Module Communication Bus Off** Supply voltage at the modules are in the normal operating range. The vehicle power mode requires serial data communications. The module setting the DTC has attempted to establish communications on the serial data circuits more than 3 times. **Possible Causes:** • Control modules the vehicle is equipped with • Control module locations on the low speed GMLAN serial data circuit • Each control module's low speed GMLAN serial data circuit terminals • Control modules the vehicle is equipped with • High speed GMLAN serial data circuit terminating resistors • Control module locations on the high speed GMLAN serial data circuits • Each control module's high speed GMLAN serial data circuit terminals
DTC: U1000 **1T ECM, MIL: Yes** **Years:** 2008, 2009 **Models:** All **Engines:** All **Transmissions:** All	**Class 2 Communication Malfunction** Modules connected to the Class 2 circuit monitor for serial data communications during normal vehicle operation. Operating information and commands are exchanged among the modules. When a module receives a message for a critical operating parameter, the module records the identification number of the module that sent the message. These Node Alive messages are used for State of Health monitoring. A critical operating parameter is one which, when not received, requires that the module use a default value for that parameter. When a module does not associate an identification number with at least one critical parameter within 5 seconds of starting data communication, DTC U1000 or U1255 is set. When more than one critical parameter does not have an identification number associated with it, the code will only set once. **Possible Causes:** • Class 2 circuit is open, shorted to ground or shorted to power • ECM ignition power circuit(s) has a high resistance condition • ECM main ground circuit(s) has a high resistance condition • SDM (module) could be shorted pulling the voltage low
DTC: U1016 **1T ECM, MIL: Yes** **Years:** 2008, 2009 **Models:** All **Engines:** All **Transmissions:** All	**No Communication With Powertrain Control Module** Key on, and a message from a learned ID number was not detected for the five seconds. Modules on the Class 2 circuit monitor for data communications during vehicle operation. When a module receives a message for critical data, the module records the identification number of the module sending the message for State of Health monitoring (Node Alive messages). Once a module learns an ID number, it checks for that module's Node Alive message. **Note: Look for this code in All modules. The one without the code is the module that has a problem, and it may have failed.** **Possible Causes:** • ECM Class 2 circuit is open, shorted to ground or to B+ • ECM ignition power circuit(s) has a high resistance condition • ECM main ground circuit(s) has a high resistance condition • ECM (module) may have failed and is pulling the circuit low
DTC: U1026 **1T ECM, MIL: Yes** **Years:** 2008, 2009 **Models:** All **Engines:** All **Transmissions:** All	**Loss of ATC Class 2 Communication** Key on or engine running; and a module detected that it could not communicate with the ATC controller for 1 second. Modules connected to the Class 2 circuit monitor for data communications during normal vehicle operation. Operating information and commands are exchanged among the modules. When a module receives a message for a critical operating parameter, the module records the identification number of the module that sent the message for State of Health monitoring (Node Alive messages). Once a module learns an identification number, it will monitor for that module's Node Alive message. Each module on the Class 2 circuit that is powered and performing functions that require detection of a communications malfunction is required to send a Node Alive message every two seconds. When no message is detected from a learned identification number for five seconds, a DTC U1xxx (XXX is equal to the 3-digit identification number) is set. **Possible Causes:** • Check for a loose connection at the ATC module • Test the main power and ground circuits to the ATC module • Check the Class 2 serial data circuit to the ATC module • ATC module may have failed

DTC	Trouble Code Title, Conditions & Possible Causes
DTC: U1041 **2T ECM, MIL:** Yes **Years:** 2008, 2009 **Models:** All **Engines:** All **Transmissions:** All	**Loss of Electronic Brake Controller Communication** Key on or engine running; and a module detected that it could not communicate with the EBCM controller for 1 second. Modules connected to the Class 2 circuit monitor for data communications during normal vehicle operation. Operating information and commands are exchanged among the modules. When a module receives a message for a critical operating parameter, the module records the identification number of the module that sent the message for State of Health monitoring (Node Alive messages). Once a module learns an identification number, it will monitor for that module's Node Alive message. Each module on the Class 2 circuit that is powered and performing functions that require detection of a communications malfunction is required to send a Node Alive message every two seconds. When no message is detected from a learned identification number for five seconds, a DTC U1xxx (XXX is equal to the 3-digit identification number) is set. **Possible Causes:** • Check for a loose connection at the EBCM (module) • Test the main power and ground circuits to the EBCM (module) • Check the Class 2 serial data circuit to the EBCM (module) • EBCM (module) may have failed
DTC: U1064 **2T ECM, MIL:** Yes **Years:** 2008, 2009 **Models:** All **Engines:** All **Transmissions:** All	**No Communication With Body Control Module** Key on, and a message from a learned ID number was not detected for the five seconds. Modules on the Class 2 circuit monitor for data communications during vehicle operation. When a module receives a message for critical data, the module records the identification number of the module sending the message for State of Health monitoring (Node Alive messages). Look for this code in All modules. The one without this code may have failed **Possible Causes:** • BCM Class 2 circuit is open, shorted to ground or to B+ • BCM ignition power circuit has a high resistance condition • BCM main ground circuit(s) has a high resistance condition • BCM (module) may have failed and is pulling the circuit low
DTC: U1088 **2T ECM, MIL:** Yes **Years:** 2008, 2009 **Models:** All **Engines:** All **Transmissions:** All	**No Communication With SDM (Restraint Module)** Key on, and a message from a learned ID number was not detected for the five seconds. Modules on the Class 2 circuit monitor for data communications during vehicle operation. When a module receives a message for critical data, the module records the identification number of the module sending the message for State of Health monitoring (Node Alive messages). Look for this code in All modules. The one without this code may have failed. **Possible Causes:** • SDM Class 2 circuit is open, shorted to ground or to B+ • SDM ignition power circuit has a high resistance condition • SDM main ground circuit(s) has a high resistance condition • SDM (module) may have failed and is pulling the circuit low
DTC: U1092 **2T ECM, MIL:** Yes **Years:** 2008, 2009 **Models:** All **Engines:** All **Transmissions:** All	**Loss of VTD (Pass Lock) Communication** Key on or engine running; and a module detected that it could not communicate with the VTD controller for 1 second. Modules connected to the Class 2 circuit monitor for data communications during normal vehicle operation. Operating information and commands are exchanged among the modules. When a module receives a message for a critical operating parameter, the module records the identification number of the module that sent the message for State of Health monitoring (Node Alive messages). Once a module learns an identification number, it will monitor for that module's Node Alive message. Each module on the Class 2 circuit that is powered and performing functions that require detection of a communications malfunction is required to send a Node Alive message every two seconds. When no message is detected from a learned identification number for five seconds, a DTC U1xxx (the X's identify the 3-digit identification number) is set. **Possible Causes:** • Check for a loose connection at the VTD module • Test the main power and ground circuits to the VTD module • Check the Class 2 serial data circuit to the VTD module • VTD module may have failed
DTC: U1096 **2T ECM, MIL:** Yes **Years:** 2008, 2009 **Models:** All **Engines:** All **Transmissions:** All	**No Communication With Instrument Panel Cluster** Key on, and a message from a learned ID number was not detected for the five seconds. Modules on the Class 2 circuit monitor for data communications during vehicle operation. When a module receives a message for critical data, the module records the identification number of the module sending the message for State of Health monitoring (Node Alive messages). Once a module learns an ID number, it checks for that module's Node Alive message. **Note: Look for this code in All modules. The one without the code is the module that has a problem, and it may have failed.** **Possible Causes:** • IPC Class 2 circuit is open, shorted to ground or to B+ • IPC ignition power circuit has a high resistance condition • IPC main ground circuit(s) has a high resistance condition • IPC (module) may have failed and is pulling the circuit low

DTC	Trouble Code Title, Conditions & Possible Causes
DTC: U1097 **2T ECM, MIL: Yes** **Years:** 2008, 2009 **Models:** All **Engines:** All **Transmissions:** All	**No Communication With Driver Information Center** Key on, and a message from a learned ID number was not detected for the five seconds. Modules on the Class 2 circuit monitor for data communications during vehicle operation. When a module receives a message for critical data, the module records the identification number of the module sending the message for State of Health monitoring (Node Alive messages). Once a module learns an ID number, it checks for that module's Node Alive message. **Note: Look for this code in All modules. The one without the code is the module that has a problem, and it may have failed.** **Possible Causes:** • DIC Class 2 circuit is open, shorted to ground or to B+ • DIC ignition power circuit has a high resistance condition • DIC main ground circuit(s) has a high resistance condition • DIC (module) may have failed and is pulling the circuit low
DTC: U1151 **2T ECM, MIL: Yes** **Years:** 2008, 2009 **Models:** All **Engines:** All **Transmissions:** All	**No Communication With Vehicle Interface Unit** Key on, and a message from a learned ID number was not detected for the five seconds. Modules on the Class 2 circuit monitor for data communications during vehicle operation. When a module receives a message for critical data, the module records the identification number of the module sending the message for State of Health monitoring (Node Alive messages). Once a module learns an ID number, it checks for that module's Node Alive message. The module without this code is the module with a problem (it has failed). **Possible Causes:** • VIU Class 2 circuit is open, shorted to ground or to B+ • VIU ignition power circuit has a high resistance condition • VIU main ground circuit(s) has a high resistance condition • VIU (module) may have failed and is pulling the circuit low
DTC: U1152 **2T ECM, MIL: Yes** **Years:** 2008, 2009 **Models:** All **Engines:** All **Transmissions:** All	**No Communication With HVAC Control Module** Key on, and a message from a learned ID number was not detected for the five seconds. Modules on the Class 2 circuit monitor for data communications during vehicle operation. When a module receives a message for critical data, the module records the identification number of the module sending the message for State of Health monitoring (Node Alive messages). Once a module learns an ID number, it checks for that module's Node Alive message. The module without this code is the module with a problem (it has failed). **Possible Causes:** • HVAC Class 2 circuit is open, shorted to ground or to B+ • HVAC ignition power circuit has a high resistance condition • HVAC main ground circuit(s) has a high resistance condition • HVAC (module) may have failed and is pulling the circuit low
DTC: U1193 **2T ECM, MIL: Yes** **Years:** 2008, 2009 **Models:** All **Engines:** All **Transmissions:** All	**Loss of Vehicle Immobilizer Module Communications** Key on or engine running; and a module detected that it could not communicate with the VIM controller for 1 second. Modules connected to the Class 2 circuit monitor for data communications during normal vehicle operation. Operating information and commands are exchanged among the modules. When a module receives a message for a critical operating parameter, the module records the identification number of the module that sent the message for State of Health monitoring (Node Alive messages). Once a module learns an identification number, it will monitor for that module's Node Alive message. Each module on the Class 2 circuit that is powered and performing functions that require detection of a communications malfunction is required to send a Node Alive message every two seconds. When no message is detected from a learned identification number for five seconds, a DTC U1xxx (XXX is equal to the 3-digit identification number) is set. **Possible Causes:** • Test the main power and ground circuits to the VIM module for a loose connection • Check the Class 2 serial data circuit to the VIM module • VTD module may have failed
DTC: U1255 **2T ECM, MIL: Yes** **Years:** 2008, 2009 **Models:** All **Engines:** All **Transmissions:** All	**Class 2 Communications Malfunction** Modules connected to the Class 2 circuit monitor for serial data communications during normal vehicle operation. Operating data and commands are exchanged among modules. When a module receives a message for a critical operating parameter, the module records the identification number of the module that sent the message. These Node Alive messages are used for State of Health monitoring. A critical operating parameter is one which, when not received, requires the module use a default value for that parameter. If a module does not associate an ID number with at least one critical parameter in 5 seconds after starting communication, U1000 or U1255 is set. If two or more are missing, the code sets at once. **Possible Causes:** • Class 2 circuit is open, shorted to ground or shorted to power • ECM ignition power circuit(s) has a high resistance condition • ECM main ground circuit(s) has a high resistance condition

DTC	Trouble Code Title, Conditions & Possible Causes
DTC: U1300 **1T ECM, MIL: Yes** **Years:** 2008, 2009 **Models:** All **Engines:** All **Transmissions:** All	**Class 2 Circuit Short to Ground** Key on or engine running; system voltage supplied to the module is in the normal operating voltage range, vehicle power mode requires serial data communication to occur, and the ECM did no detect any valid messages on the Class 2 circuit, or the voltage condition detected on the Class 2 circuit was low for 3 seconds. Modules connected to the Class 2 circuit check for data communications during normal vehicle operation. Operating information and commands are exchanged among the modules. Each module transmits Node Alive messages on the Class 2 data circuit once every 2 seconds. When the module detects a low voltage condition on the Class 2 serial data circuit for approximately 3 seconds, it sets U1300 or U1305 if it cannot identify the problem. **Note: This code is set by loss of communication. Look in All of the modules for this trouble code - the one without it has a problem** **Possible Causes:** • Class 2 serial data line was in a low state for 3 seconds due to a short to sensor ground or chassis ground • One or more modules on the Class 2 line has a short to ground
DTC: U1301 **1T ECM, MIL: Yes** **Years:** 2008, 2009 **Models:** All **Engines:** All **Transmissions:** All	**Class 2 Circuit Short to Battery** Key on or engine running; system voltage supplied to the module is in the normal operating voltage range, vehicle power mode requires serial data communication to occur, and the ECM did no detect any valid messages on the Class 2 circuit, or the voltage condition detected on the Class 2 circuit was low for 3 seconds. Modules connected to the Class 2 circuit check for data communications during normal vehicle operation. Operating information and commands are exchanged among the modules. In addition, each module transmits Node Alive messages on the Class 2 data circuit once every 2 seconds. If the module detects a high voltage condition on the Class 2 serial data circuit for 3 seconds, it sets U1300. **Note: This code is set by loss of communication. Look in All of the modules for this trouble code - the one without it has a problem.** **Possible Causes:** • Class 2 serial data line was in a high state for 3 seconds due to a short to VREF or system power • One or more modules on Class 2 line has an short to power
DTC: U1305 **1T ECM, MIL: Yes** **Years:** 2008, 2009 **Models:** All **Engines:** All **Transmissions:** All	**Class 2 Data Link High or Low** Key on or engine running; system voltage supplied to the module is in the normal operating voltage range, vehicle power mode requires serial data communication to occur, and the ECM did no detect any valid messages on the Class 2 circuit, or the voltage condition detected on the Class 2 circuit was low for 3 seconds. Modules connected to the Class 2 circuit check for data communications during normal vehicle operation. Operating information and commands are exchanged among the modules. In addition, each module transmits Node Alive messages on the Class 2 data circuit about once every 2 seconds. When the module detects a high voltage condition on the Class 2 serial data circuit for approximately 3 seconds, it sets U1300 or U1305 if it cannot identify the problem. **Possible Causes:** • Class 2 serial data line has either a high or low voltage condition on the circuit, and the module cannot identify the fault • One or more modules on Class 2 line has an short to power • One or more modules on the Class 2 line has a short to ground
DTC: U2100 **1T CCM, MIL: Yes** **Years:** 2008, 2009 **Models:** All **Engines:** All **Transmissions:** All	**Controller Area Network (CAN) Bus Communication** Supply voltage at the modules are in the normal operating range. vehicle power mode requires serial data communicationsThe module setting the DTC has attempted to establish communications on the serial data circuits more than 3 times. **Possible Causes:** • Control modules the vehicle is equipped with • Control module locations on the low speed GMLAN serial data circuit • Each control module's low speed GMLAN serial data circuit terminals • Control modules the vehicle is equipped with • High speed GMLAN serial data circuit terminating resistors • Control module locations on the high speed GMLAN serial data circuits • Each control module's high speed GMLAN serial data circuit terminals

ABS: Anti-lock braking system. An electro-mechanical braking system which is designed to minimize or prevent wheel lock-up during braking.

ABSOLUTE PRESSURE: Atmospheric (barometric) pressure plus the pressure gauge reading.

ACCELERATOR PUMP: A small pump located in the carburetor that feeds fuel into the air/fuel mixture during acceleration.

ACCUMULATOR: A device that controls shift quality by cushioning the shock of hydraulic oil pressure being applied to a clutch or band.

ACTUATING MECHANISM: The mechanical output devices of a hydraulic system, for example, clutch pistons and band servos.

ACTUATOR: The output component of a hydraulic or electronic system.

ADVANCE: Setting the ignition timing so that spark occurs earlier before the piston reaches top dead center (TDC).

ADAPTIVE MEMORY (ADAPTIVE STRATEGY): The learning ability of the TCM or PCM to redefine its decision-making process to provide optimum shift quality.

AFTER TOP DEAD CENTER (ATDC): The point after the piston reaches the top of its travel on the compression stroke.

AIR BAG: Device on the inside of the car designed to inflate on impact of crash, protecting the occupants of the car.

AIR CHARGE TEMPERATURE (ACT) SENSOR: The temperature of the airflow into the engine is measured by an ACT sensor, usually located in the lower intake manifold or air cleaner.

AIR CLEANER: An assembly consisting of a housing, filter and any connecting ductwork. The filter element is made up of a porous paper, sometimes with a wire mesh screening, and is designed to prevent airborne particles from entering the engine through the carburetor or throttle body.

AIR INJECTION: One method of reducing harmful exhaust emissions by injecting air into each of the exhaust ports of an engine. The fresh air entering the hot exhaust manifold causes any remaining fuel to be burned before it can exit the tailpipe.

AIR PUMP: An emission control device that supplies fresh air to the exhaust manifold to aid in more completely burning exhaust gases.

AIR/FUEL RATIO: The ratio of air-to-gasoline by weight in the fuel mixture drawn into the engine.

ALDL (assembly line diagnostic link): Electrical connector for scanning ECM/PCM/TCM input and output devices.

ALIGNMENT RACK: A special drive-on vehicle lift apparatus/measuring device used to adjust a vehicle's toe, caster and camber angles.

ALL WHEEL DRIVE: Term used to describe a full time four wheel drive system or any other vehicle drive system that continuously delivers power to all four wheels. This system is found primarily on station wagon vehicles and SUVs not utilized for significant off road use.

ALTERNATING CURRENT (AC): Electric current that flows first in one direction, then in the opposite direction, continually reversing flow.

ALTERNATOR: A device which produces AC (alternating current) which is converted to DC (direct current) to charge the car battery.

AMMETER: An instrument, calibrated in amperes, used to measure the flow of an electrical current in a circuit. Ammeters are always connected in series with the circuit being tested.

AMPERAGE: The total amount of current (amperes) flowing in a circuit.

AMPLIFIER: A device used in an electrical circuit to increase the voltage of an output signal.

AMP/HR. RATING (BATTERY): Measurement of the ability of a battery to deliver a stated amount of current for a stated period of time. The higher the amp/hr. rating, the better the battery.

AMPERE: The rate of flow of electrical current present when one volt of electrical pressure is applied against one ohm of electrical resistance.

ANALOG COMPUTER: Any microprocessor that uses similar (analogous) electrical signals to make its calculations.

ANODIZED: A special coating applied to the surface of aluminum valves for extended service life.

ANTIFREEZE: A substance (ethylene or propylene glycol) added to the coolant to prevent freezing in cold weather.

ANTI-FOAM AGENTS: Minimize fluid foaming from the whipping action encountered in the converter and planetary action.

ANTI-WEAR AGENTS: Zinc agents that control wear on the gears, bushings, and thrust washers.

ANTI-LOCK BRAKING SYSTEM: A supplementary system to the base hydraulic system that prevents sustained lock-up of the wheels during braking as well as automatically controlling wheel slip.

ANTI-ROLL BAR: See stabilizer bar.

ARC: A flow of electricity through the air between two electrodes or contact points that produces a spark.

ARMATURE: A laminated, soft iron core wrapped by a wire that converts electrical energy to mechanical energy as in a motor or relay. When rotated in a magnetic field, it changes mechanical energy into electrical energy as in a generator.

ATDC: After Top Dead Center.

ATF: Automatic transmission fluid.

ATMOSPHERIC PRESSURE: The pressure on the Earth's surface caused by the weight of the air in the atmosphere. At sea level, this pressure is 14.7 psi at 32°F (101 kPa at 0°C).

ATOMIZATION: The breaking down of a liquid into a fine mist that can be suspended in air.

AUXILIARY ADD-ON COOLER: A supplemental transmission fluid cooling device that is installed in series with the heat exchanger (cooler), located inside the radiator, to provide additional support to cool the hot fluid leaving the torque converter.

AUXILIARY PRESSURE: An added fluid pressure that is introduced into a regulator or balanced valve system to control valve movement. The auxiliary pressure itself can be either a fixed or a variable value. (See balanced valve; regulator valve.)

AWD: All wheel drive.

AXIAL FORCE: A side or end thrust force acting in or along the same plane as the power flow.

AXIAL PLAY: Movement parallel to a shaft or bearing bore.

AXLE CAPACITY: The maximum load-carrying capacity of the axle itself, as specified by the manufacturer. This is usually a higher number than the GAWR.

AXLE RATIO: This is a number (3.07:1, 4.56:1, for example) expressing the ratio between driveshaft revolutions and wheel revolutions. A low numerical ratio allows the engine to work easier because it doesn't have to turn as fast. A high numerical ratio means that the engine has to turn more rpm's to move the wheels through the same number of turns.

BACKFIRE: The sudden combustion of gases in the intake or exhaust system that results in a loud explosion.

BACKLASH: The clearance or play between two parts, such as meshed gears.

BACKPRESSURE: Restrictions in the exhaust system that slow the exit of exhaust gases from the combustion chamber.

BAKELITE®: A heat resistant, plastic insulator material commonly used in printed circuit boards and transistorized components.

BALANCED VALVE: A valve that is positioned by opposing auxiliary hydraulic pressures and/or spring force. Examples include mainline regulator, throttle, and governor valves. (See regulator valve.)

BAND: A flexible ring of steel with an inner lining of friction material. When tightened around the outside of a drum, a planetary member is held stationary to the transmission/transaxle case.

BALL BEARING: A bearing made up of hardened inner and outer races between which hardened steel balls roll.

BALL JOINT: A ball and matching socket connecting suspension components (steering knuckle to lower control arms). It permits rotating movement in any direction between the components that are joined.

BARO (BAROMETRIC PRESSURE SENSOR): Measures the change in the intake manifold pressure caused by changes in altitude.

BAROMETRIC MANIFOLD ABSOLUTE PRESSURE (BMAP) SENSOR: Operates similarly to a conventional MAP sensor; reads intake manifold pressure and is also responsible for determining altitude and barometric pressure prior to engine operation.

BAROMETRIC PRESSURE: (See atmospheric pressure.)

BALLAST RESISTOR: A resistor in the primary ignition circuit that lowers voltage after the engine is started to reduce wear on ignition components.

BATTERY: A direct current electrical storage unit, consisting of the basic active materials of lead and sulfuric acid, which converts chemical energy into electrical energy. Used to provide current for the operation of the starter as well as other equipment, such as the radio, lighting, etc.

BEAD: The portion of a tire that holds it on the rim.

BEARING: A friction reducing, supportive device usually located between a stationary part and a moving part.

BEFORE TOP DEAD CENTER (BTDC): The point just before the piston reaches the top of its travel on the compression stroke.

BELTED TIRE: Tire construction similar to bias-ply tires, but using two or more layers of reinforced belts between body plies and the tread.

BEZEL: Piece of metal surrounding radio, headlights, gauges or similar components; sometimes used to hold the glass face of a gauge in the dash.

BIAS-PLY TIRE: Tire construction, using body ply reinforcing cords which run at alternating angles to the center line of the tread.

BI-METAL TEMPERATURE SENSOR: Any sensor or switch made of two dissimilar types of metal that bend when heated or cooled due to the different expansion rates of the alloys. These types of sensors usually function as an on/off switch.

BLOCK: See Engine Block.

BLOW-BY: Combustion gases, composed of water vapor and unburned fuel, that leak past the piston rings into the crankcase during normal engine operation. These gases are removed by the PCV system to prevent the buildup of harmful acids in the crankcase.

BOOK TIME: See Labor Time.

BOOK VALUE: The average value of a car, widely used to determine trade-in and resale value.

BOOST VALVE: Used at the base of the regulator valve to increase mainline pressure.

BORE: Diameter of a cylinder.

BRAKE CALIPER: The housing that fits over the brake disc. The caliper holds the brake pads, which are pressed against the discs by the caliper pistons when the brake pedal is depressed.

BRAKE HORSEPOWER (BHP): The actual horsepower available at the engine flywheel as measured by a dynamometer.

BRAKE FADE: Loss of braking power, usually caused by excessive heat after repeated brake applications.

BRAKE HORSEPOWER: Usable horsepower of an engine measured at the crankshaft.

BRAKE PAD: A brake shoe and lining assembly used with disc brakes.

BRAKE PROPORTIONING VALVE: A valve on the master cylinder which restricts hydraulic brake pressure to the wheels to a specified amount, preventing wheel lock-up.

BREAKAWAY: Often used by Chrysler to identify first-gear operation in D and 2 ranges. In these ranges, first-gear operation depends on a one-way roller clutch that holds on acceleration and releases (breaks away) on deceleration, resulting in a freewheeling coast-down condition.

BRAKE SHOE: The backing for the brake lining. The term is, however, usually applied to the assembly of the brake backing and lining.

BREAKER POINTS: A set of points inside the distributor, operated by a cam, which make and break the ignition circuit.

BRINNELLING: A wear pattern identified by a series of indentations at regular intervals. This condition is caused by a lack of lube, overload situations, and/or vibrations.

BTDC: Before Top Dead Center.

BUMP: Sudden and forceful apply of a clutch or band.

BUSHING: A liner, usually removable, for a bearing; an anti-friction liner used in place of a bearing.

CALIFORNIA ENGINE: An engine certified by the EPA for use in California only; conforms to more stringent emission regulations than Federal engine.

CALIPER: A hydraulically activated device in a disc brake system, which is mounted straddling the brake rotor (disc). The caliper contains at least one piston and two brake pads. Hydraulic pressure on the piston(s) forces the pads against the rotor.

CAPACITY: The quantity of electricity that can be delivered from a unit, as from a battery in ampere-hours, or output, as from a generator.

CAMBER: One of the factors of wheel alignment. Viewed from the front of the car, it is the inward or outward tilt of the wheel. The top of the tire will lean outward (positive camber) or inward (negative camber).

CAMSHAFT: A shaft in the engine on which are the lobes (cams) which operate the valves. The camshaft is driven by the crankshaft, via a belt, chain or gears, at one half the crankshaft speed.

CAPACITOR: A device which stores an electrical charge.

CARBON MONOXIDE (CO): A colorless, odorless gas given off as a normal byproduct of combustion. It is poisonous and extremely dangerous in confined areas, building up slowly to toxic levels without warning if adequate ventilation is not available.

CARBURETOR: A device, usually mounted on the intake manifold of an engine, which mixes the air and fuel in the proper proportion to allow even combustion.

CASTER: The forward or rearward tilt of an imaginary line drawn through the upper ball joint and the center of the wheel. Viewed from the sides, positive caster (forward tilt) lends directional stability, while negative caster (rearward tilt) produces instability.

CATALYTIC CONVERTER: A device installed in the exhaust system, like a muffler, that converts harmful byproducts of combustion into carbon dioxide and water vapor by means of a heat-producing chemical reaction.

CENTRIFUGAL ADVANCE: A mechanical method of advancing the spark timing by using flyweights in the distributor that react to centrifugal force generated by the distributor shaft rotation.

CENTRIFUGAL FORCE: The outward pull of a revolving object, away from the center of revolution. Centrifugal force increases with the speed of rotation.

CETANE RATING: A measure of the ignition value of diesel fuel. The higher the cetane rating, the better the fuel. Diesel fuel cetane rating is roughly comparable to gasoline octane rating.

CHECK VALVE: Any one-way valve installed to permit the flow of air, fuel or vacuum in one direction only.

CHOKE: The valve/plate that restricts the amount of air entering an engine on the induction stroke, thereby enriching the air/fuel ratio.

CHUGGLE: Bucking or jerking condition that may be engine related and may be most noticeable when converter clutch is engaged; similar to the feel of towing a trailer.

CIRCLIP: A split steel snapring that fits into a groove to hold various parts in place.

CIRCUIT BREAKER: A switch which protects an electrical circuit from overload by opening the circuit when the current flow exceeds a pre-determined level. Some circuit breakers must be reset manually, while most reset automatically.

CIRCUIT: Any unbroken path through which an electrical current can flow. Also used to describe fuel flow in some instances.

CIRCUIT, BYPASS: Another circuit in parallel with the major circuit through which power is diverted.

CIRCUIT, CLOSED: An electrical circuit in which there is no interruption of current flow.

CIRCUIT, GROUND: The non-insulated portion of a complete circuit used as a common potential point. In automotive circuits, the ground is composed of metal parts, such as the engine, body sheet metal, and frame and is usually a negative potential.

CIRCUIT, HOT: That portion of a circuit not at ground potential. The hot circuit is usually insulated and is connected to the positive side of the battery.

CIRCUIT, OPEN: A break or lack of contact in an electrical circuit, either intentional (switch) or unintentional (bad connection or broken wire).

CIRCUIT, PARALLEL: A circuit having two or more paths for current flow with common positive and negative tie points. The same voltage is applied to each load device or parallel branch.

CIRCUIT, SERIES: An electrical system in which separate parts are connected end to end, using one wire, to form a single path for current to flow.

CIRCUIT, SHORT: A circuit that is accidentally completed in an electrical path for which it was not intended.

CLAMPING (ISOLATION) DIODES: Diodes positioned in a circuit to prevent self-induction from damaging electronic components.

CLEARCOAT: A transparent layer which, when sprayed over a vehicle's paint job, adds gloss and depth as well as an additional protective coating to the finish.

CLUTCH: Part of the power train used to connect/disconnect power to the rear wheels.

CLUTCH, FLUID: The same as a fluid coupling. A fluid clutch or coupling performs the same function as a friction clutch by utilizing fluid friction and inertia as opposed to solid friction used by a friction clutch. (See fluid coupling.)

CLUTCH, FRICTION: A coupling device that provides a means of smooth and positive engagement and disengagement of engine torque to the vehicle powertrain. Transmission of power through the clutch is accomplished by bringing one or more rotating drive members into contact with complementing driven members.

COAST: Vehicle deceleration caused by engine braking conditions.

COEFFICIENT OF FRICTION: The amount of surface tension between two contacting surfaces; identified by a scientifically calculated number.

COIL: Part of the ignition system that boosts the relatively low voltage supplied by the car's electrical system to the high voltage required to fire the spark plugs.

COMBINATION MANIFOLD: An assembly which includes both the intake and exhaust manifolds in one casting.

COMBINATION VALVE: A device used in some fuel systems that routes fuel vapors to a charcoal storage canister instead of venting them into the atmosphere. The valve relieves fuel tank pressure and allows fresh air into the tank as the fuel level drops to prevent a vapor lock situation.

COMBUSTION CHAMBER: The part of the engine in the cylinder head where combustion takes place.

COMPOUND GEAR: A gear consisting of two or more simple gears with a common shaft.

COMPOUND PLANETARY: A gearset that has more than the three elements found in a simple gearset and is constructed by combining members of two planetary gearsets to create additional gear ratio possibilities.

COMPRESSION CHECK: A test involving removing each spark plug and inserting a gauge. When the engine is cranked, the gauge will record a pressure reading in the individual cylinder. General operating condition can be determined from a compression check.

COMPRESSION RATIO: The ratio of the volume between the piston and cylinder head when the piston is at the bottom of its stroke (bottom dead center) and when the piston is at the top of its stroke (top dead center).

COMPUTER: An electronic control module that correlates input data according to prearranged engineered instructions; used for the management of an actuator system or systems.

CONDENSER: An electrical device which acts to store an electrical charge, preventing voltage surges.
2. A radiator-like device in the air conditioning system in which refrigerant gas condenses into a liquid, giving off heat.

CONDUCTOR: Any material through which an electrical current can be transmitted easily.

CONNECTING ROD: The connecting link between the crankshaft and piston.

CONSTANT VELOCITY JOINT: Type of universal joint in a halfshaft assembly in which the output shaft turns at a constant angular velocity without variation, provided that the speed of the input shaft is constant.

CONTINUITY: Continuous or complete circuit. Can be checked with an ohmmeter.

CONTROL ARM: The upper or lower suspension components which are mounted on the frame and support the ball joints and steering knuckles.

CONVENTIONAL IGNITION: Ignition system which uses breaker points.

CONVERTER: (See torque converter.)

CONVERTER LOCKUP: The switching from hydrodynamic to direct mechanical drive, usually through the application of a friction element called the converter clutch.

COOLANT: Mixture of water and anti-freeze circulated through the engine to carry off heat produced by the engine.

CORROSION INHIBITOR: An inhibitor in ATF that prevents corrosion of bushings, thrust washers, and oil cooler brazed joints.

COUNTERSHAFT: An intermediate shaft which is rotated by a mainshaft and transmits, in turn, that rotation to a working part.

COUPLING PHASE: Occurs when the torque converter is operating at its greatest hydraulic efficiency. The speed differential between the impeller and the turbine is at its minimum. At this point, the stator freewheels, and there is no torque multiplication.

CRANKCASE: The lower part of an engine in which the crankshaft and related parts operate.

CRANKSHAFT: Engine component (connected to pistons by connecting rods) which converts the reciprocating (up and down) motion of pistons to rotary motion used to turn the driveshaft.

CURB WEIGHT: The weight of a vehicle without passengers or payload, but including all fluids (oil, gas, coolant, etc.) and other equipment specified as standard.

CURRENT: The flow (or rate) of electrons moving through a circuit. Current is measured in amperes (amp).

CURRENT FLOW CONVENTIONAL: Current flows through a circuit from the positive terminal of the source to the negative terminal (plus to minus).

CURRENT FLOW, ELECTRON: Current or electrons flow from the negative terminal of the source, through the circuit, to the positive terminal (minus to plus).

CV-JOINT: Constant velocity joint.

CYCLIC VIBRATIONS: The off-center movement of a rotating object that is affected by its initial balance, speed of rotation, and working angles.

CYLINDER BLOCK: See engine block.

CYLINDER HEAD: The detachable portion of the engine, usually fastened to the top of the cylinder block and containing all or most of the combustion chambers. On overhead valve engines, it contains the valves and their operating parts. On overhead cam engines, it contains the camshaft as well.

CYLINDER: In an engine, the round hole in the engine block in which the piston(s) ride.

DATA LINK CONNECTOR (DLC): Current acronym/term applied to the federally mandated, diagnostic junction connector that is used to monitor ECM/PC/TCM inputs, processing strategies, and outputs including diagnostic trouble codes (DTCs).

DEAD CENTER: The extreme top or bottom of the piston stroke.

DECELERATION BUMP: When referring to a torque converter clutch in the applied position, a sudden release of the accelerator pedal causes a forceful reversal of power through the drivetrain (engine braking), just prior to the apply plate actually being released.

DELAYED (LATE OR EXTENDED): Condition where shift is expected but does not occur for a period of time, for example, where clutch or band engagement does not occur as quickly as expected during part throttle or wide open throttle apply of accelerator or when manually downshifting to a lower range.

DETENT: A spring-loaded plunger, pin, ball, or pawl used as a holding device on a ratchet wheel or shaft. In automatic transmissions, a detent mechanism is used for locking the manual valve in place.

DETENT DOWNSHIFT: (See kickdown.)

DETERGENT: An additive in engine oil to improve its operating characteristics.

DETONATION: An unwanted explosion of the air/fuel mixture in the combustion chamber caused by excess heat and compression, advanced timing, or an overly lean mixture. Also referred to as "ping".

DEXRON®: A brand of automatic transmission fluid.

DIAGNOSTIC TROUBLE CODES (DTCs): A digital display from the control module memory that identifies the input, processor, or output device circuit that is related to the powertrain emission/driveability malfunction detected. Diagnostic trouble codes can be read by the MIL to flash any codes or by using a handheld scanner.

DIAPHRAGM: A thin, flexible wall separating two cavities, such as in a vacuum advance unit.

DIESELING: The engine continues to run after the car is shut off; caused by fuel continuing to be burned in the combustion chamber.

DIFFERENTIAL: A geared assembly which allows the transmission of motion between drive axles, giving one axle the ability to rotate faster than the other, as in cornering.

DIFFERENTIAL AREAS: When opposing faces of a spool valve are acted upon by the same pressure but their areas differ in size, the face with the larger area produces the differential force and valve movement. (See spool valve.)

DIFFERENTIAL FORCE: (See differential areas)

DIGITAL READOUT: A display of numbers or a combination of numbers and letters.

DIGITAL VOLT OHMMETER: An electronic diagnostic tool used to measure voltage, ohms and amps as well as several other functions, with the readings displayed on a digital screen in tenths, hundredths and thousandths.

DIODE: An electrical device that will allow current to flow in one direction only.

DIRECT CURRENT (DC): Electrical current that flows in one direction only.

DIRECT DRIVE: The gear ratio is 1:1, with no change occurring in the torque and speed input/output relationship.

DISC BRAKE: A hydraulic braking assembly consisting of a brake disc, or rotor, mounted on an axle shaft, and a caliper assembly containing, usually two brake pads which are activated by hydraulic pressure. The pads are forced against the sides of the disc, creating friction which slows the vehicle.

DISPERSANTS: Suspend dirt and prevent sludge buildup in a liquid, such as engine oil.

DOUBLE BUMP (DOUBLE FEEL): Two sudden and forceful applies of a clutch or band.

DISPLACEMENT: The total volume of air that is displaced by all pistons as the engine turns through one complete revolution.

DISTRIBUTOR: A mechanically driven device on an engine which is responsible for electrically firing the spark plug at a pre-determined point of the piston stroke.

DOHC: Double overhead camshaft.

DOUBLE OVERHEAD CAMSHAFT: The engine utilizes two camshafts mounted in one cylinder head. One camshaft operates the exhaust valves, while the other operates the intake valves.

DOWEL PIN: A pin, inserted in mating holes in two different parts allowing those parts to maintain a fixed relationship.

DRIVELINE: The drive connection between the transmission and the drive wheels.

DRIVE TRAIN: The components that transmit the flow of power from the engine to the wheels. The components include the clutch, transmission, driveshafts (or axle shafts in front wheel drive), U-joints and differential.

DRUM BRAKE: A braking system which consists of two brake shoes and one or two wheel cylinders, mounted on a fixed backing plate, and a brake drum, mounted on an axle, which revolves around the assembly.

DRY CHARGED BATTERY: Battery to which electrolyte is added when the battery is placed in service.

DVOM: Digital volt ohmmeter

DWELL: The rate, measured in degrees of shaft rotation, at which an electrical circuit cycles on and off.

DYNAMIC: An application in which there is rotating or reciprocating motion between the parts.

EARLY: Condition where shift occurs before vehicle has reached proper speed, which tends to labor engine after upshift.

EBCM: See Electronic Control Unit (ECU).

ECM: See Electronic Control Unit (ECU).

ECU: Electronic control unit.

ELECTRODE: Conductor (positive or negative) of electric current.

ELECTROLYSIS: A surface etching or bonding of current conducting transmission/transaxle components that may occur when grounding straps are missing or in poor condition.

ELECTROLYTE: A solution of water and sulfuric acid used to activate the battery. Electrolyte is extremely corrosive.

ELECTROMAGNET: A coil that produces a magnetic field when current flows through its windings.

ELECTROMAGNETIC INDUCTION: A method to create (generate) current flow through the use of magnetism.

ELECTROMAGNETISM: The effects surrounding the relationship between electricity and magnetism.

ELECTROMOTIVE FORCE (EMF): The force or pressure (voltage) that causes current movement in an electrical circuit.

ELECTRONIC CONTROL UNIT: A digital computer that controls engine (and sometimes transmission, brake or other vehicle system) functions based on data received from various sensors. Examples used by some manufacturers include Electronic Brake Control Module (EBCM), Engine Control Module (ECM), Powertrain Control Module (PCM) or Vehicle Control Module (VCM).

ELECTRONIC IGNITION: A system in which the timing and firing of the spark plugs is controlled by an electronic control unit, usually called a module. These systems have no points or condenser.

ELECTRONIC PRESSURE CONTROL (EPC) SOLENOID: A specially designed solenoid containing a spool valve and spring assembly to control fluid mainline pressure. A variable current flow, controlled by the ECM/PCM, varies the internal force of the solenoid on the spool valve and resulting mainline pressure. (See variable force solenoid.)

ELECTRONICS: Miniaturized electrical circuits utilizing semiconductors, solid-state devices, and printed circuits. Electronic circuits utilize small amounts of power.

ELECTRONIFICATION: The application of electronic circuitry to a mechanical device. Regarding automatic transmissions, electrification is incorporated into converter clutch lockup, shift scheduling, and line pressure control systems.

ELECTROSTATIC DISCHARGE (ESD): An unwanted, high-voltage electrical current released by an individual who has taken on a static charge of electricity. Electronic components can be easily damaged by ESD.

ELEMENT: A device within a hydrodynamic drive unit designed with a set of blades to direct fluid flow.

ENAMEL: Type of paint that dries to a smooth, glossy finish.

END BUMP (END FEEL OR SLIP BUMP): Firmer feel at end of shift when compared with feel at start of shift.

END-PLAY: The clearance/gap between two components that allows for expansion of the parts as they warm up, to prevent binding and to allow space for lubrication.

ENERGY: The ability or capacity to do work.

ENGINE: The primary motor or power apparatus of a vehicle, which converts liquid or gas fuel into mechanical energy.

ENGINE BLOCK: The basic engine casting containing the cylinders, the crankshaft main bearings, as well as machined surfaces for the mounting of other components such as the cylinder head, oil pan, transmission, etc.

ENGINE BRAKING: Use of engine to slow vehicle by manually downshifting during zero-throttle coast down.

ENGINE CONTROL MODULE (ECM): Manages the engine and incorporates output control over the torque converter clutch solenoid. (Note: Current designation for the ECM in late model vehicles is PCM.)

ENGINE COOLANT TEMPERATURE (ECT) SENSOR: Prevents converter clutch engagement with a cold engine; also used for shift timing and shift quality.

EP LUBRICANT: EP (extreme pressure) lubricants are specially formulated for use with gears involving heavy loads (transmissions, differentials, etc.).

ETHYL: A substance added to gasoline to improve its resistance to knock, by slowing down the rate of combustion.

ETHYLENE GLYCOL: The base substance of antifreeze.

EXHAUST MANIFOLD: A set of cast passages or pipes which conduct exhaust gases from the engine.

FAIL-SAFE (BACKUP) CONTROL: A substitute value used by the PCM/TCM to replace a faulty signal from an input sensor. The temporary value allows the vehicle to continue to be operated.

FAST IDLE: The speed of the engine when the choke is on. Fast idle speeds engine warm-up.

FEDERAL ENGINE: An engine certified by the EPA for use in any of the 49 states (except California).

FEEDBACK: A circuit malfunction whereby current can find another path to feed load devices.

FEELER GAUGE: A blade, usually metal, of precisely predetermined thickness, used to measure the clearance between two parts.

FILAMENT: The part of a bulb that glows; the filament creates high resistance to current flow and actually glows from the resulting heat.

FINAL DRIVE: An essential part of the axle drive assembly where final gear reduction takes place in the powertrain. In RWD applications and north-south FWD applications, it must also change the power flow direction to the axle shaft by ninety degrees. (Also see axle ratio).

FIRING ORDER: The order in which combustion occurs in the cylinders of an engine. Also the order in which spark is distributed to the plugs by the distributor.

FIRM: A noticeable quick apply of a clutch or band that is considered normal with medium to heavy throttle shift; should not be confused with harsh or rough.

FLAME FRONT: The term used to describe certain aspects of the fuel explosion in the cylinders. The flame front should move in a controlled pattern across the cylinder, rather than simply exploding immediately.

FLARE (SLIPPING): A quick increase in engine rpm accompanied by momentary loss of torque; generally occurs during shift.

FLAT ENGINE: Engine design in which the pistons are horizontally opposed. Porsche, Subaru and some old VW are common examples of flat engines.

FLAT RATE: A dealership term referring to the amount of money paid to a technician for a repair or diagnostic service based on that particular service versus dealership's labor time (NOT based on the actual time the technician spent on the job).

FLAT SPOT: A point during acceleration when the engine seems to lose power for an instant.

FLOODING: The presence of too much fuel in the intake manifold and combustion chamber which prevents the air/fuel mixture from firing, thereby causing a no-start situation.

FLUID: A fluid can be either liquid or gas. In hydraulics, a liquid is used for transmitting force or motion.

FLUID COUPLING: The simplest form of hydrodynamic drive, the fluid coupling consists of two look-alike members with straight radial varies referred to as the impeller (pump) and the turbine. Input torque is always equal to the output torque.

FLUID DRIVE: Either a fluid coupling or a fluid torque converter. (See hydrodynamic drive units.)

FLUID TORQUE CONVERTER: A hydrodynamic drive that has the ability to act both as a torque multiplier and fluid coupling. (See hydrodynamic drive units; torque converter.)

FLUID VISCOSITY: The resistance of a liquid to flow. A cold fluid (oil) has greater viscosity and flows more slowly than a hot fluid (oil).

FLYWHEEL: A heavy disc of metal attached to the rear of the crankshaft. It smoothes the firing impulses of the engine and keeps the crankshaft turning during periods when no firing takes place. The starter also engages the flywheel to start the engine.

FOOT POUND (ft. lbs., lbs. ft. or sometimes, ft. lb.): The amount of energy or work needed to raise an item weighing one pound, a distance of one foot.

FREEZE PLUG: A plug in the engine block which will be pushed out if the coolant freezes. Sometimes called expansion plugs, they protect the block from cracking should the coolant freeze.

FRICTION: The resistance that occurs between contacting surfaces. This relationship is expressed by a ratio called the coefficient of friction (CL).

FRICTION, COEFFICIENT OF: The amount of surface tension between two contacting surfaces; expressed by a scientifically calculated number.

FRONT END ALIGNMENT: A service to set caster, camber and toe-in to the correct specifications. This will ensure that the car steers and handles properly and that the tires wear properly.

FRICTION MODIFIER: Changes the coefficient of friction of the fluid between the mating steel and composition clutch/band surfaces during the engagement process and allows for a certain amount of intentional slipping for a good "shift-feel".

FRONTAL AREA: The total frontal area of a vehicle exposed to air flow.

FUEL FILTER: A component of the fuel system containing a porous paper element used to prevent any impurities from entering the engine through the fuel system. It usually takes the form of a canister-like housing, mounted in-line with the fuel hose, located anywhere on a vehicle between the fuel tank and engine.

FUEL INJECTION: A system replacing the carburetor that sprays fuel into the cylinder through nozzles. The amount of fuel can be more precisely controlled with fuel injection.

FULL FLOATING AXLE: An axle in which the axle housing extends through the wheel giving bearing support on the outside of the housing. The front axle of a four-wheel drive vehicle is usually a full floating axle, as are the rear axles of many larger (1 ton and over) pick-ups and vans.

FULL-TIME FOUR-WHEEL DRIVE: A four-wheel drive system that continuously delivers power to all four wheels. A differential between the front and rear driveshafts permits variations in axle speeds to control gear wind-up without damage.

FULL THROTTLE DETENT DOWNSHIFT: A quick apply of accelerator pedal to its full travel, forcing a downshift.

FUSE: A protective device in a circuit which prevents circuit overload by breaking the circuit when a specific amperage is present. The device is constructed around a strip or wire of a lower amperage rating than the circuit it is designed to protect. When an amperage higher than that stamped on the fuse is present in the circuit, the strip or wire melts, opening the circuit.

FUSIBLE LINK: A piece of wire in a wiring harness that performs the same job as a fuse. If overloaded, the fusible link will melt and interrupt the circuit.

FWD: Front wheel drive.

GAWR: (Gross axle weight rating) the total maximum weight an axle is designed to carry.

GCW: (Gross combined weight) total combined weight of a tow vehicle and trailer.

GARAGE SHIFT: initial engagement feel of transmission, neutral to reverse or neutral to a forward drive.

GARAGE SHIFT FEEL: A quick check of the engagement quality and responsiveness of reverse and forward gears. This test is done with the vehicle stationary.

GEAR: A toothed mechanical device that acts as a rotating lever to transmit power or turning effort from one shaft to another. (See gear ratio.)

GEAR RATIO: A ratio expressing the number of turns a smaller gear will make to turn a larger gear through one revolution. The ratio is found by dividing the number of teeth on the smaller gear into the number of teeth on the larger gear.

GEARBOX: Transmission

GEAR REDUCTION: Torque is multiplied and speed decreased by the factor of the gear ratio. For example, a 3:1 gear ratio changes an input torque of 180 ft. lbs. and an input speed of 2700 rpm to 540 Ft. lbs. and 900 rpm, respectively. (No account is taken of frictional losses, which are always present.)

GEARTRAIN: A succession of intermeshing gears that form an assembly and provide for one or more torque changes as the power input is transmitted to the power output.

GEL COAT: A thin coat of plastic resin covering fiberglass body panels.

GENERATOR: A device which produces direct current (DC) necessary to charge the battery.

GOVERNOR: A device that senses vehicle speed and generates a hydraulic oil pressure. As vehicle speed increases, governor oil pressure rises.

GROUND CIRCUIT: (See circuit, ground.)

GROUND SIDE SWITCHING: The electrical/electronic circuit control switch is located after the circuit load.

GVWR: (Gross vehicle weight rating) total maximum weight a vehicle is designed to carry including the weight of the vehicle, passengers, equipment, gas, oil, etc.

HALOGEN: A special type of lamp known for its quality of brilliant white light. Originally used for fog lights and driving lights.

HARD CODES: DTCs that are present at the time of testing; also called continuous or current codes.

HARSH(ROUGH): An apply of a clutch or band that is more noticeable than a firm one; considered undesirable at any throttle position.

HEADER TANK: An expansion tank for the radiator coolant. It can be located remotely or built into the radiator.

HEAT RANGE: A term used to describe the ability of a spark plug to carry away heat. Plugs with longer nosed insulators take longer to carry heat off effectively.

HEAT RISER: A flapper in the exhaust manifold that is closed when the engine is cold, causing hot exhaust gases to heat the intake manifold providing better cold engine operation. A thermostatic spring opens the flapper when the engine warms up.

HEAVY THROTTLE: Approximately three-fourths of accelerator pedal travel.

HEMI: A name given an engine using hemispherical combustion chambers.

HERTZ (HZ): The international unit of frequency equal to one cycle per second (10,000 Hertz equals 10,000 cycles per second).

HIGH-IMPEDANCE DVOM (DIGITAL VOLT-OHMMETER): This styled device provides a built-in resistance value and is capable of limiting circuit current flow to safe milliamp levels.

HIGH RESISTANCE: Often refers to a circuit where there is an excessive amount of opposition to normal current flow.

HORSEPOWER: A measurement of the amount of work; one horsepower is the amount of work necessary to lift 33,000 lbs. one foot in one minute. Brake horsepower (bhp) is the horsepower delivered by an engine on a dynamometer. Net horsepower is the power remaining (measured at the flywheel of the engine) that can be used to turn the wheels after power is consumed through friction and running the engine accessories (water pump, alternator, air pump, fan etc.)

HOT CIRCUIT: (See circuit, hot; hot lead.)

HOT LEAD: A wire or conductor in the power side of the circuit. (See circuit, hot.)

HOT SIDE SWITCHING: The electrical/electronic circuit control switch is located before the circuit load.

HUB: The center part of a wheel or gear.

HUNTING (BUSYNESS): Repeating quick series of up-shifts and downshifts that causes noticeable change in engine rpm, for example, as in a 4-3-4 shift pattern.

HYDRAULICS: The use of liquid under pressure to transfer force of motion.

HYDROCARBON (HC): Any chemical compound made up of hydrogen and carbon. A major pollutant formed by the engine as a by-product of combustion.

HYDRODYNAMIC DRIVE UNITS: Devices that transmit power solely by the action of a kinetic fluid flow in a closed recirculating path. An impeller energizes the fluid and discharges the high-speed jet stream into the turbine for power output.

HYDROMETER: An instrument used to measure the specific gravity of a solution.

HYDROPLANING: A phenomenon of driving when water builds up under the tire tread, causing it to lose contact with the road. Slowing down will usually restore normal tire contact with the road.

HYPOID GEARSET: The drive pinion gear may be placed below or above the centerline of the driven gear; often used as a final drive gearset.

IDLE MIXTURE: The mixture of air and fuel (usually about 14:1) being fed to the cylinders. The idle mixture screw(s) are sometimes adjusted as part of a tune-up.

IDLER ARM: Component of the steering linkage which is a geometric duplicate of the steering gear arm. It supports the right side of the center steering link.

IMPELLER: Often called a pump, the impeller is the power input (drive) member of a hydrodynamic drive. As part of the torque converter cover, it acts as a centrifugal pump and puts the fluid in motion.

INCH POUND (inch lbs.; sometimes in. lb. or in. lbs.): One twelfth of a foot pound.

INDUCTANCE: The force that produces voltage when a conductor is passed through a magnetic field.

INDUCTION: A means of transferring electrical energy in the form of a magnetic field. Principle used in the ignition coil to increase voltage.

INITIAL FEEL: A distinct firmer feel at start of shift when compared with feel at finish of shift.

INJECTOR: A device which receives metered fuel under relatively low pressure and is activated to inject the fuel into the engine under relatively high pressure at a predetermined time.

INPUT: In an automatic transmission, the source of power from the engine is absorbed by the torque converter, which provides the power input into the transmission. The turbine drives the input(turbine)shaft.

INPUT SHAFT: The shaft to which torque is applied, usually carrying the driving gear or gears.

INTAKE MANIFOLD: A casting of passages or pipes used to conduct air or a fuel/air mixture to the cylinders.

INTERNAL GEAR: The ring-like outer gear of a planetary gearset with the gear teeth cut on the inside of the ring to provide a mesh with the planet pinions.

ISOLATION (CLAMPING) DIODES: Diodes positioned in a circuit to prevent self-induction from damaging electronic components.

IX ROTARY GEAR PUMP: Contains two rotating members, one shaped with internal gear teeth and the other with external gear teeth. As the gears separate, the fluid fills the gaps between gear teeth, is pulled across a crescent-shaped divider, and then is forced to flow through the outlet as the gears mesh.

IX ROTARY LOBE PUMP: Sometimes referred to as a gerotor type pump. Two rotating members, one shaped with internal lobes and the other with external lobes, separate and then mesh to cause fluid to flow.

JOURNAL: The bearing surface within which a shaft operates.

JUMPER CABLES: Two heavy duty wires with large alligator clips used to provide power from a charged battery to a discharged battery mounted in a vehicle.

JUMPSTART: Utilizing the sufficiently charged battery of one vehicle to start the engine of another vehicle with a discharged battery by the use of jumper cables.

KEY: A small block usually fitted in a notch between a shaft and a hub to prevent slippage of the two parts.

KICKDOWN: Detent downshift system; either linkage, cable, or electrically controlled.

KILO: A prefix used in the metric system to indicate one thousand.

KNOCK: Noise which results from the spontaneous ignition of a portion of the air-fuel mixture in the engine cylinder caused by overly advanced ignition timing or use of incorrectly low octane fuel for that engine.

KNOCK SENSOR: An input device that responds to spark knock, caused by over advanced ignition timing.

LABOR TIME: A specific amount of time required to perform a certain repair or diagnostic service as defined by a vehicle or after-market manufacturer .

LACQUER: A quick-drying automotive paint.

LATE: Shift that occurs when engine is at higher than normal rpm for given amount of throttle.

LIGHT-EMITTING DIODE (LED): A semiconductor diode that emits light as electrical current flows through it; used in some electronic display devices to emit a red or other color light.

LIGHT THROTTLE: Approximately one-fourth of accelerator pedal travel.

LIMITED SLIP: A type of differential which transfers driving force to the wheel with the best traction.

LIMP-IN MODE: Electrical shutdown of the transmission/ transaxle output solenoids, allowing only forward and reverse gears that are hydraulically energized by the manual valve. This permits the vehicle to be driven to a service facility for repair.

LIP SEAL: Molded synthetic rubber seal designed with an outer sealing edge (lip) that points into the fluid containing area to be sealed. This type of seal is used where rotational and axial forces are present.

LITHIUM-BASE GREASE: Chassis and wheel bearing grease using lithium as a base. Not compatible with sodium-base grease.

LOAD DEVICE: A circuit's resistance that converts the electrical energy into light, sound, heat, or mechanical movement.

LOAD RANGE: Indicates the number of plies at which a tire is rated. Load range B equals four-ply rating; C equals six-ply rating; and, D equals an eight-ply rating.

LOAD TORQUE: The amount of output torque needed from the transmission/transaxle to overcome the vehicle load.

LOCKING HUBS: Accessories used on part-time four-wheel drive systems that allow the front wheels to be disengaged from the drive train when four-wheel drive is not being used. When four-wheel drive is desired, the hubs are engaged, locking the wheels to the drive train.

LOCKUP CONVERTER: A torque converter that operates hydraulically and mechanically. When an internal apply plate (lockup plate) clamps to the torque converter cover, hydraulic slippage is eliminated.

LOCK RING: See Circlip or Snapring

MAGNET: Any body with the property of attracting iron or steel.

MAGNETIC FIELD: The area surrounding the poles of a magnet that is affected by its attraction or repulsion forces.

MAIN LINE PRESSURE: Often called control pressure or line pressure, it refers to the pressure of the oil leaving the pump and is controlled by the pressure regulator valve.

MALFUNCTION INDICATOR LAMP (MIL): Previously known as a check engine light, the dash-mounted MIL illuminates and signals the driver that an emission or driveability problem with the powertrain has been detected by the ECM/PCM. When this occurs, at least one diagnostic trouble code (DTC) has been stored into the control module memory.

MANIFOLD ABSOLUTE PRESSURE (MAP) SENSOR: Reads the amount of air pressure (vacuum) in the engine's intake manifold system; its signal is used to analyze engine load conditions.

MANIFOLD VACUUM: Low pressure in an engine intake manifold formed just below the throttle plates. Manifold vacuum is highest at idle and drops under acceleration.

MANIFOLD: A casting of passages or set of pipes which connect the cylinders to an inlet or outlet source.

MANUAL LEVER POSITION SWITCH (MLPS): A mechanical switching unit that is typically mounted externally to the transmission/transaxle to inform the PCM/ECM which gear range the driver has selected.

MANUAL VALVE: Located inside the transmission/transaxle, it is directly connected to the driver's shift lever. The position of the manual valve determines which hydraulic circuits will be charged with oil pressure and the operating mode of the transmission.

MANUAL VALVE LEVER POSITION SENSOR (MVLPS): The input from this device tells the TCM what gear range was selected.

MASS AIR FLOW (MAF) SENSOR: Measures the airflow into the engine.

MASTER CYLINDER: The primary fluid pressurizing device in a hydraulic system. In automotive use, it is found in brake and hydraulic clutch systems and is pedal activated, either directly or, in a power brake system, through the power booster.

MacPherson STRUT: A suspension component combining a shock absorber and spring in one unit.

MEDIUM THROTTLE: Approximately one-half of accelerator pedal travel.

MEGA: A metric prefix indicating one million.

MEMBER: An independent component of a hydrodynamic unit such as an impeller, a stator, or a turbine. It may have one or more elements.

MERCON: A fluid developed by Ford Motor Company in 1988. It contains a friction modifier and closely resembles operating characteristics of Dexron.

METAL SEALING RINGS: Made from cast iron or aluminum, their primary application is with dynamic components involving pressure sealing circuits of rotating members. These rings are designed with either butt or hook lock end joints.

METER (ANALOG): A linear-style meter representing data as lengths; a needle-style instrument interfacing with logical numerical increments. This style of electrical meter uses relatively low impedance internal resistance and cannot be used for testing electronic circuitry.

METER (DIGITAL): Uses numbers as a direct readout to show values. Most meters of this style use high impedance internal resistance and must be used for testing low current electronic circuitry.

MICRO: A metric prefix indicating one-millionth (0.000001).

MILLI: A metric prefix indicating one-thousandth (0.001).

MINIMUM THROTTLE: The least amount of throttle opening required for upshift; normally close to zero throttle.

MISFIRE: Condition occurring when the fuel mixture in a cylinder fails to ignite, causing the engine to run roughly.

MODULE: Electronic control unit, amplifier or igniter of solid state or integrated design which controls the current flow in the ignition primary circuit based on input from the pick-up coil. When the module opens the primary circuit, high secondary voltage is induced in the coil.

MODULATED: In an electronic-hydraulic converter clutch system (or shift valve system), the term modulated refers to the pulsing of a solenoid, at a variable rate. This action controls the buildup of oil pressure in the hydraulic circuit to allow a controlled amount of clutch slippage.

MODULATED CONVERTER CLUTCH CONTROL (MCCC): A pulse width duty cycle valve that controls the converter lockup apply pressure and maximizes smoother transitions between lock and unlock conditions.

MODULATOR PRESSURE (THROTTLE PRESSURE): A hydraulic signal oil pressure relating to the amount of engine load, based on either the amount of throttle plate opening or engine vacuum.

MODULATOR VALVE: A regulator valve that is controlled by engine vacuum, providing a hydraulic pressure that varies in relation to engine torque. The hydraulic torque signal functions to delay the shift pattern and provide a line pressure boost. (See throttle valve.)

MOTOR: An electromagnetic device used to convert electrical energy into mechanical energy.

MULTIPLE-DISC CLUTCH: A grouping of steel and friction lined plates that, when compressed together by hydraulic pressure acting upon a piston, lock or unlock a planetary member.

MULTI-WEIGHT: Type of oil that provides adequate lubrication at both high and low temperatures.

needed to move one amp through a resistance of one ohm.

MUSHY: Same as soft; slow and drawn out clutch apply with very little shift feel.

MUTUAL INDUCTION: The generation of current from one wire circuit to another by movement of the magnetic field surrounding a current-carrying circuit as its ampere flow increases or decreases.

NEEDLE BEARING: A bearing which consists of a number (usually a large number) of long, thin rollers.

NITROGEN OXIDE (NOx): One of the three basic pollutants found in the exhaust emission of an internal combustion engine. The amount of NOx usually varies in an inverse proportion to the amount of HC and CO.

NONPOSITIVE SEALING: A sealing method that allows some minor leakage, which normally assists in lubrication.

O2 SENSOR: Located in the engine's exhaust system, it is an input device to the ECM/PCM for managing the fuel delivery and ignition system. A scanner can be used to observe the fluctuating voltage readings produced by an O2 sensor as the oxygen content of the exhaust is analyzed.

O-RING SEAL: Molded synthetic rubber seal designed with a circular cross-section. This type of seal is used primarily in static applications.

OBD II (ON-BOARD DIAGNOSTICS, SECOND GENERATION): Refers to the federal law mandating tighter control of 1996 and newer vehicle emissions, active monitoring of related devices, and standardization of terminology, data link connectors, and other technician concerns.

OCTANE RATING: A number, indicating the quality of gasoline based on its ability to resist knock. The higher the number, the better the quality. Higher compression engines require higher octane gas.

OEM: Original Equipment Manufactured. OEM equipment is that furnished standard by the manufacturer.

OFFSET: The distance between the vertical center of the wheel and the mounting surface at the lugs. Offset is positive if the center is outside the lug circle; negative offset puts the center line inside the lug circle.

OHM'S LAW: A law of electricity that states the relationship between voltage, current, and resistance. Volts = amperes x ohms

OHM: The unit used to measure the resistance of conductor-to-electrical flow. One ohm is the amount of resistance that limits current flow to one ampere in a circuit with one volt of pressure.

OHMMETER: An instrument used for measuring the resistance, in ohms, in an electrical circuit.

ONE-WAY CLUTCH: A mechanical clutch of roller or sprag design that resists torque or transmits power in one direction only. It is used to either hold or drive a planetary member.

ONE-WAY ROLLER CLUTCH: A mechanical device that transmits or holds torque in one direction only.

OPEN CIRCUIT: A break or lack of contact in an electrical circuit, either intentional (switch) or unintentional (bad connection or broken wire).

ORIFICE: Located in hydraulic oil circuits, it acts as a restriction. It slows down fluid flow to either create back pressure or delay pressure buildup downstream.

OSCILLOSCOPE: A piece of test equipment that shows electric impulses as a pattern on a screen. Engine performance can be analyzed by interpreting these patterns.

OUTPUT SHAFT: The shaft which transmits torque from a device, such as a transmission.

OUTPUT SPEED SENSOR (OSS): Identifies transmission/transaxle output shaft speed for shift timing and may be used to calculate TCC slip; often functions as the VSS (vehicle speed sensor).

OVERDRIVE: (1.) A device attached to or incorporated in a transmission/transaxle that allows the engine to turn less than one full revolution for every complete revolution of the wheels. The net effect is to reduce engine rpm, thereby using less fuel. A typical overdrive gear ratio would be .87:1, instead of the normal 1:1 in high gear. (2.) A gear assembly which produces more shaft revolutions than that transmitted to it.

OVERDRIVE PLANETARY GEARSET: A single planetary gearset designed to provide a direct drive and overdrive ratio. When coupled to a three-speed transmission/transaxle configuration, a four-speed/overdrive unit is present.

OVERHEAD CAMSHAFT (OHC): An engine configuration in which the camshaft is mounted on top of the cylinder head and operates the valve either directly or by means of rocker arms.

OVERHEAD VALVE (OHV): An engine configuration in which all of the valves are located in the cylinder head and the camshaft is located in the cylinder block. The camshaft operates the valves via lifters and pushrods.

OVERRUNCLUTCH: Another name for a one-way mechanical clutch. Applies to both roller and sprag designs.

OVERSTEER: The tendency of some vehicles, when steering into a turn, to over-respond or steer more than required, which could result in excessive slip of the rear wheels. Opposite of under-steer.

OXIDATION STABILIZERS: Absorb and dissipate heat. Automatic transmission fluid has high resistance to varnish and sludge buildup that occurs from excessive heat that is generated primarily in the torque converter. Local temperatures as high as 6000F (3150C) can occur at the clutch plates during engagement, and this heat must be absorbed and dissipated. If the fluid cannot withstand the heat, it burns or oxidizes, resulting in an almost immediate destruction of friction materials, clogged filter screen and hydraulic passages, and sticky valves.

OXIDES OF NITROGEN: See nitrogen oxide (NOx).

OXYGEN SENSOR: Used with a feedback system to sense the presence of oxygen in the exhaust gas and signal the computer which can use the voltage signal to determine engine operating efficiency and adjust the air/fuel ratio.

PARALLEL CIRCUIT: (See circuit, parallel.)

PARTS WASHER: A basin or tub, usually with a built-in pump mechanism and hose used for circulating chemical solvent for the purpose of cleaning greasy, oily and dirty components.

PART-TIME FOUR WHEEL DRIVE: A system that is normally in the two wheel drive mode and only runs in four-wheel drive when the system is manually engaged because more traction is desired. Two or four wheel drive is normally selected by a lever to engage the front axle, but if locking hubs are used, these must also be manually engaged in the Lock position. Otherwise, the front axle will not drive the front wheels.

PASSIVE RESTRAINT: Safety systems such as air bags or automatic seat belts which operate with no action required on the part of the driver or passenger. Mandated by Federal regulations on all vehicles sold in the U.S. after 1990.

PAYLOAD: The weight the vehicle is capable of carrying in addition to its own weight. Payload includes weight of the driver, passengers and cargo, but not coolant, fuel, lubricant, spare tire, etc.

PCM: Powertrain control module.

PCV VALVE: A valve usually located in the rocker cover that vents crankcase vapors back into the engine to be reburned.

PERCOLATION: A condition in which the fuel actually "boils," due to excessive heat. Percolation prevents proper atomization of the fuel causing rough running.

PICK-UP COIL: The coil in which voltage is induced in an electronic ignition.

PING: A metallic rattling sound produced by the engine during acceleration. It is usually due to incorrect ignition timing or a poor grade of gasoline.

PINION: The smaller of two gears. The rear axle pinion drives the ring gear which transmits motion to the axle shafts.

PINION GEAR: The smallest gear in a drive gear assembly.

PISTON: A disc or cup that fits in a cylinder bore and is free to move. In hydraulics, it provides the means of converting hydraulic pressure into a usable force. Examples of piston applications are found in servo, clutch, and accumulator units.

PISTON RING: An open-ended ring which fits into a groove on the outer diameter of the piston. Its chief function is to form a seal between the piston and cylinder wall. Most automotive pistons have three rings: two for compression sealing; one for oil sealing.

PITMAN ARM: A lever which transmits steering force from the steering gear to the steering linkage.

PLANET CARRIER: A basic member of a planetary gear assembly that carries the pinion gears.

PLANET PINIONS: Gears housed in a planet carrier that are in constant mesh with the sun gear and internal gear. Because they have their own independent rotating centers, the pinions are capable of rotating around the sun gear or the inside of the internal gear.

PLANETARY GEAR RATIO: The reduction or overdrive ratio developed by a planetary gearset.

PLANETARY GEARSET: In its simplest form, it is made up of a basic assembly group containing a sun gear, internal gear, and planet carrier. The gears are always in constant mesh and offer a wide range of gear ratio possibilities.

PLANETARY GEARSET (COMPOUND): Two planetary gearsets combined together.

PLANETARY GEARSET (SIMPLE): An assembly of gears in constant mesh consisting of a sun gear, several pinion gears mounted in a carrier, and a ring gear. It provides gear ratio and direction changes, in addition to a direct drive and a neutral.

PLY RATING: A. rating given a tire which indicates strength (but not necessarily actual plies). A two-ply/four-ply rating has only two plies, but the strength of a four-ply tire.

POLARITY: Indication (positive or negative) of the two poles of a battery.

PORT: An opening for fluid intake or exhaust.

POSITIVE SEALING: A sealing method that completely prevents leakage.

POTENTIAL: Electrical force measured in volts; sometimes used interchangeably with voltage.

POWER: The ability to do work per unit of time, as expressed in horsepower; one horsepower equals 33,000 ft. lbs. of work per minute, or 550 ft. lbs. of work per second.

POWER FLOW: The systematic flow or transmission of power through the gears, from the input shaft to the output shaft.

POWER-TO-WEIGHT RATIO: Ratio of horsepower to weight of car.

POWERTRAIN: See Drivetrain.

POWERTRAIN CONTROL MODULE (PCM): Current designation for the engine control module (ECM). In many cases, late model vehicle control units manage the engine as well as the transmission. In other settings, the PCM controls the engine and is interfaced with a TCM to control transmission functions.

Ppm: Parts per million; unit used to measure exhaust emissions.

PREIGNITION: Early ignition of fuel in the cylinder, sometimes due to glowing carbon deposits in the combustion chamber. Preignition can be damaging since combustion takes place prematurely.

PRELOAD: A predetermined load placed on a bearing during assembly or by adjustment.

PRESS FIT: The mating of two parts under pressure, due to the inner diameter of one being smaller than the outer diameter of the other, or vice versa; an interference fit.

PRESSURE: The amount of force exerted upon a surface area.

PRESSURE CONTROL SOLENOID (PCS): An output device that provides a boost oil pressure to the mainline regulator valve to control line pressure. Its operation is determined by the amount of current sent from the PCM.

PRESSURE GAUGE: An instrument used for measuring the fluid pressure in a hydraulic circuit.

PRESSURE REGULATOR VALVE: In automatic transmissions, its purpose is to regulate the pressure of the pump output and supply the basic fluid pressure necessary to operate the transmission. The regulated fluid pressure may be referred to as mainline pressure, line pressure, or control pressure.

PRESSURE SWITCH ASSEMBLY (PSA): Mounted inside the transmission, it is a grouping of oil pressure switches that inputs to the PCM when certain hydraulic passages are charged with oil pressure.

PRESSURE PLATE: A spring-loaded plate (part of the clutch) that transmits power to the driven (friction) plate when the clutch is engaged.

PRIMARY CIRCUIT: The low voltage side of the ignition system which consists of the ignition switch, ballast resistor or resistance wire, bypass, coil, electronic control unit and pick-up coil as well as the connecting wires and harnesses.

PROFILE: Term used for tire measurement (tire series), which is the ratio of tire height to tread width.

PROM (PROGRAMMABLE READ-ONLY MEMORY): The heart of the computer that compares input data and makes the engineered program or strategy decisions about when to trigger the appropriate output based on stored computer instructions.

PULSE GENERATOR: A two-wire pickup sensor used to produce a fluctuating electrical signal. This changing signal is read by the controller to determine the speed of the object and can be used to measure transmission/transaxle input speed, output speed, and vehicle speed.

PSI: Pounds per square inch; a measurement of pressure.

PULSE WIDTH DUTY CYCLE SOLENOID (PULSE WIDTH MODULATED SOLENOID): A computer-controlled solenoid that turns on and off at a variable rate producing a modulated oil pressure; often referred to as a pulse width modulated (PWM) solenoid. Employed in many electronic automatic transmissions and transaxles, these solenoids are used to manage shift control and converter clutch hydraulic circuits.

PUSHROD: A steel rod between the hydraulic valve lifter and the valve rocker arm in overhead valve (OHV) engines.

PUMP: A mechanical device designed to create fluid flow and pressure buildup in a hydraulic system.

QUARTER PANEL: General term used to refer to a rear fender. Quarter panel is the area from the rear door opening to the tail light area and from rear wheel well to the base of the trunk and roof-line.

RACE: The surface on the inner or outer ring of a bearing on which the balls, needles or rollers move.

RACK AND PINION: A type of automotive steering system using a pinion gear attached to the end of the steering shaft. The pinion meshes with a long rack attached to the steering linkage.

RADIAL TIRE: Tire design which uses body cords running at right angles to the center line of the tire. Two or more belts are used to give tread strength. Radials can be identified by their characteristic sidewall bulge.

RADIATOR: Part of the cooling system for a water-cooled engine, mounted in the front of the vehicle and connected to the engine with rubber hoses. Through the radiator, excess combustion heat is dissipated into the atmosphere through forced convection using a water and glycol based mixture that circulates through, and cools, the engine.

RANGE REFERENCE AND CLUTCH/BAND APPLY CHART: A guide that shows the application of clutches and bands for each gear, within the selector range positions. These charts are extremely useful for understanding how the unit operates and for diagnosing malfunctions.

RAVIGNEAUX GEARSET: A compound planetary gearset that features matched dual planetary pinions (sets of two) mounted in a single planet carrier. Two sun gears and one ring mesh with the carrier pinions.

REACTION MEMBER: The stationary planetary member, in a planetary gearset, that is grounded to the transmission/transaxle case through the use of friction and wedging devices known as bands, disc clutches, and one-way clutches.

REACTION PRESSURE: The fluid pressure that moves a spool valve against an opposing force or forces; the area on which the opposing force acts. The opposing force can be a spring or a combination of spring force and auxiliary hydraulic force.

REACTOR, TORQUE CONVERTER: The reaction member of a fluid torque converter, more commonly called a stator. (See stator.)

REAR MAIN OIL SEAL: A synthetic or rope-type seal that prevents oil from leaking out of the engine past the rear main crankshaft bearing.

RECIRCULATING BALL: Type of steering system in which recirculating steel balls occupy the area between the nut and worm wheel, causing a reduction in friction.

RECTIFIER: A device (used primarily in alternators) that permits electrical current to flow in one direction only.

REDUCTION: (See gear reduction.)

REGULATOR VALVE: A valve that changes the pressure of the oil in a hydraulic circuit as the oil passes through the valve by bleeding off (or exhausting) some of the volume of oil supplied to the valve.

REFRIGERANT 12 (R-12) or 134 (R-134): The generic name of the refrigerant used in automotive air conditioning systems.

REGULATOR: A device which maintains the amperage and/or voltage levels of a circuit at predetermined values.

RELAY: A switch which automatically opens and/or closes a circuit.

RELAY VALVE: A valve that directs flow and pressure. Relay valves simply connect or disconnect interrelated passages without restricting the fluid flow or changing the pressure.

RELIEF VALVE: A spring-loaded, pressure-operated valve that limits oil pressure buildup in a hydraulic circuit to a predetermined maximum value.

RELUCTOR: A wheel that rotates inside the distributor and triggers the release of voltage in an electronic ignition.

RESERVOIR: The storage area for fluid in a hydraulic system; often called a sump.

RESIN: A liquid plastic used in body work.

RESIDUAL MAGNETISM: The magnetic strength stored in a material after a magnetizing field has been removed.

RESISTANCE: The opposition to the flow of current through a circuit or electrical device, and is measured in ohms. Resistance is equal to the voltage divided by the amperage.

RESISTOR SPARK PLUG: A spark plug using a resistor to shorten the spark duration. This suppresses radio interference and lengthens plug life.

RESISTOR: A device, usually made of wire, which offers a preset amount of resistance in an electrical circuit.

RESULTANT FORCE: The single effective directional thrust of the fluid force on the turbine produced by the vortex and rotary forces acting in different planes.

RETARD: Set the ignition timing so that spark occurs later (fewer degrees before TDC).

RHEOSTAT: A device for regulating a current by means of a variable resistance.

RING GEAR: The name given to a ring-shaped gear attached to a differential case, or affixed to a flywheel or as part of a planetary gear set.

ROADLOAD: grade.

ROCKER ARM: A lever which rotates around a shaft pushing down (opening) the valve with an end when the other end is pushed up by the pushrod. Spring pressure will later close the valve.

ROCKER PANEL: The body panel below the doors between the wheel opening.

ROLLER BEARING: A bearing made up of hardened inner and outer races between which hardened steel rollers move.

ROLLER CLUTCH: A type of one-way clutch design using rollers and springs mounted within an inner and outer cam race assembly.

ROTARY FLOW: The path of the fluid trapped between the blades of the members as they revolve with the rotation of the torque converter cover (rotational inertia).

ROTOR: (1.) The disc-shaped part of a disc brake assembly, upon which the brake pads bear; also called, brake disc. (2.) The device mounted atop the distributor shaft, which passes current to the distributor cap tower contacts.

ROTARY ENGINE: See Wankel engine.

RPM: Revolutions per minute (usually indicates engine speed).

RTV: A gasket making compound that cures as it is exposed to the atmosphere. It is used between surfaces that are not perfectly machined to one another, leaving a slight gap that the RTV fills and in which it hardens. The letters RTV represent room temperature vulcanizing.

RUN-ON: Condition when the engine continues to run, even when the key is turned off. See dieseling.

SEALED BEAM: A automotive headlight. The lens, reflector and filament from a single unit.

SEATBELT INTERLOCK: A system whereby the car cannot be started unless the seatbelt is buckled.

SECONDARY CIRCUIT: The high voltage side of the ignition system, usually above 20,000 volts. The secondary includes the ignition coil, coil wire, distributor cap and rotor, spark plug wires and spark plugs.

SELF-INDUCTION: The generation of voltage in a current-carrying wire by changing the amount of current flowing within that wire.

SEMI-CONDUCTOR: A material (silicon or germanium) that is neither a good conductor nor an insulator; used in diodes and transistors.

SEMI-FLOATING AXLE: In this design, a wheel is attached to the axle shaft, which takes both drive and cornering loads. Almost all solid axle passenger cars and light trucks use this design.

SENDING UNIT: A mechanical, electrical, hydraulic or electromagnetic device which transmits information to a gauge.

SENSOR: Any device designed to measure engine operating conditions or ambient pressures and temperatures. Usually electronic in nature and designed to send a voltage signal to an on-board computer, some sensors may operate as a simple on/off switch or they may provide a variable voltage signal (like a potentiometer) as conditions or measured parameters change.

SERIES CIRCUIT: (See circuit, series.)

SERPENTINE BELT: An accessory drive belt, with small multiple v-ribs, routed around most or all of the engine-powered accessories such as the alternator and power steering pump. Usually both the front and the back side of the belt comes into contact with various pulleys.

SERVO: In an automatic transmission, it is a piston in a cylinder assembly that converts hydraulic pressure into mechanical force and movement; used for the application of the bands and clutches.

SHIFT BUSYNESS: When referring to a torque converter clutch, it is the frequent apply and release of the clutch plate due to uncommon driving conditions.

SHIFT VALVE: Classified as a relay valve, it triggers the automatic shift in response to a governor and a throttle signal by directing fluid to the appropriate band and clutch apply combination to cause the shift to occur.

SHIM: Spacers of precise, predetermined thickness used between parts to establish a proper working relationship.

SHIMMY: Vibration (sometimes violent) in the front end caused by misaligned front end, out of balance tires or worn suspension components.

SHORT CIRCUIT: An electrical malfunction where current takes the path of least resistance to ground (usually through damaged insulation). Current flow is excessive from low resistance resulting in a blown fuse.

SHUDDER: Repeated jerking or stick-slip sensation, similar to chuggle but more severe and rapid in nature, that may be most noticeable during certain ranges of vehicle speed; also used to define condition after converter clutch engagement.

SIMPSON GEARSET: A compound planetary gear train that integrates two simple planetary gearsets referred to as the front planetary and the rear planetary.

SINGLE OVERHEAD CAMSHAFT: See overhead camshaft.

SKIDPLATE: A metal plate attached to the underside of the body to protect the fuel tank, transfer case or other vulnerable parts from damage.

SLAVE CYLINDER: In automotive use, a device in the hydraulic clutch system which is activated by hydraulic force, disengaging the clutch.

SLIPPING: Noticeable increase in engine rpm without vehicle speed increase; usually occurs during or after initial clutch or band engagement.

SLUDGE: Thick, black deposits in engine formed from dirt, oil, water, etc. It is usually formed in engines when oil changes are neglected.

SNAP RING: A circular retaining clip used inside or outside a shaft or part to secure a shaft, such as a floating wrist pin.

SOFT: Slow, almost unnoticeable clutch apply with very little shift feel.

SOFTCODES: DTCs that have been set into the PCM memory but are not present at the time of testing; often referred to as history or intermittent codes.

SOHC: Single overhead camshaft.

SOLENOID: An electrically operated, magnetic switching device.

SPALLING: A wear pattern identified by metal chips flaking off the hardened surface. This condition is caused by foreign particles, overloading situations, and/or normal wear.

SPARK PLUG: A device screwed into the combustion chamber of a spark ignition engine. The basic construction is a conductive core inside of a ceramic insulator, mounted in an outer conductive base. An electrical charge from the spark plug wire travels along the conductive core and jumps a preset air gap to a grounding point or points at the end of the conductive base. The resultant spark ignites the fuel/air mixture in the combustion chamber.

SPECIFIC GRAVITY (BATTERY): The relative weight of liquid (battery electrolyte) as compared to the weight of an equal volume of water.

SPLINES: Ridges machined or cast onto the outer diameter of a shaft or inner diameter of a bore to enable parts to mate without rotation.

SPLIT TORQUE DRIVE: In a torque converter, it refers to parallel paths of torque transmission, one of which is mechanical and the other hydraulic.

SPONGY PEDAL: A soft or spongy feeling when the brake pedal is depressed. It is usually due to air in the brake lines.

SPOOLVALVE: A precision-machined, cylindrically shaped valve made up of lands and grooves. Depending on its position in the valve bore, various interconnecting hydraulic circuit passages are either opened or closed.

SPRAG CLUTCH: A type of one-way clutch design using cams or contoured-shaped sprags between inner and outer races. (See one-way clutch.)

SPRUNG WEIGHT: The weight of a car supported by the springs.

SQUARE-CUT SEAL: Molded synthetic rubber seal designed with a square- or rectangular-shaped cross-section. This type of seal is used for both dynamic and static applications.

SRS: Supplemental restraint system

STABILIZER (SWAY) BAR: A bar linking both sides of the suspension. It resists sway on turns by taking some of added load from one wheel and putting it on the other.

STAGE: The number of turbine sets separated by a stator. A turbine set may be made up of one or more turbine members. A three-element converter is classified as a single stage.

STALL: In fluid drive transmission/transaxle applications, stall refers to engine rpm with the transmission/transaxle engaged and the vehicle stationary; throttle valve can be in any position between closed and wide open.

STALL SPEED: In fluid drive transmission/transaxle applications, stall speed refers to the maximum engine rpm with the transmission/transaxle engaged and vehicle stationary, when the throttle valve is wide open. (See stall; stall test.)

STALL TEST: A procedure recommended by many manufacturers to help determine the integrity of an engine, the torque converter stator, and certain clutch and band combinations. With the shift lever in each of the forward and reverse positions and with the brakes firmly applied, the accelerator pedal is momentarily pressed to the wide open throttle (WOT) position. The engine rpm reading at full throttle can provide clues for diagnosing the condition of the items listed above.

STALL TORQUE: The maximum design or engineered torque ratio of a fluid torque converter, produced under stall speed conditions. (See stall speed.)

STARTER: A high-torque electric motor used for the purpose of starting the engine, typically through a high ratio geared drive connected to the flywheel ring gear.

STATIC: A sealing application in which the parts being sealed do not move in relation to each other.

STATOR (REACTOR): The reaction member of a fluid torque converter that changes the direction of the fluid as it leaves the turbine to enter the impeller vanes. During the torque multiplication phase, this action assists the impeller's rotary force and results in an increase in torque.

STEERING GEOMETRY: Combination of various angles of suspension components (caster, camber, toe-in); roughly equivalent to front end alignment.

STRAIGHT WEIGHT: Term designating motor oil as suitable for use within a narrow range of temperatures. Outside the narrow temperature range its flow characteristics will not adequately lubricate.

STROKE: The distance the piston travels from bottom dead center to top dead center.

SUBSTITUTION: Replacing one part suspected of a defect with a like part of known quality.

SUMP: The storage vessel or reservoir that provides a ready source of fluid to the pump. In an automatic transmission, the sump is the oil pan. All fluid eventually returns to the sump for recycling into the hydraulic system.

SUN GEAR: In a planetary gearset, it is the center gear that meshes with a cluster of planet pinions.

SUPERCHARGER: An air pump driven mechanically by the engine through belts, chains, shafts or gears from the crankshaft. Two general types of supercharger are the positive displacement and centrifugal type, which pump air in direct relationship to the speed of the engine.

SUPPLEMENTAL RESTRAINT SYSTEM: See air bag.

SURGE: Repeating engine-related feeling of acceleration and deceleration that is less intense than chuggle.

SWITCH: A device used to open, close, or redirect the current in an electrical circuit.

SYNCHROMESH: A manual transmission/transaxle that is equipped with devices (synchronizers) that match the gear speeds so that the transmission/transaxle can be downshifted without clashing gears.

SYNTHETIC OIL: Non-petroleum based oil.

TACHOMETER: A device used to measure the rotary speed of an engine, shaft, gear, etc., usually in rotations per minute.

TDC: Top dead center. The exact top of the piston's stroke.

TEFLON SEALING RINGS: Teflon is a soft, durable, plastic-like material that is resistant to heat and provides excellent sealing. These rings are designed with either scarf-cut joints or as one-piece rings. Teflon sealing rings have replaced many metal ring applications.

TERMINAL: A device attached to the end of a wire or cable to make an electrical connection.

TEST LIGHT, CIRCUIT-POWERED: Uses available circuit voltage to test circuit continuity.

TEST LIGHT, SELF-POWERED: Uses its own battery source to test circuit continuity.

THERMISTOR: A special resistor used to measure fluid temperature; it decreases its resistance with increases in temperature.

THERMOSTAT: A valve, located in the cooling system of an engine, which is closed when cold and opens gradually in response to engine heating, controlling the temperature of the coolant and rate of coolant flow.

THERMOSTATIC ELEMENT: A heat-sensitive, spring-type device that controls a drain port from the upper sump area to the lower sump. When the transaxle fluid reaches operating temperature, the port is closed and the upper sump fills, thus reducing the fluid level in the lower sump.

THROTTLE POSITION (TP) SENSOR: Reads the degree of throttle opening; its signal is used to analyze engine load conditions. The ECM/PCM decides to apply the TCC, or to disengage it for coast or load conditions that need a converter torque boost.

THROTTLE PRESSURE/MODULATOR PRESSURE: A hydraulic signal oil pressure relating to the amount of engine load, based on either the amount of throttle plate opening or engine vacuum.

THROTTLE VALVE: A regulating or balanced valve that is controlled mechanically by throttle linkage or engine vacuum. It sends a hydraulic signal to the shift valve body to control shift timing and shift quality. (See balanced valve; modulator valve.)

THROW-OUT BEARING: As the clutch pedal is depressed, the throwout bearing moves against the spring fingers of the pressure plate, forcing the pressure plate to disengage from the driven disc.

TIE ROD: A rod connecting the steering arms. Tie rods have threaded ends that are used to adjust toe-in.

TIE-UP: Condition where two opposing clutches are attempting to apply at same time, causing engine to labor with noticeable loss of engine rpm.

TIMING BELT: A square-toothed, reinforced rubber belt that is driven by the crankshaft and operates the camshaft.

TIMING CHAIN: A roller chain that is driven by the crankshaft and operates the camshaft.

TIRE ROTATION: Moving the tires from one position to another to make the tires wear evenly.

TOE-IN (OUT): A term comparing the extreme front and rear of the front tires. Closer together at the front is toe-in; farther apart at the front is toe-out.

TOP DEAD CENTER (TDC): The point at which the piston reaches the top of its travel on the compression stroke.

TORQUE: Measurement of turning or twisting force, expressed as foot-pounds or inch-pounds.

TORQUE CONVERTER: A turbine used to transmit power from a driving member to a driven member via hydraulic action, providing changes in drive ratio and torque. In automotive use, it links the driveplate at the rear of the engine to the automatic transmission.

TORQUE CONVERTER CLUTCH: The apply plate (lockup plate) assembly used for mechanical power flow through the converter.

TORQUE PHASE: Sometimes referred to as slip phase or stall phase, torque multiplication occurs when the turbine is turning at a slower speed than the impeller, and the stator is reactionary (stationary). This sequence generates a boost in output torque.

TORQUE RATING (STALL TORQUE): The maximum torque multiplication that occurs during stall conditions, with the engine at wide open throttle (WOT) and zero turbine speed.

TORQUE RATIO: An expression of the gear ratio factor on torque effect. A 3:1 gear ratio or 3:1 torque ratio increases the torque input by the ratio factor of 3. Input torque (100 ft. lbs.) x 3 = output torque (300 ft. lbs.)

TRACTION: The amount of usable tractive effort before the drive wheels slip on the road contact surface.

TORSION BAR SUSPENSION: Long rods of spring steel which take the place of springs. One end of the bar is anchored and the other arm (attached to the suspension) is free to twist. The bars' resistance to twisting causes springing action.

TRACK: Distance between the centers of the tires where they contact the ground.

TRACTION CONTROL: A control system that prevents the spinning of a vehicle's drive wheels when excess power is applied.

TRACTIVE EFFORT: The amount of force available to the drive wheels, to move the vehicle.

TRANSAXLE: A single housing containing the transmission and differential. Transaxles are usually found on front engine/front wheel drive or rear engine/rear wheel drive cars.

TRANSDUCER: A device that changes energy from one form to another. For example, a transducer in a microphone changes sound energy to electrical energy. In automotive air-conditioning controls used in automatic temperature systems, a transducer changes an electrical signal to a vacuum signal, which operates mechanical doors.

TRANSMISSION: A powertrain component designed to modify torque and speed developed by the engine; also provides direct drive, reverse, and neutral.

TRANSMISSION CONTROL MODULE (TCM): Manages transmission functions. These vary according to the manufacturer's product design but may include converter clutch operation, electronic shift scheduling, and mainline pressure.

TRANSMISSION FLUID TEMPERATURE (TFT) SENSOR: Originally called a transmission oil temperature (TOT) sensor, this input device to the ECM/PCM senses the fluid temperature and provides a resistance value. It operates on the thermistor principle.

TRANSMISSION INPUT SPEED (TIS) SENSOR: Measures turbine shaft (input shaft) rpm's and compares to engine rpm's to determine torque converter slip. When compared to the transmission output speed sensor or VSS, gear ratio and clutch engagement timing can be determined.

TRANSMISSION OIL TEMPERATURE (TOT) SENSOR: (See transmission fluid temperature (TFT) sensor.)

TRANSMISSION RANGE SELECTOR (TRS) SWITCH: Tells the module which gear shift position the driver has chosen.

TRANSFER CASE: A gearbox driven from the transmission that delivers power to both front and rear driveshafts in a four-wheel drive system. Transfer cases usually have a high and low range set of gears, used depending on how much pulling power is needed.

TRANSISTOR: A semi-conductor component which can be actuated by a small voltage to perform an electrical switching function.

TREAD WEAR INDICATOR: Bars molded into the tire at right angles to the tread that appear as horizontal bars when ⅟₁₆ in. of tread remains.

TREAD WEAR PATTERN: The pattern of wear on tires which can be "read" to diagnose problems in the front suspension.

TUNE-UP: A regular maintenance function, usually associated with the replacement and adjustment of parts and components in the electrical and fuel systems of a vehicle for the purpose of attaining optimum performance.

TURBINE: The output (driven) member of a fluid coupling or fluid torque converter. It is splined to the input (turbine) shaft of the transmission.

TURBOCHARGER: An exhaust driven pump which compresses intake air and forces it into the combustion chambers at higher than atmospheric pressures. The increased air pressure allows more fuel to be burned and results in increased horsepower being produced.

TURBULENCE: The interference of molecules of a fluid (or vapor) with each other in a fluid flow.

TYPE F: Transmission fluid developed and used by Ford Motor Company up to 1982. This fluid type provides a high coefficient of friction.

TYPE 7176: The preferred choice of transmission fluid for Chrysler automatic transmissions and transaxles. Developed in 1986, it closely resembles Dexron and Mercon. Type 7176 is the recommended service fill fluid for all Chrysler products utilizing a lockup torque converter dating back to 1978.

U-JOINT (UNIVERSAL JOINT): A flexible coupling in the drive train that allows the driveshafts or axle shafts to operate at different angles and still transmit rotary power.

UNDERSTEER: The tendency of a car to continue straight ahead while negotiating a turn.

UNIT BODY: Design in which the car body acts as the frame.

UNLEADED FUEL: Fuel which contains no lead (a common gasoline additive). The presence of lead in fuel will destroy the functioning elements of a catalytic converter, making it useless.

UNSPRUNG WEIGHT: The weight of car components not supported by the springs (wheels, tires, brakes, rear axle, control arms, etc.).

UPSHIFT: A shift that results in a decrease in torque ratio and an increase in speed.

VACUUM: A negative pressure; any pressure less than atmospheric pressure.

VACUUM ADVANCE: A device which advances the ignition timing in response to increased engine vacuum.

VACUUM GAUGE: An instrument used for measuring the existing vacuum in a vacuum circuit or chamber. The unit of measure is inches (of mercury in a barometer).

VACUUM MODULATOR: Generates a hydraulic oil pressure in response to the amount of engine vacuum.

VALVES: Devices that can open or close fluid passages in a hydraulic system and are used for directing fluid flow and controlling pressure.

VALVE BODY ASSEMBLY: The main hydraulic control assembly of the transmission/transaxle that contains numerous valves, check balls, and other components to control the distribution of pressurized oil throughout the transmission.

VALVE CLEARANCE: The measured gap between the end of the valve stem and the rocker arm, cam lobe or follower that activates the valve.

VALVE GUIDES: The guide through which the stem of the valve passes.

The guide is designed to keep the valve in proper alignment.

VALVE LASH (clearance): The operating clearance in the valve train.

VALVE TRAIN: The system that operates intake and exhaust valves, consisting of camshaft, valves and springs, lifters, pushrods and rocker arms.

VAPOR LOCK: Boiling of the fuel in the fuel lines due to excess heat. This will interfere with the flow of fuel in the lines and can completely stop the flow. Vapor lock normally only occurs in hot weather.

VARIABLE DISPLACEMENT (VARIABLE CAPACITY) VANE PUMP: Slipper-type vanes, mounted in a revolving rotor and contained within the bore of a movable slide, capture and then force fluid to flow. Movement of the slide to various positions changes the size of the vane chambers and the amount of fluid flow. **Note:** GM refers to this pump design as variable displacement, and Ford terms it variable capacity.

VARIABLE FORCE SOLENOID (VFS): Commonly referred to as the electronic pressure control (EPC) solenoid, it replaces the cable/linkage style of TV system control and is integrated with a spool valve and spring assembly to control pressure. A variable computer-controlled current flow varies the internal force of the solenoid on the spool valve and resulting control pressure.

VARIABLE ORIFICE THERMAL VALVE: Temperature-sensitive hydraulic oil control device that adjusts the size of a circuit path opening. By altering the size of the opening, the oil flow rate is adapted for cold to hot oil viscosity changes.

VARNISH: Term applied to the residue formed when gasoline gets old and stale.

VCM: See Electronic Control Unit (ECU).

VEHICLE SPEED SENSOR (VSS): Provides an electrical signal to the computer module, measuring vehicle speed, and affects the torque converter clutch engagement and release.

VESPEL SEALING RINGS: Hard plastic material that produces excellent sealing in dynamic settings. These rings are found in late versions of the 4T60 and in all 4T60-E and 4T80-E transaxles.

VISCOSITY: The ability of a fluid to flow. The lower the viscosity rating, the easier the fluid will flow. 10 weight motor oil will flow much easier than 40 weight motor oil.

VISCOSITY INDEX IMPROVERS: Keeps the viscosity nearly constant with changes in temperature. This is especially important at low temperatures, when the oil needs to be thin to aid in shifting and for cold-weather starting. Yet it must not be so thin that at high temperatures it will cause excessive hydraulic leakage so that pumps are unable to maintain the proper pressures.

VISCOUS CLUTCH: A specially designed torque converter clutch apply plate that, through the use of a silicon fluid, clamps smoothly and absorbs torsional vibrations.

VOLT: Unit used to measure the force or pressure of electricity. It is defined as the pressure needed to move one amp through the resistance of one ohm.

VOLTAGE: The electrical pressure that causes current to flow. Voltage is measured in volts (V).

VOLTAGE, APPLIED: The actual voltage read at a given point in a circuit. It equals the available voltage of the power supply minus the losses in the circuit up to that point.

VOLTAGE DROP: The voltage lost or used in a circuit by normal loads such as a motor or lamp or by abnormal loads such as a poor (high-resistance) lead or terminal connection.

VOLTAGE REGULATOR: A device that controls the current output of the alternator or generator.

VOLTMETER: An instrument used for measuring electrical force in units called volts. Voltmeters are always connected parallel with the circuit being tested.

VORTEX FLOW: The crosswise or circulatory flow of oil between the blades of the members caused by the centrifugal pumping action of the impeller.

WANKEL ENGINE: An engine which uses no pistons. In place of pistons, triangular-shaped rotors revolve in specially shaped housings.

WATER PUMP: A belt driven component of the cooling system that mounts on the engine, circulating the coolant under pressure.

WATT: The unit for measuring electrical power. One watt is the product of one ampere and one volt (watts equals amps times volts). Wattage is the horsepower of electricity (746 watts equal one horsepower).

WHEEL ALIGNMENT: Inclusive term to describe the front end geometry (caster, camber, toe-in/out).

WHEEL CYLINDER: Found in the automotive drum brake assembly, it is a device, actuated by hydraulic pressure, which, through internal pistons, pushes the brake shoes outward against the drums.

WHEEL WEIGHT: Small weights attached to the wheel to balance the wheel and tire assembly. Out-of-balance tires quickly wear out and also give erratic handling when installed on the front.

WHEELBASE: Distance between the center of front wheels and the center of rear wheels.

WIDE OPEN THROTTLE (WOT): Full travel of accelerator pedal.

WORK: The force exerted to move a mass or object. Work involves motion; if a force is exerted and no motion takes place, no work is done. Work per unit of time is called power. Work = force x distance = ft. lbs. 33,000 ft. lbs. in one minute = 1 horsepower

ZERO-THROTTLE COAST DOWN: A full release of accelerator pedal while vehicle is in motion and in drive range.

ENGLISH TO METRIC CONVERSION: TORQUE

To convert foot-pounds (ft. lbs.) to Newton-meters (Nm), multiply the number of ft. lbs. by 1.36

To convert Newton-meters (Nm) to foot-pounds (ft. lbs.), multiply the number of Nm by 0.7376

ft. lbs.	Nm	ft. lbs.	Nm	ft. lbs.	Nm	ft. lbs.	Nm
0.1	0.1	34	46.2	76	103.4	118	160.5
0.2	0.3	35	47.6	77	104.7	119	161.8
0.3	0.4	36	49.0	78	106.1	120	163.2
0.4	0.5	37	50.3	79	107.4	121	164.6
0.5	0.7	38	51.7	80	108.8	122	165.9
0.6	0.8	39	53.0	81	110.2	123	167.3
0.7	1.0	40	54.4	82	111.5	124	168.6
0.8	1.1	41	55.8	83	112.9	125	170.0
0.9	1.2	42	57.1	84	114.2	126	171.4
1	1.4	43	58.5	85	115.6	127	172.7
2	2.7	44	59.8	86	117.0	128	174.1
3	4.1	45	61.2	87	118.3	129	175.4
4	5.4	46	62.6	88	119.7	130	176.8
5	6.8	47	63.9	89	121.0	131	178.2
6	8.2	48	65.3	90	122.4	132	179.5
7	9.5	49	66.6	91	123.8	133	180.9
8	10.9	50	68.0	92	125.1	134	182.2
9	12.2	51	69.4	93	126.5	135	183.6
10	13.6	52	70.7	94	127.8	136	185.0
11	15.0	53	72.1	95	129.2	137	186.3
12	16.3	54	73.4	96	130.6	138	187.7
13	17.7	55	74.8	97	131.9	139	189.0
14	19.0	56	76.2	98	133.3	140	190.4
15	20.4	57	77.5	99	134.6	141	191.8
16	21.8	58	78.9	100	136.0	142	193.1
17	23.1	59	80.2	101	137.4	143	194.5
18	24.5	60	81.6	102	138.7	144	195.8
19	25.8	61	83.0	103	140.1	145	197.2
20	27.2	62	84.3	104	141.4	146	198.6
21	28.6	63	85.7	105	142.8	147	199.9
22	29.9	64	87.0	106	144.2	148	201.3
23	31.3	65	88.4	107	145.5	149	202.6
24	32.6	66	89.8	108	146.9	150	204.0
25	34.0	67	91.1	109	148.2	151	205.4
26	35.4	68	92.5	110	149.6	152	206.7
27	36.7	69	93.8	111	151.0	153	208.1
28	38.1	70	95.2	112	152.3	154	209.4
29	39.4	71	96.6	113	153.7	155	210.8
30	40.8	72	97.9	114	155.0	156	212.2
31	42.2	73	99.3	115	156.4	157	213.5
32	43.5	74	100.6	116	157.8	158	214.9
33	44.9	75	102.0	117	159.1	159	216.2

METRIC TO ENGLISH CONVERSION: TORQUE

To convert foot-pounds (ft. lbs.) to Newton-meters (Nm), multiply the number of ft. lbs. by 1.36

To convert Newton-meters (Nm) to foot-pounds (ft. lbs.), multiply the number of Nm by 0.7376

Nm	ft. lbs.	Nm	ft. lbs.	Nm	ft. lbs.	Nm	ft. lbs.	Nm	ft. lbs.
0.1	0.1	34	25.0	76	55.9	118	86.8	160	117.6
0.2	0.1	35	25.7	77	56.6	119	87.5	161	118.4
0.3	0.2	36	26.5	78	57.4	120	88.2	162	119.1
0.4	0.3	37	27.2	79	58.1	121	89.0	163	119.9
0.5	0.4	38	27.9	80	58.8	122	89.7	164	120.6
0.6	0.4	39	28.7	81	59.6	123	90.4	165	121.3
0.7	0.5	40	29.4	82	60.3	124	91.2	166	122.1
0.8	0.6	41	30.1	83	61.0	125	91.9	167	122.8
0.9	0.7	42	30.9	84	61.8	126	92.6	168	123.5
1	0.7	43	31.6	85	62.5	127	93.4	169	124.3
2	1.5	44	32.4	86	63.2	128	94.1	170	125.0
3	2.2	45	33.1	87	64.0	129	94.9	171	125.7
4	2.9	46	33.8	88	64.7	130	95.6	172	126.5
5	3.7	47	34.6	89	65.4	131	96.3	173	127.2
6	4.4	48	35.3	90	66.2	132	97.1	174	127.9
7	5.1	49	36.0	91	66.9	133	97.8	175	128.7
8	5.9	50	36.8	92	67.6	134	98.5	176	129.4
9	6.6	51	37.5	93	68.4	135	99.3	177	130.1
10	7.4	52	38.2	94	69.1	136	100.0	178	130.9
11	8.1	53	39.0	95	69.9	137	100.7	179	131.6
12	8.8	54	39.7	96	70.6	138	101.5	180	132.4
13	9.6	55	40.4	97	71.3	139	102.2	181	133.1
14	10.3	56	41.2	98	72.1	140	102.9	182	133.8
15	11.0	57	41.9	99	72.8	141	103.7	183	134.6
16	11.8	58	42.6	100	73.5	142	104.4	184	135.3
17	12.5	59	43.4	101	74.3	143	105.1	185	136.0
18	13.2	60	44.1	102	75.0	144	105.9	186	136.8
19	14.0	61	44.9	103	75.7	145	106.6	187	137.5
20	14.7	62	45.6	104	76.5	146	107.4	188	138.2
21	15.4	63	46.3	105	77.2	147	108.1	189	139.0
22	16.2	64	47.1	106	77.9	148	108.8	190	139.7
23	16.9	65	47.8	107	78.7	149	109.6	191	140.4
24	17.6	66	48.5	108	79.4	150	110.3	192	141.2
25	18.4	67	49.3	109	80.1	151	111.0	193	141.9
26	19.1	68	50.0	110	80.9	152	111.8	194	142.6
27	19.9	69	50.7	111	81.6	153	112.5	195	143.4
28	20.6	70	51.5	112	82.4	154	113.2	196	144.1
29	21.3	71	52.2	113	83.1	155	114.0	197	144.9
30	22.1	72	52.9	114	83.8	156	114.7	198	145.6
31	22.8	73	53.7	115	84.6	157	115.4	199	146.3
32	23.5	74	54.4	116	85.3	158	116.2	200	147.1
33	24.3	75	55.1	117	86.0	159	116.9	201	147.8

ENGLISH/METRIC CONVERSION: TEMPERATURE

To convert Fahrenheit (F°) to Celsius (C°), take F° temperature and subtract 32, multiply the result by 5 and divide the result by 9
To convert Celsius (C°) to Fahrenheit (F°), take C° temperature and multiply it by 9, divide the result by 5 and add 32

F°	C°	F°	C°	C°	F°	C°	F°
-40	-40.0	150	65.6	-38	-36.4	46	114.8
-35	-37.2	155	68.3	-36	-32.8	48	118.4
-30	-34.4	160	71.1	-34	-29.2	50	122
-25	-31.7	165	73.9	-32	-25.6	52	125.6
-20	-28.9	170	76.7	-30	-22	54	129.2
-15	-26.1	175	79.4	-28	-18.4	56	132.8
-10	-23.3	180	82.2	-26	-14.8	58	136.4
-5	-20.6	185	85.0	-24	-11.2	60	140
0	-17.8	190	87.8	-22	-7.6	62	143.6
1	-17.2	195	90.6	-20	-4	64	147.2
2	-16.7	200	93.3	-18	-0.4	66	150.8
3	-16.1	205	96.1	-16	3.2	68	154.4
4	-15.6	210	98.9	-14	6.8	70	158
5	-15.0	212	100.0	-12	10.4	72	161.6
10	-12.2	215	101.7	-10	14	74	165.2
15	-9.4	220	104.4	-8	17.6	76	168.8
20	-6.7	225	107.2	-6	21.2	78	172.4
25	-3.9	230	110.0	-4	24.8	80	176
30	-1.1	235	112.8	-2	28.4	82	179.6
35	1.7	240	115.6	0	32	84	183.2
40	4.4	245	118.3	2	35.6	86	186.8
45	7.2	250	121.1	4	39.2	88	190.4
50	10.0	255	123.9	6	42.8	90	194
55	12.8	260	126.7	8	46.4	92	197.6
60	15.6	265	129.4	10	50	94	201.2
65	18.3	270	132.2	12	53.6	96	204.8
70	21.1	275	135.0	14	57.2	98	208.4
75	23.9	280	137.8	16	60.8	100	212
80	26.7	285	140.6	18	64.4	102	215.6
85	29.4	290	143.3	20	68	104	219.2
90	32.2	295	146.1	22	71.6	106	222.8
95	35.0	300	148.9	24	75.2	108	226.4
100	37.8	305	151.7	26	78.8	110	230
105	40.6	310	154.4	28	82.4	112	233.6
110	43.3	315	157.2	30	86	114	237.2
115	46.1	320	160.0	32	89.6	116	240.8
120	48.9	325	162.8	34	93.2	118	244.4
125	51.7	330	165.6	36	96.8	120	248
130	54.4	335	168.3	38	100.4	122	251.6
135	57.2	340	171.1	40	104	124	255.2
140	60.0	345	173.9	42	107.6	126	258.8
145	62.8	350	176.7	44	111.2	128	262.4

LENGTH CONVERSION

To convert inches (in.) to millimeters (mm), multiply the number of inches by 25.4
To convert millimeters (mm) to inches (in.), multiply the number of millimeters by 0.04

Inches	Millimeters	Inches	Millimeters	Inches	Millimeters	Inches	Millimeters
0.0001	0.00254	0.005	0.1270	0.09	2.286	4	101.6
0.0002	0.00508	0.006	0.1524	0.1	2.54	5	127.0
0.0003	0.00762	0.007	0.1778	0.2	5.08	6	152.4
0.0004	0.01016	0.008	0.2032	0.3	7.62	7	177.8
0.0005	0.01270	0.009	0.2286	0.4	10.16	8	203.2
0.0006	0.01524	0.01	0.254	0.5	12.70	9	228.6
0.0007	0.01778	0.02	0.508	0.6	15.24	10	254.0
0.0008	0.02032	0.03	0.762	0.7	17.78	11	279.4
0.0009	0.02286	0.04	1.016	0.8	20.32	12	304.8
0.001	0.0254	0.05	1.270	0.9	22.86	13	330.2
0.002	0.0508	0.06	1.524	1	25.4	14	355.6
0.003	0.0762	0.07	1.778	2	50.8	15	381.0
0.004	0.1016	0.08	2.032	3	76.2	16	406.4

ENGLISH/METRIC CONVERSION: LENGTH

To convert inches (in.) to millimeters (mm), multiply the number of inches by 25.4
To convert millimeters (mm) to inches (in.), multiply the number of millimeters by 0.04

Inches		Millimeters	Inches		Millimeters	Inches		Millimeters
Fraction	Decimal	Decimal	Fraction	Decimal	Decimal	Fraction	Decimal	Decimal
1/64	0.016	0.397	11/32	0.344	8.731	11/16	0.688	17.463
1/32	0.031	0.794	23/64	0.359	9.128	45/64	0.703	17.859
3/64	0.047	1.191	3/8	0.375	9.525	23/32	0.719	18.256
1/16	0.063	1.588	25/64	0.391	9.922	47/64	0.734	18.653
5/64	0.078	1.984	13/32	0.406	10.319	3/4	0.750	19.050
3/32	0.094	2.381	27/64	0.422	10.716	49/64	0.766	19.447
7/64	0.109	2.778	7/16	0.438	11.113	25/32	0.781	19.844
1/8	0.125	3.175	29/64	0.453	11.509	51/64	0.797	20.241
9/64	0.141	3.572	15/32	0.469	11.906	13/16	0.813	20.638
5/32	0.156	3.969	31/64	0.484	12.303	53/64	0.828	21.034
11/64	0.172	4.366	1/2	0.500	12.700	27/32	0.844	21.431
3/16	0.188	4.763	33/64	0.516	13.097	55/64	0.859	21.828
13/64	0.203	5.159	17/32	0.531	13.494	7/8	0.875	22.225
7/32	0.219	5.556	35/64	0.547	13.891	57/64	0.891	22.622
15/64	0.234	5.953	9/16	0.563	14.288	29/32	0.906	23.019
1/4	0.250	6.350	37/64	0.578	14.684	59/64	0.922	23.416
17/64	0.266	6.747	19/32	0.594	15.081	15/16	0.938	23.813
9/32	0.281	7.144	39/64	0.609	15.478	61/64	0.953	24.209
19/64	0.297	7.541	5/8	0.625	15.875	31/32	0.969	24.606
5/16	0.313	7.938	41/64	0.641	16.272	63/64	0.984	25.003
21/64	0.328	8.334	21/32	0.656	16.669	1/1	1.000	25.400
			43/64	0.672	17.066			

CHILTON® LABOR GUIDE

Whether you are looking for labor times in print, or on CD-ROM, Chilton is your source! Chilton's editors have carefully crafted the latest edition of the famous Chilton Labor Guide to bring you the most accurate repair information available. Chilton's editors consider warranty times, component locations, component type, the environment in which technicians work, the training they receive, and the tools they use when calculating a labor time. To allow for vehicle age, operating conditions, and type of service, the Chilton Labor Guide provides standard and severe service times, plus OEM warranty times. Vehicle makes and models conform to current Automotive Aftermarket Industry Association (AAIA) standards.

978-1-1110-3608-9 Chilton 2010 Labor Guide Manual Set (Domestic & Import)

978-1-1110-3611-9 Chilton 2010 Labor Guide CD-ROM (Domestic & Import)

CD-ROM FEATURES

- ○ access labor times for 1981-2010 import and domestic vehicle models
- ○ save time with automatically calculated labor charges, taxes, & parts as total job is estimated
- ○ create professional estimates for your customer and worksheets for your technicians, printing them whenever needed
- ○ keep track of customers, prior estimates, and your own parts or package jobs with less paper
- ○ choose part names for estimates from an industry standard database to reduce typing
- ○ estimate and track your work status with improved forms
- ○ communicate easily with customers using re-designed printouts which show all labor and parts in an easy-to-read format.
- ○ simplify adding parts to your estimate or work order with a helpful parts list
- ○ locate information quick with a keyword search engine
- ○ quickly locate work requests by day, week and month using the calendar feature

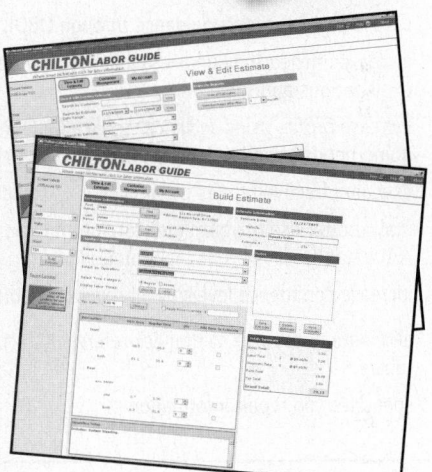

Manual FEATURES

- ○ more than 2,500 pages of updated Chilton labor times split into two volumes includes vehicle information from 1981 to 2010
- ○ trusted by more service professionals than any other labor guide
- ○ less flipping though pages with separate domestic and imported vehicle manuals
- ○ convenient tabs display contents by manufacturer and model
- ○ easy-to-find manufacturers are arranged alphabetically within each volume
- ○ search using two-indexes - labor operations and systems - in each model group
- ○ page numbers include manufacturer code so you know where you are in the book

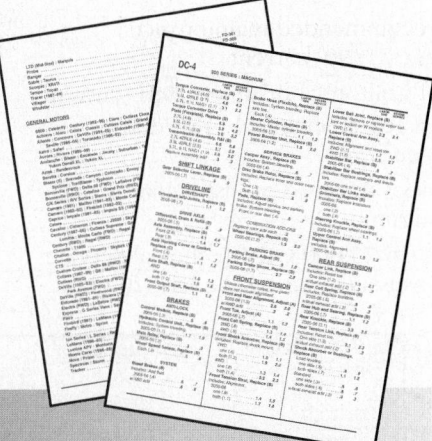

Chilton's labor times are so trusted, even a competing publisher uses them!

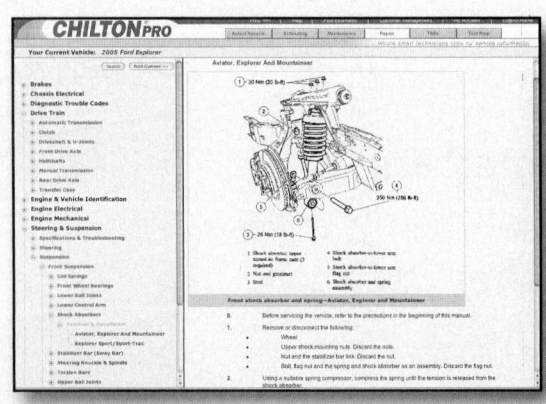

Chilton® 2010 Service Manuals

The Chilton 2010 Service Manuals now include even better graphics and expanded procedures! Chilton's editors have put together the most current automotive repair information available to assist users during daily repairs. These new manuals allow users to accurately and efficiently diagnose and repair late-model cars and trucks. Trust the step-by-step procedures and helpful illustrations that only Chilton can provide. The 2010 Service Manuals cover 2008 and 2009 models plus available 2010 models.

KEY FEATURES
- organized by vehicle manufacturer
- provides thousands of pages of expertly written content
- access new year, make, and model information without repeating previous edition's content
- comprehensive, technically detailed content, including exploded view illustrations, diagnostics and specification charts,   arranged alphabetically by model group for quick, easy access

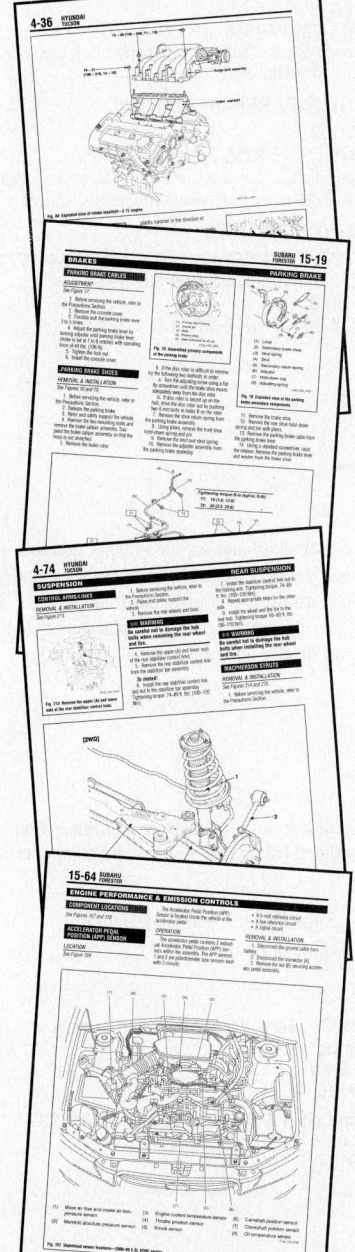

2010 EDITIONS
2010 Asian Service Manual Vol. 1*
ISBN 978-1-1110-3764-2
Part No. 163764

2010 Asian Service Manual Vol. 2*
ISBN 978-1-1110-3765-9
Part No. 163765

2010 Asian Service Manual Vol. 3*
ISBN 978-1-1110-3766-6
Part No. 163766

2010 Asian Service Manual Vol. 4*
ISBN 978-1-1110-3767-3
Part No. 163767

2010 Asian Service Manual Vol. 5*
ISBN 978-1-1110-3768-0
Part No. 163768

2010 European Service Manual*
ISBN 978-1-1110-3769-7
Part No. 163769

2010 Chrysler Service Manual, Volumes 1 & 2
ISBN 978-1-1110-3654-6
Part No. 163654

2010 Ford Service Manual, Vols. 1 & 2
ISBN 978-1-1110-3657-7
Part No. 163657

2010 General Motors Service Manuals, Vols. 1, 2, & 3
ISBN 978-1-111-03661-4
Part No. 163661

2008 EDITIONS
2008 Chrysler Service Manual, Vols. 1 & 2
ISBN 978-1-4283-2204-2
Part No. 142204

2008 Ford Service Manuals, Vols. 1 & 2
ISBN 978-1-4283-2208-0
Part No. 142208

2008 Edition General Motors Service Manuals, Vols. 1 & 2
ISBN 978-1-4283-2211-0
Part No. 142211

2008 Asian Service Manuals, Vols. 1-4
ISBN 978-1-4283-2214-1
Part No. 142214

2008 Asian Service Manual, Vol. 1
ISBN 978-1-4283-2215-8
Part No. 142215

2008 Asian Service Manual, Vol. 2
ISBN 978-1-4283-2216-5
Part No. 142216

2008 Asian Service Manual, Vol. 3
ISBN 978-1-4283-2217-2
Part No. 142217

2008 Asian Service Manual, Vol. 4
ISBN 978-1-4283-2218-9
Part No. 142218

2008 European Service Manual
ISBN 978-1-4283-2220-2
Part No. 142220

2006 EDITIONS
2006 DaimlerChrysler Diagnostic Service Manual
ISBN 978-1-4180-2118-4
Part No. 132118

2006 General Motors Diagnostic Service Manual
ISBN 978-1-4180-2120-7
Part No. 132120

2006 Asian Diagnostic Service Manual, Vol. 1
ISBN 978-1-4180-2913-5
Part No. 132913

2006 Asian Diagnostic Service Manual, Vol. 2
ISBN 978-1-4180-2914-2
Part No. 132914

2006 Asian Diagnostic Service Manual, Vol. 3
ISBN 978-1-4180-2915-9
Part No. 132915

2006 Asian Diagnostic Service Manual, 3 Vol. Set
ISBN 978-1-4180-3212-8
Part No. 132986

2006 European Diagnostic Service Manual
ISBN 978-1-4180-2924-1
Part No. 132924

2006 DaimlerChrysler Mechanical Service Manual
ISBN 978-1-4180-0600-6
Part No. 130600

2006 Asian Mechanical Service Manual, Vol. 1
ISBN 978-1-4180-0947-2
Part No. 130947

2006 Asian Mechanical Service Manual, Vol. 2
ISBN 978-1-4180-0948-9
Part No. 130948

2006 Asian Mechanical Service Manual, Vol. 3
ISBN 978-1-4180-0949-6
Part No. 130949

2006 Asian Mechanical Service Manual, 3 Vol. Set
ISBN 978-1-4180-0603-7
Part No. 130603

2006 European Mechanical Service Manual
ISBN 978- 1-4180-0604-4
Part No. 130604

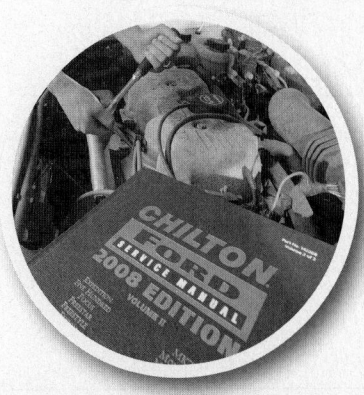

*Available December 2010

**Order Today–
Quantities
are Limited**

Chilton® Mechanical Service Manuals–Perennial Editions

These manuals contain repair and maintenance information for all major systems. Included are repair and overhaul procedures using thousands of illustrations.

CHILTON AUTO REPAIR MANUALS

1998-2002
ISBN 978-0-8019-9362-6/Part No. 9362
Covers all popular American and Canadian cars. An added feature includes scheduled maintenance interval charts.

1993-97
ISBN 978-0-8019-7919-4/Part No. 7919
Covers all popular American and Canadian cars.

1980-87
ISBN 978-0-8019-7670-4/Part No. 7670
Covers all popular American and Canadian cars.

CHILTON IMPORT AUTO REPAIR MANUALS

1998-2002
ISBN 978-0-8019-9363-3/Part No. 9363
Covers all popular Import cars. An added feature includes scheduled maintenance intervals charts.

1993-97
ISBN 978-0-8019-7920-0/Part No. 7920
Covers all popular Import cars.

1988-92
ISBN 978-0-8019-7907-1/Part No. 7907
Covers all popular Import cars.

1980-87
ISBN 978-0-8019-7672-8/Part No. 7672
Covers all popular Import cars.

CHILTON TRUCK AND VAN REPAIR MANUALS

1998-2002
ISBN 978-0-8019-9364-0/Part No. 9364
Covers popular U.S., Canadian, and Import Pick-Ups, Vans, and 4WDs. An added feature includes scheduled maintenance interval charts.

1993-97
ISBN 978-0-8019-7921-7/Part No. 7921
Covers popular U.S., Canadian, and Import Pick-Ups, Sport-Utilities, Vans, RVs and 4 wheel drives.

1991-95
ISBN 978-0-8019-7911-8/Part No. 7911
Covers popular U.S., Canadian, and Import Pick-Ups, Vans, RVs and 4 wheel drives.

1986-90
ISBN 978-08019-7902-6/Part No. 7902
Covers popular U.S., Canadian, and Import Pick-Us, Vans, RVs and 4 wheel drives.

1979-86
ISBN 978-08019-7655-1/Part No. 7655
Covers popular U.S., Canadian, and Import Pick-Ups, Vans, RVs and 4 wheel drives.

CHILTON SUV REPAIR MANUAL

1998-2002
ISBN 978-08019-9365-7/Part No. 9365
Covers popular U.S., Canadian, and import SUVs. An added feature includes scheduled maintenance intervals charts.

COLLECTOR'S SERIES

CHILTON AUTO REPAIR MANUAL 1964-1971
ISBN 978-08019-5974-5/Part No. 5974
1971-1978
ISBN 978-08019-7012-2/Part No. 7012

ISBN 978-1-4018-9880-9
Part No. 129880
544 pp, 8" x 11", SC, ©2006

Chilton Timing Belts, 1985-2005

Timing belt procedures can represent increased profits for automotive repair shops and service stations, and this manual contains all the information automotive technicians need to properly service timing belts on domestic and imported cars, vans, and light trucks through 2005 models. Clear, straightforward procedures, illustrations, and specifications help to communicate 20 years of vehicle applications for fast, accurate inspection, replacement, and tensioning of timing belts. Users will learn how to perform key procedures quickly and safely, while learning the correct labor time to charge for the service.

ALSO AVAILABLE:

Quick-Reference Manuals

The Chilton Professional Series offers *Quick-Reference Manuals* for the automotive professional, providing complete coverage on repair and maintenance, adjustments, and diagnostic procedures for specific systems and components.

KEY FEATURES

- step-by-step procedures
- detailed illustrations and exploded views
- easy-to-use manufacturer and model indexing
- handy specifications or data charts

Heater Core Service 1990-2000,
ISBN 978-0-8019-9311-4
Part No. 9311
Brake Specifications and Service 1990-2000
ISBN 978-0-8019-9312-1
Part No. 9312

Electric Cooling Fans, Accessory Drive Belts &
Water Pumps, 1995-1999,
ISBN 978-0-8019-9126-4
Part No. 9126
Powertrain Codes & Oxygen Sensors, 1990-1999,
ISBN 978-0-8019-9127-1
Part No. 9127

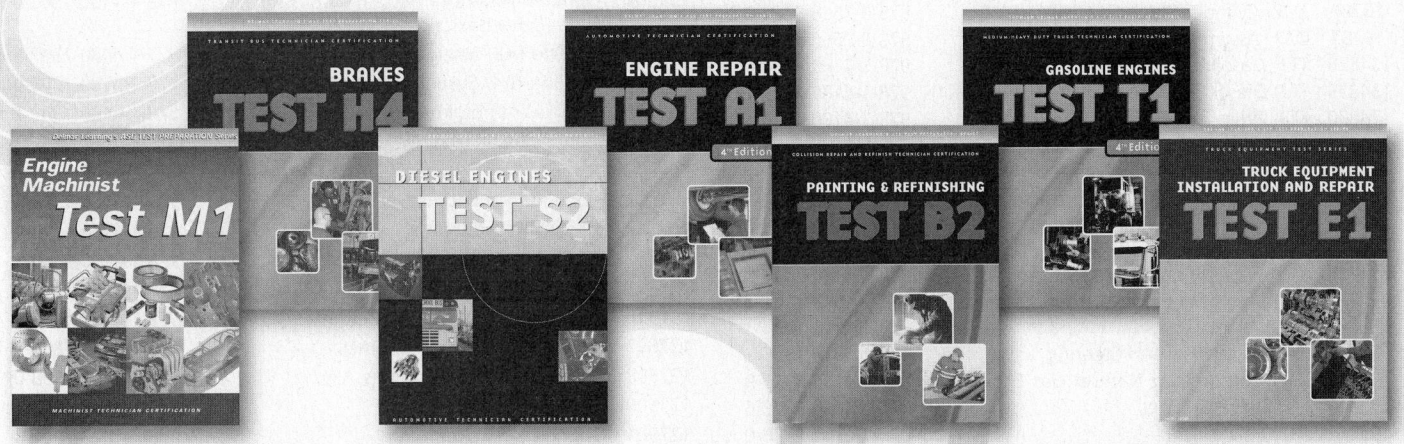

You Deserve The Best When You Are Putting Your Skills To The Test!

ASE Test Preparation Manuals

133878	(A1) Engine Repair, 4E	978-1-4180-3878-6
133879	(A2) Transmissions and Transaxles, 4E	978-1-4180-3879-3
133880	(A3) Manual Drive Train and Axles, 4E	978-1-4180-3880-9
133881	(A4) Suspension and Steering, 4E	978-1-4180-3881-6
133882	(A5) Brakes, 4E	978-1-4180-3882-3
133883	(A6) Electrical/Electronic Systems, 4E	978-1-4180-3883-0
133884	(A7) Heating and Air Conditioning, 4E	978-1-4180-3884-7
133885	(A8) Engine Performance, 4E	978-1-4180-3885-4
133888	(L1) Advanced Engine Performance, 4E	978-1-4180-3888-5
133886	(X1) Exhaust Systems, 4E	978-1-4180-3886-1
133887	(P2) Parts Specialist, 4E	978-1-4180-3887-8
133889	(C1) Service Consultant, 2E	978-1-4180-3889-2
23664	(B2) Painting and Refinishing, 3E	978-1-4018-3664-1
23665	(B3) Non Structural Analysis and Damage Repair, 3E	978-1-4018-3665-8
23666	(B4) Structural Analysis and Damage Repair, 3E	978-1-4018-3666-5
23667	(B5) Mechanical and Electrical Components, 3E	978-1-4018-3667-2
23668	(B6) Damage Analysis and Estimation, 3E	978-1-4018-3668-9
16280	(M1) Cylinder Head Specialist	978-0-7668-6280-7
16281	(M2) Cylinder Block Specialist	978-0-7668-6281-4
16282	(M3) Assembly Specialist	978-0-7668-6282-1
134828	(T1) Gasoline Engines, 4E	978-1-4180-4828-0
134829	(T2) Diesel Engines, 4E	978-1-4180-4829-7
134830	(T3) Drive Train, 4E	978-1-4180-4830-3
134831	(T4) Brakes, 4E	978-1-4180-4831-0
134832	(T5) Suspension and Steering, 4E	978-1-4180-4832-7
134834	(T6) Electrical/Electronic Systems, 4E	978-1-4180-4834-1
134835	(T7) Heating, Ventilation, and Air Conditioning, 4E	978-1-4180-4835-8
134836	(T8) Preventive Maintenance, 4E	978-1-4180-4836-5
21822	(S2) Diesel Engines	978-1-4018-1822-7
21824	(S4) Brakes	978-1-4018-1824-1
21825	(S5) Suspension and Steering	978-1-4018-1825-8
153939	(H1) Compressed Natural Gas Engines	978-1-4354-3939-9
136570	(H2) Diesel Engines	978-1-4180-6570-6
155376	(H3) Drive Train	978-1-4354-5376-0
134998	(H4) Brakes	978-1-4180-4998-0
144011	(H5) Suspension & Steering	978-1-4283-4011-4
134999	(H6) Electrical/Electronic Systems	978-1-4180-4999-7
136571	(H7) Heating, Ventilation, & Air Conditioning	978-1-4180-6571-3
153938	(H8) Preventive Maintenance	978-1-4354-3938-2
153935	(E1) Truck Equipment Installation & Repair	978-1-4354-3935-1
153936	(E2) Electronic Systems Installation & Repair	978-1-4354-3936-8
153937	(E3) Auxilary Power Systems Installation & Repair	978-1-4354-3937-5

ASE Test Preparation in Spanish

131305	Spanish (A1) Engine Repair	978-1-4018-1014-6
131305	Spanish (A2) Transmissions and Transaxles	978-1-4018-1015-3
131305	Spanish (A3) Manual Drive Train and Axles	978-1-4018-1016-0
131305	Spanish (A4) Suspension and Steering	978-1-4018-1017-7
131305	Spanish (A5) Brakes	978-1-4018-1018-4
131305	Spanish (A6) Electrical/Electronic Systems	978-1-4018-1019-1
131305	Spanish (A7) Heating and Air Conditioning	978-1-4018-1020-7
131305	Spanish (A8) Engine Performance	978-1-4018-1021-4
131305	Spanish (L1) Advanced Engine Performance	978-1-4018-1022-1
131305	Spanish (X1) Exhaust Systems	978-1-4018-1024-5
131305	Spanish (P2) Parts Specialist	978-1-4018-1023-8
29255	Spanish (B2) Painting and Refinishin	978-1-4018-9255-5
22544	Spanish (B3) Non-Structural Analysis and Damage Repair	978-1-4018-2544-7
29131	Spanish (B4) Structural Analysis and Damage Repair	978-1-4018-9131-2
27759	Spanish (B5) Mechanical and Electrical Components	978-1-4018-7759-0
26573	Spanish (B6) Damage Analysis and Estimation	978-1-4018-6573-3

Online ASE Test Preparation
Place your order online at www.techniciantestprep.com

131305	*Online (A1) Engine Repair	978-1-4180-1305-9
131306	*Online (A2) Automatic Transmissions & Transaxles	978-1-4180-1306-6
131307	*Online (A3) Manual Drive Trains & Axles	978-1-4180-1307-3
131308	*Online (A4) Suspension & Steering	978-1-4180-1308-0
131309	*Online (A5) Brakes	978-1-4180-1309-7
131310	*Online (A6) Electrical/Electronic Systems	978-1-4180-1310-3
131311	*Online (A7) Heating & Air Conditioning	978-1-4180-1311-0
131312	*Online (A8) Engine Performance	978-1-4180-1312-7
131313	*Online (X1) Exhaust Systems	978-1-4180-1313-4
131314	*Online (P2) Automobile Parts Specialist	978-1-4180-1314-1
131315	*Online (L1) Advanced Engine Performance	978-1-4180-1315-8
131316	*Online (C1) Service Consultant	978-1-4180-1316-5
127897	Online (T1) Gasoline Engines	978-1-4018-7897-9
127898	Online (T2) Diesel Engines	978-1-4018-7898-6
127900	Online (T3) Drive Train	978-1-4018-7900-6
127901	Online (T4) Brakes	978-1-4018-7901-3
127903	Online (T5) Suspension & Steering	978-1-4018-7903-7
131879	Online (T6) Electrical/Electronic Systems	978-1-4180-1879-5
131880	Online (T7) Heating, Ventilation, & Air Conditioning	978-1-4180-1880-1
127906	Online (T8) Preventive Maintenance	978-1-4018-7906-8
154748	Online (B2) Painting & Refinishing	978-1-4354-4748-6
154749	Online (B3) Non-Structural Analysis & Damage Repair	978-1-4354-4749-3
154750	Online (B4) Structural Analysis and Repair	978-1-4354-4750-9
154751	Online (B5) Mechanical & Electrical Components	978-1-4354-4751-6
154752	Online (B6) Damage Analysis & Estimating	978-1-4354-4752-3

*Switch between English & Spanish at the click of a button!

Complete Series

133954	ASE Test Preparation Manuals for Automotive (A1-A8, X1, P2, L1, C1)	978-1-4180-3954-7
136139	ASE Test Preparation Manuals for Automotive (A1-A8 & L1)	978-1-4180-6139-5
134197	ASE Test Preparation Manuals for Automotive (A1-A8, L1, & P2)	978-1-4180-4197-7
136237	ASE Test Preparation Manuals for Automotive (A1-A8)	978-1-4180-6237-8
136335	ASE Test Preparation Manuals for Automotive (A1-A8, L1, P2, & X1)	978-1-4180-6335-1
133447	Online ASE Test Preparation for Automotive (A1-A8, X1, P2, L1, C1)	978-1-4180-1344-8

Place your order online at www.techniciantestprep.com

134934	ASE Test Preparation Manuals for Medium/Heavy Duty Truck (T1-T8)	978-1-4180-4934-8
130611	Online ASE Test Preparation for Medium/Heavy Duty Truck (T1-T8)	978-1-4180-0611-2

Place your order online at www.techniciantestprep.com

125120	ASE Test Preparation Manuals for Collision (B2-B6)	978-1-4018-5120-0
24155	ASE Test Preparation Manuals for Collision in Spanish (B2-B6)	978-1-4018-4155-3
16283	ASE Test Preparation Manuals for Engine Machinist (M1-M3)	978-0-7668-6283-8

CSAT-Automotive Series

The online *Comprehensive Skill Assessment Tool-Automotive Series* helps instructors and trainers implement the necessary training programs for individual areas needing improvement over various key automotive topics. As a true skill gap analysis tool, within each key topic, strategic learning areas are measured for knowledge of theory, hands-on application, and diagnostic skill. Areas of strength and areas needing improvement are identified. The combined phases of education and training, and post-assessment allow instructors to track skill level growth and target specific areas needing development.

Courses Available in the CSAT Automotive Series

Parts Specialist
ISBN 978-1-4180-3225-8

Service Consultant
ISBN 978-1-4180-3223-4

Advanced Engine Performance
ISBN 978-1-4180-0073-8

Brakes
ISBN 978-1-4180-0069-1

Electrical/Electronic Systems
ISBN 978-1-4180-0070-7

Engine Performance
ISBN 978-1-4180-0072-1

Engine Repair
ISBN 978-1-4180-0065-3

Exhaust Systems
ISBN 978-1-4180-0074-5

Heating and Air Conditioning
ISBN 978-1-4180-0071-4

Manual Drive Train & Axles
ISBN 978-1-4180-0067-7

Suspension & Steering
ISBN 978-1-4180-0068-4

Transmissions & Transaxles
ISBN 978-1-4180-0066-0

All-in-One (contains questions from all eight core automotive areas in one product)
ISBN 978-1-4354-2825-6

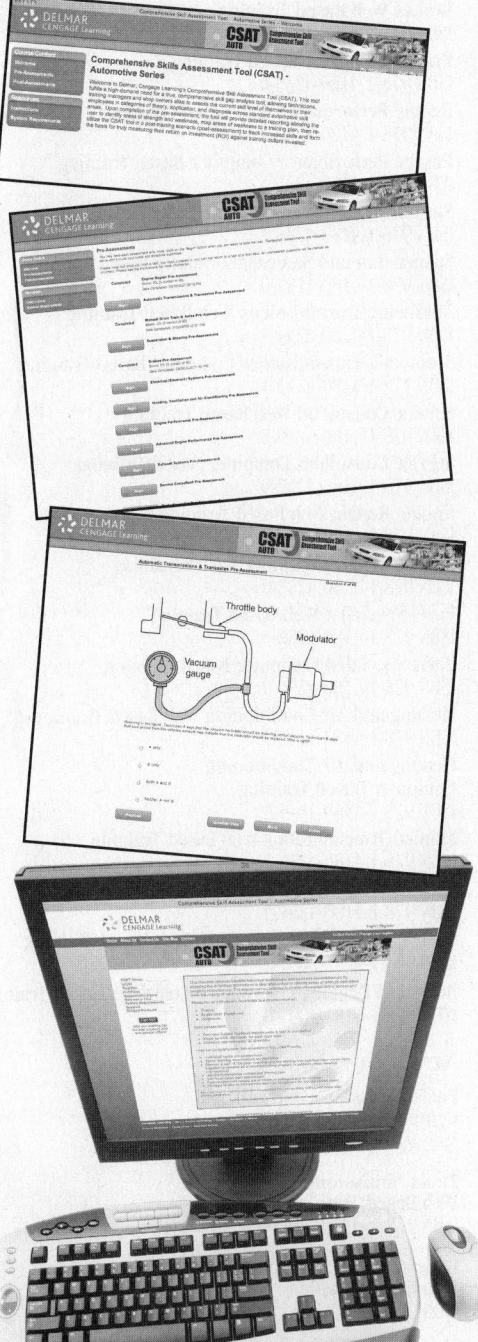

FEATURES

- available tests include Engine Repair, Transmissions and Transaxles, Manual Drive Train and Axles, Suspension and Steering, Brakes, Electrical/Electronic Systems, Heating and Air Conditioning, Engine Performance, Advanced Engine Performance, and Exhaust Systems
- can be utilized by companies to measure the technical skill level of individuals against an "ideal" to identify areas of strength and creates a skill gap analysis to help users address areas needing improvement
- questions are written and reviewed by experts in the industry and offer users the opportunity to receive instant feedback
- account set-up that enables instructors and trainers to assess and track the results of individual students
- acts as a true return on investment (ROI) tool for companies to ensure they invest their training dollars in the most appropriate areas

Visit **www.skillanalysis.com**
for a free demo!

Professional Automotive Technician Training Series: PATTS
Delmar

Delmar, the leader in providing first-rate educational materials for automotive technicians, now offers this exciting self-paced learning series. Choose the delivery method that best suits your needs– CD-ROM or Web-based product – and receive more than 8.5 hours worth of quality instruction. Combining theory, diagnosis, and repair information into one easy-to-use training tool, this highly interactive product helps technicians receive the most applicable delivery method for their needs, regardless of technical infrastructure.

KEY FEATURES

- attention-grabbing animations and learner interactions keep users interested and engaged throughout the course of the program
- bookmarking technology enables users to track their progress from beginning to end
- periodic progress checks and end-of-section reviews are integrated throughout to ensure the highest level of retention
- a certificate of completion can be printed by users achieving a score of 80% or higher on the final review of the course
- all material is completely AICC and SCORM compliant
- all material follows the latest ASE and NATEF standards

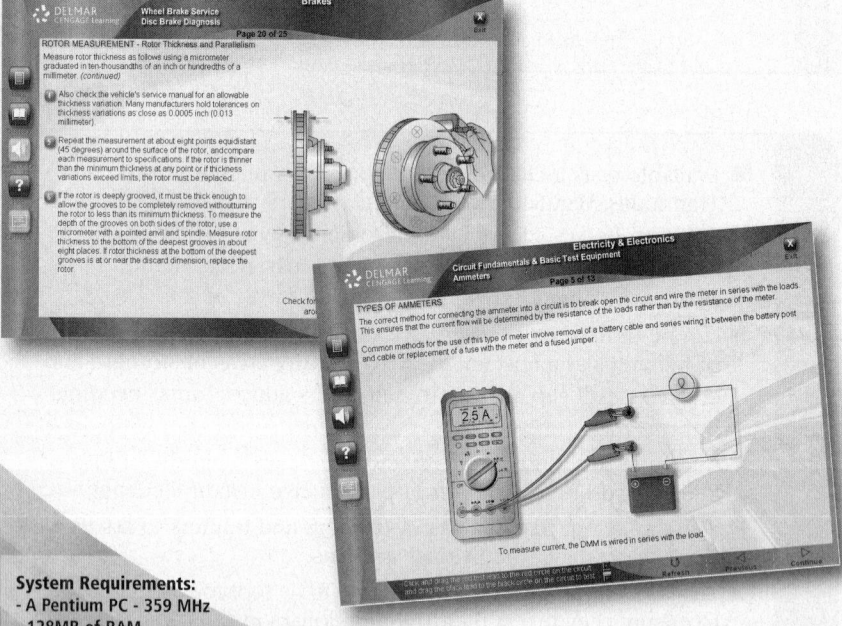

System Requirements:
- A Pentium PC - 359 MHz
- 128MB of RAM
- Windows 2000, Windows XP, Windows Vista
- Graphics adapter with Minimum 1024 x 768 display resolution, 32 bit depth
- Minimum Display Resolution 1024 x 768
- High Speed Internet Connection
- Internet Explorer 6, 7, or Firefox 2
- Not Mac Compatible

Basic Automotive Service and Maintenance Web Based Training
ISBN 978-1-4180-4101-4

Basic Automotive Service and Maintenance Computer Based Training
ISBN 978-1-4180-4100-7

Electricity and Electronics Web Based Training
ISBN 978-1-4180-4242-4

Electricity and Electronics Computer Based Training
ISBN 978-1-4180-4241-7

Brakes Web Based Training
ISBN 978-1-4180-4236-3

Brakes Computer Based Training
ISBN 978-1-4180-4235-6

Engine Performance Web Based Training
ISBN 978-1-4180-4240-0

Engine Performance Computer Based Training
ISBN 978-1-4180-4239-4

Suspension and Steering Web Based Training
ISBN 978-1-4180-4238-7

Suspension and Steering Computer Based Training
ISBN 978-1-4180-4237-0

Automatic Transmissions Web Based Training
ISBN 978-1-4180-4244-8

Automatic Transmissions Computer Based Training
ISBN 978-1-4180-4243-1

Service Consultant Web Based Training
ISBN 978-1-4180-4249-3

Service Consultant Computer Based Training
ISBN 978-1-4180-4247-9

Engine Repair Web Based Training
ISBN 978-1-4180-4254-7

Engine Repair Computer Based Training
ISBN 978-1-4180-4253-0

Parts Specialist Web Based Training
ISBN 978-1-4180-4252-3

Parts Specialist Computer Based Training
ISBN 978-1-4180-4250-9

Heating and Air Conditioning Web Based Training
ISBN 978-1-4180-4246-2

Heating and Air Conditioning Computer Based Training
ISBN 978-1-4180-4245-5

Manual Transmissions Web Based Training
ISBN 978-1-4180-4256-1

Manual Transmissions Computer Based Training
ISBN 978-1-4180-4255-4

Advanced Engine Performance Web Based Training
ISBN 978-1-4283-2098-7

Advanced Engine Performance Computer Based Training
ISBN 978-1-4283-2097-0

New Courses!

Fuels, Emissions, and Exhaust Computer Based Training
ISBN 978-1-4354-4148-4

Fuels, Emissions, and Exhaust Web Based Training
ISBN 978-1-4354-4147-7

Hybrid, Electric, and Fuel-Cell Vehicles Web Based Training
ISBN 978-1-4354-4144-6

Hybrid, Electric, and Fuel-Cell Vehicles Computer Based Training
ISBN 978-1-4354-4143-9

Visit **www.techniciantraining.com**
for a free demo!